SECTION I:
PERIODICAL LITERATURE AND ESSAYS

Sample Entry

CONFIDENTIALITY[1]

Streiffer, Robert; Rubel, Alan P.; Fagan, Julie R. [2] Medical privacy and the public's right to vote: what presidential candidates should disclose.[3] *Journal of Medicine and Philosophy* [4] 2006 August[5]; 31(4)[6]: 417-439[7]. NRCBL: 8.4; 1.3.5[8]. SC: an [9].

Abstract: We argue that while presidential candidates have the right to medical privacy, the public nature and importance of the presidency generates a moral requirement that candidates waive those rights in certain circumstances. Specifically, candidates are required to disclose information about medical conditions that are likely to seriously undermine their ability to fulfill what we call the "core functions" of the office of the presidency. This requirement exists because (1) people have the right to be governed only with their consent, (2) people's consent is meaningful only when they have access to information necessary for making informed voting decisions, (3) such information is necessary for making informed voting decisions, and (4) there are no countervailing reasons sufficiently strong to override this right. We also investigate alternative mechanisms for legally encouraging or requiring disclosure. Protecting the public's right to this information is of particular importance because of the documented history of deception and secrecy regarding the health of presidents and presidential candidates.[14]

1. Subject heading: **CONFIDENTIALITY**
2. Author(s): **Streiffer, Robert; Rubel, Alan P.; Fagan, Julie R.**
3. Title of article: Medical privacy and the public's right to vote: what presidential candidates should disclose.
4. Title of journal: *Journal of Medicine and Philosophy*
5. Date of publication: 2006 August
6. Volume and issue number (if available): 31(4)
7. Pagination: 417-439
8. NRCBL (all classification numbers): 8.4; 1.3.5
9. SC (Subject Captions): an (optional)
10. Identifiers: (optional)
11. Note: additional information (optional)
12. Conference: (optional)
13. Comments: information about related publications (optional)
14. Abstract: We argue that while presidential candidates have the right to medical privacy, the public nature and importance of the presidency generates a moral requirement that candidates waive those rights in certain circumstances. Specifically, candidates . . . . (optional)

BIBLIOGRAPHY
OF
BIOETHICS

BIBLIOGRAPHY OF BIOETHICS

Volume 33

Editors
LeRoy Walters
Tamar Joy Kahn
Doris Mueller Goldstein

Associate Editors
Frances Amitay Abramson
Richard M. Anderson
Laura Jane Bishop
Martina Darragh
Jeanne Ryan Furcron
Harriet Hutson Gray
Lucinda Fitch Huttlinger
Patricia C. Martin
Hannelore S. Ninomiya
Anita Lonnes Nolen
Leslie B. Pendley
Susan Cartier Poland

Managing Editor
Mara R. Snyder

Editorial Production
Roxie France-Nuriddin

KENNEDY INSTITUTE OF ETHICS
GEORGETOWN UNIVERSITY
Box 571212
WASHINGTON, DC 20057-1212

Publication of the annual *Bibliography of Bioethics* is a project of the Kennedy Institute of Ethics, Georgetown University. This book benefits from acquisition, classification, and database development activities funded by Contract HHSN276200553501C with the National Library of Medicine, and by Grant 5 P41 HG01115 from the National Human Genome Research Institute. It also reflects the contributions of The Anderson Partnership; Max M. and Marjorie B. Kampelman; and the National Endowment for the Humanities.

ISSN 0363-0161
ISBN 978-1-883913-14-4

This volume of the *Bibliography of Bioethics*
is dedicated to the memory of
our dear colleague and friend
Cecily Orr Nuckols
October 17, 1951 - July 22, 2006

Associate Editor of the
Bibliography of Bioethics, 1980-2002
Library and Information Services
Kennedy Institute of Ethics.

Contents

Staff

Editors

LeRoy Walters, Ph.D, Joseph P. Kennedy, Sr. Professor

Tamar Joy Kahn, M.L.S., Senior Bibliographer

Doris Mueller Goldstein, M.L.S., M.A., Director, Library and Information Services

Acquisitions Librarian

Lucinda Fitch Huttlinger, M.L.S., M.M.

System Librarians

Anita Lonnes Nolen, M.A., C.A.

Mara R. Snyder, M.S.L.S.

Bibliographers

Frances Amitay Abramson, M.A., M.S.

Jeanne Ryan Furcron, M.L.S.

Hannelore S. Ninomiya, M.L.S., M.A.

Leslie B. Pendley, M.L.I.S.

Reference Librarians

Richard M. Anderson, M.L.S.

Martina Darragh, M.L.S.

Harriet H. Gray, M.S.L.S., M.T.S.

Kathleen A. Schroeder, M.D., M.S.I.

Research Associates

Laura Jane Bishop, Ph.D.

Susan Cartier Poland, J.D.

Research Staff

Mark Clemente, B.A.

Roxie France-Nuriddin, B.A.

Ted Jackson, B.A.

Patricia C. Martin, M.A.

Io Nami-Wolk, B.S.

xiii

Editorial Advisory Board

Robert M. Veatch, Ph.D.
Senior Research Scholar, Kennedy Institute of
    Ethics; and
Professor of Medical Ethics
Georgetown University

INTRODUCTION

INTRODUCTION

The Field of Bioethics

Bioethics can be defined as the systematic study of value questions that arise in health care delivery and in biomedicine. Specific bioethical issues that have recently received national and international attention include euthanasia, assisted suicide, new reproductive technologies, cloning, human experimentation, genetic engineering, abortion, informed consent, acquired immunodeficiency syndrome (AIDS), organ donation and transplantation, and managed care and other concerns in the allocation of health care resources.

As this list of topics suggests, the field of bioethics includes several dimensions. The first is the ethics of the professional patient relationship. Traditionally, the accent has been on the duties of health professionals–duties that, since the time of Hippocrates, have frequently been delineated in codes of professional ethics. In more recent times the rights of patients have also received considerable attention. Research ethics, the study of value problems in biomedical and behavioral research, constitutes a second dimension of bioethics. During the 20th century, as both the volume and visible achievements of such research have increased, new questions have arisen concerning the investigator-subject relationship and the potential social impact of biomedical and behavioral research and technology. In recent years a third dimension of bioethics has emerged–the quest to develop reasonable public policy guidelines for both the delivery of health care and the allocation of health care resources, as well as for the conduct of research.

No single academic discipline is adequate to discuss these various dimensions of bioethics. For this reason bioethics has been, since its inception in the late 1960s, a cross-disciplinary field. The primary participants in the interdisciplinary discussion have been physicians and other health professionals, biologists, psychologists, sociologists, lawyers, historians, and philosophical and religious ethicists.

During the past thirty-two years there has been a rapid growth of academic, professional, and public interest in the field of bioethics. One evidence of this interest is the establishment of numerous research institutes and teaching programs in bioethics, both in the United States and abroad. Professional societies, federal and state legislatures, and the courts have also turned increasing attention to problems in the field. In addition, there has been a veritable explosion of literature on bioethical issues.

The literature of bioethics appears in widely scattered sources and is reported in diverse indexes which employ a bewildering variety of subject headings. This annual *Bibliography* is the product of a unique information retrieval system designed to identify the central issues of bioethics, to develop a subject classification scheme appropriate to the field, and to provide comprehensive, cross-disciplinary coverage of current English-language materials on bioethical topics.

Volume 33 of the *Bibliography* contains one year's worth of the literature garnered by this comprehensive information system. Specifically, it includes all of the citations that were acquired in 2006 by two projects at the Kennedy Institute of Ethics: the National Reference Center for Bioethics Literature (NRCBL) and the National Information Resource on Ethics & Human Genetics (NIREHG). Items selected for indexing for the bioethics subset of the U.S. National Library of Medicine's PubMed/MEDLINE journal database and the NLM Catalog, its book database, are included in this volume.

The Table of Contents includes a list of subject headings used to arrange the citations. Most citations are listed once, under their primary subject heading. Classification numbers at the end of each citation represent additional topics covered by the publication. These classification numbers are drawn from the NRCBL's Classification Scheme, reproduced on the inside front cover.

BIBLIOGRAPHY OF BIOETHICS
The Scope of the Bibliography

This thirty-third volume of the *Bibliography of Bioethics* includes materials which discuss the ethical aspects of the following major topics and subtopics:

BIOETHICS, MEDICAL ETHICS, AND
PROFESSIONAL ETHICS
- Codes of Ethics
- Commissions
- Ethicists and Ethics Committees
- Nursing Ethics and Philosophy
- Philosophy of Medicine
- Professional Ethics
- Quality and Value of Life
- Religious Perspectives

DEATH AND DYING
- Advance Directives
- Assisted Suicide
- Attitudes to Death
- Capital Punishment
- Determination of Death
- Euthanasia and Allowing to Die
- Terminal Care

GENETICS
- Behavioral Genetics
- Eugenics
- Gene Therapy
- Genetic Counseling
- Genetic Privacy
- Genetic Research
- Genetic Screening
- Genetics and Human Ancestry
- Genome Mapping
- Patents
- Recombinant DNA Research
- Sociobiology

HEALTH CARE AND PUBLIC HEALTH
- AIDS
- Care for Specific Groups
- Drug Industry
- Health, Concept of
  - Mental Health, Concept of
- Health Care
  - Health Care Economics
  - Health Care Quality
  - Occupational Health
- Organ and Tissue Donation and Transplantation
- Public Health
- Resource Allocation
- Right to Health Care

- Sexuality
- Telemedicine and Informatics

MENTAL HEALTH THERAPIES
- Behavior Control
- Electroconvulsive Therapy
- Involuntary Commitment
- Psychopharmacology
- Psychotherapy

PATIENT RELATIONSHIPS
- Confidentiality
- Informed Consent
- Sexuality
- Treatment Refusal
- Truth Disclosure

REPRODUCTION AND REPRODUCTIVE
TECHNOLOGIES
- Abortion
- Artificial Insemination and Surrogate Mothers
- Cloning
- Contraception
- Cryobanking of Sperm, Ova, and Embryos
- In Vitro Fertilization
- Population Policy
- Sex Determination
- Sterilization

RESEARCH
- Animal Experimentation
- Behavioral Research
- Biomedical Research
- Enhancement
- Human Experimentation
- Nanotechnology
- Research Ethics and Scientific Misconduct

SOCIOLOGY OF MEDICINE
- Cultural Pluralism
- Journalism and Publishing
- Malpractice and Professional Misconduct
- Medical Education
- Professional-Professional Relationship

WAR AND HUMAN RIGHTS ABUSES
- International Human Rights
- International Migration of Health Professionals
- Torture, Genocide, and War Crimes
- War and Terrorism

This volume of the *Bibliography* cites 8,779 documents (primarily in English) that discuss ethical and related public policy aspects of the topics and subtopics listed above. Documents cited in this volume include journal and newspaper articles, laws, court decisions, monographs, and chapters in books. Most of the documents listed were published since 2004. In the *Periodical Literature and Essays* section, for example, 3,874 of the 8,117 entries were published in 2006; 1,822 in 2005; and 582 in 2004; therefore, 77 per cent of the literature cited in Section I was published since 2004.

A cross-disciplinary monitoring system has been devised in an effort to secure documents falling within the subject-matter scope outlined above. Among the reference tools and databases searched for pertinent citations are the following:

AGRICOLA

All England Law Reports (subject index)

America: History & Life

ATLA Religion Database

Choice

Cumulative Index to Nursing and Allied Health Literature (CINAHL)

Current Contents: Social and Behavioral Sciences

Digital Dissertations and Theses (UMI Proquest)

Dominion Law Reports (subject index)

ERIC

GPO Access

Historical Abstracts

Index to Canadian Legal Periodical Literature

Index to Foreign Legal Periodicals

Library Journal

MEDLINE

Mental and Physical Disability Law Reporter

Month in Review (GAO reports and other publications)

New Titles in Bioethics

PAIS International

Philosopher's Index

POPLINE

PsycInfo

Social Sciences Index

Sociological Abstracts

Specialty Law Digest: Health Care

Tarlton Law Library Legal Bibliography Series

WorldCat

In addition, the *Bibliography* staff directly monitors 206 journals and newspapers for articles falling within the scope of bioethics. Those preceded by an asterisk (*) have given permission for abstracts to be included in this volume. It is important to note that the journal articles cited in this volume are actually drawn from many more journals than those listed below.

Academic Medicine

*Accountability in Research

Agriculture and Human Values

AIDS and Public Policy Journal

America

*American Journal of Bioethics

*American Journal of Law and Medicine

American Journal of Nursing

American Journal of Psychiatry

*American Journal of Public Health

Annals of Health Law

*Annals of Internal Medicine

APA Newsletter on Philosophy and Medicine

*Archives of Internal Medicine

ATLA: Alternatives to Laboratory Animals

*Bioethics

Bioethics Forum

*BMC Medical Ethics [electronic resource]

*BMJ (British Medical Journal)

British Journal of Nursing

Bulletin of Medical Ethics

Business and Professional Ethics Journal

Business Ethics Quarterly

Canadian Medical Association Journal

CCAR Journal

Cerebrum [electronic resource]

*Christian Bioethics

Christian Century

Christian Medical Society Journal

*Clinical Ethics

Community Genetics

Conservative Judaism

Criminal Justice Ethics

*CQ: Cambridge Quarterly of Healthcare Ethics

Decisions; Journal of the Federation Internationale des Associations Medicales Catholiques

DePaul Journal of Health Care Law

*Developing World Bioethics

Dolentium Hominum

Environmental Ethics

Environmental Values

Ethical Human Psychology and Psychiatry

Ethical Perspectives

Ethical Theory and Moral Practice

BIBLIOGRAPHY OF BIOETHICS

*Ethics

*Ethics and Behavior

Ethics and Intellectual Disability

Ethics and Medicine

Ethics and Medics

*Eubios Journal of Asian and International Bioethics

European Journal of Health Law

First Things: A Monthly Journal of Religion and Public Life

Formosan Journal of Medical Humanities

Free Inquiry

Genetic Testing

Genetics in Medicine

GeneWatch

*Genomics, Society and Policy [electronic resource]

Georgetown Journal of Legal Ethics

*Hastings Center Report

Health Affairs

Health and Human Rights

*Health Care Analysis

Health Care Ethics USA [electronic resource]

Health Care Financing Review

Health Law in Canada

Health Law Journal

Health Law Review

Health Matrix (Cleveland)

Health Policy [ISSN 0168-8510]

Health Progress

*HEC Forum

Human Genome News

Human Life Review

Human Reproduction

Human Reproduction and Genetic Ethics

Human Research Report

Humane Health Care [electronic resource]

Hypatia

IDHL: International Digest of Health Legislation [electronic resource]

Indian Journal of Medical Ethics [electronic resource]

International Journal of Applied Philosophy

*International Journal of Bioethics (Journal International de Bioéthique)

International Journal of Health Services

International Journal of Law and Psychiatry

International Journal of Technology Assessment in Health Care

*IRB: Ethics and Human Research

Issues in Ethics

Issues in Law and Medicine

Issues in Science and Technology

*JAMA

Jewish Medical Ethics and Halacha

*JONA's Healthcare Law, Ethics, and Regulation

Journal of Advanced Nursing

Journal of Applied Animal Welfare Science

*Journal of Applied Philosophy

*Journal of Bioethical Inquiry

Journal of Biolaw and Business

*Journal of Clinical Ethics

Journal of Contemporary Health Law and Policy

*Journal of Empirical Research on Human Research Ethics

Journal of Ethics

*Journal of Ethics in Mental Health [electronic resource]

Journal of General Internal Medicine

Journal of Genetic Counseling

Journal of Halacha and Contemporary Society

Journal of Health Care Law and Policy

*Journal of Health Politics, Policy and Law

Journal of Information Ethics

Journal of Intellectual Disability Research

Journal of Law and Health [electronic resource]

Journal of Law and Religion

*Journal of Law, Medicine and Ethics

Journal of Legal Medicine

*Journal of Medical Ethics

Journal of Medical Genetics

*Journal of Medical Humanities

*Journal of Medicine and Philosophy

Journal of Moral Education

Journal of Nursing Administration

Journal of Nursing Law

Journal of Palliative Care

Journal of Philosophy, Science and Law [electronic resource]

Journal of Professional Nursing

Journal of Psychiatry and Law

Journal of Public Health Policy

Journal of Religion and Health

Journal of Religious Ethics

Journal of Social Philosophy

Journal of the American Academy of Psychiatry and the Law

Journal of the American College of Dentists

Journal of the American Geriatrics Society

Journal of the American Medical Women's Association

Journal of the Society of Christian Ethics

Judaism

*Kennedy Institute of Ethics Journal

*Lancet

Law and the Human Genome Review (Revista de Derecho y Genoma Humano)

Legal Medical Quarterly

Linacre Quarterly

Literature and Medicine

Medical Ethics & Bioethics (Medicinska Etika & Bioetika)

*Medical Humanities

Medical Humanities Review

Medical Law International

Medical Law Review

Medical Trial Technique Quarterly

*Medicine and Law

Medicine, Conflict and Survival

*Medicine, Health Care and Philosophy

Mental Retardation [ISSN 0047-6765]

*Milbank Quarterly

Minnesota Medicine

Monash Bioethics Review

*National Catholic Bioethics Quarterly

*Nature

Nature Biotechnology

Nature Medicine

NCEHR Communiqué (National Council on Ethics in Human Research) [electronic resource]

New Atlantis

*New England Journal of Medicine

New Genetics and Society

New Scientist

New York Times

Newsweek

Notizie de Politeia

Notre Dame Journal of Law, Ethics and Public Policy

*Nursing Ethics

Omega: Journal of Death and Dying

Online Journal of Issues in Nursing [electronic resource]

Origins

*Penn Bioethics Journal

Perspectives in Biology and Medicine

Perspectives on the Professions: Ethical & Policy Issues

Pharos

*Philosophy and Public Affairs

Philosophy and Public Policy Quarterly

*Philosophy, Ethics, and Humanities in Medicine [electronic resource]

Politics and the Life Sciences

Professional Ethics Report [electronic resource]

Protecting Human Subjects

Psychiatric Services

Public Affairs Quarterly

Res Publica

Responsive Community

Review of Metaphysics

Romanian Journal of Bioethics (Revista Romana de Bioetica)

*Science

Science and Engineering Ethics

Science as Culture

Science, Technology, and Human Values

Sh'ma

Social Justice Research

Social Philosophy and Policy

*Social Science and Medicine

Social Theory and Practice

Society and Animals

Studies in Christian Ethics

*Theoretical Medicine and Bioethics

Tradition

UNOS Update

Update (Loma Linda University Ethics Center) [electronic resource]

U.S. News and World Report

Virtual Mentor: Ethics Journal of the American Medical Association [electronic resource]

Washington Post

*Women's Health Issues

Yale Journal of Health Policy, Law, and Ethics

All documents cited by the *Bibliography* are in the collection of the NRCBL.

Arrangement of the *Bibliography*

This volume of the *Bibliography of Bioethics* is divided into five parts:

1. Introduction
2. Section I: Periodical Literature and Essays — Subject Entries
3. Section II: Periodical Literature and Essays — Author Index
4. Section III: Monographs — Subject Entries
5. Section IV: Monographs — Title Index.

Sections 2 and 4 constitute the core of the *Bibliography*.

Section 1: Periodical Literature and Essays — Subject Entries

This Section, one of the two main parts of the *Bibliography*, contains usually one entry for each of the documents selected by the

BIBLIOGRAPHY OF BIOETHICS

bioethics information retrieval system during the preceding year. In Volume 33 of the *Bibliography*, entries for 8,117 documents have been included in the Section. The format of these documents is as follows:

Journal articles	6,381
Essays in books	1,067
Newspaper articles	432
Pamphlets and other materials	128
Legal documents	109

Section I is organized under 78 major subject headings, of which 16 are further divided by subheadings. Each subheading is separated from the major subject term by a slash.

Readers of the *Bibliography* should first scan the alphabetic list of subject headings in the Table of Contents to determine where citations of interest to them are likely to be found.

Section I includes cross references of two types. *See* cross references lead the reader from terms that are not used as subject headings to terms that are used. *See also* cross references suggest additional subject headings where the reader may find citations of related interest.

Citations appear alphabetically by author, with anonymous citations at the beginning of the section, sorted alphabetically by title. Entries with both corporate and personal authors are sorted by the corporate author. As explained below, the citations are accompanied by NRCBL Classification Scheme numbers as well as, in some cases, Subject Captions denoting approach or content. Subject Caption definitions can be found on page footers. Abstracts are again included in this volume. In addition, we have instituted several optional new fields in Section I that provide additional information: identifiers (such as persons, places, organizations, acronym equivalents), conference information, comments regarding related publications, and general notes.

Fourteen data elements may appear in an entry for a journal article. A sample subject heading and entry for a journal article follow:

CONFIDENTIALITY[1]
 Streiffer, Robert; Rubel, Alan P.; Fagan, Julie R.[2] Medical privacy and the public's right to vote: what presidential candidates should disclose. [3] *Journal of Medicine and Philosophy* [4] 2006 August[5]; 31(4)[6]: 417-439[7]. NRCBL: 8.4; 1.3.5[8]. SC: an [9].
  Abstract: We argue that while presidential candidates have the right to medical privacy, the public nature and importance of the presidency generates a moral requirement that candidates waive those rights in certain circumstances. Specifically, candidates are required to disclose information about medical conditions that are . . . .

  1. Subject heading: **CONFIDENTIALITY**
  2. Author(s): **Streiffer, Robert; Rubel, Alan P.; Fagan, Julie R.**
  3. Title of article: Medical privacy and the public's right to vote: what presidential candidates should disclose.
  4. Title of journal: *Journal of Medicine and Philosophy*
  5. Date of publication: 2006 August
  6. Volume and issue number (if available): 31(4)
  7. Pagination: 417-439
  8. NRCBL (all classification numbers): 8.4; 1.3.5
  9. SC (Subject Captions): an (optional)
  10. Identifiers: (optional)
  11. Note: additional information (optional)
  12. Conference: (optional)
  13. Comments: information about related publications (optional)
  14. Abstract: We argue that while presidential candidates have the right to medical privacy, the public nature and importance of . . . (optional)

The sample entry presented on the previous page displays the format and elements which appear in a journal article, the most prevalent publication type. The title field may be augmented by terms in square brackets which indicate additional aspects of the document, such as: letter, editorial, and news. The complete NRCBL Classification Scheme can be found on the inside front cover, and the Subject Captions equivalents are on alternating footers in Section I. The inside back cover displays the Subject Heading Key for Section II, leading the reader from the primary, i.e. first, NRCBL number to the corresponding Subject Heading(s) in Section I. Most citations appear only once in this volume.

Section II: Periodical Literature and Essays — Author Index

Citations in the Author Index are followed by the primary NRCBL Classification Number (Subject). Citations that have no personal or corporate author are listed at the end of the Author Index for Periodical Literature and Essays under ANONYMOUS. The two-page SUBJECT HEADING KEY FOR SECTION II appears on the inside back cover; it provides subject heading equivalents in Section I for the subject numbers appearing at the end of each citation in Section II.

Section III: Monographs — Subject Entries

These records have been derived from the annual publication of the NRCBL's *New Titles in Bioethics*, and cite monographs added to the collection in 2006 that cover bioethics and related areas of ethics and applied ethics. The NRCBL Classification Scheme (reproduced in full on the inside front cover) provides the arrangement for these citations. The Monographs section includes 662 records for books, reports, audiovisuals, special issues of journals, and new periodical subscriptions. Only subject headings actually occurring in Volume 33 are included on this list.

The monograph citations are arranged according to the primary subject category of the volume, and then, under subject category, by author, editor, producer, or title. Each citation in the Section usually appears only once. Classification numbers at the end of each citation represent additional bioethics topics covered by the publication. Monograph entries also include acquisition information, especially important for the so-called "gray literature." Monographs in foreign languages are included in the *Bibliography*.

Section IV: Monographs — Title Index

This Section provides a title index to all the entries in the Monographs Section. The title is followed by the subject section and author within which the complete citation can be found.

The *Bibliography of Bioethics*: History and Current Availability on the World Wide Web

Through December 2000, the entries in all of the annual volumes of the *Bibliography of Bioethics* were available online in BIOETHICSLINE®, a database produced for the National Library of Medicine (NLM) by the Bioethics Information Retrieval Project at the Kennedy Institute of Ethics, Georgetown University. As of 2001, NLM incorporated its subject-oriented databases–like BIOETHICSLINE– into two large databases, PubMed/MEDLINE for journal articles and related documents, and LOCATOR*plus*/NLM Catalog for books and related documents.

Bibliographic records in the BIOETHICSLINE® database were retrospectively converted to PubMed or LOCATOR*plus* records based on publication type. The Bioethics Information Retrieval Project now selects and indexes bioethics-related journal articles, newspaper articles, court decisions, and laws directly for PubMed/MEDLINE and books, book chapters, audiovisual materials, and unpublished documents for LOCATOR*plus* (also distributed as the NLM Catalog). This effort is funded by a contract with NLM, with additional support from the National Human Genome Research Institute.

Citations from the *Bibliography of Bioethics* are available on the World Wide Web via the National Library of Medicine's PubMed/MEDLINE and LOCATOR*plus* databases, where they are indexed with NLM's Medical Subject Headings (MeSH) indexing vocabulary, and via the ETHXWeb and GenETHX databases, maintained by NRCBL. Access to the NLM and NRCBL databases, along with searching information, is available through the Web gateway of the Kennedy Institute of Ethics at http://bioethics.georgetown.edu. In addition, a comprehensive NRCBL publication provides advice for database searchers: *Bioethics Searcher's Guide to Online Information Resources*. (See "Distribution" paragraph below for ordering information.)

Acknowledgments

It is a pleasure to acknowledge the assistance of several people and organizations who played significant roles in the production of this thirty-third volume of the *Bibliography of Bioethics*. Although this publication is not a direct product of federal funding, it depends upon critical support from the National Library of Medicine and the National Human Genome Research Institute, both at the National Institutes of Health. We wish to thank, in particular, our NLM Project Officers, Martha Cohn, Sara Tybaert, and Susan Von Braunsberg; our NLM Contracting Officer, Alex Navas; and Joy Boyer, Program Director, The Ethical, Legal, and Social Implications Program, National Human Genome Research Institute, for their interest and support. Other support is provided by the National Endowment for the Humanities, the Anderson Partnership, Max M. and Marjory B. Kampelman, and many publishers and individuals who contributed copies of books and journal articles to NRCBL.

Patricia Milmoe McCarrick, former reference librarian at NRCBL, continues as a library volunteer. Several Georgetown University students carried out document acquisition and data entry tasks: Diane Lois Healy, Nana Hasegawa, Larissa Hsia-Wong, Rebecca Kruser, Kevin C. Kwiatkowski, Amanda McCafferty, Vilija Mickute, Tessa Munekiyo, Ayah Nuriddin, and Kerstin Sondermann.

Distribution of the *Bibliography of Bioethics* and Related Publications

Inquiries about purchasing Volumes 10-33 of the *Bibliography* or the current edition of *Bioethics Searcher's Guide to Online Information Resources* should be directed to Library Publications, Kennedy Institute of Ethics, Georgetown University, Box 571212, Washington, DC 20057-1212, telephone 202-687-3885 or 888-BIO-ETHX (outside the Washington, DC metropolitan area); fax 202-687-6770, e-mail: bioethics@georgetown.edu.

International Bioethics Exchange Project (IBEP)

IBEP, a project of the Kennedy Institute of Ethics, promotes research and education in bioethics in the developing world by donating multiple volumes of the *Bibliography* to libraries abroad in order to encourage the development of bioethics reference resources in those countries. In turn, IBEP is eager to collect documents about bioethics from the exchange participants. Any books, policy statements, periodicals and other materials about bioethical issues in the participant countries that are donated to IBEP are added to the NRCBL collection and considered for inclusion in the *Bibliography*. This project relies upon the support of donors to underwrite the transport of the volumes to the developing country library.

To date libraries in the following countries have become participants in the project: Argentina, Brazil, Burkina Faso, The Cameroons, Costa Rica, Croatia, Eritrea, Grenada, Israel, Jamaica, Lithuania, Mexico, Papua New Guinea, Peoples Republic of China, Philippines, Poland, Portugal, Republic of Belarus, Republic of Korea, Republic of Slovenia, Republic of the Congo, Republic of Trinidad and Tobago, Romania, Rwanda, St. Lucia, Sierra Leone, Slovak Republic, South Africa, Sri Lanka, Thailand, Turkey, Uzbekistan, Venezuela, Yemen, and Zambia.

Contributions in support of an IBEP library or donations of bioethics books, reprints, audiovisual materials, and other documents should be sent to Acquisitions Librarian, Kennedy Institute of Ethics, Georgetown University, Box 571212, Washington, DC 20057-1212; Telephone 1-202-687-3885; Toll-free 1-888-BIO-ETHX (U.S. and Canada); FAX +202-687-6770; e-mail: bioethics@georgetown.edu. All donations are reviewed for inclusion in the NRCBL collection as well as for this *Bibliography*.

The staff welcomes suggestions for the improvement of future volumes of the *Bibliography of Bioethics*. Please send all comments to: Editors, *Bibliography of Bioethics*, Kennedy Institute of Ethics, Georgetown University, Box 571212, Washington, DC 20057-1212.

July 2, 2007

SECTION I:
PERIODICAL LITERATURE AND ESSAYS

SUBJECT ENTRIES

SECTION I: PERIODICAL LITERATURE AND ESSAYS SUBJECT ENTRIES

ABORTION

Abortion and our culture: an interview with Eyal Press. *Free Inquiry* 2006 June-July; 26(4): 8. NRCBL: 12.1.

Deaths after RU-486 [editorial]. *New York Times* 2006 April 10; p. A22. NRCBL: 12.1; 9.7.

Beisel, Nicola; Kay, Tamara. Abortion, race, and gender in nineteenth-century America. *American Sociological Review* 2004 August; 69(4): 498-518. NRCBL: 12.1; 9.5.4; 10; 2.2; 7.1; 15.5; 9.5.5.

Brown, Harold O.J. The victory of the abstract over the real. *Human Life Review* 2006 Spring; 32(2): 64-70. NRCBL: 12.1.

Clowes, Brian. The mathematics of applied scientific racism. *Human Life Review* 2006 Spring; 32(2): 52-63. NRCBL: 12.1; 12.5.1; 15.5.

Cook, R.J.; Dickens, B.M.; Horga, M. Safe abortion: WHO technical and policy guidance. *International Journal of Gynecology and Obstetrics* 2004 July; 86(1): 79-84. NRCBL: 12.1; 12.4.1; 21.1. Identifiers: World Health Organization.

Creinin, Mitchell D. Medical abortion regiments: historical context and overview. *American Journal of Obstetrics and Gynecology* 2000 August; 183(Supplement 2): S3-S9. NRCBL: 12.1; 9.7; 2.2.

de Costa, Caroline M. Medical abortion for Australian women: it's time. *Medical Journal of Australia* 2005 October 3; 183(7): 378-380. NRCBL: 12.1; 9.7. Identifiers: mifepristone.

Dykes, Bryan A. Proposed rights of conscience legislation: expanding to include pharmacists and other health care providers. *Georgia Law Review* 2002 Winter; 36(2): 565-597. NRCBL: 12.1; 9.7; 12.4.3; 12.3; 8.1. SC: le.

Echevarria, Laura. RU-486: a bitter pill. *Human Life Review* 2006 Summer-Fall; 32(3-4): 109-117. NRCBL: 12.1; 9.7.

Espey, Eve; Ogburn, Tony; Chavez, Alice; Qualls, Clifford; Leyba, Mario. Abortion education in medical schools: a national survey. *American Journal of Obstetrics and Gynecology* 2005 February; 192(2): 640-643. NRCBL: 12.1; 7.2. SC: em.

Grisolía, James Santiago. Stem cell grafting for epilepsy: clinical promise and ethical concerns. *Epilepsy and Behavior* 2001 August; 2(4): 318-323. NRCBL: 12.1; 19.1; 18.5.4; 15.1.

Harvey, S. Marie; Beckman, Linda J.; Satre, Sarah J. Experience and satisfaction with providing methotrexate-induced abortion services among U.S. providers. *Journal of the American Medical Women's Association* 2000; 55 (3, Supplement): 161-163. NRCBL: 12.1; 9.7; 12.5.2. SC: em.

Harvey, S. Marie; Sherman, Christy A.; Bird, Sheryl Thorburn; Warren, Jocelyn. Understanding medical abortion: policy, politics and women's health [policy statement]. *Eugene: University of Oregon. Center for the Study of Women in Society* 2002 Policy Matter #3: 50 p. [Online]. Accessed: http://csws.uoregon.edu/home/policymat3.pdf [2006 October 31]. NRCBL: 12.1; 9.7; 12.4.1; 8.3.1.

Hemmerling, Anke; Siedentopf, Friederike; Kentenich, Heribert. Emotional impact and acceptability of medical abortion with mifepristone: a German experience. *Journal of Psychosomatic Obstetrics and Gynaecology* 2005 March; 26(1): 23-31. NRCBL: 12.1; 9.7. SC: em.

Hessini, Leila. Global progress in abortion advocacy and policy: an assessment of the decade since ICPD. *Reproductive Health Matters* 2005 May; 13(25): 88-100. NRCBL: 12.1; 12.5.1; 9.1; 9.5.5; 21.1. SC: le. Identifiers: International Conference on Population and Development.

Hopkins, Nick; Zeedyk, Suzanne; Raitt, Fiona. Visualising abortion: emotion discourse and fetal imagery in a contemporary abortion debate. *Social Science and Medicine* 2005 July; 61(2): 393-403. NRCBL: 12.1; 12.5.1; 7.1; 1.3.12; 4.4. Identifiers: United Kingdom (Great Britain).

NRCBL: National Reference Center for Bioethics Literature Classification Scheme   See inside front cover for terms.

13

Jutel, Annemarie. What's in a name? Death before birth. *Perspectives in Biology and Medicine* 2006 Summer; 49(3): 425-434. NRCBL: 12.1; 9.5.5; 4.4.

Kenny, Catherine. Abortion — a reproductive right. *In:* Widdows, Heather; Idiakez, Itziar Alkorta; Cirión, Aitziber Emaldi, eds. Women's Reproductive Rights. New York: Palgrave Macmillan; 2006: 17-32. NRCBL: 12.1.

Kramlich, Maureen. The abortion debate thirty years later: from choice to coercion. *Fordham Urban Law Journal* 2004 March; 31(3): 783-804. NRCBL: 12.1; 12.4.1. SC: le.

Motluk, Alison. Science, politics, and morality collide [news]. *New Scientist* 2006 March 18-24; 189(2543): 8-9. NRCBL: 12.1; 12.4.2.

Purdy, L. Women's reproductive autonomy: medicalisation and beyond. *Journal of Medical Ethics* 2006 May; 32(5): 287-291. NRCBL: 12.1; 14.1; 9.5.5.

Abstract: Reproductive autonomy is central to women's welfare both because childbearing takes place in women's bodies and because they are generally expected to take primary responsibility for child rearing. In 2005, the factors that influence their autonomy most strongly are poverty and belief systems that devalue such autonomy. Unfortunately, such autonomy is a low priority for most societies, or is anathema to their belief systems altogether. This situation is doubly sad because women's reproductive autonomy is intrinsically valuable for women and also instrumentally valuable for the welfare of humankind. This paper takes for granted the moral and practical necessity of such autonomy and digs deeper into the question of what such a commitment might entail, focusing on the mid-level policy making that, at least in the US and Canada, plays a significant role in shaping women's options. This paper examines a large teaching hospital's policy on reduction of multifetal pregnancies. The policy permits reduction of triplets to twins, but not twins to a singleton. As there is no morally relevant difference between these two types of reduction, it is evident that inappropriate medicalisation can still limit women's autonomy in undesirable ways.

Randall, Susan. Health care reform and abortion. *Berkeley Women's Law Journal* 1994; 9: 58-76. NRCBL: 12.1; 12.4.4; 9.3.1. SC: le.

Rodgers, Sandra; Downie, Jocelyn. Abortion: ensuring access [editorial]. *CMAJ/JAMC: Canadian Medical Association Journal* 2006 July 4; 175(1): 9. NRCBL: 12.1; 9.5.5.

Sangala, Vanessa. Safe abortion: a woman's right. *Tropical Doctor* 2005 July; 35(3): 130-133. NRCBL: 12.1; 12.4.1.

Schlafly, Andrew L. Legal implications of a link between abortion and breast cancer. *Journal of American Physicians and Surgeons* 2005 Spring; 10(1): 11-14. NRCBL: 12.1; 8.3.1; 9.5.5. SC: le.

Tang, G.W.; Lau, O.W.K.; Yip, P. Further acceptability evaluation of RU 486 and ONO 802 as abortifacient agents in a Chinese population. *Contraception* 1993 September; 48(3): 267-276. NRCBL: 12.1; 9.7; 12.5.2. SC: em. Identifiers: Hong Kong.

Tang, G.W.K. A pilot study of acceptability of RU 486 and ONO 802 in Chinese population. *Contraception* 1991 November; 44(5): 523-532. NRCBL: 12.1; 9.7; 12.5.2. SC: em. Identifiers: Hong Kong.

van den Broek, Nynke. The problem of unsafe abortions [editorial]. *Tropical Doctor* 2005 July; 35(3): 129. NRCBL: 12.1; 12.5.1.

Wicclair, Mark R.; Gosman, Gabriella. Abortion. *In:* Mitcham, Carl, ed. Encyclopedia of Science, Technology, and Ethics. Farmington Hills, MI: Thomson/Gale, 2005: 1-6. NRCBL: 12.1; 21.1. SC: rv.

ABORTION/ LEGAL ASPECTS

Abortion rights in Latin America [editorial]. *New York Times* 2006 January 6; p. A20. NRCBL: 12.4.1. SC: po.

Abortion ruling in Colombia [editorial]. *New York Times* 2006 May 24; p. A26. NRCBL: 12.4.1.

Constitutional law — abortion rights — Fourth Circuit declares Virginia partial birth infanticide statute unconstitutional per se. — Richmond Medical Center for Women v. Hicks, 409 F.3d 619 (4th Cir.), reh'g and reh'g en banc denied, 422 F.3d 160 (4th Cir. 2005). *Harvard Law Review* 2005 December; 119(2): 685-692. NRCBL: 12.4.1. SC: le.

House passes abortion bill on minors. *New York Times* 2006 September 27; p. A23. NRCBL: 12.4.1. SC: le.

Togo: abortion legalized in rape and incest. *New York Times* 2006 December 29; p. A15. NRCBL: 12.4.2. SC: po. Identifiers: World briefing; Africa.

Aizenman, N.C. Nicaragua's total ban on abortion spurs critics. *Washington Post* 2006 November 28; p. A1, A13. NRCBL: 12.4.1; 9.5.5; 9.5.8.

Alan Guttmacher Institute. An overview of abortion laws. *State Policies in Brief* 2006 February 1: 3 page [Online]. Accessed: http://www.guttmacher.org/statecenter/spibs/spib_OAL.pdf [21 February 2006]. NRCBL: 12.4.1. SC: em; le.

Alan Guttmacher Institute. Refusing to provide health services. *State Policies in Brief* 2006 February 1: 3 page [Online]. Accessed: http://www.guttmacher.org/statecenter/spibs/spib_RPHS.pdf [21 February 2006]. NRCBL: 12.4.3; 9.7; 11.1; 11.3. SC: em; le.

Alan Guttmacher Institute. Restricting insurance coverage of abortion. *State Policies in Brief* 2006 February 1: 2 page [Online]. Accessed: http://guttmacher.org/statecenter/spibs/spib_RICA.pdf [21 February 2006]. NRCBL: 12.4.1; 9.3.1. SC: em; le.

Alan Guttmacher Institute. State policies on late-term abortions. *State Policies in Brief* 2006 February 1: 2 page

[Online]. Accessed: http://www.guttmacher.org/statecenter/spibs/spib_PLTA.pdf [21 February 2006]. NRCBL: 12.4.1. SC: em; le.

Appel, Jacob M. Judicial diagnosis 'conscience' vs. care how refusal clauses are reshaping the rights revolution. *Medicine and Health, Rhode Island* 2005 August; 88(8): 279-281. NRCBL: 12.4.3; 12.3; 8.1; 9.7; 11.1. SC: le.

Applebaum, David. Judges' voices in the French abortion debate of the 1970s. *E Law: Murdoch University Electronic Journal of Law* 1995 December; 2(3): 25 p. [Online]. Accessed: http://www.murdoch.edu.au/elaw/issues/v2n3/applebaum23.html [2006 June 29]. NRCBL: 12.4.1; 10; 1.3.5. SC: le.

Bailey, Barbara Jean. Congress ignores the parameters of the health exception: judicial responses to congressional evidence and partial-birth abortion in the wake of Stenberg v. Carhart. *Journal of Legal Medicine* 2006 March; 27(1): 71-85. NRCBL: 12.4.2; 9.5.5. SC: le.

Baird, Karen L. Globalizing reproductive control: consequences of the "global gag rule.". *In:* Tong, Rosemarie; Donchin, Anne; Dodds, Susan, eds. Linking Visions: Feminist Bioethics, Human Rights, and the Developing World. Lanham, MD: Rowman and Littlefield Publishers; 2004: 133-145. NRCBL: 12.4.1; 9.3.1; 13.3.

Barry, Ursula. Abortion in the republic of Ireland. *Feminist Review* 1988 Spring; (29): 57-63. NRCBL: 12.4.2.

Borgmann, Caitlin E. Winter count: taking stock of abortion rights after Casey and Carhart. *Fordham Urban Law Journal* 2004 March; 31(3): 675-716. NRCBL: 12.4.1. SC: le.

Bridges, Khiara M. A judicial bypass procedure for an adolescent's abortion. *California Law Review* 2006 January; 94(1): 215-242. NRCBL: 12.4.2; 9.5.7; 1.3.5; 21.7. SC: le.

Budnitz, Elizabeth. Not a part of her sentence: applying the Supreme Court's Johnson v. California to prison abortion policies. *Brooklyn Law Review* 2006 Spring; 71(3): 1291-1332. NRCBL: 12.4.2; 1.3.5; 9.5.5.

Catholic Church. United States Conference of Catholic Bishops [USCCB]. Brief supports partial-birth abortion ban. *Origins* 2006 June 8; 36(4): 58-63. NRCBL: 12.4.4; 12.3. SC: le.

Ceasar, Mike. Court ends Colombia's abortion ban. *Lancet* 2006 May 20-26; 367(9523): 1645-1646. NRCBL: 12.4.1. SC: le.

Chervenak, Frank A.; McCullough, Laurence B. Conscientious objection in medicine: author did not meet standards of argument based ethics [letter]. *BMJ: British Medical Journal* 2006 February 18; 332(7538): 425. NRCBL: 12.4.3; 12.3; 8.1.

Cocon Group; Moreau, Caroline; Bajos, Nathalie; Bouyer, Jean. Access to health care for induced abortions. Analysis by means of a French national survey. *European Journal of Public Health* 2004 December; 14(4): 369-374. NRCBL: 12.4.2; 12.4.3; 12.5.2. SC: em.

Coleman, Karen. The politics of abortion in Australia: freedom, church, and state. *Feminist Review* 1988 Spring; (29): 75-97. NRCBL: 12.4.2; 12.5.1.

Collett, Teresa Stanton. Transporting minors for immoral purposes: the case of the Child Custody Protection Act and the Child Interstate Abortions Notification Act. *Health Matrix: The Journal of Law-Medicine* 2006 Winter; 16(1): 107-150. NRCBL: 12.4.2; 11.2; 8.3.2. SC: le.

Crawford, Amy E. Under siege: freedom of choice and the statutory ban on abortions on military bases. *University of Chicago Law Review* 2004 Fall; 71(4): 1549-1582. NRCBL: 12.4.1; 1.3.5. SC: le.

Cupich, Blase J. Abortion and public policy: conditions for the debate. *America* 2006 September 11; 195(6): 19-20. NRCBL: 12.4.1; 12.4.4; 1.2. SC: le.

Dailard, Cynthia. What Lawrence v. Texas says about the history and future of reproductive rights. *Fordham Urban Law Journal* 2004 March; 31(3): 717-723. NRCBL: 12.4.1; 10. SC: le.

Davey, Monica. Ban on most abortions advances in South Dakota; most sweeping ban by a state in years. *New York Times* 2006 February 23; p. A14. NRCBL: 12.4.1. SC: po.

Davey, Monica. South Dakota bans abortion, setting up a battle. *New York Times* 2006 March 7; p. A1, A14. NRCBL: 12.4.1; 21.1. SC: po.

Day, Michael. Abortion should be made easier, charity says [news]. *BMJ: British Medical Journal* 2006 December 2; 333(7579): 1139. NRCBL: 12.4.1. SC: le; em. Identifiers: United Kingdom (Great Britain).

Dayton, Cornelia Hughes. Taking the trade: abortion and gender relations in an eighteenth-century New England village. *In:* Kennedy, Kathleen; Ullman, Sharon, eds. Sexual Borderlands: Constructing an American Sexual Past. Columbus: Ohio State University Press; 2003: 50-82. NRCBL: 12.4.1; 12.5.1.

Dyer, Clare. Woman loses fight for parents' right to know of abortion advice [news]. *BMJ: British Medical Journal* 2006 January 28; 332(7535): 198. NRCBL: 12.4.2; 8.4; 8.3.2. SC: le. Identifiers: United Kingdom (Great Britain).

Ehrlich, J. Shoshanna. Choosing abortion: teens who make the decision without parental involvement. *Gender Issues* 2003 Spring; 21(2): 3-39. NRCBL: 12.4.2; 8.3.2. SC: le. Identifiers: Bellotti v. Baird.

Faigman, David L. The right to be let alone: privacy and the problem of defining life and death. *In his:* Laboratory

---

NRCBL: National Reference Center for Bioethics Literature Classification Scheme   See inside front cover for terms.

15

of Justice: The Supreme Court's 200-Year Struggle To Integrate Science and the Law. New York: Times Books/ Henry Holt; 2004: 205-250. NRCBL: 12.4.1; 20.7; 20.5.1. SC: le.

Fisher, Anthony. The duties of a Catholic politician with respect to bio-lawmaking. *Notre Dame Journal of Law, Ethics and Public Policy* 2006; 20(1): 89-123. NRCBL: 12.4.1; 1.2; 1.3.5. SC: le.

Forsythe, Clarke D.; Presser, Stephen B. The tragic failure of Roe v. Wade: why abortion should be returned to the states. *Texas Review of Law and Politics* 2005 Fall; 10(1): 85-170. NRCBL: 12.4.2; 9.5.5. SC: le.

Foss, Tara D. Privacy issues for girls are in the news and in BJN [editorial]. *British Journal of Nursing* 2006 January 26-February 8; 15(2): 65. NRCBL: 12.4.2; 8.3.2; 8.4. SC: le. Identifiers: United Kingdom (Great Britain).

Gerson, Chad M. Toward an international standard of abortion rights: two obstacles. *Chicago Journal of International Law* 2005; 5: 753-761. NRCBL: 12.4.1; 21.1; 11.1. SC: le.

Gevers, Sjef. Abortion legislation and the future of the 'counseling model'. *European Journal of Health Law* 2006 April; 13(1): 27-40. NRCBL: 12.4.1; 12.5.3. SC: le.

Greenhouse, Linda. Abortion opponents win dispute. *New York Times* 2006 March 1; p. A14. NRCBL: 12.4.1. SC: po.

Greenhouse, Linda. Justices reaffirm abortion access for emergencies. *New York Times* 2006 January 19; p. A1, A18. NRCBL: 12.4.1. SC: po.

Greenhouse, Linda. Justices to review federal ban on disputed abortion method; case may hinge on Alito, Court's newest member. *New York Times* 2006 February 22; p. A1, A14. NRCBL: 12.4.1. SC: po.

Hagen, John D., Jr. Rights talk and its remedies: the jurisprudence of Mary Ann Glendon. *America* 2006 January 2-9; 194(1): 14-16. NRCBL: 12.4.1; 1.3.8; 1.2.

Harper, Cynthia C.; Henderson, Jillian T.; Darney, Philip D. Abortion in the United States. *Annual Review of Public Health* 2005 April; 26: 501-512. NRCBL: 12.4.1; 12.5.1.

Himmelweit, Susan. More than 'a woman's right to choose'? *Feminist Review* 1988 Spring; (29): 38-56. NRCBL: 12.4.2.

Hitt, Jack. Pro-life nation: what happens when you completely criminalize abortion? Over the last eight years, El Salvador has found out. *New York Times Magazine* 2006 April 9; p. 40-47, 62, 72, 74. NRCBL: 12.4.1; 12.5.1; 12.3.

Hlaca, Nenad. Abortion Act and incidence of legal abortions in the Republic of Croatia. *Bulletin of Medical Ethics*

2006 April-May; (214): 26-28. NRCBL: 12.4.1; 12.5.1. SC: em.

Hulse, Carl. Senate removes abortion option for young girls. *New York Times* 2006 July 26; p. A1, A15. NRCBL: 12.4.2; 8.3.2; 12.4.3. SC: po.

Irish Women's Abortion Support Group. Across the water. *Feminist Review* 1988 Spring; (29): 64-71. NRCBL: 12.4.2; 12.5.1.

Jorns, Amalia W. Challenging warrantless inspections of abortion providers: a new constitutional strategy. *Columbia Law Review* 2005 June; 105(5): 1563-1596. NRCBL: 12.4.4; 12.4.2. SC: le.

Joyce, Theodore; Kaestner, Robert; Colman, Silvie. Changes in abortions and births and the Texas Parental Notification Law. *New England Journal of Medicine* 2006 March 9; 354(10): 1031- 1038. NRCBL: 12.4.2; 8.3.2; 12.5.2. SC: le; em.

Abstract: BACKGROUND: On January 1, 2000, Texas began enforcement of a law that requires physicians to notify a parent of a minor child seeking an abortion at least 48 hours before the procedure. METHODS: We assessed changes in the rates in Texas of abortions and births (events per 1000 age-specific population) before enforcement of the parental notification law (1998 to 1999) and after enforcement (2000 to 2002). We did this by comparing the rate changes among minors 15 to 17 years of age at the time of conception (i.e., those who were subject to the law) with those of teens 18 years of age at the time of conception (i.e., those who were not subject to the law). RESULTS: After enforcement of the law, abortion rates fell by 11 percent among 15-year-olds (rate ratio, 0.89; 95 percent confidence interval, 0.83 to 0.94), 20 percent among 16-year-olds (rate ratio, 0.80; 95 percent confidence interval, 0.76 to 0.85), and 16 percent among 17-year- olds (rate ratio 0.84; 95 percent confidence interval, 0.80 to 0.87), relative to the rates among 18-year-olds. Among the subgroup of minors 17.50 to 17.74 years of age at the time of conception (who would have been subject to the parental notification law in early pregnancy), birth rates rose by 4 percent relative to those of teens 18.00 to 18.24 years of age (rate ratio, 1.04; 95 percent confidence interval, 1.00 to 1.08). The adjusted odds ratio for having an abortion after 12 weeks' gestation among minors 17.50 to 17.74 years of age as compared with 18-year-olds was 1.34 (95 percent confidence interval, 1.10 to 1.62). CONCLUSIONS: The Texas parental notification law was associated with a decline in abortion rates among minors from 15 to 17 years of age. It was also associated with increased birth rates and rates of abortion during the second trimester among a subgroup of minors who were 17.50 to 17.74 years of age at the time of conception. Copyright 2006 Massachusetts Medical Society.

Kaminer, Wendy. Partial-truth abortion bans [op-ed]. *Free Inquiry* 2006 June-July; 26(4): 17-18. NRCBL: 12.4.1.

Kelly, Kevin T. Carhart v. Gonzales: rethinking Stenberg and the partial-birth abortion ban. *Jurimetrics* 2006 Spring; 46(3): 353-372. NRCBL: 12.4.2. SC: le.

Kendall, Christopher C. New York v. Sullivan: shhh . . . don't say the "A" word! Another outcome-oriented abor-

---

tion decision. *John Marshall Law Review* 1990 Summer; 23(4): 753-770. NRCBL: 12.4.2. SC: le.

Kennedy, Ian; Grubb, Andrew. Abortion. *In their:* Medical Law. 3rd ed. London: Butterworths; 2005: 1405-1491. NRCBL: 12.4.1. SC: le.

Keown, John. Back to the future of abortion law: Roe's rejection of America's history and traditions. *Issues in Law and Medicine* 2006 Summer; 22(1): 3-37. NRCBL: 12.4.1; 2.2. SC: an; le.

Kissling, Frances. Should abortion be prevented? *Conscience* 2006-2007 Winter; 27(4): 13-16. NRCBL: 12.4.2; 12.3; 11.1; 12.5.1. SC: le.

Larijani, B.; Zahedi, F. Changing parameters for abortion in Iran. *Indian Journal of Medical Ethics* 2006 October-December; 3(4): 130-131. NRCBL: 12.4.1; 1.2.

Law, Nathaniel. Abortion: Supreme Court avoids disturbing abortion precedents by ruling on grounds of remedy — Ayotte v. Planned Parenthood of Northern New England. *Journal of Law, Medicine and Ethics* 2006 Summer; 34(2): 469-471. NRCBL: 12.4.1. SC: le.

Lehren, Andrew; Leland, John. Scant drop seen in abortions if parents are told. *New York Times* 2006 March 6; p. A1, A18. NRCBL: 12.4.2; 8.3.2. SC: po.

Lueck, Jared C. Roe v. Wade and its Supreme Court progeny. *Journal of Contemporary Legal Issues* 2004; 14(1): 209-214. NRCBL: 12.4.4; 12.1; 9.5.5.

Lugosi, Charles I. When abortion was a crime: a historical perspective. *University of Detroit Mercy Law Review* 2006 Winter; 83(2): 51-69. NRCBL: 12.4.2; 1.3.5. SC: le.

Maio, Monica. Labor pains: the undue burden of forcing a woman to carry a non-viable fetus to term. *Journal of Law and Family Studies* 2005; 7(2): 459-474. NRCBL: 12.4.2; 12.4.3. SC: le.

Martin, Deanna. Abortion consent law before Ind. (Indiana) legislature: doctor would say conception begins life. *Washington Post* 2006 February 12; p. A10. NRCBL: 12.4.1. SC: po.

Mavroforou, A.; Michalodimitrakis, E. The British Abortion Act (1967) and the interests of the foetus. *Medicine and Law: World Association for Medical Law* 2006 March; 25(1): 175-188. NRCBL: 12.4.2; 12.3; 4.4. SC: le.
Abstract: This article examines ethical issues on the rights and interests of the unborn foetus, an issue that remains highly contentious. Furthermore, it attempts to investigate how well the British legislation fits with the foetus and pregnant woman's rights and interests. "Pro-life" and "pro-choice" groups have provided extensive arguments for and against. One important theoretical issue rests on whether foetuses are human beings in the moral sense, in which all human beings have full and equal moral rights. What constitutes personhood is a matter of moral decision and is not one of scientific fact and thus it consists of all persons, rather than all genetically human entities. It is persons who invent moral rights and who are capable of respecting them. Legislators in Britain have sidestepped the ethical debate on abortion by opting for the pragmatic course of permitting abortion in a limited range of circumstances and thus the Abortion Act 1967 has failed to address the status of the foetus, or indeed the rights of any of the parties concerned. Thus, although the Act supports the interests of the foetus capable of free existence by lowering the foetal age to 24 weeks after which termination is not permissible, the legislators have accepted that the rights of the woman outweigh those of the foetus and if a woman's own life or health is in danger then even a late abortion is the best choice.

McDonagh, Eileen. Abortion rights after South Dakota. *Free Inquiry* 2006 June-July; 26(4): 34-38. NRCBL: 12.4.1.

McGregor, Murray; Moore, Rory. The constitutionality of abortion on request in South Africa. *E Law: Murdoch University Electronic Journal of Law* 1995 December; 2(3): 32 p. [Online]. Accessed: http://www.murdoch.edu.au/elaw/issues/v2n3/moore23.html [2006 June 29]. NRCBL: 12.4.1. SC: le.

McKinley, James C., Jr. Nicaragua eliminates last exception to strict anti-abortion law. *New York Times* 2006 November 20; p. A5. NRCBL: 12.4.1. SC: po.

McNaughton, Heathe Luz; Mitchell, Ellen M.H.; Hernandez, Emilia G.; Padilla, Karen; Blandon, Marta Maria. Patient privacy and conflicting legal and ethical obligations in El Salvador: reporting of unlawful abortions. *American Journal of Public Health* 2006 November; 96(11): 1927-1933. NRCBL: 12.4.2; 12.4.3; 8.4. SC: le.
Abstract: Postabortion care providers who breach patient confidentiality endanger women's health and violate ethics. A 1998 abortion ban in El Salvador likely spurred an increase in the number of women investigated, because many women were reported to legal authorities by health care providers. Having analyzed safeguards of confidentiality in laws and ethical guidelines, we obtained information from legal records on women prosecuted from 1998 to 2003 and identified factors that may lead to reporting through a survey of obstetrician-gynecologists (n=110). Although ethical and human rights standards oblige providers to respect patients' privacy, 80% of obstetrician-gynecologists mistakenly believed reporting was required. Most respondents (86%) knew that women delay seeking care because of fear of prosecution, yet a majority (56%) participated in notification of legal authorities.

Meehan, Mary. How the Supremes flunked history. *Human Life Review* 2006 Spring; 32(2): 41-51. NRCBL: 12.4.1; 12.4.4.

Moses, Michael F. Casey and its impact on abortion regulation. *Fordham Urban Law Journal* 2004 March; 31(3): 805-815. NRCBL: 12.4.1. SC: le.

O'Day, Ken. Intrinsic value and investment. *Utilitas* 1999 July; 11(2): 194-214. NRCBL: 12.4.2; 1.1; 1.2. SC: an.

Petersen, Kerry. Abortion in Australia: a legal misconception. *Australian Health Review* 2005 May; 29(2): 142-145. NRCBL: 12.4.1. SC: le.

NRCBL: National Reference Center for Bioethics Literature Classification Scheme   See inside front cover for terms.

17

Press, Eyal. My father's abortion war; When the abortion provider Dr. Barnett Slepian was murdered outside Buffalo, one of his colleagues decided to keep his own nearby office open. How America's most polarizing conflict came to my family's doorstep. *New York Times Magazine* 2006 January 22; p. 56-61. NRCBL: 12.4.3. SC: po.

Rabkin, Rebecca. From Kierkegaard to Kennedy: existentialist philosophy in the Supreme Court's decision in Planned Parenthood v. Casey and its effect on the right to privacy. *Hastings Constitutional Law Quarterly* 2004 Summer; 31(4): 611-635. NRCBL: 12.4.4; 1.1. SC: le.

Rafferty, Philip. Roe v. Wade: a scandal upon the court. *Rutgers Journal of Law and Religion* 2005; 7(1): pp. 84 [Online] Accessed: http://org.law.rutgers.edu/publications/law-religion/articles/7_1_1.pdf [2006 December 5]. NRCBL: 12.4.2; 9.5.5. SC: le.

Ramsey, Carolyn B. Restructuring the debate over fetal homicide laws. *Ohio State Law Journal* 2006; 67(4): 721-782. NRCBL: 12.4.2. SC: le.

Randolph, A. Raymond. Before Roe v. Wade: Judge Friendly's draft abortion opinion. *Harvard Journal of Law and Public Policy* 2006 Summer; 29(3): 1035-1062. NRCBL: 12.4.1; 12.4.2; 12.2.

Reyes, Heathe Luz McNaughton; Hord, Charlotte E.; Mitchell, Ellen M.H.; Blandon, Marta Maria. Invoking health and human rights to ensure access to legal abortion: the case of a nine-year old girl from Nicaragua. *Health and Human Rights: An International Journal* 2006; 9(2): 62-86. NRCBL: 12.4.2; 9.5.7; 21.1. SC: cs.

Richards, Erica. Loss of potential parenthood as a statutory solution to the conflict between wrongful death remedies and Roe v. Wade. *Washington and Lee Law Review* 2006 Spring; 63(2): 809-848. NRCBL: 12.4.2; 9.2. SC: le.

Rosen, Jeffrey. The day after Roe. *Atlantic Monthly* 2006 June; 297(5): 56-66. NRCBL: 12.4.2; 9.5.5. Identifiers: Roe v. Wade.

Rudoren, Jodi. Kansas' top court limits abortion record search; attorney general's inquiry will continue. *New York Times* 2006 February 4; p. A7. NRCBL: 12.4.1. SC: po.

Samant, Padmaja. Learning to be humane. *Indian Journal of Medical Ethics* 2006 April-June; 3(2): 72. NRCBL: 12.4.2; 11.2; 8.1; 7.1;. SC: cs. Comments: Conflict between the law and ethics while researching. Indian Journal of Medical Ethics 2006 April-June; 3(2): 69.

Saunders, William L., Jr. Lethal experimentation on human beings: Roe's effect on bioethics. *Fordham Urban Law Journal* 2004 March; 31(3): 817-830. NRCBL: 12.4.1; 18.5.4; 14.5; 15.1.

Sedler, Robert A. The Supreme Court will not overrule Roe v. Wade. *Hofstra Law Review* 2006 Spring; 34(3): 1207-1213. NRCBL: 12.4.1; 1.3.5.

Side, Katherine. Contract, charity, and honorable entitlement: social citizenship and the 1967 Abortion Act in Northern Ireland after the Good Friday Agreement. *Social Politics* 2006 Spring; 13(1): 89-116. NRCBL: 12.4.2; 9.5.5; 9.2; 12.5.1.

Solomon, Deborah. Abortion issue moves to states: shift on federal bench spurs governors, legislators to battle Roe. *Wall Street Journal* 2006 March 9; p. A4. NRCBL: 12.4.1. SC: po.

South Africa. Minister of Health. Choice on Termination of Pregnancy Amendment Bill [B72-2003]. Government Gazette No. 25725 2003 November 13: 1-5. NRCBL: 12.4.4. SC: le.

South Africa. The Presidency. No. 38 of 2004: Choice of Termination of Pregnancy Amendment Act, 2004 (Assented to 4 February 2005). Government of Gazette, No. 27267, 2005 February 11; (476): 5 p. NRCBL: 12.4.4. SC: le.

Spanish Women's Abortion Support Group. Spanish women and the Alton Bill. *Feminist Review* 1988 Spring; (29): 72-74. NRCBL: 12.4.2; 12.5.1; 12.4.3; 12.3; 8.1. Identifiers: Spain; European Union.

Suver, Betsy West. The obstacles to a constitutional partial birth abortion ban: how state legislatures have failed and the shortcomings of President George W. Bush's Partial Birth Abortion Ban Act of 2003. *University of Dayton Law Review* 2004-2005 Fall; 30(1): 149-169. NRCBL: 12.4.1. SC: le.

United States. Congress. An act to prohibit the procedure commonly known as partial-birth abortion. Washington, DC: U.S. G.P.O., 2003. 8 p. [Online]. Accessed: http://frwebgate.access.gpo.gov/cgi-bin/getdoc.cgi?dbname=108_cong_public_laws&docid=f: publ105.108.pdf [2007 November 5]. NRCBL: 12.4.4. SC: le. Identifiers: Partial-Birth Abortion Ban Act of 2003. Note: Public Law 108-105, 108th Congress, approved November 5, 2003. (117 Statutes at Large 1201) Codified as 18 United States Code 1531.

United States. Congress. An act to protect infants who are born alive. Washington, DC: U.S. G.P.O., 2002. 1 p. [Online]. Accessed: http://frwebgate.access.gpo.gov/cgi-bin/getdoc.cgi?dbname=107_cong_public_laws&docid=f: publ207.107.pdf [2007 March 2]. NRCBL: 12.4.4; 4.4; 9.5.8. SC: le. Identifiers: Born-Alive Infants Protection Act of 2002. Note: Public Law 107-207, 107th Congress, approved August 5, 2002. (116 Statutes at Large 926) Codified as 1 United States Code 8.

United States. Congress. House. A bill to amend title 18, United States Code, to prevent the transportation of minors in circumvention of certain laws relating to abortion. Washington, DC: U.S. G.P.O., 2005. 10 p. [Online]. Accessed: http://frwebgate.access.gpo.gov/cgi-bin/useftp.cgi?IPaddress=162.140.64.21&filename=

h748ih.pdf&directory=/diskb/wais/data/109_cong_bills [2006 July 24]. NRCBL: 12.4.2; 8.3.2; 9.5.7; 12.4.4. SC: le. Identifiers: Child Interstate Abortion Notification Act. Note: H.R. 748, 109th Congress, 1st session. Introduced by Rep. Ros-Lehtinen, February 10, 2005. Referred to the Committee on the Judiciary.

United States. Congress. House. A bill to ensure that women seeking an abortion are fully informed regarding the pain experienced by their unborn child. Washington, DC: U.S. G.P.O., 2006. 23 p. [Online]. Accessed: http://frwebgate.access.gpo.gov/cgi-bin/useftp.cgi? IPaddress=162.140.64.21&filename=h6099ih.pdf& directory=/diskb/wais/data/109_cong_bills [2006 November 20]. NRCBL: 12.4.2. SC: le. Identifiers: Unborn Child Pain Awareness Act of 2006. Note: H.R. 6099, 109th Congress, 2d session. Introduced by Rep. Smith, September 19, 2006. Referred to the Committee on Energy and Commerce.

United States. Congress. House. A bill to prohibit certain abortions. Washington, DC: U.S. G.P.O., 2005. 2 p. [Online]. Accessed: http://frwebgate.access.gpo.gov/cgi-bin/ useftp.cgi?IPaddress=162.140.64.21&filename= h3746ih.pdf&directory=/diskb/wais/data/109_cong_bills [2006 June 7]. NRCBL: 12.4.2. SC: le. Identifiers: Late Term Abortion Restriction Act. Note: H.R. 3746, 109th Congress, 1st session. Introduced by Rep. Hoyer, September 13, 2005. Referred to the Committee on Energy and Commerce and to the Committee on the Judiciary.

United States. Congress. House. A bill to provide for parental notification and intervention in the case of a minor seeking an abortion. Washington, DC: U.S. G.P.O., 2005. 4 p. [Online]. Accessed: http://frwebgate.access.gpo.gov/ cgi-bin/getdoc.cgi?dbname=109_cong_bills&docid= f:h2971ih.txt.pdf [2006 June 7]. NRCBL: 12.4.2; 8.3.2. SC: le. Identifiers: Parental Notification and Intervention Act of 2005. Note: H.R. 2971, 109th Congress, 1st session. Introduced by Rep. Musgrave, June 17, 2005. Referred to the Committee on the Judiciary.

United States. Congress. Senate. A bill to amend title 18, United States Code, to prohibit taking minors across State lines in circumvention of laws requiring the involvement of parents in abortion decisions. Washington, DC: U.S. G.P.O., 2005. 5 p. [Online]. Accessed: http://frwebgate. access.gpo.gov/cgi-bin/useftp.cgi?IPaddress=162.140.64 .21&filename=s403pcs.pdf&directory=/diskb/wais/data/ 109_cong_bills [2006 July 17]. NRCBL: 12.4.2; 8.3.2; 9.5.7; 12.4.4. SC: le. Identifiers: Child Custody Protection Act. Note: S.403, 109th Congress, 1st session. Introduced by Sen. Ensign, February 16, 2005.

United States. Congress. Senate. A bill to ensure that women seeking an abortion are fully informed regarding the pain experienced by their unborn child. Washington, DC: U.S. G.P.O., 2005. 21 p. [Online]. Accessed: http://frwebgate.access.gpo.gov/cgi-bin/useftp.cgi?

IPaddress=162.140.64.21&filename=s51is.pdf& directory=/diskb/wais/data/109_cong_bills [2006 May 8]. NRCBL: 12.4.2; 8.3.5; 9.5.5. SC: le. Identifiers: Unborn Child Pain Awareness Act of 2005. Note: S. 51, 109th Congress, 1st session. Introduced by Sen. Sam Brownback, January 24, 2005. Referred to the Committee on Health, Education, Labor, and Pensions.

United States. Congress. Senate. A bill to protect, consistent with Roe v. Wade, a woman's freedom to choose to bear a child or terminate a pregnancy, and for other purposes. Washington, DC: U.S. G.P.O., 2006. 8 p. [Online]. Accessed: http://frwebgate.access.gpo.gov/cgi-bin/ getdoc.cgi?dbname=109_cong_bills&docid= f:s2593is.txt.pdf [2006 June 7]. NRCBL: 12.4.2; 14.1; 9.5.5. SC: le. Identifiers: Freedom of Choice Act. Note: S. 2593, 109th Congress, 2nd session. Introduced by Sen. Boxer, April 6, 2006. Referred to the Committee on the Judiciary.

United States. Congress. Senate. An act to amend title 18, United States Code, to prohibit taking minors across State lines in circumvention of laws requiring the involvement of parents in abortion decisions. Washington, DC: U.S. G.P.O., 2006. 6 p. [Online]. Accessed: http://frwebgate. access.gpo.gov/cgi-bin/useftp.cgi?IPaddress=162.140.64 .21&filename=s403es.pdf&directory=/diskb/wais/ data/109_cong_bills [2006 July 25]. NRCBL: 12.4.2; 8.3.2; 9.5.7; 12.4.4. SC: le. Identifiers: Child Custody Protection Act. Note: S. 403, 109th Congress, 2d session. Passed the Senate July 25, 2006.

United States. Court of Appeals. Ninth Circuit. Planned Parenthood of Idaho v. Wasden [Date of Decision: 2004 July 16]. *Federal Reporter*, 3d Series, 2004; 376: 908-944. NRCBL: 12.4.4. SC: le.

Abstract: Court Decision: 376 Federal Reporter, 3d Series 908; 2004 July 16 (date of decision). The U.S. Court of Appeals for the Ninth Circuit reversed a lower court decision and held that Idaho's parental consent to abortion law was unconstitutional because it did not include a constitutionally valid medical emergency provision. Idaho's parental consent law contained an exception which allowed a minor to obtain an abortion without parental consent or a court order if the minor had a sudden, unexpected, and abnormal medical condition which required an immediate abortion to save her life or prevent serious risk of permanent, substantial injury. The court first rejected the state's argument that "sudden and unexpected" referred to the moment of diagnosis because the words referred to a physical condition (not a diagnosis), the word "diagnosis" did not appear in the statute, and every diagnosis could be considered sudden and unexpected. The court also noted that even a normal pregnancy could trigger a need for an immediate abortion in some or most women. Moreover, the court found that the onset of the underlying condition of many medical problems is often different from the time of diagnosis. The court declined to disregard the words "sudden," "unexpected," and "abnormal" because the words were pivotal to the meaning of the statute and held that the plain meaning of the medical emergency restriction was unconstitutionally narrow and interfered with a woman's right to undergo an abortion if her health was threatened by continuing her pregnancy. Moreover, the court held that the state's reading of the statute was neither "fairly possible" nor "readily apparent." The

NRCBL: National Reference Center for Bioethics Literature Classification Scheme   See inside front cover for terms.

19

court also held that the emergency medical provision was unconstitutional because the time period in which a decision could be rendered for a judicial bypass was open-ended, the deadline for filing a notice of appeal was unspecified, and the timeframe for the Idaho appellate process was indeterminate. Accordingly, there was no way an Idaho physician could be reasonably certain that an emergency abortion must be performed. Furthermore, the court did not find a greater interest in involving a pregnant minor's family in an emergency abortion than in any other medical emergency requiring immediate treatment and saw no reason for singling out physicians in the former situation to criminal liability. Finally, the court held that the offending provisions could not be severed from the law because the unconstitutional portion of the law was indispensable to its operation as the Legislature intended. The remainder of the law could not stand on its own because any parental consent statute must have a medical emergency exception.

University of Cape Town. Maternal and Child Health Information and Resource Centre, Child Health Unit. The Choice on Termination of Pregnancy Act, 1996: we consider the provisions of the new Act, its role in improving public health and its implementation. *MCH News* 1996 December; (4): 6-8. NRCBL: 12.4.1.

West, J. Andrew. Defining the limits of conscientious objection in health care. *Newsletter on Philosophy and Law* 2005 Fall; 05(1): 25-34. NRCBL: 12.4.3; 12.3; 8.1; 11.3; 8.3.1. SC: an.

Woliver, Laura R. Abortion politics: discourses on lives. *In her:* The Political Geographies of Pregnancy. Urbana: University of Illinois Press; 2002: 82-114. NRCBL: 12.4.1.

Wright, Alexi A.; Katz, Ingrid T. Roe versus reality — abortion and women's health. *New England Journal of Medicine* 2006 July 6; 355(1): 1-3, 5-9. NRCBL: 12.4.1; 12.1; 12.5.1. SC: le. Identifiers: Stenberg v. Carhart; Kenneth Edelin.

ABORTION/ MORAL AND RELIGIOUS ASPECTS

European court of human rights: ECHR 2003/1 Case of Pichon and Sajous v. France, 2 October 2001, no. 49853/99. *European Journal of Health Law* 2003 March; 10(1): 66-69. NRCBL: 12.3; 11.1; 9.7. SC: le. Identifiers: contraceptive pills; abortifacients.

Barclay, Linda. Rights, intrinsic values and the politics of abortion. *Utilitas* 1999 July; 11(2): 215-229. NRCBL: 12.3; 1.1. SC: an.

Beckwith, Francis J. Defending abortion philosophically: a review of David Boonin's A Defense of Abortion [book review]. *Journal of Medicine and Philosophy* 2006 April; 31(2): 177-203. NRCBL: 12.3; 1.1; 4.4.

Cahill, Lisa Sowle. Reproduction and early life. *In her:* Theological Bioethics: Participation, Justice, and Change. Washington, DC: Georgetown University Press; 2005: 169-210. NRCBL: 12.3; 1.2; 14.1.

Campbell, Pamela. Raising awareness of the ethical issues surrounding termination of pregnancy for fetal abnormalities. *In:* Bartter, Karen, ed. Ethical Issues in Advanced Nursing Practice. Boston: Butterworth-Heinemann; 2001: 51-65. NRCBL: 12.3.

Card, Robert F. Two puzzles for Marquis's conservative view on abortion. *Bioethics* 2006 September; 20(5): 264-277. NRCBL: 12.3. SC: an.

Abstract: Don Marquis argues that abortion is morally wrong in most cases since it deprives the fetus of the value of its future. I criticize Marquis's argument for the modified conservative view by adopting an argumentative strategy in which I work within his basic account: if it is granted that his fundamental idea is sound, what follows about the morality of abortion? I conclude that Marquis is faced with a dilemma: either his position must shift towards the extreme conservative view on which abortion is never morally permissible, or he must abandon any recognizably conservative view. This dilemma suggests that Marquis's view is either deeply implausible or that he cannot use this argument to successfully support his preferred position.

Eberl, Jason T.; Koch-Hershenov, Rose; Hershenov, David. The metaphysical nuances of hylomorphism [letter and reply]. *National Catholic Bioethics Quarterly* 2006 Spring; 6(1): 9-12. NRCBL: 12.3; 1.1; 4.4; 14.1.

Fogel, Susan Berke; Rivera, Lourdes A. Saving Roe is not enough: when religion controls healthcare. *Fordham Urban Law Journal* 2004 March; 31(3): 725-749. NRCBL: 12.3; 12.4.2; 9.5.5. SC: le.

Haldane, John; Lee, Patrick. Aquinas, the embryo and the ethics of abortion. *Philosophy* 2003 March; 78(2): 255-278. NRCBL: 12.3; 4.4.

Harley, Karen. The abortion issue and advanced nursing practice. *In:* Bartter, Karen, ed. Ethical Issues in Advanced Nursing Practice. Boston: Butterworth-Heinemann; 2001: 31-50. NRCBL: 12.3.

Haslett, D.W. On life, death, and abortion. *Utilitas* 1996 July; 8(2): 159-189. NRCBL: 12.3; 1.1; 20.2.1; 20.3.1. SC: an.

Hedayat, K.M.; Shooshtarizadeh, P.; Raza, M. Therapeutic abortion in Islam: contemporary views of Muslim Shiite scholars and effect of recent Iranian legislation. *Journal of Medical Ethics* 2006 November; 32(11): 652-657. NRCBL: 12.3; 1.2.

Abstract: Abortion is forbidden under normal circumstances by nearly all the major world religions. Traditionally, abortion was not deemed permissible by Muslim scholars. Shiite scholars considered it forbidden after implantation of the fertilised ovum. However, Sunni scholars have held various opinions on the matter, but all agreed that after 4 months gestation abortion was not permitted. In addition, classical Islamic scholarship had only considered threats to maternal health as a reason for therapeutic abortion. Recently, scholars have begun to consider the effect of severe fetal deformities on the mother, the families and society. This has led some scholars to reconsider the prohibition on abortion in limited circumstances. This article reviews the Islamic basis for the prohibition of abortion and the reasons for its justification. Contemporary rulings from leading Shiite scholars and from the Sunni school of thought are presented and reviewed. The status of abortion in Muslim countries is reviewed, with special emphasis on the therapeutic abortion law passed by the Iranian Parliament in 2003. This law approved therapeutic abortion before 16 weeks of gestation under limited circumstances, including medical conditions related to fetal and maternal health. Recent measures in Iran provide an opportunity for the Muslim scholars in other countries to review their traditional stance on abortion.

Hershenov, David B. Explaining the psychological appeal of viability. *National Catholic Bioethics Quarterly* 2006 Winter; 6(4): 681-686. NRCBL: 12.3; 4.4.

Joffe, Carole. It's not just abortion, stupid — progressives and abortion. *Dissent* 2005 Winter; 37(2): 91-96. NRCBL: 12.3; 21.1. SC: an.

Kaczor, Christopher. The violinist and double-effect reasoning. *National Catholic Bioethics Quarterly* 2006 Winter; 6(4): 661-669. NRCBL: 12.3; 4.4; 1.1.

Leonard Hammer. Abortion objection in the United Kingdom within the framework of the European Convention on Human Rights and Fundamental Freedoms. *European Human Rights Law Review* 1999; [1999] 6: 564-575. NRCBL: 12.3; 8.1. SC: le.

Marquis, Don. Abortion and the beginning and end of human life. *Journal of Law, Medicine, and Ethics* 2006 Spring; 34(1): 16-25. NRCBL: 12.3; 4.4. SC: le.

Marquis, Don. Does metaphysics have implications for the morality of abortion? *Southwest Philosophy Review* 2002 January; 18(1): 73-78. NRCBL: 12.3.

McMahan, Jeff. Paradoxes of abortion and prenatal injury. *Ethics* 2006 July; 116(4): 625-655. NRCBL: 12.3; 4.4; 9.5.8; 9.5.5; 12.4.2. SC: le.

Mills, Catherine. Technology, embodiment and abortion. *Internal Medicine Journal* 2005 July; 35(7): 427-428. NRCBL: 12.3; 5.1; 4.4; 12.5.1.

Murphy, Mark C. Pro-choice and presumption: a reply to Kenneth Einar Himma. *Faith and Philosophy* 2003 April; 20(2): 240-242. NRCBL: 12.3; 1.2.

Nadler, Richard. Judaism and abortion: the hijacking of a tradition. *Human Life Review* 2006 Winter; 32(1): 43-52. NRCBL: 12.3; 4.4; 1.2.

Oaks, Laury. Antiabortion positions and young women's life plans in contemporary Ireland. *Social Science and Medicine* 2003 May; 56(9): 1973-1986. NRCBL: 12.3; 9.5.5; 14.1. SC: an.

Perrett, Roy W. Buddhism, abortion and the middle way. *Asian Philosophy* 2000 July; 10(2): 101-114. NRCBL: 12.3; 1.2.

Popovsky, Mark. Mental anguish and the permissibility of abortion. *Conservative Judaism* 2006 Summer; 58(4): 3-21. NRCBL: 12.3; 1.2; 9.5.5.

Riga, Peter J. The authority of the Catholic Church over abortion. *Linacre Quarterly* 2006 May; 73(2): 194-196. NRCBL: 12.3; 1.2.

Rovie, Eric M. Abortion: approaches from virtue. *Auslegung* 2002 Winter-Spring; 25(2): 137-150. NRCBL: 12.3; 4.4; 1.1.

Shields, Jon A. Bioethical politics. *Society* 2006 March-April; 43(3): 19-24. NRCBL: 12.3; 18.5.4; 15.1.

Swope, Paul. El aborto: un fracaso de communicación [Abortion: a failure of communication]. *Persona y Bioética* 1999 February-May; 2(6): 165-176. NRCBL: 12.3.

Unsworth-Webb, John. Potential termination of pregnancy in a non-consenting minor. *Nursing Ethics* 2006 July; 13(4): 428-437. NRCBL: 12.3; 8.3.2; 8.3.4.
Abstract: The pregnancy of a 12-year-old girl provides the basis for a consideration of approaches to a dilemma brought about by conflicting expectations. Here, medical opinion is to reject action implied by the lack of Gillick competence and by a 'parental responsibility' claim adopted by the girl's mother. Construction of the dilemma and the subsequent process, which sought resolution, illustrates that the Gillick ruling, and other guidelines intended to be helpful, can prove to be less so.

Yu, Kaiming; Wang, Defen; Lin, Meili; Wang, Shixiong; Ren, Zaoriu; Qiu, Weiqin. Ethical issues of genetic counseling and artificial abortion. *In:* Döring, Ole; Chen, Renbiao, eds. Advances in Chinese Medical Ethics: Chinese and International Perspectives. Hamburg: Institut für Asienkunde; 2002: 421-426. NRCBL: 12.3; 15.2. Note: Proceedings of the Second Sino-German Interdisciplinary Symposium about Medical Ethics in China, Shanghai, 19-23 October, 1999.

ABORTION/ SOCIAL ASPECTS

Baird, Barbara. Abortion, questions, ethics, embodiment. *History Workshop Journal* 2001 Autumn; (52): 197-216. NRCBL: 12.5.1; 12.5.2. Identifiers: Australia.

Berer, Marge. Abortion: unfinished business. *Reproductive Health Matters* 1997 May; (9): 6-9. NRCBL: 12.5.1; 9.2; 12.1; 21.1. SC: le.

Berer, Marge. Whatever happened to 'a woman's right to choose'? *Feminist Review* 1988 Spring; (29): 24-37. NRCBL: 12.5.1; 12.4.2.

Bonner, Raymond. Debate on abortion pill in Australia becomes personal. *New York Times* 2006 February 10; p. A3. NRCBL: 12.5.1; 12.4.1. SC: po.

Ellwood, David. Late terminations of pregnancy — an obstetrician's perspective. *Australian Health Review* 2005 May; 29(2): 139-142. NRCBL: 12.5.2; 7.1.

Elul, Batya; Pearlman, Elizabeth; Sohaindo, Annik; Simonds, Wendy; Westhoff, Carolyn. In-depth interviews with medical abortion clients: thoughts on the

NRCBL: National Reference Center for Bioethics Literature Classification Scheme   See inside front cover for terms.

21

method and home administration of misoprostol. *Journal of the American Medical Women's Association* 2000; 55(3, Supplement): 169-172. NRCBL: 12.5.2; 9.7.

Ferree, Myra Marx. Resonance and radicalism: feminist framing in the abortion debates of the United States and Germany. *American Journal of Sociology* 2003 September; 109(2): 304-344. NRCBL: 12.5.1; 10; 21.7.

Fielding, Stephen L.; Edmunds, Emme; Schaff, Eric A. Having an abortion using mifepristone and home misoprostol: a qualitative analysis of women's experiences. *Perspectives on Sexual and Reproductive Health* 2002 January-February; 34(1): 34-40. NRCBL: 12.5.2; 9.7. SC: em.

Finer, Lawrence B.; Frohwirth, Lori F.; Dauphinee, Lindsay A.; Singh, Susheela; Moore, Ann M. Reasons U.S. women have abortions: quantitative and qualitative perspectives. *Perspectives on Sexual and Reproductive Health* 2005 September; 37(3): 110-118. NRCBL: 12.5.2. SC: em.

Finnie, Sarah; Foy, Robbie; Mather, Jean. The pathway to induced abortion: women's experiences and general practitioner attitudes. *Journal of Family Planning and Reproductive Health Care* 2006 January; 32(1): 15-18. NRCBL: 12.5.2; 9.5.5. SC: em.

Fischer, Richard L.; Schaeffer, Kathleen; Hunter, Robert L. Attitudes of obstetrics and gynecology residents toward abortion participation: a Philadelphia area survey. *Contraception* 2005 September; 72(3): 200-205. NRCBL: 12.5.2; 7.1. SC: em.

Guillaume, Agnes. The role of abortion in the fertility transition in Abidjan (Cote d'Ivoire) during the 1990s. *Population* 2003 November-December; 58(6): 657-685. NRCBL: 12.5.2; 11.1; 9.5.6.

Harvey, S. Marie; Beckman, Linda J.; Branch, Meredith Roberts. The relationship of contextual factors to women's perceptions of medical abortion. *Health Care for Women International* 2002 September; 23(6-7): 654-665. NRCBL: 12.5.2; 9.7. SC: em.

Harvey, S. Marie; Beckman, Linda J.; Castle, Mary Ann; Coeytaux, Francine. Knowledge and perceptions of medical abortion among potential users. *Family Planning Perspectives* 1995 September-October; 27(5): 203-207. NRCBL: 12.5.2; 9.7; 12.1. SC: em.

Harvey, S. Marie; Nichols, Mark D. Development and evaluation of the abortion attributes questionnaire. *Journal of Social Issues* 2005 March; 61(1): 95-107. NRCBL: 12.5.2. SC: em.

Heminger, Justin D. Big abortion: what the antiabortion movement can learn from big tobacco. *Catholic University Law Review* 2005 Summer; 54(4): 1273-1311. NRCBL: 12.5.1; 12.4.2. SC: le.

Hillier, Sheila. Women and population control in China: issues of sexuality, power and control. *Feminist Review* 1988 Spring; (29): 101-113. NRCBL: 12.5.1; 13.3.

Holmberg, Lars I.; Wahlberg, Vivian. The process of decision-making on abortion: a grounded theory study of young men in Sweden. *Journal of Adolescent Health* 2000 March; 26(3): 230-234. NRCBL: 12.5.2; 12.5.3. SC: em.

Huntington, Dale; Nawar, Laila; Abdel-Hady, Dalia. Women's perceptions of abortion in Egypt. *Reproductive Health Matters* 1997 May 5; (9): 101-107. NRCBL: 12.5.2; 12.5.1; 9.2; 1.2. Note: Abstract in English, French, and Spanish.

Hwang, Ann C.; Koyama, Atsuko; Taylor, Diana; Henderson, Jillian T.; Miller, Suellen. Advanced practice clinicians' interest in providing medical abortion: results of a California survey. *Perspectives on Sexual and Reproductive Health* 2005 June; 37(2): 92-97. NRCBL: 12.5.2; 4.1.1; 4.1.3. SC: em.

Ipas. India Country Office; Ganatra, Bela; Manning, Vinoj; Pallipamulla, Suranjeen Prasad. Medical Abortion in Bihar and Jharkhand: A Study of Service Providers, Chemists, Women and Men. Vasant, Vihar, New Delhi, India: India Country Office, Ipas, 2005; 56 p. [Online]. Accessed: http://www.ipas.org/publications/en/INDMEDAB_E05_en.pdf [2006 March 29]. NRCBL: 12.5.2; 9.7; 21.1. SC: em.

Jankowska, Hanna. The Reproductive Rights Campaign in Poland. *Women's Studies International Forum* 1993 May-June; 16(3): 291-296. NRCBL: 12.5.1; 9.5.5; 2.2.

Jebereanu, Laura. Abortion: pro and contra. *Penn Bioethics Journal* 2006; 2(2): 25-28. NRCBL: 12.5.2. SC: em.

Abstract: To kill a new life before it's born, to do an abortion. This is a problem of many generations. In the evolution of human civilization, the attitude concerning abortion was different in different cultures, periods, societies. The aim of our study is to evaluate the actual opinion and attitude of young persons, students, and residents in medicine in Timisoara city, and the situation of the whole country. We performed a questionnaire for 400 people, between the ages of 19 and 28 with superior studies. The group is composed of 320 (80%) women and 80 (20%) men. We accepted for recording and analyzing all the completed questionnaires. The questions referred to the topic of abortion in the antecedents, and asked if they had had one, how it affected the life of the women and her family, the circumstances of acceptance of abortion today, religious aspects and different other aspects.

Klick, Jonathan. Econometric analyses of U.S. abortion policy: a critical review. *Fordham Urban Law Journal* 2004 March; 31(3): 751-782. NRCBL: 12.5.1; 1.3.5; 10; 12.4.1.

Klick, Jonathan. Mandatory waiting periods for abortions and female mental health. *Health Matrix: The Journal of Law-Medicine* 2006 Winter; 16(1): 183-208. NRCBL: 12.5.3; 12.4.2. SC: em.

Levine, Phillip B. Abortion policy and the economics of fertility. *Society* 2004 May-June; 41(4): 79-85. NRCBL: 12.5.1.

Mason, Linda. Referral to a National Health Service-funded abortion clinic. *Journal of Family Planning and Reproductive Health Care* 2005 April; 31(2): 117-120. NRCBL: 12.5.1. SC: em.

Melgalve, I.; Lazdane, G.; Trapenciere, I.; Shannon, C.; Bracken, H.; Winikoff, B. Knowledge and attitudes about abortion legislation and abortion methods among abortion clients in Latvia. *European Journal of Contraception and Reproductive Health Care* 2005 September; 10(3): 143-150. NRCBL: 12.5.2; 12.4.1. SC: em.

Molyneux, Maxine. The politics of abortion in Nicaragua: revolutionary pragmatism — or feminism in the realm of necessity? *Feminist Review* 1988 Spring; (29): 114-132. NRCBL: 12.5.1; 12.4.2; 1.2.

Nie, Jing-Bao. Mainland Chinese people's moral views and experiences of abortion: a brief report. *In:* Döring, Ole; Chen, Renbiao, eds. Advances in Chinese Medical Ethics: Chinese and International Perspectives. Hamburg: Institut für Asienkunde; 2002: 279-289. NRCBL: 12.5.2. Note: Proceedings of the Second Sino-German Interdisciplinary Symposium about Medical Ethics in China, Shanghai, 19-23 October, 1999.

Oaks, Laury. Fetal spirithood and fetal personhood: the cultural construction of abortion in Japan. *Women's Studies International Forum* 1994 September-October; 17(5): 511-523. NRCBL: 12.5.1; 4.4; 2.2.

Oye-Adeniran, Boniface A.; Adewole, Isaac F.; Umoh, Augustine V.; Iwere, Ngozi; Gbadegesin, Abidoye. Induced abortion in Nigeria: findings from focus group discussion. *African Journal of Reproductive Health* 2005 April; 9(1): 133-141. NRCBL: 12.5.2; 21.1. SC: em.

Philipov, D.; Andreev, E.; Kharkova, T.; Shkolnikov, V. Induced abortion in Russia: recent trends and underreporting in surveys. *European Journal of Population* 2004; 20(2): 95-117. NRCBL: 12.5.2. SC: em.

Saleem, Sarah; Fikree, Fariyal F. The quest for small family size among Pakistani women — is voluntary termination of pregnancy a matter of choice or necessity? *Journal of the Pakistan Medical Association* 2005 July; 55(7): 288-291. NRCBL: 12.5.2; 11.1. SC: em.

Santelli, John S.; Speizer, Ilene S.; Avery, Alexis; Kendall, Carl. An exploration of the dimensions of pregnancy intentions among women choosing to terminate pregnancy or initiate prenatal care in New Orleans, Louisiana. *American Journal of Public Health* 2006 November; 96(11): 2009-2015. NRCBL: 12.5.1; 18.5.3; 12.5.2. SC: em.
  Abstract: OBJECTIVES: We examined pregnancy decisionmaking among women seeking abortion or prenatal care. METHODS: Conventional measures of pregnancy intentions were compared with newer measures in 1017 women seeking abortion. A reduced sample of abortion patients (142 African American women from New Orleans) was compared with 464 similar women entering prenatal care. RESULTS: Virtually all abortion patients reported the pregnancy as unintended; two thirds of prenatal patients reported the pregnancy as unintended. Reasons for seeking abortion related to life circumstances, including cost, readiness, not wanting any more children, marital status, relationship stability, and being too young. Abortion patients were more likely to report trying hard to avoid a pregnancy and not being in a relationship. They were less likely to report that their partner wanted a baby (odds ratio=0.10) or that they wanted a baby with their partner (odds ratio=0.13) than prenatal patients. CONCLUSIONS: Traditional measures of pregnancy intentions did not readily predict a woman's choice to continue or abort the pregnancy. Relationship with male partners, desire for a baby with the partner, and life circumstances were critical dimensions in pregnancy decisionmaking.

Simmons, Ann. Taking the judgement out of abortion. *Nursing New Zealand* 2005 February; 11(1): 26-27. NRCBL: 12.5.1. Identifiers: New Zealand.

Smyth, Lisa. Narratives of Irishness and the problem of abortion: the X case 1992. *Feminist Review* 1998 Autumn; 60: 61-83. NRCBL: 12.5.1; 12.4.2. SC: an; cs.

Szalai, Julia. Abortion in Hungary. *Feminist Review* 1988 Spring; (29): 98-100. NRCBL: 12.5.1; 12.4.2.

Wenger, Ashley A. Fetal pain legislation: subordinating sound medical findings to moral and political agendas. *Journal of Legal Medicine* 2006 December; 27(4): 459-476. NRCBL: 12.5.3; 12.4.2; 4.4. SC: le.

Wiebe, Ellen R.; Trouton, Konia J.; Fielding, Stephen L.; Klippenstein, Jodine; Henderson, Angela. Antichoice attitudes to abortion in women presenting for medical abortions. *Journal of Obstetrics and Gynaecology Canada* 2005 March; 27(3): 247-250. NRCBL: 12.5.2. SC: cs, em. Identifiers: Canada. Note: Abstract in French and English.

ADVANCE DIRECTIVES
See also DEATH AND DYING; TREATMENT REFUSAL

End-of-life lawmaking [editorial]. *New York Times* 2006 April 23; p. CY17. NRCBL: 20.5.4. SC: le.

Akufo-Tetteh, Mary. Advance directives — considerations for advanced nurse practitioners. *In:* Bartter, Karen, ed. Ethical Issues in Advanced Nursing Practice. Boston: Butterworth-Heinemann; 2001: 118-133. NRCBL: 20.5.4.

Appelbaum, Paul S. Commentary: psychiatric advance directives at a crossroads—when can PADs be overridden? *Journal of the American Academy of Psychiatry and the Law* 2006; 34(3): 395-397. NRCBL: 20.5.4; 9.5.3; 17.1; 8.3.4. SC: le. Comments: Jeffrey W. Swanson, S. Van McCrary, Marvin S. Swartz, Eric B. Elbogen, and Richard A. Van Dorn. Superseding psychiatric advance directives:

NRCBL: National Reference Center for Bioethics Literature Classification Scheme   See inside front cover for terms.

23

ethical and legal considerations. Journal of the American Academy of Psychiatry and the Law 2006; 34(3): 385-394.

Barrett, Ronald Keith. Dialogues in diversity: an invited series of papers, advance directives, DNRs, and end-of-life care for African Americans. *Omega* 2005-2006; 52(3): 249-261. NRCBL: 20.5.4; 9.5.4; 20.3.3. SC: cs.

Basanta, W. Eugene. Advance directives and life-sustaining treatment: a legal primer. *Hematology/Oncology Clinics of North America* 2002 December; 16(6): 1381-1396. NRCBL: 20.5.4; 8.3.3. SC: le.

Baumrucker, Steven J.; Carter, Greg; Morris, Gerald M.; VandeKieft, Gregg K.; Wallace, Jo-Anne R. Case study — living wills vs. the will of loved ones. *American Journal of Hospice and Palliative Medicine* 2005 July-August; 22(4): 310-314. NRCBL: 20.5.4; 8.3.3.

Belmont, Elisabeth; Felt, J. Kay; Foley, Elizabeth M.; Gadberry, Gavin J.; Miltenberger, Barbara L.; Puri, Christopher C.; Vandecaveye, Lisa Diehl. A guide to legal issues in life-limiting conditions. *Journal of Health Law* 2005 Spring; 38(2): 145-202. NRCBL: 20.5.4; 20.4.1; 9.3.1; 9.5.2. SC: le.

Berger, Jeffrey T.; Gunderson, Martin. Say what you mean and mean what you say: a patient's conflicting preferences for care [case study]. *Hastings Center Report* 2006 January-February; 36(1): 14-15. NRCBL: 20.5.4; 8.1; 8.2; 20.5.1. SC: cs.

Bernstein, Robert. Commentary: the climate for physician adherence to psychiatric advance directives. *Journal of the American Academy of Psychiatry and the Law* 2006; 34(3): 402-405. NRCBL: 20.5.4; 9.5.3; 17.1; 8.3.4; 9.8. SC: le. Comments: Jeffrey W. Swanson, S. Van McCrary, Marvin S. Swartz, Eric B. Elbogen, and Richard A. Van Dorn. Superseding psychiatric advance directives: ethical and legal considerations. Journal of the American Academy of Psychiatry and the Law 2006; 34(3): 385-394.

Brentnall, Vicki. Directing your own end-of-life care. *Medical Economics* 2005 September 16; 82(18): 54-55. NRCBL: 20.5.4.

Brody, Jane E. Medical due diligence: a living will should spell out the specifics. *New York Times* 2006 November 28; p. F7. NRCBL: 20.5.4. SC: po.

Brown, Margaret; Fisher, John W.; Brumley, David J.; Ashby, Michael A.; Milliken, Jan. Advance directives in action in a regional palliative care service: "road testing" the provisions of the Medical Treatment Act 1988 (VIC). *Journal of Law and Medicine* 2005 November; 13(2): 186-190. NRCBL: 20.5.4. SC: em.

Browne, Alister; Sullivan, Bill. Advance directives in Canada. *CQ: Cambridge Quarterly of Healthcare Ethics* 2006 Summer; 15(3): 256-260. NRCBL: 20.5.4.

Burchardi, Nicole; Rauprich, Oliver; Hecht, Martin; Beck, Marcus; Vollmann, Jochen. Discussing living wills. A qualitative study of a German sample of neurologists and ALS patients. *Journal of the Neurological Sciences* 2005 October 15; 237(1-2): 67-74. NRCBL: 20.5.4; 8.1. SC: em.

Crane, Monica K.; Wittink, Marsha; Doukas, David J. Respecting end-of-life treatment preferences. *American Family Physician* 2005 October 1; 72(7): 1263-1268. NRCBL: 20.5.4; 8.1.

Davis, John K. Surviving interests and living wills. *Public Affairs Quarterly* 2006 January; 20(1): 17-30. NRCBL: 20.5.4; 1.1; 1.2; 8.3.4.

Davison, Sara N.; Simpson, Christy. Hope and advance care planning in patients with end stage renal disease: qualitative interview study. *BMJ: British Medical Journal* 2006 October 28; 333(7574): 886-889. NRCBL: 20.5.4; 20.5.1; 20.4.1. SC: em. Identifiers: Canada.
Abstract: OBJECTIVE: To understand hope in the context of advance care planning from the perspective of patients with end stage renal disease. DESIGN: Qualitative in-depth interview study. SETTING: Outpatient department of a university affiliated nephrology programme. PARTICIPANTS: 19 patients with end stage renal disease purposively selected from the renal insufficiency, haemodialysis, and peritoneal dialysis clinics. RESULTS: Patients' hopes were highly individualised and were shaped by personal values. They reflected a preoccupation with their daily lives. Participants identified hope as central to the process of advance care planning in that hope helped them to determine future goals of care and provided insight into the perceived benefits of advance care planning and their willingness to engage in end of life discussions. More information earlier in the course of the illness focusing on the impact on daily life, along with empowerment of the patient and enhancing professional and personal relationships, were key factors in sustaining patients' ability to hope. This helped them to imagine possibilities for a future that were consistent with their values and hopes. The reliance on health professionals to initiate end of life discussions and the daily focus of clinical care were seen as potential barriers to hope. CONCLUSIONS: Facilitated advance care planning through the provision of timely appropriate information can positively enhance rather than diminish patients' hope. Current practices concerning disclosure of prognosis are ethically and psychologically inadequate in that they do not meet the needs of patients.

Dimond, Brigit. Specialist healthcare law: palliative care. *British Journal of Nursing* 2006 February 9-22; 15(3): 156-157. NRCBL: 20.5.4; 20.5.1. SC: le. Identifiers: United Kingdom (Great Britain).

Ditto, Peter H.; Hawkins, Nikki A. Advance directives and cancer decision making near the end of life. *Health Psychology* 2005 July; 24(4 Supplement): S63-S70. NRCBL: 20.5.4; 20.4.1.

Dyer, Clare. Code sets out framework for "living wills" [news]. *BMJ: British Medical Journal* 2006 March 18; 332(7542): 623. NRCBL: 20.5.4. SC: le. Identifiers: England.

Easson, Alexandra M. Should research be part of advance care planning? *Critical Care* 2005 February; 9(1): 10-11. NRCBL: 20.5.4.

Freeman, Jerome W. The bedside vigil: love and a question. *South Dakota Journal of Medicine* 2005 May; 58(5): 179-181. NRCBL: 20.5.4; 20.5.1; 8.3.3.

Froman, Robin D.; Owen, Steven V. Randomized study of stability and change in patients' advance directives. *Research in Nursing and Health* 2005 October; 28(5): 398-407. NRCBL: 20.5.4; 9.5.4. SC: em.

Harvey, Martin. Advance directives and the severely demented. *Journal of Medicine and Philosophy* 2006 February; 31(1): 47- 64. NRCBL: 20.5.4; 9.5.3. SC: an.
Abstract: Should advance directives (ADs) such as living wills be employed to direct the care of the severely demented? In considering this question, I focus primarily on the claims of Rebecca Dresser who objects in principle to the use of ADs in this context. Dresser has persuasively argued that ADs are both theoretically incoherent and ethically dangerous. She proceeds to advocate a Best Interest Standard as the best way for deciding when and how the demented ought to be treated. I put forth a compromise position: both ADs and the Best Interest Standard have roles to play in guiding the care of the severely demented.

Jakabcin, Ann G. A legal explanation of the advanced medical directive and Maryland living will. *Maryland Medicine* 2005 Spring; 6(2): 33-43. NRCBL: 20.5.4. SC: le.

Jezewski, Mary Ann; Brown, Jean K.; Wu, Yow-Wu Bill; Meeker, Mary Ann; Feng, Jui-Ying; Bu, Xiaoyan. Oncology nurses' knowledge, attitudes, and experiences regarding advance directives. *Oncology Nursing Forum* 2005 March 5; 32(2): 319-327. NRCBL: 20.5.4; 4.1.3; 8.1; 9.5.1. SC: em.

Jordens, C.; Little, M.; Kerridge, I.; McPhee, J. From advance directives to advance care planning: current legal status, ethical rationales and a new research agenda. *Internal Medicine Journal* 2005 September; 35(9): 563-566. NRCBL: 20.5.4; 20.4.1.

Kass-Bartelmes, Barbara L.; Hughes, Ronda. Advance care planning: preferences for care at the end of life. Rockville, MD: Agency for Healthcare Research and Quality [AHRQ], 2003 March; 19 p. [Online]. Accessed: http://www.ahrq.gov/research/endliferia/endria.pdf [2006 August 30]. NRCBL: 20.5.4; 20.5.1.

Kelley, Carol G.; Lipson, Amy R.; Daly, Barbara J.; Douglas, Sara L. Use of advance directives in the chronically critically ill. *JONA's Healthcare Law, Ethics, and Regulation* 2006 April-June; 8(2): 42-47. NRCBL: 20.5.4; 7.2. SC: em.
Abstract: Although it would be ideal that all patients have the presence of an advance directive documented in their medical chart, it is especially important in the chronically critically ill, a patient population with an in-hospital mortality rate of 40%. How has the documentation of advance directives in the medical chart of chronically critically ill patients changed from 1997 to 2003? This article describes the patient characteristics and patterns of death in chronically critically ill patients, with or without an advance directive, enrolled in 2 consecutive studies.

Kirschner, Kristi L. When written advance directives are not enough. *Clinics in Geriatric Medicine* 2005 February; 21(1): 193-209. NRCBL: 20.5.4.

Kjervik, Diane K. Advance directives: promoting self-determination or hampering autonomy. *In:* Cowen, Perle Slavik; Moorhead, Sue, eds. Current Issues in Nursing. 7th ed. St. Louis, MO: Mosby, 2006: 652-659. NRCBL: 20.5.4; 1.1.

Kusmin, Ben. Swing low, sweet chariot: abandoning the disinterested witness requirement for advance directives. *American Journal of Law and Medicine* 2006; 32(1): 93-116. NRCBL: 20.5.4; 8.1. SC: le.

Lewis, Penney. Medical treatment of dementia patients at the end of life: can the law accommodate the personal identity and welfare problems? *European Journal of Health Law* 2006 September; 13(3): 219-234. NRCBL: 20.5.4; 4.4; 17.1; 9.5.2. SC: le.

Lipkin, K. Michael. Brief report: identifying a proxy for health care as part of routine medical inquiry. *JGIM: Journal of General Internal Medicine* 2006 November; 21(11): 1188-1191. NRCBL: 20.5.4. SC: em.

Lo, Bernard. Advance care planning. *American Journal of Geriatric Cardiology* 2004 November- December; 13(6): 316-320. NRCBL: 20.5.4; 8.3.3; 8.3.1; 8.1. SC: le.

Lötjönen, Salla. Medical research on patients with dementia — the role of advance directives in European legal instruments. *European Journal of Health Law* 2006 September; 13(3): 235-261. NRCBL: 20.5.4; 17.1; 9.5.2; 18.5.6.

Maclean, Alasdair R. Advance directives, future selves and decision-making. *Medical Law Review* 2006 Autumn; 14(3): 291-320. NRCBL: 20.5.4; 1.1; 4.4. SC: an.

Mazur, Dennis J.; Hickam, David H. The influence of physician explanations on patient preferences about future health-care states. *Medical Decision Making* 1997 January-March; 17(1): 56-60. NRCBL: 20.5.4; 8.1; 20.5.1.

McAdam, Jennifer L.; Stotts, Nancy A.; Padilla, Geraldine; Puntillo, Kathleen. Attitudes of critically ill Filipino patients and their families toward advance directives. *American Journal of Critical Care* 2005 January; 14(1): 17-25. NRCBL: 20.5.4; 21.7. SC: em.

McLean, G.R. Thinking about the living will. *South African Medical Journal* 1995 November; 85(11): 1146- 1147. NRCBL: 20.5.4; 1.1; 20.7; 8.3.4.

Miyata, Hiroaki; Shiraishi, Hiromi; Kai, Ichiro. Survey of the general public's attitude toward advance directives in Japan: how to respect patients' preferences. *BMC Medical Ethics* 2006; 7: 11. NRCBL: 20.5.4. SC: em.

NRCBL: National Reference Center for Bioethics Literature Classification Scheme   See inside front cover for terms.

25

Moseley, Ray; Dobalian, Aram; Hatch, Robert. The problem with advance directives: maybe it is the medium, not the message. *Archives of Gerontology and Geriatrics* 2005 September-October; 41(2): 211-219. NRCBL: 20.5.4; 1.3.12.

Muller, David. Do NOT resuscitate: a well-orchestrated plan for death ends on a brutal note. *APA [American Philosophical Association] Newsletters: Newsletter on Philosophy and Medicine* 2006 Spring; 05(2): 14-16. NRCBL: 20.5.4; 20.5.1. SC: cs.

Murray, Scott A.; Sheikh, Aziz; Thomas, Keri. Advance care planning in primary care [editorial]. *BMJ: British Medical Journal* 2006 October 28; 333(7574): 868-869. NRCBL: 20.5.4; 9.1; 20.4.1. Identifiers: United Kingdom (Great Britain).

Neitzke, Gerald; Charbonnier, Ralph; Diemer, Wolf; May, Arnd T.; Wernstedt, Thela. Göttinger Thesen zur gesetzlichen Regelung des Umgangs mit Patientenverfügung und Vorsorgevollmacht [Göttingen theses on the legal regulation of advance directives and health care powers of attorney]. *Ethik in der Medizin* 2006 June; 18(2): 192-194. NRCBL: 20.5.4. SC: le.

Patton, Michael F., Jr. Personal identity, autonomy, and advance directives. *Southwest Philosophy Review* 2002 January; 18(1): 65-72. NRCBL: 20.5.4; 1.1.

Porter, Deborah. Advance directives and the persistent vegetative state in Victoria: a human rights perspective. *Journal of Law and Medicine* 2005 November; 13(2): 256-270. NRCBL: 20.5.4; 8.3.3; 4.4; 20.2.1. SC: le.

Portsmouth, Donald. Advance directives. *In:* Rai, Gurcharan S, ed. Medical Ethics and the Elderly. 2nd ed. San Francisco: Radcliffe Medical Press; 2004: 81-89. NRCBL: 20.5.4. SC: le.

Riley, James; Pristave, Robert. Legal mechanisms to protect dialysis patients' end-of-life decisions. *Nephrology News and Issues* 2005 June; 19(7): 53-54. NRCBL: 20.5.4; 20.5.1; 8.3.3. SC: le.

Rurup, Mette L.; Onwuteaka-Philipsen, Bregje D.; van der Heide, Agnes; van der Wal, Gerrit; Deeg, Dorly J.H. Frequency and determinants of advance directives concerning end-of-life care in The Netherlands. *Social Science and Medicine* 2006 March; 62(6): 1552-1563. NRCBL: 20.5.4; 20.5.1. SC: em.

Sass, Hans-Martin. Geriatric medicine and care: health literacy, health care and deathbed care. *In:* Döring, Ole; Chen, Renbiao, eds. Advances in Chinese Medical Ethics: Chinese and International Perspectives. Hamburg: Institut für Asienkunde; 2002: 433-443. NRCBL: 20.5.4. Note: Proceedings of the Second Sino-German Interdisciplinary Symposium about Medical Ethics in China, Shanghai, 19-23 October, 1999.

Sayers, Gwen M.; Kapembwa, Moses S.; Green, Mary C. Advance refusals: does the law help? *Clinical Ethics* 2006 September; 1(3): 139-145. NRCBL: 20.5.4; 1.1; 8.3.4; 8.3.3. SC: le; cs.

Schouten, Ronald. Commentary: psychiatric advance directives as tools for enhancing treatment of the mentally ill. *Journal of the American Academy of Psychiatry and the Law* 2006; 34(1): 58-60. NRCBL: 20.5.4; 9.5.3; 8.3.3. Comments: Jeffrey Swanson, Marvin Swartz, Joelle Ferron, Eric Elbogen, and Richard Van Dorn. Psychiatric advance directives among public mental health consumers in five U.S. cities: prevalence, demand, and correlates. Journal of the American Academy of Psychiatry and the Law 2006; 34(1): 43-57.

Searight, H. Russell; Gafford, Jennifer. "It's like playing with your destiny": Bosnian immigrants' views of advance directives and end-of-life decision-making. *Journal of Immigrant Health* 2005 July; 7(3): 195-203. NRCBL: 20.5.4; 21.7; 8.1. SC: em. Identifiers: Bosnia.

Sittisombut, Sudarat; Love, Edgar J.; Sitthi-amorn, Chitr. Attitudes toward advance directives and the impact of prognostic information on the preference for cardiopulmonary resuscitation in medical inpatients in Chiang Mai University Hospital, Thailand. *Nursing and Health Sciences* 2005 December; 7(4): 243-250. NRCBL: 20.5.4; 20.5.1. SC: em.

Smith, Alexander K.; Ries, Angela Poppe; Zhang, Baohui; Tulsky, James A.; Prigerson, Holly G.; Block, Susan D. Resident approaches to advance care planning on the day of hospital admission. *Archives of Internal Medicine* 2006 August 14-28; 166(15): 1597-1602. NRCBL: 20.5.4; 7.2. SC: em.

Smith, Alison P. The Schiavo legacy. *Nursing Economic* 2005 May-June; 23(3): 136-137. NRCBL: 20.5.4; 4.1.3. SC: le.

Smucker, William D.; Houts, Renate M.; Danks, Joseph H.; Ditto, Peter H.; Fagerlin, Angela; Coppola, Kristen M. Modal preferences predict elderly patients' life-sustaining treatment choices as well as patients' chosen surrogates do. *Medical Decision Making* 2000 July-September; 20(3): 271-280. NRCBL: 20.5.4; 20.5.1; 9.5.2; 8.3.3.

Swanson, Jeffrey W.; Swartz, Marvin S.; Elbogen, Eric B.; Van Dorn, Richard A.; Ferron, Joelle; Wagner, H. Ryan; McCauley, Barbara J.; Kim, Mimi. Facilitated psychiatric advance directives: a randomized trial of an intervention to foster advance treatment planning among persons with severe mental illness. *American Journal of Psychiatry* 2006 November; 163(11): 1943-1951. NRCBL: 20.5.4; 17.1. SC: em.

Swanson, Jeffrey W.; Van McCrary, S.; Swartz, Marvin S.; Elbogen, Eric B.; Van Dorn, Richard A. Su-

---

perseding psychiatric advance directives: ethical and legal considerations. *Journal of the American Academy of Psychiatry and the Law* 2006; 34(3): 385-394. NRCBL: 20.5.4; 9.5.3; 17.1; 8.3.4. SC: le.

Szmukler, George; Dawson, John. Commentary: toward resolving some dilemmas concerning psychiatric advance directives. *Journal of the American Academy of Psychiatry and the Law* 2006; 34(3): 398-401. NRCBL: 20.5.4; 9.5.3; 17.1; 8.3.4; 8.3.3. SC: le. Identifiers: Hargrave v. Vermont. Comments: Jeffrey W. Swanson, S. Van McCrary, Marvin S. Swartz, Eric B. Elbogen, and Richard A. Van Dorn. Superseding psychiatric advance directives: ethical and legal considerations. Journal of the American Academy of Psychiatry and the Law 2006; 34(3): 385-394.

Tapp, Ann. Advance directives. *Canadian Nurse* 2006 February; 102(2): 26. NRCBL: 20.5.4.

Teno, Joan M. Advance care planning for frail, older persons. *In:* Morrison, R. Sean; Meier, Diane E.; Capello, Carol, eds. Geriatric Palliative Care. New York: Oxford University Press; 2003: 307-313. NRCBL: 20.5.4; 9.5.2.

Thompson, Trevor D.B.; Barbour, Rosaline S.; Schwartz, Lisa. Health professionals' views on advance directives: a qualitative interdisciplinary study. *Palliative Medicine* 2003; 17(5): 403-409. NRCBL: 20.5.4; 8.1; 20.3.2. SC: em. Identifiers: United Kingdom (Great Britain).

Thorevska, Natalya; Tilluckdharry, Lisa; Tickoo, Sumit; Havasi, Andrea; Amoateng-Adjepong, Yaw; Manthous, Constantine A. Patients' understanding of advance directives and cardiopulmonary resuscitation. *Journal of Critical Care* 2005 March; 20(1): 26-34. NRCBL: 20.5.4; 8.3.1; 20.5.1. SC: em.

Toller, Claire A. Stark; Budge, Marc M. Compliance with and understanding of advance directives among trainee doctors in the United Kingdom. *Journal of Palliative Care* 2006 Autumn; 22(3): 141-146. NRCBL: 20.5.4. SC: em.

Treloar, A.J. Advance directives: limitations upon their applicability in elderly care. *International Journal of Geriatric Psychiatry* 1999 December; 14(12): 1039-1043. NRCBL: 20.5.4; 20.4.1. SC: le. Identifiers: United Kingdom (Great Britain).

Tyminski, Marie Ortman. The current state of advance directive law in Ohio: more protective of provider liability than patient rights. *Journal of Law and Health* 2004-2005; 19(2): 411-449. NRCBL: 20.5.4; 8.3.4; 8.5. SC: le.

Union of American Hebrew Congregations. Committee on Bio-Ethics. The Living Will/Medical Directive: Bioethics Program/Case Study: Case Study IV. New York, NY: Union of American Hebrew Congregations, 1991 Winter; 41 p. NRCBL: 20.5.4; 1.2; 20.5.1.

United States. Department of Veterans Affairs. Medical: advance health care planning. Final rule. *Federal Register* 2005 November 30; 70(229): 71772-71774. NRCBL: 20.5.4; 5.3. SC: le.

van Oorschot, B.; Simon, A. Importance of the advance directive and the beginning of the dying process from the point of view of German doctors and judges dealing with guardianship matters: results of an empirical survey. *Journal of Medical Ethics* 2006 November; 32(11): 623-626. NRCBL: 20.5.4. SC: em.
Abstract: OBJECTIVES: To analyse and compare the surveys on German doctors and judges on end of life decision making regarding their attitudes on the advance directive and on the dying process. DESIGN: The respondents were to indicate their agreement or disagreement to eight statements on the advance directive and to specify their personal view on the beginning of the dying process. PARTICIPANTS: 727 doctors (anaesthetists or intensive-care physicians, internal specialists and general practitioners) in three federal states and 469 judges dealing with guardianship matters all over Germany. MAIN MEASUREMENTS: Comparisons of means, analyses of variance, pivot tables (chi(2) test) and factor analyses (varimax with Kaiser normalisation). RESULTS: Three attitude groups on advance directive were disclosed by the analysis: the decision model, which emphasises the binding character of a situational advance directive; the deliberation model, which puts more emphasis on the communicative aspect; and the delegation model, which regards the advance directive as a legal instrument. The answers regarding the beginning of the dying process were broadly distributed, but no marked difference was observed between the responding professions. The dying process was assumed by most participants to begin with a life expectancy of only a few days. CONCLUSIONS: A high degree of valuation for advance directive was seen in both German doctors and judges; most agreed to the binding character of the situational directive. Regarding the different individual concepts of the dying process, a cross-professional discourse on the contents of this term seems to be overdue.

Willmott, L.; White, Ben; Howard, Michelle. Overriding advance refusals of life-sustaining medical treatment. *Medicine and Law: The World Association for Medical Law* 2006 December; 25(4): 647-661. NRCBL: 20.5.4; 20.5.1; 1.1. SC: le.
Abstract: The law recognises the right of a competent adult to make an advance refusal of life-sustaining medical treatment. This right is based on the principle of self-determination which dictates that a competent adult is entitled to make decisions about the kind of treatment he or she wants to receive or not to receive. However, the right to refuse life-sustaining treatment in advance is not unqualified. There are circumstances in which a health professional or a court will be entitled to disregard an advance directive and provide the life-sustaining medical treatment. This intervention is justified on the grounds of the State's interest in preserving life. Although self-determination prevails over the State's interest in life, the courts have held that an adult's wishes need only be respected if the adult has expressed them clearly and there is otherwise no uncertainty. This paper explores in some detail the common law and statutory excuses available to health professionals in Australia who do not wish to comply with directions in an advance directive to refuse life-sustaining medical treatment. At common law, the inquiry revolves around whether the adult intended his or her refusal to apply to the circumstances that have subsequently arisen. The paper considers the different situations in which it might be ar-

NRCBL: National Reference Center for Bioethics Literature Classification Scheme   See inside front cover for terms.

27

gued that an adult completed an advance directive but did not intend it to apply, thus permitting a health professional to disregard it. In contrast, the relevant Australian statutes specify a number of excuses that expressly allow a health professional not to follow an advance directive, or prohibit him or her from following it. The paper then compares the common law with those jurisdictions that have enacted legislation and critiques the different excuses available. The paper concludes by asserting that the law generally strikes the correct balance between requiring an advance directive to be followed but not enforcing a direction to refuse life-sustaining medical treatment where there is some doubt about whether it presents the adult's views. However, there are two riders to this proposition. The first is the tendency of the judiciary to err unduly in favour of the sanctity of life when it is called upon to interpret whether an advance directive can be regarded as representing the adult's wishes in the situation that subsequently arose. Secondly, comment is made about the recognition in one statutory jurisdiction of an excuse that permits a health professional to provide treatment contrary to an advance refusal based on good medical practice.

ADVISORY COMMITTEES ON BIOETHICS
See BIOETHICS AND MEDICAL ETHICS/ COMMISSIONS

AFRICAN AMERICANS AS RESEARCH SUBJECTS *See* HUMAN EXPERIMENTATION/ SPECIAL POPULATIONS

AGED *See* CARE FOR SPECIFIC GROUPS/ AGED; HUMAN EXPERIMENTATION/ SPECIAL POPULATIONS/ AGED AND TERMINALLY ILL

AIDS

Board approves position statement on the rights of the HIV-positive nurse [news]. *Pennsylvania Nurse* 1996 July; 51(7): 11. NRCBL: 9.5.6; 16.3; 6; 8.1; 4.1.3. Identifiers: Pennsylvania Nurses Association.

Condoms and the Vatican [editorial]. *Lancet* 2006 May 13-19; 367(9522): 1550. NRCBL: 9.5.6; 11.1; 1.2.

Editorial. *Canadian HIV/AIDS Policy and Law Newsletter* 1999 Spring; 4(2-3): 3-4. NRCBL: 9.5.6; 2.1. Identifiers: Canadian Strategy on HIV/AIDS.

HIV: compulsory testing and falling incidence? [editorial]. *Lancet* 2006 April 8-14; 367(9517): 1118. NRCBL: 9.5.6; 9.1; 8.3.1; 7.1; 9.5.1; 21.1; 8.3.4.

Routine testing for the AIDS virus [editorial]. *New York Times* 2006 September 25; p. A24. NRCBL: 9.5.6; 9.1. SC: po.

US—doctor settles HIV-testing case for $10,000 [news]. *Canadian HIV/AIDS Policy and Law Newsletter* 1996 October; 3(1): 40. NRCBL: 9.5.6; 8.3.1; 8.2.

Winners and losers: routine HIV testing is on the cards. Who will it really help? [editorial]. *New Scientist* 2006 July 22-28; 191(2561): 5. NRCBL: 9.5.6.

Altman, Dennis. Rights matter: structural interventions and vulnerable communities. *Health and Human Rights: An International Journal* 2005; 8(2): 203-213. NRCBL: 9.5.6; 9.5.1; 7.1; 1.1.

American Society for Reproductive Medicine [ASRM]. Ethics Committee. Human immunodeficiency virus and infertility treatment. *Fertility and Sterility* 2004 September; 82(Supplement 1): S228-S231. NRCBL: 9.5.6; 14.1.

Asian Community AIDS Services [ACAS]. Legal, ethical, and human rights issues facing East and Southeast Asian-Canadians. *Canadian HIV/AIDS Policy and Law Newsletter* 1999 Fall-Winter; 5(1): 27-29. NRCBL: 9.5.6; 21.7.

Averill, Marilyn. HIV/AIDS. *In:* Mitcham, Carl, ed. Encyclopedia of Science, Technology, and Ethics. Farmington Hills, MI: Thomson/Gale, 2005: 924-927. NRCBL: 9.5.6; 7.1.

Avrett, Sam; Collins, Chris. HIV vaccines: current challenges and future directions. *HIV/AIDS Policy and Law Review* 2002 July; 7(1): 1, 20-25. NRCBL: 9.5.6; 9.7; 21.1.

Bayer, Ronald; Fairchild, Amy L. Changing the paradigm for HIV testing — the end of exceptionalism. *New England Journal of Medicine* 2006 August 17; 355(7): 647-649. NRCBL: 9.5.6; 9.1.

Baylis, Françoise; Ginn, Diana. Expanding access to post-exposure prophylaxis: ethical and legal issues. *Canadian HIV/AIDS Policy and Law Newsletter* 1999 Summer; 4(4): 29-38. NRCBL: 9.5.6; 9.3.1.

Bell, Brian. Legal, ethical, and human rights issues raised by HIV/AIDS: a plan for 1999-2003. *Canadian HIV/AIDS Policy and Law Newsletter* 1999 Spring; 4(2-3): 5-8. NRCBL: 9.5.6; 2.1.

Benatar, Solomon. Facing ethical challenges in rolling out antiretroviral treatment in resource-poor countries: comment on "they call it 'patient selection' in Khayelitsha". *CQ: Cambridge Quarterly of Healthcare Ethics* 2006 Summer; 15(3): 322-330. NRCBL: 9.5.6; 9.5.1; 9.7; 9.4; 1.1; 9.1. Comments: Renée C. Rox, Eric Goemaere. They call it "patient selection" in Khayelitsha: the experience of médecins sans frontières-South Africa in enrolling patients to receive antiretroviral treatment for HIV/AIDS. CQ: Cambridge Quarterly of Healthcare Ethics 2006 Summer; 15(3): 302-312.

Bennett, Sara; Chanfreau, Catherine. Approaches to rationing antiretroviral treatment: ethical and equity implications. *Bulletin of the World Health Organization* 2005 July; 83(7): 541-547. NRCBL: 9.5.6; 9.7; 9.4; 21.1. SC: em. Identifiers: Mexico; Senegal; Thailand; Uganda.

Bolognesi, Natasha. Bad Medicine [news]. *Nature Medicine* 2006 July; 12(7): 723-724. NRCBL: 9.5.6; 9.7; 4.1.1. Identifiers: South Africa; AIDS; Secomet V.

Bonito, Virginio; Spada, Maria Simonetta; Locati, Francesco; Marchesi, Gianmariano; Salmoiraghi, Marco; Spinsanti, Sandro; di Bergamo, Ospedali Riuniti; Halpern, Scott D. Consent and HIV testing in critically ill patients [letter and reply]. *JAMA: The Journal of the American Medical Association* 2006 January 4; 295(1): 38. NRCBL: 9.5.6; 8.3.1.

Cameron, Edwin. Human rights, racism and AIDS: the new discrimination. *South African Journal on Human Rights* 1993; 9: 22-29. NRCBL: 9.5.6; 21.1; 9.5.10. SC: an.

Cameron, Edwin; Gupta, Alok. Global access to treatment: achievements and challenges. *HIV/AIDS Policy and Law Review* 2002 July; 7(1): 59-71. NRCBL: 9.5.6; 9.2; 21.1; 9.7.

Centers for Disease Control and Prevention [CDC] (United States). CDC Releases Revised HIV Testing Recommendations in Health-Care Settings. Atlanta, GA: Centers for Disease Control and Prevention [CDC] (United States) 2006 September; 3 p. [Online]. Accessed: http://www.cdc.gov/hiv/topics/testing/resources/factsheets/pdf/healthcare.pdf [2006 September 25]. NRCBL: 9.5.6; 9.5.1; 9.5.5; 9.5.7.

Centers for Disease Control and Prevention [CDC] (United States). Revised recommendations for HIV testing of adults, adolescents, and pregnant women in health-care settings. *MMWR: Morbidity and Mortality Weekly Report [electronic]* 2006 September 22; 55(RR-14): 17 p. Accessed: http://www.cdc.gov/hiv/topics/testing/resources/reports/pdf/rr5514.pdf [2006 September 25]. NRCBL: 9.5.6; 9.5.1; 9.5.5; 9.5.7.

Chase, Marilyn. Gates won't fund AIDS researchers unless they pool data. *Wall Street Journal* 2006 July 20; p. B1, B4. NRCBL: 9.5.6; 1.3.9. SC: po.

Clark, Peter A. Mother-to-child transmission of HIV in Botswana: an ethical perspective on mandatory testing. *Developing World Bioethics* 2006 March; 6(1): 1-12. NRCBL: 9.5.6; 9.5.5. Identifiers: Africa.
Abstract: Mother-to-child transmission (MTCT) of HIV represents a particularly dramatic aspect of the HIV epidemic with an estimated 600,000 newborns infected yearly, 90% of them living in sub-Saharan Africa. Since the beginning of the HIV epidemic, an estimated 5.1 million children worldwide have been infected with HIV. MTCT is responsible for 90% of these infections. Two-thirds of the MTCT are believed to occur during pregnancy and delivery, and about one-third through breast-feeding. As the number of women of child bearing age infected with HIV rises, so does the number of infected children. It is apparent that voluntary testing in Botswana has made some valuable inroads in decreasing perinatal HIV transmission, but the statistics showing the increased rate of HIV infection among women 15-24 years of age are not very promising. After reviewing all the pertinent scientific data it is clear that mandatory HIV testing of all pregnant women in conjunction with the implementation of a full package of interventions would save thousands of lives - mothers, newborns and others who could be infected as a result of these women not being aware of their HIV status. If the protection and preservation of human life is a prior-

ity in Botswana, then it is time to allow for mandatory HIV testing of all pregnant women, before it is too late for those who are the most vulnerable. To do less would be medically inappropriate and ethically irresponsible.

Cohen, Leonard A.; Romberg, Elaine; Grace, Edward G.; Barnes, Douglas M. Attitudes of advanced dental education students toward individuals with AIDS. *Journal of Dental Education* 2005 August; 69(8): 896-900. NRCBL: 9.5.6; 4.1.1; 7.1; 10. SC: em.

De Cock, Kevin M. HIV testing in the era of treatment scale up. *Health and Human Rights: An International Journal* 2005; 8(2): 31-35. NRCBL: 9.5.6; 9.5.1; 1.1; 21.1.

Dunfee, Thomas W. Do firms with unique competencies for rescuing victims of human catastrophes have special obligations? Corporate responsibility and the AIDS catastrophe in sub-Saharan Africa. *Business Ethics Quarterly* 2006 April; 16(2): 185-210. NRCBL: 9.5.6; 1.3.2; 6. SC: cs.

Elbe, Stefan. Should HIV/AIDS be securitized? The ethical dilemmas of linking HIV/AIDS and security. *International Studies Quarterly* 2006 March; 50(1): 119-144. NRCBL: 9.5.6; 9.1; 21.1.

Elliott, Douglas. Focus on HIV/AIDS and injection drug use. *Canadian HIV/AIDS Policy and Law Newsletter* 1997-1998 Winter; 3(4)-4(1): 1, 53-57. NRCBL: 9.5.6; 9.3.1.

El-Maaytah, M.; Al Kayed, A.; Al Qudah, M.; Al Ahmad, H.; Al-Dabbagh, K.; Jerjes, W.; Al Khawalde, M.; Abu Hammad, O.; Dar Odeh, N.; El-Maaytah, K.; Al Shmailan, Y.; Porter, S.; Scully, C. Willingness of dentists in Jordan to treat HIV-infected patients. *Oral Diseases* 2005 September; 11(5): 318-322. NRCBL: 9.5.6; 8.1; 4.1.1. SC: em; rv.

Enserink, Martin. WHO panel weighs radical ideas [news]. *Science* 2006 December 1; 314(5804): 1373. NRCBL: 9.5.6; 9.7; 9.2; 9.3.1; 21.1.

Feldman, Eric A. AIDS policy and the politics of rights. *In his:* The Ritual of Rights in Japan: Law, Society, and Health Policy. New York: Cambridge University Press, 2000: 53-81. NRCBL: 9.5.6; 21.1.

Flanigan, Timothy P.; Beckwith, Curt; Carpenter, Charles C.J.; Frieden, Thomas R.; Kellerman, Scott E.; Das-Douglas, Moupali. Public health principles for the HIV epidemic [letter and reply]. *New England Journal of Medicine* 2006 February 23; 354(8): 878. NRCBL: 9.5.6; 9.1.

Friedman, Samuel R.; Sherman, Susan G.; Frieden, Thomas R.; Kellerman, Scott E.; Das-Douglas, Moupali. Public health principles for the HIV epidemic [letter and reply]. *New England Journal of Medicine* 2006 February 23; 354(8): 877-878. NRCBL: 9.5.6; 9.1.

NRCBL: National Reference Center for Bioethics Literature Classification Scheme   See inside front cover for terms.

29

Garmaise, David. Mandatory HIV testing used to bar potential immigrants. *HIV/AIDS Policy and Law Review* 2003 April; 8(1): 20-21. NRCBL: 9.5.6; 21.1. Identifiers: Canada.

Giuliani, Michele; Lajolo, Carlo; Rezza, Giovanni; Arici, Claudio; Babudieri, Sergio; Grima, Pierfrancesco; Martinelli, Canio; Tamburrini, Enrica; Vecchiet, Jacopo; Mura, Maria Stella; Cauda, Roberto; Mario, Tumbarello. Dental care and HIV-infected individuals: are they equally treated? *Community Dentistry and Oral Epidemiology* 2005 December; 33(6): 447-453. NRCBL: 9.5.6; 8.1; 9.8; 4.1.1. Identifiers: BSAHOD study group; Italy.

Goemaere, Eric. Response to "No shortage of dilemmas". *CQ: Cambridge Quarterly of Healthcare Ethics* 2006 Summer; 15(3): 331-332. NRCBL: 9.5.6; 9.5.1; 9.7; 9.4; 1.1. Comments: Ruth Macklin. No shortage of dilemmas: comment on "they call it 'patient selection' in Khayelitsha". CQ: Cambridge Quarterly of Healthcare Ethics 2006 Summer; 15(3): 313-321.

Goodwin, Michele. Bioethical entanglements of race, religion, and AIDS. *In:* Guinn, David E., ed. Handbook of Bioethics and Religion. New York: Oxford University Press, 2006: 363-383. NRCBL: 9.5.6; 1.2; 9.5.4.

Gostin, Lawrence O. HIV screening in health care settings. *JAMA: The Journal of the American Medical Association* 2006 October 25; 296(16): 2023-2025. NRCBL: 9.5.6.

Grentholtz, Liesl; Richter, Marlise. Developments in South African law on HIV/AIDS. *HIV/AIDS Policy and Law Review* 2004 April; 9(1): 57-60. NRCBL: 9.5.6; 8.3.2; 8.3.1.

Guillot-Hurtubise, Bruno. Dentist found guilty of discrimination. *Canadian HIV/AIDS Policy and Law Newsletter* 1995 July; 1(4): 1, 14-15. NRCBL: 9.5.6.

Gupta, Manju. Occupational risk: the outrageous reaction to HIV positive public safety and health care employees in the workplace. *Journal of Law and Health* 2004-2005; 19(1): 39-73. NRCBL: 9.5.6; 16.3.

Hanlin, Rebecca. Increasing knowledge flows by linking innovation and health — the case of SAAVI. *Genomics, Society and Policy* 2006 December; 2(3): 37-48. NRCBL: 9.5.6; 9.7; 15.1. Identifiers: South African AIDS Vaccine Initiative.

Abstract: Biotechnology and genomic innovation are seen as increasingly important for achieving public health goals in Africa. In particular, vaccines based on advances in genomic technology are deemed vital in the fight against HIV/AIDS. Public-Private Partnerships (PPPs) provide a collaborative mechanism to ensure these vaccines are developed when the private sector lacks incentives to develop these products. These partnerships provide new mechanisms for transferring the knowledge required to ensure vaccine development occurs as quickly and efficiently as possible. One such vaccine partnership is the South African AIDS Vaccine Initiative (SAAVI). This has been successful in ensuring 'value added' (benefit gained by taking part) is created for those involved particularly in the area of intangible value added determinants of collaboration and knowledge capacity. This paper outlines the results of a case study of SAAVI and argues that it provides evidence of a need to strengthen our understanding of the linkage between wider conceptual 'systems' of innovation and health. In particular, it espouses the usefulness of 'Systems of Innovation' thinking as a means to ensure that more specific focus is placed on process outputs such as collaboration and knowledge capacity. This will ensure that necessary knowledge flow is transferred between those working in the vaccine project for more efficient and effective operations. The research also raises questions about the possibility of such case studies highlighting areas of attention that need addressing if greater linkage is to occur between innovation and health at a wider health research policy level.

Heywood, M.J. The routine offer of HIV counseling and testing: a human right. *Health and Human Rights: An International Journal* 2005; 8(2): 13-19. NRCBL: 9.5.6; 9.5.1; 9.2; 21.1; 8.3.1; 7.1.

Hoffmaster, Barry; Schrecker, Ted. An ethical analysis of HIV testing of pregnant women and their newborns. *Canadian HIV/AIDS Policy and Law Newsletter* 1999 Summer; 4(4): 5-11. NRCBL: 9.5.6; 9.5.8; 9.5.5. SC: an.

Hoffmaster, Barry; Schrecker, Ted. An ethical analysis of the mandatory exclusion of immigrants who test HIV-positive. *HIV/AIDS Policy and Law Review* 2000; 5(4): 1, 42-51. NRCBL: 9.5.6; 9.1.

Hood, Robert. AIDS, crisis, and activist science. *In:* Figueroa, Robert; Harding, Sandra, eds. Science and Other Cultures: Issues in Philosophies of Science and Technology. New York: Routledge; 2003: 15-25. NRCBL: 9.5.6.

Ionescu, Carmiola. Romanian parents keep HIV secret from infected children. *Lancet* 2006 May 13-19; 367(9522): 1566. NRCBL: 9.5.6; 8.3.2; 7.1; 8.2.

Jürgens, Ralf; Elliot, Richard. Rapid HIV screening at the point of care: legal and ethical issues. *Canadian HIV/AIDS Policy and Law Newsletter* 2000 Spring-Summer; 5(2-3): 28-32. NRCBL: 9.5.6; 9.7; 9.8.

Kaplan, Laura Duhan. HIV/AIDS policies: compromising the human rights of women. *In:* Tong, Rosemarie; Donchin, Anne; Dodds, Susan, eds. Linking Visions: Feminist Bioethics, Human Rights, and the Developing World. Lanham, MD: Rowman and Littlefield Publishers; 2004: 235-246. NRCBL: 9.5.6; 10; 21.1.

Kenyon, Kristi. Routine HIV testing: a view from Botswana. *Health and Human Rights: An International Journal* 2005; 8(2): 21-23. NRCBL: 9.5.6; 9.5.1; 8.3.1; 9.8; 1.1.

Kippax, Susan. A public health dilemma: a testing question. *AIDS Care* 2006 April; 18(3): 230-235. NRCBL: 9.5.6; 9.1; 21.1. Note: Based on a presentation at AIDS Impact Conference, Cape Town, 4-7 April 2005.

Kohi, Thecla W.; Makoae, Lucy; Chirwa, Maureen; Holzemer, William L.; Phetlhu, Deliwe René; Uys, Leana; Naidoo, Joanne; Dlamini, Priscilla S.; Greeff, Minrie. HIV and AIDS stigma violates human rights in five African countries. *Nursing Ethics* 2006 July; 13(4): 404-415. NRCBL: 9.5.6; 8.1; 9.2; 21.1. SC: em.

Abstract: The situation and human rights of people living with HIV and AIDS were explored through focus groups in five African countries (Lesotho, Malawi, South Africa, Swaziland and Tanzania). A descriptive qualitative research design was used. The 251 informants were people living with HIV and AIDS, and nurse managers and nurse clinicians from urban and rural settings. NVivo software was used to identify specific incidents related to human rights, which were compared with the Universal Declaration of Human Rights. The findings revealed that the human rights of people living with HIV and AIDS were violated in a variety of ways, including denial of access to adequate or no health care/services, and denial of home care, termination or refusal of employment, and denial of the right to earn an income, produce food or obtain loans. The informants living with HIV and AIDS were also abused verbally and physically. Country governments and health professionals need to address these issues to ensure the human rights of all people.

Kremer, H.; Bader, A.; O'Cleirigh, C.; Bierhoff, H.W.; Brockmeyer, N.H. The decision to forgo antiretroviral therapy in people living with HIV — compliance as paternalism or partnership? *European Journal of Medical Research* 2004; 9(2): 61-70. NRCBL: 9.5.6; 8.1; 8.3.4. SC: em. Identifiers: Germany.

Lazzarini, Zita; Von Kohorn, Jonathan E. Medical ethics and law. *In:* Mayer, Kenneth H.; Pizer, H.F. The AIDS Pandemic: Impact on Science and Society. Boston: Elsevier Academic Press; 2005: 488-510. NRCBL: 9.5.6.

Macklin, Ruth. Scaling up HIV testing: ethical issues. *Health and Human Rights: An International Journal* 2005; 8(2): 27-30. NRCBL: 9.5.6; 9.5.1; 1.1; 21.1.

Martin, Brian. The politics of a scientific meeting: the origin-of-AIDS debate at the Royal Society. *Politics and the Life Sciences* 2001 September; 20(2): 119-130. NRCBL: 9.5.6; 9.7.

McCoy, Liza. HIV-positive patients and the doctor-patient relationship: perspectives from the margins. *Qualitative Health Research* 2005 July; 15(6): 791-806. NRCBL: 9.5.6; 8.1; 9.2.

Meel, B.L. Ethical issues related to HIV/AIDS: case reports. *Journal of Clinical Forensic Medicine* 2005 June; 12(3): 149-152. NRCBL: 9.5.6; 16.3; 12.1; 8.1. SC: cs.

Nattrass, Nicoli. Rolling out antiretroviral treatment in South Africa: economic and ethical challenges. *In:* van Niekerk, Anton A.; Kopelman, Loretta M., eds. Ethics and AIDS in Africa: The Challenge to Our Thinking. Walnut Creek, CA: Left Coast Press; 2006: 39-52. NRCBL: 9.5.6; 9.3.1; 9.7. SC: an.

O'Keefe, Eileen; Chinouya, Martha. Global migrants, gendered tradition, and human rights: black Africans and HIV in the United Kingdom. *In:* Tong, Rosemarie; Donchin, Anne; Dodds, Susan, eds. Linking Visions: Feminist Bioethics, Human Rights, and the Developing World. Lanham, MD: Rowman and Littlefield Publishers; 2004: 217-234. NRCBL: 9.5.6; 10; 21.1.

Ogden, Russel. End-of-life summit in Madrid. *Canadian HIV/AIDS Policy and Law Newsletter* 1997-1998 Winter; 3(4)-4(1): 18. NRCBL: 9.5.6; 20.4.1; 21.1.

Ogden, Russel. The uncloseting of AIDS-related euthanasia [news]. *Canadian HIV/AIDS Policy and Law Newsletter* 1994 October; 1(1): 14-15. NRCBL: 9.5.6; 20.5.1.

Paxton, Susan; Gonzales, G.; Uppakaew, K.; Abraham, K.K.; Okta, S.; Green, C.; Nair, K.S.; Merati, T.P.; Thephthien, B.; Marin, M.; Quesada, A. AIDS-related discrimination in Asia. *AIDS Care* 2005 May; 17(4): 413-424. NRCBL: 9.5.6; 21.1. SC: em. Identifiers: India; Indonesia; Thailand; Philippines.

Perez-Pena, Richard. New federal policy on H.I.V. testing poses unique local challenge. *New York Times* 2006 October 2; p. B1, B5. NRCBL: 9.5.6; 21.1. SC: po.

Ratanakul, Pinit. Bioethics and AIDS in Thailand: a Buddhist perspective. *In:* Sang-yong, Song; Young-Mo, Koo; Macer, Darryl R.J., eds. Asian Bioethics in the 21st Century. Christchurch, NZ: Eubios Ethics Institute, 2002: 299-301. NRCBL: 9.5.6; 1.2. Conference: Proceedings of the Asian Bioethics Conference (ABC4), held 22-25 November 2002 in Seoul, South Korea.

Ravichandran, Balaji. AIDS: a cause for optimism? *BMJ: British Medical Journal* 2006 December 2; 333(7579): 1179. NRCBL: 9.5.6; 9.7; 9.3.1; 21.1.

Reddy, Hasini. HIV testing in pregnancy: a duty or a choice? *Canadian HIV/AIDS Policy and Law Newsletter* 1997 Spring; 3(2-3): 7-8. NRCBL: 9.5.6; 9.5.8; 9.5.5. SC: em.

Reilly, Michael; Coghlan, Andy. To know or not to know. . . . *New Scientist* 2006 July 22-28; 191(2561): 8-9. NRCBL: 9.5.6. Identifiers: routine HIV testing.

Rennie, Stuart; Behets, Frieda. AIDS care and treatment in Sub-Saharan Africa: implementation ethics. *Hastings Center Report* 2006 May-June; 36(3): 23-31. NRCBL: 9.5.6; 21.1; 9.4; 9.3.1; 9.1.

Rennie, Stuart; Behets, Frieda. Desperately seeking targets: the ethics of routine HIV testing in low-income countries. *Bulletin of the World Health Organization* 2006 January; 84(1): 52-57. NRCBL: 9.5.6; 9.1; 8.3.1; 9.5.10; 21.1.

Royal College of Physicians of London. Clinical Effectiveness and Evaluation Unit. HIV testing for patients attending general medical services: national guidelines [and patient card insert]. London: Royal College of Physicians,

NRCBL: National Reference Center for Bioethics Literature Classification Scheme   See inside front cover for terms.

31

2005 March; 10 p. NRCBL: 9.5.6; 9.8; 8.3.1. Note: includes insert: The HIV test — what you need to know.

Abstract: This series, edited by Lynne Turner-Stokes, FRCP, "covers issues that are not covered by the major guideline producers but which are likely to be encountered across several medical specialties and primary care. The guidelines are designed to allow clinicians to make rapid, informed decisions based on up-to-date, systematically reviewed and accessible evidence. Where such evidence does not exist, consensus will be used to complete the clinical pathway."

Singh, Jerome Amir. The vital importance of implementation ethics. *Hastings Center Report* 2006 May-June; 36(3): 3. NRCBL: 9.5.6; 9.7.

Singh, Zile; Banerjee, A. HIV/AIDS: social and ethical issues. *Medical Journal of the Armed Forces of India* 2004; 60(2): 107- 108. NRCBL: 9.5.6.

South Africa. Law Commission. South Africa — national policy on HIV testing and informed consent proposed. *Canadian HIV/AIDS Policy and Law Newsletter* 1997 Spring; 3(2-3): 11-12. NRCBL: 9.5.6; 8.3.1.

Stoltz, Lori; Shap, Louise. HIV testing and pregnancy: medical and legal parameters of the policy debate. *Canadian HIV/AIDS Policy and Law Newsletter* 1999 Spring; 4(2-3): 42-44. NRCBL: 9.5.6; 9.5.8; 9.5.5.

Tanaka, Tomohiro. Medical business ethics: the HIV-tainted-blood affair in Japan. *In:* Takahashi, Takao, ed. Taking Life and Death Seriously: Bioethics from Japan. Amsterdam; Boston: Elsevier JAI; 2005: 253-273. NRCBL: 9.5.6; 19.4.

Tarantola, Daniel. HIV testing: breaking the deadly cycle. *Health and Human Rights: An International Journal* 2005; 8(2): 37-41. NRCBL: 9.5.6; 9.5.1; 8.3.1; 21.1; 9.2.

UNAIDS Reference Group on HIV/AIDS and Human Rights. Ensuring a rights-based approach to HIV testing. *Health and Human Rights: An International Journal* 2005; 8(2): 43-44. NRCBL: 9.5.6; 9.5.1; 9.8; 9.2.

Unschuld, Paul U. Modern societies, medical ethics and HIV/AIDS. *In:* Döring, Ole; Chen, Renbiao, eds. Advances in Chinese Medical Ethics: Chinese and International Perspectives. Hamburg: Institut für Asienkunde; 2002: 57-72. NRCBL: 9.5.6. Note: Proceedings of the Second Sino-German Interdisciplinary Symposium about Medical Ethics in China, Shanghai, 19-23 October, 1999.

van Niekerk, Anton A. Principles of global distributive justice and the HIV/AIDS pandemic: moving beyond Rawls and Buchanan. *In:* van Niekerk, Anton A.; Kopelman, Loretta M., eds. Ethics and AIDS in Africa: The Challenge to Our Thinking. Walnut Creek, CA: Left Coast Press; 2006: 84-110. NRCBL: 9.5.6; 1.1; 9.4; 21.1.

Wang, Yanguang. Some policy recommendations based on the principle of strategic tolerance concerning HIV/AIDS in China. *In:* Döring, Ole; Chen, Renbiao, eds. Advances in Chinese Medical Ethics: Chinese and Interna-

tional Perspectives. Hamburg: Institut für Asienkunde; 2002: 298-305. NRCBL: 9.5.6. Note: Proceedings of the Second Sino-German Interdisciplinary Symposium about Medical Ethics in China, Shanghai, 19-23 October, 1999.

Whetten, Kathryn; Leserman, Jane; Whetten, Rachel; Ostermann, Jan; Thielman, Nathan; Swartz, Marvin; Stangl, Darlene. Exploring lack of trust in care providers and the government as a barrier to health service use. *American Journal of Public Health* 2006 April; 96(4): 716-721. NRCBL: 9.5.6; 8.1; 9.8.

Whyte, Susan Reynolds; Whyte, Michael A.; Meinert, Lotte; Kyaddondo, Betty. Treating AIDS: dilemmas of unequal access in Uganda. *In:* Petryna, Adriana; Lakoff, Andrew; Kleinman, Arthur, eds. Global Pharmaceuticals: Ethics, Markets, Practices. Durham: Duke University Press; 2006: 240-262. NRCBL: 9.5.6; 9.3.1; 9.7.

Worth, Heather. Unconditional hospitality: HIV, ethics and the refugee 'problem'. *Bioethics* 2006 September; 20(5): 223-232. NRCBL: 9.5.6; 21.1.

Abstract: Refugees, as forced migrants, have suffered displacement under conditions not of their own choosing. In 2000 there were thought to be 22 million refugees of whom 6 million were HIV positive. While the New Zealand government has accepted a number of HIV positive refugees from sub-Saharan Africa, this hospitality is under threat due to negative public and political opinion. Epidemic conditions raise the social stakes attached to sexual exchanges, contagion becomes a major figure in social relationships and social production, and the fears of the contagious nature of those 'just off the plane' connect refugees to an equally deep-seated fear of racial miscegenation. Jacques Derrida's notion of unconditional hospitality is a dream of a democracy which would have a cosmopolitan form. This means that one cannot decide in advance which refugees one might choose to resettle. This paper will use Derrida's notion of unconditional hospitality to emphasise the fragility of HIV positive refugees' position, caught between becoming newly made New Zealand subjects while at the same time having that subjecthood threatened. For Derrida, both ethics and politics demand both an action and a need for a thoughtful response (a questioning without limit).

Wu, Zunyou; Sun, Xinhua; Sullivan, Sheena G.; Detels, Roger. HIV testing in China. *Science* 2006 June 9; 312(5779): 1475-1476. NRCBL: 9.5.6; 9.1.

AIDS/ CONFIDENTIALITY

Discrimination and human rights abuse in Russia. *Canadian HIV/AIDS Policy and Law Newsletter* 1999 Fall-Winter; 5(1): 22-27. NRCBL: 9.5.6; 8.4; 9.2; 8.3.4. Note: An edited version of the report entitled "AIDS-Related Violations of Human Rights and the Russian Legislation," prepared by the Russian NAMES Fund.

HIV testing and confidentiality: final report. *Canadian HIV/AIDS Policy and Law Newsletter* 1999 Spring; 4(2-3): 74. NRCBL: 9.5.6; 8.4.

Hungary: a fight every step of the way for voluntary, anonymous, and free tests [news]. *HIV/AIDS Policy and Law Review* 2004 August; 9(2): 35. NRCBL: 9.5.6; 8.4; 9.3.1.

UK: court orders publication ban in case of HIV-positive health-care worker [news]. *HIV/AIDS Policy and Law Review* 2002 March; 6(3): 74. NRCBL: 9.5.6; 8.4. SC: le. Identifiers: United Kingdom (Great Britain).

Charlebois, Edwin D.; Maiorana, Andre; McLaughlin, Marisa; Koester, Kim; Gaffney, Stuart; Rutherford, George W.; Morin, Stephen F. Potential deterrent effect of name-based HIV infection surveillance. *Journal of Acquired Immune Deficiency Syndromes* 2005 June 1; 39(2): 219-227. NRCBL: 9.5.6; 8.4; 1.3.12. SC: em.

Elliott, Richard. Scaling up HIV testing: human rights and hidden costs. *HIV/AIDS Policy and Law Review* 2006 April; 11(1): 1, 5-10. NRCBL: 9.5.6; 8.4; 8.3.1; 21.1.

Elliott, Richard. US: hospital negligent for failing to warn prior patient of risk of HIV infection by transfusion. *HIV/AIDS Policy and Law Review* 2002 March; 6(3): 71-72. NRCBL: 9.5.6; 8.4; 19.4; 8.5. SC: le.

Fox, Renée C.; Goemaere, Eric. They call it "patient selection" in Khayelitsha: the experience of médecins sans frontières-South Africa in enrolling patients to receive antiretroviral treatment for HIV/AIDS. *CQ: Cambridge Quarterly of Healthcare Ethics* 2006 Summer; 15(3): 302-312. NRCBL: 9.5.6; 9.5.1; 9.7; 9.4; 8.3.4; 8.4.

Ho, Wing Wah; Brandfield, Julie; Retkin, Randye; Laraque, Danielle. Complexities in HIV consent in adolescents. *Clinical Pediatrics* 2005 July-August; 44(6): 473-478. NRCBL: 9.5.6; 9.5.7; 8.3.1; 8.3.2; 8.4; 7.1. SC: le.

Jürgens, Ralf. HIV testing and confidentiality: a discussion paper. *Canadian HIV/AIDS Policy and Law Newsletter* 1997 Spring; 3(2-3): 3-7. NRCBL: 9.5.6; 8.4.

Jürgens, Ralf. HIV testing for peacekeeping forces: legal and human rights issues. *HIV/AIDS Policy and Law Review* 2002 December; 7(2-3): 111-114. NRCBL: 9.5.6; 21.1; 8.3.4; 8.4. SC: le.

Jürgens, Ralf. Project begins work on testing and confidentiality issues. *Canadian HIV/AIDS Policy and Law Newsletter* 1996 July; 2(4): 3-7. NRCBL: 9.5.6; 8.4; 9.1.

Klitzman, Robert; Kirshenbaum, Sheri; Kittel, Lauren; Morin, Stephen; Daya, Shaira; Mastrogiacomo, Maddalena; Rotheram-Borus, Mary Jane. Naming names: perceptions of name-based HIV reporting, partner notification, and criminalization of non-disclosure among persons living with HIV. *Sexuality Research and Social Policy* 2004; 1(3): 38-57. [Online]. Accessed: http://caliber.ucpress.net/doi/pdf/10.1525/srsp.2004.1.3.38 [2006 November 27]. NRCBL: 9.5.6; 8.4; 9.1; 1.3.5.

Koester, Kimberly A.; Maiorana, Andre; Vernon, Karen; Charlebois, Edwin; Gaffney, Stuart; Lane, Tim; Morin, Stephen F. HIV surveillance in theory and practice: assessing the acceptability of California's non-name HIV surveillance regulations. *Health Policy* 2006 August 22; 78(1): 101-110. NRCBL: 9.5.6; 9.1; 8.4. SC: an.

Lowbury, Ruth; Kinghorn, George R. Criminal prosecution for HIV transmission [editorial]. *BMJ: British Medical Journal* 2006 September 30; 333(7570): 666-667. NRCBL: 9.5.6; 8.4. SC: le. Identifiers: United Kingdom (Great Britain).

Luginaah, Isaac N.; Yiridoe, Emmanuel K.; Taabazuing, Mary-Margaret. From mandatory to voluntary testing: balancing human rights, religious and cultural values, and HIV/AIDS prevention in Ghana. *Social Science and Medicine* 2005 October; 61(8): 1689-1700. NRCBL: 9.5.6; 9.1; 1.2; 8.4. SC: em.

Luxembourg. Commission Consultative Nationale d'Éthique pour les Sciences de la Vie et de la Santé [CNE]. Avis au sujet de tests de dépistage obligatoires de l'infection par le virus HIV: Avis 1992.1 [Opinion on the subject of compulsory screening tests for infection by the HIV virus: Opinion 1992.1]. Luxembourg: Commission Nationale d'Éthique, 1992 June 12; 9 p. [Online]. Accessed: http://www.cne.public.lu/publications/avis/1992_1.pdf [2006 April 7]. NRCBL: 9.5.6; 8.3.1; 8.4. Note: Adopted unanimously by commission members present at the time of the plenary session of 12 June 1992.

Macklin, Ruth. No shortage of dilemmas: comment on "they call it 'patient selection' in Khayelitsha". *CQ: Cambridge Quarterly of Healthcare Ethics* 2006 Summer; 15(3): 313-321. NRCBL: 9.5.6; 9.5.1; 9.7; 9.4; 8.3.4; 8.4; 1.1. Comments: Renée C. Rox, Eric Goemaere. They call it "patient selection" in Khayelitsha: the experience of Médecins Sans Frontières-South Africa in enrolling patients to receive antiretroviral treatment for HIV/AIDS. CQ: Cambridge Quarterly of Healthcare Ethics 2006 Summer; 15(3): 302-312.

Marceau, Emmanuelle. Australia: court orders doctors to pay damages to woman who contracted HIV from her husband [news]. *HIV/AIDS Policy and Law Review* 2003 August; 8(2): 48-51. NRCBL: 9.5.6; 8.4. SC: le.

Melchert, Timothy P.; Patterson, Michele M. Duty to warn and interventions with HIV-positive clients. *Professional Psychology: Research and Practice* 1999 April; 30(2): 180-186. NRCBL: 9.5.6; 8.1; 8.4; 17.1. SC: le.

Mills, Edward; Rennie, Stuart; Wu, Zunyou; Sun, Xinhua; Sullivan, Sheena G.; Detels, Roger. HIV testing and individual rights [letter and response]. *Science* 2006 October 20; 314(5798): 417-419. NRCBL: 9.5.6; 9.1; 8.4. Identifiers: China.

Moss, Sheila; Williams, Olwen E.; Hind, Charles R.K. Counselling for an HIV test. *Postgraduate Medical Journal* 1996 February; 72(844): 84-86. NRCBL: 9.5.6; 8.1; 8.3.1; 8.4.

NRCBL: National Reference Center for Bioethics Literature Classification Scheme   See inside front cover for terms.

33

Nelson, John. English court upholds ban on newspaper publishing identity of HIV-positive health-care worker. *HIV/AIDS Policy and Law Review* 2002 July; 7(1): 54-55. NRCBL: 9.5.6; 8.4. SC: le. Identifiers: United Kingdom (Great Britain).

Obi, Samuel N.; Ifebunandu, Ngozi A. Consequences of HIV testing without consent. *International Journal of STD and AIDS* 2006 February; 17(2): 93-96. NRCBL: 9.5.6; 8.3.1; 9.1; 8.1; 8.4. SC: em. Identifiers: Nigeria.

Sfikas, Peter M. HIV in the workplace: Workers' Compensation Act trumps privacy right in Kentucky court case. *Journal of the American Dental Association* 2005 August; 136(8): 1169-1170. NRCBL: 9.5.6; 8.4; 16.3.

Smagata, David. Workers' compensation claims and disclosure. *Canadian HIV/AIDS Policy and Law Newsletter* 1997-1998 Winter; 3(4)-4(1): 15-16. NRCBL: 9.5.6; 8.4. SC: le.

Thorne, C.; Newell, M.L.; Peckham, C.S. Disclosure of diagnosis and planning for the future in HIV-affected families in Europe. *Child: Care, Health and Development* 2000 January; 26(1): 29-40. NRCBL: 9.5.6; 9.5.7; 8.2; 8.4; 21.1. SC: em.

Warburton, Damian. Confidentiality and HIV: ethical issues in the care of patients with HIV. *British Journal of Hospital Medicine (London)* 2005 September; 66(9): 525-528. NRCBL: 9.5.6; 8.4.

Wood, Robert W.; Hopkins, Sharon G.; Peppert, John F.; Jourden, Jack. The Washington state "name-to-code" HIV reporting system: a public health perspective. *Journal of Public Health Management and Practice* 2002; 8(6): 1-14. NRCBL: 9.5.6; 9.1; 8.4; 1.3.5.

AIDS/ HUMAN EXPERIMENTATION

Compassionate access to investigational therapies. *Canadian HIV/AIDS Policy and Law Newsletter* 1996 October; 3(1): 1, 41-43. NRCBL: 9.5.6; 9.7; 18.2.

Ahmad, Khabir. Ethics of AIDS drug trials on foster children questioned [news]. *Lancet Infectious Diseases* 2005 June; 5(6): 333-334. NRCBL: 9.5.6; 9.5.7; 9.7; 18.2; 18.5.2; 1.3.5.

Alexandrova, Anna. Legal and ethical issues in microbicides research and development in Canada. *HIV/AIDS Policy and Law Review* 2004 August; 9(2): 39-42. NRCBL: 9.5.6; 9.5.5; 18.2; 9.7.

Bélisle, Jean-Pierre; Binder, Louise. Newly infected people and clinical trials: ethical issues. *Canadian HIV/AIDS Policy and Law Newsletter* 1999 Summer; 4(4): 1, 19-20. NRCBL: 9.5.6; 18.3; 18.5.1.

Bloom, Barry R.; Rothman, David J. Medical morals: an exchange [letter and reply]. *New York Review of Books* 2001 March 8; 48(4): 5 p. [Online] Accessed: http://www.nybooks.com/articles/14108 [2006 October 30]. NRCBL: 9.5.6; 1.3.9; 18.2; 18.6. Identifiers: HIV/AIDS.

Dodier, Nicolas. Transnational medicine in public arenas: AIDS treatments in the South. *Culture, Medicine and Psychiatry* 2005 September; 29(3): 285-307. NRCBL: 9.5.6; 18.5.1; 9.7; 21.1.

Institute of Medical Ethics (Great Britain). Working Party on the Ethical Implications of AIDS. AIDS, ethics, and clinical trials. *BMJ: British Medical Journal* 1992 September 19; 305(6855): 699-701. NRCBL: 9.5.6; 18.5.1; 18.2.

Jürgens, Ralf. Dublin declaration on HIV/AIDS in prisons launched. *HIV/AIDS Policy and Law Review* 2004 April; 9(1): 40-45. NRCBL: 9.5.6; 9.2; 18.5.5; 21.1.

Kirby, Michael. HIV vaccine: ethics and human rights. *Canadian HIV/AIDS Policy and Law Newsletter* 2000 Spring-Summer; 5(2-3): 16-20. NRCBL: 9.5.6; 9.7; 18.2.

Lie, Reidar K.; Emanuel, Ezekiel J.; Grady, Christine. Circumcision and HIV prevention research: an ethical analysis. *Lancet* 2006 August 5-11; 368(9534): 522-525. NRCBL: 9.5.6; 9.5.1; 10; 18.2.

Macklin, Ruth. Changing the presumption: providing ART to vaccine research patients. *American Journal of Bioethics [Online]*. 2006 January-February; 6(1): W1-W5. NRCBL: 9.5.6; 18.1; 9.7. Identifiers: Council for International Organizations of Medical Science; International Ethical Guidelines for Biomedical Research Involving Human Subjects; antiretroviral treatment.

Moutel, Grégoire; Duchange, Nathalie; Raffi, François; Sharara, Lama I.; Théodorou, Ioannis; Noël, Violaine; de Montgolfier, Sandrine; Callies, Ingrid; Bricaire, François; Hervé, Christian; Leport, Catherine. Communication of pharmacogenetic research results to HIV-infected treated patients: standpoints of professionals and patients. *European Journal of Human Genetics* 2005 September; 13(9): 1055-1062. NRCBL: 9.5.6; 15.1; 9.7; 18.5.1. SC: em.

Ogden, Russel. Ethical review in community-based HIV/AIDS research. *Canadian HIV/AIDS Policy and Law Newsletter* 1999 Fall-Winter; 5(1): 39-40. NRCBL: 9.5.6; 18.2. SC: rv.

Shaffer, D.N.; Yebei, V.N.; Ballidawa, J.B.; Sidle, J.E.; Greene, J.Y.; Meslin, E.M.; Kimaiyo, S.J.N.; Tierney, W.M. Equitable treatment for HIV/AIDS clinical trial participants: a focus group study of patients, clinical researchers, and administrators in western Kenya. *Journal of Medical Ethics* 2006 January; 32(1): 55-60. NRCBL: 9.5.6; 9.7; 18.5.1. SC: em.

Abstract: OBJECTIVES: To describe the concerns and priorities of key stakeholders in a developing country regarding ethical obligations held by researchers and perceptions of equity or "what is fair" for study participants in an HIV/AIDS clinical drug trial. DESIGN: Qualitative study with focus groups. SETTING: Teaching and referral hospital and rural health centre in Western Kenya. PARTICIPANTS: Potential HIV/AIDS clinical trial participants, clinician researchers, and administrators. RESULTS: Eighty nine individuals participated in a total of 11 focus groups over a four month period. The desire for continued drug therapy, most often life long, following an HIV/AIDS clinical trial was the most common priority expressed in all focus groups. Patients with and without HIV/AIDS also thought subsidizing of drug therapies and education were critical forms of compensation for clinical trial participation. Financial incentives were considered important primarily for purchasing drug therapy as well as obtaining food. Patients noted a concern for the potential mismanagement of any money offered. Clinician researchers and administrators felt strongly that researchers have a moral obligation to participants following a trial to provide continued drug therapy, adverse event monitoring, and primary care. Finally, clinician researchers and administrators stressed the need for thorough informed consent to avoid coercion of study participants. CONCLUSIONS: Kenyan patients, clinician researchers, and administrators believe that it would be unfair to stop antiretroviral therapy following an HIV/AIDS clinical trial and that researchers have a long term obligation to participants.

Slack, C.; Stobie, M.; Milford, C.; Lindegger, G.; Wassenaar, D.; Strode, A.; Ijsselmuiden, C. Provision of HIV treatment in HIV preventive vaccine trials: a developing country perspective. *Social Science and Medicine* 2005 March; 60(6): 1197-1208. NRCBL: 9.5.6; 9.7; 18.2; 18.5.9; 1.1.

Strode, Ann; Slack, Catherine; Mushariwa, Muriel. HIV vaccine research — South Africa's ethical-legal framework and its ability to promote the welfare of trial participants. *South African Medical Journal* 2005 August; 95(8): 598-601. NRCBL: 9.5.6; 18.5.1; 18.2; 18.6.

Thomas, Kim. HIV study among pregnant aboriginal women raises concerns. *HIV/AIDS Policy and Law Review* 2002 December; 7(2-3): 33-34. NRCBL: 9.5.6; 18.5.1; 18.5.3. Identifiers: Canada.

Weait, Matthew; Azad, Yusef. The criminalization of HIV transmission in England and Wales: questions of law and policy. *HIV/AIDS Policy and Law Review* 2005 August; 10(2): 1, 5-12. NRCBL: 9.5.6; 1.3.5; 18.4; 8.3.1. SC: le.

Wright, Alexi A.; Katz, Ingrid T. Home testing for HIV. *New England Journal of Medicine* 2006 February 2; 354(5): 437-440. NRCBL: 9.5.6; 9.1; 18.5.1.

AIDS/ LEGAL ASPECTS

El Salvador: legislature removes law allowing pre-employment HIV testing [news]. *HIV/AIDS Policy and Law Review* 2002 December; 7(2-3): 49. NRCBL: 9.5.6; 16.3. SC: le.

New York policy on HIV testing of newborns. *Canadian HIV/AIDS Policy and Law Newsletter* 1996 January; 2(2): 15. NRCBL: 9.5.6; 9.5.8; 8.3.2. SC: le.

UK: court orders publication ban in case of HIV-positive health-care worker [news]. *HIV/AIDS Policy and Law Review* 2002 March; 6(3): 74. NRCBL: 9.5.6; 8.4. SC: le. Identifiers: United Kingdom (Great Britain).

de Bruyn, Theodore; Elliott, Richard. Compulsory HIV testing after an occupational exposure. *HIV/AIDS Policy and Law Review* 2002 March; 6(3): 1, 24-31. NRCBL: 9.5.6. SC: le. Identifiers: Ontario.

Elliott, Richard. HIV testing and treatment of children. *Canadian HIV/AIDS Policy and Law Newsletter* 1999 Fall-Winter; 5(1): 1, 3-9. NRCBL: 9.5.6; 8.3.2; 9.5.8. SC: le.

Elliott, Richard. Medical treatment of children with HIV/AIDS. *Canadian HIV/AIDS Policy and Law Newsletter* 2000 Spring-Summer; 5(2-3): 5-7. NRCBL: 9.5.6; 8.3.2. SC: le.

Elliott, Richard. US: appeals court dismisses employment discrimination suit by HIV-positive dental hygienist. *HIV/AIDS Policy and Law Review* 2002 March; 6(3): 70-71. NRCBL: 9.5.6; 9.8. SC: le.

Elliott, Richard. US: hospital negligent for failing to warn prior patient of risk of HIV infection by transfusion. *HIV/AIDS Policy and Law Review* 2002 March; 6(3): 71-72. NRCBL: 9.5.6; 8.4; 19.4; 8.5. SC: le.

Elliott, Richard. US: Supreme Court refuses to hear case of fired HIV-positive dental hygienist. *HIV/AIDS Policy and Law Review* 2003 April; 8(1): 76. NRCBL: 9.5.6; 16.3. SC: le.

Fisher, Ann Hilton; Hanssens, Catherine; Schulman, David I. The CDC's routine HIV testing recommendation: legally, not so routine. *HIV/AIDS Policy and Law Review* 2006 December; 11(2-3): 17-20. NRCBL: 9.5.6; 8.3.1. SC: le. Identifiers: Centers for Disease Control and Prevention.

Fluss, Sev S. AIDS: toward a regulatory history. *Canadian HIV/AIDS Policy and Law Newsletter* 1995 January; 1(2): 10-11. NRCBL: 9.5.6; 21.1. SC: le.

Gerntholtz, Liesl. Preventing mother-to-child transmission: landmark decision by South African court. *HIV/AIDS Policy and Law Review* 2002 March; 6(3): 1, 20-24. NRCBL: 9.5.6; 9.5.8; 9.2. SC: le.

Gerntholtz, Liesl. South Africa: highest court orders government to provide antiretrovirals to prevent mother-to-child transmission. *HIV/AIDS Policy and Law Review* 2002 December; 7(2-3): 50-52. NRCBL: 9.5.6; 9.2; 9.5.8; 9.5.7. SC: le.

Gibson, Katie. Sweden's compulsory confinement order declared a violation of liberty guarantee. *HIV/AIDS Policy and Law Review* 2005 August; 10(2): 49-50. NRCBL: 9.5.6; 9.1. SC: le.

NRCBL: National Reference Center for Bioethics Literature Classification Scheme   See inside front cover for terms.

35

Hammer, Peter J. Differential pricing of essential AIDS drugs: markets, politics and public health. *Journal of International Economic Law* 2002 December; 5(4): 883-912. NRCBL: 9.5.6; 9.7; 21.1; 9.3.1. SC: le.

Ho, Wing Wah; Brandfield, Julie; Retkin, Randye; Laraque, Danielle. Complexities in HIV consent in adolescents. *Clinical Pediatrics* 2005 July-August; 44(6): 473-478. NRCBL: 9.5.6; 9.5.7; 8.3.1; 8.3.2; 8.4; 7.1. SC: le.

Jürgens, Ralf. HIV testing for peacekeeping forces: legal and human rights issues. *HIV/AIDS Policy and Law Review* 2002 December; 7(2-3): 111-114. NRCBL: 9.5.6; 21.1; 8.3.4; 8.4. SC: le.

Jürgens, Ralf. No compulsory HIV-antibody testing of persons accused or convicted of sexual assault. *Canadian HIV/AIDS Policy and Law Newsletter* 1995 April; 1(3): 1, 12-14. NRCBL: 9.5.6; 8.3.4. SC: le.

Jürgens, Ralf. Testing of pregnant women: issues and opinions. *Canadian HIV/AIDS Policy and Law Newsletter* 1997 Spring; 3(2-3): 1, 54-60. NRCBL: 9.5.6; 9.5.8; 9.5.5; 8.3.4. SC: le.

Lowbury, Ruth; Kinghorn, George R. Criminal prosecution for HIV transmission [editorial]. *BMJ: British Medical Journal* 2006 September 30; 333(7570): 666-667. NRCBL: 9.5.6; 8.4. SC: le. Identifiers: United Kingdom (Great Britain).

MacAdam, Philip. New Ontario legislation important for persons living with HIV/AIDS. *Canadian HIV/AIDS Policy and Law Newsletter* 1995 April; 1(3): 10-11. NRCBL: 9.5.6; 8.3.3. SC: le.

Marceau, Emmanuelle. Australia: court orders doctors to pay damages to woman who contracted HIV from her husband [news]. *HIV/AIDS Policy and Law Review* 2003 August; 8(2): 48-51. NRCBL: 9.5.6; 8.4. SC: le.

Martin, Erika G.; Pollack, Harold A.; Paltiel, A. David. Fact, fiction, and fairness: resource allocation under the Ryan White CARE Act. *Health Affairs* 2006 July-August; 25(4): 1103-1112. NRCBL: 9.5.6; 9.3.1; 9.4. SC: em; le.

Matiation, Stefan. HIV/AIDS and aboriginal communities: problems of jurisdiction and discrimination: a review. *Canadian HIV/AIDS Policy and Law Newsletter* 1996 October; 3(1): 1, 47-48. NRCBL: 9.5.6; 9.5.4. SC: le; rv.

Melchert, Timothy P.; Patterson, Michele M. Duty to warn and interventions with HIV-positive clients. *Professional Psychology: Research and Practice* 1999 April; 30(2): 180-186. NRCBL: 9.5.6; 8.1; 8.4; 17.1. SC: le.

Nderitu, Terri. Balancing pills and patents: intellectual property and the HIV/AIDS crisis. *E Law: Murdoch University Electronic Journal of Law* 2001 September; 8(3): 14 p. [Online]. Accessed: http://www.murdoch.edu.au/

elaw/issues/v8n3/nderitu83_text.html [2006 August 2]. NRCBL: 9.5.6; 9.7; 21.1. SC: le.

Nelson, John. English court upholds ban on newspaper publishing identity of HIV-positive health-care worker. *HIV/AIDS Policy and Law Review* 2002 July; 7(1): 54-55. NRCBL: 9.5.6; 8.4. SC: le. Identifiers: United Kingdom (Great Britain).

Nelson, John. HIV-positive child made ward of court after father refuses treatment with antiretroviral drugs. *HIV/AIDS Policy and Law Review* 2002 July; 7(1): 53-54. NRCBL: 9.5.6; 9.5.7; 8.3.2. SC: le.

Pancevski, Bojan. Swiss judge orders HIV positive woman to disclose partners' names [news]. *BMJ: British Medical Journal* 2006 April 8; 332(7545): 809. NRCBL: 9.5.6; 8.1. SC: le.

Patterson, David. Québec court finds asymptomatic HIV infection a charter "handicap": Hamel v Malaxos [news]. *Canadian HIV/AIDS Policy and Law Newsletter* 1994 October; 1(1): 1,3-4. NRCBL: 9.5.6; 8.1. SC: le.

Scheer, Rebecca. Alberta: new bill will allow for mandatory HIV testing in emergency situations [news]. *HIV/AIDS Policy and Law Review* 2004 April; 9(1): 20-21. NRCBL: 9.5.6; 8.3.4. SC: le.

Smagata, David. Workers' compensation claims and disclosure. *Canadian HIV/AIDS Policy and Law Newsletter* 1997-1998 Winter; 3(4)-4(1): 15-16. NRCBL: 9.5.6; 8.4. SC: le.

United States. Congress. House. United States Leadership Against HIV/AIDS, Tuberculosis, and Malaria Act of 2003. [approved: 2003 May 27]. United States: Public Law 108-025 [HR 1298], 117 Stat. 2003 May 27: 711-750 [Online]. Accessed: http://frwebgate.access.gpo.gov/cgi-bin/getdoc/cgi?dbname=108_cong_public_laws&docid=f:publ025.108.pdf [2006 February 22]. NRCBL: 9.5.6; 21.1; 1.3.5; 9.5.1; 9.7. SC: le. Identifiers: 108th Congress.

United States. Court of Appeals. First Circuit. Abbott v. Bragdon [Date of Decision: 1997 March 5]. *Federal Reporter*, 3d Series 1997; 107: 934-949. NRCBL: 9.5.6; 9.2; 4.2. SC: le.
 Abstract: Court Decision: 107 Federal Reporter, 3rd Series, 934; 1997 March 5 (date of decision). The United States Court of Appeals for the First Circuit held that HIV infection interferes with reproduction and is therefore a disability under the Americans with Disabilities Act. Ms. Abbott was a patient of Dr. Bragdon, a dentist. She was HIV positive and asymptomatic. Bragdon refused to fill a cavity in his office for that reason. He offered to treat her within a hospital setting, but at greater cost to her. She brought suit under the ADA alleging that her status as HIV positive was a disability. The First Circuit agreed, finding that being HIV positive had a profound impact upon her ability to engage in intimate sexual activity, gestation, childbirth, child rearing and nurturing familial relations. The Court held that these activities were all major life activities, not lifestyle choices, and that Ms. Abbott was disabled for the purposes of the ADA.

United States. District Court, District of Maine.
Bragdon v. Abbott [Date of Decision: 22 December 1995].
Federal Supplement 1995; 912: 580-596. NRCBL: 9.5.6;
9.2; 4.2. SC: le.

Abstract: Court Decision: 912 Federal Supplement 580; 1995
December 22 (date of decision). The U.S. District Court for the
District of Maine held that a dentist violated the Americans with
Disabilities Act of 1990 ("ADA") and the Maine Human Rights
Act ("MHRA") in refusing to fill the cavity of a person infected
with HIV, wholly asymptomatic. The dentist had agreed to fill
the patient's cavity, yet only in a hospital with the patient to pay
the dentist's normal fee in addition to any hospital charges. The
court held that asymptomatic HIV infection constitutes a physical impairment for the purposes of the ADA and the MHRA as it
interferes with the major life activities of reproduction. Similarly, the court held that here the dentist could not prove that the
patient or her treatment posed a direct threat to the health or
safety of others. In its analysis, the court rejected the CDC recommendations as to the employment of HIV infected health
care workers as the risk at issue was not the transmission of HIV
from worker to patient, but that of patient to dentist infection, a
case in which the professional controls the risk of infection. Finally, the court rejected the dentist's arguments that the ADA,
as applied here, violated the Interstate Commerce Clause, the
Due Process Right to freedom from unjustified intrusions on
personal security, and the Due Process Right to freedom to contract. The court enjoined the dentist from refusing to provide
treatment solely based on HIV positive status without making
an individualized assessment. [KIE/SP]

Weait, Matthew; Azad, Yusef. The criminalization of
HIV transmission in England and Wales: questions of law
and policy. *HIV/AIDS Policy and Law Review* 2005 August; 10(2): 1, 5-12. NRCBL: 9.5.6; 1.3.5; 18.4; 8.3.1. SC:
le.

ALLOCATION *See* ORGAN AND TISSUE
TRANSPLANTATION/ ALLOCATION; RE-
SOURCE ALLOCATION

ALLOWING TO DIE *See* EUTHANASIA AND
ALLOWING TO DIE

ANIMAL EXPERIMENTATION

A matter of life and death [news]. *Nature* 2006 December
14; 442(7121): 807. NRCBL: 22.2.

An open debate [editorial]. *Nature* 2006 December 14;
442(7121): 789-790. NRCBL: 22.2. Identifiers: animal
experimentation.

Last rights [editorial]. *Nature* 2006 June 1; 441(7093):
550. NRCBL: 22.2; 20.1. Identifiers: laboratory animals.

Resisting terrorism [editorial]. *Nature* 2006 September 14;
443(7108): 122. NRCBL: 22.2.

Stand up and be counted [editorial]. *New Scientist* 2006
March 4-10; 189(2541): 5. NRCBL: 22.2; 5.1.

Allen, Colin. Ethics and the science of animal minds. *Theoretical Medicine and Bioethics* 2006; 27(4): 375-394.
NRCBL: 22.1; 1.1. SC: an.

Abstract: Ethicists have commonly appealed to science to bol-
ster their arguments for elevating the moral status of nonhuman
animals. I describe a framework within which I take many
ethicists to be making such appeals. I focus on an apparent gap
in this framework between those properties of animals that are
part of the scientific consensus, and those to which ethicists typically appeal in their arguments. I will describe two different
ways of diminishing the appearance of the gap, and argue that
both of them present challenges to ethicists seeking a firm scientific basis for their claims about the moral status of animals. I
argue that more clarity about the role of appeals to science by
applied ethicists leads to questions about the effectiveness of
such appeals, and that these questions might best be pursued
empirically.

Archibald, Kathy. No need for monkeys [letter]. *New Scientist* 2006 July 1-7; 191(2558): 26. NRCBL: 22.2.

Aziz, Tipu. Essential Animals [letter]. *New Scientist* 2006
August 5-11; 191(2563): 20. NRCBL: 22.2.

Balls, Michael. Animal experimentation: should the three
Rs be abandoned? [editorial]. *ATLA: Alternatives to Laboratory Animals* 2006 May; 34(2): 139-141. NRCBL: 22.2;
22.1.

Balls, Michael. Future improvements: replacement in vitro methods. *ILAR Journal* 2002; 43(supplement):
S69-S73. NRCBL: 22.2; 22.1; 5.2.

Balls, Michael. On facing up to risk and uncertainty in relation to animal and non-animal safety testing [editorial].
ATLA: Alternatives to Laboratory Animals 2006 December; 34(6): 547-549. NRCBL: 22.2.

Balls, Michael. Primates in medical research: the plot
thickens [editorial]. *ATLA: Alternatives to Laboratory Animals* 2006 June; 34(3): 271-272. NRCBL: 22.2.

Barilan, Y. Michael. Speciesism as a precondition to justice. *Politics and the Life Sciences* 2004 March; 23(1):
22-33. NRCBL: 22.1; 1.1.

Baumans, V. Science-based assessment of animal welfare: laboratory animals. *Revue Scientifique et Technique*
2005 August; 24(2): 503-513. NRCBL: 22.2; 22.1; 15.1.
Note: Abstract in English, French, and Spanish.

Bayvel, A.C.D. The use of animals in agriculture and science: historical context, international considerations and
future direction. *Revue Scientifique et Technique* 2005 August; 24(2): 791-813. NRCBL: 22.2; 22.3. Note: Full text
in English, French, and Spanish.

Brainard, Jeffrey. An activist group's hidden-camera investigation at Chapel Hill raises issues about colleges'
oversight of animal welfare. *Chronicle of Higher Education* 2006 March 3; 52(26): A21-A23. NRCBL: 22.2;
1.3.9.

Brainard, Jeffrey. Animal-rights groups fight colleges
over access to research records. *Chronicle of Higher Education* 2006 March 31; 52(30): A29. NRCBL: 22.1; 22.2.

NRCBL: National Reference Center for Bioethics Literature Classification Scheme   See inside front cover for terms.

37

Bryant, Taimie L. Animals unmodified: defining animals/defining human obligations to animals. *University of Chicago Legal Forum* 2006: 137-194. NRCBL: 22.1; 1.1; 16.1; 1.3.9; 4.4. SC: le.

Canadian Council on Animal Care [CCAC]; Olfert, Ernest; Bhasin, Jag; Latt, Richard; Macallum; McCutcheon, Kathie, Rainnie, Don; Schunk, Michael. CCAC guidelines on: choosing an appropriate endpoint in experiments using animals for research, teaching and testing. Ottawa: Canadian Council on Animal Care 1998: 24 p. [Online]. Accessed: http://www.ccac.ca/en/CCAC_Programs/Guidelines_Policies/PDFs/APPOPEN.pdf [2006 October 4]. NRCBL: 22.2.

Carroll, Robert G. Using animals in teaching: APS position statement and rationale. *Physiologist* 2005 August; 48(4): 206-208. NRCBL: 22.2; 7.2; 6. Identifiers: American Physiological Society.

Cavalieri, Paola. The animal debate: a reexamination. *In:* Singer, Peter, ed. In Defense of Animals: The Second Wave. Malden, MA: Blackwell Pub.; 2006: 54-68. NRCBL: 22.1; 1.1.

Combes, Robert. SPEAK v. pro-test — the Newsnight animal experimentation debate — round 1 [editorial]. *ATLA: Alternatives to Laboratory Animals* 2006 October; 34(5): 463-465. NRCBL: 22.2.

Conlee, Kathleen M.; Boysen, Sarah T. Chimpanzees in research: past, present, and future. *In:* Salem, Deborah J.; Rowan, Andrew N., eds. The State of the Animals III, 2005. Washington, DC: Humane Society Press, 2005: 119-133. NRCBL: 22.2.

Cyranoski, David. Primates in the frame [news]. *Nature* 2006 December 14; 442(7121): 812-813. NRCBL: 22.2. Identifiers: Europe.

Davey, Gareth. Chinese university students' attitudes towards the ethical treatment and welfare of animals. *Journal of Applied Animal Welfare Science* 2006; 9(4): 289-297. NRCBL: 22.1. SC: em.

Day, Michael. Experts say research on primates is vital to fight disease [news]. *BMJ: British Medical Journal* 2006 December 16; 333(7581): 1235. NRCBL: 22.2. Identifiers: United Kingdom (Great Britain).

De Simone, F.; Serratosa, J. Biotechnology, animal health and animal welfare within the framework of European Union legislation. *Revue Scientifique et Technique* 2005 April; 24(1): 89-99. NRCBL: 22.2; 21.1. SC: le. Note: Abstract available in English, French, and Spanish.

DeGrazia, David. On the question of personhood beyond homo sapiens. *In:* Singer, Peter, ed. In Defense of Animals: The Second Wave. Malden, MA: Blackwell Pub.; 2006: 40-53. NRCBL: 22.1; 4.4.

DeGrazia, David. Regarding animals: mental life, moral status, and use in biomedical research: an introduction to the special issue. *Theoretical Medicine and Bioethics* 2006; 27(4): 277-284. NRCBL: 22.2; 22.1; 1.1.

Demers, Gilles; Griffin, Gilly; De Vroey, Guy; Haywood, Joseph R.; Zurlo, Joanne. Harmonization of animal care and use guidance. *Science* 2006 May 5; 312(5774): 700-701. NRCBL: 22.2; 22.1.

Dombrowski, Daniel A. Is the argument from marginal cases obtuse? *Journal of Applied Philosophy* 2006; 23(2): 223-232. NRCBL: 22.1; 1.1. SC: an. Identifiers: Elizabeth Anderson; Cora Diamond.
Abstract: Elizabeth Anderson claims that the argument from marginal cases is 'the central argument' behind the claim that nonhuman animals have rights. But she thinks, along with Cora Diamond, that the argument is 'obtuse'. Two different meanings could be intended here: that the argument from marginal cases is too blunt or dull to dissect the reasons why it makes sense to say that nonhuman animals have rights or that the argument from marginal cases is insensitive regarding nonrational human beings (the marginal cases of humanity). The purpose of the present article is to argue that, despite Anderson's and Diamond's nuanced and perceptive treatments of the argument from marginal cases, this argument is not obtuse in either sense of the term.

Doss, Sonia D. Clinical trial trouble: not responsible for reporting. *Lab Animal* 2006 June; 35(6): 16. NRCBL: 22.2; 1.3.5.

Eidgenössische Ethikkommission für die Gentechnik im ausserhumanen Bereich = Commission fédérale d'éthique pour le génie génétique dans le domaine non humain = Commissione federale d'etica per l'ingegneria genetica nei settore non umano = Swiss Ethics Committee on Non-Human Gene Technology [ECNH]. Statement on putting "the dignity of creation" into concrete terms as part of the planned revision of the Animal Protection Law. Bern, Switzerland: Swiss Ethics Committee on Non-Human Gene Technology, 1999 November 17; 10 p. [Online]. Accessed: http://www.umwelt-schweiz.ch/imperia/md/content/ekah/16.pdf [2006 April 6]. NRCBL: 22.1.; 15.1; 22.2. Identifiers: Switzerland.

Engel, Mylan, Jr. The mere considerability of animals. *Acta Analytica* 2001; 16(27): 89-107. NRCBL: 22.1; 22.2. SC: an.

Epstein, Alex. The "animal rights" movement's cruelty to humans. *Physiologist* 2005 October; 48(5): 223, 225. NRCBL: 22.1; 18.1.

European Commission. Directorate General XI [DGXI]; Close, Bryony; Banister, Keith; Baumans, Vera; Bernoth, Eva-Maria; Bromage, Niall; Bunyan, John; Erhardt, Wolff; Flecknell, Paul; Gregory, Neville; Hackbarth, Hansjoachim; Morton, David; Warwick, Clifford. Recommendations for euthanasia of experimental animals: part 1. *Laboratory Animals* 1996;

30: 293-316. [Online]. Accessed: http://www.lal.org.uk/ workp.html [2006 October 5]. NRCBL: 22.2; 20.1. SC: rv.

European Commission. Directorate General XI [DGXI]; Close, Bryony; Banister, Keith; Baumans, Vera; Bernoth, Eva-Maria; Bromage, Niall; Bunyan, John; Erhardt, Wolff; Flecknell, Paul; Gregory, Neville; Hackbarth, Hansjoachim; Morton, David; Warwick, Clifford. Recommendations for euthanasia of experimental animals: part 2. *Laboratory Animals* 1997; 31: 1-32. [Online]. Accessed: http://www.lal.org.uk/ workp.html [2006 October 5]. NRCBL: 22.2; 20.1. SC: rv.

Fellenz, Marc R. Animal experimentation. *In:* Mitcham, Carl, ed. Encyclopedia of Science, Technology, and Ethics. Farmington Hills, MI: Thomson/Gale, 2005: 72-74. NRCBL: 22.2.

Fellenz, Marc R. Animal rights. *In:* Mitcham, Carl, ed. Encyclopedia of Science, Technology, and Ethics. Farmington Hills, MI: Thomson/Gale, 2005: 74-77. NRCBL: 22.1.

Francione, Gary L. Equal consideration and the interest of nonhuman animals in continued existence: a response to Professor Sunstein. *University of Chicago Legal Forum* 2006: 231-252. NRCBL: 22.1; 1.1; 4.4. SC: le.

Fuchs, Bruce A.; Macrina, Francis L. Use of animals in biomedical experimentation. *In:* Macrina, Francis L., ed. Scientific Integrity: Text and Cases in Responsible Conduct of Research. 3rd ed. Washington, DC: ASM Press; 2005: 127-157. NRCBL: 22.2.

Garner, Robert. Animals, medical science and consumer protection. *In his:* Animals, Politics and Morality. 2nd ed. New York: Manchester University Press; 2004: 126-161. NRCBL: 22.2.

Gauthier, C.; Griffin, G. Using animals in research, testing and teaching. *Revue Scientifique et Technique* 2005 August; 24(2): 735-745. NRCBL: 22.2. Note: Abstract in English, French and Spanish.

Gilbert, Scott F.; Tyler, Anna L.; Zackin, Emily J. The ethics of animal use in research. *In their:* Bioethics and the New Embryology: Springboards for Debate. Sunderland, MA: Sinauer Associates; 2005: 241-261. NRCBL: 22.2.

Giles, Jim. Animal experiments under fire for poor design [news]. *Nature* 2006 December 21-28; 444(7122): 981. NRCBL: 22.2.

Gipson, Chester; Wigglesworth, Carol. A word from USDA and OLAW. *Lab Animal* 2006 June; 35(6): 17. NRCBL: 22.2; 1.3.5. Identifiers: Office of Laboratory Animal Welfare (OLAW).

Gluck, John P.; Bell, Jordan B.; Pearson-Bish, Melody. Confronting ethical issues in the use of animals in biomedical and behavioral research: the search for principles. *In:* O'Donohue, William; Ferguson, Kyle, eds. Handbook of

Professional Ethics for Psychologists: Issues, Questions, and Controversies. Thousand Oaks, Calif.: SAGE Publications; 2003: 257-274. NRCBL: 22.2.

Goldberg, Alan M.; Hartung, Thomas. Protecting more than animals. *Scientific American* 2006 January; 294(1): 84-91. NRCBL: 22.2. SC: em; le.

Goldenberg, Saul. Ethical aspects when using animals in research [editorial]. *Pesquisa Odontológica Brasileira/ Brazilian Oral Research* 2005 January-March; 19(1): 1-2. NRCBL: 22.2; 22.1.

Goodman, Neville. Animal welfare, human health. *British Journal of Hospital Medicine* 2005 October; 66(10): 593. NRCBL: 22.2.

Hackam, Daniel G.; Redelmeier, Donald A. Translation of research evidence from animals to humans [letter]. *JAMA: The Journal of the American Medical Association* 2006 October 11; 296(14): 1731-1732. NRCBL: 22.2. SC: em.

Hagelin, Joakim. Use of nonhuman primates in research in Sweden: 25 year longitudinal survey. *ALTEX* 2005; 22(1): 13-18. NRCBL: 22.2. SC: rv.

Hill, Lori R. Response to protocol review scenario: did the right thing. *Lab Animal* 2006 June; 35(6): 15-16. NRCBL: 22.2.

Höfer, Thomas; Gerner, Ingrid; Gundert-Remy, Ursula; Liebsch, Manfred; Schulte, Agnes; Spielmann, Horst; Vogel, Richard; Wettig, Klaus. Animal testing and alternative approaches for the human health risk assessment under the proposed new European chemicals regulation. *Archives of Toxicology* 2004 October; 78(10): 549-564. NRCBL: 22.2; 5.2; 21.1. SC: em.

Hopkin, Michael. Demo backs animal lab in Oxford [news]. *Nature* 2006 March 2; 440(7080): 10-11. NRCBL: 22.2. Identifiers: United Kingdom (Great Britain).

Hudson, Michelle; Bhogal, Nirmala. An analysis of the home office statistics of scientific procedures on living animals, Great Britain 2004. *ATLA: Alternatives to Laboratory Animals* 2006 February; 34(1): 85-103. NRCBL: 22.2; 21.1; 15.1. SC: em.

Huxley, Andrew. Testing is necessary on animals as well as in vitro [letter]. *Nature* 2006 January 12; 439(7073): 138. NRCBL: 22.2.

Ibrahim, Darian N. Reduce, refine, replace: the failure of the three R's and the future of animal experimentation. *University of Chicago Legal Forum* 2006: 195-229. NRCBL: 22.2; 1.3.9.

International Council for Laboratory Animal Science [ICLAS]. International harmonisation of guidelines on humane endpoints. Nantes, France: International Council for Laboratory Animal Science 2005 May 9: 4 p. [Online].

NRCBL: National Reference Center for Bioethics Literature Classification Scheme   See inside front cover for terms.

39

Accessed: http://www.sciencemag.org/cgi/data/312/5774/700/DC1/1 [2006 October 4]. NRCBL: 22.2; 22.1; 21.1.

International Council for Laboratory Animal Science [ICLAS]; Demers, G. First ICLAS meeting for the harmonisation of guidelines on the use of animals in science (meeting for harmonisation of guidelines). *Nantes, France: Federation of European Laboratory Animal Science Associations [FELASA], Proceedings of the Ninth FELASA Symposium, International Harmonisation of Care and Use Issues* 2004 June 13 and 14; section 2: 40-44 [Online]. Accessed: http://www.lal.org.uk/pdffiles/FELASA/Section2.pdf [2006 October 4]. NRCBL: 22.2; 22.1; 21.1.

Jukes, Nick. Ukraine and Russia: major InterNICHE outreach: training in alternatives and replacement of animal experiments. *ALTEX: Alternativen zu Experimenten* 2005; 22(4): 269-274. NRCBL: 22.2.

Kaplan, Jay. Commentary: ethical issues surrounding the use of nonhuman primates in biomedical research. *In:* Turner, Trudy R. ed. Biological Anthropology and Ethics: From Repatriation to Genetic Identity. Albany, NY: State University of New York Press; 2005: 79-90. NRCBL: 22.2.

Kast, A. Memorial stones for the souls of animals killed for human welfare in Japan. *Berliner und Munchener Tierarztliche Wochenschrift* 1994 May; 107(5): 166-171. NRCBL: 22.1; 1.2; 7.1.

Kennedy, Donald. Animal activism: out of control [editorial]. *Science* 2006 September 15; 313(5793): 1541. NRCBL: 22.1; 1.3.5.

Kolar, Roman. Animal experimentation. *Science and Engineering Ethics* 2006 January; 12(1): 111-122. NRCBL: 22.2.

Lekan, Todd M. A pragmatist case for animal advocates on institutional animal care and use committees. *In:* McKenna, Erin; Light, Andrew, eds. Animal Pragmatism: Rethinking Human-Nonhuman Relationships. Bloomington, IN: Indiana University Press; 2004: 193-209. NRCBL: 22.2; 22.1.

Leslie, Jeff. Lay persons and community values in reviewing animal experimentation. *University of Chicago Legal Forum* 2006: 113-136. NRCBL: 22.2; 5.3; 1.3.9. SC: le.

Machan, Tibor R. Why human beings may use animals. *Journal of Value Inquiry* 2002; 36(1): 9-14. NRCBL: 22.1; 1.1.

Magnotti, Lauren. Giving a voice to those who can't speak for themselves: toward greater regulation of animal experimentation. *Buffalo Environmental Law Journal* 2006 Spring; 13(2): 179-204. NRCBL: 22.2; 5.3. SC: le.

Main, D.C.J. Offering the best to patients: ethical issues associated with the provision of veterinary services. *Veterinary Record* 2006 January 14; 158(2): 62-66. NRCBL: 22.1; 4.1.1; 9.3.1; 8.1.

Mameli, M.; Bortolotti, L. Animal rights, animal minds, and human mindreading. *Journal of Medical Ethics* 2006 February; 32(2): 84-89. NRCBL: 22.1; 22.2. SC: an.
  Abstract: Do non-human animals have rights? The answer to this question depends on whether animals have morally relevant mental properties. Mindreading is the human activity of ascribing mental states to other organisms. Current knowledge about the evolution and cognitive structure of mindreading indicates that human ascriptions of mental states to non-human animals are very inaccurate. The accuracy of human mindreading can be improved with the help of scientific studies of animal minds. However, the scientific studies do not by themselves solve the problem of how to map psychological similarities (and differences) between humans and animals onto a distinction between morally relevant and morally irrelevant mental properties. The current limitations of human mindreading - whether scientifically aided or not-have practical consequences for the rational justification of claims about which rights (if any) non-human animals should be accorded.

Marris, Emma. An easy way out? *Nature* 2006 June 1; 441(7093): 570-571. NRCBL: 22.2. Identifiers: laboratory animals.

Marris, Emma. Grey matter [news]. *Nature* 2006 December 14; 442(7121): 808-810. NRCBL: 22.2.

Matfield, Mark. With one voice: as the European Union updates its legislation on animal experiments, scientists must ensure that lawmakers are well informed. *New Scientist* 2006 November 11-17; 192(2577): 24. NRCBL: 22.2. SC: le.

Matheny, Gaverick. Utilitarianism and animals. *In:* Singer, Peter, ed. In Defense of Animals: The Second Wave. Malden, MA: Blackwell Pub.; 2006: 13-25. NRCBL: 22.1.

McTighe, Maggie. Clinical trial trouble: inform OLAW. *Lab Animal* 2006 June; 35(6): 16-17. NRCBL: 22.2.

Menache, Andre. Primate problem [letter]. *New Scientist* 2006 November 25-December 1; 192(2579): 23. NRCBL: 22.2.

Mepham, Ben. Experiments on animals. *In his:* Bioethics: An Introduction for the Biosciences. Oxford; New York: Oxford University Press; 2005: 179-201. NRCBL: 22.2.

Merali, Zeeya. Animal activists flee UK clampdown [news]. *New Scientist* 2006 May 13-19; 190(2551): 6-7. NRCBL: 22.2.

Moore, Andrew. What's in store for animal research in the EU? Researchers should have little to fear from the EU's new animal-welfare directive, but the menace is in the minutiae. *EMBO Reports* 2005 July; 6(7): 606-609. NRCBL: 22.2; 1.3.5; 21.1; 22.1.

Nussbaum, Martha C. The moral status of animals. *Chronicle of Higher Education* 2006 February 3; 52(22): B6-B8. NRCBL: 22.1; 1.1.

Organization for Economic Cooperation and Development [OECD]. Guidance document on the recognition, assessment, and use of clinical signs as humane endpoints for experimental animals used in safety evaluations. Paris: Organization for Economic Cooperation and Development, OECD Environmental Health and Safety Publications 2000 December 20; (19) : 39 p. [Online]. Accessed: http://www.olis.oecd.org/olis/2000doc.nsf/LinkTo/env-jm-mono(2000)7 [2006 October 4]. NRCBL: 22.2; 22.1; 21.1.

Perry, Baroness of Southwark. A response to reviews by Russell, Festing and Patel, Hendriksen, and Thomas on the Nuffield Council on Bioethics Report, The ethics of research involving animals. *ATLA: Alternatives to Laboratory Animals* 2006 May; 34(2): 255-259. NRCBL: 22.2.

Phaosavasdi, Sukhit; Thaneepanichskul, Surasak; Tannirandorn, Yuen; Thamkhantho, Manopchai; Pruksapong, Chumsak; Kanjanapitak, Aurchart; Leong, Hugh. Animals and ethics. *Journal of the Medical Association of Thailand* 2005 February; 88(2): 287-293. NRCBL: 22.1.

Qiu, Jane. Mighty mouse [news]. *Nature* 2006 December 14; 442(7121): 814-816. NRCBL: 22.2.

Radzikowski, Czeslaw. Protection of animal research subjects. *Science and Engineering Ethics* 2006 January; 12(1): 103-110. NRCBL: 22.2. SC: le; rv.

Richmond, Jon; Fletch, Andrew; Van Tongerloo, Robert. The international symposium on regulatory testing and animal welfare: recommendations on best scientific practices for animal care committees and animal use oversight. *ILAR Journal* 2002; 43(Supplement): S129-S132. NRCBL: 22.2. SC: le.

Rollin, Bernard E. Animal research. *In his:* Science and Ethics. New York: Cambridge University Press; 2006: 99-128. NRCBL: 22.2.

Rollin, Bernard E. Animal welfare. *In:* Mitcham, Carl, ed. Encyclopedia of Science, Technology, and Ethics. Farmington Hills, MI: Thomson/Gale, 2005: 80-83. NRCBL: 22.1; 1.3.11.

Rollin, Bernard E. The regulation of animal research and the emergence of animal ethics: a conceptual history. *Theoretical Medicine and Bioethics* 2006; 27(4): 285-304. NRCBL: 22.2; 1.1; 2.2; 22.1. SC: le.
Abstract: The history of the regulation of animal research is essentially the history of the emergence of meaningful social ethics for animals in society. Initially, animal ethics concerned itself solely with cruelty, but this was seen as inadequate to late 20(th)-century concerns about animal use. The new social ethic for animals was quite different, and its conceptual bases are explored in this paper. The Animal Welfare Act of 1966 repre-

sented a very minimal and in many ways incoherent attempt to regulate animal research, and is far from morally adequate. The 1985 amendments did much to render coherent the ethic for laboratory animals, but these standards were still inadequate in many ways, as enumerated here. The philosophy underlying these laws is explained, their main provisions are explored, and future directions that could move the ethic forward and further rationalize the laws are sketched.

Rowan, Andrew N. Animal activism and intimidation of scientists [letter]. *Science* 2006 November 10; 314(5801): 923. NRCBL: 22.2. Comments: Donald Kennedy. Animal activism out of control. Science 2006 September 15; 313(5793): 1541.

Royal College of Physicians of London. Position statement on the use of animals in medical research. London: Royal College of Physicians of London 2005 April 20; 1 p. [Online]. Accessed: http://www.rcplondon.ac.uk/college/statements/statements_animal_research.htm [2006 August 18]. NRCBL: 22.2; 6. Identifiers: United Kingdom (Great Britain). Note: Includes a printed copy of the home page of the Coalition for Medical Progress on research using animals which is linked to from the electronic version of the position statement.

Ryder, Richard D. Speciesism in the laboratory. *In:* Singer, Peter, ed. In Defense of Animals: The Second Wave. Malden, MA: Blackwell Pub.; 2006: 87-103. NRCBL: 22.2. SC: le.

Saucier, Donald A.; Cain, Mary E. The foundation of attitudes about animal research. *Ethics and Behavior* 2006; 16(2): 117-133. NRCBL: 22.2; 7.1. SC: em.

Schicktanz, Silke. Ethical considerations of the human-animal-relationship under conditions of asymmetry and ambivalence. *Journal of Agricultural and Environmental Ethics* 2006; 19(1): 7-16. NRCBL: 22.1; 15.1. SC: an. Identifiers: animal biotechnology; transgenic animals.

Shalev, Moshe. USDA revises policies on licensing of facilities and IACUC membership. *Lab Animal* 2006 June; 35(6): 13. NRCBL: 22.2.; 15.1; 14.5; 1.3.5.

Shapiro, Paul. Moral agency in other animals. *Theoretical Medicine and Bioethics* 2006; 27(4): 357-373. NRCBL: 22.1; 1.1. SC: an.
Abstract: Some philosophers have argued that moral agency is characteristic of humans alone and that its absence from other animals justifies granting higher moral status to humans. However, human beings do not have a monopoly on moral agency, which admits of varying degrees and does not require mastery of moral principles. The view that all and only humans possess moral agency indicates our underestimation of the mental lives of other animals. Since many other animals are moral agents (to varying degrees), they are also subject to (limited) moral obligations, examples of which are provided in this paper. But, while moral agency is sufficient for significant moral status, it is by no means necessary.

Silverman, Jerald. Clinical trial trouble. *Lab Animal* 2006 June; 35(6): 15. NRCBL: 22.2.

NRCBL: National Reference Center for Bioethics Literature Classification Scheme   See inside front cover for terms.

41

Smith, Kerri. Caught in the middle [news]. *Nature* 2006 December 14; 442(7121): 811. NRCBL: 22.2; 4.1.1. Identifiers: United Kingdom (Great Britain).

Spielmann, Horst. The future of animal experiments in nutrition research. *Forum of Nutrition* 2003; 56: 297-299. NRCBL: 22.2. SC: le. Identifiers: European Union.

Stark, Dennis M. Animal activism and intimidation of scientists [letter]. *Science* 2006 November 10; 314(5801): 923-924. NRCBL: 22.2. Comments: Donald Kennedy. Animal activism out of control. Science 2006 September 15; 313(5793): 1541.

Stark, Dennis M. Laboratory animal-based collaborations and contracts beyond the border. *Lab Animal* 2006 June; 35(6): 37-40. NRCBL: 22.2; 5.3; 21.1. SC: le.

Swiss Committee on Animal Experimentation; Eidgenössische Ethikkommission für die Gentechnik im ausserhumanen Bereich = Swiss Ethics Committee on Non-Human Gene Technology [ECNH] = Commission fédérale d'éthique pour le génie génétique dans le domaine non humain = Commissione federale d'etica per l'ingegneria genetica nei settore non umano;. The Dignity of Animals: A joint statement by the Swiss Ethics Committee on Non-Human Gene Technology (ECNH) and the Swiss Committee on Animal Experiments (SCAE), concerning a more concrete definition of the dignity of creation with regard to animals. Bern, Switzerland: Swiss Ethics Committee on Non-Human Gene Technology, 2005 May; 12 p. NRCBL: 22.1; 15.1; 22.2. Identifiers: Switzerland.

Sztybel, David. A living will clause for supporters of animal experimentation. *Journal of Applied Philosophy* 2006; 23(2): 173-189. NRCBL: 22.2; 20.5.4; 18.1; 1.1; 18.3. SC: an.

Abstract: Many people assume that invasive research on animals is justified because of its supposed benefits and because of the supposed mental inferiority of animals. However probably most people would be unwilling to sign a living will which consigns themselves to live biomedical experimentation if they ever, through misfortune, end up with a mental capacity equivalent to a laboratory animal. The benefits would be greater by far for medical science if living will signatories were to be used, and also the mental superiority boast would no longer apply. Ultimately, it is argued that invasive biomedical experiments would be unacceptable in a democratic society whose members are philosophically self-consistent.

United States. Congress. House. A bill to provide the Department of Justice the necessary authority to apprehend, prosecute, and convict individuals committing animal enterprise terror. 109th Congress, 1st Session, H.R. 4239. Introduced by Mr. Petri on 2005 November 4. Referred to the Committee on the Judiciary; 7p. NRCBL: 22.2; 22.3. SC: le. Identifiers: Animal Enterprise Terrorism Act.

Wadman, Meredith. Neal Barnard. *Nature Medicine* 2006 June; 12(6): 602. NRCBL: 22.2. Identifiers: animal rights; PETA.

Waldau, Paul. Religion and animals. *In:* Singer, Peter, ed. In Defense of Animals: The Second Wave. Malden, MA: Blackwell Pub.; 2006: 69-83. NRCBL: 22.1; 1.2.

Walker, Rebecca L. Human and animal subjects of research: the moral significance of respect versus welfare. *Theoretical Medicine and Bioethics* 2006; 27(4): 305-331. NRCBL: 22.2; 18.2; 1.1; 22.1. SC: an.

Abstract: Human beings with diminished decision-making capacities are usually thought to require greater protections from the potential harms of research than fully autonomous persons. Animal subjects of research receive lesser protections than any human beings regardless of decision-making capacity. Paradoxically, however, it is precisely animals' lack of some characteristic human capacities that is commonly invoked to justify using them for human purposes. In other words, for humans lesser capacities correspond to greater protections but for animals the opposite is true. Without explicit justification, it is not clear why or whether this should be the case. Ethics regulations guiding human subject research include principles such as respect for persons-and related duties-that are required as a matter of justice while regulations guiding animal subject research attend only to highly circumscribed considerations of welfare. Further, the regulations guiding research on animals discount any consideration of animal welfare relative to comparable human welfare. This paper explores two of the most promising justifications for these differences between the two sets of regulations. The first potential justification points to lesser moral status for animals on the basis of their lesser capacities. The second potential justification relies on a claim about the permissibility of moral partiality as found in common morality. While neither potential justification is sufficient to justify the regulatory difference as it stands, there is possible common ground between supporters of some regulatory difference and those rejecting the current difference.

Warnock, Mary. Man and other animals. *In her:* Nature and Morality: Recollections of a Philosopher in Public Life. New York: Continuum; 2003: 149-177. NRCBL: 22.2. SC: le.

Welchman, Jennifer. Is pragmatism chauvinistic? Dewey on animal experimentation. *In:* McKenna, Erin; Light, Andrew, eds. Animal Pragmatism: Rethinking Human-Nonhuman Relationships. Bloomington, IN: Indiana University Press; 2004: 179-192. NRCBL: 22.2.

West, Chad. Economics and ethics in the genetic engineering of animals. *Harvard Journal of Law and Technology* 2006 Spring; 19(2): 413-442. NRCBL: 22.2; 15.4; 22.1.

Wolff, Jonathan; Boyd, Kenneth. Animal rights and wrongs. *New Scientist* 2006 March 11-17; 189(2542): 20. NRCBL: 22.2.

Wynn, Susan G.; Wolpe, Paul Root. The majority view of ethics and professionalism in alternative medicine. *Journal of the American Veterinary Medical Association* 2005 February 15; 226(4): 516-520. NRCBL: 22.1; 4.1.1.

Young, John D.; Bianco, Richard W.; Fung, John J.; Lackner, Andrew A. Animal activism and intimidation of scientists [letter]. *Science* 2006 November 10; 314(5801): 923. NRCBL: 22.2. Comments: Donald Kennedy. Animal activism out of control. Science 2006 September 15; 313(5793): 1541.

Zamir, Tzachi. Killing for knowledge. *Journal of Applied Philosophy* 2006; 23(1): 17-40. NRCBL: 22.2. SC: an.
Abstract: I distinguish between four arguments commonly used to justify experimentation on animals (I). After delineating the autonomy of the question of experiments from other topics within animal ethics (II), I examine and reject each of these justifications (III-VI). I then explore two arguments according to which animal-dependent experimentation should continue even if it is immoral (VII). I close with the way in which liberationists' strategic considerations modify the moral conclusions of my analysis.

Zamir, Tzachi. The moral basis of animal-assisted therapy. *Society and Animals: Journal of Human-Animal Studies* 2006; 14(2): 179-199. NRCBL: 22.1; 9.5.1; 1.1. SC: an.

ARTIFICIAL INSEMINATION AND SURROGATE MOTHERS
See also REPRODUCTIVE TECHNOLOGIES

Refusal to artificially inseminate 'unmarried' lesbian. *Nursing Law's Regan Report* 2005 December; 46(7): 1. NRCBL: 14.2; 10; 1.2; 8.1. SC: le.

Ahuja, Kamal K.; Mamiso, Julian; Emmerson, Geraldine; Bowen-Simpkins, Peter; Seaton, Angela; Simons, Eric G. Pregnancy following intracytoplasmic sperm injection treatment with dead husband's spermatozoa: ethical and policy considerations. *Human Reproduction* 1997 June; 12(6): 1360-1363. NRCBL: 14.2; 14.6; 4.4. SC: le.

Almeling, Rene. "Why do you want to be a donor?": gender and the production of altruism in egg and sperm donation. *New Genetics and Society* 2006 August; 25(2): 143-157. NRCBL: 14.2; 19.5. SC: em.

American Society for Reproductive Medicine [ASRM]. Ethics Committee. Informing offspring of their conception by gamete donation. *Fertility and Sterility* 2004 September; 82(Supplement 1): S212-S216. NRCBL: 14.2; 14.4; 8.2.

Annas, George J. Fathers anonymous: beyond the best interests of the sperm donor. *Child Welfare* 1981 March; 60(3): 161-174. NRCBL: 14.2.

Austria. Bioethikkommission beim Bundeskanzleramt = Austria. Bioethics Commission at the Federal Chancellery. Resolution of the Bioethics Commission at the Federal Chancellery, dated 10 March 2004. Statement by the Bioethics Commission on the draft Federal Legislation to Amend the Law Regulating Reproductive Medicine (FMedG) (Amendment to FMedG2004). Vienna, Austria: Bioethikkommission beim Bundeskanzleramt; 2004 March 10, 3 p. NRCBL: 14.2; 14.6; 14.5.

Bernal, Susan Kerr. The intelligent couch potato. *Journal of Andrology* 2006 March-April; 27(2): 151-152. NRCBL: 14.2; 9.5.7. SC: cs.

Berys, Flavia. Interpreting a rent-a-womb contract: how California courts should proceed when gestational surrogacy arrangements go sour. *California Western Law Review* 2006 Spring; 42(2): 321-352. NRCBL: 14.2; 1.3.5. SC: le.

Blyth, Eric. "I wanted to be interesting. I wanted to be able to say 'I've done something interesting with my life' ": interviews with surrogate mothers in Britain. *Journal of Reproductive and Infant Psychology* 1994; 12: 189- 198. NRCBL: 14.2; 14.4. SC: cs.

Blyth, Eric. 'Not a primrose path': commissioning parents' experiences of surrogacy arrangements in Britain. *Journal of Reproductive and Infant Psychology* 1995; 13: 185-196. NRCBL: 14.2. SC: em.

Blyth, Eric. Sharing genetic origins information in third party assisted conception: a case for Victorian family values? *Children and Society* 2000; 14(1): 11-22. NRCBL: 14.2; 14.4; 8.4; 14.1; 14.6.

Brewaeys, A.; Golombok, S.; Naaktgeboren, N.; de Bruyn, J.K.; van Hall, E.V. Donor insemination: Dutch parents' opinions about confidentiality and donor anonymity and the emotional adjustment of their children. *Human Reproduction* 1997 July; 12(7): 1591-1597. NRCBL: 14.2; 14.4; 8.4; 19.5. SC: em.

Burr, Jennifer. "Repellent to proper ideas about the procreation of children": procreation and motherhood in the legal and ethical treatment of the surrogate mother. *Psychology, Evolution and Gender* 2000 August; 2(2): 105-117. NRCBL: 14.2; 10; 9.3.1; 9.5.7. SC: le.

California. Court of Appeal, Second District. Johnson v. Superior Court [Date of Decision: 2000 May 18]. *California Reporter*, 2d Series 2000; 95: 864-879. NRCBL: 14.2; 8.4. SC: le.
Abstract: Court Decision: 95 California Reporter, 2d Series 864; 18 May 2000 (date of decision). The Court of Appeal, Second District held that parents and their child, conceived with sperm from an anonymous donor, could compel the donor's deposition and production of documents in an effort to discover information relevant to their action against the sperm bank, California Cryobank, Inc. Cryobank sold Diane and Ronald Johnson sperm that it falsely claimed was fully tested and genetically screened. The sperm, from donor John Doe, genetically transmitted a kidney disease to the Johnson's child. The Johnsons sought information and a deposition from Doe in their action against Cryobank; Doe refused. The court first held that communications between Cryobank and Doe were not protected under the physician-patient privilege because Doe was not a patient and he visited Cryobank with the sole purpose of selling his sperm. The court also found that the agreement between Cryobank and the Johnsons did not preclude the disclosure of Doe's identity under all circumstances because such preclusion is against public policy. Under state law, parties are allowed to inspect insemination records under certain circumstances. To prevent inspection under all circumstances conflicts

NRCBL: National Reference Center for Bioethics Literature Classification Scheme   See inside front cover for terms.

43

with a compelling state interest in the health and welfare of children. Finally, the court did not find its holding in violation of Doe's right of privacy because, although Doe's medical records are protected under the right of privacy, compelling state interests in relevant disclosure in court proceedings, seeking the truth in court proceedings, and ensuring full redress of those injured override Doe's interest. The court specified that Doe's identity need not be automatically disclosed, and suggested the trial court construct an order protecting Doe's identity as much as possible. [KIE/SP]

Canada. House of Commons. Bill C-6: an act respecting assisted reproduction and related research = Project de loi C-6: loi concernant la procréation assistée et la recherche connexe. House of Commons of Canada 2004 February 11, 3rd session, 37 Parliament, 52-53 Elizabeth 11, 2004: 37 p. [Online]. Accessed: http://www2.parl.gc.ca/content/hoc/Bills/373/Government/C-6/c-6_3/c-6_3.pdf [2007 March 6]. NRCBL: 14.2; 9.8; 4.4. SC: le.

Carbone, June; Gottheim, Paige. Markets, subsidies, regulation, and trust: building ethical understandings into the market for fertility services. *Journal of Gender, Race and Justice* 2006 Spring; 9(3): 509-547. NRCBL: 14.2; 4.4; 8.4. SC: le.

Ciccarelli, Janice C.; Beckman, Linda J. Navigating rough waters: an overview of psychological aspects of surrogacy. *Journal of Social Issues* 2005 March; 61(1): 21-43. NRCBL: 14.2; 17.1. SC: rv.

Ciccarelli, John K.; Ciccarelli, Janice C. The legal aspects of parental rights in assisted reproductive technology. *Journal of Social Issues* 2005 March; 61(1): 127-137. NRCBL: 14.2. SC: le.

Clark, Katrina. Who's your daddy? Mine was an anonymous sperm donor. That made me mad. So I decided to find him. *Washington Post* 2006 December 17; p. B1, B5. NRCBL: 14.2. SC: po.

Codd, Helen. Policing procreation: prisoners, artificial insemination and the law. *Genomics, Society and Policy* 2006 May; 2(1): 110-117. NRCBL: 14.2; 1.3.5. Identifiers: European Convention on Human Rights.
Abstract: This article explores the implications of two recent case law decisions in the UK in which prisoners and their partners have sought to utilise the European Convention of Human Rights to challenge the refusal by the Prison Service to provide access to facilities for artificial insemination. After a discussion of the facts and legal principles arising from these cases, the author goes on to consider broader questions of the rights of prisoners' partners; the contested role of the welfare principle, and the challenges posed by recent research which promotes decisional privacy and autonomy in reproductive decision-making.

Crews, Heather A. Women be warned, egg donation isn't all it's cracked up to be: the copulation of science and the courts makes multiple mommies. *North Carolina Journal of Law and Technology* 2005 Fall; 7(1): 141-156. NRCBL: 14.2; 9.5.5; 1.3.5; 14.1. SC: le.

Devereux, John. Re B and J (artificial insemination). *Journal of Law and Medicine* 1998 May; 5(4): 330-332. NRCBL: 14.2. SC: le.

Devlin, Richard F. Baby M.: the contractual legitimation of misogyny. *Reports of Family Law (3d)* 1988; 10: 4-29. NRCBL: 14.2. SC: le.

Donovan, Catherine. Genetics, fathers and families: exploring the implications of changing the law in favour of identifying sperm donors. *Social and Legal Studies* 2006 December; 15(4): 494-510. NRCBL: 14.2; 15.1. SC: le. Identifiers: Human Fertilization and Embryology Act 1990; United Kingdom (Great Britain).

Edelmann, Robert J. Surrogacy: the psychological issues. *Journal of Reproductive and Infant Psychology* 2004 May; 22(2): 123-136. NRCBL: 14.2. SC: em.

Egan, Jennifer. Wanted: a few good sperm (looking for Mr. Good Sperm). *New York Times Magazine* 2006 March 19; p. 44-51, 66, 81, 98, 100. NRCBL: 14.2. SC: po.

Field, Martha A. Response of Professor Field. *Politics and the Life Sciences* 1991 February; 9(2): 262-268. NRCBL: 14.2. Comments: John Lawrence Hill. In defense of enforcement of the surrogate contract: a reply to Field. Politics and the Life Sciences 1991 February; 9(2): 253-261.

Fox, Robin. In the matter of "Baby M": report from the Gruter Institute for Law and Behavioral Research. *Politics and the Life Sciences* 1988 August; 7(1): 77-88. NRCBL: 14.2. SC: le.

Golombok, Susan; Lycett, Emma; MacCallum, Fiona; Jadva, Vasanti; Murray, Clare; Rust, John; Jenkins, Julian; Abdalla, Hossam; Margara, Raoul. Parenting infants conceived by gamete donation. *Journal of Family Psychology* 2004 September; 18(3): 443-452. NRCBL: 14.2; 14.4; 19.5.

Golombok, Susan; Murray, Clare; Jadva, Vasanti; MacCallum, Fiona; Lycett, Emma. Families created through surrogacy arrangements: parent-child relationships in the first year of life. *Developmental Psychology* 2004 May; 40(3): 400-411. NRCBL: 14.2. SC: em.

Grady, Denise. As the use of donor sperm increases, secrecy can be a health hazard. *New York Times* 2006 June 6; p. F5, F8. NRCBL: 14.2; 19.5; 8.3.1.

Harmon, Amy. Are you my sperm donor? Few clinics will say. *New York Times* 2006 January 20; p. A1, A15. NRCBL: 14.2; 8.4. SC: po.

Henderson, Mark; Charter, David; Ahuja, Anjana; Frean, Alexandra. Sperm donors children win the right to trace their fathers. *Times* 2004 January 17; 2p. NRCBL: 14.2; 8.4; 19.5. SC: po. Identifiers: United Kingdom (Great Britain).

Heng, Boon Chin. International egg-sharing to provide donor oocytes for clinical assisted reproduction and derivation of nuclear transfer stem cells. *Reproductive BioMedicine Online [electronic]* 2005 December; 11(6): 676-678. Accessed: http://www.rbmonline.com/Article/2024 [2006 July 25]. NRCBL: 14.2; 15.1; 19.1; 19.5; 9.3.1.

Hill, John Lawrence. In defense of enforcement of the surrogate contract: a reply to Field. *Politics and the Life Sciences* 1991 February; 9(2): 253-261. NRCBL: 14.2. SC: le. Comments: Martha A. Field. The case against enforcement of surrogacy contracts. Politics and the Life Sciences 1991 February; 8(2): 199-204.

Human Fertilisation and Embryology Authority [HFEA] (Great Britain). Donor insemination. London: Human Fertilisation and Embryology Authority, 1996 March: 5 p. NRCBL: 14.2.

Human Fertilisation and Embryology Authority [HFEA] (Great Britain). Sperm and egg donors and the law. London: Human Fertilisation and Embryology Authority, 1995 January: 5 p. NRCBL: 14.2; 19.5; 8.4. SC: le.

Janssens, P.M.W.; Simons, A.H.M.; van Kooij, R.J.; Blokzijl, E.; Dunselman, G.A.J. A new Dutch law regulating provision of identifying information of donors to offspring: background, content and impact. *Human Reproduction* 2006 April; 21(4): 852-856. NRCBL: 14.2; 8.4; 19.5. SC: le.

Kruse, Katherine. Constitutionality of recognizing multiple parental rights in the surrogacy context. *Wisconsin Women's Law Journal* 1992-1993; 7-8: 67-84. NRCBL: 14.2; 8.3.2. SC: le; rv.

Leeb-Lundberg, Sara; Kjellberg, Svante; Sydsjö, Gunilla. Helping parents to tell their children about the use of donor insemination (DI) and determining their opinions about open-identity sperm donors. *Acta Obstetricia et Gynecologica Scandinavica* 2006; 85(1): 78-81. NRCBL: 14.2; 8.4; 9.5.7. SC: em. Identifiers: Sweden.

Michelmann, Hans Wilhelm; Wewetzer, Christa; Körner, Uwe. Präkonzeptionelle Geschlechtswahl: medizinische, rechtliche und ethische Aspekte [Preconceptional sex selection; medical, legal, and ethical aspects]. *Ethik in der Medizin* 2006 June; 18(2): 164-180. NRCBL: 14.3; 14.4; 15.2. SC: le. Identifiers: Germany.

Mundy, Liza. It's all in the genes, except when it isn't. *Washington Post* 2006 December 17; p. B1, B5. NRCBL: 14.2; 15.1. SC: po. Identifiers: collaborative reproduction.

Nosarka, S.; Kruger, T.F. Surrogate motherhood [editorial]. *South African Medical Journal* 2005 December; 95(12): 942, 944, 946. NRCBL: 14.2; 8.1. SC: le.

Osberg, Brendan. For your first born child: an ethical defense of the exploitation argument against commercial surrogacy. *Penn Bioethics Journal* 2006; 2(2): 42-45. NRCBL: 14.2; 1.1.

Abstract: In this essay I explore two arguments against commercial surrogacy, based on commodification and exploitation respectively. I adopt a consequentialist framework and argue that commodification arguments must be grounded in a resultant harm to either child or surrogate, and that a priori arguments which condemn the practice for puritanical reasons cannot form a basis for public law. Furthermore there is no overwhelming evidence of harm caused to either party involved in commercial surrogacy, and hence Canadian law (which forbids the practice) must (and can) be justified on exploitative grounds. Objections raised by Wilkinson based on an 'isolated case' approach are addressed when one takes into account the political implications of public policy. I argue that is precisely these implications that justify laws forbidding commercial surrogacy on the grounds of preventing systematic exploitation.

Po-Wah, Julia Tao Lai. Right-making and wrong-making in surrogate motherhood: a Confucian feminist perspective. *In:* Tong, Rosemarie; Donchin, Anne; Dodds, Susan, eds. Linking Visions: Feminist Bioethics, Human Rights, and the Developing World. Lanham, MD: Rowman and Littlefield Publishers; 2004: 157-179. NRCBL: 14.2; 1.1; 10.

Ramsey, Joanne. Fit for the 21st century? A review of surrogacy provisions within the Human Fertilisation and Embryology Act 1990. *Medical Law International* 2006; 7(4): 281-307. NRCBL: 14.2; 5.3. SC: le; rv.

Rosenberg, Helane S.; Epstein, Yakov M. Equity in egg donation. *Journal of Gender, Race and Justice* 2006 Spring; 9(3): 569-590. NRCBL: 14.2; 19.6. SC: cs.

Sifris, Adiva. Known semen donors: to be or not to be a parent. *Journal of Law and Medicine* 2005 November; 13(2): 230-244. NRCBL: 14.2; 10. SC: le.

Snyder, Steven H.; Byrn, Mary Patricia. The use of prebirth parentage orders in surrogacy proceedings. *Family Law Quarterly* 2005 Fall; 39(3): 633-662. NRCBL: 14.2. SC: le.

Spar, Debora L. Renting wombs for money and love: the emerging market for surrogacy. *In her:* The Baby Business: How Money, Science, and Politics Drive the Commerce of Conception. Boston: Harvard Business School Press; 2006: 69-96. NRCBL: 14.2; 9.3.1.

Strathern, Marilyn. Still giving nature a helping hand? Surrogacy: a debate about technology and society. *Journal of Molecular Biology* 2002 June 14; 319(4): 985-993. NRCBL: 14.2; 5.3.

Stuhmcke, Anita. For love or money: the legal regulation of surrogate motherhood. *E Law: Murdoch University Electronic Journal of Law* 1995 December; 2(3): 27 p. [Online]. Accessed: http://www.murdoch.edu.au/elaw/issues/v2n3/stuhmcke23.html [2006 June 29]. NRCBL: 14.2. SC: le. Identifiers: Australia.

NRCBL: National Reference Center for Bioethics Literature Classification Scheme   See inside front cover for terms.

45

Thomas, Hans. ¿Ética pluralismo pueden ir de acuerdo? [Can ethics and pluralism agree?]. *Persona y Bioética* 1999 February-May; 2(6): 89-112. NRCBL: 14.2; 14.4; 15.4. SC: le. Identifiers: West Germany.

Traiman, Leland. Guidelines but no guidance: GaySpermBank.com vs. FDA. *Journal of Gender, Race and Justice* 2006 Spring; 9(3): 613-620. NRCBL: 14.2; 5.3. SC: le.

United States. Social Security Administration. Office of Hearings and Appeals. In the Case of Judith C. Hart, Claim for Parent's Insurance Benefits: Notice of Decision — Fully Favorable [Date of Decision: 27 March 1997]. Unpublished Document. New Orleans, LA: SSA Office of Hearings and Appeals, 1997 March 27: 16 p. [+ 48 p. appended]. NRCBL: 14.2; 1.3.5; 14.6. Identifiers: Decision on benefits for a child conceived after her father's death. Note: Accompanied by Complaint [Hart v. Shalala, No. 94-3944] filed by William E. Rittenberg in U.S. District Court, E.D. Louisiana, 12 December 1994 (17 p.); Memorandum of Law in Support of Plaintiff's Motion for Summary Judgment [Hart v. Shalala, No. 94-3944] filed by Diane Curtis and William E. Rittenberg, 22 March 1995 (29 p.); and Stipulation of Dismissal [Hart v. Chater, No. 94-3944] filed by Shawn B. Jensen, James C. Hrdlicka and Kathryn Kolbert, 18 March 1998 (2 p.).

van den Akker, Olga. Genetic and gestational surrogate mothers' experience of surrogacy. *Journal of Reproductive and Infant Psychology* 2003 May; 21(2): 145-161. NRCBL: 14.2; 9.5.5; 4.4; 17.1. SC: em. Identifiers: United Kingdom (Great Britain).

Van Den Akker, Olga B.A. A longitudinal pre-pregnancy to post-delivery comparison of genetic and gestational surrogate and intended mothers: confidence and genealogy. *Journal of Psychosomatic Obstetrics and Gynaecology* 2005 December; 26(4): 277-284. NRCBL: 14.2; 15.1; 9.5.7; 7.1. SC: em.

Zawawi, Majdah. Third party involvement in the reproductive process: comparative aspects of the legal and ethical approaches to surrogacy. *In:* Sang-yong, Song; Young-Mo, Koo; Macer, Darryl R.J., eds. Asian Bioethics in the 21st Century. Christchurch, NZ: Eubios Ethics Institute, 2002: 389-401. NRCBL: 14.2; 1.2; 21.1. SC: le. Identifiers: Islam; Malaysia; United Kingdom; United States. Conference: Proceedings of the Asian Bioethics Conference (ABC4), held 22-25 November 2002 in Seoul, South Korea.

ARTIFICIAL NUTRITION AND HYDRATION
See EUTHANASIA AND ALLOWING TO DIE

ASSISTED REPRODUCTIVE TECHNOLO-GIES *See* REPRODUCTIVE TECHNOLOGIES

ASSISTED SUICIDE
See also EUTHANASIA AND ALLOWING TO DIE

End-of-life groups in spat over names [news]. *Bulletin of Medical Ethics* 2005 December-2006 January; (212): 3. NRCBL: 20.7; 20.5.1.

Oral argument in Gonzales v. Oregon. *Issues in Law and Medicine* 2006 Spring; 21(3): 213-237. NRCBL: 20.7; 20.5.1; 9.5.9. SC: le. Note: transcript from court proceedings.

Position statement on assisted suicide approved. *Canadian HIV/AIDS Policy and Law Newsletter* 1995 July; 1(4): 11. NRCBL: 20.7; 20.5.1; 9.5.6. Note: Approved by the AIDS committee of Toronto, Canada, 1995 May 18.

Terri Schiavo and beyond [news]. *Bulletin of Medical Ethics* 2005 March; (206): 5-6. NRCBL: 20.7; 20.5.1. SC: le.

The assisted-suicide decision [editorial]. *New York Times* 2006 January 19; p. A22. NRCBL: 20.7; 20.5.1; 8.1. SC: po.

The Belgian act on euthanasia of May 28th, 2002. *European Journal of Health Law* 2003 September; 10(3): 329-335. NRCBL: 20.7; 20.5.1; 20.5.4. SC: le.

Abdel-Khalek, Ahmed; Lester, David; Schaller, Sylvia. Attitudes toward physician-assisted suicide and death anxiety among Kuwaiti students. *Psychological Reports* 2005 June; 96(3, Part 1): 625-626. NRCBL: 20.7; 20.5.1; 20.3.1. SC: em.

Andraghetti, R.; Foran, S.; Colebunders, R.; Tomlinson, D.; Vyras, P.; Borleffs, C.J.; Fleerackers, Y.; Schrooten, W.; Borchert, M. Euthanasia: from the perspective of HIV infected persons in Europe. *HIV Medicine* 2001 January; 2(1): 3-10. NRCBL: 20.7; 20.5.1; 9.5.6. SC: em.

Annas, George J. Congress, controlled substances, and physician-assisted suicide — elephants in mouseholes. *New England Journal of Medicine* 2006 March 9; 354(10): 1079-1084. NRCBL: 20.7; 20.5.1; 8.1; 9.5.9. SC: le.

Baron, Charles H. Not DEA'd yet: Gonzales v. Oregon. *Hastings Center Report* 2006 March-April; 36(2): 8. NRCBL: 20.7; 20.5.1; 8.1. SC: le. Identifiers: Drug Enforcement Administration.

Battin, Margaret P.; Spellecy, Ryan. What kind of freedom? Szasz's misleading perception of physician-assisted suicide. *In:* Schaler, Jeffrey A., ed. Szasz Under Fire: The Psychiatric Abolitionist Faces His Critics. Chicago: Open Court; 2004: 277-290. NRCBL: 20.7; 20.5.1.

Belgium. National Medical Council. Bulletin of the National Council, 9th December 2001: euthanasia. *Acta Chirurgica Belgica* 2002 November-December; 102(6): 369- 370. NRCBL: 20.7; 20.5.1.

Belgium. National Medical Council. Opinion of the National Council on euthanasia. *Acta Chirurgica Belgica* 2002 November-December; 102(6): 368. NRCBL: 20.7; 20.5.1.

Blevins, Dean; Preston, Thomas A.; Werth, James L. Characteristics of persons approving of physician-assisted death. *Death Studies* 2005 September; 29(7): 601-623. NRCBL: 20.7; 20.5.1; 20.3.1. SC: em.

Bookman, Terry A.; Gordon, Harvey L.; Address, Richard F.; Reines, Alvin J.; Zlotowitz, Bernard; Seltzer, Sanford; Edelheit, Joseph A.; Borowitz, Eugene B.; Kahn, Yoel H.; Sinclair, David; Dorff, Elliot; Arlas, Samuel; Quill, Timothy E.; Frehof, Solomon B. Voluntary active euthanasia assisted suicide: Case No. 2. *Journal of Psychology and Judaism* 1996 Spring; 20(1): 23-57. NRCBL: 20.7; 20.5.1; 1.2; 1.1; 4.4; 9.7; 8.1. SC: le.

Bostrom, Barry A. Gonzales v. Oregon. *Issues in Law and Medicine* 2006 Spring; 21(3): 203-210. NRCBL: 20.7; 20.5.1; 9.5.9. SC: le.

Branthwaite, Margaret. Should patients be able to choose physician-assisted suicide at the end of their lives? *Lancet Oncology* 2006 July; 7(7): 602-604. NRCBL: 20.7; 20.5.1; 8.1. SC: an; le.

Brassington, I. Killing people: what Kant could have said about suicide and euthanasia but did not. *Journal of Medical Ethics* 2006 October; 32(10): 571-574. NRCBL: 20.7; 1.1; 20.5.1. SC: an.

Breitbart, William. "Unintended consequences": can legalizing physician-assisted suicide actually result in improved palliative care practices? [editorial]. *Palliative and Supportive Care* 2003 September; 1(3): 213-214. NRCBL: 20.7; 20.5.1; 8.1; 20.4.1; 1.3.5.

Burgess, Sally; Hawton, Keith. Suicide, euthanasia, and the psychiatrist. *Philosophy, Psychiatry, and Psychology* 1998 June; 5(2): 113- 126. NRCBL: 20.7; 20.5.1; 4.3; 17.1; 1.1. SC: le; cs.

Carter, Gregory T.; VandeKieft, Gregg K.; Barron, David W. Whose life is it, anyway? The federal government vs. the state of Oregon on the legality of physician-assisted suicide. *American Journal of Hospice and Palliative Care* 2005 July-August; 22(4): 249-251. NRCBL: 20.7; 20.5.1; 8.1; 1.3.5. SC: le.

Chapman, Clare. Swiss hospital lets terminally ill patients commit suicide in its beds [news]. *BMJ: British Medical Journal* 2006 January 7; 332(7532): 7. NRCBL: 20.7; 20.5.1.

Chapple, A.; Ziebland, S.; McPherson, A.; Herxheimer, A. What people close to death say about euthanasia and assisted suicide: a qualitative study. *Journal of Medical Ethics* 2006 December; 32(12): 706-710. NRCBL: 20.7; 20.5.1. SC: em.

Charatan, Fred. US Supreme Court upholds Oregon's Death with Dignity Act [news]. *BMJ: British Medical Journal* 2006 January 28; 332(7535): 195. NRCBL: 20.7; 20.5.1; 8.1. SC: le. Identifiers: United States.

Coggon, J. Arguing about physician-assisted suicide: a response to Steinbock. *Journal of Medical Ethics* 2006 June; 32(6): 339-341. NRCBL: 20.7; 20.5.1. SC: an.

Comité Consultatif de Bioéthique de Belgique. Avis no. 9 du 22 fevrier 1999 concernant l'arrêt actif de la vie des personnes incapables d'exprimer leur volonté / Notice no. 9 of 22 February 1999 concerning active termination of life of persons unable to express their will. *In:* Les Avis du Comité Consultatif de Bioéthique de Belgique 1996-2000. Brussels: De Boeck University; 2001: 93-116. NRCBL: 20.7; 20.5.1; 8.3.3. SC: le. Identifiers: Belgium.

Dahl, E.; Levy, N. The case for physician assisted suicide: how can it possibly be proven? *Journal of Medical Ethics* 2006 June; 32(6): 335-338. NRCBL: 20.7; 20.5.1. SC: an.
　Abstract: In her paper, The case for physician assisted suicide: not (yet) proven, Bonnie Steinbock argues that the experience with Oregon's Death with Dignity Act fails to demonstrate that the benefits of legalising physician assisted suicide outweigh its risks. Given that her verdict is based on a small number of highly controversial cases that will most likely occur under any regime of legally implemented safeguards, she renders it virtually impossible to prove the case for physician assisted suicide. In this brief paper, we suggest some ways that may enable us to weigh the risks and benefits of legalisation more fairly and, hopefully, allow us to close the case for physician assisted suicide.

Davis, Carol. Live and let go. *Nursing Standard* 2005 October 26-November 1; 20(7): 16-17. NRCBL: 20.7; 20.5.1; 8.1. SC: le.

Denny, Colleen C.; Emanuel, Ezekiel J. "Physician-assisted suicide among Oregon cancer patients": a fading issue. *Journal of Clinical Ethics* 2006 Spring; 17(1): 39-42. NRCBL: 20.7; 20.5.1; 20.4.1; 9.5.3.

Dimond, Bridgit. The law regarding assisted dying for the terminally ill in the UK. *International Journal of Palliative Nursing* 2005 November; 11(11): 582-583. NRCBL: 20.7; 20.5.1; 8.1.

Dyer, Clare. UK House of Lords rejects physician assisted suicide [news]. *BMJ: British Medical Journal* 2006 May 20; 332(7551): 1169. NRCBL: 20.7; 20.5.1. SC: le.

Egan, Timothy; Liptak Adam. Fraught issue, but narrow ruling in Oregon suicide case. *New York Times* 2006 January 18; p. A16. NRCBL: 20.7; 20.5.1; 1.3.8. SC: po.

Elliot, Richard. Court dismisses constitutional challenge to ban on assisted suicide. *HIV/AIDS Policy and Law Review* 2001; 6(1-2): 35-36. NRCBL: 20.7; 20.5.1. SC: le. Identifiers: Ontario; Canada; Wakeford v. Canada.

Finlay, Ilora. Why a third attempt at legislation for physician-assisted suicide in the UK failed. *Lancet Oncology*

NRCBL: National Reference Center for Bioethics Literature Classification Scheme　　　　　See inside front cover for terms.

2006 July; 7(7): 529-531. NRCBL: 20.7; 20.5.1; 8.1. SC: le.

Ganzini, Linda. Response to Denny and Emanuel. *Journal of Clinical Ethics* 2006 Spring; 17(1): 43-45. NRCBL: 20.7; 20.5.1. Identifiers: Oregon. Comments: Colleen L. Denny and Ezekial J. Emanuel. "Physician-assisted suicide among Oregon cancer patients": a fading issue. Journal of Clinical Ethics 2006 Spring; 17(1): 39-42.

Ganzini, Linda; Hamilton, N. Gregory; Hamilton, Catherine A. Physician-assisted suicide [letter and reply]. *American Journal of Psychiatry* 2006 June; 163(6): 1109-1110. NRCBL: 20.7; 20.5.1; 17.1.

Garmaise, David. Providing assistance in dying: a call for legalization. *Canadian HIV/AIDS Policy and Law Newsletter* 1999 Summer; 4(4): 39-40. NRCBL: 20.7; 20.5.1.

Garmaise, David. The case for assisted suicide and euthanasia. *Canadian HIV/AIDS Policy and Law Newsletter* 1997 Spring; 3(2-3): 20-23. NRCBL: 20.7; 20.5.1.

Gastmans, Chris; Lemiengre, Joke; van der Wal, Gerrit; Schotsmans, Paul; Dierckx de Casterlé, Bernadette. Prevalence and content of written ethics policies on euthanasia in Catholic healthcare institutions in Belgium (Flanders). *Health Policy* 2006 April; 76(2): 169-178. NRCBL: 20.7; 9.1; 20.4.1; 1.2; 8.1; 20.5.1; 7.1. SC: em.

Gilman, Daniel. Thou shalt not kill as a defeasible heuristic: law and economics and the debate over physician-assisted suicide. *Oregon Law Review* 2004; 83: 1239-1289. NRCBL: 20.7; 20.5.1; 5.2. SC: le.

Gostin, Lawrence O. Physician-assisted suicide: a legitimate medical practice? *JAMA: The Journal of the American Medical Association* 2006 April 26; 295(16): 1941-1943. NRCBL: 20.7; 20.5.1; 9.5.9. SC: le. Identifiers: Oregon Death with Dignity Act; Controlled Substances Act; Gonzales v. Oregon.

Goy, Elizabeth R.; Carlson, Bryant; Simpoulos, Nicole; Jackson, Ann; Ganzani, Linda. Determinants of Oregon hospice chaplains' views on physician-assisted suicide. *Journal of Palliative Care* 2006 Summer; 22(2): 83-90. NRCBL: 20.7; 20.5.1; 8.1; 20.4.1; 9.1; 1.2. SC: em.

Great Britain. Parliament. House of Lords. Assisted dying for the terminally ill bill [HL]. Second Reading. *In:* Parliamentary Debates (Hansard). London: The Stationery Office, 2006 May 12; 681(145): 1184-1296. NRCBL: 20.7; 20.5.1; 8.1. SC: le. Identifiers: Lord Joffe Bill; United Kingdom.

Great Britain. Parliament. House of Lords. Select Committee. Assisted dying for the terminally ill. *Bulletin of Medical Ethics* 2005 March; (206): 9-11. NRCBL: 20.7; 20.5.1; 2.4. SC: le.

Greenhouse, Linda. Justices reject U.S. bid to block assisted suicide; Court, 6-3, says attorney general was wrong in Oregon case. *New York Times* 2006 January 18; p. A1, A16. NRCBL: 20.7; 20.5.1; 1.3.8. SC: po.

Harrison, Dean; Long, Paul A.; Sedler, Robert A.; Waun, James; Price, Elizabeth; Uhlmann, Michael. Physician-assisted suicide debate at DCL/MSU Fall 1997. *Journal of Medicine and Law* 1997 Fall; 2(1): 85-115. NRCBL: 20.7; 20.5.1. SC: le. Identifiers: Detroit College of Law, Michigan State University.

Howard, Orion M.; Fairclough, Diane L.; Daniels, Elisabeth R.; Emanuel, Ezekiel J. Physician desire for euthanasia and assisted suicide: would physicians practice what they preach? *Journal of Clinical Oncology* 1997 February; 15(2): 428-432. NRCBL: 20.7; 20.5.1; 8.1. SC: em.

Jones, James W.; McCullough, Laurence B.; Richman, Bruce W. Physician-assisted suicide: has it come of age? *Surgery* 2005 July; 138(1): 105-108. NRCBL: 20.7; 20.5.1; 8.3.4; 8.1. SC: cs.

Keown, John. Considering physician-assisted suicide: an evaluation of Lord Joffe's assisted dying for the terminally ill bill. London: Care NOT Killing Alliance, 2006. 32 p. NRCBL: 20.7; 20.5.1; 8.1.

Klampfer, Friderik. Suicide, euthanasia and human dignity. *Acta Analytica* 2001; 16(27): 7-34. NRCBL: 20.7; 20.5.1; 4.4; 8.1. Identifiers: Kant; D.J. Velleman.

Kmietowicz, Zosia. Doctors backtrack on assisted suicide [news]. *BMJ: British Medical Journal* 2006 July 8; 333(7558): 64. NRCBL: 20.7; 20.5.1; 8.1; 7.1. SC: le.

Lee, Barbara Coombs. Should it be legal for physicians to expedite a death? Yes - what experience teaches about legalization of assisted dying. *Generations: Journal of the American Society on Aging* 1999 Spring; 23(1): 59-60. NRCBL: 20.7; 8.1; 20.5.1. SC: le.

Leenaars, Antoon; Connolly, John. Suicide, assisted suicide and euthanasia: international perspectives. *Irish Journal of Psychological Medicine* 2001 March; 18(1): 33-37. NRCBL: 20.7; 20.5.1; 21.1. Identifiers: International Ethical and Legal Working Group in Suicidology.

Leenen, H.J.J. Assistance to suicide and the European Court of Human Rights/ Court of Justice of the European Communities. *European Journal of Health Law* 2002 September; 9(3): 257-282. NRCBL: 20.7; 20.5.1.

Lemmens, Trudo. US appeal courts rule in favour of assisted suicide. *Canadian HIV/AIDS Policy and Law Newsletter* 1996 July; 2(4): 1, 42-43. NRCBL: 20.7; 20.5.1. SC: le.

Liao, Solomon; Arnold, Robert M. The nature of an ethics and law review article: the challenges of a paper on physician-assisted dying [editorial]. *Journal of Palliative Medicine* 2005 June; 8(3): 484-485. NRCBL: 20.7; 20.5.1; 8.1. SC: le.

Lindsay, Ronald A. Gonzales v. Oregon and the politics of medicine. *Kennedy Institute of Ethics Journal* 2006 March; 16(1): 99- 104. NRCBL: 20.7; 20.5.1; 8.1; 7.1; 9.7; 5.3.

Linzey, Andrew. Assisted dying: a critique of the theological objections. *Bulletin of Medical Ethics* 2006 April-May; (214): 21-25. NRCBL: 20.7; 20.5.1; 1.2.

MacDonald, Michael G. Attitudes of trainees in suicide intervention toward euthanasia and suicide among the nonterminally ill. *Psychological Reports* 2005 June; 96(3, Part 1): 709-712. NRCBL: 20.7; 20.5.1. SC: em. Identifiers: Canada.

Mackellar, Calum. Laws and practices relating to euthanasia and assisted suicide in 34 countries of the Council of Europe and the USA. *European Journal of Health Law* 2003 March; 10(1): 63-64. NRCBL: 20.7; 20.5.1.

Martindale, Diane. A culture of death. *Scientific American* 2005 June; 292(6): 44, 46. NRCBL: 20.7; 20.5.1; 18.2. Identifiers: Russel Ogden.

Meier, Diane E. Should it be legal for physicians to expedite a death? No — a change of heart on assisted suicide. *Generations: Journal of the American Society on Aging* 1999 Spring; 23(1): 58, 60. NRCBL: 20.7; 8.1; 20.5.1. SC: le.

Meier, Diane E.; Myers, Hattie; Muskin, Philip R. When a patient requests help committing suicide. *Generations: Journal of the American Society on Aging* 1999 Spring; 23(1): 61-68. NRCBL: 20.7; 8.1; 20.5.1; 4.4; 17.1. SC: cs.

Meisel, Alan. Ethics and law: physician-assisted dying. *Journal of Palliative Medicine* 2005 June; 8(3): 609-621. NRCBL: 20.7; 20.5.1; 8.1. SC: le.

Mitchell, David. The importance of being important: euthanasia and critical interests in Dworkin's Life's Dominion. *Utilitas* 1995 November; 7(2): 301-314. NRCBL: 20.7; 20.5.1; 20.5.4; 8.3.3. SC: an; cs.

Nathanson, V. Euthanasia, physicians and HIV infected persons [editorial]. *HIV Medicine* 2001 January; 2(1): 1-2. NRCBL: 20.7; 20.5.1; 8.1; 9.5.6.

Nicolaidis, Christina. My mother's choice. *JAMA: The Journal of the American Medical Association* 2006 August 23-30; 296(8): 907-908. NRCBL: 20.7; 20.5.1.

Nys, Herman. A presentation of the Belgian Act on euthanasia against the background of Dutch euthanasia law. *European Journal of Health Law* 2003 September; 10(3): 239-255. NRCBL: 20.7; 20.5.1; 20.5.4. SC: le.

Parkinson, Lynne; Rainbird, Katherine; Kerridge, Ian; Clover, Kerrie; Ravenscroft, Peter; Cavenagh, John; Carter, Gregory. Patients' attitudes towards euthanasia and physician-assisted suicide: a systematic review of the literature published over fifteen years. *Monash Bioethics Review* 2006 October; 25(4): 19-43. NRCBL: 20.7; 20.5.1; 20.3.1. SC: rv; em.

Quill, Timothy E.; Meier, Diane E. The big chill — inserting the DEA into end-of-life care. *New England Journal of Medicine* 2006 January 5; 354(1): 1-3. NRCBL: 20.7; 20.5.1; 20.4.1; 9.7. SC: le. Identifiers: Drug Enforcement Agency.

Royal College of Physicians of London. Assisted Dying for the Terminally Ill Bill: A Consultation. London: Royal College of Physicians of London, 2006 May 9; 2 p. [Online]. Accessed: http://www.rcplondon.ac.uk/college/statements/statements_assisted_dying_02.htm [2006 August 18]. NRCBL: 20.7; 20.5.1; 8.1. SC: em; le. Identifiers: United Kingdom(Great Britain).
   Abstract: This statement summarizes the history and results of the Royal College of Physicians [RCP] member consultation on the Assisted Dying for the Terminally Ill Bill, a revised second bill introduced by Lord Joel Joffe in Parliament in 2004.

Royal College of Physicians of London. Clarification of RCP position on the Assisted Dying Bill. London: Royal College of Physicians of London 2004 December 9; 1 p. [Online]. Accessed: http://www.rcplondon.ac.uk/college/statements/statements_assisted_dying_01.htm [2006 August 18]. NRCBL: 20.7; 20.5.1; 8.1. Identifiers: United Kingdom (Great Britain).
   Abstract: This statement clarifies the fact that the College's position of neutrality on the Assisted Dying Bill should not be interpreted as supporting the Bill.

Royal College of Physicians of London. Written evidence to the House of Lords Select Committee on the Assisted Dying for the Terminally Ill Bill [HL]: Written evidence collated by The Royal College of Physicians of London on behalf of The Academy of Medical Royal Colleges. London: Royal College of Physicians of London 2004 September 7; 3 p. [Online]. Accessed: http://www.rcplondon.ac.uk/college/statements/statements_assisted_dying.htm [2006 August 18]. NRCBL: 20.7; 20.5.1; 8.1. Identifiers: United Kingdom (Great Britain).

Royal College of Physicians of London. Committee on Ethical Issues in Medicine. Response to Patient (Assisted Dying) Bill 2003: Royal College of Physicians Committee on Ethical Issues. London: Royal College of Physicians of London 2003 July 23; 4 p. [Online]. Accessed: http://www.rcplondon.ac.uk/college/ statements/padb_response.htm [2006 August 18]. NRCBL: 20.7; 20.5.1; 8.1. Note: Transmitted to the College by Ray Tallis, Chairman of the Committee on Ethical Issues in Medicine. The Royal College of Physicians opposed the 2003 version of the Patient (Assisted Dying) Bill.

Ruger, Theodore W. The United States Supreme Court and health law: the year in review. *Journal of Law, Medicine and Ethics* 2006 Winter; 34(4): 817-820. NRCBL: 20.7; 20.5.1. SC: le.

NRCBL: National Reference Center for Bioethics Literature Classification Scheme   See inside front cover for terms.

49

Rurup, Mette L.; Muller, Martien T.; Onwuteaka-Philipsen, Bregje D.; van der Heide, Agnes; van der Wal, Gerrit; van der Maas, Paul J. Requests for euthanasia or physician-assisted suicide from older persons who do not have a severe disease: an interview study. *Psychological Medicine* 2005 May; 35(5): 665-671. NRCBL: 20.7; 20.5.1; 9.5.2; 17.1. SC: em. Identifiers: Netherlands.

Scanlon, Colleen. Assisted suicide: how nurses should respond. *International Nursing Review* 1998 September-October; 45(5): 152. NRCBL: 20.7; 20.5.1; 4.1.3.

Sneddon, Andrew. Equality, justice, and paternalism: recentreing debate about physician-assisted suicide. *Journal of Applied Philosophy* 2006; 23(4): 387-404. NRCBL: 20.7; 20.5.1; 8.1; 1.1.

Stevens, Kenneth R. Emotional and psychological effects of physician-assisted suicide and euthanasia. *Linacre Quarterly* 2006 August; 73(3): 203-216. NRCBL: 20.7; 20.5.1; 8.1; 17.1; 21.1. Identifiers: Netherlands; Oregon; United States.

Strate, John; Kiska, Timothy; Zalman, Marvin. Who favors legalizing physician-assisted suicide? The vote on Michigan's Proposal B. *Politics and the Life Sciences* 2001 September; 20(2): 155-163. NRCBL: 20.7; 20.5.1. SC: em; le.

Suarez-Almazor, Maria E.; Newman, Catherine; Hanson, John; Bruera, Eduardo. Attitudes of terminally ill cancer patients about euthanasia and assisted suicide: predominance of psychosocial determinants and beliefs over symptom distress and subsequent survival. *Journal of Clinical Oncology* 2002 April 15; 20(8): 2134-2141. NRCBL: 20.7; 20.5.1; 8.1; 1.2; 9.5.1. SC: em.

Summers, David S.; Hentoff, Nat. End-of-life issues [letter and reply]. *Free Inquiry* 2006 October-November; 26(6): 9,11. NRCBL: 20.7; 20.5.1; 20.5.4.

Szasz, Thomas. Reply to Battin and Spellecy. *In:* Schaler, Jeffrey A., ed. Szasz Under Fire: The Psychiatric Abolitionist Faces His Critics. Chicago: Open Court; 2004: 291-300. NRCBL: 20.7; 20.5.1. SC: le.

United States. Congress. Senate. A bill to clarify Federal law to prohibit the dispensing, distribution, or administration of a controlled substance for the purpose of causing, or assisting in causing, the suicide, euthanasia, or mercy killing of any individual. Washington, DC: U.S. G.P.O., 2006. 5 p. [Online]. Accessed: http://frwebgate.access.gpo.gov/cgi-bin/useftp.cgi?IPaddress=162.140.64.21&filename=s3788is.pdf&directory=/diskb/wais/data/109_cong_bills. NRCBL: 20.7; 20.5.1; 20.5.3; 9.7. SC: le. Identifiers: Assisted Suicide Prevention Act of 2006. Note: S. 3788, 109th Congress, 2d session. Introduced by Sen. Brownback, August 3, 2006. Referred to the Committee on the Judiciary.

United States. Supreme Court. Gonzales v. Oregon [Date of Decision: 17 January 2006]. Slip Opinion, No. 04-623, 57 p., 2006. NRCBL: 20.7; 20.5.1; 8.1. SC: le.

United States. Supreme Court; Lindsay, Ronald A.; Dick, Rebecca P. Alberto Gonzales, Attorney General, et al., v. State of Oregon, et al. On Writ of Certiorari to the United States Court of Appeals for the Ninth Circuit. Brief for Amici Curiae in Support of Respondents. NRCBL: 20.7; 20.5.1; 20.5.3. SC: le.

Vandenbroucke, Amy. Case brief: physician assisted suicide. *DePaul Journal of Health Care Law* 2005; 9(1): 893-904. NRCBL: 20.7; 20.5.1. SC: le.

Varelius, Jukka. Voluntary euthanasia, physician-assisted suicide, and the goals of medicine. *Journal of Medicine and Philosophy* 2006 April; 31(2): 121-137. NRCBL: 20.7; 1.1; 20.5.1.
Abstract: It is plausible that what possible courses of action patients may legitimately expect their physicians to take is ultimately determined by what medicine as a profession is supposed to do and, consequently, that we can determine the moral acceptability of voluntary euthanasia and physician-assisted suicide on the basis of identifying the proper goals of medicine. This article examines the main ways of defining the proper goals of medicine found in the recent bioethics literature and argues that they cannot provide a clear answer to the question of whether or not voluntary euthanasia and physician-assisted suicide are morally acceptable. It is suggested that to find a plausible answer to this question and to complete the task of defining the proper goals of medicine, we must determine what is the best philosophical theory about the nature of prudential value.

Vermeersch, E. The Belgian law on euthanasia: the historical and ethical background. *Acta Chirurgica Belgica* 2002 November-December; 102(6): 394-397. NRCBL: 20.7; 20.5.1.

Vining, Therese W. Assisted suicide: where do advanced practice nurses stand? *Journal of Nursing Law* 1997; 4(2): 17-22. NRCBL: 20.7; 20.5.1; 4.1.3. SC: le.

Volker, Deborah Lowe. Assisted suicide and the domain of nursing practice. *Journal of Nursing Law* 1998; 5(1): 39-50. NRCBL: 20.7; 20.5.1; 4.1.3. SC: le.

Wolf, Susan M. Physician-assisted suicide. *Clinics in Geriatric Medicine* 2005 February; 21(1): 179-192. NRCBL: 20.7; 20.5.1; 8.1.

Wolfslast, Gabriele. Rechtliche Neuordnung der Tötung auf Verlangen? *In:* Vollmann, Jochen, ed. Medizin und Ethik: Aktuelle ethische Probleme in Therapie und Forschung. Erlangen: Universitätsbund Erlangen-Nürnberg, 2003: 125-151. NRCBL: 20.7; 20.5.1. SC: le.

Ziegler, Stephen J.; Jackson, Robert A. Who's not afraid of Proposal B?: an analysis of exit-poll data from Michigan's vote on physician-assisted suicide. *Politics and the Life Sciences* 2004 March; 23(1): 42-48. NRCBL: 20.7; 20.5.1. SC: em; le.

ATTITUDES TO DEATH *See* DEATH AND DYING/ ATTITUDES TO DEATH

BEHAVIOR CONTROL

See also CARE FOR SPECIFIC GROUPS/ MENTALLY DISABLED; ELECTROCONVULSIVE THERAPY; INVOLUNTARY COMMITMENT; MENTAL HEALTH THERAPIES; PSYCHOPHARMACOLOGY; PSYCHOTHERAPY

Boire, Richard Glen. Neurocops: the politics of prohibition and the future of enforcing social policy from inside the body. *Journal of Law and Health* 2004-2005; 19(2): 215-257. NRCBL: 17.3; 9.5.9; 17.4. SC: le.

British Association of Critical Care Nurses; Bray, Kate; Hill, Karen; Robson, Wayne; Leaver, Gill; Walker, Nikki; O'Leary, Mary; Delaney, Trish; Walsh, Dominic; Gager, Melanie; Waterhouse, Catheryne. British Association of Critical Care Nurses position statement on the use of restraint in adult critical care units. *Nursing in Critical Care* 2004 September-October; 9(5): 199-212. NRCBL: 17.3; 17.4; 6; 4.1.3. SC: rv. Identifiers: United Kingdom (Great Britain).

Clark, Masharia A. Involuntary admission and the medical inpatient: judicious use of physical restraint. *Medsurg Nursing* 2005 August; 14(4): 213-219. NRCBL: 17.3; 4.1.3; 9.8. SC: cs.

Coni, Nick; Rai, Gurcharan S. The use of restraints. *In:* Rai, Gurcharan S, ed. Medical Ethics and the Elderly. 2nd ed. San Francisco: Radcliffe Medical Press; 2004: 139-145. NRCBL: 17.3; 17.4.

Draper, Heather; McDiarmaid-Gordon, Adam; Strumidlo, Laura; Teuten, Bea; Updale, Eleanor. Virtual ethics committee, case 2: can we restrain Ivy for the benefit of others? *Clinical Ethics* 2006 June; 1(2): 68-75. NRCBL: 17.3; 9.5.2; 4.3; 8.3.1; 9.6. SC: an; cs; le.

Folkes, Kathryn. Is restraint a form of abuse? *Paediatric Nursing* 2005 July; 17(6): 41-44. NRCBL: 17.3; 9.5.7; 8.3.4; 8.3.2; 4.1.3.

Haimowitz, Stephan. Legal consequences of seclusion and restraint [letter]. *Psychiatric Services* 2006 October; 57(10): 1516. NRCBL: 17.3. SC: le.

Herrera, C.D. Restraint use and autonomy in psychiatric care. *Journal of Ethics in Mental Health* 2006 November; 1(1): E5, 4 p. NRCBL: 17.3; 1.1; 8.3.1.

Liberman, Robert Paul; Smith, Gregory M.; Altenor, Aidan; Davis, Robert H.; LeBel, Janice; Huckshorn, Kevin Ann; Frueh, B. Christopher; Grubaugh, Anouk L.; Robins, Cynthia S. Elimination of seclusion and restraint: a reasonable goal? [letter and replies]. *Psychiatric Services* 2006 April; 57(4): 576-578. NRCBL: 17.3.

McLoughlin, Kris A.; Geller, Jeffrey L. The recovery model and seclusion and restraint [letter]. *Psychiatric Services* 2006 July; 57(7): 1045. NRCBL: 17.3.

Patterson, Brodie. Developing a perspective on restraint and the least intrusive intervention. *British Journal of Nursing* 2006 December 14-2007 January 10; 15(22): 1235-1241. NRCBL: 17.3; 17.7; 21.1. SC: le. Identifiers: Council of Europe; United Kingdom (Great Britain).

Rappaport, Richard G. Losing your rights: complications of misdiagnosis [editorial]. *Journal of the American Academy of Psychiatry and the Law* 2006; 34(4): 436-438. NRCBL: 17.3; 7.4; 17.7.

Suen, Lorna K.P.; Lai, C.K.Y.; Wong, T.K.S.; Chow, S.K.Y.; Kong, S.K.F.; Ho, J.L.Y.; Kong, T.K.; Leung, J.S.C.; Wong, I.Y.C. Use of physical restraints in rehabilitation settings: staff knowledge, attitudes and predictors. *Journal of Advanced Nursing* 2006 July; 55(1): 20-28. NRCBL: 17.3. SC: em.

Wright, Evangeline. Mind-control experimentation: a travesty of human rights in the United States. *Journal of Gender, Race and Justice* 2005 Fall; 9(1): 211-239. NRCBL: 17.3; 18.5.8; 18.5.2; 18.6. SC: le.

BEHAVIORAL GENETICS

Baldwin, Thomas. Behavioural genetics: prospects and challenges. *Human Fertility* 2004 March; 7(1): 11-18. NRCBL: 15.6.

Brock, Dan W. Behavioral genetics and equality. *In:* Parens, Erik; Chapman, Audrey R.; Press, Nancy, eds. Wrestling with Behavioral Genetics: Science, Ethics, and Public Conversion. Baltimore, MD: Johns Hopkins University Press; 2006: 199-219. NRCBL: 15.6; 1.1; 4.5. SC: an.

Carey, Gregory; Gottesman, Irving I. Genes and antisocial behavior: perceived versus real threats to jurisprudence. *Journal of Law, Medicine and Ethics* 2006 Summer; 34(2): 342-351. NRCBL: 15.6; 18.4; 1.3.5. SC: le.

Conrad, Peter. Public eyes and private genes: historic frames, news constructions and social problems. *Social Problems* 1997; 44: 139-154. NRCBL: 15.6; 15.5; 15.3; 1.3.7. SC: rv.

Dinwiddie, Stephen H.; Hoop, Jinger; Gershon, Elliot S. Ethical issues in the use of genetic information. *International Review of Psychiatry* 2004 November; 16(4): 320-328. NRCBL: 15.6; 15.3.

Farahany, Nita; Bernet, William. Behavioral genetics in criminal cases: past, present, and future. *Genomics, Society and Policy* 2006 May; 2(1): 72-79. NRCBL: 15.6; 1.3.5.
  Abstract: Researchers studying human behavioral genetics have made significant scientific progress in enhancing our un-

NRCBL: National Reference Center for Bioethics Literature Classification Scheme   See inside front cover for terms.

51

derstanding of the relative contributions of genetics and the environment in observed variations in human behavior. Quickly outpacing the advances in the science are its applications in the criminal justice system. Already, human behavioral genetics research has been introduced in the U.S. criminal justice system, and its use will only become more prevalent. This essay discusses the recent historical use of behavioral genetics in criminal cases, recent advances in two gene variants of particular interest in the criminal law, MAOA and SLC6A4, the recent expert testimony on behalf of criminal defendants with respect to these two gene variants, and the future direction of behavioral genetics evidence in criminal cases.

Kaplan, Jonathan. Misinformation, misrepresentation, and misuse of human behavioral genetics research. *Law and Contemporary Problems* 2006 Winter-Spring; 69(1-2): 47-80. NRCBL: 15.6; 18.4; 9.1; 3.1.

Kaye, D.H. Behavioral genetics research and criminal DNA databases. *Law and Contemporary Problems* 2006 Winter-Spring; 69(1-2): 259-299. NRCBL: 15.6; 18.4; 1.3.5; 1.3.12; 18.3; 18.2. SC: le.

Müller-Hill, Benno. Human behavioural genetics — past and future. *Journal of Molecular Biology* 2002 June 14; 319(4): 927-929. NRCBL: 15.6; 15.11. SC: an.

Press, Nancy. Social construction and medicalization: behavioral genetics in context. *In:* Parens, Erik; Chapman, Audrey R.; Press, Nancy, eds. Wrestling with Behavioral Genetics: Science, Ethics, and Public Conversion. Baltimore, MD: Johns Hopkins University Press; 2006: 131-149. NRCBL: 15.6.

Robert, Jason Scott. Genetics and behavior. *In:* Mitcham, Carl, ed. Encyclopedia of Science, Technology, and Ethics. Farmington Hills, MI: Thomson/Gale, 2005: 849-854. NRCBL: 15.6; 2.2.

Ross, Colin A. Overestimates of the genetic contribution to eating disorders. *Ethical Human Psychology and Psychiatry* 2006 Summer; 8(2): 123-131. NRCBL: 15.6. SC: em; rv.

Rothstein, Mark A. Applications of behavioural genetics: outpacing the science? *Nature Reviews Genetics* 2005 October; 6(10): 793-798. NRCBL: 15.6; 5.1; 16.3; 1.3.5; 9.31. SC: em.

Rutter, Michael. Why is the topic of genes and behavior controversial? *In his:* Genes and Behavior: Nature — Nurture Interplay Explained. Malden, MA; Oxford: Blackwell Pub.; 2006: 1-17. NRCBL: 15.6.

Schulze, Thomas G.; Fangerau, Heiner; Propping, Peter. From degeneration to genetic susceptibility, from eugenics to genethics, from Bezugsziffer to LOD score: the history of psychiatric genetics. *International Review of Psychiatry* 2004 November; 16(4): 246- 259. NRCBL: 15.6; 2.2. SC: rv.

Tsioumanis, Assterios; Mattas, Konstadinos; Tsioumani, Elsa. The ugly curve — genetic screening into

the 21st century. *In:* Árnason, Gardar; Nordal, Salvör; Árnason, Vilhjálmur, eds. Blood and Data: Ethical, Legal and Social Aspects of Human Genetic Databases. Reykjavík: University of Iceland Press; 2004: 263-268. NRCBL: 15.6; 15.3.

Wachbroit, Robert. Normality and the significance of difference. *In:* Parens, Erik; Chapman, Audrey R.; Press, Nancy, eds. Wrestling with Behavioral Genetics: Science, Ethics, and Public Conversion. Baltimore, MD: Johns Hopkins University Press; 2006: 235-253. NRCBL: 15.6; 4.2.

Yudin, Boris. Human life: genetic or social construction. *Journal International de Bioéthique = International Journal of Bioethics* 2005 September-December; 16(3-4): 89-96, 173-174. NRCBL: 15.6; 15.3; 5.3.

Abstract: I am going to discuss some present-day tendencies in the development of the very old debate on nature vs nurture. There is a widespread position describing the history of this debate as a pendulum-like process. Some three decades ago there was a time of overwhelming prevalence of the position stressing social factors in determining human character and behavior; now the pendulum has come to the opposite side and those who stress the role of biology, of genes are in favor. Yet in my view rather acute opposition of both positions still exists. Its existence depends not so much on new scientific discoveries as on some social and cultural factors which are more conservative than the development of science. More than that, we can even talk about competition of these two positions.

BEHAVIORAL RESEARCH
See also BIOMEDICAL RESEARCH; HUMAN EXPERIMENTATION

Blank, Robert H. The brain, aggression, and public policy. *Politics and the Life Sciences* 2005 March-September; 24(1-2): 12-21. NRCBL: 18.4; 15.1; 18.6.

Bortolotti, Lisa; Mameli, Matteo. Deception in psychology: moral costs and benefits of unsought self-knowledge. *Accountability in Research* 2006 July-September; 13(3): 259-275. NRCBL: 18.4; 8.2.

Abstract: Is it ethically permissible to use deception in psychological experiments? We argue that, provided some requirements are satisfied, it is possible to use deceptive methods without producing significant harm to research participants and without any significant violation of their autonomy. We also argue that methodological deception is at least at the moment the only effective means by which one can acquire morally significant information about certain behavioral tendencies. Individuals in general, and research participants in particular, gain self-knowledge which can help them improve their autonomous decision-making. The community gains collective self-knowledge that, once shared, can play a role in shaping education, informing policies and in general creating a more efficient and just society.

Chadwick, David; Privitera, Michael. How skeptical should we be about industry-sponsored studies? [editorial]. *Neurology* 2006 August 8; 67(3): 378-379. NRCBL: 18.4.

Childress, Herb. The anthropologist and the crayons: changing our focus from avoiding harm to doing good. *Journal of Empirical Research on Human Research Ethics* 2006 June; 1(2): 79-87. NRCBL: 18.4; 18.2.

Church, Jonathan T.; Shopes, Linda; Blanchard, Margaret A. For the record: should all disciplines be subject to the Common Rule? Human subjects in social science research. *Academe* 2002 May-June; 88(3): 11 p. [Online]. Accessed: http://plinks.ebscohost.com/ehost/delivery? id=12&hid=102&sid=8c8f3742-ec0b. . . [2006 October 16]. NRCBL: 18.4; 18.2; 18.6.

Dawson, Angus J. A messy business: qualitative research and ethical review. *Clinical Ethics* 2006 June; 1(2): 114-116. NRCBL: 18.4; 18.2.

DuBois, James M. Ethics in behavioral and social science research. *In:* Iltis, Ana Smith, ed. Research Ethics. New York: Routledge, 2006: 102-120. NRCBL: 18.4.

Dunn, Laura B.; Roberts, Laura Weiss. Emerging findings in ethics of schizophrenia research. *Current Opinion in Psychiatry* 2005 March; 18(2): 111-119. NRCBL: 18.4; 18.2; 18.3. SC: rv.

Epstein, William M. The lighter side of deception research in the social sciences: social work as comedy. *Journal of Information Ethics* 2006 Spring; 15(1): 11-26. NRCBL: 18.4; 1.3.7; 1.3.9; 17.3; 10.

Faden, Pamela; Minkler, Meredith; Perry, Martha; Blum, Klaus; Moore, Leroy; Rogers, Judith. Ethical challenges in community based participatory research: a case study from the San Francisco Bay area disability community. *In:* Minkler, Meredith; Wallerstein, Nina, eds. Community Based Participatory Research for Health. San Francisco, CA: Jossey-Bass; 2003: 242-262. NRCBL: 18.4; 20.7; 20.5.1.

Freeman, Anthony. Consciousness. *In:* Mitcham, Carl, ed. Encyclopedia of Science, Technology, and Ethics. Farmington Hills, MI: Thomson/Gale, 2005: 410-411. NRCBL: 18.4; 17.1.

Fry, C.L.; Madden, A.; Brogan, D.; Loff, B. Australian resources for ethical participatory processes in public health research [letter]. *Journal of Medical Ethics* 2006 March; 32(3): 186. NRCBL: 18.4; 9.7; 9.5.9.

Hallowell, Nina; Lawton, Julia. Seeking ethical approval: opening up the lines of communication. *Clinical Ethics* 2006 June; 1(2): 109-113. NRCBL: 18.4; 18.2; 7.1. SC: an.

Kleiman, Mark. The 'brain disease' idea, drug policy and research ethics. *Addiction* 2003 July; 98(7): 871-872. NRCBL: 18.4; 9.5.9; 18.5.1.

Macklin, Ruth. Unresolved issues in social science medicine. *In:* Lolas Stepke, Fernando; Agar Corbinos, Lorenzo, eds. Interfaces Between Bioethics and the Empirical Social Sciences. Buenos Aires, Argentina: World Health Organization; 2002: 67-78. NRCBL: 18.4; 18.3.

McIlfatrick, S.; Sullivan, K.; McKenna, H. Exploring the ethical issues of the research interview in the cancer context. *European Journal of Oncology Nursing* 2006 February; 10(1): 39-47. NRCBL: 18.4; 9.5.1.

Milgram, Stanley. Behavioral study of obedience. *Journal of Abnormal and Social Psychology* 1963 October; 67: 371-378. NRCBL: 18.4.

Newman, Elana; Risch, Elizabeth; Kassam-Adams, Nancy. Ethical issues in trauma-related research: a review. *Journal of Empirical Research on Human Research Ethics* 2006 September; 1(3): 29-46. NRCBL: 18.4; 18.3; 18.5.2; 18.1. SC: rv.

Redding, Richard E. Bias on prejudice? The politics of research and racial prejudice. *Psychological Inquiry* 2004; 15(4): 289-293. NRCBL: 18.4; 21.1.

Rupert, Patricia A.; Kozlowski, Neal F.; Hoffman, Laura A.; Daniels, Denise D.; Piette, Jeanne M. Practical and ethical issues in teaching psychological testing. *Professional Psychology: Research and Practice* 1999 April; 30(2): 209-214. NRCBL: 18.4; 7.2; 17.1; 8.4; 18.3; 18.5.1; 18.5.2.

Sears, David O. A perspective on implicit prejudice from survey research. *Psychological Inquiry* 2004; 15(4): 293-297. NRCBL: 18.4; 21.1.

Shaver, Frances M. Sex work research: methodological and ethical challenges. *Journal of Interpersonal Violence* 2005 March; 20(3): 296-319. NRCBL: 18.4; 18.2; 10; 18.5.1. Identifiers: Canada.

Stinson, Sara. Ethical issues in human biology behavioral research and research with children. *In:* Turner, Trudy R. ed. Biological Anthropology and Ethics: From Repatriation to Genetic Identity. Albany, NY: State University of New York Press; 2005: 139-148. NRCBL: 18.4; 18.5.2.

Tindell, Deborah R.; Bohlander, Robert W. Participants' naivete and confidentiality in psychological research. *Psychological Reports* 2005 June; 96(3 Part 2): 963-969. NRCBL: 18.4; 8.4.

Yanos, Philip T.; Ziedonis, Douglas M. The patient-oriented clinician-researcher: advantages and challenges of being a double agent. *Psychiatric Services* 2006 February; 57(2): 249-253. NRCBL: 18.4; 17.1.

BIOETHICISTS *See* ETHICISTS AND ETHICS COMMITTEES

BIOETHICS AND MEDICAL ETHICS
See also CODES OF ETHICS; NURSING ETHICS AND PHILOSOPHY; PROFESSIONAL ETHICS

NRCBL: National Reference Center for Bioethics Literature Classification Scheme   See inside front cover for terms.

53

Bioethics at the bench [editorial]. *Nature* 2006 April 27; 440(7088): 1089-1090. NRCBL: 2.1; 1.3.9; 7.3; 15.1; 9.6. Identifiers: National Institutes of Health; ELSI program.

93rd Interparliamentary Conference. Bioethics: an international challenge for the protection of human rights = 93a. Conferencia Interparlamentaria. La Bioética: un reto internacional para la protección de los derechos humanos. *Law and the Human Genome Review = Revista de Derecho y Genoma Humano* 1995 July-December; (3): 299-301. NRCBL: 2.1; 21.1; 2.3.

Abbott, Alison. A defining moment for bioethics [review of Biblioethics: A User's Dictionary, directed by Luca Ronconi]. *Nature* 2006 March 2; 440(7080): 30. NRCBL: 2.1; 7.1.

Ames, David A. Ethical dilemmas in clinical medicine: although ethical principles are normative statements and theoretical constructs can be applied to many situations, each case is unique. *Rhode Island Medical Journal* 1986 March; 69(3): 117-120. NRCBL: 2.1.

Azariah, Jayapaul. Asian bioethics in global society. *In:* Sang-yong, Song; Young-Mo, Koo; Macer, Darryl R.J., eds. Asian Bioethics in the 21st Century. Christchurch, NZ: Eubios Ethics Institute, 2002: 219-223. NRCBL: 2.1. Conference: Proceedings of the Asian Bioethics Conference (ABC4), held 22-25 November 2002 in Seoul, South Korea.

Baldwin, DeWitt C., Jr.; Bunch, Wilton H. Moral reasoning, professionalism, and the teaching of ethics to orthopaedic surgeons. *Clinical Orthopaedics and Related Research* 2000 September; (378): 97-103. NRCBL: 2.1; 7.2. SC: em.

Bankauskaite, V.; Jakusovaite, I. Dealing with ethical problems in the healthcare system in Lithuania: achievements and challenges. *Journal of Medical Ethics* 2006 October; 32(10): 584-587. NRCBL: 2.1; 8.1; 9.1.

Baron, Jonathan. Going against nature. *In his:* Against Bioethics. Cambridge, MA: MIT Press, 2006: 51-82. NRCBL: 2.1.

Baron, Jonathan. The bigger picture. *In his:* Against Bioethics. Cambridge, MA: MIT Press, 2006: 205-213. NRCBL: 2.1.

Beam, Thomas E. A proposed ethic for military medicine. *In:* Beam, Thomas E.; Sparacino, Linette R.; Pellegrino, Edmund D.; Hartle, Anthony E.; Howe, Edmund G., eds. Military Medical Ethics. Volume 2. Washington, DC: TMM Publications, Borden Institute, Walter Reed Army Medical Center; 2003: 851-868. NRCBL: 2.1; 1.3.5.

Beam, Thomas E. Medical ethics on the battlefield: the crucible of military medical ethics. *In:* Beam, Thomas E.; Sparacino, Linette R.; Pellegrino, Edmund D.; Hartle, Anthony E.; Howe, Edmund G., eds. Military Medical Ethics.

Volume 2. Washington, DC: TMM Publications, Borden Institute, Walter Reed Army Medical Center; 2003: 369-402. NRCBL: 2.1; 1.3.5; 21.2.

Benatar, D. Bioethics and health and human rights: a critical view. *Journal of Medical Ethics* 2006 January; 32(1): 17-20. NRCBL: 2.1; 21.1. SC: an.

Abstract: Recent decades have seen the emergence of two new fields of inquiry into ethical issues in medicine. These are the fields of bioethics and of health and human rights. In this critical review of these fields, the author argues that bioethics, partly because it has been construed so broadly, suffers from quality control problems. The author also argues that the field of health and human rights is superfluous because it does nothing that cannot be done by either bioethics of the law.

Benatar, Solomon R.; Landman, Willem A. Bioethics in South Africa. *CQ: Cambridge Quarterly of Healthcare Ethics* 2006 Summer; 15(3): 239-247. NRCBL: 2.1; 7.2; 2.3; 18.1; 9.5.6; 20.5.

Benatar, Solomon; Fleischer, Theodore; Macklin, Ruth. Bioethics with blinders [letter and reply]. *Hastings Center Report* 2006 September-October; 36(5): 4-5. NRCBL: 2.1; 5.3; 21.1; 9.5.5; 9.1.

Berg, Jessica; King, Nicholas. Strange bedfellows? Reflections on bioethics' role in disaster response planning. *American Journal of Bioethics* 2006 September-October; 6(5): 3-5. NRCBL: 2.1; 9.1; 9.5.1.

Bishop, Jeffrey P.; Jotterand, Fabrice. Bioethics as biopolitics. *Journal of Medicine and Philosophy* 2006 June; 31(3): 205-212. NRCBL: 2.1. SC: an.

Borry, Pascal; Schotsmans, Paul; Dierickx, Kris. Author, contributor or just a signer? A quantitative analysis of authorship trends in the field of bioethics. *Bioethics* 2006 August; 20(4): 213-220. NRCBL: 2.1; 1.3.7. SC: em.

Abstract: Publications are primarily a means of communicating scientific information to colleagues, but they are much more than that. Publications in peer reviewed journals are proof of academic competence, are used as a crucial component in evaluation criteria for academic promotion and fundraising and increase the prestige of research centres and universities. The urgent need for publications has also led to abuses in authorship. In the past the single-author article was the rule, but over the past decades, the average number of authors on scientific manuscripts has drastically increased. In the field of bioethics, however, no research has been undertaken to study whether the percentage of single-author articles is decreasing, the proportion of multi-author articles is increasing or the average number of authors per article is increasing. The objective of this research is to analyze these trends in authorship for the period 1990-2003 in peer reviewed journals in the field of bioethics. In the nine peer reviewed journals from the field of bioethics we studied, we observed a significant increase of the multi-author article and of the average number of authors. This is mainly due to the increase in the number of publications with an empirical design. This growing trend is a challenge for the editors of journals in the field of bioethics to enhance awareness about the value and definition of authorship.

Borry, Pascal; Schotsmans, Paul; Dierickx, Kris. Empirical research in bioethical journals. A quantitative analysis. *Journal of Medical Ethics* 2006 April; 32(4): 240-245. NRCBL: 2.1; 1.3.7. SC: em.

Borry, Pascal; Schotsmans, Paul; Dierickx, Kris. How international is bioethics? A quantitative retrospective study. *BMC Medical Ethics* 2006; 7(1): 6 p. [Online]. Accessed: http://www.biomedcentral.com/bmcmedethics/ [2006 February 21]. NRCBL: 2.1; 21.1; 1.3.7. SC: em.
Abstract: BACKGROUND : Studying the contribution of individual countries to leading journals in a specific discipline can highlight which countries have the most impact on that discipline and whether a geographic bias exists. This article aims to examine the international distribution of publications in the field of bioethics. METHODS : Retrospective quantitative study of nine peer reviewed journals in the field of bioethics and medical ethics (Bioethics, Cambridge Quarterly of Healthcare Ethics, Hastings Center Report, Journal of Clinical Ethics, Journal of Medical Ethics, Kennedy Institute of Ethics Journal, Nursing Ethics, Christian Bioethics, and Theoretical Medicine and Bioethics). RESULTS : In total, 4,029 articles published between 1990 and 2003 were retrieved from the nine bioethical journals under study. The United States (59.3%, n = 2390), the United Kingdom (13.5%, n = 544), Canada (4%, n = 160) and Australia (3.8%, n = 154) had the highest number of publications in terms of absolute number of publications. When normalized to population size, smaller affluent countries, such as New Zealand, Finland and Sweden were more productive than the United States. The number of studies originating from the USA was decreasing in the period between 1990 and 2003. CONCLUSION : While a lot of peer reviewed journals in the field of bioethics profile themselves as international journals, they certainly do not live up to what one would expect from an "international" journal. The fact that English speaking countries, and to a larger extent American authors, dominate the international journals in the field of bioethics is a clear geographic bias towards the bioethical discussions that are going on in these journals.

Budinger, Thomas F.; Budinger, Miriam D. Medical ethics. *In their:* Ethics of Emerging Technologies: Scientific Facts and Moral Challenges. Hoboken, NJ: John Wiley and Sons; 2006: 223-276. NRCBL: 2.1.

Bunge, Mario. Bioethics. *In his:* Philosophical Dictionary. Enlarged edition. Amherst, NY: Prometheus Books; 2003: 32. NRCBL: 2.1.

Burley, Justine; Colman, Alan. Science and philosophy: bridging the two cultures divide. *Journal of Molecular Biology* 2002 June 14; 319(4): 907-915. NRCBL: 2.1; 14.5. SC: an.

Callahan, Daniel. Bioethics and ideology. *Hastings Center Report* 2006 January-February; 36(1): 3. NRCBL: 2.1; 21.1.

Campbell, Alastair V. Public policy and the future of bioethics. *Genomics, Society and Policy* 2005 February; 1(1): 86-91. NRCBL: 2.1; 5.3.

Charon, Rita. The ethicality of narrative medicine. *In:* Hurwitz, Brian; Greenhalgh, Trisha; Skultans, Vieda, eds. Narrative Research in Health and Illness. Malden MA: BMJ Books; 2004: 23-36. NRCBL: 2.1; 8.1.

Cortina, Adela. The public role of bioethics and the role of the public. *In:* Rehmann-Sutter, Christoph; Düwell, Marcus; Mieth, Dietmar, eds. Bioethics in Cultural Contexts: Reflections on Methods and Finitude. Dordrecht: Springer, 2006: 165-174. NRCBL: 2.1.

Dausset, Jean. Bioethics and responsibility = Bioética y responsabilidad. *Law and the Human Genome Review = Revista de Derecho y Genoma Humano* 1995 July-December; (3): 23-32. NRCBL: 2.1.

De Vries, Raymond G. Toward a sociology of bioethics [review of Strangers at the Bedside: A History of How Law and Bioethics Transformed Medical Decision Making by David J. Rothman; All Gods Mistakes: Genetic Counseling in a Pediatric Hospital by Charles L. Bosk; Intensive Care: Medical Ethics and the Medical Profession by Robert Zussman; Deciding Who Lives: Fateful Choices in the Intensive-Care Nursery by Renée R. Anspach]. *Qualitative Sociology* 1995 Spring; 18(1): 119-128. NRCBL: 2.1; 7.1; 15.1.

Donchin, Anne. Integrating bioethics and human rights: toward a global feminist approach. *In:* Tong, Rosemarie; Donchin, Anne; Dodds, Susan, eds. Linking Visions: Feminist Bioethics, Human Rights, and the Developing World. Lanham, MD: Rowman and Littlefield Publishers; 2004: 31-56. NRCBL: 2.1; 10; 21.1.

Emanuel, Ezekiel J. The relevance of empirical research for bioethics. *In:* Lolas Stepke, Fernando; Agar Corbinos, Lorenzo, eds. Interfaces Between Bioethics and the Empirical Social Sciences. Buenos Aires, Argentina: World Health Organization; 2002: 99-110. NRCBL: 2.1. SC: em.

Eriksson, Stefan; Helgesson, Gert; Segerdahl, Pär. Provide expertise or facilitate ethical reflection? A comment on the debate between Cowley and Crosthwaite. *Medicine, Health Care and Philosophy* 2006; 9(3): 389-392. NRCBL: 2.1. SC: em.

Eubios Ethics Institute; Asian Bioethics Conference; Song, Sang-Yong; Koo, Young-Moo; Macer, Darryl R. J. Asian bioethics in the 21st century. Christchurch, N.Z.: Eubios Ethics Institute, 2003; 434 p. NRCBL: 2.1; 21.1. Conference: Proceedings of the Asian Bioethics Conference (ABC4); Seoul, South Korea; 2002 November 22-25.

Evans, John H. Between technocracy and democratic legitimation: a proposed compromise position for common morality public bioethics. *Journal of Medicine and Philosophy* 2006 June; 31(3): 213-234. NRCBL: 2.1. SC: an.
Abstract: In this article I explore the underlying political philosophy of public bioethics by comparing it to technocratic authority, particularly the technocratic authority claimed by economists in Mexico in the 1980s and 1990s. I find that public bioethics—at least in the dominant forms—is implicitly designed for and tries to use technocratic authority. I examine how this type of bioethics emerged and has continued. I finish by arguing that, as claims to technocratic authority go, bioethics is in an incredibly weak position, which partly explains why it has

NRCBL: National Reference Center for Bioethics Literature Classification Scheme   See inside front cover for terms.

55

never gained the degree of public legitimacy that other technocracies have gained. I conclude by arguing for a "technocracy-lite" orientation for public bioethics.

Fischer, Michael M.J. Ethnographic critique and technoscientific narratives: the old mole, ethical plateaux, and the governance of emergent biosocial polities. *Culture Medicine and Psychiatry* 2001 December; 25(4): 355-393. NRCBL: 2.1; 5.1; 5.3; 7.1; 15.1.

Frader, Joel. Becoming an ethical physician. *Atrium* 2006 Winter; 2: 12-13. NRCBL: 2.1; 2.3; 7.2.

Freeman, Jerome W.; Schellinger, Ellen; Olsen, Arthur; Harris, Mary Helen; Eidsness, LuAnn. A model for bioethics decision making: C/CPR. *South Dakota Journal of Medicine* 2005 May; 58(5): 195-196. NRCBL: 2.1. Identifiers: covenant/context, principles, and resolution.

Gert, Bernard; Culver, Charles M.; Clouser, K. Danner. Principlism. *APA Newsletters: Newsletter on Philosophy and Medicine* 2006 Spring; 05(2): 16-19. NRCBL: 2.1. SC: an.

Giordano, Simona. Paternalism v. respect for autonomy. *In her:* Understanding Eating Disorders: Conceptual and Ethical Issues in the Treatment of Anorexia and Bulimia Nervosa. New York: Oxford University Press; 2005: 33-57. NRCBL: 2.1.

Glaser, Vicki; Hurlbut, William B. An interview with William B. Hurlbut. *Rejuvenation Research* 2005 Summer; 8(2): 110-122. NRCBL: 2.1; 4.5; 9.5.2; 5.1.

Graumann, Sigrid. Experts on bioethics in biopolitics. *In:* Rehmann-Sutter, Christoph; Düwell, Marcus; Mieth, Dietmar, eds. Bioethics in Cultural Contexts: Reflections on Methods and Finitude. Dordrecht: Springer, 2006: 175-185. NRCBL: 2.1; 21.1.

Gross, Michael. Bioethics and war [editorial]. *CQ: Cambridge Quarterly of Healthcare Ethics* 2006 Fall; 15(4): 341-343. NRCBL: 2.1; 21.2.

Haimes, Erica. What can the social sciences contribute to the study of ethics?: theoretical, empirical and substantive considerations. *In:* Rehmann-Sutter, Christoph; Düwell, Marcus; Mieth, Dietmar, eds. Bioethics in Cultural Contexts: Reflections on Methods and Finitude. Dordrecht: Springer, 2006: 277-298. NRCBL: 2.1. SC: em.

Haker, Hille. Narrative bioethics. *In:* Rehmann-Sutter, Christoph; Düwell, Marcus; Mieth, Dietmar, eds. Bioethics in Cultural Contexts: Reflections on Methods and Finitude. Dordrecht: Springer, 2006: 353-376. NRCBL: 2.1.

Hill, Edward C. Your morality or mine? An inquiry into the ethics of human reproduction. *American Journal of Obstetrics and Gynecology* 1986 June; 154(6): 1173-1180. NRCBL: 2.1; 14.1. Conference: Fifty-second Annual

Meeting of the Pacific coast Obstetrical and Gynecological Society; Napa, California; 1985 September 29 - October 4.

Himma, Kenneth Einar. Natural law. *In:* Mitcham, Carl, ed. Encyclopedia of Science, Technology, and Ethics. Farmington Hills, MI: Thomson/Gale, 2005: 1289-1295. NRCBL: 2.1; 5.1.

Holm, Søren; Williams-Jones, Bryn. Global bioethics — myth or reality? *BMC Medical Ethics [electronic]* 2006; 7: 10. 10p. Accessed: http://www.biomedcentral.com/1472-6939/7/10 [nd]. NRCBL: 2.1; 21.1; 1.3.12.
Abstract: BACKGROUND: There has been debate on whether a global or unified field of bioethics exists. If bioethics is a unified global field, or at the very least a closely shared way of thinking, then we should expect bioethicists to behave the same way in their academic activities anywhere in the world. This paper investigates whether there is a 'global bioethics' in the sense of a unified academic community. METHODS: To address this question, we study the web-linking patterns of bioethics institutions, the citation patterns of bioethics papers and the buying patterns of bioethics books. RESULTS: All three analyses indicate that there are geographical and institutional differences in the academic behavior of bioethicists and bioethics institutions. CONCLUSION: These exploratory studies support the position that there is no unified global field of bioethics. This is a problem if the only reason is parochialism. But these regional differences are probably of less concern if one notices that bioethics comes in many not always mutually understandable dialects.

Howe, Edmund G. Mixed agency in military medicine: ethical roles in conflict. *In:* Beam, Thomas E.; Sparacino, Linette R.; Pellegrino, Edmund D.; Hartle, Anthony E.; Howe, Edmund G., eds. Military Medical Ethics. Volume 1. Washington, DC: TMM Publications, Borden Institute, Walter Reed Army Medical Center; 2003: 331-365. NRCBL: 2.1; 21.2; 1.3.5.

Hu, Ching-li. The World Health Organization and its role in bioethics. *In:* Döring, Ole; Chen, Renbiao, eds. Advances in Chinese Medical Ethics: Chinese and International Perspectives. Hamburg: Institut für Asienkunde; 2002: 26-37. NRCBL: 2.1; 21.1. Note: Proceedings of the Second Sino-German Interdisciplinary Symposium about Medical Ethics in China, Shanghai, 19-23 October, 1999.

Iltis, Ana Smith. Look who's talking: the interdisciplinarity of bioethics and the implications for bioethics education. *Journal of Medicine and Philosophy* 2006 December; 31(6): 629-641. NRCBL: 2.1; 2.3. SC: an.
Abstract: There are competing accounts of the birth of bioethics. Despite the differences among them, these accounts share the claim that bioethics was not born in a single disciplinary home or in a single social space, but in numerous, including hospitals, doctors' offices, research laboratories, courtrooms, medical schools, churches and synagogues, and philosophy classrooms. This essay considers the interdisciplinarity of bioethics and the contribution of new disciplines to bioethics. It also explores the implications of interdisciplinarity for bioethics education. As bioethics develops, it will be helpful to identify essential elements in the education of bioethicists and

to distinguish between members of other disciplines who make important contributions to bioethics and bioethicists.

Jonsen, Albert R. History and future of bioethics. *In:* Rehmann-Sutter, Christoph; Düwell, Marcus; Mieth, Dietmar, eds. Bioethics in Cultural Contexts: Reflections on Methods and Finitude. Dordrecht: Springer, 2006: 13-19. NRCBL: 2.1; 2.2.

Kahn, Jeffrey P. What happens when politics discovers bioethics? *Hastings Center Report* 2006 May-June; 36(3): 10. NRCBL: 2.1; 21.1.

Kavanagh, Kathryn H. Beyond the individual: healthcare ethics in diverse societies. *In:* Dinkins, Christine Sorrell; Sorrell, Jeanne Merkle, eds. Listening to the Whispers: Re-Thinking Ethics in Healthcare. Madison, WI: University of Wisconsin Press; 2006: 248-309. NRCBL: 2.1; 9.1.

Kieniewicz, Piotr H. New frontiers, new dangers: ethical perspective. *In:* Glasa, J. ed. Ethics of Human Genetics: Challenges of the (Post) Genomic Era. Bratislava, Slovak Republic: Charis [and] IMEB Foundation; 2002: 209-223. NRCBL: 2.1; 1.3.9.

Kingma, Stuart. Biomedical ethics: in search of touchstone for tough choices. *Ecumenical Review* 1980 July; 32(3): 273-280. NRCBL: 2.1.

Koch, Tom. Bioethics as ideology: conditional and unconditional values. *Journal of Medicine and Philosophy* 2006 June; 31(3): 251-267. NRCBL: 2.1. SC: an.

Abstract: For all its apparent debate bioethical discourse is in fact very narrow. The discussion that occurs is typically within limited parameters, rarely fundamental. Nor does it accommodate divergent perspectives with ease. The reason lies in its ideology and the political and economic perspectives that ideology promotes. Here the ideology of bioethics' fundamental axioms is critiqued as arbitrary and exclusive rather than necessary and inclusive. The result unpacks the ideological and political underpinnings of bioethical thinking and suggests new avenues for a broader debate over fundamentals, and a different approach to bioethical debate.

Kuszler, Patricia C. Biotechnology entrepreneurship and ethics: principles, paradigms, and products. *Medicine and Law: The World Association for Medical Law* 2006 September; 25(3): 491-502. NRCBL: 2.1; 1.3.9; 15.1; 7.3.

Abstract: Biotechnology, whether in the context of new drugs derived from DNA and genetic technology, genetically modified food, or biologics making use of living cells, raises ethical concerns at a variety of different levels. At the research level, there is concern that the very nature of research is being subverted, rather than enhanced, by entrepreneurship. This area of ethical concern has intensified in the United States as a result of the conflicts of interests resulting from the growing alliance between University academia and private industry in the research enterprise. As we travel down the research path into development of a drug or technology, ethical questions arise with respect to protecting human subjects and society from danger and exploitation by researchers. As development gives way to marketing and dissemination of a new product, government regulators are pressed to get drugs and biologics through the regulatory pipeline into the market faster, walking an ethical

tightrope between speed and safety. As new biotechnology products enter the market place, doctors and patients traverse yet another tightrope, that between unknown risk and the promise of benefit. And finally, patent protection is increasingly viewed as a unethical culprit in keeping prices high and depriving the global poor from lifesaving drugs and biologics. Bioethics has, to date, been largely a creation of Western research and medicine. As such it is wholly inadequate to respond to the cascade of ethical issues that flow from a vibrant biotechnology industry. And if biotechnology is in its infancy, as most believe, it is crucial that scientists, entrepreneurs and governments engage in dialogue about the ethical and societal questions raised on the road of scientific progress.

Lazarus, Jeremy A.; Sharfstein, Steven S. Ethics in managed care. *Psychiatric Clinics of North America* 2002 September; 25(3): 561-574. NRCBL: 2.1; 9.3.2. SC: cs.

Lerner, K. Lee; Lerner, Brenda Wilmoth, eds. Bioethics. *In their:* Medicine, Health, and Bioethics: Essential Primary Sources. Waterville, ME: Thomson Gale; 2006: 433-491. NRCBL: 2.1.

Lindemann, Hilde. Bioethics' gender. *American Journal of Bioethics [Online].* 2006 March-April; 6(2): W15-W19. NRCBL: 2.1; 10. SC: an.

Lolas Stepke, Fernando. Empirical social science studies and bioethics: an interface for the regional program on bioethics. *In:* Lolas Stepke, Fernando; Agar Corbinos, Lorenzo, eds. Interfaces Between Bioethics and the Empirical Social Sciences. Buenos Aires, Argentina: World Health Organization; 2002: 11-14. NRCBL: 2.1. SC: em.

Macklin, Ruth. The new conservatives in bioethics: who are they and what do they seek? *Hastings Center Report* 2006 January-February; 36(1): 34-43. NRCBL: 2.1; 5.3; 21.1.

Abstract: A new political movement has arisen in bioethics, self- consciously distinguished from the rest of the field and characterized by a new way of writing and arguing. Unfortunately, that new method is mean-spirited, mystical, and emotional. It claims insight into ultimate truth yet disavows reason.

Madden, William; Carter, Brian S. Physician-soldier: a moral profession. *In:* Beam, Thomas E.; Sparacino, Linette R.; Pellegrino, Edmund D.; Hartle, Anthony E.; Howe, Edmund G., eds. Military Medical Ethics. Volume 1. Washington, DC: TMM Publications, Borden Institute, Walter Reed Army Medical Center; 2003: 269-291. NRCBL: 2.1; 1.3.5; 21.2.

Martensen, Robert L. Bioethics on the brain. *Medical Humanities Review* 2004 Spring-Fall; 18(1-2): 27-45. NRCBL: 2.1; 17.1; 15.6; 2.2; 14.1.

McCullough, Laurence B. Getting back to the fundamentals of clinical ethics. *Journal of Medicine and Philosophy* 2006 February; 31(1): 1-6. NRCBL: 2.1.

McGee, Glenn. Will bioethics take the life of philosophy? [editorial]. *American Journal of Bioethics* 2006 September-October; 6(5): 1-2. NRCBL: 2.1; 4.1.

NRCBL: National Reference Center for Bioethics Literature Classification Scheme   See inside front cover for terms.

57

McNeill, Paul M.; Macklin, Ruth; Wasunna, Angela; Komesaroff, Paul A. An expanding vista: bioethics from public health, indigenous and feminist perspectives. *Medical Journal of Australia* 2005 July 4; 183(1): 8-9. NRCBL: 2.1; 9.1; 10; 21.1. Conference: "Deep listening: bridging divides in local and global ethics, "7th World Congress of Bioethics; November 2004; Sydney, Australia.

Mieth, Dietmar. The need for ethical evaluation in biomedicine and biopolitics. *In:* Rehmann-Sutter, Christoph; Düwell, Marcus; Mieth, Dietmar, eds. Bioethics in Cultural Contexts: Reflections on Methods and Finitude. Dordrecht: Springer, 2006: 21-43. NRCBL: 2.1.

Moazam, Farhat. "To eat an elephant" [editorial]. *Eastern Mediterranean Health Journal/La Revue de Santé de la Méditerranée orientale* 2006; 12(Supplement 1): S10-S12 [Online]. Accessed: http://www.emro.who.int/publications/EMHJ/12_S/PDF/2.pdf [2007 January 3]. NRCBL: 2.1; 2.3; 18.2; 18.6. Identifiers: Center of Biomedical Ethics and Culture; Pakistan.

Nelson, William A.; Pomerantz, Andrew S.; Weeks, William B. Response to commentaries on "Is there a rural ethics literature?" [letter]. *American Journal of Bioethics [Online]* 2006 July-August; 6(4): W46-W47. NRCBL: 2.1.

Nie, Jing-Bao. Feminist bioethics and the language of human rights in the Chinese context. *In:* Tong, Rosemarie; Donchin, Anne; Dodds, Susan, eds. Linking Visions: Feminist Bioethics, Human Rights, and the Developing World. Lanham, MD: Rowman and Littlefield Publishers; 2004: 73-88. NRCBL: 2.1; 10; 14.1; 21.1.

Nikku, Nina; Eriksson, Bengt Erik. Microethics in action. *Bioethics* 2006 August; 20(4): 169-179. NRCBL: 2.1. SC: em.
Abstract: The future development of bioethics has been discussed in a number of articles in recent years, principally with regard to the trend towards empirical studies. However, what is meant by empirical studies in this context and how it is to be used concretely have been subject to varying interpretations. The purpose of this article is to develop what we term the microethical approach as a concrete method for an empirically driven bioethics. By adopting a microethical perspective, we will illustrate an analytical concept for describing and demonstrating how, as a result of contextual circumstances and forms of understanding, different individuals in their everyday life adopt different coping strategies and behavior patterns in relation to ethical values. From a deepened perspective, the complexity of human behavior becomes apparent, and knowledge is gained about how moral problems are perceived and construed by those whom they in fact affect. We intend first and foremost to develop the microethical methodology by elucidating the methods and approaches that can help in clarifying moral dilemmas on a microethical level, and how the relationship between the empirical material and the ethical analysis evolves over the course of the analysis. This is exemplified by a study of caregivers' entrance into patients' private lives through the provision of care and assistance in the home.

Palmer, Larry I. Response: Jay Katz: from harm to risks. *Yale Journal of Health Policy, Law and Ethics* 2006 Summer; 6(2): 455-464. NRCBL: 2.1; 21.6; 15.10. Conference: Symposium: A World Less Silent: Celebrating Jay Katz's Contribution to Law, Medicine, and Ethics. Comments: Alexander M. Capron. Experimentation with human beings: light or only shadows? Yale Journal of Health Policy, Law and Ethics 2006 Summer; 6(2): 431-449.

Partridge, Ernest. Future generations. *In:* Mitcham, Carl, ed. Encyclopedia of Science, Technology, and Ethics. Farmington Hills, MI: Thomson/Gale, 2005: 807-810. NRCBL: 2.1; 2.2.

Pilcher, Helen. Dial 'E' for ethics [news]. *Nature* 2006 April 27; 440(7088): 1104-1105. NRCBL: 2.1; 1.3.9; 7.3; 9.6; 18.6. Identifiers: Stanford University.

Propst, Evan J.; Hales, Sarah; Masellis, Mario; Adejumo, Adebayo O.; Godkin, M. Dianne. The beginning of one's real ethical development. *Clinical and Investigative Medicine* 2006 February; 29(1): 7-9. NRCBL: 2.1.

Qui, Renzong. A vision of the role medical ethics could play in transforming Chinese society. *In:* Döring, Ole; Chen, Renbiao, eds. Advances in Chinese Medical Ethics: Chinese and International Perspectives. Hamburg: Institut für Asienkunde; 2002: 3-11. NRCBL: 2.1. Note: Proceedings of the Second Sino-German Interdisciplinary Symposium about Medical Ethics in China, Shanghai, 19-23 October, 1999.

Rapp, Rayna. The thick social matrix for bioethics: anthropological approaches. *In:* Rehmann-Sutter, Christoph; Düwell, Marcus; Mieth, Dietmar, eds. Bioethics in Cultural Contexts: Reflections on Methods and Finitude. Dordrecht: Springer, 2006: 341-351. NRCBL: 2.1.

Redman, B.K. Review of measurement instruments in clinical and research ethics, 1999-2003. *Journal of Medical Ethics* 2006 March; 32(3): 153-156. NRCBL: 2.1; 1.3.12; 8.1; 8.3.1; 18.1; 20.5.1. SC: em; rv.
Abstract: Every field of practice has the responsibility to evaluate its outcomes and to test its theories. Evidence of the underdevelopment of measurement instruments in bioethics suggests that attending to strengthening existing instruments and developing new ones will facilitate the interpretation of accumulating bodies of research as well as the making of clinical judgements. A review of 65 instruments reported in the published literature showed 10 with even a minimal level of psychometric data. Two newly developed instruments provide examples of the full use of psychometric and ethical theory. Bioethicists use a wide range of methods for knowledge development and verification; each method should meet stringent standards of quality.

Rei, Wenmay; Yeh, Jiunn-Rong. Steering in the tides: National Bioethics Committee as an institutional solution to bio-politics? *In:* Sang-yong, Song; Young-Mo, Koo; Macer, Darryl R.J., eds. Asian Bioethics in the 21st Century. Christchurch, NZ: Eubios Ethics Institute, 2002: 363-375. NRCBL: 2.1. Identifiers: Taiwan. Conference:

Proceedings of the Asian Bioethics Conference (ABC4), held 22-25 November 2002 in Seoul, South Korea.

Saniotis, Arthur. Towards an embodiment of environmental bioethics. *Eubios Journal of Asian and International Bioethics* 2006 September; 16(5): 148-151. NRCBL: 2.1; 16.1; 5.1; 4.4; 15.1.

Saunders, John. Ethics in practice [editorial]. *Clinical Medicine* 2005 July-August; 5(4): 315-316. NRCBL: 2.1; 18.2; 9.4.

Schüklenk, Udo. Ethics in bioethics [editorial]. *Bioethics* 2006 September; 20(5): iii. NRCBL: 2.1.

Schulz-Baldes, Annette; Jakovljevic, Anna-Karina. Zur möglichkeit einer kulturübergreifenden bioethik [Possibilities of a cross-cultural bioethics]. *Ethik in der Medizin* 2006 September; 18(3): 261-266. NRCBL: 2.1; 21.7.

Sherlock, Richard. Bioethics. *In:* Mitcham, Carl, ed. Encyclopedia of Science, Technology, and Ethics. Farmington Hills, MI: Thomson/Gale, 2005: 193-200. NRCBL: 2.1; 5.1; 21.1.

Sitter-Liver, Beat. Finitude — a neglected perspective in bioethics. *In:* Rehmann-Sutter, Christoph; Düwell, Marcus; Mieth, Dietmar, eds. Bioethics in Cultural Contexts: Reflections on Methods and Finitude. Dordrecht: Springer, 2006: 45-57. NRCBL: 2.1. SC: cs.

Sokol, Daniel K. Time to get streetwise: why medical ethics needs doctors. *BMJ: British Medical Journal* 2006 December 9; 333(7580): 1226. NRCBL: 2.1.

Spier, Raymond E. Reflection on the Budapest Meeting 2005 of the European Ethics Consortium [editorial]. *Science and Engineering Ethics* 2006 October; 12(4): 587-590. NRCBL: 2.1; 21.1.

Stiggelbout, A.M.; Elstein, A.S.; Molewijk, B.; Otten, W.; Kievit, J. Clinical ethical dilemmas: convergent and divergent views of two scholarly communities. *Journal of Medical Ethics* 2006 July; 32(7): 381-388. NRCBL: 2.1; 8.3.4; 9.6; 20.5.1. SC: em. Identifiers: American Society for Bioethics and Humanities; Society for Medical Decision Making.
Abstract: OBJECTIVE: To survey members of the American Society for Bioethics and Humanities (ASBH; n = 327) and of the Society for Medical Decision Making (SMDM; n = 77) to elicit the similarities and differences in their reasoning about two clinical cases that involved ethical dilemmas. Cases: Case 1 was that of a patient refusing treatment that a surgeon thought would be beneficial. Case 2 dealt with end-of-life care. The argument was whether intensive treatment should be continued of an unconscious patient with multiorgan failure. Method: Four questions, with structured multiple alternatives, were asked about each case: identified core problems, needed additional information, appropriate next steps and who the decision maker should be. Observations and RESULTS: Substantial similarities were noticed between the two groups in identifying the core problems, the information needed and the appropriate next steps. SMDM members gave more weight to outcomes and trade-offs and ASBH members had patient autonomy trump other considerations more strongly. In case 1, more than 60% of ASBH respondents identified the patient alone as the decision maker, whereas members of SMDM were almost evenly divided between having the patient as the solo decisionmaker or preferring a group of some sort as the decision maker, a significant difference (p.02). In case 2, both groups agreed that the question of discontinuing treatment should be discussed with the family and that the family alone should not be the decision maker. CONCLUSION: Despite distinctively different methods of case analysis and little communication between the two professional communities, many similarities were observed in the actual decisions they reached on the two clinical dilemmas.

Sullivan, Karen. Finding out about ethics: what sources of information do Australian psychologists find useful? *Australian Psychologist* 2005 November; 40(3): 187-189. NRCBL: 2.1; 7.3; 17.1.

Sulmasy, Daniel P. The science behind the art: empirical research on medical ethics. *In:* Beam, Thomas E.; Sparacino, Linette R.; Pellegrino, Edmund D.; Hartle, Anthony E.; Howe, Edmund G., eds. Military Medical Ethics. Volume 1. Washington, DC: TMM Publications, Borden Institute, Walter Reed Army Medical Center; 2003: 105-126. NRCBL: 2.1. SC: em.

Sumathipala, Athula. Bioethics in Sri Lanka. *Eastern Mediterranean Health Journal* 2006; 12(Supplement 1): S73-S79 [Online]. Accessed: http://www.emro.who.int/publications/EMHJ/12_S/PDF/11.pdf [2007 January 4]. NRCBL: 2.1; 2.3; 7.2. Note: Abstract in French and Arabic.

ten Have, Henk. The activities of UNESCO in the area of ethics. *Kennedy Institute of Ethics Journal* 2006 December; 16(4): 333-351. NRCBL: 2.1; 21.1; 2.4; 2.3; 5.3; 9.6; 1.3.7.
Abstract: The member states of the United Nations Educational, Scientific and Cultural Organization (UNESCO) decided in 2002 that ethics is one of the five priority areas of the organization. This article describes three categories of past and current activities in the ethics of science and technology, in particular bioethics. The first category is the global standard setting with the Universal Declaration on Bioethics and Human Rights as the most recently adopted normative instrument. The second category focuses on capacity building in order to enable member states to apply the provisions of the declarations, through, for example, the establishment of national bioethics committees, the introduction of ethics teaching programs, and drafting of legislation and guidelines. The final category of activities is awareness raising through publications, events, and conferences. The challenges and difficulties UNESCO may face in its various activities are highlighted.

Tong, Rosemarie. Feminist perspectives, global bioethics, and the need for moral language translation skills. *In:* Tong, Rosemarie; Donchin, Anne; Dodds, Susan, eds. Linking Visions: Feminist Bioethics, Human Rights, and the Developing World. Lanham, MD: Rowman and Littlefield Publishers; 2004: 89-104. NRCBL: 2.1; 10; 21.1; 21.7.

Trotter, Griffin. Bioethics and deliberative democracy: five warnings from Hobbes. *Journal of Medicine and Phi-*

NRCBL: National Reference Center for Bioethics Literature Classification Scheme   See inside front cover for terms.

59

losophy 2006 June; 31(3): 235-250. NRCBL: 2.1; 1.3.5. SC: an.

Abstract: Thomas Hobbes is one of the most ardent and thoroughgoing opponents of participatory democracy among Western political philosophers. Though Hobbes's alternative to participatory democracy-assent by subjects to rule by an absolute sovereign-no longer constitutes a viable political alternative for Westerners, his critique of participatory democracy is a potentially valuable source of insight about its liabilities. This essay elaborates five theses from Hobbes that stand as cogent warnings to those who embrace participatory democracy, especially those (such as most bioethicists) advocating for deliberative democracy based on a rational consensus model. In light of these warnings, the author suggests an alternative, modus vivendi approach to deliberative democracy that would radically alter the current practice of bioethics.

Trotter, Griffin. What the trough breaks. *American Journal of Bioethics [Online].* 2006 January-February; 6(1): W25-W26. NRCBL: 2.1.

United Nations Educational, Scientific, and Cultural Organization [UNESCO]. Universal declaration on bioethics and human rights. *Bulletin of Medical Ethics* 2005 October-November; (211): 11-15. NRCBL: 2.1; 21.1.

Verkerk, M.A.; Buise, R.V.; van Berkestijn, Th.M.G.; Doxiadis, Spyros A.; Riis, Povl; Moerkerk, H. Medical ethics. *In:* Hermans, H.E.G.M.; Casparie, A.F.; Paelinck, J.H.P., eds. Health Care in Europe After 1992. Brookfield, VT: Ashgate, 1992: 89-107. NRCBL: 2.1; 21.1; 9.5.6.

Vollmar, Lewis C. Military medicine in war: the Geneva Conventions today. *In:* Beam, Thomas E.; Sparacino, Linette R.; Pellegrino, Edmund D.; Hartle, Anthony E.; Howe, Edmund G., eds. Military Medical Ethics. Volume 2. Washington, DC: TMM Publications, Borden Institute, Walter Reed Army Medical Center; 2003: 739-771. NRCBL: 2.1; 21.2; 1.3.5.

Williams, John R. Medical ethics in contemporary clinical practice. *Journal of the Chinese Medical Association* 2005 November; 68(11): 495-499. NRCBL: 2.1; 7.3; 8.4; 18.1; 21.1.

Zhang, Daqing. Medicine as virtuous conduct: assessing the tradition of Chinese medical ethics. *In:* Döring, Ole; Chen, Renbiao, eds. Advances in Chinese Medical Ethics: Chinese and International Perspectives. Hamburg: Institut für Asienkunde; 2002: 233-254. NRCBL: 2.1; 21.7. Note: Proceedings of the Second Sino-German Interdisciplinary Symposium about Medical Ethics in China, Shanghai, 19-23 October, 1999.

BIOETHICS AND MEDICAL ETHICS/ COMMISSIONS

Anderson, Maria. Bush dismisses council members: scientific group angry at loss of Elizabeth Blackburn from group considering stem cells. *Scientist* 2004 March 3; 5(1): 6 p. [Online]. Accessed: http://www.the-scientist.com/ news/20040303/04/ [12 October 2006]. NRCBL: 2.4; 1.3.5.

Arnhart, Larry. President's Council on Bioethics. *In:* Mitcham, Carl, ed. Encyclopedia of Science, Technology, and Ethics. Farmington Hills, MI: Thomson/Gale, 2005: 1482-1486. NRCBL: 2.4; 1.2; 5.3; 18.5.4.

Austria. Bioethikkommission beim Bundeskanzleramt = Austria. Bioethics Commission at the Federal Chancellery. Erster Tätigkeitsbericht der Bioethikkommission an den Bundeskanzler 2001/2002 [First activity report of the Bioethics Commission at the Federal Chancellery 2001/2002]. Vienna, Austria: Bioethikkommission beim Bundeskanzleramt, 2002: 31 p. NRCBL: 2.4.

Austria. Bioethikkommission beim Bundeskanzleramt = Austria. Bioethics Commission at the Federal Chancellery. Tätigkeitsbericht der Bioethikkommission an den Bundeskanzler Juli 2001 - Juli 2003 [Activity report of the Bioethics Commission at the Federal Chancellery July 2001 - July 2003]. Vienna, Austria: Bioethikkommission beim Bundeskanzleramt, 2003: 35 p. NRCBL: 2.4.

Austria. Bioethikkommission beim Bundeskanzleramt = Austria. Bioethics Commission at the Federal Chancellery. Tätigkeitsbericht der Bioethikkommission an den Bundeskanzler Juli 2003 - Juli 2005 [Activity report of the Bioethics Commission at the Federal Chancellery July 2003 - July 2005]. Vienna, Austria: Bioethikkommission beim Bundeskanzleramt, 2005: 15 p. NRCBL: 2.4.

Austria. Bioethikkommission beim Bundeskanzleramt = Austria. Bioethics Commission at the Federal Chancellery. Tätigkeitsbericht der Juli 2003 - Juli 2004 [Activity report of the Bioethics Commission at the Federal Chancellery July 2003 - July 2004]. Vienna, Austria: Bioethikkommission beim Bundeskanzleramt, 2004: 13 p. NRCBL: 2.4.

Baruch, Jay M. What is the Ocean State Ethics Network? *Medicine and Health Rhode Island* 2005 April; 88(4): 123-126. NRCBL: 2.4; 18.2; 9.6.

Briggle, Adam; Mitcham, Carl. Bioethics committees and commissions. *In:* Mitcham, Carl, ed. Encyclopedia of Science, Technology, and Ethics. Farmington Hills, MI: Thomson/Gale, 2005: 202-207. NRCBL: 2.4; 2.2; 21.1.

Callahan, Daniel. Rejecting the gambler's principle [review of Rights and Liberties in the Biotech Age: Why We Need a Genetic Bill of Rights, edited by Sheldon Kimberly and Peter Shorett]. *Nature Biotechnology* 2005 October; 23(10): 1220. NRCBL: 2.4; 15.1.

Council of Europe. Directorate General I - Legal Affairs. Bioethics Department. Steering Committee on Bioethics (CDBI): Information document concerning the CDBI. Strasbourg: Council of Europe, 2006 June 20: 27 p. [Online]. Accessed: http://www.coe.int/t/e/legal_affairs/ legal_co-operation/bioethics/cdbi/INF(2006)2%20e%20

CDBI%20info%20doc1.asp#TopOfPage [2007 March 5]. NRCBL: 2.4; 21.1; 1.3.5.

Davis, F. Daniel; Gianelli, Diane M. News from the President's Council on Bioethics. *Kennedy Institute of Ethics Journal* 2006 December; 16(4): 375-377. NRCBL: 2.4.

DeGrazia, David. Moral status, human identity, and early embryos: a critique of the President's approach. *Journal of Law, Medicine, and Ethics* 2006 Spring; 34(1): 49-57. NRCBL: 2.4; 4.4; 18.5.4; 15.1. SC: an.

Dodds, Susan; Thomson, Colin. Bioethics and democracy: competing roles of national bioethics organisations. *Bioethics* 2006 November; 20(6): 326-338. NRCBL: 2.4; 21.1; 21.7.

Green, Ronald M. For richer or poorer? Evaluating the President's Council on Bioethics. *HEC (Healthcare Ethics Committee) Forum* 2006 June; 18(2): 108-124. NRCBL: 2.4; 7.1; 2.1.

Guten, Gary N.; Kohn, Harvey S.; Zoltan, Donald J.; Black, Brian B.; Coran, David L.; Schneider, John A.; Pauers, William. The role of the chief ethics officer in a physician's office. *Clinics in Sports Medicine* 2004 April; 23(2): 243-253. NRCBL: 2.4; 6; 1.1.

Human Genetics Commission [HGC] (Great Britain). Genetic information, public consultation. Second annual report of the Human Genetics Commission. London: Human Genetics Commission, 2002; 38 p. [Online]. Accessed: http://www.hgc.gov.uk/UploadDocs/DocPub/Document/annualreport_second.pdf [2006 December 19]. NRCBL: 2.4; 15.1.

Human Genetics Commission [HGC] (Great Britain). Our genes, ourselves: towards appropriate genetic testing. Third Annual Report of the Human Genetics Commission. London: Human Genetics Commission, 2003; 63 p. [Online]. Accessed: http://www.hgc.gov.uk/UploadDocs/DocPub/Document/HGC%203rd%20Annual%20Report,%20final%20PDF.pdf [2006 December 19]. NRCBL: 2.4; 15.3.

Johnson, Summer. Multiple roles and successes in public bioethics: a response to the public forum critique of bioethics commissions. *Kennedy Institute of Ethics Journal* 2006 June; 16(2): 173-188. NRCBL: 2.4; 2.1; 1.1; 7.1. SC: em.

Abstract: National bioethics commissions have been critiqued for a variety of structural, procedural, and political aspects of their work. A more recent critique published by Dzur and Levin uses political philosophy to constructively critique the work of national bioethics commissions as public deliberative forums. However, this public forum critique of bioethics commissions ignores empirical research in political science and normative claims that suggest that advisory commissions can and should have diverse of functions beyond that of being public forums. The present paper argues that the public forum critique too narrowly considers the roles that bioethics commissions can play in public bioethics and ignores the moral obligation of commissions to fulfill their mandates. Evaluations of commissions must consider that these institutions can serve in capacities other than those of a public deliberative forum and use additional measures to evaluate the multiple roles and successes of bioethics commissions in public policy.

Kaveny, M. Cathleen. Diversity and deliberation: bioethics commissions and moral reasoning. *Journal of Religious Ethics* 2006 June; 34(2): 311-337. NRCBL: 2.4; 1.3.9; 14.5; 18.5.4; 1.1; 1.2. SC: an. Identifiers: President's Council on Bioethics; NBAC.

Kaveny, M. Cathleen. The NBAC report on cloning: a case study in religion, public policy, and bioethics. *In:* Guinn, David E., ed. Handbook of Bioethics and Religion. New York: Oxford University Press, 2006: 221-251. NRCBL: 2.4; 1.2.

May, William F. Deepening a national conversation—my take on the president's council on bioethics. *Practical Bioethics* 2005 Winter; 1(1): 1-3, 7-9. NRCBL: 2.4; 14.5; 18.5.4; 15.1.

Meilaender, Gilbert. The politics of bioethics: in defense of the Kass Council. *Weekly Standard* 2004 April 12-19; 9(30): 13-14. NRCBL: 2.4.

Miralles, Angela Aparisi. Globalization of bioethics: the task of international commissions. *Georgetown Journal of International Law* 2005 Fall; 37(1): 141-151. NRCBL: 2.4; 2.1; 21.1. SC: le.

Rasmussen, Lisa M. Engineering, gerrymandering and expertise in public bioethics. *HEC (Healthcare Ethics Committee) Forum* 2006 June; 18(2): 125-130. NRCBL: 2.4; 7.1; 2.1.

Tanne, Janice Hopkins. FDA to clarify rules on advisory committee members [news]. *BMJ: British Medical Journal* 2006 August 5; 333(7562): 278. NRCBL: 2.4; 9.7; 5.2; 5.3. Identifiers: Food and Drug Administration.

Tollefsen, Christopher. The President's Council on Bioethics: overview and assessment. *HEC (Healthcare Ethics Committee) Forum* 2006 June; 18(2): 99-107. NRCBL: 2.4; 2.1; 1.1.

BIOETHICS AND MEDICAL ETHICS/ EDUCATION
See also MEDICAL EDUCATION

Bennett-Woods, Deb. Healthcare ethics: a pedagogical goldmine. *Journal of Health Administration Education* 2005 Spring; 22(2): 159-169. NRCBL: 2.3.

Blank, Robert H. Teaching biomedical policy to undergraduates. *Politics and the Life Sciences* 1986 August; 5(1): 67-74. NRCBL: 2.3; 5.1.

Bosch, Xavier. Concerns over new EU ethics panel. *Scientist* 2005 November 21; 19(22): 3 p. [Online]. Accessed: http://www.the-scientist.com/article/display/15886 [2006

NRCBL: National Reference Center for Bioethics Literature Classification Scheme   See inside front cover for terms.

61

December 3]. NRCBL: 2.3; 21.1. Identifiers: European Union.

Caplan, Arthur; Fiester, Autumn. Bioethics centers. *In:* Mitcham, Carl, ed. Encyclopedia of Science, Technology, and Ethics. Farmington Hills, MI: Thomson/Gale, 2005: 200-201. NRCBL: 2.3; 2.2.

Cobanoglu, Nesrin; Kayhan, Zeynep. Research note: an assessment of medical ethics education. *Nursing Ethics* 2006 September; 13(5): 558-561. NRCBL: 2.3; 7.2. SC: em. Identifiers: Turkey.

Cong, Yali. Consideration of medical ethics education in China from the comparison between China and the United States. *In:* Sang-yong, Song; Young-Mo, Koo; Macer, Darryl R.J., eds. Asian Bioethics in the 21st Century. Christchurch, NZ: Eubios Ethics Institute, 2002: 251-254. NRCBL: 2.3; 6. Conference: Proceedings of the Asian Bioethics Conference (ABC4), held 22-25 November 2002 in Seoul, South Korea.

Dobos, Marta; Dioszeghy, Csaba; Hauser, Balazs; Elo, Gabor. Determinant role of education in the ethical aspects of resuscitation: a German/Hungarian comparison. *Bulletin of Medical Ethics* 2005 October-November; (211): 25-30. NRCBL: 2.3; 20.5.1; 21.1. SC: em. Identifiers: Germany; Hungary.

Döring, Ole. Moral development and education in medical ethics: an attempt at a Confucian aspiration. *In:* Döring, Ole; Chen, Renbiao, eds. Advances in Chinese Medical Ethics: Chinese and International Perspectives. Hamburg: Institut für Asienkunde; 2002: 178-194. NRCBL: 2.3; 1.2; 7.2. Note: Proceedings of the Second Sino-German Interdisciplinary Symposium about Medical Ethics in China, Shanghai, 19-23 October, 1999.

Döring, Ole. Teaching medical ethics in China, cultural, social and ethical issues. *In:* Sang-yong, Song; Young-Mo, Koo; Macer, Darryl R.J., eds. Asian Bioethics in the 21st Century. Christchurch, NZ: Eubios Ethics Institute, 2002: 255-261. NRCBL: 2.3; 21.7. Conference: Proceedings of the Asian Bioethics Conference (ABC4), held 22-25 November 2002 in Seoul, South Korea.

Draper, Heather. Using case studies in clinical ethics. *Clinical Ethics* 2006 March; 1(1): 7-10. NRCBL: 2.3; 8.4; 8.3.1. SC: cs.

Glover, Jacqueline; Lynn, Joanne; Howe, Edmund; McCullough, Laurence; Secundy, Marian; Yeide, Harry. A model for interschool teaching of humanities during clinical training. *Journal of Medical Education* 1984 July; 59(7): 594-596. NRCBL: 2.3.

Gross, Michael L. Medical ethics education: to what ends? *Journal of Evaluation in Clinical Practice* 2001 November; 7(4): 387-397. NRCBL: 2.3; 1.1.

Itai, K.; Asai, A.; Tsuchiya, Y.; Onishi, M.; Kosugi, S. How do bioethics teachers in Japan cope with ethical disagreement among healthcare university students in the classroom? A survey on educators in charge. *Journal of Medical Ethics* 2006 May; 32(5): 303-308. NRCBL: 2.3; 7.2. SC: em.

Abstract: OBJECTIVE: The purpose of this study was to demonstrate how educators involved in the teaching of bioethics to healthcare university students in Japan would cope with ethical disagreement in the classroom, and to identify factors influencing them. METHODS: A cross sectional survey was conducted using self administered questionnaires mailed to a sample of university faculty in charge of bioethics curriculum for university healthcare students. RESULTS: A total of 107 usable questionnaires were returned: a response rate of 61.5%. When facing ethical disagreement in the classroom, coping behaviour differed depending on the topic of discussion, was influenced by educators' individual clear ethical attitudes regarding the topic of discussion, and was independent of many respondents' individual and social backgrounds. Among educators, it was commonly recognised that the purpose of bioethics education was to raise the level of awareness of ethical problems, to provide information about and knowledge of those issues, to raise students' sensitivity to ethical problems, and to teach students methods of reasoning and logical argument. Yet, despite this, several respondents considered the purpose of bioethics education to be to influence students about normative ethical judgments. There was no clear relationship, however, between ways of coping with ethical disagreement and educators' sense of the purpose of bioethics education. CONCLUSIONS: This descriptive study suggests that educators involved in bioethics education for healthcare university students in Japan coped in various ways with ethical disagreement. Further research concerning ethical disagreement in educational settings is needed to provide better bioethics education for healthcare students.

Johnson, Mark E.; Brems, Christiane; Warner, Teddy D.; Roberts, Laura Weiss. The need for continuing education in ethics as reported by rural and urban mental health care providers. *Professional Psychology* 2006 April; 37(2): 183-189. NRCBL: 2.3; 7.2; 17.1.

Kaya, Ayse; Aksoy, Sahin; Simsek, Zeynep; Ozbilge, Hatice; Aksoy, Nurten. An assessment of the level of knowledge of medical and nursing students on HIV/AIDS at Harran University, Sanliurfa/Turkey, and training on ethical aspects of the disease. *In:* Sang-yong, Song; Young-Mo, Koo; Macer, Darryl R.J., eds. Asian Bioethics in the 21st Century. Christchurch, NZ: Eubios Ethics Institute, 2002: 264-267. NRCBL: 2.3; 9.5.6. SC: em. Conference: Proceedings of the Asian Bioethics Conference (ABC4), held 22-25 November 2002 in Seoul, South Korea.

Kipnis, Kenneth. Professional ethics and instructional success. *Virtual Mentor* 2001 November; 3(11): 4p. NRCBL: 2.3; 7.1.

Kipnis, Kenneth. Professional ethics and instructional success. *In:* American Medical Association. Professing Medicine: strengthening the ethics and professionalism of tomorrow's physicians. Chicago: American Medical Association; 2001: 21-32. NRCBL: 2.3; 4.1.2; 7.2; 21.7.

Note: Commemorative issue of Virtual Mentor, AMA's online ethics journal.

Kumar, Nandini K. Bioethics activities in India. *Eastern Mediterranean Health Journal* 2006; 12(Supplement 1): S56-S65 [Online]. Accessed: http://www.emro.who.int/ publications/EMHJ/12_S/PDF/9.pdf [2007 January 4]. NRCBL: 2.3; 7.2; 9.7; 18.2. Note: Abstract in French and Arabic.

Liaschenko, J.; Oguz, N.Y.; Brunnquell, D. Critique of the "tragic case" method in ethics education. *Journal of Medical Ethics* 2006 November; 32(11): 672-677. NRCBL: 2.3; 7.2. SC: an.
Abstract: It is time for the noon conference. Your job is to impart a career-changing experience in ethics to a group of students and interns gathered from four different schools with varying curriculums in ethics. They have just finished 11/2 h of didactic sessions and lunch. One third of them were on call last night. Your first job is to keep them awake. The authors argue that this "tragic case" approach to ethics education is of limited value because it limits understanding of moral problems to dilemmas; negates the moral agency of the student; encourages solutions that are merely intellectual; and suggests that ethical encounters are a matter for experts. The authors propose an alternative that focuses on three issues: the provider-patient relationship, the relationships between providers in the everyday world of health work and, the social position of healthcare providers in society. In this approach, teachers are not experts but more like guides on a journey who help students to learn that much of ethical practice comprises living through difficult situations of caring for vulnerable others and who help students to navigate some of these difficulties.

Lippi, Donatella; D'Elios, Mario Milco; Benagiano, Marisa; Gensini, Gian Franco. Bioethics under the Tuscan sun. *Bulletin of Medical Ethics* 2005 March; (206): 23-24. NRCBL: 2.3; 7.2. Identifiers: Italy.

Liu, Kimberly E.; Flood, Catherine; Capstick, Valerie. Is an interdisciplinary session on ethics and law in obstetrics and gynaecology effective? *Journal of Obstetrics and Gynaecology Canada* 2005 May; 27(5): 486-490. NRCBL: 2.3; 7.2; 9.5.5; 4.1.2. SC: em; le.

Ma, Qiang; Cai, Bingliang; Song, Guofan. The role of the media for medical ethics in China. *In:* Döring, Ole; Chen, Renbiao, eds. Advances in Chinese Medical Ethics: Chinese and International Perspectives. Hamburg: Institut für Asienkunde; 2002: 358-366. NRCBL: 2.3; 1.3.7. Note: Proceedings of the Second Sino-German Interdisciplinary Symposium about Medical Ethics in China, Shanghai, 19-23 October, 1999.

Macer, Darryl R.J. The purposes of bioethics education: lessons from Japan and Asia. *In:* Sang-yong, Song; Young-Mo, Koo; Macer, Darryl R.J., eds. Asian Bioethics in the 21st Century. Christchurch, NZ: Eubios Ethics Institute, 2002: 241-250. NRCBL: 2.3; 21.7. Conference: Proceedings of the Asian Bioethics Conference (ABC4), held 22-25 November 2002 in Seoul, South Korea.

Martin, Taylor; Rayne, Karen; Kemp, Nate J.; Hart, Jack; Diller, Kenneth R. Teaching for adaptive expertise in biomedical engineering ethics. *Science and Engineering Ethics* 2005 April; 11(2): 257-276. NRCBL: 2.3; 1.3.4. SC: em; cs.

Mattick, Karen; Bligh, John. Teaching and assessing medical ethics: where are we now? *Journal of Medical Ethics* 2006 March; 32(3): 181-185. NRCBL: 2.3; 7.2. SC: em. Identifiers: United Kingdom (Great Britain).
Abstract: To characterise UK undergraduate medical ethics curricula and to identify opportunities and threats to teaching and learning. DESIGN: Postal questionnaire survey of UK medical schools enquiring about teaching and assessment, including future perspectives. PARTICIPANTS: The lead for teaching and learning at each medical school was invited to complete a questionnaire. RESULTS: Completed responses were received from 22/28 schools (79%). Seventeen respondents deemed their aims for ethics teaching to be successful. Twenty felt ethics should be learnt throughout the course and 13 said ethics teaching and learning should be fully integrated horizontally. Twenty felt variety in assessment was important and three tools was the preferred number. A shortfall in ethics core competencies did not preclude graduation in 15 schools. The most successful aspects of courses were perceived to be their integrated nature and the small group teaching; weaknesses were described as a need for still greater integration and the heavily theoretical aspects of ethics. The major concerns about how ethics would be taught in the future related to staffing and staff development. CONCLUSIONS: This study describes how ethics was taught and assessed in 2004. The findings show that, although ethics now has an accepted place in the curriculum, more can be done to ensure that the recommended content is taught and assessed optimally.

Mele, V.; Binetti, P. Bioethics, bridge to medical education. *Journal of Biological Regulators and Homeostatic Agents* 2005 January-June; 19(1-2): 49-53. NRCBL: 2.3; 7.2; 1.1.

Moreland, Lois B. On teaching biopolicy and values in selected reproductive technologies: abortion, in vitro fertilization, and surrogate motherhood. *Politics and the Life Sciences* 1986 August; 5(1): 75-82. NRCBL: 2.3; 14.1; 12.1; 14.2; 14.4; 5.1.

Obiglio, Hugo. Education and Bioethics. *Dolentium Hominum* 1994; 9(3): 53-54. NRCBL: 2.3; 4.4; 9.6. Note: ORGs publication mentioned.

Qiu, Xiangxing; Gao, Zhiyan. A retrospect on fifty years of education in medical ethics and future prospects in China. *In:* Döring, Ole; Chen, Renbiao, eds. Advances in Chinese Medical Ethics: Chinese and International Perspectives. Hamburg: Institut für Asienkunde; 2002: 393-400. NRCBL: 2.3; 7.2. Note: Proceedings of the Second Sino-German Interdisciplinary Symposium about Medical Ethics in China, Shanghai, 19-23 October, 1999.

Ramanathan, Mala; Krishnan, Suneeta; Bhan, Anant. Reporting on the First National Bioethics Conference. *Indian Journal of Medical Ethics* 2006 January-March; 3(1): 27-30. NRCBL: 2.3. Identifiers: India. Conference: First

NRCBL: National Reference Center for Bioethics Literature Classification Scheme   See inside front cover for terms.

63

National Bioethics Conference; 25-27 November 2005; Indian Journal of Medical Ethics.

Russell, C.; O'Neill, D. Ethicists and clinicians: the case for collaboration in the teaching of medical ethics. *Irish Medical Journal* 2006 January; 99(1): 25-27. NRCBL: 2.3.

Safjan, Marek. L'enseignment de la bioéthique dans la Pologne postcommuniste. *Journal International de Bioéthique = International Journal of Bioethics* 2005 September-December; 16(3-4): 97-104, 174. NRCBL: 2.3; 7.1. Identifiers: Poland.

Schonfeld, Toby L. Reflections on teaching health care ethics on the web. *Science and Engineering Ethics* 2005 July; 11(3): 481-494. NRCBL: 2.3; 1.3.1; 1.3.12.

Sgreccia, Elio. Bioethics centers and committees: cultural origins and current status. *Dolentium Hominum* 1994; 9(2): 50-60. NRCBL: 2.3; 2.2; 9.6; 2.1; 21.1; 1.2. SC: rv.

Siegler, Mark. Lessons from 30 years of teaching clinical ethics. *Virtual Mentor* 2001 October; 3(10): 3p. NRCBL: 2.3; 7.2.

Siegler, Mark. Lessons from 30 years of teaching clinical medical ethics. *In:* American Medical Association. Professing Medicine: strengthening the ethics and professionalism of tomorrow's physicians. Chicago: American Medical Association; 2001: 8-13. NRCBL: 2.3; 1.3.1; 7.2. Note: Commemorative issue of Virtual Mentor, AMA's online ethics journal.

Smythe, William E.; Malloy, David C.; Hadjistavropoulos, Thomas; Martin, Ronald R.; Bardutz, Holly A. An analysis of the ethical and linguistic content of hospital mission statements. *Health Care Management Review* 2006 April-June; 31(2): 92-98. NRCBL: 2.3; 9.1; 9.3.1.

Tai, Michael Cheng-tek. The importance of medical humanity in medical education. *In:* Döring, Ole; Chen, Renbiao, eds. Advances in Chinese Medical Ethics: Chinese and International Perspectives. Hamburg: Institut für Asienkunde; 2002: 401-405. NRCBL: 2.3; 7.2. Note: Proceedings of the Second Sino-German Interdisciplinary Symposium about Medical Ethics in China, Shanghai, 19-23 October, 1999.

Vittabai, Baby Flankitt; Azaria, Jayapaul; Macer, Darryl R.J. Bioethics education and awareness in schools in Tamil Nadu, India. *In:* Sang-yong, Song; Young-Mo, Koo; Macer, Darryl R.J., eds. Asian Bioethics in the 21st Century. Christchurch, NZ: Eubios Ethics Institute, 2002: 268-277. NRCBL: 2.3; 9.5.6; 14.5; 15.4; 16.1; 20.5.1. SC: em. Conference: Proceedings of the Asian Bioethics Conference (ABC4), held 22-25 November 2002 in Seoul, South Korea.

Wendorf, Barbara. Ethical decision-making in quality assurance. *QRB: Quality Review Bulletin* 1982 January; 8(1): 4-6. NRCBL: 2.3; 2.1. Identifiers: Hastings Center.

Zhai, Xiaomei; Döring, Ole. A method to study medical ethics. *In:* Döring, Ole; Chen, Renbiao, eds. Advances in Chinese Medical Ethics: Chinese and International Perspectives. Hamburg: Institut für Asienkunde; 2002: 409-416. NRCBL: 2.3; 7.2. Note: Proceedings of the Second Sino-German Interdisciplinary Symposium about Medical Ethics in China, Shanghai, 19-23 October, 1999.

Zucker, A. Medical ethics as therapy. *Medical Humanities* 2006 June; 32(1): 48-52. NRCBL: 2.3; 7.2.

Abstract: In this paper, the author examines a style of teaching for a medical ethics course designed for medical students in their clinical years, a style that some believe conflicts with a commitment to analytic philosophy. The author discusses (1) why some find a conflict, (2) why there really is no conflict, and (3) the approach to medical ethics through narratives. The author will also argue that basing medical ethics on the use of narratives has problems and dangers not fully discussed in the literature.

BIOETHICS AND MEDICAL ETHICS/ HISTORY

Azmi, K.A. Shafqat; Siddiqui, M.K. Islamic medical ethics with special reference to Moalejat-e-Buqratiya. *Bulletin of the Indian Institute of History of Medicine* 1999 January; 29(1): 15-27. NRCBL: 2.2; 2.1; 1.2.

Borovecki, Ana; ten Have, Hank; Oreškovic, Stjepan. Ethics and the European countries in transition — the past and the future. *Bulletin of Medical Ethics* 2006 April-May; (214): 15-20. NRCBL: 2.2; 21.1.

Broggi, Marc Antoni. Historia del <Comité de Bioética de Cataluña>. *Bioetica and Debat* 2006 April-June; 12(44): 8-10. NRCBL: 2.2. SC: le. Identifiers: Spain.

Cheek, Dennis W. Ramsey, Paul. *In:* Mitcham, Carl, ed. Encyclopedia of Science, Technology, and Ethics. Farmington Hills, MI: Thomson/Gale, 2005: 1580-1581. NRCBL: 2.2; 1.2.

Drane, James F. What is bioethics? A history. *In:* Lolas Stepke, Fernando; Agar Corbinos, Lorenzo, eds. Interfaces Between Bioethics and the Empirical Social Sciences. Buenos Aires, Argentina: World Health Organization; 2002: 15-32. NRCBL: 2.2.

Dvonch, Victoria. Ethical dilemmas: the new is old. *Clinical Orthopaedics and Related Research* 2000 September; (378): 124-128. NRCBL: 2.2; 7.1. Identifiers: Middlemarch; Madame Bovary; Frankenstein.

Geraghty, Karen. The code as expert witness. *Virtual Mentor* 2001 October; 3(10): 2p. NRCBL: 2.2. Identifiers: American Medical Association code of medical ethics.

Güner, Ahmet. A Book on Medical Ethics in Medieval Islam: Al-Tashwîk Al-Tibbî (Encouraging Medicine) of

Abu'l-Alâ Sâid B. Al-Hasan Al-Tabîb (1009-1087 A.C.) [book review]. *Eubios Journal of Asian and International Bioethics* 2006 January; 16(1): 6-9. NRCBL: 2.2; 1.2.

Haddad, Farid Sami. Arab medical ethics. *Studies in History of Medicine* 1982 June; 6: 122-136. NRCBL: 2.2; 7.1; 1.2; 21.7.

Hameed, Abdul. Medical ethics in medieval Islam. *Studies in Philosophy of Medicine* 1977 March; 1(1): 08-124. NRCBL: 2.2; 1.2.

Herrera, Stephan. Daniel Callahan. *Nature Biotechnology* 2004 December; 22(12): 1495. NRCBL: 2.2; 9.4.

Jonsen, Albert R. A history of religion and bioethics. *In:* Guinn, David E., ed. Handbook of Bioethics and Religion. New York: Oxford University Press, 2006: 23-36. NRCBL: 2.2; 1.2.

Lichterman, Boleslav L. Basic problems of medical ethics in Russia in a historical context. *Journal International de Bioéthique = International Journal of Bioethics* 2005 September-December; 16(3-4): 43-53,168-169. NRCBL: 2.2; 8.4; 8.3.1; 18.1; 12.4.1; 20.5.1; 19.5; 17.7. SC: rv.

Abstract: The paper provides a short overview of key problems of medical ethics in the Russian and Soviet contexts—confidentiality, informed consent, human experimentation, abortion, euthanasia, organ and tissue transplantation, abuse of psychiatry. In Soviet ideology common interests were declared superior to private ones. Hence, medical confidentiality was viewed as a bourgeois survival. On the other hand, diagnosis was normally not disclosed to a patient in the case of an incurable disease (especially cancer). Due to the strong paternalistic traditions of Russian medicine the idea of informed consent is still disputed by many physicians. Abortions were first legalized in Soviet Russia in 1920. A brief history of this landmark event is provided. However, abortions were forbidden in 1936 and legalized again only in 1955. Active euthanasia was legalized in Soviet Russia in 1922 but for a short period. Federal law regulating human transplantation was adopted only in 1992 and based on the presumed consent model. Until then forensic autopsy and procurement of cadaver organs were viewed as equal procedures. In 1960s-1980s there was a practice of declaring political dissidents insane in their involuntary treatment.

Lichterman, Boleslav L. Soviet medical ethics (1917-1991). *Journal International de Bioéthique = International Journal of Bioethics* 2005 September-December; 16(3-4): 33-41, 167-168. NRCBL: 2.2; 7.1; 6; 1.3.5. Identifiers: Russia.

Abstract: Russian medical ethics bears a heavy mark of seven decades of the communist regime. In 1918 the Health Care Commissariat (ministry) was formed. It was headed by Nikolai Semashko (1874-1949) who claimed that "the ethics of the Soviet physician is an ethics of our socialist motherland, an ethics of a builder of communist society; it is equal to communist moral". "Medical ethics" had been avoided until the late 1930s when it was replaced by "medical (or surgical) deontology". This "deontological" period started with "Problems of surgical deontology" written by N. Petrov, a surgeon, and lasted for almost half a century until "medical deontology" was abandoned in favor of "bioethics" in post-communist Russia. There have been five All-Union conferences on medical deontology since 1969. The story of the emergence of "The Oath of a Soviet Physician" is briefly described. The text of this Oath was approved by a special decree of the Soviet Parliament in 1971. Each graduate of medical school in USSR was obliged to take this Oath when receiving his or her medical diploma. It is concluded that such ideas of zemstvo medicine as universal access to health care and condemnation of private practice were put into practice under the communist regime.

Lichterman, Boleslav L.; Yarovinsky, Michail. Medical ethics in Russia before the October Revolution (1917). *Journal International de Bioéthique = International Journal of Bioethics* 2005 September-December; 16(3-4): 17-32,166-167. NRCBL: 2.2; 7.1; 6.

Abstract: The evolution of medical ethics in Russia was determined by several factors. First, such Russian concepts as "obshina" (community" and "sobornost" (counciliarism) determined the supremacy of the collective body over the individual body, the state over a person etc. There is no analogue for "privacy" in the Russian language. Second, Russian medical doctors with university degrees appeared only in the 18th century after the politics of westernization by Peter the Great (1672-1725).Medical ethics probably starts from Prof. Matvei Mudrov (1776-1831) of Moscow who followed the Hippocratic credo "to treat not a disease but a patient". Third, after serfdom had been abolished in 1861 medical care in many rural regions was provided by zemstva (local elected councils). Zemskie medical doctors had idealistic views of self-sacrificing for the service to society and to the people. On the other hand, while dealing with illiterate peasants paternalism was a necessity. Ethical problems of healthcare and medicine were a subject of intense discussions both in professional and popular literature. A weekly periodical "Vrach" edited by V. Manassein played an important role in this discourse. Local medical societies adopted their own ethical codes but an All-Russian code of medical ethics was never formulated because the country lacked a national medical society. "Confessions of a physician" by Vikenty Veresaev published in 1901 put problems of doctor-patient relationship and human experimentation in the centre of public debates both nationally and internationally. Two Russian editions of "Aerztliche Ethik" by Albert Moll also contributed to the discourse on medical ethics in Russia. Medicine as a money-making activity was criticized and ridiculed in Russian literature (see, for example, Tolstoy's novels and Chekhov's stories). Medical morality was generally understood as moral life in action when deeds are much more important than words (e.g. formal codes of medical ethics).

Moriaka, Masahiro. When did "bioethics" begin in each country? A proposal of a comparative study. *Eubios Journal of Asian and International Bioethics* 2003 March 13(2): 51. NRCBL: 2.2.

Navot, Orit. A historical overview of the developing medical ethics culture in the new Jewish settlement in Israel during the years 1840-1914. *Eubios Journal of Asian and International Bioethics* 2003 March 13(2): 51-53. NRCBL: 2.2; 1.2.

Oakley, Justin. Monash Centre for Human Bioethics: a brief history. *Monash Bioethics Review* 2006 January; 25(1): 85-88. NRCBL: 2.2; 2.3.

Singer, Peter; Kuhse, Helga. 1980-2005: bioethics then and now. *Monash Bioethics Review* 2006 January; 25(1): 9-14. NRCBL: 2.2; 14.4; 15.3; 20.5.1.

NRCBL: National Reference Center for Bioethics Literature Classification Scheme   See inside front cover for terms.

65

Takahashi, Takao. Introduction: a short history of bioethics in Japan. *In:* Takahashi, Takao, ed. Taking Life and Death Seriously: Bioethics from Japan. Amsterdam; Boston: Elsevier JAI; 2005: 1-18. NRCBL: 2.2.

Vlassov, Vasiliy. Russian medicine and the Nuremberg trials. *European Journal of Public Health* 2006 June; 16(3): 229. NRCBL: 2.2; 21.1; 6.

Walters, LeRoy B. Major events and publications related to the birth of bioethics, 1925-1975 with special attention to the Anglican contribution. *Anglican Theological Review* 1999 Fall; 81(4): 631-650. NRCBL: 2.2; 1.2. Conference: Presiding Bishop's Consultation on Bioethics, Washington, DC, June 8-9 1999, College of Preachers.

Wang, Yifang. Ideals and ethics: the concept of 'the art of humaneness' is not reliable. *In:* Döring, Ole; Chen, Renbiao, eds. Advances in Chinese Medical Ethics: Chinese and International Perspectives. Hamburg: Institut für Asienkunde; 2002: 266-275. NRCBL: 2.2. Note: Proceedings of the Second Sino-German Interdisciplinary Symposium about Medical Ethics in China, Shanghai, 19-23 October, 1999.

Winter, Robert B. Innovation in surgical technique: the story of spine surgery. *Clinical Orthopaedics and Related Research* 2000 September; (378): 9-14. NRCBL: 2.2; 4.1.2; 9.8.

BIOETHICS AND MEDICAL ETHICS/ LEGAL ASPECTS

Bloche, M. Gregg. The Supreme Court and the purposes of medicine. *New England Journal of Medicine* 2006 March 9; 354(10): 993- 995. NRCBL: 2.1; 20.7; 9.5.9; 8.1; 20.5.1; 7.1. SC: le.

Broggi, Marc Antoni. Historia del <Comité de Bioética de Cataluña>. *Bioetica and Debat* 2006 April-June; 12(44): 8-10. NRCBL: 2.2. SC: le. Identifiers: Spain.

Brownback, Sam. Bioethics and the future of humanity. *National Catholic Bioethics Quarterly* 2006 Autumn; 6(3): 423-430. NRCBL: 2.1; 4.4; 18.5.4; 14.5; 1.2; 15.1. SC: le.

Castignone, Silvana. The problem of limits of law in bioethical issues. *In:* Rehmann-Sutter, Christoph; Düwell, Marcus; Mieth, Dietmar, eds. Bioethics in Cultural Contexts: Reflections on Methods and Finitude. Dordrecht: Springer, 2006: 81-90. NRCBL: 2.1. SC: le.

Fallberg, Lars. Do doctors know about their legal responsibilities? [editorial]. *European Journal of Health Law* 2006 June; 13(2): 91-93. NRCBL: 2.1; 1.3.8. SC: le.

Lenoir, Noëlle. French, European and International Legislation on Bioethics = Normativa francesa, europea e internacional en materia de Bioética. *Law and the Human Genome = Revista de Derecho y Genoma Humano* 1994 July-December; (1): 71-89. NRCBL: 2.1; 2.4; 21.1. SC: le.

Liu, Kimberly E.; Flood, Catherine; Capstick, Valerie. Is an interdisciplinary session on ethics and law in obstetrics and gynaecology effective? *Journal of Obstetrics and Gynaecology Canada* 2005 May; 27(5): 486-490. NRCBL: 2.3; 7.2; 9.5.5; 4.1.2. SC: em; le.

Miola, J. The relationship between medical law and ethics. *Clinical Ethics* 2006 March; 1(1): 22-25. NRCBL: 2.1; 9.5.7; 19.2; 9.8. SC: an; le. Identifiers: Bristol Royal Infirmary Report.

Miralles, Angela Aparisi. Globalization of bioethics: the task of international commissions. *Georgetown Journal of International Law* 2005 Fall; 37(1): 141-151. NRCBL: 2.4; 2.1; 21.1. SC: le.

Nelson, Leonard J., III. Catholic bioethics and the case of Terri Schiavo. *Cumberland Law Review* 2004-2005; 35(3): 543-574. NRCBL: 2.1; 1.2; 20.5.1. SC: le.

Nys, Herman. Towards an international treaty on human rights and biomedicine? Some reflections inspired by UNESCO's Universal Declaration on Bioethics and Human Rights [editorial]. *European Journal of Health Law* 2006 April; 13(1): 5-8. NRCBL: 2.1; 21.1. SC: le.

Palacios, Marcelo. Report on the Draft Bioethics Convention = Informe sobre el Proyecto de Convenio de Bioética. *Law and the Human Genome Review = Revista de Derecho y Genoma Humano* 1995 July-December; (3): 281-291. NRCBL: 2.1; 5.3; 21.1. SC: le.

Quintana, Octavi. Human Rights and Biomedicine Convention: a consensus convention = El Convenio de Derechos Humanos y Biomedicina: un convenio de consenso. *Revista de Derecho Genoma Humano = Law and the Human Genome Review* 1997 July-December; (7): 153-160. NRCBL: 2.1; 21.1; 18.3; 15.1. SC: le.

Reusser, Ruth. The new European Convention on Human Rights and Biomedicine = El nuevo Convenio Europeo sobre Derechos Humanos y Biomedicina. *Revista de Derecho Genoma Humano = Law and the Human Genome Review* 1997 July-December; (7): 161-169. NRCBL: 2.1; 21.1; 18.3; 15.3; 18.1; 19.5. SC: le.

Smith, George P., II. Law, religion and medicine: conjunctive or disjunctive? *Macquarie Law Symposium* 2006: 9-39. NRCBL: 2.1; 1.2; 4.4; 15.4; 5.1. SC: le. Conference: Symposium: Law, Religion and Medical Science; Macquarie University, Sydney, Australia; 2006; Division of Law, Macquarie University.

United Nations Educational, Scientific, and Cultural Organization [UNESCO]. General Conference. Universal declaration on bioethics and human rights. *Revista de Derecho y Genoma Humano* 2005 July-December; (23): 227-237. NRCBL: 2.1; 21.1; 8.3.1; 18.3. SC: le.

BIOETHICS AND MEDICAL ETHICS/ PHILOSOPHICAL ASPECTS

Allmark, Peter. An argument for the use of Aristotelian method in bioethics. *Medicine, Health Care and Philosophy* 2006; 9(1): 69-79. NRCBL: 2.1; 1.1.

Abstract: The main claim of this paper is that the method outlined and used in Aristotle's Ethics is an appropriate and credible one to use in bioethics. Here "appropriate" means that the method is capable of establishing claims and developing concepts in bioethics and "credible" that the method has some plausibility, it is not open to obvious and immediate objection. It begins by suggesting why this claim matters and then gives a brief outline of Aristotle's method. The main argument is made in three stages. First, it is argued that Aristotelian method is credible because it compares favourably with alternatives. In this section it is shown that Aristotelian method is not vulnerable to criticisms that are made both of methods that give a primary place to moral theory (such as utilitarianism) and those that eschew moral theory (such as casuistry and social science approaches). As such, it compares favourably with these other approaches that are vulnerable to at least some of these criticisms. Second, the appropriateness of Aristotelian method is indicated through outlining how it would deal with a particular case. Finally, it is argued that the success of Aristotle's philosophy is suggestive of both the credibility and appropriateness of his method.

Belkin, Gary S. Misconceived bioethics?: the misconception of the "therapeutic misconception". *International Journal of Law and Psychiatry* 2006 March-April; 29(2): 75-85. NRCBL: 2.1; 2.2; 1.1; 18.1; 18.2; 18.3; 18.4.

Benn, Piers. The role of conscience in medical ethics. *In:* Athanassoulis, Nafsika, ed. Philosophical Reflections on Medical Ethics. New York: Palgrave Macmillan; 2005: 160-179. NRCBL: 2.1; 1.1. SC: an.

Breier-Mackie, Sarah. Why ethics and gastroenterology nursing? *Gastroenterology Nursing* 2005 May-June; 28(3): 248-249. NRCBL: 2.1; 9.5.1; 4.1.3.

Briggle, Adam. Double effect and dual use. *In:* Mitcham, Carl, ed. Encyclopedia of Science, Technology, and Ethics. Farmington Hills, MI: Thomson/Gale, 2005: 543-546. NRCBL: 2.1; 1.1.

Bunch, Wilton H.; Dvonch, Victoria M. Moral decisions regarding innovation: the case method. *Clinical Orthopaedics and Related Research* 2000 September; (378): 44-49. NRCBL: 2.1; 4.1.3; 1.2. SC: cs.

Bunge, Mario. Principlism. *In his:* Philosophical Dictionary. Enlarged edition. Amherst, NY: Prometheus Books; 2003: 224. NRCBL: 2.1; 1.1.

Cadoré, Bruno. A hermeneutical approach to clinical bioethics. *In:* Viafora, Corrado, ed. Clinical Bioethics: A Search for the Foundations. Dordrecht: Springer, 2005: 53-59. NRCBL: 2.1; 1.1.

Charlesworth, Max. Bioethics in ethically pluralist societies. *Internal Medicine Journal* 2006 January; 36(1): 51-53. NRCBL: 2.1; 2.3; 1.1; 21.1; 1.2.

Chen, Renbiao; Qui, Xiangxing; Gao, Zhiyan; Shen, Mingxian. The development of biomedical ethics in China. *In:* Döring, Ole; Chen, Renbiao, eds. Advances in Chinese Medical Ethics: Chinese and International Perspectives. Hamburg: Institut für Asienkunde; 2002: 12-25. NRCBL: 2.1; 4.1.2. Note: Proceedings of the Second Sino-German Interdisciplinary Symposium about Medical Ethics in China, Shanghai, 19-23 October, 1999.

Cheng, Anthony M. The real death of vitalism: implications of the Wöhler myth. *Penn Bioethics Journal* 2005 April 2; 1(1): 3p. [Online]. Accessed: http://www. bioethicsjournal.com [2005 April 19]. NRCBL: 2.1; 1.1; 7.1; 1.2.

Cheshire, William P., Jr. When eloquence is inarticulate. *Ethics and Medicine* 2006 Fall; 22(3): 135-138. NRCBL: 2.1; 1.1; 1.2. SC: an.

Cohen, Eric. Conservative bioethics and the search for wisdom. *Hastings Center Report* 2006 January-February; 36(1): 44-56. NRCBL: 2.1; 1.1; 4.4; 5.3; 21.1.

Abstract: "Conservative" bioethics is informed by a rich view of human personhood, a decent respect for the well-considered views of people across the political spectrum, and a philosophy of the state carefully calibrated to ensure that imperfect people can live together in community. The deepest disagreements between conservatives and liberals are rooted in different ways of understanding the moral ideal of equality.

Colby, Jacqueline L. Consent: moral rightness versus non-moral goodness. *American Journal of Bioethics* 2006 May-June; 6(3): 69-71; discussion W51- W53. NRCBL: 2.1; 1.1. Comments: Jonathan Baron. A decision analysis consent. American Journal of Bioethics 2006 May-June; 6(3): 46-52.

Dawson, A.; Garrard, E. In defense of moral imperialism: four equal and universal prima facie principles. *Journal of Medical Ethics* 2006 April; 32(4): 200-204. NRCBL: 2.1; 1.1. SC: an.

Day, Lisa. Boundaries of double effect. *American Journal of Critical Care* 2005 July; 14(4): 334-337. NRCBL: 2.1; 20.5.1; 1.1; 19.5.

del Pozo, Pablo Rodríguez; Fins, Joseph J. Iberian influences on pan-American bioethics: bringing Don Quixote to our shores. *CQ: Cambridge Quarterly of Healthcare Ethics* 2006 Summer; 15(3): 225-238. NRCBL: 2.1; 1.1; 7.1; 21.1.

DeMarco, Joseph P.; Ford, Paul J. Balancing in ethical deliberation: superior to specification and casuistry. *Journal of Medicine and Philosophy* 2006 October; 31(5): 483-497. NRCBL: 2.1; 1.1.

Abstract: Approaches to clinical ethics dilemmas that rely on basic principles or rules are difficult to apply because of vagueness and conflict among basic values. In response, casuistry rejects the use of basic values, and specification produces a large set of specified rules that are presumably easily applicable. Balancing is a method employed to weigh the relative importance of different and conflicting values in application. We argue

NRCBL: National Reference Center for Bioethics Literature Classification Scheme   See inside front cover for terms.

67

against casuistry and specification, claiming that balancing is superior partly because it most clearly exhibits the reasoning behind moral decision-making. Hence, balancing may be most effective in teaching bioethics to medical professionals.

Dudzinski, Denise M.; Burke, Wylie. Practicing moral medicine: patient care to public health. *American Journal of Bioethics* 2006 March-April; 6(2): 75-76. NRCBL: 2.1; 4.1.2; 15.3. Comments: Edmund D. Pellegrino. Toward a reconstruction of medical morality. American Journal of Bioethics 2006 March-April; 6(2): 65-71.

Düwell, Marcus. One moral principle or many? *In:* Rehmann-Sutter, Christoph; Düwell, Marcus; Mieth, Dietmar, eds. Bioethics in Cultural Contexts: Reflections on Methods and Finitude. Dordrecht: Springer, 2006: 93-108. NRCBL: 2.1; 1.1.

Engelhardt, H. Tristram, Jr.; Garrett, Jeremy R.; Jotterand, Fabrice. Bioethics and the philosophy of medicine: a thirty-year perspective. *Journal of Medicine and Philosophy* 2006 December; 31(6): 565-568. NRCBL: 2.1; 2.2; 4.1.2; 9.6.

English, Veronica; Hamm, Danielle; Harrison, Caroline; Sheather, Julian; Sommerville, Ann. Medical governance and the General Medical Council. *Journal of Medical Ethics* 2006 December; 32(12): 743-744. NRCBL: 2.1; 4.1.1; 8.4; 9.1; 9.7; 9.8; 18.1; 18.2. Identifiers: United Kingdom(Great Britain); General Medical Council; National Health Service; United States.

Fan, Ruiping. Towards a Confucian virtue bioethics: reframing Chinese medical ethics in a market economy. *Theoretical Medicine and Bioethics* 2006; 27(6): 541-566. NRCBL: 2.1; 1.1; 9.3.1.

Forge, John. Guest editor's introduction: what is bioethics? *Social Alternatives* 2003 Summer; 22(1): 7-11. NRCBL: 2.1; 1.1; 15.1.

Geller, Gail. A "holistic" model of the healing relationship: what would that require of physicians? *American Journal of Bioethics* 2006 March-April; 6(2): 82-85. NRCBL: 2.1; 4.1.2; 8.1. Comments: Edmund D. Pellegrino. Toward a reconstruction of medical morality. American Journal of Bioethics 2006 March-April; 6(2): 65-71.

Gert, Bernard. A brief reply to Carson Strong. *Kennedy Institute of Ethics Journal* 2006 June; 16(2): 195-197. NRCBL: 2.1; 1.1.

Abstract: Carson Strong's reply to my response to his article demonstrates what happens when there is unacknowledged disagreement about the facts of a case or about the meaning of the terms used to describe those facts. I hope that our dialogue will help reduce this disagreement.

Gert, Bernard. Making the morally relevant features explicit: a response to Carson Strong. *Kennedy Institute of Ethics Journal* 2006 March; 16(1): 59-71. NRCBL: 2.1; 1.1. SC: cs.

Abstract: Carson Strong criticizes the application of my moral theory to bioethics cases. Some of his criticisms are due to my failure to make explicit that both the irrationality or rationality of a decision and the irrationality or rationality of the ranking of evils are part of morally relevant feature 3. Other criticisms are the result of his not using the two-step procedure in a sufficiently rigorous way. His claim that I come up with a wrong answer depends upon his incorrectly regarding a weakly justified violation as one that all impartial rational persons would agree was permitted, rather than as one about which rational persons disagree.

Gert, Bernard; Culver, Charles M.; Clouser, K. Danner. Principlism. *In their:* Bioethics: A Systematic Approach. Second edition. New York: Oxford University Press; 2006: 99-127. NRCBL: 2.1; 1.1. SC: an.

Gracia, Diego. The foundation of medical ethics in the democratic evolution of modern society. *In:* Viafora, Corrado, ed. Clinical Bioethics: A Search for the Foundations. Dordrecht: Springer, 2005: 33-40. NRCBL: 2.1; 1.1.

Gray, David Emmanuel. Decision support and moral sensitivity: must one come at the expense of the other? *American Journal of Bioethics* 2006 May-June; 6(3): 59-62; discussion W51- W53. NRCBL: 2.1; 1.1. Comments: Jonathan Baron. A decision analysis consent. American Journal of Bioethics 2006 May-June; 6(3): 46-52.

Gross, Jed Adam. Trying the case against bioethics. *American Journal of Bioethics* 2006 May-June; 6(3): 71-73; discussion W51- W53. NRCBL: 2.1; 1.1; 18.3; 18.2. Comments: Jonathan Baron. A decision analysis consent. American Journal of Bioethics 2006 May-June; 6(3): 46-52.

Gross, Michael L. Medical ethics education: to what ends? *Journal of Evaluation in Clinical Practice* 2001 November; 7(4): 387-397. NRCBL: 2.3; 1.1.

Guinan, Patrick. Medical ethics versus bioethics (a.k.a. principlism). *National Catholic Bioethics Quarterly* 2006 Winter; 6(4): 651-659. NRCBL: 2.1; 2.2; 4.1.1; 1.1.

Guten, Gary N.; Kohn, Harvey S.; Zoltan, Donald J.; Black, Brian B.; Coran, David L.; Schneider, John A.; Pauers, William. The role of the chief ethics officer in a physician's office. *Clinics in Sports Medicine* 2004 April; 23(2): 243-253. NRCBL: 2.4; 6; 1.1.

Halpern, Scott D. Decisions devoid of data? *American Journal of Bioethics* 2006 May-June; 6(3): 55-56; discussion W51- W53. NRCBL: 2.1; 1.1. Comments: Jonathan Baron. A decision analysis consent. American Journal of Bioethics 2006 May-June; 6(3): 46-52.

Hannay, Alastair. What can philosophers contribute to social ethics? *Topoi* 1998 September; 17(2): 127-136. NRCBL: 2.1; 1.1.

Hansson, Sven Ove. Risk ethics. *In:* Mitcham, Carl, ed. Encyclopedia of Science, Technology, and Ethics.

Farmington Hills, MI: Thomson/Gale, 2005: 1642-1645. NRCBL: 2.1; 1.1.

Hariharan, Seetharaman; Jonnalagadda, Ramesh; Walrond, Errol; Moseley, Harley. Knowledge, attitudes and practice of healthcare ethics and law among doctors and nurses in Barbados. *BMC Medical Ethics* 2006; 7(7): E7 [Online]. Accessed: http://www.biomedcentral.com/ 1472-6939/7/7 [2006 August 15]. NRCBL: 2.1; 2.3; 4.1.3. SC: em.

Abstract: Background: The aim of the study is to assess the knowledge, attitudes and practices among healthcare professionals in Barbados in relation to healthcare ethics and law in an attempt to assist in guiding their professional conduct and aid in curriculum development. Methods: A self-administered structured questionnaire about knowledge of healthcare ethics, law and the role of an Ethics Committee in the healthcare system was devised, tested and distributed to all levels of staff at the Queen Elizabeth Hospital in Barbados (a tertiary care teaching hospital) during April and May 2003. Results: The paper analyses 159 responses from doctors and nurses comprising junior doctors, consultants, staff nurses and sisters-in-charge. The frequency with which the respondents encountered ethical or legal problems varied widely from 'daily' to 'yearly'. 52% of senior medical staff and 20% of senior nursing staff knew little of the law pertinent to their work. 11% of the doctors did not know the contents of the Hippocratic Oath whilst a quarter of nurses did not know the Nurses Code. Nuremberg Code and Helsinki Code were known only to a few individuals. 29% of doctors and 37% of nurses had no knowledge of an existing hospital ethics committee. Physicians had a stronger opinion than nurses regarding practice of ethics such as adherence to patients' wishes, confidentiality, paternalism, consent for procedures and treating violent/non-compliant patients (p = 0.01) Conclusion: The study highlights the need to identify professionals in the workforce who appear to be indifferent to ethical and legal issues, to devise means to sensitize them to these issues and appropriately training them.

Harremoës, Poul. Precautionary principle. *In:* Mitcham, Carl, ed. Encyclopedia of Science, Technology, and Ethics. Farmington Hills, MI: Thomson/Gale, 2005: 1474-1479. NRCBL: 2.1; 1.1.

Hart, Curtis W. Clinical pragmatism in bioethics: a pastoral approach. *Journal of Religion and Health* 2006 Summer; 45(2): 196-207. NRCBL: 2.1; 1.1; 1.2; 4.4. SC: cs. Identifiers: John Dewey.

Harvey, John Collins. Clinical ethics: the art of medicine. *In:* Beam, Thomas E.; Sparacino, Linette R.; Pellegrino, Edmund D.; Hartle, Anthony E.; Howe, Edmund G., eds. Military Medical Ethics. Volume 1. Washington, DC: TMM Publications, Borden Institute, Walter Reed Army Medical Center; 2003: 61-104. NRCBL: 2.1; 2.2; 1.1.

Hoffmaster, C. Barry. Against against bioethics. *American Journal of Bioethics* 2006 May-June; 6(3): 53-55; discussion W51- W53. NRCBL: 2.1; 1.1. Comments: Jonathan Baron. A decision analysis consent. American Journal of Bioethics 2006 May-June; 6(3): 46-52.

Hollman, Jay; Kilner, John. Are Christian voices needed in public bioethics debates?: Care for persons with disabil-ities as a test case. *Ethics and Medicine* 2006 Fall; 22(3): 143-150. NRCBL: 2.1; 1.1; 1.2; 9.5.3; 9.5.1.

Holm, S. The WMA on medical ethics — some critical comments. *Journal of Medical Ethics* 2006 March; 32(3): 161-162. NRCBL: 2.1; 2.3; 4.1.2; 7.2. Identifiers: World Medical Association.

Howell, Joel D. Some thoughts on history and "healing relationships". *American Journal of Bioethics* 2006 March-April; 6(2): 80-82. NRCBL: 2.1; 4.1.2; 2.2. Comments: Edmund D. Pellegrino. Toward a reconstruction of medical morality. American Journal of Bioethics 2006 March-April; 6(2): 65-71.

Hughes, Jonathan. How not to criticize the precautionary principle. *Journal of Medicine and Philosophy* 2006 October; 31(5): 447-464. NRCBL: 2.1; 1.1; 5.3; 16.1.

Abstract: The precautionary principle has its origins in debates about environmental policy, but is increasingly invoked in bioethical contexts. John Harris and Søren Holm argue that the principle should be rejected as incoherent, irrational, and representing a fundamental threat to scientific advance and technological progress. This article argues that while there are problems with standard formulations of the principle, Harris and Holm's rejection of all its forms is mistaken. In particular, they focus on strong versions of the principle and fail to recognize that weaker forms, which may escape their criticisms, are both possible and advocated in the literature.

Jacoby, Liva H. For bioethics — the role of empirical research. *American Journal of Bioethics* 2006 May-June; 6(3): 58-59; discussion W51- W53. NRCBL: 2.1; 1.1. SC: em. Comments: Jonathan Baron. A decision analysis consent. American Journal of Bioethics 2006 May-June; 6(3): 46-52.

Johnson, Summer. Multiple roles and successes in public bioethics: a response to the public forum critique of bioethics commissions. *Kennedy Institute of Ethics Journal* 2006 June; 16(2): 173-188. NRCBL: 2.4; 2.1; 1.1; 7.1. SC: em.

Abstract: National bioethics commissions have been critiqued for a variety of structural, procedural, and political aspects of their work. A more recent critique published by Dzur and Levin uses political philosophy to constructively critique the work of national bioethics commissions as public deliberative forums. However, this public forum critique of bioethics commissions ignores empirical research in political science and normative claims that suggest that advisory commissions can and should have diverse of functions beyond that of being public forums. The present paper argues that the public forum critique too narrowly considers the roles that bioethics commissions can play in public bioethics and ignores the moral obligation of commissions to fulfill their mandates. Evaluations of commissions must consider that these institutions can serve in capacities other than those of a public deliberative forum and use additional measures to evaluate the multiple roles and successes of bioethics commissions in public policy.

Jonsen, Albert R. "Life is short, Medicine is long": reflections on a bioethical insight. *Journal of Medicine and Philosophy* 2006 December; 31(6): 667-673. NRCBL: 2.1; 4.1.2; 20.5.1. SC: an.

NRCBL: National Reference Center for Bioethics Literature Classification Scheme   See inside front cover for terms.

69

Abstract: The famous first aphorism of Hippocrates, "Life is short, the art is long" was long considered a perfect summary of medical ethics. Modern physicians find the words impossible to understand. But it can be interpreted as a fundamental insight into the ethical problems of modern medicine. The technology of modern scientific medicine can sustain life, even when life is losing its vitality. How should decisions be made about the use of technology and by whom? This is the incessant question of modern medical ethics.

Justo, Luis; Villareal, Jorgelina. Autonomy as a universal expectation: a review and research proposal. *Eubios Journal of Asian and International Bioethics* 2003 March 13(2): 53-57. NRCBL: 2.1; 9.8; 1.1. SC: em.

Kaveny, M. Cathleen. Diversity and deliberation: bioethics commissions and moral reasoning. *Journal of Religious Ethics* 2006 June; 34(2): 311-337. NRCBL: 2.4; 1.3.9; 14.5; 18.5.4; 1.1; 1.2. SC: an. Identifiers: President's Council on Bioethics; NBAC.

Kenny, Nuala. Medicine's malaise: the Pellegrino prescription. *American Journal of Bioethics* 2006 March-April; 6(2): 78-80. NRCBL: 2.1; 4.1.2; 8.1. Comments: Edmund D. Pellegrino. Toward a reconstruction of medical morality. American Journal of Bioethics 2006 March-April; 6(2): 65-71.

Kettner, Matthias. Discourse ethics: Apel, Habermas, and beyond. *In:* Rehmann-Sutter, Christoph; Düwell, Marcus; Mieth, Dietmar, eds. Bioethics in Cultural Contexts: Reflections on Methods and Finitude. Dordrecht: Springer, 2006: 299-318. NRCBL: 2.1; 1.1.

Kim, Su Hyun. Confucian bioethics and cross-cultural considerations in health care decision making. *Journal of Nursing Law* 2005 Fall; 10(3): 161-166. NRCBL: 2.1; 1.1; 9.1; 21.7.

Kipnis, Kenneth. Professional ethics and instructional success. *In:* American Medical Association. Professing Medicine: strengthening the ethics and professionalism of tomorrow's physicians. Chicago: American Medical Association; 2001: 21-32. NRCBL: 2.3; 4.1.2; 7.2; 21.7. Note: Commemorative issue of Virtual Mentor, AMA's online ethics journal.

Kittay, Eva Feder. The concept of care ethics in biomedicine: the case of disability. *In:* Rehmann-Sutter, Christoph; Düwell, Marcus; Mieth, Dietmar, eds. Bioethics in Cultural Contexts: Reflections on Methods and Finitude. Dordrecht: Springer, 2006: 319-339. NRCBL: 2.1; 1.1; 9.5.3.

Komesaroff, Paul A. The relationship between law and ethics in medicine. *Internal Medicine Journal* 2001 September-October; 31(7): 413-414. NRCBL: 2.1; 1.1; 1.3.5.

Kopelman, Loretta M. Bioethics as a second-order discipline: who is not a bioethicist? *Journal of Medicine and Philosophy* 2006 December; 31(6): 601-628. NRCBL: 2.1; 1.1; 9.6. SC: an.

Abstract: A dispute exists about whether bioethics should become a new discipline with its own methods, competency standards, duties, honored texts, and core curriculum. Unique expertise is a necessary condition for disciplines. Using the current literature, different views about the sort of expertise that might be unique to bioethicists are critically examined to determine if there is an expertise that might meet this requirement. Candidates include analyses of expertise based in "philosophical ethics," "casuistry," "a theoretical or situation ethics," "conventionalist relativism," "institutional guidance," "regulatory guidance and compliance," "political advocacy," "functionalism," and "principlism." None succeed in identifying a unique area of expertise for successful bioethicists that could serve as a basis for making it a new discipline. Rather expertise in bioethics is rooted in many professions, disciplines and fields and best understood as a second-order discipline.

Kopelman, Loretta M. What is unique about the doctor and patient medical encounter? A moral and economic perspective. *American Journal of Bioethics* 2006 March-April; 6(2): 85-88. NRCBL: 2.1; 4.1.2; 8.1. Comments: Edmund D. Pellegrino. Toward a reconstruction of medical morality. American Journal of Bioethics 2006 March-April; 6(2): 65-71.

Krones, Tanja. The scope of the recent bioethics debate in Germany: Kant, crisis, and no confidence in society. *CQ: Cambridge Quarterly of Healthcare Ethics* 2006 Summer; 15(3): 273-281. NRCBL: 2.1; 1.1; 7.1; 2.2; 21.4.

Lafollette, Hugh. Living on a slippery slope. *Journal of Ethics* 2005; 9(3-4): 475-499. NRCBL: 2.1; 1.1; 20.7.

Latham, Stephen R. Some limits of decision-theory in bioethics: rights, ends, and thick concepts. *American Journal of Bioethics* 2006 May-June; 6(3): 56-58; discussion W51- W53. NRCBL: 2.1; 1.1. Comments: Jonathan Baron. A decision analysis consent. American Journal of Bioethics 2006 May-June; 6(3): 46-52.

Lebacqz, Karen. Philosophy, theology, and the claims of justice. *In:* Guinn, David E., ed. Handbook of Bioethics and Religion. New York: Oxford University Press, 2006: 253-263. NRCBL: 2.1; 1.1; 1.2.

Liu, Kimberly E.; Flood, Catherine; Capstick, Valerie. Is an interdisciplinary session on ethics and law in obstetrics and gynaecology effective? *Journal of Obstetrics and Gynaecology Canada* 2005 May; 27(5): 486-490. NRCBL: 2.3; 7.2; 9.5.5; 4.1.2. SC: em; le.

London, Alex John. What is social and global justice to bioethics or bioethics to social and global justice? *Hastings Center Report* 2006 July-August; 36(4): 3. NRCBL: 2.1; 1.1.

Louw, Stephen J.; Hughes, Julian C. Moral reasoning — the unrealized place of casuistry in medical ethics [editorial]. *International Psychogeriatrics* 2005 June; 17(2): 149-154. NRCBL: 2.1; 1.1; 17.1.

Malek, Janet. Introduction. *Journal of Medicine and Philosophy* 2006 October; 31(5): 441-446. NRCBL: 2.1; 1.1;

5.3; 9.3.1; 9.7; 21.1. Identifiers: overview of journal content.

Mason, J.K. Ethical principles and ethical practice [editorial]. *Clinical Ethics* 2006 March; 1(1): 3-6. NRCBL: 2.1; 1.1. SC: an.

Mele, V.; Binetti, P. Bioethics, bridge to medical education. *Journal of Biological Regulators and Homeostatic Agents* 2005 January-June; 19(1-2): 49-53. NRCBL: 2.3; 7.2; 1.1.

Mellon, Brad F. James Drane's More Humane Medicine: a new foundation for twenty-first century bioethics? *Christian Bioethics* 2006 December; 12(3): 301-311. NRCBL: 2.1; 2.2; 1.2; 1.1.

Abstract: James Drane's More Humane Medicine: A Liberal Catholic Bioethics is an outstanding contribution to the study of bioethics in our day. Catholics and others who are interested in the issues discussed here will benefit from this masterful treatment. The author opens with a set of definitions, starting with what he means by a "more humane medicine." Drane contends that a more humane medicine has become necessary and desired, but not because the traditional medical ethic as "a self-declared and self-imposed ethic, outlining what noble service to others entails" is no longer valid. Rather he defines it as an advance on the traditional ethic; a "new foundation" based on a "lived set of obligations derived from a felt commitment to other persons . . . an ethics based on the relationship between doctors and patients and essentially an ethics of virtue." Drane's work is a "liberal Catholic Bioethics" in which he challenges his own faith tradition, the Roman Catholic Church, on such topics as sexuality, birth control, abortion, cloning, stem cell research, aging and dying, and euthanasia and physician-assisted suicide. The present article is a critical essay that analyzes the author's statements and conclusions.

Mordacci, Roberto. Medicine as a practice and the ethics of illness. *In:* Viafora, Corrado, ed. Clinical Bioethics: A Search for the Foundations. Dordrecht: Springer, 2005: 101-113. NRCBL: 2.1; 1.1; 4.1.2.

Murray, Thomas H. Moral reasoning in social context. *Journal of Social Issues* 1993 Summer; 49(2): 185-200. NRCBL: 2.1; 2.2; 1.1. SC: an.

Nord, Erik. Utilitarian decision analysis of informed consent. *American Journal of Bioethics* 2006 May-June; 6(3): 65-67; discussion W51- W53. NRCBL: 2.1; 1.1; 8.3.1. Comments: Jonathan Baron. A decision analysis consent. American Journal of Bioethics 2006 May-June; 6(3): 46-52.

Nortvedt, Per. Medical ethics manual: does it serve its purpose? *Journal of Medical Ethics* 2006 March; 32(3): 159-160. NRCBL: 2.1; 2.3; 4.1.2; 7.2.

Abstract: World Medical Association. Ethics manual. Ferney-Voltaire: WMA, 2005. http://www.wma.net/e/ethicsunit/pdf/manual/ethics_manual.pdf (available for download). This manual of medical ethics is meant to serve the purpose of a guiding teaching aid for medical students as well as physicians. It was decided upon and planned by the World Medical Assembly in 1999 and the work was supervised and coordinated by the WMA Ethics Unit.

Parker, Michael. A deliberative approach to clinical bioethics. *In:* Viafora, Corrado, ed. Clinical Bioethics: A Search for the Foundations. Dordrecht: Springer, 2005: 61-71. NRCBL: 2.1; 1.1.

Pellegrino, Edmund D. Bioethics and politics: "doing ethics" in the public square. *Journal of Medicine and Philosophy* 2006 December; 31(6): 569-584. NRCBL: 2.1; 1.1; 2.2. SC: an.

Pellegrino, Edmund D. The "telos" of medicine and the good of the patient. *In:* Viafora, Corrado, ed. Clinical Bioethics: A Search for the Foundations. Dordrecht: Springer, 2005: 21-32. NRCBL: 2.1; 4.1.2; 8.1. SC: an.

Pellegrino, Edmund D. Toward a reconstruction of medical morality. *American Journal of Bioethics* 2006 March-April; 6(2): 65-71. NRCBL: 2.1; 4.1.2; 8.1. SC: an.

Phaosavasdi, Sukhit; Taneepanichskul, Surasak; Tannirandorn, Yuen; Thamkhantho, Manopchai; Pruksapong, Chumsak; Kanjanapitak, Aurchart. Medical ethics for senior medical doctors (episode III). *Journal of the Medical Association of Thailand* 2005 July; 88(7): 1015-1017. NRCBL: 2.1; 4.1.2; 1.3.1.

Porter, Kamilla K.; Rai, Gurcharan S. Principles of medical ethics. *In:* Rai, Gurcharan S, ed. Medical Ethics and the Elderly. 2nd ed. San Francisco: Radcliffe Medical Press; 2004: 1-7. NRCBL: 2.1; 1.1.

Price, Connie C. Decision analysis for a new bioethics. *American Journal of Bioethics* 2006 May-June; 6(3): 62-64; discussion W51- W53. NRCBL: 2.1; 1.1; 8.3.1. Comments: Jonathan Baron. A decision analysis consent. American Journal of Bioethics 2006 May-June; 6(3): 46-52.

Rajput, Vijay; Bekes, Carolyn E. Ethical issues in hospital medicine. *Medical Clinics of North America* 2002 July; 86(4): 869-886. NRCBL: 2.1; 1.1; 8.4.

Rehmann-Sutter, Christoph. Limits of bioethics. *In:* Rehmann-Sutter, Christoph; Düwell, Marcus; Mieth, Dietmar, eds. Bioethics in Cultural Contexts: Reflections on Methods and Finitude. Dordrecht: Springer, 2006: 59-79. NRCBL: 2.1; 1.1.

Renzong, Qiu. Bioethics: a search for moral diversity. *Eastern Mediterranean Health Journal* 2006; 12(Supplement 1): S21-S29 [Online]. Accessed: http://www.emro.who.int/publications/EMHJ/12_S/PDF/4.pdf [2007 January 3]. NRCBL: 2.1; 18.6; 21.7; 1.1. Note: Abstract in French and Arabic.

Rhodes, Rosamond. The ethical standard of care. *American Journal of Bioethics* 2006 March-April; 6(2): 76-78. NRCBL: 2.1; 4.1.2; 8.1. Comments: Edmund D. Pellegrino. Toward a reconstruction of medical morality. American Journal of Bioethics 2006 March-April; 6(2): 65-71.

NRCBL: National Reference Center for Bioethics Literature Classification Scheme   See inside front cover for terms.

71

Sargent, Carolyn; Smith-Morris, Carolyn. Questioning our principles: anthropological contributions to ethical dilemmas in clinical practice. *CQ: Cambridge Quarterly of Healthcare Ethics* 2006 Spring; 15(2): 123-134. NRCBL: 2.1; 21.7; 1.1; 7.1. SC: cs; an.

Schmuhl, Hans-Walter. Nationalsozialismus als Argument im aktuellen Medizinethik-Diskurs. Eine Zwischenbilanz. *In:* Frewer, Andreas; Eickhoff, Clemens, eds. "Euthanasie" und die aktuelle Sterbehilfe-Debatte: Die historischen Hintergründe medizinischer Ethik. Frankfurt; New York: Campus; 2000: 385-407. NRCBL: 2.1; 1.1; 15.5; 21.4. SC: an.

Schneiderman, Lawrence J. Medical ethics and alternative medicine. *Scientific Review of Alternative Medicine* 1998 Spring-Summer; 2(1): 63-66. NRCBL: 2.1; 4.1.1; 4.1.2.

Schöne-Seifert, Bettina. Danger and merits of principlism: meta-theoretical reflections on the Beauchamp/Childress-approach to biomedical ethics. *In:* Rehmann-Sutter, Christoph; Düwell, Marcus; Mieth, Dietmar, eds. Bioethics in Cultural Contexts: Reflections on Methods and Finitude. Dordrecht: Springer, 2006: 109-119. NRCBL: 2.1; 1.1.

Sherlock, Richard. Medical ethics. *In:* Mitcham, Carl, ed. Encyclopedia of Science, Technology, and Ethics. Farmington Hills, MI: Thomson/Gale, 2005: 1184-1188. NRCBL: 2.1; 1.1; 8.1; 12.1.

Sidel, Victor W.; Levy, Barry S. Physician-soldier: a moral dilemma? *In:* Beam, Thomas E.; Sparacino, Linette R.; Pellegrino, Edmund D.; Hartle, Anthony E.; Howe, Edmund G., eds. Military Medical Ethics. Volume 1. Washington, DC: TMM Publications, Borden Institute, Walter Reed Army Medical Center; 2003: 293-329. NRCBL: 2.1; 1.3.5; 21.2; 4.1.2.

Silverton, Louise I. Ethics examined. *Midwifery Today and Childbirth Education* 1994 Summer; (30): 12-13. NRCBL: 2.1; 4.1.1. SC: cs.

Slosar, John Paul. Teleology, the modern moral dichotomy, and postmodern bioethics in the 21st century. *In:* Dinkins, Christine Sorrell; Sorrell, Jeanne Merkle, eds. Listening to the Whispers: Re-Thinking Ethics in Healthcare. Madison, WI: University of Wisconsin Press; 2006: 138-189. NRCBL: 2.1; 1.1.

Solbakk, Jan Helge. Catharsis and moral therapy I: a Platonic account. *Medicine, Health Care and Philosophy* 2006; 9(1): 57-67. NRCBL: 2.1; 1.1.
Abstract: This paper aims at analysing the ancient Greek notions of catharsis (clearing up, cleaning), to holon (the whole) and therapeia (therapy, treatment, healing) to assess whether they may be of help in addressing a set of questions concerning the didactics of medical ethics: What do medical students actually experience and learn when they attend classes of medical ethics? How should teachers of medical ethics proceed didactically to make students benefit morally from their teaching? And finally, to what extent and in what forms and formats can the kind of cathartic treatment envisaged by Plato still be considered a necessary preliminary to moral learning? The three questions will be addressed by means of a reconstructive analysis and assessment of the Platonic notions of catharsis and holistic therapy present in the Charmides and the Sophist. Besides, the didactic potential of Plato's dialogue form and moral regimen will be tried out. The ultimate aim is to investigate the possibilities of developing a therapeutic conception of medical ethics.

Spike, Jeffrey. Bioethics now. *Philosophy Now* 2006 May-June; 55(6): 7-8 p. [Online]. Accessed: http://www.philosophynow.org/issue55/55spike.htm [2006 December 5]. NRCBL: 2.1; 1.1; 9.6; 18.1.

Strong, Carson. Continuing the dialogue: a reply to Bernard Gert. *Kennedy Institute of Ethics Journal* 2006 June; 16(2): 189-194. NRCBL: 2.1; 1.1.
Abstract: Continuing the dialogue begun in the March 2006 issue of the Kennedy Institute of Ethics Journal, I suggest that Bernard Gert's response to my paper does not adequately address the criticisms I make of his theory's application to bioethics cases.

Strong, Carson. Gert's moral theory and its application to bioethics cases. *Kennedy Institute of Ethics Journal* 2006 March; 16(1): 39-58. NRCBL: 2.1; 1.1. SC: cs.
Abstract: Bernard Gert's theory of morality has received much critical attention, but there has been relatively little commentary on its practical value for bioethics. An important test of an ethical theory is its ability to yield results that are helpful and plausible when applied to real cases. An examination of Gert's theory and his own attempts to apply it to bioethics cases reveals that there are serious difficulties with regard to its application. These problems are sufficiently severe to support the conclusion that Gert's theory is unacceptable as an approach for resolving bioethics cases, even relatively noncontroversial cases.

Strong, Carson. The limited utility of utilitarian analysis. *American Journal of Bioethics* 2006 May-June; 6(3): 67-69; discussion W51- W53. NRCBL: 2.1; 1.1; 8.3.1. Comments: Jonathan Baron. A decision analysis consent. American Journal of Bioethics 2006 May-June; 6(3): 46-52.

Swick, Herbert M.; Bryan, Charles S.; Longo, Lawrence D. Beyond the physician charter: reflections on medical professionalism. *Perspectives in Biology and Medicine* 2006 Spring; 49(2): 263-275. NRCBL: 2.1; 1.1; 4.1.2. SC: an.

Tai, Michael Cheng-tek. Natural and unnatural — an application of Taoist thought to bioethics. *In:* Sang-yong, Song; Young-Mo, Koo; Macer, Darryl R.J., eds. Asian Bioethics in the 21st Century. Christchurch, NZ: Eubios Ethics Institute, 2002: 122-128. NRCBL: 2.1; 1.1; 20.5.1. Conference: Proceedings of the Asian Bioethics Conference (ABC4), held 22-25 November 2002 in Seoul, South Korea.

Takahashi, Takao. A synthesis of bioethics and environmental ethics founded upon the concept of care: toward a

Japanese approach to bioethics. *In:* Takahashi, Takao, ed. Taking Life and Death Seriously: Bioethics from Japan. Amsterdam; Boston: Elsevier JAI; 2005: 19-45. NRCBL: 2.1; 16.1; 4.1.1.

ten Have, Henk. "A helping and caring profession": medicine as a normative practice. *In:* Viafora, Corrado, ed. Clinical Bioethics: A Search for the Foundations. Dordrecht: Springer, 2005: 75-97. NRCBL: 2.1; 1.1; 4.1.2.

ten Have, Henk. A communitarian approach to clinical bioethics. *In:* Viafora, Corrado, ed. Clinical Bioethics: A Search for the Foundations. Dordrecht: Springer, 2005: 41-51. NRCBL: 2.1; 1.1.

Thomasma, David C. Clinical bioethics in a post modern age. *In:* Viafora, Corrado, ed. Clinical Bioethics: A Search for the Foundations. Dordrecht: Springer, 2005: 3-20. NRCBL: 2.1; 1.1; 8.1.

Thomasma, David C. Theories of medical ethics: the philosophical structure. *In:* Beam, Thomas E.; Sparacino, Linette R.; Pellegrino, Edmund D.; Hartle, Anthony E.; Howe, Edmund G., eds. Military Medical Ethics. Volume 1. Washington, DC: TMM Publications, Borden Institute, Walter Reed Army Medical Center; 2003: 23-59. NRCBL: 2.1; 1.1.

Thornton, T. Judgement and the role of the metaphysics of values in medical ethics. *Journal of Medical Ethics* 2006 June; 32(6): 365-370. NRCBL: 2.1; 1.1. SC: an.
Abstract: Despite its authors' intentions, the four principles approach to medical ethics can become crudely algorithmic in practice. The first section sets out the bare bones of the four principles approach drawing out those aspects of Beauchamp and Childress's Principles of biomedical ethics that encourage this misreading. The second section argues that if the emphasis on the guidance of moral judgement is augmented by a particularist account of what disciplines it, then the danger can be reduced. In the third section, I consider how much the resultant picture diverges from Beauchamp and Childress's actual position.

Tollefsen, Christopher. The President's Council on Bioethics: overview and assessment. *HEC (Healthcare Ethics Committee) Forum* 2006 June; 18(2): 99-107. NRCBL: 2.4; 2.1; 1.1.

Tomasevic, Luka. Challenges of global bioethics and biotechnology. *Formosan Journal of Medical Humanities* 2006 June; 7(1-2): 39-55. NRCBL: 2.1; 21.7; 1.2; 1.1.

Tsai, D. F-C. The WMA Medical Ethics Manual [book review]. *Journal of Medical Ethics* 2006 March; 32(3): 163. NRCBL: 2.1; 2.3; 4.1.2; 7.2. Identifiers: World Medical Association.

Valiathan, M.S. Ethical issues in the practice of medicine. *Indian Journal of Chest Diseases and Allied Sciences* 2006 January-March; 48(1): 7-11. NRCBL: 2.1; 2.2; 4.1.2; 1.3.1; 5.3. Identifiers: India.

Varelius, Jukka. The value of autonomy in medical ethics. *Medicine, Health Care and Philosophy* 2006; 9(3): 377-388. NRCBL: 2.1; 1.1; 8.1.

Veatch, Robert M. Assessing Pellegrino's reconstruction of medical morality. *American Journal of Bioethics* 2006 March-April; 6(2): 72-75. NRCBL: 2.1; 8.1; 4.1.2. Comments: Edmund D. Pellegrino. Toward a construction of medical morality. American Journal of Bioethics 2006 March-April; 6(2): 65-71.

Veatch, Robert M. How philosophy of medicine has changed medical ethics. *Journal of Medicine and Philosophy* 2006 December; 31(6): 585-600. NRCBL: 2.1; 1.1; 2.2; 4.1.2. SC: an.
Abstract: The celebration of thirty years of publication of The Journal of Medicine and Philosophy provides an opportunity to reflect on how medical ethics has evolved over that period. The reshaping of the field has occurred in no small part because of the impact of branches of philosophy other than ethics. These have included influences from Kantian theory of respect for persons, personal identity theory, philosophy of biology, linguistic analysis of the concepts of health and disease, personhood theory, epistemology, and political philosophy. More critically, medicine itself has begun to be reshaped. The most fundamental restructuring of medicine is currently occurring—stemming, in part, from the application of contemporary philosophy of science to the medical field. There is no journal more central to these critical events of the past three decades than The Journal of Medicine and Philosophy.

Volandes, Angelo E.; Abbo, Elmer D. Toward a reconstruction of a professional medical morality. *American Journal of Bioethics* 2006 March-April; 6(2): 88-89. NRCBL: 2.1; 8.1; 4.1.2. Comments: Edmund D. Pellegrino. Toward a reconstruction of medical morality. American Journal of Bioethics 2006 March-April; 6(2): 65-71.

Volokh, Eugene. Slippery slope arguments. *In:* Mitcham, Carl, ed. Encyclopedia of Science, Technology, and Ethics. Farmington Hills, MI: Thomson/Gale, 2005: 1783-1785. NRCBL: 2.1; 1.1.

Walker, Francis O. Cultivating simple virtues in medicine. *Neurology* 2005 November 22; 65(10): 1678-1680. NRCBL: 2.1; 1.1.

Waltho, Simon. Response to Westin and Nilstun. *Health Care Analysis: An International Journal of Health Philosophy and Policy* 2006 June; 14(2): 119-122. NRCBL: 2.1; 1.1; 8.1; 9.5.1. Comments: Westin and Nilstun. Principles help to analyse but often give no solution — secondary prevention after a cardiac event. Health Care Analysis: An International Journal of Health Philosophy and Policy 2006 June; 14(2): 111-117.

Wasson, Katherine; Cook, David. Pellegrino and medicine: a critical revision. *American Journal of Bioethics* 2006 March-April; 6(2): 90-91. NRCBL: 2.1; 4.1.2. Comments: Edmund D. Pellegrino. Toward a construction of medical morality. American Journal of Bioethics 2006 March-April; 6(2): 65-71.

NRCBL: National Reference Center for Bioethics Literature Classification Scheme   See inside front cover for terms.

73

Westin, Lars; Nilstun, Tore. Principles help to analyse but often give no solution — secondary prevention after a cardiac event. *Health Care Analysis: An International Journal of Health Philosophy and Policy* 2006 June; 14(2): 111-117. NRCBL: 2.1; 1.1; 8.1; 9.5.1.

Abstract: The aim of this paper is to investigate whether or not ethical conflicts can be identified, analysed and solved using ethical principles. The relation between the physician and the patient with ischemic heart disease (IHD) as lifestyle changes are recommended in a secondary prevention program is used as an example. The principal persons affected (the patient and his or her spouse) and the ethical principles (respect for autonomy, non-maleficence, beneficence and justice) are combined in a two dimensional model. The most important person affected by the recommendations is the patient. His or her autonomy is challenged by the suggested life style changes, the purpose of which is to promote the future wellbeing and health of the patient. The spouse is indirectly involved in and affected by the process. He or she often feels neglected by caregivers. Ethical conflicts can both be identified and analysed using ethical principles, but often no solution is implied. Most (if not all) physicians would strongly encourage life style changes, but surprisingly there is no uncontroversial justification for this conclusion using principles.

Westin, Lars; Nilstun, Tore. Principlism revisited: response to Simon Waltho. *Health Care Analysis: An International Journal of Health Philosophy and Policy* 2006 December; 14(4): 247-248. NRCBL: 2.1; 1.1.

Williams, John R. Response to reviews of the World Medical Association Medical Ethics Manual. *Journal of Medical Ethics* 2006 March; 32(3): 164-165. NRCBL: 2.1; 2.3; 4.1.2; 7.2. Comments: Per Nortvedt. Medical ethics manual: does it serve its purpose? Journal of Medical Ethics 2006 March; 32(3): 159-160. S. Holm. The WMA on medical ethics — some critical comments. Journal of Medical Ethics 2006 March; 32(3): 161-162. D. F-C. Tsai. The WMA Medical Ethics Manual. Journal of Medical Ethics 2006 March; 32(3): 163.

Winter, Robert B. Innovation in surgical technique: the story of spine surgery. *Clinical Orthopaedics and Related Research* 2000 September; (378): 9-14. NRCBL: 2.2; 4.1.2; 9.8.

Yudin, Boris. Values of preservation and values of change in bioethics. *Journal International de Bioéthique = International Journal of Bioethics* 2005 September-December; 16(3-4): 71-75, 170-171. NRCBL: 2.1; 1.1; 4.4; 16.1; 15.1.

Abstract: Since its advent bioethics has been motivated and dominated by values of preservation, be it preservation of life on the Earth or preservation of human life, health, rights, dignity, autonomy etc. Bioethics of this, let us say, more traditional type, stresses the need to preserve, to protect the surrounding order of things, which can be easily and irreversibly destroyed by our rash and unreasoned actions. Now I can turn to the second value orientation in the realm of bioethics. It stresses values related with changes in the existing (natural) order of things, these changes to be directed by our interests, desires and dreams. This kind of bioethics upholds our views above the imperatives of the preservation of nature around us. Nature is perceived, first of all, as a raw material to be transformed, more or less radically changed on the basis of our designs and by means

of our technologies in order to achieve our own goals. This opposition of two value systems can be presented as opposition between the stands of a naturalist as a (pure) observer of phenomena of the outer and inner world, on the one hand, and a researcher as someone who exerts active interventions and, after all, produces changes in the world.

Zaner, Richard M. On evoking clinical meaning. *Journal of Medicine and Philosophy* 2006 December; 31(6): 655-666. NRCBL: 2.1; 1.1; 9.6; 20.5.2. SC: an.

Abstract: It was in the course of one particular clinical encounter that I came to realize the power of narrative, especially for expressing clinically presented ethical matters. In Husserlian terms, the mode of evidence proper to the unique and the singular is the very indirection that is the genius of story-telling. Moreover, the clinical consultant is unavoidably changed by his or her clinical involvement. The individuals whose situation is at issue have their own stories that need telling. Clinical ethics is in this sense a way of helping patients, families, and, yes, health providers to discover and give voice to those stories. In this way, clinical ethics is an evoking of meaning. Kierkegaard understood this well: Indirect communication is the language for the unique and the otherwise inexpressible.

BIOETHICS AND MEDICAL ETHICS/ RELIGIOUS PERSPECTIVES

Arnhart, Larry. President's Council on Bioethics. *In:* Mitcham, Carl, ed. Encyclopedia of Science, Technology, and Ethics. Farmington Hills, MI: Thomson/Gale, 2005: 1482-1486. NRCBL: 2.4; 1.2; 5.3; 18.5.4.

Aulisio, Mark. Bioethics in a global village [editorial]. *American Journal of Bioethics* 2006 January-February; 6(1): 1-4. NRCBL: 2.1; 21.1; 1.2; 9.5.6.

Azmi, K.A. Shafqat; Siddiqui, M.K. Islamic medical ethics with special reference to Moalejat-e-Buqratiya. *Bulletin of the Indian Institute of History of Medicine* 1999 January; 29(1): 15-27. NRCBL: 2.2; 2.1; 1.2.

Brownback, Sam. Bioethics and the future of humanity. *National Catholic Bioethics Quarterly* 2006 Autumn; 6(3): 423-430. NRCBL: 2.1; 4.4; 18.5.4; 14.5; 1.2; 15.1. SC: le.

Bunch, Wilton H.; Dvonch, Victoria M. Moral decisions regarding innovation: the case method. *Clinical Orthopaedics and Related Research* 2000 September; (378): 44-49. NRCBL: 2.1; 4.1.3; 1.2. SC: cs.

Cahill, Lisa Sowle. Theology's role in public bioethics. *In:* Guinn, David E., ed. Handbook of Bioethics and Religion. New York: Oxford University Press, 2006: 37-57. NRCBL: 2.1; 1.2.

Cameron, Nigel M. de S. Biotechnology and the future of humanity. *Journal of Contemporary Health Law and Policy* 2006 Spring; 22(2): 413-423. NRCBL: 2.1; 2.4; 1.2; 21.1.

Chambers, Tod. Bioethics, religion, and linguistic capital. *In:* Guinn, David E., ed. Handbook of Bioethics and Religion. New York: Oxford University Press, 2006: 81-91. NRCBL: 2.1; 1.2.

Charlesworth, Max. Bioethics in ethically pluralist societies. *Internal Medicine Journal* 2006 January; 36(1): 51-53. NRCBL: 2.1; 2.3; 1.1; 21.1; 1.2.

Cheek, Dennis W. Ramsey, Paul. *In:* Mitcham, Carl, ed. Encyclopedia of Science, Technology, and Ethics. Farmington Hills, MI: Thomson/Gale, 2005: 1580-1581. NRCBL: 2.2; 1.2.

Chen, Rongxia. Religious emotions and bioethics. *In:* Döring, Ole; Chen, Renbiao, eds. Advances in Chinese Medical Ethics: Chinese and International Perspectives. Hamburg: Institut für Asienkunde; 2002: 214-222. NRCBL: 2.1; 1.2. Note: Proceedings of the Second Sino-German Interdisciplinary Symposium about Medical Ethics in China, Shanghai, 19-23 October, 1999.

Cheng, Anthony M. The real death of vitalism: implications of the Wöhler myth. *Penn Bioethics Journal* 2005 April 2; 1(1): 3p. [Online]. Accessed: http://www.bioethicsjournal.com [2005 April 19]. NRCBL: 2.1; 1.1; 7.1; 1.2.

Cheshire, William P., Jr. When eloquence is inarticulate. *Ethics and Medicine* 2006 Fall; 22(3): 135-138. NRCBL: 2.1; 1.1; 1.2. SC: an.

Dorff, Elliot N. "These and those are the words of the living God": Talmudic sound and fury in shaping national policy. *In:* Guinn, David E., ed. Handbook of Bioethics and Religion. New York: Oxford University Press, 2006: 143-168. NRCBL: 2.1; 1.2.

Döring, Ole. Moral development and education in medical ethics: an attempt at a Confucian aspiration. *In:* Döring, Ole; Chen, Renbiao, eds. Advances in Chinese Medical Ethics: Chinese and International Perspectives. Hamburg: Institut für Asienkunde; 2002: 178-194. NRCBL: 2.3; 1.2; 7.2. Note: Proceedings of the Second Sino-German Interdisciplinary Symposium about Medical Ethics in China, Shanghai, 19-23 October, 1999.

Evans, John H. Who legitimately speaks for religion in public bioethics? *In:* Guinn, David E., ed. Handbook of Bioethics and Religion. New York: Oxford University Press, 2006: 61-79. NRCBL: 2.1; 1.2.

Gotcher, Robert F. The theology of the body: some reflections on the significance for medical professionals. *Linacre Quarterly* 2006 May; 73(2): 115-131. NRCBL: 2.1; 1.2.

Guinan, Patrick F. Evaluating Catholic medical ethics books. *Linacre Quarterly* 2006 November; 73(4): 354-360. NRCBL: 2.1; 1.2.

Güner, Ahmet. A Book on Medical Ethics in Medieval Islam: Al-Tashwîk Al-Tibbî (Encouraging Medicine) of Abu'l-Alâ Sâid B. Al-Hasan Al-Tabîb (1009-1087 A.C.)

[book review]. *Eubios Journal of Asian and International Bioethics* 2006 January; 16(1): 6-9. NRCBL: 2.2; 1.2.

Haddad, Farid Sami. Arab medical ethics. *Studies in History of Medicine* 1982 June; 6: 122-136. NRCBL: 2.2; 7.1; 1.2; 21.7.

Hameed, Abdul. Medical ethics in medieval Islam. *Studies in Philosophy of Medicine* 1977 March; 1(1): 08-124. NRCBL: 2.2; 1.2.

Hart, Curtis W. Clinical pragmatism in bioethics: a pastoral approach. *Journal of Religion and Health* 2006 Summer; 45(2): 196-207. NRCBL: 2.1; 1.1; 1.2; 4.4. SC: cs. Identifiers: John Dewey.

Hauerwas, Stanley M. Anabaptist eyes on biotechnology. *In:* Miller, Roman J.; Brubaker, Beryl H.; Peterson, James C., eds. Viewing New Creations with Anabaptist Eyes: Ethics of Biotechnology. Telford, PA: Cascadia Pub.; 2005: 243-253. NRCBL: 2.1; 1.2; 5.1.

Hinkley, Aaron E. Christianity, the culture wars, and bioethics: current debates and controversies in the Christian approach to bioethics. *Christian Bioethics* 2006 December; 12(3): 229-235. NRCBL: 2.1; 1.2; 7.1.

Hollman, Jay; Kilner, John. Are Christian voices needed in public bioethics debates?: Care for persons with disabilities as a test case. *Ethics and Medicine* 2006 Fall; 22(3): 143-150. NRCBL: 2.1; 1.1; 1.2; 9.5.3; 9.5.1.

Jonsen, Albert R. A history of religion and bioethics. *In:* Guinn, David E., ed. Handbook of Bioethics and Religion. New York: Oxford University Press, 2006: 23-36. NRCBL: 2.2; 1.2.

Kaveny, M. Cathleen. Diversity and deliberation: bioethics commissions and moral reasoning. *Journal of Religious Ethics* 2006 June; 34(2): 311-337. NRCBL: 2.4; 1.3.9; 14.5; 18.5.4; 1.1; 1.2. SC: an. Identifiers: President's Council on Bioethics; NBAC.

Kaveny, M. Cathleen. The NBAC report on cloning: a case study in religion, public policy, and bioethics. *In:* Guinn, David E., ed. Handbook of Bioethics and Religion. New York: Oxford University Press, 2006: 221-251. NRCBL: 2.4; 1.2.

Khayat, M. Haytham. Research ethics: challenges in the eastern Mediterranean region. *Eastern Mediterranean Health Journal* 2006; 12(Supplement 1): S13-S20 [Online]. Accessed: http://www.emro.who.int/publications/EMHJ/12_S/PDF/3.pdf [2007 January 3]. NRCBL: 2.1; 1.2; 18.2; 18.6. Note: Abstract in French and Arabic.

Larijani, Bagher; Malek-Afzali, Hossein; Zahedi, Farzaneh; Motevaseli, Elaheh. Strengthening medical ethics by strategic planning in the Islamic Republic of Iran. *Developing World Bioethics* 2006 May; 6(2): 106-110. NRCBL: 2.1; 2.3; 1.2.

NRCBL: National Reference Center for Bioethics Literature Classification Scheme   See inside front cover for terms.

Abstract: To bring attention to medical ethics and to enhance the quality of health care in Iran, the Ministry of Health and Medical Education has introduced a strategic plan for medical ethics at a national level. This plan was developed through the organization and running of workshops in which experts addressed important areas related to medical ethics. They analysed strengths and weaknesses, opportunities and threats, and outlined a vision, a mission and specific goals and essential activities surrounding medical ethics. The current strategic plan has six main goals that will be reviewed in this paper. Some major activities that were carried out in recent years, and some future plans, will be also reviewed.

Larijani, B.; Zahedi, F.; Malek-Afzali, H. Medical ethics in the Islamic Republic of Iran. *Eastern Mediterranean Health Journal* 2005; 11(5 and 6): 1061-1072 [Online]. Accessed: http://www.emro.who.int/publications/emhj/1105_6/PDF/24.pdf [2007 January 4]. NRCBL: 2.1; 1.2; 2.2. Note: Abstract in French and Arabic.

Leavitt, Frank J. The international impact of Asian bioethics. *In:* Sang-yong, Song; Young-Mo, Koo; Macer, Darryl R.J., eds. Asian Bioethics in the 21st Century. Christchurch, NZ: Eubios Ethics Institute, 2002: 224-228. NRCBL: 2.1; 1.2. Conference: Proceedings of the Asian Bioethics Conference (ABC4), held 22-25 November 2002 in Seoul, South Korea.

Lebacqz, Karen. Philosophy, theology, and the claims of justice. *In:* Guinn, David E., ed. Handbook of Bioethics and Religion. New York: Oxford University Press, 2006: 253-263. NRCBL: 2.1; 1.1; 1.2.

Lysaught, M. Therese. And power corrupts . . . religion and the disciplinary matrix of bioethics. *In:* Guinn, David E., ed. Handbook of Bioethics and Religion. New York: Oxford University Press, 2006: 93-127. NRCBL: 2.1; 1.2.

McLaughlin, Chris. Ethics and spirituality are not synonyms [letter]. *Family Medicine* 2005 November-December; 37(10): 686. NRCBL: 2.1; 1.2.

Mellon, Brad F. James Drane's More Humane Medicine: a new foundation for twenty-first century bioethics? *Christian Bioethics* 2006 December; 12(3): 301-311. NRCBL: 2.1; 2.2; 1.2; 1.1.

Abstract: James Drane's More Humane Medicine: A Liberal Catholic Bioethics is an outstanding contribution to the study of bioethics in our day. Catholics and others who are interested in the issues discussed here will benefit from this masterful treatment. The author opens with a set of definitions, starting with what he means by a "more humane medicine." Drane contends that a more humane medicine has become necessary and desired, but not because the traditional medical ethic as "a self-declared and self-imposed ethic, outlining what noble service to others entails" is no longer valid. Rather he defines it as an advance on the traditional ethic; a "new foundation" based on a "lived set of obligations derived from a felt commitment to other persons . . . an ethics based on the relationship between doctors and patients and essentially an ethics of virtue." Drane's work is a "liberal Catholic Bioethics" in which he challenges his own faith tradition, the Roman Catholic Church, on such topics as sexuality, birth control, abortion, cloning, stem cell research, aging and dying, and euthanasia and physician-assisted

suicide. The present article is a critical essay that analyzes the author's statements and conclusions.

Miller, Roman J. Viewing bioethics through Anabaptist eyes. *In:* Miller, Roman J.; Brubaker, Beryl H.; Peterson, James C., eds. Viewing New Creations with Anabaptist Eyes: Ethics of Biotechnology. Telford, PA: Cascadia Pub.; 2005: 85-105. NRCBL: 2.1; 1.2.

Navot, Orit. A historical overview of the developing medical ethics culture in the new Jewish settlement in Israel during the years 1840-1914. *Eubios Journal of Asian and International Bioethics* 2003 March 13(2): 51-53. NRCBL: 2.2; 1.2.

Nelson, Leonard J., III. Catholic bioethics and the case of Terri Schiavo. *Cumberland Law Review* 2004-2005; 35(3): 543-574. NRCBL: 2.1; 1.2; 20.5.1. SC: le.

Overberg, Kenneth R. Medical ethics. *In his:* Conscience in Conflict: How to Make Moral Choices. 3rd ed. revised. Cincinnati, OH: St. Anthony Messenger Press; 2006: 79-108. NRCBL: 2.1; 1.2.

Por, Yu Kam. Respecting nature and using human intelligence: elements of a Confucian bioethics. *In:* Sleeboom, Margaret, ed. Genomics in Asia: A Clash of Bioethical Interests? New York: Kegan Paul; 2004: 159-177. NRCBL: 2.1; 1.2; 15.1.

Sachedina, Abdulaziz. "No harm, no harassment": major principles of health care in Islam. *In:* Guinn, David E., ed. Handbook of Bioethics and Religion. New York: Oxford University Press, 2006: 265-289. NRCBL: 2.1; 1.2.

Sgreccia, Elio. Bioethics centers and committees: cultural origins and current status. *Dolentium Hominum* 1994; 9(2): 50-60. NRCBL: 2.3; 2.2; 9.6; 2.1; 21.1; 1.2. SC: rv.

Smith, George P., II. Law, religion and medicine: conjunctive or disjunctive? *Macquarie Law Symposium* 2006: 9-39. NRCBL: 2.1; 1.2; 4.4; 15.4; 5.1. SC: le. Conference: Symposium: Law, Religion and Medical Science; Macquarie University, Sydney, Australia; 2006; Division of Law, Macquarie University.

Smolin, David M. Does bioethics provide answers?: Secular and religious bioethics and our procreative future. *Cumberland Law Review* 2004-2005; 35(3): 473-517. NRCBL: 2.1; 1.2; 4.4; 14.4; 15.2; 14.2.

Snyder, Graydon F. Bioethics: how will Anabaptists respond? *In:* Miller, Roman J.; Brubaker, Beryl H.; Peterson, James C., eds. Viewing New Creations with Anabaptist Eyes: Ethics of Biotechnology. Telford, PA: Cascadia Pub.; 2005: 218-228. NRCBL: 2.1; 1.2.

Tishchenko, P.D. Bioethics in Russia. *Journal International de Bioéthique = International Journal of Bioethics* 2005 September-December; 16(3-4): 67-70, 170. NRCBL: 2.1; 2.3; 7.2; 1.2; 9.3.1. Identifiers:

Meditsynskoye Pravoi Eticka = Medical Law and Ethics (journal); John Dewey.

Abstract: Ten years of development in Russian bioethics presents significant progress. At the beginning of the 90s bioethics was practically unknown for Russian medical doctors, philosophers and the public. Since the year 2000 bioethics has become an obligatory course for all medical students. The Russian Orthodox Church published the same year "The Social Doctrine" that included a special part "The Church and Problems of Bioethics." Different bioethical problems are often discussed in the mass media. The development of Russian bioethics proves the basic understanding of ethics presented by John Dewey—ethics is a function of the moral life of the community. Norms are good or bad mostly as instruments that could be used in everyday life to solve real problems people meet.

Tomasevic, Luka. Challenges of global bioethics and bio-technology. *Formosan Journal of Medical Humanities* 2006 June; 7(1-2): 39-55. NRCBL: 2.1; 21.7; 1.2; 1.1.

Vogel, Lawrence. Natural law Judaism?: The genesis of bioethics in Hans Jonas, Leo Strauss, and Leon Kass. *Hastings Center Report* 2006 May-June; 36(3): 32-44. NRCBL: 2.1; 1.2.

Walters, LeRoy B. Major events and publications related to the birth of bioethics, 1925-1975 with special attention to the Anglican contribution. *Anglican Theological Review* 1999 Fall; 81(4): 631-650. NRCBL: 2.2; 1.2. Conference: Presiding Bishop's Consultation on Bioethics, Washington, DC, June 8-9 1999, College of Preachers.

Washofsky, Mark. Halachah, aggadah, and Reform Jewish bioethics: a response. *CCAR Journal: A Reform Jewish Quarterly* 2006 Summer; 53(3): 81-106. NRCBL: 2.1; 1.2.

BIOETHICS COMMISSIONS *See* BIOETHICS AND MEDICAL ETHICS/ COMMISSIONS

BIOLOGICAL WARFARE *See* WAR AND TERRORISM

BIOMEDICAL RESEARCH
See also BEHAVIORAL RESEARCH; HUMAN EXPERIMENTATION; JOURNALISM AND PUBLISHING; NANOTECHNOLOGY

Is this the bionic man? [editorial]. *Nature* 2006 July 13; 442(7099): 109. NRCBL: 5.1; 17.1; 19.1; 22.2.

Allen, Ben L. Ethical Issues at the Interface Between Orthopedics and Bioengineering. *Journal of Investigative Surgery* 1992 July-September; 5(3): 191-199. NRCBL: 5.2; 1.3.4.

Arnhart, Larry. Biotech ethics. *In:* Mitcham, Carl, ed. Encyclopedia of Science, Technology, and Ethics. Farmington Hills, MI: Thomson/Gale, 2005: 227-232. NRCBL: 5.1; 1.1; 1.2; 2.2; 15.1.

Averill, Marilyn. Unintended consequences. *In:* Mitcham, Carl, ed. Encyclopedia of Science, Technology, and

Ethics. Farmington Hills, MI: Thomson/Gale, 2005: 1995-1999. NRCBL: 5.1.

Beam, Thomas E.; Howe, Edmund G. A look toward the future. *In:* Beam, Thomas E.; Sparacino, Linette R.; Pellegrino, Edmund D.; Hartle, Anthony E.; Howe, Edmund G., eds. Military Medical Ethics. Volume 2. Washington, DC: TMM Publications, Borden Institute, Walter Reed Army Medical Center; 2003: 831-850. NRCBL: 5.1; 9.7; 21.2; 18.5.8; 18.3; 1.3.5.

Bennett, Belinda. Rewriting the future? Biomedical advances and legal dilemmas. *Journal of Law and Medicine* 2006 February; 13(3): 295-303. NRCBL: 5.2.

Bessinger, C.D. Life-Systems Ethics and Physician-Engineer Interactions. *Journal of Investigative Surgery* 1992 July-September; 5(3): 185-190. NRCBL: 5.2; 2.2; 1.3.4.

Bhardwaj, Minakshi. Developing countries participation in the global governance of biotechnology. *In:* Sang-yong, Song; Young-Mo, Koo; Macer, Darryl R.J., eds. Asian Bioethics in the 21st Century. Christchurch, NZ: Eubios Ethics Institute, 2002: 197-205. NRCBL: 5.1; 15.1; 21.1. Conference: Proceedings of the Asian Bioethics Conference (ABC4), held 2002 November 22-25 in Seoul, South Korea.

Birch, Kean. Introduction: biofutures / biopresents. *Science as Culture* 2006 September; 15(3): 173-181. NRCBL: 5.1; 5.3.

Birke, Lynda; Whitworth, Rosalind. Seeking knowledge: women, science, and Islam. *Women's Studies International Forum* 1998 March-April; 21(2): 147-159. NRCBL: 5.1; 1.3.3; 1.3.9; 1.2; 15.1; 10. SC: em. Identifiers: United Kingdom (Great Britain).

Bugliarello, George. Bioengineering ethics. *In:* Mitcham, Carl, ed. Encyclopedia of Science, Technology, and Ethics. Farmington Hills, MI: Thomson/Gale, 2005: 190-193. NRCBL: 5.1; 1.3.4; 1.3.9.

Butter, Irene H. Premature adoption and routinization of medical technology: illustrations from childbirth technology. *Journal of Social Issues* 1993 Summer; 49(2): 11-34. NRCBL: 5.2; 9.5.7; 4.1.

Calnan, Michael; Montaner, David; Horne, Rob. How acceptable are innovative health-care technologies? A survey of public beliefs and attitudes in England and Wales. *Social Science and Medicine* 2005 May; 60(9): 1937-1948. NRCBL: 5.1; 14.1; 15.1. SC: em.

Clark, Annette E. Ethics [ethics squared]: the ethics of bioethics in the biotechnology industry. *Seattle Journal for Social Justice* 2004 Fall-Winter; 3(1): 311-344. NRCBL: 5.1; 18.5.4; 15.1.

Clark, Graeme. Socioeconomics and ethics. *In:* Clark, Graeme, ed. Cochlear Implants: Fundamentals and Appli-

NRCBL: National Reference Center for Bioethics Literature Classification Scheme   See inside front cover for terms.

77

cations. New York: Springer; 2003: 767-786. NRCBL: 5.2; 4.2; 9.7; 21.7.

de Castro, Leonardo D.; Alvarez, Allen A. Playing God. *In:* Sang-yong, Song; Young-Mo, Koo; Macer, Darryl R.J., eds. Asian Bioethics in the 21st Century. Christchurch, NZ: Eubios Ethics Institute, 2002: 206-213. NRCBL: 5.1; 1.2; 2.1; 15.1. Conference: Proceedings of the Asian Bioethics Conference (ABC4), held 2002 November 22-25 in Seoul, South Korea.

Fielder, John. The Bioengineer's obligations to patients. *Journal of Investigative Surgery* 1992 July-September; 5(3): 201-208. NRCBL: 5.2; 1.3.4.

Fouché, Rayvon. Race. *In:* Mitcham, Carl, ed. Encyclopedia of Science, Technology, and Ethics. Farmington Hills, MI: Thomson/Gale, 2005: 1561-1565. NRCBL: 5.1; 15.11.

France. Comité consultatif national d'éthique pour les sciences de la vie et de la santé. Orientation de travailleurs vers un poste comportant un risque. Rôle du médicin du travail et réflexions sur l'ambiguïté du concept d'aptitude. *Journal International de Bioéthique = International Journal of Bioethics* 2005 September-December; 16(3-4): 154-160. NRCBL: 5.2; 5.3; 16.3. Identifiers: France.

Fredriksen, S. Tragedy, utopia and medical progress. *Journal of Medical Ethics* 2006 August; 32(8): 450-453. NRCBL: 5.1; 9.5.7. SC: an.

Abstract: In this article, tragedy and utopia are juxtaposed, and it is proposed that the problem of "medicalisation" is better understood in a framework of tragedy than in a utopian one. In utopia, it is presupposed that there is an error behind every setback and every side effect, whereas tragedy brings to light how side effects can be the result of irreconcilable conflicts. Medicalisation is to some extent the result of such a tragic conflict. We are given power by medical progress, but are also confronted with our fallibility, thus provoking insecurity. This situation is illustrated by the sudden infant death syndrome (SIDS). Recent epidemiological investigations have shown that infants sleeping in a prone position have a 15-20 times higher risk of dying from SIDS than infants sleeping in a supine position. A simple means of preventing infant death is suggested by this discovery, but insecurity is also created. What else has been overlooked? Perhaps a draught, or wet diapers, or clothes of wool are just as dangerous as sleeping prone? Further investigations and precautions will be needed, but medicalisation prevails.

Frewer, Lynn J.; Miles, Susan; Brennan, Mary; Kuznesof, Sharon; Ness, Mitchell; Ritson, Christopher. Public preferences for informed choice under conditions of risk uncertainty. *Public Understanding of Science* 2002 October; 11(4): 363-372. NRCBL: 5.2; 5.3; 1.3.11; 15.1; 22.3; 7.1. SC: em.

Halvorsen, Juris Marit. The use of biotechnology in medicine with particular regard to questions for family law. *In:* Meulders-Klein, Marie-Thérèse; Deech, Ruth; Vlaardingerbroek, Paul, eds. Biomedicine, the Family and

Human Rights. New York: Kluwer Law International, 2002: 459-475. NRCBL: 5.1. SC: le.

Hofmann, Bjørn; Solbakk, Jan Helge; Holm, Søren. Analogical reasoning in handling emerging technologies: the case of umbilical cord blood biobanking. *American Journal of Bioethics* 2006 November-December; 6(6): 49-57. NRCBL: 5.1; 19.4; 19.5.

Holland, Suzanne. It's not what we say, exactly. . .or is it? *American Journal of Bioethics* 2006 November-December; 6(6): 65-66; author reply W13-W14. NRCBL: 5.1; 2.1; 19.5; 19.4. Comments: Bjørn Hofmann, Jan Helge Solbakk, and Søren Holm. Analogical reasoning in handling emerging technologies: the case of umbilical cord blood biobanking. American Journal of Bioethics 2006 November-December; 6(6): 49-57.

Ikenberg, Hans; Obwegeser, Jörg; Schneider, Volker. Who controls the controllers? [letter and reply]. *Lancet* 2006 August 12-18; 368(9535): 578-579. NRCBL: 5.2; 5.3; 1.3.9.

Inaba, Maskazu; Macer, Darryl R.J. Japanese views of medical biotechnology. *In:* Sang-yong, Song; Young-Mo, Koo; Macer, Darryl R.J., eds. Asian Bioethics in the 21st Century. Christchurch, NZ: Eubios Ethics Institute, 2002: 178-196. NRCBL: 5.1. SC: em. Conference: Proceedings of the Asian Bioethics Conference (ABC4), held 22-25 November 2002 in Seoul, South Korea.

Johnson, Summer; Burger, Ingrid. Limitations and justifications for analogical reasoning. *American Journal of Bioethics* 2006 November-December; 6(6): 59-61; author reply W13-W14. NRCBL: 5.1; 2.1. Comments: Bjørn Hofmann, Jan Helge Solbakk, and Søren Holm. Analogical reasoning in handling emerging technologies: the case of umbilical cord blood biobanking. American Journal of Bioethics 2006 November-December; 6(6): 49-57.

Jones, Andrew G. Profound hypotension: ethical considerations. *Hospital Medicine* 2002 February; 63(2): 92-94. NRCBL: 5.2. SC: le.

Jost, Timothy S. Biotechnology and public policy: an Anabaptist response. *In:* Miller, Roman J.; Brubaker, Beryl H.; Peterson, James C., eds. Viewing New Creations with Anabaptist Eyes: Ethics of Biotechnology. Telford, PA: Cascadia Pub.; 2005: 213-217. NRCBL: 5.1; 9.2; 9.3.1; 9.7; 1.2.

Juengst, Eric T. Developing and delivering new medical technologies: issues beyond access. *Journal of Social Issues* 1993 Summer; 49(2): 201-210. NRCBL: 5.2; 9.4. SC: em.

Kapp, Marshall B. Life-sustaining technologies: value issues. *Journal of Social Issues* 1993 Summer; 49(2): 151-167. NRCBL: 5.2; 9.4.

Keiper, Adam. The age of neuroelectronics. *New Atlantis* 2006 Winter; 11: 4-41. NRCBL: 5.1; 4.4.

Kitcher, Philip; Cartwright, Nancy. Science and ethics: reclaiming some neglected questions. *Perspectives on Science* 1996 Summer; 4(2): 145-153. NRCBL: 5.1; 15.10.

Kotva, Joseph J. Facing biotechnology as an alternative community of worship, character, and discernment. *In:* Miller, Roman J.; Brubaker, Beryl H.; Peterson, James C., eds. Viewing New Creations with Anabaptist Eyes: Ethics of Biotechnology. Telford, PA: Cascadia Pub.; 2005: 261-289. NRCBL: 5.1; 1.2; 15.1.

Leavitt, Sarah A. National Institutes of Health. *In:* Mitcham, Carl, ed. Encyclopedia of Science, Technology, and Ethics. Farmington Hills, MI: Thomson/Gale, 2005: 1271-1274. NRCBL: 5.1; 2.2; 18.1.

Levin, Alex V. The ethics of surgical innovation: more than one answer? = L'éthique de l'innovation chirurgicale: plus qu'une simple réponse? [editorial]. *Canadian Journal of Ophthalmology* 2005 December; 40(6): 685-688. NRCBL: 5.2. Note: Complete text in English and French.

Lichty, Peter D. Human subjects risk in new nanotechnologies? *Protecting Human Subjects* 2006 Spring; (13): 1-4. NRCBL: 5.2; 4.4.

Long, Clarissa. The future of biotechnology: promises and problems. *American Enterprise* 1998 September-October; 9(5): 55-57. NRCBL: 5.1; 15.1.

López, José J. Mapping metaphors and analogies. *American Journal of Bioethics* 2006 November-December; 6(6): 61-63; author reply W13-W14. NRCBL: 5.1; 19.5; 2.1. Comments: Bjørn Hofmann, Jan Helge Solbakk, and Søren Holm. Analogical reasoning in handling emerging technologies: the case of umbilical cord blood biobanking. American Journal of Bioethics 2006 November-December; 6(6): 49-57.

Manickavel, V. Family: another dinosaur? The market driven technological fix: is there a place for family? *In:* Sang-yong, Song; Young-Mo, Koo; Macer, Darryl R.J., eds. Asian Bioethics in the 21st Century. Christchurch, NZ: Eubios Ethics Institute, 2002: 282-86. NRCBL: 5.1. Conference: Proceedings of the Asian Bioethics Conference (ABC4), held 22-25 November 2002 in Seoul, South Korea.

Maoz, Arieh. Tampering with nature: an "unended quest". *Eubios Journal of Asian and International Bioethics* 2006 September; 16(5): 140-144. NRCBL: 5.1; 16.1; 1.3.11; 1.3.3; 15.1.

Maynard, Andrew D.; Aitken, Robert J.; Butz, Tilman; Colvin, Vicki; Donaldson, Ken; Oberdörster, Günter; Philbert, Martin A.; Ryan, John; Seaton, Anthony; Stone, Vicki; Tinkle, Sally S.; Tran, Lang; Walker, Nigel J.; Warheit, David B. Safe handling of nanotechnology [commentary]. *Nature* 2006 November 16; 444(7117): 267-269. NRCBL: 5.1.

Mepham, Ben. Politics and the biosciences. *In his:* Bioethics: An Introduction for the Biosciences. Oxford; New York: Oxford University Press; 2005: 331-355. NRCBL: 5.1; 5.2.

Mepham, Ben. Risk, precaution and trust. *In his:* Bioethics: An Introduction for the Biosciences. Oxford; New York: Oxford University Press; 2005: 309-330. NRCBL: 5.2; 16.1.

Navarrete C.; Victoria Eugenia. Bioética y biotecnología = Bioethics and biotechnology. *Revista Latinoamericana de Bioética* 2003 January; (4): 100-125. NRCBL: 5.2; 15.1; 4.4. Conference: Second International Congress the Ethics of Scientific Research: Bioethics and Genetic Manipulation; Nueva Granada Military University; Bogota, Columbia.

Nguyen, Vinh-Kim. Antiretroviral globalism, biopolitics, and therapeutic citizenship. *In:* Ong, Aihwa; Collier, Stephen J., eds. Global Assemblages: Technology, Politics, and Ethics as Anthropological Problems. Malden, MA: Blackwell Pub.; 2005: 124-144. NRCBL: 5.1; 9.1; 9.5.6; 9.7; 21.1.

Pálsson, Gísli; Rabinow, Paul. The Iceland controversy: reflections on the transnational market of civic virtue. *In:* Ong, Aihwa; Collier, Stephen J., eds. Global Assemblages: Technology, Politics, and Ethics as Anthropological Problems. Malden, MA: Blackwell Pub.; 2005: 91-103. NRCBL: 5.1; 15.10; 1.3.12; 13.1; 9.3.1; 21.1; 18.3.

Piehler, Henry R. Innovation and change in medical technology: interactions between physicians and engineers. *Journal of Investigative Surgery* 1992 July-September; 5(3): 179-184. NRCBL: 5.2; 1.3.4.

Plows, Alexandra; Boddington, Paula. Troubles with biocitizenship? *Genomics, Society and Policy* 2006 December; 2(3): 115-135. NRCBL: 5.1; 15.1. SC: an.
Abstract: Genetic and other biotechnologies are starting to impact significantly upon society and individuals within it. Rose and Novas draw on an analysis of many patient groups to sketch out the broad notion of biocitizenship as a device for describing how the empowered and informed individual, group or network can engage with bioscience. In this paper, we examine critically the notion of biocitizenship, drawing on both sociological fieldwork that grounds the debate in the views of a large and varied group of concerned actors. Using work within green politics, we identify shortcomings in the concept of biocitizenship as it has so far been explicated. The value assumptions lying behind an account of biocitizenship, and its tendency to see issues through a reductive lens, are examined. Alternative views of values and goals, which may undermine any alleged rights and duties, are explored using interviews and other ethnographic data that illustrates the complexity of the terrain. The reductive lens of biocitizenship is explored through contrast with the wider scope of concerns emanating from various sources, including many within green politics. If such complexities are not recognised, there is a danger that a concept of biocitizenship may serve to create and amplify inequalities. Problems with

---

NRCBL: National Reference Center for Bioethics Literature Classification Scheme   See inside front cover for terms.

79

identity issues are key: the construction of identity is complex and many groups are explicitly rejecting the 'biological' label. We discuss the multiple relations of citizens with the biotech and pharmaceutical industries. Arguably, existing inequalities in power relationships, exploitation, commodification and ownership patterns are being perpetuated in novel ways through the new biosciences. We pose the question of whether it is possible to construct a concept of biocitizenship that overcomes these problems.

Resnik, David B. Biomedical research in the developing world: ethical issues and dilemmas. *In:* Iltis, Ana Smith, ed. Research Ethics. New York: Routledge, 2006: 132-146. NRCBL: 5.1; 21.1.

Scheitle, Christopher P. In God we trust: religion and optimism toward biotechnology. *Social Science Quarterly* 2005 December; 86(4): 846-856. NRCBL: 5.1; 1.2; 15.1. SC: em.

Sheth, S.S.; Malpani, A.N. Inappropriate use of new technology: impact on women's health. *International Journal of Gynecology and Obstetrics* 1997 July; 58(1): 159-165. NRCBL: 5.1; 9.5.5.

Siegrist, Michael. The influence of trust and perceptions of risks and benefits on the acceptance of gene technology. *Risk Analysis* 2000 April; 20(2): 195-203. NRCBL: 5.2; 15.1; 5.1; 10. SC: em. Identifiers: Switzerland.

Stoerger, Sharon. Sociological ethics. *In:* Mitcham, Carl, ed. Encyclopedia of Science, Technology, and Ethics. Farmington Hills, MI: Thomson/Gale, 2005: 1823-1827. NRCBL: 5.1.

ten Have, Henk. Retos éticos de la nueva biotecnología = Ethical challenges of the new biotechnology. *Revista Latinoamericana de Bioética* 2003 January; (4): 56-79. NRCBL: 5.2; 15.1; 4.2. Conference: Second International Congress the Ethics of Scientific Research: Bioethics and Genetic Manipulation; Nueva Granada Military University; Bogota, Columbia.

Vesilind, P. Aarne. Medicine, technology, and ethics: a historical perspective. *Journal of Investigative Surgery* 1992 July-September; 5(3): 171-178. NRCBL: 5.2; 2.2; 1.3.4.

Werntoft, Elisabet; Edberg, Anna-Karin; Rooke, Liselotte; Hermeren, Goran; Elmstahl, Solve; Hallberg, Ingalill Rahm. Older people's views of prioritization in health care. The applicability of an interview study. *Journal of Clinical Nursing* 2005 September; 14(8B): 64-74. NRCBL: 5.1; 9.5.2; 9.4. SC: em.

Winner, Langdon. Are humans obsolete? *Hedgehog Review* 2002 Fall; 4(3): 25-44 [Online]. Accessed: http://etext.lib.virginia.edu/etcbin/toccer-hh?id= WinObso4-3.xml&images=images/ modeng&data= /texts/english/modeng/parsed&tag=public∂=all [29 January 2007]. NRCBL: 5.1; 1.1; 4.4; 15.1.

Wolpert, Lewis. The Medawar Lecture 1998: is science dangerous? *Philosophical Transactions of the Royal Society of London. Series B, Biological Sciences* 2005 June 29; 360(1458): 1253-1258. NRCBL: 5.1; 15.5; 1.3.9; 5.3.

BIOMEDICAL RESEARCH/ RESEARCH ETHICS AND SCIENTIFIC MISCONDUCT
See also MALPRACTICE AND PROFESSIONAL MISCONDUCT

A universal code of ethics falls badly short [editorial]. *Lancet* 2006 January 14-20; 367(9505): 86. NRCBL: 1.3.9; 1.3.1; 6.

Are journals doing enough to prevent fraudulent publication? [editorial]. *CMAJ/JAMC: Canadian Medical Association Journal* 2006 February 14; 174(4): 431. NRCBL: 1.3.9; 1.3.7.

Beautification and fraud [editorial]. *Nature Cell Biology* 2006 February; 8(2): 101-102. NRCBL: 1.3.9; 14.5.

Conflict between the law and ethics while researching. *Indian Journal of Medical Ethics* 2006 April-June; 3(2): 69. NRCBL: 1.3.9; 8.32; 8.3.4; 7.3; 8.4; 7.4; 12.4.2; 11.2. SC: le; cs.

Dealing with disclosure [editorial]. *Nature Medicine* 2006 September; 12(9): 979. NRCBL: 1.3.9; 1.3.7; 9.3.1.

Do researchers learn to practice misbehavior? [letter]. *Hastings Center Report* 2006 March-April; 36(2): 4. NRCBL: 1.3.9; 2.3.

Ethics and fraud [editorial]. *Nature* 2006 January 12; 439(7073): 117-118. NRCBL: 1.3.9. Identifiers: Woo Suk Hwang.

Finding fraud in China [editorial]. *Nature* 2006 June 1; 441(7093): 549-550. NRCBL: 1.3.9.

Japan's research conduct [editorial]. *Nature* 2006 February 9; 439(7077): 634. NRCBL: 1.3.9.

Writing a new ending for a story of scientific fraud [editorial]. *Lancet* 2006 January 7-13; 367(9504): 1. NRCBL: 1.3.9; 18.6. SC: le.

Abramson, John; Starfield, Barbara. The effect of conflict of interest on biomedical research and clinical practice guidelines: can we trust the evidence in evidence-based medicine? *Journal of the American Board of Family Practice* 2005 September-October; 18(5): 414-418. NRCBL: 1.3.9; 7.3; 9.7; 1.3.2; 1.3.7.

Aldhous, Peter. Hwang's forgotten crime: the exploitation of women is a far worse offence than data fabrication. *New Scientist* 2006 February 4-10; 189(2537): 22. NRCBL: 1.3.9; 19.5; 14.4; 14.6; 18.5.4; 15.1. Identifiers: Korea.

Al-Marzouki, Sanaa; Roberts, Ian; Marshall, Tom; Evans, Stephen. The effect of scientific misconduct on the results of clinical trials: a Delphi survey. *Contemporary Clinical Trials* 2005 June; 26(3): 331-337. NRCBL: 1.3.9; 18.2. SC: em.

American Medical Association [AMA]. Council on Ethical and Judicial Affairs; Green, Shane K.; Taub, Sara; Morin, Karine; Higginson, Daniel. Guidelines to prevent malevolent use of biomedical research. *CQ: Cambridge Quarterly of Healthcare Ethics* 2006 Fall; 15(4): 432-447. NRCBL: 1.3.9; 5.3; 6.

American Society of Clinical Oncology [ASCO]. American Society Of Clinical Oncology: revised conflict of interest policy. *Journal of Clinical Oncology* 2006 January 20; 24(3): 519-521. NRCBL: 1.3.9; 7.3; 9.3.1; 6.

American Society of Clinical Oncology [ASCO]. Revisions of and clarifications to the ASCO conflict of interest policy. *Journal of Clinical Oncology* 2006 January 20; 24(3): 517-518. NRCBL: 1.3.9; 7.3; 6.

Anderson, Rebecca. The singular moral compass of Otto Krayer. *Molecular Interventions* 2005 December; 5(6): 324-329. NRCBL: 1.3.9; 1.1; 21.1; 21.7; 22.2; 21.4.

Armstrong, David. Financial ties to industry cloud major depression study; at issue: whether it's safe for pregnant women to stay on medication; JAMA asks authors to explain. *Wall Street Journal* 2006 July 11; p. A1, A9. NRCBL: 1.3.9; 17.4; 9.7; 9.3.1. SC: po. Identifiers: Journal of the American Medical Association.

Assael, Leon A. Lies: the cruelty of scientific and clinical dishonesty [editorial]. *Journal of Oral and Maxillofacial Surgery* 2006 April; 64(4): 569-570. NRCBL: 1.3.9; 1.3.7.

Ausman, James I. Corruption in medicine. *Surgical Neurology* 2005 October; 64(4): 375-376. NRCBL: 1.3.9; 7.3.

Avorn, Jerry. Dangerous deception — hiding the evidence of adverse drug effects. *New England Journal of Medicine* 2006 November 23; 355(21): 2169-2171. NRCBL: 1.3.9; 9.7; 18.2.

Bastable, Ruth; Bateman, Hilarie; Hibble, Arthur; Wells, Christina. Developing an educational curriculum in primary care with practitioner and manager involvement: the governance shackle. *Medical Teacher* 2005 March; 27(2): 127-129. NRCBL: 1.3.9; 7.2.

Bastian, Hilda. Non-peer review: consumer involvement in research review. *In:* Godlee, Fiona; Jefferson, Tom, eds. Peer Review in Health Sciences. 2nd ed. London: BMJ Books; 2003: 248-262. NRCBL: 1.3.9; 1.3.7.

Bedward, Julie; Davison, Ian; Field, Stephen; Thomas, Hywel. Audit, educational development and research: what counts for ethics and research governance? *Medical Teacher* 2005 March; 27(2): 99-101. NRCBL: 1.3.9; 7.2.

Berenson, Alex. Disparity emerges in Lilly data on schizophrenia drug. *New York Times* 2006 December 21; p. C1, C5. NRCBL: 1.3.7; 9.7; 7.1. Identifiers: Zyprexa.

Bevan, David. The changing face of scientific misconduct. *Clinical and Investigative Medicine* 2004 June; 27(3): 117-119. NRCBL: 1.3.9; 1.3.7.

Bird, Stephanie. Misconduct in science. *In:* Mitcham, Carl, ed. Encyclopedia of Science, Technology, and Ethics. Farmington Hills, MI: Thomson/Gale, 2005: 1205-1207. NRCBL: 1.3.9.

Bird, Stephanie J. Research ethics, research integrity and the responsible conduct of research [editorial]. *Science and Engineering Ethics* 2006 July; 12(3): 411-412. NRCBL: 1.3.9.

Bird, Stephanie J. Responsible conduct of research. *In:* Mitcham, Carl, ed. Encyclopedia of Science, Technology, and Ethics. Farmington Hills, MI: Thomson/Gale, 2005: 1624-1625. NRCBL: 1.3.9.

Bird, Stephanie J.; Briggle, Adam. Research ethics: an overview. *In:* Mitcham, Carl, ed. Encyclopedia of Science, Technology, and Ethics. Farmington Hills, MI: Thomson/Gale, 2005: 1599-1607. NRCBL: 1.3.9; 5.3; 18.6.

Bolognesi, Natasha. University shuts down virologist's work on questionable AIDS drug [news]. *Nature Medicine* 2006 September; 12(9): 982. NRCBL: 1.3.9; 9.5.6. Identifiers: University of Cape Town; South Africa; Girish Kotwal.

Bradley, S. Gaylen. Managing competing interests. *In:* Macrina, Francis L., ed. Scientific Integrity: Text and Cases in Responsible Conduct of Research. 3rd ed. Washington, DC: ASM Press; 2005: 159-185. NRCBL: 1.3.9.

Brainard, Jeffrey. Universities experiment with classes in scientific ethics. *Chronicle of Higher Education* 2006 November 10; 53(12): A22-A23. NRCBL: 1.3.9; 1.3.3.

Brender, Alan. A nation's pride turns to shame. *Chronicle of Higher Education* 2006 January 6; 52(18): A27-A29. NRCBL: 1.3.9; 18.5.4; 14.5; 15.1. Identifiers: South Korea.

Brettingham, Madeleine. Roche denies claims it sacked employee for "whistle blowing" [news]. *BMJ: British Medical Journal* 2006 May 20; 332(7551): 1175. NRCBL: 1.3.9; 1.3.2; 9.7.

Budd, John M.; Sievert, MaryEllen; Scoville, Tom R.; Scoville, Caryn. Effects of article retraction on citation and practice in medicine. *Bulletin of the Medical Library Association* 1999 October; 87(4): 437-443. NRCBL: 1.3.9; 1.3.7. SC: rv.

Budinger, Thomas F.; Budinger, Miriam D. Ethics of scientific research. *In their:* Ethics of Emerging Technolo-

---

NRCBL: National Reference Center for Bioethics Literature Classification Scheme   See inside front cover for terms.

81

gies: Scientific Facts and Moral Challenges. Hoboken, NJ: John Wiley and Sons; 2006: 39-80. NRCBL: 1.3.9.

Burgin, Eileen. Dollars, disease, and democracy: has the Director's Council of Public Representatives improved the National Institutes of Health? *Politics and the Life Sciences* 2005 March-September; 24(1-2): 43-63. NRCBL: 1.3.9; 9.3.1; 18.1; 18.6. SC: em.

Campbell, Eric G.; Weissman, Joel S.; Vogeli, Christine; Clarridge, Brian R.; Abraham, Melissa; Marder, Jessica E.; Koski, Greg. Financial relationships between institutional review board members and industry. *New England Journal of Medicine* 2006 November 30; 355(22): 2321-2329. NRCBL: 1.3.9; 18.2; 9.7; 9.3.1. SC: em.
Abstract: BACKGROUND: Little is known about the nature, extent, and consequences of financial relationships between industry and institutional review board (IRB) members in academic institutions. We surveyed IRB members about such relationships. METHODS: We surveyed a random sample of 893 IRB members at 100 academic institutions (response rate, 67.2%). The questionnaire focused on the financial relationships that the members had with industry (e.g., employment, membership on boards, consulting, receipt of royalties, and paid speaking). RESULTS: We found that 36% of IRB members had had at least one relationship with industry in the past year. Of the respondents, 85.5% said they never thought that the relationships that another IRB member had with industry affected his or her IRB-related decisions in an inappropriate way, 11.9% said they thought this occurred rarely, 2.4% thought it occurred sometimes, and 0.2% thought it occurred often. Seventy-eight respondents(15.1%) reported that at least one protocol came before their IRB during the previous year that was sponsored either by a company with which they had a relationship or by a competitor of that company, both of which could be considered conflicts of interest. Of these 78 members (62 voting members and 16 nonvoting members), 57.7% reported that they always disclosed the relationship to an IRB official, 7.7% said they sometimes did, 11.5% said they rarely did, and 23.1% said they never did. Of the 62 voting members who reported conflicts, 64.5% reported that they never voted on the protocol, 4.8% said they rarely did, 11.3% said they sometimes did, and 19.4% said they always did. Most respondents reported that the views of IRB members who had experience working with industry were beneficial in reviewing industry-sponsored protocols. CONCLUSIONS: Relationships between IRB members and industry are common, and members sometimes participate in decisions about protocols sponsored by companies with which they have a financial relationship. Current regulations and policies should be examined to be sure that there is an appropriate way to handle conflicts of interest stemming from relationships with industry. Copyright 2006 Massachusetts Medical Society.

Caplan, Arthur L. No method, thus madness? *Hastings Center Report* 2006 March-April; 36(2): 12-13. NRCBL: 1.3.9; 21.1.

Carlin, Farr A.; Caplan, Arthur L. Talking through your epistemological hat [letter and reply]. *Hastings Center Report* 2006 July-August; 36(4): 7-8. NRCBL: 1.3.9; 21.1.

Carr, A.J. Which research is to be believed? The ethics of industrial funding of orthopaedic research [editorial]. *Journal of Bone and Joint Surgery. British Volume* 2005

November; 87-B(11): 1452-1453. NRCBL: 1.3.9; 5.3; 7.3; 9.3.1.

Chalmers, Iain. Preventing scientific misconduct. *Lancet* 2006 August 5-11; 368(9534): 450. NRCBL: 1.3.9.

Chalmers, Iain. Role of systematic reviews in detecting plagiarism: case of Asim Kurjak. *BMJ: British Medical Journal* 2006 September 16; 333(7568): 594-596. NRCBL: 1.3.9; 1.3.7; 1.3.3.

Chapman, Simon. Research from tobacco industry affiliated authors: need for particular vigilance [editorial]. *Tobacco Control* 2005 August; 14(4): 217-219. NRCBL: 1.3.9; 1.3.7; 9.5.9.

Charo, R. Alta. Fear and the First Amendment. *Hastings Center Report* 2006 September-October; 36(5): 12-13. NRCBL: 1.3.9; 1.2; 5.3.

Cherry, Mark J. Financial conflicts of interest and the human passion to innovate. *In:* Iltis, Ana Smith, ed. Research Ethics. New York: Routledge, 2006: 147-164. NRCBL: 1.3.9.

Cho, Mildred K.; McGee, Glenn; Magnus, David. Lessons of the stem cell scandal. *Science* 2006 February 3; 311(5761): 614-615. NRCBL: 1.3.9; 1.3.7.

Chong, Sei. Investigations document still more problems for stem cell researchers [news]. *Science* 2006 February 10; 311(5762): 754-755. NRCBL: 1.3.9; 18.5.4; 1.3.7. Identifiers: Korea; Woo Suk Hwang.

Chong, Sei; Normile, Dennis. How young Korean researchers helped unearth a scandal. . . [news]. *Science* 2006 January 6; 311(5757): 22-23, 25. NRCBL: 1.3.9; 18.5.4; 15.1.

Clarke, Mickey; McCartney, Denise A.; Siegel, Barry A. Regulatory oversight. *In:* Schuster, Daniel P.; Powers, William J., eds. Translational and Experimental Clinical Research. Philadelphia, PA: Lippincott Williams and Wilkins; 2005: 176-188. NRCBL: 1.3.9; 18.2. SC: le.

Cola, Philip A.; Cottington, Eric M. Responsible conduct of research. *In:* Fedor, Carol A.; Cola, Philip A.; Pierre, Christine, eds. Responsible Research: A Guide for Coordinators. London; Chicago, IL: Remedics; 2006: 49-64. NRCBL: 1.3.9; 1.3.7.

Cole, Andrew. UK launches panel to tackle research misconduct [news]. *BMJ: British Medical Journal* 2006 April 15; 332(7546): 871. NRCBL: 1.3.9; 2.4.

Colman, Alan. Everyone listed on Dolly paper met established criteria for authorship. *Nature* 2006 April 27; 440(7088): 1112. NRCBL: 1.3.9; 14.5. Identifiers: Ian Wilmut.

Consoli, Luca. Scientific misconduct and science ethics: a case study based approach. *Science and Engineering Eth-*

ics 2006 July; 12(3): 533-541. NRCBL: 1.3.9; 5.1. Identifiers: endrikschön.

Cooper, Richelle J.; Gupta, Malkeet; Wilkes, Michael S.; Hoffman, Jerome R. Conflict of interest disclosure policies and practices in peer-reviewed biomedical journals. *JGIM: Journal of General Internal Medicine* 2006 December; 21(12): 1248-1252. NRCBL: 1.3.9; 1.3.7. SC: em.

Couzin, Jennifer. Breakdown of the year: scientific fraud. *Science* 2006 December 22; 314(5807): 1853. NRCBL: 1.3.9; 18.5.4; 15.1.

Couzin, Jennifer. Fake data, but could the idea still be right? *Science* 2006 July 14; 313(5784): 154. NRCBL: 1.3.9.

Couzin, Jennifer. Truth and consequences. *Science* 2006 September 1; 313(5791): 1222-1226. NRCBL: 1.3.9; 1.3.3.

Couzin, Jennifer. . . .And how the problems eluded peer reviewers and editors [news]. *Science* 2006 January 6; 311(5757): 23-24. NRCBL: 1.3.9; 1.3.7; 18.5.4; 15.1.

Couzin, Jennifer; Schirber, Michael. Fraud upends oral cancer field, casting doubt on prevention trial [news]. *Science* 2006 January 27; 311(5760): 448-449. NRCBL: 1.3.9; 1.3.5; 1.3.7.

Couzin, Jennifer; Unger, Katherine. Cleaning up the paper trail [news]. *Science* 2006 April 7; 312(5770): 38-43. NRCBL: 1.3.9; 1.3.7.

Cowell, Henry R. Ethical responsibilities of editors, reviewers, and authors. *Clinical Orthopaedics and Related Research* 2000 September; (378): 83-89. NRCBL: 1.3.9; 1.3.7.

Cyranoski, David. Hwang takes the stand at fraud trial [news]. *Nature* 2006 November 2; 444(7115): 12. NRCBL: 1.3.9; 18.5.4; 15.1; 19.1. Identifiers: Woo Suk Hwang; South Korea.

Cyranoski, David. Named and shamed [news]. *Nature* 2006 May 25; 441(7092): 392-393. NRCBL: 1.3.9. Identifiers: China.

Cyranoski, David. Verdict: Hwang's human stem cells were all fakes [news]. *Nature* 2006 January 12; 439(7073): 122-123. NRCBL: 1.3.9; 14.5; 18.5.4; 15.1; 19.1.

Dahlberg, John E.; Mahler, Christian C. The Poehlman case: running away from the truth. *Science and Engineering Ethics* 2006 January; 12(1): 157-173. NRCBL: 1.3.9. SC: cs; em.

Danish Committee on Scientific Dishonesty. Case of plagiarism: work originating from Denmark, translated into Polish and published in a Polish Journal. Four Polish scientists guilty of scientific dishonesty. *Danish Medical Bulletin* 1996 September; 43(4): 367. NRCBL: 1.3.9.

Dauphinee, W. Dale; Frecker, Richard C. Routinely collected educational data: challenges to ethics and to privacy. *Medical Education* 2005 September; 39(9): 877-879. NRCBL: 1.3.9; 1.3.3; 8.4.

Davis, Michael. Conflict of interest. *In:* Mitcham, Carl, ed. Encyclopedia of Science, Technology, and Ethics. Farmington Hills, MI: Thomson/Gale, 2005: 402-404. NRCBL: 1.3.9.

De Vries, Raymond; Anderson, Melissa S.; Martinson, Brian C. Normal misbehavior: scientists talk about the ethics of research. *Journal of Empirical Research on Human Research Ethics* 2006 March; 1(1): 43-50. NRCBL: 1.3.9. SC: em.

De Vries, Raymond; Elliott, Carl. Why disclosure? [editorial]. *JGIM: Journal of General Internal Medicine* 2006 September; 21(9): 1003-1004. NRCBL: 1.3.9; 18.1.

DeAngelis, Catherine D. The influence of money on medical science [editorial]. *JAMA: The Journal of the American Medical Association* 2006 August 23-30; 296(8): 996-998. NRCBL: 1.3.9; 1.3.7; 7.3.

DeCoursey, Thomas E. It's difficult to publish contradictory findings [letter]. *Nature* 2006 February 16; 439(7078): 784. NRCBL: 1.3.9; 1.3.7.

di Norcia, Vincent. Intellectual property and the commercialization of research and development. *Science and Engineering Ethics* 2005 April; 11(2): 203-219. NRCBL: 1.3.9; 5.3. SC: an.

Dietz, William H. Needed for NAASO: a code of ethics. *Obesity Research* 1994 March; 2(2): 164-165. NRCBL: 1.3.9; 1.3.7. Identifiers: North American Association for the Study of Obesity.

Dinan, Michaela A.; Weinfurt, Kevin P.; Friedman, Joëlle Y.; Allsbrook, Jennifer S.; Gottlieb, Julie; Schulman, Kevin A.; Hall, Mark A.; Dhillon, Jatinder K.; Sugarman, Jeremy. Comparison of conflict of interest policies and reported practices in academic medical centers in the United States. *Accountability in Research* 2006 October-December; 13(4): 325-342. NRCBL: 1.3.9. SC: em.

Drenth, Pieter J.D. Responsible conduct in research. *Science and Engineering Ethics* 2006 January; 12(1): 13-21. NRCBL: 1.3.9; 5.3.

Eaton, Lynn. Norwegian researcher admits that his data were faked [news]. *BMJ: British Medical Journal* 2006 January 28; 332(7535): 193. NRCBL: 1.3.9. Identifiers: Norway; Jon Sudbo.

Edwards, R.G. Cloning and cheating [editorial]. *Reproductive BioMedicine Online [electronic]* 2006 February; 12(2): 141. NRCBL: 1.3.9.

NRCBL: National Reference Center for Bioethics Literature Classification Scheme   See inside front cover for terms.

83

Eliades, Theodore; Athanasiou, Athanasios E.; Papadopulos, Jannis S. Ethics and fraud in science: a review of scientific misconduct and applications to craniofacial research. *World Journal of Orthodontics* 2005 Fall; 6(3): 226-232. NRCBL: 1.3.9; 7.1; 18.2; 18.3.

Emanuel, Ezekiel J. Researching a bioethical question. *In:* Gallin, John I., ed. Principles and Practice of Clinical Research. San Diego, CA: Academic Press; 2002: 27-37. NRCBL: 1.3.9; 2.1.

Farthing, Michael J.G. Authors and publication practices. *Science and Engineering Ethics* 2006 January; 12(1): 41-52. NRCBL: 1.3.9; 1.3.7.

Fisher, Celia B. Clinical trials results databases: unanswered questions. *Science* 2006 January 13; 311(5758): 180-181. NRCBL: 1.3.9; 1.3.12; 18.2; 9.7.

Freudenburg, William R. Seeding science, courting conclusions: reexamining the intersection of science, corporate cash, and the law. *Sociological Forum* 2005 March; 20(1): 3-33. NRCBL: 1.3.9; 7.3; 5.3. SC: le.

Frisina, Michael E. Commentary: the application of medical ethics in biomedical research. *CQ: Cambridge Quarterly of Healthcare Ethics* 2006 Fall; 15(4): 439-441. NRCBL: 1.3.9; 5.3; 21.2; 7.1.

Fry, Craig L.; Treloar, Carla; Maher, Lisa. Ethical challenges and responses in harm reduction research: promoting applied communitarian ethics. *Drug and Alcohol Review* 2005 September; 24(5): 449-459. NRCBL: 1.3.9; 9.5.9; 1.1.

Fuyuno, Ichiko; Cyranoski, David. Doubts over biochemist's data expose holes in Japanese fraud laws [news]. *Nature* 2006 February 2; 439(7076): 514. NRCBL: 1.3.9. Identifiers: Kazunari Taira.

Fuyuno, Ichiko; Cyranoski, David. Further accusations rock Japanese RNA laboratory [news]. *Nature* 2006 April 6; 440(7085): 720-721. NRCBL: 1.3.9.

Gardner, William. Compelled disclosure of scientific research data. *Information Society* 2004 April-June; 20(2): 141-146. NRCBL: 1.3.9; 1.3.5; 18.1. SC: le.

Gardner, William; Lidz, Charles W. Research sponsorship, financial relationships, and the process of research in pharmaceutical clinical trials. *Journal of Empirical Research on Human Research Ethics* 2006 June; 1(2): 11-18. NRCBL: 1.3.9; 9.7; 5.3. SC: em.

Gardner, William; Lidz, Charles W.; Hartwig, Kathryn C. Authors' reports about research integrity problems in clinical trials. *Contemporary Clinical Trials* 2005 April; 26(2): 244-251. NRCBL: 1.3.9; 18.2; 1.3.7. SC: em.

Garfield, Eugene; McVeigh, Marie; Muff, Marion. Preventing scientific fraud [letter]. *Annals of Internal Medicine* 2006 September 19; 145(6): 472-473. NRCBL: 1.3.9.

Gefenas, Eugenijus. The concept of risk and responsible conduct of research. *Science and Engineering Ethics* 2006 January; 12(1): 75-83. NRCBL: 1.3.9.

Gerber, Paul. What can we learn from the Hwang and Sudbø affairs? *Medical Journal of Australia* 2006 June 19; 184(12): 632-635. NRCBL: 1.3.9; 1.3.7. Identifiers: Korea; Norway.

Gewin, Virginia. Fears rise over leaks of clinical trial results. *Nature* 2005 September 8; 437(7056): 191. NRCBL: 1.3.9; 1.3.2; 7.3; 9.7.

Giles, Jim. The trouble with replication [news]. *Nature* 2006 July 27; 442(7101): 344-347. NRCBL: 1.3.9; 1.3.7.

Gold, Jennifer L. Conflict over conflicts of interest: an analysis of the new NIH rules. *Journal of Law, Medicine, and Ethics* 2006 Spring; 34(1): 105-110. NRCBL: 1.3.9; 7.3; 18.6. SC: le. Identifiers: National Institutes of Health.

Gøtzsche, Peter C. Research integrity and pharmaceutical industry sponsorship: trial registration, transparency and less reliance on industry trials are essential [editorial]. *Medical Journal of Australia* 2005 June 6; 182(11): 549-550. NRCBL: 1.3.9; 18.2; 9.7.

Group of Advisers on the Ethical Implications of Biotechnology. The ethical aspects of the fifth research framework program [guideline]. *Politics and the Life Sciences* 1998 March; 17(1): 73-76. NRCBL: 1.3.9; 15.1; 5.3.

Guston, David H. Research integrity. *In:* Mitcham, Carl, ed. Encyclopedia of Science, Technology, and Ethics. Farmington Hills, MI: Thomson/Gale, 2005: 1607-1609. NRCBL: 1.3.9.

Guterman, Lila. Digging into the roots of research ethics. *Chronicle of Higher Education* 2006 September 1; 53(2): 24-26; 28. NRCBL: 1.3.9; 1.3.11; 5.1; 18.5.9; 9.7. Identifiers: Kelly Bannister.

Guterman, Lila. Sense of injustice can lead scientists to act unethically, study finds. *Chronicle of Higher Education* 2006 April 21; 52(33): A21. NRCBL: 1.3.9; 1.3.7.

Guterman, Lila. The taint of 'misbehavior'. *Chronicle of Higher Education* 2006 February 24; 52(25): A14- A16. NRCBL: 1.3.9; 18.5.4; 1.3.7.

Hampson, Lindsay A.; Agrawal, Manish; Joffe, Steven; Gross, Cary P.; Verter, Joel; Emanuel, Ezekiel J. Patients' views on financial conflicts of interest in cancer research trials. *New England Journal of Medicine* 2006 November 30; 355(22): 2330-2337. NRCBL: 1.3.9; 5.3; 9.7; 18.1. SC: em.
  Abstract: BACKGROUND: Financial ties between researchers or medical centers and companies whose drugs are being tested have come under increasing scrutiny. METHODS: We con-

---

ducted in-person interviews with 253 patients in cancer-research trials (a 93% response rate) at five U.S. medical centers to determine their attitudes regarding potential financial conflicts of interest among researchers and medical centers. RESULTS: More than 90% of patients expressed little or no worry about financial ties that researchers or institutions might have with drug companies. Most patients said they would have enrolled in the trial even if the drug company had paid the researcher for speaking (82% of those interviewed) or consulting (75%) or if the researcher had received royalty payments (70%) or owned stock in the company (76%). Similarly, most patients would have enrolled in the trial if their cancer center had owned stock in the drug company (77%) or received royalty payments from the company (79%). Most patients believed it was ethical for researchers to receive speaking fees (81%) or consulting fees (82%) from the company. However, a substantial minority of patients wanted disclosure of the oversight system for researchers (40%) and of researchers' financial interests (31%); 17% thought no disclosure to patients was necessary. CONCLUSIONS: Most patients in cancer-research trials were not worried about financial ties between researchers or medical centers and drug companies and would still have enrolled in the trial if they had known about such financial ties. A substantial minority wanted to be informed about the oversight system to protect against financial conflicts of interest and about researchers' financial interests. Copyright 2006 Massachusetts Medical Society.

Harper, Mary G. Ethical multiculturalism: an evolutionary concept analysis. *Advances in Nursing Science* 2006 April-June; 29(2): 110-124. NRCBL: 1.3.9; 21.7. SC: an; em; rv.

Häyry, Matti; Takala, Jukka; Jallinoja, Piia; Lötjönen, Salla; Takala, Tuija. Ethicalization in bioscience — a pilot study in Finland. *CQ: Cambridge Quarterly of Healthcare Ethics* 2006 Summer; 15(3): 282-284. NRCBL: 1.3.9. SC: em.

Henry, David A.; Kerridge, Ian H.; Hill, Suzanne R.; McNeill, Paul M.; Doran, Evan; Newby, David A.; Henderson, Kim M.; Maguire, Jane; Stokes, Barrie J.; Macdonald, Graham J.; Day, Richard O. Medical specialists and pharmaceutical industry-sponsored research: a survey of the Australian experience. *Medical Journal of Australia* 2005 June 6; 182(11): 557-560. NRCBL: 1.3.9; 18.2; 9.7.

Hoeyer, Klaus; Dahlager, Lisa; Lynöe, Niels. Conflicting notions of research ethics. The mutually challenging traditions of social scientists and medical researchers. *Social Science and Medicine* 2005 October; 61(8): 1741-1749. NRCBL: 1.3.9; 1.3.1; 18.3; 7.3.

Hoeyer, Klaus; Dahlager, Lisa; Lynöe, Niels. Ethical conflicts during the social study of clinical practice: the need to reassess the mutually challenging research ethics traditions of social scientists and medical researchers. *Clinical Ethics* 2006 March; 1(1): 41-45. NRCBL: 1.3.9; 7.3; 18.3; 7.1; 18.1. SC: cs.

Holden, Constance. Schatten: Pitt panel finds 'misbehavior' but not misconduct [news]. *Science* 2006 February 17; 311(5763): 928. NRCBL: 1.3.9; 1.3.7. Identifiers: Korea; University of Pittsburgh; Woo Suk Hwang.

Holden, Constance. Scientists keep some data to themselves [news]. *Science* 2006 January 27; 311(5760): 448. NRCBL: 1.3.9.

Holden, Constance. The undisclosed background of a paper on a depression treatment. *Science* 2006 August 4; 313(5787): 598. NRCBL: 1.3.9; 1.3.7; 9.7.

Illingworth, R.; Poza, M. Fraud and other misconduct in biomedical research [editorial]. *Neurocirugia* 2005 August; 16(4): 297-300. NRCBL: 1.3.9. Note: Editorial in English, commentary in Spanish.

Ingham, Janis Costello. Research ethics 101: the responsible conduct of research. *Seminars in Speech and Language* 2003 November; 24(4): 323- 337. NRCBL: 1.3.9; 18.2; 18.3; 6; 5.3; 1.3.7. SC: cs.

Interlandi, Jeneen. An unwelcome discovery. Walter DeNino was a young lab technician who analyzed data for his mentor, Eric Poehlman. What he found was that Poehlman was not the scientist he appeared to be. *New York Times Magazine* 2006 October 22; p. 98-103. NRCBL: 1.3.9.

Itoh, Machiko; Kato, Kazuto. What should scientists do outside the laboratory? Lessons on science communication from the Japanese genome research project. *Genetics, Society, and Policy* 2005 August; 1(2): 80-93. NRCBL: 1.3.9; 15.10.

James, Jack E. "Third-party" threats to research integrity in public-private partnerships. *Addiction* 2002 October; 97(10): 1251-1255. NRCBL: 1.3.9; 9.3.1; 7.3.

Jette, Alan M. Without scientific integrity, there can be no evidence base. *Physical Therapy* 2005 November; 85(11): 1122-1123. NRCBL: 1.3.9.

Johnston, Bradley C.; Vohra, Sunita. Investigator-initiated trials are more impartial. *Nature* 2006 September 14; 443(7108): 144. NRCBL: 1.3.9; 7.3; 5.3.

Kaiser, Jocelyn. NIH rules rile scientists, survey finds [news]. *Science* 2006 November 3; 314(5800): 740. NRCBL: 1.3.9. Identifiers: National Institutes of Health.

Kaiser, Jocelyn. Researchers attack newspaper probe of trials [news]. *Science* 2006 September 22; 313(5794): 1714. NRCBL: 1.3.9; 1.3.7.

Kalichman, Michael. Ethics and science: a 0.1% solution. *Issues in Science and Technology* 2006 Fall; 23(1): 34-36. NRCBL: 1.3.9; 18.2; 7.2.

Kennedy, Donald. Editorial expression of concern [letter]. *Science* 2006 January 6; 311(5757): 36. NRCBL: 1.3.9; 18.5.4; 15.1; 1.3.7.

Kennedy, Donald. Responding to fraud [editorial]. *Science* 2006 December 1; 314(5804): 1353. NRCBL: 1.3.9; 1.3.7.

NRCBL: National Reference Center for Bioethics Literature Classification Scheme   See inside front cover for terms.

85

Keranen, Lisa. Assessing the seriousness of research misconduct: considerations for sanction assignment. *Accountability in Research* 2006 April-June; 13(2): 179-205. NRCBL: 1.3.9; 18.6.

Abstract: Federal and institutional policies recommend the criterion of "seriousness" as a guide for sanction assignment in cases where researchers have been found to have committed research misconduct. Discrepancies in assessments of seriousness for similar acts of misconduct suggest the need to clarify what might be meant by the seriousness of research misconduct and how the criterion can be used to assign sanctions. This essay demonstrates how determinations of seriousness can differ depending on the set of ethical appeals employed and argues that an expanded lexicon for talking about the seriousness of research misconduct would help to promote fairness and consistency in sanction assignment. It concludes with some policy recommendations for those charged with research misconduct sanction assignment and for those who oversee research integrity at institutional levels.

Kjeldsen, Sverre E.; Narkiewicz, Krzysztof; Cifková, Renata; Mancia, Giuseppe. ESH statement on detection and punishment of abstract fraud and poster plagiarism. *Blood Pressure* 2005; 14(6): 322-323. NRCBL: 1.3.9; 7.4. Identifiers: European Society of Hypertension.

Kjeldsen, Sverre E.; Narkiewicz, Krzysztof; Cifkova, Renata; Mancia, Giuseppe. ESH statement on detection and punishment of abstract fraud and poster plagiarism. *Journal of Hypertension* 2006 January; 24(1): 203-204. NRCBL: 1.3.9; 1.3.7; 7.3.

Kline, A. David. On complicity theory. *Science and Engineering Ethics* 2006 April; 12(2): 257-264. NRCBL: 1.3.9.

Koch, Douglas D. Truth or consequences. *Journal of Cataract and Refractive Surgery* 2005 September; 31(9): 1679-1680. NRCBL: 1.3.9; 1.3.7.

Koppelman-White, Elysa. Research misconduct and the scientific process: continuing quality improvement. *Accountability in Research* 2006 July-September; 13(3): 225-246. NRCBL: 1.3.9; 2.3. SC: an.

Abstract: The response to research misconduct involves the attempt to regulate behavior through (a) creating and enforcing a rule and (b) ethics education. The roles of each must be shaped by considerations of the nature of scientific practice. Given the nature of science, the role of (a) must be limited in scope: both in the types of behavior it covers and in the level of intent that must be present for an allegation of misconduct to be proven. Since one important role of ethics education is to fill the gaps that regulatory rules leave open, it is this limitation in scope and its source in theoretical concerns that better reveals the type and kind of education needed. It is argued that much of the current ethics education falls short. Since the gaps left by the rule are largely due to theoretical concerns about the very nature of the scientific process and the nature of that process is constantly evolving, ethics education must focus more heavily on theory and must reach a wider audience. It is argued that ethics education can be more effective if it aims, in part, in creating a discipline-specific, constantly evolving standard of care.

Krohmal, Benjamin J.; Sobolski, Gregory K. Commentary: physicians and risk of malevolent use of research.

CQ: Cambridge Quarterly of Healthcare Ethics 2006 Fall; 15(4): 441-444. NRCBL: 1.3.9; 5.3.

Lahiri, Debomoy K. Discourse among referees and editors would help [letter]. *Nature* 2006 February 16; 439(7078): 784. NRCBL: 1.3.9; 1.3.7.

Lazarus, Arthur. Individual wariness needed to spot biased drug research. *Managed Care* 2005 September; 14(9): 8, 13. NRCBL: 1.3.9; 7.3; 9.7; 9.3.1.

Lefor, Alan T. Scientific misconduct and unethical human experimentation: historic parallels and moral implications. *Nutrition* 2005 July-August; 21(7-8): 878-882. NRCBL: 1.3.9; 21.4; 15.5; 1.3.5.

Lenard, John. Two facets peer review and the proper role of study sections. *Accountability in Research* 2006 July-September; 13(3): 277-283. NRCBL: 1.3.9.

Abstract: The current National Institutes of Health study section system is under increasing criticism due to tight budgets and decreased levels of perceived competence. There is also an overemphasis on written critiques from the study section by unsuccessful applicants. It is argued that this arises from confusion between two different purposes of peer review. A system of universal participation in peer review by senior funded investigators is proposed to ameliorate these problems.

Lenzer, Jeanne. Conflicts of interest are common at FDA [news]. *BMJ: British Medical Journal* 2006 April 29; 332(7548): 991. NRCBL: 1.3.9; 9.7. SC: em. Identifiers: Food and Drug Administration.

Lenzer, Jeanne. Researcher received undisclosed payments of $300 000 from Pfizer [news]. *BMJ: British Medical Journal* 2006 December 16; 333(7581): 1237. NRCBL: 1.3.9; 9.3.1; 9.7; 18.3; 19.5. SC: le. Identifiers: Pearson Sutherland, III; United States.

Leo, Jonathan. The SSRI trials in children: disturbing implications for academic medicine. *Ethical Human Psychology and Psychiatry* 2006 Spring; 8(1): 29-41. NRCBL: 1.3.9; 1.3.7; 17.4; 18.5.2; 20.7. Identifiers: selective serotonin reuptake inhibitor.

Leydens, Jon A. Plagiarism. *In:* Mitcham, Carl, ed. Encyclopedia of Science, Technology, and Ethics. Farmington Hills, MI: Thomson/Gale, 2005: 1411-1413. NRCBL: 1.3.9.

Liang, Bryan A. The bounds of science and ethics. *Journal of Biolaw and Business* 2006; 9(1): 44-45. NRCBL: 1.3.9; 18.1.

Lindblad, William J. A matter of ethics [editorial]. *Wound Repair and Regeneration* 2005 May-June; 13(3): 217. NRCBL: 1.3.9; 7.3; 5.3. Identifiers: National Institutes of Health.

Little, M. Expressing freedom and taking liberties: the paradoxes of aberrant science. *Medical Humanities* 2006 June; 32(1): 32-37. NRCBL: 1.3.9; 1.1.

Abstract: Complete freedom does not exist, despite people's preparedness to die for it. Scientific freedom is much defended and yet much misunderstood. Scientists have limits imposed on their freedom by the disciplines and discourse communities in which they place themselves. Freedom within these socially constructed constraints needs to be distinguished from taking liberties with the rules and practices that make up these constraints, and validate the activities of special groups within society. Scientists (and the public) perceive taking liberties with science's rules and practices as aberrant science, and they often react punitively. Aberrant science can be broadly examined under four headings: wicked science, naughty science, dysfunctional science, and ideologically unacceptable science. When we examine examples of perceived aberrant science, we find that these categories of "misconduct" are connected and often confused. Scientific freedom needs to be redefined with due regard to current understandings of scientists as human beings facing powerful social pressures to deliver results of a particular kind.

Malek, Janet. Misconduct in science: biomedical science cases. *In:* Mitcham, Carl, ed. Encyclopedia of Science, Technology, and Ethics. Farmington Hills, MI: Thomson/Gale, 2005: 1207-1210. NRCBL: 1.3.9. Identifiers: William Summerlin, John Darsee, Robert Gallo, David Baltimore.

Mandell, Brian F. New CCJM policy: no manufacturer involvement in the preparation of articles. *Cleveland Clinic Journal of Medicine* 2005 March; 72(3): 169. NRCBL: 1.3.9; 7.3.

Marris, Emma. Doctor admits Lancet study is fiction [news]. *Nature* 2006 January 19; 439(7074): 248-249. NRCBL: 1.3.9; 1.3.7. Identifiers: Norway.

Marris, Emma; Check, Erika. Disgraced cloner's ally is cleared of misconduct [news]. *Nature* 2006 February 16; 439(7078): 768-769. NRCBL: 1.3.9; 14.5; 18.5.4; 15.1. Identifiers: Korea; Woo Suk Hwang; Gerald Schatter.

Marshall, Eliot. deCODE adds plagiarism allegation to its case [news]. *Science* 2006 October 27; 314(5799): 580. NRCBL: 1.3.9; 15.10; 1.3.2.

Martinson, Brian C.; Anderson, Melissa A.; Crain, A. Lauren; De Vries, Raymond. Scientists' perceptions of organizational justice and self-reported misbehaviors. *Journal of Empirical Research on Human Research Ethics* 2006 March; 1(1): 51-66. NRCBL: 1.3.9; 1.3.2; 1.1. SC: em.

Maurissen, Jacques P.; Gilbert, Steven G.; Sander, Miriam; Beauchamp, Tom L.; Johnson, Shelley; Schwetz, Bernard A.; Goozner, Merrill; Barrow, Craig S. Workshop proceedings: managing conflict of interest in science. A little consensus and a lot of controversy. *Toxicological Sciences* 2005 September; 87(1): 11-14. NRCBL: 1.3.9; 7.3.

McLachlan, John C.; McHarg, Jane. Ethical permission for the publication of routinely collected data. *Medical Education* 2005 September; 39(9): 944-948. NRCBL: 1.3.9; 1.3.3; 8.4.

McLeish, Caitríona A. Science and censorship in an age of bio-weapons threat. *Science as Culture* 2006 September; 15(3): 215-236. NRCBL: 1.3.9; 21.3; 1.3.7; 5.3.

Mepham, Ben. Bioethics in the laboratory. *In his:* Bioethics: An Introduction for the Biosciences. Oxford; New York: Oxford University Press; 2005: 357-378. NRCBL: 1.3.9; 1.3.1.

Meyer, Gitte. Journalism and science: how to erode the idea of knowledge. *Journal of Agricultural and Environmental Ethics* 2006; 19(3): 239-252. NRCBL: 1.3.9; 1.3.7; 5.3; 1.3.2. SC: an.

Michalek, Arthur M.; Wicher, Camille C. Conflicts of interest/commitment. *Journal of Cancer Education* 2005 Spring; 20(1): 8-9. NRCBL: 1.3.9. SC: cs.

Monastersky, Richard. Science journals must develop stronger safeguards against fraud, panel says. *Chronicle of Higher Education* 2006 December 8; 53(16): A15. NRCBL: 1.3.9; 1.3.7.

Mumford, Michael D.; Devenport, Lynn D.; Brown, Ryan P.; Connelly, Shane; Murphy, Stephen T.; Hill, Jason H.; Antes, Alison L. Validation of ethical decision making measures: evidence for a new set of measures. *Ethics and Behavior* 2006; 16(4): 319-345. NRCBL: 1.3.9; 18.2; 1.3.2; 1.3.7. SC: em.

Murphy, Timothy F. On being downstream from faked scientific reports. *BMJ: British Medical Journal* 2006 March 18; 332(7542): 674. NRCBL: 1.3.9; 14.5; 18.5.4; 15.1.

Musher, Daniel M.; Stone, Peter H. Undisclosed conflicts of interest [letter and reply]. *Annals of Internal Medicine* 2006 February 7; 144(3): 225-226. NRCBL: 1.3.9; 9.7. Comments: Peter H. Stone. Update in Cardiology. Annals of Internal Medicine 2005; 143: 737-743.

Nandakumar, Saranya. The cloning controversy. *Indian Journal of Medical Ethics* 2006 July-September; 3(3): 93-94. NRCBL: 1.3.9; 5.3; 18.5.4; 15.1. SC: cs. Identifiers: Hwang Woo-Suk.

Abstract: Stem cell research has captured the imagination of many, including the scientific and medical community. But the medical community received a wake-up call early this year when a well-known researcher publicly confessed to deception. While the core question relates to honesty and integrity, it is equally necessary to examine the system that made such deception possible.

National Institutes of Health [NIH] (United States). Guidelines for the Conduct of Research in the Intramural Research Program at NIH. Bethesda, MD: National Institutes of Health, 1997 January. [Online]. Accessed: http://www.nih.gov/campus/irnews/guidelines.htm [2006 July 11]; 7 p. NRCBL: 1.3.9; 18.2. Identifiers: National Institutes of Health [NIH]. Note: 3rd edition.

NRCBL: National Reference Center for Bioethics Literature Classification Scheme   See inside front cover for terms.

87

Nebal, Elizabeth G. Conflict of interest — or conflict of priorities? [editorial]. *New England Journal of Medicine* 2006 November 30; 355(22): 2365-2367. NRCBL: 1.3.9; 18.2; 5.3; 9.7; 18.1.

Ness, April C. National Institutes of Health enacts final ethics regulations. *Journal of Biolaw and Business* 2006; 9(1): 50-51. NRCBL: 1.3.9; 7.3.

Noble, David W. Preventing scientific fraud [letter]. *Annals of Internal Medicine* 2006 September 19; 145(6): 472. NRCBL: 1.3.9.

Normile, Dennis. Panel discredits findings of Tokyo University team [news]. *Science* 2006 February 3; 311(5761): 595. NRCBL: 1.3.9; 1.3.3. Identifiers: Kazunari Taira.

Nylenna, Magne; Horton, Richard. Research misconduct: learning the lessons. *Lancet* 2006 November 25-December 1; 368(9550): 1856. NRCBL: 1.3.9.

Nylenna, Magne; Simonsen, Sigmund. Scientific misconduct: a new approach to prevention. *Lancet* 2006 June 10-16; 367(9526): 1882-1884. NRCBL: 1.3.9.

Osseweijer, Patricia. A new model for science communication that takes ethical considerations into account: the three E-model: entertainment, emotion, and education [letter]. *Science and Engineering Ethics* 2006 October; 12(4): 591-593. NRCBL: 1.3.9.

Park, Sang Chul. Reactions to the Hwang scandal [letter]. *Science* 2006 February 3; 311(5761): 606. NRCBL: 1.3.9; 14.5. Identifiers: Korea.

Parrish, Debra M. On identifying research misconduct respondents [letter]. *Science and Engineering Ethics* 2005 April; 11(2): 171-172. NRCBL: 1.3.9. Identifiers: National Science Foundation (NSF); Office of Research Integrity (ORI).

Pascal, Chris B. Managing data for integrity: policies and procedures for ensuring the accuracy and quality of the data in the laboratory. *Science and Engineering Ethics* 2006 January; 12(1): 23-29. NRCBL: 1.3.9.

Pichini, Simona; Pulido, Marta; García-Algar, Óscar. Authorship in manuscripts submitted to biomedical journals: an author's position and its value [letter]. *Science and Engineering Ethics* 2005 April; 11(2): 173-175. NRCBL: 1.3.9; 1.3.7.

Plemmons, Dena K.; Brody, Suzanne A.; Kalichman, Michael W. Student perceptions of the effectiveness of education in the responsible conduct of research. *Science and Engineering Ethics* 2006 July; 12(3): 571-582. NRCBL: 1.3.9; 2.3. SC: em.

Pontifical Academy for Life = Pontificia Academia pro vita. Final communique: ethics of biomedical research. *L'Osservatore Romano* 2003 March 19: 5, 10 [Online]. Accessed: http://www.catholicculture.org/docs/doc_view. cfm?recnum=5083 [2006 September 6]. NRCBL: 1.3.9; 1.2.

Psaty, Bruce M.; Weiss, Noel S.; Furberg, Curt D. Recent trials in hypertension: compelling science or commercial speech? *JAMA: The Journal of the American Medical Association* 2006 April 12; 295(14): 1704-1706. NRCBL: 1.3.9; 9.1; 9.7; 18.1; 1.3.7.

Qazi, Yureeda. Fabrication: crime in research [letter]. *Lancet* 2006 February 25-March 3; 367(9511): 649. NRCBL: 1.3.9; 5.3; 18.6.

Qian, Wang. Chinese perspectives. *In:* Mitcham, Carl, ed. Encyclopedia of Science, Technology, and Ethics. Farmington Hills, MI: Thomson/Gale, 2005: 317-325. NRCBL: 1.3.9; 1.3.4; 2.1.

Redman, Barbara K.; Merz, Jon F. Research misconduct policies of high impact biomedical journals. *Accountability in Research* 2006 July-September; 13(3): 247-258. NRCBL: 1.3.9; 1.3.7. SC: rv; em.

Abstract: Several national and international organizations have recommended policies regarding journal responsibilities about research misconduct in submitted or published manuscripts. A search of Web sites of the fifty highest impact journals in a cluster of biomedical fields and a limited survey of their editors shows that few journals have formally adopted standards for dealing with questions of research misconduct. Publicly available policies may have a deterrent effect and can prevent arbitrariness in handling cases.

Redman, Barbara K.; Templin, Thomas N.; Merz, Jon F. Research misconduct among clinical trial staff. *Science and Engineering Ethics* 2006 July; 12(3): 481-489. NRCBL: 1.3.9. SC: em. Identifiers: Native Americans.

Reynolds, Sandra M. ORI findings of scientific misconduct in clinical trials and publicly funded research, 1992-2002. *Clinical Trials* 2004; 1(6): 509-516. NRCBL: 1.3.9; 18.2; 18.6. SC: em.

Ridker, Paul M.; Torres, Jose. Reported outcomes in major cardiovascular clinical trials funded by for-profit and not-for-profit organization: 2000-2005. *JAMA: The Journal of the American Medical Association* 2006 May 17; 295(19): 2270-2274. NRCBL: 1.3.9; 7.3; 9.7; 9.3.1; 18.1. SC: em.

Abstract: CONTEXT: In surveys based on data available prior to 2000, clinical trials funded by for-profit organizations appeared more likely to report positive findings than those funded by not-for-profit organizations. Whether this situation has changed over the past 5 years or whether similar effects are present among jointly funded trials is unknown. OBJECTIVE: To determine in contemporary randomized cardiovascular trials the association between funding source and the likelihood of reporting positive findings. DESIGN: We reviewed 324 consecutive superiority trials of cardiovascular medicine published between January 1, 2000, and July 30, 2005, in JAMA, The Lancet, and the New England Journal of Medicine. MAIN OUTCOME MEASURE: The proportion of trials favoring newer treatments over the standard of care was evaluated by funding source. RESULTS: Of the 324 superiority trials, 21 cited no funding source. Of the 104 trials funded solely by

---

not-for-profit organizations, 51 (49%)reported evidence significantly favoring newer treatments over the standard of care, whereas 53 (51%) did not (P = .80). By contrast, 92 (67.2%) of 137 trials funded solely by for-profit organizations favored newer treatments over standard of care(P001). Among 62 jointly funded trials, 35 (56.5%), an intermediate proportion, favored newer treatments. For 205 randomized trials evaluating drugs, the proportions favoring newer treatments were 39.5%, not-for-profit; 54.4%, jointly funded; and 65.5%, for-profit trials (P for trend across groups = .002). For the 39 randomized trials evaluating cardiovascular devices, the proportions favoring newer treatments were 50.0%, not-for-profit; 69.2%, jointly funded; and 82.4%, for-profit trials (P for trend across groups = .07). Regardless of funding source, trials using surrogate end points, such as quantitative angiography, intravascular ultrasound, plasma biomarkers, and functional measures were more likely to report positive findings (67%) than trials using clinical end points (54.1%; P = .02). CONCLUSIONS: Recent cardiovascular trials funded by for-profit organizations are more likely to report positive findings than trials funded by not-for-profit organizations, as are trials using surrogate rather than clinical end points. Trials jointly funded by not-for-profit and for-profit organizations appear to report positive findings at a rate approximately midway between rates observed in trials supported solely by one or the other of these entities.

Roberts, Laura Weiss; McAuliffe, Timothy L. Investigators' affirmation of ethical, safeguard, and scientific commitments in human research. *Ethics and Behavior* 2006; 16(2): 135-150. NRCBL: 1.3.9; 18.2; 7.1; 7.2. SC: em.

Rogawski, Michael A.; Suber, Peter. Support for the NIH public access policy [letter]. *Science* 2006 September 15; 313(5793): 1572. NRCBL: 1.3.9; 1.3.12. Identifiers: National Institutes of Health.

Roig, Miguel. Commentary: ethical writing should be taught. *BMJ: British Medical Journal* 2006 September 16; 333(7568): 596-597. NRCBL: 1.3.9; 1.3.7; 1.3.3.

Rosenstock, Linda. Protecting special interests in the name of "good science". *JAMA: The Journal of the American Medical Association* 2006 May 24-31; 295(20): 2407-2410. NRCBL: 1.3.9. SC: le. Identifiers: Data Quality Act.

Sarojini, N.B.; Bhattacharya, Saswati. Such research cannot be in isolation. *Indian Journal of Medical Ethics* 2006 April-June; 3(2): 70. NRCBL: 1.3.9; 8.3.2; 8.3.4; 7.3; 8.4; 7.4; 12.4.2; 11.2. SC: le; cs. Comments: Conflict between the law and ethics while researching. Indian Journal of Medical Ethics 2006 April-June; 3(2): 69.

Schechter, Alan N. Integrity in research: individual and institutional responsibility. *In:* Gallin, John I., ed. Principles and Practice of Clinical Research. San Diego, CA: Academic Press; 2002: 39-50. NRCBL: 1.3.9.

Selgelid, Michael J. Commentary: the ethics of dangerous discovery. *CQ: Cambridge Quarterly of Healthcare Ethics* 2006 Fall; 15(4): 444-447. NRCBL: 1.3.9; 5.3; 15.1; 21.3.

Shamoo, Adil E. Accountability in research. *In:* Mitcham, Carl, ed. Encyclopedia of Science, Technology, and Ethics.

Farmington Hills, MI: Thomson/Gale, 2005: 6-7. NRCBL: 1.3.9.

Shamoo, Adil E. Data audit would reduce unethical behaviour [letter]. *Nature* 2006 February 16; 439(7078): 784. NRCBL: 1.3.9.

Sharp, Richard R.; Yarborough, Mark. Informed trust and the financing of biomedical research. *Journal of Law, Medicine and Ethics* 2006 Summer; 34(2): 460-464. NRCBL: 1.3.9; 7.3; 5.3.

Siegel-Itzkovich, Judy. Israel looks into claims of "illegal medical experiment" [news]. *BMJ: British Medical Journal* 2006 July 22; 333(7560): 165. NRCBL: 1.3.9; 1.3.7; 18.2.

Siegel-Itzkovich, Judy. Israeli doctors are arrested in investigation [news]. *BMJ: British Medical Journal* 2006 October 21; 333(7573): 823. NRCBL: 1.3.9; 18.5.7.

Slingsby, Brian Taylor; Kodama, Satoshi; Akabayashi, Akira. Scientific misconduct in Japan: the present paucity of oversight policy. *CQ: Cambridge Quarterly of Healthcare Ethics* 2006 Summer; 15(3): 294-297. NRCBL: 1.3.9; 5.3.

Smith, Anthony J. Scientific freedom. *Journal of Dental Research* 2004 December; 83(12): 895. NRCBL: 1.3.9.

Snyder, Evan Y.; Loring, Jeanne F. Beyond fraud — stem-cell research continues. *New England Journal of Medicine* 2006 January 26; 354(4): 321-324. NRCBL: 1.3.9; 18.5.4; 15.1; 14.5; 19.5; 19.1.

Sonfield, Adam. The uses and abuses of science in sexual and reproductive health policy debates. *Guttmacher Report on Public Policy* 2005 November; 8(4): 1-3. NRCBL: 1.3.9; 1.3.7; 11.1; 12.1; 10.

Sox, Harold C.; Rennie, Drummond. Preventing scientific fraud [response]. *Annals of Internal Medicine* 2006 September 19; 145(6): 472-473. NRCBL: 1.3.9.

Sox, Harold C.; Rennie, Drummond. Research misconduct, retraction, and cleansing the medical literature: lessons from the Poehlman case. *Annals of Internal Medicine* 2006 April 18; 144(8): 609-613. NRCBL: 1.3.9; 1.3.7.

Sprague, Robert L.; Mitcham, Carl. Misconduct in science: social science cases. *In:* Mitcham, Carl, ed. Encyclopedia of Science, Technology, and Ethics. Farmington Hills, MI: Thomson/Gale, 2005: 1213-1215. NRCBL: 1.3.9; 18.4.

Squires, Bruce. Editorial policy: the right to medical information [editorial]. *CMAJ/JAMC: Canadian Medical Association Journal* 2006 September 12; 175(6): 557. NRCBL: 1.3.9; 1.3.12.

Steneck, Nicholas H. Fostering integrity in research: definitions, current knowledge, and future directions. *Science*

NRCBL: National Reference Center for Bioethics Literature Classification Scheme   See inside front cover for terms.

89

and Engineering Ethics 2006 January; 12(1): 53-74. NRCBL: 1.3.9. SC: em.

Stephens, Joe. Harvard research in China is faulted: safety, ethics problems of tests noted. *Washington Post* 2003 March 30: A06. NRCBL: 1.3.9.

Sterba, Sonya K. Misconduct in the analysis and reporting of data: bridging methodological and ethical agendas for change. *Ethics and Behavior* 2006; 16(4): 305-318. NRCBL: 1.3.9; 18.2; 17.1; 6; 18.4.

Stossel, Thomas; Shaywitz, David. What's wrong with money in science. *Washington Post* 2006 July 2; p. B3. NRCBL: 1.3.9. SC: po.

Streiffer, Robert. Academic freedom and academic-industry relationships in biotechnology. *Kennedy Institute of Ethics Journal* 2006 June; 16(2): 129-149. NRCBL: 1.3.9; 15.8; 5.3; 1.1; 1.3.2; 1.3.3. SC: le.

Abstract: Commercial academic-industry relationships (AIRs) are widespread in biotechnology and have resulted in a wide array of restrictions on academic research. Objections to such restrictions have centered on the charge that they violate academic freedom. I argue that these objections are almost invariably unsuccessful. On a consequentialist understanding of the value of academic freedom, they rely on unfounded empirical claims about the overall effects that AIRs have on academic research. And on a rights-based understanding of the value of academic freedom, they rely on excessively lavish assumptions about the kinds of activities that academic freedom protects.

Sugarman, Jeremy. Lying, cheating and stealing in clinical research [editorial]. *Clinical Trials* 2004; 1(6): 475-476. NRCBL: 1.3.9; 18.2; 18.6.

Thekkuveettil, Anoopkumar. Where is the girl in all the decision making? *Indian Journal of Medical Ethics* 2006 April-June; 3(2): 71. NRCBL: 1.3.9; 8.3.2; 7.3; 18.2; 12.4.2; 11.2. SC: cs. Comments: Conflict between the law and ethics while researching. Indian Journal of Medical Ethics 2006 April-June; 3(2): 69.

Tong, S.; Olsen, J. The threat to scientific integrity in environmental and occupational medicine. *Occupational and Environmental Medicine* 2005 December; 62(12): 843-846. NRCBL: 1.3.9; 16.1; 16.3; 1.3.2.

University of Pittsburgh. Summary Investigative Report on Allegations of Possible Scientific Misconduct on the Part of Gerald P. Schatten, Ph.D., February 8, 2006. Pittsburgh, PA: University of Pittsburgh, 2006 February 8; 9. p.[Online]. Accessed: http://newsbureau.upmc.com/PDF/Final%20 Public%20Report%202.08.pdf. NRCBL: 1.3.9; 14.5. Comments: W. S. Hwang, et al. Patient-Specific Embryonic Stem Cells Derived from Human SCNT Blastocysts. Science 2005 June 17; 308(5729): 1777-1783.

Abstract: This report was written by a University of Pittsburgh panel established to investigate the role of its professor Gerald P. Schatten, Ph.D., Professor of Obstetrics, Gynecology and Reproductive Sciences and Director, Pittsburgh Development Center, in the collaboration with Korean scientist Woo-Suk
Hwang, who falsified data concerning derivation of stem cells from cloned human embryos. Dr. Schatten was co-corresponding and senior author on the Science paper. [KIE]

Van Norman, Gail A.; Palmer, Susan K.; Jackson, Stephen H. The ethical role of medical journal editors [letter]. *Anesthesia and Analgesia* 2005 February; 100(2): 603-604. NRCBL: 1.3.9; 18.2; 1.3.7. SC: em.

Vogel, Gretchen. Fraud investigation clouds paper on early cell fate [news]. *Science* 2006 December 1; 314(5804): 1367-1368. NRCBL: 1.3.9. Identifiers: R. Michael Roberts.

Vogeli, Christine; Yucel, Recai; Bendavid, Eran; Jones, Lisa M.; Anderson, Melissa S.; Louis, Karen Seashore; Campbell, Eric G. Data withholding and the next generation of scientists: results of a national survey. *Academic Medicine* 2006 February; 81(2): 128-136. NRCBL: 1.3.9. SC: em.

Wachbroit, Robert. Research as a profession. *Philosophy and Public Policy Quarterly* 2006 Winter-Spring; 26(1-2): 18-20. NRCBL: 1.3.9; 18.1; 8.1.

Wade, Nicholas. Cancer study was made up, journal says. *New York Times* 2006 January 19; p. A16. NRCBL: 1.3.9; 1.3.7. SC: po.

Wade, Nicholas. It may look authentic; here's how to tell it isn't: a scientific journal shows the way in a new offensive against fraud. *New York Times* 2006 January 24; p. F1, F6. NRCBL: 1.3.9; 1.3.7. SC: po.

Wade, Nicholas. Science academy creating panel to monitor stem-cell research. *New York Times* 2006 February 16; p. A21. NRCBL: 1.3.9; 18.5.4; 18.1. SC: po.

Wade, Nicholas; Sang-Hun, Choe. Human cloning was all faked, Koreans report. *New York Times* 2006 January 10; p. A1, A12. NRCBL: 1.3.9; 14.5. SC: po.

Wadman, Meredith. A few good scientists. *Nature Medicine* 2006 September; 12(9): 986-987. NRCBL: 1.3.9; 1.3.7; 9.3.1. Identifiers: conflicts of interest.

Wadman, Meredith. Agency accused of 'illusion of integrity' [news]. *Nature* 2006 September 21; 443(7109): 252-253. NRCBL: 1.3.9; 1.3.5; 7.3. Identifiers: National Institutes of Health.

Wang, Qizhi. Misconduct: China needs university ethics courses. *Nature* 2006 July 13; 442(7099): 132. NRCBL: 1.3.9; 1.3.3.

Webster, Andrew. Social science ethics: the changing context for research. *Clinical Ethics* 2006 March; 1(1): 39-40. NRCBL: 1.3.9; 5.2; 18.2. Identifiers: Research Ethics Framework (REF).

Weiss, Rick. "Serious misconduct" by NIH expert found: scientist did not report sending tissues to drug firm and getting paid, report says. *Washington Post* 2006 June 14; p. A6. NRCBL: 1.3.9. SC: po. Identifiers: Trey Sunderland.

Weiss, Rick. Government health researchers pressed to share data at no charge. *Washington Post* 2006 March 10; p. A17. NRCBL: 1.3.9; 1.3.5; 1.3.12. SC: po.

Wells, Frank. Fraud and misconduct in clinical research. *In:* Di Giovanna, Ignazio; Hayes, Gareth, eds. Principles of Clinical Research. Philadelphia: Wrightson Biomedical Pub.; 2001: 507-528. NRCBL: 1.3.9.

Wilbanks, John. Another reason for opening access to research. *BMJ: British Medical Journal* 2006 December 23-30; 333(7582): 1306-1308. NRCBL: 1.3.9; 1.3.7; 1.3.12.

Wolpert, Lewis. Is science dangerous? *Journal of Molecular Biology* 2002 June 14; 319(4): 969-972. NRCBL: 1.3.9; 15.5; 14.5. SC: an.

Wu, Guosheng. Misconduct: forum should not be used to settle scores. *Nature* 2006 July 13; 442(7099): 132. NRCBL: 1.3.9. Identifiers: China.

Xin, Hao. Online sleuths challenge cell paper [news]. *Science* 2006 December 15; 314(5806): 1669. NRCBL: 1.3.9. Identifiers: Taiwan; Ban-Yang Chang.

Xin, Hao. Scandals shake Chinese science. *Science* 2006 June 9; 312(5779): 1464-1466. NRCBL: 1.3.9.

Yang, Xiangzhong. A simple system of checks and balances to cut fraud [letter]. *Nature* 2006 February 16; 439(7078): 782. NRCBL: 1.3.9; 1.3.7.

Yang, Xiangzhong. Hwang's fraud adds impetus to ES cell research [letter]. *Nature Biotechnology* 2006 April; 24(4): 393. NRCBL: 1.3.9; 14.5; 18.5.4; 15.1. Identifiers: embryonic stem.

Yano, Eiji. Japanese spousal smoking study revisited: how a tobacco industry funded paper reached erroneous conclusions. *Tobacco Control* 2005 August; 14(4): 227-235. NRCBL: 1.3.9; 9.5.9; 1.3.7. SC: em.

Zamiska, Nicholas. Scientist rebels against WHO over bird flu [Ilaria Capua]. *Wall Street Journal* 2006 March 13; p B1, B2. NRCBL: 1.3.9; 9.1. SC: po. Identifiers: World Health Organization.

BIOMEDICAL RESEARCH/ SOCIAL CONTROL OF SCIENCE AND TECHNOLOGY

Ahmed, Amer S. The last twist of the knife: encouraging the regulation of innovative surgical procedures. *Columbia Law Review* 2005 June; 105(5): 1529-1562. NRCBL: 5.3; 9.1; 9.7. SC: le; an.

Austria. Bioethikkommission beim Bundeskanzleramt = Austria. Bioethics Commission at the Federal Chan-
cellery. Decision of the Bioethics Commission at the Federal Chancellery of 11 February 2002 concerning the recommendation for Austria's accession to the Biomedicine Convention of the Council of Europe. Vienna, Austria: Bioethikkommission beim Bundeskanzleramt, 2002 February 11: 6 p. NRCBL: 5.3; 21.1. SC: le. Identifiers: Convention for the Protection of Human Rights and Dignity of the Human Being with Regard to the Application of Biology and Medicine; European Convention on Human Rights and Biomedicine.

Barie, Philip S. Temporary insanity? [editorial]. *Surgical Infections* 2005; 6(2): 181-184. NRCBL: 5.3; 7.3; 1.3.9; 9.7; 1.3.2.

Billings, Paul R. A medical geneticist's view. *World Watch* 2002 July-August; 15(4): 16. NRCBL: 5.3; 15.1. SC: po.

Brown, David. Johns Hopkins scales down its deal with cosmetics firm after criticism [news]. *BMJ: British Medical Journal* 2006 April 22; 332(7547): 929. NRCBL: 5.3; 18.2; 18.5.3; 9.7; 1.3.2.

Camilleri, Michael; Gamble, Gail L.; Kopecky, Stephen L.; Wood, Michael B.; Hockema, Marianne L. Principles and process in the development of the Mayo Clinic's individual and institutional conflict of interest policy. *Mayo Clinic Proceedings* 2005 October; 80(10): 1340-1346. NRCBL: 5.3; 1.3.9.

Campbell, Eric G.; Blumenthal, David. Academic industry relationships in biotechnology: a primer on policy and practice. *Cloning* 2000; 2(3): 129-136. NRCBL: 5.3; 15.1.

Cohen, Eric. Biotechnology and the spirit of capitalism. *New Atlantis* 2006 Spring; 12: 9-23. NRCBL: 5.3; 4.4; 9.3.1.

Cook-Deegan, Robert. The urge to commercialize: interactions between public and private research development. *In:* Esanu, Julie M.; Uhlir, Paul F., eds. The Role of Scientific and Technical Data and Information in the Public Domain: Proceedings of a Symposium. Washington, DC: National Academies Press; 2002: 87-94. NRCBL: 5.3. Note: "The symposium was held on September 5-6, 2002, at the National Academics in Washington, DC.".

Davies, Keith G.; Wolf-Phillips, Jonathan. Scientific citizenship and good governance: implications for biotechnology. *Trends in Biotechnology* 2006 February; 24(2): 57-61. NRCBL: 5.3; 1.3.9.

Delaney, Brendan. Commentary: is society losing control of the medical research agenda. *BMJ: British Medical Journal* 2006 May 6; 332(7549): 1063-1064. NRCBL: 5.3; 18.1; 9.3.1. Comments: British Medical Journal. 2006 May 6; 332(7549): 1061-4.

NRCBL: National Reference Center for Bioethics Literature Classification Scheme   See inside front cover for terms.

91

Elliot, Kevin C. An ethics of expertise based on informed consent. *Science and Engineering Ethics* 2006 October; 12(4): 637-661. NRCBL: 5.3; 8.3.1; 1.3.9.

Faden, Ruth. The road to balanced oversight [editorial]. *Science* 2006 August 18; 313(5789): 891. NRCBL: 5.3; 18.5.4; 15.1. Identifiers: Hinxton Group; stem cell research.

Freschi, Gina C. Navigating the research exemption's safe harbor: Supreme Court to clarify scope-implications for stem cell research in California. *Santa Clara Computer and High Technology Law Journal* 2005; 21: 855-901. NRCBL: 5.3; 18.5.4; 15.1. SC: le.

Fukuyama, Francis. How to regulate science. *Public Interest* 2002 Winter; 146: 3-22. NRCBL: 5.3; 14.1; 15.1; 21.1.

Gauthier, Clement. Principles and guidelines for the development of a science- based decision making process facilitating the implementation of the 3Rs by governmental regulators. *ILAR Journal* 2002; 43(Supplement): S99-S104. NRCBL: 5.3; 22.2; 21.1.

Gerlach, Neil; Hamilton, Sheryl N. From mad scientist to bad scientist: Richard Seed as biogovernmental event. *Communication Theory* 2005 February; 15(1): 78-99. NRCBL: 5.3; 1.3.7; 14.5; 1.3.5; 5.2. SC: an.

Gleicher, Norbert. Reflections and comments on regulations of biotechnologies that touch the beginning of human life. *Journal of Assisted Reproduction and Genetics* 2005 January; 22(1): 41-46. NRCBL: 5.3; 14.4; 14.5.

Gruning, Thilo; Gilmore, Anna B.; McKee, Martin. Tobacco industry influence on science and scientists in Germany. *American Journal of Public Health* 2006 January; 96(1): 20-32. NRCBL: 5.3; 1.3.2; 9.5.9; 1.3.9.
Abstract: Using tobacco industry documents, we examined how and why the tobacco industry sought to influence science and scientists in Germany as a possible factor in explaining the German opposition to stricter tobacco regulation. Smoking and health research programs were organized both separately by individual tobacco companies and jointly through their German trade organization. An extensive network of scientists and scientific institutions with tobacco industry links was developed. Science was distorted in 5 ways: suppression, dilution, distraction, concealment, and manipulation. The extent of tobacco industry influence over the scientific establishment in Germany is profound. The industry introduced serious bias that probably influenced scientific and public opinion in Germany. This influence likely undermined efforts to control tobacco use.

Halweil, Brian; Bell, Dick. Beyond cloning: the larger agenda of human engineering. *World Watch* 2002 July-August; 15(4): 8-10. NRCBL: 5.3; 15.5; 15.4. SC: po.

Hilgartner, Stephen. Acceptable intellectual property. *Journal of Molecular Biology* 2002 June 14; 319(4): 943-946. NRCBL: 5.3; 5.2; 15.1. SC: an.

Holden, Constance. Scientists object to Massachusetts rules [news]. *Science* 2006 September 8; 313(5792): 1372. NRCBL: 5.3; 18.5.4; 15.1.

Holm, Søren. Reply to Sandin: the paradox of precaution is not dispelled by attention to context. *CQ: Cambridge Quarterly of Healthcare Ethics* 2006 Spring; 15(2): 184-187. NRCBL: 5.3; 5.2; 1.1; 16.1; 21.1. SC: le.

Hudson, Michelle. The EU Physical Agents (EMF) Directive and its impact on MRI imaging in animal experiments: a submission by FRAME to the HSE. *ATLA: Alternatives to Laboratory Animals* 2006 June; 34(3): 343-347. NRCBL: 5.3; 22.2. SC: le.

Jasanoff, Sheila. The life sciences and the rule of law. *Journal of Molecular Biology* 2002 June 14; 319(4): 891-899. NRCBL: 5.3; 15.8. SC: le.

Johnston, Josephine. Field notes: small. *Hastings Center Report* 2006 November-December; 36(6): inside cover. NRCBL: 5.3; 5.4. Identifiers: nanotechnology.

Kesselheim, Aaron S.; Avorn, Jerry. Biomedical patents and the public's health: is there a role for eminent domain? *JAMA: The Journal of the American Medical Association* 2006 January 25; 295(4): 434-437. NRCBL: 5.3; 9.7. SC: le.

Kesselheim, Aaron S.; Mello, Michelle M. Medical-process patents — monopolizing the delivery of health care. *New England Journal of Medicine* 2006 November 9; 355(19): 2036-2041. NRCBL: 5.3; 9.1; 9.3.1; 1.3.9. SC: le.

Khan, Robyna, I. Paying the price of research. *SciDev.Net (Science and Development Network)* 2004 November 10: 3 pages [Online] Accessed: http://www.scidev.net/dossiers/index.cfm?fuseaction=printarticle&dossier=5&type=3&itemid=331&language-1 [2005 December 2]. NRCBL: 5.3; 18.2; 8.1. Identifiers: Pakistan.

Krohn, Wolfgang. Enquete commissions. *In:* Mitcham, Carl, ed. Encyclopedia of Science, Technology, and Ethics. Farmington Hills, MI: Thomson/Gale, 2005: 641-644. NRCBL: 5.3; 21.1. Identifiers: Germany.

Leroux, Thérèse; Hirtle, Marie; Fortin, Louis-Nicolas. An overview of public consultation mechanisms developed to address the ethical and social issues raised by biotechnology. *Journal of Consumer Policy* 1998 December; 21(4): 445-481. NRCBL: 5.3; 21.1; 18.2; 15.1. SC: rv.

Levin, Yuval. The moral challenge of modern science. *New Atlantis* 2006 Fall; 14: 32-46. NRCBL: 5.3; 1.3.9.

Marchant, Gary E.; Sylvester, Douglas J. Transnational models for regulation of nanotechnology. *Journal of Law, Medicine and Ethics* 2006 Winter; 34(4): 714-725. NRCBL: 5.3; 5.4; 21.1. SC: an.
Abstract: Like all technologies, nanotechnology will inevitably present risks, whether they result from unintentional effects of otherwise beneficial applications, or from the malevolent mis-

use of technology. Increasingly, risks from new and emerging technologies are being regulated at the international level, although governments and private experts are only beginning to consider the appropriate international responses to nanotechnology. In this paper, we explore both the potential risks posed by nanotechnology and potential regulatory frameworks that law may impose. In so doing, we also explore the various rationales for international regulation including the potential for cross-boundary harms, sharing of regulatory expertise and resources, controlling protectionism and trade conflicts, avoiding a "race to the bottom" in which governments seek economic advantage through lax regulation, and limiting the "nano divide" between North and South. Finally, we examine some models for international regulation and offer tentative thoughts on the prospects for each.

Mayor, Susan. Publicly funded research in the UK must be freely accessible [news]. *BMJ: British Medical Journal* 2006 July 15; 333(7559): 112. NRCBL: 5.3.

Monbiot, George. Exposed: the secret corporate funding behind health research. *Guardian* 2006 February 7 [Online]. Accessed: http://www.guardian.co.uk/print/ 0,,5393221-103390,00.html [2006 February 8]. NRCBL: 5.3; 8.2; 1.3.2.

Parry, Odette; Mauthner, Natasha S. Whose data are they anyway? Practical, legal and ethical issues in archiving qualitative research data. *Sociology* 2004 February; 38(1): 139-152. NRCBL: 5.3; 8.4; 1.3.12.

Patsopoulos, Nikolaos A.; Analatos, Apostolos A.; Ioannidis, John P.A. Origin and funding of the most frequently cited papers in medicine: database analysis. *BMJ: British Medical Journal* 2006 May 6; 332(7549): 1061-1063. NRCBL: 5.3; 18.1; 9.3.1; 21.1. SC: em.
Abstract: Objective To evaluate changes in the role of academics and the sources of funding for the medical research cited most frequently over the past decade. Design Database analysis. Data sources Web of Knowledge database. Methods For each year from 1994 to 2003, articles in the domain of clinical medicine that had been cited most often by the end of 2004 were identified. Changes in authors' affiliations and funding sources were evaluated. Results Of the 289 frequently cited articles, most had at least one author with a university (76%) or hospital (57%) affiliation, and the proportion of articles with each type of affiliation was constant over time. Government or public funding was most common (60% of articles), followed by industry (36%). The proportion of most frequently cited articles funded by industry increased over time (odds ratio 1.17 per year, P = 0.001) and was equal to the proportion funded by government or public sources by 2001. 65 of the 77 most cited randomised controlled trials received funding from industry, and the proportion increased significantly over time (odds ratio 1.59 per year, P = 0.003). 18 of the 32 most cited trials published after 1999 were funded by industry alone. Conclusion Academic affiliations remain prominent among the authors of the most frequently cited medical research. Such research is increasingly funded by industry, often exclusively so. Academics may be losing control of the clinical research agenda.

Raza, Mohshin. Collaborative healthcare research: some ethical considerations. *Science and Engineering Ethics* 2005 April; 11(2): 177-186. NRCBL: 5.3; 21.1.

Rudoren, Jodi. Stem cell work gets states' aid after Bush veto. *New York Times* 2006 July 25; p. A1, A16. NRCBL: 5.3; 18.5.4; 15.1. SC: po.

Sandin, Per. A paradox out of context: Harris and Holm on the precautionary principle. *CQ: Cambridge Quarterly of Healthcare Ethics* 2006 Spring; 15(2): 175-183. NRCBL: 5.3; 5.2; 1.1; 16.1; 21.1. SC: le.

Sarewitz, Daniel. Governance of science. *In:* Mitcham, Carl, ed. Encyclopedia of Science, Technology, and Ethics. Farmington Hills, MI: Thomson/Gale, 2005: 878-882. NRCBL: 5.3; 15.1.

Skene, Loane. Bioscience, community expectations and the law [forum]. *University of New South Wales Law Journal* 2003; 26(3): 799- 806. NRCBL: 5.3; 15.1; 8.4; 1.3.5. SC: le. Identifiers: Australia.

Smith, Shane; Neaves, William; Teitelbaum, Steven. Adult stem cell treatments for diseases? [letter]. *Science* 2006 July 28; 313(5786): 439. NRCBL: 5.3; 18.5.1; 15.1.

Stiglitz, Joseph E. Scrooge and intellectual property rights: a medical prize fund could improve the financing of drug innovations. *BMJ: British Medical Journal* 2006 December 23-30; 333(7582): 1279-1280. NRCBL: 5.3; 1.3.9; 1.3.7; 9.3.1.

Sullivan, E. Thomas; Juengst, Eric T.; Charo, R. Alta; McCabe, Edward R.B. Risks posed by new biomedical technologies: how do we analyze, communicate and regulate risk? *Medical Ethics Newsletter* 2006 Fall; 13(3): 5-8. NRCBL: 5.3; 4.5; 18.5.4; 15.1; 15.10.

Tucker, Jonathan B.; Zilinskas, Raymond A. The promise and perils of synthetic biology. *New Atlantis* 2006 Spring; 12: 25-45. NRCBL: 5.3; 15.1; 15.7; 21.3.

United States. Congress. Senate. A bill to amend the Federal Food, Drug, and Cosmetic Act to create a new three-tiered approval system for drugs, biological products, and devices that is responsive to the needs of seriously ill patients, and for other purposes. Washington, DC: U.S. G.P.O., 2005. 24 p. [Online]. Accessed: http:// frwebgate.access.gpo.gov/cgi-bin/useftp.cgi? IPaddress=162.140.64.21&filename=s1956is.pdf& directory=/diskb/wais/data/109_cong_bills [2006 November 21]. NRCBL: 5.3; 9.7. SC: le. Identifiers: Access, Compassion, Care, and Ethics for Seriously Ill Patients Act (ACCESS Act). Note: S. 1956, 109th Congress, 1st session. Introduced by Sen. Brownback, November 3, 2005. Referred to the Committee on Health, Education, Labor, and Pensions.

Vedantam, Shankar. Group says FDA, advisory panels show bias toward drug approvals. *Washington Post* 2006 August 29; p. A13. NRCBL: 5.3; 9.7. SC: po. Identifiers: Food and Drug Administration.

NRCBL: National Reference Center for Bioethics Literature Classification Scheme   See inside front cover for terms.

93

Wade, Nicholas. In new method for stem cells, viable embryos; objections to use remain; development could raise the level of debate in midterm elections. *New York Times* 2006 August 24; p. A1, A23. NRCBL: 5.3; 18.5.4; 19.1.

Wade, Nicholas. Some scientists see shift in stem cell hopes. *New York Times* 2006 August 14; p. A18. NRCBL: 5.3; 18.5.4; 19.1. SC: po.

BIOMEDICAL TECHNOLOGIES *See* ENHANCEMENT; ORGAN AND TISSUE TRANSPLANTATION; REPRODUCTIVE TECHNOLOGIES

BLACKS AS RESEARCH SUBJECTS *See* HUMAN EXPERIMENTATION/ SPECIAL POPULATIONS

BLOOD DONATION AND TRANSFUSION
See also ORGAN AND TISSUE TRANSPLANTATION

Bekker, Linda-Gail; Wood, Robin. Blood safety — at what cost? [editorial]. *JAMA: The Journal of the American Medical Association* 2006 February 1; 295(5): 557-558. NRCBL: 19.4; 9.8. SC: le.

Bramstedt, Katrina A. Transfusion contracts for Jehovah's Witnesses receiving organ transplants: ethical necessity or coercive pact? *Journal of Medical Ethics* 2006 April; 32(4): 193-195. NRCBL: 19.4; 1.2; 8.3.4; 19.6.

Burton, Thomas M. Biopure moves to sell blood substitute in Europe. *Wall Street Journal* 2006 July 12; p. D2. NRCBL: 19.4. SC: po.

Burton, Thomas M. Blood-substitute study is criticized by U.S. agency. *Wall Street Journal* 2006 March 10; p. A3. NRCBL: 19.4; 5.3. SC: po.

Burton, Thomas M. FDA to weigh test of blood substitute out of public view. *Wall Street Journal* 2006 July 11; p. D3. NRCBL: 19.4; 18.5.1. SC: po.

Burton, Thomas M. FDA to weigh using fake blood in trauma trial. *Wall Street Journal* 2006 July 6; p. B1, B2. NRCBL: 19.4; 18.5.1. SC: po. Identifiers: Food and Drug Administration.

Burton, Thomas M. Use of substitution for blood draws ethics challenge. *Wall Street Journal* 2006 March 20; p. A2. NRCBL: 19.4; 18.3.

Busby, Helen. Consent, trust and ethics: reflections on the findings of an interview based study with people donating blood for genetic research for research within the NHS. *Clinical Ethics* 2006 December; 1(4): 211-215. NRCBL: 19.4; 18.1; 15.1. SC: em.

Carassiti, M.; Tambone, V.; Agrò, F.E. Blood transfusion and the principle of the double effect act: proposal of a

new ethical view for Jehovah's Witnesses. *Clinica Terapeutica* 2003 November-December; 154(6): 447. NRCBL: 19.4; 1.2.

Chan, S. Cord blood banking: what are the real issues? [editorial]. *Journal of Medical Ethics* 2006 November; 32(11): 621-622. NRCBL: 19.4; 9.5.7.

Dougherty, Anne Hamilton. Letter to the editor: in defense of the PolyHeme® trial [letter]. *American Journal of Bioethics [Online]* 2006 September-October; 6(5): W35-W37. NRCBL: 19.4; 18.2.

Edozien, Leroy C. NHS maternity units should not encourage commercial banking of umbilical cord blood. *BMJ: British Medical Journal* 2006 October 14; 333(7572): 801-804. NRCBL: 19.4; 9.5.7; 9.3.1. Identifiers: United Kingdom(Great Britain); National Health Service.

Elhence, Priti. Ethical issues in transfusion medicine. *Indian Journal of Medical Ethics* 2006 July-September; 3(3): 87-89. NRCBL: 19.4; 7.1; 8.3.1; 8.3.4.
Abstract: The practice of transfusion medicine involves a number of ethical issues because blood comes from human beings and is a precious resource with a limited shelf life. In 1980 the International Society of Blood Transfusion endorsed its first formal code of ethics, which was adopted by the World Health Organisation and the League of Red Crescent Societies. A revised code of ethics for donation and transfusion was endorsed in 2000. Blood donation as a gift, donor confidentiality, donor notification and donor consent, consent for transfusion, the right to refuse blood transfusion, the right to be informed if harmed, and ethical principles for establishments, are discussed in the international and Indian contexts.

Farrell, Anne-Maree. Is the gift still good? Examining the politics and regulation of blood safety in the European Union. *Medical Law Review* 2006 Summer; 14(2): 155-179. NRCBL: 19.4; 19.6; 9.8; 21.1; 4.4; 9.5.6. SC: an; le.

Fisk, Nicholas M.; Roberts, Irene A.G.; Markwald, Roger; Mironov, Vladimir. Can routine commercial cord blood banking be scientifically and ethically justified? *PLoS Medicine* 2005 February; 2(2): 0087-0090. NRCBL: 19.4; 9.5.7; 9.3.1.

Gohel, M.S.; Bulbulia, R.A.; Slim, F.J.; Poskitt, K.R.; Whyman, M.R. How to approach major surgery where patients refuse blood transfusion (including Jehovah's Witnesses). *Annals of the Royal College of Surgeons of England* 2005 January; 87(1): 3-14. NRCBL: 19.4; 8.3.4; 1.2. Identifiers: United Kingdom (Great Britain).

Gyamfi, Cynthia; Gyamfi, Mavis M.; Berkowitz, Richard L. Ethical and medicolegal considerations in the obstetric care of a Jehovah's Witness. *Obstetrics and Gynecology* 2003 July; 102(1): 173-180. NRCBL: 19.4; 1.2; 9.5.5.

Hewitt, P.E.; Moore, C.; Soldan, K. vCJD donor notification exercise: 2005. *Clinical Ethics* 2006 September; 1(3): 172-178. NRCBL: 19.4; 19.5; 9.1. SC: em.

Holloway, Karla F.C. Accidental communities: race, emergency medicine, and the problem of PolyHeme. *American Journal of Bioethics* 2006 May-June; 6(3): 7-17; discussion W46- W48. NRCBL: 19.4; 9.5.4; 18.5.1; 18.2; 18.6.

Hutchon, David J.R.; Carpenter, Robert James, Jr. Commercial cord blood banking: immediate cord clamping is not safe: public cord blood banking should be more widely adopted [letters]. *BMJ: British Medical Journal* 2006 October 28; 333(7574): 919. NRCBL: 19.4; 9.5.7; 9.3.1. Identifiers: United Kingdom (Great Britain); United States.

Iffy, L.; Varadi, V.; Portuondo, N.; Ende, N. Collection of fetal blood for stem cell research and therapy. *Medicine and Law: The World Association for Medical Law* 2006 September; 25(3): 553-561. NRCBL: 19.4; 9.5.8; 8.3.2. SC: le.

Abstract: Stem cell research has generated novel therapeutic opportunities at the expense of new ethical and legal problems. Its promoters recommended early clamping of the umbilical cord to maximize the amount of acquired fetal blood. Fear has been expressed, therefore, that the donor could be compromised by this approach. Actually, the problem is more complex than generally assumed. In certain clinical situations the neonate may benefit from or become harmed by additional blood volume. Gravity influences the direction of umbilical blood flow and, thus the consequences of early or delayed cord clamping. Therefore, vaginal birth promotes blood flow from the placenta to the fetus, whereas delivery by cesarean section usually has the opposite effect. Largely ignored in the course of the relevant debates, the above facts require consideration. The controversy may be beneficial in the long run by drawing attention to this relatively neglected aspect of perinatal medicine.

Kurtzberg, Joanne; Lyerly, Anne Drapkin; Sugarman, Jeremy. Untying the Gordian knot: policies, practices, and ethical issues related to banking of umbilical cord blood. *Journal of Clinical Investigation* 2005 October; 115(10): 2592-2597. NRCBL: 19.4; 9.5.7; 19.5.

LeFebour, Patricia A.; Elliot, Douglas. Ontario court rules on notification of blood donors: Canadian AIDS Society v Her Majesty the Queen in Right of Ontario, Dr Richard Schabas and the Canadian Red Cross Society. *Canadian HIV/AIDS Policy and Law Newsletter* 1995 January; 1(2): 1, 13-14. NRCBL: 19.4; 9.5.6; 8.3.1; 8.4. SC: le.

Neal, Karama C. Analogical trends in umbilical cord blood legislation in the United States. *American Journal of Bioethics* 2006 November-December; 6(6): 68-70l author reply W13-W14. NRCBL: 19.4; 19.5. Comments: Bjørn Hofmann, Jan Helge Solbakk, and Søren Holm. Analogical reasoning in handling emerging technologies: the case of umbilical cord blood biobanking. American Journal of Bioethics 2006 November- December; 6(6): 49-57.

Samuel, Gabrielle N.; Ankeny, Rachel A.; Kerridge, Ian H. Mixing metaphors in umbilical cord blood transplantation. *American Journal of Bioethics* 2006 November-December; 6(6): 58-59; author reply W13-W14.

NRCBL: 19.4; 19.5; 15.1. Comments: Bjørn Hofmann, Jan Helge Solbakk, and Søren Holm. Analogical reasoning in handling emerging technologies: the case of umbilical cord blood biobanking. American Journal of Bioethics 2006 November-December; 6(6): 49-57.

Sazama, Kathleen. Managing infectious or untested autologous blood components: the ethical dilemma of private rights versus public safety [editorial]. *Archives of Pathology and Laboratory Medicine* 2005 October; 129(10): 1212-1213. NRCBL: 19.4; 8.4; 9.8.

Sheremeta, Lorraine; Plant, Margo; Knoppers, Bartha Maria. The future of cord blood banking in Canada. *Health Law Review* 2006; 14(3): 51-56. NRCBL: 19.4; 19.5; 9.5.8. SC: em.

Strauss, Ronald G.; Lipton, Karen Shoos. Glucocorticoid stimulation of neutrophil donors: a medical, scientific, and ethical dilemma [editorial]. *Transfusion* 2005 November; 45(11): 1697-1699. NRCBL: 19.4; 9.7. SC: em.

Trimmel, Michael; Lattacher, Helene; Janda, Monika. Voluntary whole-blood donors, and compensated platelet donors and plasma donors: motivation to donate, altruism and aggression. *Transfusion and Apheresis Science* 2005 October; 33(2): 147-155. NRCBL: 19.4; 9.3.1; 1.1. SC: em.

White, Gladys B. Analogical power and Aristotle's model of persuasion. *American Journal of Bioethics* 2006 November-December; 6(6): 67-68; author reply W13-W14. NRCBL: 19.4; 19.5; 1.1. Comments: Bjørn Hofmann, Jan Helge Solbakk, and Søren Holm. Analogical reasoning in handling emerging technologies: the case of umbilical cord blood biobanking. American Journal of Bioethics 2006 November-December; 6(6): 49-57.

Wolfson, Rachel K.; Kahana, Madelyn D.; Nachman, James B.; Lantos, John. Extracorporeal membrane oxygenation after stem cell transplant: clinical decision-making in the absence of evidence. *Pediatric Critical Care Medicine* 2005 March; 6(2): 200-203. NRCBL: 19.4; 18.5.2; 20.5.2; 8.3.2. SC: cs.

CAPITAL PUNISHMENT

Amateur night [editorial]. *Nature* 2006 May 4; 441(7089): 2. NRCBL: 20.6.

Lethal injection on trial [editorial]. *Lancet* 2006 March 4-10; 367(9512): 703. NRCBL: 20.6; 4.4; 7.3.

North Carolina, using medical monitoring device, executes killer. *New York Times* 2006 April 22; p. A13. NRCBL: 20.6. SC: le.

Bhan, Anant. Killing for the state: death penalty and the medical profession: a call for action in India. *National*

NRCBL: National Reference Center for Bioethics Literature Classification Scheme   See inside front cover for terms.

95

Medical Journal of India 2005 July-August; 18(4): 205-208. NRCBL: 20.6; 4.1.2.

Bonchek, Lawrence I.; Gawande, Atul. Why physicians participate in executions [letter and reply]. *New England Journal of Medicine* 2006 July 6; 355(1): 99-100. NRCBL: 20.6; 8.1.

Broder, John M. Questions over method lead to delay of execution. *New York Times* 2006 February 22; p. A11. NRCBL: 20.6. SC: po.

Clark, Peter A. Physician participation in executions: care giver or executioner? *Journal of Law, Medicine, and Ethics* 2006 Spring; 34(1): 95-104. NRCBL: 20.6. SC: le.

Davey, Monica. Missouri says it can't comply on executions. *New York Times* 2006 July 15; p. A1, A11. NRCBL: 20.6. SC: po.

Ellerin, Bruce E.; Gawande, Atul. Why physicians participate in executions [letter and reply]. *New England Journal of Medicine* 2006 July 6; 355(1): 99-100. NRCBL: 20.6; 8.1.

Ewing, Charles Patrick. Diagnosing and treating "insanity" on death row: legal and ethical perspectives. *Behavioral Sciences and the Law* 1987 Spring; 5(2): 175-185. NRCBL: 20.6; 17.2; 4.3. SC: le.

Fields, Gary. Criminal mind: on death row, fate of mentally ill is thorny problem; can states execute inmates made sane only by drugs? medical, legal quandary; a test case is Mr. Thompson. *Wall Street Journal* 2006 December 14; p. A1, A8. NRCBL: 20.6; 17.8. SC: po. Identifiers: Gregory Thompson; Tennessee.

Gabos, Kelly A. The perils of Singleton v. Norris: ethics and beyond. *American Journal of Law and Medicine* 2006; 32(1): 117-132. NRCBL: 20.6; 8.3.4; 8.1; 9.5.3. SC: le.

Gawande, Atul. When law and ethics collide — why physicians participate in executions. *New England Journal of Medicine* 2006 March 23; 354(12): 1221-1229. NRCBL: 20.6; 4.1.2. SC: le.

Goodman, Brenda. Judge allows device to be used for monitoring lethal injection. *New York Times* 2006 April 18; p. A18. NRCBL: 20.6; 9.7. SC: le.

Gottleib, Michael K. Singleton v. Norris: precursor to Abu Ghraib? The importance of role integrity in medicine. *APA Newsletter on Philosophy and Law* 2005 Fall; 05(1): 11-25. NRCBL: 20.6; 17.8; 17.7; 1.3.5; 8.3.4. SC: le.

Gottlieb, Michael K. Executions and torture: the consequences of overriding professional ethics. *Yale Journal of Health Policy, Law and Ethics* 2006 Summer; 6(2): 351-389. NRCBL: 20.6; 17.4; 17.8; 21.4; 7.1. SC: le.

Grady, Denise. Doctors see way to cut risks of suffering in lethal injection. *New York Times* 2006 June 23; p. A1, A24. NRCBL: 20.6. SC: po.

Heilbrun, Kirk S. The assessment of competency for execution: an overview. *Behavioural Sciences and the Law* 1987 Autumn; 5(4): 385-396. NRCBL: 20.6; 4.3; 17.2. SC: le; rv.

Kramers, Cornelis; Deinum, Jaap; Gawande, Atul. Why physicians participate in executions [letter and reply]. *New England Journal of Medicine* 2006 July 6; 355(1): 99-100. NRCBL: 20.6; 8.1.

Liptak, Adam. Citing risk of missteps, judges set hurdles for lethal injection. *New York Times* 2006 April 12; p. A1, A18. NRCBL: 20.6. SC: le.

Liptak, Adam. State proposes using device, not doctors, in execution. *New York Times* 2006 April 13; p. A14. NRCBL: 20.6; 9.7.

Marris, Emma. Will medics' qualms kill the death penalty? [news]. *Nature* 2006 May 4; 441(7089): 8-9. NRCBL: 20.6; 4.1.2.

McCarthy, Michael. Lethal injection challenged as "cruel and unusual" fate. *Lancet* 2006 March 4-10; 367(9512): 717. NRCBL: 20.6; 4.4; 7.3. Identifiers: California.

Spencer, Steven S.; Gawande, Atul. Why physicians participate in executions [letter and reply]. *New England Journal of Medicine* 2006 July 6; 355(1): 100. NRCBL: 20.6; 8.1.

Steinbrook, Robert. New technology, old dilemma — monitoring EEG activity during executions. *New England Journal of Medicine* 2006 June 15; 354(24): 2525-2527. NRCBL: 20.6. Identifiers: electroencephalogram.

Stone, Alan A. Forensic ethics and capital punishment: is there a special problem? [editorial]. *Journal of Forensic Psychiatry* 2002 December; 13(3): 487-493. NRCBL: 20.6; 17.2; 1.3.5. SC: le.

Ulmer, Nicholas C. Doctors and the death penalty: hippocratic and hypocritical? *Christianity and Crisis* 1981 April 13; 41: 109-119. NRCBL: 20.6; 4.1.2.

Yaes, Robert J.; Gawande, Atul. Why physicians participate in executions [letter and reply]. *New England Journal of Medicine* 2006 July 6; 355(1): 99-100. NRCBL: 20.6; 8.1.

CARE FOR SPECIFIC GROUPS
See also HUMAN EXPERIMENTATION/ SPECIAL POPULATIONS

Aitkenhead, Decca. Nip/tuck nation. *In:* Miller, Paul; Wilsdon, James, eds. Better Humans?: The Politics of Human Enhancement and Life Extension. London: Demos, 2006: 103-113. NRCBL: 9.5.1; 4.5.

Anderson-Shaw; Lisa. Rural health care ethics: networking and resources can lead to original research. *American Journal of Bioethics* 2006 March-April; 6(2): 61-62.

NRCBL: 9.5.1; 2.1; 1.3.9. Comments: William Nelson, Gili Lushkov, Andrew Pomerantz and William B. Weeks. Rural health care ethics: is there a literature? American Journal of Bioethics 2006 March-April; 6(2): 44-50.

Aultman, Julie M. A foreigner in my own country: forgetting the heterogeneity of our national community. *American Journal of Bioethics* 2006 March-April; 6(2): 56-59. NRCBL: 9.5.1; 1.3.9; 1.3.7. Comments: William Nelson, Gili Lushkov, Andrew Pomerantz and William B. Weeks. Rural health care ethics: is there a literature? American Journal of Bioethics 2006 March-April; 6(2): 44-50.

Beach, Mary Catherine; Sugarman, Jeremy; Johnson, Rachel L.; Arbelaez, Jose J.; Duggan, Patrick S.; Cooper, Lisa A. Do patients treated with dignity report higher satisfaction, adherence, and receipt of preventive care? *Annals of Family Medicine* 2005 July-August; 3(4): 331-338. NRCBL: 9.5.1; 4.4; 8.1; 8.3.1.

Berger, Jeffrey T.; Gorski, Matthew; Cohen, Todd. Advance health planning and treatment preferences among recipients of implantable cardioverter defibrillators: an exploratory study. *Journal of Clinical Ethics* 2006 Spring; 17(1): 72-78. NRCBL: 9.5.1; 5.1; 18.5.7; 8.1; 8.3.4; 20.5.4.

Bernstein, Joseph; Perlis, Clifford; Bartolozzi, Arthur R. Ethics in sports medicine. *Clinical Orthopaedics and Related Research* 2000 September; (378): 50-60. NRCBL: 9.5.1; 8.3.1; 8.4; 9.4; 9.5.7. SC: cs.

Birmingham, Luke; Wilson, Simon; Adshead, Gwen. Prison medicine: ethics and equivalence [editorial]. *British Journal of Psychiatry* 2006 January; 188: 4-6. NRCBL: 9.5.1; 1.3.5; 7.1; 8.1; 9.2. Identifiers: England; Wales.

Boncz, Imre; Sebestyén, Andor. Compensation for vaccine injury in Hungary. *Lancet* 2006 April 8-14; 367(9517): 1144. NRCBL: 9.5.1; 9.7; 8.5; 9.3.1.

Brassington, I. Body art and medical need. *Journal of Medical Ethics* 2006 January; 32(1): 13-16. NRCBL: 9.5.1. SC: an.
Abstract: A company called Biojewelry has proposed to take a sample of bone tissue from a couple and to grow this sample into wedding rings. One of the ethical problems that such a proposal faces is that it implies surgery without medical need. To this end, only couples with a prior need for surgery are being considered. This paper examines the question of whether such a stipulation is necessary. It is suggested that, though medical need and the provision of health and wellbeing is overwhelmingly the warrant for surgical intervention, there is no reason in principle why other, non-medical, projects such as jewelry creation might not also warrant surgical intervention. Implicitly, this line of thought forces us to consider the proper place of surgical intervention- — that is, to ask what surgeons are for.

Braun, Lundy. Reifying human difference: the debate on genetics, race, and health. *International Journal of Health Services* 2006; 36(3): 557-573. NRCBL: 9.5.1; 9.5.4; 15.11; 13.1; 18.5.1. SC: an.

Brentlinger, Paula E. Health, human rights, and malaria control: historical background and current challenges. *Health and Human Rights: An International Journal* 2006; 9(2): 11-38. NRCBL: 9.5.1; 21.1; 7.1.

Burke, Suzanne M. The case manager's view. *Journal of Clinical Ethics* 2006 Spring; 17(1): 83-84. NRCBL: 9.5.1; 8.1; 8.3.4; 20.4.1. SC: cs.

Byron, Margaret; Cockshott, Zoë; Brownett, Hilary; Ramkalawan, Tina. What does 'disability' mean for medical students? An exploration of the words medical students associate with the term 'disability'. *Medical Education* 2005 February; 39(2): 176-183. NRCBL: 9.5.1; 7.2. SC: em.

Carey, Benedict. Doctors say electric pulses aided brain-damaged man. *New York Times* 2006 October 16; p. A14. NRCBL: 9.5.1; 8.3.1; 4.4. SC: po.

Charuvastra, Anthony; Friedmann, Peter D.; Stein, Michael D. Physician attitudes regarding the prescription of medical marijuana. *Journal of Addictive Diseases* 2005; 24(3): 87-93. NRCBL: 9.5.1; 9.7; 9.5.9; 7.1. SC: em.

Chatterjee, J.S. From compliance to concordance in diabetes. *Journal of Medical Ethics* 2006 September; 32(9): 507-510. NRCBL: 9.5.1; 8.1; 8.3.4.
Abstract: Compliance is a key concept in health care and affects all areas of health care including diabetes. Non-compliance has previously been a label attached to many patients without much thought having been given to the causes of poor compliance. Over the last few decades there has been a large volume of research focusing on compliance that has exposed the multitude of factors affecting compliance. Even the definition is not clear cut and so comparability between studies is not without difficulties. A better understanding of the factors affecting compliance, including the doctor/patient relationship, has allowed the evolution of "concordance". Concordance views the patient as being the equal of the healthcare provider and as having a right to make informed decisions. In a condition such as diabetes, which has many potential long term complications, it is vital that concordance is embraced in the healthcare system in order to improve care.

Coghlan, Andy. A contentious cut: unethical mutilation in the name of medicine or a procedure that might save millions of lives in Africa? [news]. *New Scientist* 2006 November 25-December 1; 192(2579): 8-9. NRCBL: 9.5.1; 10.

Cohen, Peter J. Medical marijuana, compassionate use, and public policy: expert opinion or vox populi? *Hastings Center Report* 2006 May-June; 36(3): 19-22. NRCBL: 9.5.1; 9.7; 9.5.9. SC: le.

Colgrove, James. The ethics and politics of compulsory HPV vaccination. *New England Journal of Medicine* 2006 December 7; 355(23): 2389-2391. NRCBL: 9.5.1; 9.7; 9.5.7; 9.5.5; 8.3.4; 10.

Collins, Timothy P. Human technology manufacturing platforms. *National Catholic Bioethics Quarterly* 2006

NRCBL: National Reference Center for Bioethics Literature Classification Scheme   See inside front cover for terms.

97

Autumn; 6(3): 497-515. NRCBL: 9.5.1; 9.7; 18.5.4; 12.3; 1.2. SC: an.

Cook, Ann Freeman; Hoas, Helena. Re-framing the question: what do we really want to know about rural health care ethics? *American Journal of Bioethics* 2006 March-April; 6(2): 51-53. NRCBL: 9.5.1; 8.1; 2.1; 7.1. Comments: William Nelson, Gili Lushkov, Andrew Pomerantz and William B. Weeks. Rural health care ethics: is there a literature? American Journal of Bioethics 2006 March-April; 6(2): 44-50.

Derksen, Jim; Chochinov, Harvey Max. Disability and end-of-life care: let the conversation begin. *Journal of Palliative Care* 2006 Autumn; 22(3): 175-182. NRCBL: 9.5.1; 20.5.1; 20.4.1; 7.1; 8.1.

Dudzinski, Denise M.; Shannon, Sarah E.; Tong, Rosemarie. Competent refusal of nursing care [case study]. *Hastings Center Report* 2006 March-April; 36(2): 14-15. NRCBL: 9.5.1; 4.1.3; 20.5.1. SC: cs.

Edwards, Steven D.; McNamee, Mike. Why sports medicine is not medicine. *Health Care Analysis: An International Journal of Health Philosophy and Policy* 2006 June; 14(2): 103-109. NRCBL: 9.5.1; 4.1.2; 4.4.

Abstract: Sports Medicine as an apparent sub-class of medicine has developed apace over the past 30 years. Its recent trajectory has been evidenced by the emergence of specialist international research journals, standard texts, annual conferences, academic appointments and postgraduate courses. Although this field of enquiry and practice lays claim to the title 'sports medicine' this paper queries the legitimacy of that claim. Depending upon how 'sports medicine' and 'medicine' are defined, a plausible-sounding case can be made to show that sports medicine is not in fact a branch of medicine. Rather, it is sometimes closer to practices such as non-therapeutic cosmetic surgery. The argument of the paper is as follows. It begins with a brief statement concerning methodology. We then identify and subscribe to a plausible defining goal of medicine taken from a recognised authority in the field. Then two representative, authoritative, definitions of sports medicine are discussed. It is then shown that acceptance of these definitions of sports medicine generates a problem in that if they are accepted, no necessary commitment to the defining goal of medicine is present within sports medicine. It seems to follow that sports medicine is not medicine. In the final part of the paper a critical response to that conclusion is presented and rebutted. The response is one which rejects the identification of the defining goal of medicine upon which our argument rests.

Elliott, Richard. Ontario appellate court denies HIV-positive man's constitutional claim to medical marijuana. *HIV/AIDS Policy and Law Review* 2002 March; 6(3): 56-58. NRCBL: 9.5.1; 9.7; 9.5.9. SC: le.

Emanuel, Ezekiel J.; Wertheimer, Alan. The ethics of influenza vaccination: response [letters]. *Science* 2006 August 11; 313(5788): 758-759. NRCBL: 9.5.1; 9.4; 9.7.

Enserink, Martin. Selling the stem cell dream. *Science* 2006 July 14; 313(5784): 160-163. NRCBL: 9.5.1; 1.3.2; 18.5.4; 9.3.1; 15.1.

Foley, Kathleen M.; Szalavitz, Maia. Why not a national institute on pain research? *Cerebrum: The Dana Forum on Brain Science* 2006 February: 1-14. NRCBL: 9.5.1; 9.7; 9.5.9; 4.4.

Frey, Harvey S. The ethics of influenza vaccination [letter]. *Science* 2006 August 11; 313(5788): 758. NRCBL: 9.5.1; 9.4; 9.7.

Fryer-Edwards, Kelly. On cattle and casseroles. *American Journal of Bioethics* 2006 March-April; 6(2): 55-56. NRCBL: 9.5.1; 8.4. SC: le. Identifiers: Health Insurance Portability and Accountability Act of 1996; Wyoming. Comments: William Nelson, Gili Lushkov, Andrew Pomerantz and William B. Weeks. Rural health care ethics: is there a literature? American Journal of Bioethics 2006 March-April; 6(2): 44-50.

Galvani, Alison P.; Medlock, Jan; Chapman, Gretchen B. The ethics of influenza vaccination [letter]. *Science* 2006 August 11; 313(5788): 758. NRCBL: 9.5.1; 9.4; 9.7.

General Medical Council [GMC](Great Britain). Serious Communicable Diseases. London: General Medical Council, 1998; 14 p. NRCBL: 9.5.1; 9.5.6; 8.3.1; 8.4; 7.1;. Note: Approved September 1997. Replaces the guidance booklet "HIV and AIDS.".

Geppert, Cynthia M.A.; Arora, Sanjeev. Ethical issues in the treatment of hepatitis C. *Clinical Gastroenterology and Hepatology* 2005 October; 3(10): 937-944. NRCBL: 9.5.1; 9.2; 9.4. SC: em.

Gill, Carol J. Disability, constructed vulnerability, and socially conscious palliative care. *Journal of Palliative Care* 2006 Autumn; 22(3): 183-189. NRCBL: 9.5.1; 4.4; 7.1; 20.4.1; 20.5.1.

Giordano, Simona. Autonomy and control in eating disorders. *In her:* Understanding Eating Disorders: Conceptual and Ethical Issues in the Treatment of Anorexia and Bulimia Nervosa. New York: Oxford University Press; 2005: 211-234. NRCBL: 9.5.1; 1.1.

Giordano, Simona. Eating or treating? Legal and ethical issues surrounding eating disorders. *In her:* Understanding Eating Disorders: Conceptual and Ethical Issues in the Treatment of Anorexia and Bulimia Nervosa. New York: Oxford University Press; 2005: 179-210. NRCBL: 9.5.1.

Goering, Sara. Conformity through cosmetic surgery: the medical erasure of race and disability. *In:* Figueroa, Robert; Harding, Sandra, eds. Science and Other Cultures: Issues in Philosophies of Science and Technology. New York: Routledge; 2003: 172-188. NRCBL: 9.5.1; 4.2.

Good, Grace. Sick to death. *Journal of Clinical Ethics* 2006 Spring; 17(1): 80-82. NRCBL: 9.5.1; 9.5.3; 8.3.4; 8.1; 8.4. SC: cs.

Gould, Donald. Castrating into conformity. *New Statesman (London, England:* 1957) 1967 October 27; 74: 540. NRCBL: 9.5.1; 10; 1.3.5; 1.3.1. Identifiers: Germany.

Greene, Wallace. Dispensing medical marijuana: some halachic parameters. *Judaism* 2006 Summer-Fall; 55(1-2): 28-38. NRCBL: 9.5.1; 9.7; 9.5.9; 1.2.

Haisma, H.J.; de Hon, O. Gene doping. *International Journal of Sports Medicine* 2006 April; 27(4): 257-266. NRCBL: 9.5.1; 15.1; 4.5; 9.7.

Hall, Peter. Failed asylum seekers and health care [editorial]. *BMJ: British Medical Journal* 2006 July 15; 333(7559): 109-110. NRCBL: 9.5.1; 9.3.1; 21.1. SC: le. Identifiers: United Kingdom (Great Britain).

Hammett, Theodore M. Making the case for health interventions in correctional facilities. *Journal of Urban Health* 2001 June; 78(2): 236-240. NRCBL: 9.5.1; 1.3.5; 9.5.6; 9.1.

Hancock, Debbie. Influenza vaccinations: should they be mandatory for nurses? *MCN: The American Journal of Maternal Child Nursing* 2006 March-April; 31(2): 77. NRCBL: 9.5.1; 9.7; 4.1.3.

Hardwig, John. Rural health care ethics: what assumptions and attitudes should drive the research? *American Journal of Bioethics* 2006 March-April; 6(2): 53-54. NRCBL: 9.5.1; 2.1; 1.3.9; 1.3.7. Comments: William Nelson, Gili Lushkov, Andrew Pomerantz and William B. Weeks. Rural health care ethics: is there a literature? American Journal of Bioethics 2006 March-April; 6(2): 44-50.

Herrmann, Beate. Schönheitsideal und medizinische Körpermanipulation: invasive Selbstgestaltung als Ausdruck autonomer Entscheidung oder "sozialer Unterwerfung" = Ideals of beauty and the medical manipulation of the body between free choice and coercion. *Ethik in der Medizin* 2006 March; 18(1): 71-80. NRCBL: 9.5.1; 1.1; 4.5.

Hess, David. Cancer. *In:* Mitcham, Carl, ed. Encyclopedia of Science, Technology, and Ethics. Farmington Hills, MI: Thomson/Gale, 2005: 285-288. NRCBL: 9.5.1; 18.5.1; 18.6.

Holt, Graeme; Wheelan, Kerry; Gregori, Alberto. The ethical implications of recent innovations in knee arthroplasty. *Journal of Bone and Joint Surgery. American Volume* 2006 January; 88(1): 226-229. NRCBL: 9.5.1; 5.1; 1.1.

Howe, P. David. Investigating sports medicine: medical anthropology in context. *In his:* Sport, Professionalism and Pain: Ethnographies of Injury and Risk. New York: Routledge; 2004: 13-32. NRCBL: 9.5.1; 7.1.

Iezzoni, Lisa I. Going beyond disease to address disability. *New England Journal of Medicine* 2006 September 7; 355(10): 976-979. NRCBL: 9.5.1; 8.1; 7.2.

Ingram, David. Antidiscrimination, welfare, and democracy: toward a discourse-ethical understanding of disability law. *Social Theory and Practice* 2006 April; 32(2): 213-248. NRCBL: 9.5.1; 7.1; 4.2; 1.1. SC: le.

Johnson, Rob. The unique ethics of sports medicine. *Clinics in Sports Medicine* 2004 April; 23(2): 175-182. NRCBL: 9.5.1; 8.1; 8.4; 8.3.1; 9.5.9; 9.4; 1.3.1.

Jones, James W.; McCullough, Laurence B.; Richman, Bruce W. Ethics of operative scheduling: fiduciary patient responsibilities and more. *Journal of Vascular Surgery* 2003 July; 38(1): 204-205. NRCBL: 9.5.1; 1.3.2; 9.1. SC: cs.

Kennedy, Allison M.; Brown, Cedric J.; Gust, Deborah A. Vaccine beliefs of parents who oppose compulsory vaccination. *Public Health Reports* 2005 May-June; 120(3): 252-258. NRCBL: 9.5.1; 9.7; 8.3.2; 8.3.4. SC: em.

Kidd, Maria. Ethical considerations in childhood immunizations for the advanced nurse practitioner. *In:* Bartter, Karen, ed. Ethical Issues in Advanced Nursing Practice. Boston: Butterworth-Heinemann; 2001: 66-79. NRCBL: 9.5.1; 9.7.

Kirschner, Kristi L. Unequal stakeholders: "for you, it's an academic exercise; for me, it's my life". *American Journal of Bioethics* 2006 September-October; 6(5): 30-32; discussion W30-W32. NRCBL: 9.5.1; 9.5.4; 20.5.1. Comments: Mary Ellen Wojtasiewicz. Damage compounded: disparities, distrust, and disparate impact in end-of-life conflict resolution policies. American Journal of Bioethics 2006 September-October; 6(5): 8-12.

Kittay, Eva Feder; Jennings, Bruce; Wasunna, Angela A. Dependency, difference and the global ethic of longterm care. *Journal of Political Philosophy* 2005 December; 13(4): 443-469. NRCBL: 9.5.1; 21.1; 1.1.

Klugman, Craig M. Have and have nots. *American Journal of Bioethics* 2006 March-April; 6(2): 63-64. NRCBL: 9.5.1; 2.1; 1.3.9. Comments: William Nelson, Gili Lushkov, Andrew Pomerantz and William B. Weeks. Rural health care ethics: is there a literature? American Journal of Bioethics 2006 March-April; 6(2): 44-50.

Kolata, Gina. Study questions colonoscopy effectiveness. *New York Times* 2006 December 14; p. A36. NRCBL: 9.5.1; 9.8; 9.3.1. SC: po; em.

Kordsmeier, Julie. Influenza vaccinations: should they be mandatory for nurses? *MCN: The American Journal of Maternal Child Nursing* 2006 March-April; 31(2): 76. NRCBL: 9.5.1; 9.7; 7.1.

Laureys, Steven; Pellas, Frédéric; Van Eeckhout, Philippe; Ghorbel, Sofiane; Schnakers, Caroline;

NRCBL: National Reference Center for Bioethics Literature Classification Scheme   See inside front cover for terms.

99

Perrin, Fabian; Berré, Jacques; Faymonville, Marie-Elisabeth; Pantke, Karl-Heinz; Damas, Francois; Lamy, Maurice; Moonen, Gustave; Goldman, Serge. The locked-in syndrome : what is it like to be conscious but paralyzed and voiceless? *Progress in Brain Research* 2005; 150: 495-511. NRCBL: 9.5.1; 20.5.1; 4.4. SC: em.

Little, Miles. Chronic illness and the experience of surviving cancer. *Internal Medicine Journal* 2004 April; 34(4): 201-202. NRCBL: 9.5.1; 4.4.

Ljungqvist, Arne. The international anti-doping policy and its implementation. *In:* Tamburrini, Claudio; Tännsjö, Torbjörn, eds. Genetic Technology and Sport: Ethical Questions. London; New York: Routledge; 2005: 13-18. NRCBL: 9.5.1; 9.5.9.

Lo, Bernard. HPV vaccine and adolescents' sexual activity [editorial]. *BMJ: British Medical Journal* 2006 May 13; 332(7550): 1106-1107. NRCBL: 9.5.1; 9.7; 10; 9.5.7.

Lu, David W.; Matz, Kenneth A. Declining use of the eponym "Reiter's syndrome" in the medical literature, 1998-2003. *Journal of the American Academy of Dermatology* 2005 October; 53(4): 720-723. NRCBL: 9.5.1; 21.4. SC: em.

Luño, Angel Rodríguez. Ethical reflections on vaccines using cells from aborted fetuses. *National Catholic Bioethics Quarterly* 2006 Autumn; 6(3): 453-459. NRCBL: 9.5.1; 9.7; 18.5.4; 12.3.

Mathias, Michael B. The competing demands of sport and health: an essay on the history of ethics in sports medicine. *Clinics in Sports Medicine* 2004 April; 23(2): 195-214. NRCBL: 9.5.1; 1.3.1; 7.1.

Mensah, George A. Eliminating disparities in cardiovascular health: six strategic imperatives and a framework for action. *Circulation* 2005 March 15; 111(10): 1332-1336. NRCBL: 9.5.1.

Miller, Jessica Prata. Defining "research" in rural health care ethics. *American Journal of Bioethics* 2006 March-April; 6(2): 59-61. NRCBL: 9.5.1; 1.3.7; 2.1; 1.3.9. Comments: William Nelson, Gili Lushkov, Andrew Pomerantz and William B. Weeks. Rural health care ethics: is there a literature? American Journal of Bioethics 2006 March-April; 6(2): 44-50.

Mitchell, Christine; Truog, Robert. When a village is not enough. *Journal of Clinical Ethics* 2006 Spring; 17(1): 79. NRCBL: 9.5.1; 9.5.3; 9.6; 8.1. SC: cs.

Mitrany, Edith; Melamed, Yuval. Compulsory treatment of anorexia nervosa. *Israel Journal of Psychiatry and Related Sciences* 2005; 42(3): 185-190. NRCBL: 9.5.1; 17.7; 8.3.4. SC: le. Identifiers: Israel; Law for the Treatment of the Mentally Ill.

Morton, B.; Richardson, A.; Duncan, S. Sudden unexpected death in epilepsy (SUDEP): don't ask, don't tell?

Journal of Neurology, Neurosurgery, and Psychiatry 2006 February; 77(2): 199-202. NRCBL: 9.5.1; 8.2; 20.1; 17.1. SC: em.

Nelson, William; Lushkov, Gili; Pomerantz, Andrew; Weeks, William B. Rural health care ethics: is there a literature? *American Journal of Bioethics* 2006 March-April; 6(2): 44-50. NRCBL: 9.5.1; 1.3.9; 8.2; 2.1; 7.1. SC: em.

Newell, Christopher. Disability, bioethics, and rejected knowledge. *Journal of Medicine and Philosophy* 2006 June; 31(3): 269-283. NRCBL: 9.5.1; 2.1. SC: an.
Abstract: In this article I explore disability as far more than individual private tragedy, suggesting it has a social location and reproduction. Within this context we look at the power relations associated with bioethics and its largely uncritical use of the biomedical model. Within that context the topics of genetics, euthanasia, and biotechnology are explored. In examining these topics a social account of disability is proposed as rejected knowledge. Accordingly we explore the political nature of bioethics as a project.

Nowak, Rachel. When looks can kill: the nip and tuck generation faces a danger far worse than the operation going wrong. *New Scientist* 2006 October 21-27; 192(2574): 18-21. NRCBL: 9.5.1; 20.7.

Omer, Saad B.; Pan, William K.Y.; Halsey, Neal A.; Stokley, Shannon; Moulton, Lawrence H.; Navar, Ann Marie; Pierce, Mathew; Salmon, Daniel A. Nonmedical exemptions to school immunization requirements: secular trends and association of state policies with pertussis incidence. *JAMA: The Journal of the American Medical Association* 2006 October 11; 296(14): 1757-1763. NRCBL: 9.5.1; 9.5.7; 9.7. SC: em.
Abstract: School immunization requirements have played a major role in controlling vaccine-preventable diseases in the United States. Most states offer nonmedical exemptions to school requirements (religious or personal belief). Exemptors are at increased risk of acquiring and transmitting disease. The role of exemption policies may be especially important for pertussis, which is endemic in the United States. OBJECTIVE: To determine if (1) the rates of nonmedical exemptions differ and have been increasing in states that offer only religious vs personal belief exemptions; (2) the rates of nonmedical exemptions differ and have been increasing in states that have easy vs medium and easy vs difficult processes for obtaining exemptions; and (3) pertussis incidence is associated with policies of granting personal belief exemptions, ease of obtaining exemptions, and acceptance of parental signature as sufficient proof of compliance with school immunization requirements. DESIGN, SETTING, AND PARTICIPANTS: We analyzed 1991 through 2004 state-level rates of nonmedical exemptions at school entry and 1986 through 2004 pertussis incidence data for individuals aged 18 years or younger. MAIN OUTCOME MEASURES: State-level exemption rates and pertussis incidence. RESULTS: From 2001 through 2004, states that permitted personal belief exemptions had higher nonmedical exemption rates than states that offered only religious exemptions, and states that easily granted exemptions had higher nonmedical exemption rates in 2002 through 2003 compared with states with medium and difficult exemption processes. The mean exemption rate increased an average of 6% per year, from 0.99% in 1991 to 2.54% in 2004, among states that offered personal belief exemptions. In states that easily granted exemptions, the rate increased 5% per

year, from 1.26% in 1991 to 2.51% in 2004. No statistically significant change was seen in states that offered only religious exemptions or that had medium and difficult exemption processes. In multivariate analyses adjusting for demographics, easier granting of exemptions (incidence rate ratio = 1.53; 95% confidence interval, 1.10-2.14) and availability of personal belief exemptions (incidence rate ratio =1.48; 95% confidence interval, 1.03-2.13) were associated with increased pertussis incidence. CONCLUSIONS: Permitting personal belief exemptions and easily granting exemptions are associated with higher and increasing nonmedical US exemption rates. State policies granting personal belief exemptions and states that easily grant exemptions are associated with increased pertussis incidence. States should examine their exemption policies to ensure control of pertussis and other vaccine-preventable diseases.

Orenstein, Walter A.; Hinman, Alan R. The immunization system in the United States — the role of school immunization laws. *Vaccine* 1999; 17(Supplement 3): S19-S24. NRCBL: 9.5.1; 9.7; 1.3.5.

Pan American Health Organization. Women, Health and Development Program; Onyango, Christine. Gender equity in health sector reform: a review of the literature. *Pan American Health Organization* 2001 July: 1-42 [Online].Accessed: http://www.paho.org/English/DPM/ GPP/GH/ReformLitReview.pdf [2006 March 14]. NRCBL: 9.5.1; 9.5.5; 10; 21.1; 9.2; 9.3.1. SC: rv. Note: Regional Office of the World Health Organization.

Pan American Health Organization. Women, Health, and Development Program. Gender equity in health. Washington, DC: Pan American Health Organization n.d. [Online]. Accessed: http://www.paho.org/English/AD/ GE/GEHFactSheet.pdf [2006 March 14]. NRCBL: 9.5.1; 9.5.5; 10.

Phadke, Anant. Restricted availability of free anti-rabies vaccine in public health facilities in India: unethical and criminal. *Indian Journal of Medical Ethics* 2006 April-June; 3(2): 48-49. NRCBL: 9.5.1; 9.7; 9.4; 21.1.

Pontifical Academy for Life. Moral reflections on vaccines prepared from cells derived from aborted human fetuses. *National Catholic Bioethics Quarterly* 2006 Autumn; 6(3): 541-550. NRCBL: 9.5.1; 9.7; 18.5.4; 12.3; 1.2.

Pruss, Alexander R. Complicity, fetal tissue, and vaccines. *National Catholic Bioethics Quarterly* 2006 Autumn; 6(3): 461-470. NRCBL: 9.5.1; 9.7; 18.5.4; 12.3; 4.1.2; 1.2.

Raffle, Angela E. Information about screening — is it to achieve high uptake or to ensure informed choice? *Health Expectations* 2001 June; 4(2): 92-98. NRCBL: 9.5.1; 8.3.1; 15.3; 8.1; 5.2; 9.1.

Ressler-Maerlender, Jessamyn; Sorensen, Robyn E. Circumcision: an informed choice. *AWHONN Lifelines* 2005 April-May; 9(2): 146-150. NRCBL: 9.5.1; 10; 8.3.2.

Rifkin, Dena. The elephant in the room. *Hastings Center Report* 2006 March-April; 36(2): 9. NRCBL: 9.5.1; 8.1. SC: cs.

Ritchie, Elspeth Cameron; Mott, Robert L. Military humanitarian assistance: the pitfalls and promise of good intentions. *In:* Beam, Thomas E.; Sparacino, Linette R.; Pellegrino, Edmund D.; Hartle, Anthony E.; Howe, Edmund G., eds. Military Medical Ethics. Volume 2. Washington, DC: TMM Publications, Borden Institute, Walter Reed Army Medical Center; 2003: 805-830. NRCBL: 9.5.1; 21.1; 1.3.5.

Robinson, Ellen M.; Hamel-Nardozzi, Marguerite. Stories of the silent: advocating for a disabled woman at end of life. *Topics in Stroke Rehabilitation* 2005 Summer; 12(3): 82-86. NRCBL: 9.5.1; 20.5.1; 8.1; 4.4. SC: cs.

Rold, William J. 30 years after Estelle v. Gamble: a legal retrospective. *CorrectCare* 2006 Summer; 20(3): 7, 18. NRCBL: 9.5.1; 1.3.5. SC: le.

Salmon, Daniel A.; Teret, Stephen P.; MacIntyre, C. Raina; Salisbury, David; Burgess, Margaret A.; Halsey, Neal A. Compulsory vaccination and conscientious or philosophical exemptions: past, present, and future. *Lancet* 2006 February 4-10; 367(9508): 436-442. NRCBL: 9.5.1; 9.7; 7.1; 9.8; 21.1. SC: le.
Abstract: Compulsory vaccination has contributed to the success of immunisation programmes in the USA and Australia, yet the benefits from compulsory vaccination are not universally recognised. Some people—experts and the public alike—believe that the benefits of compulsory vaccination are outweighed by the associated ethical problems. A review of vaccination legislation in the UK, Australia, and the USA raises four main points. First, compulsory vaccination may be effective in preventing disease outbreaks, reaching and sustaining high immunisation coverage rates, and expediting the introduction of new vaccines. Second, to be effective, compulsory programmes must have a reliable supply of safe and effective vaccines and most people must be willing to be vaccinated. Third, allowance of exemptions to compulsory vaccination may limit public backlash. Finally, compulsory vaccination may increase the burden on governments to ensure the safety of vaccines. Nevertheless, although compulsory immunisation can be very effective, it might not be acceptable in some countries where high coverage has been achieved through other approaches or efforts, such as in Sweden, Norway, Denmark, the Netherlands, and the UK. These factors should be considered when compulsory vaccinations are being introduced or immunisation laws refined. Lessons learned from compulsory vaccination could be useful to other public-health programmes.

Sandman, Lars; Nordmark, Anders. Ethical conflicts in prehospital emergency care. *Nursing Ethics* 2006 November; 13(6): 592-607. NRCBL: 9.5.1. SC: em. Identifiers: Sweden.

Santora, Marc. In diabetes fight, raising cash and keeping trust. *New York Times* 2006 November 25; p. A1, B4. NRCBL: 9.5.1; 1.3.2; 9.1. SC: po. Identifiers: American Diabetes Association.

NRCBL: National Reference Center for Bioethics Literature Classification Scheme   See inside front cover for terms.

101

Saul, Stephanie. Profit and questions as doctors offer prostate cancer therapy. *New York Times* 2006 December 1; p. A1, C7. NRCBL: 9.5.1; 9.3.1; 8.1.

Sibbald, Robert W.; Lazar, Neil M. Bench-to-bedside review: ethical challenges for those in directing roles in critical care units. *Critical Care* 2005 February; 9(1): 76-80. NRCBL: 9.5.1; 1.3.2; 9.4.

Silverstein, Robin P. The ethics of influenza vaccination [letter]. *Science* 2006 August 11; 313(5788): 758. NRCBL: 9.5.1; 9.4; 9.7.

Siminoff, Laura A.; Step, Mary M. A communication model of shared decision making: accounting for cancer treatment decisions. *Health Psychology* 2005 July; 24(4 Supplement): S99-S105. NRCBL: 9.5.1; 9.4; 8.1.

Singh, Ritupriya; Singh, Kaushal K. Ethical aspects of the tuberculosis programme. *Health Administrator* 2003 January-July; 15(1-2): 156-168. NRCBL: 9.5.1. Identifiers: India.

Slevin, Maurice. Funding of patients' groups. *Lancet* 2006 July 15-21; 368(9531): 202. NRCBL: 9.5.1; 9.3.1; 9.7.

Srivastava, Ranjana. No refuge for the ailing. *New England Journal of Medicine* 2006 August 3; 355(5): 443-445. NRCBL: 9.5.1; 20.4.1; 9.2; 1.3.5.

Stanley, Jay. Societal influences and the ethics of military healthcare. *In:* Beam, Thomas E.; Sparacino, Linette R.; Pellegrino, Edmund D.; Hartle, Anthony E.; Howe, Edmund G., eds. Military Medical Ethics. Volume 2. Washington, DC: TMM Publications, Borden Institute, Walter Reed Army Medical Center; 2003: 719-738. NRCBL: 9.5.1; 1.3.5; 9.5.5; 9.5.6.

Trivedi, Amal N.; Ayanian, John Z. Perceived discrimination and use of preventive health services. *JGIM: Journal of General Internal Medicine* 2006 June; 21(6): 553-558. NRCBL: 9.5.1; 9.3.1; 9.4.5; 10. SC: em.

Tucker, Andrew M. Ethics and the professional team physician. *Clinics in Sports Medicine* 2004 April; 23(2): 227-241. NRCBL: 9.5.1; 8.1; 8.4; 1.3.2.

Tuite, Helen; Browne, Katherine; O'Neill, Desmond. Prisoners in general hospitals: doctors' attitudes and practice [letter]. *BMJ: British Medical Journal* 2006 March 4; 332(7540): 548-549. NRCBL: 9.5.1; 8.1. SC: em. Identifiers: Ireland.

Verweij, Marcel; Dawson, Angus. Ethical principles for collective immunisation programmes. *Vaccine* 2004 August 13; 22(23-24): 3122-3126. NRCBL: 9.5.1; 9.7; 9.1.

Warner, Teddy D.; Monaghan-Geernaert, Pamela; Battaglia, John; Brems, Christiane; Johnson, Mark E.; Roberts, Laura Weiss. Ethical considerations in rural health care: a pilot study of clinicians in Alaska and New

Mexico. *Community Mental Health Journal* 2005 February; 41(1): 21-33. NRCBL: 9.5.1; 8.1; 8.4. SC: em.

Wenkel, David H. Separation of conjoined twins and the principle of double effect. *Christian Bioethics* 2006 December; 12(3): 291-300. NRCBL: 9.5.1; 1.1; 9.5.7.
Abstract: This article examines the relationship between the principle of double effect and justification for separation surgeries for conjoined twins. First, the principle of double effect is examined in light of its historical context. It is argued that it can only operate under an absolutist view of good and evil that is compatible with the Bible. Given this foundation for application, scenarios for separating conjoined twins are considered against the criteria for the principle of double effect. It is concluded that the principle of double effect cannot be applied to cases wherein one of the twins must be killed. However, it is noted that this does not leave decision makers without options.

Whaley, Arthur L. Ethnicity/race, ethics, and epidemiology. *Journal of the National Medical Association* 2003 August; 95(8): 736-742. NRCBL: 9.5.1; 9.5.4; 7.1; 21.7.

Wroe, Abigail L.; Bhan, Angela; Salkovskis, Paul; Bedford, Helen. Feeling bad about immunising our children. *Vaccine* 2005 February 10; 23(12): 1428-1433. NRCBL: 9.5.1; 9.7; 8.3.2. SC: em.

Yan, Qingshan. Removing obstacles — ethics of the public welfare payments for the disabled. *In:* Döring, Ole; Chen, Renbiao, eds. Advances in Chinese Medical Ethics: Chinese and International Perspectives. Hamburg: Institut für Asienkunde; 2002: 315-321. NRCBL: 9.5.1; 9.3.1. Note: Proceedings of the Second Sino-German Interdisciplinary Symposium about Medical Ethics in China, Shanghai, 19-23 October, 1999.

Zajtchuk, Joan T. Military medicine in humanitarian missions. *In:* Beam, Thomas E.; Sparacino, Linette R.; Pellegrino, Edmund D.; Hartle, Anthony E.; Howe, Edmund G., eds. Military Medical Ethics. Volume 2. Washington, DC: TMM Publications, Borden Institute, Walter Reed Army Medical Center; 2003: 773-804. NRCBL: 9.5.1; 21.1; 1.3.5.

Zimmerman, Richard K. If pneumonia is the "old man's friend", should it be prevented by vaccination? An ethical analysis. *Vaccine* 2005 May 31; 23(29): 3843-3849. NRCBL: 9.5.1; 9.7; 9.5.2; 9.4.

CARE FOR SPECIFIC GROUPS/ AGED

Banks, Daniel; Crow, Sue. Helping residents in nursing homes find peace. *Linacre Quarterly* 2006 November; 73(4): 302-317. NRCBL: 9.5.2; 1.2; 4.1.3.

Barron, Jeremy S.; Duffey, Patricia L.; Byrd, Linda Jo; Campbell, Robin; Ferrucci, Luigi. Informed consent for research participation in frail older persons. *Aging Clinical and Experimental Research* 2004 February; 16(1): 79-85. NRCBL: 9.5.2; 18.2; 18.3; 18.5.7.

Berdes, Celia; Emanuel, Linda. Creative adaptation in aging and dying: ethical imperative or impossible dream?

In: Jansen, Lynn A., ed. Death in the Clinic. Lanham, MD: Rowman and Littlefield; 2006: 97-117. NRCBL: 9.5.2; 20.4.1.

Birrell, J.; Thomas, D.; Jones, C.A. Promoting privacy and dignity for older patients in hospital. *Nursing Standard* 2006 January 11-17; 20(18): 41-46. NRCBL: 9.5.2; 8.4.

Bolmsjö, Ingrid Ågren; Sandman, Lars; Andersson, Edith. Everyday ethics in the care of elderly people. *Nursing Ethics* 2006 May; 13(3): 249-263. NRCBL: 9.5.2. SC: em. Identifiers: Sweden.

Bowling, Ann. Quality of life in healthcare decisions. *In:* Rai, Gurcharan S, ed. Medical Ethics and the Elderly. 2nd ed. San Francisco: Radcliffe Medical Press; 2004: 147-154. NRCBL: 9.5.2.

Cahn, Ellen. Dementia and the nursing home decision. *Conservative Judaism* 2006 Summer; 58(4): 32-50. NRCBL: 9.5.2; 8.1; 7.1; 9.5.3; 1.2.

Eckenwiler, Lisa A. A missed opportunity: the President's Council on Bioethics report on ethical caregiving. *American Journal of Bioethics [Online].* 2006 March-April; 6(2): W20-W23. NRCBL: 9.5.2; 2.4.

Edwards, Nancy. Legal, ethical, and moral considerations in caring for individuals with Alzheimer's disease. *In:* Cowen, Perle Slavik; Moorhead, Sue, eds. Current Issues in Nursing. 7th ed. St. Louis, MO: Mosby, 2006: 645-651. NRCBL: 9.5.2; 17.1.

Emanuel, Linda; Iris, Madelyn A.; Webster, James R. Ethical aspects of geriatric palliative care. *In:* Morrison, R. Sean; Meier, Diane E.; Capello, Carol, eds. Geriatric Palliative Care. New York: Oxford University Press; 2003: 55-78. NRCBL: 9.5.2; 2.1; 20.4.1.

Ersin, Fatma; Cevik, Ebru; Aksoy, Sahin; Aksoy, Nurten. Aging and nursing in Turkey: an ethical perspective. *In:* Sang-yong, Song; Young-Mo, Koo; Macer, Darryl R.J., eds. Asian Bioethics in the 21st Century. Christchurch, NZ: Eubios Ethics Institute, 2002: 118-121. NRCBL: 9.5.2; 8.1. Conference: Proceedings of the Asian Bioethics Conference (ABC4), held 22-25 November 2002 in Seoul, South Korea.

Fan, Ruiping. Confucian filial piety and long term care for aged parents. *HEC (Healthcare Ethics Committee) Forum* 2006 March; 18(1): 1-17. NRCBL: 9.5.2; 1.1; 7.1.

Franklin, Lise-Lotte; Ternestedt, Britt-Marie; Nordenfelt, Lennart. Views on dignity of elderly nursing home residents. *Nursing Ethics* 2006 March; 13(2): 130-146. NRCBL: 9.5.2; 4.4. SC: em. Identifiers: Sweden.
Abstract: Discussion about a dignified death has almost exclusively been applied to palliative care and people dying of cancer. As populations are getting older in the western world and living with chronic illnesses affecting their everyday lives, it is relevant to broaden the definition of palliative care to include other groups of people. The aim of the study was to explore the views on dignity at the end of life of 12 elderly people living in two nursing homes in Sweden. A hermeneutic approach was used to interpret the material, which was gathered during semi-structured interviews. A total of 39 interviews were transcribed. The analysis revealed three themes: (1) the unrecognizable body; (2) fragility and dependency; and (3) inner strength and a sense of coherence.

Fried, Terri R.; Byers, Amy L.; Gallo, William T.; Van Ness, Peter H.; Towle, Virginia R.; O'Leary, John R.; Dubin, Joel A. Prospective study of health status preferences and changes in preferences over time in older adults. *Archives of Internal Medicine* 2006 April 24; 166(8): 890-895. NRCBL: 9.5.2; 20.5.4. SC: em.

Gastmans, Chris; Milisen, K. Use of physical restraint in nursing homes: clinical-ethical considerations. *Journal of Medical Ethics* 2006 March; 32(3): 148-152. NRCBL: 9.5.2; 17.3.
Abstract: This article gives a brief overview of the state of the art concerning physical restraint use among older persons in nursing homes. Within this context we identify some essential values and norms that must be observed in an ethical evaluation of physical restraint. These values and norms provide the ethical foundation for a number of concrete recommendations that could give clinical and ethical support to caregivers when they make decisions about physical restraint. Respect for the autonomy and overall wellbeing of older persons, a proportional assessment of the advantages and disadvantages, a priority focus on the alternatives to physical restraint, individualised care, interdisciplinary decision making, and an institutional policy are the central points that make it possible to deal responsibly with the use of physical restraint for older persons in nursing homes.

Goldstein, Nathan E.; Lynn, Joanne. Trajectory of end-stage heart failure: the influence of technology and implications for policy change. *Perspectives on Biology and Medicine* 2006 Winter; 49(1): 10-18. NRCBL: 9.5.2; 20.5.4; 20.4.1; 4.4; 9.4.

Guptha, S.H.; Owusu-Agyei, P. Ageism in services for transient ischaemic attack and stroke: clinical leadership is key in changing practice [letter]. *BMJ: British Medical Journal* 2006 September 23; 333(7569): 656. NRCBL: 9.5.2; 9.4.

Johri, Mira; Damschroder, Laura J.; Zikmund-Fisher, Brian J.; Ubel, Peter A. The importance of age in allocating health care resources: does intervention-type matter? *Health Economics* 2005 July; 14(7): 669-678. NRCBL: 9.5.2; 4.4; 9.3.1; 9.4.

Jost, Timothy Stoltzfus. Racial and ethnic disparities in Medicare: what the Department of Health and Human Services and the Centers for Medicare and Medicaid services can, and should, do. *DePaul Journal of Health Care Law* 2005; 9(1): 667-718. NRCBL: 9.5.2; 9.5.4; 9.3.1.

Kirkpatrick, James N.; Kim, Antony Y. Heart failure ethics: overview of an emerging need. *Perspectives on Biology and Medicine* 2006 Winter; 49(1): 1-9. NRCBL: 9.5.2; 4.4; 20.4.1.

NRCBL: National Reference Center for Bioethics Literature Classification Scheme   See inside front cover for terms.

Knapp, Samuel; VandeCreek, Leon. Ethical and patient management issues with older, impaired drivers. *Professional Psychology: Research and Practice* 2005 April; 36(2): 197-202. NRCBL: 9.5.2. SC: cs.

Körtner, Ulrich H.J. Frailty: medizinethische Überlegungen zur Gebrechlichkeit des alten Menschen [Frailty: medical ethical considerations about the frailty of the elderly]. *Ethik in der Medizin* 2006 June; 18(2): 108-119. NRCBL: 9.5.2.

Levy, Roger N. Does cost containment create conflict in the care of the elderly patient? *Clinical Orthopaedics and Related Research* 2000 September; (378): 66-70. NRCBL: 9.5.2; 9.3.2; 9.4.

Liao, Solomon. Unmet activity of daily living needs: elder mistreatment and ethics in geriatric research [letter]. *Journal of the American Geriatrics Society* 2006 October; 54(10): 1622-1623. NRCBL: 9.5.2; 18.5.7.

Lloyd, Liz. Mortality and morality: ageing and the ethics of care. *Ageing and Society* 2004 March; 24(2): 235-256. NRCBL: 9.5.2; 20.4.1; 1.1; 10. SC: an.

McConnel, Charles; Turner, Leigh. Medicine, ageing and human longevity: the economics and ethics of anti-ageing interventions. *EMBO Reports* 2005 July; 6(Special Issue): S59-S62. NRCBL: 9.5.2; 9.3.1.

McDowall, Michael A. Ageism in services for transient ischaemic attack and stroke: ageism or cost-benefit analysis? [letter]. *BMJ: British Medical Journal* 2006 September 23; 333(7569): 656. NRCBL: 9.5.2; 9.4.

O'Dowd, Adrian. Doctors charged with ensuring dignity for older patients [news]. *BMJ: British Medical Journal* 2006 April 29; 332(7548): 993. NRCBL: 9.5.2. Identifiers: United Kingdom (Great Britain).

Rockwood, Kenneth. Capacity, population aging and professionalism [editorial]. *CMAJ/JAMC: Canadian Medical Association Journal* 2006 June 6; 174(12): 1689. NRCBL: 9.5.2; 8.3; 1.1.

Sabat, Steven R. Capacity for decision-making in Alzheimer's disease: selfhood, positioning and semiotic people. *Australian and New Zealand Journal of Psychiatry* 2005 November-December; 39(11-12): 1030-1035. NRCBL: 9.5.2; 4.4; 9.4; 8.3.3; 9.5.3.

Saga, Tadashi. Care for the elderly in Japan: past, present and future. *In:* Takahashi, Takao, ed. Taking Life and Death Seriously: Bioethics from Japan. Amsterdam; Boston: Elsevier JAI; 2005: 139-173. NRCBL: 9.5.2.

Sass, Hans-Martin; Wang, Yanguang. Geriatric medicine and care: ethical issues in providing and withholding treatment. *In:* Döring, Ole; Chen, Renbiao, eds. Advances in Chinese Medical Ethics: Chinese and International Perspectives. Hamburg: Institut für Asienkunde; 2002: 378-390. NRCBL: 9.5.2. Note: Proceedings of the Second

Sino-German Interdisciplinary Symposium about Medical Ethics in China, Shanghai, 19-23 October, 1999.

Schwark, C.; Schellinger, Peter D. Is old age really a reason to withhold thrombolytic therapy? [editorial]. *Journal of Neurology, Neurosurgery, and Psychiatry* 2006 March; 77(3): 289. NRCBL: 9.5.2; 9.2; 9.4.

Sorrell, Jeanne Merkle. Listening in thin places: ethics in the care of persons with Alzheimer's Disease. *Advances in Nursing Science* 2006 April-June; 29(2): 152-160. NRCBL: 9.5.2; 4.3; 4.1.3; 1.1; 4.4. SC: an.

Stuck, A.E. Autonomy and appropriate care for older disabled older people: guidelines of the Swiss Academy of Medical Sciences: commentary. *Journal of Nutrition, Health and Aging* 2005 July-August; 9(4): 287. NRCBL: 9.5.2; 1.1.

Swiss Academy of Medical Sciences; Stuck, Andreas; Amstad, Hermann; Baumann-Hölzle, Ruth; Fankhauser, Angeline; Kesselring, Annemarie; Leuba, Audrey; Rapin, Charles-Henri; Schmitt, Regula; Schönenberg, Hansruedi; Wirz, Urban; Vallotton, Michel. Treatment and care of elderly persons who are in need of care: medical-ethical guidelines and recommendations. *Journal of Nutrition, Health and Aging* 2005 July-August; 9(4): 288-295. NRCBL: 9.5.2; 6; 9.4. Identifiers: Switzerland.

Teeri, Sari; Leino-Kilpi, Helena; Valimaki, Maritta. Long-term nursing care of elderly people: identifying ethically problematic experiences among patients, relatives and nurses in Finland. *Nursing Ethics* 2006 March; 13(2): 116-129. NRCBL: 9.5.2; 8.1. SC: em.

Abstract: The aim of this study was to explore ethically problematic situations in the long-term nursing care of elderly people. It was assumed that greater awareness of ethical problems in caring for elderly people helps to ensure ethically high standards of nursing care. To obtain a broad perspective on the current situation, the data for this study were collected among elderly patients, their relatives and nurses in one long-term care institution in Finland. The patients (n = 10) were interviewed, while the relatives, (n = 17) and nurses (n = 9) wrote an essay. Interpretation of the data was based on qualitative content analysis. Problematic experiences were divided into three categories concerning patients' psychological, physical and social integrity. In the case of psychological integrity, the problems were seen as being related to treatment, self-determination and obtaining information; for physical integrity, they were related to physical abuse and lack of individualized care; and for social integrity, to loneliness and social isolation. This study provided no information on the prevalence of ethical problems. However, it is clear from the results that patient integrity warrants more attention in the nursing care of elderly patients.

Watson, Alison. Ethical dilemma: an elderly man and getting home. *Perspectives* 2005 Winter; 29(4): 13-15. NRCBL: 9.5.2; 10.

Weaver, Glenn. Embodied spirituality: experiences of identity and spiritual suffering among persons with Alzheimer's dementia. *In:* Jeeves, Michael, ed. From Cells to

Souls — and Beyond: Changing Portraits of Human Nature. Grand Rapids, MI: W.B. Eerdmans; 2004: 77-101. NRCBL: 9.5.2; 1.2; 17.1.

Young, John. Ageism in services for transient ischaemic attack and stroke [editorial]. *BMJ: British Medical Journal* 2006 September 9; 333(7567): 508-509. NRCBL: 9.5.2; 9.4. Identifiers: United Kingdom(Great Britain).

CARE FOR SPECIFIC GROUPS/ FETUSES
See also HUMAN EXPERIMENTATION/ SPECIAL POPULATIONS/ EMBRYOS AND FETUSES

Chervenak, Frank A.; McCullough, Laurence B.; Skupski, Daniel; Chasen, Stephen T. Ethical issues in the management of pregnancies complicated by fetal anomalies. *Obstetrical and Gynecological Survey* 2003 July; 58(7): 473-483. NRCBL: 9.5.8; 9.5.5; 18.5.4; 12.1; 1.1; 7.2. SC: rv.

Couzin, Jennifer. Desperate measures. *Science* 2006 August 18; 313(5789): 904-907. NRCBL: 9.5.8; 9.5.5; 18.5.4; 15.1. Identifiers: fetal surgery.

Davis, John Jefferson. The moral status of the embryonic human: religious perspectives. *Ethics and Medicine* 2006 Spring; 22(1): 9-21. NRCBL: 9.5.8; 4.4; 1.2; 14.1.

Latson, Larry A. Aortic valvuloplasty in the fetus: technically possible but is it ready for prime time? *Journal of Pediatrics* 2005 October; 147(4): 424-426. NRCBL: 9.5.8; 9.5.5; 9.8.

Lees, C.; Baumgartner, H. The TRUFFLE study — a collaborative publicly funded project from concept to reality: how to negotiate an ethical, administrative and funding obstacle course in the European Union[editorial]. *Ultrasound in Obstetrics and Gynecology* 2005 February; 25(2): 105-107. NRCBL: 9.5.8; 18.5.4; 15.1. Identifiers: Trial of Umbilical and Fetal Flow in Europe.

Marks, Lee Ann. The "Seymour Report" on Fetal Welfare and the Law in Australia. *E Law: Murdoch University Electronic Journal of Law* 1995 December; 2(3): 4 p. [Online]. Accessed: http://www.murdoch.edu.au/elaw/issues/v2n3/marks23.html [2006 June 29]. NRCBL: 9.5.8. SC: le.

Mendoza, Fátima Flores. The offence of foetal injuries in Spain's Penal Code of 1995 = El delito de lesiones al feto en el Código español de 1995. *Law and the Human Genome Review = Revista de Derecho y Genoma Humano* 1996 July-December; (5): 157-183. NRCBL: 9.5.8; 4.4; 15.1; 1.3.5.

Schenker, Joseph G.; Gdansky, Efraim. Ethical dilemmas in modern obstetrics [editorial]. *Prenatal and Neonatal Medicine* 1998 June; 3(3): 279-280. NRCBL: 9.5.8; 9.5.5; 8.1.

Shapiro, Carla. Our neighbors to the north: a Canadian perspective on perinatal ethics. *Newborn and Infant Nursing Review* 2005 June; 5(2): 82-86. NRCBL: 9.5.8; 9.5.5; 9.5.9; 4.4.

Sytsma, Sharon E. The ethics of using dexamethasone to prevent virilization of female fetuses. *In:* Sytsma, Sharon E., ed. Ethics and Intersex. Dordrecht: Springer, 2006: 241-258. NRCBL: 9.5.8; 9.7; 10.

Tighe, Mark. Fetuses can feel pain [letter]. *BMJ: British Medical Journal* 2006 April 29; 332(7548): 1036. NRCBL: 9.5.8; 4.4. Comments: British Medical Journal. 2006 Apr 15; 332(7546): 909-12.

CARE FOR SPECIFIC GROUPS/ INDIGENTS

Hospital charged with dumping homeless patient. *New York Times* 2006 November 17; p. A29. NRCBL: 9.5.10; 9.2; 9.3.1; 1.3.2. SC: po. Identifiers: Kaiser Permanente; patient dumping.

Geraghty, Karen. The obligation to provide charity care. *Virtual Mentor* 2001 October; 3(10): 3p. NRCBL: 9.5.10.

Geraghty, Karen. The obligation to provide charity care. *In:* American Medical Association. Professing Medicine: strengthening the ethics and professionalism of tomorrow's physicians. Chicago: American Medical Association; 2001: 57-61. NRCBL: 9.5.10; 4.1.2. Note: Commemorative issue of Virtual Mentor, AMA's online ethics journal.

Glaser, John W. "Covering the uninsured" is a flawed moral frame. *Health Progress* 2006 March-April; 87(2): 4-9. NRCBL: 9.5.10; 9.3.1.

Groves, Sara. Health care for the poor and underserved. *In:* Cowen, Perle Slavik; Moorhead, Sue, eds. Current Issues in Nursing. 7th ed. St. Louis, MO: Mosby, 2006: 639-644. NRCBL: 9.5.10.

CARE FOR SPECIFIC GROUPS/ MENTALLY DISABLED
See also BEHAVIOR CONTROL; ELECTROCONVULSIVE THERAPY; INVOLUNTARY COMMITMENT; MENTAL HEALTH THERAPIES; PSYCHOPHARMACOLOGY; PSYCHOTHERAPY

Aronson, Jane. Silenced complaints, suppressed expectations: the cumulative effects of home care rationing. *International Journal of Health Services* 2006; 36(3): 535-556. NRCBL: 9.5.3; 9.5.5; 9.4; 9.8; 9.3.2. SC: em. Identifiers: Canada.

Baldwin, Clive. Narrative, ethics and people with severe mental illness. *Australian and New Zealand Journal of Psychiatry* 2005 November-December; 39(11-12): 1022-1029. NRCBL: 9.5.3; 4.4; 4.3; 8.1.

NRCBL: National Reference Center for Bioethics Literature Classification Scheme   See inside front cover for terms.

105

Chur-Hansen, Anna; Zion, Deborah. 'Let's fix the chemical imbalance first, and then we can work on the problems second': an exploration of ethical implications of prescribing an SSRI for 'depression'. *Monash Bioethics Review* 2006 January; 25(1): 15-30. NRCBL: 9.5.3; 9.7; 8.1. Identifiers: Australia; Monash University; selective serotonin reuptake inhibitors.

Dudzinski, Denise M. Compounding vulnerability: pregnancy and schizophrenia. *American Journal of Bioethics [Online].* 2006 March-April; 6(2): W1-W14. NRCBL: 9.5.3; 9.5.9; 17.1; 12.4.2.

Dyer, Clare. UK government scraps mental health bill [news]. *BMJ: British Medical Journal* 2006 April 1; 332(7544): 748. NRCBL: 9.5.3; 17.1. SC: le. Identifiers: England.

Eastman, Nigel. Reforming mental health law in England and Wales: the government's recent climb down is not a victory: the real battle is about to begin [editorial]. *BMJ: British Medical Journal* 2006 April 1; 332(7544): 737-738. NRCBL: 9.5.3; 17.1; 21.1. SC: le.

Erwin, Cheryl; Philibert, Robert. Shocking treatment: the use of tasers in psychiatric care. *Journal of Law, Medicine, and Ethics* 2006 Spring; 34(1): 116-120. NRCBL: 9.5.3; 17.3.

French, Catherine M. Protecting the "right" to choose of women who are incompetent: ethical, doctrinal, and practical arguments against fetal representation. *Case Western Reserve Law Review* 2005 Winter; 56(2): 511-546. NRCBL: 9.5.3; 12.4.2; 9.5.5; 8.3.3. SC: le.

Gill, Chandler E.; Taylor, Henry M.; Lin, K.T.; Padaliya, Bimal B.; Newman, William J.; Abramovitch, Anna I.; Richardson, CaraLee R.; Charles, P. David. Difficulty in securing treatment for degenerative hip disease in a patient with Down syndrome: the gap remains open. *Journal of the National Medical Association* 2006 January; 98(1): 93-96. NRCBL: 9.5.3; 9.5.1; 9.8. SC: cs.

Glover-Thomas, N. Treating the vulnerable in England and Wales: the impact of law reform and changing policy. *International Journal of Law and Psychiatry* 2006 January-February; 29(1): 22-35. NRCBL: 9.5.3; 17.8; 8.3.3; 8.3.4. SC: le. Identifiers: Mental Health Act 1983; Mental Capacity Act 2005.

Hoffer, L. John. Tube feeding in advanced dementia: the metabolic perspective. *BMJ: British Medical Journal* 2006 December 9; 333(7580): 1214-1215. NRCBL: 9.5.3; 9.5.2; 20.5.1.

Nelson, Lawrence J. Respect for the developmentally disabled and forgoing life-sustaining treatment. *Mental Retardation and Developmental Disabilities Research Reviews* 2003; 9(1): 3-9. NRCBL: 9.5.3; 20.5.1; 8.3.3; 4.4; 8.3.4. SC: cs.

Nelson, Robert M. Imagining the developmentally disabled and mentally retarded: an introduction. *Mental Retardation and Developmental Disabilities Research Reviews* 2003; 9(1): 1-2. NRCBL: 9.5.3; 8.3.3; 2.1.

Parish, Colin. Profession reacts to allegations of inappropriate control and restraint. *Nursing Standard* 2005 July 20; 19(45): 14-15. NRCBL: 9.5.3; 9.8.

Patel, Vikram; Saraceno, Benedetto; Kleinman, Arthur. Beyond evidence: the moral case for international mental health [editorial]. *American Journal of Psychiatry* 2006 August; 163(8): 1312-1315. NRCBL: 9.5.3; 21.1.

Phillips, Lorraine J.; Phillips, Win. Better reproductive healthcare for women with disabilities: a role for nursing leadership. *Advances in Nursing Science* 2006 April-June; 29(2): 134-151. NRCBL: 9.5.3; 9.5.5; 9.8. SC: an.

Pollack, Daniel. The capacity of a mentally challenged person to consent to abortion and sterilization. *Health and Social Work* 2005 August; 30(3): 253-257. NRCBL: 9.5.3; 8.3.3; 12.4.2; 11.3. SC: le.

Post, Stephen G. Respectare: moral respect for the lives of the deeply forgetful. *In:* Hughes, Julian C.; Louw, Stephen J.; Sabat, Steven R., eds. Dementia: Mind, Meaning, and the Person. New York: Oxford University Press, 2006: 223-234. NRCBL: 9.5.3; 4.4.

Rock, Patricia J. Eugenics and euthanasia: a cause for concern for disabled people, particularly disabled women. *Disability and Society* 1996 March; 11(1): 121-127. NRCBL: 9.5.3; 9.5.5; 20.5.1.

Rossetti, Jeanette; Fox, Patricia G.; Burns, Kenneth. Advocating for the rights of the mentally ill: a global issue. *International Journal of Psychiatric Nursing Research* 2005 September; 11(1): 1211-1217. NRCBL: 9.5.3; 21.1; 4.1.3.

Schostak, Zev. Alzheimer's and dementia in the elderly: Halachic perspectives. *Journal of Halacha and Contemporary Society* 2006 Fall; (52): 83-109. NRCBL: 9.5.3; 9.5.2; 4.3; 20.5.4; 1.2.

Sjöström, Stefan. Invocation of coercion context in compliance communication — power dynamics in psychiatric care. *International Journal of Law and Psychiatry* 2006 January-February; 29(1): 36-47. NRCBL: 9.5.3; 17.7; 17.8; 8.3.4; 8.1. SC: le.

Sturmey, Peter. Ethical dilemmas and the most effective therapies. *In:* Jacobson, John W.; Foxx, Richard M.; Mulick, James A., eds. Controversial Therapies for Developmental Disabilities: Fad, Fashion, and Science in Professional Practice. Mahwah, NJ: L. Erlbaum Associates; 2005: 435-449. NRCBL: 9.5.3; 4.1.1.

Yamin, Alicia Ely; Rosenthal, Eric. Out of the shadows: using human rights approaches to secure dignity and well-being for people with mental disabilities. *PLoS Medi-*

cine 2005 April; 2(4): 0296-0298. NRCBL: 9.5.3; 4.4; 21.1.

CARE FOR SPECIFIC GROUPS/ MINORITIES

Banks, Angela D.; Malone, Ruth E. Accustomed to enduring: experiences of African-American women seeking care for cardiac symptoms. *Heart and Lung* 2005 January-February; 34(1): 13-21. NRCBL: 9.5.4; 9.55.; 9.5.1. SC: em; cs.

Beller, George A. Disparities in health care in racial and ethnic minorities. *Journal of Nuclear Cardiology* 2005 November-December; 12(6): 617-619. NRCBL: 9.5.4; 9.4; 9.2.

Bhopal, Raj. Race and ethnicity: responsible use from epidemiological and public health perspectives. *Journal of Law, Medicine and Ethics* 2006 Fall; 34(3): 500-507. NRCBL: 9.5.4; 7.1; 9.1; 13.1; 15.11; 18.2. SC: le.

Abstract: While the concepts of race and ethnicity have been abused historically, they are potentially invaluable in epidemiology and public health. Epidemiology relies upon variables that help differentiate populations by health status, thereby refining public health and health care policy, and offering insights for medical science. Race and ethnicity are powerful tools for doing this. The prerequisite for their responsible use is a society committed to reducing inequalities and inequities in health status. When this condition is met, it is irresponsible not to utilize these concepts.

Bird, Sheryl Thorburn; Bogart, Laura M. Perceived race-based and socio-economic status (SES)-based discrimination in interactions with health care providers. *Ethnicity and Disease* 2001 Autumn; 11(3): 554-563. NRCBL: 9.5.4; 8.1; 9.8. SC: em.

Bronx Health REACH Coalition. Action Committee; Calman, Neil S.; Golub, Maxine; Ruddock, Charmaine; Le, Lan; Hauser, Diane. Separate and unequal care in New York City. *Journal of Health Care Law and Policy* 2006; 9(1): 105-120. NRCBL: 9.5.4; 9.3.1. SC: em. Conference: Symposium; Bridging the racial divide in health care: eliminating racial and ethnic disparities in health status; Baltimore, Maryland; 2005 March 11; University of Maryland School of Law's Law and Health Care Program.

Cho, Mildred K. Racial and ethnic categories in biomedical research: there is no baby in the bathwater. *Journal of Law, Medicine and Ethics* 2006 Fall; 34(3): 497-499. NRCBL: 9.5.4; 7.1; 18.2; 18.5.1; 15.11.

Abstract: The use of racial categories in biomedicine has had a long history in the United States. However, social hierarchy and discrimination, justified by purported scientific differences, has also plagued the history of racial categories. Because "race" has some correlation with biological and genetic characteristics, there has been a call not to "throw the baby out with the bathwater" by eliminating race as a research or clinical category. I argue that race is too undefined and fluid to be useful as a proxy for biology or genetics.

Clancy, Carolyn M. Closing the health care disparities gap: turning evidence into action. *Journal of Health Care Law and Policy* 2006; 9(1): 121-135. NRCBL: 9.5.4; 9.1. Conference: Symposium; Bridging the Racial Divide in Health Care: Eliminating Racial and Ethnic Disparities in Health Status; Baltimore, Maryland; 2005 March 11; University of Maryland School of Law, Law and Health Care Program.

Clark, Brietta R. Hospital flight from minority communities: how our existing civil rights framework fosters racial inequality in healthcare. *DePaul Journal of Health Care Law* 2005; 9(2): 1023-1100. NRCBL: 9.5.4; 9.2; 9.3.1; 9.8. SC: le.

Danis, Marion; Lavizzo-Mourey, Risa. Respecting diversity. *In:* Morrison, R. Sean; Meier, Diane E.; Capello, Carol, eds. Geriatric Palliative Care. New York: Oxford University Press; 2003: 79-90. NRCBL: 9.5.4; 20.4.1; 9.5.2.

Dula, Annette; Williams, September. When race matters. *Clinics in Geriatric Medicine* 2005 February; 21(1): 239-253. NRCBL: 9.5.4; 20.5.1. SC: cs.

Duster, Troy. Lessons from history: why race and ethnicity have played a major role in biomedical research. *Journal of Law, Medicine and Ethics* 2006 Fall; 34(3): 487-496. NRCBL: 9.5.4; 7.1; 2.2; 18.2; 18.5.1; 15.11.

Abstract: Before any citizen enters the role of scientist, medical practitioner, lawyer, epidemiologist, and so on, each and all grow up in a society in which the categories of human differentiation are folk categories that organize perceptions, relations, and behavior. That was true during slavery, during Reconstruction, the eugenics period, the two World Wars, and is no less true today. While every period understandably claims to transcend those categories, medicine, law, and science are profoundly and demonstrably influenced by the embedded folk notions of race and ethnicity.

Elster, Nanette R. ART for the masses? Racial and ethnic inequality in assisted reproductive technologies. *DePaul Journal of Health Care Law* 2005; 9(1): 719-733. NRCBL: 9.5.4; 14.4; 14.2; 19.1; 9.3.1.

Fennell, Mary L. Racial disparities in care: looking beyond the clinical encounter [editorial]. *Health Services Research* 2005 December; 40(6, Part 1): 1713-1721. NRCBL: 9.5.4; 8.1; 9.8; 9.5.2.

Gamble, Vanessa Northington. Trust, medical care, and racial and ethnic minorities. *In:* Satcher, David; Pamies, Rubens J., eds. Multicultural medicine and health disparities. New York: McGraw-Hill, 2006: 437-448. NRCBL: 9.5.4; 8.1.

Gibbons, M.C. Common ground: exploring policy approaches to addressing racial disparities from the left and right. *Journal of Health Care Law and Policy* 2006; 9(1): 48-76. NRCBL: 9.5.4; 7.1; 9.1. Conference: Symposium; Bridging the racial divide in health care: eliminating racial and ethnic disparities in health status; Baltimore, Mary-

---

NRCBL: National Reference Center for Bioethics Literature Classification Scheme   See inside front cover for terms.

107

land; 2005 March 11; University of Maryland School of Law's Law and Health Care Program.

Halbert, Chanita Hughes; Armstrong, Katrina; Gandy, Oscar H., Jr.; Shaker, Lee. Racial differences in trust in health care providers. *Archives of Internal Medicine* 2006 April 24; 166(8): 896-901. NRCBL: 9.5.4; 8.1. SC: em.

Halfmann, Drew; Rude, Jess; Ebert, Kim. The biomedical legacy in minority health policy-making, 1975-2002. *In:* Kronenfeld, Jennie Jacobs, ed. Health Care Services, Racial and Ethnic Minorities and Underserved Populations: Patient and Provider Perspectives. Boston: Elsevier JAI, 2005: 245-275. NRCBL: 9.5.4.

Hoffman, Sharona. "Racially-tailored" medicine unraveled. *American University Law Review* 2005 December; 55(2): 395-452. NRCBL: 9.5.4; 9.7; 15.1; 18.5.1; 18.2. SC: le. Identifiers: BiDil.

Ikemoto, Lisa C. Race to health: racialized discourses in a transhuman world. *DePaul Journal of Health Care Law* 2005; 9(2): 1101-1129. NRCBL: 9.5.4; 15.10; 14.5; 4.4.

Jacobs, Elizabeth A.; Rolle, Italia; Ferrans, Carol Estwing; Whitaker, Eric E.; Warnecke, Richard B. Understanding African Americans' views of the trustworthiness of physicians. *JGIM: Journal of General Internal Medicine* 2006 June; 21(6): 642-647. NRCBL: 9.5.4; 8.1. SC: em.

Johnston, Trevor. In one's own image: ethics and the reproduction of deafness. *Journal of Deaf Studies and Deaf Education* 2005 Fall; 10(4): 426-441. NRCBL: 9.5.4; 15.2; 14.4. SC: an.

Kahn, Jonathan. Genes, race, and population: avoiding a collision of categories. *American Journal of Public Health* 2006 November; 96(11): 1965-1970. NRCBL: 9.5.4; 15.1; 9.7; 18.5.1.

Abstract: A wide array of federal mandates have a profound impact on the use of racial and ethnic categories in biomedical research, clinical practice, product development, and health policy. Current discussions over the appropriate use of racial and ethnic categories in biomedical contexts have largely focused on the practices of individual researchers. By contrast, our discussion focuses on relations between the daily practices of biomedical professionals and federal regulatory mandates. It draws upon the legal doctrine of equal protection to move beyond such debates and to propose guidelines to address the structural forces imposed by federal regulations that mandate how data about race and ethnicity are used in biomedical research. It offers a framework to manage the tension involved in using existing federally mandated categories of race and ethnicity alongside new scientific findings about human genetic variation.

Ladenheim, Kala; Groman, Rachel. State legislative activities related to elimination of health disparities. *Journal of Health Politics, Policy and Law* 2006 February; 31(1): 153-183. NRCBL: 9.5.4; 9.4; 9.1. SC: le.

Abstract: How have state legislatures acted to address racial and ethnic disparities in health care? This article examines trends over time in state legislation related to disparities in care and access, proposed legislation during one biennial session, and contemporary legislative attitudes and awareness of the issue. The mix of strategies adopted across the states reflects the differing ways that states understand gaps in minority health and changing strategies over time. Historically, California, Florida, and Louisiana (all states with substantial minority populations) have been the most active in dealing with minority health issues through statutes. In the eighteen months of the 2001-2002 legislative session that we studied, the most common bills called for studies of disparities and appropriations for identifiable minority health initiatives. Measures that successfully cleared the legislature include measures related to cultural competence and minority health awareness month. Finally, the article discusses issues and limitations in using legislative action to measure the level of state policy activity with regard to health disparities. To ground the description of trends in disparity legislation, the authors integrated comments by state legislators with a discussion of problems in interpreting legislative activity.

Lindsay, Ronald A. Why should we be concerned with disparate impact? *American Journal of Bioethics* 2006 September-October; 6(5): 23-24; discussion W30-W32. NRCBL: 9.5.4; 20.5.1; 9.4. Comments: Mary Ellen Wojtasiewicz. Damage compounded: disparities, distrust, and disparate impact in end-of-life conflict resolution policies. American Journal of Bioethics 2006 September-October; 6(5): 8-12.

Lurie, Nicole; Fremont, Allen; Jain, Arvind K.; Taylor, Stephanie L.; McLaughlin, Rebecca; Peterson, Eric; Kong, B. Waine; Ferguson, T. Bruce, Jr. Racial and ethnic disparities in care: the perspectives of cardiologists. *Circulation* 2005 March 15; 111(10): 1264-1269. NRCBL: 9.5.4; 9.5.1; 9.8. SC: em.

Malinowski, Michael J. Could biobanking be a means to include "health care have-nots" in the genomics revolution? *DePaul Journal of Health Care Law* 2005; 9(2): 1005-1022. NRCBL: 9.5.4; 15.1; 19.1; 18.6. SC: le.

Mallinger, Julie B.; Fisher, Susan G.; Brown, Theodore; Lamberti, J. Steven. Racial disparities in the use of second-generation antipsychotics for the treatment of schizophrenia. *Psychiatric Services* 2006 January; 57(1): 133-136. NRCBL: 9.5.4; 17.4. SC: em.

Matthew, Dayna Bowen. A new strategy to combat racial inequality in American health care delivery. *DePaul Journal of Health Care Law* 2005; 9(1): 793-853. NRCBL: 9.5.4; 9.3.1. SC: le.

Outterson, Kevin. Tragedy and remedy: reparations for disparities in black health. *DePaul Journal of Health Care Law* 2005; 9(1): 735-791. NRCBL: 9.5.4; 9.3.1. SC: le.

Petersen, Laura A.; Wright, Steven M.; Peterson, Eric D.; Daley, Jennifer. Impact of race on cardiac care and outcomes in veterans with acute myocardial infarction. *Medical Care* 2002 January; 40(1 Supplement):I86-I96. NRCBL: 9.5.4; 9.5.1; 9.2; 9.4.

Petsko, Gregory A. Color blind. *Genome Biology [electronic]* 2004 November 26; 5(12): 119, 3 p. Accessed: http://genomebiology.com/2004/5/12/119 [2006 January 22]. NRCBL: 9.5.4; 3.1; 15.11; 15.1.

Pittman, Larry J. A Thirteenth Amendment challenge to both racial disparities in medical treatment and improper physicians' informed consent disclosures. *Saint Louis University Law Journal* 2003 Fall; 48(1): 131-189. NRCBL: 9.5.4; 8.3.1. SC: le.

Pohl, Lynn Marie. Long waits, small spaces, and compassionate care: memories of race and medicine in a mid-twentieth-century southern community. *Bulletin of the History of Medicine* 2000 Spring; 74(1): 107-137. NRCBL: 9.5.4; 8.1; 7.1.

Randall, Vernellia R. Eliminating racial discrimination in health care: a call for state health care anti-discrimination law. *DePaul Journal of Health Care Law* 2006 Fall; 10(1): 1-25. NRCBL: 9.5.4. SC: le.

Reiheld, Alison. Erasure of past: how failure to remember can be a morally blameworthy act. *American Journal of Bioethics* 2006 September-October; 6(5): 25-26; discussion W30-W32. NRCBL: 9.5.4; 9.4; 1.1; 20.5.1. Comments: Mary Ellen Wojtasiewicz. Damage compounded: disparities, distrust, and disparate impact in end-of-life conflict resolution policies. American Journal of Bioethics 2006 September-October; 6(5): 8-12.

Root, Michael. The problem of race in medicine. *Philosophy of the Social Sciences* 2001 March; 31(1): 20-39 [Online] Accessed: http://pos.sagepub.com/cgi/reprint/31/1/20 [2007 February 6]. NRCBL: 9.5.4; 7.1; 9.1; 15.1.

Rouse, Carol Moxley. Paradigms and politics: shaping health care access for sickle cell patients through the discursive regimes of biomedicine. *Culture Medicine and Psychiatry* 2004 September; 28(3): 369-399. NRCBL: 9.5.4; 9.2. SC: cs.

Salles, Arleen L.F. Bioethics, difference, and rights. *In:* Tong, Rosemarie; Donchin, Anne; Dodds, Susan, eds. Linking Visions: Feminist Bioethics, Human Rights, and the Developing World. Lanham, MD: Rowman and Littlefield Publishers; 2004: 57-72. NRCBL: 9.5.4; 21.7.

Singh, Swaran P.; Burns, Tom. Race and mental health: there is more to race than racism. *BMJ: British Medical Journal* 2006 September 23; 333(7569): 648-651. NRCBL: 9.5.4; 9.5.3; 17.7; 17.1.

Smith, David Barton. Healthcare's hidden civil rights legacy. *St. Louis University Law Journal* 2003 Fall; 48(1): 37-60. NRCBL: 9.5.4; 9.2. SC: le.

Stone, Deborah. Reframing the racial disparities issue for state governments. *Journal of Health Politics, Policy and Law* 2006 February; 31(1): 127-152. NRCBL: 9.5.4; 9.1; 9.4; 1.1.

Abstract: Although racial and ethnic disparities in health have been on the federal government's agenda since 1985, no policy reforms have significantly reduced disparities. The question arises whether states can effectively address this issue without waiting for solutions from the national government. The purpose of this article is to propose ways of reframing the disparities issue that might give state policy makers more leverage and might strengthen political will to address the issue. I suggest a moral frame based on a concept of distributive justice in which medical care must be distributed according to need. I explain the rationales for such a frame and consider its strategic advantages and disadvantages. In the last section, I suggest some policies based on this framing that are within the power of state legislatures.

United States. Congress. Senate. A bill to amend the Public Health Service Act to improve the health and healthcare of racial and ethnic minority and other health disparity populations. Washington, DC: U.S. G.P.O., 2006. 131 p.[Online]. Accessed: http://frwebgate.access.gpo.gov/cgi-bin/useftp.cgi?IPaddress=162.140.64.21&filename=s4024is.pdf&directory=/diskb/wais/data/109_cong_bills [2006 December 5]. NRCBL: 9.5.4. SC: le. Identifiers: Minority Health Improvement and Health Disparity Elimination Act. Note: S. 4024, 109th Congress, 2d session. Introduced by Sen. Frist, September 29 2006. Referred to the Committee on Health, Education, Labor and Pensions.

van Ryn, Michelle; Burgess, Diana; Malat, Jennifer; Griffin, Joan. Physicians' perceptions of patients' social and behavioral characteristics and race disparities in treatment recommendations for men with coronary artery disease. *American Journal of Public Health* 2006 February; 96(2): 351- 357. NRCBL: 9.5.4; 8.1. SC: em.

Abstract: OBJECTIVES: A growing body of evidence suggests that provider decisionmaking contributes to racial/ethnic disparities in care. We examined the factors mediating the relationship between patient race/ethnicity and provider recommendations for coronary artery bypass graft surgery. METHODS: Analyses were conducted with a data set that included medical record, angiogram, and provider survey data on postangiogram encounters with patients who were categorized as appropriate candidates for coronary artery bypass graft surgery. RESULTS: Race significantly influenced physician recommendations among male, but not female, patients. Physicians' perceptions of patients' education and physical activity preferences were significant predictors of their recommendations, independent of clinical factors, appropriateness, payer, and physician characteristics. Furthermore, these variables mediated the effects of patient race on provider recommendations. CONCLUSIONS: Our findings point to the importance of research and intervention strategies addressing the ways in which providers' beliefs about patients mediate disparities in treatment. In addition, they highlight the need for discourse and consensus development on the role of social factors in clinical decisionmaking.

Werner, Rachel M.; Asch, David A.; Polsky, Daniel. Racial profiling: the unintended consequences of coronary artery bypass graft report cards. *Circulation* 2005 March 15; 111(10): 1257-1263. NRCBL: 9.5.4; 9.8; 9.2. SC: em.

Westmoreland, Timothy M.; Watson, Kathryn R. Redeeming hollow promises: the case for mandatory spending on health care for American Indians and Alaska

NRCBL: National Reference Center for Bioethics Literature Classification Scheme   See inside front cover for terms.

109

Natives. *American Journal of Public Health* 2006 April; 96(4): 600-605. NRCBL: 9.5.4; 9.3.1.

Abstract: The reliance on discretionary spending for American Indian/ Alaska Native health care has produced a system that is insufficient and unreliable and is associated with ongoing health disparities. Moreover, the gap between mandatory spending on a Medicare beneficiary and discretionary spending on an American Indian/Alaska Native beneficiary has grown dramatically, thus compounding the problem. The budget classification for American Indian/Alaska Native health services should be changed, and health care delivery to this population should be designated as mandatory spending. If a correct structure is in place, mandatory spending is more likely to provide adequate funding that keeps pace with changes in costs and need.

CARE FOR SPECIFIC GROUPS/ MINORS

The rights of the child in the context of HIV/AIDS. *Canadian HIV/AIDS Policy and Law Newsletter* 1997-1998 Winter; 3(4)-4(1): 59. NRCBL: 9.5.7; 20.5.6; 21.1. Note: reprinted from the United Nations Convention on the Rights of the Child.

Allen, David B.; Fost, Norman. hGH for short stature: ethical issues raised by expanded access. *Journal of Pediatrics* 2004 May; 144(5): 648-652. NRCBL: 9.5.7; 9.5.1; 15.1; 4.5. Identifiers: human growth hormone.

Arnold, L. Eugene. Turn-of-the-century ethical issues in child psychiatric research. *Current Psychiatry Reports* 2001 April; 3(2): 109-114. NRCBL: 9.5.7; 17.4; 18.2; 18.5.2.

Beals, Katharine P. The ethics of autism: what's wrong with the dominant paradigms and how to fix them. *Mental Retardation and Developmental Disabilities Research Reviews* 2003; 9(1): 32-39. NRCBL: 9.5.7; 17.1; 7.1.

Björn, Gunilla Jarkman; Björn, Åke. Ethical aspects when treating traumatized refugee children and their families. *Nordic Journal of Psychiatry* 2004; 58(3): 193-198. NRCBL: 9.5.7; 17.2; 21.1; 1.1. SC: cs.

Bramwell, R.; Weindling, M. Families' views on ward rounds in neonatal units. *Archives of Disease in Childhood Fetal and Neonatal Edition* 2005 September; 90(5): F429-F431. NRCBL: 9.5.7; 8.1; 8.4. SC: em. Identifiers: United Kingdom (Great Britain).

Chang, Cindy. Health care for undocumented immigrant children: special members of an underclass. *Washington University Law Quarterly* 2005; 83(4): 1271-1294. NRCBL: 9.5.7; 9.5.10; 9.2; 9.3.1; 9.4. SC: le.

Clafflin, Carol J.; Barbarin, Oscar A. Does "telling" less protect more? Relationships among age, information disclosure, and what children with cancer see and feel. *Journal of Pediatric Psychology* 1991 April; 16(2): 169-191. NRCBL: 9.5.7; 9.5.1; 8.2; 8.1.

Clark, Peter A. To circumcise or not to circumcise? *Health Progress* 2006 September-October; 87(5): 30-39. NRCBL: 9.5.7; 10.

Clayton, Ellen Wright. Talking with parents before newborn screening. *Journal of Pediatrics* 2005 September; 147(3, Supplement): S26-S29. NRCBL: 9.5.7; 8.3.2; 15.3.

Craig, Amber. North Carolina Medicaid and the funding of routine non- therapeutic circumcisions. *In:* Denniston, George C.; Hodges, Frederick Mansfield; Milos, Marilyn Fayre, eds. Flesh and Blood: Perspectives on the Problems of Circumcision in Contemporary Society. New York: Kluwer Academic/Plenum Publishers; 2004: 207-216. NRCBL: 9.5.7; 10; 9.3.1.

Dhondt, Jean-Louis. Implementation of informed consent for a cystic fibrosis newborn screening program in France: low refusal rates for optional testing. *Journal of Pediatrics* 2005 September; 147(3, Supplement): S106-S108. NRCBL: 9.5.7; 8.3.2; 15.3. SC: em.

Edwards, James C. Concepts of technology and their role in moral reflection. *In:* Parens, Erik, ed. Surgically Shaping Children: Technology, Ethics, and the Pursuit of Normality. Baltimore, MD: Johns Hopkins University Press; 2006: 51-67. NRCBL: 9.5.7; 1.1; 5.1.

Eide, Brock L.; Eide, Fernette F. The mislabeled child. *New Atlantis* 2006 Spring; 12: 46-59. NRCBL: 9.5.7; 4.3.

Elliott, Carl. Attitudes, souls, and persons: children with severe neurological impairment. *Mental Retardation and Developmental Disabilities Research Reviews* 2003; 9(1): 16-20. NRCBL: 9.5.7; 4.4; 20.4.2.

Feder, Ellen K. "In their best interests": parents' experience of atypical genitalia. *In:* Parens, Erik, ed. Surgically Shaping Children: Technology, Ethics, and the Pursuit of Normality. Baltimore, MD: Johns Hopkins University Press; 2006: 189-210. NRCBL: 9.5.7; 10.

Fegran, Liv; Helseth, Solvi; Slettebo, Ashild. Nurses as moral practitioners encountering parents in neonatal intensive care units. *Nursing Ethics* 2006 January; 13(1): 52-64. NRCBL: 9.5.7; 1.1; 7.1; 8.1.

Abstract: Historically, the care of hospitalized children has evolved from being performed in isolation from parents to a situation where the parents and the child are regarded as a unit, and parents and nurses as equal partners in the child's care. Parents are totally dependent on professionals' knowledge and expertise, while nurses are dependent on the children's emotional connection with their parents in order to provide optimal care. Even when interdependency exists, nurses as professionals hold the power to decide whether and to what extent parents should be involved in their child's care. This article focuses on nurses' responsibility to act ethically and reflectively in a collaborative partnership with parents. To illuminate the issue of nurses as moral practitioners, we present an observation of contemporary child care, and discuss it from the perspective of the Danish moral philosopher KE Logstrup and his book The ethical demand [sic; The Ethical Demand].

Foreman, D.M. Attention deficit hyperactivity disorder: legal and ethical aspects. *Archives of Disease in Childhood* 2006 February; 91(2): 192-194. NRCBL: 9.5.7; 2.1; 7.1; 8.1.

Franck, Linda S.; Spencer, Caroline. Informing parents about anaesthesia for children's surgery: a critical literature review. *Patient Education and Counseling* 2005 November; 59(2): 117-125. NRCBL: 9.5.7; 8.3.2. SC: rv; em.

Frize, Monique; Yang, Lan; Walker, Robin C.; O'Connor, Annette M. Conceptual framework of knowledge management for ethical decision-making support in neonatal intensive care. *IEEE Transactions on Information Technology in Biomedicine* 2005 June; 9(2): 205-215. NRCBL: 9.5.7; 20.5.2; 8.1; 9.4. SC: em.

Gilbert, Steven G. Ethical, legal, and social issues: our children's future. *NeuroToxicology* 2005 August; 26(4): 521-530. NRCBL: 9.5.7; 16.1; 5.1.

Hardy, Linda. Informed consent: adolescent minors, surrogate decision- making, and the school nurse. *School Nurse News* 2003 September; 20(4): 28-31. NRCBL: 9.5.7; 8.3.1; 8.3.2; 7.1; 8.1.

Hodges, Frederick Mansfield. Bodily integrity in the biotech era: placing human rights and medical ethics in historical context. *In:* Denniston, George C.; Hodges, Frederick Mansfield; Milos, Marilyn Fayre, eds. Flesh and Blood: Perspectives on the Problems of Circumcision in Contemporary Society. New York: Kluwer Academic/Plenum Publishers; 2004: 1-15. NRCBL: 9.5.7; 10.

Hofvander, Yngve. Circumcision of boys: time for doctors to reconsider. *In:* Denniston, George C.; Hodges, Frederick Mansfield; Milos, Marilyn Fayre, eds. Flesh and Blood: Perspectives on the Problems of Circumcision in Contemporary Society. New York: Kluwer Academic/Plenum Publishers; 2004: 109-117. NRCBL: 9.5.7; 10.

Kachoyeanos, Mary K.; Zollo, Mary Bess. Ethics in pain management of infants and children. *MCN: The American Journal of Maternal Child Nursing* 1995 May-June; 20(3): 142-147. NRCBL: 9.5.7; 4.4; 7.1.

Lauritzen, Paul. Response to Richard B. Miller's "children, ethics, and modern medicine" [book review]. *Journal of Religious Ethics* 2006 March; 34(1): 151-161. NRCBL: 9.5.7; 2.1; 1.1; 9.6; 18.2. SC: an.

Liddon, Nicole; Pulley, LeaVonne; Cockerham, William C.; Lueschen, Guenther; Vermund, Sten H.; Hook, Edward W. Parents'/guardians' willingness to vaccinate their children against genital herpes. *Journal of Adolescent Health* 2005 September; 37(3): 187-193. NRCBL: 9.5.7; 9.7; 8.3.2; 10. SC: em.

Lindemann, Hilde. The power of parents and the agency of children. *In:* Parens, Erik, ed. Surgically Shaping Children: Technology, Ethics, and the Pursuit of Normality.

Baltimore, MD: Johns Hopkins University Press; 2006: 176-188. NRCBL: 9.5.7.

Llewellyn, David. Penile torts in the courts. *In:* Denniston, George C.; Hodges, Frederick Mansfield; Milos, Marilyn Fayre, eds. Flesh and Blood: Perspectives on the Problems of Circumcision in Contemporary Society. New York: Kluwer Academic/Plenum Publishers; 2004: 69-79. NRCBL: 9.5.7; 10. SC: le.

Marsh, Jeffrey L. To cut or not to cut?: a surgeon's perspective on surgically shaping children. *In:* Parens, Erik, ed. Surgically Shaping Children: Technology, Ethics, and the Pursuit of Normality. Baltimore, MD: Johns Hopkins University Press; 2006: 113-124. NRCBL: 9.5.7.

Miller, Paul Steven. Toward truly informed decisions about appearance-normalizing surgeries. *In:* Parens, Erik, ed. Surgically Shaping Children: Technology, Ethics, and the Pursuit of Normality. Baltimore, MD: Johns Hopkins University Press; 2006: 211-226. NRCBL: 9.5.7.

Miller, Richard B. On medicine, culture, and children's basic interests: a reply to three critics. *Journal of Religious Ethics* 2006 March; 34(1): 177-189. NRCBL: 9.5.7; 8.3.2; 1.1. SC: cs.

Mohrmann, Margaret E. Whose interests are they, anyway? [review of Children, Ethics, and Modern Medicine by Richard B. Miller]. *Journal of Religious Ethics* 2006 March; 34(1): 141-150. NRCBL: 9.5.7; 2.1; 8.3.2; 20.5.2; 1.2. SC: an.

Mouradian, Wendy E. What's special about the surgical context? *In:* Parens, Erik, ed. Surgically Shaping Children: Technology, Ethics, and the Pursuit of Normality. Baltimore, MD: Johns Hopkins University Press; 2006: 125-140. NRCBL: 9.5.7; 4.2.

Nowak, Rachel. Ear implant success sparks culture war. *New Scientist* 2006 November 25-December 1; 192(2579): 16-17. NRCBL: 9.5.7; 5.2.

Olusanya, B.O.; Luxon, L.M.; Wirz, S.L. Ethical issues in screening for hearing impairment in newborns in developing countries. *Journal of Medical Ethics* 2006 October; 32(10): 588-591. NRCBL: 9.5.7; 9.1; 9.5.1.

Pattison, S.; Evans, H.M. Cause for concern: the absence of consideration of public and ethical interest in British public policy. *Journal of Medical Ethics* 2006 December; 32(12): 711-714. NRCBL: 9.5.7; 1.3.5. Identifiers: United Kingdom (Great Britain).

Paul, M.; Newns, K.; Creedy, K.V. Some ethical issues that arise from working with families in the National Health Service. *Clinical Ethics* 2006 June; 1(2): 76-81. NRCBL: 9.5.7; 8.3.2; 1.1; 8.4; 8.1. SC: cs. Identifiers: Justice.

Pérez-Cárceles, M.D.; Pereñiguez, J.E.; Osuna, E.; Pérez-Flores, D.; Luna, A. Primary care confidentiality

---

NRCBL: National Reference Center for Bioethics Literature Classification Scheme   See inside front cover for terms.

for Spanish adolescents: fact or fiction? *Journal of Medical Ethics* 2006 June; 32(6): 329-334. NRCBL: 9.5.7; 8.4. SC: em; le.

Abstract: BACKGROUND: By providing healthcare to adolescents, a major opportunity is created to help them cope with the challenges in their lives, develop healthy behaviour and become responsible healthcare consumers. Confidentiality is a major issue in adolescent healthcare, and its perceived absence may be the main barrier to an adolescent seeking medical care. Little is known, however, about confidentiality for adolescents in primary care practices in Spain. OBJECTIVE: To ascertain the attitudes of Spanish family doctors towards the right of adolescents to confidentiality in different healthcare situations and in the prescription of treatment. Method: A descriptive postal questionnaire was self-administered by family doctors. RESULTS: Parents of patients under 18 years are always informed by 18.5% of family doctors, whereas parents of those under 16 years are informed by 38.8% of doctors. The patients are warned of this likelihood by 79.3% of doctors. The proportion of doctors supporting confidentiality for adolescents increases with the age and maturity of the patients, whereas workload and previous training has a negative effect. CONCLUSIONS: Spanish laws on adolescent healthcare are not reflected by the paternalistic attitude that Spanish primary care doctors have towards their adolescent patients. Doctors need to be provided with up-to-date and clinically relevant explanations on contemporary legal positions. In primary care, more attention should be paid to adolescents' rights to information, privacy and confidentiality. Doctors should be more aware of the need to encourage communication between teenagers and their parents, while also safeguarding their patients' rights to confidential care.

Pinnock, Ralph; Crosthwaite, Jan. When parents refuse consent to treatment for children and young persons. *Journal of Paediatrics and Child Health* 2005 July; 41(7): 369-373. NRCBL: 9.5.7; 8.3.2; 8.3.4; 9.6.

Schachter, Debbie; Kleinman, Irwin; Harvey, William. Informed consent and adolescents. *Canadian Journal of Psychiatry* 2005 August; 50(9): 534-540. NRCBL: 9.5.7; 8.3.1; 8.3.2; 17.1. SC: rv.

Sheela, S.R.; Latha, M.; Liu, P.; Lem, K.; Kaler, S.G. Copper-replacement treatment for symptomatic Menkes disease: ethical considerations. *Clinical Genetics* 2005 September; 68(3): 278-283. NRCBL: 9.5.7; 8.3.2; 7.1. SC: cs.

Sigafoos, J. Self-determination: can we let the child determine the 'best' treatment? [editorial]. *Pediatric Rehabilitation* 2006 January-March; 9(1): 1-2. NRCBL: 9.5.7; 8.3.2; 8.3.1.

Simonds, Anita K. Ethical aspects of home long term ventilation in children with neuromuscular disease. *Paediatric Respiratory Reviews* 2005 September; 6(3): 209-214. NRCBL: 9.5.7; 2.1; 9.4.

Skinner, S. Rachel; Ng, Cindy; McDonald, Ann; Walters, Tamara. A patient with autism and severe depression: medical and ethical challenges for an adolescent medicine unit. *Medical Journal of Australia* 2005 October

17; 183(8): 422-424. NRCBL: 9.5.7; 17.1; 11.3; 8.1; 8.3.2. SC: cs.

Southall, David P.; Samuels, Martin P. CNEP needs to return. *Lancet* 2006 April 1-7; 367(9516): 1033-1035. NRCBL: 9.5.7; 9.8; 18.6. Identifiers: continuous negative extrathoracic-pressure ventilation.

Tanne, Janice Hopkins. Vaccines against cervical cancer provoke US controversy [news]. *BMJ: British Medical Journal* 2006 April 8; 332(7545): 814. NRCBL: 9.5.7; 9.7; 10; 9.5.5.

Twiss, Sumner B. On cross-cultural conflict and pediatric intervention [review of "Children, Ethics, and Modern Medicine" by Richard B. Miller]. *Journal of Religious Ethics* 2006 March; 34(1): 163-175. NRCBL: 9.5.7; 8.3.2; 21.7; 8.3.4. SC: cs.

Tyson, Jon E.; Stoll, Barbara J. Evidence-based ethics and the care and outcome of extremely premature infants. *Clinics in Perinatology* 2003 June; 30(2): 363-387. NRCBL: 9.5.7; 9.4; 20.5.2; 8.1. SC: rv.

Watson, Michael S.; Mann, Marie Y.; Lloyd-Puryear, Michele A.; Rinaldo, Piero; Howell, R. Rodney. Newborn screening: toward a uniform screening panel and system. Executive summary. *Genetics in Medicine* 2006 May; 8(Supplement 1): 1S-11S. NRCBL: 9.5.7; 9.1; 15.3. SC: em.

Watson, Michael S.; Mann, Marie Y.; Lloyd-Puryear, Michele A.; Rinaldo, Piero; Howell, R. Rodney. Newborn screening: toward a uniform screening panel and system. Main report. *Genetics in Medicine* 2006 May; 8(Supplement 1): 12S-52S. NRCBL: 9.5.7; 9.1; 15.3. SC: em.

Weinberg, Aviva. Pediatric cochlear implants: the great debate. *Penn Bioethics Journal* 2005 April 2; 1(1): 4p. [Online]. Accessed: http://www.bioethicsjournal.com [2005 April 19]. NRCBL: 9.5.7; 5.1; 4.2; 7.1.

Wheeler, Robert. Gillick or Fraser? A plea for consistency over competence in children [editorial]. *BMJ: British Medical Journal* 2006 April 8; 332(7545): 807. NRCBL: 9.5.7; 8.3.2; 11.2. SC: le. Identifiers: England.

Winter, Karen. The participation rights of looked after children in their health care: a critical review of the research. *International Journal of Children's Rights* 2006; 14(1): 77-95. NRCBL: 9.5.7; 8.3.2; 1.3.5; 9.2. SC: le.

Worthington, Roger. Standards of healthcare and respecting children's rights. *Journal of the Royal Society of Medicine* 2006 April; 99(4): 208-210. NRCBL: 9.5.7; 9.2; 8.1; 8.4.

Yu, Victor Y. Is neonatal intensive care justified in all preterm infants? *Croatian Medical Journal* 2005 October; 46(5): 744-750. NRCBL: 9.5.7; 9.4; 20.5.2. SC: rv.

Zwi, Anthony B.; Grove, Natalie J.; Kelly, Paul; Gayer, Michelle; Ramos-Jimenez, Pilar; Sommerfeld, Johannes. Child health in armed conflict: time to rethink. *Lancet* 2006 June 10-16; 367(9526): 1886-1888. NRCBL: 9.5.7; 21.2; 8.3.2.

CARE FOR SPECIFIC GROUPS/ SUBSTANCE ABUSERS

Bremberg, Stefan; Nilstun, Tore. Justifications of physicians' choice of action: attitudes among the general public, GPs, and oncologists in Sweden. *Scandinavian Journal of Primary Health Care* 2005 June; 23(2): 102-108. NRCBL: 9.5.9; 8.1. SC: em.

Chapman, Charlotte. Dual relationships in substance abuse treatment: ethical implications. *Alcoholism Treatment Quarterly* 1997; 15(2): 73-79. NRCBL: 9.5.9; 17.2; 8.1.

Deibert, Ryan J.; Goldbaum, Gary; Parker, Theodore R.; Hagan, Holly; Marks, Robert; Hanrahan, Michael; Thiede, Hanne. Increased access to unrestricted pharmacy sales of syringes in Seattle- King County, Washington: structural and individual-level changes, 1996 versus 2003. *American Journal of Public Health* 2006 August; 96(8): 1347-1353. NRCBL: 9.5.9; 9.7; 8.1. SC: em.

Dobson, Roger. Study shows that tobacco firms covertly hired scientists [news]. *BMJ: British Medical Journal* 2006 February 11; 332(7537): 321. NRCBL: 9.5.9; 1.3.2; 9.6; 1.3.9; 21.1.

Foddy, Bennett; Savulescu, Julian. Addiction and autonomy: can addicted people consent to the prescription of their drug of addiction? *Bioethics* 2006 February; 20(1): 1-15. NRCBL: 9.5.9; 8.3.1; 1.1; 18.3. SC: an.

Abstract: It is often claimed that the autonomy of heroin addicts is compromised when they are choosing between taking their drug of addiction and abstaining. This is the basis of claims that they are incompetent to give consent to be prescribed heroin. We reject these claims on a number of empirical and theoretical grounds. First we argue that addicts are likely to be sober, and thus capable of rational thought, when approaching researchers to participate in research. We reject behavioural evidence purported to establish that addicts lack autonomy. We present an argument that extrinsic forces must be irresistible in order to make a choice non-autonomous. We argue that heroin does not present such an irresistible force. We make a case that drug-oriented desires are strong regular appetitive desires, which do not compromise consent. Finally we argue that an addict's apparent desire to engage in a harmful act cannot be construed as evidence of irrational or compulsive thought. On these arguments, a sober heroin addict must be considered competent, autonomous and capable of giving consent. More generally, any argument against legalisation of drugs or supporting infringement of the liberty of those desiring to take drugs of addiction must be based on considerations of harm and paternalism, and not on false claims that addicts lack freedom of the will.

Foddy, Bennett; Savulescu, Julian. Autonomy, addiction and the drive to pleasure: designing drugs and our biology: a reply to Neil Levy. *Bioethics* 2006 February; 20(1): 21-23. NRCBL: 9.5.9; 18.3; 1.1.

Fox, Brion J. Framing tobacco control efforts within an ethical context. *Tobacco Control* 2005 August; 14(Supplement 2): ii38-ii44. NRCBL: 9.5.9; 9.1; 1.1; 2.1.

Fry, Craig L.; Hall, Wayne; Ritter, Alison; Jenkinson, Rebecca. The ethics of paying drug users who participate in research: a review and practical recommendations. *Journal of Empirical Research on Human Research Ethics* 2006 December; 1(4): 21-35. NRCBL: 9.5.9; 18.5.1; 9.3.1. SC: rv.

Gillies, John; Sheehan, Mark. Commentary: when should patients be held responsible for their lifestyle choices? [response]. *BMJ: British Medical Journal* 2006 February 4; 332(7536): 279. NRCBL: 9.5.9; 9.4. Comments: Stuart McPherson and Colin John Rees. An alcoholic patient who continues to drink: case outcome. BMJ: British Medical Journal 2006 February 4; 332(7536): 276.

Haber, Paul. Commentary: challenge for doctors and policy makers [response]. *BMJ: British Medical Journal* 2006 February 4; 332(7536): 277-278. NRCBL: 9.5.9; 9.5.3; 9.4. Comments: Stuart McPherson and Colin John Rees. An alcoholic patient who continues to drink: case outcome. BMJ: British Medical Journal 2006 February 4; 332(7536): 276.

Hammond, David; Collishaw, Neil E.; Callard, Cynthia. Secret science: tobacco industry research on smoking behaviour and cigarette toxicity. *Lancet* 2006 March 4-10; 367(9512): 781-787. NRCBL: 9.5.9; 1.3.9; 1.3.2; 7.1; 5.3; 21.1.

Abstract: A lack of scientific data remains the principal obstacle to regulating cigarette toxicity. In particular, there is an immediate need to improve our understanding of the interaction between smoking behaviour and product design, and its influence on cigarette deliveries. This article reviews internal tobacco industry documents on smoking behaviour research undertaken by Imperial Tobacco Limited (ITL) and British-American Tobacco (BAT). BAT documents indicate that smokers vary their puffing behaviour to regulate nicotine levels and compensate for low- yield cigarettes by smoking them more intensely. BAT research also shows that the tar and nicotine delivered to smokers is substantially greater than the machine-smoked yields reported to consumers and regulators. Internal documents describe a strategy to maximise this discrepancy through product design. In particular, BAT developed elastic cigarettes that produced low yields under standard testing protocols, whereas in consumers' hands they elicited more intensive smoking and provided higher concentrations of tar and nicotine to smokers. Documents also show that BAT pursued this product strategy despite the health risks to consumers and ethical concerns raised by senior scientists, and paired it with an equally successful marketing campaign that promoted these cigarettes as low-tar alternatives for health-concerned smokers. Overall, the documents seem to reveal a product strategy intended to exploit the limitations of the testing protocols and to intentionally conceal from consumers and regulators the potential toxicity of BAT products revealed by BAT's own research. Tobacco industry research underscores the serious limitations of the

NRCBL: National Reference Center for Bioethics Literature Classification Scheme   See inside front cover for terms.

113

current cigarette testing protocols and the documents describe deceptive business practices that remain in place.

Harris, Gardiner. F.D.A. dismisses medical benefit from marijuana; political fight widens; agency reply to Congress contradicts '99 report by top scientists. *New York Times* 2006 April 21; p. A1, A23. NRCBL: 9.5.9; 5.3. SC: le.

Keane, Helen. Moral frameworks, ethical engagement and harm reduction: commentary on 'Ethical challenges and responses in harm reduction research: promoting applied communitarian ethics' by C.L. Fry, C. Treloar and L. Maher. *Drug and Alcohol Review* 2005 November; 24(6): 551-552. NRCBL: 9.5.9; 7.1; 1.3.1; 1.1.

Klag, Stefanie; O'Callaghan, Frances; Creed, Peter. The use of legal coercion in the treatment of substance abusers: an overview and critical analysis of thirty years of research. *Substance Use and Misuse* 2005; 40(12): 1777-1795. NRCBL: 9.5.9; 8.3.4. SC: le.

Kozlowski, Lynn T.; Edwards, B.Q. "Not safe" is not enough: smokers have a right to know more than there is no safe tobacco product. *Tobacco Control* 2005 August; 14(Supplement 2): ii3-ii7. NRCBL: 9.5.9; 8.2; 9.1; 1.1.

Levy, Neil. Addiction, autonomy and ego-depletion: a response to Bennett Foddy and Julian Savulescu. *Bioethics* 2006 February; 20(1): 16-20. NRCBL: 9.5.9; 18.3; 18.5.6; 8.3.1.

Lovell, Anne M. Addiction markets: the case of high-dose Buprenorphine in France. *In:* Petryna, Adriana; Lakoff, Andrew; Kleinman, Arthur, eds. Global Pharmaceuticals: Ethics, Markets, Practices. Durham: Duke University Press; 2006: 136-170. NRCBL: 9.5.9; 1.3.2; 9.3.1; 9.7.

Mackenzie, Robin. Addiction in public health and criminal justice system governance: neuroscience, enhancement and happiness research. *Genomics, Society and Policy* 2006 May; 2(1): 92-109. NRCBL: 9.5.9; 15.1; 4.5.
Abstract: Present regulations and prohibitions relating to psychoactive substances rest upon socio-historically contingent and hence arguably irrational foundations. New evidence bases located in post-genomic genetics and neuroscience hold the potential to disrupt them through demonstrating a lack of congruence between the regulations and prohibitions and the alleged and actual harms. How far might we use such knowledge to drive policy? What limits, if any, should be placed on our choices, and what attempts to influence these may be seen as acceptable? This article seeks to address these questions in relation to criminal justice system and public health governance of psychoactive substance use. It will explore the implications of justifications employed in both areas to restrict free choice on the grounds of harm to the self and to others. The central argument made is that the current categorisation of psychoactive substances as lawful or unlawful is likely to become disrupted as the result of several separate discourses which converge over psychoactive substance use: enhancement, cognitive liberty and the degree to which subjective experiences of pleasure, well being and happiness might enable us to improve and maintain our health as individuals and that of society as a whole. In my view, the strategic deployment of concepts of addiction

which has enabled the public health and criminal justice systems to be able to share governance over psychoactive substance use is likely to become destabilised by these discursive developments. In that policy in the United Kingdom and elsewhere now draws upon happiness research, while reformers advocate freedom of choice over means of enhancing our states of being, a new focus upon the rational evaluation of psychoactive substances governance seems plausible.

McPherson, Stuart; Rees, Colin John. An alcoholic patient who continues to drink: case outcome. *BMJ: British Medical Journal* 2006 February 4; 332(7536): 276. NRCBL: 9.5.9; 8.1; 9.4.

Miller, Peter. Harm reduction ethics: a promising basis for drug policy. *Drug and Alcohol Review* 2005 November; 24(6): 553-554. NRCBL: 9.5.9; 9.1; 7.1.

Miller, Peter; Moore, David; Strang, John. The regulation of research by funding bodies: an emerging ethical issue for the alcohol and other drug sector? *International Journal of Drug Policy* 2006 January; 17(1): 12-16. NRCBL: 9.5.9; 9.3.1; 18.6; 18.5.1.

Nilssen, Even. Coercion and justice: a critical analysis of compulsory intervention towards adult substance abusers in Scandinavian social law. *International Journal of Social Welfare* 2005 April; 14(2): 134-144. NRCBL: 9.5.9; 1.1; 21.1. SC: le. Identifiers: Denmark; Sweden; Norway.

Novotny, Thomas E.; Carlin, D. Ethical and legal aspects of global tobacco control. *Tobacco Control* 2005 August; 14(Supplement 2): ii26-ii30. NRCBL: 9.5.9; 21.1; 9.1.

Parascandola, Mark. Science, industry, and tobacco harm reduction: a case study of tobacco industry scientists' involvement in the National Cancer Institute's Smoking and Health Program, 1964-1980. *Public Health Reports* 2005 May-June; 120(3): 338-349. NRCBL: 9.5.9; 1.3.2; 1.3.9; 7.3.

Preston, Julia. Texas hospitals' separate paths reflect the debate on immigration. *New York Times* 2006 July 18; p. A1, A18. NRCBL: 9.5.9; 9.4; 9.3.1. SC: po.

Roy, David. Access to sterile needles for young people under the age of 14: an ethical analysis [letter]. *Canadian HIV/AIDS Policy and Law Newsletter* 1996 April; 2(3): 4. NRCBL: 9.5.9; 9.5.7; 9.5.6.

Scott, Christy K.; White, William L. Ethical issues in the conduct of longitudinal studies of addiction treatment. *Journal of Substance Abuse Treatment* 2005; 28(Supplement 1): S91-S101. NRCBL: 9.5.9; 18.3; 18.5.1; 18.5.2; 9.3.1; 8.4;. SC: cs; le.

Solai, Sandra; Dubois-Arber, Françoise; Benninghoff, Fabienne; Benaroyo, Lazare. Ethical reflections emerging during the activity of a low threshold facility with supervised drug consumption room in Geneva, Switzerland. *International Journal of Drug Policy* 2006 January; 17(1): 17-22. NRCBL: 9.5.9; 7.1; 8.1; 9.2.

Wilson, Nick; Thomson, George. Tobacco taxation and public health: ethical problems, policy responses. *Social Science and Medicine* 2005 August; 61(3): 649-659. NRCBL: 9.5.9; 1.3.5; 9.1; 1.1.

Zernike, Kate. F.D.A.'s report illuminates wide divide on marijuana. *New York Times* 2006 April 22; p. A11. NRCBL: 9.5.9; 5.3. SC: le.

CARE FOR SPECIFIC GROUPS/ WOMEN

American College of Obstetricians and Gynecologists [ACOG]. Committee on Ethics. ACOG Committee Opinion #321: maternal decision making, ethics, and the law. *Obstetrics and Gynecology* 2005 November; 106(5 Part 1): 1127-1137. NRCBL: 9.5.5; 9.5.8; 8.3.4; 9.5.9.

Armstrong, David. Baby talk: Drug firm's cash sways debate over test for pregnant women; Glaxo funds lectures urging herpes screening — an idea widely rejected by experts; at issue: virus's risk to infants. *Wall Street Journal* 2006 December 13; p. A1, A12. NRCBL: 9.5.5; 9.7; 9.3.1; 7.2. SC: po.

Brakman, Sarah-Vaughn; Scholz, Sally J. Adoption, ART, and a re-conception of the maternal body: toward embodied maternity. *Hypatia: A Journal of Feminist Philosophy* 2006 Winter; 21(1): 54-73. NRCBL: 9.5.5; 10; 14.1.

Büken, Nüket Örnek; Sahinoglu, Serap. Violence against women in Turkey and the role of women physicians. *Nursing Ethics* 2006 March; 13(2): 197-205. NRCBL: 9.5.5; 7.1; 10.

Callister, Lynn Clark. Perinatal ethics: state of the science. *Journal of Perinatal and Neonatal Nursing* 2006 January-March; 20(1): 37-39. NRCBL: 9.5.5; 14.1; 4.1.3.

Cantor, Julie D.; Reisman, Neal R. When an adult female seeks ritual genital alteration: ethics, law, and the parameters of participation. *Plastic and Reconstructive Surgery* 2006 April; 117(4): 1158-1166. NRCBL: 9.5.5; 9.5.7; 10; 8.3.1; 21.1.

Chandis, V.; Williams, T. The patient, the doctor, the fetus, and the court-compelled cesarean: why courts should address the question through a bioethical lens. *Medicine and Law: The World Association for Medical Law* 2006 December; 25(4): 729-746. NRCBL: 9.5.5; 8.3.4; 2.1. SC: le.

Abstract: Court-ordered Cesarean sections are a relatively recent phenomenon in the intersection of law and medicine. Existing jurisprudence utilizes a legal balancing test when addressing conflicts that arise between physicians and patients regarding obstetrical treatment and care. The authors contend that courts' analyses lack a fundamental element—a bioethical framework. Therefore, the authors believe that in order to better assess such conflicts, courts should incorporate a bioethical framework such as the Georgetown mantra to help complement their legal analyses.

Coleman, P.K.; Reardon, D.C.; Lee, M.B. Women's preferences for information and complication seriousness ratings related to elective medical procedures. *Journal of Medical Ethics* 2006 August; 32(8): 435-438. NRCBL: 9.5.5; 8.3.1. SC: em.

Abstract: OBJECTIVE: To study the preferences of patients for information related to elective procedures. METHODS: A survey was carried out using a sample of 187 women. The majority of whom were on a low-income, who obtained obstetric or gynaecological services at St Joseph Regional Medical Center in Milwaukee, Wisconsin, while they were in a waiting room. RESULTS: Many of the complications, including those that are uncommon and less serious, were considered to be relevant to the medical decisions of most patients. Average seriousness ratings associated with complications of various elective procedures were in the range of moderate to high. A frequency of complications of 1:100 or higher would factor into most women's elective treatment decisions. Women indicated a preference for receiving as much or more information pertaining to complications associated with particular elective obstetric or gynaecological procedures as other elective procedures. CONCLUSION: Most women wish to be informed of risks and treatment alternatives, rate many complications as serious, and are likely to use information provided to make elective treatment decisions.

Conroy, Ronán M. Female genital mutilation: whose problem, whose solution? [editorial]. *BMJ: British Medical Journal* 2006 July 15; 333(7559): 106-107. NRCBL: 9.5.5; 9.5.7; 10; 21.7.

Coors, Marilyn E.; Townsend, Susan F. Supporting pregnant women through difficult decisions: a case of prenatal diagnosis of osteogenesis imperfecta. *Journal of Clinical Ethics* 2006 Fall; 17(3): 266-274. NRCBL: 9.5.5; 15.2; 8.1; 4.1.2.

Craven, Christa. Claiming respectable American motherhood: homebirth mothers, medical officials, and the state. *Medical Anthropology Quarterly* 2005 June; 19(2): 194-215. NRCBL: 9.5.5; 4.1.3.

Dalton, Kevin J. Refusal of interventions to protect the life of the viable fetus—a case-based Transatlantic overview. *Medico-Legal Journal* 2006; 74(Part 1): 16-24. NRCBL: 9.5.5; 9.5.8; 8.3.4; 1.2; 9.5.6. SC: le. Identifiers: United States; Untied Kingdom (Great Britain).

Danerek, Margaretha; Uden, Giggi; Dykes, Anna-Karin. Sympathetic responsibility in ethically difficult situations. *Acta Obstetricia Gynecologica Scandinavica* 2005 December; 84(12): 1164-1171. NRCBL: 9.5.5; 9.5.8; 4.1.2; 8.1. Identifiers: Sweden.

Dixon-Woods, Mary; Williams, S.J.; Jackson, C.J.; Akkad, A.; Kenyon, S.; Habiba, M. Why women consent to surgery, even when they don't want to: a qualitative study. *Clinical Ethics* 2006 September; 1(3): 153-158. NRCBL: 9.5.5; 8.3.1; 2.1; 7.1. SC: em.

Dyer, Clare. Patient is to appeal High Court ruling on breast cancer drug [news]. *BMJ: British Medical Journal*

NRCBL: National Reference Center for Bioethics Literature Classification Scheme   See inside front cover for terms.

115

2006 February 25; 332(7539): 443. NRCBL: 9.5.5; 9.7; 9.4. SC: le.

Dyer, Clare. Trusts can take cost into account when deciding drug treatment [news]. *BMJ: British Medical Journal* 2006 April 22; 332(7547): 928. NRCBL: 9.5.5; 9.7; 9.3.1; 9.4. SC: le. Identifiers: United Kingdom (Great Britain).

Fey, Toby Schonfeld. Regulating radiology: ethical issues in mammography and federal legislation. *Journal of Women's Health and Gender-Based Medicine* 2000 December; 9(10): 1113-1118. NRCBL: 9.5.5; 5.3; 7.1; 1.3.5.

Fraser, Alisdair. Female genital mutilation and Baker Brown [letter]. *Journal of the Royal Society of Medicine* 1997 October; 90(10): 586-587. NRCBL: 9.5.5; 10; 7.1.

Halperin, Mordechai. Dysfunctional uterine bleeding: new approaches. *In:* Rosner, Fred, ed. Medicine and Jewish Law. Volume III. Brooklyn, NY: Yashar Books, Inc.; 2005: 191-200. NRCBL: 9.5.5; 1.2.

Happe, Kelly E. Heredity, gender and the discourse of ovarian cancer. *New Genetics and Society* 2006 August; 25(2): 171-196. NRCBL: 9.5.5; 9.5.1; 15.3; 10; 16.3.

Hebbar, Shripad; Nayak, Sathisha. Ethical issues in laparoscopic hysterectomy. *Indian Journal of Medical Ethics* 2006 January-March; 3(1): 19-20. NRCBL: 9.5.5; 8.3.1; 9.3.1.

Hulsey, Tara. Prenatal drug use: the ethics of testing and incarcerating pregnant women. *Newborn and Infant Nursing Review* 2005 June; 5(2): 93-96. NRCBL: 9.5.5; 9.5.9; 9.5.8; 17.7.

Hyams, Ross. Who gets to choose? Responses to the foetal/maternal conflict. *E Law: Murdoch University Electronic Journal of Law* 1995 December; 2(3): 8 p. [Online]. Accessed: http://www.murdoch.edu.au/elaw/issues/v2n3/hyams23.html [2006 June 29]. NRCBL: 9.5.5; 9.5.8; 10; 14.1. SC: le. Identifiers: United States; Canada.

International Community of Women Living with HIV/AIDS. The International Community of Women Living with HIV/AIDS: point of view. *Health and Human Rights: An International Journal* 2005; 8(2): 25-26. NRCBL: 9.5.5; 9.5.6; 7.1; 8.3.1; 9.5.7.

Kalish, R.B.; McCullough, L.B.; Chervenak, F.A. Decision-making about caesarean delivery. *Lancet* 2006 March 18-24; 367(9514): 883-885. NRCBL: 9.5.5; 5.2; 8.3.1; 1.1; 4.2.

Kauffman, Robert P.; Castracane, V. Daniel; Van Hook, Catherine L. Postmenopausal hormone therapy and informed consent: a call for common sense. *Journal of Women's Health* 2005 September; 14(7): 592-594. NRCBL: 9.5.5; 8.3.1.

Lam, Wendy; Fielding, Richard; Chan, Miranda; Chow, Louis; Ho, Ella. Participation and satisfaction with surgical treatment decision-making in breast cancer among Chinese women. *Breast Cancer Research and Treatment* 2003 July; 80(2): 171-180. NRCBL: 9.5.5; 9.5.1; 8.3.1. SC: em. Identifiers: Hong Kong.

Layne, Linda L. Unhappy endings: a feminist reappraisal of the women's health movement from the vantage of pregnancy loss. *Social Science and Medicine* 2003 May; 56(9): 1881-1891. NRCBL: 9.5.5; 14.1; 10. SC: an.

Leszczynska, Katarzyna; Dymczyk, K.; Wac, K.; Krajewska, K. Obeying patient's rights on the basis of maternity ward. *Roczniki Akademii Medycznej w Bialymstoku* 2005; 50(Supplement 1): 70-73. NRCBL: 9.5.5; 8.1; 9.2.

Linder, Erin N. Punishing prenatal alcohol abuse: the problems inherent in utilizing civil commitment to address addiction. *University of Illinois Law Review* 2005; 2005(3): 873-901. NRCBL: 9.5.5; 9.5.8; 9.5.9; 1.3.5. SC: le.

Minkoff, Howard; Paltrow, Lynn M. The rights of "unborn children" and the value of pregnant women. *Hastings Center Report* 2006 March-April; 36(2): 26-28. NRCBL: 9.5.5; 9.5.8; 1.3.5. SC: le.

Montazeri, Ali; Haji-Mahmoodi, Mehregan; Jarvandi, Soghra. Breast self-examination: do religious beliefs matter? A descriptive study. *Journal of Public Health Medicine* 2003 June; 25(2): 154-155. NRCBL: 9.5.5; 9.5.1; 1.2. SC: em. Identifiers: Islam; Iran.

Mostafa, S.R.A.; El Zeiny, N.A.M.; Tayel, S.E.S.; Moubarak, E.L. What do medical students in Alexandria know about female genital mutilation? *Eastern Mediterranean Health Journal = La Revue de Santé de la Méditerranéeorientale* 2006; 12(Supplement 2): S78-S92 [Online]. Accessed: http://www.emro.who.int/publications/emhj/12_S2/PDF/8.pdf [2007 January 4]. NRCBL: 9.5.5; 10; 7.2; 7.1. SC: em. Note: Abstract in French and Arabic.

Nelson, Erin. Reconceiving pregnancy: expressive choice and legal reasoning. *McGill Law Journal* 2004; 49: 593-634. NRCBL: 9.5.5; 9.5.8; 8.3.4; 12.4.2. SC: le.

Noland, Lynn R. Informing patients of the risks and benefits of hormone replacement therapy: nephrologists' ethical obligation. *Advances in Chronic Kidney Disease* 2004 October; 11(4): 387-390. NRCBL: 9.5.5; 9.7; 8.2; 7.3. SC: cs.

Nusbaum, Julie. Childbirth in modern Athens: the transition from homebirth to hospital birth. *Penn Bioethics Journal* 2006; 2(2): 33-37. NRCBL: 9.5.5; 9.5.7; 7.1; 4.2. SC: em.

Abstract: The transition of birthing practices in Greece from a homebirth culture, in which women deliver at home surrounded by family and under the supervision of a typically female birth attendant, to a biomedical birth model, in which women deliver in a hospital with numerous forms of medical intervention and

---

under the control of a physician, has been unusually rapid. Today, Western biomedicine not only dominates the health care system in Greece but has an essential hegemony on women's health care. My research examines whether the pervasive utilization of biomedical environments for birthing can be explained by a lack of alternatives or by women's satisfaction with the technology and care available in hospitals. I also examine how women retain control over their experience of pregnancy and childbirth within the biomedical context and attempt to explain the emerging construction of a "natural" discourse on pregnancy and childbirth in Athens. Major themes that emerged from interviews with Athenian women were the lack of consent for medical intervention during birth, limited infrastructure to support women who seek non-medical alternatives, and limited emotional support and collective education for mothers in the urban environment of Athens. Also, women described choosing the right caregiver as essential to maintaining a sense of control over their pregnancy and, more generally, over their life. In light of women's apparent interest in improving women's experience of pregnancy and childbirth in Athens, it is recommended that researchers further explore the interaction of medical and non-medical discourses on pregnancy and childbirth.

Parker, Kelly. Pregnant women inmates: evaluating their rights and identifying opportunities for improvements in their treatment. *Journal of Law and Health* 2004-2005; 19(2): 259-295. NRCBL: 9.5.5; 9.2; 18.5.5. SC: le.

Pector, Elizabeth A. Ethical issues of high-order multiple births. *Newborn and Infant Nursing Reviews* 2005 June; 5(2): 69-76. NRCBL: 9.5.5; 9.3.1; 14.4; 12.1; 8.1; 1.3.7. SC: em.

Queenan, John T. Elective cesarean delivery [editorial]. *Obstetrics and Gynecology* 2004 June; 103(6): 1135-1136. NRCBL: 9.5.5; 9.5.7; 8.3.1.

Rabin, Roni. A new vaccine for girls, but should it be compulsory? *New York Times* 2006 July 18; p. F5, F7. NRCBL: 9.5.5; 9.7; 8.3.4. SC: po.

Renker, Paula Rinard; Tonkin, Peggy. Women's views of prenatal violence screening: acceptability and confidentiality issues. *Obstetrics and Gynecology* 2006 February; 107(2, Part 1): 348-354. NRCBL: 9.5.5; 11.4. SC: em.

Sharma, Geeta; Gold, Heather T.; Chervenak, Frank A.; McCullough, Laurence; Alt, Abigail K.; Chasen, Stephen T. Patient preference regarding first-trimester aneuploidy risk assessment. *American Journal of Obstetrics and Gynecology* 2005 October; 193(4): 1429-1436. NRCBL: 9.5.5; 8.3.1; 12.1. SC: em.

Sheldon, Tony. Dutch insurers pay midwives to refer fewer to hospital [news]. *BMJ: British Medical Journal* 2006 November 18; 333(7577): 1034. NRCBL: 9.5.5; 4.1.3; 9.3.1; 9.8.

Simonstein, Frida. Pressures on women to reproduce and the drive towards assisted reproductive technologies. *Medicine and Law: The World Association for Medical Law* 2006 June; 25(2): 355-363. NRCBL: 9.5.5; 14.4; 18.1.

Abstract: This paper explores the role of assisted reproductive technology in the management of infertility from an Israeli

viewpoint. The author discusses the effects of the generous provision of IVF facilities in Israel when compared with other countries and explains the apparent conflict between the service and research functions of these practices.

Sisters of St. Francis Health Services, Inc. Management of extrauterine pregnancy [policy statement]. *Ethics and Medics* 2006 March; 31(3): 4. NRCBL: 9.5.5; 1.2; 12.1. Identifiers: ectopic pregnancy; Catholics.

Stein, Rob. Institute practices reproductive medicine — and Catholicism. *Washington Post* 2006 October 31; p. A14. NRCBL: 9.5.5; 11.1; 1.2. SC: po.

Sulmasy, Daniel P. Emergency contraception for women who have been raped: must Catholics test for ovulation, or is testing for pregnancy morally sufficient? *Kennedy Institute of Ethics Journal* 2006 December; 16(4): 305-331. NRCBL: 9.5.5; 10; 11.1; 1.2; 1.1.

Abstract: On the grounds that rape is an act of violence, not a natural act of intercourse, Roman Catholic teaching traditionally has permitted women who have been raped to take steps to prevent pregnancy, while consistently prohibiting abortion even in the case of rape. Recent scientific evidence that emergency contraception (EC) works primarily by preventing ovulation, not by preventing implantation or by aborting implanted embryos, has led Church authorities to permit the use of EC drugs in the setting of rape. Doubts about whether an abortifacient effect of EC drugs has been completely disproven have led to controversy within the Church about whether it is sufficient to determine that a woman is not pregnant before using EC drugs or whether one must establish that she has not recently ovulated. This article presents clinical, epidemiological, and ethical arguments why testing for pregnancy should be morally sufficient for a faith community that is strongly opposed to abortion.

Thampapillai, Dilan. Court-ordered obstetrical intervention and the rights of a pregnant woman. *Journal of Law and Medicine* 2005 May; 12(4): 455-461. NRCBL: 9.5.5; 9.5.8; 8.3.4; 8.3.1; 4.4. SC: le. Identifiers: Australia.

United States. Congress. House. A bill to provide for programs that reduce the need for abortion, help women bear healthy children, and support new parents. Washington, DC: U.S. G.P.O., 2006. 46 p. [Online]. Accessed: http://frwebgate.access.gpo.gov/cgi-bin/useftp.cgi?IPaddress=162.140.64.21&filename=h6145ih.pdf&directory=/diskb/wais/data/109_cong_bills [2006 December 05]. NRCBL: 9.5.5; 12.1. SC: le. Identifiers: Pregnant Women Support Act. Note: H.R. 6145, 109th Congress, 2d session. Introduced by Rep. Davis, September 21, 2006. Referred to the Committee on Energy and Commerce, and in addition to the Committees on Education and the Workforce, Ways and Means, and Agriculture.

Unnithan-Kumar, Maya. Conception technologies, local healers and negotiations around childbearing in Rajasthan. *In:* Unnithan-Kumar, Maya, ed. Reproductive Agency, Medicine and the State: Cultural Transformations in Childbearing. New York: Berghahn Books; 2004: 59-81. NRCBL: 9.5.5; 14.1; 21.7.

NRCBL: National Reference Center for Bioethics Literature Classification Scheme   See inside front cover for terms.

117

Van Der Weyden, Martin B. Retrospective ethical approval [reply]. *Medical Journal of Australia* 2001 September 3; 175(5): 286. NRCBL: 9.5.5; 8.3.1; 7.1; 9.6.

Wax, Joseph R.; Cartin, Angelina; Pinette, Michael G.; Blackstone, Jacquelyn. Patient choice cesarean: an evidence-based review. *Obstetrical and Gynecological Survey* 2004 August; 59(8): 601-616. NRCBL: 9.5.5. SC: rv.

Wilkinson, Sue; Kitzinger, Celia. Whose breast is it anyway? A feminist consideration of advice and 'treatment' for breast cancer. *Women's Studies International Forum* 1993 May-June; 16(3): 229-238. NRCBL: 9.5.5; 4.1.1.

Williams, Clare; Sandall, Jane; Lewando-Hundt, Gillian; Heyman, Bob; Spencer, Kevin; Grellier, Rachel. Women as moral pioneers? Experiences of first trimester antenatal screening. *Social Science and Medicine* 2005 November; 61(9): 1983-1992. NRCBL: 9.5.5; 15.2; 1.1. SC: em. Identifiers: United Kingdom (Great Britain).

Young, Diony. Confrontation in Kansas City: elective cesareans and maternal choice [editorial]. *Birth* 2000 September; 27(3): 153-155. NRCBL: 9.5.5.

CARING *See* NURSING ETHICS AND PHILOSOPHY; PHILOSOPHY OF MEDICINE; PATIENT RELATIONSHIPS

CIVIL COMMITMENT *See* INVOLUNTARY COMMITMENT

CLINICAL ETHICISTS *See* ETHICISTS AND ETHICS COMMITTEES

CLINICAL ETHICS *See* BIOETHICS AND MEDICAL ETHICS; ETHICISTS AND ETHICS COMMITTEES; NURSING ETHICS AND PHILOSOPHY; PROFESSIONAL ETHICS

CLINICAL ETHICS COMMITTEES *See* ETHICISTS AND ETHICS COMMITTEES

CLINICAL TRIALS *See* BIOMEDICAL RESEARCH; HUMAN EXPERIMENTATION

CLONING
See also HUMAN EXPERIMENTATION/ SPECIAL POPULATIONS/ EMBRYOS AND FETUSES; REPRODUCTIVE TECHNOLOGIES

Considerations of the Holy See on human cloning. *United Nations: General Assembly* 2004 October 7; A/C.6/59/INF/1: 4 p. [Online]. Accessed: http://daccessdds.un.org/doc/UNDOC/LTD/N04/541/26/PDF/N0454126.pdf?OpenElement [2007 February 12]. NRCBL: 14.5; 1.2; 5.3.

Drop the c-word [news]. *New Scientist* 2006 October 21-27; 192(2574): 7. NRCBL: 14.5. Identifiers: cloning.

Human cloning and scientific corruption: the South Korea scandal and the future of the stem cell debate. *New Atlantis* 2006 Winter; 11: 113-117. NRCBL: 14.5; 1.3.9.

Proceed with caution [editorial]. *Nature Biotechnology* 2005 July; 23(7): 763. NRCBL: 14.5; 18.5.6; 15.4; 18.1.

Abdur Rab, M.; Khayat, M.H. Human cloning: Eastern Mediterranean region perspective. *Eastern Mediterranean Health Journal* 2006; 12(Supplement 2): S29-S37 [Online]. Accessed: http://www.emro.who.int/publications/EMHJ/12_S2/PDF/4.pdf [2007 January 4]. NRCBL: 14.5; 1.2; 15.1; 18.5.4; 21.1. SC: rv. Note: Abstract in French and Arabic.

Aldhous, Peter; Coghlan, Andy. Ten years on, has the cloning dream died? *New Scientist* 2006 July 1-7; 191(2558): 8-10. NRCBL: 14.5; 15.1.

Aldhous, Peter; Coghlan, Andy. Therapeutic cloning set back by hype and fraud. *New Scientist* 2006 July 1-7; 191(2558): 11. NRCBL: 14.5; 18.5.4; 15.1; 19.1.

American Society for Reproductive Medicine [ASRM]. Ethics Committee. Human somatic cell nuclear transfer (cloning). *Fertility and Sterility* 2004 September; 82(Supplement 1): S236-S239. NRCBL: 14.5; 14.1; 15.1.

Austria. Bioethikkommission beim Bundeskanzleramt = Austria. Bioethics Commission at the Federal Chancellery. Interim report on so-called reproductive cloning with regard to a detailed opinion on the application of human cloning, embryo protection and embryo research, preimplantation diagnosis as well as additional issues concerning reproductive medicine. Vienna, Austria: Bioethikkommission beim Bundeskanzleramt, 2003 February 12: 3 p. NRCBL: 14.5; 18.5.4; 15.2. Note: Decision of the Bioethics Commission at the Federal Chancellery of 12 February 2003.

Babu, M.N. Human cloning: an ethically negative feat in genetic engineering. *Philosophy and Social Action* 1998 April-June; 24(2): 46-55. NRCBL: 14.5.

Barnoy, Sivia; Ehrenfeld, Malka; Sharon, Rina; Tabak, Nili. Knowledge and attitudes toward human cloning in Israel. *New Genetics and Society* 2006 April; 25(1): 21-31. NRCBL: 14.5; 1.2. SC: em.

Basak, Jyotish C. Cloning: social or scientific priority? *Indian philosophical quarterly* 2002 October; 29(4): 517-528. NRCBL: 14.5; 5.1.

Best, Steven; Kellner, Douglas. Biotechnology, ethics and the politics of cloning. *Democracy and Nature* 2002 November; 8(3): 439-465. NRCBL: 14.5; 5.1; 18.5.4; 15.1.

Best, Steven; Kellner, Douglas. Biotechnology, ethics, and the politics of cloning. *In:* Stehr, Nico, ed. Biotechnology Between Commerce and Civil Society. New Brunswick, NJ: Transaction Publishers; 2004: 53-88. NRCBL: 14.5; 15.1; 22.3.

Birnbacher, Dieter. Human cloning and human dignity. *Reproductive BioMedicine Online [electronic]* 2005 March; 10(Supplement 1): 50-55. NRCBL: 14.5; 4.4; 5.2; 9.5.7; 15.1. SC: an. Conference: Ethics, Law and Moral Philosophy of Reproductive Biomedicine; London, UK; 2004 September 30 - October 1; Royal Society.

Birnbacher, Dieter. Zentrale Ethikkommission der Bundesärztekammer veröffentlicht Stellungnahme zum Forschungsklonen mit dem Ziel therapeutischer Anwendungen [Central Ethics Committee of the German Medical Association publishes statement on research cloning with the goal of therapeutic applications]. *Ethik in der Medizin* 2006 June; 18(2): 189-191. NRCBL: 14.5; 2.4.

Byrne, Mary. Ethics, assisted reproductive technologies and cloning. *Reform* 2001 Spring; 79: 22-26, 71. NRCBL: 14.5; 14.1; 9.5.3.

Cameron, Nigel M. de S. "On one path or the other": cloning, religion, and the making of U.S. biopolicy. *In:* Guinn, David E., ed. Handbook of Bioethics and Religion. New York: Oxford University Press, 2006: 305-327. NRCBL: 14.5; 1.2; 5.3.

Campbell, Courtney. Prophecy and citizenry: the case of human cloning. *Sunstone* 1998 June; 21: 11-15. NRCBL: 14.5; 1.2; 2.1.

Caplan, Arthur L. Human cloning and stem cell research. *In his:* Smart Mice, Not-So-Smart People: An Interesting and Amusing Guide to Bioethics. Lanham, MD: Rowman & Littlefield, 2007: 95-118. NRCBL: 14.5; 1.3.9; 18.5.4; 15.1. SC: po.

Carvalho, Ana Sofia; Machado, Pedro; Malcata, Francisco Xavier. Public perception of science: cloning in the Portuguese press. *In:* Glasa, J., ed. Ethics of Human Genetics: Challenges of the (Post) Genomic Era. Bratislava, Slovak Republic: Charis [and] IMEB Foundation; 2002: 203-208. NRCBL: 14.5.

Check, Erika. The rocky road to success [news]. *Nature* 2005 September 8; 437(7056): 185-186. NRCBL: 14.5; 18.5.4; 15.1; 19.1. Identifiers: Kevin Eggan.

Choo, Dong-Ryul. Two master arguments in the ethics of human cloning: the procreative right of couples vs. autonomy of the future clones. *In:* Sang-yong, Song; Young-Mo, Koo; Macer, Darryl R.J., eds. Asian Bioethics in the 21st Century. Christchurch, NZ: Eubios Ethics Institute, 2002: 402-417. NRCBL: 14.5; 14.1; 1.1; 4.5. SC: an. Conference: Proceedings of the Asian Bioethics Conference (ABC4), held 2002 November 22-25 in Seoul, South Korea.

Claxton, John; Sachez, Elena; Matthiessen-Guyader, Line. Ethical, legal, and social aspects of farm animal cloning in the 6th Framework Programme for Research. *Cloning and Stem Cells* 2004; 6(2): 178-181. NRCBL: 14.5; 22.2; 5.3. Identifiers: European Commission.

Cobbe, N. Why the apparent haste to clone humans? *Journal of Medical Ethics* 2006 May; 32(5): 298-302. NRCBL: 14.5; 18.5.4; 15.1.

Cui, Ke-Hui. Three concepts of cloning in human beings. *Reproductive BioMedicine Online [electronic]* 2005 July; 11(1): 16-17. Accessed: http://www.rbmonline.com/Article/1763 [2005 December 16]. NRCBL: 14.5; 15.1.

Cyranoski, David. No end in sight for stem-cell odyssey. *Nature* 2006 February 9; 439(7077): 658-659. NRCBL: 14.5; 18.5.4; 15.1; 19.1.

Davion, Victoria. Coming down to earth on cloning: an ecofeminist analysis of homophobia in the current debate. *Hypatia: A Journal of Feminist Philosophy* 2006 Fall; 21(4): 58-76. NRCBL: 14.5; 1.1; 10; 16.1; 15.6.

De Anna, Gabriele. Cloning, begetting, and making children. *HEC (Healthcare Ethics Committee) Forum* 2006 June; 18(2): 172-188. NRCBL: 14.5; 4.4; 14.1; 1.1. SC: an. Comments: Matteo Galletti. Begetting, cloning and being human: two national commission reports against human cloning from Italy and the U.S.A. HEC (Healthcare Ethics Committee) Forum 2006 June; 18(2): 172-188.

Dennis, Carina. Cloning: what now? Mining the secrets of the egg. *Nature* 2006 February 9; 439(7077): 652-655. NRCBL: 14.5; 18.5.4; 15.1; 19.1.

Doerflinger, Richard M. The many casualties of cloning. *New Atlantis* 2006 Spring; 12: 60-70. NRCBL: 14.5; 1.3.9; 1.2.

Elsner, D. Just another reproductive technology? The ethics of human reproductive cloning as an experimental medical procedure. *Journal of Medical Ethics* 2006 October; 32(10): 596-600. NRCBL: 14.5; 14.4; 18.1. SC: an.

Essed, Philomena; Goldberg, David Theo. Cloning cultures: the social injustices of sameness. *Ethnic and Racial Studies* 2002 November 1; 25(6): 1066-1082. NRCBL: 14.5; 5.1. SC: an.

Fost, Norman. The great stem cell debate: where are we now? Cloning, chimeras, and cash. *WMJ: official publication of the State Medical Society of Wisconsin* 2006 June; 105(4): 16-17. NRCBL: 14.5; 15.1; 18.5.4; 22.3.

Galletti, Matteo. Begetting, cloning and being human: two national commission reports against human cloning from Italy and the U.S.A. *HEC (Healthcare Ethics Committee) Forum* 2006 June; 18(2): 156-171. NRCBL: 14.5; 2.4; 21.1; 4.4; 1.1; 7.1. SC: an.

Garrafa, Volnei. Crítica bioética: a um nascimento anunciado = Crítica bioética: de un nacimiento anunciado = Bioethical critique: of a foretold birth. *Revista*

NRCBL: National Reference Center for Bioethics Literature Classification Scheme   See inside front cover for terms.

119

Latinoamericana de Bioética 2003 January; (4): 18-37. NRCBL: 14.5; 22.2; 18.5.1; 18.5.4; 15.1. Conference: Second International Congress on the Ethics of Scientific Research: Bioethics and Genetic Manipulation; Nueva Granada Military University; Bogota, Columbia.

Garzón Díaz, Fabio Alberto. Clonaid: ¿fraude y/o negocio? = Clonaid: fraud and/or business? [editorial]. *Revista Latinoamericana de Bioética* 2003 January; (4): 12-17. NRCBL: 14.5. Conference: Second International Congress on the Ethics of Scientific Research: Bioethics and Genetic Manipulation; Nueva Granada Military University; Bogota, Columbia.

Gazzaniga, Michael. All clones are not the same (opinion). *New York Times* 2006 February 16; p. A33. NRCBL: 14.5; 5.3. SC: po.

Giarelli, Ellen. Images of cloning and stem cell research in editorial cartoons in the United States. *Qualitative Health Research* 2006 January; 16(1): 61-78. NRCBL: 14.5; 18.5.4; 15.1. SC: rv; em.

Gilbert, Scott F.; Tyler, Anna L.; Zackin, Emily J. Ethics and policies for human cloning. *In their:* Bioethics and the New Embryology: Springboards for Debate. Sunderland, MA: Sinauer Associates; 2005: 125-140. NRCBL: 14.5.

Gillon, Raanan. Human reproductive cloning — a look at the arguments against it and a rejection of most of them. *Journal of the Royal Society of Medicine* 1999 January; 92(1): 3-12. NRCBL: 14.5; 1.1.

Gómez-Lobo, Alfonso. Human cloning: potential and ethical issues. *Estudios Publicos* 2003 Summer; (89): 1-8 [Online]. Accessed: http://www.cepchile.cl/dms/archivo_3180_1626/rev89_gomezlobo_ing.pdf [2007 January 25]. NRCBL: 14.5; 1.1.

Gurdon, J.B. Reproductive cloning: past, present and future. *Reproductive BioMedicine Online [electronic]* 2005 March; 10(Supplement 1): 43-44. NRCBL: 14.5; 22.2; 18.5.4; 15.1. Conference: Ethics, Law and Moral Philosophy of Reproductive Biomedicine; London, UK; 2004 September 30 - October 1; Royal Society.

Gurnham, David. The mysteries of human dignity and the brave new world of human cloning. *Social and Legal Studies* 2005 June; 14(2): 197 [Online]. Accessed: http://sls.sagepub.com/cgi/reprint/14/2/197 [2007 January 23]. NRCBL: 14.5; 1.1; 4.4.

Gusman, Adam. An appropriate legislative response to cloning for biomedical research: the case against a criminal ban. *Annals of Health Law* 2005 Summer; 14(2): 361-394. NRCBL: 14.5; 18.5.4; 18.6; 5.3; 15.1.

Harris, John; Patrizio, Pasquale; Gurdon, John; Strong, Carson; Birnbacher, Dieter; Robertson, John; McLaren, Anne; Holm, Søren; Isasi, Rosario; Edwards, Robert; Lockwood, Gillian; White, Gladys; Galton, David; McMahan, Jeff. Discussion (day 1 session 3): moral philosophy of human reproductive cloning. *Reproductive BioMedicine Online [electronic]* 2005 March; 10(Supplement 1): 56-59. NRCBL: 14.5; 14.4; 5.2; 9.5.7; 4.4; 18.5.4; 15.1. SC: an. Conference: Ethics, Law and Moral Philosophy of Reproductive Biomedicine; London, UK; 2004 September 30 - October 1; Royal Society.

Hawes, Susan; Oakley, Justin. Ethics of using employees' eggs in cloning research. *Nature* 2006 April 20; 440(7087): 992. NRCBL: 14.5; 14.4; 14.6.

Hongladarom, Soraj. Human cloning in a Thai novel: Wimon Sainimnuan's Amata and Thai cultural attitudes toward biotechnology. *In:* Sleeboom, Margaret, ed. Genomics in Asia: A Clash of Bioethical Interests? New York: Kegan Paul; 2004: 85-105. NRCBL: 14.5; 1.2.

Hopkins, Patrick D. Protecting God from science and technology: how religious criticisms of biotechnologies backfire. *Zygon* 2002 June; 37(2): 317-343. NRCBL: 14.5; 15.1; 1.2.

Hornig Priest, Susanna. Cloning: a study in news production. *Public Understanding of Science* 2001 January 1; 10(1): 59-69. NRCBL: 14.5; 1.3.7; 5.1.

Horst, Maja. Cloning sensations: mass mediated articulation of social responses to controversial biotechnology. *Public Understanding of Science* 2005 April; 14(2): 185-200. NRCBL: 14.5; 5.1; 1.3.7. Identifiers: Denmark.

Hurlbut, William B. Altered nuclear transfer: scientific, legal, and ethical foundations. *Journal of Contemporary Health Law and Policy* 2006 Spring; 22(2): 458-475. NRCBL: 14.5; 4.4; 2.4.

Jaenisch, Rudolf; Meissner, Alex; Solter, Davor. Politically correct human embryonic stem cells? [letter and reply]. *New England Journal of Medicine* 2006 March 16; 354(11): 1208-1209. NRCBL: 14.5.

Jamieson, J.W. The case for cloning. *Mankind Quarterly* 1998 Fall; 39(1): 95-107. NRCBL: 14.5; 15.5.

Jensen, Eric; Weasel, Lisa H. Abortion rhetoric in American news coverage of the human cloning debate. *New Genetics and Society* 2006 December; 25(3): 305-323. NRCBL: 14.5; 12.3; 1.3.7; 1.2. SC: em.

Kavanaugh, John F. Cloning, by whatever name, smells bad. *America* 2006 June 19-26; 194(21): 9. NRCBL: 14.5; 18.5.4; 1.2; 18.5.1; 4.4.

Kaveny, M. Cathleen. Rhetoric, public reason, and bioethics: the President's Council on Bioethics and Human Cloning [review of Human Cloning and Human Dignity: The Report of the President's Council on Bioethics]. *Journal of Law and Politics* 2004 Summer; 20(3): 489-503. NRCBL: 14.5; 2.4.

Kirk, E.P.; Cregan, K. Ethics of therapeutic cloning [letter and reply]. *Internal Medicine Journal* 2005 August; 35(8): 500-501. NRCBL: 14.5; 18.5.4; 19.5; 15.1.

Korean Academy of Medical Sciences. Incident of "human cloning" from Kyunghee University Medical Center [editorial]. *Journal of Korean Medical Science* 1999 February; 14(1): 1. NRCBL: 14.5; 18.5.4; 5.3; 15.1.

Lane, Robert. Safety, identity and consent: a limited defense of reproductive human cloning. *Bioethics* 2006 June; 20(3): 125-135. NRCBL: 14.5. SC: an.
  Abstract: Some opponents of reproductive human cloning have argued that, because of its experimental nature, any attempt to create a child by way of cloning would risk serious birth defects or genetic abnormalities and would therefore be immoral. Some versions of this argument appeal to the consent of the person to be conceived in this way. In particular, they assume that if an experimental reproductive technology has not yet been shown to be safe, then, before we use it, we are morally obligated to get either the actual consent or the presumed consent of the person to be conceived. In this article, I attempt to explain the appeal of such consent-based arguments as deriving from a mistaken view of personal identity. I then argue that since this view is false, such arguments are unsound. Finally, I argue that even if reproductive cloning is unsafe, it may still be morally permissible in some circumstances.

Ledford, Heidi. A breed apart. *Nature* 2006 November 9; 444(7116): 137. NRCBL: 14.5; 22.3; 15.1.

Lee, Martin Lishexian. The inadequacies of absolute prohibition of reproductive cloning. *Journal of Law and Medicine* 2004 February; 11(3): 351-372. NRCBL: 14.5; 18.5.4; 5.2; 18.6; 15.1.

Lewontin, Richard C. The confusion over cloning. *New York Review of Books* 1997 October 23; 44(16): 20-23. NRCBL: 14.5; 15.1; 18.6; 1.2.

Magney, Alix. Cloning me, cloning you: reflections on the ethics of cloning for individuals, families and society. *Social Alternatives* 2003 Summer; 22(1): 19-26. NRCBL: 14.5; 1.1. SC: cs.

McGee, Glenn. Human cloning. *In:* Mitcham, Carl, ed. Encyclopedia of Science, Technology, and Ethics. Farmington Hills, MI: Thomson/Gale, 2005: 938-942. NRCBL: 14.5; 2.2.

Mendieta, Eduardo. Habermas on human cloning: the debate on the future of the species. *Philosophy and Social Criticism* 2004 September; 30(5-6): 721-743. NRCBL: 14.5; 1.1; 15.2; 14.4. SC: an.

Minsky, Marvin. Notes on reading Kazuo Ishiguro's "Never Let Me Go" [response]. *Perspectives in Biology and Medicine* 2006 Autumn; 49(4): 628-630. NRCBL: 14.5; 19.5; 4.4.

Morgan, Carol A. Tissue harvesting for cloning: an ethical perspective for veterinarians / Prélèvement de tissus aux fins de clonage: une perspective déontologique à l'intention des vétérinaires. *Canadian Veterinary Journal* 2005 April; 46(4): 358-363. NRCBL: 14.5; 22.3. Note: Full text in English and French.

Morgan, Rose M. Cloning a human. *In her:* The Genetics Revolution: History, Fears, and Future of a Life-Altering Science. Westport, CT: Greenwood Press; 2006: 175-191. NRCBL: 14.5; 15.5; 2.2; 2.4.

Morgan, Rose M. Reproductive cloning. *In her:* The Genetics Revolution: History, Fears, and Future of a Life-Altering Science. Westport, CT: Greenwood Press; 2006: 159-173. NRCBL: 14.5; 2.2; 22.3; 15.7; 22.2; 21.1.

National Bioethics Advisory Commission. Cloning human beings: report and recommendations of the National Bioethics Advisory Commission. *Jurimetrics* 1997 Fall; 38(1): 3-10. NRCBL: 14.5; 2.4.

Normile, Dennis; Vogel, Gretchen; Couzin, Jennifer. South Korean team's remaining human stem cell claim demolished [news]. *Science* 2006 January 13; 311(5758): 156-157. NRCBL: 14.5; 1.3.9; 1.3.7; 15.1; 18.5.4; 19.5; 8.1.

Oakley, Justin. Reproductive cloning and arguments from potential. *Monash Bioethics Review* 2006 January; 25(1): 42-47. NRCBL: 14.5; 14.1.

Panno, Joseph. Ethics of animal cloning. *In his:* Animal Cloning: The Science of Nuclear Transfer. New York: Facts of File, 2005: 66-73. NRCBL: 14.5; 22.3.

Pennings, Guido; de Wert, Guido M.W.R. Cloned embryos: in search of criteria to determine their moral status. *Nature Review Genetics* 2005 March; 6(3): 161. NRCBL: 14.5; 4.4; 15.1.

Pollack, Andrew; Martin, Andrew. FDA tentatively declares food from cloned animals to be safe; critics say risks have not been fully weighed. *New York Times* 2006 December 29; p. A1, A23. NRCBL: 14.5; 22.3; 9.1; 5.3. SC: po.

Rollin, Bernard E. Biotechnology and ethics III: cloning, xenotransplantation, and stem cells. *In his:* Science and Ethics. New York: Cambridge University Press; 2006: 185-214. NRCBL: 14.5; 19.1; 22.2; 18.5.4.

Rosen, Gary. What would a clone say? A humanist case against therapeutic cloning. *New York Times Magazine* 2005 November 27; p. 19, 20. NRCBL: 14.5. SC: po.

Sanchez-Sweatman, L.R. Reproductive cloning and human health: an ethical, international, and nursing perspective. *International Nursing Review* 2000 March; 47(1): 28-37. NRCBL: 14.5; 6; 4.1.3.

Schramm, Fermin Roland. The Dolly case, the Polly drug, and the morality of human cloning. *Cadernos de Saúde Pública* 1999; 15 (suppl. 1): 51-64. NRCBL: 14.5; 15.1.

NRCBL: National Reference Center for Bioethics Literature Classification Scheme   See inside front cover for terms.

121

Spar, Debora L. Return to the forbidden past: issues in human cloning. *In her:* The Baby Business: How Money, Science, and Politics Drive the Commerce of Conception. Boston: Harvard Business School Press; 2006: 129-158. NRCBL: 14.5.

Sparrow, Robert. Cloning, parenthood, and genetic relatedness. *Bioethics* 2006 November; 20(6): 308-318. NRCBL: 14.5; 14.1; 15.1. SC: an.

Stabile, Bonnie. National determinants of cloning policy. *Social Science Quarterly* 2006 June; 87(2): 449-458. NRCBL: 14.5; 21.7. SC: em.

Steel, Michael. Brain, mind, and person: cloning and questions of identity. *In:* Jeeves, Michael, ed. From Cells to Souls — and Beyond: Changing Portraits of Human Nature. Grand Rapids, MI: W.B. Eerdmans; 2004: 1-10. NRCBL: 14.5; 4.4.

Strong, Carson. The ethics of human reproductive cloning. *Reproductive BioMedicine Online [electronic]* 2005 March; 10(Supplement 1): 45-49. NRCBL: 14.5; 5.2; 9.5.7; 15.1; 4.4. SC: an. Conference: Ethics, Law and Moral Philosophy of Reproductive Biomedicine; London, UK; 2004 September 30 - October 1; Royal Society.

Tzamalouka, Georgia S.; Papadakaki, Maria; Soultatou, Pelagia; Chatzifotiou, Sevasti; Tarlatzis, Basil; Chliaoutakis, Joannes El. Predicting human cloning acceptability: a national Greek survey on the beliefs of the public. *Journal of Assisted Reproduction and Genetics* 2005 October; 22(9-10): 315-322. NRCBL: 14.5; 5.1. SC: em.

Tzamalouka, Georgia S.; Soultatou, Pelagia; Papadakaki, Maria; Chatzifotiou, Sevasti; Tarlatzis, Basil; Chliaoutakis, Joannes El. Identifying the public's knowledge and intention to use human cloning in Greek urban areas. *Journal of Assisted Reproduction and Genetics* 2005 February; 22(2): 47-56. NRCBL: 14.5; 14.4; 5.1. SC: em.

Union of American Hebrew Congregations. Committee on Bio-Ethics. Cloning: Bioethics Program/Case Study: Program Guide X. New York, NY: Union of American Hebrew Congregations, 1998 Summer; 66 p. NRCBL: 14.5; 1.2; 1.3.5; 14.4; 18.5.4.

van Gend, David. Prometheus, Pandora and the myths of cloning. *Human Life Review* 2006 Summer-Fall; 32(3-4): 15-27. NRCBL: 14.5; 15.1; 18.5.4.

Van Steendam, Guido; Dinnyés, András; Mallet, Jacques; Meloni, Rolando; Casabona, Carlos Romeo; González, Jorge Guerra; Kure, Josef; Szathmáry, Eörs; Vorstenbosch, Jan; Molnár, Péter; Edbrooke, David; Sándor, Judit; Oberfrank, Ferenc; Cole-Turner, Ron; Hargittai, István; Littig, Beate; Ladikas, Miltos; Mordini, Emilio; Roosendaal, Hans E.; Salvi, Maurizio; Gulyás, Balázs; Malpede, Diana. The Budapest Meeting 2005 intensified networking on ethics of science: the case of reproductive cloning, germline gene therapy and human dignity. *Science and Engineering Ethics* 2006 October; 12(4): 731-793. NRCBL: 14.5; 15.1; 15.4; 2.3; 4.4; 21.1. Identifiers: Reprogenetics Project.

Wade, Nicholas. University panel faults cloning co-author. *New York Times* 2006 February 11; p. A12. NRCBL: 14.5; 1.3.9; 1.3.3. SC: po.

Young, Lorraine E. Scientific hazards of human reproductive 'cloning'. *Human Fertility* 2003 May; 6(2): 59-63. NRCBL: 14.5; 22.2; 15.3. Identifiers: United Kingdom (Great Britain).

CLONING/ LEGAL ASPECTS

Atwill, Nicole. Human cloning: French legislation and European initiatives. *International Journal of Legal Information* 2000 Winter; 28(3): 500-504. NRCBL: 14.5; 21.1; 1.3.5. SC: le.

Gottweis, Herbert; Triendl, Robert. South Korean policy failure and the Hwang debacle. *Nature Biotechnology* 2006 February; 24(2): 141-143. NRCBL: 14.5; 18.5.4; 15.1; 19.5; 1.3.9. SC: le.

Guimerá, Juan-Felipe Higuera. Juridico-penal considerations on human embryo cloning (I) = Consideraciones jurídico-penales sobre las conductas de clonación en los embriones humanos (I). *Law and the Human Genome = Revista de Derecho y Genoma Humano* 1994 July-December; (1): 49-70. NRCBL: 14.5; 21.1; 15.1; 18.5.4. SC: le.

Hidalgo, Soraya Nadia. Cloning or serial reproduction of human beings, a twenty-first century alternative? = Clonación o reproducción en serie de seres humanos, ¿una alternativa del siglo XXI? *Law and the Human Genome Review =Revista de Derecho y Genoma Humano* 1996 January-June; (4): 39-58. NRCBL: 14.5; 21.1; 18.5.4; 14.1; 15.1. SC: le.

Isasi, Rosario M.; Annas, George J. To clone alone: the United Nations' Human Cloning Declaration. *Revista de Derecho y Genoma Humano = Law and the Human Genome Review* 2006 January-June; (24): 13-26. NRCBL: 14.5; 21.1. SC: le.

Lim, Linda. Singapore cloning bill [news brief]. *Nature Biotechnology* 2004 October; 22(10): 1199. NRCBL: 14.5. SC: le.

Liu, Athena. Human embryo cloning prohibited in Hong Kong. *Journal of Assisted Reproduction and Genetics* 2005 December; 22(11-12): 369-378. NRCBL: 14.5; 18.5.4; 22.3; 15.1. SC: le.

Luxembourg. Commission Consultative Nationale d'Éthique pour les Sciences de la Vie et de la Santé [CNE]. Le clonage reproductif d'êtres humains: Avis 2004.1 [Reproductive cloning of humans: Opinion 2004: 1]. Luxembourg: Commission Nationale d'Éthique, 2004;

23 p. [Online]. Accessed: http://www.cne.public. lu/publications/avis/2004_1.pdf [2006 April 7]. NRCBL: 14.5. SC: le.

Missouri Bishops; Burke, Raymond; Finn, Robert; Gaydos, John; Leibrecht, John; Hermann, Robert; Boland, Raymond. Cloning and embryonic stem-cells: ballot initiative opposed. *Origins* 2006 October 19; 36(19): 293-296. NRCBL: 14.5; 18.5.4; 1.2; 15.1. SC: le.

Missouri. *Laws, statutes, etc.* Cloning — use of state funds prohibited [Approved: 10 July 1998; Effective 1 January 1999]. Missouri Revised Statutes, Section 1.217 (28 August 2003) 1 p. [Online]. Accessed: http://www.moga.state.mo.us/statutes/c000-099/0010000217.htm [2007 March 9]. NRCBL: 14.5. SC: le.

Montgomery, John Warwick. The human embryo cloning danger in European context. *Philosophia Christi Series 2:* 2002; 4(1): 215-229. NRCBL: 14.5; 18.6. SC: le.

Panno, Joseph. Legal issues. *In his:* Animal Cloning: The Science of Nuclear Transfer. New York: Facts on File, 2005: 74-77. NRCBL: 14.5; 22.3. SC: le.

Perry, Anthony C.F. Nuclear transfer cloning and the United Nations. *Nature Biotechnology* 2004 December; 22(12): 1506-1508. NRCBL: 14.5; 21.1; 18.6. SC: le.

Romeo Casabona, Carlos María. Legal limitations on research and its results? The cloning paradigm = ¿Límites jurídicos a la investigación y sus consecuencias? El paradigma de la clonación. *Revista de Derecho Genoma Humano = Law and the Human Genome Review* 1997 January-June; (6): 21-27. NRCBL: 14.5; 15.1. SC: le.

Steinbock, Bonnie. Reproductive cloning: another look. *University of Chicago Legal Forum* 2006: 87-111. NRCBL: 14.5; 5.2; 2.4; 4.4; 15.1. SC: le.

United States. Congress. House. A bill to amend title 18, United States Code, to prohibit human cloning. Washington, DC: U.S. G.P.O., 2003. 5 p. [Online]. Accessed: http://frwebgate.access.gpo.gov/cgi-bin/getdoc.cgi?dbname=108_cong_bills&docid= f:h234ih.txt.pdf [2007 March 8]. NRCBL: 14.5. SC: le. Identifiers: Human Cloning Prohibition Act of 2003. Note: H.R. 234, 108th Congress, 1st session. Introduced by Rep. Weldon on January 8, 2003. Referred to the Committee on the Judiciary and the Committee on Energy and Commerce.

United States. Congress. House. A bill to prohibit human cloning. Washington, DC: U.S. G.P.O., 2005. 4 p. [Online]. Accessed: http://frwebgate.access.gpo.gov/cgi-bin/useftp.cgi?IPaddress=162.140.64.21&filename=h3932ih.pdf&directory=/diskb/wais/data/109_cong_bills [2006 November 21]. NRCBL: 14.5; 15.1. SC: le. Identifiers: Human Cloning Ban Act of 2005. Note: H.R. 3932, 109th Congress, 1st session. Introduced by Rep. Bono, September 28, 2005. Referred to the Committee on the Judiciary.

United States. Congress. House. A bill to prohibit human cloning and protect stem cell research. Washington, DC: U.S. G.P.O., 2005. 11 p. [Online]. Accessed: http://frwebgate.access.gpo.gov/cgi-bin/useftp.cgi?IPaddress=162.140.64.21&filename=h1822ih.pdf&directory=/diskb/wais/data/109_cong_bills [2006 May 10]. NRCBL: 14.5; 18.5.4; 15.1; 14.4; 19.5. SC: le. Identifiers: Human Cloning Ban and Stem Cell Research Protection Act of 2005; United States. Federal Food, Drug, and Cosmetic Act. Note: H.R. 1822, 109th Congress, 1st session. Introduced by Rep. Bono, April 26, 2005. Referred to the Committee on Energy and Commerce.

United States. Congress. Senate. A bill to amend the Public Health Service Act to prohibit human cloning. Washington, DC: U.S. G.P.O., 2003. 5 p. [Online]. Accessed: http://frwebgate.access.gpo.gov/cgi-bin/getdoc.cgi?dbname=108_cong_bills&docid=f:s245is.txt.pdf [2007 March 8]. NRCBL: 14.5. SC: le. Identifiers: Human Cloning Prohibition Act of 2003. Note: S. 245, 108th Congress, 1st session. Introduced by Sen. Brownback on January 29, 2003. Referred to the Committee on Health, Education, Labor, and Pensions.

United States. Congress. Senate. A bill to ban human cloning while protecting stem cell research. Washington, DC: U.S. G.P.O., 2002. 3 p. [Online]. Accessed: http://frwebgate.access.gpo.gov/cgi-bin/getdoc.cgi?dbname=107_cong_bills&docid= f:s1893is.txt.pdf [2007 March 8]. NRCBL: 14.5; 18.5.4; 15.1. SC: le. Identifiers: Human Cloning Ban and Stem Cell Research Protection Act of 2002. Note: S. 1893, 107th Congress, 2nd session. Introduced by Sen. Harkin on January 24, 2002. Referred to the Committee on Health, Education, Labor, and Pensions.

United States. Congress. Senate. A bill to prohibit human cloning. Washington, DC: U.S. G.P.O., 2005. 4 p. [Online]. Accessed: http://frwebgate.access.gpo.gov/cgi-bin/useftp.cgi?IPaddress=162.140.64.21&filename=s1520is.pdf&directory=/diskb/wais/data/109_cong_bills [2006 November 21]. NRCBL: 14.5; 15.1. SC: le. Identifiers: Human Cloning Ban Act of 2005. Note: S. 1520, 109th Congress, 1st session. Introduced by Sen. Feinstein, July 27, 2005. Referred to the Committee on the Judiciary.

United States. Congress. Senate. A bill to prohibit human cloning and protect stem cell research. Washington, DC: U.S. G.P.O., 2003. 11 p. [Online]. Accessed: http://frwebgate.access.gpo.gov/cgi-bin/getdoc.cgi?dbname=108_cong_bills&docid=f:s303is.txt.pdf [2007 March 8]. NRCBL: 14.5; 18.5.4; 15.1. SC: le. Identifiers: Human Cloning Ban and Stem Cell Research Protection Act of 2003. Note: S. 303, 108th Congress, 1st session. Introduced by Sen. Hatch on February 5, 2003. Referred to the Committee on the Judiciary.

United States. Congress. Senate. A bill to prohibit human cloning and protect stem cell research. Washington, DC:

NRCBL: National Reference Center for Bioethics Literature Classification Scheme   See inside front cover for terms.

123

U.S. G.P.O., 2005. 11 p. [Online]. Accessed: http://frwebgate.access.gpo.gov/cgi-bin/useftp.cgi? IPaddress=162.140.64.21&file name=s876is.pdf& directory=/diskb/wais/data/109_cong_bills [2006 May 10]. NRCBL: 14.5; 18.5.4; 15.1; 14.4; 19.5. SC: le. Identifiers: Human Cloning Ban and Stem Cell Research Protection Act of 2005. Note: S. 876, 109th Congress, 1st session. Introduced by Sen. Hatch, April 21, 2005. Referred to the Committee on the Judiciary.

Wohn, D. Yvette; Normile, Dennis. Korean cloning scandal: prosecutors allege elaborate deception and missing funds [news]. *Science* 2006 May 19; 312(5776): 980-981. NRCBL: 14.5; 1.3.9. SC: le.

CODES OF ETHICS

Code of ethics for the health education profession. *Health Education and Behavior* 2002 February; 29(1): 11. NRCBL: 6; 7.2.

Disclosure of confidential information: amendments to the Code of Ethics of Nurses. *Perspective Infirmiere* 2005 September-October; 3(1): 9. NRCBL: 6; 4.1.3; 8.4.

Disclosure of medical errors. *Annals of Emergency Medicine* 2004 March; 43(3): 432. NRCBL: 6; 9.8; 8.2. Identifiers: American College of Emergency Physicians.

Enforcement Procedure for Occupational Therapy Code of Ethics (2000). *American Journal of Occupational Therapy* 2000 November-December; 54(6): 617-621. NRCBL: 6; 9.8; 16.3.

Principles of occupational therapy ethics. *American Journal of Occupational Therapy* 1984 December 1; 38(12): 799-802. NRCBL: 6. Note: Adopted by the American Occupational Therapy Association, April 1977; Adopted, Revised, April 1979.

American Academy of Neurology [AAN]; Williams, M.A.; Mackin, G.A.; Beresford, H.R.; Gordon, J.; Jacobson, P.L.; McQuillen, M.P.; Reimschisel, T.E.; Taylor, R.M.; Bernat, J.L.; Rizzo, M.; Snyder, R.D.; Sagsveen, M.G.; Amery, M.; Brannon, W.L., Jr. American Academy of Neurology qualifications and guidelines for the physician expert witness. *Neurology* 2006 January 10; 66(1): 13-14. NRCBL: 6; 7.3; 1.3.5.

American Academy of Pain Medicine [AAPM]. Council on Ethics. Ethics charter from American Academy of Pain Medicine. *Pain Medicine* 2005 May-June; 6(3): 203-212. NRCBL: 6; 4.4; 4.1.2; 1.3.1.

American Academy of Psychiatry and the Law [AAPL]. American Academy of Psychiatry and the Law ethical guidelines for the practice of forensic psychiatry. *Bloomfield, CT: American Academy of Psychiatry and the Law,* 1995: 5 p.[Online]. Accessed: http://www.aapl.org/ ethics.htm [14 December 2005]. NRCBL: 6; 17.1; 1.3.5.

American College of Surgeons [ACS]. Task Force on Professionalism. Code of professional conduct. *Journal of the American College of Surgeons* 2004 November; 199(5): 734-735. NRCBL: 6.

American College of Surgeons [ACS]. Task Force on Professionalism; Barry, Linda; Blair, Patrice Gabler; Cosgrove, Ellen M.; Cruess, Richard L.; Cruess, Sylvia R.; Eastman, A. Brent; Fabri, P. Jeffrey; Kirksey, Thomas D.; Liscum, Kathleen R.; Morrison, Rosemary; Sachdeva, Ajit K.; Svahn, David S.; Russell, Thomas R.; Dickey, Jamie; Ungerleider, Ross M.; Harken, Alden H. One year, and counting, after publication of our ACS "Code of Professional Conduct". *Journal of the American College of Surgeons* 2004 November; 199(5): 736-740. NRCBL: 6.

American Health Information Management Association. Professional Ethics Committee. American Health Information Management Association code of ethics. *Journal of AHIMA* 2004 November-December; 75(10): 80A-80D. NRCBL: 6; 1.3.12.

American Occupational Therapy Association [AOTA]. Enforcement procedures for the Occupational Therapy Code of Ethics. *American Journal of Occupational Therapy* 2005 November-December; 59(6): 643-652. NRCBL: 6; 16.3.

American Society of Human Genetics [ASHG]. Code of ethics. Bethesda, MD: American Society of Human Genetics, 2006 March; 2 p. [Online]. Accessed: http://genetics. faseb.org/genetics/ashg/pubs/policy/pol-49.pdf [2007 February 7]. NRCBL: 6; 15.1; 8.4.

Aravind, K.; Kannappan, J.G. Hippocratic oath in the modern times. *Indian Journal of Dental Research* 2005 April-June; 16(2): 37-41. NRCBL: 6; 4.1.2; 2.2. Identifiers: Louis Lasagna.

Benatar, Solomon R.; Berwick, Donald M.; Bisognano, Maureen; Dalton, James; Davidoff, Frank; Frenk, Julio; Hiatt, Howard; Hurwitz, Brian; Janeway, Penny; Marshall, Margaret H.; Norling, Richard; Rocklage, Mary Roch; Scott, Hilary; Sen, Amartya; Smith, Richard; Sommerville, Ann. A shared statement of ethical principles. *Nursing Standard* 1999 January 27-February 2; 13(19): 34-36. NRCBL: 6; 4.1.3; 9.1. Identifiers: Tavistock Group; United Kingdom (Great Britain); June Andrews.

Blickle, Gerhard. Professional ethics needs a theoretical background. *European Psychologist* 2004 December; 9(4): 273-274. NRCBL: 6; 17.1; 21.1. Identifiers: International Union of Psychological Sciences. Comments: Jean L. Pettifor. Professional Ethics Across National Boundaries.

California Dental Association. California Dental Association: Code of Ethics. *Journal of the California Dental Association* 2006 January; 34(1): 57-62. NRCBL: 6; 4.1.1.

Canadian College of Health Service Executives. Code of ethics. *Healthcare Management Forum* 2005 Winter; 18(4): 22-25. NRCBL: 6; 9.1; 1.3.2. Note: Full text in English and French.

Canelloupou-Bottis, Maria. Recent developments in health law in Greece. *European Journal of Health Law* 2006 June; 13(2): 107-113. NRCBL: 6; 4.1.1; 9.8. SC: an.

Davis, Michael. Codes of ethics. *In:* Mitcham, Carl, ed. Encyclopedia of Science, Technology, and Ethics. Farmington Hills, MI: Thomson/Gale, 2005: 350-353. NRCBL: 6.

Dubois, Michel Y. The birth of an ethics charter for pain medicine [editorial]. *Pain Medicine* 2005 May-June; 6(3): 201-202. NRCBL: 6; 4.4; 2.1.

Dubois, Michel Y.; Banja, John; Brushwood, David; Fine, Perry G.; Gallagher, Rollin M.; Gilbert, Hugh; Hamaty, Daniel; Jansen, Lynn; Joranson, David; Lebovits, Allen H.; Lippe, Philipp M.; Murphy, Timothy F.; Orr, Robert; Rich, Ben A. Ethics Charter from American Academy of Pain Medicine. *Pain Medicine* 2005 May-June; 6(3): 203-212. NRCBL: 6; 4.4; 2.1.

Fisher, Celia B. Challenges in constructing a cross-national ethics code for psychologists. *European Psychologist* 2004 December; 9(4): 275-277. NRCBL: 6; 17.1; 21.1. Identifiers: International Union of Psychological Science. Comments: Jean L. Pettifor's Professional Ethics Across National Boundaries.

International Commission on Occupational Health [ICOH]. International code of ethics for occupational health professionals. Update 2002 March. Rome, Italy: International Commission on Occupational Health. Secretariat General. Update. 2002 March; 26 p. [Online]. Accessed: http://www.icohweb.org/core_docs/code_ethics_eng.pdf [2006 October 16]. NRCBL: 6.

Knapp, Samuel; VandeCreek, Leon. A principle-based analysis of the 2002 American Psychological Association Ethics Code. *Psychotherapy* 2004 Fall; 41(3): 247-254. NRCBL: 6; 1.1.

Kuhar, Michael J. Should codes of ethics include expectations of others? [letter]. *Science and Engineering Ethics* 2006 July; 12(3): 413-414. NRCBL: 6.

Marks, Ray; Shive, Steven E. Improving our application of the health education code of ethics. *Health Promotion Practice* 2006 January; 7(1): 23-25. NRCBL: 6; 7.2; 2.3.

Morris, Kathleen. Codes of ethics for nurses and continuing education. *Ohio Nurses Review* 2005 November-December; 80(6): 7. NRCBL: 6; 4.1.3; 7.2.

Myers, Wade C.; Hall, Richard C.W.; Eth, Spencer. AAPL's new ethics guidelines [letter]. *AAPL (American Academy of Psychiatry and the Law) Newsletter* 2006 April; 31(2): 12-13. NRCBL: 6.

Pedersen, Paul B. The cultural context of the American Counseling Association code of ethics. *Journal of Counseling and Development* 1997 Winter; 76(1): 23-28. NRCBL: 6; 17.1.

Pettifor, Jean L. Professional ethics across national boundaries. *European Psychologist* 2004 December; 9(4): 264-272. NRCBL: 6; 17.1; 21.1. Identifiers: International Union of Psychological Sciences.

Pipes, Randolph B.; Holstein, Jaymee E.; Aguirre, Maria G. Examining the personal-professional distinction: ethics codes and the difficulty of drawing a boundary. *American Psychologist* 2005 May-June; 60(4): 325-334. NRCBL: 6; 17.1; 7.1.

Reitz, S. Maggie; Arnold, Melba; Franck, Linda Gabriel; Austin, Darryl J.; Hill, Diane; McQuade, Lorie J.; Knox, Daryl K.; Slater, Deborah Yarett. Occupational Therapy Code of Ethics (2005). *American Journal of Occupational Therapy* 2005 November-December; 59(6): 639-642. NRCBL: 6; 18.3.

Thompson, Linda W. Nursing ethics: the ANA code for nurses. *Tennessee Nurse* 1998 December; 61(6): 23, 25-29. NRCBL: 6; 4.1.3. Identifiers: American Nurses' Association.

Westerveld, H.E.; Briet, J.W.; Houwaart, E.S.; Legemaate, J.; Meerman, T.J.A.M.; Breetvelt, E.J.; van der Wall, E. Dutch medical oath. *Netherlands Journal of Medicine* 2005 October; 63(9): 368-371. NRCBL: 6; 4.1.2; 1.3.1.

Wolinsky, Howard. Bioethics for the world. *EMBO Reports* 2006 April; 7(4): 354-358. NRCBL: 6; 2.4; 21.1. Identifiers: Universal Declaration on Bioethics and Human Rights.

COMMISSIONS ON BIOETHICS *See* BIOETHICS AND MEDICAL ETHICS/ COMMISSIONS

CONFIDENTIALITY
See also AIDS/ CONFIDENTIALITY

Should a doctor tell? *Economist* 1971 March 13; 238: 25. NRCBL: 8.4; 8.3.2; 11.2. Identifiers: United Kingdom (Great Britain).

Striking the right balance between privacy and public good [editorial]. *Lancet* 2006 January 28-February 3; 367(9507): 275. NRCBL: 8.4; 1.3.9; 1.3.12; 18.3; 18.6.

The new threat to your medical privacy. *Consumer Reports* 2006 March; 71(3): 39-42. NRCBL: 8.4; 1.3.12.

NRCBL: National Reference Center for Bioethics Literature Classification Scheme   See inside front cover for terms.

125

Abbo, Elmer D.; Volandes, Angelo E. Rare but routine: the physician's obligation to protect third parties. *American Journal of Bioethics* 2006 March-April; 6(2): 34-36. NRCBL: 8.4; 9.5.6. Identifiers: Tarasoff v. Regents of University of California. Comments: Kenneth Kipnis. A defense of unqualified medical confidentiality. American Journal of Bioethics 2006 March-April; 6(2): 7-18.

Alpert, Sheri A. Protecting medical privacy: challenges in the age of genetic information. *Journal of Social Issues* 2003; 59(2): 301-322. NRCBL: 8.4; 1.3.12; 15.1; 15.3. SC: rv. Identifiers: HIPAA.

Baker, Robert. Confidentiality in professional medical ethics. *American Journal of Bioethics* 2006 March-April; 6(2): 39-41. NRCBL: 8.4; 6; 2.2. Identifiers: American Medical Association. Comments: Kenneth Kipnis. A defense of unqualified medical confidentiality. American Journal of Bioethics 2006 March-April; 6(2): 7-18.

Balint, John. Should confidentiality in medicine be absolute? *American Journal of Bioethics* 2006 March-April; 6(2): 19-20. NRCBL: 8.4; 9.5.6. Comments: Kenneth Kipnis. A defense of unqualified medical confidentiality. American Journal of Bioethics 2006 March-April; 6(2): 7-18.

Banja, John D. Qualifying confidentiality obligations. *American Journal of Bioethics* 2006 March-April; 6(2): 28-29. NRCBL: 8.4; 9.5.6. Comments: Kenneth Kipnis. A defense of unqualified medical confidentiality. American Journal of Bioethics 2006 March-April; 6(2): 7-18.

Barrett, Geraldine; Cassell, Jackie A.; Peacock, Janet L.; Coleman, Michel P. National survey of British public's views on use of identifiable medical data by the National Cancer Registry. *BMJ: British Medical Journal* 2006 May 6; 332(7549): 1068-1070. NRCBL: 8.4; 1.3.12. SC: em.
> Abstract: Objectives: To describe the views of the British public on the use of personal medical data by the National Cancer Registry without individual consent, and to assess the relative importance attached by the public to personal privacy in relation to public health uses of identifiable health data. Design: Cross sectional, face to face interview survey. Setting England, Wales, and Scotland. Participants 2872 respondents, 97% of those who took part in the Office for National Statistics' omnibus survey, a national multistage probability sample, in March and April 2005 (response rates 62% and 69%, respectively).Results: 72% (95% confidence interval 70% to 74%) of all respondents did not consider any of the following to be an invasion of their privacy by the National Cancer Registry: inclusion of postcode, inclusion of name and address, and the receipt of a letter inviting them to a research study on the basis of inclusion in the registry. Only 2% (2% to 3%) of the sample considered all of these to amount to an invasion of privacy. Logistic regression analysis showed that the proportions not concerned about invasion of privacy varied significantly by country, ethnicity, socioeconomic status, and housing tenure, although in all subgroups examined most respondents had no concerns. 81% (79% to 83%) of all respondents said that they would support a law making cancer registration statutory. Conclusions: Most of the British public considers the confidential use of personal,

identifiable patient information by the National Cancer Registry for the purposes of public health research and surveillance not to be an invasion of privacy.

Baumer, David; Earp, Julia Brande; Payton, Fay Cobb. Privacy of medical records: IT implications of HIPAA. *In:* Tavani, Herman T., ed. Ethics, Computing, and Genomics. Sudbury, MA: Jones and Bartlett; 2006: 137-152. NRCBL: 8.4.

Berg, Jessica. A qualified defense of legal disclosure requirements. *American Journal of Bioethics* 2006 March-April; 6(2): 25-26. NRCBL: 8.4. Comments: Kenneth Kipnis. A defense of unqualified medical confidentiality. American Journal of Bioethics 2006 March-April; 6(2): 7-18.

Bird, Sara. A GP's duty of confidentiality. *Australian Family Physician* 2005 October; 34(10): 881. NRCBL: 8.4; 7.1. SC: cs.

Bird, Sara. Epilepsy, driving and confidentiality. *Australian Family Physician* 2005 December; 34(12): 1057-1058. NRCBL: 8.4; 8.1; 17.1. SC: cs.

Bompiani, Andriano. Genetic data and regulations on protection of personal data in Italy. *European Journal of Health Law* 2001 March; 8(1): 41-50. NRCBL: 8.4; 15.1; 8.3.1. SC: le.

Bossi, Jeanne. European Directive of October 24, 1995 and protection of medical data: the consequences of the law governing data processing and freedoms. *European Journal of Health Law* 2002 September; 9(3): 201-206. NRCBL: 8.4; 1.3.12; 18.3; 8.2. SC: le.

Boylan, Michael. The duty to rescue and the limits of confidentiality. *American Journal of Bioethics* 2006 March-April; 6(2): 32-34. NRCBL: 8.4; 4.1.2; 1.3.1; 1.1. Comments: Kenneth Kipnis. A defense of unqualified medical confidentiality. American Journal of Bioethics 2006 March-April; 6(2): 7-18.

Broderick, Pia; Walker, Iain. Donor gametes and embryos: who wants to know what about whom, and why? *Politics and the Life Sciences* 2001 March; 20(1): 29-42. NRCBL: 8.4; 14.1; 19.5. Identifiers: Australia.

Brownstein, John S.; Cassa, Christopher A.; Mandl, Kenneth D. No place to hide — reverse identification of patients from published maps [letter]. *New England Journal of Medicine* 2006 October 19; 355(16): 1741-1742. NRCBL: 8.4; 1.3.9; 5.1. SC: em.

Büken, Erhan; Sahinoglu, Serap; Büken, Nüket Örnek. Statutory disclosure in article 280 of the Turkish Penal Code. *Nursing Ethics* 2006 November; 13(6): 573-580, discussion 580-591. NRCBL: 8.4; 1.3.5. SC: le.

Canellopoulou-Bottis, Maria. The implementation of European Directive 95/46/EC in Greece and medical/genetic data. *European Journal of Health Law* 2002 September; 9(3): 207-218. NRCBL: 8.4; 1.3.12; 15.1; 18.3. SC: le.

Capron, Alexander M. Addressing an ethical dilemma dialogically rather than (merely) logically. *American Journal of Bioethics* 2006 March-April; 6(2): 36-39. NRCBL: 8.4; 9.5.6. Comments: Kenneth Kipnis. A defense of unqualified medical confidentiality. American Journal of Bioethics 2006 March-April; 6(2): 7-18.

Carey, Ruth. Recent developments in privacy legislation. *HIV/AIDS Policy and Law Review* 2003 August; 8(2): 1, 11-17. NRCBL: 8.4. SC: le.

Carlisle, J.; Shickle, D.; Cork, M.; McDonagh, A. Concerns over confidentiality may deter adolescents from consulting their doctors. A qualitative exploration. *Journal of Medical Ethics* 2006 March; 32(3): 133-137. NRCBL: 8.4; 9.5.7. SC: em.

Abstract: Young people who are concerned that consultations may not remain confidential are reluctant to consult their doctors, especially about sensitive issues. This study sought to identify issues and concerns of adolescents, and their parents, in relation to confidentiality and teenagers' personal health information. SETTING: Recruitment was conducted in paediatric dermatology and general surgery outpatient clinics, and on general surgery paediatric wards. Interviews were conducted in subjects' own homes. METHODS: Semistructured interviews were used for this exploratory qualitative study. Interviews were carried out with 11 young women and nine young men aged 14-17. Parents of 18 of the young people were interviewed separately. Transcripts of tape recorded interviews provided the basis for a framework analysis. RESULTS: Young women were more concerned than young men, and older teenagers more concerned than younger teenagers, about people other than their general practitioner(GP) having access to their health information. Young people with little experience of the healthcare system were less happy than those with greater knowledge of the National Health Service (NHS) for non-medical staff to access their health information. As they grow older, adolescents become increasingly concerned that their health information should remain confidential. CONCLUSION: Young people's willingness to be open in consultations could be enhanced by doctors taking time to explain to them that their discussion is completely confidential. Alternatively, if for any reason confidentiality cannot be assured, doctors should explain why.

Carulla, Santiago Ripol. The protection of medical and genetic data in the Council of Europe's normative texts (Part I) = La protección de los datos médicos y genéticos en la normativa del Consejo de Europa (Parte I). *Law and the Human Genome Review = Revista de Derecho y Genoma Humano* 1996 July-December; (5): 109-120. NRCBL: 8.4; 1.3.12; 15.1; 21.1; 4.4. SC: le.

Charles-Edwards, Imelda; Brotchie, Jane. Privacy: what does it mean for children's nurses? *Paediatric Nursing* 2005 June; 17(5): 38-43. NRCBL: 8.4; 9.5.7; 8.3.2; 4.1.3.

Churchill, Jack L. What's a dentist to do? To say or not to say. *Northwest Dentistry* 2006 January-February; 85(1): 39-40. NRCBL: 8.4; 8.3.2; 4.1.1; 9.5.6; 6. SC: cs.

Clark, Alexander M.; Findlay, Iain N. Attaining adequate consent for the use of electronic patient records: an opt-out strategy to reconcile individuals' rights and public benefit. *Public Health* 2005 November; 119(11): 1003-1010. NRCBL: 8.4; 1.3.12; 8.3.1.

Clarke, Angus; Richards, Martin; Kerzin-Storrar, Lauren; Halliday, Jane; Young, Mary Anne; Simpson, Sheila A.; Featherstone, Katie; Forrest, Karen; Lucassen, Anneke; Morrison, Patrick J.; Quarrell, Oliver W.J.; Stewart, Helen. Genetic professionals' reports of nondisclosure of genetic risk information within families. *European Journal of Human Genetics* 2005 May; 13(5): 556-562. NRCBL: 8.4; 8.1; 15.3; 15.2; 8.3.1. SC: em.

Coleman, David L. Who's guarding medical privacy? *Business and Health* 1999 March; 17(3): 29-30, 32, 37-8. NRCBL: 8.4; 1.3.12; 5.3.

Collins, Nerida; Knowles, Ann D. Adolescents' attitudes towards confidentiality between the school counsellor and the adolescent client. *Australian Psychologist* 1995 November; 30(3): 179-182. NRCBL: 8.4; 7.1; 17.1; 9.5.7; 10; 9.5.9; 4.3.

Collins-Nakai, Ruth. "Patient information — sacred trust". *Health Law in Canada* 2006 March; 26(3): 36-39. NRCBL: 8.4; 8.1. SC: le.

Conti, A. The recent Italian consolidation act on privacy: new measures for data protection. *Medicine and Law: World Association for Medical Law* 2006 March; 25(1): 127-138. NRCBL: 8.4; 9.1; 1.3.12. SC: le.

Abstract: In the light of the new Consolidation Act on privacy, in effect since January 2004, the author has made some observations in relation to the protection of data concerning health. Special focus has been given to an overall view of the new regulations. "Sensitive data" are seen as differing from health data, while always respecting the rights, the fundamental freedom and the dignity of the person involved. A central role continues to be played by the Controller, who has regulating and control powers.

Dada, Mahomed A.; McQuoid-Mason, David J. Medico-legal aspects of pathology — current dilemmas regarding confidentiality and disclosure. *South African Medical Journal* 2005 November; 95(11): 875-877. NRCBL: 8.4; 1.3.12. SC: le.

Davidson, Graham. The ethics of confidentiality: introduction. *Australian Psychologist* 1995 November; 30(3): 153-157. NRCBL: 8.4; 17.2; 6; 9.5.7; 7.1; 18.5.2.

de Wolf, Virginia A.; Sieber, Joan E.; Steel, Philip M.; Zarate, Alvan O. Part II: HIPAA and disclosure risk issues. *IRB: Ethics and Human Research* 2006 January-February; 28(1): 6-11. NRCBL: 8.4; 1.3.12; 8.3.1. SC: le. Identifiers: Health Insurance Portability and Accountability Act of 1996.

NRCBL: National Reference Center for Bioethics Literature Classification Scheme   See inside front cover for terms.

127

de Wolf, Virginia A.; Sieber, Joan E.; Steel, Philip M.; Zarate, Alvan O. Part III: meeting the challenge when data sharing is required. *IRB: Ethics and Human Research* 2006 March-April; 28(2): 10- 15. NRCBL: 8.4; 18.2; 18.3.

DeCew, Judith Wagner. Alternatives for protecting privacy while respecting patient care and public health needs. *Ethics and Information Technology* 1999; 1(4): 249-255. NRCBL: 8.4; 9.1; 1.3.12.

Dimond, Bridgit. Legal aspects of continence: disclosure of a medical condition. *British Journal of Nursing* 2006 April 27-May 10; 15(8): 467-468. NRCBL: 8.4; 9.5.1. SC: le.

Dondorp, Wybo; Legemaate, Johan; Van de Klippe, Hanneke. The retention of medical records: Dutch Health Council report in favour of statutory change. *European Journal of Health Law* 2004 September; 11(3): 273-282. NRCBL: 8.4; 1.3.12; 15.1. SC: le.

Dorr, David A.; Rowan, Belle; Weed, Matt; James, Brent; Clayton, Paul. Physicians' attitudes regarding patient access to electronic medical records. *AMIA Symposium Proceedings* 2003; p. 832. NRCBL: 8.4; 1.3.12. SC: em.

Draper, Heather; MacDiarmaid-Gordon, Adam; Strumidlo, Laura; Teuten, Bea; Updale, Eleanor. Virtual clinical ethics committee, case 3: confidentiality — what are our obligations to dead patients? *Clinical Ethics* 2006 September; 1(3): 121-129. NRCBL: 8.4; 9.5.6; 9.6. SC: cs.

Duncan, Rony E.; Newson, Ainsley J. Clinical genetics and the problem with unqualified confidentiality. *American Journal of Bioethics* 2006 March-April; 6(2): 41-43. NRCBL: 8.4; 15.3; 9.5.6. Comments: Kenneth Kipnis. A defense of unqualified medical confidentiality. American Journal of Bioethics 2006 March-April; 6(2): 7-18.

Dyer, Clare. Crime victims are given right to object to disclosure of their medical records to courts [news]. *BMJ: British Medical Journal* 2006 July 15; 333(7559): 115. NRCBL: 8.4; 1.3.12; 1.3.5. Identifiers: United Kingdom (Great Britain).

Engelschion, Sverre. The implementation of Directive 95/46/EC in Norway, especially with regard to medical data. *European Journal of Health Law* 2002 September; 9(3): 189-200. NRCBL: 8.4; 1.3.12; 15.1; 18.3; 8.2. SC: le.

Erde, E.; Pomerantz, S.C.; Saccocci, M.; Kramer-Feely, V.; Cavalieri, T.A. Privacy and patient-clergy access: perspectives of patients admitted to hospital. *Journal of Medical Ethics* 2006 July; 32(7): 398-402. NRCBL: 8.4; 9.1; 1.2. SC: em.
  Abstract: BACKGROUND: For patients admitted to hospital both pastoral care and privacy or confidentiality are important. Rules related to each have come into conflict recently in the US. Federal laws and other rules protect confidentiality in ways that countermand hospitals' methods for facilitating access to pastoral care. This leads to conflicts and poses an unusual type of dilemma-one of conflicting values and rights. As interests are elements necessary for establishing rights, it is important to explore patients' interests in privacy compared with their desire for attention from a cleric. AIM: To assess the willingness of patients to have their names and rooms included on a list by religion, having that information given to clergy without their consent, their sense of privacy violation if that were done and their views about patients' privacy rights. Methods and PARTICIPANTS: 179 patients, aged 18-92 years, admitted to hospital in an acute care setting, were interviewed and asked about their preferences for confidentiality and pastoral support. RESULTS: Most (57%) patients did not want to be listed by religion; 58% did not think hospitals should give lists to clergy without their consent and 84% welcomed a visit by their own clergy even if triggered from a hospital list. CONCLUSIONS: Values related to confidentiality or privacy and pastoral care were found to be inconsistent and more complicated than expected. Balancing the right to privacy and the value of religious support continue to present a challenge for hospitals. Patients' preferences support the importance of providing balance in a way that protects rights while offering comprehensive services.

Francis, Theo. Medical dilemma: spread of records stirs patient fears of privacy erosion; Ms. Galvin's insurer studies psychotherapist's notes; a dispute over the rules; complaint tally hits 23,896. *Wall Street Journal* 2006 December 26; p. A1, A8. NRCBL: 8.4; 1.3.12. SC: po.

Furlong, Allannah. Confidentiality with respect to third parties: a psychoanalytic view. *International Journal of Psychoanalysis* 2005 April; 86(Part 2): 375-394. NRCBL: 8.4; 17.2.

Gibson, Elaine. Medical confidentiality and protection of third party interests. *American Journal of Bioethics* 2006 March-April; 6(2): 23-25. NRCBL: 8.4; 9.5.6; 1.1. Comments: Kenneth Kipnis. A defense of unqualified medical confidentiality. American Journal of Bioethics 2006 March-April; 6(2): 7-18.

Gilbert, Robert E. Coping with presidential disability: the proposal for a standing medical commission. *Politics and the Life Sciences* 2003 March 22(1): 2-13. NRCBL: 8.4; 4.4; 1.3.5; 9.5.1.

Gold, Liza H.; Metzner, Jeffrey L. Psychiatric employment evaluations and the Health Insurance Portability and Accountability Act. *American Journal of Psychiatry* 2006 November; 163(11): 1878-1882. NRCBL: 8.4; 8.2; 17.1.

Goldblatt, Peter. Evidence will help achieve consensus. *BMJ: British Medical Journal* 2006 January 21; 332(7534): 169. NRCBL: 8.4; 8.3.1; 7.1. SC: le. Comments: Amy Iverson, Kathleen Liddell, Nicole Fear, Matthew Hotopf, and Simon Wessely. Consent, confidentiality, and the Data Protection Act. BMJ: British Medical Journal 2006 January 21; 332(7534): 165-169.

Greenough, Anne; Graham, Helen. Protecting and using patient information: the role of the Caldicott Guardian. *Clinical Medicine* 2004 May-June; 4(3): 246-249. NRCBL: 8.4; 8.3.1; 1.3.12; 6. Identifiers: United Kingdom (Great Britain); Caldicott Committee.

Guedj, M.; Muñoz Sastre, M.T.; Mullet, E.; Sorum, P.C. Do French lay people and health professionals find it acceptable to breach confidentiality to protect a patient's wife from a sexually transmitted disease? *Journal of Medical Ethics* 2006 July; 32(7): 414-419. NRCBL: 8.4; 8.1; 10. SC: em.

Abstract: OBJECTIVE: To determine under what conditions lay people and health professionals find it acceptable for a physician to breach confidentiality to protect the wife of a patient with a sexually transmitted disease (STD). METHODS: In a study in France, breaching confidentiality in 48 scenarios were accepted by 144 lay people, 10 psychologists and 7 physicians. The scenarios were all possible combinations of five factors: severity of the disease (severe, lethal); time taken to discuss this with (little time, much time); intent to inform the spouse about the disease (none, one of these days, immediately); intent to adopt protective behaviours (no intent, intent); and decision to consult an expert in STDs (yes, no), 2 x 2 x 3 x2 x 2. The importance and interactions of each factor were determined, at the group level, by performing analyses of variance and constructing graphs. RESULTS: The concept of breaching confidentiality to protect a wife from her husband's STD was favoured much more by lay people and psychologists than by physicians (mean ratings 11.76, 9.28 and 2.90, respectively, on a scale of 0-22). The patient's stated intentions to protect his wife and to inform her of the disease had the greatest impact on acceptability. A cluster analysis showed groups of lay participants who found breaching confidentiality "always acceptable" (n = 14), "depending on the many circumstances" (n = 87), requiring "consultation with an expert" (n = 30) and "never acceptable(n = 13)". CONCLUSIONS: Most people in France are influenced by situational factors when deciding if a physician should breach confidentiality to protect the spouse of a patient infected with STD.

Han, Juliana. The Tenth Circuit finds a constitutionally protected-right to privacy in prescription drug records. *Journal of Law, Medicine, and Ethics* 2006 Spring; 34(1): 134-136. NRCBL: 8.4; 9.7. SC: le.

Handberg, R.B. Talking about the unspeakable in a secretive institution: health and disability among Supreme Court justices. *Politics and the Life Sciences* 1989 August; 8(1): 70-73. NRCBL: 8.4; 1.3.5. Identifiers: United States Supreme Court.

Heikkinen, Anne; Wickström, Gustav; Leino-Kilpi, Helena. Understanding privacy in occupational health services. *Nursing Ethics* 2006 September; 13(5): 515-530. NRCBL: 8.4; 16.3. SC: em. Identifiers: Finland.

Abstract: The aim of this study was to gain a deeper understanding of privacy in occupational health services. Data were collected through in-depth theme interviews with occupational health professionals (n = 15), employees (n = 15) and employers (n = 14). Our findings indicate that privacy, in this context, is a complex and multilayered concept, and that companies as well as individual employees have their own core secrets. Co-operation between the three groups proved challenging: occupational health professionals have to consider carefully in which situations and how much they are entitled to release private information on individual employees for the benefit of the whole company. Privacy is thus not an absolute right of an individual, but involves the idea of sharing responsibility. The findings open up useful new perspectives on ethical questions of privacy and on the development of occupational health practices.

Hodge, James G. The legal and ethical fiction of "pure" confidentiality. *American Journal of Bioethics* 2006 March-April; 6(2): 21-22. NRCBL: 8.4; 9.5.6. Comments: Kenneth Kipnis. A defense of unqualified medical confidentiality. *American Journal of Bioethics* 2006 March-April; 6(2): 7-18.

Hooghiemstra, Theo. Introduction to the special privacy issue. *European Journal of Health Law* 2002 September; 9(3): 181-188. NRCBL: 8.4; 1.3.12; 15.1; 18.3. SC: le.

Hooghiemstra, Theo. The implementation of Directive 95/46/EC in the Netherlands, with special regard to medical data. *European Journal of Health Law* 2002 September; 9(3): 219-227. NRCBL: 8.4; 1.3.12; 15.1; 18.3; 8.2. SC: le.

Ikegaya, H.; Kawai, K.; Kikuchi, Y.; Yoshida, K. Does informed consent exempt Japanese doctors from reporting therapeutic deaths? *Journal of Medical Ethics* 2006 February; 32(2): 114-116. NRCBL: 8.4; 8.3.1. SC: em; le.

Abstract: The Japanese Medical Act section 21 states that doctors must report unnatural deaths to the police, even though the term "unnatural death" is not defined by law. However, many doctors are reluctant to report potential therapeutic deaths (PTDs). The Japanese Society of Legal Medicine has submitted guidelines for unnatural death, including PTD. These define a PTD as an unexpected death, the cause of which is unknown, but which is potentially related to medical practice. Such deaths are "reportable" to the coroner in the UK. In this study, we addressed the question of whether physicians would report each of eight hypothetical PTDs. Although the clinical societies (the Japan Society of Internal Medicine and the Japan Surgical Society) declare that doctors must report deaths due to gross negligence, 60% of the participants said that they would not report gross negligence involving an overdose in cases where they had obtained informed consent or had provided an explanation after the death occurred. This can be accounted for by the mistaken belief on the part of the participants that obtaining informed consent exempts Japanese physicians from the duty of reporting PTDs. The attitude of Japanese physicians is caused by the death investigation system, which is designed to discover whether a crime has been committed rather than focusing on the cause of death. Accordingly, the Japanese Government has decided to commission a pilot study from an independent organisation in which medical specialists will investigate PTDs in order to prevent deaths occurring as a result of gross negligence.

Iverson, Amy; Liddell, Kathleen; Fear, Nicole; Hotopf, Matthew; Wessely, Simon. Consent, confidentiality, and the Data Protection Act. *BMJ: British Medical Journal* 2006 January 21; 332(7534): 165-169. NRCBL: 8.4; 8.3; 7.1. SC: le.

Jeffords, James M. Confidentiality of medical information: protecting privacy in an electronic age. *Professional Psychology: Research and Practice* 1999 April; 30(2): 115-116. NRCBL: 8.4; 1.3.12; 17.1. SC: le.

Jenkin, Annie; Millward, Jennifer. A moral dilemma in the emergency room: confidentiality and domestic violence. *Accident and Emergency Nursing* 2006 January; 14(1): 38-42. NRCBL: 8.4; 9.1; 9.5.5.

NRCBL: National Reference Center for Bioethics Literature Classification Scheme   See inside front cover for terms.

129

Johnson, Andrea N. The federal psychotherapist-patient privilege, the purported "dangerous patient" exception, and its impact on African American access to mental health services. *Howard Law Journal* 2005; 48(3): 1025-1051. NRCBL: 8.4; 17.2; 4.3; 9.5.4. SC: le.

Kaiser, Jocelyn. Rule to protect records may doom long-term heart study [news]. *Science* 2006 March 17; 311(5767): 1547-1548. NRCBL: 8.4; 1.3.12.

Karro, Jonathan; Dent, Andrew W.; Farish, Stephen. Patient perceptions of privacy infringements in an emergency department. *Emergency Medicine Australasia* 2005 April; 17(2): 117-123. NRCBL: 8.4; 9.5.1. SC: em. Identifiers: Australia.

Kennedy, Ian; Grubb, Andrew. Confidentiality. *In their:* Medical Law. 3rd ed. London: Butterworths; 2005: 1047-1136. NRCBL: 8.4. SC: le.

Kienle, Thomas. New forms of medical data collection — should be complemented by a new European privacy standard? *European Journal of Health Law* 2001 March; 8(1): 27-39. NRCBL: 8.4; 1.3.12; 21.1. SC: le.

Kipnis, Kenneth. A defense defended [letter]. *American Journal of Bioethics [Online].* 2006 March-April; 6(2): W32-W34. NRCBL: 8.4; 9.5.6. Identifiers: medical confidentiality.

Kipnis, Kenneth. A defense of unqualified medical confidentiality. *American Journal of Bioethics* 2006 March-April; 6(2): 7-18. NRCBL: 8.4; 9.5.6; 4.1.2; 1.3.1; 1.1. Identifiers: Tarasoff v. Regents of University of California.

Klitzman, Robert. Qualifying confidentiality: historical and empirical issues. *American Journal of Bioethics* 2006 March-April; 6(2): 26-27. NRCBL: 8.4; 9.5.6. Comments: Kenneth Kipnis. A defense of unqualified medical confidentiality. American Journal of Bioethics 2006 March-April; 6(2): 7-18.

Knowles, Ann D.; McMahon, Marilyn. Expectations and preferences regarding confidentiality in the psychologist-client relationship. *Australian Psychologist* 1995 November; 30(3): 175-178. NRCBL: 8.4; 17.2; 8.1; 7.1; 9.5.7. SC: em.

Koocher, Gerald P. Confidentiality in psychological practice. *Australian Psychologist* 1995 November; 30(3): 158-163. NRCBL: 8.4; 4.3; 17.2; 8.3.1; 9.3.1; 1.3.12. SC: le.

Kuitenbrouwer, Frank. Privacy and its fallacies [editorial]. *European Journal of Health Law* 2002 September; 9(3): 173-179. NRCBL: 8.4; 1.3.12. SC: le.

Lagay, Faith. Resuscitating privacy in emergency settings. *Virtual Mentor* 2001 November; 3(11): 2p. NRCBL: 8.4; 8.1.

Lenzer, Jeanne. Doctors outraged at Patriot Act's potential to seize medical records [news]. *BMJ: British Medical Journal* 2006 January 14; 332(7533): 69. NRCBL: 8.4; 1.3.12; 1.3.5.

Levanon, Ayelet; Sobol, Limor; Tzur, Hila. Medical confidentiality and use of medical information in Israel. *Journal of Biolaw and Business* 2006; 9(4): 20-28. NRCBL: 8.4; 18.2; 18.3; 6. SC: le; rv.

Levine, Carol. HIPAA and talking with family caregivers: what does the law really say? *AJN: American Journal of Nursing* 2006 August; 106(8): 51-53. NRCBL: 8.4. Identifiers: Health Insurance Portability and Accountability Act (HIPAA).

Li, Mingyan; Poovendran, Radha; Narayanan, Sreeram. Protecting patient privacy against unauthorized release of medical images in a group communication environment. *Computerized Medical Imaging and Graphics* 2005 July; 29(5): 367-383. NRCBL: 8.4; 1.3.12.

Liang, Bryan A. Medical information, confidentiality, and privacy. *Hematology/Oncology Clinics of North America* 2002 December; 16(6): 1433-1447. NRCBL: 8.4; 1.3.12. SC: le.

Lyren, Anne; Kodish, Eric; Lazebnik, Rina; O'Riordan, Mary Ann. Understanding confidentiality: perspectives of African American adolescents and their parents. *Journal of Adolescent Health: Official Publication of the Society for Adolescent Medicine* 2006 August; 39(2): 261-265. NRCBL: 8.4; 8.3.2; 9.5.4; 9.5.7. SC: em.

MacIntosh, Tracy. Ethical considerations for clinical photography in the Global South. *Developing World Bioethics* 2006 May; 6(2): 81-88. NRCBL: 8.4; 1.3.7; 1.3.9; 18.3; 21.1; 18.6.

Abstract: Clinical photography is an important tool for teaching practitioners and field workers about the clinical manifestations of famine and under nutrition, particularly with respect to the Global South. Current international guidelines for clinical photography are not consistently applied or enforced, which has led to violations of privacy and rights, particularly for patients and victims of disaster in the Global South. Combining existing clinical photography guidelines from the North with ongoing clinical ethics debates in the South, this paper explores approaches to establishing photography guidelines throughout the world that will be sensitive to the privacy and dignities of all patients and victims of emergencies.

Maehle, Andreas-Holger. Protecting patient privacy or serving public interests? Challenges to medical confidentiality in imperial Germany. *Social History of Medicine* 2003 December; 16(3): 383-401. NRCBL: 8.4; 8.1; 9.5.1; 7.1. SC: le.

Markovitz, Barry P.; Goodman, Kenneth W. Case reports on the web redux: confidentiality still in jeopardy. *AMIA Symposium Proceedings* 2003; p. 926. NRCBL: 8.4; 18.3; 1.3.12. SC: em.

Marks, Patricia D. Reaching a balance between privacy, privilege and planning: a look at barriers to obtaining information for patients with criminal involvement. *Psychiatric Quarterly* 2004 Summer; 75(2): 127-138. NRCBL: 8.4; 17.1; 1.3.5. SC: le.

McAdam, Catherine; Rai, Gurcharan S. Confidentiality. *In:* Rai, Gurcharan S, ed. Medical Ethics and the Elderly. 2nd ed. San Francisco: Radcliffe Medical Press; 2004: 9-17. NRCBL: 8.4; 8.3.1.

McGregor, Joan. No moral absolutes. *American Journal of Bioethics* 2006 March-April; 6(2): 29-30. NRCBL: 8.4; 4.1.2; 1.1. Comments: Kenneth Kipnis. A defense of unqualified medical confidentiality. American Journal of Bioethics 2006 March-April; 6(2): 7-18.

McHale, Jean. Confidentiality and psychiatry: dilemmas of disclosure [editorial]. *Journal of Forensic Psychiatry* 2000 September; 11(2): 255-259. NRCBL: 8.4; 17.1. SC: le. Identifiers: United Kingdom (Great Britain).

McMahon, Marilyn; Knowles, Ann D. Confidentiality in psychological practice: a decrepit concept? *Australian Psychologist* 1995 November; 30(3): 164-168. NRCBL: 8.4; 17.2; 7.1; 6; 9.5.6. SC: em; le.

McSherry, Bernadette. Consenting to shared electronic health records: the proposed HealthConnect system. *Journal of Law and Medicine* 2004 February; 11(3): 269-273. NRCBL: 8.4; 1.3.12. SC: le.

Meier, Barry. U.S. shields doctor data in implants. *New York Times* 2006 July 10; p. C1, C5. NRCBL: 8.4; 7.1. SC: po.

Meyer, Gregg S. Privacy versus progress: the international debate over medical records research. *Nutrition* 1999 January; 15(1): 81-82. NRCBL: 8.4; 1.3.12; 5.3.

Michel, L.; Van Damme, H. The challenge of electronic medical prescriptions to the rule of confidentiality and to the respect of patient's privacy. *Acta Chirurgica Belgica* 2005 September-October; 105(5): 455-456. NRCBL: 8.4; 1.3.12.

Miller, Robert D. Health care information. *In his:* Problems in Health Care Law. Ninth edition. Sudbury, MA: Jones and Bartlett Publishers; 2006: 427-491. NRCBL: 8.4; 1.3.12.

Milne, Janet. An analysis of the law of confidentiality with special reference to the counselling of minors. *Australian Psychologist* 1995 November; 30(3): 169-174. NRCBL: 8.4; 17.2; 9.5.7; 6; 4.3. SC: le.

Mitrevski, Julia P. Psychotherapist patient privilege. Applying Jaffee v. Redmond: communications to a psychotherapist are not privileged if they occur outside the course of diagnosis or treatment. *Journal of the American Academy of Psychiatry and the Law* 2006; 34(2): 245-246. NRCBL: 8.4; 17.1. SC: le.

Moor, James H. Using genetic information while protecting the privacy of the soul. *Ethics and Information Technology* 1999; 1(4): 257-263. NRCBL: 8.4; 15.1; 1.3.12.

Moor, James H. Using genetic information while protecting the privacy of the soul. *In:* Tavani, Herman T., ed. Ethics, Computing, and Genomics. Sudbury, MA: Jones and Bartlett; 2006: 109-119. NRCBL: 8.4; 15.1.

Murray, George. Privacy issues and Plan B: the Canadian Pharmacists Association responds [letter]. *CMAJ/JAMC: Canadian Medical Association Journal* 2006 January 3; 174(1): 64-65. NRCBL: 8.4; 11.1; 9.7; 7.3.

Neubauer, Richard L.; Cruess, Sylvia R.; Cruess, Richard L. Paranoia over privacy. *Annals of Internal Medicine* 2006 August 1; 145(3): 228-230. NRCBL: 8.4. SC: le. Identifiers: HIPAA (Health Insurance Portability and Accountability Act).

Nordal, Salvör. Privacy in public. *In:* Árnason, Gardar; Nordal, Salvör; Árnason, Vilhjálmur, eds. Blood and Data: Ethical, Legal and Social Aspects of Human Genetic Databases. Reykjavík: University of Iceland Press; 2004: 249-254. NRCBL: 8.4; 15.1.

Nosowsky, Rachel; Giordano, Thomas J. The Health Insurance Portability and Accountability Act of 1996 (HIPAA) privacy rule: implications for clinical research. *Annual Review of Medicine* 2006; 57: 575-590. NRCBL: 8.4. SC: le.

Olsen, Douglas P.; Dixon, Jane Karpe; Grey, Margaret; Deshefy-Longhi, Terry; Demarest, Jo Cecille. Privacy concerns of patients and nurse practitioners in primary care — an APRNet study. *Journal of the American Academy of Nurse Practitioners* 2005 December; 17(12): 527-534. NRCBL: 8.4; 4.1.3. SC: em.

Olson, Karen L.; Grannis, Shaun J.; Mandl, Kenneth D. Privacy protection versus cluster detection in spatial epidemiology. *American Journal of Public Health* 2006 November; 96(11): 2002-2008. NRCBL: 8.4; 1.3.9.
Abstract: OBJECTIVES: Patient data that includes precise locations can reveal patients' identities, whereas data aggregated into administrative regions may preserve privacy and confidentiality. We investigated the effect of varying degrees of address precision (exact latitude and longitude vs the center points of zip code or census tracts) on detection of spatial clusters of cases. METHODS: We simulated disease outbreaks by adding supplementary spatially clustered emergency department visits to authentic hospital emergency department syndromic surveillance data. We identified clusters with a spatial scan statistic and evaluated detection rate and accuracy. RESULTS: More clusters were identified, and clusters were more accurately detected, when exact locations were used. That is, these clusters contained at least half of the simulated points and involved few additional emergency department visits. These results were especially apparent when the synthetic clustered points crossed administrative boundaries and fell into multiple zip code or census tracts. CONCLUSIONS: The spatial cluster detection algorithm performed better when addresses were analyzed as exact locations than when they were analyzed as center points of zip code or census tracts, particularly when the clustered points

NRCBL: National Reference Center for Bioethics Literature Classification Scheme   See inside front cover for terms.

131

crossed administrative boundaries. Use of precise addresses offers improved performance, but this practice must be weighed against privacy concerns in the establishment of public health data exchange policies.

Peterson, Candida C.; Siddle, David A.T. Confidentiality issues in psychological research. *Australian Psychologist* 1995 November; 30(3): 187-190. NRCBL: 8.4; 18.4; 18.2; 6; 17.1.

Platt, Priscilla. The individual's right of access to his or her own personal health information. *Health Law in Canada* 2006 March; 26(3): 44-59. NRCBL: 8.4; 8.1. SC: le. Identifiers: Canada.

Prudil, Lukas. Privacy and confidentiality — old concept, new challenges. *Medicine and Law: The World Association for Medical Law* 2006 September; 25(3): 573-580. NRCBL: 8.4; 15.1; 1.1; 18.6. SC: le.
Abstract: This paper concerns a privacy and confidentiality problem in cases of exceptional situations. It is primarily aimed at using DNA samples, and at a breach of genetic data protection. European legal provisions are especially mentioned.

Requejo, M. Teresa. Legal analysis of the Spanish basic law 41/2002 on the autonomy of the patient and the rights and obligations with regard to clinical information and documentation. *European Journal of Health Law* 2003 September; 10(3): 257-269. NRCBL: 8.4; 20.5.4; 8.3.1. SC: le.

Robertson, Christopher. The consequences of qualified confidentiality. *American Journal of Bioethics* 2006 March-April; 6(2): 31-32. NRCBL: 8.4; 9.5.6. Comments: Kenneth Kipnis. A defense of unqualified medical confidentiality. American Journal of Bioethics 2006 March-April; 6(2): 7-18.

Robins, Robert S.; Rothschild, Henry. Ethical dilemmas of the president's physician. *Politics and the Life Sciences* 1988 August; 7(1): 3-11. NRCBL: 8.4; 1.3.5; 8.1; 2.1.

Rogers, Wendy A. Pressures on confidentiality. *Lancet* 2006 February 18-24; 367(9510): 553-554. NRCBL: 8.4; 8.3.1. SC: em.

Rosner, Fred. Medical confidentiality and patient privacy: the Jewish perspective. *Cancer Investigation* 2006 February; 24(1): 113-115. NRCBL: 8.4; 1.2; 2.1.

Rothstein, Mark A.; Schneider, Carl E. Is HIPAA flawed, or unnecessary? [letter and reply]. *Hastings Center Report* 2006 July-August; 36(4): 6-7. NRCBL: 8.4; 1.3.12.

Rothstein, Mark A.; Talbott, Meghan K. Compelled disclosure of health information: protecting against the greatest potential threat to privacy. *JAMA: The Journal of the American Medical Association* 2006 June 28; 295(24): 2882-2885. NRCBL: 8.4; 1.3.12. SC: le. Identifiers: National Health Information Network (NHIN).

Ruebner, Ralph; Reis, Leslie Ann. Hippocrates to HIPAA: a foundation for a federal physician-patient privilege. *Temple Law Review* 2004 Fall; 77(3): 505-576. NRCBL: 8.4. SC: le.

Sanci, Lena A.; Sawyer, Susan M.; Kang, Melissa S.-L.; Haller, Dagmar M.; Patton, George C. Confidential health care for adolescents: reconciling clinical evidence with family values. *Medical Journal of Australia* 2005 October 17; 183(8): 410-414. NRCBL: 8.4; 9.5.7; 8.3.2. SC: le.

Savage, Anne. Confidentiality versus public duty. *Journal of the Royal Society of Medicine* 2006 February; 99(2): 99-100. NRCBL: 8.4; 9.5.10; 9.5.7.

Schneider, Carl E. HIPAA-cracy. *Hastings Center Report* 2006 January-February; 36(1): 10-11. NRCBL: 8.4; 1.3.12. SC: le. Identifiers: Health Insurance Portability and Accountability Act.

Schwartz, Myrna F.; Brecher, Adelyn R.; Whyte, John; Klein, Mary G. A patient registry for cognitive rehabilitation research: a strategy for balancing patients' privacy rights with researchers' need for access. *Archives of Physical Medicine and Rehabilitation* 2005 September; 86(9): 1807-1814. NRCBL: 18.2; 8.4. SC: em.

Shumak, Steven L.; Sen, Mithu; Gregson, Daniel; Lewis, James; Hoey, John. Unnecessary exposure? [letter and response]. *CMAJ/JAMC: Canadian Medical Association Journal* 2006 February 14; 174(4): 499-500. NRCBL: 8.4.

Silfen, Molly. I want my information back: evidentiary privilege following the partial birth abortion cases. *Journal of Health Law* 2005 Winter; 38(1): 121-135. NRCBL: 8.4; 12.1; 1.3.12; 1.3.5. SC: le.

Slovenko, Ralph. Breach of confidentiality. *In his:* Psychiatry in Law/Law in Psychiatry. Volume 2. New York: Brunner-Routledge; 2002: 689-710. NRCBL: 8.4; 17.1. SC: le.

Slowther, Anne-Marie. Sharing information in health care: the nature and limits of confidentiality. *Clinical Ethics* 2006 June; 1(2): 82-84. NRCBL: 8.4; 8.3.1.

Sokol, Daniel K.; Car, J. Patient confidentiality and telephone consultations: time for a password. *Journal of Medical Ethics* 2006 December; 32(12): 688-689. NRCBL: 8.4.

Somerville, Margaret A. "Doing ethics" in the context of sharing patients' personal health information. *Canadian Journal on Aging / La Revue Canadienne du Vieillissement* 2004 Fall; 23(3): 197-202. NRCBL: 8.4; 7.3; 8.1; 8.3.3. Note: Abstract in French and English.

Stone, Margaret A.; Redsell, Sarah A.; Ling, Jennifer T.; Hay, Alastair D. Sharing patient data: competing demands of privacy, trust and research in primary care [interview]. *British Journal of General Practice* 2005 October;

55(519): 783-789. NRCBL: 8.4; 1.3.12; 9.1. Identifiers: United Kingdom (Great Britain).

Streiffer, Robert; Rubel, Alan P.; Fagan, Julie R. Medical privacy and the public's right to vote: what presidential candidates should disclose. *Journal of Medicine and Philosophy* 2006 August; 31(4): 417-439. NRCBL: 8.4; 1.3.5. SC: an.

> Abstract: We argue that while presidential candidates have the right to medical privacy, the public nature and importance of the presidency generates a moral requirement that candidates waive those rights in certain circumstances. Specifically, candidates are required to disclose information about medical conditions that are likely to seriously undermine their ability to fulfill what we call the "core functions" of the office of the presidency. This requirement exists because (1) people have the right to be governed only with their consent, (2) people's consent is meaningful only when they have access to information necessary for making informed voting decisions, (3) such information is necessary for making informed voting decisions, and (4) there are no countervailing reasons sufficiently strong to override this right. We also investigate alternative mechanisms for legally encouraging or requiring disclosure. Protecting the public's right to this information is of particular importance because of the documented history of deception and secrecy regarding the health of presidents and presidential candidates.

Terry, Nicolas P. Privacy and the health information domain: properties, models and unintended results. *European Journal of Health Law* 2003 September; 10(3): 223-237. NRCBL: 8.4; 1.3.12; 7.1. SC: an; le.

Thomson, Colin J.H. Protecting health information privacy in research: how much law do Australians need? *Medical Journal of Australia* 2005 September 19; 183(6): 315-317. NRCBL: 8.4; 18.1; 1.3.5. SC: le.

Trachtman, Howard. The secret sharer [letter]. *American Journal of Bioethics [Online].* 2006 March-April; 6(2): W35. NRCBL: 8.4. Comments: Kenneth Kipnis. A defense of unqualified medical confidentiality. American Journal of Bioethics 2006 March-April; 6(2): 7-18.

Tracy, C. Shawn; Drummond, Neil; Ferris Lorraine E.; Globerman, Judith; Hébert, Philip C.; Pringle, Dorothy M.; Cohen, Carole A. To tell or not to tell? Professional and lay perspectives on the disclosure of personal health information in community-based dementia care. *Canadian Journal on Aging = La Revue Canadienne du Vieillissement* 2004 Fall; 23(3): 203-215. NRCBL: 8.4; 7.3; 8.1; 9.5.2; 17.1. SC: em. Note: Abstract in French and English.

United States. Congress. House. A bill to protect the privacy of health information in the age of genetic and other new technologies, and for other purposes. Washington, DC: U.S. G.P.O., 1999. 73 p. [Online]. Accessed: http://frwebgate.access.gpo.gov/cgi-bin/getdoc.cgi?dbname=106_cong_bills&docid= f:h2878ih.txt.pdf [2007 March 8]. NRCBL: 8.4; 15.1. SC: le. Identifiers: Medical Privacy in the Age of New Technologies Act of 1999. Note: H.R. 2878, 106th Congress, 1st Session. Introduced by Rep. McDermott on September 15, 1999. Referred to

the Committee on Commerce and the Committee on Government Reform.

United States. Congress. House. A bill to provide individuals with access to health information of which they are a subject, ensure personal privacy with respect to health-care-related information, impose criminal and civil penalties for unauthorized use of protected health information, to provide for the strong enforcement of these rights, and to protect States' rights. Washington, DC: U.S. G.P.O., 1999. 81 p. [Online]. Accessed: http://frwebgate.access.gpo.gov/cgi-bin/getdoc.cgi?dbname=106_cong_bills&docid= f:h1057ih.txt.pdf [2007 March 2]. NRCBL: 8.4. SC: le. Note: H.R. 1057, 106th Congress, 1st session. Introduced by Rep. Markey on March 10, 1999. Referred to the Committee on Commerce, and the Committee on the Judiciary.

United States. Congress. Senate. A bill to provide individuals with access to health information of which they are a subject, ensure personal privacy with respect to health-care-related information, impose criminal and civil penalties for unauthorized use of protected health information, to provide for the strong enforcement of these rights, and to protect State's rights. Washington, DC: U.S. G.P.O., 1999. 81 p. [Online]. Accessed: http://frwebgate.access.gpo.gov/cgi-bin/getdoc.cgi?dbname=106_cong_bills&docid=f:s573is.txt.pdf [2007 March 2]. NRCBL: 8.4. SC: le. Note: S. 573, 106th Congress, 1st session. Introduced by Sen. Leahy on March 10, 1999. Referred to the Committee on Health, Education, Labor, and Pensions.

United States. Congress. Senate. A bill to provide individuals with access to health information of which they are the subject, ensure personal privacy with respect to personal medical records and health care-related information, impose criminal and civil penalties for unauthorized use of personal health information, and to provide for the strong enforcement of these rights. Washington, DC: U.S. G.P.O., 1997. 78 p. [Online]. Accessed: http://frwebgate. access.gpo.gov/cgi-bin/getdoc.cgi?dbname= 105_cong_bills&docid= f:s1368is.txt.pdf [2007 March 2]. NRCBL: 8.4. SC: le. Note: S. 1368, 105th Congress, 1st session. Introduced by Sen. Leahy on November 4, 1997. Referred to the Committee on Labor and Human Resources.

van den Hoven, Jeroen. Privacy. *In:* Mitcham, Carl, ed. Encyclopedia of Science, Technology, and Ethics. Farmington Hills, MI: Thomson/Gale, 2005: 1490-1492. NRCBL: 8.4.

Van Overstraeten, M.; Michel, Luc. The protection of the patient's private life: a vast normative landscape. First part. *Acta Chirurgica Belgica* 2005 September-October; 105(5): 457-463. NRCBL: 8.4.

Van Overstraeten, M.; Michel, Luc. The protection of the patient's private life: the computer challenge. Second

---

NRCBL: National Reference Center for Bioethics Literature Classification Scheme   See inside front cover for terms.

part. *Acta Chirurgica Belgica* 2005 September-October; 105(5): 464-470. NRCBL: 8.4; 1.3.12; 1.3.5; 21.1.

Vargese, Sunny T.; George, Sapna Ann. Doctors and the electronic media [letter]. *Indian Journal of Medical Ethics* 2006 October-December; 3(4): 145. NRCBL: 8.4; 1.3.7.

Vaughan, N.J.A.; Fogarty, L. Confidentiality and diabetes 'registers' — a dilemma? *Diabetic Medicine* 2000 August; 17(8): 563-564. NRCBL: 8.4; 1.3.12; 9.5.1.

Vermaas, Albert. Forced HIV-testing: a blessing for the physician or a worst case scenario for the patient? *Medicine and Law: The World Association for Medical Law* 2006 June; 25(2): 241-247. NRCBL: 8.4; 8.3.4; 9.5.6. SC: le.
Abstract: A ruling by the Court of Appeal in Amsterdam on 18 April 2002 has emphasized that a patient not only has rights but also responsibilities. The issue was whether a physician can violate his medical confidentiality in the patient-doctor relationship as a result of fear of infection with the HIV-virus after an accidental cut during surgery. The aim of the physician was for the award of his claim that the patient be forced to take an HIV-test. The ruling by the Court of Appeal has been noted by health lawyers and has been received positively (not unexpectedly) by the medical profession.

Walley, Tom. Using personal health information in medical research. *BMJ: British Medical Journal* 2006 January 21; 332(7534): 130-131. NRCBL: 8.4; 8.3.1; 7.1. SC: le.

Waltz, Emily. New York's scheme to track diabetes stirs privacy concerns [news]. *Nature Medicine* 2006 February; 12(2): 155. NRCBL: 8.4; 9.5.1; 1.3.12.

Westin, Alan F. Public attitudes toward electronic health records. *AHIP Coverage* 2005 July-August; 46(4): 22-25. NRCBL: 8.4; 1.3.12.

Whiteman, David C. Privacy and medical research [editorial]. *Internal Medicine Journal* 2005 August; 35(8): 441-442. NRCBL: 8.4; 18.1. SC: le.

Wilson, Jennifer Fisher. Health Insurance Portability and Accountability Act privacy rule causes ongoing concerns among clinicians and researchers. *Annals of Internal Medicine* 2006 August 15; 145(4): 313-316. NRCBL: 8.4. SC: le.

Wolfberg, Douglas M.; Wirth, Stephen R. Do EMS ride-along programs violate patient privacy? How to ensure your program measures up to HIPAA's privacy rule. *JEMS: A Journal of Emergency Medical Services* 2006 January; 31(1): 36-41. NRCBL: 8.4. SC: le. Identifiers: Health Insurance Portability and Accountability Act.

Woogara, Jay. Privacy and dignity of cancer patients: a qualitative study of patients privacy in UK National Health Service patient care settings. *Journal of Cancer Education* 2005 Summer; 20(2): 119-123. NRCBL: 8.4; 9.5.1. SC: em.

Wynaden, Dianne; Orb, Angelica. Impact of patient confidentiality on carers of people who have a mental disorder. *International Journal of Mental Health Nursing* 2005 September; 14(3): 166-171. NRCBL: 8.4; 17.1. SC: em. Identifiers: Australia.

CONTRACEPTION
See also POPULATION POLICY; STERILIZATION

Manitoba pharmacists' association clarifies Plan B regulations [news]. *CMAJ/JAMC: Canadian Medical Association Journal* 2006 April 11; 174(8): 1078. NRCBL: 11.1; 8.4; 9.7.

Ontario pharmacists drop Plan B screening form [news]. *Canadian Medical Association Journal* 2006 January 17; 174(2): 149-150. NRCBL: 11.1; 9.7; 8.4. Identifiers: Ontario College of Pharmacists.

Alan Guttmacher Institute. Minors' access to contraceptive services. *State Policies in Brief* 2006 February 1: 3 pages [Online]. Accessed: http://www.guttmacher.org/statecenter/spibs/spib_MACS.pdf [21 February 2006]. NRCBL: 11.2. SC: em; le.

Albiston, Catherine. The social meaning of the Norplant condition: constitutional considerations of race, class, and gender. *Berkeley Women's Law Journal* 1994; 9: 9-57. NRCBL: 11.1; 9.7; 9.5.5; 9.5.4; 1.3.5. SC: le.

American Pharmacists Association [APhA]. APhA Statement on FDA's Recent Approval of Plan B for OTC Status. Washington, DC: American Pharmacists Association, 2006 August 24: 1 p. [Online]. Accessed: http://www.aphanet.org/AM/Template.cfm?Template=CM/ContentDisplay.cfm&ContentID=6569 [2006 September 26]. NRCBL: 11.1; 9.7; 9.5.5; 9.5.7. Identifiers: levonorgestrel; over the counter.

Asch, Adrienne. Two cheers for conscience exceptions. *Hastings Center Report* 2006 November-December; 36(6): 11-12. NRCBL: 11.1; 1.2; 9.7; 8.1.

Ballard, Megan J. A practical analysis of the constitutional and legal infirmities of Norplant as a condition of probation. *Wisconsin Women's Law Journal* 1992-1993; 7-8: 85-106. NRCBL: 11.1; 9.7; 1.3.5. SC: le.

Barbaro, Michael. In reversal, Wal-Mart will sell contraceptive. *New York Times* 2006 March 4; p. C4. NRCBL: 11.1; 1.3.2; 9.7. SC: po.

Bartholomew, Terence P.; Carvalho, Tatiana. General practitioners' competence and confidentiality determinations with a minor who requests the oral contraceptive pill. *Journal of Law and Medicine* 2005 November; 13(2): 191-203. NRCBL: 11.2; 8.4. SC: em.

Beckman, Linda J.; Harvey, S. Marie; Sherman, Christy A.; Petitti, Diana B. Changes in providers' views and practices about emergency contraception: an HMO based intervention. *Obstetrics and Gynecology* 2001 June; 97(6): 942-946. NRCBL: 11.1; 9.7; 7.2. SC: em.

Bird, Sheryl Thorburn; Harvey, S. Marie; Beckman, Linda J. Emergency contraceptive pills: an exploratory study of knowledge and perceptions among Mexican women from both sides of the border. *Journal of American Medical Women's Association* 1998 Fall; 53(5, Supplement 2): 262-265. NRCBL: 11.1; 9.7; 9.5.4. SC: em.

Bovens, L. The rhythm method and embryonic death. *Journal of Medical Ethics* 2006 June; 32(6): 355-356. NRCBL: 11.1; 4.4. SC: an.
  Abstract: Some proponents of the pro-life movement argue against morning after pills, IUDs, and contraceptive pills on grounds of a concern for causing embryonic death. What has gone unnoticed, however, is that the pro-life line of argumentation can be extended to the rhythm method of contraception as well. Given certain plausible empirical assumptions, the rhythm method may well be responsible for a much higher number of embryonic deaths than some other contraceptive techniques.

Briggs, Gerald G. Comment: pharmacist critique was ill-informed. *Annals of Pharmacotherapy* 2006 July-August; 40: 1474-1475. NRCBL: 11.1; 9.7; 4.1.1; 7.2.

Cahill, Judith A.; Maddux, Michael S.; Gans, John A.; Manasse, Henri R. Pharmacist critique woefully outdated and uninformed [letter]. Washington, DC: American Pharmacists Association 2006: 2 p. NRCBL: 11.1; 9.7; 4.1.1.

California. Supreme Court. Catholic Charities of Sacramento County v. Superior Court of Sacramento County [Date of Decision: 2004 March 1]. *Pacific Reporter*, 3d Series, 2004; 85: 67-108. NRCBL: 11.1; 9.2; 1.2. SC: le.
  Abstract: Court Decision: 85 Pacific Reporter, 3d Series 67; 2004 March 1 (date of decision). The California Supreme Court agreed with a lower court decision that the state's Women's Contraception Equity Act (WCEA) requires employers who provide prescription drug benefits in their health care insurance plans to include prescription contraception coverage. Catholic Charities of Sacramento challenged the constitutionality of the provision, specifically with regard to its right to the free exercise of religion. The court held that Catholic Charities was not entitled to an exemption as it did not meet the criteria of a "religious employer" as delineated in WCEA. Furthermore, WCEA "served a compelling state interest in the elimination of. . . gender discrimination in the provision of health benefits"; had a "secular legislative purpose"; was valid and neutral; and neither advanced or inhibited religion.

Collins, Mary K. Conscience clauses and oral contraceptives: conscientious objection or calculated obstruction? *Annals of Health Law* 2006 Winter; 15(1): 37-60. NRCBL: 11.1; 12.4.3; 12.3; 9.7; 1.2. SC: le.

Comparetto, C.; Giudici, S.; Coccia, M.E.; Scarselli, G.; Borruto, F. Clinical, ethical, and medical legal considerations on emergency contraception. *Clinical and Experimental Obstetrics and Gynecology* 2005; 32(2): 107-110. NRCBL: 11.1; 9.7; 12.1. SC: em.

Connolly, June. Contraception and the under 16s — legal and ethical implications for the advanced nurse practitioner. *In:* Bartter, Karen, ed. Ethical Issues in Advanced Nursing Practice. Boston: Butterworth-Heinemann; 2001: 16-30. NRCBL: 11.2. SC: le.

Davidoff, Frank. Sex, politics, and morality at the FDA: reflections on the Plan B decision. *Hastings Center Report* 2006 March-April; 36(2): 20-25. NRCBL: 11.1; 9.7; 12.1; 1.3.5. Identifiers: Food and Drug Administration.

Davidoff, Frank; Trussell, James. Plan B and the politics of doubt. *JAMA: The Journal of the American Medical Association* 2006 October 11; 296(14): 1775-1777. NRCBL: 11.1; 5.3.

de Melo-Martín, Inmaculada; Briggle, Adam. Birth control. *In:* Mitcham, Carl, ed. Encyclopedia of Science, Technology, and Ethics. Farmington Hills, MI: Thomson/Gale, 2005: 232-237. NRCBL: 11.1; 2.2.

Delbanco, Suzanne F.; Stewart, Felicia H.; Koenig, Jacqueline D.; Parker, Molly L.; Hoff, Tina; McIntosh, Mary. Are we making progress with emergency contraception? Recent findings on American adults and health professionals. *Journal of the American Medical Women's Association* 1998 Fall; 53(5, Supplement 2): 242-246. NRCBL: 11.1; 9.7. SC: em.

Duvall, Melissa. Pharmacy conscience clause statutes: constitutional religious "accommodations" or unconstitutional "substantial burdens" on women? *American University Law Review* 2006 June; 55(5): 1485-1522. NRCBL: 11.1; 9.7; 8.1; 1.2. SC: le.

Eide, Karissa. Can a pharmacist refuse to fill birth control prescriptions on moral or religious grounds? *California Western Law Review* 2005 Fall; 42(1): 121-148. NRCBL: 11.1; 9.7; 8.1; 1.2. SC: le; an.

Ellerston, Charlotte; Trussell, James; Stewart, Felicia H.; Winikoff, Beverly. Should emergency contraceptive pills be available without prescription? *Journal of the American Medical Women's Association* 1998 Fall; 53(5, Supplement 2): 226-229, 232. NRCBL: 11.1; 9.7. SC: an.

Fielder, John H. Pharmacists refuse to fill emergency contraception prescriptions. *IEEE Engineering in Medicine and Biology Magazine* 2005 July-August; 24(4): 88-91. NRCBL: 11.1; 9.7; 12.1; 8.1.

Garside, Ruth; Ayres, Richard; Owen, Mike; Pearson, Virginia A.H.; Roizen, Judith. Anonymity and confidentiality: rural teenagers' concerns when accessing sexual health services. *Journal of Family Planning and Reproductive Health Care* 2002 January; 28(1): 23-26. NRCBL: 11.2; 8.4; 9.5.7. SC: em.

Gee, Rebekah E. Plan B, reproductive rights, and physician activism. *New England Journal of Medicine* 2006 July 6; 355(1): 4-5. NRCBL: 11.1; 9.7; 8.1; 9.1. SC: le.

NRCBL: National Reference Center for Bioethics Literature Classification Scheme   See inside front cover for terms.

135

Glasier, Anna. Emergency contraception: is it worth all the fuss? [editorial]. *BMJ: British Medical Journal* 2006 September 16; 333(7568): 560-561. NRCBL: 11.1; 9.7; 12.1; 21.1.

Golden, Neville H.; Seigel, Warren M.; Fisher, Martin; Schneider, Marcie; Quijano, Emilyn; Suss, Amy; Bergeson, Rachel; Seitz, Michele; Saunders, Deborah. Emergency contraception: pediatricians' knowledge, attitudes, and opinions. *Pediatrics* 2001 February; 107(2): 287-292. NRCBL: 11.1; 9.7; 11.2. SC: em.

Grimes, David A. Emergency contraception and fire extinguishers: a prevention paradox. *American Journal of Obstetrics and Gynecology* 2002 December; 187(6): 1536-1538. NRCBL: 11.1; 9.7. SC: an.

Grimes, David A.; Raymond, Elizabeth G.; Scott Jones, Bonnie. Emergency contraception over-the-counter: the medical and legal imperatives. *Obstetrics and Gynecology* 2001 July; 98(1): 151-155. NRCBL: 11.1; 9.7. SC: le.

Harper, Cynthia C.; Ellertson, Charlotte E. The emergency contraceptive pill: a survey of knowledge and attitudes among students at Princeton University. *American Journal of Obstetrics and Gynecology* 1995 November; 173(5): 1438-1445. NRCBL: 11.1; 9.7. SC: em. Note: Journal of Social Issues 2005 March; 61(1): 153.

Harris, Gardiner. F.D.A. approves broader access to next-day pill; sales over the counter; change just for adults — contraceptive still tied to abortion battle. *New York Times* 2006 August 25; p. A1, A18. NRCBL: 11.1; 5.3. SC: po. Identifiers: Food and Drug Administration.

Hepler, Charles D. Balancing pharmacists' conscientious objections with their duty to serve [editorial]. *Journal of the American Pharmacists Association* 2005 July-August; 45(4): 434-436. NRCBL: 11.1; 9.7; 1.2; 4.1.1.

Hutchings, Jane; Wrinkler, Jennifer L.; Fuller, Timothy S.; Gardner, Jacqueline S.; Wells, Elisa S.; Downing, Don; Shafer, Rod. When the morning after is Sunday: pharmacist prescribing of emergency contraceptive pills. *Journal of the American Medical Women's Association* 1998 Fall; 53(5, Supplement 2): 230-232. NRCBL: 11.1; 9.7.

Jackson, Rebecca; , Bimla Schwartz, Eleanor ; Freedman, Lori; Darney, Philip. Knowledge and willingness to use emergency contraceptive among low-income post-partum women. *Contraception* 2000 June; 61(6): 351-357. NRCBL: 11.1; 9.5.5; 9.5.4; 9.7. SC: em.

Jacobs, Russell A. Conee and Marquis on contraception. *Southwest Philosophy Review* 2002 July; 18(2): 101-105. NRCBL: 11.1; 12.3.

Jones, Rachel K.; Boonstra, Heather. Confidential reproductive health care for adolescents. *Current Opinion in Obstetrics and Gynecology* 2005 October; 17(5): 456-460. NRCBL: 11.2; 8.3.2. SC: le; rv.

Karpa, Kelly Dowhower. Pharmacist critique was ill-formed. *Annals of Pharmacotherapy* 2006 July-August; 40: 1441-1444. NRCBL: 11.1; 9.7; 4.1.1.

Kaufman, Marc. Plan B battles embroil states; proposals mirror red-blue divide. *Washington Post* 2006 February 27; p. A1, A7. NRCBL: 11.1; 9.7; 1.3.5. SC: po.

Kennedy, Ian; Grubb, Andrew. Contraception and sterilisation. *In their:* Medical Law. 3rd ed. London: Butterworths; 2005: 1139-1210. NRCBL: 11.2; 11.3; 9.5.3. SC: le.

Kissling, Frances. Does church doctrine trump rape victims' needs? *Conscience* 2006 Autumn; 27(3): 17. NRCBL: 11.1; 9.7; 12.1; 1.2.

Kuehn, Bridget M. Group backs emergency contraception. *JAMA: The Journal of the American Medical Association* 2006 June 21; 295(23): 2708-2709. NRCBL: 11.1. Identifiers: American College of Obstetricians and Gynecologists(ACOG).

LeDoux, Allison. Truth about emergency contraception. *Ethics and Medics* 2006 December; 31(12): 1-2. NRCBL: 11.1; 9.7; 12.1.

Lowell, Staci D. Striking a balance: finding a place for religious conscience clauses in contraceptive equity legislation. *Cleveland State Law Review* 2005; 52: 441-465. NRCBL: 11.1; 9.3.1; 1.2; 9.7.

Lumpkin, Cristina Arana. Does a pharmacist have the right to refuse to fill a prescription for birth control? *University of Miami Law Review* 2005-2006; 60: 105-130. NRCBL: 11.1; 9.7; 8.1; 1.2. SC: le.

Mellick, Erica S. Time for Plan B: increasing access to emergency contraception and minimizing conflicts of conscience. *Journal of Health Care Law and Policy* 2006; 9(2): 402-440. NRCBL: 11.1; 9.7; 12.1; 8.3.4; 1.2. SC: le.

Monastersky, Nicole; Landau, Sharon Cohen. Future of emergency contraception lies in pharmacists' hands. *Journal of the American Pharmacists Association* 2006 January-February; 46(1): 84-88. NRCBL: 11.1; 9.7; 7.2.

Mubaraki, Maharukh. The constitutionality of court imposed contraception as a condition of probation. *Criminal Justice Journal* 1992 Fall; 14(2): 385-405. NRCBL: 11.1; 9.7; 1.3.5. SC: le.

Nguyen, Thuan. Science and journalism: never the two shall meet? [letter]. *CMAJ/JAMC: Canadian Medical Association Journal* 2006 April 11; 174(8): 1132. NRCBL: 11.1; 8.4; 9.7. Comments: CMAJ/JAMC: Canadian Medical Journal Association 2005 December 6; 173(12): 1435-1436.

Oleson, Christopher. Nature, "naturalism", and the immorality of contraception: a critique of Fr. Rhonheimer on condom use and contraceptive intent. *National Catholic Bioethics Quarterly* 2006 Winter; 6(4): 719-721. NRCBL: 11.1; 1.2; 4.4.

Patterson, Angela. Carey v. Population Services International: minor's rights to access contraceptives. *Journal of Contemporary Legal Issues* 2004; 14(1): 469-475. NRCBL: 11.2. SC: le.

Pineda, Rafael Luis. "Contracepción de emergencia" un mal llamado método contraceptivo ["Emergency contraception": a misnamed method of contraception]. *Persona y Bioética* 1999 February-May; 2(6): 1-23. NRCBL: 11.1; 9.7.

Ponte, Charles D. Comment: pharmacist critique was ill-informed. *Annals of Pharmacotherapy* 2006 July-August; 40: 1475-1476. NRCBL: 11.1; 9.7; 4.1.1.

Pruitt, Sandi L.; Mullen, Patricia Dolan. Contraception or abortion? Inaccurate descriptions of emergency contraception in newspaper articles, 1992-2002. *Contraception* 2005 January; 71(1): 14-21. NRCBL: 11.1; 12.5.1; 1.3.7. SC: em.

Pruitt, Sandi L.; Mullen, Patricia Dolan. Response to letters to the editor regarding contraception or abortion? Inaccurate descriptions of emergency contraception in newspaper articles, 1992-2002 [letter]. *Contraception* 2005 November; 72(5): 396-397. NRCBL: 11.1; 8.3.1; 1.3.7.

Repenshek, Mark. The mechanism of action in intrauterine devices (IUD) as it relates to physician billing services. *Health Care Ethics USA* 2006; 14(2): E2 [Online]. Accessed: http://chce.slu.edu/Partnerships_HCE_Intro.html[2006 November 17]. NRCBL: 11.1; 1.2; 9.3.1.

Rodriguez, Pablo; Shields, Wayne C. Religion and medicine [editorial]. *Contraception* 2005 April; 71(4): 302-303. NRCBL: 11.1; 8.1; 1.2.

Rubin, Susan E.; Grumet, Surah; Prine, Linda. Hospital religious affiliation and emergency contraceptive prescribing practices. *American Journal of Public Health* 2006 August; 96(8): 1398-1401. NRCBL: 11.1; 9.7; 9.1; 1.2. SC: em.

Abstract: With access to reproductive health care eroding, examination of prescribing of contraception, including emergency contraception (EC), is important. We examined whether working in a family practice affiliated with a religious institution changes the likelihood of a provider prescribing EC. Our survey asked about EC prescribing practices in a range of situations. As predicted, practitioners in non-religiously affiliated practices reported higher rates of prescribing EC than those in religiously affiliated practices. In both cases, however, the practitioners' prescribing patterns were inadequate.

Rudd, Gene. Avoiding pregnancy: "a plan" versus Plan B. *Annals of Pharmacotherapy* 2004 September; 38(9): 1535-1536. NRCBL: 11.1; 9.7.

Saul, Stephanie. FDA shifts view on next-day pill; moves toward backing its sale over the counter. *New York Times* 2006 August 1; p. A1, A12. NRCBL: 11.1; 5.3. SC: po.

Schaffer, Amanda. A philosopher's take on the rhythm method is rattling opponents of abortion. *New York Times* 2006 June 13; p. F5, F8. NRCBL: 11.1; 1.1. SC: po. Identifiers: Luc Bovens.

Schorn, Mavis N. Emergency contraception for sexual assault victims: an advocacy coalition framework. *Policy, Politics and Nursing Practice* 2005 November; 6(4): 343-353. NRCBL: 11.1; 10; 9.5.5; 1.3.5. SC: le; cs.

Shacter, Hannah. Emergency contraception: balancing a patient's right to medication with a pharmacist's right of conscientious objection. *Penn Bioethics Journal* 2006; 2(1): 3p. [Online]. Accessed: http://www.bioethicsjournal.com [2006 February 21]. NRCBL: 11.1; 9.7; 4.1.1; 1.3.1; 1.2; 9.2.

Sherman, Christy A. Emergency contraception: the politics of post-coital contraception. *Journal of Social Issues* 2005 March; 61(1): 139-157. NRCBL: 11.1; 9.7; 12.1; 21.1.

Shi, Chih-Wen; Ganiats, Theodore G. The debate about over-the-counter emergency contraceptive pills. *Journal of Midwifery and Women's Health* 2005 September-October; 50(5): 423-426. NRCBL: 11.1; 9.7; 9.2.

Shorto, Russell. Contra-contraception: a growing number of conservatives see birth control as part of an ailing culture that overemphasizes sex and devalues human life; Is this the beginning of the next culture war? *New York Times Magazine* 2006 May 7; p. 48-55, 68, 83. NRCBL: 11.1; 21.1.

Stabile, Susan J. State attempts to define religion: the ramifications of applying mandatory prescription contraceptive coverage statutes to religious employers. *Harvard Journal of Law and Public Policy* 2005 Summer; 28(3): 741-780. NRCBL: 11.1; 1.2; 9.3.1; 9.7. SC: le.

Stanford, Joseph B.; Larimore, Walter L. Description of emergency contraception in the media [letter]. *Contraception* 2005 November; 72(5): 394-395. NRCBL: 11.1; 1.3.7; 8.3.1.

Tanne, Janice Hopkins. FDA appointment is stalled as revelations emerge over Plan B [news]. *BMJ: British Medical Journal* 2006 August 12; 333(7563): 317. NRCBL: 11.1; 9.7; 5.3; 1.3.5.

Tanne, Janice Hopkins. FDA finally approves plan B — but with restrictions [news]. *BMJ: British Medical Journal* 2006 September 2; 333(7566): 461. NRCBL: 11.1; 9.7; 11.2. SC: le. Identifiers: United States.

Tanne, Janice Hopkins. FDA rejected contraception for political reasons [news]. *BMJ: British Medical Journal*

NRCBL: National Reference Center for Bioethics Literature Classification Scheme   See inside front cover for terms.

137

2006 March 18; 332(7542): 624. NRCBL: 11.1; 9.7; 1.3.5. SC: le. Identifiers: Food and Drug Administration.

Templeton, Sarah-Kate. Mother sues for veto on daughter's morning-after pill. *Sunday Times* 2005 May 15: 1 p. [Online]. http://infoweb.newsbank.com/iw-search/we/InfoWeb/?p_action=print&p_docid=10. . . [5 October 2006]. NRCBL: 11.2; 8.3.2; 9.7; 11.1.

United States. Congress. House. A bill to provide for the provision by hospitals of emergency contraceptives to women who are survivors of sexual assault. Washington, DC: U.S. G.P.O., 2005. 7 p. [Online]. Accessed: http://frwebgate.access.gpo.gov/cgi-bin/useftp.cgi?IPaddress=162.140.64.21&filename=h2928ih.pdf&directory=/diskb/wais/data/109_cong_bills [2006 November 27]. NRCBL: 11.1. SC: le. Identifiers: Compassionate Assistance for Rape Emergencies Act. Note: H.R. 2928, 109th Congress, 1st session. Introduced by Rep. Rothman, June 15, 2005. Referred to the Committee on Energy and Commerce and the Committee on Ways and Means.

United States. Congress. House. A bill to require the Commissioner of Food and Drugs to determine whether to allow the marketing of Plan B as a prescription drug for women 15 years of age or younger and a nonprescription drug for women 16 years of age or older. Washington, DC: U.S. G.P.O., 2005. 7 p. [Online]. Accessed: http://frwebgate.access.gpo.gov/cgi-bin/useftp.cgi?IPaddress=162.140.64.21&file name=h4229ih.pdf&directory=/diskb/wais/data/109_cong_bills [2006 November 21]. NRCBL: 11.1; 11.2; 9.7. SC: le. Identifiers: Plan B for Plan B Act of 2005. Note: H.R. 4229, 109th Congress, 1st session. Introduced by Rep. Maloney, November 3, 2005. Referred to the Committee on Energy and Commerce.

United States. Congress. Senate. Expressing the sense of the Senate concerning Griswold v. Connecticut. Washington, DC: U.S. G.P.O., 2005. 4 p. [Online]. Accessed: http://frwebgate.access.gpo.gov/cgi-bin/useftp.cgi?IPaddress=162.140.64.21&file name=sr162is.pdf&directory=/diskb/wais/data/109_cong_bills [2006 June 7]. NRCBL: 11.1; 8.4; 9.5.5. SC: le. Note: S. Res. 162, 109th Congress, 1st session. On June 7, 2005 Sen. Snowe submitted the following resolution. Referred to the Committee on the Judiciary.

Van Riper, Kristi K.; Hellerstedt, Wendy L. Emergency contraceptive pills: dispensing practices, knowledge and attitudes of South Dakota pharmacists. *Perspectives on Sexual and Reproductive Health* 2005 March; 37(1): 19-24. NRCBL: 11.1; 9.7. SC: em.

Wall, L. Lewis; Brown, Douglas. Refusals by pharmacists to dispense emergency contraception: a critique. *Obstetrics and Gynecology* 2006 May; 107(5): 1148-1151. NRCBL: 11.1; 9.7; 4.1.1.

Weil, Elizabeth. A wrongful birth? *New York Times Magazine* 2006 March 12; p. 48-53. NRCBL: 11.4; 12.1; 15.2; 14.4. SC: po.

Wellbery, Caroline. Emergency contraception: an ongoing debate [editorial]. *American Family Physician* 2004 August 15; 70(4): 655-659. NRCBL: 11.1; 9.7; 9.2.

White, Matthew. Conscience clauses for pharmacists: the struggle to balance conscience rights with the rights of patients and institutions. *Wisconsin Law Review* 2005; 2005(6): 1611-1648. NRCBL: 11.1; 9.7; 8.1; 1.2; 4.1.1. SC: le.

Winckler, Susan C.; Gans, John A. Conscientious objection and collaborative practice: conflicting or complementary initiatives? *Journal of the American Pharmacists Association* 2006 January-February; 46(1): 12-13. NRCBL: 11.1; 9.7; 8.1.

W., Barbara. Counter attack [letter]. *Canadian Medical Association Journal* 2006 January 17; 174(2): 211-212. NRCBL: 11.1; 11.2.

Zhou, Jianping. Ethics and practice of family planning and reproductive health in China. *In:* Döring, Ole; Chen, Renbiao, eds. Advances in Chinese Medical Ethics: Chinese and International Perspectives. Hamburg: Institut für Asienkunde; 2002: 322-326. NRCBL: 11.1. Note: Proceedings of the Second Sino-German Interdisciplinary Symposium about Medical Ethics in China, Shanghai, 19-23 October, 1999.

COST OF HEALTH CARE *See* HEALTH CARE ECONOMICS

CRYOBANKING OF SPERM, OVA, AND EMBRYOS

Ahuja, K.K.; Simons, E.G. Advanced oocyte cryopreservation will not undermine the practice of ethical egg sharing. *Reproductive BioMedicine Online [electronic]* 2006 March; 12(3): 282-283. NRCBL: 14.6. SC: em.

American Society for Reproductive Medicine [ASRM]. Ethics Committee. Oocyte donation to postmenopausal women. *Fertility and Sterility* 2004 September; 82(Supplement 1): S254-S255. NRCBL: 14.6; 19.5; 9.5.5; 9.5.2.

American Society for Reproductive Medicine [ASRM]. Ethics Committee. Posthumous reproduction. *Fertility and Sterility* 2004 September; 82(Supplement 1): S260-S262. NRCBL: 14.6; 20.1; 8.3.1; 19.5.

Amoroso, Kimberly. Frozen embryo adoption and the United States government. *Newsletter on Philosophy and Medicine* 2005 Fall; 05(1): 3-5. NRCBL: 14.6; 14.4; 19.5; 1.2; 9.3.1; 12.3. SC: le.

Annett, Tim. Balancing competing interests over frozen embryos: the judgment of Solomon? Evans v. United

Kingdom. *Medical Law Review* 2006 Autumn; 14(3): 425-433. NRCBL: 14.6. SC: le.

Apel, Susan B. Cryopreserved embryos: a response to "forced parenthood" and the role of intent. *Family Law Quarterly* 2005 Fall; 39(3): 663-681. NRCBL: 14.6. SC: le.

Bankowski, Brandon J.; Lyerly, Anne D.; Faden, Ruth R.; Wallach, Edward E. The social implications of embryo cryopreservation. *Fertility and Sterility* 2005 October; 84(4): 823-832. NRCBL: 14.6. SC: rv.

Bergues, Ulrike; Sèle, Bernard. Destruction of cryopreserved embryos: what fate lies in store for the cryopreserved human embryos in France? The French law leaves uncertainties. *Human Reproduction* 1997 February; 12(2): 207-208. NRCBL: 14.6; 1.3.5.

Bernal, Susan Kerr. Trite but true, better safe than sorry. *Journal of Andrology* 2005 September-October; 26(5): 559-562. NRCBL: 14.6; 10; 19.5; 1.3.5. Identifiers: Food and Drug Administration.

Blyth, Eric. Access to information about gamete and embryo donors in the UK [editorial]. *Obstetrics and Gynaecology Today* 2003 March; 8(3): 109-112. NRCBL: 14.6; 14.1; 8.4; 1.3.5. Identifiers: United Kingdom (Great Britain);Human Fertilisation and Embryology Act.

Blyth, Eric. Secrets and lies: barriers to the exchange of genetic origins information following donor assisted conception. *Adoption and Fostering* 1999; 23(1): 49-58. NRCBL: 14.6; 14.2; 14.1; 18.5.4; 8.4; 15.1.

Bonaccorso, Monica M. E. Programmes of gamete donation: strategies in (private) clinics of assisted conception. *In:* Unnithan-Kumar, Maya, ed. Reproductive Agency, Medicine and the State: Cultural Transformations in Childbearing. New York: Berghahn Books; 2004: 83-101. NRCBL: 14.6; 19.5. SC: em.

Brulliard, Karin. In competitive marketplace, Asian egg donors in demand. *Washington Post* 2006 November 19; p. A1, A7. NRCBL: 14.6; 19.5; 21.7. SC: po.

Caplan, Arthur. Lies in embryo [op-ed]. *Free Inquiry* 2006 June-July; 26(4): 15-16. NRCBL: 14.6.

Connors, Rachel. Y v Austin Health and the Royal Women's Hospital. *Journal of Law and Medicine* 2006 February; 13(3): 292-294. NRCBL: 14.6; 19.5; 14.4. SC: le.

Connors, Rachel. Yz v Infertility Treatment Authority. *Journal of Law and Medicine* 2006 February; 13(3): 289-291. NRCBL: 14.6; 19.5; 14.4. SC: le.

Dawson, K.J. The storage of human embryos. *Human Reproduction* 1997 January; 12(1): 6. NRCBL: 14.6; 8.3.1. SC: le. Comments: R.G. Edwards and Helen K. Beard. Destruction of cryopreserved embryos: U.K. law dictated the

destruction of 3000 cryopreserved human embryos. Human Reproduction 1997 January; 12(1): 3-5.

Deech, Ruth. A reply from the chairman of the HFEA. *Human Reproduction* 1997 January; 12(1): 5-6. NRCBL: 14.6; 8.3.1; 5.3. SC: le. Identifiers: Human Fertilisation and Embryology Authority. Comments: R.G. Edwards and Helen K. Beard. Destruction of cryopre- served embryos: U.K. law dictated the destruction of 3000 cryopreserved human embryos. Human Reproduction 1997 January; 12(1): 3-5.

Edwards, R.G.; Beard, Helen K. Destruction of cryopreserved embryos: U.K. law dictated the destruction of 3000 cryopreserved human embryos. *Human Reproduction* 1997 January; 12(1): 3-5. NRCBL: 14.6; 8.3.1; 5.3. SC: le.

Englert, Y.; Revelard, Ph. Isn't it "who decides" rather than "what to do" with spare embryos? *Human Reproduction* 1997 January; 12(1): 8-10. NRCBL: 14.6; 8.3.1; 5.3. SC: le. Comments: R.G. Edwards and Helen K. Beard. Destruction of cryopreserved embryos: U.K. law dictated the destruction of 3000 cryopreserved human embryos. Human Reproduction 1997 January; 12(1): 3-5.

ESHRE Task Force on Ethics and Law; Pennings, G.; de Wert, G.; Shenfield, F.; Cohen, J.; Devroey, P.; Tarlatzis, B. ESHRE Task Force on Ethics and Law 11: posthumous assisted reproduction. *Human Reproduction* 2006 December; 21(12): 3050-3053. NRCBL: 14.6; 2.1; 20.1. SC: an; le.

Ferraretti, Anna Pia; Pennings, Guido; Gianaroli, Luca; Magli, Maria Cristina. Semen donor recruitment in an oocyte donation programme. *Human Reproduction* 2006 October; 21(10): 2482-2485. NRCBL: 14.6; 19.5.

Halperin, Mordechai. Post-mortem sperm retrieval. *In:* Rosner, Fred, ed. Medicine and Jewish Law. Volume III. Brooklyn, NY: Yashar Books, Inc.; 2005: 41-51. NRCBL: 14.6; 1.2; 20.1.

Hartshorne, Geraldine. Future regulation of fertility banking in the UK. *Human Fertility* 2003 May; 6(2): 71-73. NRCBL: 14.6; 1.3.5; 19.5. Identifiers: United Kingdom (Great Britain).

Heng, Boon Chin. Advances in oocyte cryopreservation technology will eventually blur the ethical and moral boundaries between compensated egg sharing and commercialized oocyte donation. *Reproductive BioMedicine Online [electronic]* 2006 March; 12(3): 280-281. NRCBL: 14.6; 9.3.1.

Human Fertilisation and Embryology Authority [HFEA] (Great Britain). Embryo storage. London: Human Fertilisation and Embryology Authority, 1996 May; 6 p. NRCBL: 14.6; 8.3.1.

Katz, Katheryn D. Parenthood from the grave: protocols for retrieving and utilizing gametes from the dead or dying.

NRCBL: National Reference Center for Bioethics Literature Classification Scheme   See inside front cover for terms.

139

University of Chicago Legal Forum 2006: 289-316. NRCBL: 14.6; 19.5; 20.1. SC: le.

Kemelmajer de Carlucci, Aida Rosa. Genetic material and assisted reproduction. Case law reaction (Part II) = Material genético y reproducción asistida. Reacción jurisprudencial (Parte II). *Revista de Derecho Genoma Humano = Law and the Human Genome Review* 1997 July-December; (7): 173-186. NRCBL: 14.6; 20.1; 14.4. SC: le.

Kindregan, Charles P., Jr.; McBrien, Maureen. Posthumous reproduction. *Family Law Quarterly* 2005 Fall; 39(3): 579-597. NRCBL: 14.6; 19.5; 8.3.3; 4.4. SC: le.

Langley, Laura S.; Blackston, Joseph W. Sperm, egg, and a petri dish: unveiling the underlying property issues surrounding cryopreserved embryos. *Journal of Legal Medicine* 2006 June; 27(2): 167-206. NRCBL: 14.6; 4.4. SC: le.

Lui, S.C.; Weaver, S.M. Attitudes and motives of semen donors and non-donors. *Human Reproduction* 1996 September; 11(9): 2061-2066. NRCBL: 14.6. SC: em.

Nachtigall, Robert D.; Becker, Gay; Friese, Carrie; Butler, Anneliese; MacDougall, Kirstin. Parents' conceptualization of their frozen embryos complicates the disposition decision. *Fertility and Sterility* 2005 August; 84(2): 431-434. NRCBL: 14.6; 4.4; 18.5.4; 15.1. SC: em.

Premo-Hopkins, Mark W. Between organs and adoption: why pre-embryo donors should not be allowed to discriminate against recipients. *University of Chicago Legal Forum* 2006: 441-470. NRCBL: 14.6; 4.4; 19.5. SC: le.

Robertson, John A. Regulation of assisted reproduction: the need for flexibility. *Human Reproduction* 1997 January; 12(1): 7-8. NRCBL: 14.6; 8.3.1; 5.3. SC: le. Comments: R.G. Edwards and Helen K. Beard. Destruction of cryopreserved embryos: U.K. law dictated the destruction of 3000 cryopreserved human embryos. Human Reproduction 1997 January; 12(1): 3-5.

Ron-El, R. Assisted reproductive technology and embryo production. *Human Reproduction* 1997 January; 12(1): 10. NRCBL: 14.6; 5.3. SC: le. Comments: R.G. Edwards and Helen K. Beard. Destruction of cryopreserved embryos: U.K. law dictated the destruction of 3000 cryopreserved human embryos. Human Reproduction 1997 January; 12(1): 3-5.

Rosenwaks, Zev; Davis, Owen K. On the disposition of cryopreserved human embryos: an opinion. *Human Reproduction* 1997 June; 12(6): 1121. NRCBL: 14.6; 1.3.5; 4.4. SC: le. Identifiers: United Kingdom (Great Britain).

Ruiz, Amparo; Perez, Inmaculada; Pellicer, Antonio. Cryostorage of human embryos: time to decide. *Human Reproduction* 1996 April; 11(4): 703-705. NRCBL: 14.6. Identifiers: United Kingdom (Great Britain).

Schäfer, D.; Kettner, M. Moral concern over cryopreserved human embryos: too much or too little? *Human Reproduction* 1997 January; 12(1): 10-11. NRCBL: 14.6; 8.3.1; 5.3. SC: le. Comments: R.G. Edwards and Helen K. Beard. Destruction of cryopreserved embryos: U.K. law dictated the destruction of 3000 cryopreserved human embryos. Human Reproduction 1997 January; 12(1): 3-5.

Skouvakis, Fotini Antonia. Defining the undefined: using a best interest approach to decide the fate of cryopreserved preembryos in Pennsylvania. *Penn State Law Review* 2005 Winter; 109(3): 885-905. NRCBL: 14.6; 4.4. SC: le.

Smith, Amanda J. J.B. v. M.B. new evidence that contracts need to be reevaluated as the method of choice for resolving frozen embryo disputes. *North Carolina Law Review* 2003 January; 81(2): 878-1011. NRCBL: 14.6; 1.1. SC: le.

Strong, Carson. Gamete retrieval after death or irreversible unconsciousness: what counts as informed consent? *CQ: Cambridge Quarterly of Healthcare Ethics* 2006 Spring; 15(2): 161-171. NRCBL: 14.6; 8.3.3; 20.1.

Tober, Diane M. Semen as gift, semen as goods: reproductive workers and the market in altruism. *In:* Scheper-Hughes, Nancy; Wacquant, Loïc, eds. Commodifying Bodies. Thousand Oaks, CA: SAGE Publications; 2002: 137-160. NRCBL: 14.6; 9.3.1.

Vogel, Gretchen. Ethical oocytes: available for a price. *Science* 2006 July 14; 313(5784): 155. NRCBL: 14.6; 9.3.1; 19.5; 18.5.4; 15.1.

CULTURAL PLURALISM

Bailes, Marion J.; Minas, I. Harry; Klimidis, Steven. Mental health research, ethics and multiculturalism. *Monash Bioethics Review* 2006 January; 25(1): 53-63. NRCBL: 21.7; 18.2; 18.5.9; 9.5.4. SC: em.

Chacko, Ninan. Autonomy or economy? A paper written more to provoke re-thinking, than to enlighten or educate! *Humane Health Care International* 2006; 6(1): 1-6 [Online]. Accessed: http://www.humanehealthcare.com/volume_page.asp?id=164 [2006 July 18]. NRCBL: 21.7; 1.1; 8.3.4.

Elliot, Ann Christy. Health care ethics: cultural relativity of autonomy. *Journal of Transcultural Nursing* 2001 October; 12(4): 326-330. NRCBL: 21.7; 8.1; 1.1. SC: cs.

Engelhardt, H. Tristram. Public discourse and reasonable pluralism: rethinking the requirements of neutrality. *In:* Guinn, David E., ed. Handbook of Bioethics and Religion. New York: Oxford University Press, 2006: 169-194. NRCBL: 21.7.

Ford, Valerie; Furlong, Beth. Health systems and health promotion programs — the necessity of cultural competence: an ethical analysis. *In:* Kronenfeld, Jennie Jacobs, ed. Health Care Services, Racial and Ethnic Minorities and Underserved Populations: Patient and Provider Perspectives. Boston: Elsevier JAI, 2005: 233-243. NRCBL: 21.7; 9.1.

Hallenbeck, James; Goldstein, Mary K. Decisions at the end of life: cultural considerations beyond medical ethics. *Generations: Journal of the American Society on Aging* 1999 Spring; 23(1): 24-29. NRCBL: 21.7; 20.3.1; 2.1; 20.5.4.

McKendrick, Jane H.; Bennett, Pamela Aratukutuku. Health research across cultures — an ethical dilemma? *Monash Bioethics Review* 2006 January; 25(1): 64-71. NRCBL: 21.7; 18.2; 9.5.4.

Mooney, Gavin. Why not community values in all health research and for all cultures? *Monash Bioethics Review* 2006 January; 25(1): 72-74. NRCBL: 21.7; 18.5.9; 18.2.

Tilbury, Farida. Ethical dilemmas: principles and practice in research with African refugees. *Monash Bioethics Review* 2006 January; 25(1): 75-84. NRCBL: 21.7; 18.2; 18.5.9; 9.5.4.

Tishchenko, Pavel. Dimensions of cultural diversity of medical ethics. *In:* Rehmann-Sutter, Christoph; Düwell, Marcus; Mieth, Dietmar, eds. Bioethics in Cultural Contexts: Reflections on Methods and Finitude. Dordrecht: Springer, 2006: 211-227. NRCBL: 21.7.

Waldman, Ellen. Cultural priorities revealed: the development and regulations of assisted reproduction in the United States and Israel. *Health Matrix: The Journal of Law-Medicine* 2006 Winter; 16(1): 65-106. NRCBL: 21.7; 14.4; 14.2; 14.6. SC: le.

White, Karolyn; McGrath, Catherine; Kerridge, Ian. Multicultural medicine: ethical issues encountered when perspectives differ. *Eubios Journal of Asian and International Bioethics* 2006 January; 16(1): 4-6. NRCBL: 21.7; 4.1.1; 7.1; 8.1. Identifiers: complementary and alternative medicine; conventional medicine.

Yeo, Gwen. Ethical considerations in Asian and Pacific Island elders. *Clinics in Geriatric Medicine* 1995 February; 11(1): 139-151. NRCBL: 21.7; 9.5.2.

Yu, Kam-por. The alleged Asian values and their implications for bioethics. *In:* Sang-yong, Song; Young-Mo, Koo; Macer, Darryl R.J., eds. Asian Bioethics in the 21st Century. Christchurch, NZ: Eubios Ethics Institute, 2002: 232-237. NRCBL: 21.7; 1.1. SC: em. Conference: Proceedings of the Asian Bioethics Conference (ABC4), held 22-25 November 2002 in Seoul, South Korea.

DEATH AND DYING

Barilan, Y. Michael. Bodyworlds and the ethics of using human remains: a preliminary discussion. *Bioethics* 2006 September; 20(5): 233-247. NRCBL: 20.1; 20.3.1. SC: an.
Abstract: Accepting the claim that the living have some moral duties with regard to dead bodies, this paper explores those duties and how they bear on the popular traveling exhibition Bodyworlds. I argue that the concept of informed consent presupposes substantial duties to the dead, namely duties that reckon with the meaning of the act in question. An attitude of respect and not regarding human remains as mere raw material are non-alienable substantial duties. I found the ethos of Bodyworlds premature but full of promises such as public attitudes to organ donations. At the practical level I conclude that Bodyworlds should use only willed donations or unclaimed bodies for which dignified funerals are not available. In the case of live donations, Bodyworlds has a duty to participate in the medical care of needy donors. However, secrecy with regard to the source of cadavers seems to be the most troublesome aspect of Bodyworlds.

Baron, Jonathan. Death and the value of life. *In his:* Against Bioethics. Cambridge, MA: MIT Press, 2006: 83-96. NRCBL: 20.1; 4.4.

Borthwick, Jane. Something for every body. *Lancet* 2006 June 17-23; 367(9527): 1971-1972. NRCBL: 20.1; 7.1; 7.2; 4.4.

Burton, J.L.; Underwood, J.C.E. Necropsy practice after the "organ retention scandal": requests, performance, and tissue retention. *Journal of Clinical Pathology* 2003 July; 56(7): 537-541. NRCBL: 20.1; 8.3.3; 19.5. SC: em. Identifiers: United Kingdom (Great Britain).

Catholic Church. National Conference of Catholic Bishops [NCCB]. Committee on Science and Human Values. Dialogue Group of Scientists and Catholic Bishops. The Manner of Our Dying. Washington, DC: United States Catholic Conference, 1998. NRCBL: 20.1; 1.2.

Hammer, Eric T.; Mitcham, Carl. Death and dying. *In:* Mitcham, Carl, ed. Encyclopedia of Science, Technology, and Ethics. Farmington Hills, MI: Thomson/Gale, 2005: 476-481. NRCBL: 20.1.

Hayden, Deborah. Alas, poor Yorick: digging up the dead to make medical diagnoses. *PLoS Medicine* 2005 March; 2(3): 0184-0186. NRCBL: 20.1; 15.1.

Mattulat, Martin; Frewer, Andreas. Pathologie, politik und moral: Georg B. Gruber als medizinethiker und die zustimmung zur section [Pathology, politics, and morality: George B. Gruber as medical ethicist and the consent to autopsy]. *Ethik in der Medizin* 2006 September; 18(3): 238-250. NRCBL: 20.1; 2.2; 15.5; 21.1; 21.4.

Richards, Norvin. Choosing when to die. *Journal of Ethics* 2005; 9(3-4): 517-531. NRCBL: 20.1; 1.1.

NRCBL: National Reference Center for Bioethics Literature Classification Scheme   See inside front cover for terms.

141

Ruddick, William. "Biographical lives" revisited and extended. *Journal of Ethics* 2005; 9(3-4): 501-515. NRCBL: 20.1; 1.1.

Sulmasy, Daniel P. Death, dignity, and the theory of value. *In:* Schotsmans, Paul; Meulenbergs, Tom, eds. Euthanasia and Palliative Care in the Low Countries. Dudley, MA: Peeters, 2005: 95-119. NRCBL: 20.1; 4.4.

Woods, John. Privatizing death: metaphysical discouragements of ethical thinking. *Midwest Studies in Philosophy* 2000 August; 24: 199-218. NRCBL: 20.1; 1.1. SC: an.

DEATH AND DYING/ ATTITUDES TO DEATH

See also ADVANCE DIRECTIVES; ASSISTED SUICIDE; EUTHANASIA AND ALLOWING TO DIE

Albert, S.M.; Rabkin, J.G.; Del Bene, M.L.; Tider, T.; O'Sullivan, I.; Rowland, L.P.; Mitsumoto, H. Wish to die in end-stage ALS. *Neurology* 2005 July 12; 65(1): 68-74. NRCBL: 20.3.1; 20.5.1. SC: em.

Becker, Janet E. Oncology social workers' attitudes toward hospice care and referral behavior. *Health and Social Work* 2004 February; 29(1): 36-45. NRCBL: 20.3.2; 1.3.10.

Cahill, Lisa Sowle. Decline and dying: cultural and theological interpretations. *In her:* Theological Bioethics: Participation, Justice, and Change. Washington, DC: Georgetown University Press; 2005: 70-101. NRCBL: 20.3.1; 20.4.1; 20.5.1; 1.2.

Catt, Susan; Blanchard, Martin; Addington-Hall, Julia; Zis, Maria; Blizard, Bob; King, Michael. The development of a questionnaire to assess the attitudes of older people to end-of-life issues (AEOLI). *Palliative Medicine* 2005; 19(5): 397-401. NRCBL: 20.3.1; 20.4.1; 20.5.1. SC: em. Identifiers: United Kingdom (Great Britain).

Catt, Susan; Blanchard, Martin; Addington-Hall, Julia; Zis, Maria; Blizard, Robert; King, Michael. Older adults' attitudes to death, palliative treatment and hospice care. *Palliative Medicine* 2005 July; 19(5): 402-410. NRCBL: 20.3.1; 9.5.2; 9.5.1; 20.4.1. SC: em.

Curtis, Joy. Multidisciplinary input on institutional ethics committees: a nursing perspective. *QRB: Quality Review Bulletin* 1984 July; 10(7): 199-202. NRCBL: 20.3.2; 20.5.1.

Duffy, Sonia A.; Jackson, Frances C.; Schim, Stephanie M.; Ronis, David L.; Fowler, Karen E. Racial/ethnic preferences, sex preferences, and perceived discrimination related to end-of-life care. *Journal of the American Geriatrics Society* 2006 January; 54(1): 150-157. NRCBL: 20.3.1; 9.5.4; 20.4.1; 20.5.1. SC: em.

Einav, S.; Avidan, A.; Brezis, M.; Rubinow, A. Attitudes of medical practitioners towards "do not resuscitate" orders. *Medicine and Law: World Association for Medical Law* 2006 March; 25(1): 219-228. NRCBL: 20.3.2; 20.5.1. SC: em.

Abstract: When the desires of a patient are unknown or cannot be ascertained, cardio-pulmonary resuscitation (CPR) is the default procedure. Explicit, Do Not Resuscitate (DNR), orders are required to prevent implementation of CPR. We studied the response of general medical internists in specific clinical situations demanding consideration of DNR orders and respect for patient preferences; their current practice regarding slow codes and participation in CPR attempts considered futile provide information as to how often they discuss DNR issues with patients or families. Eighty-five internists attending the monthly meeting of the Internal Medicine Forum participated in the study. The physicians demonstrated their consent to participate by accepting a remote transmitter that elicited a response 2-3 minutes following the presentation of case vignettes or practice-related questions. The survey showed that 73% of the physicians agreed to assign a DNR order for a terminally ill patient unable to express her preferences. Only 55% agreed to do the same for a competent patient who specifically requested that CPR be withheld in the event of a cardiopulmonary arrest (p.05). 77% reported to have performed CPR, at least three times, in situations where they expected no benefit. 59% affirmed that their team had performed a partial CPR (slow code) at least once. Only 28% discussed the subject of DNR with patients or family more than 5 times a year. Paternalism, disregard for patients' preferences and poor communication skills influence normative behaviour in end-of-life decision-making.

Henig, Robin Marantz. Will we ever arrive at the good death? Almost 40 years after the birth of the hospice movement, and despite the rise of living wills and palliative care, the end of life remains anxious and hypermedicalized. Goldie Gold's struggle, and ours, to come to a dignified end. *New York Times Magazine* 2005 August 7; p. 26-35, 40, 68. NRCBL: 20.3.1; 20.4.1. SC: po.

Lübbe, Andreas S. Persisting misconceptions about patients' attitudes at the end of life [editorial]. *Supportive Care in Cancer* 2005 April; 13(4): 203-205. NRCBL: 20.3.1; 20.4.1; 4.4; 9.5.1. Identifiers: Germany.

Mayo, David J. Some reflections on whether death is bad. *In:* Jansen, Lynn A., ed. Death in the Clinic. Lanham, MD: Rowman and Littlefield; 2006: 17-26. NRCBL: 20.3.1.

McMullen, Greg. Breaking the trance? Enabling dissenting views on immortalism. *Health Law Review* 2006; 15(1): 47-49. NRCBL: 20.3.1.

Robinson, Ellen M.; Good, Grace; Burke, Suzanne. Talking with Lorraine's mother and sister, five months after her death. *Journal of Clinical Ethics* 2006 Spring; 17(1): 94-96. NRCBL: 20.3.3; 20.4.1; 8.1. SC: cs.

Shih, Fun-Jin; Gau, Meei-Ling; Lin, Yaw-Sheng; Pong, Suang-Jing; Lin, Hung-Ru. Death and help expected from nurses when dying. *Nursing Ethics* 2006 July; 13(4): 360-375. NRCBL: 20.3.2; 7.2; 20.4.1. SC: em.

Abstract: This project was undertaken to ascertain the perceptions of a group of Taiwan's fourth-year bachelor of science in

---

nursing (BSN) students regarding death and help expected from nurses during the dying process. Within the Chinese culture, death is one of the most important life issues. However, in many Chinese societies it is difficult for people to reveal their deepest feelings to their significant others or loved ones. It was in this context that this project was developed because little is known about how Taiwan's nursing students perceive death and the dying process. Using an open-ended, self-report questionnaire, 110 senior BSN students recorded their thoughts on: (1) their fears before physical death; (2) afterlife destinations; and (3) the help they would expect from nurses when dying. The data were analyzed using a three-layer qualitative thematic analysis. The students' reported needs during the dying process were directed towards three main goals: (1) help in reaching the 'triple targets of individual life'; (2) help in facilitating in-depth support so that both the dying person and significant others can experience a blessed farewell; and (3) help in reaching a destination in the afterlife. The results support the belief of dying as a transition occurring when life weans itself from the mortal world and prepares for an afterlife.

Stevens, Kenneth R. Emotional and psychological effect of physician-assisted suicide and euthanasia on participating physicians. *Issues in Law and Medicine* 2006 Spring; 21(3): 187-200. NRCBL: 20.3.2; 20.7; 20.5.1. SC: rv.

Štifanic, Mirko. Mistanasia in a society in transition. *Formosan Journal of Medical Humanities* 2006 June; 7(1-2): 81-89. NRCBL: 20.3.1; 20.5.1; 21.7.

Timmermans, Stefan. Death brokering: constructing culturally appropriate deaths. *Sociology of Health and Illness* 2005 November; 27(7): 993-1013. NRCBL: 20.3.2; 20.1; 8.1; 21.7.

Werner, Perla; Carmel, Sara; Ziedenberg, Hanna. Nurses' and social workers' attitudes and beliefs about and involvement in life-sustaining treatment decisions. *Health and Social Work* 2004 February; 29(1): 27-35. NRCBL: 20.3.2; 20.5.1; 1.3.10; 20.4.1. SC: em.

DEATH AND DYING/ DETERMINATION OF DEATH

Benjamin, Martin. Determining death. *In his:* Philosophy and This Actual World: An Introduction to Practical Philosophical Inquiry. Lanham, MD: Rowman and Littlefield Publishers; 2003: 149-169. NRCBL: 20.2.1.

Bernat, James L. Defining death. *In:* Jansen, Lynn A., ed. Death in the Clinic. Lanham, MD: Rowman and Littlefield; 2006: 27-46. NRCBL: 20.2.1.

Bernat, James L. The concept and practice of brain death. *Progress in Brain Research* 2005; 150: 369-379. NRCBL: 20.2.1; 19.5; 1.1; 1.2.

Burck, Russell; Anderson-Shaw, Lisa; Sheldon, Mark; Egan, Erin A. The clinical response to brain death: a policy proposal. *JONA's Healthcare Law, Ethics, and Regulation* 2006 April-June; 8(2): 53-59. NRCBL: 20.2.1.

Abstract: The ethical and scientific literature reflects a certain amount of controversy and confusion surrounding the concept of death by neurological criteria, or brain death. The issues surrounding brain death occur with limited frequency for those working in acute critical care settings. Even so, the literature and our own experiences evidence the discomfort of caregivers and policymakers when dealing with brain-dead patients and their family and loved ones. One particular area in which there seems to be significant diversity of opinion is what should occur when death by neurological criteria is pronounced. At some hospitals, when the patient is pronounced dead by neurological criteria, the support equipment is removed from the body immediately and the body is prepared for visitation by family or is transported to the morgue. In other hospitals, support equipment is maintained for a certain limited period to allow the family to be present when the equipment is ultimately removed. In general, however, it appears that institutional guidelines and policy are vague, at best, or often silent about the issue of when, how, and, to some extent, who decides what is done with the body. This policy paper discusses the confusion of care providers as well as lay persons related to the general concepts of death by neurological criteria. In addition, alternative approaches to the withdrawal of support equipment are examined. This article may also allow nursing administrators to better understand the importance of establishing specific clinical guidelines for their staff related to patients declared dead by neurological criteria. Our conclusion is that a universal policy should be adopted whereby all institutions develop the same guidelines concerning when and how treatment modalities should be withdrawn on their brain-dead patients. Such policy guidelines may not extinguish the misconceptions, misunderstandings, and discomforts that are present with a diagnosis of brain death, but it would certainly allow for more consistent actions on the part of the caregivers. Consistency would substantially benefit caregivers, families, and society alike.

Curry, S.; Ravelingien, A.; Braeckman, J.; Mortier, F.; Mortier, E.; Kerremans, I. Living patients in a permanent vegetative state as legitimate research subjects [letter and reply]. *Journal of Medical Ethics* 2006 October; 32(10): 606-607, 609-611. NRCBL: 20.2.1; 4.4; 18.3; 18.5.1; 19.1; 22.2.

Draper, H.; Ravelingien, A.; Braeckman, J.; Mortier, F.; Mortier, E.; Kerremans, I. Research and patients in a permanent vegetative state [letter and reply]. *Journal of Medical Ethics* 2006 October; 32(10): 607,609-611. NRCBL: 20.2.1; 4.4; 18.3; 18.5.1.

Farragher, Rachel A.; Laffey, John G. Maternal brain death and somatic support. *Neurocritical Care* 2005; 3(2): 99-106. NRCBL: 20.2.1; 9.5.8; 9.5.5. SC: em.

Farragher, R.; Marsh, B.; Laffey, J.G. Maternal brain death — an Irish perspective. *Irish Journal of Medical Science* 2005 October-December; 174(4): 55-59. NRCBL: 20.2.1; 9.5.5; 9.5.8; 20.5.1; 2.1. SC: rv.

Gert, Bernard; Chiong, Winston. Matters of "life" and "death" [letter and reply]. *Hastings Center Report* 2006 May-June; 36(3): 4, 5-6. NRCBL: 20.2.1.

Gert, Bernard; Culver, Charles M.; Clouser, K. Danner. Death. *In their:* Bioethics: A Systematic Approach. Second edition. New York: Oxford University Press; 2006: 283-308. NRCBL: 20.2.1. SC: an.

NRCBL: National Reference Center for Bioethics Literature Classification Scheme   See inside front cover for terms.

143

Gómez, Euclides Eslava. Controversias sobre muerte cerebral [Controversies in brain death]. *Persona y Bioética* 1999 February-May; 2(6): 43-55. NRCBL: 20.2.1.

Hershenov, David B. The death of a person. *Journal of Medicine and Philosophy* 2006 April; 31(2): 107-120. NRCBL: 20.2.1; 1.4; 4.4.

Abstract: Drawing upon Lynne Baker's idea of the person derivatively possessing the properties of a constituting organism, I argue that even if persons aren't identical to living organisms, they can each literally die a biological death. Thus we can accept that we're not essentially organisms and can still die without having to admit that there are two concepts and criteria of death as Jeff McMahan and Robert Veatch do. Furthermore, we can accept James Bernat's definition of "death"without having to insist, as he does, that persons are identical to organisms or that persons can only die metaphorical deaths.

Joffe, Ari R.; Anton, Natalie. Brain death: understanding of the conceptual basis by pediatric intensivists in Canada. *Archives of Pediatrics and Adolescent Medicine* 2006 July; 160: 747-752. NRCBL: 20.2.1; 20.3.2. SC: em.

Kennedy, Ian; Grubb, Andrew. Death and dead bodies. *In their:* Medical Law. 3rd ed. London: Butterworths; 2005: 2191-2263. NRCBL: 20.2.1. SC: le.

Kim, Jung Ran; Fisher, Murray John; Elliott, Doug. Attitudes of intensive care nurses towards brain death and organ transplantation: instrument development and testing. *Journal of Advanced Nursing* 2006 March; 53(5): 571-582. NRCBL: 20.2.1; 19.5; 20.3.2. SC: em. Identifiers: Korea.

Kim, Jung Ran; Fisher, Murray; Elliott, Doug. Knowledge levels of Korean intensive care nurses towards brain death and organ transplantation. *Journal of Clinical Nursing* 2006 May; 15(5): 574-580. NRCBL: 20.2.1; 4.1.3; 21.7. SC: em.

Laureys, Steven. Science and society: death, unconsciousness and the brain. *Nature Reviews Neuroscience* 2005 November; 6(11): 899-909. NRCBL: 20.2.1; 20.5.1; 1.2; 1.3.5.

Levy, N.; Ravelingien, A.; Braeckman, J.; Mortier, F.; Mortier, E.; Kerremans, I. Respecting rights . . . to death [letter and reply]. *Journal of Medical Ethics* 2006 October; 32(10): 608-609, 609-611. NRCBL: 20.2.1; 4.4; 18.3; 18.5.1; 19.1; 22.2.

Lizza, John P.; Chiong, Winston. Matters of "life" and "death" [letter and reply]. *Hastings Center Report* 2006 May-June; 36(3): 4-5, 5-6. NRCBL: 20.2.1.

Machado, Calixto. The first organ transplant from a brain-dead donor. *Neurology* 2005 June 14; 64(11): 1938-1942. NRCBL: 20.2.1; 19.5; 19.1.

McMahan, Jeff. An alternative to brain death. *Journal of Law, Medicine, and Ethics* 2006 Spring; 34(1): 44-48. NRCBL: 20.2.1; 4.4.

Miller, Robert D. Death and dead bodies. *In his:* Problems in Health Care Law. Ninth edition. Sudbury, MA: Jones and Bartlett Publishers; 2006: 765-787. NRCBL: 20.2.1; 19.5; 19.6. SC: le.

National Health and Medical Research Council [NHMRC] (Australia). Certifying death: the brain function criterion. Canberra, ACT: The Council, 1997; 25 p. NRCBL: 20.2.1.

New York Academy of Medicine. Committee on Public Health and Committee on Medicine in Society. Statement and resolution on the definition of death [Approved: May 1984]. *Bulletin of the New York Academy of Medicine* 1984 November; 60(9): 955-958. NRCBL: 20.2.1.

Paris, John J.; Cranford, Ronald E. Definition of brain death. *Theology Today* 1983 April; 40(1983-1984): 5-14. NRCBL: 20.2.1; 19.5. SC: le. Identifiers: Richard Berger.

Pediatric Reference Group; Neonatal Reference Group; Shemie, Sam D.; Doig, Christopher; Dickens, Bernard; Byrne, Paul; Wheelock, Brian; Rocker, Graeme; Baker, Andrew; Seland, T. Peter; Guest, Cameron; Cass, Dan; Jefferson, Rosella; Young, Kimberly; Teitelbaum, Jeanne. Severe brain injury to neurological determination of death: Canadian forum recommendations. *CMAJ/JAMC: Canadian Medical Association Journal* 2006 March 14; 174(6, Supplement): S1-S12. NRCBL: 20.2.1.

Resnicoff, Steven H. The legal and halachic ramifications of brain death. *In:* Rosner, Fred, ed. Medicine and Jewish Law. Volume III. Brooklyn, NY: Yashar Books, Inc.; 2005: 91-109. NRCBL: 20.2.1; 1.2.

Rosen, Michael. Defining death: the interaction of ethics and Halachah. *CCAR Journal: A Reform Jewish Quarterly* 2006 Fall; 53(4): 44-61. NRCBL: 20.2.1; 20.5.1; 1.2.

Sassower, Raphael; Grodin, Michael A. Epistemological questions concerning death. *Death Studies* 1986 July-August; 10(4): 341-353. NRCBL: 20.2.1.

Schlotzhauer, Anna V.; Liang, Bryan A. Definitions and implications of death. *Hematology/Oncology Clinics of North America* 2002 December; 16(6): 1397-1413. NRCBL: 20.2.1; 19.5. SC: le.

Shepherd, Lois. In respect of people living in a permanent vegetative state — and allowing them to die. *Health Matrix: The Journal of Law-Medicine* 2006 Summer; 16(2): 631-691. NRCBL: 20.2.1; 20.5.1. SC: le.

Sparrow, Robert. Right of the living dead? Consent to experimental surgery in the event of cortical death. *Journal of Medical Ethics* 2006 October; 32(10): 601-605. NRCBL: 20.2.1; 4.4; 18.3; 18.5.1; 19.1; 22.2. SC: an.

Thompson, J.; Ravelingien, A.; Braeckman, J.; Mortier, F.; Mortier, E.; Kerremans, I. Relatives of the living dead [letter and reply]. *Journal of Medical Ethics*

2006 October; 32(10): 607-608, 609-611. NRCBL: 20.2.1; 4.4; 18.3; 18.5.1.

Winkler, David I. Conceptual issues in the definition of death: a guide to public policy. *In:* Rosner, Fred, ed. Medicine and Jewish Law. Volume III. Brooklyn, NY: Yashar Books, Inc.; 2005: 111-129. NRCBL: 20.2.1.

Wisemann, Claudia. The contributions of medical history to medical ethics: the case of brain death. *In:* Rehmann-Sutter, Christoph; Düwell, Marcus; Mieth, Dietmar, eds. Bioethics in Cultural Contexts: Reflections on Methods and Finitude. Dordrecht: Springer, 2006: 187-196. NRCBL: 20.2.1; 7.1.

Youngner, Stuart J. Brain death. *In:* Mitcham, Carl, ed. Encyclopedia of Science, Technology, and Ethics. Farmington Hills, MI: Thomson/Gale, 2005: 245-247. NRCBL: 20.2.1; 2.2.

Youngner, Stuart; Chiong, Winston. Matters of "life" and "death" [letter and reply]. *Hastings Center Report* 2006 May-June; 36(3): 5, 5-6. NRCBL: 20.2.1.

DEATH AND DYING/ TERMINAL CARE

A letter from the children. *Journal of Clinical Ethics* 2006 Winter; 17(4): 339. NRCBL: 20.4.1; 9.5.3.

Adenipekun, A.; Onibokun, A.; Elumelu, T.N.; Soyannwo, O.A. Knowledge and attitudes of terminally ill patients and their family to palliative care and hospice services in Nigeria. *Nigerian Journal of Clinical Practice* 2005 June; 8(1): 19-22. NRCBL: 20.4.1. SC: em.

Aksoy, Sahin. Ethical considerations on the end of life issues in Turkey. *In:* Sang-yong, Song; Young-Mo, Koo; Macer, Darryl R.J., eds. Asian Bioethics in the 21st Century. Christchurch, NZ: Eubios Ethics Institute, 2002: 79-83. NRCBL: 20.4.1; 20.5.1. Conference: Proceedings of the Asian Bioethics Conference (ABC4), held 22-25 November 2002 in Seoul, South Korea.

American Association for Hospice and Palliative Medicine. Position statement on sedation at the end-of-life. *In:* Tännsjö, Torbjörn, ed. Terminal Sedation: Euthanasia in Disguise? Boston: Kluwer Academic Publishers; 2004: 129-131. NRCBL: 20.4.1; 9.7.

American Association for Hospice and Palliative Medicine. Position statement on sedation at the end-of-life. *In:* Tännsjö, Torbjörn, ed. Terminal Sedation: Euthanasia in Disguise? Boston: Kluwer Academic Publishers; 2004: 127-128. NRCBL: 20.4.1; 9.7.

Anderman, Jonathan. Right to access experimental drugs. *American Journal of Law and Medicine* 2006; 32(4): 611-614. NRCBL: 20.4.1; 9.2; 18.2. SC: le.

Au, Derrick K.S. A case of terminal metastic carcinoma of the lung: who makes the decision for terminal sedation? *In:* Döring, Ole; Chen, Renbiao, eds. Advances in Chinese Medical Ethics: Chinese and International Perspectives. Hamburg: Institut für Asienkunde; 2002: 417-420. NRCBL: 20.4.1; 9.7. Note: Proceedings of the Second Sino-German Interdisciplinary Symposium about Medical Ethics in China, Shanghai, 19-23 October, 1999.

Bakitas, Marie A. Self-determination: analysis of the concept and implications for research in palliative care. *Canadian Journal of Nursing Research* 2005 June; 37(2): 22-49. NRCBL: 20.4.1; 4.4; 8.1.

Barnard, David. The skull at the banquet. *In:* Jansen, Lynn A., ed. Death in the Clinic. Lanham, MD: Rowman and Littlefield; 2006: 66-80. NRCBL: 20.4.1.

Baron, Carol; Blicker, Ilena J.; Levy, Michael H.; Moss, Steven; Kozberg, Cary; Hill, C. Stratton, Jr.; Quill, Timothy E.; Tendler, Moshe; Rosner, Fred; Jacob, Walter; Freehof, Solomon B. The role of pain and suffering in decisionmaking: case no. 3. *Journal of Psychology and Judaism* 1996 Spring; 20(1): 59-97. NRCBL: 20.4.1; 4.4; 1.2; 9.5.3; 9.5.2; 9.7; 20.7; 20.5.1; 8.1; 1.1.

Basta, Lofty L. Ethical issues in the management of geriatric cardiac patients: a hospital's ethics committee decides to not give analgesics to a terminally ill patient to relieve her pain. *American Journal of Geriatric Cardiology* 2005 May-June; 14(3): 150-151. NRCBL: 20.4.1; 9.5.2; 4.4.

Basta, Lofty L. Ethical issues in the management of geriatric cardiac patients: the cardiologist acted in good faith, which resulted in losing the legal battle, the support of the hospital administration, and the friendship of the pulmonologist. *American Journal of Geriatric Cardiology* 2005 November-December; 14(6): 331-332. NRCBL: 20.4.1; 9.5.2; 8.5. SC: cs.

Baumrucker, Steven J.; Longenecker, Paul D.; Carter, Greg; Morris, Gerald M.; Stolick, Matt; Sheldon, Joanne E. SPTS — how soon is too soon? [case study and commentaries]. *American Journal of Hospice and Palliative Medicine* 2005 May-June; 22(3): 233-236. NRCBL: 20.4.1; 4.4; 17.1. SC: cs. Identifiers: sedation for palliation of terminal symptoms.

Beckstrand, Renea L.; Callister, Lynn Clark; Kirchhoff, Karin T. Providing a "good death": critical care nurses' suggestions for improving end-of-life care. *American Journal of Critical Care* 2006 January; 15(1): 38-46. NRCBL: 20.4.1; 20.5.1. SC: em.

Beider, Shay. An ethical argument for integrated palliative care. *Evidence-Based Complementary and Alternative Medicine* 2005; 2(2): 227-231. NRCBL: 20.4.1; 4.4.

Bendiksen, Robert. Death, dying and bioethics: current issues in the USA. *In:* Charmaz, Kathy; Howarth, Glennys; Kellehear, Allan, eds. The Unknown Country: Death in Australia, Britain and the USA. New York: St. Martin's Press; 1997: 198-212. NRCBL: 20.4.1; 20.4.2; 20.5.1; 20.5.2; 20.7.

NRCBL: National Reference Center for Bioethics Literature Classification Scheme   See inside front cover for terms.

145

Benedict, James. "Goses, Terefah, and Kiddush Ha-Shem" exceptions in Jewish bioethics regarding the preservation of life. *Brethren Life and Thought* 1998 Winter-Spring; 43(1 and 2): 43-53. NRCBL: 20.4.1; 1.2.

Berger, Jeffrey T. Suffering in advanced dementia: diagnostic and treatment challenges and questions about palliative sedation. *Journal of Clinical Ethics* 2006 Winter; 17(4): 364-366. NRCBL: 20.4.1; 9.5.3.

Bern-Klug, Mercedes. The ambiguous dying syndrome. *Health and Social Work* 2004 February; 29(1): 55-65. NRCBL: 20.4.1; 20.3.1.

Biggs, Hazel; Mackenzie, Robin. End of life decision-making, policy and the criminal justice system: untrained carers assuming responsibility [UCARes] and their uncertain legal liabilities. *Genomics, Society and Policy* 2006 May; 2(1): 118-128. NRCBL: 20.4.1; 20.5.1; 1.3.5. SC: le.

Abstract: This article will explore some previously unrecognised legal and ethical issues associated with informal care-giving and criminal justice in the context of end of life decision-making. It was prompted by a recent case in Leeds Crown Court, which raises important issues for the people who care for their loved ones at home and for the criminal justice system more generally. Government figures estimate that over 5.2 million Britons are responsible for the care of relatives or loved ones. In order to evaluate some of the ways in which they might find themselves exposed to unexpected criminal liability we have characterised this group as untrained carers who assume responsibility (UCARes).

Birchall, Melissa. Decision-making in palliative care: a reflective case study. *Contemporary Nurse* 2005 July-August; 19(1-2): 253-263. NRCBL: 20.4.1; 4.1.3. SC: cs.

Bonito, V.; Caraceni, A.; Borghi, L.; Marcello, N.; Mori, M.; Porteri, C.; Casella, G.; Causarano, R.; Gasparini, M.; Colombi, L.; Defanti, C.A. The clinical and ethical appropriateness of sedation in palliative neurological treatments = La sedazione nelle cure palliative neurologiche: appropriatezza clinica ed etica. *Neurological Sciences* 2005 December; 26(5): 370-385. NRCBL: 20.4.1; 20.5.1; 9.7; 1.1. Note: Full text in English and Italian.

Bosshard, Georg; de Stoutz, Noémi; Bär, Walter. Eine gesetzliche Regulierung des Umgangs mit Opiaten und Sedativa bei medizinischen Entscheidungen am Lebensende? [Legal regulation of opiate and sedative use in medical end-of-life decisions]. *Ethik in der Medizin* 2006 June; 18(2): 120-132. NRCBL: 20.4.1; 1.1; 9.5.9; 20.5.1. SC: le. Identifiers: Europe.

Brock, Dan W. Terminal sedation from the moral rights' perspective. *In:* Tännsjö, Torbjörn, ed. Terminal Sedation: Euthanasia in Disguise? Boston: Kluwer Academic Publishers; 2004: 71-79. NRCBL: 20.4.1; 9.7; 20.5.1. SC: an.

Broeckaert, Bert; Janssens, Rien. Palliative care and euthanasia: Belgian and Dutch perspectives. *In:* Schotsmans, Paul; Meulenbergs, Tom, eds. Euthanasia and Palliative Care in the Low Countries. Dudley, MA: Peeters, 2005: 35-69. NRCBL: 20.4.1; 20.5.1; 20.3.1; 21.1.

Burggraeve, Roger. You shall not let anyone die alone: responsible care for suffering and dying people. *In:* Schotsmans, Paul; Meulenbergs, Tom, eds. Euthanasia and Palliative Care in the Low Countries. Dudley, MA: Peeters, 2005: 147-173. NRCBL: 20.4.1; 4.4; 20.3.1.

Callahan, Daniel. A commentary — putting autonomy in its place: developing effective guidelines. *Gerontologist* 2002 October; 42(Special Issue 3): 129-131. NRCBL: 20.4.1; 1.1.

Callahan, Daniel. Terminal sedation and the artefactual fallacy. *In:* Tännsjö, Torbjörn, ed. Terminal Sedation: Euthanasia in Disguise? Boston: Kluwer Academic Publishers; 2004: 93-102. NRCBL: 20.4.1; 9.7; 20.5.1. SC: an.

Casarett, David J.; Teno, Joan; Higginson, Irene. How should nations measure the quality of end-of-life care for older adults? Recommendations for an international minimum data set. *Journal of American Geriatrics Society* 2006 November; 54(11): 1765-1771. NRCBL: 20.4.1; 21.1. SC: em.

Casarett, David; Van Ness, Peter H.; O'Leary, John R.; Fried, Terri R. Are patient preferences for life-sustaining treatment really a barrier to hospice enrollment for older adults with serious illness? *Journal of the American Geriatrics Society* 2006 March; 54(3): 472-478. NRCBL: 20.4.1; 20.5.1. SC: em.

Cessario, Romanus. Catholic considerations on palliative care. *National Catholic Bioethics Quarterly* 2006 Winter; 6(4): 639-650. NRCBL: 20.4.1; 1.2; 20.5.1; 4.4; 20.7.

Christmas, Colleen; Finucane, Tom. Artificial nutrition and hydration. *In:* Morrison, R. Sean; Meier, Diane E.; Capello, Carol, eds. Geriatric Palliative Care. New York: Oxford University Press; 2003: 36-45. NRCBL: 20.4.1; 9.5.2; 9.5.3; 20.5.1.

Clark, David. Cradle to the grave? Terminal care in the United Kingdom, 1948-67. *Mortality* 1999; 4(3): 225-247. NRCBL: 20.4.1; 2.2.

Clayton, Josephine M.; Butow, Phyllis N.; Arnold, Robert M.; Tattersall, Martin H.N. Discussing end-of-life issues with terminally ill cancer patients and their carers: a qualitative study. *Supportive Care in Cancer* 2005 August; 13(8): 589-599. NRCBL: 20.4.1; 8.1; 9.5.1; 20.3.1. SC: em. Identifiers: Australia.

Coni, Nick; McAdam, Catherine. Achieving and good death. *In:* Rai, Gurcharan S, ed. Medical Ethics and the Elderly. 2nd ed. San Francisco: Radcliffe Medical Press; 2004: 113-123. NRCBL: 20.4.1; 20.5.1; 20.5.4; 8.2.

Correa, Francisco Javier Léon. Bioética de la atención de enfermería al enfermo terminal [Bioethics of nursing care for the terminally ill]. *Persona y Bioética* 1999 February-May; 2(6): 123-142. NRCBL: 20.4.1.

Cripe, Larry D. Hope is the thing with feathers. *JAMA: The Journal of the American Medical Association* 2006 October 18; 296(15): 1815-1816. NRCBL: 20.4.1; 20.5.1. Identifiers: terminal illness.

Davis, Mellar P. Should experimental therapy be made available off-study for terminally ill patients? *Lancet Oncology* 2006 July; 7(7): 531-533. NRCBL: 20.4.1; 18.2.

Doron, Israel. Caring for the dying: from a "negative" to a "positive" legal right to die at home. *Care Management Journals* 2005 Spring; 6(1): 22-28. NRCBL: 20.4.1; 9.2. SC: le.

Drought, Theresa S.; Koenig, Barbara A. "Choice" in end-of-life decision making: researching fact or fiction? *Gerontologist* 2002 October; 42(Special Issue 3): 114-128. NRCBL: 20.4.1; 18.5.7; 9.4.

Duffy, James. Rediscovering the meaning in medicine: lessons from the dying on the ethics of experience. *Palliative and Supportive Care* 2004 June; 2(2): 207-211. NRCBL: 20.4.1; 4.1.2; 7.1.

Eckerdal, Gunnar. Sedation in palliative care — the doctor's perspective. *In:* Tännsjö, Torbjörn, ed. Terminal Sedation: Euthanasia in Disguise? Boston: Kluwer Academic Publishers; 2004: 37-41. NRCBL: 20.4.1; 9.7.

Emanuel, Linda. Relief of suffering is the business of every discipline [editorial]. *Archives of Internal Medicine* 2006 January 23; 166(2): 149- 150. NRCBL: 20.4.1; 4.4.

Engelberg, Ruth A.; Patrick, Donald L.; Curtis, J. Randall. Correspondence between patients' preferences and surrogates' understandings for dying and death. *Journal of Pain and Symptom Management* 2005 December; 30(6): 498-509. NRCBL: 20.4.1; 8.1. SC: em.

EURELD Consortium; Bilsen, Johan; Norup, Michael; Deliens, Luc; Miccinesi, Guido; van der Wal, Gerrit; Löfmark, Rurik; Faisst, Karin; van der Heide, Agnes. Drugs used to alleviate symptoms with life shortening as a possible side effect: end-of-life care in six European countries. *Journal of Pain and Symptom Management* 2006 February; 31(2): 111-121. NRCBL: 20.4.1; 20.5.1; 9.7; 21.1. SC: em.

Furrow, Barry R. Pain management and liability issues. *Hematology/Oncology Clinics of North America* 2002 December; 16(6): 1483-1494. NRCBL: 20.4.1; 8.5; 8.3.1. SC: le.

Garces-Foley, Kathleen. Hospice and the politics of spirituality. *Omega* 2006; 53(1-2): 117-136. NRCBL: 20.4.1; 1.2.

Gastmans, Chris. Caring for dignified end of life in a Christian health care institution: the view of Caritas Catholica Flanders. *In:* Schotsmans, Paul; Meulenbergs, Tom, eds. Euthanasia and Palliative Care in the Low Countries. Dudley, MA: Peeters, 2005: 205-225. NRCBL: 20.4.1; 1.2; 4.4.

González Barón, Manuel; Gómez Raposo, César; Pinto Marín, Álvaro. Sedation in clinical oncology. *Clinical and Translational Oncology* 2005 August; 7(7): 295-301. NRCBL: 20.4.1; 8.3; 20.5.1.

Gormally, Luke. Terminal sedation and the doctrine of the sanctity of life. *In:* Tännsjö, Torbjörn, ed. Terminal Sedation: Euthanasia in Disguise? Boston: Kluwer Academic Publishers; 2004: 81-91. NRCBL: 20.4.1; 4.4; 9.7; 20.5.1. SC: an.

Goy, Elizabeth R.; Jackson, Ann; Harvath, Theresa A.; Miller, Lois L.; Delorit, Molly A.; Ganzini, Linda. Oregon hospice nurses and social workers' assessment of physician progress in palliative care over the past 5 years. *Palliative and Supportive Care* 2003 September; 1(3): 215-219. NRCBL: 20.4.1; 7.1; 4.1.3; 1.3.10. SC: em.

Grady, Denise. Medical and ethical questions raised on deaths of critically ill patients. *New York Times* 2006 July 20; p. A18. NRCBL: 20.4.1; 20.5.1. SC: po; le. Identifiers: Hurricane Katrina 2005.

Grady, Denise. The fuzzy gray place in a killing zone. *New York Times* 2006 August 13; p. WK3. NRCBL: 20.4.1; 1.1. SC: po. Identifiers: Double effect.

Grünwald, Hans W. Hospice care for the terminally ill: an absolute necessity [editorial]. *Cancer Investigation* 2005; 23(3): 283. NRCBL: 20.4.1; 4.4; 1.2.

Guinn, David E. The heart of the matter: religion and spirituality at the end of life. *In:* Guinn, David E., ed. Handbook of Bioethics and Religion. New York: Oxford University Press, 2006: 345-357. NRCBL: 20.4.1; 1.2.

Hampton, James W. End-of-life issues for American Indians: a commentary. *Journal of Cancer Education* 2005 Spring; 20(1 Supplement): 37-40. NRCBL: 20.4.1; 9.5.4; 21.7.

Han, Paul K.; Arnold, Robert M. Palliative care services, patient abandonment, and the scope of physicians' responsibilities in end-of-life care. *Journal of Palliative Medicine* 2005 December; 8(6): 1238-1245. NRCBL: 20.4.1; 9.3.1; 9.2; 8.1. SC: cs.

Haverkamp, Margje H.; van Delden, Johannes J.M. Une mort tres douce: end-of-life decisions in France; reflections from a Dutch perspective. *Medicine, Health Care and Philosophy* 2006; 9(3): 367-376. NRCBL: 20.4.1; 20.5.1.

Hildén, H-M.; Honkasalo, M-L.; Louhiala, P. Finnish doctors and the realisation of patient autonomy in the context of end of life decision making. *Journal of Medical Eth-*

NRCBL: National Reference Center for Bioethics Literature Classification Scheme   See inside front cover for terms.

147

ics 2006 June; 32(6): 316-320. NRCBL: 20.4.1; 1.1; 8.1. SC: em.

Abstract: Patient autonomy is a fundamental principle in end of life decision making. However, its realisation may take a variety of forms. Discourse analysis was conducted in a qualitative interview study of 19 physicians. The physicians made use of three different discourses, each of which contained a specific understanding of patient autonomy and a physician's proper activities in the context of end of life decision making.

Hill, Jill M. Forcina. Hospice utilization: political, cultural, and legal issues. *Journal of Nursing Law* 2005 Winter; 10(4): 216-224. NRCBL: 20.4.1; 21.7. SC: le.

Holman, Julieta Bleichmar; Brendel, David H. The ethics of palliative care in psychiatry. *Journal of Clinical Ethics* 2006 Winter; 17(4): 333-338. NRCBL: 20.4.1; 9.5.3; 9.6.

Hurst, Samia A.; Mauron, Alex. The ethics of palliative care and euthanasia: exploring common values. *Palliative Medicine* 2006 March; 20(2): 107-112. NRCBL: 20.4.1; 20.5.1; 4.4; 20.7.

Hwang, Shirley S.; Chang, Victor T.; Cogswell, Janet; Srinivas, Shanthi; Kasimis, Basil. Knowledge and attitudes toward end-of-life care in veterans with symptomatic metastatic cancer. *Palliative and Supportive Care* 2003 September; 1(3): 221-230. NRCBL: 20.4.1; 20.3.1; 9.5.1. SC: em.

Ivanyushkin, A.Y.; Khetagurova, A.K. Palliative care in Russia. *Journal International de Bioéthique = International Journal of Bioethics* 2005 September-December; 16(3-4): 55-63, 169. NRCBL: 20.4.1; 2.2; 9.5.6; 9.5.7.

Abstract: The article addresses the history of establishing hospices in Russia complying with international WHO documents. The article also presents the ethics of palliative medicine in the Russian Federation with an objective analysis of the diseases affecting patients with special highlights on social problems.

Kaufman, Sharon R. A commentary: hospital experience and meaning at the end of life. *Gerontologist* 2002 October; 42(Special Issue 3): 34-39. NRCBL: 20.4.1; 20.5.1.

Kelly, Brian J.; Varghese, Francis T.; Pelusi, Dan. Countertransference and ethics: a perspective on clinical dilemmas in end-of-life decisions. *Palliative and Supportive Care* 2003 December; 1(4): 367-375. NRCBL: 20.4.1; 8.1; 9.4; 20.7; 20.5.1.

Kompanje, Erwin J.O.; van Zuylen, Lia; van der Rijt, C.C.D. Karin. Morphine is not a sedative and does not shorten life. *Archives of Internal Medicine* 2006 October 9; 166(18): 2047-2048. NRCBL: 20.4.1; 9.7; 20.5.1.

Kuczewski, Mark G. Our cultures, our selves: toward an honest dialogue on race and end of life decisions. *American Journal of Bioethics* 2006 September-October; 6(5): 13-17; discussion W30-W32. NRCBL: 20.4.1; 9.4; 9.5.4. Comments: Mary Ellen Wojtasiewicz. Damage compounded: disparities, distrust, and disparate impact in end-of-life conflict resolution policies. American Journal of Bioethics 2006 September-October; 6(5): 8-12.

Kuhse, Helga. Why terminal sedation is no solution to the voluntary euthanasia debate. *In:* Tännsjö, Torbjörn, ed. Terminal Sedation: Euthanasia in Disguise? Boston: Kluwer Academic Publishers; 2004: 57-70. NRCBL: 20.4.1; 9.7; 20.5.1. SC: an.

Kuschner, Ware; Lo, Bernard; Rubenfeld, Gordon. Dying patients and palliative sedation [letter and reply]. *JAMA: The Journal of the American Medical Association* 2006 March 15; 295(11): 1250. NRCBL: 20.4.1; 9.7.

Kushel, Margot B.; Miaskowski, Christine. End-of-life care for homeless patients: "she says she is there to help me in any situation". *JAMA: The Journal of the American Medical Association* 2006 December 27; 296(24): 2959-2966. NRCBL: 20.4.1; 9.5.10; 20.5.4.

Abstract: Homelessness annually affects an estimated 2.3 million to 3.5 million individuals living in the United States. Homeless people face difficulties in meeting their basic needs. Many have substance abuse problems and mental illness, lack social support, and have no medical insurance. These challenges complicate the homeless patient's ability to engage in end-of-life advanced planning, adhere to medications, and find an adequate site to receive terminal care. Employing a multidisciplinary team to care for homeless patients can help address their needs and improve care. For patients who continue to use illicit substances while receiving end-of-life care, experts recommend scheduling frequent clinic visits, using long-acting pain medications, dispensing small quantities of medications at a time, and using a written pain agreement. Homeless people are less likely to have a surrogate decision maker. Clinicians should have frequent, well-documented conversations with these patients about end-of-life wishes. Homeless people can rarely use hospice services because they lack the financial resources for inpatient hospice and have neither the home nor the social support required for home hospice. Developing inpatient palliative care services at hospitals that serve many homeless people could improve the end-of-life care homeless people receive.

Lindström, Irma; Gaston-Johansson, Fannie; Danielson, Ella. Documentation of patients' participation in care at the end of life. *Nursing Ethics* 2006 July; 13(4): 394-403. NRCBL: 20.4.1; 1.3.12; 8.1. SC: em. Identifiers: Sweden.

Abstract: The aim of this study was to describe how patients' participation in the care they received was documented in their health care records during the last three months of their lives. Two hundred and twenty-nine deceased adult persons were randomly identified from 12 municipalities in a Swedish county and their records were selected from different health care units. Content analysis was used to analyse the text. Four categories of patient participation were described: refusing offered care and treatments; appealing for relief; desire for everyday life; and making personal decisions. The most common way for these patients to be involved in their care at the end of their life was by refusal of the treatment and care offered. Characteristic of the different ways of participation were the diverse activities represented. The description of patients' involvement in their life situation at this time indicated their dissociation from the health care offered more than consenting to it.

Luptak, Marilyn. Social work and end-of-life care for older people: a historical perspective. *Health and Social Work* 2004 February; 29(1): 7-15. NRCBL: 20.4.1; 20.3.2; 9.5.2; 2.2; 1.3.10. SC: le.

MacPherson, Cheryl Cox. Healthcare development requires stakeholder consultation: palliative care in the Caribbean. *CQ: Cambridge Quarterly of Healthcare Ethics* 2006 Summer; 15(3): 248-255. NRCBL: 20.4.1; 4.4; 20.5.1.

Magnusson, Roger S. The devil's choice: re-thinking law, ethics, and symptom relief in palliative care. *Journal of Law, Medicine and Ethics* 2006 Fall; 34(3): 559-569. NRCBL: 20.4.1; 20.5.2. SC: le.
   Abstract: Health professionals do not always have the luxury of making "right" choices. This article introduces the "devil's choice" as a metaphor to describe medical choices that arise in circumstances where all the available options are both unwanted and perverse. Using the devil's choice, the paper criticizes the principle of double effect and provides a re-interpretation of the conventional legal and ethical account of symptom relief in palliative care.

Martone, Marilyn. What does society owe those who are minimally conscious? *Journal of the Society of Christian Ethics* 2006 Fall-Winter; 26(2): 201-217. NRCBL: 20.4.1; 9.5.1; 4.4.

Materstvedt, Lars Johan. Palliative care on the 'slippery slope' towards euthanasia? *Palliative Medicine* 2003; 17(5): 387-392. NRCBL: 20.4.1; 20.5.1; 9.4. SC: an. Identifiers: Norway.

McMahon, Robin L. An ethical dilemma in a hospice setting. *Palliative and Supportive Care* 2003 March; 1(1): 79-87. NRCBL: 20.4.1; 20.5.1; 20.7; 1.3.10; 2.1. SC: cs.

Mitchell, Christine. "Margaret's" children remember [interview]. *Journal of Clinical Ethics* 2006 Winter; 17(4): 349-357. NRCBL: 20.4.1; 9.5.3; 9.6.

Mitchell, Christine. A mother's death: the story of "Margaret's" children. *Journal of Clinical Ethics* 2006 Winter; 17(4): 331-332. NRCBL: 20.4.1; 9.5.3; 9.6.

Moneymaker, Kathleen. Comfort measures only. *Journal of Palliative Medicine* 2005 June; 8(3): 688. NRCBL: 20.4.1. Identifiers: palliative care.

Morita, Tatsuya; Chinone, Yoshikazu; Ikenaga, Masayuki; Miyoshi, Makoto; Nakaho, Toshimichi; Nishitateno, Kenji; Sakonji, Mitsuaki; Shima, Yasuo; Suenaga, Kazuyuki; Takigawa, Chizuko; Kohara, Hiroyuki; Tani, Kazuyuki; Kawamura, Yasuo; Matsubara, Tatsuhiro; Watanabe, Akihiko; Yagi, Yasuo; Sasaki, Toru; Higuchi, Akiko; Kimura, Hideyuki; Abo, Hirofumi; Ozawa, Taketoshi; Kizawa, Yoshiyuki; Uchitomi, Yosuke. Ethical validity of palliative sedation therapy: a multicenter, prospective, observational study conducted on specialized palliative care units in Japan. *Journal of*

Pain and Symptom Management 2005 October; 30(4): 308-319. NRCBL: 20.4.1; 4.4; 9.7. SC: em.

Morita, Toshiko. Nursing of dying patients: from the viewpoint of cultural background of attending death. *In:* Takahashi, Takao, ed. Taking Life and Death Seriously: Bioethics from Japan. Amsterdam; Boston: Elsevier JAI; 2005: 175-208. NRCBL: 20.4.1; 20.3.2; 21.7.

Morrin, Peter A.F. Death and dying in the Canadian health-care system. *Ontario Medical Review* 1993 December: 55-57. NRCBL: 20.4.1; 20.3.2.

Moss, Ralph W. No way to save a life. *New Scientist* 2006 June 3-9; 190(2554): 21. NRCBL: 20.4.1; 9.7; 9.8; 18.6. SC: le.

Mystakidou, Kyriaki; Rosenfeld, Barry; Parpa, Efi; Tsilika, Eleni; Katsouda, Emmanuela; Galanos, Antonis; Vlahos, Lambros. The schedule of attitudes toward hastened death: validation analysis in terminally ill cancer patients. *Palliative and Supportive Care* 2004 December; 2(4): 395-402. NRCBL: 20.4.1; 9.5.1; 20.5.1; 20.3.1. SC: em.

Nolan, Marie T.; Hughes, Mark; Narendra, Derek Paul; Sood, Johanna R.; Terry, Peter B.; Astrow, Alan B.; Kub, Joan; Thompson, Richard E.; Sulmasy, Daniel P. When patients lack capacity: the roles that patients with terminal diagnoses would choose for their physicians and loved ones in making medical decisions. *Journal of Pain and Symptom Management* 2005 October; 30(4): 342-353. NRCBL: 20.4.1; 8.1; 8.3.3. SC: em.

Norwegian Medical Association. Guidelines on palliative sedation. *In:* Tännsjö, Torbjörn, ed. Terminal Sedation: Euthanasia in Disguise? Boston: Kluwer Academic Publishers; 2004: 132-133. NRCBL: 20.4.1; 9.7.

Okon, Tomasz R. "Nobody understands": on a cardinal phenomenon of palliative care. *Journal of Medicine and Philosophy* 2006 February; 31(1): 13-46. NRCBL: 20.4.1; 8.1; 1.1.
   Abstract: In the clinical practice of palliative medicine, recommended communication models fail to approximate the truth of suffering associated with an impending death. I provide evidence from patients' stories and empiric research alike to support this observation. Rather than attributing this deficiency to inadequate training or communication skills, I examine the epistemological premises of the biomedical language governing the patient-physician communication. I demonstrate that the contemporary biomedicine faces a fundamental aporetic occlusion in attempting to examine death. This review asserts that the occlusion defines, rather than simply complicating, palliative care. Given the defining place of aporia in the care for the dying, I suggest that this finding shape the clinicians' responses to the needs of patients in clinical care and in designing palliative research. Lastly, I briefly signal that a genuinely apophatic voice construing the occlusion as a mystery rather than an aporia may be superior to the present communication and empathy models.

NRCBL: National Reference Center for Bioethics Literature Classification Scheme   See inside front cover for terms.

149

Olthuis, Gert; Dekkers, Wim; Leget, Carlo; Vogelaar, Paul. The caring relationship in hospice care: an analysis based on the ethics of the caring conversation. *Nursing Ethics* 2006 January; 13(1): 29-40. NRCBL: 20.4.1; 8.1.

Abstract: Good nursing is more than exercising a specific set of skills. It involves the personal identity of the nurse. The aim of this article is to answer two questions: (1) what kind of person should the hospice nurse be? and (2) how should the hospice nurse engage in caring conversations? To answer these questions we analyse a nurse's story that is intended to be a profile of an exemplary hospice nurse. This story was constructed from an analysis of five semistructured interviews with hospice nurses, based on the 'ethics of the caring conversation', which is inspired by the ethical perspective of Paul Ricoeur. The research questions concentrate on the norms of respect, responsibility and reciprocity, which are integral parts of the 'ethics of the caring conversation'.

Perkins, Henry S.; de Souza, Emi Pouce; Cortez, Josie D.; Hazuda, Helen P. Comments on Skrank et al. focus group findings about the influence of culture on communication preferences in end-of-life care [letter]. *JGIM: Journal of General Internal Medicine* 2006 April; 21(4): 399-400. NRCBL: 20.4.1; 9.5.4.

Pomerantz, Sherry C.; Bhatt, Himani; Brodsky, Nancy L.; Lurie, Deborah; Ciesielski, Janice; Cavalieri, Thomas A. Physicians' practices related to the use of terminal sedation: moral and ethical concerns. *Palliative and Supportive Care* 2004 March; 2(1): 15-21. NRCBL: 20.4.1; 20.5.1; 7.1; 4.1.2. SC: em.

Puri, Vinod K. Death in the ICU: feelings of those left behind. *Chest* 2003 July; 124(1): 11-12. NRCBL: 20.4.1; 8.1; 4.4; 20.3.3. Identifiers: intensive care unit.

Purtilo, Ruth B. Attention to caregivers and hope: overlooked aspects of ethics consultation. *Journal of Clinical Ethics* 2006 Winter; 17(4): 358-363. NRCBL: 20.4.1; 9.5.3; 9.6; 20.3.3.

Reid, Coleen. Medicating "Margaret". *Journal of Clinical Ethics* 2006 Winter; 17(4): 340-343. NRCBL: 20.4.1; 9.5.3; 9.7.

Rich, Ben A.; Casarett, David; Battin, Margaret P. Ethics forum. 75-year-old man has end-stage prostate cancer with metastases to bone. *Pain Medicine* 2005 November-December; 6(6): 459-463. NRCBL: 20.4.1; 4.4; 8.3.3; 8.1. SC: cs.

Rietjens, Judith A.C.; van Delden, Johannes J.M.; van der Heide, Agnes; Vrakking, Astrid M.; Onwuteaka-Philipsen, Bregje D.; van der Maas, Paul J.; van der Waal, Gerrit. Terminal sedation and euthanasia. *Archives of Internal Medicine* 2006 April 10; 166(7): 749-753. NRCBL: 20.4.1; 9.7; 20.5.1. SC: em. Identifiers: Netherlands.

Abstract: BACKGROUND: An important issue in the debate about terminal sedation is the extent to which it differs from euthanasia. We studied clinical differences and similarities between both practices in the Netherlands. METHODS: Personal interviews were held with a nationwide stratified sample of 410 physicians (response rate, 85%) about the most recent cases in which they used terminal sedation, defined as administering drugs to keep the patient continuously in deep sedation or coma until death without giving artificial nutrition or hydration (n = 211), or performed euthanasia, defined as administering a lethal drug at the request of a patient with the explicit intention to hasten death (n = 123). We compared characteristics of the patients, the decision-making process, and medical care of both practices. RESULTS: Terminal sedation and euthanasia both mostly concerned patients with cancer. Patients receiving terminal sedation were more often anxious (37%) and confused (24%) than patients receiving euthanasia (15% and 2%, respectively). Euthanasia requests were typically related to loss of dignity and a sense of suffering without improving, whereas requesting terminal sedation was more often related to severe pain. Physicians applying terminal sedation estimated that the patient's life had been shortened by more than 1 week in 27% of cases, compared with 73% in euthanasia cases. CONCLUSIONS: Terminal sedation and euthanasia both are often applied to address severe suffering in terminally ill patients. However, terminal sedation is typically used to address severe physical and psychological suffering in dying patients, whereas perceived loss of dignity during the last phase of life is a major problem for patients requesting euthanasia.

Rosner, Fred. Hospice care for the terminally ill: help or hindrance [editorial]. *Cancer Investigation* 2005; 23(3): 281-282. NRCBL: 20.4.1; 4.4; 1.2.

Ross, Heather M. Islamic tradition at the end of life. *MedSurg Nursing* 2001 April; 10(2): 83-87. NRCBL: 20.4.1; 1.2; 20.5.1.

Rousseau, Paul. The ethics of palliative sedation. *Caring* 2004 November; 23(11): 14-19. NRCBL: 20.4.1; 4.4; 20.5.1.

Ryan, Rosemary. Palliative care for "Margaret". *Journal of Clinical Ethics* 2006 Winter; 17(4): 344-348. NRCBL: 20.4.1; 9.5.3.

Sachs, Magna Andreen. Sedation — unconsciousness — anaesthesia! What are we talking about? *In:* Tännsjö, Torbjörn, ed. Terminal Sedation: Euthanasia in Disguise? Boston: Kluwer Academic Publishers; 2004: 31-35. NRCBL: 20.4.1; 9.7.

Sahm, S.; Will, R.; Hommel, G. What are cancer patients' preferences about treatment at the end of life, and who should start talking about it? A comparison with healthy people and medical staff. *Supportive Care in Cancer* 2005 April; 13(4): 206-214. NRCBL: 20.4.1; 20.5.1; 20.5.4; 9.5.1; 8.1.

Shugarman, Lisa R.; Lorenz, Karl; Lynn, Joanne. End-of-life care: an agenda for policy improvement. *Clinics in Geriatric Medicine* 2005 February; 21(1): 255-272. NRCBL: 20.4.1; 9.8.

Sokol, Daniel K. What is false hope? *Journal of Clinical Ethics* 2006 Winter; 17(4): 367-368. NRCBL: 20.4.1; 8.1; 8.2.

Stein, Gary L. Improving our care at life's end: making a difference. *Health and Social Work* 2004 February; 29(1): 77-79. NRCBL: 20.4.1; 1.3.10; 9.8.

Stienstra, Deborah; Chochinov, Harvey Max. Vulnerability, disability, and palliative end-of-life care. *Journal of Palliative Care* 2006 Autumn; 22(3): 166-174. NRCBL: 20.4.1; 9.5.1; 4.4; 20.5.1.

Switankowsky, Irene Sonia. Successful dying for cancer patients. *Humane Health Care International* 2006; 6(2): 3p. NRCBL: 20.4.1.

Tang, Siew Tzuh; Liu, Tsang-Wu; Lai, Mei-Shu; Liu, Li-Ni; Chen, Chen-Hsiu. Concordance of preferences for end-of-life care between terminally ill cancer patients and their family caregivers in Taiwan. *Journal of Pain and Symptom Management* 2005 December; 30(6): 510-518. NRCBL: 20.4.1; 8.1; 9.5.1. SC: em.

Tännsjö, Torbjörn. Terminal sedation: a substitute for euthanasia? *In:* Tännsjö, Torbjörn, ed. Terminal Sedation: Euthanasia in Disguise? Boston: Kluwer Academic Publishers; 2004: 15-30. NRCBL: 20.4.1; 9.7; 20.5.1. SC: an.

Thorns, Andrew; Garrard, Eve. Ethical issues in care of the dying. *In:* Ellershaw, John; Wilkinson, Susie, eds. Care of the Dying: A Pathway to Excellence. New York: Oxford University Press; 2003: 62-73. NRCBL: 20.4.1.

United States. Congress. House. A bill to amend the Controlled Substances Act to promote pain management and palliative care without permitting assisted suicide and euthanasia, and for other purposes. Washington, DC: U.S. G.P.O., 2000. 12 p. [Online]. Accessed: http://frwebgate.access.gpo.gov/cgi-bin/getdoc.cgi?dbname=106_cong_bills&docid=f:h5544ih.txt.pdf [2007 March 2]. NRCBL: 20.4.1; 9.7; 4.4. SC: le. Note: H.R. 5544, 106th Congress, 2nd session. Introduced by Rep. Hyde on October 25, 2000. Referred to the Committee on Commerce and the Committee on the Judiciary.

United States. Congress. Senate. A bill to promote pain management and palliative care without permitting assisted suicide and euthanasia, and for other purposes. Washington, DC: U.S. G.P.O., 2000. 12 p. [Online]. Accessed: http://frwebgate.access.gpo.gov/cgi-bin/getdoc.cgi?dbname=106_cong_bills&docid=f:s2607is.txt.pdf [2007 March 02]. NRCBL: 20.4.1; 9.7; 4.4. SC: le. Note: S. 2607, 106th Congress, 2nd session. Introduced by Sen. Wyden on May 23, 2000. Referred to Committee on Health, Education, Labor, and Pensions.

van Delden, Johannes J.M. Terminal sedation: different practice, different evaluations. *In:* Tännsjö, Torbjörn, ed. Terminal Sedation: Euthanasia in Disguise? Boston: Kluwer Academic Publishers; 2004: 103-113. NRCBL: 20.4.1; 9.7; 20.5.1. SC: em.

Vernooij-Dassen, Myrra J.F.J.; Osse, Bart H.P.; Schade, Egbert; Grol, Richard P.T.M. Patient autonomy problems in palliative care: systematic development and evaluation of a questionnaire. *Journal of Pain and Symptom Management* 2005 September; 30(3): 264-270. NRCBL: 20.4.1; 1.1; 8.1.

Volker, Deborah Lowe; Kahn, David; Penticuff, Joy H. Patient control and end-of-life care Part I: the advanced practice nurse perspective. *Oncology Nursing Forum* 2004 September 17; 31(5): 945-953. NRCBL: 20.4.1; 8.1; 4.1.3; 9.5.1. SC: em.

Volker, Deborah Lowe; Kahn, David; Penticuff, Joy H. Patient control and end-of-life care Part II: the patient perspective. *Oncology Nursing Forum* 2004 September 17; 31(5): 954-960. NRCBL: 20.4.1; 8.1; 9.5.1. SC: em.

Wojtasiewicz, Mary Ellen. Damage compounded: disparities, distrust, and disparate impact in end-of-life conflict resolution policies. *American Journal of Bioethics* 2006 September-October; 6(5): 8-12. NRCBL: 20.4.1; 9.5.4; 9.4.

Woods, Simon. Terminal sedation: a nursing perspective. *In:* Tännsjö, Torbjörn, ed. Terminal Sedation: Euthanasia in Disguise? Boston: Kluwer Academic Publishers; 2004: 43-56. NRCBL: 20.4.1; 9.7; 20.5.1. SC: le.

DEATH AND DYING/ TERMINAL CARE FOR MINORS

Burns, Jeffrey P. Is there any consensus about end-of-life care in pediatrics? *Archives of Pediatrics and Adolescent Medicine* 2005 September; 159(9): 889-891. NRCBL: 20.4.2; 20.5.2; 1.1; 8.3.2. Identifiers: double effect.

D'Almeida, Michelle; Hume, Roderick F., Jr.; Lathrop, Anthony; Njoku, Adaku; Calhoun, Byron C. Perinatal hospice: family-centered care of the fetus with a lethal condition. *Journal of American Physicians and Surgeons* 2006 Summer; 11(2): 52-55. NRCBL: 20.4.2; 20.5.2; 15.2; 17.1. SC: em.

Darnill, Stephanie; Gamage, Bernadette. The patient's journey: palliative care — a parent's view. *BMJ: British Medical Journal* 2006 June 24; 332(7556): 1494-1495. NRCBL: 20.4.2.

Hays, Ross M.; Valentine, Jeanette; Haynes, Gerri; Geyer, J. Russell; Villareale, Nanci; McKinstry, Beth; Varni, James W.; Churchill, Shervin S. The Seattle Pediatric Palliative Care Project: effects on family satisfaction and health-related quality of life. *Journal of Palliative Medicine* 2006 June; 9(3): 716-728. NRCBL: 20.4.2; 9.5.7; 8.1; 9.8.

Jacobs, Hollye Harrington. Ethics in pediatric end-of-life care: a nursing perspective. *Journal of Pediatric Nursing* 2005 October; 20(5): 360-369. NRCBL: 20.4.2; 4.1.3; 2.1.

NRCBL: National Reference Center for Bioethics Literature Classification Scheme   See inside front cover for terms.

151

Keough, William J. Towards the development of ethical practices in paediatric clinical trials: the special position of the terminally ill child. *Journal of Law and Medicine* 2006 February; 13(3): 370-386. NRCBL: 20.4.2; 18.2; 18.5.2. SC: le.

Powers, Denise V. Perinatal hospice. *Conscience* 2006 Autumn; 27(3): 31-33. NRCBL: 20.4.2; 15.2; 12.4.2.

Rascher, Wolfgang. Ethische Fragen bei der Behandlung von Früh- und Neugeborenen. *In:* Vollmann, Jochen, ed. Medizin und Ethik: Aktuelle ethische Probleme in Therapie und Forschung. Erlangen: Universitätsbund Erlangen-Nürnberg, 2003: 15-30. NRCBL: 20.4.2; 20.5.2.

DELIVERY OF HEALTH CARE *See* CARE FOR SPECIFIC GROUPS

DETERMINATION OF DEATH *See* DEATH AND DYING/ DETERMINATION OF DEATH

DISCLOSURE *See* CONFIDENTIALITY; IN-FORMED CONSENT; HUMAN EXPERIMENTATION/ INFORMED CONSENT; TRUTH DISCLOSURE

DISTRIBUTIVE JUSTICE *See* RESOURCE ALLOCATION

DIVERSITY *See* CULTURAL PLURALISM

DNA FINGERPRINTING *See* GENETICS/ LEGAL ASPECTS

DONATION *See* BLOOD DONATION AND TRANSFUSION; ORGAN AND TISSUE TRANSPLANTATION/ DONATION AND PROCUREMENT

DRUG INDUSTRY

A special relationship [editorial]. *New Scientist* 2006 October 28-November 3; 192(2575): 5. NRCBL: 9.7; 7.1; 9.1; 9.3.1. Identifiers: pharmaceutical industry; patient groups.

Fill this prescription. *Scientific American* 2005 October; 293(4): 6. NRCBL: 9.7; 9.2; 12.4.3; 12.3; 8.1.

Funding of patients' groups [editorial]. *Lancet* 2006 July 1-7; 368(9529): 2. NRCBL: 9.7; 1.3.2; 9.3.1.

Playing down the risks of a drug [editorial]. *New York Times* 2006 December 19; p. 32. NRCBL: 9.7; 7.1; 8.3.1. SC: po.

Seducing the medical profession [editorial]. *New York Times* 2006 February 2; p. A22. NRCBL: 9.7; 1.3.2; 9.3.1. SC: po.

Abelson, Reed. Charities tied to doctors get drug industry gifts. *New York Times* 2006 June 28; p. A1, C4. NRCBL: 9.7; 1.3.2; 9.3.1.

Abelson, Reed. New nerve test, a moneymaker, divides doctors. *New York Times* 2006 October 20; p. A1, C6. NRCBL: 9.7; 9.3.1. SC: po. Identifiers: Neurometrix.

Aiello, Allison E.; King, Nicholas B.; Foxman, B. Ethical conflicts in public health research and practice: antimicrobial resistance and the ethics of drug development. *American Journal of Public Health* 2006 November; 96(11): 1910-1914. NRCBL: 9.7; 9.3.1; 1.3.2; 9.1.
Abstract: Since the 1960s, scientists and pharmaceutical representatives have called for the advancement and development of new antimicrobial drugs to combat infectious diseases. In January 2005, Senate Majority Leader Bill Frist (R-TN), MD, introduced a biopreparedness bill that included provisions for patent extensions and tax incentives to stimulate industry research on new antimicrobials. Although government stimulus for private development of new antimicrobials is important, it does not resolve long-standing conflicts of interest between private entities and society. Rising rates of antimicrobial resistance have only exacerbated these conflicts. We used methicillin-resistant Staphylococcus aureus as a case study for reviewing these problems, and we have suggested alternative approaches that may halt the vicious cycle of resistance and obsolescence generated by the current model of antimicrobial production.

Aldhous, Peter. Do drug firm links sway psychiatry? *New Scientist* 2006 April 29-May 5; 190(2549): 14. NRCBL: 9.7; 7.3; 17.4.

American Pharmacists Association [APhA]; MacLean, Linda Garrelts. Freedom of Conscience for Small Pharmacies. Submitted to the House Small Business Committee. Testimony of the American Pharmacists Association. Washington, DC: The Association [APhA] 2005 July 25; 10 p. [Online]. Accessed: http://www.aphanet.org/AM/Template.cfm?Section=Home&CONTENTID=3565&Template=/cm/CONTENTDisplay.cfm [2006 September 18]. NRCBL: 9.7; 11.1; 8.1. Note: Testimony by Linda Garrelts McLean RPh, CDE.

Andersen, Morten; Kragstrup, Jakob; Søndergaard, Jens. How conducting a clinical trial affects physicians' guideline adherence and drug preferences. *JAMA: The Journal of the American Medical Association* 2006 June 21; 295(23): 2759-2764. NRCBL: 9.7; 1.3.9; 7.3. SC: em.

Applbaum, Kalman. Educating for global mental health: the adoption of SSRIs in Japan. *In:* Petryna, Adriana; Lakoff, Andrew; Kleinman, Arthur, eds. Global Pharmaceuticals: Ethics, Markets, Practices. Durham: Duke University Press; 2006: 85-110. NRCBL: 9.7; 1.3.2; 9.3.1; 17.4.

Arnold, Robert M.; Han, Paul K.J.; Seltzer, Deborah. Opioid contracts in chronic nonmalignant pain management: objectives and uncertainties. *American Journal of Medicine* 2006 April; 119(4): 292-296. NRCBL: 9.7; 4.4; 8.1.

Berenson, Alex. Drug files show maker promoted unapproved use; Lilly's marketing effort; company denies aiming schizophrenia pills at dementia patients. *New York*

Times 2006 December 18; p. A1, A26. NRCBL: 9.7; 7.1. SC: po; le. Identifiers: Off-label prescription.

Bergquist, Amy. Pharmacist refusals: dispensing (with) religious accommodation under Title VII. *Minnesota Law Review* 2006 April; 90(4): 1073-1105. NRCBL: 9.7; 11.2; 1.2; 8.1. SC: le.

Blech, Jörg. The illness industry. *New Scientist* 2006 July 22-28; 191(2561): 24. NRCBL: 9.7; 4.2; 4.3; 17.4. Identifiers: pharmaceutical industry.

Blumsohn, Aubrey; Mansfield, Peter R.; Pimazoni, Augusto. Doctors as lapdogs to drug firms [letters]. *BMJ: British Medical Journal* 2006 November 25; 333(7578): 1121-1122. NRCBL: 9.7; 1.3.2; 9.3.1.

Borrego, Matthew E.; Short, Jennifer; House, Naomi; Gupchup, Gireesh; Naik, Rupali; Cuellar, Denise. New Mexico pharmacists' knowledge, attitudes, and beliefs toward prescribing oral emergency contraception. *Journal of the American Pharmacists Association* 2006 January-February; 46(1): 33-43. NRCBL: 9.7; 7.1; 11.1. SC: em.

Breen, Kerry J. The medical profession and the pharmaceutical industry: when will we open our eyes? *Medical Journal of Australia* 2004 April 19; 180(8): 409-410. NRCBL: 9.7; 7.3; 1.3.2; 9.3.1. SC: em.

Breggin, Peter R. Court filing makes public my previously suppressed analysis of Paxil's effects. *Ethical Human Psychology and Psychiatry* 2006 Spring; 8(1): 77-84. NRCBL: 9.7; 17.4. SC: le.

Breggin, Peter R. How GlaxoSmithKline suppressed data on Paxil-Induced Akathisia: implications for suicidality and violence. *Ethical Human Psychology and Psychiatry* 2006 Summer; 8(2): 91-100. NRCBL: 9.7; 17.4; 20.7. SC: le.

Brehany, John F. Ethics in vaccine development and production: transforming health care. *Health Care Ethics USA* 2006; 14(3): E2. NRCBL: 9.7; 1.2; 12.1; 18.5.4; 15.1.

Brey, Philip. Prosthetics. *In:* Mitcham, Carl, ed. Encyclopedia of Science, Technology, and Ethics. Farmington Hills, MI: Thomson/Gale, 2005: 1527-1532. NRCBL: 9.7; 2.1.

Brodkey, Amy C. The role of the pharmaceutical industry in teaching psychopharmacology: a growing problem. *Academic Psychiatry* 2005 May-June; 29(2): 222-229. NRCBL: 9.7; 17.4; 7.2; 1.3.2; 1.3.3.

Brody, Howard. The company we keep: why physicians should refuse to see pharmaceutical representatives. *Annals of Family Medicine* 2005 January-February; 3(1): 82-85. NRCBL: 9.7; 1.3.2; 9.3.1. SC: an.

Brotzman, Gregory L.; Mark, David H. Policies regulating the activities of pharmaceutical representatives in

residency programs. *Journal of Family Practice* 1992 January; 34(1): 54-57. NRCBL: 9.7; 1.3.2; 7.2; 7.3. SC: em.

Busfield, Joan. Pills, power, people: sociological understandings of the pharmaceutical industry. *Sociology* 2006 April; 40(2): 297-314. NRCBL: 9.7; 18.2; 21.1; 5.3.

Campbell, Nancy D. Drugs. *In:* Mitcham, Carl, ed. Encyclopedia of Science, Technology, and Ethics. Farmington Hills, MI: Thomson/Gale, 2005: 546-549. NRCBL: 9.7; 15.1; 21.1.

Carey, Benedict. Study cites links to firms by psychiatrists. *New York Times* 2006 April 20; p. A23. NRCBL: 9.7; 17.1; 1.3.2. SC: em.

Carreyrou, John. Cephalon used improper tactics to sell drug, probe finds. *Wall Street Journal* 2006 November 21; p. B1, B2. NRCBL: 9.7; 1.3.2; 9.5.1. SC: po.

Carreyrou, John. Seizures of Canadian drugs rise as Congress, Customs spar. *Wall Street Journal* 2006 July 24; p. B1, B8. NRCBL: 9.7; 12.7. SC: po.

Cassels, Alan. Canada may be forced to allow direct to consumer advertising [news]. *BMJ: British Medical Journal* 2006 June 24; 332(7556): 1469. NRCBL: 9.7; 1.3.2.

Chang, Pepe Lee. Who's in the business of saving lives? *Journal of Medicine and Philosophy* 2006 October; 31(5): 465-482. NRCBL: 9.7; 21.1. SC: an.
Abstract: There are individuals, including children, dying needlessly in poverty-stricken third world countries. Many of these deaths could be prevented if pharmaceutical companies provided the drugs needed to save their lives. Some believe that because pharmaceutical companies have the power to save lives, and because they can do so with little effort, they have a special obligation. I argue that there is no distinction, with respect to obligations and responsibilities, between pharmaceutical companies and other types of companies. As a result, to hold pharmaceutical companies especially responsible for saving lives in third world countries is unjustified.

Check, Erika. Universities urged to do more for poor nations [news]. *Nature* 2006 November 23; 444(7118): 412-413. NRCBL: 9.7; 1.3.3; 21.1.

Cline, Rebecca J. Welch; Young, Henry N. Direct-to-consumer print ads for drugs: do they undermine the physician-patient relationship? *Journal of Family Practice* 2005 December; 54(12): 1049-1057. NRCBL: 9.7; 1.3.7; 9.8; 8.1.

Coleman, David L.; Kazdin, Alan E.; Miller, Lee Ann; Morrow, Jon S.; Udelsman, Robert. Guidelines for interactions between clinical faculty and the pharmaceutical industry: one medical school's approach. *Academic Medicine* 2006 February; 81(2): 154-160. NRCBL: 9.7; 1.3.2; 9.3.1; 7.2.

Collier, Joe. Big pharma and the U.K. government. *Lancet* 2006 January 14-20; 367(9505): 97-98. NRCBL: 9.7; 5.3.

NRCBL: National Reference Center for Bioethics Literature Classification Scheme   See inside front cover for terms.

153

Crowinshield, Roy. The orthopaedic profession and industry: conflict or convergence of interests. *Clinical Orthopaedics and Related Research* 2003 July; (412): 8-13. NRCBL: 9.7; 1.3.2; 2.2; 7.2; 7.3.

Dailard, Cynthia. Beyond the issue of pharmacist refusals: pharmacies that won't sell emergency contraception. *Guttmacher Report on Public Policy* 2005 August; 8(3): 10-12. NRCBL: 9.7; 11.1; 8.1. SC: le.

Day, Michael. Industry association suspends drug company for entertaining doctors. *BMJ: British Medical Journal* 2006 February 18; 332(7538): 381. NRCBL: 9.7; 7.3.

Diamond, Eugene F. The licit use of methotrexate: managing extrauterine gestation. *Ethics and Medics* 2006 March; 31(3): 3. NRCBL: 9.7; 1.2; 9.5.5; 12.3. Identifiers: ectopic pregnancy; Catholics.

Dockhorn, Robert J. Orphan drugs provide needed treatment options. *Maryland Medicine* 2005 Winter; 6(1): 26-29. NRCBL: 9.7; 9.3.1; 1.3.2.

Donohue, Julie. A history of drug advertising: the evolving roles of consumers and consumer protection. *Milbank Quarterly* 2006; 84(4): 659-699. NRCBL: 9.7; 9.3.1.

Dresser, Rebecca. Pharmaceutical company gifts: from voluntary standards to legal demands. *Hastings Center Report* 2006 May-June; 36(3): 8-9. NRCBL: 9.7; 1.3.2; 9.3.1. SC: le.

Dyer, Owen. GSK breached marketing code [news]. *BMJ: British Medical Journal* 2006 August 19; 333(7564): 368. NRCBL: 9.7; 1.3.2. Identifiers: GlaxoSmithKline.

Dyer, Owen. Industry group suspends drug company for breaching code [news]. *BMJ: British Medical Journal* 2006 October 7; 333(7571): 717. NRCBL: 9.7; 1.3.2. Identifiers: United Kingdom (Great Britain).

Eichaker, Peter Q.; Natanson, Charles; Danner, Robert L. Surviving sepsis — practice guidelines, marketing campaigns, and Eli Lilly. *New England Journal of Medicine* 2006 October 19; 355(16): 1640-1642. NRCBL: 9.7; 9.5.1; 9.3.1; 1.3.2; 5.2; 18.2; 8.3.1; 9.8; 1.3.9.

Elliott, Carl. The drug pushers. *Atlantic Monthly* 2006 April; 297(3): 82-84, 86, 88-93. NRCBL: 9.7; 1.3.2; 9.3.1. Identifiers: pharmaceutical sales representatives.

Epps, Charles H., Jr. Ethical guidelines for orthopaedists and industry. *Clinical Orthopaedics and Related Research* 2003 July; (412): 14-20. NRCBL: 9.7; 1.3.2; 5.3; 7.2; 7.3; 9.3.1.

Epstein, Charles J. Genetic testing: hope or hype? *Genetics in Medicine* 2004 July-August; 6(4): 165-172. NRCBL: 9.7; 15.1.

Fielder, John H. The Vioxx debacle. *IEEE Engineering in Medicine and Biology Magazine* 2005 March-April; 24(2): 106-109. NRCBL: 9.7.

Figueiras, Adolfo; Tato, Fernando; Fontaiñas, Jesus; Takkouche, Bahi; Gestal-Otero, Juan Jesus. Physicians' attitudes towards voluntary reporting of adverse drug events. *Journal of Evaluation in Clinical Practice* 2001 November; 7(4): 347-354. NRCBL: 9.7; 8.2; 7.1. SC: em. Identifiers: Spain.

Fijn, Roel; van Epenhuysen, L. Sara; Peijnenburg, A. Jeanne M.; de Jong-van den Berg, Lolkje T.W.; Brouwers, Jacobus R.B.J. Introducing ethics in hospital drug resource allocation decisions: keep expectations modest and beware of unintended effects. Part I: an explorative overview. *Pharmacoepidemiology and Drug Safety* 2002 September; 11(6): 523-527. NRCBL: 9.7; 9.4; 9.2.

Fijn, Roel; van Epenhuysen, L. Sara; Peijnenburg, A. Jeanne M.; de Jong-van den Berg, Lolkje T.W.; Brouwers, Jacobus R.B.J. Introducing ethics in hospital drug resource allocation decisions: keep expectations modest and beware of unintended effects. Part II: the use of ethics. *Pharmacoepidemiology and Drug Safety* 2002 October-November; 11(7): 617-620. NRCBL: 9.7; 9.4; 9.2.

Flanagan-Klygis, Erin A.; Sharp, Lisa; Frader, Joel E. Dismissing the family who refuses vaccines: a study of pediatrician attitudes. *Archives of Pediatrics and Adolescent Medicine* 2005 October; 159(10): 929-934. NRCBL: 9.7; 9.5.7; 8.3.2; 8.3.4; 8.1. SC: em.

Fries, James F.; Krishnan, Eswar. Equipoise, design bias, and randomized controlled trials: the elusive ethics of new drug development. *Arthritis Research and Therapy* 2004; 6(3): R250-R255. NRCBL: 9.7; 18.2; 18.5.1.

Gebhardt, D.O.E.; van Burenlaan, Anna. The generic-patent medicine conflict flares up again in the Netherlands [letter]. *Journal of Medical Ethics* 2006 September; 32(9): 555. NRCBL: 9.7.

Gilbody, S.; Wilson, P.; Watt, I. Benefits and harms of direct to consumer advertising: a systematic review. *Quality and Safety in Health Care* 2005 August; 14: 246-250. NRCBL: 9.7; 1.3.2. SC: em; rv.

Gill, D.G. "Anything you can do, I can do bigger?": the ethics and equity of growth hormone for small normal children. *Archives of Disease in Childhood* 2006 March; 91(3): 270-272. NRCBL: 9.7; 9.5.7. SC: an.

Goetz, Thomas. The thin pill. *Wired* 2006 October: 150-157. NRCBL: 9.7; 1.3.2; 4.2; 5.1. Identifiers: metabolic syndrome; pharmaceutical industry; marketing.

Goodman, Robert L.; Carrasquillo, Olveen. The corporate co-author, the ghost writer, and the medical society: an object lesson (June, 2005 issue) [letter]. *JGIM: Journal of General Internal Medicine* 2006 January; 21(1): 102. NRCBL: 9.7; 1.3.7; 7.3.

Grabowski, Henry. Patents, innovation and access to new pharmaceuticals. *Journal of International Economic Law* 2002 December; 5(4): 849-860. NRCBL: 9.7; 5.3; 21.1; 9.5.6. SC: le.

Guðmundsson, Sigurður. Doctors and drug companies: the beauty and the beast? [editorial]. *Acta Ophthalmologica Scandinavica* 2005 August; 83(4): 407-408. NRCBL: 9.7; 1.3.2; 9.3.1.

Halpern, Georges M. COX-2 inhibitors: a story of greed, deception and death. *Inflammopharmacology* 2005; 13(4): 419-425. NRCBL: 9.7.

Harris, Gardiner. In article, doctors back ban on drug companies' gifts; concerns cited on quality of patient care. *New York Times* 2006 January 25; p. A14. NRCBL: 9.7; 1.3.2; 9.3.1. SC: po.

Harris, Gardiner; Pear, Robert. Drug maker's efforts to compete in lucrative insulin market are under scrutiny. *New York Times* 2006 January 28; p. A14. NRCBL: 9.7. SC: po.

Harvey, Ken J.; Vitry, Agnes I.; Roughead, Elizabeth; Aroni, Rosalie; Ballenden, Nicola; Faggotter, Ralph. Pharmaceutical advertisements in prescribing software: an analysis. *Medical Journal of Australia* 2005 July 18; 183(2): 75-79. NRCBL: 9.7; 1.3.2; 1.3.12. SC: em.

Hasman, Andreas; Holm, Søren. Direct-to-consumer advertising: should there be a free market in healthcare information? *CQ: Cambridge Quarterly of Healthcare Ethics* 2006 Winter; 15(1): 42-49. NRCBL: 9.7; 1.3.2; 5.3; 21.1; 1.3.7.

Healy, David. Did regulators fail over selective serotonin reuptake inhibitors? *BMJ: British Medical Journal* 2006 July 8; 333(7558): 92-95. NRCBL: 9.7; 18.1; 18.6; 5.3. Identifiers: United States; United Kingdom (Great Britain).

Healy, David. The new medical oikumene. *In:* Petryna, Adriana; Lakoff, Andrew; Kleinman, Arthur, eds. Global Pharmaceuticals: Ethics, Markets, Practices. Durham: Duke University Press; 2006: 61-84. NRCBL: 9.7; 1.3.2; 9.3.1; 17.4.

Hendricks, J.W. Does immunization refusal warrant discontinuing a physician-patient relationship? *Archives of Pediatrics and Adolescent Medicine* 2005 October; 159(10): 994. NRCBL: 9.7; 8.3.2; 8.3.4; 8.1.

Herrling, Paul. Experiments in social responsibility. *Nature* 2006 January 19; 439(7074): 267-268. NRCBL: 9.7.

Hill, Kevin P. Free Lunch? [editorial]. *American Journal of Psychiatry* 2006 April; 163(4): 569-570. NRCBL: 9.7; 1.3.2; 9.3.1. Identifiers: pharmaceutical industry; gifts to physicians.

Jack, Andrew. Too close for comfort? [news]. *BMJ: British Medical Journal* 2006 July 1; 333(7557): 13. NRCBL: 9.7; 9.1; 1.3.2. Identifiers: Pharmaceutical industry; patient groups.

Jørgensen, Anders W.; Hilden, Jørgen; Gøtzsche, Peter C. Cochrane reviews compared with industry supported meta-analyses and other meta-analyses of the same drugs: systematic review. *BMJ: British Medical Journal* 2006 October 14; 333(7572): 782-785. NRCBL: 9.7; 1.3.9. SC: em.

Jutel, Annemarie. Conflicted encounters: theoretical considerations in the understanding of disease-mongering. *Monash Bioethics Review* 2006 July; 25(3): 7-23. NRCBL: 9.7; 4.2; 1.3.2. SC: an.

Kälvemark Sporrong, Sofia; Höglund, Anna T.; Hansson, Mats G.; Westerholm, Peter; Arnetz, Bengt. "We are white coats whirling round"—moral distress in Swedish pharmacies. *Pharmacy World and Science* 2005 June; 27(3): 223-229. NRCBL: 9.7; 4.1.1; 1.3.1; 7.1. SC: em.

Kapp, Marshall B. Drug companies, dollars, and the shaping of American medical practice. *Southern Illinois University Law Journal* 2005 Winter; 29(2): 237-262. NRCBL: 9.7; 1.3.2; 9.3.1. SC: le.

Kmietowicz, Zosia. Advertisements highlight MSD's inappropriate hospitality [news]. *BMJ: British Medical Journal* 2006 September 30; 333(7570): 671. NRCBL: 9.7; 1.3.2; 9.3.1. Identifiers: United Kingdom (Great Britain); MerckSharp and Dohme.

Knestout, Brian P. An essential prescription: why pharmacist-inclusive conscience clauses are necessary. *Journal of Contemporary Health Law and Policy* 2006 Spring; 22(2): 349-382. NRCBL: 9.7; 8.3.4; 7.3. SC: le.

Kondro, Wayne. Conflicts cause FDA to review advisory committees. *CMAJ/JAMC: Canadian Medical Association Journal* 2006 July 4; 175(1): 23-24. NRCBL: 9.7; 1.3.9.

Lakoff, Andrew. High contact: gifts and surveillance in Argentina. *In:* Petryna, Adriana; Lakoff, Andrew; Kleinman, Arthur, eds. Global Pharmaceuticals: Ethics, Markets, Practices. Durham: Duke University Press; 2006: 111-135. NRCBL: 9.7; 1.3.2; 9.3.1; 17.4.

Lakoff, Andrew. The private life of numbers: pharmaceutical marketing in post-welfare Argentina. *In:* Ong, Aihwa; Collier, Stephen J., eds. Global Assemblages: Technology, Politics, and Ethics as Anthropological Problems. Malden, MA: Blackwell Pub.; 2005: 194-213. NRCBL: 9.7; 1.3.2.

Lansing, Paul; Fricke, Michael. Pharmaceutical advertising to consumers: corporate profits vs. public safety. *Business and Professional Ethics Journal* 2005 Fall; 24(3): 23-26. NRCBL: 9.7; 1.3.7; 5.3; 1.3.2. SC: an.

NRCBL: National Reference Center for Bioethics Literature Classification Scheme   See inside front cover for terms.

155

Leiva, Rene. A brief history of human diploid cell strains. *National Catholic Bioethics Quarterly* 2006 Autumn; 6(3): 443-451. NRCBL: 9.7; 9.5.1; 18.5.4; 12.3.

Levinson, Wendy; Laupacis, Andreas. A call for fairness in formulary decisions [editorial]. *Archives of Internal Medicine* 2006 January 9; 166(1): 16-18. NRCBL: 9.7; 9.3.1.

Lurie, Peter; Almeida, Cristina M.; Stine, Nicholas; Stine, Alexander R.; Wolfe, Sidney M. Financial conflict of interest disclosure and voting patterns at Food and Drug Administration drug advisory committee meetings. *JAMA: The Journal of the American Medical Association* 2006 April 26; 295(16): 1921-1928. NRCBL: 9.7; 1.3.5; 5.3; 7.3. SC: le.

Abstract: CONTEXT: In January 2002, the US Food and Drug Administration (FDA) issued a draft guidance requiring more detailed financial conflict of interest disclosure at advisory committee meetings. OBJECTIVES: To characterize financial conflict disclosures at drug-related meetings, and to assess the relationship between conflicts and voting behavior at meetings that considered specific products. DESIGN AND SETTING: Cross-sectional study using agendas and transcripts from all FDA Drug Advisory Committee meetings (2001-2004) listed on the FDA Web site. MAIN OUTCOME MEASURES: Conflict rates, type, and size. The relationship between having a conflict and voting in favor of the index drug was described for each voter using Mantel-Haenszel relative risks and Monte Carlo simulations; Spearman rho was used for a meeting-level analysis comparing rates of conflict with voting patterns. The impact of the removal of persons with conflicts of interest on the vote margins was also evaluated. RESULTS: A total of 221 meetings held by 16 advisory committees were included in the study. In 73% of the meetings, at least 1 advisory committee member or voting consultant disclosed a conflict; only 1% of advisory committee members were recused. For advisory committee members (n = 1957) and voting consultants combined (n = 990), 28% (n = 825)disclosed a conflict. The most commonly specified conflicts were consulting arrangements, contracts/grants, and investments. Nineteen percent of consulting arrangements involved over 10,000 dollars, 23% of contracts/grants exceeded 100,000 dollars, and 30% of investments were over 25,000 dollars. The meeting-level analysis did not show a statistically significant relationship between conflict rates ("index conflict," "competitor conflict," or "any conflict") and voting patterns, but a weak, statistically significant positive relationship was apparent for competitor conflict and any conflict in the Mantel-Haenszel analyses. The Monte Carlo analyses produced similar findings in the competitor conflict analysis only. In all 3 conflict categories, the exclusion of advisory committee members and voting consultants with conflicts would have produced margins less favorable to the index drug in the majority of meetings, but this would not have changed whether the majority favored or opposed the drug. CONCLUSIONS: Disclosures of conflicts of interest at drug advisory committee meetings are common, often of considerable monetary value, and rarely result in recusal of advisory committee members. A weak relationship between certain types of conflicts and voting behaviors was detected, but excluding advisory committee members and voting consultants with conflicts would not have altered the overall vote outcome at any meeting studied.

Magotra, Ratna. The controversy of drug-eluting cardiac stents. *Indian Journal of Medical Ethics* 2006 January-March; 3(1): 25-26. NRCBL: 9.7; 9.8; 21.1.

Mahowald, Mark W.; Cramer Bornemann, Michel A. What? Influenced by industry? Not me! [editorial]. *Sleep Medicine* 2005 September; 6(5): 389-390. NRCBL: 9.7; 1.3.2; 9.3.1; 1.3.9; 1.3.7.

Marshall, Jessica; Aldhous, Peter. Swallowing the best advice? *New Scientist* 2006 October 28-November 3; 192(2575): 18-22. NRCBL: 9.7; 7.1; 9.1; 9.3.1. Identifiers: pharmaceutical industry; donations to patient groups.

Mathews, Anna Wilde. Fraud, errors taint key study of widely used Sanofi drug; despite some faked results, FDA approves antibiotic; one doctor's cocaine use; company defends safety. *Wall Street Journal* 2006 May 1; p. A1, A12. NRCBL: 9.7; 1.3.9. SC: po.

Mathews, Anna Wilde; Westphal, Sylvia Pagan. Tricky FDA debate: should a risky drug be approved again? *Wall Street Journal* 2006 February 24; p. B1, B4. NRCBL: 9.7. SC: po.

McKinney, Rose; Korn, David. Should an institution that has commercial rights in a new drug or device be allowed to evaluate the technology? *PLoS Medicine* 2005 January; 2(1): 0005-0008. NRCBL: 9.7; 1.3.3; 1.3.2; 9.3.1.

Meichtry, Stacy. Religious order runs drug lab for cures, ethics. *Wall Street Journal* 2006 October 7; p. B1, B8. NRCBL: 9.7; 1.2. SC: po. Identifiers: Nerviano Medical Science [NMS]; Congregation of the Children of the Immaculate Conception.

Meier, Barry. Guidant consultant advised company to release data on defects. *New York Times* 2006 March 9; p. C3. NRCBL: 9.7; 8.4. SC: po; le.

Miller, Jed. The unconscionability of conscience clauses: pharmacists' consciences and women's access to contraception. *Health Matrix: The Journal of Law-Medicine* 2006 Winter; 16(1): 237-278. NRCBL: 9.7; 11.2; 12.4.3; 9.5.5. SC: le.

Minhas, Rubin. New ethical framework for pharmaceutical physicians [letter]. *BMJ: British Medical Journal* 2006 April 29; 332(7548): 1034. NRCBL: 9.7; 1.3.7.

Mintzberg, Henry. Patent nonsense: evidence tells of an industry out of social control. *CMAJ/JAMC: Canadian Medical Association Journal* 2006 August 15; 175(4): 374-376. NRCBL: 9.7; 13.2; 5.3.

Moynihan, Ray. Roche defends buying lavish meals for doctors at Sydney's restaurants [news]. *BMJ: British Medical Journal* 2006 July 22; 333(7560): 169. NRCBL: 9.7; 9.3.1; 1.3.2.

Muir, Hazel. Dicing with death. *New Scientist* 2006 July 29-August 4; 191(2562): 38-41. NRCBL: 9.7. Identifiers: off-label prescription drugs.

National Reference Center for Bioethics Literature [NRCBL]. Pharmacists and conscientious objection. *Ken-*

nedy Institute of Ethics Journal 2006 December; 16(4): 379-396. NRCBL: 9.7; 1.1; 11.1; 1.2; 4.1.1; 1.3.1.

Naughton, Michelle J.; Jones, Alison Snow; Shumaker, Sally A. When practices, promises, profits, and policies outpace hard evidence: the post-menopausal hormone debate. *Journal of Social Issues* 2005 March; 61(1): 159-179. NRCBL: 9.7; 9.5.5; 5.2.

Newland, Shelby E. The role of bioethics in the international prescription drug market: economics and global justice. *Penn Bioethics Journal* 2006; 2(2): 8-12. NRCBL: 9.7; 21.1; 9.3.1; 5.3.

Abstract: In terms of health care access, bioethics has an important role to inform and shape policy issues and develop interdisciplinary ideas and interventions. The rising price of prescription drugs presents one of the most looming barriers to health care access in the world today. Including both theoretical and practical features of the pharmaceutical industry's behavior is necessary to find ethical solutions towards increasing access. Bioethics can evaluate global justice by weighing human rights theory and future innovation at the macro level, and by addressing market forces and responsibilities at the micro level. Inherent structural features of pharmaceuticals, such as its reliance on research and development, cause the industry to employ pricing strategies that seem counter-intuitive to conventional wisdom, but that result in producing a just allocation as defined by market forces. Parallel trade and drug exportation/reimportation threaten the saliency of the industry's differential pricing scheme; a case-study of a single "Euro-price" within the European Union illustrates how this will actually create harm to the most needy member states. This complex situation requires solutions weighing arguments from human rights theory with those from economic theory to arrive at the most globally just allocation of prescription drugs in the global marketplace, as well as to ensure future innovation and scientific progress. Bioethicists as well as economists need to partake urgently in this discourse for the betterment of the global injustices in the international prescription drug market.

Nissen, Steven. An audience with . . . Steven Nissen [interview]. *Nature Reviews Drug Discovery* 2006 February; 5(2): 98. NRCBL: 9.7; 5.2; 18.2; 18.5.1; 21.1.

Nutt, David J. Informed consent — a new approach to drug regulation? [editorial]. *Journal of Psychopharmacology* 2006 January; 20(1): 3-4. NRCBL: 9.7; 8.3.1.

Okie, Susan. Access before approval — a right to take experimental drugs? *New England Journal of Medicine* 2006 August 3; 355(5): 437-440. NRCBL: 9.7; 20.4.1; 18.2. SC: le.

Pollack, Andrew. Genentech caps cost of cancer drug for some patients. *New York Times* 2006 October 12; p C2. NRCBL: 9.7; 9.3.1; 9.5.10. SC: po.

Pollack, Andrew. Stanford to ban drug makers' gifts to doctors, even pens. *New York Times* 2006 September 12; p. C2. NRCBL: 9.7; 1.3.2; 9.3.1; 7.2. SC: po.

Pollack, Andrew. Take your pills, all your pills: drug makers nag patients to stay the course. *New York Times* 2006 March 11; p. C1, C13. NRCBL: 9.7; 8.1; 9.5.1.

Pollack, Andrew; Abelson, Reed. Why the data diverge on the dangers of Vioxx: even in medical journals, statistics can be subject to broad interpretation. *New York Times* 2006 May 22; p. C1, C5. NRCBL: 9.7; 1.3.9; 1.3.7. SC: em.

Price, Andrew. Antibiotics. *In:* Mitcham, Carl, ed. Encyclopedia of Science, Technology, and Ethics. Farmington Hills, MI: Thomson/Gale, 2005: 84-86. NRCBL: 9.7.

Prystay, Cris; Hiebert, Murray; Linebaugh, Kate. Companies face ethical issues over Tamiflu. *Wall Street Journal* 2006 January 16; p. B1, B3. NRCBL: 9.7. SC: po.

Psaty, Bruce M.; Rennie, Drummond. Clinical trial investigators and their prescribing patterns: another dimension to the relationship between physician investigators and the pharmaceutical industry [editorial]. *JAMA: The Journal of the American Medical Association* 2006 June 21; 295(23): 2787-2790. NRCBL: 9.7; 1.3.9; 7.3.

Ray, Wayne A.; Stein, C. Michael. Reform of drug regulation — beyond an independent drug-safety board. *New England Journal of Medicine* 2006 January 12; 354(2): 194-201. NRCBL: 9.7; 5.3.

Regis, Catherine. Direct-to-consumer advertising for prescription drugs in Canada: beyond good or evil. *Health Law Review* 2006; 14(2): 28-33. NRCBL: 9.7; 1.3.2; 7.2.

Resnik, David. Access to affordable medication in the developing world: social responsibility vs. profit. *In:* van Niekerk, Anton A.; Kopelman, Loretta M., eds. Ethics and AIDS in Africa: The Challenge to Our Thinking. Walnut Creek, CA: Left Coast Press; 2006: 111-126. NRCBL: 9.7; 1.3.2; 21.1.

Rosner, Fred. Gifts to physicians from drug companies. *In:* Rosner, Fred, ed. Medicine and Jewish Law. Volume III. Brooklyn, NY: Yashar Books, Inc.; 2005: 177-190. NRCBL: 9.7; 1.3.2; 9.3.1.

Royal College of Physicians of London. The relationship between physicians and the biomedical industries: advice of the Royal College of Physicians. London: Royal College of Physicians of London 2004 December 6; 4 p. [Online]. Accessed: http://www.rcplondon.ac.uk/college/statements/advice_biomedIndustry.htm [2006 August 18]. NRCBL: 9.7; 1.3.2; 9.3.1; 6; 7.3. Identifiers: United Kingdom (Great Britain). Note: Replaces the guidance published by the College in 2002 in its report: The Relationship between Physicians and the Biomedical Industries.

Ruff, Tilman A.; Haikal-Mukhtar, Hadia. Doctors, drugs, information and ethics: a never-ending story [editorial]. *Medical Journal of Australia* 2005 July 18; 183(2): 73-74. NRCBL: 9.7; 1.3.2; 6; 7.3; 8.1.

Rutledge, Philip; Crookes, David; McKinstry, Brian; Maxwell, Simon R.J. Do doctors rely on pharmaceutical

NRCBL: National Reference Center for Bioethics Literature Classification Scheme   See inside front cover for terms.

157

industry funding to attend conferences and do they perceive that this creates a bias in their drug selection? Results from a questionnaire survey. *Pharmacoepidemiology and Drug Safety* 2003 December; 12(8): 663-667. NRCBL: 9.7; 7.3; 1.3.2; 9.3.1.

Sarmiento, Augusto. The relationship between orthopaedics and industry must be reformed. *Clinical Orthopaedics and Related Research* 2003 July; (412): 38-44. NRCBL: 9.7; 1.3.2; 7.3; 9.3.1.

Saul, Stephanie. Doctors object as drug makers learn who's prescribing what. *New York Times* 2006 May 4; p. A1, C4. NRCBL: 9.7; 8.4; 7.1.

Saul, Stephanie. Drug makers pay for lunch as they pitch. *New York Times* 2006 July 28; p. A1, C7. NRCBL: 9.7; 1.3.2; 9.3.1. SC: po.

Saul, Stephanie. Unease on industry's role in hypertension debate. *New York Times* 2006 May 20; p. A1, C9. NRCBL: 9.7; 1.3.2; 9.3.1.

Sauri, Michael. Influence and drug marketing. *Maryland Medicine* 2005 Winter; 6(1): 24-25. NRCBL: 9.7; 1.3.2; 1.3.7; 9.3.1.

Sauri, Michael A. The politics of vaccine production. *Maryland Medicine* 2005 Winter; 6(1): 19-22. NRCBL: 9.7; 21.1; 5.2; 9.1. SC: le.

Scherer, F.M.; Watal, Jayashree. Post-TRIPS options for access to patented medicines in developing nations. *Journal of International Economic Law* 2002 December; 5(4): 913-939. NRCBL: 9.7; 21.1; 5.3; 9.3.1. SC: le. Identifiers: Trade-Related Aspects of Intellectual Property.

Shenk, David. Money + science = ethics problems on campus. *Nation* 1999 March 22; 268(11): 11-18. NRCBL: 9.7; 9.3.1; 5.2; 5.3.

Shuchman, Miriam. Delaying generic competition — corporate payoffs and the future of Plavix. *New England Journal of Medicine* 2006 September 28; 355(13): 1297-1300. NRCBL: 9.7; 9.3.1; 1.3.2. SC: le.

Sinha, Gunjan. Drug companies accused of stalling tailored therapies [news]. *Nature Medicine* 2006 September; 12(9): 983. NRCBL: 9.7; 15.1.

South Dakota State Medical Association. Committee on Ethics and Judicial Affairs; Holm, Richard P. Prescribing ethics, and self care. *South Dakota Medicine* 2006 February; 59(2): 69. NRCBL: 9.7; 8.1.

Spier, R.E. Vaccines and vaccination. *In:* Mitcham, Carl, ed. Encyclopedia of Science, Technology, and Ethics. Farmington Hills, MI: Thomson/Gale, 2005: 2015-2020. NRCBL: 9.7; 2.2; 9.1.

Spurgeon, David. FDA regulations make it harder to sue drug companies [news]. *BMJ: British Medical Journal* 2006 June 10; 332(7554): 1350. NRCBL: 9.7; 18.1; 9.3.1. SC: em. Identifiers: Food and Drug Administration.

Srinivasan, Sandhya. The draft national pharmaceuticals policy: concerns relating to data exclusivity and price control [editorial]. *Indian Journal of Medical Ethics* 2006 October-December; 3(4): 118-119. NRCBL: 9.7; 5.3.

Steinbrook, Robert. For sale: physicians' prescribing data. *New England Journal of Medicine* 2006 June 29; 354(26): 2745-2747. NRCBL: 9.7; 1.3.12; 9.3.1.

Stiles, Gary L. Wyeth Pharmaceutical's perspective on vaccine production. *Maryland Medicine* 2005 Winter; 6(1): 22-23. NRCBL: 9.7. SC: le.

Swartz, Martha S. "Conscience clauses" or "unconscionable clauses": personal beliefs versus professional responsibilities. *Yale Journal of Health Policy, Law and Ethics* 2006 Summer; 6(2): 269-350. NRCBL: 9.7; 8.3.4; 7.3. SC: le.

Tanne, Janice Hopkins. Former FDA commissioner pleads guilty to two charges [news]. *BMJ: British Medical Journal* 2006 October 28; 333(7574): 874. NRCBL: 9.7; 1.3.5; 1.3.9. SC: le. Identifiers: United States.

Tanne, Janice Hopkins. NEJM editor gives pretrial evidence in Vioxx case [news]. *BMJ: British Medical Journal* 2006 February 4; 332(7536): 255. NRCBL: 9.7; 1.3.7; 1.3.9. SC: le. Identifiers: New England Journal of Medicine.

Tengilimoglu, Dilaver; Kisa, Adnan; Ekiyor, Aykut. The pharmaceutical sales rep/physician relationship in Turkey: ethical issues in an international context. *Health Marketing Quarterly* 2004; 22(1): 21-39. NRCBL: 9.7; 7.3; 1.3.2; 9.3.1; 4.1.2; 1.3.1. SC: em.

Tesoriero, Heather Won. Vioxx doctors wooed by Merck are now its foes. *Wall Street Journal* 2006 March 10; p. B1, B3. NRCBL: 9.7; 9.3.1; 8.1. SC: po.

United States. Congress. House. A bill to prevent abusive practices by pharmaceutical benefit managers (PBMs). Washington, DC: U.S. G.P.O., 2006. 2 p. [Online]. Accessed: http://frwebgate.access.gpo.gov/cgi-bin/useftp. cgi?IPaddress=162.140.64.21&filename=h5979ih.pdf& directory=/diskb/wais/data/109_cong_bills [2006 November 27]. NRCBL: 9.7; 9.3.1. SC: le. Identifiers: Pharmaceutical Benefit Manager Abuse Prevention Act of 2006. Note: H.R. 5979, 109th Congress, 2nd session. Introduced by Rep. Boozman, July 28, 2006. Referred to the Committee on the Energy and Commerce.

United States. Congress. House. A bill to suspend further implementation of the Department of Defense anthrax vaccination program until the vaccine is determined to be safe and effective and to provide for a study by the National Institutes of Health of that vaccine. Washington, DC: U.S. G.P.O., 1999. 8 p. [Online]. Accessed: http://frwebgate.

access.gpo.gov/cgi-bin/getdoc.cgi?dbname=106_cong_bills&docid= f:h2548ih.txt.pdf [2007 March 2]. NRCBL: 9.7; 18.5.8. SC: le. Note: H.R. 2548, 106th Congress, 1st session. Introduced by Rep. Gilman on July 19, 1999. Referred to the Committee on Armed Services and the Committee on Commerce.

United States. Congress. House. A bill to amend the Federal Food, Drug, and Cosmetic Act to prohibit the approval of any drug that infringes the right to life, and for other purposes. Washington, DC: U.S. G.P.O., 2005. 2 p.[Online]. Accessed: http://frwebgate.access.gpo.gov/cgi-bin/getdoc.cgi?dbname=109_cong_bills&docid=f:h3553ih.txt.pdf [2006 June 7]. NRCBL: 9.7; 4.4; 12.1; 20.7; 20.5.1. SC: le. Note: H.R. 3553, 109th Congress, 1st session. Introduced by Rep. Gingrey, July 28, 2005. Referred to the Committee on Energy and Commerce.

United States. Congress. House. A bill to amend the Federal Food, Drug, and Cosmetic Act with respect to drug advertising, and for other purposes. Washington, DC: U.S. G.P.O., 2005. 9. [Online]. Accessed: http://frwebgate. access.gpo.gov/cgi-bin/useftp.cgi?IPaddress=162.140.64 .21&filename=h3950ih.pdf&directory=/diskb/wais/data/109_cong_bills [2006 June 7]. NRCBL: 9.7; 1.3.2. SC: le. Identifiers: Responsibility in Drug Advertising Act of 2005. Note: H.R. 3950, 109th Congress, 1st session. Introduced by Rep. DeLauro, September 29, 2005. Referred to the Committee on Energy and Commerce.

United States. Congress. House. A bill to require prescription drug manufacturers, packers, and distributors to disclose certain gifts provided in connection with detailing, promotional, or other marketing activities, and for other purposes. Washington, DC: U.S. G.P.O., 2006. 5 p. [Online]. Accessed: http://frwebgate.access.gpo.gov/cgi-bin/useftp.cgi?IPaddress=162.140.64.21&filename=h4718ih.pdf&directory=/diskb/wais/data/109_cong_bills [2006 June 7]. NRCBL: 9.7; 1.3.2; 5.3. SC: le. Identifiers: Drug Company Gift Disclosure Act. Note: H.R. 4718; 109th Congress, 2nd session. Introduced by Rep. DeFazio, February 8, 2006. Referred to the Committee on Energy and Commerce.

United States. Congress. Senate. A bill to establish certain duties for pharmacies when pharmacists employed by the pharmacies refuse to fill valid prescriptions for drugs or devices on the basis of personal beliefs, and for other purposes. Washington, DC: U.S. G.P.O., 2005. 7 p. [Online]. Accessed: http://frwebgate.access.gpo.gov/cgi-bin/useftp.cgi?IPaddress=162.140.64.21&filename=s809is.pdf&directory=/diskb/wais/data/109_cong_bills [2006 November 21]. NRCBL: 9.7; 1.2; 11.1; 8.1. SC: le. Identifiers: Access to Legal Pharmaceuticals Act. Note: S. 809, 109th Congress, 1st session. Introduced by Sen. Lautenberg, April 14, 2005. Referred to the Committee on Health, Education, Labor and Pensions.

Victoroff, Michael S. When personal and professional collide. *Managed Care* 2005 August; 14(8): 18, 21. NRCBL: 9.7; 11.1; 8.1.

Vischer, Robert K. Conscience in context: pharmacist rights and the eroding moral marketplace. *Stanford Law and Policy Review* 2006; 17(1): 83-119. NRCBL: 9.7; 8.3.4; 7.3. SC: le.

Wadman, Meredith. Spitzer sues drug giant for deceiving doctors [news]. *Nature* 2004 June 10; 429(6992): 589. NRCBL: 9.7; 1.3.9; 17.4. Identifiers: GlaxoSmithKline; Paxil.

Walthall, Arron. Legal pressure to incorporate pharmacogenetics in the U.K. *Jurimetrics* 2006 Spring; 46(3): 263-279. NRCBL: 9.7; 15.1; 8.5. SC: le.

Wazana, Ashley; Primeau, Francois. Ethical considerations in the relationship between physicians and the pharmaceutical industry. *Psychiatric Clinics of North America* 2002 September; 25(3): 647-663. NRCBL: 9.7; 1.3.2; 7.3.

Wenger, Neil S.; Lieberman, Jay R. The orthopaedic surgeon and industry: ethics and industry incentives. *Clinical Orthopaedics and Related Research* 2000 September; (378): 39-43. NRCBL: 9.7; 1.3.2; 9.3.1.

Whyte, Susan Reynolds; van der Geest, Sjaak; Hardon, Anita. Drug vendors and their market: the commodification of health. *In their:* Social Lives of Medicines. New York: Cambridge University Press; 2002: 79-90. NRCBL: 9.7.

Wicclair, Mark R. Pharmacies, pharmacists, and conscientious objection. *Kennedy Institute of Ethics Journal* 2006 September; 16(3): 225-250. NRCBL: 9.7; 1.1; 9.2; 11.1; 7.1; 4.1.1; 1.3.1.

Wilan, Ken. Finding the moral high ground [news]. *Nature Biotechnology* 2006 March; 24(3): 237-239. NRCBL: 9.7; 1.3.2; 7.3; 15.1.

Wolinsky, Howard. Disease mongering and drug marketing: does the pharmaceutical industry manufacture diseases as well as drugs? *EMBO Reports* 2005 July; 6(7): 612-614. NRCBL: 9.7; 1.3.2; 4.2.

Wood, Alastair J.J. A proposal for radical changes in the drug-approval process. *New England Journal of Medicine* 2006 August 10; 355(6): 618-623. NRCBL: 9.7; 1.3.9; 1.3.2; 18.2; 18.6.

Wurth, Gene R.; Sherr, Judy H.; Coffman, Thomas M. Orthopaedic research and education foundation and industry. *Clinical Orthopaedics and Related Research* 2003 July; (412): 54-56. NRCBL: 9.7; 1.3.2; 7.2.

Zindrick, Michael R. Orthopaedic surgery and Food and Drug Administration off-label uses. *Clinical Orthopaedics and Related Research* 2000 September; (378): 31-38. NRCBL: 9.7; 5.3; 8.1.; 9.8.

NRCBL: National Reference Center for Bioethics Literature Classification Scheme   See inside front cover for terms.

159

Zipkin, Daniella A.; Steinman, Michael A. Response to "interactions between pharmaceutical representatives and doctors in training: a thematic review" [letter]. *JGIM: Journal of General Internal Medicine* 2006 January; 21(1): 103. NRCBL: 9.7; 1.3.2; 7.2.

Zoltan, Andrew. Jacobson revisited: mandatory polio vaccination as an unconstitutional condition. *George Mason Law Review* 2005 Spring; 13(3): 735-765. NRCBL: 9.7; 9.1; 9.5.1. SC: le.

Zuckerman, Diana M. FDA advisory committees: does approval mean safety? Washington, DC: National Research Center for Women and Families, 2006; 48 p.[Online]. Accessed: http://www.center4research.org/pdf/FDA_Report_9-2006.pdf [2006 September 28]. NRCBL: 9.7; 5.2; 1.3.5; 9.8; 7.1. SC: em. Identifiers: Food and Drug Administration.

DURABLE POWER OF ATTORNEY *See* ADVANCE DIRECTIVES

ECONOMICS *See* GENETIC SCREENING/ ECONOMIC ASPECTS; HEALTH CARE ECONOMICS; ORGAN AND TISSUE TRANSPLANTATION/ DONATION AND PROCUREMENT/ ECONOMIC ASPECTS

EDUCATION *See* BIOETHICS AND MEDICAL ETHICS/ EDUCATION; MEDICAL EDUCATION

ELECTROCONVULSIVE THERAPY

See also BEHAVIOR CONTROL; CARE FOR SPECIFIC GROUPS/ MENTALLY DISABLED; MENTAL HEALTH THERAPIES

Byrne, Peter; Cassidy, Brendan; Higgins, Patrick. Knowledge and attitudes toward electroconvulsive therapy among health care professionals and students. *Journal of ECT* 2006 June; 22(2): 133-138. NRCBL: 17.5; 4.1.3. SC: em.

Chatterjee, A. The promise and predicament of cosmetic neurology. *Journal of Medical Ethics* 2006 February; 32(2): 110-113. NRCBL: 17.5. SC: an.

Fink, Max. Is the practice of ECT ethical? *World Journal of Biological Psychiatry* 2005; 6(Supplement 2): 38-43. NRCBL: 17.5; 1.1.

Ford, Paul J.; Kubu, Cynthia S. Stimulating debate: ethics in a multidisciplinary functional neurosurgery committee. *Journal of Medical Ethics* 2006 February; 32(2): 106-109. NRCBL: 17.5. SC: an.
  Abstract: Multidisciplinary healthcare committees meet regularly to discuss patients' candidacy for emerging functional neurosurgical procedures, such as Deep Brain Stimulation(DBS). Through debate and discussion around the surgical candidacy of particular patients, functional neurosurgery programs begin to mold practice and policy supported both by scientific evidence and clear value choices. These neurosurgical

decisions have special considerations not found in non-neurologic committees. The professional time used to resolve these conflicts provides opportunities for the emergence of careful, ethical practices simultaneous with the expansion of therapy applications.

Frank, Leonard Roy. The electroshock quotationary. *Ethical Human Psychology and Psychiatry* 2006 Summer; 8(2): 157-177. NRCBL: 17.5; 2.2. SC: rv.

Freeman, Scott A.; McCall, W. Vaughn. High-risk electroconvulsive therapy and patient autonomy: a response to Dr. McCall's editorial [letter and reply]. *Journal of ECT* 2005 March; 21(1): 52-53. NRCBL: 17.5; 8.1; 1.1.

Harris, Victoria. Electroconvulsive therapy: administration codes, legislation, and professional recommendations. *Journal of the American Academy of Psychiatry and the Law* 2006; 34(3): 406-411. NRCBL: 17.5; 8.3.1; 8.3.3; 8.3.4. SC: le.

Lauber, Christoph; Nordt, Carlos; Falcato, Luis; Rössler, Wulf. Can a seizure help? The public's attitude toward electroconvulsive therapy. *Psychiatry Research* 2005 April 15; 134(2): 205-209. NRCBL: 17.5; 17.3. SC: em. Identifiers: Switzerland.

EMBRYOS *See* CARE FOR SPECIFIC GROUPS/ FETUSES; CRYOBANKING OF SPERM, OVA AND EMBRYOS; HUMAN EXPERIMENTATION/ SPECIAL POPULATIONS/ EMBRYOS AND FETUSES

ENHANCEMENT

As evolution intended. *New Scientist* 2006 August 26-September 1; 19(2566): 25. NRCBL: 4.5.

Berry, Roberta M. Beyond therapy, beyond the beltway: an opening argument for a public debate on enhancement biotechnologies. *HEC (Healthcare Ethics Committee) Forum* 2006 June; 18(2): 131-155. NRCBL: 4.5; 1.1; 7.1; 2.4; 5.3.

Bostrom, Nick. Welcome to a world of exponential change. *In:* Miller, Paul; Wilsdon, James, eds. Better Humans?: The Politics of Human Enhancement and Life Extension. London: Demos, 2006: 40-50. NRCBL: 4.5.

Budinger, Thomas F.; Budinger, Miriam D. Ethics of enhancement technologies. *In their:* Ethics of Emerging Technologies: Scientific Facts and Moral Challenges. Hoboken, NJ: John Wiley and Sons; 2006: 383-432. NRCBL: 4.5; 5.1.

Buyx, Alena M. Jenseits der Therapie [Beyond therapy]. *Ethik in der Medizin* 2006 September; 18(3): 267-272. NRCBL: 4.5.

Cantor, Julie. Cosmetic dermatology and physicians' ethical obligations: more than just hope in a jar. *Seminars in*

Cutaneous Medicine and Surgery 2005 September; 24(3): 155-160. NRCBL: 4.5; 4.1.2; 1.3.

Caplan, Arthur. Bioengineering and self-improvement. *Free Inquiry* 2006 April-May; 26(3): 20-21. NRCBL: 4.5.

Caplan, Arthur. Is it wrong to try to improve human nature? *In:* Miller, Paul; Wilsdon, James, eds. Better Humans?: The Politics of Human Enhancement and Life Extension. London: Demos, 2006: 31-39. NRCBL: 4.5.

Cerullo, Michael A. Cosmetic pyschopharmacology and the President's Council on Bioethics. *Perspectives in Biology and Medicine* 2006 Autumn; 49(4): 515-523. NRCBL: 4.5; 17.4; 2.4.

Cetina, Karin Knorr. The rise of a culture of life: the biological sciences are encouraging the move away from the ideals of the Enlightenment towards an idea of individual perfectibility and enhancement. *EMBO Reports* 2005 July; 6(Special Issue): S76-S80. NRCBL: 4.5; 5.1; 1.1; 4.4.

Cloud, David S. Perfect vision, via surgery, is helping and hurting Navy. *New York Times* 2006 June 20; p. A1, A15. NRCBL: 4.5. SC: po.

Franklin, Sarah. Better by design? *In:* Miller, Paul; Wilsdon, James, eds. Better Humans?: The Politics of Human Enhancement and Life Extension. London: Demos, 2006: 86-94. NRCBL: 4.5.

Gesang, Bernward. "Enhancement" zwischen Selbstbetrug und Selbstverwirklichung / Enhancement between self-realization and self-deception. *Ethik in der Medizin* 2006 March; 18(1): 10-26. NRCBL: 4.5; 1.1; 9.5.7.

Gibson, T.M. The bioethics of enhancing human performance for spaceflight. *Journal of Medical Ethics* 2006 March; 32(3): 129-132. NRCBL: 4.5.

Abstract: There are many ways of enhancing human performance. For military aviation in general, and for spaceflight in particular, the most important tools are selection, training, equipment, pharmacology, and surgery. In the future, genetic manipulation may be feasible. For each of these tools, the specific modalities available range from the ethically acceptable to the ethically unacceptable. Even when someone consents to a particular procedure to enhance performance, the action may be ethically unacceptable to society as a whole and the burden of risk for the individual may be too great. In addition, there are several characteristics that define the quality and the acceptability of the consent. Each method of enhancing performance will be examined in the context of the principles of medical ethics in a western society: autonomy, non-maleficence, beneficence, and justice. The aim is to draw the attention of aeromedical practitioners to the complexities of ethical dilemmas such as this particular one in order to help them to develop a morally justifiable code of practice that balances society's needs against individual ambitions and corporate goals.

Giordano, Simona; Harris, John. What is gender equality in sports? *In:* Tamburrini, Claudio; Tännsjö, Torbjörn, eds. Genetic Technology and Sport: Ethical Questions. London; New York: Routledge; 2005: 209-217. NRCBL: 4.5; 9.5.1; 9.5.9; 15.4; 10.

Greely, Henry T. Man and superman. *New Scientist* 2006 August 5-11; 191(2563): 19. NRCBL: 4.5.

Hogle, Linda F. Enhancement technologies and the body. *Annual Review of Anthropology* 2005; 34: 695-716. NRCBL: 4.5; 1.3.1; 15.1; 17.1.

Hook, C. Christopher. The techno sapiens are coming. *Christianity Today* 2004 January; 48(1): 36-40. NRCBL: 4.5; 5.1; 1.2. Identifiers: transhumanist philosophy; bioengineering.

Hurst, Rachel. The perfect crime. *In:* Miller, Paul; Wilsdon, James, eds. Better Humans?: The Politics of Human Enhancement and Life Extension. London: Demos, 2006: 114-121. NRCBL: 4.5; 20.5.1.

Jones, D.G. Enhancement: are ethicists excessively influenced by baseless speculations? *Medical Humanities* 2006 December; 32(2): 77-81. NRCBL: 4.5; 15.5. SC: an.

Kaebnick, Gregory E. Wonderful children [editorial]. *Hastings Center Report* 2006 November-December; 36(6): 2. NRCBL: 4.5; 9.5.7.

Kettner, Matthias. "Wunscherfüllende Medizin" zwischen Kommerz und Patientendienlichkeit / "Medicine of desire" between commercialization and patient-centeredness. *Ethik in der Medizin* 2006 March; 18(1): 81-91. NRCBL: 4.5; 9.5.1; 9.3.1.

Kettner, Matthias. Assistenz zum guten Leben: der Trend zur wunscherfüllenden Medizin / Assistance for a good life: the trend towards wish-fulfilling medicine [editorial]. *Ethik in der Medizin* 2006 March; 18(1): 5-9. NRCBL: 4.5.

Klerkx, Greg. The transhumanists as tribe. *In:* Miller, Paul; Wilsdon, James, eds. Better Humans?: The Politics of Human Enhancement and Life Extension. London: Demos, 2006: 59-66. NRCBL: 4.5.

Lawton, Graham. The incredibles. *New Scientist* 2006 May 13-19; 190(2551): 32-38. NRCBL: 4.5. SC: rv. Identifiers: human enhancement.

Le Page, Michael. Only drugs can stop sports cheats. *New Scientist* 2006 August 19-25; 191(2565): 18-19. NRCBL: 4.5; 9.5.1; 9.7; 15.1.

Loland, Sigmund. The vulnerability thesis and use of bio-medical technology in sport. *In:* Tamburrini, Claudio; Tännsjö, Torbjörn, eds. Genetic Technology and Sport: Ethical Questions. London; New York: Routledge; 2005: 158-164. NRCBL: 4.5; 9.5.1; 9.5.9.

McNamee, M.J.; Edwards, S.D. Transhumanism, medical technology and slippery slopes. *Journal of Medical Ethics* 2006 September; 32(9): 513-518. NRCBL: 4.5; 1.1. SC: an.

NRCBL: National Reference Center for Bioethics Literature Classification Scheme   See inside front cover for terms.

161

Abstract: In this article, transhumanism is considered to be a quasi-medical ideology that seeks to promote a variety of therapeutic and human-enhancing aims. Moderate conceptions are distinguished from strong conceptions of transhumanism and the strong conceptions are found to be more problematic than the moderate ones. A particular critique of Bostrom's defence of transhumanism is presented. Various forms of slippery slope arguments that may be used for and against transhumanism are discussed and one particular criticism, moral arbitrariness, that undermines both weak and strong transhumanism is highlighted.

Miah, Andy. Gene doping: the shape of things to come. *In:* Tamburrini, Claudio; Tännsjö, Torbjörn, eds. Genetic Technology and Sport: Ethical Questions. London; New York: Routledge; 2005: 42-53. NRCBL: 4.5; 9.5.1; 15.4.

Miller, Paul; Wilsdon, James. Stronger, longer, smarter, faster. *In their:* Better Humans?: The Politics of Human Enhancement and Life Extension. London: Demos, 2006: 13-27. NRCBL: 4.5.

Miller, Paul; Wilsdon, James. The man who wants to live forever. *In their:* Better Humans?: The Politics of Human Enhancement and Life Extension. London: Demos, 2006: 51-58. NRCBL: 4.5; 20.5.1.

Munthe, Christian. Ethical aspects of controlling genetic doping. *In:* Tamburrini, Claudio; Tännsjö, Torbjörn, eds. Genetic Technology and Sport: Ethical Questions. London; New York: Routledge; 2005: 107-125. NRCBL: 4.5; 9.5.1; 15.3; 15.4.

Mykytyn, Courtney Everts. Anti-aging medicine: predictions, moral obligations, and biomedical intervention. *Anthropological Quarterly* 2006 Winter; 79(1): 5-31. NRCBL: 4.5; 5.3; 9.5.2; 9.7. SC: rv.

Persaud, Raj. Does smarter mean happier? *In:* Miller, Paul; Wilsdon, James, eds. Better Humans?: The Politics of Human Enhancement and Life Extension. London: Demos, 2006: 129-136. NRCBL: 4.5; 17.1.

Persson, Ingmar. What's wrong with admiring athletes and other people? *In:* Tamburrini, Claudio; Tännsjö, Torbjörn, eds. Genetic Technology and Sport: Ethical Questions. London; New York: Routledge; 2005: 70-81. NRCBL: 4.5; 9.5.1; 9.5.9; 15.4.

Rose, Steven. Brain gain. *In:* Miller, Paul; Wilsdon, James, eds. Better Humans?: The Politics of Human Enhancement and Life Extension. London: Demos, 2006: 69-78. NRCBL: 4.5; 17.1.

Sandberg, David E. Growth hormone treatment for short stature: inferences from FDA decisions and clinical practice. *Atrium* 2006 Fall; 3: 13-15. NRCBL: 4.5; 9.7; 9.5.7.

Schneider, Angela J.; Friedman, Theodore. Gene transfer in sports: an opening scenario for genetic enhancement of normal "human traits". *In their:* Gene Doping in Sports: The Science and Ethics of Genetically Modified Athletes.

Boston: Elsevier Academic Press, 2006: 37-49. NRCBL: 4.5; 15.1; 9.5.1.

Silvers, Anita. Pure enhancement [letter]. *National Catholic Bioethics Quarterly* 2006 Autumn; 6(3): 405-408. NRCBL: 4.5; 3.1; 15.1; 1.2.

Simonstein, Frida. Stem cells and the ethics of indefinitely prolonged lives. *In:* Sang-yong, Song; Young-Mo, Koo; Macer, Darryl R.J., eds. Asian Bioethics in the 21st Century. Christchurch, NZ: Eubios Ethics Institute, 2002: 65-72. NRCBL: 4.5; 18.5.4; 15.1; 20.5.1. Conference: Proceedings of the Asian Bioethics Conference (ABC4), held 22-25 November 2002 in Seoul, South Korea.

Synofzik, Matthis. Kognition à la carte? Der Wunsch nach kognitionsverbessernden Psychopharmaka in der Medizin = Cognition on demand? — The wish for cognition-enhancing drugs in medicine. *Ethik in der Medizin* 2006 March; 18(1): 37-50. NRCBL: 4.5; 4.2; 17.4.

Tamburrini, Claudio. Education or genetic blueprints, what's the difference? *In:* Tamburrini, Claudio; Tännsjö, Torbjörn, eds. Genetic Technology and Sport: Ethical Questions. London; New York: Routledge; 2005: 82-90. NRCBL: 4.5; 9.5.1; 15.4.

Tännsjö, Torbjörn. Genetic engineering and elitism in sport. *In:* Tamburrini, Claudio; Tännsjö, Torbjörn, eds. Genetic Technology and Sport: Ethical Questions. London; New York: Routledge; 2005: 57-69. NRCBL: 4.5; 9.5.1; 15.4.

Turner, Danielle; Sahakian, Barbara. The cognition-enhanced classroom. *In:* Miller, Paul; Wilsdon, James, eds. Better Humans?: The Politics of Human Enhancement and Life Extension. London: Demos, 2006: 79-85. NRCBL: 4.5; 17.4.

Turney, Jon. More life. *In:* Miller, Paul; Wilsdon, James, eds. Better Humans?: The Politics of Human Enhancement and Life Extension. London: Demos, 2006: 95-103. NRCBL: 4.5; 20.5.1.

van Hilvoorde, Ivo. Sport and genetics: moral and educational considerations regarding 'athletic predestination.'. *In:* Tamburrini, Claudio; Tännsjö, Torbjörn, eds. Genetic Technology and Sport: Ethical Questions. London; New York: Routledge; 2005: 91-103. NRCBL: 4.5; 9.5.1; 15.4.

Volandes, Angelo. Envying Cinderella and the future of medical enhancements. *Medical Humanities* 2006 December; 32(2): 73-76. NRCBL: 4.5; 9.3.1. SC: an.

Walcher-Andris, Elfriede. Ethische Aspekte des pharmakologischen "cognition enhancement" am Beispiel des Gebrauchs von Psychostimulanzien durch Kinder und Jugendliche / Ethical aspects of pharmacological cognition enhancement and the use of psychostimulants by children and young persons. *Ethik in der Medizin* 2006 March; 18(1): 27-36. NRCBL: 4.5; 9.5.7; 17.4.

Wolbring, Gregor. The unenhanced underclass. *In:* Miller, Paul; Wilsdon, James, eds. Better Humans?: The Politics of Human Enhancement and Life Extension. London: Demos, 2006: 122-128. NRCBL: 4.5; 9.5.4.

ETHICISTS AND ETHICS COMMITTEES

Aroskar, Mila Ann. Healthcare organizations as moral communities. *Journal of Clinical Ethics* 2006 Fall; 17(3): 255-256. NRCBL: 9.6; 4.1.3; 8.1; 7.2.

Bayley, Carol. Ethics Committee DX: failure to thrive. *HEC (Healthcare Ethics Committee) Forum* 2006 December; 18(4): 357-367. NRCBL: 9.6; 9.1; 1.3.2; 9.3.2; 9.8; 7.1.

Bernt, Francis; Clark, Peter; Starrs, Josita; Talone Patricia. Ethics committees in Catholic hospitals. *Health Progress* 2006 March-April; 87(2): 18-25. NRCBL: 9.6; 1.2. SC: em.

Boitte, Pierre. For an ethical function in hospitals. *In:* Viafora, Corrado, ed. Clinical Bioethics: A Search for the Foundations. Dordrecht: Springer, 2005: 169-180. NRCBL: 9.6.

Borovecki, Ana; ten Have, Henk; Oreškovic, Stjepan. Ethics committees in Croatia in the healthcare institutions: the first study about their structure and functions, and some reflections on the major issues and problems. *HEC(Healthcare Ethics Committee) Forum* 2006 March; 18(1): 49-60. NRCBL: 9.6.

Borovecki, A.; ten Have, H.; Oreškovic, S. Education of ethics committee members: experience from Croatia. *Journal of Medical Ethics* 2006 March; 32(3): 138-142. NRCBL: 9.6; 2.3. SC: em.

Abstract: To study knowledge and attitudes of hospital ethics committee members at the first workshop for ethics committees in Croatia. DESIGN: Before/after cross-sectional study using a self administered questionnaire. SETTING: Educational workshop for members of hospital ethics committees, Zagreb, 2003. Main outcome measurements: Knowledge and attitudes of participants before and after the workshop; everyday functioning of hospital ethics committees. RESULTS: The majority of the respondents came from committees with at least five members. The majority of ethics committees were appointed by the governing bodies of their hospitals. Most committees were founded after the implementation of the law on health protection in 1997. Membership structure (three physicians and two members from other fields) and functions were established on the basis of that law. Analysis of research protocols was the main part of their work. Other important functions-education, case analysis, guidelines formation-were neglected. Members' level of knowledge was not sufficient for the complicated tasks they were supposed to perform. However, it was significantly higher after the workshop. Most respondents felt their knowledge should be improved by additional education. Their views on certain issues and bioethical dilemmas displayed a high level of paternalism and over protectiveness, which did not change after the workshop. CONCLUSIONS: The committees developed according to bureaucratic requirements. Furthermore, there are concerns about members' knowledge levels. More efforts need to be made to use education to improve the quality of the work.

Additional research is necessary to explore ethics committees' work in Croatia especially in the hospital setting.

Caenepeel, Didier; Jobin, Guy. Discursivité et co-autorité en éthique clinique: regard critique sur le rôle et les fonctions de la délibération éthique en comité = Discursiveness and co-authority in clinical ethics: A critical look at the role and functions of ethics committee deliberations. *Journal International de Bioéthique = International Journal of Bioethics* 2005 September-December; 16(3-4): 107-133, 174-175. NRCBL: 9.6; 1.1.

Christopher, Myra. Role of ethics committees, ethics networks, and ethics centers in improving end-of-life care. *Pain Medicine* 2001 June; 2(2): 162-168. NRCBL: 9.6; 20.4.1; 9.8. Identifiers: Midwest Bioethics Center.

Collier, Julie; Rorty, Mary; Sandborg, Christy. Rafting the ethical rapids. *HEC (Healthcare Ethics Committee) Forum* 2006 December; 18(4): 332-341. NRCBL: 9.6; 9.1; 1.3.2; 9.4.

Conrad, Ellison. Terminal success. *HEC (Healthcare Ethics Committee) Forum* 2006 December; 18(4): 287-290. NRCBL: 9.6; 9.1; 1.3.2. SC: cs.

Craig, Jana M.; May, Thomas. Evaluating the outcomes of ethics consultation. *Journal of Clinical Ethics* 2006 Summer; 17(2): 168-180. NRCBL: 9.6; 9.8.

Davis, Walter. Failure to thrive or refusal to adapt? Missing links in the evolution from ethics committee to ethics program. *HEC (Healthcare Ethics Committee) Forum* 2006 December; 18(4): 291-297. NRCBL: 9.6; 9.1; 1.3.2; 2.3.

DeRenzo, Evan G.; Mokwunye, Nneka; Lynch, John J. Rounding: how everyday ethics can invigorate a hospital's ethics committee. *HEC (Healthcare Ethics Committee) Forum* 2006 December; 18(4): 319-331. NRCBL: 9.6; 2.3; 9.8. Identifiers: Washington Hospital Center.

Dickenson, Donna. Gender and ethics committees: where's the 'different voice'? *Bioethics* 2006 June; 20(3): 115-124. NRCBL: 9.6; 10; 21.1.

Abstract: Prominent international and national ethics commissions such as the UNESCO International Bioethics Committee rarely achieve anything remotely resembling gender equality, although local research and ethics committees are somewhat more egalitarian. Under-representation of women is particularly troubling when the subject matter of modern bioethics so disproportionately concerns women's bodies, and when such committees claim to derive 'universal' standards. Are women missing from many ethics committees because of relatively straightforward, if discriminatory, demographic factors? Or are the methods of analysis and styles of ethics to which these bodies are committed somehow 'anti-female'? It has been argued, for example, that there is a 'different voice' in ethical reasoning, not confined to women but more representative of female experience. Similarly, some feminist writers, such as Evelyn Fox Keller and Donna Haraway, have asked difficult epistemological questions about the dominant 'masculine paradigm' in science. Perhaps the dominant paradigm in ethics committee deliberation is similarly gendered? This article provides a pre-

NRCBL: National Reference Center for Bioethics Literature Classification Scheme   See inside front cover for terms.

163

liminary survey of women's representation on ethics committees in eastern and western Europe, a critical analysis of the supposed 'masculinism' of the principlist approach, and a case example in which a 'different voice' did indeed make a difference.

Draper, Heather; MacDiarmaid-Gordon, Adam; Strumidlo, Laura; Teuten, Bea; Updale, Eleanor. Virtual ethics committee, case 1: should our hospital have a policy of telling patients about near misses? *Clinical Ethics* 2006 March; 1(1): 11-17. NRCBL: 9.6; 8.2; 9.1; 8.1.

Ells, Carolyn. Healthcare ethics committees' contribution to review of institutional policy. *HEC (Healthcare Ethics Committee) Forum* 2006 September; 18(3): 265-275. NRCBL: 9.6; 9.1; 1.3.2.

Finegold, David; Moser, Allison. Ethical decision-making in bioscience firms. *Nature Biotechnology* 2006 March; 24(3): 285-290. NRCBL: 9.6; 1.3.2; 18.2; 9.7; 5.1; 15.1. SC: em.

Foglia, Mary Beth; Pearlman, Robert A. Integrating clinical and organizational ethics. *Health Progress* 2006 March-April; 87(2): 31-35. NRCBL: 9.6; 7.1; 20.1.

Frikovic, Aleksandra; Gosic, Nada. Practical experience in the work of institutional ethics committees in Croatia on the example of the ethics committee at Clinical Hospital Center Rijeka. *HEC (Healthcare Ethics Committee)Forum* 2006 March; 18(1): 37-48. NRCBL: 9.6; 2.3. SC: cs.

Gastmans, Chris; Van Neste, Fernand; Schotsmans, Paul. Pluralism and ethical dialogue in Christian healthcare institutions: the view of Caritas Catholica Flanders. *Christian Bioethics* 2006 December; 12(3): 265-280. NRCBL: 9.6; 1.2; 21.7; 7.1; 4.4.

Abstract: In this article, the place and the nature of an ethical dialogue that develops within Christian healthcare institutions in Flanders, Belgium is examined. More specifically, the question is asked how Christian healthcare institutions should position themselves ethically in a context of a pluralistic society. The profile developed by Caritas Catholica Flanders must take seriously not only the external pluralistic context of our society and the internal pluralistic worldviews by personnel/employees and patients, but also the inherent inspiration of a Christian healthcare institution. This article concludes with ten general orientations that could shape the ethical dialogue from a Christian inspiration in a pluralistic context.

Gordon, Elisa J.; Hamric, Ann B. The courage to stand up: the cultural politics of nurses' access to ethics consultation. *Journal of Clinical Ethics* 2006 Fall; 17(3): 231-254. NRCBL: 9.6; 4.1.3; 7.1. SC: em ;cs.

Guerrier, M. Hospital based ethics, current situation in France: between "espaces" and committees. *Journal of Medical Ethics* 2006 September; 32(9): 503-506. NRCBL: 9.6.

Abstract: Unlike research ethics committees, which were created in 1988, the number of functioning hospital based ethical organisations in France, such as clinical ethics committees, is unknown. The objectives of such structures are diverse. A recent law created regional ethical forums, the objectives of which are education, debate, and research in relation to healthcare ethics. This paper discusses the current situation in France and the possible evolution and conflicts induced by this law. The creation of official healthcare ethics structures raises several issues.

Hoy, Janet; Feigenbaum, Erika. Making the case for ethics consults in community mental health centers. *Community Mental Health Journal* 2005 June; 41(3): 235-250. NRCBL: 9.6; 17.7.

Hubert, Robert M.; Freeman, Larry T. Report of the ACA Ethics Committee: 2002-2003. *Journal of Counseling and Development* 2004 Spring; 82(2): 248- 251. NRCBL: 9.6; 17.1. Identifiers: American Counseling Association.

Hurst, Samia A.; Chevrolet, Jean-Claude; Loew, François. Methods in clinical ethics: a time for eclectic pragmatism? *Clinical Ethics* 2006 September; 1(3): 159-164. NRCBL: 9.6. SC: em.

Longstaff, Holly; Burgess, Michael; Lewis, Patrick. Comparing methods for ethical consultation for biotechnology related issues. *Health Law Review* 2006; 15(1): 37-38. NRCBL: 9.6. SC: em.

Mayle, Kathy. Nurses and ethics consultation: growing beyond a rock and a hard place. *Journal of Clinical Ethics* 2006 Fall; 17(3): 257-259. NRCBL: 9.6; 4.1.3; 9.3.2; 7.2.

McCruden, Patrick; Kuczewski, Mark. Is organizational ethics the remedy for failure to thrive? Toward an understanding of mission leadership. *HEC (Healthcare Ethics Committee) Forum* 2006 December; 18(4): 342-348. NRCBL: 9.6; 9.1; 1.3.2; 9.3.1.

McGrath, Pam. Multidisciplinary insights on the evolving role of the ethics committee in an Australian regional hospital. *Monash Bioethics Review* 2006 July; 25(3): 59-72. NRCBL: 9.6. SC: em. Identifiers: Australia.

Miller, Jessica Prata. Feminist values and bioethics practice: strangers at the bedside? *American Philosophical Association Newsletter on Feminism and Philosophy* 2006 Spring; 5(2): 3-8. [Online]. Accessed: http://www. apaonline.org/publications/newsletters/Vol05n2/ Feminism.pdf [18 October 2006]. NRCBL: 9.6; 10; 1.1.

Mills, Ann E.; Rorty, Mary V.; Spencer, Edward M. Introduction: ethics committees and failure to thrive. *HEC (Healthcare Ethics Committee) Forum* 2006 December; 18(4): 279-286. NRCBL: 9.6; 9.1; 1.3.2; 9.8; 2.3.

Milmore, Don. Hospital ethics committees: a survey in upstate New York. *HEC (Healthcare Ethics Committee) Forum* 2006 September; 18(3): 222-244. NRCBL: 9.6. SC: em.

Moreno, Jonathan D. Ethics committees: beyond benign neglect. *HEC (Healthcare Ethics Committee) Forum* 2006 December; 18(4): 368-369. NRCBL: 9.6; 2.2; 9.1; 1.3.2.

Murphy, Kevin. A "next generation" ethics committee. *Health Progress* 2006 March-April; 87(2): 26-30. NRCBL: 9.6.

Nelson, William A. Defining ethics: how to determine whether a conflict falls under your ethics committee's purview. *Healthcare Executive* 2006 July-August; 21(4): 38-39. NRCBL: 9.6; 9.5.2. SC: em.

Nelson, William; Weeks, William B. Rural and non-rural differences in membership of the American Society of Bioethics and Humanities. *Journal of Medical Ethics* 2006 July; 32(7): 411-413. NRCBL: 9.6. SC: em.

Abstract: OBJECTIVE: To determine whether bioethicists are distributed along a rural-to-urban continuum in a way that reflects potential need of those resources as determined by the general population, hospital facilities and hospital beds. METHODS: US members of a large, multidisciplinary professional society, the American Society of Bioethics and Humanities (ASBH), the US population, hospital facilities and hospital beds were classified across a four-tier rural-to-urban continuum. The proportion of each group in rural settings was compared with that in urban settings, and odds ratios were calculated with 95% confidence intervals. RESULTS: Although 91% of ASBH members live or work in urban settings, only 66% of the US population did so. In contrast, 2% of ASBH members live or work in rural settings compared with 13% of the population. ASBH members were 10.7 times (95% CI 6.6 to 17.3) as likely to be represented in urban than in rural settings when compared with the general population, 25.6 times (95% CI 15.8 to 41.5) and 6.9 times (95% CI 4.3 to 11.1) as likely with regard to hospital facilities and hospital beds, respectively. CONCLUSIONS: Using various comparisons it was found that ASBH members are under-represented in rural as compared with urban settings. Although not all bioethicists are ASBH members, these findings suggest that the availability of professional bioethical resources may be inadequate in rural America. The disparities that were found may have considerable effect on ethics scholarship, research, ethical committees and education, and adds to the argument that rural American communities are under-served.

Nilson, Elizabeth G.; Fins, Joseph J. Reinvigorating ethics consultations: an impetus from the "quality" debate. *HEC (Healthcare Ethics Committee) Forum* 2006 December; 18(4): 298-304. NRCBL: 9.6; 9.8.

O'Brien, Linda A. Establishing and educating a long-term care regional ethics committee: the NJ model. *Journal of the American Medical Directors Association* 2005 January-February; 6(1): 66-67. NRCBL: 9.6; 9.5.1. Identifiers: New Jersey.

O'Toole, Brian. St. Louis system has corporate ethics committee. *Health Progress* 2006 March-April; 87(2): 42-45. NRCBL: 9.6; 9.1.

Orlowski, J.P.; Hein, S.; Christensen, J.A.; Meinke, R.; Sincich, T. Why doctors use or do not use ethics consultation. *Journal of Medical Ethics* 2006 September; 32(9): 499-502. NRCBL: 9.6. SC: em.

Abstract: Ethics consultation is used regularly by some doctors, whereas others are reluctant to use these services. AIM: To determine factors that may influence doctors to request or not request ethics consultation. METHODS: A survey questionnaire was distributed to doctors on staff at the University Community Hospital in Tampa, Florida, USA. The responses to the questions on the survey were arranged in a Likert Scale, from strongly disagree, somewhat disagree, neither agree nor disagree, somewhat agree to strongly agree. Data were analysed with the Wilcoxon test for group comparisons, the chi2 test to compare proportions and a logistic regression analysis. RESULTS: Of the 186 surveys distributed, 121 were returned, giving a 65% response rate. Demographic data were similar between the groups saying yes (I do/would use ethics consultation when indicated) and no (I do not/would not use ethics consultation when indicated). No statistically significant differences were observed between the user and non-user groups in terms of opinions about ethics consultants having extensive training in ethics or participating in ethics educational opportunities. On the issue "Ethics committee members or consultants cannot grasp the full picture from the outside", the non-users were neutral, whereas the users somewhat disagreed (p=0.012). Even more significant was the difference between surgeons and non-surgeons, where, by logistic regression analysis, surgeons who believed that ethics consultants could not grasp the full picture from the outside were highly likely to not use (p=0.0004). Non-users of ethics consultations thought that it was their responsibility to resolve issues with the patient or family (72.2% agree, p.05). Users of ethics consultation believed in shared decision making or the importance of alternate points of view (90.8% agree, p.05). IMPLICATIONS: Ethics consultations are used by doctors who believe in shared decision making. Doctors who did not use ethics consultation tended to think that it was their responsibility to resolve issues with patients and families and that they were already proficient in ethics

Orr, Robert D. Clinical ethics consultation: to intubate or not to intubate — Part I of a series. *Today's Christian Doctor* 2006 Fall; 37(3): 30-31. NRCBL: 9.6; 20.5.1; 8.3.3; 9.3.4. SC: cs.

Pape, Deborah; Manning, Suzanne. The educational ladder model for ethics committees: confidence and change flourishing through core competency development. *HEC (Healthcare Ethics Committee) Forum* 2006 December; 18(4): 305-318. NRCBL: 9.6; 9.8; 2.3. SC: le.

Pustovit, Svitlana V. Some methodological aspects of ethics committees' expertise: the Ukrainian example. *Science and Engineering Ethics* 2006 January; 12(1): 85-94. NRCBL: 9.6; 21.1. SC: en.

Racine, E.; Hayes, K. The need for a clinical ethics service and its goals in a community healthcare service centre: a survey. *Journal of Medical Ethics* 2006 October; 32(10): 564-566. NRCBL: 9.6. SC: em. Identifiers: Quebec.

Ribas, Salvador Ribas. Empirical studies on healthcare ethics committees in the USA. A bibliographic review. *Formosan Journal of Medical Humanities* 2006 June; 7(1-2): 67-80. NRCBL: 9.6. SC: em.

Saunders, John. Developing clinical ethics committees. *Clinical Medicine* 2004 May-June; 4(3): 232-234. NRCBL: 9.6. Identifiers: United Kingdom (Great Britain).

Schneiderman, Lawrence J.; Gilmer, Todd; Teetzel, Holly D.; Dugan, Daniel O.; Goodman-Crews, Paula;

NRCBL: National Reference Center for Bioethics Literature Classification Scheme   See inside front cover for terms.

165

Cohn, Felicia. Dissatisfaction with ethics consultations: the Anna Karenina principle. *CQ: Cambridge Quarterly of Healthcare Ethics* 2006 Winter; 15(1): 101-106. NRCBL: 9.6; 9.8. SC: em.

Svehla, Carolyn J.; Anderson-Shaw, Lisa. Hospital ethics committees: is it time to expand our access to managed care organizations? *JONA's Healthcare Law, Ethics, and Regulation* 2006 January-March; 8(1): 15-19. NRCBL: 9.6; 9.3.2.

Tarzian, Anita J.; Hoffmann, Diane E.; Volbrecht, Rose Mary; Meyers, Judy L. The roles of healthcare ethics committee networks in shaping healthcare policy and practices. *HEC (Healthcare Ethics Committee) Forum* 2006 March; 18(1): 85-94. NRCBL: 9.6; 9.1; 7.1.

Thompson, Richard E. The hospital ethics committee — then and now. *Physician Executive* 2006 May-June; 32(3): 60-62. NRCBL: 9.6; 2.2.

Tuohey, John. Ethics consultation in Portland. *Health Progress* 2006 March-April; 87(2): 36-41. NRCBL: 9.6.

Updale, Eleanor. The challenge of lay membership of clinical ethics committees. *Clinical Ethics* 2006 March; 1(1): 60-62. NRCBL: 9.6.

Vahrman, Julian. Placebo controls [letter]. *Journal of the Royal Society of Medicine* 1995 October; 88(10): 603. NRCBL: 9.6; 2.3.

Viafora, Corrado. The ethical function in the health care institutions: clinical ethics committees. *In:* Viafora, Corrado, ed. Clinical Bioethics: A Search for the Foundations. Dordrecht: Springer, 2005: 181-192. NRCBL: 9.6.

Walsh, Raoul A.; Cholowski, Krystyna; Tzelepis, Flora. Surveying university students: variability in ethics committee requirements [letter]. *Australian and New Zealand Journal of Public Health* 2006 February; 30(1): 84-85. NRCBL: 9.6; 18.2; 18.3; 18.5.2.

Watson, A.R. Ethics support in clinical practice. *Archives of Disease in Childhood* 2005 September; 90(9): 943-946. NRCBL: 9.6. Identifiers: United Kingdom (Great Britain).

Watts, Geoff. Combating chaos [news]. *BMJ: British Medical Journal* 2006 September 30; 333(7570): 674. NRCBL: 9.6; 2.4. Identifiers: United Kingdom (Great Britain).

Weston, Christine M.; O'Brien, Linda A.; Goldfarb, Neil I.; Roumm, Adam R.; Isele, William P.; Hirschfeld, Kathryn. The NJ SEED project: evaluation of an innovative initiative for ethics training in nursing homes. *Journal of the American Medical Directors Association* 2005 January-February; 6(1): 68-75. NRCBL: 9.6; 2.3; 7.2; 9.5.1. SC: em. Identifiers: New Jersey Stein Ethics Education and Development.

White, Earl D., II. Reflections on the success of hospital ethics committees in my health system. *HEC (Healthcare Ethics Committee) Forum* 2006 December; 18(4): 349-356. NRCBL: 9.6; 9.8; 2.3. Identifiers: Sentara Healthcare.

ETHICS COMMITTEES *See* ETHICISTS AND ETHICS COMMITTEES; HUMAN EXPERIMENTATION/ ETHICS COMMITTEES AND POLICY GUIDELINES

EUGENICS

A.M. Carr-Saunders on eugenics and the declining birth rate. *Population and Development Review* 2004 March; 30(1): 147-157. NRCBL: 15.5; 7.1; 13.3; 21.1.

Agar, Nicholas; Prusak, Bernard G. The debate over liberal eugenics [letter and reply]. *Hastings Center Report* 2006 March-April; 36(2): 4-5, 6-7. NRCBL: 15.5; 4.5; 4.4; 1.1.

Allen, Garland E. Genetics, eugenics and the medicalization of social behavior: lessons from the past. *Endeavour* 1999; 23(1): 10-19. NRCBL: 15.5; 7.1; 15.6.

Aultman, Julie M. Eugenomics: eugenics and ethics in the 21st century. *Genomics, Society and Policy* 2006 August; 2(2): 28-49. NRCBL: 15.5; 15.10; 5.1.
Abstract: With a shift from genetics to genomics, the study of organisms in terms of their full DNA sequences, the resurgence of eugenics has taken on a new form. Following from this new form of eugenics, which I have termed "eugenomics", is a host of ethical and social dilemmas containing elements patterned from controversies over the eugenics movement throughout the 20 th century. This paper identifies these ethical and social dilemmas, drawing upon an examination of why eugenics of the 20th century was morally wrong. Though many eugenic programs of the early 20 th century remain in the dark corners of our history and law books and scientific journals, not all of these programs have been, nor should be, forgotten. My aim is not to remind us of the social and ethical abuses from past eugenics programs, but to draw similarities and dissimilarities from what we commonly know of the past and identify areas where genomics may be eugenically beneficial and harmful to our global community. Is how that our ethical and social concerns are not taken as seriously as they should be by the scientific community, political and legal communities, and by the international public; as eugenomics is quickly gaining control over our genetic futures, ethics, I argue, is lagging behind and going considerably unnoticed. In showing why ethics is lagging behind I propose a framework that can provide us with a better understanding of genomics with respect to our pluralistic, global values.

Bix, Amy Sue. Experiences and voices of eugenics fieldworkers: "women's work" in biology. *Social Studies of Science* 1997 August; 27(4): 625-668. NRCBL: 15.5; 10; 2.2. SC: rv.

Brock, Dan W.; Prusak, Bernard G. The debate over liberal eugenics [letter and reply]. *Hastings Center Report* 2006 March-April; 36(2): 5-6, 6-7. NRCBL: 15.5; 1.1; 4.5; 4.4; 8.3.3.

Cirión, Aitziber Emaldi. Genetics and the current eugenic trends: the new law in the People's Republic of China = La genética y las actuales corrientes eugenésicas: la nueva Ley de la República Popular China. *Law and the Human Genome Review = Revista de Derecho y Genoma Humano* 1996 July-December; (5): 147-156. NRCBL: 15.5; 15.2; 21.1. SC: le.

Cot, Annie L. "Breed out the unfit and breed in the fit": Irving Fisher, economics, and the science of heredity. *American Journal of Economics and Sociology* 2005 July; 64(3): 793-826. NRCBL: 15.5; 2.2.

Cullen, David O'Donald. Nature versus nurture: eugenics. *Choice* 2005 November; 43(3): 405-413. NRCBL: 15.5; 2.2; 3.2; 15.9; 1.3.5; 21.4; 11.3. SC: rv.

Dorsey, Michael. The new eugenics. *World Watch* 2002 July-August; 15(4): 21-23. NRCBL: 15.5; 5.3; 15.1. SC: po.

Elks, Martin A. Visual indictment: a contextual analysis of the Kallikak Family photographs. *Mental Retardation* 2005 August; 43(4): 268-280. NRCBL: 15.5; 15.6; 2.2; 17.1. Identifiers: Henry Herbert Goddard.

Fäßler, Peter. Sozialhygiene-Rassenhygiene- Euthanasie: 'Volksgesundheitspflege' im Raum Dresden. *In his:* Dresden unterm Hakenkreuz. Ed. by Reiner Pommerin. Koln: Böhlau Verlag, 1998: 193-207. NRCBL: 15.5; 1.3.5; 2.2; 20.5.1; 21.4.

Galton, D.J. Eugenics: some lessons from the past. *Reproductive BioMedicine Online [electronic]* 2005 March; 10(Supplement 1): 133-136. NRCBL: 15.5; 2.2; 14.4; 1.3.5. SC: le. Conference: Ethics, Law and Moral Philosophy of Reproductive Biomedicine; London, UK; 2004 September 30 - October 1; Royal Society.

German Society of Human Genetics [GfH]. Committee for Public Relations and Ethical Issues. Statement on the new Chinese law concerning maternal and child health care. *Medizinische Genetik* 1995; 7: 419 (2 p.). [Online]. Accessed: http://www.medgenetik.de/sonderdruck/en/Chinese_law.pdf [2006 July 31]. NRCBL: 15.5; 13.3; 14.1; 21.1. SC: le. Identifiers: China; Law on Maternal and Infant Health Care.

Gerodetti, Natalia. From science to social technology: eugenics and politics in twentieth-century Switzerland. *Social Politics* 2006 Spring; 13(1): 59-88. NRCBL: 15.5; 1.3.5; 10.

Glad, John. The reviving debate on eugenics: eugenics publications 2003-early 2005 and eugenics data bases. *Mankind Quarterly* 2005 Summer; 45(4): 427-466. NRCBL: 15.5; 1.3.12.

Gordijn, Bert. Converging NBIC technologies for improving human performance: a critical assessment of the novelty and the prospects of the project. *Journal of Law,* *Medicine and Ethics* 2006 Winter; 34(4): 726-732. NRCBL: 15.5; 5.4; 4.4. SC: an. Identifiers: nanotechnology, biotechnology, information technology, and cognitive science.

Abstract: This contribution focuses on two claims advanced by the proponents of the project of "Converging Technologies for Improving Human Performance." Firstly, it is maintained that this project represents something genuinely new and quite unique. Secondly, it is argued that the future prospects of the project are extraordinarily positive. In order to critically assess both claims this paper first focuses on the question of whether there is actually anything genuinely new about the project of improving human performance by means of converging NBIC technologies. In addition it is analyzed whether the project warrants that we be optimistic about its future prospects.

Harper, Peter S., ed. The geneticists' manifesto. *In his:* Landmarks in Medical Genetics: Classic Papers with Commentaries. Oxford; New York: Oxford University Press; 2004: 298-301. NRCBL: 15.5; 1.3.9; 2.2.

Jamieson, J.W. Intellectual ability, evolution and eugenics. *Mankind Quarterly* 1996 Spring-Summer; 36(3 and 4): 381-392. NRCBL: 15.5; 3.2.

Laughlin, Harry H. Report of the Committee to study and to report on the best practical means of cutting off the defective germ-plasm in the American population — Volume I: the scope of the committee's work. Cold Spring Harbor, New York: Eugenics Record Office Bulletin No. 10A 1914; 64 p. NRCBL: 15.5; 2.2.

Lauritzen, Paul; Prusak, Bernard G. The debate over liberal eugenics [letter and reply]. *Hastings Center Report* 2006 March-April; 36(2): 6-7. NRCBL: 15.5; 21.1; 11.3; 1.1.

Neri, Demetrio. On the concept of eugenics: preliminaries to a critical appraisal. *Cadernos de Saúde Pública* 1999; 15 (suppl. 1): 27-34. NRCBL: 15.5; 15.1. SC: an.

Nunes, Rui. Deafness, genetics and dysgenics. *Medicine, Health Care, and Philosophy* 2006; 9(1): 25-31. NRCBL: 15.5; 9.5.1. SC: an.

Abstract: It has been argued by some authors that our reaction to deaf parents who choose deafness for their children ought to be compassion, not condemnation. Although I agree with the reasoning proposed I suggest that this practice could be regarded as unethical. In this article, I shall use the term "dysgenic" as a culturally imposed genetic selection not to achieve any improvement of the human person but to select genetic traits that are commonly accepted as a disabling condition by the majority of the social matrix; in short as a handicap. As in eugenics, dysgenics can be achieved in a positive and a negative way. Positive dysgenics intends to increase the overall number of people with a particular genetic trait. Marriage between deaf people or conceiving deaf children through reproductive technology are examples of positive dysgenics. Negative dysgenics can be obtained through careful prenatal or pre-implantation selection and abortion (or discarding) of normal embryos and foetuses. Only deaf children would be allowed to live. If dysgenics is seen as a programmed genetic intervention that undesirably shapes the human condition—like deliberately creating deaf or dwarf people—the professionals involved in reproductive technologies should answer the question if this should be an

NRCBL: National Reference Center for Bioethics Literature Classification Scheme   See inside front cover for terms.

167

accepted ethical practice because the basic human right to an open future is violated.

Oakley, Ann. Eugenics, Social Medicine and the Career of Richard Titmuss in Britain 1935-50. *British Journal of Sociology* 1991 June; 42(2): 165-194. NRCBL: 15.5.

Ost, Suzanne. Doctors and nurses of death: a case study of eugenically motivated killing under the Nazi 'euthanasia' programme. *Liverpool Law Review* 2006 April; 27(1): 5-30. NRCBL: 15.5; 20.5.1; 7.1; 17.1; 20.4. SC: cs.

Pollack, Robert. Natural design and moral constraints in science. *GeneWatch* 2006 July-August; 19(4): 3-7. NRCBL: 15.5.

Proctor, Robert N. Naziärzte, Rassenmedizin und "lebensunwertes Leben" — von der Ideologie zur "Euthanasie". *In:* Frewer, Andreas; Eickhoff, Clemens, eds. "Euthanasie" und die aktuelle Sterbehilfe-Debatte: Die historischen Hintergründe medizinischer Ethik. Frankfurt; New York: Campus; 2000: 65-89. NRCBL: 15.5; 1.3.5; 2.2; 20.5.1; 21.4.

Rembis, Michael A. "I ain't been reading while on parole": experts, mental tests, and eugenic commitment law in Illinois, 1890-1940. *History of Psychology* 2004; 7(3): 225-247. NRCBL: 15.5; 17.7. SC: cs; rv.

Rushton, J. Philippe. The pioneer fund and the scientific study of human differences. *Albany Law Review* 2002; 66: 207-262. NRCBL: 15.5; 15.6; 17.1. SC: an.

Savulescu, Julian; Hemsley, Melanie; Newson, Ainsley; Foddy, Bennett. Behavioral genetics: why eugenic selection is preferable to enhancement. *Journal of Applied Philosophy* 2006; 23(2): 157-171. NRCBL: 15.5; 15.6; 15.1; 4.5. SC: an.
  Abstract: Criminal behaviour is but one behavioural tendency for which a genetic influence has been suggested. Whilst this research certainly raises difficult ethical questions and is subject to scientific criticism, one recent research project suggests that for some families, criminal tendency might be predicted by genetics. In this paper, supposing this research is valid, we consider whether intervening in the criminal tendency of future children is ethically justifiable. We argue that, if avoidance of harm is a paramount consideration, such an intervention is acceptable when genetic selection is employed instead of genetic enhancement. Moreover, other moral problems in avoiding having children with a tendency to criminal behaviour, such as the prospect of social discrimination, can also be overcome.

Schröter, Sonja. Die Heil- und Pflegeanstalt Waldheim in Sachsen 1933-1938. *In her:* Psychiatrie in Waldheim/Sachsen (1716-1946): ein Beitrag zur Geschichte der forensischen Psychiatrie in Deutschland. Frankfurt am Main: Mabuse; 2003: 71-120. NRCBL: 15.5; 1.3.5; 2.2; 21.4.

Selden, Steven. Transforming Better Babies into Fitter Families: archival resources and the history of American eugenics movement, 1908-1930. *Proceedings of the American Philosophical Society* 2005 June; 149(2): 199-225. NRCBL: 15.5; 15.1.

Shakespeare, Tom. Manifesto for genetic justice. *Social Alternatives* 1999 January; 18(1): 29-32. NRCBL: 15.5; 15.1; 4.5.

Shelden, Randall G. Gene warfare. *Social Justice* 2000 Summer; 27(2): 162-167. NRCBL: 15.5; 15.6.

Steinberg, Deborah Lynn. A most selective practice: the eugenic logic of IVF. *Women's Studies International Forum* 1997; 20(1): 33-48. NRCBL: 15.5; 14.4. SC: em.

Su, Baoq; Macer, Darryl R.J. Ethical dilemmas in genetics and reproductive decisions from the views of Chinese people. *In:* Sang-yong, Song; Young-Mo, Koo; Macer, Darryl R.J., eds. Asian Bioethics in the 21st Century. Christchurch, NZ: Eubios Ethics Institute, 2002: 380-388. NRCBL: 15.5; 5.1; 9.5.3. SC: em. Conference: Proceedings of the Asian Bioethics Conference (ABC4), held 22-25 November 2002 in Seoul, South Korea.

Swedin, Eric G. Designing babies: a eugenics race with China? *Futurist* 2006 May-June; 40(3): 18-21. NRCBL: 15.5; 15.1; 2.2. SC: po.

Wang, Yanguang. Chinese 'eugenics': definition, practice and cultural values. *In:* Sleeboom, Margaret, ed. Genomics in Asia: A Clash of Bioethical Interests? New York: Kegan Paul; 2004: 281-299. NRCBL: 15.5; 15.2; 15.3.

Weikart, Richard. Eugenics. *In:* Mitcham, Carl, ed. Encyclopedia of Science, Technology, and Ethics. Farmington Hills, MI: Thomson/Gale, 2005: 707-710. NRCBL: 15.5; 2.2.

Weiss, Sheila F. Is biotechnological medicine a curse or a blessing? Lessons learned from the international eugenics movement, 1900-1945. *In:* Döring, Ole; Chen, Renbiao, eds. Advances in Chinese Medical Ethics: Chinese and International Perspectives. Hamburg: Institut für Asienkunde; 2002: 85-97. NRCBL: 15.5; 15.1. Note: Proceedings of the Second Sino-German Interdisciplinary Symposium about Medical Ethics in China, Shanghai, 19-23 October, 1999.

Wilkinson, Stephen. Eugenics, embryo selection, and the Equal Value Principle. *Clinical Ethics* 2006 March; 1(1): 46-51. NRCBL: 15.5; 15.2.

Wong, Benjamin. Eugenics from an East Asian perspective. *Mankind Quarterly* 2002 Spring; 42(3): 231-262. NRCBL: 15.5; 21.7.

Zanskas, Steve; Coduti, Wendy. Eugenics, euthanasia, and physician assisted suicide: an overview for rehabilitation professionals. *Journal of Rehabilitation* 2006 January-March; 72(1): 27-34. NRCBL: 15.5; 20.5.1; 20.7; 8.1.

EUTHANASIA AND ALLOWING TO DIE
See also ADVANCE DIRECTIVES; ASSISTED SUICIDE; DEATH AND DYING

Artificial feeding for a child with a degenerative disorder: a family's view. *Archives of Disease in Childhood* 2005 September; 90(9): 979. NRCBL: 20.5.1; 8.3.2; 20.5.2.

Australia—doctors admit to performing assisted suicide and euthanasia [news]. *Canadian HIV/AIDS Policy and Law Newsletter* 1997-1998 Winter; 3(4)-4(1): 47. NRCBL: 20.5.1; 20.3.2.

Empirical studies in bioethics [review]. *Bulletin of Medical Ethics* 2005 March; (206): 13-22. NRCBL: 20.5.1; 18.1. SC: em; rv.

Euthanasia: a "kit" sold in Belgian pharmacies. *Prescrire International* 2005 October; 14(79): 197. NRCBL: 20.5.1; 9.7; 1.3.5.

Flickers of consciousness [editorial]. *Nature* 2006 September 14; 443(7108): 121-122. NRCBL: 20.5.1; 17.1.

Reporting euthanasia in Holland [news]. *European Journal of Cancer Care* 2003 December; 12(4): 302. NRCBL: 20.5.1; 7.4.

The minimally conscious state: a call for guidelines [editorial]. *Lancet* 2006 July 15-21; 368(9531): 176. NRCBL: 20.5.1; 9.8. Identifiers: Terry Wallis.

Adchalingam, K.; Kong, W.H.; Zakiah, M.A.; Zaini, M.; Wong, Y.L.; Lang, C.C. Attitudes of medical students towards euthanasia in a multicultural setting. *Medical Journal of Malaysia* 2005 March; 60(1): 46-49. NRCBL: 20.5.1; 7.2; 21.7. SC: em. Identifiers: Malaysia.

Adeyemo, W.L. Sigmund Freud: smoking habit, oral cancer and euthanasia. *Nigerian Journal of Medicine* 2004 April-June; 13(2): 189-195. NRCBL: 20.5.1; 20.7; 2.2; 8.1. SC: cs.

Adhikary, Sanjib Das; Raviraj, R. Do not resuscitate orders [case study]. *Indian Journal of Medical Ethics* 2006 July-September; 3(3): 100-101. NRCBL: 20.5.1. SC: cs.

Ahmed, A.M.; Kheir, M.M. Attitudes towards euthanasia among final-year Khartoum University medical students. *Eastern Mediterranean Health Journal* 2006; 12(3 and 4): 391-397 [Online]. Accessed: http://www.emro.who.int/publications/emhj/1203_4/PDF/16.pdf [2007 January 4]. NRCBL: 20.5.1; 7.2; 20.3.2. Note: Abstract in French and Arabic.

American Osteopathic Association; End-of-Life Care Committee. American Osteopathic Association's policy statement on end-of-life care. *Journal of the American Osteopathic Association* 2005 November; 105(11, Supplement 5): S32-S34. NRCBL: 20.5.1.

Aminoff, Bechor Zvi. Overprotection phenomenon with dying dementia patients [editorial]. *American Journal of Hospice and Palliative Medicine* 2005 July-August; 22(4): 247-248. NRCBL: 20.5.1; 17.1; 9.5.2. SC: cs.

Angelucci, Patricia A. Grasping the concept of medical futility. *Nursing Management* 2006 February; 37(2): 12, 14. NRCBL: 20.5.1; 9.4; 8.1.

Appel, Jacob M. A duty to kill? A duty to die? Rethinking the euthanasia controversy of 1906. *Bulletin of the History of Medicine* 2004 Fall; 78(3): 610-634. NRCBL: 20.5.1; 20.7; 8.1; 1.3.5.

Aquilina, Carmelo; Greaves, Suki; Al-Saadi, Mohammed; Parmentier, Henk; Tarrant, Joyce; Wantoch, Elaine. Please do not resuscitate: automatic refusal is as harmful as offering resuscitation to all [letter]. *BMJ: British Medical Journal* 2006 March 11; 332(7541): 608- 609. NRCBL: 20.5.1; 8.1. Identifiers: United Kingdom (Great Britain). Comments: S.P. Conroy, T. Luxton, R.H. Harwood, and J.R. Gladman. Cardiopulmonary resuscitation in continuing care settings: time for a rethink? BMJ: British Medical Journal 2006 February 25; 332(7539): 479-482.

Arnold, Elizabeth Mayfield. Factors that influence consideration of hastening death among people with life-threatening illnesses. *Health and Social Work* 2004 February; 29(1): 17-26. NRCBL: 20.5.1; 20.3.1; 20.7; 1.3.10. SC: em.

Ashby, Michael A.; Kellehear, Allan; Stoffell, Brian F. Resolving conflict in end-of-life care: we need to acknowledge the inevitability of death to have some choice in the manner of our dying [editorial]. *Medical Journal of Australia* 2005 September 5; 183(5): 230-231. NRCBL: 20.5.1; 20.3.2; 20.3.3; 20.4.1. SC: em.

Athanassoulis, Nafsika. The treatment that leaves something to luck. *In:* Athanassoulis, Nafsika, ed. Philosophical Reflections on Medical Ethics. New York: Palgrave Macmillan; 2005: 180-197. NRCBL: 20.5.1. SC: an.

Bagheri, Alireza; Asai, Atsushi; Ida, Ryuichi. Experts' attitudes towards medical futility: an empirical survey from Japan. *BMC Medical Ethics [electronic]* 2006; 7: 8. Accessed: http://www.biomedcentral.com/1472-6939/7/8nd. NRCBL: 20.5.1; 20.3.2. SC: em.
Abstract: BACKGROUND The current debate about medical futility is mostly driven by theoretical and personal perspectives and there is a lack of empirical data to document experts and public attitudes towards medical futility. METHODS: To examine the attitudes of the Japanese experts in the fields relevant to medical futility a questionnaire survey was conducted among the members of the Japan Association for Bioethics. A total number of 108 questionnaires returned filled in, giving a response rate of 50.9%. Among the respondents 62% were healthcare professionals (HCPs) and 37% were non-healthcare professionals (Non-HCPs). RESULTS: The majority of respondents (67.6 %) believed that a physician's refusal to provide or continue a treatment on the ground of futility judgment could

NRCBL: National Reference Center for Bioethics Literature Classification Scheme   See inside front cover for terms.

169

never be morally justified but 22.2% approved such refusal with conditions. In the case of physiologically futile care, three-quarters believed that a physician should inform the patient/family of his futility judgment and it would be the patient who could decide what should be done next, based on his/her value judgment. However more than 10% said that a physician should ask about a patient's value and goals, but the final decision was left to the doctor not the patient. There was no statistically significant difference between HCPs and Non-HCPs (p = 0.676). Of respondents 67.6% believed that practical guidelines set up by the health authority would be helpful in futility judgment. CONCLUSION: The results show that there is no support for the physicians' unilateral decision-making on futile care. This survey highlights medical futility as an emerging issue in Japanese healthcare and emphasizes on the need for public discussion and policy development.

Bailey, Susan. Decision making in acute care: a practical framework supporting the 'best interests' principle. *Nursing Ethics* 2006 May; 13(3): 284-291. NRCBL: 20.5.1; 4.4; 8.3.3.

Baily, Mary Ann. How do we avoid compounding the damage? *American Journal of Bioethics* 2006 September-October; 6(5): 36-38; discussion W30-W32. NRCBL: 20.5.1; 9.4. Comments: Mary Ellen Wojtasiewicz. Damage compounded: disparities, distrust, and disparate impact in end-of-life conflict resolution policies. American Journal of Bioethics 2006 September-October; 6(5): 8-12.

Barrett, Ronald Keith. Recommendations for culturally competent end-of-life care giving. *Virtual Mentor* 2001 December; 3(12): 4p. NRCBL: 20.5.1; 21.7.

Bartlow, Bruce. End of life: lessons learned from Terri Schiavo. *Nephrology News and Issues* 2005 June; 19(7): 55, 57-58. NRCBL: 20.5.1; 20.5.4; 19.3.

Baskett, Peter J.F.; Steen, Petter A.; Bossaert, Leo. European Resuscitation Council guidelines for resuscitation 2005. Section 8. The ethics of resuscitation and end-of-life decisions. *Resuscitation* 2005 December; 67(Supplement 1): S171-S180. NRCBL: 20.5.1; 9.8.

Basta, Lofty L. End-of-life medical treatment of older cardiac patients. *American Journal of Geriatric Cardiology* 2004 November- December; 13(6): 313-315. NRCBL: 20.5.1; 9.5.2; 9.8; 20.5.4; 17.1.

Basta, Lofty L. Ethical issues in the management of geriatric cardiac patients: an 89-year-old terminally ill cardiac patient asks you to undertake every possible intervention to keep him alive. *American Journal of Geriatric Cardiology* 2004 November-December; 13(6): 327-328. NRCBL: 20.5.1; 9.5.2; 8.1; 8.3.1; 9.4. Identifiers: Project GRACE [Guidelines for Resuscitation and Care at End-of-Life].

Bastian, Till. Die "wilde" Euthanasie. *In his:* Furchtbare Ärzte: medizinische Verbrechen im Dritten Reich. München: Verlag C.H. Beck; 1995: 58-63. NRCBL: 20.5.1; 1.3.5; 2.2; 15.5; 21.4.

Bastian, Till. Die Aktion "T4.". *In his:* Furchtbare Ärzte: medizinische Verbrechen im Dritten Reich. München:

Verlag C.H. Beck; 1995: 49-57. NRCBL: 20.5.1; 1.3.5; 2.2; 15.5; 21.4.

Bastian, Till. Selektion und andere Verbrechen in den Konzentrationslagern. *In his:* Furchtbare Ärzte: medizinische Verbrechen im Dritten Reich. München: Verlag C.H. Beck; 1995: 64-71. NRCBL: 20.5.1; 1.3.5; 2.2; 15.5; 21.4.

Baume, Peter; O'Malley, Emma. Euthanasia: attitudes and practices of medical practitioners. *Medical Journal of Australia* 1994 July 18; 161: 137-144. NRCBL: 20.5.1; 20.7; 7.1. SC: em.

Baumgartner, Fritz; Cochrane, Thomas I.; Truog, Robert D. The ethical requirement to provide hydration and nutrition [letter and reply]. *Archives of Internal Medicine* 2006 June 26; 166(12): 1324-1325. NRCBL: 20.5.1.

Baumrucker, Steven J. Case study: honoring the patient's wishes or passive euthanasia? *American Journal of Hospice and Palliative Medicine* 2004 May-June; 21(3): 233-236. NRCBL: 20.5.1; 20.5.4; 8.3.1. SC: cs.

Baumrucker, Steven J.; Carter, Greg; Morris, Gerald M.; VandeKieft, Gregg K.; Owens, Darrell. Case study: advisability of partial-code orders. *American Journal of Hospice and Palliative Medicine* 2006 January-February; 23(1): 59-64. NRCBL: 20.5.1. SC: rv.

Baumrucker, Steven J.; Davis, Mellar P.; Paganini, Emil; Morris, Gerald M.; Stolick, Matt; Sheldon, Joanne E. Case study: dementia, quality of life, and appropriate treatment. *American Journal of Hospice and Palliative Medicine* 2005 September-October; 22(5): 385-391. NRCBL: 20.5.1; 19.3; 17.1; 9.5.2. SC: cs.

Bernal, Ellen W. What we do not know about racial/ethnic discrimination in end-of-life treatment decisions. *American Journal of Bioethics* 2006 September-October; 6(5): 21-23; discussion W30-W32. NRCBL: 20.5.1; 9.5.4. Comments: Mary Ellen Wojtasiewicz. Damage compounded: disparities, distrust, and disparate impact in end-of-life conflict resolution policies. American Journal of Bioethics 2006 September-October; 6(5): 8-12.

Bernat, James L. Chronic disorders of consciousness. *Lancet* 2006 April 8-14; 367(9517): 1181-1192. NRCBL: 20.5.1. SC: rv.

Bernat, James L. Medical futility: definition, determination, and disputes in critical care. *Neurocritical Care* 2005; 2(2): 198-205. NRCBL: 20.5.1; 9.4; 8.1.

Biedrzycki, Barbara A. Artificial nutrition and hydration at the end of life: whose decision is it? *ONS News* 2005 November; 20(12): 8, 10. NRCBL: 20.5.1; 8.1.

Birnbacher, Dieter. Eine ethische Bewertung der Unterschiede in der Praxis der Sterbehilfe in den Niederlanden und in Deutschland. *In:* Gordijn, Bert; ten Have, Henk, eds. Medizinethik und Kultur: Grenzen

---

medizinischen Handelns in Deutschland und den Niederlanden. Stuttgart: Frommann-Holzboog; 2000: 419-432. NRCBL: 20.5.1.

Bishop, J.P. Euthanasia, efficiency, and the historical distinction between killing a patient and allowing a patient to die. *Journal of Medical Ethics* 2006 April; 32(4): 220-224. NRCBL: 20.5.1; 20.7. SC: an.

Bishop, J.P. Framing euthanasia. *Journal of Medical Ethics* 2006 April; 32(4): 225-228. NRCBL: 20.5.1; 20.7. SC: an.

Bond, Alex. Where nowhere can lead you. *Hastings Center Report* 2006 November-December; 36(6): 22-24. NRCBL: 20.5.1. SC: cs.

British Columbia Persons with AIDS Society. Position statement on euthanasia released [news]. *Canadian HIV/AIDS Policy and Law Newsletter* 1994 October; 1(1): 15. NRCBL: 20.5.1; 20.3.2; 9.5.6.

Brown, James Henderson; Hentelheff, Paul; Barakat, Samia; Rowe, Cheryl June. Is it normal for terminally ill patients to desire death? *American Journal of Psychiatry* 1986 February; 143(2): 208-211. NRCBL: 20.5.1; 20.3.1; 17.1; 20.7. SC: em.

Burleigh, Michael. Die Nazi-Analogie und die Debatten zur Euthanasie. *In:* Frewer, Andreas; Eickhoff, Clemens, eds. "Euthanasie" und die aktuelle Sterbehilfe-Debatte: Die historischen Hintergründe medizinischer Ethik. Frankfurt; New York: Campus; 2000: 408-423. NRCBL: 20.5.1; 2.2; 1.3.5; 15.5; 21.4. SC: an.

Cahill, Lisa Sowle. Bioethics. *Theological Studies* 2006 March; 67(1): 120-142. NRCBL: 20.5.1; 20.4.1; 9.3.1; 9.2; 4.4.

Callahan, Daniel. Living and dying with medical technology. *Critical Care Medicine* 2003 May; 31(5 Supplement): S344-S346. NRCBL: 20.5.1; 5.2; 9.5.1.

Carey, Benedict. Mental activity seen in a brain gravely injured. *New York Times* 2006 September 8; p. A1, A6. NRCBL: 20.5.1; 4.4. SC: po.

Chambers, John C. Please do not resuscitate: do we perform cardiopulmonary resuscitation on living or dead people? [letter]. *BMJ: British Medical Journal* 2006 March 11; 332(7541): 608. NRCBL: 20.5.1. Identifiers: United Kingdom (Great Britain). Comments: S.P. Conroy, T. Luxton, R.H. Harwood, and J.R. Gladman. Cardiopulmonary resuscitation in continuing care settings: time for a rethink? BMJ: British Medical Journal 2006 February 25; 332(7539): 479-482.

Christmas, Colleen; Finucane, Tom. Artificial nutrition and hydration. *In his:* Is Human Life Special?: Religious and Philosophical Perspectives on the Principle of Human Dignity. New York: P. Lang; 2002: 175-187. NRCBL: 20.5.1.

Cochrane, Thomas I.; Perry, Joshua E.; Kirshner, Howard S.; Churchill, Larry R. Relevance of patient diagnosis to analysis of the Terri Schiavo case [letter and reply]. *Annals of Internal Medicine* 2006 February 21; 144(4): 305- 306. NRCBL: 20.5.1. Comments: Joshua E. Perry, Howard S. Kirshner, and Larry R. Churchill. The Terri Schiavo case: legal, ethical, and medical perspectives. Annals of Internal Medicine 2005; 143: 744-748.

Cochrane, Thomas I.; Truog, Robert D.; Casarett, David; Kapo, Jennifer; Caplan, Arthur. Appropriate use of artificial nutrition and hydration [letter and reply]. *New England Journal of Medicine* 2006 March 23; 354(12): 1320-1321. NRCBL: 20.5.1.

Cohen, Lewis M. A medical revolution in death-hastening decisions. *Palliative and Supportive Care* 2003 December; 1(4): 377-379. NRCBL: 20.5.1; 19.3; 20.3.1.

Cohen, Lewis M. Pulling the plug. *Palliative and Supportive Care* 2003 September; 1(3): 279-283. NRCBL: 20.5.1; 20.4.1; 20.3.2.

Cohen, Simon; Sprung, Charles; Sjokvist, Peter; Lippert, Anne; Ricou, Bara; Baras, Mario; Hovilehto, Seppo; Maia, Paulo; Phelan, Dermot; Reinhart, Konrad; Werdan, Karl; Bulow, Hans-Henrik; Woodcock, Tom. Communication of end-of-life decisions in European intensive care units. *Intensive Care Medicine* 2005 September; 31(9): 1215-1221. NRCBL: 20.5.1; 9.4; 8.1; 21.1. SC: em.

Comby, M.C.; Filbet, M. The demand for euthanasia in palliative care units: a prospective study in seven units of the 'Rhône-Alpes' region. *Palliative Medicine* 2005 December; 19(8): 587-593. NRCBL: 20.5.1; 20.4.1; 4.4. SC: em. Identifiers: France.

Conroy, Simon P.; Luxton, Tony; Dingwall, Robert; Harwood, Rowan H.; Gladman, John R. F. Cardiopulmonary resuscitation in continuing care settings: time for a rethink? *BMJ: British Medical Journal* 2006 February 25; 332(7539): 479-482. NRCBL: 20.5.1; 9.5.2; 4.4.

Cosman, Madeleine Pelner. Frogs, crabs, and the culture of death: lessons from the Schiavo case. *Journal of American Physicians and Surgeons* 2005 Summer; 10(2): 55-57. NRCBL: 20.5.1; 9.2; 9.3.1; 9.4.

Coulehan, Jack. "They wouldn't pay attention": death without dignity. *American Journal of Hospice and Palliative Medicine* 2005 September-October; 22(5): 339-343. NRCBL: 20.5.1; 20.4.1; 4.4. SC: cs.

Craig, Gillian; Janssens, Rien M.J.P.A.; Olthuis, Gert; Dekkers, Wim; Harvath, Theresa A.; Smyth, Dion. Sedation without hydration can seriously damage your health [debate]. *International Journal of Palliative Nursing* 2005 July; 11(7): 333-337. NRCBL: 20.5.1.

NRCBL: National Reference Center for Bioethics Literature Classification Scheme   See inside front cover for terms.

171

Crippen, David; Hawryluck, Laura. Pro/con clinical debate: life support should have a special status among therapies, and patients or their families should have a right to insist on this treatment even if it will not improve outcome. *Critical Care* 2004 August; 8(4): 231-233. NRCBL: 20.5.1; 9.4.

Culberson, John; Levy, Cari; Lawhorne, Larry. Do not hospitalize orders in nursing homes: a pilot study. *Journal of the American Medical Directors Association* 2005 January-February; 6(1): 22-26. NRCBL: 20.5.1; 9.5.2. SC: em.

Dane, Francis C.; Parish, David C. Ethical issues in registry research: in-hospital resuscitation as a case study. *Journal of Empirical Research on Human Research Ethics* 2006 December; 1(4): 69-76. NRCBL: 20.5.1; 1.3.12.

De Dijn, Herman. Euthanasia and pluralism. *In:* Schotsmans, Paul; Meulenbergs, Tom, eds. Euthanasia and Palliative Care in the Low Countries. Dudley, MA: Peeters, 2005: 227-238. NRCBL: 20.5.1; 21.7.

de Grey, Aubrey D.N.J. The ethical status of efforts to postpone aging: a reply to Hurlbut [editorial]. *Rejuvenation Research* 2005 Fall; 8(3): 129-130. NRCBL: 20.5.1; 9.5.2; 4.5.

Dekkers, Wim. Die Euthanasiedebatte und die Nazi-Ideologie: eine philosophische Analyse einer Diskussion. *In:* Gordijn, Bert; ten Have, Henk, eds. Medizinethik und Kultur: Grenzen medizinischen Handelns in Deutschland und den Niederlanden. Stuttgart: Frommann-Holzboog; 2000: 345-373. NRCBL: 20.5.1.

Delkeskamp-Hayes, Corinna. Freedom-costs of canonical individualism: enforced euthanasia tolerance in Belgium and the problem of European liberalism. *Journal of Medicine and Philosophy* 2006 August; 31(4): 333-362. NRCBL: 20.5.1; 21.7.

Abstract: Belgium's policy of not permitting Catholic hospitals to refuse euthanasia services rests on ethical presuppositions concerning the secular justification of political power which reveal the paradoxical character of European liberalism: In endorsing freedom as a value (rather than as a side constraint), liberalism prioritizes first-order intentions, thus discouraging lasting moral commitments and the authority of moral communities in supporting such commitments. The state itself is thus transformed into a moral community of its own. Alternative policies (such as an explicit moral diversification of public healthcare or the greater tolerance for Christian institutions in the Netherlands) are shown to be incompatible with Europe's liberal concern with securing social and material freedom resources, as well as the concern with equality of opportunity, as embodied in the European Union's anti-discrimination labor law. The essay's argument for the preferability of a libertarian solution closes with the challenge that only if the provision of public healthcare can be shown to be rationally indispensable for a morally justified polity, could the exposed incoherence of modern European liberalism be generously discounted.

Dennehy, Christine. Analysis of patients' rights: dementia and PEG insertion. *British Journal of Nursing* 2006 January 12-25; 15(1): 18-20. NRCBL: 20.5.1; 9.5.2; 17.1. Identifiers: percutaneous endoscopic gastronomy.

Derse, Arthur R. Limitation of treatment at the end-of-life: withholding and withdrawal. *Clinics in Geriatric Medicine* 2005 February; 21(1): 223-238. NRCBL: 20.5.1; 8.3.3.

Deschepper, Reginald; Vander Stichele, Robert; Bernheim, Jan L.; De Keyser, Els; Van Der Kelen, Greta; Mortier, Freddy; Deliens, Luc. Communication on end-of-life decisions with patients wishing to die at home: the making of a guideline for GPs in Flanders, Belgium. *British Journal of General Practice* 2006 January; 56(522): 14-19. NRCBL: 20.5.1; 8.1.

Diamond, Eugene F. Terminal sedation. *Linacre Quarterly* 2006 May; 73(2): 172-175. NRCBL: 20.5.1.

Druart, M.L. Euthanasia. *Acta Chirurgica Belgica* 2002 November-December; 102(6): 365-367. NRCBL: 20.5.1.

Du, Zhizheng. An ethical defense for withdrawing medical treatment. *In:* Döring, Ole; Chen, Renbiao, eds. Advances in Chinese Medical Ethics: Chinese and International Perspectives. Hamburg: Institut für Asienkunde; 2002: 306-314. NRCBL: 20.5.1. Note: Proceedings of the Second Sino-German Interdisciplinary Symposium about Medical Ethics in China, Shanghai, 19-23 October, 1999.

Duncan, O.D.; Parmelee, L.F. Trends in public approval of euthanasia and suicide in the US, 1947-2003. *Journal of Medical Ethics* 2006 May; 32(5): 266-272. NRCBL: 20.5.1; 20.7. SC: em.

Dunet-Larousse, Emmanuel. L'euthanasie: signification et qualification au regard du droit pénal / Euthanasia: definition and distinctions with regard to criminal law. *Revue de Droit Sanitaire et Social* 1998 April-June; 34(2): 265-283. NRCBL: 20.5.1; 20.7; 1.3.5.

Eachempati, Soumitra R.; Hydo, Lynn; Shou, Jian; Barie, Philip S. Sex differences in creation of do-not-resuscitate orders for critically ill elderly patients following emergency surgery. *Journal of Trauma* 2006 January; 60(1): 193-198. NRCBL: 20.5.1; 9.5.2. SC: em.

Eidelman, L.A.; Jakobson, D.J.; Pizov, R.; Geber, D.; Leibovitz, L.; Sprung, C.L. Forgoing life-sustaining treatment in an Israeli ICU. *Intensive Care Medicine* 1998 February; 24(2): 162-166. NRCBL: 20.5.1; 9.5.1. SC: em.

Erbguth, Frank; Lipp, Volker; Nagel, Michael Benedikt. Zum problem ausreichender Gründe für eine Behandlungsbegrenzung [The problem of adequate reasons for limiting treatment. Commentaries I and II]. *Ethik in der Medizin* 2006 June; 18(2): 181-188. NRCBL: 20.5.1. SC: cs.

Erlen, Judith A. When patients and families disagree. *Orthopaedic Nursing* 2005 July-August; 24(4): 279-282. NRCBL: 20.5.1; 8.1. SC: cs.

Ewy, Gordon A. Cardiac resuscitation — when is enough enough? [editorial]. *New England Journal of Medicine* 2006 August 3; 355(5): 510-512. NRCBL: 20.5.1; 9.5.1.

Fairchild, Alysa; Kelly, Karie-Lynn; Balogh, Alex. In pursuit of an artful death: discussion of resuscitation status on an inpatient radiation oncology service. *Supportive Care in Cancer* 2005 October; 13(10): 842-849. NRCBL: 20.5.1; 8.3.1. SC: em.

Farber, Neil J.; Simpson, Pamela; Salam, Tabassum; Collier, Virginia U.; Weiner, Joan; Boyer, E. Gil. Physicians' decisions to withhold and withdraw life-sustaining treatment. *Archives of Internal Medicine* 2006 March 13; 166(5): 560-564. NRCBL: 20.5.1. SC: em.

Farber, Stuart; Shaw, Jim; Mero, Jeff; Maloney, W. Hugh. Withholding resuscitation: a new approach to prehospital end-of-life decisions [letter]. *Annals of Internal Medicine* 2006 November 21; 145(10): 788. NRCBL: 20.5.1.

Faulstich, Heinz. Die Zahl der "Euthanasie"-Opfer. *In:* Frewer, Andreas; Eickhoff, Clemens, eds. "Euthanasie" und die aktuelle Sterbehilfe-Debatte: Die historischen Hintergründe medizinischer Ethik. Frankfurt; New York: Campus; 2000: 218-234. NRCBL: 20.5.1; 1.3.5; 2.2; 15.5; 21.4. SC: em.

Feder, Sylvia; Matheny, Roger L.; Loveless, Robert S.; Rea, Thomas D. Withholding resuscitation: a new approach to prehospital end-of-life decisions [editorial]. *Annals of Internal Medicine* 2006 May 2; 144(9): 634-640. NRCBL: 20.5.1. SC: em.

Feldman, Eric A. Asserting rights, legislating death. *In his:* The Ritual of Rights in Japan: Law, Society, and Health Policy. New York: Cambridge University Press, 2000: 82-109. NRCBL: 20.5.1.

Fidler, H.; Thompson, C.; Freeman, A.; Hogan, D.; Walker, G.; Weinman, J. Barriers to implementing a policy not to attempt resuscitation in acute medical admissions: prospective cross sectional study of a successive cohort. *BMJ: British Medical Journal* 2006 February 25; 332(7539): 461-462. NRCBL: 20.5.1; 8.1. SC: em. Identifiers: England.

Fins, Joseph J.; Schiff, Nicholas D. Shades of gray: new insights into the vegetative state. *Hastings Center Report* 2006 November-December; 36(6): 8. NRCBL: 20.5.1.

Fisher, Ian. Italian poet dies with help from a doctor. *New York Times* 2006 December 22; p. A3. NRCBL: 20.5.1. SC: po. Identifiers: Piergiorgio Welby; Italy.

Fissell, Rachel B.; Bragg-Gresham, Jennifer L.; Lopes, Antonio Alberto; Cruz, José Miguel; Fukuhara, Shunichi; Asano, Yasushi; Brown, Wendy Weinstock; Keen, Marcia L.; Port, Friedrich K.; Young, Eric W. Factors associated with "do not resuscitate" orders and rates of withdrawal from hemodialysis in the international DOPPS. *Kidney International* 2005 September; 68(3): 1282-1288. NRCBL: 20.5.1; 19.3. SC: em. Identifiers: Dialysis Outcomes and Practice Pattern Study.

Frewer, Andreas. Die Euthanasie-Debatte in der Zeitschrift Ethik 1922-1938: Zur Anatomie des medizinethischen Diskurses. *In:* Frewer, Andreas; Eickhoff, Clemens, eds. "Euthanasie" und die aktuelle Sterbehilfe-Debatte: Diehistorischen Hintergründe medizinischer Ethik. Frankfurt; New York: Campus; 2000: 90-119. NRCBL: 20.5.1; 1.3.5; 2.2; 15.5; 21.4.

Frey, Ray. Passive death. *In:* Athanassoulis, Nafsika, ed. Philosophical Reflections on Medical Ethics. New York: Palgrave Macmillan; 2005: 198-207. NRCBL: 20.5.1; 20.7. SC: an.

Frey, R.G. Intending and causing. *Journal of Ethics* 2005; 9(3-4): 465-474. NRCBL: 20.5.1; 20.7.

Fry, Sara. Guidelines for making end-of-life decisions. *International Nursing Review* 1998 September-October; 45(5): 143-144, 151. NRCBL: 20.5.1.

Ganz, F.D.; Benbenishty, J.; Hersch, M.; Fischer, A.; Gurman, G.; Sprung, C.L. The impact of regional culture on intensive care end of life decision making: an Israeli perspective from the ETHICUS study. *Journal of Medical Ethics* 2006 April; 32(4): 196-199. NRCBL: 20.5.1; 21.7. SC: em.

Ganzini, Linda; Beer, Tomasz M.; Brouns, Matthew; Mori, Motomi; Hsieh, Yi-Ching. Interest in physician-assisted suicide among Oregon cancer patients. *Journal of Clinical Ethics* 2006 Spring; 17(1): 27-38. NRCBL: 20.5.1; 20.7. SC: em.

Gattellari, Melina; Voigt, Katie J.; Butow, Phyllis N.; Tattersall, Martin H.N. When the treatment goal is not cure: are cancer patients equipped to make informed decisions? *Journal of Clinical Oncology* 2002 January 15; 20(2): 503-513. NRCBL: 20.5.1; 8.3.1; 9.5.1. SC: em. Identifiers: Australia.

Georges, Jean-Jacques; Onwuteaka-Philipsen, Bregje D.; van der Heide, Agnes; van der Wal, Gerrit; van der Maas, Paul J. Requests to forgo potentially life-prolonging treatment and to hasten death in terminally ill cancer patients: a prospective study. *Journal of Pain and Symptom Management* 2006 February; 31(2): 100-110. NRCBL: 20.5.1; 8.1; 8.3.4; 9.5.1; 7.1. SC: em.

Georges, Jean-Jacques; Onwuteaka-Philipsen, Bregje D.; van der Wal, Gerrit; van der Heide, Agnes; van der Maas, Paul J. Differences between terminally ill cancer patients who died after euthanasia had been performed and terminally ill cancer patients who did not request euthana-

---

NRCBL: National Reference Center for Bioethics Literature Classification Scheme   See inside front cover for terms.

173

sia. *Palliative Medicine* 2005 December; 19(8): 578-586. NRCBL: 20.5.1; 20.4.1; 9.5.1. SC: em. Identifiers: Netherlands.

Gert, Bernard; Culver, Charles M.; Clouser, K. Danner. Euthanasia. *In their:* Bioethics: A Systematic Approach. Second edition. New York: Oxford University Press; 2006: 309-345. NRCBL: 20.5.1.

Giacomini, M.; Cook, D.; DeJean, D.; Shaw, R.; Gedge, E. Decision tools for life support: a review and policy analysis. *Critical Care Medicine* 2006 March; 34(3): 864-870. NRCBL: 20.5.1. SC: em; rv.

Gillick, Muriel R. The ethics of artificial nutrition and hydration—a practical guide. *Practical Bioethics* 2006 Spring-Summer; 2(2-3): 1, 5-7. NRCBL: 20.5.1; 8.1.

Glick, Shimon M.; Casarett, David; Kapo, Jennifer; Caplan, Arthur. Appropriate use of artificial nutrition and hydration [letter and reply]. *New England Journal of Medicine* 2006 March 23; 354(12): 1320-1321. NRCBL: 20.5.1.

Goldblatt, David. The gift: when a patient chooses to die. *Perspectives in Biology and Medicine* 2006 Autumn; 49(4): 537-541. NRCBL: 20.5.1.

Gordijn, Bert. Die Debatte um Euthanasie in den Niederlanden und Deutschland: ein Vergleich aus historischer Sicht. *In:* Gordijn, Bert; ten Have, Henk, eds. Medizinethik und Kultur: Grenzen medizinischen Handelns in Deutschland und den Niederlanden. Stuttgart: Frommann-Holzboog; 2000: 303-343. NRCBL: 20.5.1; 21.1.

Gordon, M.; Sheehan, K. Artificial intelligence: making decisions about artificial nutrition and hydration. *Journal of Nutrition, Health and Aging* 2004; 8(4): 254-256. NRCBL: 20.5.1. SC: cs. Identifiers: Canada.

Gould, Donald. New doctor's dilemma. *New Statesman (London, England) 1957)* 1967 September 29; 74: 399. NRCBL: 20.5.1; 5.3; 4.4. Identifiers: United Kingdom (Great Britain).

Grant, Richard E.; Boylan, Michael. Just end-of-life policies and patient dignity. *American Journal of Bioethics* 2006 September-October; 6(5): 32-33; discussion W30-W32. NRCBL: 20.5.1; 9.5.4. Comments: Mary Ellen Wojtasiewicz. Damage compounded: disparities, distrust, and disparate impact in end-of-life conflict resolution policies. American Journal of Bioethics 2006 September-October; 6(5): 8-12.

Gray, Alastair. The advanced nurse practitioner: empowerment in witnessed resuscitation. *In:* Bartter, Karen, ed. Ethical Issues in Advanced Nursing Practice. Boston: Butterworth-Heinemann; 2001: 101-117. NRCBL: 20.5.1.

Halpern, Scott D.; Hansen-Flaschen, John. Terminal withdrawal of life-sustaining supplemental oxygen.

JAMA: The Journal of the American Medical Association 2006 September 20; 269(11): 1397-1400. NRCBL: 20.5.1.

Hamano, Kenzo. Should euthanasia be legalized in Japan? The importance of the attitude towards life. *In:* Sang-yong, Song; Young-Mo, Koo; Macer, Darryl R.J., eds. Asian Bioethics in the 21st Century. Christchurch, NZ: Eubios Ethics Institute, 2002: 110-117. NRCBL: 20.5.1; 21.7. Conference: Proceedings of the Asian Bioethics Conference (ABC4), held 22-25 November 2002 in Seoul, South Korea.

Hamilton, Richard. The law on dying. *Journal of the Royal Society of Medicine* 2002 November; 95(11): 565-566. NRCBL: 20.5.1; 20.7; 1.3.5. SC: cs.

Hansen, Lissi; Archbold, Patricia G.; Stewart, Barbara; Westfall, Una Beth; Ganzini, Linda. Family caregivers making life-sustaining treatment decisions: factors associated with role strain and ease. *Journal of Gerontological Nursing* 2005 November; 31(11): 28-35. NRCBL: 20.5.1; 8.1. SC: em.

Hanson, Laura C. Honoring Ms. Burke's wishes. *Practical Bioethics* 2006 Spring-Summer; 2(2-3): 13. NRCBL: 20.5.1; 8.1. SC: cs.

Hanson, Laura C. Honoring Ms. Burke's wishes—a commentary. *Practical Bioethics* 2006 Spring-Summer; 2(2-3): 14-15. NRCBL: 20.5.1; 8.1. SC: cs.

Hargrove, Marion D., Jr. A five-step approach to settling a dispute over futile care. *Journal of the Louisiana State Medical Society* 1994 October; 146(10): 439-440. NRCBL: 20.5.1; 9.8; 8.1.

Harrington, Michael D.; Luebke, D.L.; Lewis, W.R.; Auliso, M.P.; Johnson, N.J. Implantable cardioverter defibrillator (ICD) at end of life #112. *Journal of Palliative Medicine* 2005 October; 8(5): 1056-1057. NRCBL: 20.5.1; 9.7.

Hayflick, Leonard. Aging and regenerative medicine. *In:* Mitcham, Carl, ed. Encyclopedia of Science, Technology, and Ethics. Farmington Hills, MI: Thomson/Gale, 2005: 34-37. NRCBL: 20.5.1; 4.5; 18.3; 18.5.4; 19.5.

Heland, Melodie. Fruitful or futile: intensive care nurses' experiences and perceptions of medical futility. *Australian Critical Care* 2006 February; 19(1): 25-31. NRCBL: 20.5.1.

Heß, Marga. Zur Geschichte der Entschädigung von Euthanasie-Opfern: Gedenken und Handeln. *In:* Frewer, Andreas; Eickhoff, Clemens, eds. "Euthanasie" und die aktuelle Sterbehilfe-Debatte: die historischen Hintergründe medizinischer Ethik. Frankfurt; New York: Campus; 2000: 370-382. NRCBL: 20.5.1; 2.2; 9.3.1; 11.3; 15.5; 21.4.

Hook, C. Christopher; Mueller, Paul S. The Terri Schiavo saga: the making of a tragedy and lessons learned.

Mayo Clinic Proceedings 2005 November; 80(11): 1449-1460. NRCBL: 20.5.1; 8.3.3.

Hopkin, Michael. 'Vegetative' patient shows signs of conscious thought [news]. *Nature* 2006 September 14; 443(7108): 132-133. NRCBL: 20.5.1; 17.1.

Hopson, Laura R.; Hirsh, Emily; Delgado, Joao; Domeier, Robert M.; McSwain, Norman E., Jr.; Krohmer, Jon. Guidelines for withholding or termination of resuscitation in prehospital traumatic cardiopulmonary arrest: a joint position paper from the National Association of EMS Physicians Standards and Clinical Practice Committee and the American College of Surgeons Committee on Trauma. *Prehospital Emergency Care* 2003 January-March; 7(1): 141-146. NRCBL: 20.5.1; 6.

Horrobin, Steven. Immortality, human nature, the value of life and the value of life extension. *Bioethics* 2006 November; 20(6): 279-292. NRCBL: 20.5.1; 4.5; 4.4.

Hu, Joan S. Are you alive in there? *Current Surgery* 2004 July-August; 61(4): 393-394. NRCBL: 20.5.1; 4.4. SC: cs.

Hunter, Joanna K.; Dean, Tamsin; Gowan, Jenny. Death with dignity: devising a withdrawal of treatment process. *British Journal of Nursing* 2006 February 9-22; 15(3): 138-140. NRCBL: 20.5.1.

Hurst, Samia A. "Agreed boundaries": are we asking the right question? [letter]. *Archives of Internal Medicine* 2006 January 9; 166(1): 126- 127. NRCBL: 20.5.1; 20.7; 21.1.

International Council for Laboratory Animal Science [ICLAS]. International harmonisation of guidelines on euthanasia. Nantes, France: International Council for Laboratory Animal Science 2004 November 8: 4 p. [Online]. Accessed: http://www.sciencemag.org/cgi/data/312/5774/700/DC1/1 [2006 October 4]. NRCBL: 20.5.1; 22.2; 22.1; 21.1.

Jacobs, Barbara Bennett; Taylor, Carol. Medical futility in the natural attitude. *ANS: Advances in Nursing Science* 2005 October-December; 28(4): 288-305. NRCBL: 20.5.1; 9.4. SC: rv.

Jans, Jan. Churches in the Low Countries on euthanasia: background, argumentation and commentary. *In:* Schotsmans, Paul; Meulenbergs, Tom, eds. Euthanasia and Palliative Care in the Low Countries. Dudley, MA: Peeters, 2005: 175-204. NRCBL: 20.5.1; 21.1.

Jansen, Lynn A. Hastening death and the boundaries of the self. *Bioethics* 2006 April; 20(2): 105-111. NRCBL: 20.5.1; 19.1; 4.4. SC: an.

Abstract: When applying moral principles to concrete cases, we assume a background shared understanding of the boundaries of the persons to whom the principles apply. In most contexts, this assumption is unproblematic. However, in end-of-life contexts, when patients are receiving 'artificial' life-support, judgments about where a person's self begins and ends can become controversial. To illustrate this possibility, this paper presents a case in which a decision must be made whether to deactivate a patient's pacemaker as a means to hasten his death. After discussing some common moral principles that are often applied to resolve ethical problems at the end of life and after explaining why they are of no help here, the paper argues that the correct analysis of this case, and of cases of this sort, turns on considerations that relate to the constitution of the self. These considerations, the paper further argues, sometimes resist resolution. The constitution of the self is fixed in large measure by our concepts and social conventions, and these do not always provide determinate grounds for delimiting the boundaries of the self.

Janssen, Fanny; van der Heide, Agnes; Kunst, Anton E.; Mackenbach, Johan P. End-of-life decisions and old-age mortality: a cross-country analysis. *Journal of the American Geriatrics Society* 2006 December; 54(12): 1951-1953. NRCBL: 20.5.1; 20.4.1. SC: em.

Johansen, Sissel; Holen, Jacob C.; Kaasa, Stein; Loge, Jon Håvard; Materstvedt, Lars Johan. Attitudes towards, and wishes for, euthanasia in advanced cancer patients at a palliative medicine unit. *Palliative Medicine* 2005 September; 19(6): 454-460. NRCBL: 20.5.1; 20.7; 8.1; 9.5.1.

Joshi, Shalaka R. Whose life is it, anyway? The evolving face of euthanasia [editorial]. *Journal of the Association of Physicians of India* 2005 April; 53: 279-281. NRCBL: 20.5.1.

Kampits, Peter. A case study. *In:* Döring, Ole; Chen, Renbiao, eds. Advances in Chinese Medical Ethics: Chinese and International Perspectives. Hamburg: Institut für Asienkunde; 2002: 427-432. NRCBL: 20.5.1. Note: Proceedings of the Second Sino-German Interdisciplinary Symposium about Medical Ethics in China, Shanghai, 19-23 October, 1999.

Kaufman, Sharon R. Death by design. *In her:* . . .And a Time to Die: How American Hospitals Shape the End of Life. New York: Scribner; 2005: 207-235. NRCBL: 20.5.1.

Kaufman, Sharon R. Hidden places: the zone of indistinction as a way of life. *In her:* . . .And a Time to Die: How American Hospitals Shape the End of Life. New York: Scribner; 2005: 273-317. NRCBL: 20.5.1; 4.4; 20.4.1.

Kaufman, Sharon R. Life support. *In her:* . . .And a Time to Die: How American Hospitals Shape the End of Life. New York: Scribner; 2005: 236-272. NRCBL: 20.5.1.

Kellermann, Arthur; Lynn, Joanne. Withholding resuscitation in prehospital care. *Annals of Internal Medicine* 2006 May 2; 144(9): 692-693. NRCBL: 20.5.1.

Keown, John. Mr. Marty's muddle: a superficial and selective case for euthanasia in Europe. *Journal of Medical Ethics* 2006 January; 32(1): 29-33. NRCBL: 20.5.1; 20.7.

Abstract: In April 2004 the Parliamentary Assembly of the Council of Europe debated a report from its Social, Health and Family Affairs Committee (the Marty Report), which questioned the Council of Europe's opposition to legalising euthana-

---

NRCBL: National Reference Center for Bioethics Literature Classification Scheme   See inside front cover for terms.

175

sia. This article exposes the Report's flaws, not least its superficiality and selectivity.

Kerwin, Jeanne; Bauman, Susan. Out-of-hospital do-not-resuscitate (DNR) orders: the New Jersey protocol. *New Jersey Medicine* 2003 November; 100(11): 21-22. NRCBL: 20.5.1.

Kimsma, Gerrit K.; van Leeuwen, Evert. Euthanasie in den Niederlanden: Historische Entwicklung, Argumente und heutige Lage. *In:* Frewer, Andreas; Eickhoff, Clemens, eds. "Euthanasie" und die aktuelle Sterbehilfe-Debatte: Diehistorischen Hintergründe medizinischer Ethik. Frankfurt; New York: Campus; 2000: 276-312. NRCBL: 20.5.1; 2.2.

Kimsma, Gerrit; van Leeuwen, Evert. Euthanasie und Beihilfe zum Suizid in den Niederlanden. *In:* Gordijn, Bert; ten Have, Henk, eds. Medizinethik und Kultur: Grenzen medizinischen Handelns in Deutschland und den Niederlanden. Stuttgart: Frommann-Holzboog; 2000: 71-103. NRCBL: 20.5.1; 20.7.

Knoepffler, Nikolaus. Konfliktfälle am Lebensende. *In his:* Menschenwürde in der Bioethik. New York: Springer; 2004: 139-170. NRCBL: 20.5.1; 19.5; 20.7.

Knox, Crissy; Vereb, John A. Allow natural death: a more humane approach to discussing end-of-life directives. *Journal of Emergency Nursing* 2005 December; 31(6): 560-561. NRCBL: 20.5.1.

Kristjanson, Linda J.; Christakis, Nicholas. Investigating euthanasia: methodological, ethical and clinical considerations [editorial]. *Palliative Medicine* 2005 December; 19(8): 575-577. NRCBL: 20.5.1; 20.4.1.

Kwak, Jung; Haley, William E. Current research findings on end-of-life decision making among racially or ethnically diverse groups. *Gerontologist* 2005 October; 45(5): 634-641. NRCBL: 20.5.1; 7.1; 8.1; 9.5.4; 20.5.4; 21.7. SC: rv.

Lagay, Faith. Resuscitating privacy in emergency settings. *In:* American Medical Association. Professing Medicine: strengthening the ethics and professionalism of tomorrow's physicians. Chicago: American Medical Association; 2001: 75-79. NRCBL: 20.5.1; 8.4; 9.5.1. Note: Commemorative issue of Virtual Mentor, AMA's online ethics journal.

Lanier, William L. Medical interventions at the end of life: what is appropriate and who is responsible? *Mayo Clinic Proceedings* 2005 November; 80(11): 1411-1413. NRCBL: 20.5.1; 8.3.3.

Lavery, James V.; Van Laethem, Marlene L.P.; Slutsky, Arthur S. Monitoring and oversight in critical care research. *Critical Care* 2004 December; 8(6): 403-405. NRCBL: 20.5.1; 18.2. Identifiers: Canada.

Lazaruk, Tina. The CPR question. *Canadian Nurse* 2006 February; 102(2): 22-24; discussion 23-24. NRCBL: 20.5.1; 9.5.2.

Levin, Phillip D.; Sprung, Charles L. Withdrawing and withholding life-sustaining therapies are not the same. *Critical Care* 2005 June; 9(3): 230-232. NRCBL: 20.5.1.

Lin, Richard J. Withdrawing life-sustaining medical treatment — a physician's personal reflection. *Mental Retardation and Developmental Disabilities Research Reviews* 2003; 9(1): 10-15. NRCBL: 20.5.1; 9.5.7; 8.1; 7.1.

Lishman, Gordon. Please do not resuscitate: communication is key [letter]. *BMJ: British Medical Journal* 2006 March 11; 332(7541): 609. NRCBL: 20.5.1; 8.1. Identifiers: United Kingdom (Great Britain). Comments: S.P. Conroy, T. Luxton, R.H. Harwood, and J.R. Gladman. Cardiopulmonary resuscitation in continuing care settings: time for a rethink? BMJ: British Medical Journal 2006 February 25; 332(7539): 479-482.

Loeben, Greg. Understanding futility: why trust and disparate impact matter as much as what works. *American Journal of Bioethics* 2006 September-October; 6(5): 38-39; discussion W30-W32. NRCBL: 20.5.1; 9.4; 9.5.4. Comments: Mary Ellen Wojtasiewicz. Damage compounded: disparities, distrust, and disparate impact in end-of-life conflict resolution policies. American Journal of Bioethics 2006 September-October; 6(5): 8-12.

Lohiya, Ghan-Shyam; Tan-Figueroa, Lilia; Crinella, Francis M. End-of-life care for a man with developmental disabilities. *Journal of the American Board of Family Practice* 2003 January-February; 16(1): 58-62. NRCBL: 20.5.1; 9.5.1; 8.3.3; 8.1. SC: cs.

Louhiala, P.; Hildén, H.-M. Attitudes of Finnish doctors towards euthanasia in 1993 and 2003. *Journal of Medical Ethics* 2006 November; 32(11): 627-628. NRCBL: 20.5.1. SC: em.

Lunshof, Jeantine E.; Simon, Alfred. Die Diskussion um Sterbehilfe und Euthanasie in Deutschland von 1945 bis in die Gegenwart. *In:* Frewer, Andreas; Eickhoff, Clemens, eds. "Euthanasie" und die aktuelle Sterbehilfe-Debatte: Die historischen Hintergründe medizinischer Ethik. Frankfurt; New York: Campus; 2000: 237-249. NRCBL: 20.5.1; 2.2. SC: em.

Maio, Giovanni. Reanimieren oder nicht?: Ethische Überlegungen zur deutschen Diskussion über den Therapieverzicht. *In:* Gordijn, Bert; ten Have, Henk, eds. Medizinethik und Kultur: Grenzen medizinischen Handelns in Deutschland und den Niederlanden. Stuttgart: Frommann-Holzboog; 2000: 105-139. NRCBL: 20.5.1. SC: an.

Mak, Yvonne; Elwyn, Glyn. Use of hermeneutic research in understanding the meaning of desire for euthanasia. *Pal-*

liative Medicine 2003; 17(5): 395-402. NRCBL: 20.5.1; 20.4.1. SC: em. Identifiers: Hong Kong.

Mak, Yvonne; Elwyn, Glyn. Voices of the terminally ill: uncovering the meaning of desire for euthanasia. *Palliative Medicine* 2005 June; 19(4): 343-350. NRCBL: 20.5.1; 4.4; 20.3.1. SC: em. Identifiers: Hong Kong.

Manninen, B.A. A case for justified non-voluntary active euthanasia: exploring the ethics of the Groningen Protocol. *Journal of Medical Ethics* 2006 November; 32(11): 643-651. NRCBL: 20.5.1; 20.5.2. SC: an. Identifiers: Netherlands.

Abstract: One of the most recent controversies to arise in the field of bioethics concerns the ethics for the Groningen Protocol: the guidelines proposed by the Groningen Academic Hospital in The Netherlands, which would permit doctors to actively euthanise terminally ill infants who are suffering. The Groningen Protocol has been met with an intense amount of criticism, some even calling it a relapse into a Hitleresque style of eugenics, where people with disabilities are killed solely because of their handicaps. The purpose of this paper is threefold. First, the paper will attempt to disabuse readers of this erroneous understanding of the Groningen Protocol by showing how such a policy does not aim at making quality-of-life judgements, given that it restricts euthanasia to suffering and terminally ill infants. Second, the paper illustrates that what the Groningen Protocol proposes to do is both ethical and also the most humane alternative for these suffering and dying infants. Lastly, responses are given to some of the worries expressed by ethicists on the practice of any type of non-voluntary active euthanasia.

Manno, Edward M.; Wijdicks, Eelco F.M. The declaration of death and the withdrawal of care in the neurologic patient. *Neurologic Clinics* 2006 February; 24(1): 159-169. NRCBL: 20.5.1; 20.2.1; 17.1.

Manthous, Constantine A. Critical care physicians' practices and attitudes and applicable statutes regarding withdrawal of life-sustaining therapies. *Connecticut Medicine* 2005 August; 69(7): 395-400. NRCBL: 20.5.1. SC: em.

Marco, C.A. Ethical issues of resuscitation: an American perspective. *Postgraduate Medical Journal* 2005 September; 81(959): 608-612. NRCBL: 20.5.1; 2.1; 20.4.1; 9.5.1.

Marcoux, Isabelle; Onwuteaka-Philipsen, Bregje D.; Jansen-van der Weide, Marijke C.; van der Wal, Gerrit. Withdrawing an explicit request for euthanasia or physician-assisted suicide: a retrospective study on the influence of mental health status and other patient characteristics. *Psychological Medicine* 2005 September; 35(9): 1265-1274. NRCBL: 20.5.1; 20.7; 8.1; 17.1. SC: em. Identifiers: Netherlands.

Mareiniss, Darren P.; Casarett, David; Kapo, Jennifer; Caplan, Arthur. Appropriate use of artificial nutrition and hydration [letter and reply]. *New England Journal of Medicine* 2006 March 23; 354(12): 1320-1321. NRCBL: 20.5.1.

Marker, Rita L. Euthanasia and assisted suicide today. *Society* 2006 May-June; 43(4): 59-67. NRCBL: 20.5.1; 20.7; 21.1; 8.1.

Marshall, Jennifer. Life extension research: an analysis of contemporary biological theories and ethical issues. *Medicine, Health Care and Philosophy* 2006; 9(1): 87-96. NRCBL: 20.5.1; 9.5.2. SC: an.

Abstract: Many opinions and ideas about aging exist. Biological theories have taken hold of the popular and scientific imagination as potential answers to a "cure" for aging. However, it is not clear what exactly is being cured or whether aging could be classified as a disease. Some scientists are convinced that aging will be biologically alterable and that the human life span will be vastly extendable. Other investigators believe that aging is an elusive target that may only be "statistically" manipulatable through a better understanding of the operational principles of systems situated within complex environments. Not only is there confusion over definitions but also as to the safety of any potential intervention. Curing cell death, for example, may lead to cell cancer. The search for a cure for aging is not a clearly beneficial endeavour. This paper will first, describe contemporary ideas about aging processes and second, describe several current life extension technologies. Third, it analyses these theories and technologies, focusing on two representative and differing scientific points of view. The paper also considers the public health dilemma that arises from life extension research and examines two issues, risk/benefit ratio and informed consent, that are key to developing ethical guidelines for life extension technologies.

Martin, Norah. Physician-assisted suicide and euthanasia: weighing feminist concerns. *In:* Fiore, Robin N.; Nelson, Helen Lindemann, eds. Recognition, Responsibility, and Rights: Feminist Ethics and Social Theory. Lanham, MD: Rowman and Littlefield; 2003: 131-142. NRCBL: 20.5.1; 20.7.

Mayda, Atilla Senih; Özkara, Erdem; Çorapçioglu, Funda. Attitudes of oncologists toward euthanasia in Turkey. *Palliative and Supportive Care* 2005 September; 3(3): 221-225. NRCBL: 20.5.1; 7.1; 9.5.1; 9.2. SC: em.

McCullough, Laurence B.; Richman, Bruce W.; Jones, James W. Withdrawal of life-sustaining low-burden care. *Journal of Vascular Surgery* 2005 July; 42(1): 176-177. NRCBL: 20.5.1; 8.3.4; 20.3.2; 20.7.

McMahon, M. Molly; Hurley, Daniel L.; Kamath, Patrick S.; Mueller, Paul S. Medical and ethical aspects of long-term enteral tube feeding. *Mayo Clin Proceedings* 2005 November; 80(11): 1461-1476. NRCBL: 20.5.1; 8.1; 4.4; 9.5.2.

McQuoid-Mason, David. Pacemakers and end-of-life decisions. *South African Medical Journal* 2005 August; 95(8): 566, 568. NRCBL: 20.5.1; 20.5.4; 21.1. Identifiers: South Africa.

Mercurio, Mark R. The Conscientious Practice Policy: a futility policy for acute care hospitals. *Connecticut Medicine* 2005 August; 69(7): 417-419. NRCBL: 20.5.1; 9.4; 8.1.

NRCBL: National Reference Center for Bioethics Literature Classification Scheme   See inside front cover for terms.

177

Messinger-Rapport, Barbara J.; Kamel, Hosam K. Predictors of do not resuscitate orders in the nursing home. *Journal of the American Medical Directors Association* 2005 January-February; 6(1): 18-21. NRCBL: 20.5.1; 9.5.2. SC: em.

Misch, Donald A. The physician's counsel. *JAMA: the Journal of the American Medical Association* 2006 July 19; 296(3): 259-260. NRCBL: 20.5.1; 8.1; 20.4.1.

Miura, Yasuhiko; Asai, Atsushi; Matsushima, Masato; Nagata, Shizuko; Onishi, Motoki; Shimbo, Takuro; Hosoya, Tatsuo; Fukuhara, Shunichi. Families' and physicians' predictions of dialysis patients' preferences regarding life-sustaining treatments in Japan. *American Journal of Kidney Diseases* 2006 January; 47(1): 122-130. NRCBL: 20.5.1; 8.1; 8.3.3; 20.5.4. SC: em.

Miya, Pamela A. Do not resuscitate: when nurses' duties conflict with patients' rights. *Dimensions of Critical Care Nursing* 1984 September-October; 3(5): 293-298. NRCBL: 20.5.1; 8.3.4. SC: cs.

Mongodin, Bertrand. Toward an end-of-life "treatment"? *Canadian HIV/AIDS Policy and Law Newsletter* 1996 October; 3(1): 22-23. NRCBL: 20.5.1; 4.4.

Morrison, Laurie J.; Visentin, Laura M.; Kiss, Alex; Theriault, Rob; Eby, Don; Vermeulen, Marian; Sherbino, Jonathan; Verbeek, P. Richard. Validation of a rule for termination of resuscitation in out-of-hospital cardiac arrest. *New England Journal of Medicine* 2006 August 3; 355(5): 478-487. NRCBL: 20.5.1; 9.5.1. SC: em.

Abstract: BACKGROUND: We prospectively evaluated a clinical prediction rule to be used by emergency medical technicians (EMTs) trained in the use of an automated external defibrillator for the termination of basic life support resuscitative efforts during out-of-hospital cardiac arrest. The rule recommends termination when there is no return of spontaneous circulation, no shocks are administered, and the arrest is not witnessed by emergency medical-services personnel. Otherwise, the rule recommends transportation to the hospital, in accordance with routine practice. METHODS: The study included 24 emergency medical systems in Ontario, Canada. All patients 18 years of age or older who had an arrest of presumed cardiac cause and who were treated by EMTs trained in the use of an automated external defibrillator were included. The patients were treated according to standard guidelines. Characteristics of diagnostic tests for the prediction rule were calculated. These characteristics include sensitivity, specificity, and positive and negative predictive values. RESULTS: Follow-up data were obtained for all 1240 patients. Of 776 patients with cardiac arrest for whom the rule recommended termination, 4 survived (0.5 percent). The rule had a specificity of 90.2 percent for recommending transport of survivors to the emergency department and had a positive predictive value for death of 99.5 percent when termination was recommended. Implementation of this rule would result in a decrease in the rate of transportation from 100 percent of patients to 37.4 percent. The addition of other criteria (a response interval greater than eight minutes or a cardiac arrest not witnessed by a bystander) would further improve both the specificity and positive predictive value of the rule but would result in the transportation of a larger proportion of patients. CONCLUSIONS: The use of a clinical prediction rule

for the termination of resuscitation may help clinicians decide whether to terminate basic life support resuscitative efforts in patients having an out-of-hospital cardiac arrest. Copyright 2006 Massachusetts Medical Society.

Moseley, Kathryn L.; Silveira, Maria J.; Goold, Susan Dorr. Futility in evolution. *Clinics in Geriatric Medicine* 2005 February; 21(1): 211-222. NRCBL: 20.5.1; 9.4; 4.4; 8.1.

Naccache, Lionel. Is she conscious? *Science* 2006 September 8; 313(5792): 1395-1396.`NRCBL: 20.5.1.

Nava, Stefano. Ethics, attitude and practice in end-of-life care decision: a European perspective. *Monaldi Archives for Chest Disease* 2004 January-March; 61(1): 50-57. NRCBL: 20.5.1; 8.3.3. SC: rv.

Ogden, Russel. Euthanasia: a reply. *Canadian HIV/AIDS Policy and Law Newsletter* 1996 April; 2(3): 20-22. NRCBL: 20.5.1; 4.4.

Onwuteaka-Philipsen, Bregje D.; Fisher, Susanne; Cartwright, Colleen; Deliens, Luc; Miccinesi, Guido; Norup, Michael; Nilstun, Tore; van der Heide, Agnes; van der Wal, Gerrit. End-of-life decision making in Europe and Australia. *Archives of Internal Medicine* 2006 April 24; 166(8): 921-929. NRCBL: 20.5.1; 21.1. SC: em.

Owen, Adrian M.; Coleman, Martin R.; Boly, Melanie; Davis, Matthew H.; Laureys, Steven; Prickard, John D. Detecting awareness in the vegetative state. *Science* 2006 September 8; 313(5792): 1402. NRCBL: 20.5.1.

Palda, Valerie A.; Bowman, Kerry W.; McLean, Richard F.; Chapman, Martin G. "Futile" care: do we provide it? Why? A semistructured, Canada-wide survey of intensive care unit doctors and nurses. *Journal of Critical Care* 2005 September; 20(3): 207-213. NRCBL: 20.5.1; 9.4. SC: em.

Pandya, Sunil K. The team had no options [response]. *Indian Journal of Medical Ethics* 2006 July-September; 3(3): 102. NRCBL: 20.5.1. Comments: Sanjib Das Adhikary and R. Raviraj. Do not resuscitate orders. Indian Journal of Medical Ethics 2006 July-September; 3(3): 100-101.

Paris, John J.; Schreiber, Michael D.; Fogerty, Robert. Rage, rage against the dying of the light: not a metaphor for end-of-life care. *In:* Jansen, Lynn A., ed. Death in the Clinic. Lanham, MD: Rowman and Littlefield; 2006: 118-132. NRCBL: 20.5.1.

Peccarelli, Anthony M. A response to Irwin Kramer's reply. *John Marshall Law Review* 1990 Summer; 23(4): 585-589. NRCBL: 20.5.1.

Pedley, D.K.; Johnston, M. Death with dignity in the accident and emergency short stay ward [letter]. *Emergency Medicine Journal* 2001 January; 18(supplement 1): 76-77. NRCBL: 20.5.1. SC: em.

Pellegrino, Edmund D. Decisions at the end of life — the abuse of the concept of futility. *Practical Bioethics* 2005 Summer; 1(3): 3-6. NRCBL: 20.5.1; 9.4; 8.1.

Phillips, Helen. A life or death dilemma. *New Scientist* 2006 July 8-14; 19(2559): 6-7. NRCBL: 20.5.1.

Potter, Robert L.; Flanigan, Rosemary. A family divided. *Practical Bioethics* 2005 Summer; 1(3): 9. NRCBL: 20.5.1; 9.4; 8.1. SC: cs.

Poulton, B.; Ridley, S.; Mackenzie-Ross, R.; Rizvi, S. Variation in end-of-life decision making between critical care consultants. *Anaesthesia* 2005 November; 60(11): 1101-1105. NRCBL: 20.5.1; 20.4.1; 9.8. SC: em. Identifiers: United Kingdom (Great Britain).

Powis, Rachel; Stewart, Kevin; Rai, Gurcharan S. Cardiopulmonary resuscitation. *In:* Rai, Gurcharan S, ed. Medical Ethics and the Elderly. 2nd ed. San Francisco: Radcliffe Medical Press; 2004: 61-69. NRCBL: 20.5.1; 8.3.1; 8.3.3.

Price, Connie C.; Olufemi Sodeke, Stephen. Letter to the editor: end-of-life care and racial disparities: all social and health care sectors must respond! [letter]. *American Journal of Bioethics [Online]* 2006 September-October; 6(5): W33-W34. NRCBL: 20.5.1. Comments: Mary Ellen Wojtasiewicz. Damage compounded: disparities, distrust, and disparate impact in end-of-life conflict resolution policies. American Journal of Bioethics 2006 September-October; 6(5): 8-12.

Prigmore, Samantha. End-of-life decisions and respiratory disease. *Nursing Times* 2006 February 14-20; 102(7): 56, 59, 61. NRCBL: 20.5.1. SC: cs.

Quill, Timothy E.; Lo, Bernard; Brock, Dan W. Palliative options of last resort: a comparison of voluntary stopping eating and drinking, terminal sedation, physician-assisted suicide, and voluntary active euthanasia. *In:* Tännsjö, Torbjörn, ed. Terminal Sedation: Euthanasia in Disguise? Boston: Kluwer Academic Publishers; 2004: 1-14. NRCBL: 20.5.1; 9.7; 20.4.1; 20.7. SC: an.

Ramírez, Amparo Vélez. La eutanasia: el debat actual [Euthanasia: the current debate]. *Persona y Bioética* 1999 February-May; 2(6): 143-149. NRCBL: 20.5.1.

Randall, Fiona; Downie, R.S. Resuscitation and advance statements. *In their:* The Philosophy of Palliative Care: Critique and Reconstruction. New York: Oxford University Press, 2006: 125-148. NRCBL: 20.5.1; 20.5.4.

Reeder, Jean M. Withdrawal of life support in a competent patient. *AORN Journal* 1986 September; 44(3): 380, 382, 384. NRCBL: 20.5.1.

Reese, Kimberly. Family presence at cardiopulmonary resuscitation: considerations in a rehabilitation hospital. *Topics in Stroke Rehabilitation* 2005 Spring; 12(2): 82-88. NRCBL: 20.5.1; 8.1.

Regnard, Claud. Please do not resuscitate: solution is flawed [letter]. *BMJ: British Medical Journal* 2006 March 11; 332(7541): 608. NRCBL: 20.5.1. Identifiers: United Kingdom (Great Britain). Comments: S.P. Conroy, T. Luxton, R.H. Harwood, and J.R. Gladman. Cardiopulmonary resuscitation in continuing care settings: time for a rethink? BMJ: British Medical Journal 2006 February 25; 332(7539): 479-482.

Regnard, Claud; Randall, Fiona. A framework for making advance decisions on resuscitation. *Clinical Medicine* 2005 July-August; 5(4): 354-360. NRCBL: 20.5.1; 9.4; 20.4.1.

Reiver, Joanna. The modern art of dying: a history of euthanasia in the United States by Shai J. Lavi [book review]. *Journal of Legal Medicine* 2006 March; 27(1): 109-118. NRCBL: 20.5.1; 2.2.

Ricciardi-von Platen, Alice. Die Wurzeln des Euthanasiegedankens in Deutschland. *In:* Frewer, Andreas; Eickhoff, Clemens, eds. "Euthanasie" und die aktuelle Sterbehilfe-Debatte: Die historischen Hintergründe medizinischer Ethik. Frankfurt; New York: Campus; 2000: 46-64. NRCBL: 20.5.1; 1.3.5; 2.2; 15.5; 21.4.

Rodriguez, K.L.; Young, A.J. Perceptions of patients in utility or futility of end-of-life treatment. *Journal of Medical Ethics* 2006 August; 32(8): 444-449. NRCBL: 20.5.1; 8.1; 9.4; 18.5.8. SC: em.
Abstract: BACKGROUND AND OBJECTIVES: Definitions of medical futility, offered by healthcare professionals, bioethicists and other experts, have been rigorously debated by many investigators, but the perceptions of patients of futility have been explored only by a few. Patients were allowed to discuss their concerns about end-of-life care, so that their ideas about treatment futility or utility could be extrapolated by us. METHODS: In this cross-sectional study, in-depth, semistructured interviews were conducted with 30 elderly people who were receiving outpatient care in a large, urban Veterans Affairs medical centre in the US. Each of their healthcare providers was also interviewed. Participants were asked to consider four terms commonly used in advance directive forms (ie, life-sustaining treatment, terminal condition, state of permanent unconsciousness and decision-making capacity) and to discuss what these terms meant to them. Audiotapes of the open-ended interviews were transcribed and responses were coded and categorised by constant comparison, a commonly used qualitative method. RESULTS: The following four factors were taken into account by the participants when discussing end-of-life interventions and outcomes: (1)expected quality of life; (2) emotional and financial costs of treatment; (3) likelihood of treatment success; and (4) expected effect on longevity. CONCLUSIONS: Although the terms "utility" or "futility" were not generally used by the participants, segments of speech indicating their perceptions of these terms were identified. Treatment was not always discussed in the same way by patients and providers, but seemed to reflect the same four concerns. Therefore, it may be fruitful for providers to focus on these concerns when discussing end-of-life treatment options with their patients.

NRCBL: National Reference Center for Bioethics Literature Classification Scheme   See inside front cover for terms.

179

Rosell, Tarris D. After Terri—an ethics of reciprocity. *Practical Bioethics* 2006 Spring-Summer; 2(2-3): 8-10, 12. NRCBL: 20.5.1; 8.1.

Saunders, John. Assisted dying: considerations in the continuing debate. *Clinical Medicine* 2005 November-December; 5(6): 543-547. NRCBL: 20.5.1; 20.7. Identifiers: United Kingdom (Great Britain).

Schaller, C.; Kessler, M. On the difficulty of neurosurgical end of life decisions. *Journal of Medical Ethics* 2006 February; 32(2): 65-69. NRCBL: 20.5.1; 20.4.1; 17.1; 21.6. SC: em.
Abstract: OBJECTIVE: To analyse the process of end of life decisions in a neurosurgical environment. METHODS: All 113 neurosurgical patients, who were subject to so called end of life decisions within a one year period were prospectively enrolled in a computerised data bank. Decision pathways according to patient and physician related parameters were assessed. RESULTS: Leading primary diagnoses of the patients were traumatic brain injury and intracranial haemorrhage. Forty-five patients had undergone an emergency neurosurgical operation prior to end of life decision, N = 69 were conservatively treated, which included intracranial pressure recording, or they were not offered neurosurgical care because of futile prognosis. N = 111 died after a median of two (zero to nine) days. Two, in whom the end of life decisions were revised, survived. Clear decisions to terminate further treatment were made by a senior staff member on call being informed by the senior resident on call (27.4%),difficult decisions on the basis of extensive round discussions (71.7%), and very difficult decision by an interdisciplinary ethical consult (0.9%). Decisions were further substantiated by electrophysiological examinations in N = 59. CONCLUSION: End of life decisions are to be considered standard situations for neurosurgeons. These decisions may reach a high rate of "positive" prediction, if substantiated by electrophysiological examinations as well as on the grounds of clinical experience and respect for the assumed will of the patient. The fact that patients may survive following revision of an end of life decision underlines the necessity for repeated reassessment of these decisions. Ethical training for neurosurgeons is to be encouraged.

Schildmann, J.; Doyal, L.; Cushing, A.; Vollmann, J. Decisions at the end of life: an empirical study on the involvement, legal understanding and ethical views of pre-registration house officers. *Journal of Medical Ethics* 2006 October; 32(10): 567-570. NRCBL: 20.5.1. SC: em. Identifiers: United Kingdom (Great Britain).

Schloendorn, John. Making the case for human life extension: personal arguments. *Bioethics* 2006 August; 20(4): 191-202. NRCBL: 20.5.1; 4.5; 4.4; 7.1. SC: an.
Abstract: In the close to medium future, the life sciences might permit a vast extension of the human life span. I will argue that this is a very desirable development for the individual person. The question whether death is a harm to the dying is irrelevant here. All it takes is that being alive is good for the living person and not being alive is not good for anyone. Thus, living persons who expect to live on happily are rationally required to want to stay alive. Eventual uncertainty whether it will be possible to be happy in the future provides no objection, but rather an incentive to try. This view, however, may be naive in assuming that persons are unchanging entities that exist separately from their psychological information. Objections have been derived from reductionistic views that value our future experiences in a way

that declines with time, so that there will be a future point beyond which only negligible value accrues. If we adopt such a view, then we cannot now be concerned to have experiences beyond that point. I argue that these arguments fail to take into account all the reasons we might have to be concerned for the future and all kinds of such concern that come from them. The adoption of a plausible reductionistic account can arguably weaken our concern for the future and certainly change its quality in important ways. But this provides no objection to the desire to live forever, nor to live at all.

Schockenhoff, Eberhard. Töten oder Sterbenlassen: Worauf es in der Euthanasiediskussion ankommt. *In:* Gordijn, Bert; ten Have, Henk, eds. Medizinethik und Kultur: Grenzen medizinischen Handelns in Deutschland und den Niederlanden. Stuttgart: Frommann-Holzboog; 2000: 459-476. NRCBL: 20.5.1.

Schwerdt, Ruth; Merkel, Reinhard. Schön warm zudecken [Cover up warmly]. *Ethik in der Medizin* 2006 September; 18(3): 251-260. NRCBL: 20.5.1. SC: cs.

Setness, Peter A. Embracing life, accepting limits: a physician's position is unique when a loved one faces death [editorial]. *Postgraduate Medicine* 2003 August; 114(2): 9-10. NRCBL: 20.5.1.

Shannon, Sarah E. Damage compounded or damage lessened? Disparate impact or the compromises of multiculturalism. *American Journal of Bioethics* 2006 September-October; 6(5): 27-28; discussion W30-W32. NRCBL: 20.5.1; 9.5.4; 9.4. Comments: Mary Ellen Wojtasiewicz. Damage compounded: disparities, distrust, and disparate impact in end-of-life conflict resolution policies. American Journal of Bioethics 2006 September-October; 6(5): 8-12.

Shen, Mingxian. Euthanasia and Chinese traditional culture. *In:* Döring, Ole; Chen, Renbiao, eds. Advances in Chinese Medical Ethics: Chinese and International Perspectives. Hamburg: Institut für Asienkunde; 2002: 255-265. NRCBL: 20.5.1. Note: Proceedings of the Second Sino-German Interdisciplinary Symposium about Medical Ethics in China, Shanghai, 19-23 October, 1999.

Shepardson, Laura B.; Youngner, Stuart J.; Speroff, Theodore; Rosenthal, Gary E. Increased risk of death in patients with do-not-resuscitate orders. *Medical Care* 1999 August; 37(8): 727-737. NRCBL: 20.5.1; 9.8; 20.1; 7.1. SC: em.

Siegel, Mark D. Alone at life's end: trying to protect the autonomy of patients without surrogates or decision-making capacity. *Critical Care Medicine* 2006 August; 34(8): 2238-2239. NRCBL: 20.5.1; 4.4; 8.3.3; 9.5.10.

Skipp, Catharine; Campo-Flores, Arian. What the doctor did: in Katrina's wake, a deadly hospital mystery unfolds. *Newsweek* 2006 July 31; 148(5): 49. NRCBL: 20.5.1; 8.1. SC: po.

Smith, Gary B.; Poplett, Nicola; Williams, Derek. Staff awareness of a 'do not attempt resuscitation' policy in a district general hospital. *Resuscitation* 2005 May; 65(2): 159-163. NRCBL: 20.5.1; 9.8; 8.3.3. SC: em. Identifiers: United Kingdom (Great Britain).

Smith, Martin L. Should possible disparities and distrust trump do-no-harm? *American Journal of Bioethics* 2006 September-October; 6(5): 28-30; discussion W30-W32. NRCBL: 20.5.1; 9.5.4. Comments: Mary Ellen Wojtasiewicz. Damage compounded: disparities, distrust, and disparate impact in end-of-life conflict resolution policies. American Journal of Bioethics 2006 September-October; 6(5): 8-12.

Snead, O. Carter. Dynamic complementarity: Terri's law and separation of powers principles in the end-of-life context. *Florida Law Review* 2005 January; 57(1): 53-89. NRCBL: 20.5.1; 1.3.5; 8.3.3; 20.5.4.

Sorta-Bilajac, Iva; Pessini, Leo; Dobrila-Dintinjana, Renata; Hozo, Izet. Dysthanasia: the (il)legitimacy of artificially postponed death. *Medicinski Arhiv* 2005; 59(3): 199-202. NRCBL: 20.5.1; 4.4; 21.1.

Spike, Jeffrey P. Persistent vegetative state. *In:* Mitcham, Carl, ed. Encyclopedia of Science, Technology, and Ethics. Farmington Hills, MI: Thomson/Gale, 2005: 1396-1399. NRCBL: 20.5.1.

Stapleton, Renee D.; Nielsen, Elizabeth L.; Engelberg, Ruth A.; Patrick, Donald L.; Curtis, J. Randall. Ethics in cardiopulmonary medicine — association of depression and life-sustaining treatment preferences in patients with COPD. *Chest* 2005 January; 127(1): 328-334. NRCBL: 20.5.1; 17.1; 4.4. SC: em. Identifiers: chronic obstructive pulmonary disease.

Starks, Helene; Pearlman, Robert A.; Hsu, Clarissa; Back, Anthony L.; Gordon, Judith R.; Bharucha, Ashok J. Why now? Timing and circumstances of hastened deaths. *Journal of Pain and Symptom Management* 2005 September; 30(3): 215-226. NRCBL: 20.5.1; 20.7; 20.3.1; 20.4.1. SC: em.

Stobäus, Ricarda. "Euthanasie" im Nationalsozialismus: Gottfried Ewald und der Protest gegen die "Aktion T4.". *In:* Frewer, Andreas; Eickhoff, Clemens, eds. "Euthanasie" und die aktuelle Sterbehilfe-Debatte: Die historischen Hintergründe medizinischer Ethik. Frankfurt; New York: Campus; 2000: 177-192. NRCBL: 20.5.1; 1.3.5; 2.2; 15.5; 21.4.

Sugerman, Noah. Person in PVS: an oxymoronic bioethical issue. *Penn Bioethics Journal* 2006; 2(1): 4p. [Online]. Accessed: http://www.bioethicsjournal.com [2006 February 21]. NRCBL: 20.5.1; 4.4; 20.2.1. Identifiers: persistent vegetative state.

Suk, Han Sung. The ethical dilemma of patients in a vegetative state. *International Nursing Review* 1998 September-October; 45(5): 142. NRCBL: 20.5.1.

Sulch, David; Kalra, Lalit. Ethical issues in stroke management. *In:* Rai, Gurcharan S, ed. Medical Ethics and the Elderly. 2nd ed. San Francisco: Radcliffe Medical Press; 2004: 91-101. NRCBL: 20.5.1; 9.5.1.

Sulmasy, Daniel P.; Sood, Johanna R.; Texiera, Kenneth; McAuley, Ruth L.; McGugins, Jennifer; Ury, Wayne A. A prospective trial of a new policy eliminating signed consent for do not resuscitate orders. *JGIM: Journal of General Internal Medicine* 2006 December; 21(12): 1261-1268. NRCBL: 20.5.1; 8.3.1. SC: em.

Svantesson, Mia; Sjokvist, Peter; Thorsen, Hakan; Ahlstrom, Gerd. Nurses' and physicians' opinions on aggressiveness of treatment for general ward patients. *Nursing Ethics* 2006 March; 13(2): 147-162. NRCBL: 20.5.1; 20.3.2. SC: em. Identifiers: Sweden.
Abstract: The aim of this study was to evaluate agreement between nurses' and physicians' opinions regarding aggressiveness of treatment and to investigate and compare the rationales on which their opinions were based. Structured interviews regarding 714 patients were performed on seven general wards of a university hospital. The data gathered were then subjected to qualitative and quantitative analyses. There was 86% agreement between nurses' and physicians' opinions regarding full or limited treatment when the answers given as 'uncertain' were excluded. Agreement was less (77%) for patients with a life expectancy of less than one year. Disagreements were not associated with professional status because the physicians considered limiting life-sustaining treatment as often as the nurses. A broad spectrum of rationales was given but the results focus mostly on those for full treatment. The nurses and the physicians had similar bases for their opinions. For the majority of the patients, medical rationales were used, but age and quality of life were also expressed as important determinants. When considering full treatment, nurses used quality-of-life rationales for significantly more patients than the physicians. Respect for patients' wishes had a minor influence.

Tännsjö, Torbjörn. The sanctity of life and the active/passive distinction: a final reflection. *In:* Tännsjö, Torbjörn, ed. Terminal Sedation: Euthanasia in Disguise? Boston: Kluwer Academic Publishers; 2004: 115-125. NRCBL: 20.5.1; 4.4.

Taub, Sara. Images of healing and learning. *Virtual Mentor* 2001 July; 3(7): 2p. NRCBL: 20.5.1. Identifiers: Nancy Beth Cruzan.

Thelen, Mary. End-of-life decision making in intensive care. *Critical Care Nurse* 2005 December; 25(6): 28-38. NRCBL: 20.5.1; 9.4; 8.1; 7.1.

Thompson, Richard E. The Terri Schiavo dilemma: an ethics report card with a few surprises. *Physician Executive* 2005 September-October; 31(5): 60-61. NRCBL: 20.5.1; 2.1; 2.3.

Tijmes, Pieter. Euthanasia in the Netherlands. *In:* Mitcham, Carl, ed. Encyclopedia of Science, Technology, and Ethics. Farmington Hills, MI: Thomson/Gale, 2005: 713-715. NRCBL: 20.5.1.

NRCBL: National Reference Center for Bioethics Literature Classification Scheme   See inside front cover for terms.

181

Todres, I. David; Armstrong, Anne; Lally, Patricia; Cassem, Edwin H. Negotiating end-of-life issues. *New Horizons* 1998 November; 6(4): 374-382. NRCBL: 20.5.1; 20.5.2; 20.4.2; 8.3.3; 2.1; 8.1.

Tomlinson, Tom. Ethical issues. *In:* Kuebler, Kim K.; Davis, Mellar P.; Moore, Crystal Dea, eds. Palliative Practices: An Interdisciplinary Approach. St. Louis, MO: Elsevier Mosby; 2005: 291-307. NRCBL: 20.5.1. SC: cs.

Truog, Robert D.; Mitchell, Christine. Futility — from hospital policies to state laws. *American Journal of Bioethics* 2006 September-October; 6(5): 19-21; discussion W30-W32. NRCBL: 20.5.1; 9.6. Comments: Mary Ellen Wojtasiewicz. Damage compounded: disparities, distrust, and disparate impact in end-of-life conflict resolution policies. American Journal of Bioethics 2006 September-October; 6(5): 8-12.

United Kingdom. Department of Health. HSC 2000/028: resuscitation policy. London: Department of Health. Health Service Circular 2000 September: 2 p. [Online]. Accessed: http://www.dh.gov.uk/assetRoot/04/01/21/84/04012184.pdf [2006 October 3]. NRCBL: 20.5.1; 9.2; 9.3.1.

van der Steen, Jenny T.; van der Wal, Gerrit; Mehr, David R.; Ooms, Marcel E.; Ribbe, Miel W. End-of-life decision making in nursing home residents with dementia and pneumonia: Dutch physicians' intentions regarding hastening death. *Alzheimer Disease and Associated Disorders* 2005 July-September; 19(3): 148-155. NRCBL: 20.5.1; 9.5.2; 17.1; 9.4. SC: em.

van Dijk, Mara; Widdershoven, Guy A.M.; Meershoek, Agnes M. Reporting euthanasia: physicians' experiences with a Dutch regional evaluation committee. *In:* Schotsmans, Paul; Meulenbergs, Tom, eds. Euthanasia and Palliative Care in the Low Countries. Dudley, MA: Peeters, 2005: 71-82. NRCBL: 20.5.1. SC: em. Identifiers: The Netherlands.

Van Gijn, J. Euthanasia and trust [letter]. *Clinical Medicine* 2005 May-June; 5(3): 299. NRCBL: 20.5.1; 8.1. Identifiers: Netherlands.

van Willigenburg, Theo. Tod, wo ist dein Stachel?: eine internatistische Sicht des Wertes des Lebens und der Drohung des Todes. *In:* Gordijn, Bert; ten Have, Henk, eds. Medizinethik und Kultur: Grenzen medizinischen Handelns in Deutschland und den Niederlanden. Stuttgart: Frommann-Holzgoog; 2000: 477-494. NRCBL: 20.5.1; 4.4; 20.3.1.

VandeKieft, Gregg. Who decides? An ethics case consult for Terri Schiavo. *American Journal of Hospice and Palliative Medicine* 2005 May-June; 22(3): 175-177. NRCBL: 20.5.1; 20.5.4; 8.1.

Velleman, J. David. Against the right to die. *In:* Jansen, Lynn A., ed. Death in the Clinic. Lanham, MD: Rowman and Littlefield; 2006: 49-65. NRCBL: 20.5.1. SC: an.

Verhagen, A.A.E.; Sauer, P.J.J. End-of-life decisions in newborns: an approach from the Netherlands. *Pediatrics* 2005 September; 116(3): 736-739. NRCBL: 20.5.1; 20.5.2. Identifiers: Groningen Protocol.

Vernon, Martin J.; Gaillemin, Olivier. Decisions on life-sustaining therapy: nutrition and fluid. *In:* Rai, Gurcharan S, ed. Medical Ethics and the Elderly. 2nd ed. San Francisco: Radcliffe Medical Press; 2004: 33-48. NRCBL: 20.5.1; 9.5.2.

Verweij, Marcel. Die Debatte in Sachen Nichtreanimations-entscheidungen in den Niederlanden. *In:* Gordijn, Bert; ten Have, Henk, eds. Medizinethik und Kultur: Grenzen medizinischen Handelns in Deutschland und den Niederlanden. Stuttgart: Frommann-Holzboog; 2000: 141-158. NRCBL: 20.5.1.

Vincent, Jean-Louis. Outcome and ethics in severe brain damage. *Progress in Brain Research* 2005; 150: 555-563. NRCBL: 20.5.1; 20.2.1; 8.1; 20.5.4; 9.5.1.

Vincent, Jean-Louis. Withdrawing may be preferable to withholding. *Critical Care* 2005 June; 9(3): 226-229. NRCBL: 20.5.1.

Vollmann, Jochen. Patientselbstbestimmung und "aktive Sterbehilfe": Klinische und ethische Probleme. *In:* Vollmann, Jochen, ed. Medizin und Ethik: Aktuelle ethische Probleme in Therapie und Forschung. Erlangen: Universitätsbund Erlangen-Nürnberg, 2003: 107-123. NRCBL: 20.5.1.

Walter, James J. Medical futility—an ethical issue for clinicians and patients. *Practical Bioethics* 2005 Summer; 1(3): 1, 6-8. NRCBL: 20.5.1; 9.4; 8.1.

Weissman, David. Do not resuscitate orders: a call for reform. *Virtual Mentor* 2001 July; 3(7): 3p. NRCBL: 20.5.1; 9.4; 8.1.

Wenger, Nanette K.; Weber, Michael A.; Scheidt, Stephen. Hippocrates, Maimonides, and end-of-life issues [editorial]. *American Journal of Geriatric Cardiology* 2004 November-December; 13(6): 291-292. NRCBL: 20.5.1; 9.5.2; 8.1.

Wesley, Carol A. Social Work and End-of-Life Decisions: Self-Determination and the Common Good. *Health and Social Work* 1996 May; 21(2): 115-121. NRCBL: 20.5.1; 1.3.10; 6.

White, Douglas B.; Curtis, J. Randall; Lo, Bernard; Luce, John M. Decisions to limit life-sustaining treatment for critically ill patients who lack both decision-making capacity and surrogate decision-makers. *Critical Care Medicine* 2006 August; 34(8): 2053-2059. NRCBL: 20.5.1; 8.3.3; 9.5.10. SC: em.

White, Mary Terrell. Diagnosing PVS and minimally conscious state: the role of tacit knowledge and intuition. *Journal of Clinical Ethics* 2006 Spring; 17(1): 62-71. NRCBL: 20.5.1; 20.5.3; 20.2.1; 20.3.3; 8.1. Identifiers: Terri Schiavo.

Widdershoven, G. Commentary: euthanasia in Europe: a critique of the Marty report. *Journal of Medical Ethics* 2006 January; 32(1): 34-35. NRCBL: 20.5.1; 20.7. Comments: John Keown. Mr. Marty's muddle: a superficial and selective case for euthanasia in Europe. Journal of Medical Ethics 2006 January; 32(1): 29-33.

Wiesing, Urban. Reanimieren/Nicht Reanimieren aus philosophischer Sicht. *In:* Gordijn, Bert; ten Have, Henk, eds. Medizinethik und Kultur: Grenzen medizinischen Handelns in Deutschland und den Niederlanden. Stuttgart: Frommann-Holzboog; 2000: 375-390. NRCBL: 20.5.1.

Wunder, Michael. Medizin und Gewissen — Die neue Euthanasie-Debatte in Deutschland vor dem historischen und internationalen Hintergrund. *In:* Frewer, Andreas; Eickhoff, Clemens, eds. "Euthanasie" und die aktuelle Sterbehilfe-Debatte: Die historischen Hintergründe medizinischer Ethik. Frankfurt; New York: Campus; 2000: 250-275. NRCBL: 20.5.1; 2.2; 21.1.

Wunsch, Hannah; Harrison, David A.; Harvey, Sheila; Rowan, Kathryn. End-of-life decisions: a cohort study of the withdrawal of all active treatment in intensive care units in the United Kingdom. *Intensive Care Medicine* 2005 June; 31(6): 823-831. NRCBL: 20.5.1; 9.4. SC: em.

Youngner, Stuart J.; O'Toole, Elizabeth; Stellato, Tom. Two times what? Quantity and quality of life in tube feeding decisions [editorial]. *Journal of General Internal Medicine* 1997 February; 12(2): 134-135. NRCBL: 20.5.1; 4.4.

Zimmermann, Volker. Die "Heiligkeit des Lebens" — Geschichte der Euthanasie in Grundzügen. *In:* Frewer, Andreas; Eickhoff, Clemens, eds. "Euthanasie" und die aktuelle Sterbehilfe-Debatte: Die historischen Hintergründemedizinischer Ethik. Frankfurt; New York: Campus; 2000: 27-45. NRCBL: 20.5.1; 2.2; 15.5.

Zimmermann-Acklin, Markus. "Der Schrecken nutzt sich ab" — Zur Wechselwirkung von Geschichte und Ethik in der gegenwärtigen Euthanasie-Diskussion. *In:* Frewer, Andreas; Eickhoff, Clemens, eds. "Euthanasie" und die aktuelle Sterbehilfe-Debatte: Die historischen Hintergründe medizinischer Ethik. Frankfurt; New York: Campus; 2000: 448-470. NRCBL: 20.5.1; 2.2.

EUTHANASIA AND ALLOWING TO DIE/ LEGAL ASPECTS

Australia — lenient sentence in euthanasia case. *Canadian HIV/AIDS Policy and Law Newsletter* 1996 July; 2(4): 25-26. NRCBL: 20.5.1; 9.5.6. SC: le.

Case timeline. *In:* Caplan, Arthur L.; McCartney, James J.; Sisti, Dominic A., eds. The Case of Terri Schiavo: Ethics at the End of Life. Amherst, NY: Prometheus Books; 2006: 325-345. NRCBL: 20.5.1. SC: le.

Adams, Maurice; Nys, Herman. Euthanasia in the low countries: comparative reflections on the Belgian and Dutch Euthanasia Act. *In:* Schotsmans, Paul; Meulenbergs, Tom, eds. Euthanasia and Palliative Care in the Low Countries. Dudley, MA: Peeters, 2005: 5-33. NRCBL: 20.5.1; 21.1. SC: le.

Aita, Kaoruko; Kai, Ichiro. Withdrawal of care in Japan. *Lancet* 2006 July 1-7; 368(9529): 12-14. NRCBL: 20.5.1; 8.3.3; 20.4.1; 7.1. SC: le.

Allen, Michael P. Congress and Terri Schiavo: a primer on the American Constitutional order? *West Virginia Law Review* 2005 Winter; 108(2): 309-360. NRCBL: 20.5.1; 1.3.5. SC: le.

Allen, Michael P. Terri's law and democracy. *Stetson Law Review* 2005 Fall; 35(1): 179-193. NRCBL: 20.5.1; 8.3.3. SC: le; an.

Allen, William. Erring too far on the side of life: déjà vu all over again in the Schiavo saga. *Stetson Law Review* 2005 Fall; 35(1): 123-145. NRCBL: 20.5.1; 8.3.3; 2.1; 4.4. SC: le; an.

Annas, George J. "I want to live": medicine betrayed by ideology in the political debate over Terri Schiavo. *Stetson Law Review* 2005 Fall; 35(1): 49-80. NRCBL: 20.5.1; 8.3.3; 2.1; 1.2; 2.4. SC: le.

Bagaric, Mirko. The Kuhse-Singer euthanasia survey: why it fails to undermine the slippery slope argument comparing apples and apples. *European Journal of Health Law* 2002 September; 9(3): 229-241. NRCBL: 20.5.1; 21.7; 1.1. SC: an; le.

Bagaric, Mirko; Amarasekara, Kumar. Euthanasia: why does it matter (much) what the doctor thinks and why there is no suggestion that doctors should have a duty to kill. *Journal of Law and Medicine* 2002 November; 10(2): 221-231. NRCBL: 20.5.1; 7.1; 1.1; 9.2. SC: le.

Barie, Philip S. The arrogance of power unchecked — the terrible, grotesque tragedy of the case of Terri Schiavo [editorial]. *Surgical Infections* 2005 Spring; 6(1): 1-5. NRCBL: 20.5.1; 20.5.4; 1.3.5. SC: le.

Baumrucker, Steven J.; Craig, Gillian; Stolick, Matt; Morris, Gerald M.; Sheldon, Joanne. Sedation for palliation of terminal symptoms (SPTS), and nutrition and hydration at end of life [case study and commentaries]. *American Journal of Hospice and Palliative Medicine* 2005 March-April; 22(2): 153-157. NRCBL: 20.5.1; 20.4.1; 1.1. SC: cs; le.

Beauchamp, Tom L. The right to die as the triumph of autonomy. *Journal of Medicine and Philosophy* 2006 De-

---

NRCBL: National Reference Center for Bioethics Literature Classification Scheme   See inside front cover for terms.

183

cember; 31(6): 643-654. NRCBL: 20.5.1; 1.1; 8.3.1; 8.3.4; 2.2; 20.7. SC: an; le. Identifiers: Oregon; Death with Dignity Act.

Benzenhöfer, Udo. Geschichte im Recht: NS-Euthanasie in neueren Gerichtsbeschlüssen zum Thema "Behandlungsbegrenzung" (AG Hanau 1995, OLG Frankfurt 1998). *In:* Frewer, Andreas; Eickhoff, Clemens, eds. "Euthanasie" und dieaktuelle Sterbehilfe-Debatte: Die historischen Hintergründe medizinischer Ethik. Frankfurt; New York: Campus; 2000: 356-369. NRCBL: 20.5.1; 2.2; 21.4. SC: le.

Biggs, Hazel. In whose best interests: who knows? *Clinical Ethics* 2006 June; 1(2): 90-93. NRCBL: 20.5.1; 1.1; 20.5.4. SC: an; le. Identifiers: Leslie Burke.

Bolin, Jane N. Pernicious encroachment into end-of-life decision making: federal intervention in palliative pain treatment. *American Journal of Bioethics* 2006 September-October; 6(5): 34-36; discussion W30-W32. NRCBL: 20.5.1; 20.4.1; 9.7. SC: le. Comments: Mary Ellen Wojtasiewicz. Damage compounded: disparities, distrust, and disparate impact in end-of-life conflict resolution policies. American Journal of Bioethics 2006 September-October; 6(5): 8-12.

Browne, Alister. Causation, intention, and active euthanasia. *CQ: Cambridge Quarterly of Healthcare Ethics* 2006 Winter; 15(1): 71-80. NRCBL: 20.5.1; 1.1. SC: le.

Bruce, J.C. Trauma patients' rights during resuscitation. *Curationis: South African Journal of Nursing* 2000 March; 23(1): 53-56. NRCBL: 20.5.1; 2.1; 21.1. SC: le. Identifiers: South African Bill of Rights.

Buckley, Tom; Crippen, David; DeWitt, Anthony L.; Fisher, Malcolm; Liolios, Antonios; Scheetz, Christine L.; Whetstine, Leslie M. Ethics roundtable debate: withdrawal of tube feeding in a patient with persistent vegetative state where the patient's wishes are unclear and there is family dissension. *Critical Care* 2004 April; 8(2): 79-84. NRCBL: 20.5.1; 8.3.3; 8.1. SC: cs; le.

Cantor, Norman L. Déjà vu all over again: the false dichotomy between sanctity of life and quality of life. *Stetson Law Review* 2005 Fall; 35(1): 81-100. NRCBL: 20.5.1; 8.3.3; 4.4. SC: le.

Castledine, George. Are nurses concerned over legalizing euthanasia? *British Journal of Nursing* 2006 May 25-June 7; 15(10): 587. NRCBL: 20.5.1; 20.7. SC: em; le.

Cerminara, Kathy. 2005-2006 National Health Law Moot Court competition: problem. *Journal of Legal Medicine* 2006 December; 27(4): 377-394. NRCBL: 20.5.1; 8.3.3. SC: le.

Cerminara, Kathy L. Tracking the storm: the far-reaching power of the forces propelling the Schiavo cases. *Stet-*

son Law Review 2005 Fall; 35(1): 147-178. NRCBL: 20.5.1; 8.3.3. SC: le; an.

Clarfield, A. Mark. Enteral feeding tubes in end-stage dementia patients: to insert or not to insert? Administrative and financial aspects [editorial]. *Israel Medical Association Journal* 2005 July; 7(7): 467-469. NRCBL: 20.5.1; 9.5.2; 8.3.3. SC: le.

Coggon, John. Could the right to die with dignity represent a new right to die in English law? *Medical Law Review* 2006 Summer; 14(2): 219-237. NRCBL: 20.5.1; 20.2.1; 4.4. SC: le.

Comité Consultatif de Bioéthique de Belgique. Avis no. 1 du 12 mai 1997 concernant l'opportunité d'un règlement légal de l'euthanasie / Notice no. 1 of 12th May, 1997 concerning the chance of legal regulation of euthanasia. *In:* Les Avis du Comité Consultatif de Bioéthique de Belgique 1996-2000. Brussels: De Boeck University; 2001: 11-15. NRCBL: 20.5.1. SC: le. Identifiers: Belgium.

Connor, Kenneth. Connor on Schiavo. *Stetson Law Review* 2005 Fall; 35(1): 31-38. NRCBL: 20.5.1; 8.3.3. SC: le.

Council of Europe. Parliamentary Assembly. Social, Health and Family Affairs Committee; Marty, Dick. Euthanasia: report [draft resolution]. Strasbourg, France: Council of Europe, 2003 September 10; 16 p. [Online]. Accessed: http://assembly.coe.int/Documents/WorkingDocs/Doc03/EDOC9898.htm [2006 June 13]. NRCBL: 20.5.1; 20.7; 8.1. SC: le; em.

Council of Europe. Steering Committee on Bioethics [CDBI]. Replies to the questionnaire for member states relating to euthanasia. Strasbourg, France: Council of Europe, 2003 January 20; 66 p. [Online]. Accessed: http://www.coe.int/t/e/legal_affairs/legal_co-operation/bioethics/activities/ euthanasia/INF(2003)8e_replies_euthanasia.pdf [2006 September 21]. NRCBL: 20.5.1; 20.7; 21.1. SC: em; le.

Abstract: "In response to a request by the Committee of Ministers of the Council of Europe, in the light of Recommendation 1418(1999) of the Parliamentary Assembly on the protection of the human rights and dignity of the terminally ill and dying, the Steering Committee on Bioethics sent a questionnaire in 2001 to the Council of Europe member states concerning aspects of their law and practice relating to euthanasia and other end of life decisions. This document contains an analysis of the responses of the 35 member states that replied."

Darr, Kurt. Terri Schindler Schiavo: end-game. *Hospital Topics* 2005 Spring; 83(2): 29-31. NRCBL: 20.5.1; 8.3.3. SC: le.

DeLegge, Mark H.; McClave, Stephen A.; DiSario, James A.; Baskin, William N.; Brown, Russel D.; Fang, John C.; Ginsberg Gregory G. Ethical and medicolegal aspects of PEG-tube placement and provision of artificial nutritional therapy. *Gastrointestinal Endoscopy* 2005 December; 62(6): 952-959. NRCBL: 20.5.1; 2.1; 9.7; 4.4. SC: le. Identifiers: percutaneous endoscopic gastronomy.

Dimond, Bridgit. Mental capacity requirement and a patient's right to die. *British Journal of Nursing* 2006 November 9-22; 15(20): 1130-1131. NRCBL: 20.5.1; 8.3.3; 20.7. SC: le.

Dombi, William A. Lessons from Schiavo —beyond the legal. *Caring* 2005 May; 24(5): 28-31. NRCBL: 20.5.1; 20.4.1. SC: le.

Doyal, Len. Dignity in dying should include the legalization of non-voluntary euthanasia [editorial]. *Clinical Ethics* 2006 June; 1(2): 65-67. NRCBL: 20.5.1; 20.7; 4.3; 4.4; 8.1. SC: an; le.

Dyer, Clare. Woman in PVS can die, rules judge [news]. *BMJ: British Medical Journal* 2006 December 16; 333(7581): 1238. NRCBL: 20.5.1. SC: le. Identifiers: persistent vegetative state; United Kingdom (Great Britain).

Faunce, Thomas A.; Stewart, Cameron. The Messiha and Schiavo cases: third-party ethical and legal interventions in futile care disputes. *Medical Journal of Australia* 2005 September 5; 183(5): 261-263. NRCBL: 20.5.1; 8.3.3; 9.4; 8.1. SC: le; em.

Felos, George. Felos on Schiavo. *Stetson Law Review* 2005 Fall; 35(1): 9-15. NRCBL: 20.5.1; 8.3.3. SC: le.

Feuillet-Le Mintier, Brigitte. The journey from ethics to law: the case of euthanasia. *In:* Rehmann-Sutter, Christoph; Düwell, Marcus; Mieth, Dietmar, eds. Bioethics in Cultural Contexts: Reflections on Methods and Finitude. Dordrecht: Springer, 2006: 121-128. NRCBL: 20.5.1. SC: le.

Finlay, Ilora. The flip side to 'assisted dying' — why the Lords were wise to reject Lord Joffe's Bill [editorial]. *Clinical Ethics* 2006 September; 1(3): 118-120. NRCBL: 20.5.1; 20.4.1. SC: le.

Finlay, I.G.; Wheatley, Victoria J.; Izdebski, C. The House of Lords Select Committee on the Assisted Dying for the Terminally Ill Bill: implications for specialist palliative care. *Palliative Medicine* 2005 September; 19(6): 444-453. NRCBL: 20.5.1; 20.7; 8.1; 1.3.5. SC: le.

Fisher, Malcolm M.; Raper, Raymond F. Courts, doctors and end-of-life care [editorial]. *Intensive Care Medicine* 2005 June; 31(6): 762-764. NRCBL: 20.5.1; 7.1; 8.1; 9.4. SC: le.

Frank, Pamela; Cruise, Peter L.; Parsons, Sharon K.; Stutes, Ronald; Fruchter, Scott. State, heal thy physicians: an assessment of the Louisiana Natural Death Act. *Journal of Health and Human Services Administration* 2004 Winter; 27(3): 242-275. NRCBL: 20.5.1; 20.5.4. SC: le.

Freckelton, Ian. Withdrawal of artificial life support [editorial]. *Journal of Law and Medicine* 2004 February; 11(3): 265-268. NRCBL: 20.5.1. SC: le.

Gertz, Renate; Harmon, Shawn; Laurie, Graeme; Pradella, Geoff. Developments in medical law in the United Kingdom in 2005 and 2006. *European Journal of Health Law* 2006 June; 13(2): 143-158. NRCBL: 20.5.1; 18.3; 18.2; 18.5.4; 14.4; 15.1; 1.3.12; 8.4; 14.6. SC: le.

Gevers, J.K.M. Terminal sedation: between pain relief, withholding treatment and euthanasia. *Medicine and Law: The World Association for Medical Law* 2006 December; 25(4): 747-751. NRCBL: 20.5.1; 20.4.1. SC: le.
　　Abstract: In the last five to ten years there has been increasing debate on terminal sedation, a medical practice that is difficult to place between other decisions at the end of life, like alleviating pain, withholding treatment, and (in jurisdictions where this is allowed) euthanasia or physician-assisted suicide. Terminal sedation is the administration of sedative drugs with the aim to reduce the consciousness of a terminal patient in order to relieve distress. It is frequently accompanied by the withdrawal (or withholding) of life-sustaining interventions, such as hydration and nutrition. It is typically a measure of the last resort, to be considered in situations where all other measures to reduce pain and suffering have failed. While similar to palliative measures as far as the sedation itself is concerned, withholding of hydration and nutrition brings terminal sedation into the realm of non treatment decisions. At the same time, to the extent that the combination of these two measures may shorten the patient's life, the practice may be easily associated with euthanasia. It is no surprise therefore, that terminal sedation has been called (and has been disqualified as) 'slow euthanasia' or 'backdoor euthanasia'. This paper addresses the question how terminal sedation may be looked upon from a legal point of view. Is it indeed a disguised form of euthanasia, or should it be considered as a practice in its own right? In the latter case, what does it imply in legal terms, and under which conditions and safeguards could it be legally justified? To answer these questions, I will look first at the different clinical realities that may be brought under the heading 'terminal sedation'. Then I will deal with its two components—sedation on the one hand, and withholding artificial feeding on the other—in a legal perspective. The paper ends with conclusions on terminal sedation as a whole.

Gibbs, David C., III. Gibbs on Schiavo. *Stetson Law Review* 2005 Fall; 35(1): 17-29. NRCBL: 20.5.1; 8.3.3. SC: le.

Girbes, Armand R.J. End-of-life decisions in the Netherlands: false euthanasia and false murder [news]. *Intensive Care Medicine* 2005 April; 31(4): 588. NRCBL: 20.5.1. SC: le.

Girsh, Faye J. Physician aid in dying: a proposed law for California. *Criminal Justice Journal* 1992 Fall; 14(2): 333-344. NRCBL: 20.5.1; 20.7. SC: le.

Guinn, David E.; Keyserlingk, Edward W.; Morton, Wendy. Law and bioethics in Rodriguez v. Canada. *In:* Guinn, David E., ed. Handbook of Bioethics and Religion. New York: Oxford University Press, 2006: 199-220. NRCBL: 20.5.1. SC: le.

NRCBL: National Reference Center for Bioethics Literature Classification Scheme　　　　See inside front cover for terms.

185

Gurnham, David. Losing the wood for the trees: Burke and the Court of Appeal: R (on the application of Oliver Leslie Burke) v. the General Medical Council. *Medical Law Review* 2006 Summer; 14(2): 253-263. NRCBL: 20.5.1; 1.1; 21.1. SC: le.

Hanks, Geoffrey. The proposed Assisted Dying Bill in the UK [editorial]. *Palliative Medicine* 2005 September; 19(6): 441. NRCBL: 20.5.1; 20.7; 8.1; 1.3.5. SC: le.

Hartling, O.J. Euthanasia — the illusion of autonomy. *Medicine and Law: World Association for Medical Law* 2006 March; 25(1): 189-199. NRCBL: 20.5.1; 1.1. SC: le.
Abstract: The paper deals with some of the more common arguments used for the legalisation of voluntary euthanasia. It looks at these arguments from an ethical and philosophical point of view. First, the argument that to offer a person the possibility of euthanasia is to respect that person's autonomy is questionable. Can a person's decision on euthanasia be really autonomous? If euthanasia were legal everybody would be conscious of this option: the patient, the doctor, the family and the nursing staff. Thus, there could be indirect pressure on the patient to make a decision. The choice is meant to be free but the patient is not free not to make the choice. Secondly, a choice that seeks to alleviate suffering and thus improve life by annihilating it is irrational. Thirdly, autonomy as to one's own death is hardly exercised freely. Even an otherwise competent person may not be competent in deciding on his own death on account of despair, hopelessness, fear or maybe a feeling of being weak, superfluous and unwanted. This is a very uncertain base for decision-making, especially in the irrevocable decision of euthanasia. Finally, a competent person usually makes any choice in a responsible way and after due consideration; a 'good' decision should consider and respect the wishes and feelings of others. This will be no less the case in making a decision on the so-called free choice of euthanasia. Thus 'normal' behaviour in decision making will only add to the tendency of the already depressed person to feel a burden on his family, the staff and even on society.

Higham, Helen. Artificial nutrition and hydration: managing the practicalities. *Clinical Ethics* 2006 June; 1(2): 86-89. NRCBL: 20.5.1; 4.4; 9.5.1. SC: cs; le. Identifiers: Leslie Burke.

Hoffman, Jan. The last word on the last breath. *New York Times* 2006 October 10; p. F1. NRCBL: 20.5.1. SC: po; le.

Hubben, Joep. Sterbehilfe in den Niederlanden: Das Verhältnis zwischen Gesetzgebung und Rechtsprechung. *In:* Gordijn, Bert; ten Have, Henk, eds. Medizinethik und Kultur: Grenzen medizinischen Handelns in Deutschland und den Niederlanden. Stuttgart: Frommann-Holzboog; 2000: 267-281. NRCBL: 20.5.1. SC: le.

Jans, Jan. The Belgian "Act on Euthanasia": clarifying context, legislation, and practice from an ethical point of view". *Journal of the Society of Christian Ethics* 2005 Fall-Winter; 25(2): 163-177. NRCBL: 20.5.1; 21.1; 2.4; 1.2. SC: le.

Jennett, Bryan. Thirty years of the vegetative state: clinical, ethical and legal problems. *Progress in Brain Research* 2005; 150: 537-543. NRCBL: 20.5.1. SC: le; em.

Jessiman, Ian; Morgan, Derek. Withdrawing nutrition and hydration [letter and reply]. *Clinical Medicine* 2004 May-June; 4(3): 288. NRCBL: 20.5.1; 8.3.3. SC: le.

Jotkowitz, Alan; Steinberg, Avraham. Multiculturalism and end-of-life care: the new Israeli law for the terminally ill patient. *American Journal of Bioethics* 2006 September-October; 6(5): 17-19; discussion W30-W32. NRCBL: 20.5.1; 20.4.1; 9.4. SC: le. Comments: Mary Ellen Wojtasiewicz. Damage compounded: disparities, distrust, and disparate impact in end-of-life conflict resolution policies. American Journal of Bioethics 2006 September-October; 6(5): 8-12.

Kamat, Vijaylaxmi. Guiding light at the end of the tunnel [response]. *Indian Journal of Medical Ethics* 2006 July-September; 3(3): 103-104. NRCBL: 20.5.1; 20.5.4; 8.3.3. SC: le. Comments: Sanjib Das Adhikary and R. Raviraj. Do not resuscitate orders. Indian Journal of Medical Ethics 2006 July-September; 3(3): 100-101.

Kennedy, Ian; Grubb, Andrew. The end(ing) of life: the competent patient. *In their:* Medical Law. 3rd ed. London: Butterworths; 2005: 1907-2088. NRCBL: 20.5.1; 20.5.4; 20.7. SC: le.

Kennedy, Ian; Grubb, Andrew. The end(ing) of life: the incompetent patient. *In their:* Medical Law. 3rd ed. London: Butterworths; 2005: 2089-2190. NRCBL: 20.5.1. SC: le.

Kimsma, G.K. Euthanasia for existential reasons. *Medical Ethics Newsletter [Lahey Clinic]* 2006 Winter; 13(1): 1-2, 12. NRCBL: 20.5.1; 20.7; 8.1. SC: le. Identifiers: Netherlands.

Kingsbury, Brett. A line already drawn: the case for voluntary euthanasia after the withdrawal of life-sustaining hydration and nutrition. *Columbia Journal of Law and Social Problems* 2004 Winter; 38(2): 201-250. NRCBL: 20.5.1; 20.7. SC: le.

Koch, Hans-Georg. Aktuelle Rechtsfragen der Sterbehilfe im deutschen Recht. *In:* Gordijn, Bert; ten Have, Henk, eds. Medizinethik und Kultur: Grenzen medizinischen Handelns in Deutschland und den Niederlanden. Stuttgart: Frommann-Holzboog; 2000: 225-265. NRCBL: 20.5.1. SC: le.

Kramer, Irwin R. Life and death decisions: a reply to Judge Peccarelli. *John Marshall Law Review* 1990 Summer; 23(4): 569-583. NRCBL: 20.5.1. SC: le.

Landman, Willem A. Legalizing assistance with dying in South Africa. *South African Medical Journal = Suid-Afrikaanse Tydskrif Vir Geneeskunde* 2000 February; 90(2): 113-116. NRCBL: 20.5.1; 20.7; 1.3.5. SC: le.

Legemaate, Johan. The Dutch Euthanasia Act and related issues. *Journal of Law and Medicine* 2004 February; 11(3): 312-323. NRCBL: 20.5.1; 21.1. SC: le.

Lemmens, Trudo. Euthanasia. *Canadian HIV/AIDS Policy and Law Newsletter* 1995 October; 2(1): 7-9. NRCBL: 20.5.1; 4.4. SC: le.

Lewis, Penney. Assisted dying in France: the evolution of assisted dying in France: a third way? *Medical Law Review* 2006 Spring; 14(1): 44-72. NRCBL: 20.5.1; 8.3.4; 21.7. SC: le.

Llewellyn, David L., Jr. Licensed to kill: the "death with dignity" initiative. *Criminal Justice Journal* 1992 Fall; 14(2): 309-332. NRCBL: 20.5.1; 20.7. SC: le.

Loewy, Erich H. Sterbehilfe und Euthanasie-Debatte in den Vereinigten Staaten. *In:* Frewer, Andreas; Eickhoff, Clemens, eds. "Euthanasie" und die aktuelle Sterbehilfe-Debatte: Die historischen Hintergründe medizinischer Ethik. Frankfurt; New York: Campus; 2000: 313-335. NRCBL: 20.5.1; 20.7. SC: le.

Lyons, Edward C. In incognito: the principle of double effect in American Constitutional Law. *Florida Law Review* 2005 July; 57(3): 469-563. NRCBL: 20.5.1; 1.1. SC: le. Identifiers: Mary and Jodie.

Maggiore, Salvatore Maurizio; Antonelli, Massimo. Euthanasia, therapeutic obstinacy or something else? An Italian case [news]. *Intensive Care Medicine* 2005 July; 31(7): 997-998. NRCBL: 20.5.1; 20.2.1. SC: le; cs.

Majumdar, Abhik. The right to die: the Indian experience. *Australian Journal of Asian Law* 2004 August; 6(2): 157-175. NRCBL: 20.5.1; 20.7. SC: le.

Makin, Andrew. Taking resuscitation decisions in the nursing home setting. *Nursing Times* 2005 October 11-17; 101(41): 28-30. NRCBL: 20.5.1; 9.5.2; 8.3.3. SC: le. Identifiers: United Kingdom (Great Britain); Mental Capacity Act.

Marks, Thomas C., Jr. A dissenting opinion, Bush v. Schiavo, 885 So. 2d 321 (Fla. 2004). *Stetson Law Review* 2005 Fall; 35(1): 195-205. NRCBL: 20.5.1; 8.3.3. SC: le.

Martyn, Susan R.; Jacobs, Lynn Balshone. Legislating advance directives for the terminally ill: the living will and durable power of attorney. *Nebraska Law Review* 1984; 63(4): 779-809. NRCBL: 20.5.1. SC: le.

Mathes, Michele. Terri Schiavo and end-of-life decisions: can law help us out? *Medsurg Nursing* 2005 June; 14(3): 200-202. NRCBL: 20.5.1; 8.3.3; 20.5.4. SC: le.

McCrary, S. Van; Swanson, Jeffrey W.; Coulehan, Jack; Faber-Langendoen, K.; Olick, Robert S.; Belling, Catherine. Physicians' legal defensiveness in end-of-life treatment decisions: comparing attitudes and knowledge in states with different laws. *Journal of Clinical Ethics* 2006 Spring; 17(1): 15-26. NRCBL: 20.5.1; 20.5.3; 20.4.1; 20.7; 7.2. SC: le; em. Identifiers: New York; Texas.

McLean, Sheila A.M. Permanent vegetative state: the legal position. *Neuropsychological Rehabilitation* 2005 July-September; 15(3-4): 237-250. NRCBL: 20.5.1; 1.1. SC: le. Identifiers: United Kingdom (Great Britain).

Mendelson, Danuta; Ashby, Michael. The medical provision of hydration and nutrition: two very different outcomes in Victoria and Florida. *Journal of Law and Medicine* 2004 February; 11(3): 282-291. NRCBL: 20.5.1; 20.4.1. SC: le; an.

Miller, Eric C. Listening to the disabled: end-of-life medical decision making and the never competent. *Fordham Law Review* 2006 April; 74(5): 2889-2925. NRCBL: 20.5.1; 9.5.4; 9.4; 8.3.3; 4.4. SC: le.

Moore, Amanda; Tzovarras, Hunter. 2005-2006 National Health Law Moot Court competition: best brief. *Journal of Legal Medicine* 2006 December; 27(4): 395-425. NRCBL: 20.5.1; 8.3.3. SC: le.

National Conference of Commissioners on Uniform State Laws. Uniform Health-Care Decisions Act. *Issues in Law and Medicine* 2006 Summer; 22(1): 83-97. NRCBL: 20.5.1; 8.3.3; 20.5.4. SC: le.

Nys, Herman. Recent developments in health law in Belgium. *European Journal of Health Law* 2006 June; 13(2): 95-99. NRCBL: 20.5.1. SC: le.

Ogden, Russel. Euthanasia law and policy. *Canadian HIV/AIDS Policy and Law Newsletter* 1995 January; 1(2): 9-10. NRCBL: 20.5.1. SC: le.

Oppenheim, Elliott B. A doctor's perspective on what the law should be for end-of-life issues. *Journal of Medicine and Law* 1997 Fall; 2(1): 11-18. NRCBL: 20.3.2; 20.5.1. SC: le.

Pang, Samantha Mei-che. Editorial comment. *Nursing Ethics* 2006 March; 13(2): 103-104. NRCBL: 20.5.1. SC: le. Identifiers: Hong Kong; proposed bill on assisted dying in the United Kingdom.

Parrot, Anny; Gomez, M.; Herrenschmidt, Maurice; Carnein, Stéphane; Wary, Bernard; Van Der Beken, Jacques. L'euthanasie = Euthanasia. *Overtures* 1999; (93): 2-14. NRCBL: 20.5.1; 9.5.2; 20.7; 1.2. SC: le.

Peccarelli, Anthony M. A moral dilemma: the role of judicial intervention in withholding or withdrawing nutrition and hydration. *John Marshall Law Review* 1990 Summer; 23(4): 537-568. NRCBL: 20.5.1; 20.2.1. SC: le.

Perry, Joshua E. Biblical biopolitics: judicial process, religious rhetoric, Terri Schiavo and beyond. *Health Matrix: The Journal of Law-Medicine* 2006 Summer; 16(2): 553-630. NRCBL: 20.5.1; 1.2; 2.1; 7.1. SC: le.

Robertson, John A. Schiavo and its (in)significance. *Stetson Law Review* 2005 Fall; 35(1): 101-121. NRCBL: 20.5.1; 8.3.3; 2.1. SC: le; rv.

NRCBL: National Reference Center for Bioethics Literature Classification Scheme   See inside front cover for terms.

187

Rothschild, Alan. Gardner; Re BWV: resolved and unresolved issues at end of life. *Journal of Law and Medicine* 2004 February; 11(3): 292-311. NRCBL: 20.5.1; 20.4.1. SC: le; an.

Saini, Pushpinder. The doctrine of double effect and the law of murder. *Medico-Legal Journal* 1999; 67(Part 3): 106-120. NRCBL: 20.5.1; 20.7; 1.1. SC: le.

Samuels, Alec. Can the doctor do nothing? Can the doctor be compelled to administer treatment? Can the doctor refuse or withhold or withdraw treatment? *Medico-Legal Journal* 2005; 73(Part 3): 112-114. NRCBL: 20.5.1; 20.5.4; 8.1. SC: le.

Sayers, G.M.; Lloyd, D.A.; Gabe, S.M. Parenteral nutrition: ethical and legal considerations. *Postgraduate Medical Journal* 2006 February; 82(964): 79-83. NRCBL: 20.5.1; 8.1; 8.3.3. SC: cs; le.

Schneider, Carl E. Drugged. *Hastings Center Report* 2006 July-August; 36(4): 10-11. NRCBL: 20.5.1; 9.7; 1.3.5; 9.1. SC: le. Identifiers: Gonzalez v. Oregon.

Schulz-Baldes, Anette; Splett, Thomas. Entscheidungen am lebensende in der modernen medizin: ethik, recht, ökonomie und klinik [Decisions at the end of life in modern medicine: ethics, law, economics, and clinical practice]. *Ethik in der Medizin* 2006 June; 18(2): 195-200. NRCBL: 20.5.1; 9.3.1. SC: le.

Sclar, David. U.S. Supreme Court ruling in Gonzales v. Oregon upholds the Oregon Death with Dignity Act. *Journal of Law, Medicine and Ethics* 2006 Fall; 34(3): 639-645. NRCBL: 20.5.1. SC: le.

Shepherd, Lois. Shattering the neutral surrogate myth in end-of-life decisionmaking: Terri Schiavo and her family. *Cumberland Law Review* 2004-2005; 35(3): 575-595. NRCBL: 20.5.1; 8.3.3; 20.5.4. SC: le.

Silverman, Henry J. Withdrawal of feeding-tubes from incompetent patients: the Terri Schiavo case raises new issues regarding who decides in end-of-life decision making [news]. *Intensive Care Medicine* 2005 March; 31(3): 480-481. NRCBL: 20.5.1. SC: le.

Skene, Loane. The Schiavo and Korp cases: conceptualising end-of-life decision-making. *Journal of Law and Medicine* 2005 November; 13(2): 223-229. NRCBL: 20.5.1; 8.3.3. SC: le.

Sleeboom, Margaret. The limitations of the Dutch concept of euthanasia. *Eubios Journal of Asian and International Bioethics* 2003 January 13(1): 20-26. NRCBL: 20.5.1; 2.2. SC: cs; le. Identifiers: Netherlands.

Sleeboom-Faulkner, Margaret. Chinese concepts of euthanasia and health care. *Bioethics* 2006 August; 20(4): 203-212. NRCBL: 20.5.1; 20.7; 9.4; 21.1. SC: an; le. Identifiers: China; Netherlands.

Abstract: This article argues that taking concepts of euthanasia out of their political and economic contexts leads to violations of the premises on which the Stoic ideal of euthanasia is based: 'a quick, gentle and honourable death.' For instance, the transplantation of the narrowly defined concept of euthanasia developed under the Dutch welfare system into a developing country, such as the People's Republic of China (PRC), seems inadequate. For it cannot deal with questions of anxiety about degrading forms of dying and suffering without reference to its economic rationale, demanded by a scarcity (unequal distribution) of health care resources. The weakness of health care provisions for the terminally ill in Mainland China has become increasingly poignant since the collapse of collective health care institutions in the countryside since the reforms of the late-1980s. As in most cases where health care facilities are wanting, it is difficult to apply the criteria of gentleness and dignity at reaching death. Its solution lies not in a faster relief from suffering by euthanasia, but in extending the quality of life through distributive justice within Chinese healthcare policy-making. This paper begins with a brief description of the Dutch euthanasia law, after which it discusses Chinese conceptions of euthanasia in biomedical textbooks, the media and in surveys. It concludes by pointing out the need for a transnational framework in which both the specifics and generalities of euthanasia can be discussed.

Stith, Marah. The semblance of autonomy: treatment of persons with disabilities under the Uniform Health-Care Decisions Act. *Issues in Law and Medicine* 2006 Summer; 22(1): 39-80. NRCBL: 20.5.1; 1.1; 20.5.4. SC: le.

Tauh, Sara. "Departed Jan 11, 1983; at peace Dec 26, 1990." *In:* American Medical Association. Professing Medicine: strengthening the ethics and professionalism of tomorrow's physicians. Chicago: American Medical Association; 2001: 108-110. NRCBL: 20.5.1. SC: le. Note: Commemorative issue of Virtual Mentor, AMA's online ethics journal.

Thompson, William. Terri's law: the limit of the Florida legislature to decide an individual's right to die. *New England Journal on Criminal and Civil Confinement* 2005; 31: 485-518. NRCBL: 20.5.1; 8.3.4. SC: le.

Turone, Fabio. Italy debates end of life decisions [news]. *BMJ: British Medical Journal* 2006 October 7; 333(7571): 719. NRCBL: 20.5.1. SC: le. Identifiers: Piergiorgio Welby.

United States. Congress. An act for the relief of the parents of Theresa Marie Schiavo. Washington, DC: U.S. G.P.O., 2005. 2 p. [Online]. Accessed: http://frwebgate. access.gpo.gov/cgi-bin/getdoc.cgi?dbname=109_cong_ public_laws&docid=f:publ003.109.pdf [2007 March 2]. NRCBL: 20.5.3. SC: le. Identifiers: Theresa Marie Schiavo.

Üstun, Cagatay. Passive euthanasia [letter]. *Nursing Ethics* 2006 May; 13(3): 323-324. NRCBL: 20.5.1. SC: le. Identifiers: Turkey.

van der Arend, Arie J.G. Euthanasia and assisted suicide in The Netherlands: clarifying the practice and the nurse's role. *International Nursing Review* 1998 September-October; 45(5): 145-151. NRCBL: 20.5.1; 20.7; 20.3.2. SC: em; le.

van Leeuwen, Evert; Kimsma, Gerrit. Probleme im Zusammenhang mit der ethischen Rechtfertigung zur medizinischen Sterbehilfe: Auseinandersetzung mit der Euthanasie und ärztlichen Suizidbeihilfe. *In:* Gordijn, Bert; ten Have, Henk, eds. Medizinethik und Kultur: Grenzen medizinischen Handelns in Deutschland und den Niederlanden. Stuttgart: Frommann-Holzboog; 2000: 433-457. NRCBL: 20.5.1; 20.7. SC: le.

Vohra, Sameer S. An American Muslim's right to die: incorporating Islamic law into the debate. *Journal of Legal Medicine* 2006 September; 27(3): 341-359. NRCBL: 20.5.1; 20.7; 1.2. SC: le.

Vollmann, Jochen. Die deutsche Diskussion über ärztliche Tötung auf Verlangen und Beihilfe zum Suizid: Eine Übersicht medizinethischer und rechtlicher Aspekte. *In:* Gordijn, Bert; ten Have, Henk, eds. Medizinethik und Kultur: Grenzen medizinischen Handelns in Deutschland und den Niederlanden. Stuttgart: Frommann-Holzgoog; 2000: 31-70. NRCBL: 20.5.1; 20.7. SC: le.

White, S.M.; Baldwin, T.J. Withholding life-prolonging treatment [letter]. *Anaesthesia* 2005 April; 60(4): 417-418. NRCBL: 20.5.1. SC: le. Identifiers: United Kingdom(Great Britain).

Willmott, Lindy; White, Ben. Charting a course through difficult legislative waters: tribunal decisions on life-sustaining measures. *Journal of Law and Medicine* 2005 May; 12(4): 441-454. NRCBL: 20.5.1; 20.5.4; 8.3.3; 1.3.5. SC: le. Identifiers: Australia.

Willmott, Lindy; White, Ben; Cooper, Donna. The Schiavo decision: emotional, but legally controversial? *Bond Law Review* 2006 June; 18(1): 132-159. NRCBL: 20.5.1; 20.5.3; 1.3.5. SC: le. Identifiers: Queensland, Australia.

Willmott, L.; White, B. A model for decision making at the end-of-life: Queensland and beyond. *Medicine and Law: World Association for Medical Law* 2006 March; 25(1): 201-217. NRCBL: 20.5.1; 8.3.3. SC: an; le.
Abstract: This paper addresses when it is legal to withdraw or withhold medical treatment that is needed to keep a patient alive. It draws on cases and legislation from the common law world (including Australia, England and New Zealand) and considers the various legal tests applied in the different jurisdictions. Two of the most common tests employed in this situation are the "best interests of the patient" test and the "substituted judgment" test. Some jurisdictions also include other criteria as well, such as a requirement that withdrawing or withholding of medical treatment is "not inconsistent with good medical practice". This paper analyses these different legal tests, and after identifying the factors that are judged to be legally relevant to consider when deciding to withdraw or withhold treatment, outlines a preferred model. This model addresses who the relevant decision maker should be, and the criteria that should govern their decision. It suggests that family members are better equipped and more appropriate to act as decision makers than

health professionals, and also questions the appropriateness of responsible medical opinion as the decisive factor in such cases, preferring instead an approach more consistent with the principles of self determination. The model also proposes a method for resolving any disputes that arise.

Wolfson, Jay. The rule in Terri's case: an essay on the public death of Theresa Marie Schiavo. *Stetson Law Review* 2005 Fall; 35(1): 39-47. NRCBL: 20.5.1; 8.3.3. SC: le.

Woodcock, Tom; Wheeler, Robert. Glass v. United Kingdom and Burke v. General Medical Council. Judicial interpretations of European Convention Rights for patients in the United Kingdom facing decisions about life-sustaining treatment limitations [news]. *Intensive Care Medicine* 2005 June; 31(6): 885. NRCBL: 20.5.1; 20.5.2; 8.3.2; 17.1. SC: le.

Zlotowitz, Bernard M.; Golden, Gerald S.; Koretzky, Roselyn B. Termination of treatment: case no. 1 [study topic with commentaries]. *Journal of Psychology and Judaism* 1996 Spring; 20(1): 3-22. NRCBL: 20.5.1; 1.2; 20.2.1; 8.3.3; 20.5.4. SC: le.

Zuckerman, Connie. Looking beyond the law to improve end-of-life care. *Generations: Journal of the American Society on Aging* 1999 Spring; 23(1): 30-35. NRCBL: 20.5.1; 20.5.4; 8.1; 8.5. SC: le.

EUTHANASIA AND ALLOWING TO DIE/ MINORS

Britain: report suggests no care for early babies. *New York Times* 2006 November 15; p. A8. NRCBL: 20.5.2. Identifiers: Nuffield Council on Bioethics.

The ethics of premature delivery [editorial]. *Lancet* 2006 November 25-December 1; 368(9550): 1844. NRCBL: 20.5.2; 20.4.2.

Was this 'irreversible coma' really irreversible? *Nursing Law's Regan Report* 2006 January; 46(8): 1. NRCBL: 20.5.2. SC: le.

Antommaria, Armand H. Matheny. "Who Should Survive?: One of the Choices on our Conscience": Mental retardation and the history of contemporary bioethics. *Kennedy Institute of Ethics Journal* 2006 September; 16(3): 205-224. NRCBL: 20.5.2; 9.5.3; 2.2; 7.1.

Arlettaz, Romaine; Mieth, Dieto; Bucher, Hans-Ulrich; Duc, Gabriel; Fauchère, Jean-Claude. End-of-life decisions in delivery room and neonatal intensive care unit. *Acta Paediatrica* 2005 November; 94(11): 1626-1631. NRCBL: 20.5.2.

Atkinson, Leigh. Ethics and conjoined twins. *Child's Nervous System* 2004 August; 20(8-9): 504-507. NRCBL: 20.5.2; 9.4; 5.2; 4.4.

Barton, Lorayne; Hodgman, Joan E. The contribution of withholding or withdrawing care to newborn mortality.

NRCBL: National Reference Center for Bioethics Literature Classification Scheme   See inside front cover for terms.

189

Pediatrics 2005 December; 116(6): 1487-1491. NRCBL: 20.5.2; 9.5.7. SC: em. Identifiers: United Kingdom (Great Britain).

Bastek, Tara K.; Richardson, Douglas K.; Zupancic, John A.F.; Burns, Jeffrey P. Prenatal consultation practices at the border of viability: a regional survey. *Pediatrics* 2005 August; 116(2): 407-413. NRCBL: 20.5.2; 8.1; 8.3.2; 9.4. SC: em.

Baumann-Hölzle, Ruth; Maffezzoni, Marco; Bucher, Hans Ulrich. A framework for ethical decision making in neonatal intensive care. *Acta Paediatrica* 2005 December; 94(12): 1777-1783. NRCBL: 20.5.2; 20.4.2; 9.4. SC: em.

Bearison, David J. Withholding and withdrawing curative treatments. *In his:* When Treatment Fails: How Medicine Cares for Dying Children. New York: Oxford University Press; 2006: 109-145. NRCBL: 20.5.2; 20.4.2.

Beyleveld, Deryck. Rationality in bioethics: reasonable adjudication in a life and death case of the separation of conjoined twins. *In:* Rehmann-Sutter, Christoph; Düwell, Marcus; Mieth, Dietmar, eds. Bioethics in Cultural Contexts: Reflections on Methods and Finitude. Dordrecht: Springer, 2006: 145-162. NRCBL: 20.5.2; 9.5.7.

Brinchmann, Berit Støre; Torstein, Vik. Parents' involvement in life-and-death decisions in neonatal intensive care: Norwegian attitudes. *Newborn and Infant Nursing Reviews* 2005 June; 5(2): 77-81. NRCBL: 20.5.2; 8.3.2; 9.5.7. SC: em.

Byrne, Steven; Goldsmith, Jay P. Non-initiation and discontinuation of resuscitation. *Clinics in Perinatology* 2006 March; 33(1): 197-218. NRCBL: 20.5.2. SC: em.

Cadge, Wendy; Catlin, Elizabeth A. Making sense of suffering and death: how health care providers' construct meanings in a neonatal intensive care unit. *Journal of Religion and Health* 2006 Summer; 45(2): 248-263. NRCBL: 20.5.2; 4.4; 1.2; 20.3.2; 7.1. SC: em.

Campbell, Matthew. Holland to allow 'baby euthanasia'. *Sunday Times* 2006 March 5: 3 p. [Online]. Accessed: http://infoweb.newsbank.com/iw-search/we/InfoWeb/?p _action=print&p_docid=1. . . [2006 November 27]. NRCBL: 20.5.2; 8.3.4; 4.4. SC: cs.

Carnevale, Franco A.; Canouï, Pierre; Hubert, Philippe; Farrell, Catherine; Leclerc, Francis; Doussau, Amélie; Seguin, Marie-Josée; Lacroix, Jacques. The moral experience of parents regarding life-support decisions for their critically-ill children: a preliminary study in France. *Journal of Child Health Care* 2006 March; 10(1): 69-82. NRCBL: 20.5.2; 8.3.2; 8.1; 9.5.5; 17.1. SC: em.

Chervenak, Frank A.; McCullough, Laurence B.; Arabin, Birgit. Why the Groningen Protocol should be re-

jected. *Hastings Center Report* 2006 September-October; 36(5): 30-33. NRCBL: 20.5.2; 20.7; 4.4; 15.2.

Collste, Göran. Infanticide and the principle of human dignity. *In his:* Is Human Life Special?: Religious and Philosophical Perspectives on the Principle of Human Dignity. New York: P. Lang; 2002: 175-187. NRCBL: 20.5.2; 4.4.

Cooper, Peter; Collins, John; Leveaux, Viviane; Isaacs, David; Kilham, Henry; Tobin, Bernadette. Rebecca's story. *Journal of Paediatrics and Child Health* 2005 August; 41(8): 453-455. NRCBL: 20.5.2; 20.4.2; 7.1.

Dahl, Matthias. "Vollständig bildungs- und arbeitsunfähig" — Kinder- "Euthanasie" während des Nationalsozialismus und die Sterbehilfe-Debatte. *In:* Frewer, Andreas; Eickhoff, Clemens, eds. "Euthanasie" und die aktuelle Sterbehilfe-Debatte: Die historischen Hintergründe medizinischer Ethik. Frankfurt; New York: Campus; 2000: 144-176. NRCBL: 20.5.2; 1.3.5; 2.2; 15.5; 21.4.

de Leeuw, Richard; de Beaufort, Arnout J.; de Kleine, Martin J.; van Harrewijin, Karin; Kollée, Louis A.A. Foregoing intensive care treatment in newborn infants with extremely poor prognoses: a study in four neonatal intensive care units in the Netherlands. *Journal of Pediatrics* 1996 November; 129(5): 661-666. NRCBL: 20.5.2; 20.4.2.

Devictor, Denis J. Toward an ethics of communication among countries [editorial]. *Pediatric Critical Care Medicine* 2004 May; 5(3): 290-291. NRCBL: 20.5.2; 21.1.

Devictor, Denis J.; Nguyen, Duc Tinh. Forgoing life-sustaining treatments in children: a comparison between northern and southern European intensive care units. *Pediatric Critical Care Medicine* 2004 May; 5(3): 211-215. NRCBL: 20.5.2; 21.1; 8.3.2. SC: em.

Dyer, Clare. Judge rules that baby boy should not be allowed to die [news]. *BMJ: British Medical Journal* 2006 March 25; 332(7543): 685. NRCBL: 20.5.2. SC: le.

Eaton, Lynn. Ethics group rules on treating premature babies [news]. *BMJ: British Medical Journal* 2006 November 18; 333(7577): 1033. NRCBL: 20.5.2; 20.4.2. Identifiers: United Kingdom (Great Britain).

Elias-Jones, A.C.; Samanta, J. The implications of the David Glass case for future clinical practice in the UK. *Archives of Disease in Childhood* 2005 August; 90(8): 822-825. NRCBL: 20.5.2; 8.3.4; 8.3.2; 8.3.1; 9.8. SC: le.

Fauriel, Isabelle; Moutel, Grégoire; Duchange, Nathalie; Montuclard, Luc; Moutard, Marie-Laure; Cochat, Pierre; Hervé, Christian. Decision making concerning life-sustaining treatment in paediatric nephrology: professionals' experiences and values. *Nephrology Dialy-*

sis Transplantation 2005 December; 20(12): 2746-2750. NRCBL: 20.5.2; 7.1; 8.1; 21.1. SC: em.

Fiedler, Leslie A. On infanticide. *Journal of Popular Culture* 1981 Spring; 14: 676-680. NRCBL: 20.5.2; 7.1.

Fine, Robert L.; Whitfield, Jonathan M.; Carr, Barbara L.; Mayo, Thomas W. Medical futility in the neonatal intensive care unit: hope for a resolution. *Pediatrics* 2005 November; 116(5): 1219-1222. NRCBL: 20.5.2; 9.4; 8.3.2. SC: cs; le.

Fovargue, S. Editorial. *Clinical Ethics* 2006 June; 1(2): 85. NRCBL: 20.5.2; 4.4; 8.1.

Frader, Joel E. Forgoing life support across borders: who decides and why? [editorial]. *Pediatric Critical Care Medicine* 2004 May; 5(3): 289-290. NRCBL: 20.5.2; 21.1.

Gevers, Sjef. The European Court of Human Rights and the incompetent patients [editorial]. *European Journal of Health Law* 2004 September; 11(3): 225-229. NRCBL: 20.5.2; 8.3.2.

Glover, Jonathan. Should the child live? Doctors, families and conflict. *Clinical Ethics* 2006 March; 1(1): 52-59. NRCBL: 20.5.2; 8.1; 4.4; 12.3. SC: cs. Identifiers: Charlotte Wyatt; Luke Winston-Jones.

Gould, Donald. Baby doomed to live. *New Statesman (London, England:* 1957) 1972 October 27; 84: 595. NRCBL: 20.5.2; 8.3.2; 4.4. SC: le. Identifiers: United Kingdom (Great Britain).

Gunderman, Richard B.; Engle, William A. Ethics and the limits of neonatal viability [editorial]. *Radiology* 2005 August; 236(2): 427-429. NRCBL: 20.5.2; 8.3.2; 4.4; 9.4.

Gunn, Scott; Hashimoto, Satoru; Karakozov, Michael; Marx, Thomas; Tan, Ian K.S.; Thompson, Dan R.; Vincent, Jean-Louis. Ethics roundtable debate: child with severe brain damage and an underlying brain tumour. *Critical Care* 2004 August; 8(4): 213-218. NRCBL: 20.5.2; 9.4.

Haack, Susan. Limitation of treatment decisions for unwanted neonate. *Ethics and Medicine* 2006 Fall; 22(3): 139-141. NRCBL: 20.5.2; 8.3.3; 7.1; 9.5.9. SC: cs.

Huntoon, Lawrence R. The perilous vegetative state [editorial]. *Journal of American Physicians and Surgeons* 2005 Summer; 10(2): 35-36. NRCBL: 20.5.2.

Hurst, Irene. The legal landscape at the threshold of viability for extremely premature infants: a nursing perspective, part I. *JONA's Healthcare Law, Ethics, and Regulation* 2006 January-March; 8(1): 20-28. NRCBL: 20.5.2. SC: le.

Janvier, Annie; Barrington, Keith J. The ethics of neonatal resuscitation at the margins of viability: informed consent and outcomes. *Journal of Pediatrics* 2005 November; 147(5): 579-585. NRCBL: 20.5.2; 8.3.2.

Johnson, Dana E.; Thompson, Theodore R.; Aroskar, Mila; Cranford, Ronald E. Baby Doe' rules: there are alternatives. *American Journal of Diseases of Children* 1984 June; 138(6): 523-529. NRCBL: 20.5.2.

Jotkowitz, A.B.; Glick, S. The Groningen protocol: another perspective. *Journal of Medical Ethics* 2006 March; 32(3): 157-158. NRCBL: 20.5.2. Identifiers: Netherlands.
  Abstract: The Groningen protocol allows for the euthanasia of severely ill newborns with a hopeless prognosis and unbearable suffering. We understand the impetus for such a protocol but have moral and ethical concerns with it. Advocates for euthanasia in adults have relied on the concept of human autonomy, which is lacking in the case of infants. In addition, biases can potentially influence the decision making of both parents and physicians. It is also very difficult to weigh the element of quality of life on the will to live. We feel an important line has been crossed if the international medical community consents to the active euthanasia of severely ill infants and are concerned about the extension of the policy to other at risk groups.

Kavanaugh, Karen; Savage, Teresa; Kilpatrick, Sarah; Kimura, Rob; Hershberger, Patricia. Life support decisions for extremely premature infants: report of a pilot study. *Journal of Pediatric Nursing* 2005 October; 20(5): 347-359. NRCBL: 20.5.2; 8.1; 8.3.2. SC: em.

Kipper, Delio Jose; Piva, Jefferson Pedro; Garcia, Pedro Celiny Ramos; Einloft, Paulo Roberto; Bruno, Francisco; Lago, Patricia; Rocha, Tais; Schein, Alaor Ernst; Fontela, Patricia Scolari; Gava, Debora Hendler; Guerra, Luciano; Chemello, Keli; Bittencourt, Roney; Sudbrack, Simone; Mulinari, Evandro Freddy; Morais, Joao Feliz Duarte. Evolution of the medical practices and modes of death on pediatric intensive care units in southern Brazil. *Pediatric Critical Care Medicine* 2005 May; 6(3): 258-263. NRCBL: 20.5.2; 20.4.2. SC: em.

Larcher, Vic; Goldman, Ann. Living well and dying well — facing the challenges at a children's hospital. *Clinical Ethics* 2006 September; 1(3): 165-171. NRCBL: 20.5.2; 20.3.2; 20.3.3. SC: le; cs.

Leask, K. The role of the courts in clinical decision making. *Archives of Disease in Childhood* 2005 December; 90(12): 1256-1258. NRCBL: 20.5.2; 8.3.2; 8.3.4; 9.4. SC: le.

Little, George; Kahn, Richard; Green, Ronald M. Parental dreams, dilemmas, and decision-making in Cinéma Vérité. *Journal of Perinatology* 1999 April-May; 19(3): 194-196. NRCBL: 20.5.2; 8.3.2; 7.1; 8.1.

Lorenz, John M. Ethical dilemmas in the care of the most premature infants: the waters are murkier than ever. *Current Opinion in Pediatrics* 2005 April; 17(2): 186-190. NRCBL: 20.5.2; 8.3.3. SC: rv.

Lorenz, J.M. Prenatal counseling and resuscitation decisions at extremely premature gestation [editorial]. *Journal*

NRCBL: National Reference Center for Bioethics Literature Classification Scheme   See inside front cover for terms.

191

of Pediatrics 2005 November; 147(5): 567-568. NRCBL: 20.5.2; 8.3.2.

McCullough, Laurence B. Neonatal ethics at the limits of viability. *Pediatrics* 2005 October; 116(4): 1019-1021. NRCBL: 20.5.2; 1.3.5. SC: le.

Miljeteig, Ingrid; Norheim, Ole Frithjof. My job is to keep him alive, but what about his brother and sister? How Indian doctors experience ethical dilemmas in neonatal medicine. *Developing World Bioethics* 2006 March; 6(1): 23-32. NRCBL: 20.5.2. SC: em. Identifiers: India.

Abstract: Background: Studies from Western countries show that doctors working in neonatal intensive care units (NICUs) find withdrawal of treatment to be their most difficult ethical dilemma. There is less knowledge of how this is experienced in other economic, cultural, religious and educational contexts. Objectives: To explore and describe how Indian doctors experience ethical dilemmas concerning the withdrawal of treatment among critically sick and/or premature neonates. Method: Qualitative data from interviews was analysed according to Giorgi's phenomenological approach. The subjects were 14 doctors with various levels of neonatal experience, recruited from two state-owned NICUs in India. Main outcome measures: description reflecting the nature of ethical dilemmas and how they are experienced. Results: All doctors reported situations where the question of withdrawal of treatment was experienced as the worst part of their job. They felt that they lacked training in how to handle such dilemmas, and some had never talked about ethics before. They were especially concerned about non-medical considerations that do not feature in current treatment guidelines. In describing their personal experiences, the informants mentioned their sense of responsibility in situations where they were aware that their decisions would influence a family's economy and reputation, availability of food and education for siblings, other children's access to equipment in the unit, and the use of resources in an underprivileged population. Sometimes lack of resources, usually ventilators, forced them to make decisions about which babies should get the chance to live. Other reported dilemmas included difficulties co-operating with uneducated and poor parents. Conclusion: While Western doctors seem to focus on the rights and problems of the individual child, Indian doctors tend to refer to consequences for other children, for parents and society. There is a need for further research in this field, and for the development of guidelines on how to cope with differences in resources, and how to handle different patient groups' cultural and religious concerns.

Orzalesi, Marcello; Cuttini, Marina. Ethical considerations in neonatal respiratory care. *Biology of the Neonate* 2005; 87(4): 345-353. NRCBL: 20.5.2; 8.3.2. SC: rv.

Parker, Terri L. I didn't even raise my hand: a mother's retrospective journey through end-of-life decisionmaking at the "threshold of viability". *Stetson Law Review* 2005 Fall; 35(1): 207-225. NRCBL: 20.5.2; 8.3.2. SC: le.

Pearce, Eugene W.J.; Lewis, Patti. A hospice for the pre-born and newborn. *Health Progress* 2006 September-October; 87(5): 56-61. NRCBL: 20.5.2; 1.2; 15.2; 20.4.1.

Purdy, Isabell B. Embracing bioethics in neonatal intensive care, part I: evolving toward neonatal evidence-based ethics. *Neonatal Network* 2006 January-February; 25(1): 33-42. NRCBL: 20.5.2. SC: em; rv.

Purdy, Isabell B.; Wadhwani, Rita T. Embracing bioethics in neonatal intensive care, part II: case histories in neonatal ethics. *Neonatal Network* 2006 January-February; 25(1): 43-53. NRCBL: 20.5.2; 2.1. SC: cs.

Rashotte, Judy. Relational ethics in critical care [editorial]. *Australian Critical Care* 2006 February; 19(1): 4-5. NRCBL: 20.5.2; 1.1.

Rock, Melanie. Discounted lives? Weighing disability when measuring health and ruling on "compassionate" murder. *Social Science and Medicine* 2000; 51(3): 407-417. NRCBL: 20.5.2; 4.4. SC: le. Identifiers: Canada; Robert Latimer; Disability-Adjusted Life Year (DALY).

Rozovsky, L.E.; Rozovsky, F.A. The Stephen Dawson case: judging the right to survive. *Canadian Doctor* 1983 June; 49(6): 48-50. NRCBL: 20.5.2.

Sarnaik, Ashok P.; Daphtary, Kshama; Sarnaik, Ajit A. Ethical issues in pediatric intensive care in developing countries: combining western technology and eastern wisdom. *Indian Journal of Pediatrics* 2005 April; 72(4): 339-342. NRCBL: 20.5.2; 2.1; 4.4; 19.5. Identifiers: India.

Saugstad, Ola Didrik. When newborn infants are bound to die. *Acta Paediatrica* 2005 November; 94(11): 1535-1537. NRCBL: 20.5.2.

Sayeed, Sadath A. The marginally viable newborn: legal challenges, conceptual inadequacies, and reasonableness. *Journal of Law, Medicine and Ethics* 2006 Fall; 34(3): 600-610. NRCBL: 20.5.2; 20.4.2; 8.3.2. SC: le.

Abstract: Decisions to provide life-sustaining medical care for marginally viable newborns present a unique set of morally complex challenges for providers and parents in the United States. This article examines recent legal trends that restrict discretionary decision-making, and critiques commonly employed ethical justifications offered to support permitting such discretion.

Schmidt, Ulf. Kriegsausbruch und "Euthanasie": Neue Forschungsergebnisse zum "Knauer Kind" im Jahre 1939. *In:* Frewer, Andreas; Eickhoff, Clemens, eds. "Euthanasie" und die aktuelle Sterbehilfe-Debatte: Die historischen Hintergründe medizinischer Ethik. Frankfurt; New York: Campus; 2000: 120-143. NRCBL: 20.5.2; 1.3.5; 2.2; 15.5; 21.4.

Siden, Harold B. The emerging issue of euthanasia [editorial]. *Archives of Pediatric and Adolescent Medicine* 2005 September; 159(9): 887-889. NRCBL: 20.5.2.

Solomon, Mildred Z.; Sellers, Deborah E.; Heller, Karen S.; Dokken, Deborah L.; Levetown, Marcia; Rushton, Cynda; Truog, Robert D.; Fleischman, Alan R. New and lingering controversies in pediatric end-of-life care. *Pediatrics* 2005 October; 116(4): 872-883. NRCBL: 20.5.2; 20.3.2. SC: em.

Streiner, David L.; Saigal, Saroj; Burrows, Elizabeth; Stoskopf, Barbara; Rosenbaum, Peter. Attitudes of parents and health care professionals toward active treatment of extremely premature infants. *Pediatrics* 2001 July; 108(1): 152-157. NRCBL: 20.5.2; 7.1; 9.3.1; 8.1. SC: em.

Tovino, Stacey A.; Winslade, William J. A primer on the law and ethics of treatment, research, and public policy in the context of severe traumatic brain injury. *Annals of Health Law* 2005 Winter; 14(1): 1-53. NRCBL: 20.5.2; 8.3.3; 9.3.1; 18.3; 18.5.6; 20.3.1. SC: le.

Tripp, J.; McGregor, D. Withholding and withdrawing of life sustaining treatment in the newborn. *Archives of Disease in Childhood. Fetal Neonatal Edition* 2006 January; 91(1): F67-F71. NRCBL: 20.5.2; 8.1; 8.3.2; 8.3.4.

van Zuuren, Florence J.; van Manen, Eeke. Moral dilemmas in neonatology as experienced by health care practitioners: a qualitative approach. *Medicine, Health Care and Philosophy* 2006; 9(3): 339-347. NRCBL: 20.5.2. SC: em. Identifiers: Netherlands.

Verhagen, A.A.E. Developments with regard to end-of-life decisions in newborns [editorial]. *West Indian Medical Journal* 2005 October; 54(5): 277-278. NRCBL: 20.5.2; 9.4.

Verhagen, A.A.E. End of life decisions in newborns in the Netherlands: medical and legal aspects of the Groningen protocol. *Medicine and Law: The World Association for Medical Law* 2006 June; 25(2): 399-407. NRCBL: 20.5.2; 9.8; 2.4.

Abstract: The international press has been full of blood chilling accounts concerning a supposedly new practice in the Netherlands of terminating the life of severely defective newborn babies with a protocol. Our aim is to give insight into the medical and legal aspects of this protocol and to describe its contents. The legal developments concerning termination of life in newborns in the Netherlands are being discussed.

Vrakking, Astrid M.; van der Heide, Agnes; Arts, Willem Frans; Pieters, Rob; van der Voort, Edwin; Rietjens, Judith A.C.; Onwuteaka-Philipsen, Bregje D.; van der Maas, Paul J.; van der Wal, Gerrit. Medical end-of-life decisions for children in the Netherlands. *Archives of Pediatric and Adolescent Medicine* 2005 September; 159(9): 802-809. NRCBL: 20.5.2; 8.1; 8.3.2.

Walther, Frans J. Withholding treatment, withdrawing treatment, and palliative care in the neonatal intensive care unit. *Early Human Development* 2005 December; 81(12): 965-972. NRCBL: 20.5.2; 20.4.2; 8.1; 9.4.

Waltman, Patricia A.; Schenk, Laura K. Neonatal ethical decision making: where does the NNP fit in? *Neonatal Network* 1999 December; 18(8): 27-32. NRCBL: 20.5.2; 9.3.1; 9.4; 4.1.3. Identifiers: neonatal nurse practitioner.

Wilkinson, D. Is it in the best interests of an intellectually disabled infant to die? *Journal of Medical Ethics* 2006 August; 32(8): 454-459. NRCBL: 20.5.2; 9.5.3. SC: an.

Abstract: One of the most contentious ethical issues in the neonatal intensive care unit is the withdrawal of life-sustaining treatment from infants who may otherwise survive. In practice, one of the most important factors influencing this decision is the prediction that the infant will be severely intellectually disabled. Most professional guidelines suggest that decisions should be made on the basis of the best interests of the infant. It is, however, not clear how intellectual disability affects those interests. Why should intellectual disability be more important than physical disability to the future interests of an infant? Is it discriminatory to base decisions on this? This paper will try to unravel the above questions. It seems that if intellectual disability does affect the best interests of the child it must do so in one of three ways. These possibilities will be discussed as well as the major challenges to the notion that intellectual disability should have a role in such decisions. The best interests of the child can be affected by severe or profound intellectual disability. It is, though, not as clear-cut as some might expect.

EUTHANASIA AND ALLOWING TO DIE/ PHILOSOPHICAL ASPECTS

Matter of ethics. *Economist* 1967 September 30; 224: 1170. NRCBL: 20.5.1; 4.1.1. Identifiers: United Kingdom (Great Britain).

Ach, Johann S.; Gaidt, Andreas. Wehret den Anfängen? Anmerkungen zum Argument der "schiefen Ebene" in der gegenwätigen Euthanasie-Debatte. *In:* Frewer, Andreas; Eickhoff, Clemens, eds. "Euthanasie" und die aktuelle Sterbehilfe-Debatte: Die historischen Hintergründe medizinischer Ethik. Frankfurt; New York: Campus; 2000: 424-447. NRCBL: 20.5.1; 1.1.

Ackerman, Felicia. "For now have I my death": the "duty to die" versus the duty to help the ill stay alive. *Midwest Studies in Philosophy* 2000 August; 24: 172-185. NRCBL: 20.5.1; 1.1. SC: an.

Andrews, Maria; Marian, Mary. Ethical framework for the registered dietitian in decisions regarding withholding/withdrawing medically assisted nutrition and hydration. *Journal of the American Dietetic Association* 2006 February; 106(2): 206-208. NRCBL: 20.5.1; 1.1; 6; 2.1.

Bagaric, Mirko. The Kuhse-Singer euthanasia survey: why it fails to undermine the slippery slope argument comparing apples and apples. *European Journal of Health Law* 2002 September; 9(3): 229-241. NRCBL: 20.5.1; 21.7; 1.1. SC: an; le.

Bagaric, Mirko; Amarasekara, Kumar. Euthanasia: why does it matter (much) what the doctor thinks and why there is no suggestion that doctors should have a duty to kill. *Journal of Law and Medicine* 2002 November; 10(2): 221-231. NRCBL: 20.5.1; 7.1; 1.1; 9.2. SC: le.

Baumrucker, Steven J.; Craig, Gillian; Stolick, Matt; Morris, Gerald M.; Sheldon, Joanne. Sedation for palliation of terminal symptoms (SPTS), and nutrition and hydration at end of life [case study and commentaries]. *American Journal of Hospice and Palliative Medicine*

NRCBL: National Reference Center for Bioethics Literature Classification Scheme   See inside front cover for terms.

193

2005 March-April; 22(2): 153-157. NRCBL: 20.5.1; 20.4.1; 1.1. SC: cs; le.

Beauchamp, Tom L. The right to die as the triumph of autonomy. *Journal of Medicine and Philosophy* 2006 December; 31(6): 643-654. NRCBL: 20.5.1; 1.1; 8.3.1; 8.3.4; 2.2; 20.7. SC: an; le. Identifiers: Oregon; Death with Dignity Act.

Biggs, Hazel. In whose best interests: who knows? *Clinical Ethics* 2006 June; 1(2): 90-93. NRCBL: 20.5.1; 1.1; 20.5.4. SC: an; le. Identifiers: Leslie Burke.

Borthwick, Chris. Ethics and the vegetative state. *Neuropsychological Rehabilitation* 2005 July-September; 15(3-4): 257-263. NRCBL: 20.5.1; 1.1.

Breier-Mackie, Sarah. Ethics, artificial nutrition, and anorexia nervosa. *Practical Bioethics* 2006 Spring-Summer; 2(2-3): 3-5. NRCBL: 20.5.1; 1.1.

Browne, Alister. Causation, intention, and active euthanasia. *CQ: Cambridge Quarterly of Healthcare Ethics* 2006 Winter; 15(1): 71-80. NRCBL: 20.5.1; 1.1. SC: le.

Caplan, Arthur L. Death as an unnatural process: why is it wrong to seek a cure for ageing? *EMBO Reports* 2005 July; 6(Special Issue): S72-S75. NRCBL: 20.5.1; 4.4; 1.1; 4.5.

Chadwick, Ruth. Euthanasia. *In:* Mitcham, Carl, ed. Encyclopedia of Science, Technology, and Ethics. Farmington Hills, MI: Thomson/Gale, 2005: 710-713. NRCBL: 20.5.1; 1.1.

Chadwick, Ruth. Right to die. *In:* Mitcham, Carl, ed. Encyclopedia of Science, Technology, and Ethics. Farmington Hills, MI: Thomson/Gale, 2005: 1634-1635. NRCBL: 20.5.1; 1.1.

Cohen, Lewis; Ganzini, Linda; Mitchell, Christine; Arons, Stephen; Goy, Elizabeth; Cleary, James. Accusations of murder and euthanasia in end-of-life care [editorial]. *Journal of Palliative Medicine* 2005 December; 8(6): 1096-1104. NRCBL: 20.5.1; 20.7; 8.1; 1.1; 20.4.1; 2.1.

de Briey, Laurent. Euthanasie et autonomie = Euthanasia and autonomy. *Revue Philosophique de Louvain* 2003 February; 101(1): 26-42. NRCBL: 20.5.1; 1.1; 20.7. Identifiers: Belgium. Note: Abstract in English.

Dierckx de Casterlé, B.; Verpoort, C.; De Bal, N.; Gastmans, C. Nurses' views on their involvement in euthanasia: a qualitative study in Flanders (Belgium). *Journal of Medical Ethics* 2006 April; 32(4): 187-192. NRCBL: 20.5.1; 4.1.3. SC: em.

Dines, Alison. Does the distinction between killing and letting die justify some forms of euthanasia? *Journal of Advanced Nursing* 1995 May; 21(5): 911-916. NRCBL: 20.5.1; 1.1. SC: cs.

Ferrand, E.; Jabre, P.; Fernandez-Curiel, S.; Morin, F.; Vincent-Genod, C.; Duvaldestin, P.; Lemaire, F.; Hervé, C.; Marty, J. Participation of French general practitioners in end-of-life decisions for their hospitalised patients. *Journal of Medical Ethics* 2006 December; 32(12): 683-687. NRCBL: 20.5.1; 4.1.2; 8.3.3. SC: em.

Frawley, Theresa; Begley, Cecily M. Ethical issues in caring for people with carotid artery rupture. *British Journal of Nursing* 2006 January 26-February 8; 15(2): 100-103. NRCBL: 20.5.1; 1.1; 8.3.1; 20.4.1.

Goldblum, Peter B.; Martin, David J. Principles for the discussion of life and death options with terminally ill clients with HIV. *Professional Psychology: Research and Practice* 1999 April; 30(2): 187-197. NRCBL: 20.5.1; 9.5.6; 20.4.1; 4.1.1; 17.1; 20.7.

Gurnham, David. Losing the wood for the trees: Burke and the Court of Appeal: R (on the application of Oliver Leslie Burke) v. the General Medical Council. *Medical Law Review* 2006 Summer; 14(2): 253-263. NRCBL: 20.5.1; 1.1; 21.1. SC: le.

Hanser, Matthew F. Killing, letting die and preventing people from being saved. *Utilitas* 1999 November; 11(3): 277-295. NRCBL: 20.5.1; 1.1.

Hartling, O.J. Euthanasia — the illusion of autonomy. *Medicine and Law: World Association for Medical Law* 2006 March; 25(1): 189-199. NRCBL: 20.5.1; 1.1. SC: le.
Abstract: The paper deals with some of the more common arguments used for the legalisation of voluntary euthanasia. It looks at these arguments from an ethical and philosophical point of view. First, the argument that to offer a person the possibility of euthanasia is to respect that person's autonomy is questionable. Can a person's decision on euthanasia be really autonomous? If euthanasia were legal everybody would be conscious of this option: the patient, the doctor, the family and the nursing staff. Thus, there could be indirect pressure on the patient to make a decision. The choice is meant to be free but the patient is not free not to make the choice. Secondly, a choice that seeks to alleviate suffering and thus improve life by annihilating it is irrational. Thirdly, autonomy as to one's own death is hardly exercised freely. Even an otherwise competent person may not be competent in deciding on his own death on account of despair, hopelessness, fear or maybe a feeling of being weak, superfluous and unwanted. This is a very uncertain base for decision-making, especially in the irrevocable decision of euthanasia. Finally, a competent person usually makes any choice in a responsible way and after due consideration; a 'good' decision should consider and respect the wishes and feelings of others. This will be no less the case in making a decision on the so-called free choice of euthanasia. Thus 'normal' behaviour in decision making will only add to the tendency of the already depressed person to feel a burden on his family, the staff and even on society.

Herranz, Gonzalo. Euthanasia: an uncontrollable power over death. *National Catholic Bioethics Quarterly* 2006 Summer; 6(2): 263-269. NRCBL: 20.5.1; 20.7; 20.3.1; 4.4; 4.1.2; 1.2.

Hildén, Hanna-Mari; Honkasalo, Marja-Liisa. Finnish nurses' interpretations of patient autonomy in the context of end-of-life decision making. *Nursing Ethics* 2006 January; 13(1): 41-51. NRCBL: 20.5.1; 1.1; 7.1; 8.1; 20.4.1. SC: em.

Abstract: Our aim was to study how nurses interpret patient autonomy in end-of-life decision making. This study built on our previous quantitative study, which evaluated the experiences of and views on end-of-life decision making of a representative sample of Finnish nurses taken from the whole country. We performed qualitative interviews with 17 nurses and analysed these using discourse analysis. In their talk, the nurses demonstrated three different discourses, namely the 'supporter', the 'analyst' and the 'practical' discourses, each of which outlined a certain position for patients and relatives, and a certain identity for the nurses in end-of-life decision making. The nurses' talk showed notable differences when compared with that of physicians, highlighting the differences that take place in respect of the image of a person's work, professional culture, professional identification and responsibilities. An important finding was that the nurses often described their participation in end-of-life decision making in terms of indirect influence.

Ho, Kwok M.; English, Sonya; Bell, Jeanette. The involvement of intensive care nurses in end-of-life decisions: a nationwide survey. *Intensive Care Medicine* 2005 May; 31(5): 668-673. NRCBL: 20.5.1; 4.1.3; 8.1. SC: em. Identifiers: New Zealand.

Hsin-Chen, Hsin. Effects of family-centered values in elder's end-of-life decision making—perspectives of seniors in Taiwan and compared to seniors in New Zealand. *Formosan Journal of Medical Humanities* 2006 June; 7(1-2): 179-190. NRCBL: 20.5.1; 20.3.3; 1.1; 9.5.2.

Jacobs, Barbara Bennett; Taylor, Carol. "Seeing" artificial hydration and nutrition through an ethical lens. *Home Healthcare Nurse* 2005 November; 23(11): 739-742. NRCBL: 20.5.1; 4.1.3; 9.4. SC: cs.

Johnson, Arnold L. Towards a modified cardiopulmonary resuscitation policy. *Canadian Journal of Cardiology* 1998 February; 14(2): 203-208. NRCBL: 20.5.1; 9.4; 9.2; 1.1. SC: em.

King, Dorothy. Lessons learned: what the Terri Schiavo case has taught us thus far. *Health Care Food and Nutrition Focus* 2005 September; 22(9): 1, 3-6. NRCBL: 20.5.1; 4.1.1; 20.5.4.

Leget, C. Boundaries, borders, and limits. A phenomenological reflection on ethics and euthanasia. *Journal of Medical Ethics* 2006 May; 32(5): 256-259. NRCBL: 20.5.1; 1.1. SC: an.

Abstract: The subject of euthanasia divides both people and nations. It will always continue to do so because the arguments for and against this issue are intrinsically related to each other. This paper offers an analysis of the interrelation of the arguments, departing from a phenomenology of boundaries. From the participant perspective the boundary of euthanasia appears as a limit. From a helicopter perspective it appears as a border. Reflecting on both perspectives they turn out to complement other: the positive effects of the former correspond to the negative effects of the latter. In order to see how this interrelation of viewpoints works out in the case of euthanasia a paradigmatic case is analysed from the perspective of the patient, the doctor, and the family. This phenomenological analysis does not directly lead to normative conclusions. It helps by both paying attention to, and dealing with, the complexity of the issue with intellectual honesty.

Lyons, Edward C. In incognito- the principle of double effect in America constitution law. *Florida Law Review* 2005 July; 57(3): 469-563. NRCBL: 20.5.3; 1.1. SC: le. Identifiers: Mary and Jodie.

Mauron, Alex. The choosy reaper: from the myth of eternal youth to the reality of unequal death. *EMBO Reports* 2005 July; 6(Special Issue): S67-S71. NRCBL: 20.5.1; 4.4; 4.5; 1.2; 1.1.

McCormack, Paula. Quality of life and the right to die: an ethical dilemma. *Journal of Advanced Nursing* 1998 July; 28(1): 63-69. NRCBL: 20.5.1; 4.4; 1.1. SC: cs.

McLean, Sheila A.M. Permanent vegetative state: the legal position. *Neuropsychological Rehabilitation* 2005 July-September; 15(3-4): 237-250. NRCBL: 20.5.1; 1.1. SC: le. Identifiers: United Kingdom (Great Britain).

McMahan, Jeff. Killing and equality. *Utilitas* 1995 May; 7(1): 1-29. NRCBL: 20.5.1; 1.1; 12.3. SC: an.

Melltorp, G.; Nilstun, T. The difference between withholding and withdrawing life-sustaining treatment. *Intensive Care Medicine* 1997 December; 23(12): 1264-1267. NRCBL: 20.5.1; 1.1. SC: em. Identifiers: Sweden.

Mick, JoAnn. The ethical dilemma of medical futility: the case of Mr. X. *Clinical Journal of Oncology Nursing* 2005 October; 9(5): 611-616. NRCBL: 20.5.1; 1.1; 4.1.3; 9.4; 20.5.4. SC: cs.

Moody, Harry R. Intimations of prolongevity [book reviews]. *Gerontologist* 2004 June; 44(3): 432-436. NRCBL: 20.5.1; 1.1; 9.5.2; 1.5.1.

Needham, Andrea. Patients' right to decide whether to be resuscitated. *Nursing Times* 2005 July 26-August 1; 101(30): 26-27. NRCBL: 20.5.1; 8.3.4; 8.1; 4.1.3. Identifiers: United Kingdom (Great Britain).

Patterson, Rachael; George, Katrina. Euthanasia and assisted suicide: a liberal approach versus the traditional moral view. *Journal of Law and Medicine* 2005 May; 12(4): 494-510. NRCBL: 20.5.1; 20.7; 4.4; 1.1. SC: cs. Identifiers: Australia.

Rocker, Graeme M.; Cook, Deborah J.; O'Callaghan, Christopher J.; Pichora, Deborah; Dodek, Peter M.; Conrad, Wendy; Kutsogiannis, Demetrios J.; Heyland, Daren K. Canadian nurses' and respiratory therapists' perspectives on withdrawal of life support in the intensive care unit. *Journal of Critical Care* 2005 March; 20(1): 59-65. NRCBL: 20.5.1; 20.3.2; 4.1.3. SC: em.

NRCBL: National Reference Center for Bioethics Literature Classification Scheme   See inside front cover for terms.

195

Roman, Linda M.; Metules, Terri J. What we can learn from the Schiavo case. *RN* 2005 August; 68(8): 53-57, 60. NRCBL: 20.5.1; 4.1.3.

Saini, Pushpinder. The doctrine of double effect and the law of murder. *Medico-Legal Journal* 1999; 67(Part 3): 106-120. NRCBL: 20.5.1; 20.7; 1.1. SC: le.

Saliga, Christopher M. Freedom at the end of life: voluntary death versus human flourishing. *National Catholic Bioethics Quarterly* 2006 Summer; 6(2): 253-262. NRCBL: 20.5.1; 20.4.1; 20.3.1; 1.1; 4.4.

Slowther, Anne-Marie. Medical futility and 'do not attempt resuscitation' orders. *Clinical Ethics* 2006 March; 1(1): 18-20. NRCBL: 20.5.1; 5.2; 1.1.

Stith, Marah. The semblance of autonomy: treatment of persons with disabilities under the Uniform Health-Care Decisions Act. *Issues in Law and Medicine* 2006 Summer; 22(1): 39-80. NRCBL: 20.5.1; 1.1; 20.5.4. SC: le.

Teisseyre, Nathalie; Mullet, Etienne; Sorum, Paul Clay. Under what conditions is euthanasia acceptable to lay people and health professionals? *Social Science and Medicine* 2005 January; 60(2): 357-368. NRCBL: 20.5.1; 8.1; 20.7; 1.1; 19.5; 7.1. SC: em. Identifiers: France.

Tulloch, Gail. A feminist utilitarian perspective on euthanasia: from Nancy Crick to Terri Schiavo. *Nursing Inquiry* 2005 June; 12(2): 155-160. NRCBL: 20.5.1; 10; 20.7; 8.1; 1.1.

Turiel, Judith Steinberg. End of life. *In her:* Our Parents, Ourselves: How American Health Care Imperils Middle Age and Beyond. Berkeley: University of California Press; 2005: 179-224. NRCBL: 20.5.1; 1.1; 8.1; 20.4.1; 20.7.

Union of American Hebrew Congregations. Committee on Bio-Ethics. Autonomy: My Right to Live or Die: Bioethics Program/Case Study: Case Study II. New York, NY: Union of American Hebrew Congregations, 1989 April; 30 p. NRCBL: 20.5.1; 1.1; 1.2; 9.4; 9.5.2; 20.5.4. SC: cs. Note: Case Study: An Elderly Patient Refuses Dialysis.

Vincent, Jean-Louis; Berre, J.; Creteur, J. Withholding and withdrawing life prolonging treatment in the intensive care unit: a current European perspective. *Chronic Respiratory Disease* 2004; 1(2): 115-120. NRCBL: 20.5.1; 1.1; 21.1. SC: em.

Widdershoven, Guy A.M. Beyond autonomy and beneficience: the moral basis of euthanasia in the Netherlands. *In:* Schotsmans, Paul; Meulenbergs, Tom, eds. Euthanasia and Palliative Care in the Low Countries. Dudley, MA: Peeters, 2005: 83-93. NRCBL: 20.5.1; 1.1; 2.1.

EUTHANASIA AND ALLOWING TO DIE/ RELIGIOUS ASPECTS

Ankeny, Rachel A.; Clifford, Ross; Jordens, Christopher F.C.; Kerridge, Ian H.; Benson, Rod. Religious perspectives on withdrawal of treatment from patients with multiple organ failure. *Medical Journal of Australia* 2005 December 5-19; 183(11-12): 616-621. NRCBL: 20.5.1; 1.2.

Annas, George J. "I want to live": medicine betrayed by ideology in the political debate over Terri Schiavo. *Stetson Law Review* 2005 Fall; 35(1): 49-80. NRCBL: 20.5.1; 8.3.3; 2.1; 1.2; 2.4. SC: le.

Breier-Mackie, Sarah J. PEGs and ethics revisited: a timely reflection in the wake of the Terri Schiavo case. *Gastroenterology Nursing* 2005 July-August; 28(4): 292-297. NRCBL: 20.5.1; 2.1; 9.7; 1.2. Identifiers: percutaneous endoscopic gastronomy.

Bretzke, James T. A burden of means: interpreting recent Catholic magisterial teaching on end-of-life issues. *Journal of the Society of Christian Ethics* 2006 Fall-Winter; 26(2): 183-200. NRCBL: 20.5.1; 1.2; 4.4.

Bruce, Donald. To everything there is a season? Time, eternity and the promise of extending human life. *EMBO Reports* 2005 July; 6(Special Issue): S63-S66. NRCBL: 20.5.1; 4.4; 4.5; 1.2.

Caddell, David P.; Newton, Rae R. Euthanasia: American attitudes toward the physician's role. *Social Science and Medicine* 1995 June; 40(12): 1671-1681. NRCBL: 20.5.1; 7.1; 20.3.1; 1.2. SC: em.

Cahill, Lisa Sowle. Decline and dying: principles of analysis and practices of solidarity. *In her:* Theological Bioethics: Participation, Justice, and Change. Washington, DC: Georgetown University Press; 2005: 102-130. NRCBL: 20.5.1; 1.2.

Carlson, Bryant; Simopolous, Nicole; Goy, Elizabeth R.; Jackson, Ann; Ganzini, Linda. Oregon hospice chaplains' experiences with patients requesting physician-assisted suicide. *Journal of Palliative Medicine* 2005 December; 8(6): 1160-1166. NRCBL: 20.5.1; 20.7; 8.1; 20.4.1; 1.2. SC: em.

Cherry, Mark J. How should Christians make judgments at the edge of life and death? *Christian Bioethics* 2006 April; 12(1): 1-10. NRCBL: 20.5.1; 1.2.

Clark, Peter. Tube feedings and persistent vegetative state patients: ordinary and extraordinary means? *Christian Bioethics* 2006 April; 12(1): 43-64. NRCBL: 20.5.1; 1.2. Abstract: This article looks at the late John Paul II's allocution on artificial nutrition and hydration (ANH) and the implications his statement will have on the ordinary-extraordinary care distinction. The purpose of this article is threefold: first, to examine the medical condition of a persistent vegetative state (PVS); second, to examine and analyze the Catholic Church's tradition on the ordinary-extraordinary means distinction; and third, to analyze the ethics behind the pope's recent allocation in regards to PVS patients as a matter of conscience. Rather than providing clarification, I argue that the papal allocation has raised many difficult questions. People in situations where decisions must be made about withdrawal or continued ANH are in need of guidance. Moreover, additional analysis is needed to determine whether the papal allocation is in conflict with the traditional Catholic medical ethics understanding of the ordinary-extraordinary care distinction.

Drane, James F. Stopping nutrition and hydration technologies: a conflict between traditional Catholic ethics and Church authority. *Christian Bioethics* 2006 April; 12(1): 11-28. NRCBL: 20.5.1; 1.2.

Abstract: This article focuses on the troubling effects of the secular values of individual freedom and autonomy and their impact on laws regarding suicide and euthanasia. The author argues that in an increasingly secularized culture, death and dying are losing their meaning and are not thought of within a moral framework. The debate regarding the provision of artificial nutrition and hydration is critically considered in light of the history of Catholic morality as well as within the modern healthcare context, and finally with new insight from the recent statements made by the late pope. Drane argues that the pope's insistence on providing artificial nutrition and hydration despite irreversible persistent vegetative states is unconvincing.

Flanigan, Rosemary. Artificial food and hydration—defending a tradition. *Practical Bioethics* 2006 Spring-Summer; 2(2-3): 11-12. NRCBL: 20.5.1; 1.2.

Garcia, Jorge L.A. A Catholic perspective on the ethics of artificially providing food and water. *Linacre Quarterly* 2006 May; 73(2): 132-152. NRCBL: 20.5.1; 1.2. Identifiers: Pope John Paul II; Evangelium Vitae.

Gastmans, Chris; Lemiengre, Joke; Dierckx de Casterlé, Bernadette. Role of nurses in institutional ethics policies on euthanasia. *Journal of Advanced Nursing* 2006 April; 54(1): 53-61. NRCBL: 20.5.1; 1.2; 1.3.2; 7.1; 9.1. SC: em. Identifiers: Belgium.

Gordon, Michael. Ethical and clinical issues in cardiopulmonary resuscitation (CPR) in the frail elderly with dementia: a Jewish perspective. *Journal of Ethics in Mental Health* 2006 November; 1(1): E4, 4 p. NRCBL: 20.5.1; 17.1; 9.5.2; 1.2.

Harvey, John Collins. The burdens-benefits ratio consideration for medical administration of nutrition and hydration to persons in the persistent vegetative state. *Christian Bioethics* 2006 April; 12(1): 99-106. NRCBL: 20.5.1; 1.2.

Abstract: In this article, Harvey notes the initial confusion about the statement made by the pope concerning artificial nutrition and hydration on patients suffering persistent vegetative states (PVS) due to misunderstanding through the translation of the pope's words. He clarifies and assesses what was meant by the statement. He also discusses the problems of terminology concerned with the subject of PVS. Harvey concludes that the papal allocation was in line with traditional Catholic bioethics, and that while maintaining the life of a patient is favorable, in

particular cases this presumption wanes when it is clear that this treatment modality would be futile or very burdensome.

Herranz, Gonzalo. Euthanasia: an uncontrollable power over death. *National Catholic Bioethics Quarterly* 2006 Summer; 6(2): 263-269. NRCBL: 20.5.1; 20.7; 20.3.1; 4.4; 4.1.2; 1.2.

Hynds, James. Reconsidering Catholic teaching on withdrawal of artificial nutrition and hydration. *Health Care Ethics USA* 2006; 14(3): E4. NRCBL: 20.5.1; 1.2.

Iltis, Ana Smith. On the impermissibility of euthanasia in Catholic healthcare organizations. *Christian Bioethics* 2006 December; 12(3): 281-290. NRCBL: 20.5.1; 1.2; 20.4.1; 4.4.

Abstract: Roman Catholic healthcare institutions in the United States face a number of threats to the integrity of their missions, including the increasing religious and moral pluralism of society and the financial crisis many organizations face. These organizations in the United States often have fought fervently to avoid being obligated to provide interventions they deem intrinsically immoral, such as abortion. Such institutions no doubt have made numerous accommodations and changes in how they operate in response to the growing pluralism of our society, but they have resisted crossing certain lines and providing particular interventions deemed objectively wrong. Catholic hospitals in Belgium have responded differently to pluralism. In response to a growing diversity of moral views and to the Belgian Act of Euthanasia of 2002, Catholic hospitals in Belgium now engage in euthanasia. This essay examines a defense that has been offered of this practice of euthanasia in Catholic hospitals and argues that it is misguided.

Jans, Jan. The Belgian "Act on Euthanasia": clarifying context, legislation, and practice from an ethical point of view". *Journal of the Society of Christian Ethics* 2005 Fall-Winter; 25(2): 163-177. NRCBL: 20.5.3; 21.1; 2.4; 1.2. SC: le.

Mauron, Alex. The choosy reaper: from the myth of eternal youth to the reality of unequal death. *EMBO Reports* 2005 July; 6(Special Issue): S67-S71. NRCBL: 20.5.1; 4.4; 4.5; 1.2; 1.1.

Meidl, Erik J. A case studies approach to assisted nutrition and hydration. *National Catholic Bioethics Quarterly* 2006 Summer; 6(2): 319-336. NRCBL: 20.5.1; 20.4.1; 1.2.

O'Rourke, Kevin. Reflections on the papal allocution concerning care for persistent vegetative state patients. *Christian Bioethics* 2006 April; 12(1): 83-97. NRCBL: 20.5.1; 1.2.

Abstract: This article critically examines the recent papal allocution on patients in a persistent vegetative state with regard to the appropriate conditions for considering "reformable statements." In the first part of the article, the purpose and meaning of the allocution are assessed. O'Rourke concludes that give consideration of the individual patient's best interest, prolonging artificial nutrition and hydration is not, in every case, the best option. Although he stresses favorability for preservation of the life of the patient through artificial nutrition and hydration, costs and benefits to the patient should be weighed. Ultimately, he argues in favor of leaving the decision to the

NRCBL: National Reference Center for Bioethics Literature Classification Scheme   See inside front cover for terms.

197

patient, his caregivers, and others immediately involved in the case.

Parrot, Anny; Gomez, M.; Herrenschmidt, Maurice; Carnein, Stéphane; Wary, Bernard; Van Der Beken, Jacques. L'euthanasie = Euthanasia. *Overtures* 1999; (93): 2-14. NRCBL: 20.5.1; 9.5.2; 20.7; 1.2. SC: le.

Perry, Joshua E. Biblical biopolitics: judicial process, religious rhetoric, Terri Schiavo and beyond. *Health Matrix: The Journal of Law-Medicine* 2006 Summer; 16(2): 553-630. NRCBL: 20.5.1; 1.2; 2.1; 7.1. SC: le.

Place, Michael. Nutrition, hydration and the "persistent vegetative state". *Origins* 2006 May 25; 36(2): 17-24. NRCBL: 20.5.1; 1.2; 4.4; 20.5.3.

Rosner, Fred. The Terri Schiavo case in Jewish law [op-ed]. *Cancer Investigation* 2005; 23(7): 652. NRCBL: 20.5.1; 1.2; 20.1.

Sacred Congregation for the Doctrine of the Faith. Declaration on euthanasia. *In:* Tännsjö, Torbjörn, ed. Terminal Sedation: Euthanasia in Disguise? Boston: Kluwer Academic Publishers; 2004: 134-140. NRCBL: 20.5.1; 1.2.

Shannon, Thomas A. Nutrition and hydration: an analysis of the recent papal statement in the light of the Roman Catholic bioethical tradition. *Christian Bioethics* 2006 April; 12(1): 29-41. NRCBL: 20.5.1; 1.2.
Abstract: This article discusses the unexpectedly firm stance professed by John Paul II on the provision of artificial nutrition and hydration to patients who are in a persistent vegetative state, and it implications on previously held standards of judging medical treatments. The traditional ordinary/extraordinary care distinction is assessed in light of complexities of the recent allocation as well as its impact on Catholic individuals and in Catholic health care facilities. Shannon concludes that the papal allocution infers that the average Catholic patient is incapable of making proper judgments about their own care. Shannon sees the preservation of life at all costs as at least highly troubling, if not as a radical move against the Catholic medical ethics tradition.

Sullivan, Scott M. A history of extraordinary means. *Ethics and Medics* 2006 November; 31(11): 3-4. NRCBL: 20.5.1; 1.2.

Sullivan, Scott M. A history of extraordinary means: second of a three-part series. *Ethics and Medics* 2006 October; 31(10): 3-4. NRCBL: 20.5.1; 20.7; 1.2.

Sulmasy, Daniel P. End-of-life care revisited. *Health Progress* 2006 July-August; 87(4): 50-56. NRCBL: 20.5.1; 1.2.

Tanida, Noritoshi. Implications of Japanese religions in the genomic age: a survey on attitudes towards life and death within Shinto, Buddhist and Christian groups. *In:* Sleeboom, Margaret, ed. Genomics in Asia: A Clash of Bioethical Interests? New York: Kegan Paul; 2004: 107-134. NRCBL: 20.5.1; 1.2. SC: em.

Tanida, Noritoshi. Implications of Japanese religious views toward life and death in medicine. *In:* Sang-yong, Song; Young-Mo, Koo; Macer, Darryl R.J., eds. Asian Bioethics in the 21st Century. Christchurch, NZ: Eubios Ethics Institute, 2002: 288-93. NRCBL: 20.5.1; 1.2. SC: em. Conference: Proceedings of the Asian Bioethics Conference (ABC4), held 22-25 November 2002 in Seoul, South Korea.

Union of American Hebrew Congregations. Committee on Bio-Ethics. Autonomy: My Right to Live or Die: Bioethics Program/Case Study: Case Study II. New York, NY: Union of American Hebrew Congregations, 1989 April; 30 p. NRCBL: 20.5.1; 1.1; 1.2; 9.4; 9.5.2; 20.5.4. SC: cs. Note: Case Study: An Elderly Patient Refuses Dialysis.

Union of American Hebrew Congregations. Committee on Bio-Ethics. Termination of Treatment: Bioethics Program Case Study: Case Study III. New York, NY: Union of American Hebrew Congregations, 1990 April; 28 p. NRCBL: 20.5.1; 1.2; 9.4; 20.5.4. SC: cs.
Abstract: Includes: Termination of treatment based on Rabbinic sources, by Bernard M. Zlotowitz; Termination of treatment: medical aspects, by Gerald S. Golden; Termination of treatment: a look a Jewish, medical, and legal positions of removing treatment from a patient: an examination of the philosophy of the living will: the legal perspective, by Roselyn B. Koretzky

Union of American Hebrew Congregations. Committee on Bio-Ethics. Voluntary Active Euthanasia — Assisted Suicide: Bioethics Program/Case Study: Bio-Ethics Case VI. New York, NY: Union of American Hebrew Congregations, 1993 Summer; 47 p. NRCBL: 20.5.1; 20.7; 1.2.

Vohra, Sameer S. An American Muslim's right to die: incorporating Islamic law into the debate. *Journal of Legal Medicine* 2006 September; 27(3): 341-359. NRCBL: 20.5.1; 20.7; 1.2. SC: le.

Wasserman, Jason; Clair, Jeffery Michael; Ritchey, Ferris J. Racial differences in attitudes toward euthanasia. *Omega* 2005-2006; 52(3): 263-287. NRCBL: 20.5.1; 9.5.4; 1.2. SC: em.

Zientek, David M. The impact of Roman Catholic moral theology on end-of-life care under the Texas Advance Directives Act. *Christian Bioethics* 2006 April; 12(1): 65-82. NRCBL: 20.5.1; 20.5.4; 1.2.
Abstract: This essay reviews the Roman Catholic moral tradition surrounding treatments at the end of life together with the challenges presented to that tradition by the Texas Advance Directives Act. The impact on Catholic health care facilities and physicians, and the way in which the moral tradition should be applied under this statute, particularly with reference to the provision dealing with conflicts over end-of-life treatments, will be critically assessed. I will argue, based on the traditional treatment of end-of-life issues, that Catholic physicians and institutions should appeal to the conflict resolution process of the Advance Directives Act only under a limited number of circumstances. The implications, under the Texas statute, of varied interpretations of Pope John Paul II's recent allocution on

artificial feeding and hydration in the persistent vegetative state will also be considered.

Zlotowitz, Bernard M.; Golden, Gerald S.; Koretzky, Roselyn B. Termination of treatment: case no. 1 [study topic with commentaries]. *Journal of Psychology and Judaism* 1996 Spring; 20(1): 3-22. NRCBL: 20.5.1; 1.2; 20.2.1; 8.3.3; 20.5.4. SC: le.

FETUSES *See* CARE FOR SPECIFIC GROUPS/ FETUSES; HUMAN EXPERIMENTATION/ SPECIAL POPULATIONS/ EMBRYOS AND FETUSES
See also TREATMENT REFUSAL

FORCE FEEDING OF PRISONERS

Annas, George J. Hunger strikes at Guantanamo — medical ethics and human rights in a "legal black hole". *New England Journal of Medicine* 2006 September 28; 355(13): 1377-1382. NRCBL: 21.5; 2.1; 1.3.5; 21.1.

Dyer, Owen. Force feeding at Guantanamo breaches ethics, doctors say [news]. *BMJ: British Medical Journal* 2006 March 11; 332(7541): 569. NRCBL: 21.5; 8.3.4; 7.4.

Golden, Tim. Tough U.S. steps in hunger strike at camp in Cuba; force-feeding detainees; steps to avert a death — lawyers for prisoners protest treatment. *New York Times* 2006 February 9; pl A1, A20. NRCBL: 21.5; 20.7. SC: po.

Nicholl, David J.; Atkinson, Holly G.; Kalk, John; Hopkins, William; Elias, Elwyn; Siddiqui, Adnan; Cranford, Ronald E.; Sacks, Oliver. Forcefeeding and restraint of Guantanamo Bay hunger strikers [letter]. *Lancet* 2006 March 11-17; 367(9513): 811. NRCBL: 21.5.

Nicholl, David J.; Wilks, Michael. Guantanamo: a call for action: good men need to do something [letter and reply]. *BMJ: British Medical Journal* 2006 April 8; 332(7545): 854-855. NRCBL: 21.5; 7.1.

Röggla, Georg. Medically enforced feeding of detained asylum seekers on hunger strike [letter]. *Wiener Klinische Wochenschrift* 2005 June; 117(11-12): 436. NRCBL: 21.5. SC: le. Identifiers: Austria.

Rosendorff, C. Voluntary total fasting: ethical-medical considerations. *World Medical Journal* 1989; 36: 82-83. NRCBL: 21.5.

FOREIGN NATIONALS *See* HUMAN EXPERIMENTATION/ SPECIAL POPULATIONS/ FOREIGN NATIONALS

GENE THERAPY

Risks and ethics of gene transfer. *Reproductive BioMedicine Online [electronic]* 2005 March; 10(3): 309 Accessed: http://www.rbmonline.com [2005 September 30]. NRCBL: 15.4; 5.2.

Abbott, Alison. Questions linger about unexplained gene-therapy trial death [news]. *Nature Medicine* 2006 June; 12(6): 597. NRCBL: 15.4; 18.1; 20.1. Identifiers: Germany.

Bacchetta, Matthew; Richter, Gerd. Contemporary ethical analysis: a shortfall in scientific knowledge. *Politics and the Life Sciences* 1998 March; 17(1): 11-12. NRCBL: 15.4. Comments: Andrea Bonnicksen. Transplanting nuclei between human eggs: implications for germ-line genetics. Politics and the Life Sciences 1998 March; 17(1): 3-10.

Baylis, Françoise; Robert, Jason Scott. Gene therapy. *In:* Mitcham, Carl, ed. Encyclopedia of Science, Technology, and Ethics. Farmington Hills, MI: Thomson/Gale, 2005: 829-831. NRCBL: 15.4; 2.2.

Beach, Judith E. The new RAC: restructuring of the National Institutes of Health Recombinant DNA Advisory Committee. *Food and Drug Law Journal* 1999; 54(1): 49-53. NRCBL: 15.4; 18.2; 18.6.

Berger, Edward M. IVONT and the trojan horse. *Politics and the Life Sciences* 1998 March; 17(1): 13-14. NRCBL: 15.4; 14.5. Identifiers: in vitro ovum nuclear transfer. Comments: Andrea Bonnicksen. Transplanting nuclei between human eggs: implications for germ-line genetics. Politics and the Life Sciences 1998 March; 17(1): 3-10.

Bonnicksen, Andrea. Egg cell nuclear transfer continued: infertility treatment [response]. *Politics and the Life Sciences* 1998 March; 17(1): 36-38. NRCBL: 15.4; 14.5. Comments: Politics and the Life Sciences 1998 March; 17(1): 11-35.

Bonnicksen, Andrea L. Transplanting nuclei between human eggs: implications for germ-line genetics. *Politics and the Life Sciences* 1998 March; 17(1): 3-10. NRCBL: 15.4; 14.1; 14.5.

Bostrom, Nick. Human genetic enhancements: a transhumanist perspective. *Journal of Value Inquiry* 2003; 37(4): 493-506. NRCBL: 15.4; 4.4; 4.2; 1.1. SC: an.

Breivik, Gunnar. Sport, gene doping and ethics. *In:* Tamburrini, Claudio; Tännsjö, Torbjörn, eds. Genetic Technology and Sport: Ethical Questions. London; New York: Routledge; 2005: 165-177. NRCBL: 15.4; 9.5.1.

Bruce, Donald M. Moral and ethical issues in gene therapy. *Human Reproduction and Genetic Ethics: An International Journal* 2006; 12(1): 16-23. NRCBL: 15.4; 1.2; 5.3; 15.5.

Cahill, Lisa Sowle. Genetics in context: beyond anatomy and the market. *Politics and the Life Sciences* 1998 March; 17(1): 14-16. NRCBL: 15.4; 14.5; 18.5.4. Comments: Andrea Bonnicksen. Transplanting nuclei between human eggs: implications for germ-line genetics. Politics and the Life Sciences 1998 March; 17(1): 3-10.

NRCBL: National Reference Center for Bioethics Literature Classification Scheme   See inside front cover for terms.

199

Caplan, Arthur. Commentary: improving quality of life is a morally important goal for gene therapy. *Human Gene Therapy* 2006 December; 17(2): 1164. NRCBL: 15.4; 4.4; 18.5.1; 18.1.

Caplan, Arthur; Elliott, Carl. Is it ethical to use enhancement technologies to make us better than well? *PLoS Medicine* 2004 December; 1(3): 172-175. NRCBL: 15.4; 15.1; 4.4.

Carmen, Ira H. A death in the laboratory: the politics of the Gelsinger aftermath. *Molecular Therapy* 2001 April; 3(4): 425-428. NRCBL: 15.4; 18.3; 18.5.1.

Chadwick, Ruth. Nutrigenomics, individualism and sports. *In:* Tamburrini, Claudio; Tännsjö, Torbjörn, eds. Genetic Technology and Sport: Ethical Questions. London; New York: Routledge; 2005: 126-135. NRCBL: 15.4; 9.5.1.

Chadwick, Ruth; Wilson, Sarah. Bio-Amazons — a comment. *In:* Tamburrini, Claudio; Tännsjö, Torbjörn, eds. Genetic Technology and Sport: Ethical Questions. London; New York: Routledge; 2005: 205-208. NRCBL: 15.4; 9.5.1; 10.

Chan, Sarah; Harris, John. The ethics of gene therapy. *Current Opinion in Molecular Therapeutics* 2006 October; 8(5): 377-383. NRCBL: 15.4; 4.5.

Check, Erika. Gene therapists hopeful as trials resume with childhood disease [news]. *Nature* 2004 June 10; 429(6992): 587. NRCBL: 15.4; 18.5.2; 18.6. Identifiers: France.

Comité Consultatif de Bioéthique de Belgique. Avis no. 33 du 7 novembre 2005 relatif aux modifications géniques somatiques et germinales à visées thérapeutiques et/ ou mélioratives [Opinion no. 33 of Nov. 7, 2005 concerning somatic and germ cell gene therapy for therapeutic or enhancement purposes]. *Bioethica Belgica* 2006 March; (25): 3-37. NRCBL: 15.4; 18.5.4. SC: pc. Identifiers: Belgium.

European Society of Gene Therapy [ESGT]. Position paper on social, ethical and public awareness issues in gene therapy. Stockholm, Sweden: European Society of Gene Therapy, 2002 November: 10 p. [Online]. Accessed: http://www.congrex.se/esgt/downloads/position_2.pdf [2006 July 27]. NRCBL: 15.4.

Gänsbacher, Bernd. Policy statement on the social, ethical and public awareness issues in gene therapy. *Journal of Gene Medicine* 2002 November-December; 4(6): 687-691. NRCBL: 15.4; 18.6; 21.1.

Gert, Bernard; Culver, Charles M. Therapy and enhancement. *In:* Mitcham, Carl, ed. Encyclopedia of Science, Technology, and Ethics. Farmington Hills, MI: Thomson/Gale, 2005: 1938-1942. NRCBL: 15.4; 1.1; 4.5; 1.3.11; 15.1; 22.3.

Gonin, P.; Buchholz, C.J.; Pallardy, M.; Mezzina, M. Gene therapy bio-safety: scientific and regulatory issues. *Gene Therapy* 2005 October; 12(Supplement 1): S146-S152. NRCBL: 15.4; 18.1.

Grande, Lydia Feito. Putting ethics in motion: basic elements for analysis of human gene therapy = Poner en marcha la ética: elementos básicos para el análisis de la terapia génica humana. *Law and the Human Genome Review =Revista de Derecho y Genoma Humano* 1996 January-June; (4): 125-139. NRCBL: 15.4; 4.4.

Graumann, Sigrid. Die somatische Gentherapie in der Krise: Kritsche Fragen an ein experimentelles Therapiekonzept. *In:* Rehmann-Sutter, Christoph; Müller, Hansjakob, eds. Ethik und Gentherapie: zum praktischen Diskurs um die molekulare Medizin. 2nd ed. Tübingen: Francke Verlag; 2003: 117-133. NRCBL: 15.4; 18.1.

Graumann, Sigrid; Haker, Hille. Some conceptual and ethical comments on egg cell nuclear transfer. *Politics and the Life Sciences* 1998 March; 17(1): 17-19. NRCBL: 15.4; 14.5. Comments: Andrea Bonnicksen. Transplanting nuclei between human eggs: implications for germ-line genetics. Politics and the Life Sciences 1998 March; 17(1): 3-10.

Guo, Jerry; Xin, Hao. Splicing out the West? [news]. *Science* 2006 November 24; 314(5803): 1232-1235. NRCBL: 15.4; 9.7. Identifiers: China.

Henderson, Gail E.; Easter, Michele M.; Zimmer, Catherine; King, Nancy M.P.; Davis, Arlene M.; Rothschild, Barbra Bluestone; Churchill, Larry R.; Wilfond, Benjamin S.; Nelson, Daniel K. Therapeutic misconception in early phase gene transfer trials. *Social Science and Medicine* 2006 January; 62(1): 239-253. NRCBL: 15.4; 18.3. SC: em.

Holtug, Nils. Identity, integrity, and nuclei transplantation. *Politics and the Life Sciences* 1998 March; 17(1): 20-21. NRCBL: 15.4; 14.1. Comments: Andrea Bonnicksen. Transplanting nuclei between human eggs: implications for germ-line genetics. Politics and the Life Sciences 1998 March; 17(1): 3-10.

Hurwitz, Richard L. [A death in the laboratory: the politics of the Gelsinger aftermath] [letter]. *Molecular Therapy* 2001 July; 4(1): 4. NRCBL: 15.4; 18.3; 18.5.1. Comments: Ira H. Carmen. A death in the laboratory: the politics of the Gelsinger aftermath. Molecular Therapy 2001 April; 3(4): 425-428.

Ip, Po-Keung. The ethics of human enhancement gene therapy. *In:* Döring, Ole; Chen, Renbiao, eds. Advances in Chinese Medical Ethics: Chinese and International Perspectives. Hamburg: Institut für Asienkunde; 2002: 119-132. NRCBL: 15.4; 4.5. Note: Proceedings of the Second Sino-German Interdisciplinary Symposium about Medical Ethics in China, Shanghai, 19-23 October, 1999.

Jaffé, A.; Prasad, S.A.; Larcher, V.; Hart, S. Gene therapy for children with cystic fibrosis — who has the right to choose? *Journal of Medical Ethics* 2006 June; 32(6): 361-364. NRCBL: 15.4; 18.5.2; 8.3.3; 18.3.

Kim, S.Y.H.; Holloway, R.G.; Frank, S.; Beck, C.A.; Zimmerman, C.; Wilson, R.; Kieburtz, K. Volunteering for early phase gene transfer research in Parkinson disease. *Neurology* 2006 April 11; 66(7): 1010-1015. NRCBL: 15.4; 18.3; 18.5.1; 17.1. SC: em.

Knoppers, Bartha Maria. Geneticism and germ line: between courage and caution. *Politics and the Life Sciences* 1998 March; 17(1): 22-24. NRCBL: 15.4; 14.1; 21.1. Comments: Andrea Bonnicksen. Transplanting nuclei between human eggs: implications for germ-line genetics. Politics and the Life Sciences 1998 March; 17(1): 3-10.

Lacadena, Juan Ramón. Genetic manipulation offences in Spain's new Penal Code: a genetic commentary = Delitos relativos a la manipulación genética en el nuevo Código Penal español: un comentario genético. *Law and the Human Genome Review = Revista de Derecho y Genoma Humano* 1996 July-December; (5): 195-203. NRCBL: 15.4; 1.3.5. SC: le.

Lachs, John. Researchers and their subjects as neighbors. *Politics and the Life Sciences* 1998 March; 17(1): 24-25. NRCBL: 15.4; 14.1. Comments: Andrea Bonnicksen. Transplanting nuclei between human eggs: implications for germ-line genetics. Politics and the Life Sciences 1998 March; 17(1): 3-10.

Lagay, Faith. Genetic difference: unfair or only unfortunate? *Virtual Mentor* 2001 November; 3(11): 3p. NRCBL: 15.4; 1.1.

Lesch, Walter. Gentherapie und Körperbilder: Anthropologische und ethische Denkanstösse. *In:* Rehmann-Sutter, Christoph; Müller, Hansjakob, eds. Ethik und Gentherapie: zum praktischen Diskurs um die molekulare Medizin. 2nd ed. Tübingen: Francke Verlag; 2003: 251-260. NRCBL: 15.4; 1.1.

Luchsinger, Thomas; Schmid, Hermann. Gentherapie aus juristischer Sicht: Schweizerische und internationale Tendenzen. *In:* Rehmann-Sutter, Christoph; Müller, Hansjakob, eds. Ethik und Gentherapie: zum praktischen Diskurs um die molekulare Medizin. 2nd ed. Tübingen: Francke Verlag; 2003: 169-186. NRCBL: 15.4. SC: le.

Lunshof, Jeantine E. Lücken in der Regulierung?: Zur Kritik der Begutachtungsverfahren. *In:* Rehmann-Sutter, Christoph; Müller, Hansjakob, eds. Ethik und Gentherapie: zum praktischen Diskurs um die molekulare Medizin. Tübingen: Attempto Verlag; 1995: 118-136. NRCBL: 15.4; 18.2; 18.6.

Lunshof, Jeantine E. Lücken in der Regulierung?: Zur Kritik der Begutachtungsverfahren. *In:* Rehmann-Sutter, Christoph; Müller, Hansjakob, eds. Ethik und

Gentherapie: zum praktischen Diskurs um die molekulare Medizin. 2nd ed. Tübingen: Francke Verlag; 2003: 151-167. NRCBL: 15.4; 18.6. SC: le.

Mantovani, Ferrando. Genetic manipulation, legal interests under threat, control systems and techniques of protection = Manipulaciones genéticas, bienes jurídicos amenazados, sistemas de control y técnicas de tutela. *Law and the Human Genome = Revista de Derecho y Genoma Humano* 1994 July-December; (1): 91-117. NRCBL: 15.4; 14.1; 14.5; 1.1; 4.4; 8.3.1. SC: le.

Mauron, Alex; Rehmann-Sutter, Christoph. Gentherapie: Ein Katalog offener ethischer Fragen. *In:* Rehmann-Sutter, Christoph; Müller, Hansjakob, eds. Ethik und Gentherapie: Zum praktischen Diskurs um die molekulare Medizin. Tübingen: Attempto Verlag; 1995: 22-33. NRCBL: 15.4.

McGee, Glenn; McGee, Daniel B. Nuclear meltdown: ethics of the need to transfer genes. *Politics and the Life Sciences* 1998 March; 17(1): 26-28. NRCBL: 15.4; 14.1. Comments: Andrea Bonnicksen. Transplanting nuclei between human eggs: implications for germ-line genetics. Politics and the Life Sciences 1998 March; 17(1): 3-10.

McKnight, Reese. RNA interference: a critical analysis of the regulatory and ethical issues encountered in the development of a novel therapy. *Albany Law Journal of Science and Technology* 2004; 15(1): 73-108. NRCBL: 15.4; 5.3; 18.2; 18.3.

Mendell, Jerry R.; Clark, K. Reed. Risks, benefits, and consent in the age of gene therapy [editorial]. *Neurology* 2006 April 11; 66(7): 964-965. NRCBL: 15.4; 18.3; 18.2.

Nyberg, Kara; Carter, Barrie J.; Chen, Theresa; Dunbar, Cynthia; Flotte, Terrence R.; Rose, Stephen; Rosenblum, Daniel; Simek, Stephanie L.; Wilson, Carolyn. Workshop on long-term follow-up of participants in human gene transfer research. *Molecular Therapy* 2004 December; 10(6): 976-980. NRCBL: 15.4; 18.2; 1.3.12; 18.6.

Panno, Joseph. Ethics of gene therapy. *In his:* Gene Therapy: Treating Disease by Repairing Genes. New York: Facts on File, 2005: 71-78. NRCBL: 15.4.

Panno, Joseph. Legal issues. *In his:* Gene Therapy: Treating Disease by Repairing Genes. New York: Facts on File, 2005: 79-86. NRCBL: 15.4. SC: le.

Rehmann-Sutter, Christoph. Das soziale Design der Hoffnungen. *In:* Rehmann-Sutter, Christoph; Müller, Hansjakob, eds. Ethik und Gentherapie: zum praktischen Diskurs um die molekulare Medizin. 2nd ed. Tübingen: Francke Verlag; 2003: 275-286. NRCBL: 15.4.

Rehmann-Sutter, Christoph. Keimbahnveränderungen in Nebenfolge?: Ethische Überlegungen zur Abgrenzbarkeit der somatischen Gentherapie. *In:*

NRCBL: National Reference Center for Bioethics Literature Classification Scheme   See inside front cover for terms.

201

Rehmann-Sutter, Christoph; Müller, Hansjakob, eds. Ethik und Gentherapie: zum praktischen Diskurs um die molekulare Medizin. Tübingen: Attempto Verlag; 1995: 154-175. NRCBL: 15.4.

Rehmann-Sutter, Christoph. Keimbahnveränderungen in Nebenfolge?: Ethische Überlegungen zur Abgrenzbarkeit der somatischen Gentherapie. *In:* Rehmann-Sutter, Christoph; Müller, Hansjakob, eds. Ethik und Gentherapie: zum praktischen Diskurs um die molekulare Medizin. 2nd ed. Tübingen: Francke Verlag; 2003: 187-205. NRCBL: 15.4.

Rehmann-Sutter, Christoph. Politik der genetischen Identität: Gute und schlechte Gründe auf Keimbahntherapie zu verzichten. *In:* Rehmann-Sutter, Christoph; Müller, Hansjakob, eds. Ethik und Gentherapie: zum praktischen Diskurs um die molekulare Medizin. Tübingen: Attempto Verlag; 1995: 176-187. NRCBL: 15.4.

Rehmann-Sutter, Christoph. Politik der genetischen Identität: Gute und schlechte Gründe auf Keimbahntherapie zu verzichten. *In:* Rehmann-Sutter, Christoph; Müller, Hansjakob, eds. Ethik und Gentherapie: zum praktischen Diskurs um die molekulare Medizin. 2nd ed. Tübingen: Francke Verlag; 2003: 225-236. NRCBL: 15.4.

Resnik, David B. Germ-line manipulations, private industry, and secrecy. *Politics and the Life Sciences* 1998 March; 17(1): 29-30. NRCBL: 15.4; 14.1. Comments: Andrea Bonnicksen. Transplanting nuclei between human eggs: implications for germ-line genetics. Politics and the Life Sciences 1998 March; 17(1): 3-10.

Rose, Hilary. A welcome alert to backdoor germ-line therapy. *Politics and the Life Sciences* 1998 March; 17(1): 34-35. NRCBL: 15.4; 14.1. Comments: Andrea Bonnicksen. Transplanting nuclei between human eggs: implications for germ-line genetics. Politics and the Life Sciences 1998 March; 17(1): 3-10.

Rubenstein, Donald S. The fears of looking in the mirror. *Politics and the Life Sciences* 1998 March; 17(1): 31-32. NRCBL: 15.4. Comments: Andrea Bonnicksen. Transplanting nuclei between human eggs: implications for germ-line genetics. Politics and the Life Sciences 1998 March; 17(1): 3-10.

Sadler, Troy D.; Zeidler, Dana L. The morality of socioscientific issues: construal and resolution of genetic engineering dilemmas. *Science Education* 2004 January; 88(1): 4-27. NRCBL: 15.4; 2.1; 14.5. SC: em.

Scharschmidt, Tiffany; Lo, Bernard. Clinical trial design issues raised during recombinant DNA. Advisory committee review of gene transfer protocols. *Human Gene Therapy* 2006 April; 17(4): 448-454. NRCBL: 15.4; 18.2; 18.3. SC: em.

Schmid, Hermann. Gentherapie aus juristischer Sicht — schweizerische und internationale Tendenzen. *In:* Rehmann-Sutter, Christoph; Müller, Hansjakob, eds. Ethik und Gentherapie: Zum praktischen Diskurs um die molekulare Medizin. Tübingen: Attempto Verlag; 1995: 137-153. NRCBL: 15.4; 21.1. SC: le.

Schmidt, Kurt W. Ethische Überlegungen zur klinischen Durchführung somatischer Gentherapien. *In:* Rehmann-Sutter, Christoph; Müller, Hansjakob, eds. Ethik und Gentherapie: Zum praktischen Diskurs um die molekulare Medizin. Tübingen: Attempto Verlag; 1995: 83-108. NRCBL: 15.4; 18.2.

Schneider, Angela J. Genetic enhancement of athletic performance. *In:* Tamburrini, Claudio; Tännsjö, Torbjörn, eds. Genetic Technology and Sport: Ethical Questions. London; New York: Routledge; 2005: 32-41. NRCBL: 15.4; 9.5.1.

Schroeder-Kurth, Traute M. Verfahrensfragen der klinischen Prüfung bei somatischer Gentherapie. *In:* Rehmann-Sutter, Christoph; Müller, Hansjakob, eds. Ethik und Gentherapie: Zum praktischen Diskurs um die molekulare Medizin. Tübingen: Attempto Verlag; 1995: 109-117. NRCBL: 15.4; 18.2.

Scully, Jackie Leach. Gentherapieethik aus Patientensicht. *In:* Rehmann-Sutter, Christoph; Müller, Hansjakob, eds. Ethik und Gentherapie: zum praktischen Diskurs um die molekulare Medizin. 2nd ed. Tübingen: Francke Verlag; 2003: 207-223. NRCBL: 15.4. SC: em.

Senior, Kathryn. Germline gene transfer during gene therapy: reassessing the risks [news]. *Molecular Medicine Today* 1999 September; 5(9): 371. NRCBL: 15.4; 15.1; 18.2.

Sherwin, Susan; Schwartz, Meredith. Resisting the emergence of Bio-Amazons. *In:* Tamburrini, Claudio; Tännsjö, Torbjörn, eds. Genetic Technology and Sport: Ethical Questions. London; New York: Routledge; 2005: 199-204. NRCBL: 15.4; 9.5.1; 10.

Sisti, Dominic A.; Caplan, Arthur L. Back to basics in der post-Gelsinger-Ära: Ethik und Aufsicht der Gentherapieforschung seit dem Todesfall von J. Gelsinger. *In:* Rehmann-Sutter, Christoph; Müller, Hansjakob, eds. Ethik und Gentherapie: zum praktischen Diskurs um die molekulare Medizin. 2nd ed. Tübingen: Francke Verlag; 2003: 135-149. NRCBL: 15.4; 18.6. SC: le.

Sneddon, Andrew. Rawlsian decisionmaking and genetic engineering. *CQ: Cambridge Quarterly of Healthcare Ethics* 2006 Winter; 15(1): 35-41. NRCBL: 15.4; 1.1; 4.5.

Swazo, Norman K. Calculating risk/benefit in X-linked severe combined immune deficiency disorder (X-SCID) gene therapy trials: the task of ethical evaluation. *Journal of Medicine and Philosophy* 2006 October; 31(5): 533-564. NRCBL: 15.4; 18.5.2. SC: an.

Abstract: In response to adverse events in retroviral gene therapy clinical trials conducted in France to correct for X-linked severe combined immune deficiency disorder (X-SCID), an advisory committee of the Food and Drug Administration convened in October 2002, February 2003, and March 2005, to deliberate and provide recommendations for similarly sponsored research in the United States. A similar National Institutes of Health committee met in February 2003. In this article, I review the transcripts and/or minutes of these meetings to evaluate the extent to which the ethical dimension of the research was engaged even as the molecular and clinical evidence was reviewed. I then provide representative ethical arguments to demonstrate the sort of ethical reasoning that should be included as part of the agenda of such committee meetings.

Szebik, Imre. Moral dilemmas of gene transfer techniques. *In:* Sándor, Judit, ed. Society and Genetic Information: Codes and Laws in the Genetic Era. Budapest, Hungary; New York: CEU Press; 2003: 95-100. NRCBL: 15.4; 15.1.

Tamburrini, Claudio; Tännsjö, Torbjörn. The genetic design of a new Amazon. *In:* Tamburrini, Claudio; Tännsjö, Torbjörn, eds. Genetic Technology and Sport: Ethical Questions. London; New York: Routledge; 2005: 181-198. NRCBL: 15.4; 9.5.1; 10.

Thévoz, Jean-Marie. Die Evolution wissenschaftlicher und ethicscher Paradigmen in der Gentherapie. *In:* Rehmann-Sutter, Christoph; Müller, Hansjakob, eds. Ethik und Gentherapie: Zum praktischen Diskurs um die molekulare Medizin. Tübingen: Attempto Verlag; 1995: 34-40. NRCBL: 15.4; 2.2.

Warner, Carol M. Genetic engineering of human eggs and embryos: prelude to cloning. *Politics and the Life Sciences* 1998 March; 17(1): 33-34. NRCBL: 15.4; 14.5. Comments: Andrea Bonnicksen. Transplanting nuclei between human eggs: implications for germ-line genetics. Politics and the Life Sciences 1998 March; 17(1): 3-10.

Xin, Hao. Gendicine's efficacy: hard to translate [news]. *Science* 2006 November 24; 314(5803): 1233. NRCBL: 15.4; 9.7.

Zhang, Xinqing. Germ-line gene therapy from the lens of Confucian ethics. *In:* Sang-yong, Song; Young-Mo, Koo; Macer, Darryl R.J., eds. Asian Bioethics in the 21st Century. Christchurch, NZ: Eubios Ethics Institute, 2002: 61-64. NRCBL: 15.4; 1.1. Conference: Proceedings of the Asian Bioethics Conference (ABC4), held 22-25 November 20002 in Seoul, South Korea.

GENETIC COUNSELING

See also GENETIC SCREENING; SEX DETERMINATION

Ethics of preimplantation genetic diagnosis for cancer. *Lancet Oncology* 2006 August; 7(8): 611. NRCBL: 15.2; 14.4.

No easy answers [editorial]. *Nature* 2006 May 18; 441(7091): 255. NRCBL: 15.2; 14.4; 15.5. Identifiers:

United Kingdom (Great Britain); Human Fertilisation and Embryology Authority.

Ackmann, Elizabeth A. Prenatal testing gone awry: the birth of a conflict of ethics and liability. *Indiana Health Law Review* 2005; 2(1): 199-224. NRCBL: 15.2; 12.4.2; 8.5.

Albar, M.A. Counselling about genetic disease: an Islamic perspective. *Eastern Mediterranean Health Journal* 1999; 5(6): 1129-1133. NRCBL: 15.2; 1.2; 14.4.

Alonso Bedate, Carlos. Ethical and legal implications of the use of molecular biology in the clinic. *Journal of Pediatric Endocrinology and Metabolism* 2005 December; 18(Supplement 1): 1137-1143. NRCBL: 15.2; 15.1; 5.3; 8.4.

American Society for Reproductive Medicine [ASRM]. Ethics Committee. Sex selection and preimplantation genetic diagnosis. *Fertility and Sterility* 2004 September; 82(Supplement 1): S245-S248. NRCBL: 15.2; 14.4; 14.3.

Anstey, Kyle W. Prenatal testing and disability: the need for a participatory approach to research. *In:* Sang-yong, Song; Young-Mo, Koo; Macer, Darryl R.J., eds. Asian Bioethics in the 21st Century. Christchurch, NZ: Eubios Ethics Institute, 2002: 347-356. NRCBL: 15.2; 4.2; 9.5.3; 9.5.10. SC: em. Conference: Proceedings of the Asian Bioethics Conference (ABC4), held 22-25 November 2002 in Seoul, South Korea.

Babay, Z.A. Attitudes of a high-risk group of pregnant Saudi Arabian women to prenatal screening for chromosomal anomalies. *Eastern Mediterranean Health Journal* 2004 July-September; 10(4-5): 522-527. NRCBL: 15.2; 12.5.2; 1.2. SC: em.

Basu, Maitraye. Are the present day "designer babies" a threat to humankind? *Eubios Journal of Asian and International Bioethics* 2006 September; 16(5): 151-152. NRCBL: 15.2; 14.4.

Bellamy, Stephen. Lives to save lives — the ethics of tissue typing. *Human Fertility* 2005 March; 8(1): 5-11. NRCBL: 15.2; 14.4; 1.2. Identifiers: United Kingdom (Great Britain).

Braude, Peter. Preimplantation diagnosis for genetic susceptibility. *New England Journal of Medicine* 2006 August 10; 355(6): 541-543. NRCBL: 15.2; 14.4; 15.3. SC: le.

Bromage, D.I. Prenatal diagnosis and selective abortion: a result of the cultural turn? *Medical Humanities* 2006 June; 32(1): 38-42. NRCBL: 15.2; 12.3.
Abstract: There is a growing trend in obstetric medicine of prenatal diagnosis and the selective abortion of foetuses that are likely to be born with a disability. Reasons commonly given to explain this trend include the financial implications of screening and testing policies, the disruption to families caused by the birth of a child with a disability, and the potential quality of life

NRCBL: National Reference Center for Bioethics Literature Classification Scheme   See inside front cover for terms.

203

of the unborn child. This paper reflects upon another possible reason for this. It is argued that it is, in part, a consequence of our attitudes towards disability and a pursuit of aesthetic perfection. These attitudes arise from a social context that may be explained by considering the effect on the disabled community of the transition from modernity to postmodernity. This shift is demonstrated by inspecting some of the synonymous developments in art history. It is suggested that this "cultural turn" may have both helped and hindered people with disabilities, but the hypothesis requires further testing. This could best be achieved with a qualitative study of what motivates parental decision making in the obstetric unit.

Browner, C.H.; Preloran, H. Mabel. Interpreting low-income Latinas' amniocentesis refusals. *Hispanic Journal of Behavioral Sciences* 2000 August 1; 22(3): 346-368. NRCBL: 15.2; 12.5.2; 9.5.4; 21.7. SC: em.

Browner, C.H.; Preloran, H. Mabel; Casado, Maria Christina; Bass, Harold N.; Walker, Ann P. Genetic counseling gone awry: miscommunication between prenatal genetic service providers and Mexican-origin clients. *Social Science and Medicine* 2003 May; 56(9): 1933-1946. NRCBL: 15.2; 8.1; 8.3.4; 21.7; 7.1. SC: em.

Carey, Kristen N. Wrongful life and wrongful birth: legal aspects of failed genetic testing in oocyte donation. *Penn Bioethics Journal* 2005 April 2; 1(1): 4p. [Online]. Accessed: http://www.bioethicsjournal.com [2005 April 19]. NRCBL: 15.2; 14.4; 14.6. SC: le.

Casabona, Carlos María Romeo. Legal aspects of genetic counselling = Aspectos jurídicos del consejo genético. *Law and the Human Genome = Revista de Derecho y Genoma Humano* 1994 July-December; (1): 149-172. NRCBL: 15.2; 15.3; 8.4. SC: le.

Chiang, H-H; Chao, Y-M (Yu); Yuh, Y-S. Informed choice of pregnant women in prenatal screening tests for Down's syndrome. *Journal of Medical Ethics* 2006 May; 32(5): 273-277. NRCBL: 15.2; 9.5.5. SC: em. Identifiers: Taiwan.
  Abstract: BACKGROUND: Although maternal serum screening (MSS) for Down's syndrome has become routinely available in most obstetric clinics in many countries, few studies have addressed the reasons why women agree to undergo the MSS test. OBJECTIVES: The aims of this study were to describe the circumstances in which MSS was offered to pregnant women and their reasons for undertaking it. METHODS: Participant observation and in depth interviews were used in this study; specifically, the experiences of women who had a positive result for MSS and who then followed this up with amniocentesis were examined. The interviewees were twenty six mothers aged between 22 and 35 years. The interviews were audio taped and transcribed for analysis. The results were analysed by the constant comparative method. RESULTS: This study identified the reasons on which pregnant women appeared to base their decisions when undergoing MSS. The reasons were first, the recognition that the procedure was a prenatal routine procedure; second, the need to avoid the risk of giving birth to a baby with Down's syndrome, and third, a trust in modern technology and in the professional authorities. CONCLUSIONS: This study offers insights into the informed choice made by women with a positive MSS result. The reasons for undergoing MSS might help health professionals and policy makers to reflect on their practice and this may, in turn, improve the quality of prenatal care during MSS.

Chipman, Peter. The moral implications of prenatal genetic testing. *Penn Bioethics Journal* 2006; 2(2): 13-16. NRCBL: 15.2; 4.2; 4.4; 12.3; 12.4.2.
  Abstract: The advance of medical technology now permits many genetic tests to be administered to a fetus in the womb. The goal of this testing is to determine the potential for genetically based disorders and disabilities. The use of these tests has major implications on the decision of a parent to abort a child based on what information they find in the prospective child's genes. Advocates of prenatal testing argue that it enables the families of these prospective children to make an informed decision when faced with the possibility of disability. I argue that this choice is drastically limited by social coercion through a discriminatory and stereotyped perception of the disabled community. Permitting an uncontrolled barrage of prenatal genetic tests will further promote the stereotype of a disabled life, and thus hinders our societal goal to recognise and promote equality and individuality. Which disabilities to test for, or what genes to search for, is a judgement that should be made only through extensive consultation with members of the disabled community, including individuals who have suffered from or who have been directly associated with the disability which is said to be tested.

Cirion, Aitziber Emaldi. Preimplantation diagnosis: problems and future perspectives. *In:* Widdows, Heather; Idiakez, Itziar Alkorta; Cirión, Aitziber Emaldi, eds. Women's Reproductive Rights. New York: Palgrave Macmillan; 2006: 140-150. NRCBL: 15.2; 14.4.

Colah, Roshan; Surve, Reema; Nadkarni, Anita; Gorakshakar, Ajit; Phanasgaonkar, Supriya; Satoskar, Poornima; Mohanty, Dipika. Prenatal diagnosis of sickle syndromes in India: dilemmas in counselling. *Prenatal Diagnosis* 2005 May; 25(5): 345-349. NRCBL: 15.2.

Costich, Julia Field. The Perruche case and the issue of compensation for the consequences of medical error. *Health Policy* 2006 August 22; 78(1): 8-16. NRCBL: 15.2; 8.5; 9.5.7; 9.3.1; 9.8. SC: le. Identifiers: France.

Crockin, Susan L. Reproduction, genetics and the law. *Reproductive BioMedicine Online [electronic]* 2005 June; 10(6): 692-704. Accessed: http://www.rbmonline.com/Article/1726 [2005 December 16]. NRCBL: 15.2; 14.4; 11.4; 15.3; 14.6; 16.3; 8.4; 4.4. SC: le; rv.

de Ángel Yáguez, Ricardo. Prenatal genetic diagnosis and responsibility (Part I) = Diagnósticos genéticos prenatales y responsabilidad (Parte I). *Law and the Human Genome Review = Revista de Derecho y Genoma Humano* 1996 January-June; (4): 93-104. NRCBL: 15.2. SC: le. Identifiers: Spain.

Dörries, Andrea. Genetic prenatal testing: the doctor's and the patient's dilemma. *In:* Glasa, J., ed. Ethics of Human Genetics: Challenges of the (Post) Genomic Era. Bratislava, Slovak Republic: Charis [and] IMEB Foundation; 2002: 107-116. NRCBL: 15.2; 15.3.

Duke, Katy. Belgian loophole allows Swiss parents a "saviour" baby. *Lancet* 2006 July 29-August 4; 368(9533): 355-356. NRCBL: 15.2; 14.4; 19.5; 9.8; 21.1. SC: le.

Duncan, Rony E.; Foddy, Bennett; Delatycki, Martin B. Refusing to provide a prenatal test: can it ever be ethical? *BMJ: British Medical Journal* 2006 November 18; 333(7577): 1066-1068. NRCBL: 15.2; 15.3; 8.1; 12.1.

Eckert, Susan LaRusse; Katzen, Heather; Roberts, J. Scott; Barber, Melissa; Ravdin, Lisa D.; Relkin, Norman R.; Whitehouse, Peter J.; Green, Robert C. Recall of disclosed Apolipoprotein E genotype and lifetime risk estimate for Alzheimer's disease: the REVEAL Study. *Genetics in Medicine* 2006 December; 8(12): 746-751. NRCBL: 15.2; 15.3. SC: em. Identifiers: Risk Evaluation and Education for Alzheimer's Disease.

El-Hazmi, Mohsen A.F. Ethics of genetic counseling — basic concepts and relevance to Islamic communities. *Annals of Saudi Medicine* 2004 March-April; 24(2): 84-92. NRCBL: 15.2; 1.2; 15.3.

Erikson, Susan L. Post-diagnostic abortion in Germany: reproduction gone awry, again? *Social Science and Medicine* 2003 May; 56(9): 1987-2001. NRCBL: 15.2; 12.1; 15.3; 1.2; 7.1. SC: em.

Ettorre, Elizabeth. Comparing the practice of reproductive genetics in Greece, UK, Finland, and The Netherlands: constructing "expert" claims while marking "reproductive" time. *In:* Stehr, Nico, ed. Biotechnology Between Commerce and Civil Society. New Brunswick, NJ: Transaction Publishers; 2004: 299-319. NRCBL: 15.2; 15.3; 21.1. SC: em.

European Society of Human Genetics [ESHG]; European Society of Human Reproduction and Embryology [ESHRE]. The need for interaction between assisted reproduction technology and genetics: recommendations of the European Societies of Human Genetics and Human Reproduction and Embryology. *Human Reproduction* 2006 August; 21(8): 1971-1973. NRCBL: 15.2; 14.4.

Fahrenkrog, Aaron R. A comparison of international regulation of preimplantation genetic diagnosis and a regulatory suggestion for the United States. *Transnational Law and Contemporary Problems* 2006 Spring; 15(2): 757-781. NRCBL: 15.2; 14.4; 1.3.5; 5.3.

Fanos, Joanna H.; Spangner, Kerstin A.; Musci, Thomas J. Attitudes toward prenatal screening and testing for Fragile X. *Genetics in Medicine* 2006 February; 8(2): 129-133. NRCBL: 15.2; 15.3.

Fernández-Suárez, A.; Cordero Fernández, C.; García Lozano, R.; Pizarro, A.; Garzón, M.; Núnez Roldán, A. Clinical and ethical implications of genetic counselling in familial adenomatous polyposis=Implicaciones clínicas y éticas deconsejo genético en la poliposis adenomatosa familiar. *Revista Espanola Enfermedades Digestivas* 2005 September; 97(9): 654- 659; 660-665. NRCBL: 15.2. Identifiers: Spain. Note: Pages 654-659 English; Pages 660-665 Spanish.

Fujiki, Norio. Bioethics and medical genetics in Japan. *In:* Sleeboom, Margaret, ed. Genomics in Asia: A Clash of Bioethical Interests? New York: Kegan Paul; 2004: 225-253. NRCBL: 15.2. SC: em.

Geller, Gail; Holtzman, Neil A. A qualitative assessment of primary care physicians' perceptions about the ethical and social implications of offering genetic testing. *Qualitative Health Research* 1995 February; 5(1): 97-116. NRCBL: 15.2; 8.1; 8.4. SC: cs; em.

Gitter, Donna M. Am I my brother's keeper? The use of preimplantation genetic diagnosis to create a donor of transplantable stem cells for an older sibling suffering from a genetic disorder. *George Mason Law Review* 2005-2006 Fall/Winter; 13(5): 975-1035. NRCBL: 15.2; 19.5; 15.1.

Godre, Neha S. Refusing to provide a prenatal test: can it ever be ethical?: Ethics or humanity? *BMJ: British Medical Journal* 2006 December 2; 333(7579): 1174. NRCBL: 15.2; 15.3; 8.1.

Grob, Rachel. Parenting in the genomic age: the "cursed blessing" of newborn screening. *New Genetics and Society* 2006 August; 25(2): 159-170. NRCBL: 15.2; 9.5.7; 8.3.2; 9.4.

Gunawardana, Nushan P. Refusing to provide a prenatal test: can it ever be ethical?: the darker side of medicine [letter]. *BMJ: British Medical Journal* 2006 December 2; 333(7579): 1174. NRCBL: 15.2; 15.3; 8.1; 1.1.

Harmon, Amy. Couples cull embryos to halt heritage of cancer. *New York Times* 2006 September 3; p. A1, A20. NRCBL: 15.2; 14.4; 15.3. SC: po. Identifiers: preimplantation genetic diagnosis [PGD].

Harris, John. The moral choice. *New Scientist* 2006 June 17-23; 190(2556): 24. NRCBL: 15.2; 14.4. Identifiers: United Kingdom (Great Britain); Human Fertilisation and Embryology Authority.

Herissone-Kelly, Peter. Genetic screening, prospective parenthood, and the internal perspective. *In:* Árnason, Gardar; Nordal, Salvör; Árnason, Vilhjálmur, eds. Blood and Data: Ethical, Legal and Social Aspects of Human Genetic Databases. Reykjavík: University of Iceland Press; 2004: 257-262. NRCBL: 15.2; 4.4; 14.4; 15.3. SC: an.

Herissone-Kelly, P. Procreative beneficence and the prospective parent. *Journal of Medical Ethics* 2006 March; 32(3): 166-169. NRCBL: 15.2; 14.4; 14.1; 1.1. SC: an.

Abstract: Julian Savulescu has given clear expression to a principle-that of "procreative beneficence"-which underlies the thought of many contemporary writers on bioethics. The principle of procreative beneficence (PPB) holds that parents or single reproducers are at least prima facie obliged to select the child, out of a range of possible children they might have, who will be likely to lead the best life. My aim in this paper is to ar-

NRCBL: National Reference Center for Bioethics Literature Classification Scheme   See inside front cover for terms.

205

gue that prospective parents, just by dint of their being prospective parents, are in fact not obliged to act on PPB. That is, there is something about their filling the role of prospective parents that exempts them from selecting the child with the best life. I urge that it is more realistic to view prospective parents as bound by a principle of acceptable outlook, which holds that they ought not to select children whose lives will contain an unacceptable amount of suffering.

Hlaca, Nenad. Genetic counseling and the best interest of the child. *Revista de Derecho Genoma Humano = Law and the Human Genome Review* 1999 July-December; (11): 85-94. NRCBL: 15.2; 21.1; 15.3; 9.5.7. SC: le.

Holt, Kathryn. What do we tell the children? Contrasting the disclosure choices of two HD families regarding risk status and predictive genetic testing. *Journal of Genetic Counseling* 2006 August; 15(4): 253-265. NRCBL: 15.2; 15.3; 8.2; 8.1. SC: em. Identifiers: Huntington's disease.

Hopkins, Michael M. The hidden research system: the evolution of cytogenetic testing in the National Health Service. *Science as Culture* 2006 September; 15(3): 253-276. NRCBL: 15.2; 7.1; 5.3.

Hull, Richard J. Cheap listening? — Reflections on the concept of wrongful disability. *Bioethics* 2006 April; 20(2): 55-63. NRCBL: 15.2; 4.2; 12.3. SC: an.
Abstract: This paper investigates the concept of wrongful disability. That concept suggests that parents are morally obligated to prevent the genetic transmission of certain conditions and so, if they do not, any resulting disability is 'wrongful'. In their book From Chance to Choice, Buchanan, Brock, Daniels and Wikler defend the concept of wrongful disability using the principle of avoidability via substitution. That principle is scrutinised here. It is argued that the idea of avoidability via substitution is both conceptually problematic and rather insensitive. Instead, it is suggested that the question of whether or not bringing a particular disability about is wrongful does not simply hinge on whether or not substitution takes place. Rather, it involves an evaluation of parental aspirations and responsibilities. It is argued that the desire need not be responsible for creating challenges for others that lie outside what is perceived to be an acceptable range provides a justification for termination of pregnancy on the grounds of projected disability that neither commits one to wrongful life claim, nor requires that one substitute a non-disabled child instead. The ramifications of such an approach are explored. The paper concludes by suggesting that the question of what is considered to be an acceptable range of human capability is an increasingly important one. It is argued that, when addressing that question, we should be acutely aware of the social context that may go some way to define what we consider to be an acceptable range.

Isikoglu, M.; Senol, Y.; Berkkanoglu, M.; Ozgur, K.; Donmez, L.; Stones-Abbasi, A. Public opinion regarding oocyte donation in Turkey: first data from a secular population among the Islamic world. *Human Reproduction* 2006 January; 21(1): 318-323. NRCBL: 15.2; 1.2; 19.5. SC: em.

Jallinoja, Piia T. Ethics of clinical genetics: the spirit of the profession and trials of suitability from 1970 to 2000. *Critical Public Health* 2002; 12(2): 103-118. NRCBL: 15.2; 2.1; 18.2; 21.1. SC: an.

Jones, Maggie. The mystery of my eggs [PGD]. *New York Times Magazine* 2003 March 16; p. 44-46. NRCBL: 15.2.

Kalfoglou, Andrea L.; Doksum, Teresa; Bernhardt, Barbara; Geller, Gail; LeRoy, Lisa; Mathews, Debra J.H.; Evans, John H.; Doukas, David J.; Reame, Nancy; Scott, Joan; Hudson, Kathy. Opinions about new reproductive genetic technologies: hopes and fears for our genetic future. *Fertility and Sterility* 2005 June; 83(6): 1612-1621. NRCBL: 15.2; 14.4; 15.3; 15.4; 14.3; 7.1. SC: em.

Kalfoglou, Andrea L.; Scott, Joan; Hudson, Kathy. PGD patients' and providers' attitudes to the use and regulation of preimplantation genetic diagnosis. *Reproductive BioMedicine Online [electronic]* 2005 October; 11(4): 486-496. NRCBL: 15.2; 14.4; 5.3. SC: em. Identifiers: preimplantation genetic diagnosis.

Kapterian, Gisele. Harriton, Waller and Australian negligence law: is there a place for wrongful life? *Journal of Law and Medicine* 2006 February; 13(3): 336-351. NRCBL: 15.2; 8.5; 14.4. SC: le.

Kelly, Paul D. Refusing to provide a prenatal test: can it ever be ethical?: Time to re-think the autonomy of future individuals [letter]. *BMJ: British Medical Journal* 2006 December 2; 333(7579): 1173. NRCBL: 15.2; 15.3; 8.1; 1.1.

Khoshnood, Babak; De Vigan, Catherine; Vodovar, Véronique; Bréart, Gérard; Goffinet, François; Blondel, Béatrice. Advances in medical technology and creation of disparities: the case of Down syndrome. *American Journal of Public Health* 2006 December; 96(12): 2139-2144. NRCBL: 15.2; 9.5.3; 9.3.1; 9.4; 9.5.4. SC: em.

Klipstein, Sigal. Preimplantation genetic diagnosis: technological promise and ethical perils. *Fertility and Sterility* 2005 May; 83(5): 1347-1353. NRCBL: 15.2; 14.4.

Knoppers, Bartha Maria. Human genetics: parental, professional and political responsibility. *Health Law Journal* 1993; 1(1): 13-23. NRCBL: 15.2; 8.1; 8.4. SC: le. Identifiers: Picard Lecture in Health Law — 1992; Canada.

Kuppermann, Miriam; Norton, Mary E. Prenatal testing guidelines: time for a new approach? *Gynecologic and Obstetric Investigation* 2005; 60(1): 6-10. NRCBL: 15.2; 8.3.1; 9.2.

Lagay, Faith. Preimplantation genetic diagnosis. *Virtual Mentor* 2001 August; 3(8): 3p. NRCBL: 15.2; 14.4.

Lalor, Joan; Begley, Cecily. Fetal anomaly screening: what do women want to know? *Journal of Advanced Nursing* 2006 July; 55(1): 11-19. NRCBL: 15.2. SC: em.

Lam, Stephen T.S. Informed consent in genetic counseling and pediatric genetics. A View from Hong Kong. *In:* Döring, Ole; Chen, Renbiao, eds. Advances in Chinese Medical Ethics: Chinese and International Perspectives.

Hamburg: Institut für Asienkunde; 2002: 133-140. NRCBL: 15.2; 15.3; 8.3.1; 8.3.2. Note: Proceedings of the Second Sino-German Interdisciplinary Symposium about Medical Ethics in China, Shanghai, 19-23 October, 1999.

Leach, Gerald. Qualitative birth control. *New Statesman (London, England:* 1957) 1965 June 11: 906. NRCBL: 15.2; 9.5.8; 4.4; 12.1.

Lenoir, Noëlle. Legal and ethical aspects of prenatal diagnosis: the law and current practices in France and certain other countries (Part II) = Aspectos jurídicos y éticos del diagnóstico prenatal: el derecho y las prácticas vigentes en Francia y otros países (y II). *Law and the Human Genome Review = Revista de Derecho y Genoma Humano* 1995 July-December; (3): 123-141. NRCBL: 15.2; 21.1; 8.3.1; 8.4. SC: le.

Mayor, Susan. Babies born after preimplantation genetic diagnosis need follow-up [news]. *BMJ: British Medical Journal* 2006 February 4; 332(7536): 254. NRCBL: 15.2; 14.4.

McGivern, Brenda. Bioethics and the law — the impact of genetic technology on prenatal management. *E Law: Murdoch University Electronic Journal of Law* 1995 December; 2(3): 35 p. [Online]. Accessed: http://www. murdoch.edu.au/elaw/issues/v2n3mcgivern23.html [2006 June 29]. NRCBL: 15.2; 15.3; 12.4.1; 15.10; 8.4; 12.1. SC: le. Identifiers: Australia.

McLaughlin, Janice. Screening networks: shared agendas in feminist and disability movement challenges to antenatal screening and abortion. *Disability and Society* 2003 May; 18(3): 297-310. NRCBL: 15.2; 9.5.1; 10. SC: an.

McMahan, Jeff; Cohen, Jacques; Ko, Minoru; Johnson, Martin; Robertson, John; Murphy, Timothy; Brinsden, Peter; Hussein, Fatima; Savulescu, Julian; McLaren, Anne; McLean, Sheila; Harris, John; Schulman, Joe; Edwards, Robert; Pedersen, Roger; Stock, Gregory; Grudzinskas, Gedis; Boivin, Jacky. Discussion (day 2 session 2): modern genetics and the human embryo in vitro. *Reproductive BioMedicine Online [electronic]* 2005 March; 10(Supplement 1): 107-110. NRCBL: 15.2; 14.4; 10. Conference: Ethics, Law and Moral Philosophy of Reproductive Biomedicine; London, UK; 2004 September 30 - October 1; Royal Society.

McMahon, William M.; Baty, Bonnie Jeanne; Botkin, Jeffrey. Genetic counseling and ethical issues for autism. *American Journal of Medical Genetics. Part C, Seminars in Medical Genetics* 2006 February 15; 142(1): 52-57. NRCBL: 15.2; 15.3; 17.1.

Meidl, Susan Marie. EIFWAIL and psychological distress: no support for early induction. *Ethics and Medics* 2006 April; 31(4): 1-2. NRCBL: 15.2; 9.5.5; 17.1; 12.5.1; 9.5.8. Identifiers: Early induction of fetuses with abnormalities incompatible with life (EIFWAIL).

Miola, José. Autonomy ruled ok?: Al Hamwi v. Johnston and Another. *Medical Law Review* 2006 Spring; 14(1): 108-114. NRCBL: 15.2; 8.3.1. SC: le.

Modra, Lucy. Prenatal genetic testing kits sold at your local pharmacy: promoting autonomy or promoting confusion? *Bioethics* 2006 September; 20(5): 254-263. NRCBL: 15.2; 15.3; 9.3.1; 9.7. SC: an.
Abstract: Research groups around the world are developing non-invasive methods of prenatal genetic diagnosis, in which foetal cells are obtained by maternal blood test. Meanwhile, an increasing number of genetic tests are sold directly to the public. I extrapolate from these developments to consider a scenario in which PNGD self-testing kits are sold directly to the public. Given the opposition to over-the-counter genetic tests and the continuing controversy surrounding PNGD, it is reasonable to expect objections to PNGD self-testing kits. I focus on one potential objection, that PNGD self-testing kits would undermine the autonomy of potential test subjects. More specifically, that 'direct to the public' PNGD would fail to ensure that consumers exercise authority in the following PNGD-related choices: Should I use PNGD? Based on the results of the PNGD test, should I continue or terminate my pregnancy? Under the current system, PNGD is provided by health care practitioners, who are required to counsel women both before and after the test. In contrast, 'direct to the public' PNGD would allow women to make their PNGD-related decisions outside the context of the health care system. I compare these two decision-making contexts, arguing that the health care system is not unequivocally better at promoting the autonomy of potential test subjects. Therefore the promotion of autonomy does not constitute a strong argument against such test kits. Other objections may be more persuasive, so I do not offer an overall assessment of the acceptability of 'direct to the public' PNGD.

Morain, William D. Sometimes both the palates and the ethics are cleft [editorial]. *Annals of Plastic Surgery* 2005 June; 54(6): 681-682. NRCBL: 15.2; 2.1; 9.5.7; 12.1.

Moyer, Anne; Brown, Beth; Gates, Elena; Daniels, Molly; Brown, Halle D.; Kuppermann, Miriam. Decisions about prenatal testing for chromosomal disorders: perceptions of a diverse group of pregnant women. *Journal of Women's Health and Gender-Based Medicine* 1999 May; 8(4): 521-531. NRCBL: 15.2; 9.5.5; 8.3.1.

Nahman, Michal. Materializing Israeliness: difference and mixture in transnational ova donation. *Science as Culture* 2006 September; 15(3): 199-213. NRCBL: 15.2; 21.1; 4.5; 14.1; 7.1.

National Advisory Commission on Biomedical Ethics (Switzerland) [NEK-CNE] = Nationale Ethikkommission im Bereich Humanmedizin = Commission nationale d'éthique pour la médecine humaine = Commissione nazionale d'etica per la medicina. Preimplantation Genetic Diagnosis:. Bern, Switzerland: Swiss National Advisory Commission on Biomedical Ethics; 2005 December, 19 p. NRCBL: 15.2; 14.4. Note: Opinion no. 10/2005, abridged version (Chapters III and IV only), translated by Jeff Acheson. Opinion was adopted by the Commission on 3 November 2005. Full report is available

NRCBL: National Reference Center for Bioethics Literature Classification Scheme   See inside front cover for terms.

207

in German and French; abridged versions are available in English and Italian.

National Society of Genetic Counselors [NSGC] (United States). Code of ethics of the National Society of Genetic Counselors. *Journal of Genetic Counseling* 2006 October; 15(5): 309-311. NRCBL: 15.2; 6.

National Society of Genetic Counselors [NSGC] (United States). Definition Task Force; Resta, Robert; Bowles Biesecker, Barbara; Bennett, Robin L.; Blum, Sandra; Estabrooks Hahn, Susan; Strecker, Michelle N.; Williams, Janet L. A new definition of genetic counseling: National Society of Genetic Counselors' Task Force report. *Journal of Genetic Counseling* 2006 April; 15(2): 77-83. NRCBL: 15.2.

National Society of Genetic Counselors [NSGC] (United States). Code of Ethics Work Group; Bennett, R.L.; Callanan, N.; Gordon, E.; Karns, L.; Mooney, K.H.; Ruzicka, R.; Schmerler, S.; Weissman, S. Code of ethics of the National Society of Genetic Counselors: Explication of Revisions. *Journal of Genetic Counseling* 2006 October; 15(5): 313-323. NRCBL: 15.2; 6.

Newson, Ainsley. Should parental refusals of newborn screening be respected? *CQ: Cambridge Quarterly of Healthcare Ethics* 2006 Spring; 15(2): 135-146. NRCBL: 15.2; 8.3.4. SC: le.

Nicolaides, Kypros H.; Chervenak, Frank A.; McCullough, Laurence B.; Avgidou, Kyriaki; Papageorghiou, Aris. Evidence-based obstetric ethics and informed decision-making by pregnant women about invasive diagnosis after first-trimester assessment of risk for trisomy 21. *American Journal of Obstetrics and Gynecology* 2005 August; 193(2): 322-326. NRCBL: 15.2; 9.5.5; 8.1. SC: em.

Nippert, Irmgard. International perspectives on abortion and genetic counselling. A European perspective. *In:* Döring, Ole; Chen, Renbiao, eds. Advances in Chinese Medical Ethics: Chinese and International Perspectives. Hamburg: Institut für Asienkunde; 2002: 141-158. NRCBL: 15.2; 12.5.2. Note: Proceedings of the Second Sino-German Interdisciplinary Symposium about Medical Ethics in China, Shanghai, 19-23 October, 1999.

Offit, Kenneth; Sagi, Michal; Hurley, Karen. Preimplantation genetic diagnosis for cancer syndromes. *JAMA: The Journal of the American Medical Association* 2006 December 13; 296(22): 2727-2730. NRCBL: 15.2; 14.4.

Pieterse, Arwen H.; van Dulmen, Sandra; van Dijk, Sandra; Bensing, Jozien M.; Ausems, Margreet G.E.M. Risk communication in completed series of breast cancer genetic counseling visits. *Genetics in Medicine* 2006 November; 8(11): 688-696. NRCBL: 15.2; 8.1.

Pilnick, Alison. What "most people" do: exploring the ethical implications of genetic counselling. *New Genetics and Society* 2002 December; 21(3): 339-350. NRCBL: 15.2; 1.1; 8.1. SC: em.

Ram, N.R. Britain's new preimplantation tissue typing policy: an ethical defense. *Journal of Medical Ethics* 2006 May; 32(5): 278-282. NRCBL: 15.2; 14.4; 19.5. Identifiers: United Kingdom(Great Britain).

Ramer-Chrastek, Joan; Thygeson, Megan V. A perinatal hospice for an unborn child with a life-limiting condition [case study]. *International Journal of Palliative Nursing* 2005 June; 11(6): 274-276. NRCBL: 15.2; 9.5.8; 20.4.2; 9.5.5. SC: cs.

Rao, Radhika. Preimplantation genetic diagnosis and reproductive equality. *Gender Medicine* 2004 December; 1(2): 64-69. NRCBL: 15.2; 14.4; 14.3; 9.2. SC: le.

Ray, Pierre F. Ethics and genetics of carrier embryos [letter]. *Human Reproduction* 2006 October; 21(10): 2722-2723. NRCBL: 15.2; 14.4; 5.2.

Raz, Aviad E.; Atar, Marcela. Upright generations of the future: tradition and medicalization in community genetics. *Journal of Contemporary Ethnography* 2004 June; 33(3): 296-322 [Online]. Accessed: http://jce.sagepub.com/cgi/reprint/33/3/296 [2007 January 24]. NRCBL: 15.2; 10; 15.3; 21.7. SC: em. Identifiers: Israel; Bedouins.

Reiner, William G. Prenatal gender imprinting and medical decision-making: genetic male neonates with severely inadequate penises. *In:* Sytsma, Sharon E., ed. Ethics and Intersex. Dordrecht: Springer, 2006: 153-163. NRCBL: 15.2.

Riddell, Mary. We have seen the future: genetically perfect children. What we need to see next are laws and regulations to ensure that time never arrives. *New Statesman (London, England: 1996)* 1997 February 21; 126: 19. NRCBL: 15.2. SC: po.

Robertson, John A. Ethics and the future of preimplantation genetic diagnosis. *Reproductive BioMedicine Online [electronic]* 2005 March; 10(Supplement 1): 97-101. NRCBL: 15.2; 4.4; 15.5; 14.3; 9.5.1. Conference: Ethics, Law and Moral Philosophy of Reproductive Biomedicine; London, UK; 2004 September 30 - October 1; Royal Society.

Samerski, Silja. Genetic counseling. *In:* Mitcham, Carl, ed. Encyclopedia of Science, Technology, and Ethics. Farmington Hills, MI: Thomson/Gale, 2005: 838-841. NRCBL: 15.2; 2.2; 5.1; 1.3.1.

Samerski, Silja. The unleashing of genetic terminology: how genetic counselling mobilizes for risk management. *New Genetics and Society* 2006 August; 25(2): 197-208. NRCBL: 15.2; 15.1; 9.5.5; 7.1; 5.2.

Scott, Rosamund. Choosing between possible lives: legal and ethical issues in preimplantation genetic diagnosis. *Oxford Journal of Legal Studies* 2006 Spring; 26(1): 153-178. NRCBL: 15.2; 14.4. SC: le; an.

Shahine, Lora K.; Caughey, Aaron B. Preimplantation genetic diagnosis: the earliest form of prenatal diagnosis. *Gynecologic and Obstetric Investigation* 2005; 60(1): 39-46. NRCBL: 15.2; 14.4.

Shakespeare, Tom W. Refusing to provide a prenatal test: can it ever be ethical?: Rights of future children [letter]. *BMJ: British Medical Journal* 2006 December 2; 333(7579): 1173-1174. NRCBL: 15.2; 15.3; 8.1; 1.1.

Sharpe, Neil F.; Carter, Ronald F. Prenatal screening and diagnosis. *In their:* Genetic Testing: Care, Consent, and Liability. Hoboken, NJ: Wiley-Liss; 2006: 163-218. NRCBL: 15.2; 8.3.1. SC: le.

Shaw, Alison. Attitudes to genetic diagnosis and to the use of medical technologies in pregnancy: some British Pakistani perspectives. *In:* Unnithan-Kumar, Maya, ed. Reproductive Agency, Medicine and the State: Cultural Transformations in Childbearing. New York: Berghahn Books; 2004: 25-41. NRCBL: 15.2; 20.5.2; 21.7. SC: em; cs.

Shinoki, Eri; Matsuda, Ichiro. Changes of bioethics perspective of Japanese clinical geneticists about repro-genetics during 1995-2001. *In:* Takahashi, Takao, ed. Taking Life and Death Seriously: Bioethics from Japan. Amsterdam; Boston: Elsevier JAI; 2005: 85-112. NRCBL: 15.2. SC: em.

Siddiqui, Faraz. Assessing the ethicality of pre-implantation genetic diagnosis beyond the discourse of eugenics. *Penn Bioethics Journal* 2006; 2(1): 4p. [Online]. Accessed: http://www.bioethicsjournal.com [2006 February 21]. NRCBL: 15.2; 15.5; 7.1.

Simon, Alex; Schenker, Joseph G. Ethical consideration of intentioned preimplantation genetic diagnosis to enable future tissue transplantation. *Reproductive BioMedicine Online [electronic]* 2005 March; 10(3): 320-324. Accessed: http://www.rbmonline.com/Article/1615 [2005 September 34]. NRCBL: 15.2; 14.4; 19.5; 18.5.4; 4.4; 1.1.

Sipr, Kvetoslav. Prenatal diagnosis and respect for autonomy. *In:* Glasa, J., ed. Ethics of Human Genetics: Challenges of the (Post) Genomic Era. Bratislava, Slovak Republic: Charis [and] IMEB Foundation; 2002: 117-121. NRCBL: 15.2.

Sokol, Daniel K.; Bergson, Gilian. Genetic counselling and the "new genetics". *In their:* Medical Ethics and Law: Surviving on the Wards and Passing Exams. London: Trauma Pub., 2005: 133-148. NRCBL: 15.2.

Stemerding, Dirk; Nelis, Annemiek. Cancer genetics and its "different faces of autonomy". *New Genetics and Society* 2006 April; 25(1): 1-19. NRCBL: 15.2; 1.1; 15.3; 9.5.1.

Stock, Gregory. Germinal choice technology and the human future. *Reproductive BioMedicine Online [electronic]* 2005 March; 10(Supplement 1): 27-35. NRCBL: 15.2; 15.4; 14.5; 15.5; 15.1; 4.5. Conference: Ethics, Law and Moral Philosophy of Reproductive Biomedicine; London, UK; 2004 September 30 - October 1; Royal Society.

Thomas, Cordelia. Preimplantation genetic diagnosis: development and regulation. *Medicine and Law: The World Association for Medical Law* 2006 June; 25(2): 365-378. NRCBL: 15.2; 14.4; 4.4; 5.3. SC: le. Identifiers: Human Fertilisation and Embryology Authority (HFEA); United Kingdom; New Zealand.

Abstract: Pre-implantation genetic diagnosis (PGD) is used to biopsy and analyse embryos created through in vitro fertilisation (IVF) to avoid implanting an embryo affected by a mutation or chromosomal abnormality associated with serious illness. It reduces the chance that the parents will be faced with a difficult decision of whether to terminate the pregnancy, if the disorder is detected during the course of gestation. PGD is widely accepted for this purpose although there have been suggestions that such procedures have the effect of de-valuing persons in the community with disabilities. PGD potentially has other more controversial purposes, including the selection of the sex of the baby for personal preferences such as balancing the family, rather than to avoid a sex-linked disorder. Recently PGD has become available to create a donor child who is Human Leukocyte Antigen (HLA) matched with a sibling in need of stem cell transplant. In most cases the intention is to utilise the cord blood. However, an HLA-matched child could potentially be required to be a donor of tissues and organs throughout life. This may arise should the initial cord blood donation fail for any one of several reasons, such as inadequate cord blood cell dose, graft failure after cord blood transplant, or the recipient child experiencing a recurrence of the original illness after transplant. However, such on-going demands could also arise if a HLA-matched child was fortuitously conceived by natural means. As such, the issue is not PGD, but rather whether to harvest bone marrow or a solid organ from a child. This raises the question of whether there should be limits and procedures to protect such children from exploitation until they achieve sufficient competence to be able to make mature and autonomous decisions about whether to donate, even if the consequence may in some cases be that it is too late to save the sibling. Additionally, the parents may not be able to make a dispassionate decision, when they have a conflict of interests between their children. As such, parents may not be the best proxy decision-makers in this area and the decision might be better made by an independent authority or court. This paper considers ethical and legal issues arising from PGD. It will compare the willingness of the HFEA in the United Kingdom to allow this process to be used even in cases where the condition suffered by the sibling is non-heritable, with the more restrictive guidelines in New Zealand and questions the constitutional basis on which ethics committees develop policy in the absence of a legislative framework.

Thomas, Cordelia. Pre-implantation testing and the protection of the "saviour sibling". *Deakin Law Review* 2004; 9(1): 119-143. NRCBL: 15.2; 8.3.2; 19.5; 14.4; 9.5.7. SC: le. Identifiers: Australia; New Zealand.

NRCBL: National Reference Center for Bioethics Literature Classification Scheme   See inside front cover for terms.

209

Turone, Fabio. Italian court upholds ban on pre-implantation diagnosis [news]. *BMJ: British Medical Journal* 2006 November 4; 333(7575): 934. NRCBL: 15.2; 14.4; 14.6. SC: le.

Ulrich, Hans G. Ethische Konflikte bei der Präimplantationsdiagnostik (Preimplantation-Genetic-Diagnosis). *In:* Vollmann, Jochen, ed. Medizin und Ethik: Aktuelle ethische Probleme in Therapie und Forschung. Erlangen: Universitätsbund Erlangen-Nürnberg, 2003: 31-59. NRCBL: 15.2; 14.4.

Vassy, Carine. How prenatal diagnosis became acceptable in France. *Trends in Biotechnology* 2005 May; 23(5): 246-249. NRCBL: 15.2; 9.5.8; 8.3.1; 4.4; 12.1. SC: cs.

Veach, Patricia McCarthy; LeRoy, Bonnie S.; Bartels, Dianne M. Behaving ethically. *In their:* Facilitating the Genetic Counseling Process: A Practice Manual. New York: Springer, 2003: 222-241. NRCBL: 15.2.

Veach, Patricia McCarthy; LeRoy, Bonnie S.; Bartels, Dianne M. National Society of Genetic Counselors Code of Ethics. *In their:* Facilitating the Genetic Counseling Process: A Practice Manual. New York: Springer, 2003: 285-287. NRCBL: 15.2; 6.

Walther, J.-U. Genetische Beratung und ihre Normen. Ethische Überlegungen [Genetic counselling in a sociocultural framework. Ethical considerations]. *Monatsschrift Kinderheilkunde* 2004; 152: 1217-1224. NRCBL: 15.2; 1.1; 2.1; 8.4. SC: cs.

Weil, Jon; Ormond, Kelly; Peters, June; Peters, Kathryn; Bowles Biesecker, Barbara; LeRoy, Bonnie. The relationship of nondirectiveness to genetic counseling: report of a workshop at the 2003 NSGC Annual Education Conference. *Journal of Genetic Counseling* 2006 April; 15(2): 85-93. NRCBL: 15.2. Identifiers: National Society of Genetic Counselors.

White, Mary Terrell. Religious and spiritual concerns in genetic testing and decision making: an introduction for pastoral and genetic counselors. *Journal of Clinical Ethics* 2006 Summer; 17(2): 158-167. NRCBL: 15.2; 15.3; 1.2; 8.1.

Williams, Clare; Alderson, Priscilla; Farsides, Bobbie. 'Drawing the line' in prenatal screening and testing: health practitioners' discussions. *Health Risk and Society* 2002 March; 4(1): 61-75. NRCBL: 15.2. SC: em. Identifiers: United Kingdom (Great Britain); Down's syndrome.

Yágüez, Ricardo de Ángel. Prenatal genetic diagnosis and responsibility (Part II) = Diagnósticos genéticos prenatales y responsabilidad (Parte II). *Law and the Human Genome Review = Revista de Derecho y Genoma Humano* 1996 July-December; (5): 129-143. NRCBL: 15.2. SC: le. Identifiers: Spain.

GENETIC PRIVACY

Genome privacy [editorial]. *Nature Medicine* 2006 July; 12(7): 717. NRCBL: 15.10; 18.3.

Task Force Report on Genetic Information and Health Insurance = Informe del Grupo Trabajo sobre Información Genética y Seguros de Salud. *Law and the Human Genome = Revista de Derecho y Genoma Humano* 1994 July-December; (1): 221-232. NRCBL: 15.1; 9.3.1; 15.3; 8.4.

The Domesday project [editorial]. *New Scientist* 2006 January 21-27; 189(2535): 5. NRCBL: 15.1; 1.3.12; 8.4.

Abel, Elizabeth; Horner, Sharon D.; Tyler, Diane; Innerarity, Sheryl A. The impact of genetic information on policy and clinical practice. *Policy, Politics, and Nursing Practice* 2005 February; 6(1): 5-14. NRCBL: 15.3; 8.4; 9.2; 9.1; 9.3.1.

Adalsteinsson, Ragnar. The constitutionality of the Icelandic Act on a health sector database. *In:* Sándor, Judit, ed. Society and Genetic Information: Codes and Laws in the Genetic Era. Budapest, Hungary; New York: CEU Press; 2003: 203-211. NRCBL: 15.1; 8.4.

Agich, George. A phenomenological approach to bioethics. *In:* Ashcroft, Richard; Lucassen, Anneke; Parker, Michael; Verkerk, Marian; Widderhoven, Guy, eds. Case Analysis in Clinical Ethics. New York: Cambridge University Press; 2005: 187-200. NRCBL: 15.3; 8.4; 1.1. SC: an.

Almarsdóttir, Anna Birna; Traulsen, Janine Morgall; Björnsdóttir, Ingunn. "We don't have that many secrets" — the lay perspective on privacy and genetic data. *In:* Árnason, Gardar; Nordal, Salvör ; Árnason, Vilhjálmur, eds. Blood and Data: Ethical, Legal and Social Aspects of Human Genetic Databases. Reykjavík: University of Iceland Press; 2004: 193-200. NRCBL: 15.1; 1.3.12; 8.4. SC: em.

Almond, Brenda. Genetic profiling of newborns: ethical and social issues. *Nature Reviews Genetics* 2006 January; 7(1): 67-71. NRCBL: 15.3; 1.3.12; 8.3.2; 8.4.

Alonso Bedate, Carlos. Ethical and legal implications of the use of molecular biology in the clinic. *Journal of Pediatric Endocrinology and Metabolism* 2005 December; 18(Supplement 1): 1137-1143. NRCBL: 15.2; 15.1; 5.3; 8.4.

American Society of Human Genetics [ASHG]. Should family members about whom you collect only medical history information for your research be considered 'human subjects'? [policy statement]. Bethesda, MD: American Society of Human Genetics, 2000 March: 3 p. [Online]. Accessed: http://www.ashg.org/genetics/ashg/pubs/policy/pol-38.htm [2006 July 25]. NRCBL: 15.1; 18.3; 18.2; 8.4.

Ashcroft, Richard. 'Power, corruption and lies': ethics and power. *In:* Ashcroft, Richard; Lucassen, Anneke; Parker, Michael; Verkerk, Marian; Widderhoven, Guy, eds. Case Analysis in Clinical Ethics. New York: Cambridge University Press; 2005: 77-94. NRCBL: 15.3; 8.4. SC: an.

Auray-Blais, Christiane; Patenaude Johane. A biobank management model applicable to biomedical research. *BMC Medical Ethics [Online].* 2006; 7(4): 9 p. Accessed: http://www.biomedcentral.com/bmcmedethics/ [15 June 2006]. NRCBL: 15.1; 18.2; 8.4.

Abstract: BACKGROUND : The work of Research Ethics Boards (REBs), especially when involving genetics research and biobanks, has become more challenging with the growth of biotechnology and biomedical research. Some REBs have even rejected research projects where the use of a biobank with coded samples was an integral part of the study, the greatest fear being the lack of participant protection and uncontrolled use of biological samples or related genetic data. The risks of discrimination and stigmatization are a recurrent issue. In light of the increasing interest in biomedical research and the resulting benefits to the health of participants, it is imperative that practical solutions be found to the problems associated with the management of biobanks: namely, protecting the integrity of the research participants, as well as guaranteeing the security and confidentiality of the participant's information. METHODS : We aimed to devise a practical and efficient model for the management of biobanks in biomedical research where a medical archivist plays the pivotal role as a data-protection officer. The model had to reduce the burden placed on REBs responsible for the evaluation of genetics projects and, at the same time, maximize the protection of research participants. RESULTS : The proposed model includes the following: 1) a means of protecting the information in biobanks, 2) offers ways to provide follow-up information requested about the participants, 3) protects the participant's confidentiality and 4) adequately deals with the ethical issues at stake in biobanking. CONCLUSION : Until a governmental governance body is established in Quebec to guarantee the protection of research participants and establish harmonized guidelines for the management of biobanks in medical research, it is definitely up to REBs to find solutions that the present lack of guidelines poses. The model presented in this article offers a practical solution on a day-to-day basis for REBs, as well as researchers by promoting an archivist to a pivotal role in the process. It assures protection of all participants who altruistically donate their samples to generate and improve knowledge for better diagnosis and medical treatment.

Beckman, Ludvig. Genetic privacy from Locke's point of view. *Journal of Value Inquiry* 2004; 38(2): 241-251. NRCBL: 15.3; 8.4; 4.4. SC: ph.

Biedrzycki, Barbara A. Genetic discrimination: it could happen to you. *ONS News* 2005 December; 20(13): 8-9. NRCBL: 15.1; 8.4.

Black, Michael. Genetics in the courtroom [forum]. *University of New South Wales Law Journal* 2003; 26(3): 755-763. NRCBL: 15.1; 8.3.1; 8.4; 8.2; 9.5.1. SC: cs; le. Identifiers: Australia.

Blank, Robert H. Genethics. *In:* Mitcham, Carl, ed. Encyclopedia of Science, Technology, and Ethics. Farmington

Hills, MI: Thomson/Gale, 2005: 831-836. NRCBL: 15.1; 8.4; 9.4.

Boggio, Andrea. Charitable trusts and human research genetic databases: the way forward? *Genetics, Society, and Policy* 2005 August; 1(2): 41-49. NRCBL: 15.1; 15.3; 1.3.12; 8.4.

Burke, Wylie; Diekema, Douglas S. Ethical issues arising from the participation of children in genetic research. *Journal of Pediatrics* 2006 July; 149(1, Supplement): S34-S38. NRCBL: 15.1; 18.5.2; 8.4; 15.6; 1.3.12.

Campbell, Alastair. A virtue-ethics approach. *In:* Ashcroft, Richard; Lucassen, Anneke; Parker, Michael; Verkerk, Marian; Widderhoven, Guy, eds. Case Analysis in Clinical Ethics. New York: Cambridge University Press; 2005: 45-56. NRCBL: 15.3; 8.4. SC: an.

Casabona, Carlos María Romeo. Legal aspects of genetic counselling = Aspectos jurídicos del consejo genético. *Law and the Human Genome = Revista de Derecho y Genoma Humano* 1994 July-December; (1): 149-172. NRCBL: 15.2; 15.3; 8.4. SC: le.

Caulfield, Timothy. Perceptions of risk and human genetic databases: consent and confidentiality policies. *In:* Árnason, Gardar; Nordal, Salvör; Árnason, Vilhjálmur, eds. Blood and Data: Ethical, Legal and Social Aspects of Human Genetic Databases. Reykjavík: University of Iceland Press; 2004: 283-289. NRCBL: 15.1; 1.3.12; 8.4; 18.3.

Coghlan, Andy. One million people, one medical gamble [news]. *New Scientist* 2006 January 21-27; 189(2535): 8-9. NRCBL: 15.1; 1.3.12; 8.4.

Colorado. *Laws, statutes, etc.* An act concerning genetic privacy [Approved: 1 June 2002]. Colorado: General Assembly, 2002. 2 p. [Online]. Accessed: http://www.state. co.us/gov_dir/leg_dir/olls/sl2002a/sl.262.pdf 2007 March 8]. NRCBL: 15.3; 8.3.1. SC: le. Note: Senate Bill 02-78, 63rd General Assembly, 2nd regular session. Introduced on January 11, 2002. Approved June 1, 2002.

Crockin, Susan L. Reproduction, genetics and the law. *Reproductive BioMedicine Online [electronic]* 2005 June; 10(6): 692-704. Accessed: http://www.rbmonline.com/ Article/1726 [2005 December 16]. NRCBL: 15.2; 14.4; 11.4; 15.3; 14.6; 16.3; 8.4; 4.4. SC: le; rv.

Crolla, Domenic A. Reflections on the legal, social, and ethical implications of pharmacogenomic research. *Jurimetrics* 2006 Spring; 46(3): 239-248. NRCBL: 15.1; 9.7; 8.4; 15.10; 1.3.12; 13.1; 21.1. SC: le.

Cutter, Anthony Mark. To clear or convict? The role of genomics in criminal justice. *Genomics, Society and Policy* 2006 May; 2(1): 1-15. NRCBL: 15.1; 1.3.5.

Abstract: Recognising that the advent of new scientific or technological developments is often met with conflicting reactions, this paper explores the various attitudes to police uses of DNA.

NRCBL: National Reference Center for Bioethics Literature Classification Scheme   See inside front cover for terms.

211

Using the National DNA Database of England and Wales (NDNAD) as a vehicle for analysis, this paper identifies the need to balance the utility of the database, and others like it, with issues relating to the privacy of those whose data is contained within it. As the paper explores the impact of the NDNAD, and by association other databases designed for the same purpose, we are faced with complex utopian visions of a criminal justice service armed with an all powerful database for the benefit of society, contrasted with the dystopian vision of a criminal justice service, armed with the identical, all powerful database intent on mischief to our detriment. In conclusion, the paper observes that governance of such databases is difficult in the face of conflicting and competing interests, and suggests a theoretical framework that would seek to create a database that has the maximum utility, but protects those within it from harm.

de Melo-Martín, Inmaculada. Furthering injustices against women: genetic information, moral obligations, and gender. *Bioethics* 2006 November; 20(6): 301-307. NRCBL: 15.3; 15.1; 8.4; 10. SC: an.

de Sola, Carlos. Privacy and genetic data cases of conflict (I) = Privacidad y datos genéticos. Situaciones de conflicto (I). *Law and the Human Genome = Revista de Derecho y Genoma Humano* 1994 July-December; (1): 173-184. NRCBL: 15.1; 8.4. SC: le.

de Wert, Guido. Cascade screening: whose information is it anyway? *European Journal of Human Genetics* 2005 April; 13(4): 397-398. NRCBL: 15.3; 8.4; 8.3.1.

DeCew, Judith Wagner. Privacy and policy for genetic research. *Ethics and Information Technology* 2004; 6(1): 5-14. NRCBL: 15.1; 18.1; 8.4.

DeCew, Judith Wagner. Privacy and policy for genetic research. *In:* Tavani, Herman T., ed. Ethics, Computing, and Genomics. Sudbury, MA: Jones and Bartlett; 2006: 121-135. NRCBL: 15.1; 8.4.

District of Columbia. *Laws, statutes, etc.* An act to amend the Human Rights Act of 1977 to prohibit employment discrimination based on genetic information; to prohibit an employer, employment agency, or labor organization from requesting or requiring a genetic test of, or administering a genetic test to, an employee or applicant for employment or membership; to prohibit an employer, employment agency, or labor organization from seeking to obtain, obtaining, or using genetic information of an employee or applicant for employment; to provide an exemption that allows the use of genetic testing or information with the written and informed consent of the employee or applicant for employment to determine the existence of a bonafide occupational qualification, investigate a workers' compensation or disability compensation claim, or determine an employee's susceptibility or exposure to potentially toxic substances in the workplace; to prohibit health benefit plans and health insurers from using genetic information as a condition of eligibility or in setting premium rates; and to prohibit health benefit plans and health insurers from requesting or requiring genetic testing [Approved: 3 January 2005]. Washington, DC: Council of the District of Colum-

bia, 2005. 4 p. [Online]. Accessed: http://www.dccouncil. washington.dc.us/images/00001/20041217111559.pdf [2007 March 9]. NRCBL: 15.1; 15.3; 8.4. SC: le. Identifiers: Human Rights Genetic Information Amendment Act of 2004. Note: Act 15-648. Introduced by council members Graham and Patterson on January 7, 2003. Approved on January 3, 2005.

Duguet, A.M. Genetic research: between freedom in research and the patient's rights: contribution of the Declaration of Helsinki [editorial]. *European Journal of Health Law* 2001 September; 8(3): 203-206. NRCBL: 15.1; 8.4; 18.3; 15.3. SC: le.

Elger, Bernice S.; Harding, Timothy W. Should children and adolescents be tested for Huntington's disease? Attitudes of future lawyers and physicians in Switzerland. *Bioethics* 2006 June; 20(3): 158-167. NRCBL: 15.3; 9.5.7; 8.3.2. SC: em.
Abstract: The objective of the study was to identify future lawyers' and physicians' views on testing children for Huntington's disease (HD) against parents' wishes. After receiving general information about HD, patient autonomy and confidentiality, law students and advanced medical students were shown an interview with a mother suffering from HD who is opposed to informing and testing her two children (aged 10 and 16) for HD. Students then filled out questionnaires concerning their agreement with testing. No significant differences were found between medical and law students or between students from different courses concerning the adolescent son. Three quarters of students thought that he should be told about his mother's disease, and 91% thought the adolescent son should have the opportunity of genetic testing for HD himself. However, significant differences were found concerning the 10-year old son, with 44% of law students and 30% of medical students in favour of testing the child for HD. Students raised some important ethical issues in their elective comments. In conclusion, we found highly positive attitudes towards informing a 16-year old of his mother's HD and offering to test him. These attitudes were not in tune with guidelines. Students did not consider several practical and ethical issues of genetic testing of children and adolescents. Specific education should ensure that attitudes are based on sufficiently detailed knowledge about all aspects of genetic testing of children to discourage pressures on persons at risk of HD.

Faden, Ruth R.; Kass, Nancy E. Genetic screening technology: ethical issues in access to tests by employers and health insurance companies. *Journal of Social Issues* 1993 Summer; 49(2): 75-88. NRCBL: 15.3; 1.3.2; 8.4; 9.3.1.

Falcâo de Oliveira, Guilherme Freire. Juridical implications on genome knowledge (Part II) = Implicaciones jurídicas del conocimiento del genoma (Parte II). *Revista de Derecho Genoma Humano = Law and the Human Genome Review* 1997 July-December; (7): 59-98. NRCBL: 15.3; 15.2; 8.4.

Figueroa Yañez, Gonzalo. UNESCO Draft Universal Declaration on the Human Genome = El Proyecto de Declaración Universal sobre el Genoma Humano de la UNESCO. *Revista de Derecho Genoma Humano = Law and the Human Genome Review* 1997 July-December; (7):

113-120. NRCBL: 15.10; 21.1; 18.3; 2.4; 4.4; 9.3.1; 8.4. SC: le.

France. Comité consultatif national d'éthique pour les sciences de la vie et de la santé. Problèmes éthiques posés par les collections de matériel biologique et les données d'information associées: "biobanques", "biothèques" =Ethical problems posed by biological specimen collections and their associated data: "biobanks", "bioethics". *Journal International de Bioéthique = International Journal of Bioethics* 2005 September-December; 16(3-4): 141-151. NRCBL: 15.1; 1.3.12; 8.4; 9.3.1.

Frist, Bill. Open sesame. Congress must establish boundaries to protect privacy and promote ethical uses of new genetic information. *Forum for Applied Research and Public Policy* 2000 Spring; 15(1): 44-48. NRCBL: 15.1; 8.4. SC: an.

Gatensby, Anne. Privacy, property, and social relations in bioinformatics research. *In:* Árnason, Gardar; Nordal, Salvör; Árnason, Vilhjálmur, eds. Blood and Data: Ethical, Legal and Social Aspects of Human Genetic Databases. Reykjavík: University of Iceland Press; 2004: 28-27. NRCBL: 15.1; 8.4; 15.8.

Geller, Gail; Holtzman, Neil A. A qualitative assessment of primary care physicians' perceptions about the ethical and social implications of offering genetic testing. *Qualitative Health Research* 1995 February; 5(1): 97-116. NRCBL: 15.2; 8.1; 8.4. SC: cs; em.

Gerards, Janneke H.; Janssen, Heleen L. Regulation of genetic and other health information in a comparative perspective. *European Journal of Health Law* 2006 December; 13(4): 339-398. NRCBL: 15.1; 8.4; 9.3.1; 21.1. SC: rv; le.

German Society of Human Genetics [GfH]. Commission for Standpoints and Ethical Questions. DNA banking and personal data in biomedical research: technical, social, and ethical questions. *Medizinische Genetik* 2004; 16: 347-350. [Online]. Accessed: http://www.medgenetik. de/sonderdruck/en/DNA%20Banking_engl_060605.pdf [2006 July 31]. NRCBL: 15.1; 1.3.12; 18.1; 18.3; 8.3.1; 8.4.

Gertz, Renate. Is it 'me' or 'we'? Genetic relations and the meaning of 'personal data' under the Data Protection Directive. *European Journal of Health Law* 2004 September; 11(3): 231-244. NRCBL: 15.1; 1.3.12; 17.1; 8.4. SC: le.

Gillon, Raanan. Families and genetic testing: the case of Jane and Phyllis from a four- principles perspectives. *In:* Ashcroft, Richard; Lucassen, Anneke; Parker, Michael; Verkerk, Marian; Widderhoven, Guy, eds. Case Analysis in Clinical Ethics. New York: Cambridge University Press; 2005: 165-185. NRCBL: 15.3; 8.4; 2.1. SC: an.

Godard, Beatrice; Raeburn, Sandy; Pembrey, Marcus; Bobrow, Martin; Farndon, Peter; Ayme, Segolene. Genetic information and testing in insurance and employment: technical, social and ethical issues. *European Journal of Human Genetics* 2003 December; 11(Supplement 2): S123-S142. NRCBL: 15.3; 9.3.1; 8.4; 21.1. SC: rv.

Godard, Beatrice; Schmidtke, Jorg; Cassiman, Jean-Jacques; Ayme, Segolene. Data storage and DNA banking for biomedical research: informed consent, confidentiality, quality issues, ownership, return of benefits. A professional perspective. *European Journal of Human Genetics* 2003 December; 11(Supplement 2): S88-S122. NRCBL: 15.10; 1.3.12; 13.1; 18.3; 8.4; 21.1. SC: rv.

Guzauskas, Gregory F.; Lebel, Robert Roger. The duty to re-contact for newly appreciated risk factors: Fragile X premutation. *Journal of Clinical Ethics* 2006 Spring; 17(1): 46-52. NRCBL: 15.3; 15.2; 15.6; 9.5.3; 8.4.

Hawaii. *Laws, statutes, etc.* An act relating to genetic information and genetic testing [Approved: 1 July 2002]. Hawaii: State Legislature, 2002. 3 p. [Online]. Accessed: http://www.capitol.hawaii.gov/session2002/bills/ SB2180_hd1_.htm [2007 March 9]. NRCBL: 15.1; 8.4. SC: le. Note: Senate Bill 2180, 21st Legislature, regular session. Introduced by Sen. Nakata on January 18, 2002. Approved on July 1, 2002.

Herzog, Antonia V.; Frankel, Mark S. A model ethical protocol as a guidance document for human genome research. *Revista de Derecho Genoma Humano = Law and the Human Genome Review* 1999 January-June; (10): 21-40. NRCBL: 15.11; 21.1; 15.8; 18.3; 8.4. Identifiers: Human Genome Diversity Project (HGDP).

Hlaca, Nenad. Human genome and protection of human rights in Croatia. *Revista de Derecho y Genoma Humano = Law and the Human Genome Review* 2006 January-June; (24): 65-73. NRCBL: 15.3; 8.4; 15.10. SC: le.

Hoedemaekers, Rogeer; Gordijn, Bert; Pijnenburg, Martien. Does an appeal to the common good justify individual sacrifices for genomic research? *Theoretical Medicine and Bioethics* 2006; 27(5): 415-431. NRCBL: 15.10; 15.1; 18.3; 8.4; 1.3.1.

Hofmann, Bjørn. Forensic uses and misuses of DNA: a case report from Norway. *Genomics, Society and Policy* 2006 May; 2(1): 129-131. NRCBL: 15.1; 1.3.5.
Abstract: New technology generates fantastic possibilities which challenge traditional distinctions between good and bad. Genetic analysis of DNA for forensic purposes is but one example of this. Here society's need for convicting criminals can conflict with the same society's need to assure the confidentiality of information about its members and their trust in its institutions. In order to illustrate the complexity of such challenges, a case report from Norway is presented. The point is to reflect on the way we handle trailblazing health technologies in general and on cases where law and order is gained by means that can be conceived of as immoral in particular. The case calls for careful ethical reflection.

NRCBL: National Reference Center for Bioethics Literature Classification Scheme   See inside front cover for terms.

213

Holm, Søren. An empirical approach. *In:* Ashcroft, Richard; Lucassen, Anneke; Parker, Michael; Verkerk, Marian; Widderhoven, Guy, eds. Case Analysis in Clinical Ethics. New York: Cambridge University Press; 2005: 201-211. NRCBL: 15.3; 8.4. SC: an; em.

Human Genetics Commission [HGC] (Great Britain). Public attitudes to human genetic information: People's Panel quantitative study conducted for the Human Genetics Commission. London: Human Genetics Commission, 2001 March. 68 p. [Online]. Accessed: http://www.hgc.gov.uk/UploadDocs/DocPub/Document/morigeneticattitudes.pdf [2006 July 26]. NRCBL: 15.1; 15.3; 8.4; 1.3.5. SC: em. Note: This volume contains the summary findings of a quantitative survey of a representative sample from the People's Panel conducted by MORI Social Research on behalf of the Human Genetics Commission [HGC].

Hurwitz, Brian. Family access to shared genetic information: an analysis of the narrative. *In:* Ashcroft, Richard; Lucassen, Anneke; Parker, Michael; Verkerk, Marian; Widderhoven, Guy, eds. Case Analysis in Clinical Ethics. New York: Cambridge University Press; 2005: 27-43. NRCBL: 15.3; 8.4. SC: an.

Iceland. Supreme Court. Ragnhildur Gumðundsdóttir vs. The State of Iceland. (Thursday, 27 November 2003, No. 151/2003). *European Journal of Health Law* 2004 September; 11(3): 283-291. Subject: 15.1; 1.3.12; 17.1; 8.4. SC: le.

Idaho. *Laws, statutes, etc.* An act relating to genetic testing privacy; amending title 39, Idaho Code, by the addition of a new chapter 83, title 39, Idaho Code, to provide a short title, to define terms, to set forth restrictions regarding genetic testing information applicable to employers, to provide for a private right of action and to provide for enforcement; and amending section 41-1313, Idaho Code, to prohibit insurers from discriminating on the basis of a genetic test or private genetic information for certain purposes [Approved: 31 March 2006]. Idaho: State Legislature, 2006. 8 p. [Online]. Accessed: http://www3.state.id.us/oasis/2006/S1423.html [2007 March 9]. NRCBL: 15.3; 15.1; 8.4. SC: le. Identifiers: Genetic Testing Privacy Act. Note: Senate Bill No. 1423, 58th Legislature, 2nd regular session. Introduced on March 2, 2006. Approved on March 31, 2006.

Javitt, Gail H. Policy implications of genetic testing: not just for geneticists anymore. *Advances in Chronic Kidney Disease* 2006 April; 13(2): 178-182. NRCBL: 15.3; 5.3; 8.4; 16.3. SC: le.

Jenkins, Jean F.; Lea, Dale Halsey. My hopes and fears: how I feel about genetic research. *In their:* Nursing Care in the Genomic Era: A Case-Based Approach. Sudbury, MA: Jones and Bartlett Publishers, 2005: 287-316. NRCBL: 15.1; 8.4; 9.7; 18.3.

Joh, Elizabeth E. Reclaiming "abandoned" DNA: the Fourth Amendment and genetic privacy. *Northwestern University Law Review* 2006 Winter; 100(2): 857-884. NRCBL: 15.1; 8.4; 1.3.5. SC: le.

Joly, Yann. Life insurers' access to genetic information: a way out of the stalemate? *Health Law Review* 2006; 14(3): 14-21. NRCBL: 15.1; 8.4. SC: le.

Joly, Yann; Knoppers, Bartha M. Pharmacogenomic data sample collection and storage: ethical issues and policy approaches. *Pharmacogenomics* 2006 March; 7(2): 219-226. NRCBL: 15.10; 9.7; 1.3.12; 8.4; 18.3; 21.1.

Kakuk, Péter. Genetic information in the age of genohype. *Medicine, Health Care and Philosophy* 2006; 9(3): 325-337. NRCBL: 15.1; 1.1; 8.4; 15.3. SC: an.

Kaye, Jane. Police collection and access to DNA samples. *Genomics, Society and Policy* 2006 May; 2(1): 16-27. NRCBL: 15.1; 1.3.5.
Abstract: As forensic techniques continue to improve, reports on the success of the police in using DNA analysis for solving past and present criminal cases are becoming an everyday occurrence in the media. There are two avenues by which police can collect and obtain access to DNA samples. The first is on the basis of legislation that allows the police to forcibly collect samples in some situations. The second is through an access order granted by the court, which allows access to samples from existing collections held by other parties. The purpose of this paper is to compare these two legal mechanisms that allow the police to acquire and access DNA samples. My concern is the increase in collection of DNA samples for genetic research, the moves to standardise data collection and the computerisation of medical records, may make research collections more attractive to the police. Are we are prepared for research collections to become an extension of the National DNA Database used for crime detection? In the USA a decision has been made that the police should not be allowed access to samples and information derived from 'sensitive' research. This article considers 'the certificates of confidentiality' that have been instigated by the National Institute of Health in the USA in order to prohibit such uses of research collections by the police. In this article I consider whether certificates of confidentiality should be used in the UK, as a way of providing greater protection to researchers and participants in research.

Knoppers, Bartha Maria. Human genetics: parental, professional and political responsibility. *Health Law Journal* 1993; 1(1): 13-23. NRCBL: 15.2; 8.1; 8.4. SC: le. Identifiers: Picard Lecture in Health Law — 1992; Canada.

Knoppers, Bartha Maria; Fecteau, Claudine. Human genomic databases: a global public good? *European Journal of Health Law* 2003 March; 10(1): 27-41. NRCBL: 15.10; 1.3.12; 13.1; 8.4; 15.8; 21.1. SC: le.

Knoppers, Bartha Maria; Saginur, Madelaine. The Babel of genetic data terminology. *Nature Biotechnology* 2005 August; 23(8): 925-927. NRCBL: 15.1; 8.4; 18.2; 21.1. SC: le.

Lazer, David; Mayer-Schönberger, Viktor. Statutory frameworks for regulating information flows: drawing lessons for the DNA data banks from other government data systems. *Journal of Law, Medicine and Ethics* 2006 Summer; 34(2): 366-374. NRCBL: 15.1; 1.3.12; 13.1; 8.4. SC: le.

Lea, Dale Halsey; Williams, Janet; Donahue, M. Patricia. Ethical issues in genetic testing. *Journal of Midwifery and Women's Health* 2005 May-June; 50(3): 234-240. NRCBL: 15.3; 1.1; 8.4.

Lenoir, Noëlle. Legal and ethical aspects of prenatal diagnosis: the law and current practices in France and certain other countries (Part II) = Aspectos jurídicos y éticos del diagnóstico prenatal: el derecho y las prácticas vigentes en Francia y otros países (y II). *Law and the Human Genome Review = Revista de Derecho y Genoma Humano* 1995 July-December; (3): 123-141. NRCBL: 15.2; 21.1; 8.3.1; 8.4. SC: le.

LeVine, Harry. Problems, controversies, and solutions. *In his:* Genetic Engineering: A Reference Handbook. 2nd ed. Santa Barbara, CA: ABC-CLIO, 2006: 47-81. NRCBL: 15.1; 1.2; 1.3.11; 8.4; 9.3.1; 14.5; 16.3.

Liddell, Kathy. Did the watchdog bark, bite or whimper? UK report on the use of personal genetic information. *European Journal of Health Law* 2002 September; 9(3): 243-256. NRCBL: 15.1; 2.4; 18.3; 8.4. SC: le.

Lin, Zhen; Altman, Russ B.; Owen, Art B. Confidentiality in genome research [letter]. *Science* 2006 July 28; 313(5786): 441-442. NRCBL: 15.10; 8.4.

Lucassen, Anneke. Families and genetic testing: the case of Jane and Phyllis. *In:* Ashcroft, Richard; Lucassen, Anneke; Parker, Michael; Verkerk, Marian; Widderhoven, Guy, eds. Case Analysis in Clinical Ethics. New York: Cambridge University Press; 2005: 7-26. NRCBL: 15.3; 8.4. SC: cs.

Lucassen, Anneke; Parker, Michael; Wheeler, Robert. Implications of data protection legislation for family history. *BMJ: British Medical Journal* 2006 February 4; 332(7536): 299-301. NRCBL: 15.1; 1.3.12; 8.4; 8.3.1.

Maryland. *Laws, statutes, etc.* An act for the purpose of prohibiting the use of certain genetic information to deny or otherwise affect a health insurance policy or contract; prohibiting the request or requirement of certain genetic information as a basis for issuing or renewing health benefits coverage; prohibiting the disclosure of certain genetic information to certain persons without certain authorization of the individual from whom the genetic information was obtained; identifying certain permissible purposes for disclosure of genetic information; defining certain terms; repealing the termination date of certain provisions of law that relate to the use of genetic tests; and generally relating to prohibiting discrimination on the basis of genetic information in health insurance [Approved: 13 April 1999]. Maryland: General Assembly, 1999. 4 p. [Online]. Accessed: http://mlis.state.md.us/PDF-Documents/1999rs/bills/sb/sb0774t.PDF [2007 March 9]. NRCBL:

15.1; 8.4. SC: le. Identifiers: Genetic Information Nondiscrimination in Health Insurance Act of 1999. Note: Senate Bill 774, 1999 regular session. Introduced on March 5, 1999. Approved on April 13, 1999.

Massachusetts. *Laws, statutes, etc.* An act relative to insurance and genetic testing and privacy protection [Approved: 22 August 2000]. Massachusetts: House Bill 5416, Acts of 2000, Chapter 254. 10 p. [Online]. Accessed: http://www.mass.gov/legis/laws/seslaw00/sl000254.htm [2007 March 9]. NRCBL: 15.1; 8.4. SC: le.

McCall Smith, Alexander. Genetic privacy and discrimination. *In:* Glasa, J., ed. Ethics of Human Genetics: Challenges of the (Post) Genomic Era. Bratislava, Slovak Republic: Charis [and] IMEB Foundation; 2002: 81-87. NRCBL: 15.3; 8.4.

McGivern, Brenda. Bioethics and the law — the impact of genetic technology on prenatal management. *E Law: Murdoch University Electronic Journal of Law* 1995 December; 2(3): 35 p. [Online]. Accessed: http://www.murdoch.edu.au/elaw/issues/v2n3mcgivern23.html [2006 June 29]. NRCBL: 15.2; 15.3; 12.4.1; 15.10; 8.4; 12.1. SC: le. Identifiers: Australia.

McLean, Sheila A.M. Mapping the human genome — friend or foe? *Social Science and Medicine* 1994 November; 39(9): 1221-1227. NRCBL: 15.10; 5.3; 15.3; 8.4.

Mesters, Ilse; Ausems, Marlein; Eichhorn, Sophie; Vasen, Hans. Informing one's family about genetic testing for hereditary non-polyposis colorectal cancer (HNPCC): a retrospective exploratory study. *Familial Cancer* 2005; 4(2): 163-167. NRCBL: 15.3; 8.1; 8.4. SC: em. Identifiers: Netherlands.

Montana. *Laws, statutes, etc.* An act establishing standards for the collection, use, and disclosure of genetic information in issuing insurance; prohibiting insurers from requiring genetic testing except as otherwise required by-law; prohibiting discrimination on the basis of genetic traits by insurers, health service corporations, health maintenance organizations, fraternal benefit societies, and other issuers of individual or group policies or certificates of insurance; prohibiting the solicitation of genetic information for nontherapeutic purposes; and amending sections 2-18-812 and 33-31-111, MCA [Approved: 19 April 1999]. Montana: State Legislature, 1999. 5 p. [Online]. Accessed: http://data.opi.state.mt.us/bills/billhtml/HB0111.htm [2007 March 9]. NRCBL: 15.1; 8.4. SC: le. Note: House Bill 111, 1999 regular session. Introduced by Rep. Guggenheim on December 18, 1998. Approved on April 19, 1999.

New Jersey. *Laws, statutes, etc.* An act concerning genetic testing and genetic privacy. New Jersey: Senate Bill 695; Public Laws 1996-1997, Chapter 126. 16 p. [Online]. Accessed http://www.njleg.state.nj.us/9697/Bills/

NRCBL: National Reference Center for Bioethics Literature Classification Scheme   See inside front cover for terms.

215

PL96/126_.PDF [9 March 2007]. NRCBL: 15.1; 8.4. SC: le. Identifiers: Genetic Privacy Act.

New Mexico. *Laws, statutes, etc.* An act relating to genetic information; prohibiting the use of genetic information in nonmedical contexts [Approved: 6 April 2005]. New Mexico: State Legislature, 2005. 4 p. [Online]. Accessed: http://legis.state.nm.us/Sessions/05%20Regular/ final/HB0183.pdf [2007 March 9]. NRCBL: 15.1; 8.4. SC: le. Note: House Bill 183, 47th Legislature, 2005 regular session. Introduced by Rep. Picraux. Approved on April 6, 2005.

Newson, Ainsley J.; Humphries, Steve E. Cascade testing in familial hypercholesterolaemia: how should family members be contacted? *European Journal of Human Genetics* 2005 April; 13(4): 401-408. NRCBL: 15.3; 8.4; 8.3.1; 8.1.

Nielsen, Linda. Genetic testing and privacy: a European perspective = Pruebas genéticas y derecho a la intimidad: una perspectiva europea. *Law and the Human Genome Review = Revista de Derecho y Genoma Humano* 1996 January-June; (4): 59-76. NRCBL: 15.3; 21.1; 8.4. SC: le. Identifiers: Europe.

Nõmper, Ants. What is wrong with using anonymized data and tissue for research purposes? *In:* Árnason, Gardar; Nordal, Salvör; Árnason, Vilhjálmur, eds. Blood and Data: Ethical, Legal and Social Aspects of Human Genetic Databases. Reykjavík: University of Iceland Press; 2004: 121-126. NRCBL: 15.1; 1.3.9; 8.4; 18.1.

Ossorio, Pilar N. Letting the gene out of the bottle: a comment on returning individual research results to participants. *American Journal of Bioethics* 2006 November-December; 6(6): 24-25; author reply W10-W12. NRCBL: 15.1; 18.2; 8.4; 8.1. Comments: Vardit Ravitsky and Benjamin S. Wilfond. Disclosing individual genetic results to research participants. American Journal of Bioethics 2006 November-December; 6(6): 8-17.

Otlowski, Margaret. Essentially yours: the protection of human genetic information in Australia. *GeneWatch* 2006 January-February; 19(1): 9-12. NRCBL: 15.3; 8.4.

Otlowski, Margaret. Genetic discrimination: meeting the challenges of an emerging issue [forum]. *University of New South Wales Law Journal* 2003; 26(3): 764-769. NRCBL: 15.3; 8.4; 9.3.1; 9.5.4. SC: le. Identifiers: Australia.

Otlowski, Margaret F.A.; Williamson, Robert. Ethical and legal issues and the "new genetics". *Medical Journal of Australia* 2003 June 2; 178(11): 582-585. NRCBL: 15.3; 8.4; 15.2; 7.1.

Parker, Michael. A conversational approach to the ethics of genetic testing. *In:* Ashcroft, Richard; Lucassen, Anneke; Parker, Michael; Verkerk, Marian; Widderhoven, Guy, eds. Case Analysis in Clinical Ethics. New York:

Cambridge University Press; 2005: 149-164. NRCBL: 15.3; 8.4; 15.2. SC: an.

Parthasarathy, Shobita. Regulating risk: defining genetic privacy in the United States and Britain. *Science, Technology, and Human Values* 2004 Summer; 29(3): 332-352. NRCBL: 15.3; 8.4; 9.3.1.

Petersen, Alan. Securing our genetic health: engendering trust in UK Biobank. *Sociology of Health and Illness* 2005 March; 27(2): 271-292. NRCBL: 15.1; 1.3.12; 8.3.1; 9.1; 1.3.5; 8.4. Identifiers: United Kingdom (Great Britain).

Phua, Kai-Lit. The Human Genome Project and genetic research: what are the implications for ethics and equity? *Critical Public Health* 2004 June; 14(2): 191-200. NRCBL: 15.10; 15.1; 8.4.

Pickens, K.L. Don't judge me by my genes: a survey of federal genetic discrimination legislation. *Tulsa Law Journal* 1998 Fall; 34(1): 161-181. NRCBL: 15.1; 8.4; 15.10. SC: le.

Rabino, Isaac. Research scientists surveyed on ethical issues in genetic medicine: a comparison of attitudes of US and European researchers. *New Genetics and Society* 2006 December; 25(3): 325-342. NRCBL: 15.3; 8.4; 15.4; 21.1. SC: em.

Ravitsky, Vardit; Wilfond, Benjamin S. Disclosing individual genetic results to research participants. *American Journal of Bioethics* 2006 November-December; 6(6): 8-17. NRCBL: 15.1; 18.2; 8.1; 18.3; 8.4.

Renegar, Gaile; Webster, Christopher J.; Stuerzebecher, Steffen; Harty, Lea; Ide, Susan E.; Balkite, Beth; Rogalski- Salter, Taryn A.; Cohen, Nadine; Spear, Brian B.; Barnes, Diane M.; Brazell, Celia. Returning genetic research results to individuals: points-to-consider. *Bioethics* 2006 February; 20(1): 24-36. NRCBL: 15.1; 8.2; 9.7.

Abstract: This paper is intended to stimulate debate amongst stakeholders in the international research community on the topic of returning individual genetic research results to study participants. Pharmacogenetics and disease genetics studies are becoming increasingly prevalent, leading to a growing body of information on genetic associations for drug responsiveness and disease susceptibility with the potential to improve health care. Much of these data are presently characterized as exploratory (non-validated or hypothesis-generating). There is, however, a trend for research participants to be permitted access to their personal data if they so choose. Researchers, sponsors, patient advocacy groups, ethics committees and regulatory authorities are consequently confronting the issue of whether, and how, study participants might receive their individual results. Noted international ethico-legal guidelines and public policy positions in Europe and the United States are reviewed for background. The authors offer 'Points-to-Consider' regarding returning results in the context of drug development trials based on their knowledge and experience. Theses considerations include: the clinical relevance of data, laboratory qualifications, informed consent procedures, confidentiality of medical information and the competency of persons providing results to participants. The discussion is framed as a benefit-to-risk assessment to balance the potential positive versus negative consequences to participants, while maintaining the integrity and feasibility of conducting genetic research studies.

Ripol Carulla, Santiago. The protection of medical and genetic data in the Council of Europe's normative texts (part II) = La protección de los datos médicos y genéticos en la normativa del Consejo de Europa (Parte II). *Revista de Derecho Genoma Humano = Law and the Human Genome Review* 1997 January-June; (6): 101-127. NRCBL: 15.1; 8.4; 21.1; 1.3.9. SC: le.

Rizzo, Robert F. Safeguarding genetic information: privacy, confidentiality, and security? *In:* Davis, John B., ed. The Social Economics of Health Care. New York: Routledge; 2001: 257-284. NRCBL: 15.1; 8.4.

Roche, Patricia A.; Annas, George J. DNA testing, banking, and genetic privacy. *New England Journal of Medicine* 2006 August 10; 355(6): 545-546. NRCBL: 15.3; 15.1; 1.3.12; 8.4; 19.5.

Rothstein, Mark A.; Talbott, Meghan K. The expanding use of DNA in law enforcement: what role for privacy? *Journal of Law, Medicine and Ethics* 2006 Summer; 34(2): 153-164. NRCBL: 15.1; 1.3.5; 1.3.12; 1.1. SC: le.

Sabatier, Sandrine. Steering Committee on Bioethics (CDBI): Working Party on Human Genetics (CDBI-CO-GT4). Strasbourg: Council of Europe [COE]. Steering Committee on Bioethics, 1997 October 27: 40 p. [Online]. Accessed: http://www.coe.int/t/e/legal_affairs/legal_co-operation/bioethics/texts_and_documents/DIR-JUR (97)13Genetics.pdf [2007 March 5]. NRCBL: 15.3; 15.2; 18.3; 8.4.

Sándor, Judit. Genetic data: old and new challenges in data protection. *In:* Glasa, J., ed. Ethics of Human Genetics: Challenges of the (Post) Genomic Era. Bratislava, Slovak Republic: Charis [and] IMEB Foundation; 2002: 89-97. NRCBL: 15.3; 8.4. SC: le.

Savulescu, Julian. A utilitarian approach. *In:* Ashcroft, Richard; Lucassen, Anneke; Parker, Michael; Verkerk, Marian; Widderhoven, Guy, eds. Case Analysis in Clinical Ethics. New York: Cambridge University Press; 2005: 115-131. NRCBL: 15.3; 8.4; 1.1. SC: an.

Schmitz, Dagmar; Wiesing, Urban. Just a family medical history? *BMJ: British Medical Journal* 2006 February 4; 332(7536): 297-299. NRCBL: 15.1; 15.11; 8.3.1; 8.4; 15.3.

Schneider, Katherine A.; Chittenden, Anu B.; Branda, Kelly J.; Keenan, Meredith A.; Joffe, Steven; Patenaude, Andrea Farkas; Reynolds, Hazel; Dent, Karin; Eubanks, Sonja; Goldman, Jill; Leroy, Bonnie; Warren, Nancy Steinberg; Taylor, Kelly; Vockley, Cate Walsh; Garber, Judy E. Ethical issues in cancer genetics: 1) whose information is it? *Journal of Genetic Counseling*

2006 December; 15(6): 491-503. NRCBL: 15.3; 15.2; 8.4. SC: cs.

Schwarz, Pascal. The collection and management of confidential genetic data: an evaluation of deCODE genetics based on the principle of autonomy. *In:* Árnason, Gardar; Nordal, Salvör; Árnason, Vilhjálmur, eds. Blood and Data: Ethical, Legal and Social Aspects of Human Genetic Databases. Reykjavík: University of Iceland Press; 2004: 231-235. NRCBL: 15.1; 1.1; 1.3.12; 8.4.

Sharpe, Neil F.; Carter, Ronald F. Confidentiality, disclosure, and recontact. *In their:* Genetic Testing: Care, Consent, and Liability. Hoboken, NJ: Wiley-Liss; 2006: 398-424. NRCBL: 15.3; 8.4.

Sharpe, Neil F.; Carter, Ronald F. New genetics and the protection of information. *In their:* Genetic Testing: Care, Consent, and Liability. Hoboken, NJ: Wiley-Liss; 2006: 425-442. NRCBL: 15.1; 8.4.

Sild, Tarmo; Mullari, Tambet. Population based genetic research: Estonian answer to the legal challenge. *European Journal of Health Law* 2001 December; 8(4): 363-371. NRCBL: 15.1; 1.3.12; 13.1; 19.1; 8.4. SC: le.

Simoncelli, Tania. Dangerous excursions: the case against expanding forensic DNA databases to innocent persons. *Journal of Law, Medicine and Ethics* 2006 Summer; 34(2): 390-397. NRCBL: 15.1; 1.3.5; 1.3.12; 8.4. SC: le.

Sismondo, Lauren J. GINA, what could you do for me one day?: The potential of the Genetic Information Nondiscrimination Act to protect the American public. *Washington University Journal of Law and Policy* 2006; 21: 459-481. NRCBL: 15.3; 8.4; 9.3.1; 16.3. SC: le.

Skrikerud, Anne Maria. Monozygotic autonomy and genetic privacy. *In:* Árnason, Gardar; Nordal, Salvör; Árnason, Vilhjálmur, eds. Blood and Data: Ethical, Legal and Social Aspects of Human Genetic Databases. Reykjavík: University of Iceland Press; 2004: 243-247. NRCBL: 15.1; 1.1; 8.4. SC: an.

Slaughter, Louise McIntosh. Genetic testing and discrimination: how private is your information? *Stanford Law and Policy Review* 2006; 17(1): 67-81. NRCBL: 15.1; 15.3; 8.4. SC: le.

Smith, Michael E. Let's make the DNA identification database as inclusive as possible. *Journal of Law, Medicine and Ethics* 2006 Summer; 34(2): 385-389. NRCBL: 15.1; 1.3.5; 1.3.12; 8.4. SC: le.

South Carolina. *Laws, statutes, etc.* An act to amend title 38, Code of Laws of South Carolina, 1976, relating to insurance, by adding chapter 93 so as to enact provisions regulating the privacy of genetic information [Approved: 26 May 1998]. South Carolina: General Assembly Bill 535. 4 p. [Online]. Accessed: http://www.scstatehouse.net/sess112_1997-1998/bills/535.htm [2007 March 9].

NRCBL: National Reference Center for Bioethics Literature Classification Scheme   See inside front cover for terms.

217

NRCBL: 15.1; 8.4. SC: le. Identifiers: Privacy of Genetic Information. Note: General Assembly Bill 535, 112th session, 1997-1998. Introduced on March 12, 1997. Approved on May 26, 1998.

Stulic, Mathew. Genetic non-discrimination, privacy and property rights. *E Law: Murdoch University Electronic Journal of Law* 2000 June; 7(2): 26 p. [Online]. Accessed: http://www.murdoch.edu.au/elaw/issues/v4n3/stulic72.html[2006 June 29]. NRCBL: 15.1; 15.8. SC: le. Identifiers: Australia. Genetic Privacy and Non-Discrimination Bill 1998.

Takala, Tuija. Why we should not relax ethical rules in the age of genetics. *In:* Árnason, Gardar; Nordal, Salvör; Árnason, Vilhjálmur, eds. Blood and Data: Ethical, Legal and Social Aspects of Human Genetic Databases. Reykjavík: University of Iceland Press; 2004: 135-140. NRCBL: 15.1; 8.4; 18.3.

Taupitz, Jochen. Genetic analysis and the right to self-determination in German Civil War = Análisis genético y derecho de autodeterminación en el Derecho Civil Alemán. *Law and the Human Genome Review = Revista de Derecho y Genoma Humano* 1996 January-June; (4): 77-90. NRCBL: 15.3; 8.3.1; 8.4. SC: le.

Tavani, Herman T. Genomic research and data-mining technology: implications for personal privacy and informed consent. *Ethics and Information Technology* 2004; 6(1): 15-28. NRCBL: 15.1; 18.3; 1.3.12; 8.4.

Trent, Ronald J.A. Essentially yours: the protection of human genetic information in Australia — the impact on clinical practice and the 'new genetics'. *University of New South Wales Law Journal* 2003; 26(3): 807-812. NRCBL: 15.3; 8.4; 1.3.5; 7.3. SC: le.

Tucker, Diane C.; Acton, Ronald, T.; Press, Nancy; Ruggiero, Andrea; Reiss, Jacob A.; Walker, Ann P.; Wenzel, Lari; Harrison, Barbara; Fadojutimi-Akinsiku, Margaret; Harrison, Helen; Adams, Paul; Crabb, Jennifer A.; Anderson, Roger; Thomson, Elizabeth. Predictors of belief that genetic test information about hemochromatosis should be shared with family members. *Genetic Testing* 2006 Spring; 10(1): 50-59. NRCBL: 15.3; 8.4; 8.2; 8.1; 7.1. SC: em.

United States. Congress. House. A bill to amend the Public Health Service Act to prohibit health discrimination against individuals and their family members on the basis of genetic information, and for other purposes. Washington, DC: U.S. G.P.O., 2003. 7 p. [Online]. Accessed: http://frwebgate.access.gpo.gov/cgi-bin/useftp.cgi?IPaddress=162.140.64.21&file name=h3636ih.pdf& directory=/disk2/wais/data/108_cong_bills [2006 November 20]. NRCBL: 15.3. SC: le. Identifiers: Genetic Privacy and Nondiscrimination Act of 2003. Note: H.R. 3636, 108th Congress, 1st session. Introduced by Rep. Stearns,

November 26, 2003. Referred to the Committee on Energy and Commerce.

United States. Congress. House. A bill to establish limitations with respect to disclosure and use of genetic information in connection with group health plans and health insurance coverage, to provide for consistent standards applicable in connection with hospital care and medical services provided under title 38 of the United States Code, to prohibit employment discrimination on the basis of genetic information and genetic testing, and for other purposes. Washington, DC: U.S. G.P.O.; 1998. 22 p. [Online]. Accessed: http://frwebgate.access.gpo.gov/cgi-bin/useftp.cgi?IPaddress=162.140.64.122&filename=h3299ih.pdf&directory=/diskc/wais/data/105_cong_bills [2007 March 6]. NRCBL: 15.1; 8.4; 9.3.1. SC: le. Identifiers: Family Genetic Privacy and Protection Act. Note: H.R. 3299, 105th Congress, 2d session. Introduced by Rep. Smith, February 26, 1998. Referred to the Committee on Commerce, and in addition to the Committees on Education and the Workforce, and Veterans' Affairs.

United States. Congress. House. A bill to establish limitations with respect to disclosure and use of genetic information, and for other purposes. Washington, DC: U.S. G.P.O.; 1997. 8 p. [Online]. Accessed: http://frwebgate.access.gpo.gov/cgi-bin/useftp.cgi?IPaddress=162.140.64.122&filename=h341ih.pdf&directory=/diskc/wais/data/105_cong_bills [2007 March 5]. NRCBL: 15.1; 8.4. SC: le. Identifiers: Genetic Privacy and Nondiscrimination Act of 1997. Note: H.R. 341, 105th Congress, 1st session. Introduced by Rep. Stearns, January 7, 1997. Referred to the Committee on Commerce, and in addition to the Committees on Government Reform and Oversight and Education and the Workforce.

United States. Congress. House. A bill to prohibit discrimination by group health plans and employers based on genetic information. Washington, DC: U.S. G.P.O., 2006. 10 p. [Online]. Accessed: http://frwebgate.access.gpo.gov/cgi-bin/useftp.cgi?IPaddress=162.140.64.21&filename=h6125ih.pdf&directory=/diskb/wais/data/109_cong_bills [2006 November 1]. NRCBL: 15.3; 8.4. SC: le. Identifiers: Taxpayer Protection from Genetic Discrimination Act of 2006. Note: H.R. 6125, 109th Congress, 2d session. Introduced by Rep. Paul, September 20, 2006. Referred to the Committee on Government Reform and to the Committees on Education and the Workforce, Energy and Commerce, and Ways and Means.

United States. Congress. House. A bill to prohibit discrimination on the basis of genetic information with respect to health insurance. Washington, DC: U.S. G.P.O., 2003, 75 p. [Online]. Accessed: http://frwebgate.access.gpo.gov/cgi-bin/useftp.cgi?IPaddress=162.140.64.21&filename=h1910ih.pdf&directory=/disk2/wais/data/108_cong_bills [2006 November 27]. NRCBL: 15.3; 8.4; 9.3.1; 15.1. SC: le. Identifiers: Genetic Nondiscrimination in Health Insurance and Employment Act. Note:

H.R. 1910, 108th Congress, 1st session. Introduced by Rep. Slaughter, May 1, 2003. Referred to the Committee on Energy and Commerce and in addition to the Committees on Ways and Means and Education and the Workforce.

United States. Congress. House. A bill to prohibit discrimination on the basis of genetic information with respect to health insurance. Washington, DC: U.S. G.P.O., 2001. 69 p. [Online]. Accessed: http://frwebgate.access. gpo.gov/cgi-bin/getdoc.cgi?dbname=107_cong_bills& docid=f:h602ih.txt. pdf [2007 March 8]. NRCBL: 15.3; 8.4; 9.3.1. SC: le. Identifiers: Genetic Nondiscrimination in Health Insurance and Employment Act. Note: H.R. 602, 107th Congress, 1st session. Introduced by Rep. Slaughter on February 13, 2001. Referred to the Committee on Energy and Commerce in addition to the Committees on Ways and Means, and Education and the Workforce.

United States. Congress. House. A bill to prohibit discrimination on the basis of genetic information with respect to health insurance and employment. Washington, DC: U.S. G.P.O., 2005. 81 p. [Online]. Accessed: http://frwebgate.access.gpo.gov/cgi-bin/useftp.cgi? IPaddress=162.140.64.21&filename=h1227ih.pdf& directory=/diskb/wais/data/109_cong_bills [2006 December 6]. NRCBL: 15.3; 8.4; 9.3.1; 15.1. SC: le. Identifiers: Genetic Information Nondiscrimination Act of 2005. Note: H.R. 1227, 109th Congress, 1st session. Introduced by Rep. Biggert, March 10, 2005. Referred to the Committee on Education and the Workforce, and in addition to the Committees on Energy and Commerce, and Ways and Means.

United States. Congress. House. A bill to prohibit health insurance and employment discrimination against individuals and their family members on the basis of predictive genetic information or genetic services. Washington, DC: U.S.G.P.O., 1999. 70 p. [Online]. Accessed: http://frwebgate.access.gpo.gov/cgi-bin/getdoc.cgi? dbname=106_cong_bills&docid= f:h2457ih.txt.pdf [2007 March 8]. NRCBL: 15.3; 8.4; 9.3.1. SC: le. Identifiers: Genetic Nondiscrimination in Health Insurance and Employment Act of 1999. Note: H.R. 2457, 106th Congress, 1st session. Introduced by Rep. Slaughter in the House of Representatives on July 1, 1999. Referred to the Committee on Commerce, and in addition to the Committees on Ways and Means, and Education in the Workforce.

United States. Congress. Senate. A bill to prohibit discrimination on the basis of genetic information with respect to health insurance. Washington, DC: U.S. G.P.O.; 2001. 28 p. [Online]. Accessed: http://frwebgate.access. gpo.gov/cgi-bin/useftp.cgi?IPaddress=162.140.64.31& filename=s382is.pdf&directory=/disk2/wais/ data/107_cong_bills [2007 March 6]. NRCBL: 15.1; 8.4; 9.3.1. SC: le. Identifiers: Genetic Information Nondiscrimination in Health Insurance Act of 2001. Note: S. 382, 107th Congress, 1st session. Introduced by Rep. Snowe,

February 15, 2001. Referred to the Committee on Health, Education, Labor, and Pensions.

United States. Congress. Senate. A bill to prohibit discrimination on the basis of genetic information with respect to health insurance. Washington, DC: U.S. G.P.O., 1999. 27 p. [Online]. Accessed: http://frwebgate.access. gpo.gov/cgi-bin/getdoc.cgi?dbname=106_cong_bills& docid=f:s543is.txt. pdf [2007 March 8]. NRCBL: 15.1; 8.4; 9.3.1. SC: le. Identifiers: Genetic Information Nondiscrimination in Health Insurance Act of 1999. Note: S. 543, 106th Congress, 1st session. Introduced by Sen. Snowe on March 4, 1999. Referred to the Committee on Health, Education, Labor, and Pensions.

United States. Congress. Senate. A bill to prohibit discrimination on the basis of genetic information with respect to health insurance and employment. Washington, DC: U.S. G.P.O., 2002. 45 p. [Online]. Accessed: http://frwebgate.access.gpo.gov/cgi-bin/getdoc.cgi? dbname=107_cong_bills&docid= f:s1995is.txt.pdf [2007 March 8]. NRCBL: 15.1; 8.4; 9.3.1. SC: le. Identifiers: Genetic Information Nondiscrimination Act of 2002. Note: S. 1995, 107th Congress, 2nd session. Introduced by Sen. Snowe on March 6, 2002. Referred to the Committee on Health, Education, Labor and Pensions.

United States. Congress. Senate. A bill to prohibit discrimination on the basis of genetic information with respect to health insurance and employment. Washington, DC: U.S. G.P.O., 2001. 73 p. [Online]. Accessed: http://frwebgate.access.gpo.gov/cgi-bin/getdoc.cgi? dbname=107_cong_bills&docid= f:s318is.txt. pdf [2007 March 8]. NRCBL: 15.1; 8.4; 9.3.1. SC: le. Identifiers: Genetic Nondiscrimination in Health Insurance and Employment Act. Note: S. 318, 107th Congress, 1st session. Introduced by Sen. Daschle on February 13, 2001. Referred to the Committee on Health, Education, Labor, and Pensions.

United States. Congress. Senate. A bill to prohibit health insurance and employment discrimination against individuals and their family members on the basis of predictive genetic information or genetic services. Washington, DC: U.S.G.P.O., 1999. 70 p. [Online]. Accessed: http://frwebgate.access.gpo.gov/cgi-bin/getdoc.cgi? dbname=106_cong_bills&docid= f:s1322is.txt.pdf [2007 March 8]. NRCBL: 15.1; 8.4; 9.3.1. SC: le. Identifiers: Genetic Nondiscrimination in Health Insurance and Employment Act of 1999. Note: S. 1322, 106th Congress, 1st session. Introduced by Sen. Daschle on July 1, 1999. Referred to the Committee on Health, Education, Labor, and Pensions.

United States. Congress. Senate. A bill to protect the genetic privacy of individuals, and for other purposes. Washington, DC: U.S. G.P.O., 1996. 42 p. [Online]. Accessed: http://frwebgate.access.gpo.gov/cgi-bin/getdoc.cgi? dbname=104_cong_bills&docid= f:s1898is.txt.pdf [2007

NRCBL: National Reference Center for Bioethics Literature Classification Scheme   See inside front cover for terms.

219

March 8]. NRCBL: 15.1; 8.4. SC: le. Identifiers: Genetic Confidentiality and Nondiscrimination Act of 1996. Note: S. 1898, 104th Congress, 2nd session. Introduced by Sen. Domenici on June 24, 1996. Referred to the Committee on Labor and Human Resources.

United States. Congress. Senate. An act to prohibit discrimination on the basis of genetic information with respect to health insurance and employment. Washington, DC: U.S. G.P.O., 2003. 86 p. [Online]. Accessed: http://frwebgate.access.gpo.gov/cgi-bin/useftp.cgi?IPaddress=162.140.64.21&filename=s1053es.pdf&directory=/disk2/wais/data/108_cong_bills [2006 November 27]. NRCBL: 15.3; 15.1; 8.4; 9.3.1. SC: le. Identifiers: Genetic Information Nondiscrimination Act of 2003 (Engrossed as Agreed to or Passed by Senate). Note: S. 1053, 108th Congress, 1st session. Passed the Senate October 14, 2003.

United States. Congress. Senate. A bill to prohibit discrimination on the basis of genetic information with respect to health insurance and employment. Washington, DC: U.S. G.P.O., 2005. 85 p. [Online]. Accessed: http://frwebgate.access.gpo.gov/cgi-bin/useftp.cgi?IPaddress=162.140.64.21&filename=s306es.pdf&directory=/diskb/wais/data/109_cong_bills. NRCBL: 15.3; 8.4. SC: le. Identifiers: Genetic Information Nondiscrimination Act of 2005.

Verkerk, Marian. A feminist care-ethics approach to genetics. *In:* Ashcroft, Richard; Lucassen, Anneke; Parker, Michael; Verkerk, Marian; Widderhoven, Guy, eds. Case Analysis in Clinical Ethics. New York: Cambridge University Press; 2005: 133-148. NRCBL: 15.3; 8.4; 10; 4.1.1. SC: an.

Virginia. *Laws, statutes, etc.* An act to amend an reenact section 38.2-613 of the Code of Virginia and to amend the Code of Virginia by adding a section numbered 38.2-508.4 relating to insurance; genetic information privacy[Approved 6 April 1996; Expires 1 July 1998]. Virginia: Senate Bill 335; Acts of Assembly, Chapter 704. [Online]. 5 p. Accessed http://leg1.state.va.us/cgi-bin/legp504.exe?961+ful+CHAP0704 [2007 March 9]. NRCBL: 15.1; 8.4. SC: le.

Walther, J.-U. Genetische Beratung und ihre Normen. Ethische Überlegungen [Genetic counselling in a sociocultural framework. Ethical considerations]. *Monatsschrift Kinderheilkunde* 2004; 152: 1217-1224. NRCBL: 15.2; 1.1; 2.1; 8.4. SC: cs.

Webster, Dianne. Storage and use of residual dried blood spots. *Southeast Asian Journal of Tropical Medicine and Public Health* 2003; 34(Supplement 3): 49-51. NRCBL: 15.3; 9.5.7; 8.3.2; 8.4. Identifiers: Australia; New Zealand.

Weeden, Jeffrey Lawrence. Genetic liberty, genetic property: protecting genetic information. *Ave Maria Law Re-*

view 2006 Summer; 4(2): 611-664. NRCBL: 15.8; 15.10; 8.4. SC: le.

Weisbrot, David. Mad science or modern miracles? *Reform* 2001 Spring; 79: 5-9. NRCBL: 15.3; 8.4; 1.3.12. SC: le. Identifiers: Protection of Human Genetic Information; Australian Law Reform Commission [ALRC]; Australian Health Ethics Committee [AHEC].

Weldon, Sue; Levitt, Mairi. "Public databases and privat(ized) property?": a UK study of public perceptions of privacy in relation to population based human genetic databases. *In:* Árnason, Gardar; Nordal, Salvör; Árnason, Vilhjálmur, eds. Blood and Data: Ethical, Legal and Social Aspects of Human Genetic Databases. Reykjavík: University of Iceland Press; 2004: 181-186. NRCBL: 15.1; 1.3.12; 8.4. SC: em.

Widdershoven, Guy. Interpretation and dialogue in hermeneutic ethics. *In:* Ashcroft, Richard; Lucassen, Anneke; Parker, Michael; Verkerk, Marian; Widderhoven, Guy, eds. Case Analysis in Clinical Ethics. New York: Cambridge University Press; 2005: 57-75. NRCBL: 15.3; 8.4; 1.1. SC: an.

Withers, Rob. Reading the genes. *In:* Ashcroft, Richard; Lucassen, Anneke; Parker, Michael; Verkerk, Marian; Widderhoven, Guy, eds. Case Analysis in Clinical Ethics. New York: Cambridge University Press; 2005: 95-114. NRCBL: 15.3; 8.4. SC: an.

Worrall, Bradford B.; Chen, Donna T.; Brown, Robert D., Jr.; Brott, Thomas G.; Meschia, James F. A survey of the SWISS researchers on the impact of sibling privacy protections on pedigree recruitment. *Neuroepidemiology* 2005; 25(1): 32-41. NRCBL: 15.1; 8.4; 18.2; 18.3. SC: em. Identifiers: Siblings With Ischemic Stroke Study.

Wyoming. *Laws, statutes, etc.* An act relating to group health insurance; limiting the use of genetic testing results by group insurers as specified; and providing for an effective date [Approved: 2003 March 3]. Wyoming: State Legislature, 2003. 3 p. [Online]. Accessed: http://legisweb.state.wy.us/2003/enroll/hb0024.pdf [2007 March 9]. NRCBL: 15.1; 8.4. SC: le. Note: House Bill No. 24, 57th Legislature, 2003 general session. Introduced by Reps. Tipton and Meuli on January 15, 2003. Approved March 3, 2003.

Yanes, Pedro. Personal insurance and genetic information (I) = Seguros de personas e información genética (I). *Law and the Human Genome = Revista de Derecho y Genoma Humano* 1994 July-December; (1): 185-194. NRCBL: 15.1; 8.4. SC: le.

Zhang, Bao-Hong. The completion of the human genome nucleotide sequence raises privacy concerns [letter]. *Bulletin of the World Health Organization* 2000; 78(11): 1373. NRCBL: 15.1; 8.4.

GENETIC RESEARCH
See also GENOME MAPPING; RECOMBINANT DNA RESEARCH

Human Genome Research Act (Latvia, 2003). *In:* Sándor, Judit, ed. Society and Genetic Information: Codes and Laws in the Genetic Era. Budapest, Hungary; New York: CEU Press; 2003: 375-388. NRCBL: 15.1. SC: le.

Achter, Paul; Parrott, Roxanne; Silk, Kami. African Americans' opinions about human-genetics research. *Politics and the Life Sciences* 2004 March; 23(1): 60-66. NRCBL: 15.1; 18.5.1. SC: em.

American Society of Human Genetics [ASHG]. Should family members about whom you collect only medical history information for your research be considered 'human subjects'? [policy statement]. Bethesda, MD: American Society of Human Genetics, 2000 March: 3 p. [Online]. Accessed: http://www.ashg.org/genetics/ashg/pubs/policy/pol-38.htm [2006 July 25]. NRCBL: 15.1; 18.3; 18.2; 8.4.

American Society of Human Genetics [ASHG]. Ad Hoc Committee on Consumer Issues. Genetic lay advocacy groups: significant others in the conduct of human genetics research. Committee Report. Bethesda, MD: American Society of Human Genetics, 2001 October 18. 9 p. [Online]. Accessed: http://genetics.faseb.org/genetics/ashg/pubs/policy/pol_46.pdf [2006 July 24]. NRCBL: 15.1; 18.2; 18.6. Note: Revised Version. The original document was prepared in October 1999. Revised versions were issued November 10, 2000 and October 18, 2001.

Appel, Jacob M. The monster's laws: a legal history of chimera research. *GeneWatch* 2006 March-April; 19(2): 12-16. NRCBL: 15.1; 22.1; 18.1.

Auray-Blais, Christiane; Patenaude Johane. A biobank management model applicable to biomedical research. *BMC Medical Ethics [Online].* 2006; 7(4): 9 p. Accessed: http://www.biomedcentral.com/bmcmedethics/ [15 June 2006]. NRCBL: 15.1; 18.2; 8.4.

Abstract: BACKGROUND : The work of Research Ethics Boards (REBs), especially when involving genetics research and biobanks, has become more challenging with the growth of biotechnology and biomedical research. Some REBs have even rejected research projects where the use of a biobank with coded samples was an integral part of the study, the greatest fear being the lack of participant protection and uncontrolled use of biological samples or related genetic data. The risks of discrimination and stigmatization are a recurrent issue. In light of the increasing interest in biomedical research and the resulting benefits to the health of participants, it is imperative that practical solutions be found to the problems associated with the management of biobanks: namely, protecting the integrity of the research participants, as well as guaranteeing the security and confidentiality of the participant's information. METHODS : We aimed to devise a practical and efficient model for the management of biobanks in biomedical research where a medical archivist plays the pivotal role as a data-protection officer. The model had to reduce the burden placed on REBs responsible for the evaluation of genetics projects and, at the same time, maximize the protection of research participants. RESULTS : The proposed model includes the following: 1) a means of protecting the information in biobanks, 2) offers ways to provide follow-up information requested about the participants, 3) protects the participant's confidentiality and 4) adequately deals with the ethical issues at stake in biobanking. CONCLUSION : Until a governmental governance body is established in Quebec to guarantee the protection of research participants and establish harmonized guidelines for the management of biobanks in medical research, it is definitely up to REBs to find solutions that the present lack of guidelines poses. The model presented in this article offers a practical solution on a day-to-day basis for REBs, as well as researchers by promoting an archivist to a pivotal role in the process. It assures protection of all participants who altruistically donate their samples to generate and improve knowledge for better diagnosis and medical treatment.

Bates, Benjamin R.; Lynch, John A.; Bevan, Jennifer L.; Condit, Celeste M. Warranted concerns, warranted outlooks: a focus group study of public understandings of genetic research. *Social Science and Medicine* 2005 January; 60(2): 331-344. NRCBL: 15.1; 5.3; 15.7; 7.1. SC: em.

Beskow, Laura M. Considering the nature of individual research results. *American Journal of Bioethics* 2006 November-December; 6(6): 38-40; author reply W10-W12. NRCBL: 15.1; 18.2; 8.1; 8.2. Comments: Vardit Ravitsky and Benjamin S. Wilfond. Disclosing individual genetic results to research participants. American Journal of Bioethics 2006 November-December; 6(6): 8-17.

Boggio, Andrea. Charitable trusts and human research genetic databases: the way forward? *Genetics, Society, and Policy* 2005 August; 1(2): 41-49. NRCBL: 15.1; 15.3; 1.3.12; 8.4.

Burke, Wylie; Diekema, Douglas S. Ethical issues arising from the participation of children in genetic research. *Journal of Pediatrics* 2006 July; 149(1, Supplement): S34-S38. NRCBL: 15.1; 18.5.2; 8.4; 15.6; 1.3.12.

Burke, Wylie; Khoury, Muin J.; Stewart, Alison; Zimmern, Ronald L. The path from genome-based research to population health: development of an international public health genomics network. *Genetics in Medicine* 2006 July; 8(7): 451-458. NRCBL: 15.1; 15.10; 21.1; 9.1.

Chalmers, D.; Otlowski, M.; Nicol, D.; Skene, Loane. Legal and ethical implications of human genetic research: Australian perspectives = Implicaciones legales y éticas de la investigación genética humana: perspectivas australianas. *Law and the Human Genome Review = Revista de Derecho y Genoma Humano* 1995 July-December; (3): 211-220. NRCBL: 15.1; 15.4; 15.3; 15.10; 15.8. SC: le.

Coleman, Carl H.; Menikoff, Jerry A.; Goldner, Jesse A.; Dubler, Nancy Neveloff. Genetics research. *In their:* The Ethics and Regulation of Research with Human Subjects: Teacher's Manual. Newark, NJ: LexisNexis, 2005: 209-219. NRCBL: 15.1.

NRCBL: National Reference Center for Bioethics Literature Classification Scheme   See inside front cover for terms.

221

Coleman, Carl H.; Menikoff, Jerry A.; Goldner, Jesse A.; Dubler, Nancy Neveloff. Genetics research. *In their:* The Ethics and Regulation of Research with Human Subjects. Newark, NJ: LexisNexis, 2005: 697-746. NRCBL: 15.1.

Cooper, Zachary N.; Nelson, Robert M.; Ross, Lainie F. Informed consent for genetic research involving pleiotropic genes: an empirical study of ApoE research. *IRB: Ethics and Human Research* 2006 September-October; 28(5): 1-11. NRCBL: 15.1; 18.3; 18.2. SC: em. Identifiers: apolipoprotein E.

Council of Europe. Committee of Ministers. Recommendation Rec(2006)4 of the Committee of Ministers to member states on research on biological materials of human origin. *Genetics in Medicine* 2006 September; 13(3): 302-310. NRCBL: 15.1; 1.3.12; 18.6; 18.2; 18.3. SC: le.

Crolla, Domenic A. Reflections on the legal, social, and ethical implications of pharmacogenomic research. *Jurimetrics* 2006 Spring; 46(3): 239-248. NRCBL: 15.1; 9.7; 8.4; 15.10; 1.3.12; 13.1; 21.1. SC: le.

de Bouvet, Armelle; Deschamps, Claude; Boitte, Pierre; Boury, Dominique. Bioinformation: the philosophical and ethical issues at stake in a new modality of research practices. *Medicine, Health Care and Philosophy* 2006; 9(2): 201-209. NRCBL: 15.1; 1.1. SC: an.
Abstract: This article deals with the integration of ethical reflection into the research practices of the project at the Lille Nord-Pas-de-Calais genopole: "Multifactorial genetic pathologies and therapeutic innovations". The general hypothesis of this text is that changes in research practices in biology (mainly through the use of bioinformatics) imply changes in medical practices, which require critical reflection. This hypothesis could be broken down into three sub-hypotheses: (1)Research in biology is undergoing a complete transformation; (2) Research in biology is a cultural practice, which cannot be reduced to a simple cognitive action; (3) Research in biology is a techno-scientific practice. As for the method, the aim of our research at the Medical Ethics Centre is to elucidate the philosophical and ethical range of biomedical practices. This work entails a double task for reflection. On the one hand, from the revelation of ethical tensions present in these practices, we have to think about what is at stake in these practices, and more broadly in society. On the other hand, we have to analyse the conditions enabling the actors to assume the significance of ethical reflection in their practices. The method set up to undertake this double task could be qualified as "narrative hermeneutics", as its aim is to attempt to interpret the stakes in practices from proximity with these practices and from what their actors have to say about them. The text then goes on to analyse more specifically the emergence and place of bioinformatics in present-day biomedical research.

de Melo-Martín, Inmaculada. Genetic research and technology. *In:* Mitcham, Carl, ed. Encyclopedia of Science, Technology, and Ethics. Farmington Hills, MI: Thomson/Gale, 2005: 841-849. NRCBL: 15.1; 2.2; 1.3.11.

DeCew, Judith Wagner. Privacy and policy for genetic research. *Ethics and Information Technology* 2004; 6(1): 5-14. NRCBL: 15.1; 18.1; 8.4.

DeCew, Judith Wagner. Privacy and policy for genetic research. *In:* Tavani, Herman T., ed. Ethics, Computing, and Genomics. Sudbury, MA: Jones and Bartlett; 2006: 121-135. NRCBL: 15.1; 8.4.

Dressler, Lynn G.; Juengst, Eric T. Thresholds and boundaries in the disclosure of individual genetic research results. *American Journal of Bioethics* 2006 November-December; 6(6): 18-20; author reply W10-W13. NRCBL: 15.1; 18.2; 1.3.9; 8.1. Comments: Vardit Ravitsky and Benjamin S. Wilfond. Disclosing individual genetic results to research participants. American Journal of Bioethics 2006 November-December; 6(6): 8-17.

Duguet, A.M. Genetic research: between freedom in research and the patient's rights: contribution of the Declaration of Helsinki [editorial]. *European Journal of Health Law* 2001 September; 8(3): 203-206. NRCBL: 15.1; 8.4; 18.3; 15.3. SC: le.

Elger, Bernice S.; Caplan, Arthur L. Consent and anonymization in research involving biobanks. *EMBO Reports* 2006 July; 7(7): 661-666. NRCBL: 15.1; 1.3.12; 18.2; 18.3. SC: an; rv. Identifiers: Office of Human Research Protections.

Eriksson, Stefan; Helgesson, Gert. Potential harms, anonymization, and the right to withdraw consent to biobank research. *European Journal of Human Genetics* 2005 September; 13(9): 1071-1076. NRCBL: 15.1; 1.3.12; 18.2. Identifiers: Sweden.

Fernandez, Conrad V.; Weijer, Charles. Obligations in offering to disclose genetic research results. *American Journal of Bioethics* 2006 November-December; 6(6): 44-46. NRCBL: 15.1; 18.2; 8.2. Comments: Vardit Ravitsky and Benjamin S. Wilfond. Disclosing individual genetic results to research participants. American Journal of Bioethics 2006 November-December; 6(6): 8-17.

Gatensby, Anne. Privacy, property, and social relations in bioinformatics research. *In:* Árnason, Gardar; Nordal, Salvör; Árnason, Vilhjálmur, eds. Blood and Data: Ethical, Legal and Social Aspects of Human Genetic Databases. Reykjavík: University of Iceland Press; 2004: 28-27. NRCBL: 15.1; 8.4; 15.8.

German Society of Human Genetics [GfH]. Commission for Standpoints and Ethical Questions. DNA banking and personal data in biomedical research: technical, social, and ethical questions. *Medizinischegenetik* 2004; 16: 347-350. [Online]. Accessed: http://www.medgenetik.de/sonderdruck/en/DNA%20Banking_engl_060605.pdf [2006 July 31]. NRCBL: 15.1; 1.3.12; 18.1; 18.3; 8.3.1; 8.4.

Gillam, L.; Poulakis, Z.; Tobin, S.; Wake, M. Enhancing the ethical conduct of genetic research: investigating views of parents on including their healthy children in a study on mild hearing loss. *Journal of Medical Ethics* 2006 September; 32(9): 537-541. NRCBL: 15.1; 15.3; 18.3; 18.5.2.

Abstract: Clinical genetic research is often regarded as more ethically problematic than other forms of research, and in some countries is subject to specific regulation, requiring researchers to follow specialised guidelines. In this paper, an approach to enhancing the ethical conduct of genetic research is proposed, which is believed to be more effective than simply attempting to follow general guidelines. The potential concerns, likely areas of misunderstanding and negative reactions of the participant group are systematically investigated before starting a study on genetics. This would constitute, in effect, an ethical pilot study, similar to a feasibility pilot study to test equipment, procedures and logistics. The findings of the ethical pilot study would be used to help in designing ethically important aspects of research protocol, such as recruitment procedures, written and other information for potential participants, informed consent processes and reporting of results including ambiguous or uncertain results.

Glasa, Jozef. Ethics of pharmacogenetic and pharmacogenomic research: problems and perspectives. *In his:* Ethics of Human Genetics: Challenges of the (Post) Genomic Era. Bratislava, Slovak Republic: Charis [and] IMEB Foundation; 2002: 153-169. NRCBL: 15.1; 9.7; 18.2.

Goodenough, Trudy; Williamson, Emma; Kent, Julie; Ashcroft, Richard. Ethical protection in research: including children in the debate. *In:* Smyth, Marie; Williamson, Emma, eds. Researchers and Their 'Subjects': Ethics, Power, Knowledge and Consent. Bristol, UK: Policy Press; 2004: 55-72. NRCBL: 15.1; 18.5.2.

Halbert, Chanita Hughes; Gandy, Oscar H., Jr.; Collier, Aliya; Shaker, Lee. Intentions to participate in genetics research among African American smokers. *Cancer Epidemiology, Biomarkers and Prevention* 2006 January; 15(1): 150-153. NRCBL: 15.1; 18.3; 15.3; 18.5.1. SC: em.

Harmon, Shawn H.E. The recommendation on research on biological materials of human origin: another brick in the wall. *European Journal of Health Law* 2006 September; 13(3): 293-301. NRCBL: 15.1; 1.3.12; 18.6; 18.2; 18.3. SC: le.

Hjörleifsson, Stefán; Schei, Edvin. Scientific rationality, uncertainty and the governance of human genetics: an interview study with researchers at deCODE genetics. *European Journal of Human Genetics: EJHG* 2006 July; 14(7): 802-808. NRCBL: 15.1; 1.3.12; 18.6. SC: em. Identifiers: Iceland.

Hoedemaekers, Rogeer; Gordijn, Bert; Hekster, Y.; van Agt, F.;. The complexities of ethical evaluation of genomics research. *HEC (Healthcare Ethics Committee) Forum* 2006 March; 18(1): 18-36. NRCBL: 15.1; 5.2; 18.3; 18.2; 18.6.

Hoeyer, Klaus. Studying ethics as policy: the naming and framing of moral problems in genetic research. *Current Anthropology* 2005 December; 46(supplement 5): S71-S90. NRCBL: 15.1; 1.3.12; 18.1. Identifiers: Sweden.

Jenkins, Jean F.; Lea, Dale Halsey. My hopes and fears: how I feel about genetic research. *In their:* Nursing Care in the Genomic Era: A Case-Based Approach. Sudbury, MA: Jones and Bartlett Publishers, 2005: 287-316. NRCBL: 15.1; 8.4; 9.7; 18.3.

Kanellopoulou, Nadja K. Gift or duty? A normative discussion for participation in human genetic databases research. *In:* Árnason, Gardar; Nordal, Salvör; Árnason, Vilhjálmur, eds. Blood and Data: Ethical, Legal and Social Aspects of Human Genetic Databases. Reykjavík: University of Iceland Press; 2004: 95-99. NRCBL: 15.1; 1.3.12.

Kristinsson, Sigurdur. Databases and informed consent: can broad consent legitimate research? *In:* Árnason, Gardar; Nordal, Salvör; Árnason, Vilhjálmur, eds. Blood and Data: Ethical, Legal and Social Aspects of Human Genetic Databases. Reykjavík: University of Iceland Press; 2004: 111-119. NRCBL: 15.1; 1.3.12; 18.3.

Laurie, Graeme; Hunter, Kathryn G. Benefit-sharing and public trust in genetic research. *In:* Árnason, Gardar; Nordal, Salvör; Árnason, Vilhjálmur, eds. Blood and Data: Ethical, Legal and Social Aspects of Human Genetic Databases. Reykjavík: University of Iceland Press; 2004: 323-331. NRCBL: 15.1; 1.1; 1.3.12.

Manolio, Teri A. Taking our obligations to research participants seriously: disclosing individual results of genetic research. *American Journal of Bioethics* 2006 November-December; 6(6): 32-34; author reply W10-W12. NRCBL: 15.1; 18.2; 8.1; 15.2. Comments: Vardit Ravitsky and Benjamin S. Wilfond. Disclosing individual genetic results to research participants. American Journal of Bioethics 2006 November-December; 6(6): 8-17.

Marshall, Patricia A.; Adebamowo, Clement A.; Adeyemo, Adebowale A.; Ogundiran, Temidayo O.; Vekich, Mirjana; Strenski, Teri; Zhou, Jie; Prewitt, Elaine; Cooper, Richard S.; Rotimi, Charles N. Voluntary participation and informed consent to international genetic research. *American Journal of Public Health* 2006 November; 96(11): 1989-1995. NRCBL: 15.1; 9.5.4; 18.5.9; 18.3. SC: em.

Abstract: OBJECTIVES: We compared voluntary participation and comprehension of informed consent among individuals of African ancestry enrolled in similarly designed genetic studies of hypertension in the United States and Nigeria. METHODS: Survey questionnaires were used to evaluate factors associated with voluntariness (the number of people volunteering) and understanding of the study's genetic purpose. A total of 655 individuals (United States: 348; Nigeria: 307) were interviewed after participation in the genetic studies. RESULTS: Most US respondents (99%), compared with 72% of Nigerian respondents, reported being told the study purpose. Fewer than half of the respondents at both sites reported that the study purpose was to learn about genetic inheritance of hypertension. Most respondents indicated that their participation was voluntary. In the United States, 97% reported that they could withdraw, compared with 67% in Nigeria. In Nigeria, nearly half the married women reported asking permission from husbands to enroll in the hypertension study; no respondents sought permission from

NRCBL: National Reference Center for Bioethics Literature Classification Scheme   See inside front cover for terms.

223

local elders to participate in the study. CONCLUSIONS: Our findings highlight the need for more effective approaches and interventions to improve comprehension of consent for genetic research among ethnically and linguistically diverse populations in all settings.

Marturano, Antonio. Molecular biologists as hackers of human data: rethinking intellectual property rights for bioinformatics research. *In:* Tavani, Herman T., ed. Ethics, Computing, and Genomics. Sudbury, MA: Jones and Bartlett; 2006: 235-245. NRCBL: 15.1; 1.3.9.

Meltzer, Leslie A. Undesirable implications of disclosing individual genetic results to research participants. *American Journal of Bioethics* 2006 November-December; 6(6): 28-30; author reply W10-W12. NRCBL: 15.1; 18.2; 1.1. Comments: Vardit Ravitsky and Benjamin S. Wilfond. Disclosing individual genetic results to research participants. American Journal of Bioethics 2006 November-December; 6(6): 8-17.

Nilstun, Tore; Hermerén, Göran. Human tissue samples and ethics — attitudes of the general public in Sweden to biobank research. *Medicine, Health Care and Philosophy* 2006; 9(1): 81-86. NRCBL: 15.1; 1.3.12; 19.5. SC: em.
Abstract: PURPOSE: To survey the attitudes of the general public in Sweden to biobank research and to discuss the findings in the light of some well-known ethical principles. METHODS: A questionnaire was used to survey the opinions of the general public in Sweden, and an ethical analysis (using the principles of autonomy, non-maleficence, beneficence and justice) was performed to discuss the possible conditions of such research. FINDINGS: Between 3 and 9% answered that they did not want their samples to be collected and stored in a biobank. Many respondents required information about the purpose of the research and wanted to be able to consent or refuse. About one third of the respondents said they would have answered differently if financial gain was involved and those who commented indicated a more negative attitude. The principle of autonomy maintains that the right to self-determination should be respected, and the principles of non-maleficence and beneficence that the probable harms and benefits resulting from a particular project by using samples from a biobank should be balanced. The general public disagree about how these principles are to be balanced. INTERPRETATION: In the light of the findings different interpretations of the situation as well as possible alternatives are discussed in this paper.

Nõmper, Ants. Estonian Human Research Act and its implementation. *In:* Glasa, J., ed. Ethics of Human Genetics: Challenges of the (Post) Genomic Era. Bratislava, Slovak Republic: Charis [and] IMEB Foundation; 2002: 99-104. NRCBL: 15.1. SC: le.

Nõmper, Ants. What is wrong with using anonymized data and tissue for research purposes? *In:* Árnason, Gardar; Nordal, Salvör; Árnason, Vilhjálmur, eds. Blood and Data: Ethical, Legal and Social Aspects of Human Genetic Databases. Reykjavík: University of Iceland Press; 2004: 121-126. NRCBL: 15.1; 1.3.9; 8.4; 18.1.

O'Rourke, Dennis H.; Hayes, M. Geoffrey; Carlyle, Shawn. The consent process and a DNA research: contrasting approaches in North America. *In:* Turner, Trudy R.

ed. Biological Anthropology and Ethics: From Repatriation to Genetic Identity. Albany, NY: State University of New York Press; 2005: 231-240. NRCBL: 15.1; 18.3; 18.5.9.

Onay, Ozan. The true ramifications of genetic criminality research for free will in the criminal justice system. *Genomics, Society and Policy* 2006 May; 2(1): 80-91. NRCBL: 15.1; 1.3.5; 15.6.
Abstract: There is an explicit belief – evident in jurisprudential literature – that developments in behavioural genetics in the very near future will necessitate a dramatic revolution in common law criminal justice systems. This paper considers what is truly shown by behavioural genetics in relation to free will, and the effect of such conclusions on criminal justice systems which rely upon the concept of free will as a foundation element. This paper ultimately concludes that it is unlikely that criminal justice systems will be shaken – or indeed substantially influenced – by past or future discoveries in genetics. Three major arguments are employed: (1) that theses connecting genetic traits with criminal free will exhibit a naïve conception of partial genetic determinism; (2) that theses connecting genetic traits with criminal free will have been unduly motivated by discoveries in behavioural genetics which are disreputable or misleading; and (3) that even should an unexpected discovery be made exhibiting a strong causal connection between genetics and criminal behaviour, this will not prove to be an intolerable novelty for any criminal justice system which otherwise assumes free will to exist.

Ormond, Kelly E. Disclosing genetic research results: examples from practice. *American Journal of Bioethics* 2006 November-December; 6(6): 30-32; author reply W10-W12. NRCBL: 15.1; 15.3; 18.2. Comments: Vardit Ravitsky and Benjamin S. Wilfond. Disclosing individual genetic results to research participants. American Journal of Bioethics 2006 November-December; 6(6): 8-17.

Ossorio, Pilar N. Letting the gene out of the bottle: a comment on returning individual research results to participants. *American Journal of Bioethics* 2006 November-December; 6(6): 24-25; author reply W10-W12. NRCBL: 15.1; 18.2; 8.4; 8.1. Comments: Vardit Ravitsky and Benjamin S. Wilfond. Disclosing individual genetic results to research participants. American Journal of Bioethics 2006 November-December; 6(6): 8-17.

Pardo, Juan Bautista. Genetic research in the service of mankind: reflections of a lawyer = La investigación genética al servicio del hombre: reflexiones de un jurista. *Law and the Human Genome = Revista de Derecho y Genoma Humano* 1994 July-December; (1): 25-27. NRCBL: 15.1. SC: le.

Parker, Lisa S.; Broyles, Lauren Matukaitis. Ethical issues in the conduct of genetic research. *In:* Iltis, Ana Smith, ed. Research Ethics. New York: Routledge, 2006: 32-60. NRCBL: 15.1.

Pelias, Mary Kay. Research in human genetics: the tension between doing no harm and personal autonomy. *Clinical Genetics* 2005 January; 67(1): 1-5. NRCBL: 15.1; 18.2; 18.3; 18.6; 1.1. SC: rv.

Ravitsky, Vardit; Wilfond, Benjamin S. Disclosing individual genetic results to research participants. *American Journal of Bioethics* 2006 November-December; 6(6): 8-17. NRCBL: 15.1; 18.2; 8.1; 18.3; 8.4.

Renegar, Gaile; Webster, Christopher J.; Stuerzebecher, Steffen; Harty, Lea; Ide, Susan E.; Balkite, Beth; Rogalski- Salter, Taryn A.; Cohen, Nadine; Spear, Brian B.; Barnes, Diane M.; Brazell, Celia. Returning genetic research results to individuals: points-to-consider. *Bioethics* 2006 February; 20(1): 24-36. NRCBL: 15.1; 8.2; 9.7.

Abstract: This paper is intended to stimulate debate amongst stakeholders in the international research community on the topic of returning individual genetic research results to study participants. Pharmacogenetics and disease genetics studies are becoming increasingly prevalent, leading to a growing body of information on genetic associations for drug responsiveness and disease susceptibility with the potential to improve health care. Much of these data are presently characterized as exploratory (non-validated or hypothesis-generating). There is, however, a trend for research participants to be permitted access to their personal data if they so choose. Researchers, sponsors, patient advocacy groups, ethics committees and regulatory authorities are consequently confronting the issue of whether, and how, study participants might receive their individual results. Noted international ethico-legal guidelines and public policy positions in Europe and the United States are reviewed for background. The authors offer 'Points-to-Consider' regarding returning results in the context of drug development trials based on their knowledge and experience. Theses considerations include: the clinical relevance of data, laboratory qualifications, informed consent procedures, confidentiality of medical information and the competency of persons providing results to participants. The discussion is framed as a benefit-to-risk assessment to balance the potential positive versus negative consequences to participants, while maintaining the integrity and feasibility of conducting genetic research studies.

Rice, James A. Taking ourselves seriously: the relevance of Dworkinian principlism in genetic research. *Journal of Philosophy, Science and Law* 2006 March 20; 6: 14 p. NRCBL: 15.1; 1.1. SC: an; le.

Sankar, Pamela. Hasty generalisation and exaggerated certainties: reporting genetic findings in health disparities research. *New Genetics and Society* 2006 December; 25(3): 249-264. NRCBL: 15.1; 9.5.4.

Schüklenk, Udo; Kleinsmidt, Anita. North-south benefit sharing arrangements in bioprospecting and genetic research: a critical ethical and legal analysis. *Developing World Bioethics* 2006 December; 6(3): 122-134. NRCBL: 15.1; 9.4; 21.1. SC: an.

Abstract: Most pharmaceutical research carried out today is focused on the treatment and management of the lifestyle diseases of the developed world. Diseases that affect mainly poor people are neglected in research advancements in treatment because they cannot generate large financial returns on research and development costs. Benefit sharing arrangements for the use of indigenous resources and genetic research could only marginally address this gap in research and development in diseases that affect the poor. Benefit sharing as a strategy is conceptually problematic, even if one, as we do, agrees that impoverished indigenous communities should not be exploited and that they should be assisted in improving their living conditions. The accepted concept of intellectual property protection envisages clearly defined originators and owners of knowledge, whereas the concept of community membership is fluid and indigenous knowledge is, by its very nature, open, with the originator(s) lost in the mists of time. The delineation of 'community' presents serious conceptual and practical difficulties as few communities form discrete, easily discernable groups, and most have problematic leadership structures. Benefit sharing is no substitute for governments' responsibility to uplift impoverished communities. Benefit sharing arrangements may be fraught with difficulties but considerations of respect and equity demand that prior informed consent and consultation around commercialisation of knowledge take place with the source community and their government.

Sethe, Sebastian. Cell line research with UK Biobank: why the new British biobank is not just another population genetic database. *In:* Árnason, Gardar; Nordal, Salvör; Árnason, Vilhjálmur, eds. Blood and Data: Ethical, Legal and Social Aspects of Human Genetic Databases. Reykjavík: University of Iceland Press; 2004: 313-319. NRCBL: 15.1; 1.3.12.

Sharp, Richard R.; Foster, Morris W. Clinical utility and full disclosure of genetic results to research participants. *American Journal of Bioethics* 2006 November-December; 6(6): 42-44. NRCBL: 15.1; 18.2; 8.2. Comments: Vardit Ravitsky and Benjamin S. Wilfond. Disclosing individual genetic results to research participants. American Journal of Bioethics 2006 November-December; 6(6): 8-17.

Sild, Tarmo; Mullari, Tambet. Population based genetic research: Estonian answer to the legal challenge. *European Journal of Health Law* 2001 December; 8(4): 363-371. NRCBL: 15.1; 1.3.12; 13.1; 19.1; 8.4. SC: le.

Solbakk, Jan Helge; Holm, Søren; Lobato de Faria, Paula; Harris, Jennifer; Cambon-Thomsen, Anne; Halvorsen, Marit; Stoltenberg, Camilla; Strand, Roger; Hofmann, Bjørn; Skrikerud, Anne Maria; Karlsen, Jan Reinert. Mapping the language of research-biobanks and health registries: from traditional biobanking to research biobanking. *In:* Árnason, Gardar; Nordal, Salvör; Árnason, Vilhjálmur, eds. Blood and Data: Ethical, Legal and Social Aspects of Human Genetic Databases. Reykjavík: University of Iceland Press; 2004: 299-306. NRCBL: 15.1; 1.3.12; 19.5.

Tano, Mervyn L. Interrelationships among native peoples, genetic research, and the landscape: need for further research into ethical, legal, and social issues. *Journal of Law, Medicine and Ethics* 2006 Summer; 34(2): 301-309. NRCBL: 15.1; 1.3.5; 16.1.

Tavani, Herman T. Genomic research and data-mining technology: implications for personal privacy and informed consent. *Ethics and Information Technology* 2004; 6(1): 15-28. NRCBL: 15.1; 18.3; 1.3.12; 8.4.

Wade, Christopher H.; Kalfoglou, Andrea L. When do genetic researchers have a duty to recontact study partici-

---

NRCBL: National Reference Center for Bioethics Literature Classification Scheme   See inside front cover for terms.

225

pants? *American Journal of Bioethics* 2006 November-December; 6(6): 26-27; author reply W10-W12. NRCBL: 15.1; 15.3; 8.1; 18.2. Comments: Vardit Ravitsky and Benjamin S. Wilfond. Disclosing individual genetic results to research participants. American Journal of Bioethics 2006 November-December; 6(6): 8-17.

Williams, Sloan R. A case study of ethical issues in genetic research: the Sally Hemings-Thomas Jefferson story. *In:* Turner, Trudy R. ed. Biological Anthropology and Ethics: From Repatriation to Genetic Identity. Albany, NY: State University of New York Press; 2005: 185-208. NRCBL: 15.1; 14.1.

Worrall, Bradford B.; Chen, Donna T.; Brown, Robert D., Jr.; Brott, Thomas G.; Meschia, James F. A survey of the SWISS researchers on the impact of sibling privacy protections on pedigree recruitment. *Neuroepidemiology* 2005; 25(1): 32-41. NRCBL: 15.1; 8.4; 18.2; 18.3. SC: em. Identifiers: Siblings With Ischemic Stroke Study.

GENETIC SCREENING
See also DNA FINGERPRINTING; GENETIC COUNSELING; GENOME MAPPING

Ågård, Anders; Bolmsjö, Ingrid Ågren; Hermerén, Göran; Wahlstöm, Jan. Familial hypercholesterolemia: ethical, practical and psychological problems from the perspective of patients. *Patient Education and Counseling* 2005 May; 57(2): 162-167. NRCBL: 15.3; 8.3.1; 4.2. SC: em. Identifiers: Sweden.

Agich, George. A phenomenological approach to bioethics. *In:* Ashcroft, Richard; Lucassen, Anneke; Parker, Michael; Verkerk, Marian; Widderhoven, Guy, eds. Case Analysis in Clinical Ethics. New York: Cambridge University Press; 2005: 187-200. NRCBL: 15.3; 8.4; 1.1. SC: an.

Almond, Brenda. Genetic profiling of newborns: ethical and social issues. *Nature Reviews Genetics* 2006 January; 7(1): 67-71. NRCBL: 15.3; 1.3.12; 8.3.2; 8.4.

Andrews, Lesley; Mireskandari, Shab; Jessen, Jaime; Thewes, Belinda; Solomon, Michael; Macrae, Finlay; Meiser, Bettina. Impact of familial adenomatous polyposis on young adults: attitudes toward genetic testing, support, and information needs. *Genetics in Medicine* 2006 November; 8(11): 697-703. NRCBL: 15.3; 15.2; 9.5.7. SC: em.

Arar, Nedal H.; Hazuda, Helen; Steinbach, Rebecca; Arar, Mazen Y.; Abboud, Hanna E. Ethical issues associated with conducting genetic family studies of complex disease. *Annals of Epidemiology* 2005 October; 15(9): 712-719. NRCBL: 15.3; 18.3; 15.1; 8.1. SC: em.

Ashcroft, Richard. 'Power, corruption and lies': ethics and power. *In:* Ashcroft, Richard; Lucassen, Anneke; Parker, Michael; Verkerk, Marian; Widderhoven, Guy,

eds. Case Analysis in Clinical Ethics. New York: Cambridge University Press; 2005: 77-94. NRCBL: 15.3; 8.4. SC: an.

Barlow-Stewart, Kristine. New genetics: benefits and burdens for families. *Reform* 2001 Spring; 79: 14-18, 74. NRCBL: 15.3; 15.2.

Beckman, Ludvig. Genetic privacy from Locke's point of view. *Journal of Value Inquiry* 2004; 38(2): 241-251. NRCBL: 15.3; 8.4; 4.4. SC: ph.

Berg, Kare. Ethical aspects of early diagnosis of genetic disease. *World Health* 1996 September-October; 49(5): 20-21. NRCBL: 15.3; 8.1; 9.5.1.

Bernhardt, Barbara A.; Tambor, Ellen S.; Fraser, Gertrude; Wissow, Lawrence S.; Geller, Gail. Parents' and children's attitudes toward the enrollment of minors in genetic susceptibility research: implications for informed consent. *American Journal of Medical Genetics* 2003 February 1; 116A(4): 315-323. NRCBL: 15.3; 18.5.2; 18.3. SC: em.

Birnbacher, Dieter. Predictive medicine — the right to know and the right not to know. *Acta Analytica* 2001; 16(27): 35-47. NRCBL: 15.3; 8.2; 1.1; 8.1. SC: an. Identifiers: autonomy.

Blackburn, Laura. Genetic testing: U.K. embryos may be screened for cancer risk [news]. *Science* 2006 May 19; 312(5776): 984. NRCBL: 15.3.

Bleich, J. David. Genetic screening. *In:* Rosner, Fred, ed. Medicine and Jewish Law. Volume III. Brooklyn, NY: Yashar Books, Inc.; 2005: 55-82. NRCBL: 15.3; 1.2.

Botkin, Jeffrey R. Research for newborn screening: developing a national framework. *Pediatrics* 2005 October; 116(4): 862-871. NRCBL: 15.3; 18.5.2; 9.5.7; 18.2.

Bowen, Deborah J.; Battuello, Kathryn M.; Raats, Monique. Marketing genetic tests: empowerment or snake oil? *Health Education and Behavior* 2005 October; 32(5): 676-685. NRCBL: 15.3; 5.3; 1.3.2. SC: an; em.

Bowman, James E. Genetic screening programs and public policy. *Phylon* 1977 June; 38(2): 117-142. NRCBL: 15.3; 15.11; 15.6; 9.5.4; 9.1. Identifiers: African-Americans; sickle cell anemia.

Bradley, A.N. Utility and limitations of genetic testing and information. *Nursing Standard* 2005 October 12-18; 20(5): 52-55. NRCBL: 15.3; 15.1.

Burton, Sarah K.; Withrow, Kara; Arnos, Kathleen S.; Kalfoglou, Andrea L.; Pandya, Arti. A focus group study of consumer attitudes toward genetic testing and newborn screening for deafness. *Genetics in Medicine* 2006 December; 8(12): 779-783. NRCBL: 15.3; 9.5.7; 9.1. SC: em.

Campbell, Alastair. A virtue-ethics approach. *In:* Ashcroft, Richard; Lucassen, Anneke; Parker, Michael; Verkerk, Marian; Widderhoven, Guy, eds. Case Analysis in Clinical Ethics. New York: Cambridge University Press; 2005: 45-56. NRCBL: 15.3; 8.4. SC: an.

Canadian Paediatric Society. Ethics Committee; Arbour, Laura. Guidelines for genetic testing of healthy children [policy statement]. Ottawa, Ontario, Canada: Canadian Society of Medical Geneticists, 2002 October 28. 11 p. [Online]. Accessed: http://ccmg.medical.org/pdf/cps_gentestchild.pdf [2006 July 26]. NRCBL: 15.3. Note: Canadian Paediatric Society Position Statement, approved by Canadian College of Medical Geneticists [CCMG] Board.

Carter, Ross E. Psychological evaluation a consideration in the ethics of genetic testing for breast cancer. *Psychiatric Annals* 2004 February; 34(2): 119-124. NRCBL: 15.3; 15.2; 17.1; 2.1.

Carter, Sarah; Taylor, David; Bates, Ian. Institutionalized paternalism? Stakeholders' views on public access to genetic testing. *Journal of Health Services Research and Policy.* 2006 July; 11(3): 155-161. NRCBL: 15.3; 9.1. SC: em. Identifiers: United Kingdom (Great Britain).

Catholic Church. National Conference of Catholic Bishops [NCCB]. Committee on Science and Human Values. The Promise and Peril of Genetic Screening. Washington, DC: United States Catholic Conference, 1997. NRCBL: 15.3; 1.2.

Council for Responsible Genetics. Genetic testing: preliminary policy guidelines [guideline]. *GeneWatch* 2006 July-August; 19(4): 15-18. NRCBL: 15.3. Identifiers: CRG.

Cowan, Ruth Schwartz. Eugenics, genetic screening, and the slippery slope. *In:* Miller, Roman J.; Brubaker, Beryl H.; Peterson, James C., eds. Viewing New Creations with Anabaptist Eyes: Ethics of Biotechnology. Telford, PA: Cascadia Pub.; 2005: 149-167. NRCBL: 15.3; 15.5.

d'Agincourt-Canning, Lori. Genetic testing for hereditary breast and ovarian cancer: responsibility and choice. *Qualitative Health Research* 2006 January; 16(1): 97-118. NRCBL: 15.3; 9.5.1. SC: em.

Davey, Angela; French, Davina; Dawkins, Hugh; O'Leary, Peter. New mothers' awareness of newborn screening, and their attitudes to the retention and use of screening samples for research purposes. *Genomics, Society and Policy* 2005 December; 1(3): 41-51. NRCBL: 15.3; 8.3.2; 18.3. SC: em.

de Melo-Martín, Inmaculada. Furthering injustices against women: genetic information, moral obligations, and gender. *Bioethics* 2006 November; 20(6): 301-307. NRCBL: 15.3; 15.1; 8.4; 10. SC: an.

de Wert, Guido. Cascade screening: whose information is it anyway? *European Journal of Human Genetics* 2005 April; 13(4): 397-398. NRCBL: 15.3; 8.4; 8.3.1.

DeLisi, Lynn E.; Bertisch, Hilary. A preliminary comparison of the hopes of researchers, clinicians, and families for the future ethical use of genetic findings on schizophrenia. *American Journal of Medical Genetics Part B* 2006 January 5; 141(1): 110-115. NRCBL: 15.3; 15.2; 17.14. SC: em.

Elger, Bernice S.; Harding, Timothy W. Should children and adolescents be tested for Huntington's disease? Attitudes of future lawyers and physicians in Switzerland. *Bioethics* 2006 June; 20(3): 158-167. NRCBL: 15.3; 9.5.7; 8.3.2. SC: em.

Abstract: The objective of the study was to identify future lawyers' and physicians' views on testing children for Huntington's disease (HD) against parents' wishes. After receiving general information about HD, patient autonomy and confidentiality, law students and advanced medical students were shown an interview with a mother suffering from HD who is opposed to informing and testing her two children (aged 10 and 16) for HD. Students then filled out questionnaires concerning their agreement with testing. No significant differences were found between medical and law students or between students from different courses concerning the adolescent son. Three quarters of students thought that he should be told about his mother's disease, and 91% thought the adolescent son should have the opportunity of genetic testing for HD himself. However, significant differences were found concerning the 10-year old son, with 44% of law students and 30% of medical students in favour of testing the child for HD. Students raised some important ethical issues in their elective comments. In conclusion, we found highly positive attitudes towards informing a 16-year old of his mother's HD and offering to test him. These attitudes were not in tune with guidelines. Students did not consider several practical and ethical issues of genetic testing of children and adolescents. Specific education should ensure that attitudes are based on sufficiently detailed knowledge about all aspects of genetic testing of children to discourage pressures on persons at risk of HD.

Emery, Jon. Is informed choice in genetic testing a different breed of informed decision-making? A discussion paper. *Health Expectations* 2001 June; 4(2): 81-86. NRCBL: 15.3; 15.2; 8.3.1; 8.1; 7.1.

Etchegary, Holly. Genetic testing for Huntington's disease: how is the decision taken? *Genetic Testing* 2006 Spring; 10(1): 60-67. NRCBL: 15.3; 8.1. SC: em.

European Society of Human Genetics [ESHG]. Population genetic screening programmes: technical, social and ethical issues. *European Journal of Human Genetics* 2003 December; 11(Supplement 2): S5-S7. NRCBL: 15.3; 13.1; 1.3.12.

European Society of Human Genetics [ESHG]. Public and Professional Policy Committee [PPPC]. Population genetic screening programmes: technical, social and ethical issues. *European Journal of Human Genetics* 2003 December; 11(12): 903-905. NRCBL: 15.3; 6.

NRCBL: National Reference Center for Bioethics Literature Classification Scheme See inside front cover for terms.

227

Evans, Gareth; Harris, Rodney. The ethics of testing for cancer-predisposition genes. *In:* Eeles, R.A., Ponder, B.A.J.; Horwich, A.; Easton, D.F., eds. Genetic Predisposition to Cancer. London: Chapman and Hare; 1996 June: 383-393. NRCBL: 15.3; 9.5.1; 9.1.

Evans, James P.; Skrzynia, Cécile; Susswein, Lisa; Harlan, Megan. Genetics and the young woman with breast cancer. *Breast Disease* 2005-2006; 23: 17-29. NRCBL: 15.3; 9.5.1.

Falcâo de Oliveira, Guilherme Freire. Juridical implications on genome knowledge (Part II) = Implicaciones jurídicas del conocimiento del genoma (Parte II). *Revista de Derecho Genoma Humano = Law and the Human Genome Review* 1997 July-December; (7): 59-98. NRCBL: 15.3; 15.2; 8.4.

Fryer, Alan. The genetic testing of children. *Journal of the Royal Society of Medicine* 1997 August; 90(8): 419-421. NRCBL: 15.3; 9.5.7. Identifiers: United Kingdom (Great Britain).

Gaff, Clara L.; Cowan, Ruth; Meiser, Bettina; Lindeman, Geoffrey. Genetic services for men: the preferences of men with a family history of prostate cancer. *Genetics in Medicine* 2006 December; 8(12): 771-780. NRCBL: 15.3; 9.5.7; 9.1. SC: em.

Gason, Alexandra A.; Delatycki, Martin B.; Metcalfe, Sylvia A.; Aitken, MaryAnne. It's "back to school" for genetic screening. *European Journal of Human Genetics* 2006 April; 14(4): 384-389. NRCBL: 15.3; 9.5.7. Identifiers: Australia.

Gason, A.A.; Aitken, M.A.; Metcalfe, S.A.; Allen, K.J.; Delatycki, M.B. Genetic susceptibility screening in schools: attitudes of the school community towards hereditary haemochromatosis. *Clinical Genetics* 2005 February; 67(2): 166-174. NRCBL: 15.3; 9.5.7; 8.3.2. SC: em. Identifiers: Australia.

German Society of Human Genetics [GfH]. Committee for Public Relations and Ethical Issues. Statement on postnatal predictive genetic diagnosis [position statement]. *Medizinische Genetik* 1991; 3(2): 10-11. [Online]. Accessed: http://www.medgenetik.de/sonderdruck/en/Predictive_diagnosis.pdf [2006 July 31]. NRCBL: 15.3; 8.3.1.

Gillon, Raanan. Families and genetic testing: the case of Jane and Phyllis from a four- principles perspectives. *In:* Ashcroft, Richard; Lucassen, Anneke; Parker, Michael; Verkerk, Marian; Widderhoven, Guy, eds. Case Analysis in Clinical Ethics. New York: Cambridge University Press; 2005: 165-185. NRCBL: 15.3; 8.4; 2.1. SC: an.

Godard, Beatrice; ten Kate, Leo; Evers-Kiebooms, Gerry; Ayme, Segolene. Population genetic screening programmes: principles, techniques, practices, and policies. *European Journal of Human Genetics* 2003 December; 11(Supplement 2): S49-S87. NRCBL: 15.3; 13.1; 9.1; 21.1. SC: rv.

Goelen, Guido; Rigo, Adelheid; Bonduelle, Maryse; De Greve, Jacques. BRCA 1/2 gene mutation testing-based cancer prevention and the moral concerns of different types of patients. *Annals of the New York Academy of Sciences* 1999; 889: 240-243. NRCBL: 15.3; 15.2; 9.5.1.; 8.1. SC: em. Identifiers: Belgium.

Grosse, Scott D.; Khoury, Muin J. What is the clinical utility of genetic testing? *Genetics in Medicine* 2006 July; 8(7): 448-450. NRCBL: 15.3.

Guillemin, Marilys; Gillam, Lynn. Attitudes to genetic testing for deafness: the importance of informed choice. *Journal of Genetic Counseling* 2006 February; 15(1): 51-59. NRCBL: 15.3; 15.2; 8.3.1; 12.1. SC: em.

Guzauskas, Gregory F.; Lebel, Robert Roger. The duty to re-contact for newly appreciated risk factors: Fragile X premutation. *Journal of Clinical Ethics* 2006 Spring; 17(1): 46-52. NRCBL: 15.3; 15.2; 15.6; 9.5.3; 8.4.

Halbert, Chanita Hughes; Kessler, Lisa; Stopfer, Jill E.; Domchek, Susan; Wileyto, E. Paul. Low rates of acceptance of BRCA1 and BRCA2 test results among African American women at increased risk for hereditary breast-ovarian cancer. *Genetics in Medicine* 2006 September; 8(9): 576-582. NRCBL: 15.3; 9.5.4; 9.5.5; 15.2. SC: em.

Hargreaves, Katrina M.; Stewart, Ruth J.; Oliver, Sandy R. Informed choice and public health screening for children: the case of blood spot screening. *Health Expectations* 2005 June; 8(2): 161-171. NRCBL: 15.3; 9.5.7; 8.3.2; 9.1. SC: em. Identifiers: United Kingdom (Great Britain).

Haydon, J. Genetics: uphold the rights of all clients to informed decision-making and voluntary action. *Nursing Standard* 2005 September 28-October 4; 20(3): 48-51. NRCBL: 15.3; 15.2; 8.1; 4.1.3. SC: em; cs.

Hedera, Peter. Ethical principles and pitfalls of genetic testing for dementia. *Journal of Geriatric Psychiatry and Neurology* 2001 Winter; 14(4): 213-221. NRCBL: 15.3; 17.1; 9.5.2. SC: em.

Hegwer, G.; Fairley, C.; Charrow, J.; Ormond, K.E. Knowledge and attitudes toward a free education and Ashkenazi Jewish Carrier Testing Program. *Journal of Genetic Counseling* 2006 February; 15(1): 61-70. NRCBL: 15.3; 1.3.3; 1.2. SC: em.

Heller, Jan C.; Wallington, Maria. Cardiology and genomics: an ethical view. *Health Progress* 2006 March-April; 87(2): 51-53. NRCBL: 15.3; 15.10; 1.2.

Henneman, Lidewij; Timmermans, Danielle R.M.; van der Wal, Gerrit. Public attitudes toward genetic testing:

perceived benefits and objections. *Genetic Testing* 2006 Summer; 10(2): 139-145. NRCBL: 15.3. SC: em.

Hoff, Timothy; Hoyt, Adrienne; Therrell, Brad; Ayoob, Maria. Exploring barriers to long-term follow-up in newborn screening programs. *Genetics in Medicine* 2006 September; 8(9): 563-570. NRCBL: 15.3; 9.5.7; 9.1. SC: em.

Holm, Søren. An empirical approach. *In:* Ashcroft, Richard; Lucassen, Anneke; Parker, Michael; Verkerk, Marian; Widderhoven, Guy, eds. Case Analysis in Clinical Ethics. New York: Cambridge University Press; 2005: 201-211. NRCBL: 15.3; 8.4. SC: an; em.

Holtzman, Neil A. The diffusion of new genetic tests for predicting disease. *FASEB Journal* 1992 July; 6: 2806-2812. NRCBL: 15.3; 15.2; 8.1.

Hudson, Kathy L. Genetic testing oversight [editorial]. *Science* 2006 September 29; 313(5795): 1853. NRCBL: 15.3.

Hudson, Kathy L.; Murphy, Juli A.; Kaufman, David J.; Javitt, Gail H.; Katsanis, Sara H.; Scott, Joan. Oversight of US genetic testing laboratories. *Nature Biotechnology* 2006 September; 24(9): 1083-1090. NRCBL: 15.3; 9.7; 9.8; 5.3. SC: em.

Hurley, Ann C.; Harvey, Rose; Roberts, J. Scott; Wilson-Chase, Chantel; Lloyd, Stephanie; Prest, Janalyn; Lock, Margaret; Horvath, Kathy J.; Green, Robert C. Genetic susceptibility for Alzheimer's disease: why did adult offspring seek testing? *American Journal of Alzheimer's Disease and Other Dementias* 2005 November-December; 20(6): 374-381. NRCBL: 15.3; 17.1. SC: em.

Hurwitz, Brian. Family access to shared genetic information: an analysis of the narrative. *In:* Ashcroft, Richard; Lucassen, Anneke; Parker, Michael; Verkerk, Marian; Widderhoven, Guy, eds. Case Analysis in Clinical Ethics. New York: Cambridge University Press; 2005: 27-43. NRCBL: 15.3; 8.4. SC: an.

Hutson, Stu. Troubling times for embryo gene tests [news]. *New Scientist* 2006 March 18-24; 189(2543): 14-15. NRCBL: 15.3; 15.2; 9.8.

Jenkins, Jean F.; Lea, Dale Halsey. Connecting genomics to health benefits: genetic testing. *In their:* Nursing care in the Genomic Era: A Case-Based Approach. Sudbury, MA.: Jones and Bartlett Publishers, 2005: 69-110. NRCBL: 15.3.

Johnson, Alissa. Predictive genetic testing of minors. *NCSL Legisbrief* 2006 April-May; 14(19): 1-2. NRCBL: 15.3; 9.5.7.

Kalb, Claudia; Underwood, Anne; Mummolo, Jonathan. Peering into the future. Genetic testing is transforming medicine — and the way families think about their health. As science unlocks the intricate secrets of DNA, we face difficult choices and new challenges. *Newsweek* 2006 December 11; 148(24): 52-54, 56-57, 60-61. NRCBL: 15.3; 15.2. SC: po.

Kasparian, Nadine A.; Meiser, Bettina; Butow, Phyllis N.; Job, R.F. Soames; Mann, Graham J. Better the devil you know? High-risk individuals' anticipated psychological responses to genetic testing for melanoma susceptibility. *Journal of Genetic Counseling* 2006 December; 15(6): 433-447. NRCBL: 15.3; 17.1; 9.5.1. SC: em.

Kent, Alastair. We can change the future. *EMBO Reports* 2005 September; 6(9): 801-804. NRCBL: 15.3; 9.5.7; 9.8.

Kinney, Anita Yeomans; Croyle, Robert T.; Dudley, William N.; Bailey, Christine A.; Pelias, Mary Kay; Neuhausen, Susan L. Knowledge, attitudes, and interest in breast-ovarian cancer gene testing: a survey of a large African-American kindred with a BRCA1 mutation. *Preventive Medicine* 2001 December; 33(6): 543-551. NRCBL: 15.3; 9.5.4; 9.5.1. SC: em.

Klatt, Edward C.; Florell, Scott R.; Rodgers, George M. Genetic testing in autopsies [letter and reply]. *American Journal of Clinical Pathology* 2000 February; 113(2): 311-312. NRCBL: 15.3; 20.1.

Klemp, Jennifer R.; O'Dea, Anne; Chamberlain, Carolyn; Fabian, Carol J. Patient satisfaction of BRCA1/2 genetic testing by women at high risk for breast cancer participating in a prevention trial. *Familial Cancer* 2005; 4(4): 279-284. NRCBL: 15.3; 9.5.5; 15.2. SC: em.

Klitzman, Robert. Genetic testing creates new versions of ancient dilemmas. *New York Times* 2006 January 17; p. F5. NRCBL: 15.3; 8.3.4. SC: po.

Kmietowicz, Zosia. Sickle cell screening makes genetic counselling everybody's business [news]. *BMJ: British Medical Journal* 2006 March 11; 332(7541): 570. NRCBL: 15.3; 15.2; 9.5.7; 9.1. Identifiers: United Kingdom (Great Britain).

Kohane, Isaac S.; Masys, Daniel R.; Altman, Russ B. The incidental ome: a threat to genomic medicine. *JAMA: the Journal of the American Medical Association* 2006 July 12; 296(2): 212-215. NRCBL: 15.3.

Lea, Dale Halsey; Williams, Janet; Donahue, M. Patricia. Ethical issues in genetic testing. *Journal of Midwifery and Women's Health* 2005 May-June; 50(3): 234-240. NRCBL: 15.3; 1.1; 8.4.

Longenecker, Randall L. The face of overpowering knowledge. *In:* Miller, Roman J.; Brubaker, Beryl H.; Peterson, James C., eds. Viewing New Creations with Anabaptist Eyes: Ethics of Biotechnology. Telford, PA: Cascadia Pub.; 2005: 205-208. NRCBL: 15.3; 15.2.

Lucassen, Anneke. Families and genetic testing: the case of Jane and Phyllis. *In:* Ashcroft, Richard; Lucassen, Anneke; Parker, Michael; Verkerk, Marian; Widderhoven,

NRCBL: National Reference Center for Bioethics Literature Classification Scheme   See inside front cover for terms.

229

Guy, eds. Case Analysis in Clinical Ethics. New York: Cambridge University Press; 2005: 7-26. NRCBL: 15.3; 8.4. SC: cs.

Luxembourg. Commission Consultative Nationale d'Éthique pour les Sciences de la Vie et de la Santé [CNE]. Avis concernant un projet de recherche sur les anomalies de l'hémoglobine lors de l'examen prénuptial: Avis 1/1990 [Opinion concerning a research project on the anomalies of hemoglobin at the time of a premarital examination: Opinion 1/1990]. Luxembourg: Commission Nationale d'Éthique, 1990; 2 p. [Online]. Accessed: http://www.cne.public.lu/publications/avis/1990_1.PDF [2006 April 7]. NRCBL: 15.3; 15.2.

Malpas, Phillipa. The right to remain in ignorance about genetic information—can such a right be defended in the name of autonomy? *New Zealand Medical Journal* 2005 August 12; 118(1220); 8 p. NRCBL: 15.3; 8.3.1; 1.1; 8.1. SC: cs.

Malpas, P.J. Why tell asymptomatic children of the risk of an adult-onset disease in the family but not test them for it? *Journal of Medical Ethics* 2006 November; 32(11): 639-642. NRCBL: 15.3; 8.2; 9.5.7. SC: an.

Abstract: This paper first considers why it is important to give children genetic information about hereditary conditions in the family, which will go on to affect their lives in a salient way. If it is important to inform children that they are at risk for an adult-onset disease that exists in the family, why should they not also grow up knowing whether they actually carry the genetic mutation? Central to this discussion is the importance of the process of disclosure and the environment in which genetic information is divulged. It is concluded that the reasons given for defending disclosure of genetic conditions in the family to children are also important reasons to cautiously defend predictive genetic testing of children for adult-onset diseases.

Matsuda, Ichiro. Bioethical considerations in neonatal screening: Japanese experiences. *Southeast Asian Journal of Tropical Medicine and Public Health* 2003; 34(Supplement 3): 46-48. NRCBL: 15.3; 9.5.7; 8.3.2; 8.3.4.

Matsuda, Ichiro. Genetic health care services, present and near future in Japan. *Eubios Journal of Asian and International Bioethics* 2003 March 13(2): 57-59. NRCBL: 15.3; 15.2.

McCall Smith, Alexander. Genetic privacy and discrimination. *In:* Glasa, J., ed. Ethics of Human Genetics: Challenges of the (Post) Genomic Era. Bratislava, Slovak Republic: Charis [and] IMEB Foundation; 2002: 81-87. NRCBL: 15.3; 8.4.

McLean, Sheila A.M. The genetic testing of children. *In:* Sándor, Judit, ed. Society and Genetic Information: Codes and Laws in the Genetic Era. Budapest, Hungary; New York: CEU Press; 2003: 145-160. NRCBL: 15.3; 9.5.7.

McMahan, Jeff. The morality of screening for disability. *Reproductive BioMedicine Online [electronic]* 2005 March; 10(Supplement 1): 129-132. NRCBL: 15.3; 9.5.1;

9.5.7. SC: an. Conference: Ethics, Law and Moral Philosophy of Reproductive Biomedicine; London, UK; 2004 September 30 - October 1; Royal Society.

Mepham, Ben. Reproductive choices. *In his:* Bioethics: An Introduction for the Biosciences. Oxford; New York: Oxford University Press; 2005: 124-149. NRCBL: 15.3; 14.1.

Mesters, Ilse; Ausems, Marlein; Eichhorn, Sophie; Vasen, Hans. Informing one's family about genetic testing for hereditary non-polyposis colorectal cancer (HNPCC): a retrospective exploratory study. *Familial Cancer* 2005; 4(2): 163-167. NRCBL: 15.3; 8.1; 8.4. SC: em. Identifiers: Netherlands.

Michie, Susan; di Lorenzo, Elena; Lane, Ruth; Armstrong, Kevin; Sanderson, Saskia. Genetic information leaflets: influencing attitudes towards genetic testing. *Genetics in Medicine* 2004 July-August; 6(4): 219-225. NRCBL: 15.3; 17.1; 15.1; 7.1. SC: em.

Middleton, Anna. Parents' attitudes towards genetic testing and the impact of deafness in the family. *In:* Stephens, Dafydd; Jones, Lesley, eds. The Impact of Genetic Hearing Impairment. London; Philadelphia: Whurr; 2005: 11-53. NRCBL: 15.3; 12.5.2; 15.2.

Mirkes, Renée. Newborn screening: toward a just system. *Ethics and Medicine* 2006 Fall; 22(3): 163-175. NRCBL: 15.3; 9.5.7; 9.2.

Newson, Ainsley J.; Humphries, Steve E. Cascade testing in familial hypercholesterolaemia: how should family members be contacted? *European Journal of Human Genetics* 2005 April; 13(4): 401-408. NRCBL: 15.3; 8.4; 8.3.1; 8.1.

Nordin, Karin; Björk, Jan; Berglund, Gunilla. Factors influencing intention to obtain a genetic test for a hereditary disease in an affected group and in the general public. *Preventive Medicine* 2004 December; 39(6): 1107-1114. NRCBL: 15.3. SC: em. Identifiers: Sweden.

Otlowski, Margaret. Essentially yours: the protection of human genetic information in Australia. *GeneWatch* 2006 January-February; 19(1): 9-12. NRCBL: 15.3; 8.4.

Otlowski, Margaret F.A.; Williamson, Robert. Ethical and legal issues and the "new genetics". *Medical Journal of Australia* 2003 June 2; 178(11): 582-585. NRCBL: 15.3; 8.4; 15.2; 7.1.

Panicola, Michael R.; Hamel, Ronald P. Conscience, cooperation, and full disclosure. *Health Progress* 2006 January-February; 87(1): 52-59. NRCBL: 15.3; 14.1; 1.2; 9.5.1.

Parens, Erik; Asch, Adrienne. Disability rights critique of prenatal genetic testing: reflections and recommendations. *Mental Retardation and Developmental Disabilities*

Research Reviews 2003; 9(1): 40-47. NRCBL: 15.3; 15.2; 9.5.1; 14.1; 7.1. SC: an.

Parker, Michael. A conversational approach to the ethics of genetic testing. *In:* Ashcroft, Richard; Lucassen, Anneke; Parker, Michael; Verkerk, Marian; Widderhoven, Guy, eds. Case Analysis in Clinical Ethics. New York: Cambridge University Press; 2005: 149-164. NRCBL: 15.3; 8.4; 15.2. SC: an.

Patenaude, Andrea Farkas. The genetic testing of children for cancer susceptibility: ethical, legal, and social issues. *Behavioral Sciences and the Law* 1996 Autumn; 14(4): 393-410. NRCBL: 15.3; 9.5.7; 8.3.2; 8.1.

Paulson, Henry L. Diagnostic testing in neurogenetics. Principles, limitations, and ethical considerations. *Neurologic Clinics of North America* 2002 August 1; 20(3): 627-643. NRCBL: 15.3; 17.1; 15.2.

Peters, June A.; Vadaparampil, Susan T.; Kramer, Joan; Moser, Richard P.; Peterson, Lori Jo; Loud, Jennifer; Greene, Mark H. Familial testicular cancer: interest in genetic testing among high-risk family members. *Genetics in Medicine* 2006 December; 8(12): 760-770. NRCBL: 15.3; 9.5.1. SC: em.

Pollack, Andrew. The wide, wild world of genetic testing. *New York Times* 2006 September 12; p. NYT4. NRCBL: 15.3. SC: po.

Rabino, Isaac. Research scientists surveyed on ethical issues in genetic medicine: a comparison of attitudes of US and European researchers. *New Genetics and Society* 2006 December; 25(3): 325-342. NRCBL: 15.3; 8.4; 15.4; 21.1. SC: em.

Ramsey, Scott D.; Yoon, Paula; Moonesinghe, Ramal; Khoury, Muin J. Population-based study for the prevalence of family history of cancer: implications for cancer screening and prevention. *Genetics in Medicine* 2006 September; 8(9): 571-575. NRCBL: 15.3; 9.5.1; 9.1. SC: em.

Riordan, Sara Hammer; Loescher, Lois J. Medical students' attitudes toward genetic testing of minors. *Genetic Testing* 2006 Spring; 10(1): 68-73. NRCBL: 15.3; 9.5.7; 7.2. SC: em.

Roche, Patricia A.; Annas, George J. DNA testing, banking, and genetic privacy. *New England Journal of Medicine* 2006 August 10; 355(6): 545-546. NRCBL: 15.3; 15.1; 1.3.12; 8.4; 19.5.

Rogausch, Anja; Prause, Daniela; Schallenberg, Anne; Brockmoller, Jurgen; Himmel, Wolfgang. Patients' and physicians' perspectives on pharmacogenetic testing. *Pharmacogenomics* 2006 January; 7(1): 49-59. NRCBL: 15.3; 9.7; 8.1. SC: em.

Root, Michael. The use of race in medicine as a proxy for genetic differences. *Philosophy of Science* 2003 December; 70(5): 1173-1183. NRCBL: 15.3; 9.5.4; 9.2; 9.4; 3.1.

Ross, Lainie Friedman. Heterozygote carrier testing in high schools abroad: what are the lessons for the U.S.? *Journal of Law, Medicine and Ethics* 2006 Winter; 34(4): 753-764. NRCBL: 15.3; 8.3.2; 9.5.7. SC: an.

Abstract: The main value of carrier detection in the general population is to determine reproductive risks. In this manuscript I examine the practice of providing carrier screening programs in the school setting. While the data show that high school screening programs can achieve high uptake, I argue that this may reflect a lack of full understanding about risks, benefits, and alternatives, and the right not to know. It may also reflect the inherent coercion in group testing, particularly for adolescents who are prone to peer pressure. The problem of carrier screening in the schools is compounded when the condition has a predilection for certain groups based on race, ethnicity or religion. I examine programs around the world that seek to test high school students for Tay Sachs and Cystic Fibrosis carrier status. I argue that carrier programs should be designed so as to minimize stigma and to allow individuals to refuse. The mandatory school environment cannot achieve this. Rather, I conclude that screening programs should be designed to attract young adults and not adolescents to participate in a more voluntary venue.

Royse, Susan D. Implications of genetic testing for sudden cardiac death syndrome. *British Journal of Nursing* 2006 November 9-22; 15(20): 1104-1107. NRCBL: 15.3.

Russo, Gene. Home health tests are 'genetic horoscopes' [news]. *Nature* 2006 August 3; 442(7102): 497. NRCBL: 15.3; 9.7.

Sacchini, Dario; Di Pietro, Maria Luisa; Spagnolo, Antonio G. Genetic screening: benefits and pitfalls. *In:* Glasa, J., ed. Ethics of Human Genetics: Challenges of the (Post) Genomic Era. Bratislava, Slovak Republic: Charis [and] IMEB Foundation; 2002: 131-151. NRCBL: 15.3.

Sanghavi, Darshak M. Wanting babies like themselves, some parents choose genetic defects. *New York Times* 2006 December 5; p. F5, F8. NRCBL: 15.3; 14.4; 4.2.

Sankar, Pamela; Cho, Mildred K.; Wolpe, Paul Root; Schairer, Cynthia. What is in a cause? Exploring the relationship between genetic cause and felt stigma. *Genetics in Medicine* 2006 January; 8(1): 33-42. NRCBL: 15.3; 4.2; 7.1. SC: em.

Savulescu, Julian. A utilitarian approach. *In:* Ashcroft, Richard; Lucassen, Anneke; Parker, Michael; Verkerk, Marian; Widderhoven, Guy, eds. Case Analysis in Clinical Ethics. New York: Cambridge University Press; 2005: 115-131. NRCBL: 15.3; 8.4; 1.1. SC: an.

Savulescu, Julian. Compulsory genetic testing for APOE Epsilon 4 and boxing. *In:* Tamburrini, Claudio; Tännsjö, Torbjörn, eds. Genetic Technology and Sport: Ethical Questions. London; New York: Routledge; 2005: 136-146. NRCBL: 15.3; 9.5.1.

Savulescu, Julian; Foddy, Bennett. Comment: genetic test available for sports performance. *British Journal of Sports Medicine* 2005 August; 39(8): 472. NRCBL: 15.3; 4.5; 5.1.

NRCBL: National Reference Center for Bioethics Literature Classification Scheme   See inside front cover for terms.

231

Schlich-Bakker, Kathryn J.; ten Kroode, Herman F.J.; Ausems, Margreet G.E.M. A literature review of the psychological impact of genetic testing on breast cancer patients. *Patient Education and Counseling* 2006 July; 62(1): 13-20. NRCBL: 15.3; 9.5.1. SC: em; rv.

Schneider, Katherine A.; Chittenden, Anu B.; Branda, Kelly J.; Keenan, Meredith A.; Joffe, Steven; Patenaude, Andrea Farkas; Reynolds, Hazel; Dent, Karin; Eubanks, Sonja; Goldman, Jill; Leroy, Bonnie; Warren, Nancy Steinberg; Taylor, Kelly; Vockley, Cate Walsh; Garber, Judy E. Ethical issues in cancer genetics: 1) whose information is it? *Journal of Genetic Counseling* 2006 December; 15(6): 491-503. NRCBL: 15.3; 15.2; 8.4. SC: cs.

Segal, Mary E.; Sankar, Pamela; Reed, Danielle R. Research issues in genetic testing of adolescents for obesity. *Nutrition Reviews* 2004 August; 62(8): 307-320. NRCBL: 15.3; 8.3.2; 9.5.7. SC: rv.

Sharpe, Neil F.; Carter, Ronald F. Confidentiality, disclosure, and recontact. *In their:* Genetic Testing: Care, Consent, and Liability. Hoboken, NJ: Wiley-Liss; 2006: 398-424. NRCBL: 15.3; 8.4.

Sharpe, Neil F.; Carter, Ronald F. Susceptibility testing. *In their:* Genetic Testing: Care, Consent, and Liability. Hoboken, NJ: Wiley-Liss; 2006: 268-291. NRCBL: 15.3.

Skirton, Heather; Frazier, Lorraine Q.; Calvin, Amy O.; Cohen, Marlene Z. A legacy for the children — attitudes of older adults in the United Kingdom to genetic testing. *Journal of Clinical Nursing* 2006 May; 15(5): 565-573. NRCBL: 15.3; 9.5.2. SC: em. Identifiers: United Kingdom (Great Britain).

Slosar, John Paul. Genomics and neurology: an ethical view. *Health Progress* 2006 January-February; 87(1): 68-72. NRCBL: 15.3; 1.2.

Strange, Charlie; Moseley, Mary Allison; Jones, Yonge; Schwarz, Laura; Xie, Lianqi; Brantly, Mark L. Genetic testing of minors for alpha1-antitrypsin deficiency. *Archives of Pediatrics and Adolescent Medicine* 2006 May; 160(5): 531-534. NRCBL: 15.3; 9.5.7. SC: em.

Suthers, G.K.; Armstrong, J.; McCormack, J.; Trott, D. Letting the family know: balancing ethics and effectiveness when notifying relatives about genetic testing for a familial disorder. *Journal of Medical Genetics* 2006 August; 43(8): 665-670. NRCBL: 15.3; 8.1. SC: em.

Swiss Society of Medical Genetics [SSGM]. Informed choice in diagnostic genetic testing. Binningen, Switzerland: Swiss Society of Medical Genetics, 2003. 3p [Online]. Accessed: http://www.ssgm.ch/sections/pdf/current/publications/SSGM_eng%20v1.pdf [2006 July 31]. NRCBL: 15.3; 8.3.1.

Therrell, Bradford L., Jr. Ethical, legal and social issues in newborn screening in the United States. *Southeast Asian Journal of Tropical Medicine and Public Health* 2003; 34(Supplement 3): 52-58. NRCBL: 15.3; 9.5.7; 8.3.2; 8.3.4; 1.3.5.

Tremain, Shelley. Reproductive freedom, self-regulation, and the government of impairment in utero. *Hypatia: A Journal of Feminist Philosophy* 2006 Winter; 21(1): 35-53. NRCBL: 15.3; 5.2; 15.2; 9.5.5; 9.5.8; 1.3.5; 10. SC: an.

Tucker, Diane C.; Acton, Ronald, T.; Press, Nancy; Ruggiero, Andrea; Reiss, Jacob A.; Walker, Ann P.; Wenzel, Lari; Harrison, Barbara; Fadojutimi-Akinsiku, Margaret; Harrison, Helen; Adams, Paul; Crabb, Jennifer A.; Anderson, Roger; Thomson, Elizabeth. Predictors of belief that genetic test information about hemochromatosis should be shared with family members. *Genetic Testing* 2006 Spring; 10(1): 50-59. NRCBL: 15.3; 8.4; 8.2; 8.1; 7.1. SC: em.

Union of American Hebrew Congregations. Committee on Bio-Ethics. Genetic Screening and the Human Genome Project: Bioethics Program/Case Study: Program Guide V. New York, NY: Union of American Hebrew Congregations, 1992 Spring; 35p. NRCBL: 15.3; 1.2; 15.10.

Union of American Hebrew Congregations. Committee on Bio-Ethics. Genetic Testing: Bioethics Study Guide XII. New York, NY: Union of American Hebrew Congregations, 2001; 70 p. NRCBL: 15.3; 1.2; 9.5.7; 9.5.5. SC: cs.

United States. Government Accountability Office [GAO]; Kutz, Gregory. Nutrigenetic Testing: Tests Purchased from Four Web sites Mislead Consumers. Testimony before the Special Committee on Aging, U.S. Senate. Statement of Gregory Kutz, Managing Director Forensic Audits and Special Investigations. Washington, DC: Government Accountability Office [GAO], 2006 July 27; 23 p. [Online]. Accessed: http://www.gao.gov/cgi-bin/getrpt?GAO-06-977T [2006 August 3]. NRCBL: 15.3; 9.1.

van den Berg, Matthijs; Timmermans, Danielle, R.M.; Kleinveld, Johanna H.; Garcia, Elisa; van Vugt, John M.G.; van der Wal, Gerrit. Accepting or declining the offer of prenatal screening for congenital defects: test uptake and women's reasons. *Prenatal Diagnosis* 2005 January; 25(1): 84-90. NRCBL: 15.3; 15.2; 9.5.3. SC: em. Identifiers: Netherlands.

van Korlaar, I.M.; Vossen, C.Y.; Rosendaal, F.R.; Bovill, E.G.; Naud, S.; Cameron, L.D.; Kaptein, A.A. Attitudes toward genetic testing for thrombophilia in asymptomatic members of a large family with heritable protein C deficiency. *Journal of Thrombosis and Haemostasis* 2005 November; 3(11): 2437-2444. NRCBL: 15.3; 7.1; 5.2; 17.1. SC: em.

Vassy, Carine. From a genetic innovation to mass health programmes: the diffusion of Down's Syndrome prenatal screening and diagnostic techniques in France. *Social Science and Medicine* 2006 October; 63(8): 2041-2051. NRCBL: 15.3.

Verkerk, Marian. A feminist care-ethics approach to genetics. *In:* Ashcroft, Richard; Lucassen, Anneke; Parker, Michael; Verkerk, Marian; Widderhoven, Guy, eds. Case Analysis in Clinical Ethics. New York: Cambridge University Press; 2005: 133-148. NRCBL: 15.3; 8.4; 10; 4.1.1. SC: an.

Visco, Frances M.; Skolnick, Mark; Collins, Francis S. Commentary on the ASCO Statement on Genetic Testing for Cancer Susceptibility. *Journal of Clinical Oncology* 1996 May; 14(5): 1737-1740. NRCBL: 15.3; 9.5.5; 9.5.1; 8.1. Identifiers: National Action Plan on Breast Cancer; American Society of Clinical Oncology.

Wasson, Katherine; Cook, E. David; Helzlsour, Kathy. Direct-to-consumer online genetic testing and the four principles: an analysis of the ethical issues. *Ethics and Medicine* 2006 Summer; 22(2): 83-91. NRCBL: 15.3; 1.3.2; 1.1; 2.1.

Webster, Dianne. Storage and use of residual dried blood spots. *Southeast Asian Journal of Tropical Medicine and Public Health* 2003; 34(Supplement 3): 49-51. NRCBL: 15.3; 9.5.7; 8.3.2; 8.4. Identifiers: Australia; New Zealand.

Weiss, Rick. Human embryos in Britain may be screened for cancer risk. *Washington Post* 2006 May 11; p. A12. NRCBL: 15.3; 9.5.8. SC: po.

Widdershoven, Guy. Interpretation and dialogue in hermeneutic ethics. *In:* Ashcroft, Richard; Lucassen, Anneke; Parker, Michael; Verkerk, Marian; Widderhoven, Guy, eds. Case Analysis in Clinical Ethics. New York: Cambridge University Press; 2005: 57-75. NRCBL: 15.3; 8.4; 1.1. SC: an.

William-Jones, Bryn. "Be ready against cancer, now": direct-to-consumer advertising for genetic testing. *New Genetics and Society* 2006 April; 25(1): 89-107. NRCBL: 15.3; 1.3.2; 9.7; 1.3.12.

Withers, Rob. Reading the genes. *In:* Ashcroft, Richard; Lucassen, Anneke; Parker, Michael; Verkerk, Marian; Widderhoven, Guy, eds. Case Analysis in Clinical Ethics. New York: Cambridge University Press; 2005: 95-114. NRCBL: 15.3; 8.4. SC: an.

Wolinsky, Howard. Do-it-yourself diagnosis. *EMBO Reports* 2005 September; 6(9): 805-807. NRCBL: 15.3; 15.2; 9.8.

Woliver, Laura R. The Human Genome Project: designer genes. *In her:* The Political Geographies of Pregnancy. Urbana: University of Illinois Press; 2002: 45-81. NRCBL: 15.3; 15.10.

Wonkam, Ambroise; Njamnshi, Alfred K.; Angwafo, Fru F., III. Knowledge and attitudes concerning medical genetics amongst physicians and medical students in Cameroon (sub-Saharan Africa). *Genetics in Medicine* 2006 June; 8(6): 331-338. NRCBL: 15.3; 15.2; 12.1; 7.1; 7.2. SC: em.

GENETIC SCREENING/ ECONOMIC ASPECTS

Abel, Elizabeth; Horner, Sharon D.; Tyler, Diane; Innerarity, Sheryl A. The impact of genetic information on policy and clinical practice. *Policy, Politics, and Nursing Practice* 2005 February; 6(1): 5-14. NRCBL: 15.3; 8.4; 9.2; 9.1; 9.3.1.

Ackerman, Terrence F. Ethical issues in genetic testing for cancer susceptibility. *In:* Ellis, C.N., ed. Inherited Cancer Syndromes: Current Clinical Management. New York: Springer-Verlag, 2004: 61-82. NRCBL: 15.3; 8.3.1; 1.1; 8.3.2; 9.3.1; 9.5.1.

Boddington, Paula; Hogben, Susan. Working up policy: the use of specific disease exemplars in formulating general principles governing childhood genetic testing. *Health Care Analysis: An International Journal of Health Philosophy and Policy* 2006 March; 14(1): 1-13. NRCBL: 15.3; 9.5.7.

Abstract: Non-therapeutic genetic testing in childhood presents a "myriad of ethical questions"; questions which are discussed and resolved in professional policy and position statements. In this paper we consider an underdiscussed but strongly influential feature of policy-making, the role of selective case and exemplar in the production of general recommendations. Our analysis, in the tradition of rhetoric and argumentation, examines the predominate use of three particular disease exemplar (Huntington's disease, Tay-Sachs disease and sickle cell disease) to argue for or against particular genetic tests (predictive testing and testing for carrier status). We discuss the influence these choices have on the type and strength of subsequent recommendations. We argue that there are lessons to be drawn about how genetic diseases are conceptualised and we caution against the geneticisation of medical policy making.

Breheny, Nikki; Geelhoed, Elizabeth; Goldblatt, Jack; O'Leary, Peter. Cost-effectiveness of predictive genetic tests for familial breast and ovarian cancer. *Genetics, Society, and Policy* 2005 August; 1(2): 67-79. NRCBL: 15.3; 9.3.1.

Cole, Andrew. Genetic tests and staff are cut to save money [news]. *BMJ: British Medical Journal* 2006 December 16; 333(7581): 1238. NRCBL: 15.3; 9.3.1. Identifiers: United Kingdom (Great Britain).

Cutter, Mary Ann G. Managing genetic testing information: legal, ethical, and social challenges. *Revista de Derecho Genoma Humano = Law and the Human Genome Review* 1999 July-December; 11: 167-185. NRCBL: 15.3; 15.1; 9.3.1. SC: le.

NRCBL: National Reference Center for Bioethics Literature Classification Scheme   See inside front cover for terms.

233

Daniel, Caroline. Locking the sick out in the cold. *New Statesman (London, England:* 1996) 1997 February 21; 126: 22-23. NRCBL: 15.3; 9.3.1. SC: po. Identifiers: United Kingdom (Great Britain).

European Society of Human Genetics [ESHG]. Public and Professional Policy Committee [PPPC]. Genetic information and testing in insurance and employment: technical, social and ethical issues. *European Journal of Human Genetics* 2003 December; 11(12): 909-910. NRCBL: 15.3; 6; 16.3; 9.3.1.

Faden, Ruth R.; Kass, Nancy E. Genetic screening technology: ethical issues in access to tests by employers and health insurance companies. *Journal of Social Issues* 1993 Summer; 49(2): 75-88. NRCBL: 15.3; 1.3.2; 8.4; 9.3.1.

Flynn, Gillian. To test or not: genetic mapping poses ethical dilemmas for employers. *Workforce* 2000 December; 79(12): 108-112. NRCBL: 15.3; 16.3; 9.3.1.

Fulda, K.G.; Lykens, K. Ethical issues in predictive genetic testing: a public health perspective. *Journal of Medical Ethics* 2006 March; 32(3): 143-147. NRCBL: 15.3; 15.2; 1.1; 9.1; 8.1; 2.1.
Abstract: As a result of the increase in genetic testing and the fear of discrimination by insurance companies, employers, and society as a result of genetic testing, the disciplines of ethics, public health, and genetics have converged. Whether relatives of someone with a positive predictive genetic test should be notified of the results and risks is a matter urgently in need of debate. Such a debate must encompass the moral and ethical obligations of the diagnosing physician and the patient. The decision to inform or not will vary depending on what moral theory is used. Utilising the utilitarian and libertarian theories produces different outcomes. The principles of justice and non-maleficence will also play an important role in the decision.

Godard, Beatrice; Raeburn, Sandy; Pembrey, Marcus; Bobrow, Martin; Farndon, Peter; Ayme, Segolene. Genetic information and testing in insurance and employment: technical, social and ethical issues. *European Journal of Human Genetics* 2003 December; 11(Supplement 2): S123-S142. NRCBL: 15.3; 9.3.1; 8.4; 21.1. SC: rv.

Golomb, Meredith R.; Garg, Bhuwan P.; Walsh, Laurence E.; Williams, Linda S. Perinatal stroke in baby, prothrombotic gene in mom: does this affect maternal health insurance? *Neurology* 2005 July 12; 65(1): 13-16. NRCBL: 15.3; 9.3.1. SC: em.

Green, Nancy S.; Dolan, Siobhan, M.; Murray, Thomas H. Newborn screening: complexities in universal genetic testing. *American Journal of Public Health* 2006 November; 96(11): 1955-1959. NRCBL: 15.3; 9.5.7; 9.1.
Abstract: Newborn screening (NBS)—in which each newborn infant is screened for up to 50 specific metabolic disorders for early detection and intervention—is the first program of population wide genetic testing. As a public health intervention, NBS has greatly improved the lives of thousands of affected children. New technologies and new economic and social forces pose significant ethical and clinical challenges to NBS. Two primary challenges concern (1) accommodating clinical and ethical standards to rapid technological developments in NBS and (2) preparing public health systems to respond to the medical advances and social forces driving expansion of NBS programs. We describe and analyze these challenges through consideration of 3 disorders: phenylketonuria, medium-chain acyl-CoA dehydrogenase deficiency, and cystic fibrosis.

Hübner, D. Genetic testing and private insurance—a case of "selling one's body"? *Medicine, Health Care and Philosophy* 2006 March; 9(1): 43-55. NRCBL: 15.3; 9.3.1. SC: an.
Abstract: Arguments against the possible use of genetic test results in private health and life insurance predominantly refer to the problem of certain gene carriers failing to obtain affordable insurance cover. However, some moral intuitions speaking against this practice seem to be more fundamental than mere concerns about adverse distributional effects. In their perspective, the central ethical problem is not that some people might fail to get insurance cover because of their 'bad genes',but rather that some people would manage to get insurance cover because of their 'good genes'. This paper tries to highlight the ethical background of these intuitions. Their guiding idea appears to be that, by pointing to his favourable test results, a customer might make an attempt to 'sell his body'. The rationale of this concept is developed and its applicability to the case at issue is critically investigated. The aim is to clarify an essential objection against the use of genetic information in private insurance which has not yet been openly addressed in the academic debate of the topic.

Idaho. *Laws, statutes, etc.* An act relating to genetic testing privacy; amending title 39, Idaho Code, by the addition of a new chapter 83, title 39, Idaho Code, to provide a short title, to define terms, to set forth restrictions regarding genetic testing information applicable to employers, to provide for a private right of action and to provide for enforcement; and amending section 41-1313, Idaho Code, to prohibit insurers from discriminating on the basis of a genetic test or private genetic information for certain purposes [Approved: 31 March 2006]. Idaho: State Legislature, 2006. 8 p. [Online]. Accessed: http://www3.state.id.us/oasis/2006/S1423.html [2007 March 9]. NRCBL: 15.3; 15.1; 8.4. SC: le. Identifiers: Genetic Testing Privacy Act. Note: Senate Bill No. 1423, 58th Legislature, 2nd regular session. Introduced on March 2, 2006. Approved on March 31, 2006.

Javitt, Gail H. Policy implications of genetic testing: not just for geneticists anymore. *Advances in Chronic Kidney Disease* 2006 April; 13(2): 178-182. NRCBL: 15.3; 5.3; 8.4; 16.3. SC: le.

Knudsen, Lisbeth Ehlert. Workplace genetic screening. *In:* Westerholm, Peter; Nilstun, Tore; Øvretveit, John, eds. Practical Ethics in Occupational Health. San Francisco: Radcliffe Medical Press; 2004: 223-239. NRCBL: 15.3; 16.3.

Magnusson, Roger S. A short history of the next thirty years: genetic testing, clinical care and personal choices [forum]. *University of New South Wales Law Journal*

2003; 26(3): 743- 754. NRCBL: 15.3; 4.5; 9.1; 9.3.1; 2.2; 5.2. Identifiers: Australia.

Murthy, Anant; Dixon, Anna; Mossialos, Elias. Genetic testing and insurance. *Journal of the Royal Society of Medicine* 2001 February; 94(2): 57-60. NRCBL: 15.3; 9.3.1.

Nevada. *Laws, statutes, etc.* An act relating to genetic information; providing that it is an unlawful employment practice for an employer, a labor organization or an employment agency to discriminate against a person based on genetic information; and providing other matters properly relating thereto [Approved: 9 June 1999]. Nevada: State Legislature, 1999. 2 p. [Online]. Accessed: http://www.leg.state.nv.us/70th/bills/SB/SB16_EN.pdf [2007 March 9]. NRCBL: 15.3; 15.1. SC: le. Note: Senate Bill 16, 70th session, 1999 session. Introduced on January 18, 1999. Approved on June 9, 1999.

Otlowski, Margaret. Genetic discrimination: meeting the challenges of an emerging issue [forum]. *University of New South Wales Law Journal* 2003; 26(3): 764-769. NRCBL: 15.3; 8.4; 9.3.1; 9.5.4. SC: le. Identifiers: Australia.

Parthasarathy, Shobita. Regulating risk: defining genetic privacy in the United States and Britain. *Science, Technology, and Human Values* 2004 Summer; 29(3): 332-352. NRCBL: 15.3; 8.4; 9.3.1.

Raeburn, J.A. Genetic tests and insurance in the UK. *Reform* 2001 Spring; 79: 32-36, 72. NRCBL: 15.3; 9.3.1.

Sabatier, Sandrine. Steering Committee on Bioethics (CDBI): Working Party on Human Genetics (CDBI-CO-GT4). Strasbourg: Council of Europe [COE]. Steering Committee on Bioethics, 1997 October 27: 40 p. [Online]. Accessed: http://www.coe.int/t/e/legal_affairs/ legal_co-operation/bioethics/texts_and_documents/ DIR-JUR (97)13Genetics.pdf [2007 March 5]. NRCBL: 15.3; 15.2; 18.3; 8.4.

Simon, Jürgen. Insurance and genetic testing in Germany and the international context. *In:* Sándor, Judit, ed. Society and Genetic Information: Codes and Laws in the Genetic Era. Budapest, Hungary; New York: CEU Press; 2003: 185-199. NRCBL: 15.3; 9.3.1; 21.1. SC: le.

Simon, Jürgen; Ravenstein, Christian. Gene tests and employees in an international comparison. *Revista de Derecho y Genoma Humano* 2005 July-December; (23): 167-190. NRCBL: 15.3; 16.3; 21.1. SC: le. Identifiers: Austria; Switzerland; United Kingdom (Great Britain).

Sismondo, Lauren J. GINA, what could you do for me one day?: The potential of the Genetic Information Nondiscrimination Act to protect the American public. *Washington University Journal of Law and Policy* 2006; 21: 459-481. NRCBL: 15.3; 8.4; 9.3.1; 16.3. SC: le.

Smith, Richard; Raithatha, Nick. Why disclosure of genetic tests for health insurance should be voluntary. *Journal of Health Services Research and Policy* 2006 July; 11(3): 184-186. NRCBL: 15.3; 9.3.1. Identifiers: United Kingdom (Great Britain).

United States. Congress. House. A bill to prohibit discrimination by group health plans and employers based on genetic information. Washington, DC: U.S. G.P.O., 2006. 10 p. [Online]. Accessed: http://frwebgate.access.gpo. gov/cgi-bin/useftp.cgi?IPaddress=162.140.64.21& filename=h6125ih.pdf&directory=/diskb/wais/data/109_ cong_bills [2006 November 1]. NRCBL: 15.3; 8.4. SC: le. Identifiers: Taxpayer Protection from Genetic Discrimination Act of 2006. Note: H.R. 6125, 109th Congress, 2d session. Introduced by Rep. Paul, September 20, 2006. Referred to the Committee on Government Reform and to the Committees on Education and the Workforce, Energy and Commerce, and Ways and Means.

United States. Congress. House. A bill to prohibit discrimination on the basis of genetic information with respect to health insurance. Washington, DC: U.S. G.P.O., 2003, 75 p. [Online]. Accessed: http://frwebgate.access. gpo.gov/cgi-bin/useftp.cgi?IPaddress=162.140.64.21& filename=h1910ih.pdf&directory=/disk2/wais/ data/108_cong_bills [2006 November 27]. NRCBL: 15.3; 8.4; 9.3.1; 15.1. SC: le. Identifiers: Genetic Nondiscrimination in Health Insurance and Employment Act. Note: H.R. 1910, 108th Congress, 1st session. Introduced by Rep. Slaughter, May 1, 2003. Referred to the Committee on Energy and Commerce and in addition to the Committees on Ways and Means and Education and the Workforce.

United States. Congress. House. A bill to prohibit discrimination on the basis of genetic information with respect to health insurance. Washington, DC: U.S. G.P.O., 2001. 69 p. [Online]. Accessed: http://frwebgate.access. gpo.gov/cgi-bin/getdoc.cgi?dbname=107_cong_bills& docid= f:h602ih.txt.pdf [2007 March 8]. NRCBL: 15.3; 8.4; 9.3.1. SC: le. Identifiers: Genetic Nondiscrimination in Health Insurance and Employment Act. Note: H.R. 602, 107th Congress, 1st session. Introduced by Rep. Slaughter on February 13, 2001. Referred to the Committee on Energy and Commerce in addition to the Committees on Ways and Means, and Education and the Workforce.

United States. Congress. House. A bill to prohibit discrimination on the basis of genetic information with respect to health insurance and employment. Washington, DC: U.S. G.P.O., 2005. 81 p. [Online]. Accessed: http://frwebgate.access.gpo.gov/cgi-bin/useftp.cgi? IPaddress=162.140.64.21&file name=h1227ih.pdf& directory=/diskb/wais/data/109_cong_bills [2006 December 6]. NRCBL: 15.3; 8.4; 9.3.1; 15.1. SC: le. Identifiers: Genetic Information Nondiscrimination Act of 2005. Note: H.R. 1227, 109th Congress, 1st session. Introduced by Rep. Biggert, March 10, 2005. Referred to the Committee on Education and the Workforce, and in addition to the

---

NRCBL: National Reference Center for Bioethics Literature Classification Scheme   See inside front cover for terms.

Committees on Energy and Commerce, and Ways and Means.

United States. Congress. House. A bill to prohibit health insurance and employment discrimination against individuals and their family members on the basis of predictive genetic information or genetic services. Washington, DC: U.S.G.P.O., 1999. 70 p. [Online]. Accessed: http://frwebgate.access.gpo.gov/cgi-bin/getdoc.cgi?dbname=106_cong_bills&docid=f:h2457ih.txt.pdf [2007 March 8]. NRCBL: 15.3; 8.4; 9.3.1. SC: le. Identifiers: Genetic Nondiscrimination in Health Insurance and Employment Act of 1999. Note: H.R. 2457, 106th Congress, 1st session. Introduced by Rep. Slaughter in the House of Representatives on July 1, 1999. Referred to the Committee on Commerce, and in addition to the Committees on Ways and Means, and Education in the Workforce.

United States. Congress. Senate. An act to prohibit discrimination on the basis of genetic information with respect to health insurance and employment. Washington, DC: U.S. G.P.O., 2003. 86 p. [Online]. Accessed: http://frwebgate.access.gpo.gov/cgi-bin/useftp.cgi?IPaddress=162.140.64.21&file name=s1053es.pdf&directory=/disk2/wais/data/108_cong_bills [2006 November 27]. NRCBL: 15.3; 15.1; 8.4; 9.3.1. SC: le. Identifiers: Genetic Information Nondiscrimination Act of 2003 (Engrossed as Agreed to or Passed by Senate). Note: S. 1053, 108th Congress, 1st session. Passed the Senate October 14, 2003.

United States. Congress. Senate. A bill to prohibit discrimination on the basis of genetic information with respect to health insurance and employment. Washington, DC: U.S. G.P.O., 2005. 85 p. [Online]. Accessed: http://frwebgate.access.gpo.gov/cgi-bin/useftp.cgi?IPaddress=162.140.64.21&file name=s306es.pdf&directory=/diskb/wais/data/109_cong_bills. NRCBL: 15.3; 8.4. SC: le. Identifiers: Genetic Information Nondiscrimination Act of 2005.

Washington. *Laws, statutes, etc.* An act relating to genetic testing as a condition of employment; and adding a new section to chapter 49.44 of the Revised Code of Washington [Approved: 11 March 2004]. Washington: State Legislature, 2004. 3 p. [Online]. Accessed: http://www.leg.wa.gov/pub/billinfo/2003-04/Pdf/Bills/Session%20Law%202004/6180. SL.pdf [2007 March 9]. NRCBL: 15.3; 15.1. SC: le. Note: Senate Bill 6180, 58th Legislature, 2004 regular session. Introduced on January 14, 2004. Approved on March 11, 2004.

Wolfberg, Adam J. Genes on the web — direct-to-consumer marketing of genetic testing. *New England Journal of Medicine* 2006 August 10; 355(6): 543-545. NRCBL: 15.3; 9.3.1; 1.3.2; 15.2.

GENETIC SCREENING/ LEGAL ASPECTS
See also GENETICS/ LEGAL ASPECTS

Bernat, Erwin. Legal aspects of developments in human genetics: an Austrian viewpoint = Aspectos legales de los avances en genética humana. Un punto de vista austriaco. *Law and the Human Genome Review = Revista de Derecho y Genoma Humano* 1995 July-December; (3): 35-42. NRCBL: 15.3; 15.2; 15.4; 21.1. SC: le. Identifiers: Austria; Germany.

Colorado. *Laws, statutes, etc.* An act concerning genetic privacy [Approved: 1 June 2002]. Colorado: General Assembly, 2002. 2 p. [Online]. Accessed: http://www.state.co.us/gov_dir/leg_dir/olls/sl2002a/sl.262.pdf [2007 March 8]. NRCBL: 15.3; 8.3.1. SC: le. Note: Senate Bill 02-78, 63rd General Assembly, 2nd regular session. Introduced on January 11, 2002. Approved June 1, 2002.

Cutter, Mary Ann G. Managing genetic testing information: legal, ethical, and social challenges. *Revista de Derecho Genoma Humano = Law and the Human Genome Review* 1999 July-December; 11: 167-185. NRCBL: 15.3; 15.1; 9.3.1. SC: le.

Hlaca, Nenad. Human genome and protection of human rights in Croatia. *Revista de Derecho y Genoma Humano = Law and the Human Genome Review* 2006 January-June; (24): 65-73. NRCBL: 15.3; 8.4; 15.10. SC: le.

Human Genetics Commission [HGC] (Great Britain). The supply of genetic tests direct to the public: a consultation document. London: Human Genetics Commission, Dept. of Health, 2002 July. 27 p. [Online]. Accessed: http://www.hgc.gov.uk/UploadDocs/DocPub/Document/testingconsultation.pdf [27 July 2006]. NRCBL: 15.3; 5.3. SC: le.

Ibarreta, Dolores; Elles, Robert; Cassiman, Jean-Jacques; Rodriguez-Cerezo, Emilio; Dequeker, Elisabeth. Towards quality assurance and harmonization of genetic testing services in the European Union. *Nature Biotechnology* 2004 October; 22(10): 1230-1235. NRCBL: 15.3; 21.1. SC: le; em.

Idaho. *Laws, statutes, etc.* An act relating to genetic testing privacy; amending title 39, Idaho Code, by the addition of a new chapter 83, title 39, Idaho Code, to provide a short title, to define terms, to set forth restrictions regarding genetic testing information applicable to employers, to provide for a private right of action and to provide for enforcement; and amending section 41-1313, Idaho Code, to prohibit insurers from discriminating on the basis of a genetic test or private genetic information for certain purposes [Approved: 31 March 2006]. Idaho: State Legislature, 2006. 8 p. [Online]. Accessed: http://www3.state.id.us/oasis/2006/S1423.html [2007 March 9]. NRCBL: 15.3; 15.1; 8.4. SC: le. Identifiers: Genetic Testing Privacy Act. Note: Senate Bill No. 1423, 58th Legislature, 2nd regular session. Introduced on March 2, 2006. Approved on March 31, 2006.

Javitt, Gail H. Policy implications of genetic testing: not just for geneticists anymore. *Advances in Chronic Kidney Disease* 2006 April; 13(2): 178-182. NRCBL: 15.3; 5.3; 8.4; 16.3. SC: le.

Lemke, Thomas. Beyond genetic discrimination. Problems and perspectives of a contested notion. *Genomics, Society and Policy* 2005 December; 1(3): 22-40. NRCBL: 15.3; 4.2. SC: le; an.

Lucassen, A.; Kaye, J. Genetic testing without consent: the implications of the new Human Tissue Act 2004. *Journal of Medical Ethics* 2006 December; 32(12): 690-692. NRCBL: 15.3; 8.3.1. SC: le. Identifiers: Human Tissue Act 2004; United Kingdom (Great Britain).

Nebraska. *Laws, statutes, etc.* An act relating to genetic testing [Approved: 25 May 2001]. Nebraska: Legislative Bill 432, 97th Legislature. Slip Laws 2001-2002. 7 p. [Online]. Accessed: http://srvwww.unicam.state.ne.us/ unicamAllDrafting.html. NRCBL: 15.3. SC: le.

Nevada. *Laws, statutes, etc.* An act relating to genetic information; providing that it is an unlawful employment practice for an employer, a labor organization or an employment agency to discriminate against a person based on genetic information; and providing other matters properly relating thereto [Approved: 9 June 1999]. Nevada: State Legislature, 1999. 2 p. [Online]. Accessed: http://www.leg.state.nv.us/70th/bills/SB/SB16_EN.pdf [2007 March 9]. NRCBL: 15.3; 15.1. SC: le. Note: Senate Bill 16, 70th session, 1999 session. Introduced on January 18, 1999. Approved on June 9, 1999.

Nielsen, Linda. Genetic testing and privacy: a European perspective = Pruebas genéticas y derecho a la intimidad: una perspectiva europea. *Law and the Human Genome Review = Revista de Derecho y Genoma Humano* 1996 January-June; (4): 59-76. NRCBL: 15.3; 21.1; 8.4. SC: le. Identifiers: Europe.

Otlowski, Margaret. Genetic discrimination: meeting the challenges of an emerging issue [forum]. *University of New South Wales Law Journal* 2003; 26(3): 764-769. NRCBL: 15.3; 8.4; 9.3.1; 9.5.4. SC: le. Identifiers: Australia.

Paradise, Jordan. European opposition to exclusive control over predictive breast cancer testing and the inherent implications for U.S. patent law and public policy: a case study of the Myriad Genetics' BRCA patent controversy. *Food and Drug Law Journal* 2004; 59(1): 133-154. NRCBL: 15.3; 15.8; 1.3.5; 5.2; 5.3. SC: le. Identifiers: United States.

Sándor, Judit. Genetic data: old and new challenges in data protection. *In:* Glasa, J., ed. Ethics of Human Genetics: Challenges of the (Post) Genomic Era. Bratislava, Slovak Republic: Charis [and] IMEB Foundation; 2002: 89-97. NRCBL: 15.3; 8.4. SC: le.

Simon, Jürgen. Insurance and genetic testing in Germany and the international context. *In:* Sándor, Judit, ed. Society and Genetic Information: Codes and Laws in the Genetic Era. Budapest, Hungary; New York: CEU Press; 2003: 185-199. NRCBL: 15.3; 9.3.1; 21.1. SC: le.

Simon, Jürgen; Ravenstein, Christian. Gene tests and employees in an international comparison. *Revista de Derecho y Genoma Humano* 2005 July-December; (23): 167-190. NRCBL: 15.3; 16.3; 21.1. SC: le. Identifiers: Austria; Switzerland; United Kingdom (Great Britain).

Sismondo, Lauren J. GINA, what could you do for me one day?: The potential of the Genetic Information Nondiscrimination Act to protect the American public. *Washington University Journal of Law and Policy* 2006; 21: 459-481. NRCBL: 15.3; 8.4; 9.3.1; 16.3. SC: le.

Somek, Alexander. This is about ourselves: or, what makes genetic discrimination interesting. *In:* Stehr, Nico, ed. Biotechnology Between Commerce and Civil Society. New Brunswick, NJ: Transaction Publishers; 2004: 195-216. NRCBL: 15.3. SC: le.

STRATA Expert Group. Ethical, legal and social implications of genetic testing: research, development and clinical applications. *European Journal of Health Law* 2004 September; 11(3): 309-317. NRCBL: 15.3; 2.4; 18.2; 21.1. SC: le.

Taupitz, Jochen. Genetic analysis and the right to self-determination in German Civil War = Análisis genético y derecho de autodeterminación en el Derecho Civil Alemán. *Law and the Human Genome Review = Revista de Derecho y Genoma Humano* 1996 January-June; (4): 77-90. NRCBL: 15.3; 8.3.1; 8.4. SC: le.

Taylor, Mark J. Problems with targeting law reform at genetic discrimination. *In:* Árnason, Gardar; Nordal, Salvör; Árnason, Vilhjálmur, eds. Blood and Data: Ethical, Legal and Social Aspects of Human Genetic Databases. Reykjavík: University of Iceland Press; 2004: 347-352. NRCBL: 15.3. SC: le.

Trent, Ronald J.A. Essentially yours: the protection of human genetic information in Australia — the impact on clinical practice and the 'new genetics'. *University of New South Wales Law Journal* 2003; 26(3): 807-812. NRCBL: 15.3; 8.4; 1.3.5; 7.3. SC: le.

United States. Congress. House. A bill to amend the Public Health Service Act to prohibit health discrimination against individuals and their family members on the basis of genetic information, and for other purposes. Washington, DC: U.S. G.P.O., 2003. 7 p. [Online]. Accessed: http://frwebgate.access.gpo.gov/cgi-bin/useftp.cgi? IPaddress=162.140.64.21&file name=h3636ih.pdf& directory=/disk2/wais/data/108_cong_bills [2006 November 20]. NRCBL: 15.3. SC: le. Identifiers: Genetic Privacy and Nondiscrimination Act of 2003. Note: H.R. 3636, 108th Congress, 1st session. Introduced by Rep. Stearns,

---

NRCBL: National Reference Center for Bioethics Literature Classification Scheme   See inside front cover for terms.

237

November 26, 2003. Referred to the Committee on Energy and Commerce.

United States. Congress. House. A bill to prohibit discrimination by group health plans and employers based on genetic information. Washington, DC: U.S. G.P.O., 2006. 10 p. [Online]. Accessed: http://frwebgate.access.gpo.gov/cgi-bin/useftp.cgi?IPaddress=162.140.64.21&filename=h6125ih.pdf&directory=/diskb/wais/data/109_cong_bills [2006 November 1]. NRCBL: 15.3; 8.4. SC: le. Identifiers: Taxpayer Protection from Genetic Discrimination Act of 2006. Note: H.R. 6125, 109th Congress, 2d session. Introduced by Rep. Paul, September 20, 2006. Referred to the Committee on Government Reform and to the Committees on Education and the Workforce, Energy and Commerce, and Ways and Means.

United States. Congress. House. A bill to prohibit discrimination on the basis of genetic information with respect to health insurance. Washington, DC: U.S. G.P.O., 2003, 75 p. [Online]. Accessed: http://frwebgate.access.gpo.gov/cgi-bin/useftp.cgi?IPaddress=162.140.64.21&filename=h1910ih.pdf&directory=/disk2/wais/data/108_cong_bills [2006 November 27]. NRCBL: 15.3; 8.4; 9.3.1; 15.1. SC: le. Identifiers: Genetic Nondiscrimination in Health Insurance and Employment Act. Note: H.R. 1910, 108th Congress, 1st session. Introduced by Rep. Slaughter, May 1, 2003. Referred to the Committee on Energy and Commerce and in addition to the Committees on Ways and Means and Education and the Workforce.

United States. Congress. House. A bill to prohibit discrimination on the basis of genetic information with respect to health insurance. Washington, DC: U.S. G.P.O., 2001. 69 p. [Online]. Accessed: http://frwebgate.access.gpo.gov/cgi-bin/getdoc.cgi?dbname=107_cong_bills&docid= f:h602ih.txt.pdf [2007 March 8]. NRCBL: 15.3; 8.4; 9.3.1. SC: le. Identifiers: Genetic Nondiscrimination in Health Insurance and Employment Act. Note: H.R. 602, 107th Congress, 1st session. Introduced by Rep. Slaughter on February 13, 2001. Referred to the Committee on Energy and Commerce in addition to the Committees on Ways and Means, and Education and the Workforce.

United States. Congress. House. A bill to prohibit discrimination on the basis of genetic information with respect to health insurance and employment. Washington, DC: U.S. G.P.O., 2005. 81 p. [Online]. Accessed: http://frwebgate.access.gpo.gov/cgi-bin/useftp.cgi?IPaddress=162.140.64.21&filename=h1227ih.pdf&directory=/diskb/wais/data/109_cong_bills [2006 December 6]. NRCBL: 15.3; 8.4; 9.3.1; 15.1. SC: le. Identifiers: Genetic Information Nondiscrimination Act of 2005. Note: H.R. 1227, 109th Congress, 1st session. Introduced by Rep. Biggert, March 10, 2005. Referred to the Committee on Education and the Workforce, and in addition to the Committees on Energy and Commerce, and Ways and Means.

United States. Congress. House. A bill to prohibit health insurance and employment discrimination against individuals and their family members on the basis of predictive genetic information or genetic services. Washington, DC: U.S.G.P.O., 1999. 70 p. [Online]. Accessed: http://frwebgate.access.gpo.gov/cgi-bin/getdoc.cgi?dbname=106_cong_bills&docid=f:h2457ih.txt.pdf [2007 March 8]. NRCBL: 15.3; 8.4; 9.3.1. SC: le. Identifiers: Genetic Nondiscrimination in Health Insurance and Employment Act of 1999. Note: H.R. 2457, 106th Congress, 1st session. Introduced by Rep. Slaughter in the House of Representatives on July 1, 1999. Referred to the Committee on Commerce, and in addition to the Committees on Ways and Means, and Education in the Workforce.

United States. Congress. Senate. An act to prohibit discrimination on the basis of genetic information with respect to health insurance and employment. Washington, DC: U.S. G.P.O., 2003. 86 p. [Online]. Accessed: http://frwebgate.access.gpo.gov/cgi-bin/useftp.cgi?IPaddress=162.140.64.21&filename=s1053es.pdf&directory=/disk2/wais/data/108_cong_bills [2006 November 27]. NRCBL: 15.3; 15.1; 8.4; 9.3.1. SC: le. Identifiers: Genetic Information Nondiscrimination Act of 2003 (Engrossed as Agreed to or Passed by Senate). Note: S. 1053, 108th Congress, 1st session. Passed the Senate October 14, 2003.

United States. Congress. Senate. A bill to prohibit discrimination on the basis of genetic information with respect to health insurance and employment. Washington, DC: U.S. G.P.O., 2005. 85 p. [Online]. Accessed: http://frwebgate.access.gpo.gov/cgi-bin/useftp.cgi?IPaddress=162.140.64.21&filename=s306es.pdf&directory=/diskb/wais/data/109_cong_bills. NRCBL: 15.3; 8.4. SC: le. Identifiers: Genetic Information Nondiscrimination Act of 2005.

van Voorhees, Alexander. Truth in testing laws: a shot in the arm for designer gene tests. *Health Matrix: The Journal of Law-Medicine* 2006 Summer; 16(2): 797-829. NRCBL: 15.3; 8.3.1. SC: le.

Washington. *Laws, statutes, etc.* An act relating to genetic testing as a condition of employment; and adding a new section to chapter 49.44 of the Revised Code of Washington [Approved: 11 March 2004]. Washington: State Legislature, 2004. 3 p. [Online]. Accessed: http://www.leg.wa.gov/pub/billinfo/2003-04/Pdf/Bills/ Session%20Law%202004/6180. SL.pdf [2007 March 9]. NRCBL: 15.3; 15.1. SC: le. Note: Senate Bill 6180, 58th Legislature, 2004 regular session. Introduced on January 14,2004. Approved on March 11, 2004.

Weisbrot, David. Mad science or modern miracles? *Reform* 2001 Spring; 79: 5-9. NRCBL: 15.3; 8.4; 1.3.12. SC: le. Identifiers: Protection of Human Genetic Information; Australian Law Reform Commission [ALRC]; Australian Health Ethics Committee [AHEC].

Wolbring, Gregor. A disability rights approach to genetic discrimination. *In:* Sándor, Judit, ed. Society and Genetic Information: Codes and Laws in the Genetic Era. Budapest, Hungary; New York: CEU Press; 2003: 161-184. NRCBL: 15.3; 15.2. SC: le.

GENETICS

Genes for sale? = ¿Genes a la venta? [editorial]. *Revista de Derecho y Genoma Humano = Law and the Human Genome Review* 1998 January-June; (8): 15-18. NRCBL: 15.1; 9.3.1; 15.8.

Illuminating BiDil [editorial]. *Nature Biotechnology* 2005 August; 23(8): 903. NRCBL: 15.1; 9.7; 1.3.5; 15.11. Identifiers: Food and Drug Administration (FDA).

Legal and ethical norms in the field of genetics: a selection of international and national legal documents, reports, and policy recommendations. *In:* Sándor, Judit, ed. Society and Genetic Information: Codes and Laws in the Genetic Era. Budapest, Hungary; New York: CEU Press; 2003: 267-281. NRCBL: 15.1.

New international prospects for human rights and the human genome [editorial] = Nuevas perspectivas para los derechos humanos y el genoma humano en el ámbito internacional. *Revista de Derecho Genoma Humano = Law and the Human Genome Review* 1997 July-December; (7): 15-21. NRCBL: 15.1; 21.1. Identifiers: UNESCO.

Policing ourselves [editorial]. *Nature* 2006 May 25; 441(7092): 383. NRCBL: 15.1; 1.3.9; 5.3; 15.7. Identifiers: synthetic biology.

Proposed international guidelines on ethical issues in medical genetics and genetic services (Part I). *Revista de Derecho y Genoma Humano = Law and the Human Genome Review* 1998 January-June; (8): 219-233. NRCBL: 15.1; 21.1.

The debate on establishing a Taiwan biobank. *Formosan Journal of Medical Humanities* 2006 June; 7(1-2): 1-2. NRCBL: 15.1; 1.3.12.

Abraham, Abraham S. Genetic engineering and cloning. *In:* Rosner, Fred, ed. Medicine and Jewish Law. Volume III. Brooklyn, NY: Yashar Books, Inc.; 2005: 83-88. NRCBL: 15.1; 14.5; 1.2.

Abrams, Jerold J. Pragmatism, artificial intelligence, and posthuman bioethics: Shusterman, Rorty, Foucault. *Human Studies* 2004 September; 27(3): 241-258. NRCBL: 15.1; 1.1.

Aldhous, Peter. Tailored medicines for rich and poor alike. *New Scientist* 2006 September 9-15; 191(2568): 13. NRCBL: 15.1; 9.7; 21.1.

Alvarez-Castillo, Fatima; Feinholz, Dafna. Women in developing countries and benefit sharing. *Developing World Bioethics* 2006 December; 6(3): 113-121. NRCBL: 15.1; 1.1; 10; 21.1. SC: an.

Abstract: The aim of this paper is to show that any process of benefit sharing that does not guarantee the representation and participation of women in the decision-making process, as well as in the distribution of benefits, contravenes a central demand of social justice. It is argued that women, particularly in developing countries, can be excluded from benefits derived from genetic research because of existing social structures that promote and maintain discrimination. The paper describes how the structural problem of gender-based inequity can impact on benefit sharing processes. At the same time, examples are given of poor women's ability to organise themselves and to achieve social benefits for entire communities. Relevant international guidelines (e.g. the Convention on Biodiversity) recognise the importance of women's contributions to the protection of biodiversity and thereby, implicitly, their right to a share of the benefits, but no mechanism is outlined on how to bring this about. The authors make a clear recommendation to ensure women's participation in benefit sharing negotiations by demanding seats at the negotiation table.

Andorno, Roberto. Seeking common ground on genetic issues: the UNESCO Declaration on the Human Genome. *In:* Sándor, Judit, ed. Society and Genetic Information: Codes and Laws in the Genetic Era. Budapest, Hungary; New York: CEU Press; 2003: 105-123. NRCBL: 15.1.

Ayres, Ed. A landmark issue. *World Watch* 2002 July-August; 15(4): 3. NRCBL: 15.1. SC: po. Identifiers: genetic engineering.

Baccarini, Elvio. A liberal argument on the topic of genetic engineering. *Acta Analytica* 2001; 16(27): 49-66. NRCBL: 15.1; 1.1; 14.5. SC: an.

Bane, Audra; Brown, Lesli; Carter, Joy; Cote, Chris; Crider, Karin; de la Forest, Suzanne; Livingston, Michelle; Montero, Darrel. Life and death decisions: America's changing attitudes towards genetic engineering, genetic testing and abortion, 1972-98. *International Social Work* 2003 April; 46(2): 209-219. NRCBL: 15.1; 2.2; 12.5.2. SC: rv; em.

Banner, Michael; Suk, Jonathan E. Genomics in the UK: mapping the social science landscape. *Genomics, Society and Policy* 2006 August; 2(2): 1-27. NRCBL: 15.1; 1.3.12; 5.1; 1.1; 5.3. SC: em; rv. Identifiers: United Kingdom (Great Britain).

Abstract: This paper has been prepared from the perspective of the ESRC Genomics Policy and Research Forum, which has the particular mandate of linking social science research on genomics with ongoing public and policy debates. It is intended as a contribution to discussions about the future agenda for social scientific analyses of genomics. Given its scope, this paper is necessarily painted with a broad brush. It is presented in the hope that it can serve both as a useful reference for those less familiar with the themes and foci of UK-based social science research about genomics and, for those more engaged in the field, as a foundation for discussions about the future social sciences agenda in this area. This paper has four parts. The first identifies the boundaries of the topic. It is suggested that the boundaries of genomics are properly regarded by social scientists as soft rather than hard, and as encompassing far more than genomics as narrowly understood. In the second part, the UK context for

NRCBL: National Reference Center for Bioethics Literature Classification Scheme   See inside front cover for terms.

239

social science research is briefly described before proceeding to part three, which offers a survey of the major areas and patterns of research. This is organised by reference to the themes of globalisation, governance and regulation, and refers to 129 current or recently completed projects (surveyed during the winter of 2005) that address these themes. Part four proposes some appropriate areas for future research, drawing on and advancing what has been achieved thus far. Social scientific analyses of the nature and consequences of genomic science, it is claimed, have been crucially framed by the institutionalising of non-scientific considerations under the heading of ELSA/ELSI (Ethical, Legal and Social Aspects/Implications).It is suggested that an understanding of the limitations and consequences of this framing provides a vital starting point in considering future research agendas.

Barula, Archana. Designing humans. *Eubios Journal of Asian and International Bioethics* 2006 September; 16(5): 154-158. NRCBL: 15.1; 4.5.

Bauer, Martin W. Long-term trends in public sensitivities about genetic identification: 1973-2002. *In:* Árnason, Gardar; Nordal, Salvör; Árnason, Vilhjálmur, eds. Blood and Data: Ethical, Legal and Social Aspects of Human Genetic Databases. Reykjavík: University of Iceland Press; 2004: 143-159. NRCBL: 15.1; 1.3.7; 15.3; 21.1. SC: em.

Baumann-Hölzle, Ruth. Das menschliche Genom, eine zu bewahrende Ressource oder manipulierbares Material? *In:* Rehmann-Sutter, Christoph; Müller, Hansjakob, eds. Ethik und Gentherapie: Zum praktischen Diskurs um die molekulare Medizin. Tübingen: Attempto Verlag; 1995: 188-194. NRCBL: 15.1.

Beckwith, Jon. A historical view of social responsibility in genetics. *Bioscience* 1993 May; 43(5): 187-193. NRCBL: 15.1; 15.5; 15.6; 15.10; 7.1; 3.1.

Belicza, Biserka. Teaching about ethical aspects in human genetics to medical professionals: experience in Croatia. *In:* Glasa, J., ed. Ethics of Human Genetics: Challenges of the (Post) Genomic Era. Bratislava, Slovak Republic: Charis [and] IMEB Foundation; 2002: 41-52. NRCBL: 15.1; 2.3; 7.2.

Bengtsson, Karin Erika. Policy for human genetic resources as compared to environmental genetic resources. *In:* Árnason, Gardar; Nordal, Salvör; Árnason, Vilhjálmur, eds. Blood and Data: Ethical, Legal and Social Aspects of Human Genetic Databases. Reykjavík: University of Iceland Press; 2004: 339-346. NRCBL: 15.1; 1.3.12.

Berg, Thomas. Human brain cells in animal brains: philosophical and moral considerations. *National Catholic Bioethics Quarterly* 2006 Spring; 6(1): 89-107. NRCBL: 15.1; 18.1; 18.5.4; 22.1; 4.4; 1.1; 1.2; 5.3.

Bibeau, Gilles. Quel humanism pour un âge post-génomique?/ What kind of humanism in the post-genomique era? *Anthropologie et Sociétés* 2003; 27(3): 93-113 [Online]. Accessed: http://www.erudit.org/revue/as/2003/v27/n3/007926ar.pdf [25 January 2007]. NRCBL: 15.1; 15.4; 4.5; 1.3.1. SC: an.

Biesecker, Leslie G. Human genetics therapies and manipulations. *In:* Miller, Roman J.; Brubaker, Beryl H.; Peterson, James C., eds. Viewing New Creations with Anabaptist Eyes: Ethics of Biotechnology. Telford, PA: Cascadia Pub.; 2005: 39-57. NRCBL: 15.1; 15.4.

Birch, Kean. The neoliberal underpinnings of the bioeconomy: the ideological discourses and practices of economic competitiveness. *Genomics, Society and Policy* 2006 December; 2(3): 1-15. NRCBL: 15.1; 1.3.2.
   Abstract: When we talk about ideology and new genetics we tend to think of concepts like geneticisation and genetic essentialism, which present genetics and biology in deterministic terms. However, the aim of this article is to consider how a particular economic ideology – neoliberalism – has affected the bioeconomy rather than assuming that it is the inherent qualities of biotechnology that determine market value. In order to do this, the paper focuses on the discourses and practices of economic competitiveness that pervade biotechnology policy-making in the UK, Europe and the USA. Finally it will consider how the manufacture of scarcity – in order to produce the bioeconomy – has led to a problematic focus on a specific innovation paradigm that may prove detrimental to the development and distribution of new biotechnologies.

Blukis, Uldis. Diversity is protection against our ignorance. *World Watch* 2002 September-October; 15(5): 6. NRCBL: 15.1; 4.5. Identifiers: inheritable genetic modification.

Blumenthal, David; Campbell, Eric G.; Gokhale, Manjusha; Yucel, Recai; Clarridge, Brian; Hilgartner, Stephen; Holtzman, Neil A. Data withholding in genetics and other life sciences: prevalences and predictors. *Academic Medicine* 2006 February; 81(2): 137-145. NRCBL: 15.1; 1.3.9. SC: em.

Bosch, Xavier. Group ponders genomics and public health. *JAMA: The Journal of the American Medical Association* 2006 April 19; 295(15): 1762. NRCBL: 15.1; 9.1. Identifiers: European Union.

Bostrom, Nick; Ord, Toby. The reversal test: eliminating status quo bias in applied ethics. *Ethics* 2006 July; 116(4): 656-679. NRCBL: 15.1; 4.5; 5.2; 15.4. Identifiers: cognitive genetic enhancement.

Bovenberg, Jasper A. Blood, sweat, and grants—'honest Jim' and the European database-right. *Genetics, Society, and Policy* 2005 August; 1(2): 1-28. NRCBL: 15.1; 1.3.12; 1.3.9; 5.3.

Bovenberg, Jasper A. Towards an international system of ethics and governance of biobanks: a "special status" for genetic data? *Critical Public Health* 2005 December; 15(4): 369-383. NRCBL: 15.1; 1.3.12; 18.1. Identifiers: UNESCO Declaration on Human Genetic Data.

Brandt-Rauf, Sherry I.; Raveis, Victoria H.; Drummond, Nathan F.; Conte, Jill A.; Rothman, Sheila M. Ashkenazi Jews and breast cancer: the consequences of linking ethnic identity to genetic disease. *American Jour-*

nal of Public Health 2006 November; 96(11): 1979-1988. NRCBL: 15.1; 9.5.4.

Abstract: We explored the advantages and disadvantages of using ethnic categories in genetic research. With the discovery that certain breast cancer gene mutations appeared to be more prevalent in Ashkenazi Jews, breast cancer researchers moved their focus from high-risk families to ethnicity. The concept of Ashkenazi Jews as genetically unique, a legacy of Tay-Sachs disease research and a particular reading of history, shaped this new approach even as methodological imprecision and new genetic and historical research challenged it. Our findings cast doubt on the accuracy and desirability of linking ethnic groups to genetic disease. Such linkages exaggerate genetic differences among ethnic groups and lead to unequal access to testing and therapy.

Brewer, Janet K. Individual boundaries and the impact of genetic databases upon collectivist cultures: molecular, cognitive and philosophical views. *In:* Árnason, Gardar; Nordal, Salvör; Árnason, Vilhjálmur, eds. Blood and Data: Ethical, Legal and Social Aspects of Human Genetic Databases. Reykjavík: University of Iceland Press; 2004: 291-296. NRCBL: 15.1; 1.3.12; 21.7.

Bruce, Ann; Tait, Joyce. Interests, values, and genetic databases. *In:* Árnason, Gardar; Nordal, Salvör; Árnason, Vilhjálmur, eds. Blood and Data: Ethical, Legal and Social Aspects of Human Genetic Databases. Reykjavík: University of Iceland Press; 2004: 211-216. NRCBL: 15.1; 1.3.12.

Bruce, Donald. Categorizing genes: commodifying people? *In:* Árnason, Gardar; Nordal, Salvör; Árnason, Vilhjálmur, eds. Blood and Data: Ethical, Legal and Social Aspects of Human Genetic Databases. Reykjavík: University of Iceland Press; 2004: 269-273. NRCBL: 15.1; 1.2; 4.5; 15.3.

Brunk, Conrad G. Biotechnology and the future. *In:* Miller, Roman J.; Brubaker, Beryl H.; Peterson, James C., eds. Viewing New Creations with Anabaptist Eyes: Ethics of Biotechnology. Telford, PA: Cascadia Pub.; 2005: 257-260. NRCBL: 15.1; 1.2.

Brunk, Conrad G. The biotechnology vision: insight from Anabaptist values. *In:* Miller, Roman J.; Brubaker, Beryl H.; Peterson, James C., eds. Viewing New Creations with Anabaptist Eyes: Ethics of Biotechnology. Telford, PA: Cascadia Pub.; 2005: 106-121. NRCBL: 15.1; 1.2; 1.3.11.

Budinger, Thomas F.; Budinger, Miriam D. Ethics of genetically modified organisms. *In their:* Ethics of Emerging Technologies: Scientific Facts and Moral Challenges. Hoboken, NJ: John Wiley and Sons, 2006: 186-222. NRCBL: 15.1; 1.3.11.

Burack, Jeffrey H. Jewish reflections on genetic enhancement. *Journal of Society of Christian Ethics* 2006 Spring-Summer; 26(1): 137-161. NRCBL: 15.1; 4.5; 1.2; 4.4.

Burk, Dan L. Bioinformatics lessons from the open source movement. *In:* Tavani, Herman T., ed. Ethics, Com-

puting, and Genomics. Sudbury, MA: Jones and Bartlett; 2006: 247-254. NRCBL: 15.1; 1.3.12.

Busby, Helen. UK biobank: social and political landscapes. *In:* Árnason, Gardar; Nordal, Salvör; Árnason, Vilhjálmur, eds. Blood and Data: Ethical, Legal and Social Aspects of Human Genetic Databases. Reykjavík: University of Iceland Press; 2004: 307-311. NRCBL: 15.1; 1.3.12; 19.4.

Busby, Helen; Martin, Paul. Biobanks, national identity and imagined communities: the case of UK biobank. *Science as Culture* 2006 September; 15(3): 237-251. NRCBL: 15.1; 1.3.12; 13.1; 18.3; 7.1.

Butzel, Henry M. Teaching at the interface between genetics and law. *Politics and the Life Sciences* 1986 August; 5(1): 54-58. NRCBL: 15.1; 5.1; 2.3.

Byers, Peter H. 2005 ASHG Presidential Address. If only we spoke the same language—we would have so much to discuss. *American Journal of Human Genetics* 2006 March; 78(3): 368-372. NRCBL: 15.1; 15.3; 18.2. Identifiers: American Society of Human Genetics.

Cahill, Lisa Sowle. Biotechnology, genes, and justice. *In her:* Theological Bioethics: Participation, Justice, and Change. Washington, DC: Georgetown University Press; 2005: 211-251. NRCBL: 15.1; 1.2.

Calnan, Michael; Wainwright, David; Glasner, Peter; Newbury-Ecob, Ruth; Ferlie, Ewan. 'Medicine's next goldmine?' The implications of new genetic health technologies for the health service. *Medicine, Health Care, and Philosophy* 2006; 9(1): 33-41. NRCBL: 15.1; 15.3; 15.4; 9.1.

Abstract: There is considerable uncertainty about the implications of the new genetics for health services. These [sic; There] are the enthusiasts who argue that molecular genetics will transform health care and others argue that the scope for genetic interventions is limited. The aim of this paper is to examine some of the questions, tensions and difficulties which face health care providers particularly in developed countries as they try to come to terms with the dilemmas raised by new genetic health care technologies (NGHTs). It identifies questions for research which may help the development of robust and flexible strategies for implementation.

Caplan, Arthur L. Engineering plants, microbes, and animals. *In his:* Smart Mice, Not-So-Smart People: An Interesting and Amusing Guide to Bioethics. Lanham, MD: Rowman & Littlefield, 2007: 47-58. NRCBL: 15.1; 1.3.11; 22.3. SC: po.

Caulfield, Timothy. Perceptions of risk and human genetic databases: consent and confidentiality policies. *In:* Árnason, Gardar; Nordal, Salvör; Árnason, Vilhjálmur, eds. Blood and Data: Ethical, Legal and Social Aspects of Human Genetic Databases. Reykjavík: University of Iceland Press; 2004: 283-289. NRCBL: 15.1; 1.3.12; 8.4; 18.3.

NRCBL: National Reference Center for Bioethics Literature Classification Scheme   See inside front cover for terms.

241

Chadwick, Ruth; Marturano, Antonio. Computing, genetics, and policy: theoretical and practical considerations. *In:* Tavani, Herman T., ed. Ethics, Computing, and Genomics. Sudbury, MA: Jones and Bartlett; 2006: 75-83. NRCBL: 15.1.

Chai, Jianhua. Human genetic resources, genetic information and medical ethics. *In:* Döring, Ole; Chen, Renbiao, eds. Advances in Chinese Medical Ethics: Chinese and International Perspectives. Hamburg: Institut für Asienkunde; 2002: 159-163. NRCBL: 15.1. Note: Proceedings of the Second Sino-German Interdisciplinary Symposium about Medical Ethics in China, Shanghai, 19-23 October, 1999.

Check, Erika. Synthetic biologists try to calm fears [news]. *Nature* 2006 May 25; 441(7092): 388-389. NRCBL: 15.1; 1.3.9; 5.1; 15.7.

Cheng, Wan-Chiung; Li, Wan-Ping. A study on the ethical, legal, and social aspects of the Chinese genetic database in Taiwan. *In:* Árnason, Gardar; Nordal, Salvör; Árnason, Vilhjálmur, eds. Blood and Data: Ethical, Legal and Social Aspects of Human Genetic Databases. Reykjavík: University of Iceland Press; 2004: 45-49. NRCBL: 15.1; 1.3.12.

Cody, Jannine D. Creating partnerships and improving health care: the role of genetic advocacy groups. *Genetics in Medicine* 2006 December; 8(12): 797-799. NRCBL: 15.1; 9.5.1.

Cole, Simon A. The myth of fingerprints: the legacy of forensic fingerprinting and arrestee. *GeneWatch* 2006 November-December; 19(6): 3-6. NRCBL: 15.1; 1.3.5; 1.3.12. Identifiers: California.

Conrad, Peter. Use of expertise: sources, quotes, and voice in the reporting of genetics in the news. *Public Understanding of Science* 1999; 8: 285-302. NRCBL: 15.1; 1.3.7; 5.1. SC: em.

Coors, Marilyn E. Considering chimeras: the confluence of genetic engineering and ethics. *National Catholic Bioethics Quarterly* 2006 Spring; 6(1): 75-87. NRCBL: 15.1; 18.1; 22.1; 5.3; 4.4; 1.1; 3.2.

Council for Responsible Genetics. Intelligence and genetic determinism. *GeneWatch* 2006 November-December; 19(6): 9-12. NRCBL: 15.1.

Council for Responsible Genetics. Sexual orientation and genetic discrimination. *GeneWatch* 2006 July-August; 19(4): i-iv. NRCBL: 15.1; 10.

Cutter, Anthony Mark. Genetic databases and what the rat won't do: what is dignity at law? *In:* Árnason, Gardar; Nordal, Salvör; Árnason, Vilhjálmur, eds. Blood and Data: Ethical, Legal and Social Aspects of Human Genetic Databases. Reykjavík: University of Iceland Press; 2004: 217-222. NRCBL: 15.1; 1.3.12; 4.4; 18.2.

Cutter, Anthony Mark. To clear or convict? The role of genomics in criminal justice. *Genomics, Society and Policy* 2006 May; 2(1): 1-15. NRCBL: 15.1; 1.3.5.
Abstract: Recognising that the advent of new scientific or technological developments is often met with conflicting reactions, this paper explores the various attitudes to police uses of DNA. Using the National DNA Database of England and Wales (NDNAD) as a vehicle for analysis, this paper identifies the need to balance the utility of the database, and others like it, with issues relating to the privacy of those whose data is contained within it. As the paper explores the impact of the NDNAD, and by association other databases designed for the same purpose, we are faced with complex utopian visions of a criminal justice service armed with an all powerful database for the benefit of society, contrasted with the dystopian vision of a criminal justice service, armed with the identical, all powerful database intent on mischief to our detriment. In conclusion, the paper observes that governance of such databases is difficult in the face of conflicting and competing interests, and suggests a theoretical framework that would seek to create a database that has the maximum utility, but protects those within it from harm.

De Jonge, Bram; Korthals, Michiel. Vicissitudes of benefit sharing of crop genetic resources: downstream and upstream. *Developing World Bioethics* 2006 December; 6(3): 144-157. NRCBL: 15.1; 1.1; 1.3.11; 9.4; 21.1. SC: an.
Abstract: In this article, we will first give a historic overview of the concept of benefit sharing and its appearance in official agreements, particularly with respect to crop genetic resources. It will become clear that, at present, benefit sharing is primarily considered as an instrument of compensation or exchange, and thus refers to commutative justice. However, we believe that such a narrow interpretation of benefit sharing disregards, and even undermines, much of its (historical)content and potency, especially where crop genetic resources are concerned. We argue that benefit sharing should not be based merely on commutative justice but rather on a broader model that is also grounded in the concept of distributive justice. This has repercussions for the application of benefit sharing, which we try to clarify by distinguishing between downstream and upstream benefit sharing. Upstream benefit sharing is not so much inspired by compensation for actions done, or the distribution downstream of benefits developed, but by the idea of shared decision-making on the research and development of resources fundamental to human welfare. Going upstream in the research process of crop genetic resources, and determining research agendas and improving crops according to the needs of the poor, benefit sharing may well be a tool to contribute to world food security and global justice. We concretize our ideas on upstream benefit sharing by introducing a set of criteria that determine the success of consultations on agricultural research agenda setting.

de Melo-Martín, Inmaculada; Hanks, Craig. Genetics technologies and women: the importance of context. *Bulletin of Science, Technology and Society* 2001 October 1; 21(5): 354-360. NRCBL: 15.1; 10.

de Rosnay, Joël. Biology, power and responsibility. *Diogenes (International Council for Philosophy and Humanistic Studies)* 1980 Spring; (109): 77-91. NRCBL: 15.1; 1.3.9; 5.3.

de Vries, Rob. Genetic engineering and the integrity of animals. *Journal of Agricultural and Environmental Ethics* 2006; 19(5): 469-493. NRCBL: 15.1; 22.1. SC: an.

de Vries, R. Ethical concepts regarding the genetic engineering of laboratory animals. *Medicine, Health Care and Philosophy* 2006; 9(2): 211-225. NRCBL: 15.1; 22.2; 22.3. SC: an; em.

Abstract: Intrinsic value and animal integrity are two key concepts in the debate on the ethics of the genetic engineering of laboratory animals. These concepts have, on the one hand, a theoretical origin and are, on the other hand, based on the moral beliefs of people not directly involved in the genetic modification of animals. This 'external' origin raises the question whether these concepts need to be adjusted or extended when confronted with the moral experiences and opinions of people directly involved in the creation or use of transgenic laboratory animals. To answer this question, 35 persons from the practice of biomedical research who are directly involved in genetic engineering (scientists, biotechnicians, animal caretakers and laboratory animal scientists) were interviewed. They were asked to give their moral opinion on different aspects of the genetic engineering of animals and to react to statements about the concepts of intrinsic value and animal integrity. Analysis of the interviews showed that, contrary to what is often assumed, the respondents embraced these concepts, even those senses that (more) specifically apply to genetic engineering. And although the respondents raised some objections that go beyond issues of animal welfare, these objections could quite well be expressed in terms of the concepts of intrinsic value and animal integrity. In short, the results of the present study strongly suggest that these concepts do not have to be adjusted or extended in the light of the moral experiences and opinions from practice.

Degregori, Thomas R. Genetically modified foods. *In:* Mitcham, Carl, ed. Encyclopedia of Science, Technology, and Ethics. Farmington Hills, MI: Thomson/Gale, 2005: 836-838. NRCBL: 15.1; 1.3.11; 5.1.

Dickens, Bernard M. Genetics and artificial procreation in Canada. *In:* Meulders-Klein, Marie-Thérèse; Deech, Ruth; Vlaardingerbroek, Paul, eds. Biomedicine, the Family and Human Rights. New York: Kluwer Law International, 2002: 87-105. NRCBL: 15.1.

Dissanayake, V.H.W.; Simpson, R.; Jayasekara, R.W. Attitudes towards the new genetic and assisted reproductive technologies in Sri Lanka: a preliminary report. *New Genetics and Society* 2002 March; 21(1): 65-74. NRCBL: 15.1; 14.1; 12.5.2; 7.1. SC: em.

Döring, Ole. Human genetics and ethics in China. *Eubios Journal of Asian and International Bioethics* 1997 September; 7: 3 p. [Online]. Accessed: http://www.biol.tsukuba.ac.jp/~macer/EJ75/ej75c.html [2005 July 21]. NRCBL: 15.1; 21.1; 21.7.

Doyle, Alan; Rawle, Frances; Greenaway, Peter. The UK Biobank. *In:* Sándor, Judit, ed. Society and Genetic Information: Codes and Laws in the Genetic Era. Budapest, Hungary; New York: CEU Press; 2003: 247-263. NRCBL: 15.1.

Dundes, Lauren. Is the American public ready to embrace DNA as a crime-fighting tool? A survey assessing public support for DNA database. *Bulletin of Science, Technology and Society* 2001 October 1; 21(5): 369-375. NRCBL: 15.1; 1.3.12; 1.3.5.

Egziabher, Berehan Gebre; Benatar, Soloman; Annas, George J.; Agam, Hasmy; Arya, Sadhana; Menon, Nivedita; Lokaneeta, Jinee; Pratt, Dave; Ho, Mae-Wan; Zhu, Yifei; Blackwelder, Brent; Dubois, Mark; Hayes, Randy; Kennedy, Robert F., Jr.; Knox, John A.; Musil, Robert K.; Passacantando, John; Perrault, Michele; Ritchie, Mark. Views from around the world. *World Watch* 2002 July-August; 15(4): 24-25. NRCBL: 15.1; 21.7. SC: po. Identifiers: genetic engineering.

Ellison, George T.H.; Jones, Ian Rees. Social identities and the 'new genetics': scientific and social consequences. *Critical Public Health* 2002; 12(3): 265-282. NRCBL: 15.1; 15.6; 18.1; 18.6.

European Parliament. Temporary Committee on Human Genetics and Other New Technologies in Modern Medicine. Final report on the ethical, legal, economic and social implications of human genetics. Strasbourg/Brussels/Luxembourg: European Parliament [A5- 0391/2001], 2001 November 8: 1-118. NRCBL: 15.1; 15.3; 18.2; 18.6; 21.1.

European Society of Human Genetics [ESHG]. Genetic information and testing in insurance and employment: technical, social and ethical issues. *European Journal of Human Genetics* 2003 December; 11(Supplement 2): S11-S12. NRCBL: 15.1; 9.3.1.

Evans, John H. Stratification in knowledge production: author prestige and the influence of an American academic debate. *Poetics* 2005 April; 33(2): 111-133. NRCBL: 15.1; 5.1. SC: em.

Facio, Flavia M. One size does not fit all. *American Journal of Bioethics* 2006 November-December; 6(6): 40-42; author reply W10-W12. NRCBL: 15.1; 18.2; 8.1. Comments: Vardit Ravitsky and Benjamin S. Wilfond. Disclosing individual genetic results to research participants. American Journal of Bioethics 2006 November-December; 6(6): 8-17.

Featherstone, Carol. Testing gene therapy vectors in healthy volunteers [news]. *Molecular Medicine Today* 1997 July; 3(7): 277. NRCBL: 15.1; 18.5.1.

Fenton, Elizabeth. Liberal eugenics and human nature: against Habermas. *Hastings Center Report* 2006 November-December; 36(6): 35-42. NRCBL: 15.1; 4.5; 15.5; 1.1. Identifiers: Food and Drug Administration.

Fleising, Usher. Genetic essentialism, mana, and the meaning of DNA. *New Genetics and Society* 2001 April; 20(1): 43-57. NRCBL: 15.1; 1.3.1.

Forbes, Ian. States of uncertainty: governing the empire of biotechnology. *New Genetics and Society* 2006 April; 25(1): 69-88. NRCBL: 15.1; 1.3.5; 5.1.

NRCBL: National Reference Center for Bioethics Literature Classification Scheme   See inside front cover for terms.

243

Foster, M.W.; Royal, C.D.M.; Sharp, R.R. The routinisation of genomics and genetics: implications for ethical practices. *Journal of Medical Ethics* 2006 November; 32(11): 635-638. NRCBL: 15.1. SC: an.

Abstract: Among bioethicists and members of the public, genetics is often regarded as unique in its ethical challenges. As medical researchers and clinicians increasingly combine genetic information with a range of non-genetic information in the study and clinical management of patients with common diseases, the unique ethical challenges attributed to genetics must be re-examined. A process of genetic routinisation that will have implications for research and clinical ethics, as well as for public conceptions of genetic information, is constituted by the emergence of new forms of genetic medicine, in which genetic information is interpreted in a multifactorial frame of reference. Although the integration of genetics in medical research and treatment may be a helpful corrective to the mistaken assumptions of genetic essentialism or determinism, the routinisation of genetics may have unintended consequences for the protection of genetic information, perceptions of non-genetic information and the loss of genetic research as a laboratory for exploring issues in research and clinical ethics. Consequently, new ethical challenges are presented by the increasing routinisation of genetic information in both biomedical and public spheres.

Foster, M.W.; Sharp, R.R. Will investments in biobanks, prospective cohorts, and markers of common patterns of variation benefit other populations for drug response and disease susceptibility gene discovery? *Pharmacogenomics Journal* 2005; 5(2): 75-80. NRCBL: 15.1; 9.7.

Friedlaender, Jonathan S. Commentary: changing standards of informed consent: raising the bar. *In:* Turner, Trudy R. ed. Biological Anthropology and Ethics: From Repatriation to Genetic Identity. Albany, NY: State University of New York Press; 2005: 263-274. NRCBL: 15.1; 18.3; 18.5.9.

Fryer-Edwards, Kelly; Fullerton, Stephanie M. Relationships with test-tubes: where's the reciprocity? *American Journal of Bioethics* 2006 November-December; 6(6): 36-38; author reply W10-W12. NRCBL: 15.1; 8.1; 8.2. Comments: Vardit Ravitsky and Benjamin S. Wilfond. Disclosing individual genetic results to research participants. American Journal of Bioethics 2006 November-December; 6(6): 8-17.

Fuchs-Kittowski, Klaus; Rosenthal, Hans A.; Rosenthal, André. Die Entschlüsselung des Humangenoms — ambivalente Auswirkungen auf Gesellschaft und Wissenschaft = Decoding the human genome — ambivalent effects on society and science. *Erwägen Wissen Ethik* 2005; 16(2): 149-234. NRCBL: 15.1; 15.10; 14.1.

Fukuyama, Francis. In defense of nature, human and non-human. *World Watch* 2002 July-August; 15(4): 30-32. NRCBL: 15.1; 5.3. SC: po.

Ganache, Isabelle. "Commercial revolution" of science: the complex reality and experience of genetic and genomic scientists. *Genomics, Society and Policy* 2006 December; 2(3): 96-114. NRCBL: 15.1; 5.3; 15.8; 21.1. SC: em.

Abstract: According to advocates and authors from different disciplines interested in biomedicine, biomedical research in genetics and genomics has the potential to transform medicine, the economy, society, and humanity as a whole. Believing in this potential, biomedical scientists produce knowledge and participate in the decisions concerning the orientation of this research and its applications. Through a qualitative analysis of scientists' practice-related discourse, we identified three main sources of complexity in their involvement in the "commercial revolution" of science. First, scientists insist on the existence of different types of university-industry relationships. Second, they urge that the multiple realities of genetic and genomic research be acknowledged. Third, they present themselves as individuals in a diverse scientific community, each with a unique position in this commercial revolution. This paper draws attention to these complexities because they must be considered when engaging in a study of genetics and genomics advances from a research ethics perspective.

Gandhi, Gursatej. Impact of modern genetics: a Sikh perspective. *In:* Sleeboom, Margaret, ed. Genomics in Asia: A Clash of Bioethical Interests? New York: Kegan Paul; 2004: 51-65. NRCBL: 15.1; 1.2; 15.3.

García-Sancho, Miguel. The rise and fall of the idea of genetic information (1948-2006). *Genomics, Society and Policy* 2006 December; 2(3): 16-36. NRCBL: 15.1; 15.10.

Abstract: On 26 June 2000, during the presentation of the Human Genome Project's first draft, Bill Clinton, then President of the United States, claimed that "today we are learning the language in which God created life". Behind his remarks lay a story of more than half a century involving the understanding of DNA as information. This paper analyses that story, discussing the origins of the informational view of our genes during the early 1950s, how such a view affected the research on the genetic code (1950s and '60s) and the transformation of the information idea in the context of DNA sequencing and bioinformatics ('80s and '90s). I suggest that the concept of DNA as information reached a climax with the proposal of the Human Genome Project (HGP), but is currently facing a crisis coinciding with the questioning of the information society. Finally, I discuss the emergence of systems biology as an alternative paradigm.

Genetic Interest Group [GIG]; Mehta, Pritti. Promoting equity of access to genetic healthcare: a guide to the development of linguistically and culturally competent communication services. London: Genetic Interest Group [GIG], 2005 November: 38 p. [Online]. Accessed: http://gig.org.uk/docs/promotingaccess.pdf [2006 July 26]. NRCBL: 15.1; 9.2. Note: The Translation Project is a core activity of the London IDEAS Genetic Knowledge Park, funded by the Department of Health and the Department of Trade and Industry, and is collaboration between GIG and the North West Thames Regional Genetics Service.

German Society of Human Genetics [GfH]. Committee for Public Relations and Ethical Issues. Position paper of the German Society of Human Genetics. *Med Genetik* 1996; 8: 125-130 (13 pages) [Online]Accessed:

http://www.medgenetik.de/sondedruck/en/Position_paper.pdf [2005 December 2]. NRCBL: 15.1.

Gilbert, Scott F.; Tyler, Anna L.; Zackin, Emily J. New perspectives on old issues: genetic essentialism. *In their:* Bioethics and the New Embryology: Springboards for Debate. Sunderland, MA: Sinauer Associates; 2005: 227-239. NRCBL: 15.1.

Gilbert, Scott F.; Tyler, Anna L.; Zackin, Emily J. Should we modify the human genome?: should we allow the genetic engineering of human beings? *In their:* Bioethics and the New Embryology: Springboards for Debate. Sunderland, MA: Sinauer Associates; 2005: 199-212. NRCBL: 15.1; 4.5; 15.3.

González, Javier García. Penal regulation of gene technologies in Portugal. A case of normative standstill = Regulación penal de las genotecnologías: Portugal. Un ejemplo de inmovilismo normativo. *Law and the Human Genome Review= Revista de Derecho y Genoma Humano* 1996 July-December; (5): 185-193. NRCBL: 15.1; 14.1; 1.3.5.

Grace, Eric S. Ethical issues. *In his:* Biotechnology Unzipped: Promises and Realities. Revised second edition. Washington, DC: Joseph Henry Press; 2006: 191-223. NRCBL: 15.1; 1.3.11; 14.5.

Gracia Guillén, Diego. Pharmacogen-ethics. *In:* Lolas Stepke, Fernando; Agar Corbinos, Lorenzo, eds. Interfaces Between Bioethics and the Empirical Social Sciences. Buenos Aires, Argentina: World Health Organization; 2002: 53-65. NRCBL: 15.1; 9.7; 1.1.

Greely, Henry T. The revolution in human genetics: implications for human societies. *South Carolina Law Review* 2001 Winter; 52(2): 377-381. NRCBL: 15.1; 15.3; 5.3.

Gremmen, Bart. Genomics and the intrinsic value of plants. *Genomics, Society and Policy* 2005 December; 1(3): 1-7. NRCBL: 15.1; 1.3.11.

Griffiths, Paul E.; Stotz, Karola. Genes in the postgenomic era. *Theoretical Medicine and Bioethics* 2006; 27(6): 499-521. NRCBL: 15.1; 3.1. SC: an.

Gudding, Gabriel. The phenotype/genotype distinction and the disappearance of the body. *Journal of the History of Ideas* 1996 July; 57(3): 525-545. NRCBL: 15.1; 2.2; 4.4.

Haga, Susanne B. Policy implications of defining race and more by genome profiling. *Genomics, Society and Policy* 2006 May; 2(1): 57-71. NRCBL: 15.1; 3.1; 15.11.
Abstract: The genome revolution has provided the basis for many new applications in diverse areas such as health, food and agriculture, and forensics. While standard DNA profiling has become the paramount form of identification in forensics, expansion of genomic applications is being considered and tested to provide more descriptive information to facilitate the capture of perpetrators. Two major applications are being explored and tested: 1) ancestry profiling from which race can be inferred; and 2) profiling for physical traits to provide a genetic-based description or sketch. The use and incorporation of these new applications raises several logistical questions and ethical issues. This article will explore some of the policy implications in the use of expanded genome profiling for forensics purposes.

Hale, Benjamin. The moral considerability of invasive transgenic animals. *Journal of Agricultural and Environmental Ethics* 2006; 19(4): 337-366. NRCBL: 15.1; 22.2; 19.1; 16.1. SC: an. Identifiers: xenotransplantation genetically modified animals (XGMA).

Halweil, Brian. The war of words and images. *World Watch* 2002 July-August; 15(4): 37-39. NRCBL: 15.1. SC: po. Identifiers: human genetic modification.

Harvey, Rosemary D. Pioneers of genetics: a comparison of the attitudes of William Bateson and Erwin Baur to eugenics. *Notes and Records of the Royal Society of London* 1995 January; 49(1): 105-117. NRCBL: 15.1; 15.5.

Harvey-Blakenship, Michele; Hocking, Barbara Ann. Genetic restitution?: DNA, compensation, and biological families. *In:* Tong, Rosemarie; Donchin, Anne; Dodds, Susan, eds. Linking Visions: Feminist Bioethics, Human Rights, and the Developing World. Lanham, MD: Rowman and Littlefield Publishers; 2004: 203-234. NRCBL: 15.1; 1.3.5.

Hathout, H. An Islamic perspective on human genetic and reproductive technologies. *Eastern Mediterranean Health Journal* 2006; 12(Supplement 2): S22-S28 [Online]. Accessed: http://www.emro.who.int/publications/EMHJ/12_S2/PDF/3.pdf [2007 January 4]. NRCBL: 15.1; 1.2; 14.1. Note: Abstract in French and Arabic.

Hayes, Richard. The science and politics of genetically modified humans. *World Watch* 2002 July-August; 15(4): 11-12. NRCBL: 15.1. SC: po.

Häyry, Matti. Do regulations address concerns? *In:* Árnason, Gardar; Nordal, Salvör; Árnason, Vilhjálmur, eds. Blood and Data: Ethical, Legal and Social Aspects of Human Genetic Databases. Reykjavík: University of Iceland Press; 2004: 201-207. NRCBL: 15.1; 1.3.12.

Hedgecoe, Adam; Martin, Paul. The drugs don't work: expectations and the shaping of the pharmacogenetics. *Social Studies of Science* 2003 June; 33(3): 327-364. NRCBL: 15.1; 9.7; 2.1; 5.1. SC: an; rv.

Heffernan, Teresa. Bovine anxieties, virgin births, and the secret of life. *Cultural Critique* 2003 Winter; (53): 116-133. NRCBL: 15.1; 22.2; 14.5; 4.4; 1.3.9.

Hindmarsh, Richard. The problems of genetic engineering. *Peace Review* 2000 December; 12(4): 541-547. NRCBL: 15.1; 18.6; 5.2.

Hoeyer, Klaus; Tutton, Richard. "Ethics was here": studying the language-games of ethics in the case of UK

NRCBL: National Reference Center for Bioethics Literature Classification Scheme   See inside front cover for terms.

245

Biobank. *Critical Public Health* 2005 December; 15(4): 385-397. NRCBL: 15.1; 1.3.12; 18.1; 2.1.

Hoffman, Paul W. The brethren discuss genetic engineering. *Brethren Life and Thought* 1986 Autumn; 31(4): 201-208. NRCBL: 15.1; 1.2.

Hofmann, Bjørn. Do biobanks promote paternalism? On the loss of autonomy in the quest for individual independence. *In:* Árnason, Gardar; Nordal, Salvör; Árnason, Vilhjálmur, eds. Blood and Data: Ethical, Legal and Social Aspects of Human Genetic Databases. Reykjavík: University of Iceland Press; 2004: 237-242. NRCBL: 15.1; 1.1; 1.3.12.

Hofmann, Bjørn. Forensic uses and misuses of DNA: a case report from Norway. *Genomics, Society and Policy* 2006 May; 2(1): 129-131. NRCBL: 15.1; 1.3.5.
Abstract: New technology generates fantastic possibilities which challenge traditional distinctions between good and bad. Genetic analysis of DNA for forensic purposes is but one example of this. Here society's need for convicting criminals can conflict with the same society's need to assure the confidentiality of information about its members and their trust in its institutions. In order to illustrate the complexity of such challenges, a case report from Norway is presented. The point is to reflect on the way we handle trailblazing health technologies in general and on cases where law and order is gained by means that can be conceived of as immoral in particular. The case calls for careful ethical reflection.

Hofmann, Bjørn; Solbakk, Jan Helge; Holm, Søren. Teaching old dogs new tricks: the role of analogies in bioethical analysis and argumentation concerning new technologies. *Theoretical Medicine and Bioethics* 2006; 27(5): 397-413. NRCBL: 15.1; 1.3.12. SC: an.

Holm, Søren. Informed consent and bio-banking of material from children. *Genomics, Society and Policy* 2005 February; 1(1): 16-26. NRCBL: 15.1; 1.3.12; 18.5.2; 15.3. SC: an.
Abstract: This paper considers the ethical issues raised by biobanking of material from children who are not mature enough to give ethically valid consent. The first part considers consent requirements for entry of such materials into the biobank, whereas the second part looks at the issues that arise when a competent child later wants to withdraw previously stored materials, and at the issues that arise when there is informational entanglement between information about a parent and information about a child. The paper argues for three main conclusions: 1. That it is in most cases acceptable for parents to give proxy consent to entry of material from their children into biobanks, even though this is not strictly speaking in the best interest of the child; 2. that a right to withdraw from the biobank is more important when material has been entered with proxy consent; and 3. that disputes about the withdrawal of entangled information, i.e. information that is both about a parent and a child, should be resolved in favour of the child.

Horlick-Jones, Tom; Walls, John; Rowe, Gene; Pidgeon, Nick; Poortinga, Wouter; O'Riordan, Tim. On evaluating the GM Nation? Public debate about the commercialisation of transgenic crops in Britain. *New Genetics and Society* 2006 December; 25(3): 265-288.

NRCBL: 15.1; 1.3.11. Identifiers: genetically modified crops.

Howell, Nancy R. Co-creation, co-redemption, and genetics. *American Journal of Theology and Philosophy* 1999 May; 20(2): 147-163. NRCBL: 15.1; 1.2; 3.2.

Iklé, Fred Charles. The deconstruction of death: the coming politics of biotechnology. *National Interest* 2000-2001 Winter; 62: 87-95. NRCBL: 15.1; 4.5; 15.5.

Isasi, Rosario. The human rights perspective. *World Watch* 2002 July-August; 15(4): 32. NRCBL: 15.1. SC: po. Identifiers: human genetic engineering.

Jenkins, Jean F.; Lea, Dale Halsey. Connecting genomics to history. *In their:* Nursing Care in the Genomic Era: A Case-Based Approach. Sudbury, MA: Jones and Bartlett Publishers, 2005: 247-266. NRCBL: 15.1; 13.1; 15.11.

Jenkins, Jean F.; Lea, Dale Halsey. Connecting genomics to society: spirituality and religious traditions. *In their:* Nursing Care in the Genomic Era: A Case-Based Approach. Sudbury, MA: Jones and Bartlett Publishers, 2005: 267-285. NRCBL: 15.1; 1.2.

Jennings, Lance. To enhance, or not to enhance. *Futurist* 2004 March-April; 38(2): 68, 66. NRCBL: 15.1; 4.5. SC: po.

Jiayin, Min. A philosophical meditation on genomics. *In:* Sleeboom, Margaret, ed. Genomics in Asia: A Clash of Bioethical Interests? New York: Kegan Paul; 2004: 201-223. NRCBL: 15.1.

Jonas, Hans. Technik, Ethik und biogenetische Kunst: Betrachtungen zur neuen Schöpferrolle des Menschen. *In:* Klein, Adolf, ed. Verantwortung in Naturwissenschaft und Technik: ein Textbuch. Bonn: Dümmler; 1989: 83-99. NRCBL: 15.1.

Jones, Dan. All about me. *New Scientist* 2006 August 19-25; 191(2565): 28-36. NRCBL: 15.1; 15.6. Identifiers: personal genome; Craig Venter.

Kaiser, Jocelyn. U.S. hospital launches large biobank of children's DNA [news]. *Science* 2006 June 16; 312(5780): 1584-1585. NRCBL: 15.1; 1.3.12.

Kanamori, Osamu. Ethics of genetic life designs. *In:* Sang-yong, Song; Young-Mo, Koo; Macer, Darryl R.J., eds. Asian Bioethics in the 21st Century. Christchurch, NZ: Eubios Ethics Institute, 2002: 157-164. NRCBL: 15.1. Conference: Proceedings of the Asian Bioethics Conference (ABC4), held 22-25 November 2002 in Seoul, South Korea.

Kaye, Jane. Broad consent — the only option for population genetic databases? *In:* Árnason, Gardar; Nordal, Salvör; Árnason, Vilhjálmur, eds. Blood and Data: Ethical, Legal and Social Aspects of Human Genetic Databases.

Reykjavík: University of Iceland Press; 2004: 103-109.
NRCBL: 15.1; 1.3.12; 18.3.

Kaye, Jane. Police collection and access to DNA samples.
Genomics, Society and Policy 2006 May; 2(1): 16-27.
NRCBL: 15.1; 1.3.5.
Abstract: As forensic techniques continue to improve, reports
on the success of the police in using DNA analysis for solving
past and present criminal cases are becoming an everyday occurrence in the media. There are two avenues by which police
can collect and obtain access to DNA samples. The first is on the
basis of legislation that allows the police to forcibly collect
samples in some situations. The second is through an access order granted by the court, which allows access to samples from
existing collections held by other parties. The purpose of this
paper is to compare these two legal mechanisms that allow the
police to acquire and access DNA samples. My concern is the
increase in collection of DNA samples for genetic research, the
moves to standardise data collection and the computerisation of
medical records, may make research collections more attractive
to the police. Are we are prepared for research collections to become an extension of the National DNA Database used for
crime detection? In the USA a decision has been made that the
police should not be allowed access to samples and information
derived from 'sensitive' research. This article considers 'the
certificates of confidentiality' that have been instigated by the
National Institute of Health in the USA in order to prohibit such
uses of research collections by the police. In this article I consider whether certificates of confidentiality should be used in
the UK, as a way of providing greater protection to researchers
and participants in research.

Kean, Sam. NIH proposes genetic database [news].
Chronicle of Higher Education 2006 September 15; 53(4):
A27. NRCBL: 15.1; 15.10; 15.11.

**Kearnes, Matthew; Grove-White, Robin;
MacNaghten, Phil; Wilsdon, James; Wynne, Brian.**
From bio to nano: learning lessons from the UK agricul-
tural biotechnology controversy. *Science as Culture* 2006
December; 15(4): 291-307. NRCBL: 15.1; 1.3.11; 5.1; 5.2;
7.1; 5.3.

**Kent, Julie; Faulkner, Alex; Geesink, Ingrid;
Fitzpatrick, David.** Culturing cells, reproducing and reg-
ulating the self. *Body and Society* 2006 June; 12(2): 1-23
[Online]. Accessed: http://bod.sagepub.com/cgi/reprint/
12/2/1[2007 January 23]. NRCBL: 15.1; 4.5; 5.1; 19.1.
Identifiers: United Kingdom (Great Britain).

Kerr, Anne. Genetics and citizenship. *Society* 2003 September-October; 40(6): 44-50. NRCBL: 15.1; 5.1; 15.3.

Kerr, Anne. Genetics and citizenship. *In:* Stehr, Nico, ed.
Biotechnology Between Commerce and Civil Society.
New Brunswick, NJ: Transaction Publishers; 2004:
159-174. NRCBL: 15.1.

Kerr, Anne. Rights and responsibilities in the new genetics era. *Critical Social Policy* 2003 May; 23(2): 208-226
[Online]. Accessed: http://csp.sagepub.com/cgi/reprint/
23/2/208 [2007 January 25]. NRCBL: 15.1; 4.4; 5.3.

Khazova, Olga A. Genetics and artificial procreation in
Russia. *In:* Meulders-Klein, Marie-Thérèse; Deech, Ruth;

Vlaardingerbroek, Paul, eds. Biomedicine, the Family and
Human Rights. New York: Kluwer Law International,
2002: 377-391. NRCBL: 15.1; 14.1.

Khoon, Chan Chee. Genomics, health, and society: a
view from the South. *In:* Sleeboom, Margaret, ed.
Genomics in Asia: A Clash of Bioethical Interests? New
York: Kegan Paul; 2004: 301-316. NRCBL: 15.1; 9.1.

Kishore, R.R. Human genome: the promises, concerns
and controversies (part I) = El Genoma Humano:
promesas, preocupaciones y controversias (Parte I).
*Revista de Derecho Genoma Humano = Law and the Hu-
man Genome Review* 1997 January-June; (6): 171-180.
NRCBL: 15.1; 15.10; 15.11.

Klitzman, Robert. Questions, complexities, and limita-
tions in disclosing individual genetic results. *American
Journal of Bioethics* 2006 November-December; 6(6):
34-36; author reply W10-W12. NRCBL: 15.1; 18.2; 8.1.
Comments: Vardit Ravitsky and Benjamin S. Wilfond.
Disclosing individual genetic results to research partici-
pants. American Journal of Bioethics 2006
November-December; 6(6): 8-17.

Knoepffler, Nikolaus. Konfliktfälle bei gentechnischen
Eingriffen am Menschen. *In his:* Menschenwürde in der
Bioethik. New York: Springer; 2004: 171-182. NRCBL:
15.1; 4.5; 15.4.

Koch, Lene. The government of genetic knowledge. *In:*
Lundin, Susanne; Åkesson, Lynn, eds. Gene Technology
and Economy. Lund: Nordic Academic Press; 2002:
92-103. NRCBL: 15.1.

Koo, Mi Jung; Yang, Jae Sub. Reflections on the human
dignity in genetics. *In:* Sang-yong, Song; Young-Mo, Koo;
Macer, Darryl R.J., eds. Asian Bioethics in the 21st Century. Christchurch, NZ: Eubios Ethics Institute, 2002:
165-171. NRCBL: 15.1; 4.4. Conference: Proceedings of
the Asian Bioethics Conference (ABC4), held 22-25 November 2002 in Seoul, South Korea.

Korts, Külliki. Becoming masters of our genes: public acceptance of the Estonian Genome Project. *In:* Árnason,
Gardar; Nordal, Salvör; Árnason, Vilhjálmur, eds. Blood
and Data: Ethical, Legal and Social Aspects of Human Genetic Databases. Reykjavík: University of Iceland Press;
2004: 187-192. NRCBL: 15.1; 1.3.12; 15.10. SC: em.

Kutukdjian, Georges B. Genética y ética: implicaciones
internacionales = Genetics and ethics: international implications. *Revista Latinoamericana de Bioética* 2003 January; (4): 38-55. NRCBL: 15.1; 15.10; 15.8; 15.2; 15.3.
Conference: Second International Congress on the Ethics
of Scientific Research: Bioethics and Genetic Manipulation; Nueva Granada Military University; Bogota,
Columbia.

**La commission de l'éthique de la science et de la
technologie [Québec].** Pour une gestion éthique des

NRCBL: National Reference Center for Bioethics Literature Classification Scheme   See inside front cover for terms.

247

OGM: mises en garde. *Journal International de Bioéthique = International Journal of Bioethics* 2005 September-December; 16(3-4): 137-140. NRCBL: 15.1; 1.3.11; 22.3; 2.4. Identifiers: Quebec; Canada.

Lagay, Faith. Genetic disparity: unfortunate or unfair? *In:* American Medical Association. Professing Medicine: strengthening the ethics and professionalism of tomorrow's physicians. Chicago: American Medical Association; 2001: 114-117. NRCBL: 15.1. Note: Commemorative issue of Virtual Mentor, AMA's online ethics journal.

Langlois, Adèle. The governance of genomic information: will it come of age? *Genomics, Society and Policy* 2006 December; 2(3): 49-63. NRCBL: 15.1; 15.10; 5.3; 21.1.

Abstract: The completion of the Human Genome Project has opened up unprecedented possibilities in healthcare, but also ethical and social dilemmas in terms of how these can be achieved. Genomic information can be seen as a "global public good" (GPG), in that it is represented by knowledge in the public domain and across national boundaries. Lack of investment, infrastructure and expertise in developing countries means that they are unable to take advantage of these GPG characteristics to address their health needs, fuelling fears of a growing "genomics divide". Some have suggested an international knowledge sharing and capacity building network, a Global Genomics Initiative, as a means to harness the potential of genomics to reduce inequalities in health between North and South. Three UNESCO declarations also call for cooperation between developed and developing countries in genomics research and science and technology in general. Using international relations theories around global governance and networks as a conceptual framework, this paper examines whether these initiatives are likely to succeed in providing effective governance of genomics.

Lassen, Jesper; Jamison, Andrew. Genetic technologies meet the public: the discourses of concern. *Science, Technology, and Human Values* 2006 January; 31(1): 8-28. NRCBL: 15.1; 5.2; 1.3.2; 16.1; 5.1. SC: em.

Lavieri, Robert R.; Garner, Samual A. Ethical considerations in the communication of unexpected information with clinical implications. *American Journal of Bioethics* 2006 November-December; 6(6): 46-48. NRCBL: 15.1; 18.2; 8.2. Comments: Vardit Ravitsky and Benjamin S. Wilfond. Disclosing individual genetic results to research participants. American Journal of Bioethics 2006 November-December; 6(6): 8-17.

Le Roux, Nadège; Cussenot, Olivier. La génétique au coeur du débat ethique? = Genetics at the heart of the ethical debate? *Progres en Urologie* 2000 November; 10(5): 1053-1084. NRCBL: 15.1; 18.5.4; 15.3; 15.10; 15.2; 15.4; 14.4. SC: rv.

Lee, Shui Chuen. Biotechnology and responsibility to future generations: a Confucian perspective. *In:* Sleeboom, Margaret, ed. Genomics in Asia: A Clash of Bioethical Interests? New York: Kegan Paul; 2004: 145-158. NRCBL: 15.1; 1.2.

LePage, Michael. Tools you can trust. *New Scientist* 2006 June 10-16; 190(2555): 38-41. NRCBL: 15.1; 15.4. Identifiers: genetic engineering.

Lerner, Evan. Editorial. *GeneWatch* 2006 November-December; 19(6): 2, 17. NRCBL: 15.1; 1.3.5; 1.3.12. Identifiers: DNA databases.

Levidow, Les. The GM crops debate: utilitarian bioethics? *Capitalism, Nature, Socialism* 2001 March; 12(1): 44-55. NRCBL: 15.1; 1.3.11. SC: an.

LeVine, Harry. Problems, controversies, and solutions. *In his:* Genetic Engineering: A Reference Handbook. 2nd ed. Santa Barbara, CA: ABC-CLIO, 2006: 47-81. NRCBL: 15.1; 1.2; 1.3.11; 8.4; 9.3.1; 14.5; 16.3.

LeVine, Harry. Worldwide perspective. *In his:* Genetic Engineering: A Reference Handbook. 2nd ed. Santa Barbara, CA: ABC-CLIO, 2006: 83-94. NRCBL: 15.1; 5.3; 21.1.

Levine, Judith. What human genetic modification means for women. *World Watch* 2002 July-August; 15(4): 26-29. NRCBL: 15.1; 10; 12.1. SC: po.

Levitt, Mairi. UK Biobank: a model for public engagement? *Genomics, Society and Policy* 2005 December; 1(3): 78-81. NRCBL: 15.1; 1.3.12; 5.3; 18.1.

Levitt, Mairi; Tomasini, Floris. Bar-coded children: an exploration of issues around the inclusion of children on the England and Wales national DNA database. *Genomics, Society and Policy* 2006 May; 2(1): 41-56. NRCBL: 15.1; 1.3.5; 8.3.2; 1.3.12.

Abstract: The forensic database of England and Wales is the largest in the world with profiles from over 3 million people. Samples can be taken without consent, not only from convicted criminals, but, also from all those arrested on suspicion of a recordable offence even if they are not subsequently charged. There has been little public debate on the database, in contrast to other applications of genetic technology, and, in particular, a lack of discussion on the inclusion of children despite the UN Convention on the Rights of the Child and the debate around children's consent. The paper begins by briefly introducing the significance of the inclusion of children on the England and Wales National DNA database (NDNAD) in the context of current law. Next there is a report of the findings of a small focus group study carried out with children aged 10-12 and one of their parents, who were contacted through their schools. The study explored issues related to the inclusion of children on the NDNAD, including children's responsibility and independence, and gathered responses to real life case studies about the taking of DNA samples from children. These findings are used to further support multi-disciplinary arguments on why the inclusion of children, between the ages of 10-12, may be considered controversial.

Levitt, Mairi; Weldon, Sue. A well placed trust? Public perceptions of the governance of DNA databases. *Critical Public Health* 2005 December; 15(4): 311-321. NRCBL: 15.1; 1.3.12. Identifiers: United Kingdom (Great Britain).

Levitt, Mairi; Weldon, Sue. Genetic databases and public trust. *In:* Árnason, Gardar; Nordal, Salvör; Árnason,

Vilhjálmur, eds. Blood and Data: Ethical, Legal and Social Aspects of Human Genetic Databases. Reykjavík: University of Iceland Press; 2004: 175-179. NRCBL: 15.1; 1.3.12. SC: em.

Lipton, Peter. Genetic and generic determinism: a new threat to free will? *In:* Rees, Dai; Rose, Steven, eds. The New Brain Sciences: Perils and Prospects. New York: Cambridge University Press; 2004: 88-100. NRCBL: 15.1; 1.1.

Lipton, Peter. Nuffield Council on Bioethics consultation. *Pharmacogenomics* 2003 January; 4(1): 91-95. NRCBL: 15.1; 9.7.

Lissemore, James L. Linkage of genetics and ethics: more crossing over is needed. *Biology of the Cell* 2005 July; 97(7): 599-604. NRCBL: 15.1; 1.3.12; 2.1.

Lorenzo, Salomé Santos; González, Aránzazu San José. Second Council of Europe Symposium on Bioethics ('Ethics and Human Genetics') = Segundo Simposio del Consejo de Europa sobre Bioética (<Etica y Genética Humana>). *Law and the Human Genome = Revista de Derecho y Genoma Humano* 1994 July-December; (1): 233-236. NRCBL: 15.1; 21.1; 15.8.

Lucassen, Anneke; Parker, Michael. The UK Genethics Club: clinical ethics support for genetic services. *Clinical Ethics* 2006 December; 1(4): 219-223. NRCBL: 15.1; 2.3; 7.2. SC: cs.

Lundin, Susanne. The body is worth investing in. *In:* Lundin, Susanne; Åkesson, Lynn, eds. Gene Technology and Economy. Lund: Nordic Academic Press; 2002: 104-115. NRCBL: 15.1.

Luxembourg. Commission Consultative Nationale d'Éthique pour les Sciences de la Vie et de la Santé [CNE]. Avis concernant les directives de la CEE sur la dissémination d'organismes génétiquement modifiés: Avis 2/1990 [Opinion concerning the directives of the CEE on the release of genetically modified organisms: Opinion 2/1990]. Luxembourg: Commission Nationale d'Éthique, 1990; 14 p. [Online]. Accessed: http://www.cne.public.lu/publications/avis/1990_2.PDF [2006 April 7]. NRCBL: 15.1; 1.3.11. Identifiers: CEE — Communauté Economique Européenne [European Union].

M'charek, Amade. Technologies of similarities and differences, or how to do politics with DNA. *In his:* The Human Genome Diversity Project: An Ethnography of Scientific Practice. Cambridge; New York: Cambridge University Press; 2005: 148-185. NRCBL: 15.1; 21.1.

Macnaghten, Phil. Animals in their nature: a case study on public attitudes to animals, genetic modification and "nature". *Sociology* 2004 July 1; 38(3): 533-551. NRCBL: 15.1; 5.3; 22.1; 22.2.

Mahlknecht, Ulrich; Voelter-Mahlknecht, Susanne. Pharmacogenomics: questions and concerns. *Current Medical Research and Opinion* 2005 July; 21(7): 1041-1047. NRCBL: 15.1; 9.7; 15.3; 16.3; 21.1; 9.3.1.

Malmqvist, Erik. The notion of health and the morality of genetic intervention. *Medicine, Health Care and Philosophy* 2006; 9(2): 181-192. NRCBL: 15.1; 4.5; 15.4; 4.2; 1.1. SC: an.

Abstract: In the present paper it is argued that genetic interventions on human embryos are in principle permissible if they promote the health of the persons that these embryos will one day become and impermissible if they compromise their health. This so called health-intervention principle is reached by, inter alia, rejecting alternative approaches to the problem of the permissibility of genetic intervention. The health-intervention principle can be interpreted in different ways depending on how the notion of health is understood. The central part of the paper is an attempt to find a concept of health which is such that it makes the health-intervention principle normatively plausible. For this purpose I examine two influential competing theories of health: Cristopher Boorse's biostatistical theory of health and Lennart Nordenfelt's welfare theory of health. I argue that the health-intervention principle is more plausible if health is understood in the latter sense, although it is not ruled out that the principle may be given an even more plausible explication in terms of some other notion of health.

March, Ruth; Cheeseman, Kevin; Doherty, Michael. Pharmacogenetics — legal, ethical and regulatory considerations [editorial]. *Pharmacogenomics* 2001 November; 2(4): 317-327. NRCBL: 15.1; 9.7.

Markl, Hubert. Man's place in nature: evolutionary past and genomic future. *Journal of Molecular Biology* 2002 June 14; 319(4): 869-876. NRCBL: 15.1; 3.1; 16.1. SC: an.

Marsden, Wendy. Analyzing multiple discourses in the establishment of genetic databases. *In:* Árnason, Gardar; Nordal, Salvör; Árnason, Vilhjálmur, eds. Blood and Data: Ethical, Legal and Social Aspects of Human Genetic Databases. Reykjavík: University of Iceland Press; 2004: 167-173. NRCBL: 15.1; 1.3.12.

Martin, Paul. Genetic governance: the risks, oversight, and regulation of genetic databases in the UK. *New Genetics and Society* 2001 August; 20(2): 157-183. NRCBL: 15.1; 1.3.12; 18.6. SC: an.

Marturano, Antonio; Chadwick, Ruth. How the role of computing is driving new genetics' public policy. *Ethics and Information Technology* 2004; 6(1): 43-53. NRCBL: 15.1; 1.3.12; 5.3.

Mathews, Debra J.; Kalfoglou, Andrea; Hudson, Kathy. Geneticists' views on science policy formation and public outreach. *American Journal of Medical Genetics Part A* 2005 August 30; 137(2): 161-169. NRCBL: 15.1; 5.1; 5.3; 7.1. SC: em.

Mauron, Alex. Genomic metaphysics. *Journal of Molecular Biology* 2002 June 14; 319(4): 957-962. NRCBL: 15.1.

NRCBL: National Reference Center for Bioethics Literature Classification Scheme   See inside front cover for terms.

249

Mauron, Alex. Genom-Metaphysik. *In:* Rehmann-Sutter, Christoph; Müller, Hansjakob, eds. Ethik und Gentherapie: zum praktischen Diskurs um die molekulare Medizin. 2nd ed. Tübingen: Francke Verlag; 2003: 237-249. NRCBL: 15.1; 1.1; 4.4.

Mauron, Alex. Renovating the house of being: genomes, souls, and selves. *Annals of the New York Academy of Sciences* 2003 October; 1001: 240-252. NRCBL: 15.1; 1.1; 15.10; 4.4.

McConnaha, Scott. Genomics and the ministry: the executive perspective. *Health Progress* 2006 May-June; 87(3): 56-60. NRCBL: 15.1; 1.2.

McCullough, Laurence B.; Wilson, Nancy L.; Rhymes, Jill A.; Teasdale, Thomas A. Ethical issues in genetics and aging: diagnosis, treatment, and prevention in the era of molecular medicine. *Generations* 2000 Spring; 24(1): 72-78. NRCBL: 15.1; 9.5.2; 15.3.

McGee, Glenn. Spare the genes, spoil the child? The not-so-deadly sins of genetic enhancement = ¿Escatimar genes, estropear a los hijos? Los pecados no tan capitales de la mejora genética. *Revista de Derecho Genoma Humano = Law and the Human Genome Review* 1997 July-December; (7): 199-217. NRCBL: 15.1; 4.5; 15.3.

McKibben, Bill. Why environmentalists should be concerned. *World Watch* 2002 July-August; 15(4): 40-41. NRCBL: 15.1. SC: po.

Mehta, Michael D.; Gair, Julie J. Social, political, legal and ethical areas of inquiry in biotechnology and genetic engineering. *Technology in Society* 2001 April; 23(2): 241-264. NRCBL: 15.1; 5.1. SC: rv.

Miah, Andy. Gene-doping: sport, values, and bioethics. *In:* Glasa, J., ed. Ethics of Human Genetics: Challenges of the (Post) Genomic Era. Bratislava, Slovak Republic: Charis [and] IMEB Foundation; 2002: 171-180. NRCBL: 15.1; 4.5.

Miringoff, Marque-Luisa. Dissecting people and ignoring social structure: an analysis of individualism, public policy, and genetic labeling. *Behavioral Sciences and the Law* 1996 Autumn; 14(4): 433-442. NRCBL: 15.1; 15.6; 9.5.7. SC: an.

Mirkes, Reneé. Is it ethical to generate human-animal chimeras? *National Catholic Bioethics Quarterly* 2006 Spring; 6(1): 109-130. NRCBL: 15.1; 18.1; 22.1; 18.5.4; 4.4; 1.1.

Mooney, Pat. Making well people "better". *World Watch* 2002 July-August; 15(4): 13-16, 43. NRCBL: 15.1; 5.3; 9.7. SC: po. Identifiers: human performance enhancement drugs.

Moore, Adam D. Intellectual property, genetic information, and gene enhancement techniques. *In:* Tavani, Herman T., ed. Ethics, Computing, and Genomics. Sudbury, MA: Jones and Bartlett; 2006: 197-211. NRCBL: 15.1; 4.5; 15.8.

Moses, Alan. Intelligent design: playing with the building blocks of biology. *Berkeley Science Review* 2005 Spring; 5(1): 34-40. NRCBL: 15.1; 5.3; 21.1. SC: po. Identifiers: synthetic design.

Moss, Lenny. The question of questions: what is a gene? Comments on Rolston and Griffiths and Stotz. *Theoretical Medicine and Bioethics* 2006; 27(6): 523-534. NRCBL: 15.1; 3.1. SC: an.

Munro, Cindy L. Genetic technology and scientific integrity. *In:* Macrina, Francis L. Scientific Integrity: Text and Cases in Responsible Conduct of Research. 3rd ed. Washington, DC: ASM Press; 2005: 247-267. NRCBL: 15.1; 15.3; 15.4.

Myskja, Bjørn K. The moral difference between intragenic and transgenic modification of plants. *Journal of Agricultural and Environmental Ethics* 2006; 19(3): 225-238. NRCBL: 15.1; 13.1.11; 15.7; 5.3.

Nasim, Anwar. Ethical issues: an Islamic perspective. *In:* Sleeboom, Margaret, ed. Genomics in Asia: A Clash of Bioethical Interests? New York: Kegan Paul; 2004: 29-50. NRCBL: 15.1; 1.2; 18.5.4.

Ng, Mary Ann Chen; Macer, Darryl. Attitudes toward biotechnology and bioethics in the Philippines: a pilot study. *In:* Sleeboom, Margaret, ed. Genomics in Asia: A Clash of Bioethical Interests? New York: Kegan Paul; 2004: 255-279. NRCBL: 15.1. SC: em.

Nõmper, Ants; Kruuv, Krista. The Estonian Genome Project. *In:* Sándor, Judit, ed. Society and Genetic Information: Codes and Laws in the Genetic Era. Budapest, Hungary; New York: CEU Press; 2003: 213-224. NRCBL: 15.1.

Nuffield Council on Bioethics. Forensic use of bioinformation: ethical issues. Consultation paper. London: Nuffield Council on Bioethics, 2006 November; 28 p. [Online]. Accessed: http://www.nuffieldbioethics.org/fileLibrary/pdf/Consultation_FINAL001.pdf [2006 November 29]. NRCBL: 15.1; 1.3.5; 1.3.12. Identifiers: United Kingdom (Great Britain). Note: The consultation closes on 30th January 2007. Respondent form and related information may be found at http://www.nuffieldbioethics.org/go/textonly/ourwork/bioinformationuse/page_848.html.

O'Neill, Onora. DNA and ethics. *In:* Krude, Torsten, ed. DNA: Changing Science and Society. Cambridge, UK; New York: Cambridge University Press; 2004: 166-182. NRCBL: 15.1.

Oderberg, David S. Towards and natural law critique of genetic engineering. *In:* Athanassoulis, Nafsika, ed. Philosophical Reflections on Medical Ethics. New York:

Palgrave Macmillan; 2005: 109-134. NRCBL: 15.1. SC: an.

Ogundiran, Temidayo O. Africa must come on board with the genomics bandwagon. *Genomics, Society and Policy* 2005 December; 1(3): 66-77. NRCBL: 15.1; 1.3.11; 5.1; 9.1; 21.1.

Pálsson, Gílsi. The Iceland biogenetic project. *In:* Stehr, Nico, ed. Biotechnology Between Commerce and Civil Society. New Brunswick, NJ: Transaction Publishers; 2004: 277-297. NRCBL: 15.1; 15.3; 15.10.

Parker, Lisa S. Best laid plans for offering results go awry. *American Journal of Bioethics* 2006 November-December; 6(6): 22-23; author reply W10-W12. NRCBL: 15.1; 18.2; 8.1; 18.3. Comments: Vardit Ravitsky and Benjamin S. Wilfond. Disclosing individual genetic results to research participants. American Journal of Bioethics 2006 November-December; 6(6): 8-17.

Patel, Rajeev; Torres, Robert J.; Rosset, Peter. Genetic engineering in agriculture and corporate engineering in public debate: risk, public relations, and public debate over genetically modified crops. *International Journal of Occupational and Environmental Health* 2005 October-December; 11(4): 428-436. NRCBL: 15.1; 1.3.11; 1.3.2. SC: an. Identifiers: Monsanto.

Peters, Ted. Playing God. *In:* Mitcham, Carl, ed. Encyclopedia of Science, Technology, and Ethics. Farmington Hills, MI: Thomson/Gale, 2005: 1424-1427. NRCBL: 15.1; 5.1; 2.1; 1.2; 4.5.

Petersen, Alan. Securing our genetic health: engendering trust in UK Biobank. *Sociology of Health and Illness* 2005 March; 27(2): 271-292. NRCBL: 15.1; 1.3.12; 8.3.1; 9.1; 1.3.5; 8.4. Identifiers: United Kingdom (Great Britain).

Pirags, Valdis; Grens, Elmars. The Latvian Genome Project. *In:* Sándor, Judit, ed. Society and Genetic Information: Codes and Laws in the Genetic Era. Budapest, Hungary; New York: CEU Press; 2003: 225-231. NRCBL: 15.1.

Pokorski, Robert J. Genetic information and life insurance risk classification and antiselection (first of two parts). *Journal of Insurance Medicine* 1994-1995 Winter; 26(4): 413-419. NRCBL: 15.1; 1.3.2.

Porter, Gerard. The wolf in sheep's clothing: informed consent forms as commercial contracts. *In:* Árnason, Gardar; Nordal, Salvör; Árnason, Vilhjálmur, eds. Blood and Data: Ethical, Legal and Social Aspects of Human Genetic Databases. Reykjavík: University of Iceland Press; 2004: 85-93. NRCBL: 15.1; 18.3.

Puckrein, Gary; Yancy, Clyde W. BiDil's impact [letter and response]. *Nature Biotechnology* 2005 November; 23(11): 1343-1344. NRCBL: 15.1; 9.7; 15.11.

Purdy, Jedediah S. Dolly and Madison. *American Prospect* 1998 May-June; 38: 88-94. NRCBL: 15.1; 5.3.

Putnina, Aivita. Population genome project in Latvia: exploring the articulation of agency. *In:* Sándor, Judit, ed. Society and Genetic Information: Codes and Laws in the Genetic Era. Budapest, Hungary; New York: CEU Press; 2003: 233-245. NRCBL: 15.1.

Regalado, Antonio. Scientist's study of brain genes sparks a backlash; Dr. Lahn connects evolution in some groups to IQ; debate on race and DNA; "Speculating is dangerous". *Wall Street Journal* 2006 June 16; p. A1, A12. NRCBL: 15.1; 3.1. SC: po.

Resnik, David B.; Vorhaus, Daniel B. Genetic modification and genetic determinism. *Philosophy, Ethics, and Humanities in Medicine* 2006; 1(9): 11 p. NRCBL: 15.1; 4.5; 1.1; 14.5. SC: an.

Ries, Nola M.; Caulfield, Timothy. First pharmacogenomics, next nutrigenomics: genohype or genohealthy? *Jurimetrics* 2006 Spring; 46(3): 281-308. NRCBL: 15.1; 9.7; 4.1.1; 1.3.2.

Robb, J. Wesley. The Christian and the new biology. *Encounter* 1981 Summer; 42(3): 197-205. NRCBL: 15.1; 14.4; 1.2; 2.1.

Robert, Jason Scott; Kirk, Dwayne D. Ethics, biotechnology, and global health: the development of vaccines in transgenic plants. *American Journal of Bioethics [Online]* 2006 July-August; 6(4): W29-W41. NRCBL: 15.1; 1.3.11; 9.1; 9.7; 15.7; 21.1.

Robins, Rosemary. Overburdening risk: policy frameworks and the public uptake of gene technology. *Public Understanding of Science* 2001 January; 10(1): 19-36. NRCBL: 15.1; 5.3; 5.2.

Rollin, Bernard E. Biotechnology and ethics I: is genetic engineering intrinsically wrong? *In his:* Science and Ethics. New York: Cambridge University Press; 2006: 129-154. NRCBL: 15.1.

Rollin, Bernard E. Biotechnology and ethics II: rampaging monsters and suffering animals. *In his:* Science and Ethics. New York: Cambridge University Press; 2006: 155-184. NRCBL: 15.1; 22.2.

Rolston, Holmes, III. What is a gene? From molecules to metaphysics. *Theoretical Medicine and Bioethics* 2006; 27(6): 471-497. NRCBL: 15.1; 3.1. SC: an.

Rothman, Barbara Katz. A sociological skeptic in the brave new world. *Gender and Society* 1998 October; 12(5): 501-504. NRCBL: 15.1; 5.3. SC: an.

Roughgarden, Joan. Genetic engineering versus diversity. *In her:* Evolution's Rainbow: Diversity, Gender, and Sexuality in Nature and People. Berkeley: University of California Press; 2004: 306-326. NRCBL: 15.1; 10; 9.5.4.

NRCBL: National Reference Center for Bioethics Literature Classification Scheme   See inside front cover for terms.

251

Rowe, John W.; Gatz, Margaret. Implications of genetic knowledge for public policy. *Generations: Journal of the American Society of Aging* 2000 Spring; 24(1): 79-83. NRCBL: 15.1; 9.5.2.

Russell, Alex. A hidden xenophobia of our own? (Does "The Commons" hide a fear of the new diversity genetic engineering might bring?). *World Watch* 2002 September-October; 15(5): 7-8. NRCBL: 15.1; 14.5; 4.5.

Ryan, Maura. Justice and genetics: whose holy grail? *Health Progress* 2006 May-June; 87(3): 46-56. NRCBL: 15.1; 1.1; 21.1; 9.1.

Ryen, Tind Shepper. Human genome organization. *In:* Mitcham, Carl, ed. Encyclopedia of Science, Technology, and Ethics. Farmington Hills, MI: Thomson/Gale, 2005: 942-944. NRCBL: 15.1; 5.1; 21.1.

Sade, Robert M. Issues of social policy and ethics in gene technology. *Methods and Findings in Experimental and Clinical Pharmacology* 1994 September; 16(7): 477-489. NRCBL: 15.1; 5.3; 15.3; 15.8; 15.4; 7.1.

Sakamoto, Hyakudai. Genome, artificial evolution and global community. *In:* Sleeboom, Margaret, ed. Genomics in Asia: A Clash of Bioethical Interests? New York: Kegan Paul; 2004: 135-144. NRCBL: 15.1.

Salter, Brian; Jones, Mavis. Biobanks and bioethics: the politics of legitimation. *Journal of European Public Policy* 2005 August; 12(4): 710-732. NRCBL: 15.1; 1.3.12; 18.6; 21.1.

Savulescu, Julian. New breeds of humans: the moral obligation to enhance. *Reproductive BioMedicine Online [electronic]* 2005 March; 10(Supplement 1): 36-39. NRCBL: 15.1; 4.5; 15.5. SC: an. Conference: Ethics, Law and Moral Philosophy of Reproductive Biomedicine; London, UK; 2004 September 30 - October 1; Royal Society.

Schaefer, G. Bradley; Dunston, Georgia M. Health-care disparities in medical genetics. *In:* Satcher, David; Pamies, Rubens J., eds. Multicultural medicine and health disparities. New York: McGraw-Hill, 2006: 471-484. NRCBL: 15.1; 9.2.

Schaub, Diana J. Chimeras: from poetry to science. *National Catholic Bioethics Quarterly* 2006 Spring; 6(1): 29-35. NRCBL: 15.1; 18.1; 22.1; 4.4; 5.3.

Schneider, Angela J.; Friedman, Theodore. International cooperation and regulation: the Banbury Workshop (2002). *In their:* Gene Doping in Sports: The Science and Ethics of Genetically Modified Athletes. Boston: Elsevier Academic Press, 2006: 65-78. NRCBL: 15.1; 4.5; 5.3; 9.5.1.

Schneider, Angela J.; Friedman, Theodore. Some ethical aspects of "harm" in sport. *In their:* Gene Doping in Sports: The Science and Ethics of Genetically Modified Athletes. Boston: Elsevier Academic Press, 2006: 89-93. NRCBL: 15.1; 4.5; 9.5.1.

Schroeder, Doris. Benefit sharing: from obscurity to common knowledge [editorial]. *Developing World Bioethics* 2006 December; 6(3): ii. NRCBL: 15.1; 1.1; 9.4.

Abstract: Benefit sharing has been a recurrent theme in international debates for the past two decades. However, despite its prominence in law, medical ethics and political philosophy, the concept has never been satisfactorily defined. In this conceptual paper, a definition that combines current legal guidelines with input from ethics debates is developed. Philosophers like boxes; protective casings into which they can put concisely-defined concepts. Autonomy is the human capacity for self-determination; beneficence denotes the virtue of good deeds, coercion is the intentional threat of harm and so on. What about benefit sharing? Does the concept have a box and are the contents clearly defined? The answer to this question has to be no. The concept of benefit sharing is almost unique in that various disciplines use it regularly without precise definitions. In this article, a definition for benefit sharing is provided, to eliminate unnecessary ambiguity.

Schroeder, Doris; Lasén-Díaz, Carolina. Sharing the benefits of genetic resources: from biodiversity to human genetics. *Developing World Bioethics* 2006 December; 6(3): 135-143. NRCBL: 15.1; 9.4; 21.1. SC: an.

Abstract: Benefit sharing aims to achieve an equitable exchange between the granting of access to a genetic resource and the provision of compensation. The Convention on Biological Diversity (CBD), adopted at the 1992 Earth Summit in Rio de Janeiro, is the only international legal instrument setting out obligations for sharing the benefits derived from the use of biodiversity. The CBD excludes human genetic resources from its scope, however, this article considers whether it should be expanded to include those resources, so as to enable research subjects to claim a share of the benefits to be negotiated on a case-by-case basis. Our conclusion on this question is: 'No, the CBD should not be expanded to include human genetic resources.' There are essential differences between human and non-human genetic resources, and, in the context of research on humans, an essentially fair exchange model is already available between the health care industry and research subjects. Those who contribute to research should receive benefits in the form of accessible new health care products and services, suitable for local health needs and linked to economic prosperity (e.g. jobs). When this exchange model does not apply, as is often the case in developing countries, individually negotiated benefit sharing agreements between researchers and research subjects should not be used as 'window dressing'. Instead, national governments should focus their finances on the best economic investment they could make; the investment in population health and health research as outlined by the World Health Organization's Commission on Macroeconomics and Health; whilst international barriers to such spending need to be removed.

Schulte, Paul A. Interpretation of genetic data for medical and public health uses. *In:* Árnason, Gardar; Nordal, Salvör; Árnason, Vilhjálmur, eds. Blood and Data: Ethical, Legal and Social Aspects of Human Genetic Databases. Reykjavík: University of Iceland Press; 2004: 277-282. NRCBL: 15.1.

Scully, Jackie Leach. Nothing like a gene. *In:* Neumann-Held, Eva M.; Rehmann-Sutter, Christoph, eds. Genes in Development: Re-reading the Molecular Paradigm. Durham, N.C.: Duke University Press; 2006: 349-364. NRCBL: 15.1.

Service, Robert F. Synthetic biologists debate policing themselves [news]. *Science* 2006 May 26; 312(5777): 1116. NRCBL: 15.1.

Seyfer, Tara L. An overview of chimeras and hybrids. *National Catholic Bioethics Quarterly* 2006 Spring; 6(1): 37-49. NRCBL: 15.1; 18.1; 22.1; 4.4; 1.1; 1.2.

Shakespeare, Tom. Parental diagnosis, disability equality, and freedom of choice. *Reform* 2001 Spring; 79: 19-21, 71. NRCBL: 15.2; 12.1.

Sherlock, Richard. Nature's end: the theological meaning of the new genetics. *Ethics and Medicine* 2006 Spring; 22(1): 47-56. NRCBL: 15.1; 4.4; 1.1. Identifiers: Aristotle; David Hume.

Sherlock, Richard; Morrey, John D. Ethical issues in transgenics. *Cloning* 2000; 2(3): 137-144. NRCBL: 15.1; 22.2; 22.3; 14.5; 1.3.9; 5.3.

Shildrick, Margrit. Genetics, normativity, and ethics: some bioethical concerns. *Feminist Theory* 2004 August; 5(2): 149-165 [Online]. Accessed: http://fty.sagepub. com/cgi/reprint/5/2/149 [2007 January 24]. NRCBL: 15.1; 1.1; 4.4; 10; 15.10. Identifiers: Human Genome Project.

Shiva, Vandana. Biopirates and the poor. *World Watch* 2002 July-August; 15(4): 25. NRCBL: 15.1. SC: po. Identifiers: gene piracy.

Silva, Vesta T. In the beginning was the gene: the hegemony of genetic thinking in contemporary culture. *Communication Theory* 2005 February; 15(1): 100-123. NRCBL: 15.1; 5.3; 1.3.7; 15.6; 15.3.

Silverman, Paul H. Rethinking genetic determinism: with only 30,000 genes, what is it that makes humans human? *Scientist* 2004 May 24; 18(10): 32-33. NRCBL: 15.1; 15.10.

Simoncelli, Tania; Wallace, Helen. Expanding databases, declining liberties. *GeneWatch* 2006 January-February; 19(1): 3-8, 18. NRCBL: 15.1; 21.1; 1.3.12; 1.3.5. Identifiers: United States; United Kingdom (Great Britain).

Singer, Eleanor; Corning, Amy; Lamias, Mark. The polls — trends: genetic testing, engineering, and therapy: awareness and attitudes. *Public Opinion Quarterly* 1998 Winter; 62(4): 633-664. NRCBL: 15.1. SC: em.

Singer, Peter. Shopping at the genetic supermarket. *In:* Sang-yong, Song; Young-Mo, Koo; Macer, Darryl R.J., eds. Asian Bioethics in the 21st Century. Christchurch, NZ: Eubios Ethics Institute, 2002: 143-156. NRCBL: 15.1; 9.3.1. Conference: Proceedings of the Asian Bioethics Conference (ABC4), held 22-25 November 2002 in Seoul, South Korea.

Snyder, Graydon F. Theological reflections on genetic engineering. *Brethren Life and Thought* 1986 Autumn; 31(4): 209-214. NRCBL: 15.1; 1.2.

St. Louis, Brett. Sport, genetics and the "natural athlete": the resurgence of racial science. *Body and Society* 2003 June; 9(2): 75-95 [Online]. Accessed: http://bod. sagepub.com/cgi/reprint/9/2/75 [2007 January 25]. NRCBL: 15.1; 3.1; 4.4.

Stempsey, William E. The geneticization of diagnostics. *Medicine, Health Care and Philosophy* 2006; 9(2): 193-200. NRCBL: 15.1; 4.2; 1.1. SC: an.
  Abstract: "Geneticization" is a term used to describe the ways in which the science of genetics is influencing society at large and medicine in particular; it has important implications for the process of diagnostics. Because genetic diagnostics produces knowledge about genetic disease and predisposition to disease, it is essentially influenced by these innovations in the disease concept. In this paper, I argue that genetic diagnostics presents new ethical challenges not because the diagnostic process or method in genetic diagnostics is ethically different in kind from traditional medical diagnostics, but because it relies on a neo-ontological concept of disease in a context of genetic reductionism. Geneticization has not produced a radically new concept of disease, however, but has introduced innovations into the classical ontological concept of disease. When this new concept of disease is held in tandem with genetic reductionism, we are led to the absurd conclusion that disease is the very essence of the human being. I argue that neither the neo-ontological concept of disease nor genetic reductionism is necessary for a proper understanding of genetic diagnostics.

Stephen, Sarah. Letters to unborn daughters: exploring the implications of genetic engineering. *Futuris* 2004 March-April; 38(2): 37-39. NRCBL: 15.1; 4.5. SC: po.

Steuernagel, Trudy. Marcuse and biotechnology. *Negations* 1998 Winter; 3: 44-55 [Online]. Accessed: http://www.datawranglers.com/negations/issues/98w/ steurnagel_01.html [2007 January 31]. NRCBL: 15.1; 14.4; 5.1; 10; 14.5.

Strauss, Bernard S. Getting around. *DNA Repair* 2005 August 15; 4(9): 951-957. NRCBL: 15.1; 5.1; 1.3.7; 1.3.9.

Sulmasy, Daniel P. The logos of the genome: genomes as parts of organisms. *Theoretical Medicine and Bioethics* 2006; 27(6): 535-540. NRCBL: 15.1; 3.1. SC: an.

Suzuki, David. A little knowledge. . . . *New Scientist* 2006 September 23-29; 191(2570): 18. NRCBL: 15.1; 15.7. Identifiers: genetic engineering.

Svendsen, Mette Nordahl; Koch, Lene. Genetics and prevention: a policy in the making. *New Genetics and Society* 2006 April; 25(1): 51-68. NRCBL: 15.1; 9.5.1; 15.2; 8.3.1; 7.1.

Tammpuu, Piia. Making genes commonly meaningful: implications of national self-images on human genetic databases. *In:* Árnason, Gardar; Nordal, Salvör; Árnason, Vilhjálmur, eds. Blood and Data: Ethical, Legal and Social Aspects of Human Genetic Databases. Reykjavík: Univer-

NRCBL: National Reference Center for Bioethics Literature Classification Scheme   See inside front cover for terms.

253

sity of Iceland Press; 2004: 161-165. NRCBL: 15.1; 1.3.7; 1.3.12.

Tavani, Herman T. Environmental genomics, data mining, and informed consent. *In his:* Ethics, Computing, and Genomics. Sudbury, MA: Jones and Bartlett; 2006: 167-185. NRCBL: 15.1; 1.3.12; 8.3.1.

Tavani, Herman T. Ethics at the intersection of computing and genomics. *In his:* Ethics, Computing, and Genomics. Sudbury, MA: Jones and Bartlett; 2006: 5-26. NRCBL: 15.1; 1.3.12.

Terry, Sharon F.; Terry, Patrick F. A consumer perspective on forensic DNA banking. *Journal of Law, Medicine and Ethics* 2006 Summer; 34(2): 408-414. NRCBL: 15.1; 1.3.12; 18.5.1; 13.1. Identifiers: Genetic Alliance Biobank; PXE International.

Thorgeirsdóttir, Sigrídur. The controversy on consent in the Icelandic database case and narrow bioethics. *In:* Árnason, Gardar; Nordal, Salvör; Árnason, Vilhjálmur, eds. Blood and Data: Ethical, Legal and Social Aspects of Human Genetic Databases. Reykjavík: University of Iceland Press; 2004: 67-77. NRCBL: 15.1; 1.3.12; 18.3.

Townend, David M.R. Who owns genetic information? *In:* Sándor, Judit, ed. Society and Genetic Information: Codes and Laws in the Genetic Era. Budapest, Hungary; New York: CEU Press; 2003: 125-144. NRCBL: 15.1.

Townsley, Michael; Smith, Chloe; Pease, Ken. First impressions count: serious detections arising from criminal justice samples. *Genomics, Society and Policy* 2006 May; 2(1): 28-40. NRCBL: 15.1; 1.3.5.

Abstract: DNA samples on the England and Wales national database matching those found at scenes of serious violent or sexual crimes were identified. The earlier offence leading the sample to appear on the database was noted. The bulk (60-84% according to inclusion criteria) involved theft, drug or other offending. The result, indicating offender versatility, is consistent with most research on criminal careers. Its importance for operational police lies in identifying the contribution made by DNA samples taken after less serious offences in clearing subsequent serious crime, and the importance of taking such samples from as wide a list of apparently 'trivial' crime types as possible. Examining specific relationships between early and later offences revealed a significant link between providing a DNA sample following a drug offence and subsequently committing murder.

Turner, Trudy R. Commentary: data sharing and access to information. *In:* Turner, Trudy R. ed. Biological Anthropology and Ethics: From Repatriation to Genetic Identity. Albany, NY: State University of New York Press; 2005: 281-287. NRCBL: 15.1; 1.3.12.

Väliverronen, Esa. Expert, healer, reassurer, hero and prophet: framing genetics and medical scientists in television news. *New Genetics and Society* 2006 December; 25(3): 233-247. NRCBL: 15.1; 1.3.7. Identifiers: Finland.

Van Steendam, Guido; Dinnyés, András; Mallet, Jacques; Meloni, Rolando; Casabona, Carlos Romeo;

González, Jorge Guerra; Kure, Josef; Szathmáry, Eörs; Vorstenbosch, Jan; Molnár, Péter; Edbrooke, David; Sándor; Oberfrank, Ferenc; Cole-Turner, Ron; Hargittai, István; Littig, Beate; Ladikas, Miltos; Mordini, Emilio; Roosendaal, Hans E.; Salvi, Maurizio; Gulyás, Balázs; Malpede, Diana. Summary: the Budapest Meeting 2005 intensified networking on ethics of science: the case of reproductive cloning, germline gene therapy, and human dignity. *Science and Engineering Ethics* 2006 July; 12(3): 415-420. NRCBL: 15.1; 14.5.

Varsha. DNA fingerprinting in the criminal justice system: an overview. *DNA and Cell Biology* 2006 March; 25(3): 181-188. NRCBL: 15.1; 1.3.5.

Vogel, F. Human genetics: the molecular revolution and its ethical consequences. *International Journal of Human Genetics* 2001; 1(1): 1-9. NRCBL: 15.1; 14.1; 9.3.1.

Wallace, Helen. Permanently detained: as the U.K.'s database expands, crimes solved with DNA drop. *GeneWatch* 2006 November-December; 19(6): 13-18. NRCBL: 15.1; 1.3.5; 1.3.12.

Walter, James J. The bioengineering of planet Earth: some scientific, moral, and theological considerations. *New Theology Review* 2002 August; 15: 41-54. NRCBL: 15.1; 1.2; 1.3.11; 21.1.

Walters, LeRoy B. The ethics of human gene therapy. *Brethren Life and Thought* 1986 Autumn; 31(4): 215-222. NRCBL: 15.1; 15.4.

Wasserman, David. This old house: the human genome and human body as objects of historic preservation. *Politics and the Life Sciences* 2003 March 22(1): 43-47. NRCBL: 15.1; 4.4.

Watts, Geoff. Will UK biobank pay off? [news]. *BMJ: British Medical Journal* 2006 May 6; 332(7549): 1052. NRCBL: 15.1; 1.3.12.

Welin, Stellan. The value of life. *In:* Lundin, Susanne; Åkesson, Lynn, eds. Gene Technology and Economy. Lund: Nordic Academic Press; 2002: 85-91. NRCBL: 15.1; 4.4.

Wichmann, H.-E. Genetic epidemiology in Germany — from biobanking to genetic statistics. *Methods of Information in Medicine* 2005; 44(4): 584-589. NRCBL: 15.1; 1.3.12; 13.1. SC: em.

Wilkie, Tom. When man plays God. *New Statesman (London, England:* 1996) 1998 June 12; 127(4389): 14-15. NRCBL: 15.1; 1.3.11; 5.3. Identifiers: genetically modified foods.

Williams, Carolyn. Australian attitudes to DNA sample banks and genetic screening. *Current Medical Research and Opinion* 2005 November; 21(11): 1773-1775. NRCBL: 15.1; 1.3.12; 18.1.

Williams, Garrath. Bioethics and large-scale biobanking: individualistic ethics and collective projects. *Genetics, Society, and Policy* 2005 August; 1(2): 50-66. NRCBL: 15.1; 1.3.12; 18.3; 1.3.5.

Wilson, Leland. Toward regulating genetic engineering. *Brethren Life and Thought* 1986 Autumn; 31(4): 241-248. NRCBL: 15.1; 2.2; 5.3.

Wilson, Philip K. Confronting "hereditary" disease: eugenic attempts to eliminate tuberculosis in progressive era America. *Journal of Medical Humanities* 2006 Spring; 27(1): 19-37. NRCBL: 15.5; 9.5.1; 4.2; 9.1; 2.2.

Abstract: Tuberculosis was clearly one of the most predominant diseases of the early twentieth century. At this time, Americans involved in the eugenics movement grew increasingly interested in methods to prevent this disease's potential hereditary spread. To do so, as this essay examines, eugenicists' attempted to shift the accepted view that tuberculosis arose from infection and contagion to a view of its heritable nature. The methods that they employed to better understand the propagation and control of tuberculosis are also discussed. Finally, the essay explores the interpretative analyses of data that the Eugenics Record Office used in an attempt to convince contemporaries of the hereditary transmission of tuberculosis.

Wilson, Sarah. Biobanks and the "social" in social justice. *In:* Árnason, Gardar; Nordal, Salvör; Árnason, Vilhjálmur, eds. Blood and Data: Ethical, Legal and Social Aspects of Human Genetic Databases. Reykjavík: University of Iceland Press; 2004: 333-338. NRCBL: 15.1; 1.1; 1.3.12.

Wolfson, Adam. Biodemocracy in America. *Public Interest* 2002 Winter; 40(146): 23-37. NRCBL: 15.1; 14.5; 21.1; 4.5.

Yang, Huanming. In the name of humanity — a brief introduction to the Universal Declaration on the Human Genome and Human Rights. *In:* Döring, Ole; Chen, Renbiao, eds. Advances in Chinese Medical Ethics: Chinese and International Perspectives. Hamburg: Institut für Asienkunde; 2002: 38-53. NRCBL: 15.1. Note: Proceedings of the Second Sino-German Interdisciplinary Symposium about Medical Ethics in China, Shanghai, 19-23 October, 1999.

Zwick, Michael. Genetic engineering: risks and hazards as perceived by the German public. *New Genetics and Society* 2000 December; 19(3): 269-281. NRCBL: 15.1.

GENETICS/ LEGAL ASPECTS
See also GENETIC SCREENING/ LEGAL ASPECTS

The appropriateness of criminal law to prevent misguided genetic interventions = Sobre la idoneidad del Derecho penal para prevenir intervenciones genéticas desviadas. *Law and the Human Genome Review = Revista de Derecho y Genoma Humano* 1996 July-December; (5): 15-17. NRCBL: 15.1; 1.3.5. SC: le.

Arzamendi, José Luis de la Cuesta. The so called 'genetic manipulation' offences in the new Spanish Criminal Code of 1995 = Los llamados delitos de <manipulación genética> en el nuevo Código Penal español de 1995. *Law and the Human Genome Review = Revista de Derecho y Genoma Humano* 1996 July-December; (5): 47-72. NRCBL: 15.1; 14.1. SC: le.

Balmaseda, María Angeles Egusquiza. The legal role of biological proof and refusal to undergo testing in investigations of paternity (Part II) = El papel jurídico de las pruebas biológicas y la negativa a su sometimiento en la investigación de la paternidad (y II). *Law and the Human Genome Review = Revista de Derecho y Genoma Humano* 1995 July-December; (3): 43-66. NRCBL: 15.1; 14.1. SC: le.

Bernal Villegas, Jaime Eduardo. Retos de la manipulación genética a los países del tercer mundo / Challenges of genetic manipulation for third-world countries. *Revista Latinoamericana de Bioética* 2003 January; (4): 80-99. NRCBL: 15.1; 4.4; 1.3.11. SC: le.

Black, Michael. Genetics in the courtroom [forum]. *University of New South Wales Law Journal* 2003; 26(3): 755-763. NRCBL: 15.1; 8.3.1; 8.4; 8.2; 9.5.1. SC: cs; le. Identifiers: Australia.

Bovenberg, Jasper. Whose tissue is it anyway? *Nature Biotechnology* 2005 August; 23(8): 929-933. NRCBL: 15.1; 4.4; 18.1; 15.8; 5.1. SC: le.

Casado, María. The conflict between legal interests in clinical genetics: public health requirements and the safeguarding of human dignity = El conflicto entre bienes jurídicos en el campo de la genética clínica: exigencias de saludpública y salvaguarda de la dignidad humana. *Law and the Human Genome Review = Revista de Derecho y Genoma Humano* 1996 January-June; (4): 23-37. NRCBL: 15.1; 2.1; 1.1; 9.1. SC: le. Identifiers: Spain.

De Francesco, Laura. Genetic profiteering [news]. *Nature Biotechnology* 2006 August; 24(8): 888-890. NRCBL: 15.1; 15.3; 9.1. SC: le.

de Sola, Carlos. Privacy and genetic data cases of conflict (I) = Privacidad y datos genéticos. Situaciones de conflicto (I). *Law and the Human Genome = Revista de Derecho y Genoma Humano* 1994 July-December; (1): 173-184. NRCBL: 15.1; 8.4. SC: le.

District of Columbia. *Laws, statutes, etc.* An act to amend the Human Rights Act of 1977 to prohibit employment discrimination based on genetic information; to prohibit an employer, employment agency, or labor organization from requesting or requiring a genetic test of, or administering a genetic test to, an employee or applicant for employment or membership; to prohibit an employer, employment agency, or labor organization from seeking to obtain, obtaining, or using genetic information of an employee or applicant for employment; to provide an exemption that

NRCBL: National Reference Center for Bioethics Literature Classification Scheme   See inside front cover for terms.

255

allows the use of genetic testing or information with the written and informed consent of the employee or applicant for employment to determine the existence of a bonafide occupational qualification, investigate a workers' compensation or disability compensation claim, or determine an employee's susceptibility or exposure to potentially toxic substances in the workplace; to prohibit health benefit plans and health insurers from using genetic information as a condition of eligibility or in setting premium rates; and to prohibit health benefit plans and health insurers from requesting or requiring genetic testing [Approved: 3 January 2005]. Washington, DC: Council of the District of Columbia, 2005. 4 p. [Online]. Accessed: http://www.dccouncil. washington.dc.us/images/00001/20041217111559.pdf [2007 March 9]. NRCBL: 15.1; 15.3; 8.4. SC: le. Identifiers: Human Rights Genetic Information Amendment Act of 2004. Note: Act 15-648. Introduced by council members Graham and Patterson on January 7, 2003. Approved on January 3, 2005.

Etzioni, Amitai. A communitarian approach: a viewpoint on the study of the legal, ethical and policy considerations raised by DNA tests and databases. *Journal of Law, Medicine and Ethics* 2006 Summer; 34(2): 214-221. NRCBL: 15.1; 1.3.5; 1.3.12. SC: le.

Gaensslen, R. E. Should biological evidence or DNA be retained by forensic science laboratories after profiling? No, except under narrow legislatively-stipulated conditions. *Journal of Law, Medicine and Ethics* 2006 Summer; 34(2): 375-379. NRCBL: 15.1; 18.3; 18.2. SC: le.

Gerards, Janneke H.; Janssen, Heleen L. Regulation of genetic and other health information in a comparative perspective. *European Journal of Health Law* 2006 December; 13(4): 339-398. NRCBL: 15.1; 8.4; 9.3.1; 21.1. SC: rv;le.

Gertz, Renate. Is it 'me' or 'we'? Genetic relations and the meaning of 'personal data' under the Data Protection Directive. *European Journal of Health Law* 2004 September; 11(3): 231-244. NRCBL: 15.1; 1.3.12; 17.1; 8.4. SC: le.

Greely, Henry T.; Riordan, Daniel P.; Garrison, Nanibaa' A.; Mountain, Joanna L. Family ties: the use of DNA offender databases to catch offenders' kin. *Journal of Law, Medicine and Ethics* 2006 Summer; 34(2): 248-262. NRCBL: 15.1; 1.3.5; 1.3.12; 13.1. SC: le.

Grodsky, Jamie A. Genetics and environmental law: redefining public health. *California Law Review* 2005 January; 93(1): 171-269. NRCBL: 15.1; 9.1; 16.1. SC: le.

Haesler, Andrew. DNA and policing. *Reform* 2001 Spring; 79: 27-31. NRCBL: 15.1; 1.3.5. SC: le.

Haimes, Erica. Social and ethical issues in the use of familial searching in forensic investigations: insights from family and kinship studies. *Journal of Law, Medicine and Ethics* 2006 Summer; 34(2): 263-276. NRCBL: 15.1; 1.3.5; 1.3.12; 13.1. SC: le.

Hansson, Sven Ove; Björkman, Barbro. Bioethics in Sweden. *CQ: Cambridge Quarterly of Healthcare Ethics* 2006 Summer; 15(3): 285-293. NRCBL: 15.1; 1.3; 12; 1.3.5; 18.3. SC: cs; le.

Hawaii. *Laws, statutes, etc.* An act relating to genetic information and genetic testing [Approved: 1 July 2002]. Hawaii: State Legislature, 2002. 3 p. [Online]. Accessed: http://www.capitol.hawaii.gov/session2002/bills/ SB2180_hd1_.htm [2007 March 9]. NRCBL: 15.1; 8.4. SC: le. Note: Senate Bill 2180, 21st Legislature, regular session. Introduced by Sen. Nakata on January 18, 2002. Approved on July 1, 2002.

Hunter, Kathryn G. DNA as taxable property — the elephant in the room or a red herring? *European Journal of Health Law* 2006 September; 13(3): 263-277. NRCBL: 15.1; 4.4; 18.6. SC: le.

Iceland. Supreme Court. Ragnhildur Gumðundsdóttir vs. The State of Iceland. (Thursday, 27 November 2003, No. 151/2003). *European Journal of Health Law* 2004 September; 11(3): 283-291. Subject: 15.1; 1.3.12; 17.1; 8.4. SC: le.

Inayatullah, Sohail; Fitzgerald, Jennifer. Gene discourses: politics, culture, law, and futures. *Technological Forecasting and Social Change* 1996 June-July; 52(2-3): 161-183. NRCBL: 15.1; 5.1; 10. SC: le; an.

Jaffe, Gregory. Regulatory slowdown on GM crop decision [letter]. *Nature Biotechnology* 2006 July; 24(7): 748-749. NRCBL: 15.1; 1.3.11; 5.3. SC: le.

Joh, Elizabeth E. Reclaiming "abandoned" DNA: the Fourth Amendment and genetic privacy. *Northwestern University Law Review* 2006 Winter; 100(2): 857-884. NRCBL: 15.1; 8.4; 1.3.5. SC: le.

Joly, Yann. Life insurers' access to genetic information: a way out of the stalemate? *Health Law Review* 2006; 14(3): 14-21. NRCBL: 15.1; 8.4. SC: le.

Kaye, D.H. Who needs special needs? On the constitutionality of collecting DNA and other biometric data from arrestees. *Journal of Law, Medicine and Ethics* 2006 Summer; 34(2): 188-198. NRCBL: 15.1; 1.3.5; 19.5; 1.3.12. SC: le.

Kent, Julie; Faulkner, A.; Geesink, I.; FitzPatrick, D. Towards governance of human tissue engineered technologies in Europe: framing the case for a new regulatory regime. *Technological Forecasting and Social Change* 2006 January; 73(1): 41-60. NRCBL: 15.1; 19.5; 5.3; 21.1. SC: le.

Knoppers, Bartha Maria. Genetics and common law. *In:* Meulders-Klein, Marie-Thérèse; Deech, Ruth; Vlaardingerbroek, Paul, eds. Biomedicine, the Family and Human Rights. New York: Kluwer Law International, 2002: 397-414. NRCBL: 15.1. SC: le.

Knoppers, Bartha Maria; Saginur, Madelaine. The Babel of genetic data terminology. *Nature Biotechnology* 2005 August; 23(8): 925-927. NRCBL: 15.1; 8.4; 18.2; 21.1. SC: le.

Knoppers, Bartha Maria; Saginur, Madelaine; Cash, Howard. Ethical issues in secondary uses of human biological materials from mass disasters. *Journal of Law, Medicine and Ethics* 2006 Summer; 34(2): 352-365. NRCBL: 15.1; 1.3.12; 18.5.1; 18.3; 21.1. SC: le.

Komel, Radovan. Practical and legal aspects and public debate on ethics in human genetics in Slovenia. *In:* Glasa, J., ed. Ethics of Human Genetics: Challenges of the (Post) Genomic Era. Bratislava, Slovak Republic: Charis [and] IMEB Foundation; 2002: 33-40. NRCBL: 15.1. SC: le.

Lazer, David; Mayer-Schönberger, Viktor. Statutory frameworks for regulating information flows: drawing lessons for the DNA data banks from other government data systems. *Journal of Law, Medicine and Ethics* 2006 Summer; 34(2): 366-374. NRCBL: 15.1; 1.3.12; 13.1; 8.4. SC: le.

LeVine, Harry. Facts, data, and opinion. *In his:* Genetic Engineering: A Reference Handbook. 2nd ed. Santa Barbara, CA: ABC-CLIO, 2006: 141-200. NRCBL: 15.1; 1.3.2; 5.3; 14.5; 18.5.4. SC: em; le.

Liddell, Kathy. Did the watchdog bark, bite or whimper? UK report on the use of personal genetic information. *European Journal of Health Law* 2002 September; 9(3): 243-256. NRCBL: 15.1; 2.4; 18.3; 8.4. SC: le.

Manson, Neil C. What is genetic information, and why is it significant? A contextual, contrastive, approach. *Journal of Applied Philosophy* 2006; 23(1): 1-16. NRCBL: 15.1. SC: le.

Abstract: Is genetic information of special ethical significance? Does it require special regulation? There is considerable contemporary debate about this question (the 'genetic exceptionalism' debate). 'Genetic information' is an ambiguous term and, as an aid to avoiding conflation in the genetic exceptionalism debate, a detailed account is given of just how and why 'genetic information' is ambiguous. Whilst ambiguity is a ubiquitous problem of communication, it is suggested that 'genetic information' is ambiguous in a particular way, one that gives rise to the problem of 'significance creep' (i.e., where claims about the significance of certain kinds of genetic information in one context influence our thinking about the significance of other kinds of genetic information in other contexts). A contextual and contrastive methodology is proposed: evaluating the significance of genetic information requires us to be sensitive to the polysemy of 'genetic information' across contexts and then examine the contrast in significance (if any) of genetic, as opposed to nongenetic, information within contexts. This, in turn, suggests that a proper solution to the regulatory question requires us to pay more attention to how and why information, and its acquisition, possession and use, come to be of ethical significance.

Maryland. *Laws, statutes, etc.* An act for the purpose of prohibiting the use of certain genetic information to deny or otherwise affect a health insurance policy or contract; prohibiting the request or requirement of certain genetic information as a basis for issuing or renewing health benefits coverage; prohibiting the disclosure of certain genetic information to certain persons without certain authorization of the individual from whom the genetic information was obtained; identifying certain permissible purposes for disclosure of genetic information; defining certain terms; repealing the termination date of certain provisions of law that relate to the use of genetic tests; and generally relating to prohibiting discrimination on the basis of genetic information in health insurance [Approved: 13 April 1999]. Maryland: General Assembly, 1999. 4 p. [Online]. Accessed: http://mlis.state.md.us/PDF-Documents/1999rs/bills/sb/sb0774t.PDF [2007 March 9]. NRCBL: 15.1; 8.4. SC: le. Identifiers: Genetic Information Nondiscrimination in Health Insurance Act of 1999. Note: Senate Bill 774, 1999 regular session. Introduced on March 5, 1999. Approved on April 13, 1999.

Massachusetts. *Laws, statutes, etc.* An act relative to insurance and genetic testing and privacy protection [Approved: 22 August 2000]. Massachusetts: House Bill 5416, Acts of 2000, Chapter 254. 10 p. [Online]. Accessed: http://www.mass.gov/legis/laws/seslaw00/sl000254.htm [2007 March 9]. NRCBL: 15.1; 8.4. SC: le.

McGuire, Amy L.; Gibbs, Richard A. Currents in contemporary ethics. *Journal of Law, Medicine and Ethics* 2006 Winter; 34(4): 809-812. NRCBL: 15.1; 18.2; 18.3. SC: le.

Michaud, Jean. Bioethics and recent French law developments = Las nuevas leyes francesas sobre Bioética. *Law and the Human Genome Review = Revista de Derecho y Genoma Humano* 1995 July-December; (3): 277-279. NRCBL: 15.1; 2.1. SC: le.

Montana. *Laws, statutes, etc.* An act establishing standards for the collection, use, and disclosure of genetic information in issuing insurance; prohibiting insurers from requiring genetic testing except as otherwise required by law; prohibiting discrimination on the basis of genetic traits by insurers, health service corporations, health maintenance organizations, fraternal benefit societies, and other issuers of individual or group policies or certificates of insurance; prohibiting the solicitation of genetic information for nontherapeutic purposes; and amending sections 2-18-812 and 33-31-111, MCA [Approved: 19 April 1999]. Montana: State Legislature, 1999. 5 p. [Online]. Accessed: http://data.opi.state.mt.us/bills/billhtml/HB0111.htm [2007 March 9]. NRCBL: 15.1; 8.4. SC: le. Note: House Bill 111, 1999 regular session. Introduced by Rep. Guggenheim on December 18, 1998. Approved on April 19, 1999.

New Jersey. *Laws, statutes, etc.* An act concerning genetic testing and genetic privacy. New Jersey: Senate Bill 695; Public Laws 1996-1997, Chapter 126. 16 p. [Online]. Accessed http://www.njleg.state.nj.us/9697/Bills/PL96/

NRCBL: National Reference Center for Bioethics Literature Classification Scheme   See inside front cover for terms.

257

126_.PDF [9 March 2007]. NRCBL: 15.1; 8.4. SC: le. Identifiers: Genetic Privacy Act.

New Mexico. *Laws, statutes, etc.* An act relating to genetic information; prohibiting the use of genetic information in nonmedical contexts [Approved: 6 April 2005]. New Mexico: State Legislature, 2005. 4 p. [Online]. Accessed: http://legis.state.nm.us/Sessions/05%20 Regular/final/HB0183.pdf [2007 March 9]. NRCBL: 15.1; 8.4. SC: le. Note: House Bill 183, 47th Legislature, 2005 regular session. Introduced by Rep. Picraux. Approved on April 6, 2005.

Ossorio, Pilar N. About face: forensic genetic testing for race and visible traits. *Journal of Law, Medicine and Ethics* 2006 Summer; 34(2): 277-292. NRCBL: 15.1; 1.3.5; 1.3.12; 9.5.4; 15.10. SC: le.

Pickens, K.L. Don't judge me by my genes: a survey of federal genetic discrimination legislation. *Tulsa Law Journal* 1998 Fall; 34(1): 161-181. NRCBL: 15.1; 8.4; 15.10. SC: le.

Rich, Robert F.; Ziegler, Julian. Genetic discrimination in health insurance — comprehensive legal solutions for a (not so) special problem? *Indiana Health Law Review* 2005; 2(1): 1-47. NRCBL: 15.1; 4.2; 9.3.1. SC: le.

Ripol Carulla, Santiago. The protection of medical and genetic data in the Council of Europe's normative texts (part II) = La protección de los datos médicos y genéticos en la normativa del Consejo de Europa (Parte II). *Revista de Derecho Genoma Humano = Law and the Human Genome Review* 1997 January-June; (6): 101-127. NRCBL: 15.1; 8.4; 21.1; 1.3.9. SC: le.

Rospigliosi, Enrique Varsi. Genetic Law in Peru = El Derecho genético en el Perú. *Law and the Human Genome Review = Revista de Derecho y Genoma Humano* 1996 July-December; (5): 121-125. NRCBL: 15.1. SC: le.

Rothstein, Mark A.; Talbott, Meghan K. The expanding use of DNA in law enforcement: what role for privacy? *Journal of Law, Medicine and Ethics* 2006 Summer; 34(2): 153-164. NRCBL: 15.1; 1.3.5; 1.3.12; 1.1. SC: le.

Salter, Brian; Jones, Mavis. Regulating human genetics: the changing politics of biotechnology governance in the European Union. *Health, Risk and Society* 2002 November; 4(3): 325-340. NRCBL: 15.1; 21.1. SC: le.

Schneider, Carl E.; Wardle, Lynn D. Genetics and artificial procreation in the U.S.A. *In:* Meulders-Klein, Marie-Thérèse; Deech, Ruth; Vlaardingerbroek, Paul, eds. Biomedicine, the Family and Human Rights. New York: Kluwer Law International, 2002: 55-86. NRCBL: 15.1; 14.1. SC: le.

Scott, Christopher Thomas. Chimeras in the crosshairs [news]. *Nature Biotechnology* 2006 May; 24(5): 487-490. NRCBL: 15.1; 18.1; 22.1. SC: le.

Sebatier, Sandrine. Ethical questions raised by human genetics. A personal contribution to the preparation of a legal instrument of the Council of Europe on human genetics (Part I). *Revista de Derecho y Genoma Humano = Law and the Human Genome Review* 1998 January-June; (8): 187-203. NRCBL: 15.1; 15.3; 15.2; 14.4. SC: le.

Shapiro, Julie. A lesbian centered critique of "genetic parenthood". *Journal of Gender, Race and Justice* 2006 Spring; 9(3): 591-612. NRCBL: 15.1; 10; 14.2. SC: an; le.

Silvers, Anita; Stein, Michael Ashley. Essentially empirical: the roles of biological and legal classification in effectively prohibiting genetic discrimination. *In:* Figueroa, Robert; Harding, Sandra, eds. Science and Other Cultures: Issues in Philosophies of Science and Technology. New York: Routledge; 2003: 129-153. NRCBL: 15.1. SC: em; le.

Simoncelli, Tania. Dangerous excursions: the case against expanding forensic DNA databases to innocent persons. *Journal of Law, Medicine and Ethics* 2006 Summer; 34(2): 390-397. NRCBL: 15.1; 1.3.5; 1.3.12; 8.4. SC: le.

Slaughter, Louise McIntosh. Genetic testing and discrimination: how private is your information? *Stanford Law and Policy Review* 2006; 17(1): 67-81. NRCBL: 15.1; 15.3; 8.4. SC: le.

Smith, Michael E. Let's make the DNA identification database as inclusive as possible. *Journal of Law, Medicine and Ethics* 2006 Summer; 34(2): 385-389. NRCBL: 15.1; 1.3.5; 1.3.12; 8.4. SC: le.

South Carolina. *Laws, statutes, etc.* An act to amend title 38, Code of Laws of South Carolina, 1976, relating to insurance, by adding chapter 93 so as to enact provisions regulating the privacy of genetic information [Approved: 26 May 1998]. South Carolina: General Assembly Bill 535. 4 p. [Online]. Accessed: http://www.scstatehouse.net/sess112_1997-1998/bills/535.htm [2007 March 9]. NRCBL: 15.1; 8.4. SC: le. Identifiers: Privacy of Genetic Information. Note: General Assembly Bill 535, 112th session, 1997-1998. Introduced on March 12, 1997. Approved on May 26, 1998.

Stulic, Mathew. Genetic non-discrimination, privacy and property rights. *E Law: Murdoch University Electronic Journal of Law* 2000 June; 7(2): 26 p. [Online]. Accessed: http://www.murdoch.edu.au/elaw/issues/v4n3/stulic72.html[2006 June 29]. NRCBL: 15.1; 15.8. SC: le. Identifiers: Australia. Genetic Privacy and Non-Discrimination Bill 1998.

Sullivan, Rebecca. An embryonic nation: life against health in Canadian biotechnological discourse. *Communication Theory* 2005 February; 15(1): 39-58. NRCBL: 15.1; 5.1; 4.4; 10; 18.5.4; 19.1; 22.2. SC: an; le.

Thable, Daman. With great knowledge comes great responsibilities: an examination of genetic discrimination in

---

Canada. *Health Law Review* 2006; 14(3): 22-31. NRCBL: 15.1; 4.2. SC: le.

Toom, Victor. DNA fingerprinting and the right to inviolability of the body and bodily integrity in the Netherlands: convincing evidence and proliferating body parts. *Genomics, Society and Policy* 2006 December; 2(3): 64-74. NRCBL: 15.1; 1.3.5; 4.4. SC: le; an.

Abstract: The completion of the Human Genome Project has opened up unprecedented possibilities in healthcare, but also ethical and social dilemmas in terms of how these can be achieved. Genomic information can be seen as a "global public good" (GPG), in that it is represented by knowledge in the public domain and across national boundaries. Lack of investment, infrastructure and expertise in developing countries means that they are unable to take advantage of these GPG characteristics to address their health needs, fuelling fears of a growing "genomics divide". Some have suggested an international knowledge sharing and capacity building network, a Global Genomics Initiative, as a means to harness the potential of genomics to reduce inequalities in health between North and South. Three UNESCO declarations also call for cooperation between developed and developing countries in genomics research and science and technology in general. Using international relations theories around global governance and networks as a conceptual framework, this paper examines whether these initiatives are likely to succeed in providing effective governance of genomics.

United States. Congress. House. A bill to establish limitations with respect to disclosure and use of genetic information in connection with group health plans and health insurance coverage, to provide for consistent standards applicable in connection with hospital care and medical services provided under title 38 of the United States Code, to prohibit employment discrimination on the basis of genetic information and genetic testing, and for other purposes. Washington, DC: U.S. G.P.O.; 1998. 22 p. [Online]. Accessed: http://frwebgate.access.gpo.gov/cgi-bin/useftp.cgi?IPaddress=162.140.64.122&filename=h3299ih.pdf&directory=/diskc/wais/data/ 105_cong_bills [2007 March 6]. NRCBL: 15.1; 8.4; 9.3.1. SC: le. Identifiers: Family Genetic Privacy and Protection Act. Note: H.R. 3299, 105th Congress, 2d session. Introduced by Rep. Smith, February 26, 1998. Referred to the Committee on Commerce, and in addition to the Committees on Education and the Workforce, and Veterans' Affairs.

United States. Congress. House. A bill to establish limitations with respect to disclosure and use of genetic information, and for other purposes. Washington, DC: U.S. G.P.O.; 1997. 8 p. [Online]. Accessed: http://frwebgate.access.gpo.gov/cgi-bin/useftp.cgi?IPaddress=162.140.64.122&filename=h341ih.pdf&directory=/diskc/wais/data/ 105_cong_bills [2007 March 5]. NRCBL: 15.1; 8.4. SC: le. Identifiers: Genetic Privacy and Nondiscrimination Act of 1997. Note: H.R. 341, 105th Congress, 1st session. Introduced by Rep. Stearns, January 7, 1997. Referred to the Committee on Commerce, and in addition to the Committees on Government Reform and Oversight and Education and the Workforce.

United States. Congress. Senate. A bill to amend Title 18, United States Code, to prohibit human chimeras. Washington, DC: U.S. G.P.O., 2005. 5 p. [Online]. Accessed: http://frwebgate.access.gpo.gov/cgi-bin/getdoc.cgi?dbname=109_cong_bills&docid=f:s659is.txt.pdf [2006 April 28]. NRCBL: 15.1; 18.1; 22.1. SC: le. Identifiers: Human Chimera Prohibition Act of 2005. Note: S. 659, 109th Congress, 1st session. Introduced by Sen. Brownback on March 17, 2005. Referred to the Committee on the Judiciary.

United States. Congress. Senate. A bill to prohibit discrimination on the basis of genetic information with respect to health insurance. Washington, DC: U.S. G.P.O.; 2001. 28 p. [Online]. Accessed: http://frwebgate.access.gpo.gov/cgi-bin/useftp.cgi?IPaddress=162.140.64.31&filename=s382is.pdf&directory=/disk2/wais/data/ 107_cong_bills [2007 March 6]. NRCBL: 15.1; 8.4; 9.3.1. SC: le. Identifiers: Genetic Information Nondiscrimination in Health Insurance Act of 2001. Note: S. 382, 107th Congress, 1st session. Introduced by Rep. Snowe, February 15, 2001. Referred to the Committee on Health, Education, Labor, and Pensions.

United States. Congress. Senate. A bill to prohibit discrimination on the basis of genetic information with respect to health insurance. Washington, DC: U.S. G.P.O., 1999. 27 p. [Online]. Accessed: http://frwebgate.access.gpo.gov/cgi-bin/getdoc.cgi?dbname=106_cong_bills&docid=f:s543is.txt.pdf [2007 March 8]. NRCBL: 15.1; 8.4; 9.3.1. SC: le. Identifiers: Genetic Information Nondiscrimination in Health Insurance Act of 1999. Note: S. 543, 106th Congress, 1st session. Introduced by Sen. Snowe on March 4, 1999. Referred to the Committee on Health, Education, Labor, and Pensions.

United States. Congress. Senate. A bill to prohibit discrimination on the basis of genetic information with respect to health insurance and employment. Washington, DC: U.S. G.P.O., 2002. 45 p. [Online]. Accessed: http://frwebgate.access.gpo.gov/cgi-bin/getdoc.cgi?dbname=107_cong_bills&docid= f:s1995is.txt.pdf [2007 March 8]. NRCBL: 15.1; 8.4; 9.3.1. SC: le. Identifiers: Genetic Information Nondiscrimination Act of 2002. Note: S. 1995, 107th Congress, 2nd session. Introduced by Sen. Snowe on March 6, 2002. Referred to the Committee on Health, Education, Labor and Pensions.

United States. Congress. Senate. A bill to prohibit discrimination on the basis of genetic information with respect to health insurance and employment. Washington, DC: U.S. G.P.O., 2001. 73 p. [Online]. Accessed: http://frwebgate.access.gpo.gov/cgi-bin/getdoc.cgi?dbname=107_cong_bills&docid=f:s318is.pdf [2007 March 8]. NRCBL: 15.1; 8.4; 9.3.1. SC: le. Identifiers: Genetic Nondiscrimination in Health Insurance and Employment Act. Note: S. 318, 107th Congress, 1st session. Introduced by Sen. Daschle on February 13, 2001. Re-

NRCBL: National Reference Center for Bioethics Literature Classification Scheme See inside front cover for terms.

259

ferred to the Committee on Health, Education, Labor, and Pensions.

United States. Congress. Senate. A bill to prohibit health insurance and employment discrimination against individuals and their family members on the basis of predictive genetic information or genetic services. Washington, DC: U.S.G.P.O., 1999. 70 p. [Online]. Accessed: http://frwebgate.access.gpo.gov/cgi-bin/getdoc.cgi? dbname=106_cong_bills&docid= f:s1322is.txt.pdf [2007 March 8]. NRCBL: 15.1; 8.4; 9.3.1. SC: le. Identifiers: Genetic Nondiscrimination in Health Insurance and Employment Act of 1999. Note: S. 1322, 106th Congress, 1st session. Introduced by Sen. Daschle on July 1, 1999. Referred to the Committee on Health, Education, Labor, and Pensions.

United States. Congress. Senate. A bill to protect the genetic privacy of individuals, and for other purposes. Washington, DC: U.S. G.P.O., 1996. 42 p. [Online]. Accessed: http://frwebgate.access.gpo.gov/cgi-bin/getdoc.cgi? dbname=104_cong_bills&docid= f:s1898is.txt.pdf [2007 March 8]. NRCBL: 15.1; 8.4. SC: le. Identifiers: Genetic Confidentiality and Nondiscrimination Act of 1996. Note: S. 1898, 104th Congress, 2nd session. Introduced by Sen. Domenici on June 24, 1996. Referred to the Committee on Labor and Human Resources.

United States. Congress. Senate. A bill to improve access to and appropriate utilization of valid, reliable and accurate molecular genetic tests by all populations thus helping to secure the promise of personalized medicine for all Americans. Washington, DC: U.S. G.P.O., 2006. 43 p. [Online]. Accessed: http://frwebgate.access.gpo.gov/cgi-bin/getdoc.cgi?dbname=109_cong_bills&docid=f:s3822is.txt.pdf [2006 July 17]. NRCBL: 15.1; 15.3; 9.7; 3.1. SC: le. Identifiers: Genomics and Personalized Medicine Act of 2006. Note: S.3822. 109th Congress, 2nd session. Introduced by Sen. Obama, August 3, 2006. Referred to the Committee on Finance.

Uranga, Amelia Martín. European legislation on genetically modified organisms = La normativa en Europa sobre los organismos modificados genéticamente. *Law and the Human Genome Review = Revista de Derecho y Genoma Humano* 1996 July-December; (5): 205-223. NRCBL: 15.1; 21.1; 15.7; 21.1. SC: le.

Virginia. *Laws, statutes, etc.* An act to amend an reenact section 38.2-613 of the Code of Virginia and to amend the Code of Virginia by adding a section numbered 38.2-508.4 relating to insurance; genetic information privacy[Approved 6 April 1996; Expires 1 July 1998]. Virginia: Senate Bill 335; Acts of Assembly, Chapter 704. [Online]. 5 p. Accessed http://leg1.state.va.us/cgi-bin/legp504.exe? 961+ful+CHAP0704 [2007 March 9]. NRCBL: 15.1; 8.4. SC: le.

Weiss, Marcia J. Beware! Uncle Sam has your DNA; legal fallout from its use and misuse in the U.S. *Ethics and Information Technology* 2004; 6(1): 55-63. NRCBL: 15.1; 1.3.12; 5.3. SC: le.

Wyoming. *Laws, statutes, etc.* An act relating to group health insurance; limiting the use of genetic testing results by group insurers as specified; and providing for an effective date [Approved: 2003 March 3]. Wyoming: State Legislature, 2003. 3 p. [Online]. Accessed: http://legisweb. state.wy.us/2003/enroll/hb0024.pdf [2007 March 9]. NRCBL: 15.1; 8.4. SC: le. Note: House Bill No. 24, 57th Legislature, 2003 general session. Introduced by Reps. Tipton and Meuli on January 15, 2003. Approved March 3, 2003.

Yagüe, Francisco Lledó. Compulsory paternity: on the recent 19 January 1994 judgement of the Spanish Constitutional Court = La paternidad forzada: a propósito de la reciente sentencia del Tribunal Constitucional de 19 enero de 1994. *Law and the Human Genome = Revista de Derecho y Genoma Humano* 1994 July-December; (1): 197-202. NRCBL: 15.1; 14.1. SC: le.

Yanes, Pedro. Personal insurance and genetic information (I) = Seguros de personas e información genética (I). *Law and the Human Genome = Revista de Derecho y Genoma Humano* 1994 July-December; (1): 185-194. NRCBL: 15.1; 8.4. SC: le.

GENETICS AND HUMAN ANCESTRY

Declaration of Indigenous Peoples of the Western Hemisphere regarding the Human Genome Diversity Project. Phoenix (Arizona), on February 19 of 1995 = Declaración de los Pueblos Indígenas del Hemisferio Occidental enrelación con el Proyecto de Diversidad del Genoma Humano. Fénix (Arizona), 19 de febrero de 1995. *Law and the Human Genome Review = Revista de Derecho y Genoma Humano* 1996 January-June; (4): 209-211. NRCBL: 15.11.

The ethical and legal debate on the Human Genome Diversity Project: are all the perspectives reconcilable? = El debate ético y jurídico en torno al Proyecto Genoma Humano sobre Diversidad ¿son conciliables todas las perspectivas? [editorial]. *Law and the Human Genome Review = Revista de Derecho y Genoma Humano* 1996 January-June; (4): 13-15. NRCBL: 15.11; 21.1.

Azevêdo, Eliane S.; Tavares-Neto, José. Black identity and registries in Brazil: a question of rights and justice. *Eubios Journal of Asian and International Bioethics* 2006 January; 16(1): 22-24. NRCBL: 15.11; 9.5.4.

Birenbaum-Carmeli, D. On the prevalence of population groups in the human-genetics research literature. *Politics and the Life Sciences* 2004 March; 23(1): 34-41. NRCBL: 15.11; 13.1. SC: an; em.

Brewer, Rose M. Thinking critically about race and genetics. *Journal of Law, Medicine and Ethics* 2006 Fall; 34(3): 513-519. NRCBL: 15.11; 9.5.4; 15.10; 3.1; 7.2.

Abstract: We must critically rethink race and genetics in the context of the new genetic breakthroughs and haplotype mapping. We must avoid the slippery slope of turning socially constructed racial categories into genetic realities. It is a potentially dangerous arena given the history of racialized science in the United States and globally. Indeed, the new advances must be viewed in the context of a long history of racial inequality, continuing into the current period. This is more than a question of how carefully we use categories of analysis such as race. Justice and equity must be core to our considerations. There is a community stake in this work that must be seriously considered and included in decision making. A progressive and critical analysis is in order.

Brodwin, Paul. "Bioethics in action" and human population genetics research. *Culture, Medicine and Psychiatry* 2005 June; 29(2): 145-178. NRCBL: 15.11; 2.1; 21.7; 21.1; 18.3. Identifiers: Human Genome Diversity Project; Melungeons.

Brugada, Ramon. Genetics, ethics and ethnicity [editorial]. *Heart Rhythm* 2004 November; 1(5): 608-609. NRCBL: 15.11; 15.3; 9.5.4.

Calderón, Rosario. The Human Genome Diversity Project: ethical aspects = El Proyecto Genoma Humano sobre Diversidad: aspectors éticos. *Law and the Human Genome Review = Revista de Derecho y Genoma Humano* 1996 January-June;(4): 107-123. NRCBL: 15.11; 21.1; 13.1; 15.1; 9.3.1.

Condit, Celeste Michelle; Parrott, Roxanne; Harris, Tina M. Lay understandings of the relationship between race and genetics: development of a collectivized knowledge through shared discourse. *Public Understanding of Science* 2002 October; 11(4): 373-387. NRCBL: 15.11; 5.3; 15.1. SC: em.

Dyson, Simon M. "Race," ethnicity and haemoglobin disorders. *Social Science and Medicine* 1998 June 1; 47(1): 121-131. NRCBL: 15.11; 15.3; 9.5.4. Identifiers: United Kingdom (Great Britain).

Ferreira, Luzitano Brandão. Population genetics and the power of discrimination. *Eubios Journal of Asian and International Bioethics* 2006 January; 16(1): 25-27. NRCBL: 15.11; 15.3.

Fleming, John I. Ethics and the Human Genome Diversity Project = La ética y el Proyecto Genoma Humano sobre Diversidad. *Law and the Human Genome Review = Revista de Derecho y Genoma Humano* 1996 January-June; (4): 141-164. NRCBL: 15.11; 21.1; 15.10; 15.5; 9.3.1. SC: le.

Harmon, Amy. DNA gatherers hit a snag: the tribes don't trust them. *New York Times* 2006 December 10; p. A1, A38. NRCBL: 15.11; 18.2; 18.5.9. Identifiers: Genographic Project.

Harmon, Amy. Seeking ancestry and privilege in DNA ties uncovered by tests. *New York Times* 2006 April 12; p. A1, A17. NRCBL: 15.11; 15.3.

Hasian, Marouf, Jr. The Internet and the human genome. *Peace Review* 2001 September; 13(3): 375-380. NRCBL: 15.11; 1.3.1; 21.1; 1.3.12. Identifiers: Human Genome Diversity Project.

Herzog, Antonia V.; Frankel, Mark S. A model ethical protocol as a guidance document for human genome research. *Revista de Derecho Genoma Humano = Law and the Human Genome Review* 1999 January-June; (10): 21-40. NRCBL: 15.11; 21.1; 15.8; 18.3; 8.4. Identifiers: Human Genome Diversity Project (HGDP).

Kahn, Jonathan. From disparity to difference: how race-specific medicines may undermine policies to address inequalities in health care. *Southern California Interdisciplinary Law Journal* 2005 Fall; 15(1): 105-130. NRCBL: 15.11; 9.7; 9.1.

Kahn, Jonathan. Race, pharmacogenomics, and marketing: putting BiDil in context. *American Journal of Bioethics [Online]* 2006 September-October; 6(5): W1-W5. NRCBL: 15.11; 9.5.4; 9.7; 9.3.1. Identifiers: United States; Food and Drug Administration; African-American Heart Failure Trial (A-HEFT).

Kahn, Jonathan; Sankar, Pamela. Being specific about race-specific medicine. *Health Affairs* 2006 July-November; (Web Exclusives): 375-377. NRCBL: 15.11; 9.5.4; 9.7. Identifiers: African Americans.

Kraft, Dina. A hunt for genes that betrayed a desert people. *New York Times* 2006 March 21; p. F1, F4. NRCBL: 15.11; 15.3; 15.2; 9.5.1; 21.7. Identifiers: Bedoin.

Parrott, Roxanne L.; Silk, Kami J.; Dillow, Megan R.; Krieger, Janice L.; Harris, Tina M.; Condit, Celeste M. Development and validation of tools to assess genetic discrimination and genetically based racism. *Journal of the National Medical Association* 2005 July; 97(7): 980-990. NRCBL: 15.11; 15.1; 3.1; 9.5.4. SC: em.

Pearson, Roger. The concept of heredity in Western thought: part three: the revival of interest in genetics. *Mankind Quarterly* 1995 Fall; 36(1): 73-103. NRCBL: 15.11; 21.1; 3.2.

Puckrein, Gary. BiDil: from another vantage point. *Health Affairs* 2006 July-November; (Web Exclusives): 368-374. NRCBL: 15.11; 9.5.4; 9.7. Identifiers: African Americans; race-specific medicine.

Reardon, Jenny. Group consent and the informed, volitional subject. *In her:* Race to the Finish: Identity and Governance in an Age of Genomics. Princeton, NJ: Princeton University Press; 2005: 98-125. NRCBL: 15.11; 15.10; 18.3.

Shanawani, H.; Dame, L.; Schwartz, D.A.; Cook-Deegan, R. Non-reporting and inconsistent reporting of race and ethnicity in articles that claim associations among genotype, outcome, and race or ethnicity. *Journal of Medi-*

NRCBL: National Reference Center for Bioethics Literature Classification Scheme   See inside front cover for terms.

261

cal Ethics 2006 December; 32(12): 724-728. NRCBL: 15.11; 1.3.7. SC: em.

Suda, Eiko; Macer, Darryl R.J. Ethical challenges of conducting the Hap Map Genetics project in Japan. *In:* Sang-yong, Song; Young-Mo, Koo; Macer, Darryl R.J., eds. Asian Bioethics in the 21st Century. Christchurch, NZ: Eubios Ethics Institute, 2003: 31-45. NRCBL: 15.11. Conference: Proceedings of the Asian Bioethics Conference (ABC4), held 22-25 November 2002 in Seoul, South Korea.

Weiss, Kenneth M. Coming to terms with human variation. *Annual Review of Anthropology* 1998; 27: 273-300. NRCBL: 15.11; 15.10; 1.3.12; 1.3.1. SC: rv.

Winston, Cynthia E.; Kittles, Rick A. Psychological and ethical issues related to identity and inferring ancestry of African Americans. *In:* Turner, Trudy R. ed. Biological Anthropology and Ethics: From Repatriation to Genetic Identity. Albany, NY: State University of New York Press; 2005: 209-229. NRCBL: 15.11.

GENOCIDE *See* TORTURE, GENOCIDE, AND WAR CRIMES

GENOME MAPPING
See also GENETIC RESEARCH; GENETIC SCREENING; RECOMBINANT DNA RESEARCH

Genome privacy [editorial]. *Nature Medicine* 2006 July; 12(7): 717. NRCBL: 15.10; 18.3.

International Workshop on Legal Aspects of the Human Genome Project. Bilbao Declaration (Spain) = Reunión Internacional sobre el Derecho ante el Proyecto Genoma Humano. La Declaración de Bilbao. *Law and the Human Genome = Revista de Derecho y Genoma Humano* 1994 July-December; (1): 205-209. NRCBL: 15.10; 21.1.

Statement on the Principled Conduct of Genetic Research. Statement approved by HUGO Council on 21 March 1996, Heidelberg (Federal Republic of Germany) = Declaración sobre los Principios de Actuación en la Investigación Genética. Aprobada por el Consejo de HUGO en Heidelberg (República Federal de Alemania), 21 marzo de 1996. *Law and the Human Genome Review = Revista de Derecho y Genoma Humano* 1996 July-December; (5): 235-237. NRCBL: 15.10; 15.1. Identifiers: Human Genome Project; Human Genome Organization (HUGO).

The genetic starting line. *Economist* 2000 July 1; 356: 21-22. NRCBL: 15.10. SC: po.

Althanasiou, Tom; Darnovsky, Marcy. The genome as a commons. *World Watch* 2002 July-August; 15(4:) 33-36. NRCBL: 15.10; 15.1; 14.5.

Badagliacco, Joanna M.; Ruiz, Carey D. Impoverished Appalachia and Kentucky genomes: what is at stake? How

to do feminists reply? *New Genetics and Society* 2006 August; 25(2): 209-226. NRCBL: 15.10; 9.5.10; 9.5.5; 15.5.

Barker, Joanne. The Human Genome Diversity Project: "peoples", "populations" and the cultural politics of identification. *Cultural Studies* 2004 July; 18(4): 571-606. NRCBL: 15.10; 13.1; 21.1.

Bergel, Salvador Darío. UNESCO Declaration on the Protection of the Human Genome = El Proyecto de Declaración de la UNESCO sobre Protección del Genoma Humano. *Revista de Derecho Genoma Humano = Law and the Human Genome Review* 1997 July-December; (7): 31-57. NRCBL: 15.10; 21.1; 15.5.

Blanck, Peter David; Marti, Mollie Weighner. Genetic discrimination and the employment provisions of the Americans with Disabilities Act: emerging legal, empirical and policy implications. *Behavioral Sciences and the Law* 1996 Autumn; 14(4): 411-432. NRCBL: 15.10; 15.1.

Bostanci, Adam. Two drafts, one genome? Human diversity and human genome research. *Science as Culture* 2006 September; 15(3): 183-198. NRCBL: 15.10; 5.3; 1.3.7.

Brand, Angela. Public health and genetics — a dangerous combination? *European Journal of Public Health* 2005 April; 15(2): 114-116. NRCBL: 15.10; 9.1.

Caplan, Arthur L. Mapping ourselves. *In his:* Smart Mice, Not-So-Smart People: An Interesting and Amusing Guide to Bioethics. Lanham, MD: Rowman & Littlefield, 2007: 119-138. NRCBL: 15.10. SC: po.

Caron, Lorraine; Karkazis, Katrina; Raffin, Thomas A.; Swan, Gary; Koenig, Barbara A. Nicotine addiction through a neurogenomic prism: ethics, public health, and smoking. *Nicotine and Tobacco Research* 2005 April; 7(2): 181-197. NRCBL: 15.10; 17.1; 9.5.9; 9.1. SC: rv.

Casabona, Carlos María Romeo. The UNESCO Outline of a Declaration on the Protection of the Human Genome: comments on a necessary initiative = El Proyecto de Declaración de la UNESCO sobre la Protección del Genoma Humano: observaciones a una iniciativa necesaria. *Law and the Human Genome Review = Revista de Derecho y Genoma Humano* 1995 July-December; (3): 153-165. NRCBL: 15.10; 5.3; 21.1. SC: le.

Clayton, Ellen. Ethical concerns in HapMap project. *Protecting Human Subjects* 2006 Spring; (13): 9-11. NRCBL: 15.10; 1.3.12.

Collins, Francis S.; Mansoura, Monique K. The Human Genome Project: revealing the shared inheritance of all humankind. *Cancer* 2001 January 1; 91(1, Supplement): 221-225. NRCBL: 15.10; 15.11.

Espiell, Héctor Gros. The common heritage of humanity and the human genome = El patrimonio común de la humanidad y el genoma humano. *Law and the Human Genome Review = Revista de Derecho y Genoma Humano*

1995 July-December;(3): 89-101. NRCBL: 15.10; 4.4. SC: le.

Ettorre, Elizabeth; Katz Rothman, Barbara; Steinberg, Deborah Lynn. Feminism confronts the genome: introduction. *New Genetics and Society* 2006 August; 25(2): 133-142. NRCBL: 15.10; 10.

European Society of Human Genetics [ESHG]. Data storage and DNA banking for biomedical research: technical, social and ethical issues. *European Journal of Human Genetics* 2003 December; 11(Supplement 2): S8-S10. NRCBL: 15.10; 13.1; 18.3.

Falcâo de Oliveira, Guilherme Freire. Juridical implications on genome knowledge (Part I) = Impliciones jurídicas del conocimiento del genoma (Parte I). *Revista de Derecho Genoma Humano = Law and the Human Genome Review* 1997 January-June; (6): 51-62. NRCBL: 15.10; 15.1; 1.3.5. SC: le.

Figueroa Yañez, Gonzalo. UNESCO Draft Universal Declaration on the Human Genome = El Proyecto de Declaración Universal sobre el Genoma Humano de la UNESCO. *Revista de Derecho Genoma Humano = Law and the Human Genome Review* 1997 July-December; (7): 113-120. NRCBL: 15.10; 21.1; 18.3; 2.4; 4.4; 9.3.1; 8.4. SC: le.

Foster, Morris W.; Mulvihill, John J.; Sharp, Richard R. Investments in cancer genomes: who benefits and who decides. *American Journal of Public Health* 2006 November; 96(11): 1960-1964. NRCBL: 15.10; 9.3.1; 9.4.
Abstract: The Cancer Genome Atlas—formerly the Human Cancer Genome Project—provides an opportunity for considering how social concerns about resource allocation are interrelated with practical decisions about specific research strategies—part of a continuing convergence between scientific and public evaluations of priorities for biomedical research funding. For example, the manner, order, and extent that The Cancer Genome Atlas selects tumor types and populations to be sampled will determine who benefits most from its findings. Those choices will be determined on the basis of both scientific and social values. By soliciting public involvement and conducting rigorous policy analysis in the design of large scientific projects such as The Cancer Genome Atlas, cancer researchers can help democratize the allocation of scientific resources and foster public confidence in biomedical research.

Friend, William B. Scientific, ethical and legal perspectives on human genome research: Plenary Session of the Pontifical Academy of Sciences = Perspectivas científicas, éticas y legales de las investigaciones sobre el genoma humano: Sesión Plenaria de la Academia Pontificia de Ciencias, aspectos postorales. *Law and the Human Genome Review = Revista de Derecho y Genoma Humana* 1995 July-December; (3): 221-243. NRCBL: 15.10; 1.2; 15.2; 8.3.1.

Gert, Bernard. Moral theory and the Human Genome Project. *In:* Tavani, Herman T., ed. Ethics, Computing, and Genomics. Sudbury, MA: Jones and Bartlett; 2006: 33-54. NRCBL: 15.10; 1.1.

Godard, Beatrice; Schmidtke, Jorg; Cassiman, Jean-Jacques; Ayme, Segolene. Data storage and DNA banking for biomedical research: informed consent, confidentiality, quality issues, ownership, return of benefits. A professional perspective. *European Journal of Human Genetics* 2003 December; 11(Supplement 2): S88-S122. NRCBL: 15.10; 1.3.12; 13.1; 18.3; 8.4; 21.1. SC: rv.

Greenhough, Beth. Decontextualised? Dissociated? Detached? Mapping the networks of bioinformatics exchange. *Environment and Planning* 2006 March; 38(3): 445-463. NRCBL: 15.10; 1.3.12; 13.1. Identifiers: Iceland; deCode.

Gros Espiell, Héctor. UNESCO's Draft Universal Declaration on the Human Genome and Human Rights = El Proyecto de Declaración Universal sobre el Genoma Humano y los Derechos de la Persona Humana de la UNESCO. *Revista de Derecho Genoma Humano = Law and the Human Genome Review* 1997 July-December; (7): 121-148. NRCBL: 15.10; 21.1; 2.4. SC: le.

Hasian, Marouf, Jr.; Plec, Emily. The cultural, legal, and scientific arguments in the Human Genome Diversity debate. *Howard Journal of Communications* 2002 October-December; 13(4): 301-319. NRCBL: 15.10; 13.1; 21.1.

Hjörleifsson, Stefán; Strand, Roger; Schei, Edvin. Health as a genetic planning project: enthusiasm and second thoughts among biomedical researchers and their research subjects. *Genomics, Society and Policy* 2005 December; 1(3): 52-65. NRCBL: 15.10; 5.3; 1.3.12; 4.2. SC: em.

Hoedemaekers, Rogeer; Gordijn, Bert; Pijnenburg, Martien. Does an appeal to the common good justify individual sacrifices for genomic research? *Theoretical Medicine and Bioethics* 2006; 27(5): 415-431. NRCBL: 15.10; 15.1; 18.3; 8.4; 1.3.1.

Hoeyer, Klaus; Lynöe, Niels. Is informed consent a solution to contractual problems? A comment on the article '"Iceland Inc"?: On the Ethics of Commercial Population Genomics' by Jon F. Merz, Glenn E. McGee, and Pamela Sankar. *Social Science and Medicine* 2004 March; 58(6): 1211. NRCBL: 15.10; 1.3.12; 13.1. Identifiers: deCode. Comments: Jon F. Merz, Glenn E. McGee, and Pamela Sankar. "Iceland Inc"?: on the ethics of commercial population genomics.

Joly, Yann; Knoppers, Bartha M. Pharmacogenomic data sample collection and storage: ethical issues and policy approaches. *Pharmacogenomics* 2006 March; 7(2): 219-226. NRCBL: 15.10; 9.7; 1.3.12; 8.4; 18.3; 21.1.

Kauwell, Gail P. Emerging concepts in nutrigenomics: a preview of what is to come. *Nutrition in Clinical Practice* 2005 February; 20(1): 75-87. NRCBL: 15.10; 15.1; 4.1.1. SC: rv.

NRCBL: National Reference Center for Bioethics Literature Classification Scheme   See inside front cover for terms.

263

Kirby, Michael. Human freedom and the human genome (Part I). *Revista de Derecho Genoma Humano = Law and the Human Genome Review* 1999 January-June; (10): 107-114. NRCBL: 15.10; 21.1.

Kirby, Michael. Human freedom and the human genome (Part II). *Revista de Derecho Genoma Humano = Law and the Human Genome Review* 1999 July-December; (11): 71-84. NRCBL: 15.10; 21.1; 14.5; 4.4; 5.3.

Kirby, Michael. Meeting our friend, the genome. *Revista de Derecho y Genoma Humano = Law and the Human Genome Review* 1998 January-June; (8): 60-70. NRCBL: 15.10; 15.5; 15.1. SC: le.

Kirby, Michael. The human genome and patent law. *Reform* 2001 Spring; 79: 10-13, 70. NRCBL: 15.10. SC: le.

Kirby, Michael. The Human Genome Project and its challenges to society = Proyecto Genoma Humano y su desafío a la sociedad. *Law and the Human Genome Review = Revista de Derecho y Genoma Humano* 1996 July-December; (5): 73-85. NRCBL: 15.10; 15.11. SC: le.

Kirkman, Maggie. Public health and the challenge of genomics. *Australian and New Zealand Journal of Public Health* 2005 April; 29(2): 163-165. NRCBL: 15.10; 15.5; 9.1.

Knoppers, Bartha Maria; Fecteau, Claudine. Human genomic databases: a global public good? *European Journal of Health Law* 2003 March; 10(1): 27-41. NRCBL: 15.10; 1.3.12; 13.1; 8.4; 15.8; 21.1. SC: le.

La Caze, Adam. Does pharmacogenomics provide an ethical challenge to the utilisation of cost-effectiveness analysis by public health systems? *Pharmacoeconomics* 2005; 23(5): 445-447. NRCBL: 15.10; 9.7; 9.3.1; 9.4. Identifiers: Australia.

Lin, Zhen; Altman, Russ B.; Owen, Art B. Confidentiality in genome research [letter]. *Science* 2006 July 28; 313(5786): 441-442. NRCBL: 15.10; 8.4.

Loeppky, Rodney D. Control from within? Power, identity, and the Human Genome Project. *Alternatives: Social Transformation and Human Governance* 1998 April-June; 18(2): 205-233. NRCBL: 15.10; 15.5; 10. SC: an.

Lone Dog, Leota. Whose genes are they? The Human Genome Diversity Project. *Journal of Health and Social Policy* 1999; 10(4): 51-66. NRCBL: 15.10; 15.8; 15.11.

Manasse, Henri R., Jr. The other side of the human genome. *American Journal of Health-System Pharmacy* 2005 May 15; 62(10): 1080-1086. NRCBL: 15.10; 15.5; 2.2; 21.4.

McCain, Lauren. Informing technology policy decisions: the US Human Genome Project's ethical, legal, and social implications programs as a critical case. *Technology in So-*

ciety 2002 January-April; 24(1-2): 111-132. NRCBL: 15.10; 2.2.

McKenzie, Michael. Genetics and Christianity: an uneasy but necessary partnership. *Christian Research Journal* 1995 Fall; 18: 1-8. NRCBL: 15.10; 1.2; 15.7.

McLean, Sheila A.M. Mapping the human genome — friend or foe? *Social Science and Medicine* 1994 November; 39(9): 1221-1227. NRCBL: 15.10; 5.3; 15.3; 8.4.

Merz, J.F.; McGee, G.E.; Sankar, P. Response from Jon F. Merz, Glenn E. McGee, and Pamela Sankar to Hoeyer and Lynöe's commentary on their article "'Iceland Inc.'? On the Ethics of Commercial Genomics". *Social Science and Medicine* 2004 March; 58(6): 1213. NRCBL: 15.10; 1.3.12; 13.1. Identifiers: deCode.

Moreno Muñoz, Miguel. The debate on the legal implications of the Human Genome Project: epistemological contributions = Aportaciones epistemológicas al debate sobre las implicaciones jurídicas del Proyecto Genoma Humano. *Revista de Derecho Genoma Humano = Law and the Human Genome Review* 1997 January-June; (6): 181-209. NRCBL: 15.10; 15.5.

Morgan, Rose M. The HGDP debate. *In her:* The Genetics Revolution: History, Fears, and Future of a Life-Altering Science. Westport, CT: Greenwood Press; 2006: 105-128. NRCBL: 15.10; 13.1; 21.1.

Olson, Maynard V. The Human Genome Project: a player's perspective. *Journal of Molecular Biology* 2002 June 14; 319(4): 931-942. NRCBL: 15.10. SC: rv.

Owens, Kelly N.; Harvey-Blankenship, Michelle; King, Mary-Claire. Genomic sequencing in the service of human rights. *International Journal of Epidemiology* 2002 February; 31(1): 53-58. NRCBL: 15.10; 21.1. SC: em.

Pálsson, Gísli. Medical databases: the Icelandic case. *In:* Lundin, Susanne; Åkesson, Lynn, eds. Gene Technology and Economy. Lund: Nordic Academic Press; 2002: 22-41. NRCBL: 15.10; 1.3.12; 13.1.

Pálsson, Gísli; Harðardóttir, Kristín E. For whom the cell tolls: debates about biomedicine. *Current Anthropology* 2002 April; 43(2): 271-301. NRCBL: 15.10; 1.3.12; 13.1. Identifiers: Iceland; deCode.

Pálsson, Gísli; Rabinow, Paul. The Icelandic genome debate. *Trends in Biotechnology* 2001 May 1; 19(5): 166-171. NRCBL: 15.10; 1.3.12; 18.6; 15.8; 4.4.

Pandikattu, Kuruvilla. For a collective human future project. *Peace Review* 2000 December; 12(4): 579-585. NRCBL: 15.10; 4.5.

Perpich, Joseph G. The dawn of genomics and regenerative medicine: new paradigms for medicine, the public's health, and society. *Technology in Society* 2004 April-August; 26(2-3): 405-414. NRCBL: 15.10; 18.5.4; 5.3; 15.1.

Phua, Kai-Lit. The Human Genome Project and genetic research: what are the implications for ethics and equity? *Critical Public Health* 2004 June; 14(2): 191-200. NRCBL: 15.10; 15.1; 8.4.

Racine, Eric; Gareau, Isabelle; Doucet, Hubert; Laudy, Danielle; Jobin, Guy; Schradeley-Desmond, Pamela. Hyped biomedical science or uncritical reporting? Press coverage of genomics (1992-2001) in Quebec. *Social Science and Medicine* 2006 March; 62(5): 1278-1290. NRCBL: 15.10; 1.3.7. SC: em.

Reardon, Jenny. The Human Genome Diversity Project: a case study in coproduction. *Social Studies of Science* 2001 June; 31(3): 357-388. NRCBL: 15.10; 13.1; 21.1. SC: em; rv.

Simm, Kadri. Benefit-sharing: an inquiry regarding the meaning and limits of the concept in human genetics research. *Genetics, Society, and Policy* 2005 August; 1(2): 29-40. NRCBL: 15.10; 1.1; 5.3.

SoRelle, Ruth. Who owns your DNA? Who will own it? *Circulation* 2000 February 8; 101(5): e67-e68. NRCBL: 15.10; 5.3.

Tennant, Agnieszka. The genome doctor: an interview with Francis Collins. *Christianity Today* 2001 October 1: 42-46. NRCBL: 15.10; 1.2.

Thomson, Elizabeth; McMillan, Ian. Genethics: The Human Genome Project has profound implications for society. Ian McMillan talked to Elizabeth Thomson about its importance for nurses. *Nursing Standard* 1998 December 9-15; 13(12): 21-22. NRCBL: 15.10. Identifiers: Human Genome Project; ELSI.

Tupasela, Aaro. Locating tissue collections in tissue economies — deriving value from biomedical research. *New Genetics and Society* 2006 April; 25(1): 33-49. NRCBL: 15.10; 1.3.12; 13.1; 7.1. SC: cs; em.

United Nations Educational, Scientific, and Cultural Organization [UNESCO]. International Bioethics Committee. Outline of a declaration on the human genome and its protection in relation to human dignity and human rights = El Borrador de Declaración sobre el genoma humano y su protección en relación con la dignidad humana y los derechos humanos. *Law and the Human Genome Review = Revista de Derecho y Genoma Humano* 1995 July-December; (3): 303-307. NRCBL: 15.10; 21.1.

United Nations. Expert group meeting on disability-sensitive policy and programme monitoring and evaluation; Avard, Denise. Human genetics research and practice: implications for people with disabilities. New York: United Nations Headquarters. Expert group meeting on disability-sensitive policy and programme monitoring and evaluation; 2002 January 14; 9 p. [Online]. Accessed: http://www.un.org/esa/socdev/enable/disid2001e.

htm#top [2006 August 15]. NRCBL: 15.10; 18.5.6. Identifiers: Human Genome Project. Conference: Expert group meeting on disability-sensitive policy and programme monitoring and evaluation. UNHQ, New York 2001 December 3-5.

Van Rinsum, Henk J.; Tangwa, Godfrey, B. Colony of genes, genes of the colony: diversity, differences and divide. *Third World Quarterly* 2004 September; 25(6): 1031-1043. NRCBL: 15.10; 5.1. Identifiers: African American; Africa.

Wade, Nicholas. The quest for the $1,000 human genome: DNA sequencing in the doctor's office? At birth? It may be coming closer. *New York Times* 2006 July 18; p. F1, F3. NRCBL: 15.10; 9.3.1.

Waltz, Emily. Informed consent issues hobble cancer genome scheme [news]. *Nature Medicine* 2006 July; 12(7): 719. NRCBL: 15.10; 18.3.

Winickoff, David E.; Neumann, Larissa B. Towards a social contract for genomics: property and the public in the "biotrust" model. *Genomics, Society and Policy* 2005; 1(3): 8-21. NRCBL: 15.10; 1.3.12; 4.4; 15.1; 15.8; 19.1; 19.5; 9.3.1.

Zongliang, Xu. Ethical challenges of human genome diversity research. *Eubios Journal of Asian and International Bioethics* 2003 January 13(1): 8-10. NRCBL: 15.10; 15.3; 15.11.

Zwart, Hub. The Language of God: a Scientist Presents Evidence for Belief, by Francis Collins [book review]. *Genomics, Society and Policy* 2006 December; 2(3): 136-141. NRCBL: 15.10; 1.2; 3.2.

HEALTH CARE

See also CARE FOR SPECIFIC GROUPS; HEALTH CARE ECONOMICS; HEALTH CARE QUALITY; RESOURCE ALLOCATION; RIGHT TO HEALTH CARE

Allmark, P. Choosing Health and the inner citadel. *Journal of Medical Ethics* 2006 January; 32(1): 3-6. NRCBL: 9.1; 1.1. SC: an. Identifiers: United Kingdom (Great Britain).

Abstract: It is argued in this paper that the latest UK government white paper on public health, Choosing Health, is vulnerable to a charge of paternalism. For some years libertarians have levelled this charge at public health policies. The white paper tries to avoid it by constant reference to informed choice and choice related terms. The implication is that the government aims only to inform the public of health issues; how they respond is up to them. It is argued here, however, that underlying the notion of informed choice is a Kantian, "inner citadel" view of autonomy. According to this view, each of us acts autonomously only when we act in accord with reason. On such a view it is possible to justify coercing, cajoling, and conning people on the basis that their current behaviour is not autonomous because it is subject to forces that cause irrational choice, such as addiction. "Informed choice" in this sense is compatible with paternalism.

NRCBL: National Reference Center for Bioethics Literature Classification Scheme   See inside front cover for terms.

265

This paternalism can be seen in public health policies such as deceptive advertising and the treatment of "bad habits" as addictions. Libertarians are bound to object to this. In the concluding section, however, it is suggested that public health can, nonetheless, find ethical succour from alternative approaches.

Asada, Yukiko. Is health inequality across individuals of moral concern? *Health Care Analysis: An International Journal of Health Philosophy and Policy* 2006 March; 14(1): 25-36. NRCBL: 9.1; 1.1.

Abstract: The history of the documentation of health inequality is long. The way in which health inequality has customarily been documented is by comparing differences in the average health across groups, for example, by sex or gender, income, education, occupation, or geographic region. In the controversial World Health Report 2000, researchers at the World Health Organization criticized this traditional practice and proposed to measure health inequality across individuals irrespective of individuals' group affiliation. They defended its proposal on the moral grounds without clear explanation. In this paper I ask: is health inequality across individuals of moral concern, and, if so, why? Clarification of these questions is crucial for meaningful interpretation of health inequality measured across individuals. Only if there was something morally problematic in health inequality across individuals, its reduction would be good news. Specifically, in this paper I provide three arguments for the moral significance of health inequality across individuals: (a) health is special, (b) health equity plays an important and unique role in the general pursuit of justice, and (c) health inequality is an indicator of general injustice in society. I then discuss three key questions to examine the validity of these arguments: (i) how special is health?, (ii) how good is health as an indicator?, and (iii) what do we mean by injustice? I conclude that health inequality across individuals is of moral interest with the arguments (b) and (c).

Axon, A.T.R.; Beilenhoff, U.; James, T.; Ladas, S.D.; Larsen, E.; Neumann, C.S.; Nowak, A.; Schofl, R.; Tveit, K.M. Legal and ethical considerations: group 4 report. *Endoscopy* 2004 April; 36(4): 362-365. NRCBL: 9.1; 9.5.1. Conference: ESGE/UEGF Colorectal Cancer, Public Awareness Campaign: The Public/Professional Interface Workshop; Oslo, Norway; 2003 June 20-22;.

Bayley, Carol; Boyle, Philip; Heller, Jan C.; McCruden, Patrick J.; O'Brien, Dan. Shedding light on organizational ethics: five ethicists help define and contextualize an elusive topic. *Health Progress* 2006 November-December; 87(6): 28-33. NRCBL: 9.1; 1.3.2.

Bloche, M. Gregg. WTO deference to national health policy: toward an interpretive principle. *Journal of International Economic Law* 2002 December; 5(4): 825-848. NRCBL: 9.1; 9.7; 21.1. SC: an; le. Identifiers: World Trade Organization.

Bohannon, John. Fighting words from WHO's new malaria chief [news]. *Science* 2006 February 3; 311(5761): 599. NRCBL: 9.1; 9.7; 21.1. Identifiers: World Health Organization.

Breeze, Jayne. Can paternalism be justified in mental health care? *Journal of Advanced Nursing* 1998 August; 28(2): 260-265. NRCBL: 9.1; 17.1; 1.1; 8.3.3. SC: cs.

Brinkmann, Bill; Maines, T. Dean; Naughton, Michael J.; Stebbins, J. Michael; Weimerskirch, Arnold. Bridging the gap: Catholic health care organizations need concrete ways to connect social principles to practice. *Health Progress* 2006 November-December; 87(6): 43-50. NRCBL: 9.1; 1.3.2.

Brock, Dan W.; Ho, William; Robinson, Walter. In the line of duty: SARS and physician responsibility in epidemics [forum]. *Medical Ethics Newsletter* 2006 Spring; 13(2): 5-8. NRCBL: 9.1; 8.1; 7.1; 2.2. Identifiers: severe acute respiratory syndrome.

Bruhn, John G. Looking good, but behaving badly: leader accountability and ethics failure. *Health Care Manager* 2005 July-September; 24(3): 191-199. NRCBL: 9.1; 1.3.2.

Buchanan, Allen; Decamp, Matthew. Responsibility for global health. *Theoretical Medicine and Bioethics* 2006; 27(1): 95-114. NRCBL: 9.1; 21.1; 1.3.1.

Abstract: There are several reasons for the current prominence of global health issues. Among the most important is the growing awareness that some risks to health are global in scope and can only be countered by global cooperation. In addition, human rights discourse and, more generally, the articulation of a coherent cosmopolitan ethical perspective that acknowledges the importance of all persons, regardless of where they live, provide a normative basis for taking global health seriously as a moral issue. In this paper we begin the task of translating the vague commitment to doing something to improve global health into a coherent set of more determinate obligations. One chief conclusion of our inquiry is that the responsibilities of states regarding global health are both more determinate and more extensive than is usually assumed. We also argue, however, that institutional innovation will be needed to achieve a more comprehensive, fair distribution of concrete responsibilities regarding global health and to provide effective mechanisms for holding various state and nonstate actors accountable for fulfilling them.

Cahill, Lisa Sowle. National and international health access reform. *In her:* Theological Bioethics: Participation, Justice, and Change. Washington, DC: Georgetown University Press; 2005: 131-168. NRCBL: 9.1; 1.2.

Carney, Marie. Positive and negative outcomes from values and beliefs held by healthcare clinician and non-clinician managers. *Journal of Advanced Nursing* 2006 April; 54(1): 111-119. NRCBL: 9.1; 1.3.2. SC: em. Identifiers: Ireland.

Chiang, Chun. The social capital theory research of the public medical service about relations of caring for patients. *Formosan Journal of Medical Humanities* 2006 June; 7(1-2): 159-177. NRCBL: 9.1; 8.1; 1.3.5.

Chilton, Mariana. Developing a measure of dignity for stress-related health outcomes. *Health and Human Rights: An International Journal* 2006; 9(2): 209-233. NRCBL: 9.1; 21.1; 4.4; 9.8.

Cochran, Clarke E. Catholic health care in the public square: tension on the frontier. *In:* Guinn, David E., ed.

Handbook of Bioethics and Religion. New York: Oxford University Press, 2006: 403-425. NRCBL: 9.1; 1.2.

Comeau, Pauline. Conscription fears accompany threat of pandemic [news]. *CMAJ/JAMC: Canadian Medical Association Journal* 2006 April 25; 174(9): 1245-1246. NRCBL: 9.1; 9.5.1. Identifiers: Canada; Ontario Medical Association; Emergency Management and Civil Protection Act.

Crigger, Bette-Jane. e-Medicine: policy to shape the future of health care. *Hastings Center Report* 2006 January-February; 36(1): 12-13. NRCBL: 9.1; 1.3.12.

Daniels, Norman. Toward ethical review of health system transformations. *American Journal of Public Health* 2006 March; 96(3): 447-451. NRCBL: 9.1; 18.2.
  Abstract: Efforts to transform health systems constitute social experiments on a population. Like clinical research, they deploy measures that are unproven in the context of the reform, and they often impose significant risks on some people in order to achieve a social goal: the improvement of health delivery. The rationale for proactively evaluating clinical experimentation on human subjects also applies to these social experiments. We used the "benchmarks of fairness" methodology to illustrate the elements such an evidence-based review should encompass, leaving open the question of who should perform it. The review must include the ethical objectives of reform, namely, an integrated approach to equity, accountability, and efficiency; the fit between measures taken and these objectives; and the governance of the reform.

Daniels, Norman. Why justice is good for our health. *In:* Lolas Stepke, Fernando; Agar Corbinos, Lorenzo, eds. Interfaces Between Bioethics and the Empirical Social Sciences. Buenos Aires, Argentina: World Health Organization; 2002: 37-52. NRCBL: 9.1; 1.1.

Daniels, Norman; Flores, Walter; Pannarunothai, Supasit; Ndumbe, Peter N.; Bryant, John H.; Ngulube, T.J.; Wang, Yuankun. An evidence-based approach to benchmarking the fairness of health-sector reform in developing countries. *Bulletin of the World Health Organization* 2005 July; 83(7): 534-540. NRCBL: 9.1; 21.1; 1.1. SC: em.

Dean, Wesley; Scott, H. Morgan. Emergent infectious diseases. *In:* Mitcham, Carl, ed. Encyclopedia of Science, Technology, and Ethics. Farmington Hills, MI: Thomson/Gale, 2005: 610-614. NRCBL: 9.1; 21.1.

Deaton, Angus. Equity and population health [letter]. *Hastings Center Report* 2006 September-October; 36(5): 5-6. NRCBL: 9.1; 1.1; 21.1.

DeBakey, Michael E. The role of government in health care: a societal issue [editorial]. *American Journal of Surgery* 2006 February; 191(2): 145-157. NRCBL: 9.1; 1.3.5.

DeDonato, David M.; Mathis, Rick D. Religious and cultural considerations in military healthcare. *In:* Beam, Thomas E.; Sparacino, Linette R.; Pellegrino, Edmund D.; Hartle, Anthony E.; Howe, Edmund G., eds. Military Med-

ical Ethics. Volume 2. Washington, DC: TMM Publications, Borden Institute, Walter Reed Army Medical Center; 2003: 687-718. NRCBL: 9.1; 1.3.5; 1.2; 21.7.

Dell'Oro, Roberto. Interpreting clinical judgment: epistemological notes on the praxis of medicine. *In:* Viafora, Corrado, ed. Clinical Bioethics: A Search for the Foundations. Dordrecht: Springer, 2005: 155-168. NRCBL: 9.1; 1.1; 4.1.2.

English, Joel; Klein, Rob; Niehaus, Tess; Ross, Joyce M. Health hazard? *Marketing Health Services* 2005 Winter; 25(4): 14, 16-19. NRCBL: 9.1; 1.3.2.

Fairchild, Amy L. Diabetes and disease surveillance. *Science* 2006 July 14; 313(5784): 175-176. NRCBL: 9.1; 1.3.12; 8.4; 5.3.

Fairchild, Amy L.; Colgrove, James; Jones, Marian Moser. The challenge of mandatory evacuation: providing for and deciding for. *Health Affairs* 2006 July-August; 25(4): 958-967. NRCBL: 9.1; 16.1. SC: le.

Forbes, James A., Jr. Religious perspectives on access to health care: a Protestant perspective. *Mount Sinai Journal of Medicine* 1997 March; 64(2): 75-79. NRCBL: 9.1; 1.2; 9.4.

Fox, Daniel M. America's ecumenical health policy: a century of consensus. *Mount Sinai Journal of Medicine* 1997 March; 64(2): 72-74. NRCBL: 9.1; 1.2; 2.1; 9.3.1.

Gallagher, John A. "Like shining from shook foil": a "virtuous organization" is prepared to test both the body and the soul. *Health Progress* 2006 November-December; 87(6): 18-23. NRCBL: 9.1; 1.3.2.

Getz, Linn; Kirkengen, Anna Luise; Hetlevik, Irene; Sigurdsson, Johann A. Individually based preventive medical recommendations — are they sustainable and responsible? A call for ethical reflection [editorial]. *Scandinavian Journal of Primary Health Care* 2005 June; 23(2): 65-67. NRCBL: 9.1; 4.1.2.

Glicksman, Gail Gaisin; Glicksman, Allen. Apples and oranges: a critique of current trends in the study of religion, spirituality, and health. *In:* Guinn, David E., ed. Handbook of Bioethics and Religion. New York: Oxford University Press, 2006: 333-343. NRCBL: 9.1; 1.2.

Gostin, Lawrence O. Federal executive power and communicable disease control: CDC quarantine regulations. *Hastings Center Report* 2006 March-April; 36(2): 10-11. NRCBL: 9.1; 1.3.5. SC: le.

Gostin, Lawrence O. Medical countermeasures for pandemic influenza: ethics and the law. *JAMA: The Journal of the American Medical Association* 2006 February 1; 295(5): 554-556. NRCBL: 9.1; 9.4; 9.5.1; 9.7. SC: le.

NRCBL: National Reference Center for Bioethics Literature Classification Scheme   See inside front cover for terms.

267

Gostin, Lawrence O. Property rights and the common good. *Hastings Center Report* 2006 September-October; 36(5): 10-11. NRCBL: 9.1; 1.3.5. SC: le.

Grabenstein, John D. The value of immunization for God's people. *National Catholic Bioethics Quarterly* 2006 Autumn; 6(3): 433-442. NRCBL: 9.1; 9.5.1; 9.7; 1.2.

Gruen, Russell L.; Campbell, Eric G.; Blumenthal, David. Public roles of US physicians: community participation, political involvement, and collective advocacy. *JAMA: The Journal of the American Medical Association* 2006 November 22-29; 296(20): 2467-2475. NRCBL: 9.1; 7.1. SC: em.

Abstract: CONTEXT: Whether physicians have a professional responsibility to address health-related issues beyond providing care to individual patients has been vigorously debated. Yet little is known about practicing physicians' attitudes about or the extent to which they participate in public roles, which we defined as community participation, political involvement, and collective advocacy. OBJECTIVES: To determine the importance physicians assign to public roles, their participation in related activities, and sociodemographic and practice factors related to physicians' rated levels of importance and activity. DESIGN, SETTING, AND PARTICIPANTS: Mail survey conducted between November 2003 and June 2004 of 1662 US physicians engaged indirect patient care selected from primary care specialties (family practice, internal medicine, pediatrics) and 3 non-primary care specialties (anesthesiology, general surgery, cardiology). MAIN OUTCOME MEASURES: Rated importance of community participation, political involvement, collective advocacy, and relevant self-reported activities encompassing the previous 3 years; rated importance of physician action on different issues. RESULTS: Community participation, political involvement, and collective advocacy were rated as important by more than 90% of respondents, and a majority rated community participation and collective advocacy as very important. Nutrition, immunization, substance abuse, and road safety issues were rated as very important by more physicians than were access-to-care issues, unemployment, or illiteracy. Two thirds of respondents had participated in at least 1 of the 3 types of activities in the previous 3 years. Factors independently related to high overall rating of importance (civic-mindedness) included age, female sex, underrepresented race/ethnicity, and graduation from a non-US or non-Canadian medical school. Civic mindedness, medical specialty, practice type, underrepresented race/ethnicity, preceptors of physicians in training, rural practice, and graduation from a non-US or non-Canadian medical school were independently related to civic activity. CONCLUSIONS: Public roles are definable entities that have widespread support among physicians. Civic-mindedness is associated primarily with sociodemographic factors, but civic action is associated with specialty and practice-based factors.

Hall, Mark A. A corporate ethic of 'care' in health care. *Seattle Journal for Social Justice* 2004 Fall-Winter; 3(1): 417-428. NRCBL: 9.1; 1.3.2.

Hamel, Ron. Organizational ethics: why bother? [editorial]. *Health Progress* 2006 November-December; 87(6): 4-5. NRCBL: 9.1; 1.3.2.

Heller, Jan C. Moral mistakes that leaders make. *Health Care Ethics USA* 2006; 14(1): E3 [Online]. Accessed: http://chce.slu.edu/Partnerships_HCE_Intro.html [2006 November 17]. NRCBL: 9.1; 1.3.2.

Irwig, Les; McCaffery, Kirsten; Salkeld, Glenn; Bossuyt, Patrick. Informed choice for screening: implications for evaluation. *BMJ: British Medical Journal* 2006 May 13; 332(7550): 1148-1150. NRCBL: 9.1; 8.3.1. Identifiers: United Kingdom (Great Britain).

Jacobson, Michael F. Lifting the veil of secrecy from industry funding of nonprofit health organizations. *International Journal of Occupational and Environmental Health* 2005 October-December; 11(4): 349-355. NRCBL: 9.1; 1.3.2; 9.3.1; 7.3.

Jakušovaite, Irayda; Darulis, Žilvinas; Žekas, Romualdas. Lithuanian health care in transitional state: ethical problems. *BMC Public Health* 2005 November 9; 5: 117: 8 p. NRCBL: 9.1.

Jochemsen, H.; Hoogland, J.; Polder, J. Maintaining integrity in times of scarce resources. *In:* Viafora, Corrado, ed. Clinical Bioethics: A Search for the Foundations. Dordrecht: Springer, 2005: 139-152. NRCBL: 9.1; 1.1. SC: an.

Jørgensen, Karsten Juhl; Gøtzsche, Peter C. Content of invitations for publicly funded screening mammography. *BMJ: British Medical Journal* 2006 March 4; 332(7540): 538-541. NRCBL: 9.1; 9.5.5; 5.2; 8.3.1; 21.1. SC: em. Identifiers: United Kingdom (Great Britain).

Koivusalo, Meri. The impact of economic globalisation on health. *Theoretical Medicine and Bioethics* 2006; 27(1): 13-34. NRCBL: 9.1; 9.3.1; 21.1.

Abstract: The analysis of the impact of economic globalisation on health depends on how it is defined and should consider how it shapes both health and health policies. I first discuss the ways in which economic globalisation can and has been defined and then why it is important to analyse its impact both in terms of health and health policies. I then explore the ways in which economic globalisation influences health and health policies and how this relates to equity, social justice, and the role of values and social rights in societies. Finally, I argue that the process of economic globalisation provides a common challenge for all health systems across the globe and requires a broader debate on values, accountability, and policy approaches.

Krause, Joan H. Ethical lawyering in the gray areas: health care fraud and abuse. *Journal of Law, Medicine, and Ethics* 2006 Spring; 34(1): 121-125. NRCBL: 9.1; 1.3.8; 9.3.1. SC: le.

LaFrance, Arthur B. Merger of religious and public hospitals: render unto Caesar. . . . *Seattle Journal for Social Justice* 2004 Fall-Winter; 3(1): 229-310. NRCBL: 9.1; 1.3.2; 1.3.5. SC: le.

Lavery, J.V.; Upshur, R.E.; Sharp, R.R.; Hofman, K.J. Ethical issues in international environmental health research. *International Journal of Hygiene and Environmental Health* 2003 August; 206(4-5): 453-463. NRCBL: 9.1; 16.1; 21.1.

Lee, Connal; Rogers, Wendy A. Ethics, pandemic planning and communications. *Monash Bioethics Review* 2006 October; 25(4): 9-18. NRCBL: 9.1; 7.1; 8.1; 1.3.7; 21.1.

Lee, Philip; Oliver, Thomas; Benjamin, A.E.; Lee, Dorothy. Politics, health policy, and the American character. *Stanford Law and Policy Review* 2006; 17(1): 7-32. NRCBL: 9.1; 1.1; 9.4; 7.2; 9.3.1. SC: le.

Lee, Simon J. Craddock. Ethics of articulation: constituting organizational identity in a Catholic hospital system. *In:* Dinkins, Christine Sorrell; Sorrell, Jeanne Merkle, eds. Listening to the Whispers: Re-Thinking Ethics in Healthcare. Madison, WI: University of Wisconsin Press; 2006: 69-137. NRCBL: 9.1; 1.2.

Mann, Jonathan. Health and human rights: if not now, when? *American Journal of Public Health* 2006 November; 96(11): 1940-1943. NRCBL: 9.1; 21.1. Note: Excerpted from Jonathan M. Mann. Health and human rights: if not now, when? Health and Human Rights 1997; 2(3): 113-120.

McDaniel, Charlotte; Veledar, Emir; LeConte, Stephen; Peltier, Scott; Maciuba, Agata. Ethical environment, healthcare work, and patient outcomes. *American Journal of Bioethics [Online]* 2006 September-October; 6(5):W17-W29. NRCBL: 9.1; 21.1; 9.8. SC: em. Identifiers: Finland; United States.

McKee, Martin. Values, beliefs, and implications. *In:* Marinker, Marshall, ed. Health Targets in Europe: Polity, Progress and Promise. London: BMJ Books; 2002: 181-205. NRCBL: 9.1.

Newman, Janet; Vidler, Elizabeth. Discriminating customers, responsible patients, empowered users: consumerism and the modernisation of health care. *Journal of Social Policy* 2006 April; 35(2): 193-209. NRCBL: 9.1; 7.1; 8.1. Identifiers: United Kingdom (Great Britain).

Oliver, J. Eric. The politics of pathology: how obesity became an epidemic disease. *Perspectives in Biology and Medicine* 2006 Autumn; 49(4): 611-627. NRCBL: 9.1; 4.2; 7.1; 9.5.1.

Olsan, Tobie H. Corporatization and the institutional aspects of morality in home care. *In:* Dinkins, Christine Sorrell; Sorrell, Jeanne Merkle, eds. Listening to the Whispers: Re-Thinking Ethics in Healthcare. Madison, WI: University of Wisconsin Press; 2006: 10-68. NRCBL: 9.1; 4.1.3.

Ozar, David T. Finding a voice: like individuals, organizations are moral speakers and actors. *Health Progress* 2006 November-December; 87(6): 24-27. NRCBL: 9.1; 1.3.2.

Patel, Salil H. Present and future challenges in medical data management: economics, ethics, and the law. *Studies in Health Technology and Informatics* 2005; 118: 43-51. NRCBL: 9.1; 9.3.1; 1.3.12.

Pesut, Barbara. Fundamental or foundational obligation? Problematizing the ethical call to spiritual care in nursing. *Advances in Nursing Science* 2006 April-June; 29(2): 125-133. NRCBL: 9.1; 1.2; 8.1. SC: an.

Powell, John; Fitton, Richard; Fitton, Caroline. Sharing electronic health records: the patient view. *Informatics in Primary Care* 2006; 14(1): 55-57. NRCBL: 9.1; 1.3.12; 8.4. SC: em. Identifiers: United Kingdom (Great Britain).

Rice, Thomas. Should consumer choice be encouraged in health care? *In:* Davis, John B., ed. The Social Economics of Health Care. New York: Routledge; 2001: 9-39. NRCBL: 9.1; 1.3.2.

Rogers, Sharon. Why can't I visit? The ethics of visitation restrictions — lessons learned from SARS. *Critical Care* 2004 October; 8(5): 300-302. NRCBL: 9.1; 7.1.

Ross, John K.; Ross, Sherry K.; McClung, Bruce A. Ethical decision making and organizational behavior: a case of life and death. *HEC (Healthcare Ethics Committee) Forum* 2006 September; 18(3): 193-206. NRCBL: 9.1; 1.3.1; 1.3.2; 9.7; 7.3. SC: cs.

Sarra, Janis. Contemporary corporate theory applied to the health care sector: a Canadian perspective. *Seattle Journal for Social Justice* 2004 Fall-Winter; 3(1): 345-385. NRCBL: 9.1; 1.3.2. Identifiers: Canada.

Setness, Peter A. When privacy and the public good collide: does the collection of health data for research harm individual patients? [editorial]. *Postgraduate Medicine* 2003 January; 113(5): 15-16, 19. NRCBL: 9.1; 8.4; 9.8.

Specter, Michael. Political science: the Bush administration's war on the laboratory. *New Yorker* 2006 March 13: 58, 60-67. NRCBL: 9.1; 9.7; 9.5.5; 1.3.5; 10.

Steinbrook, Robert. Imposing personal responsibility for health. *New England Journal of Medicine* 2006 August 24; 355(8): 753-756. NRCBL: 9.1; 7.1; 9.3.1; 9.5.10.

Sulmasy, Daniel P. On the current state of clinical ethics. *Pain Medicine* 2001 June; 2(2): 97-105. NRCBL: 9.1; 2.1; 7.2.

Talone, Patricia A. Starting an organizational ethics committee: an ethicist suggests some practical and concrete steps. *Health Progress* 2006 November-December; 87(6): 34-37. NRCBL: 9.1; 1.3.2.

Taylor, Gary; Hawley, Helen. Health promotion and the freedom of the individual. *Health Care Analysis: An International Journal of Health Philosophy and Policy* 2006 March; 14(1): 15-24. NRCBL: 9.1; 1.1; 7.1.
Abstract: This article considers the extent to which health promotion strategies pose a threat to individual freedom. It begins by taking a look at health promotion strategies and at the historical development of health promotion in Britain. A theoretical context is then developed in which Berlin's distinction between negative and positive liberty is used alongside the ideas of John Stuart Mill, Charles Taylor and T.H. Green to discuss the poli-

NRCBL: National Reference Center for Bioethics Literature Classification Scheme   See inside front cover for terms.

269

tics of health promotion and to identify the implications of conflicting perspectives on freedom. The final section looks at current health promotion policy in Britain and beyond and argues that, if freedom is seen in terms of empowerment, health promotion can enhance individual freedom.

Thompson, Alison K.; Faith, Karen; Gibson, Jennifer L.; Upshur, Ross E.G. Pandemic influenza preparedness: an ethical framework to guide decision-making. *BMC Medical Ethics* 2006; 7: 12. NRCBL: 9.1; 9.5.1; 21.1. Identifiers: Ontario Ministry of Health and Long Term Care.

Tovino, Stacey A. Hospital chaplaincy under the HIPAA Privacy rule: health care or "just visiting the sick"? *Indiana Health Law Review* 2005; 2(1): 49-92. NRCBL: 9.1; 1.2; 8.4. SC: le. Identifiers: Health Insurance Portability and Accountability Act.

Tuffs, Annette. Germany will penalise cancer patients who do not undergo regular screening [news]. *BMJ: British Medical Journal* 2006 October 28; 333(7574): 877. NRCBL: 9.1; 9.5.1; 9.3.1.

Tuffs, Annette. Sponsorship of patients' groups by drug companies should be made transparent [news]. *BMJ: British Medical Journal* 2006 December 16; 333(7581): 1238. NRCBL: 9.1; 9.7; 1.3.2. Identifiers: Germany.

Watson, Rory. Cancer group denies company funding will influence its agenda [news]. *BMJ: British Medical Journal* 2006 October 28; 333(7574): 874. NRCBL: 9.1; 9.7; 9.3.1; 9.5.1. Identifiers: Europe.

Weber, David O. Unethical business practices in U.S. health care alarm physician leaders. *Physician Executive* 2005 March-April; 31(2): 6-13. NRCBL: 9.1; 1.3.2. SC: em.

Wynia, Matthew K. Routine screening: informed consent, stigma and the waning of HIV exceptionalism. *American Journal of Bioethics* 2006 July-August; 6(4): 5-8. NRCBL: 9.1; 9.5.6; 8.3.1. Identifiers: Centers for Disease Control (CDC); United States.

Zoloth, Laurie; Zoloth, Stephen. Don't be chicken: bioethics and avian flu [editorial]. *American Journal of Bioethics* 2006 January-February; 6(1): 5-8. NRCBL: 9.1; 9.7; 9.4.

HEALTH CARE/ HEALTH CARE ECONOMICS
See also RESOURCE ALLOCATION

Choice policies must focus on reducing health inequalities [editorial]. *Lancet* 2006 January 14-20; 367(9505): 85. NRCBL: 9.3.1; 8.1; 9.4.

Rationing is essential in tax-funded health systems. *Lancet* 2006 October 21-27; 368(9545): 1394. NRCBL: 9.3.1; 9.21; 7.1.

Abelson, Reed. Heart procedure is off the charts in an Ohio city. *New York Times* 2006 August 18; p. A1, C4. NRCBL: 9.3.1; 7.1. SC: po.

Alsever, Jennifer. Basking on the beach, or maybe on the operating table. *New York Times* 2006 October 15; p. BU5. NRCBL: 9.3.1; 9.5.1; 9.8. SC: po. Identifiers: Medical tourism.

Altman, Stuart H.; Doonan, Michael. Can Massachusetts lead the way in health care reform? *New England Journal of Medicine* 2006 May 18; 354(20): 2093-2095. NRCBL: 9.3.1.

Angrosino, Michael V. Catholic social policy and U.S. health care reform: a relationship revisited. *Medical Anthropology Quarterly* 2001 September; 15(3): 312-328. NRCBL: 9.3.1; 2.1. SC: rv.

Baily, Mary Ann; Menzel, Paul; Light, Donald W. Talking to each other about universal health care: do values belong in the discussion? [letter and reply]. *Hastings Center Report* 2006 November-December; 36(6): 4-5. NRCBL: 9.3.1; 9.2; 21.1; 1.1.

Ballard, Dustin W.; Derlet, Robert W.; Rich, Ben A.; Lowe, Robert A. EMTALA, two decades later: a descriptive review of fiscal year 2000 violations. *American Journal of Emergency Medicine* 2006 March; 24(2): 197-205. NRCBL: 9.3.1; 9.5.1; 8.1. SC: em; le. Identifiers: Emergency Medical Treatment and Active Labor Act.

Bayley, Carol. Pay for performance: the next best thing. *Hastings Center Report* 2006 January-February; 36(1): inside back cover. NRCBL: 9.3.1; 9.1.

Berenson, Alex. A cancer drug shows promise, at a price that many can't pay. *New York Times* 2006 February 15; p. A1, C2. NRCBL: 9.3.1; 9.7; 9.5.1. SC: po.

Bishop, Gene; Brodkey, Amy C. Personal responsibility and physician responsibility — West Virginia's Medicaid plan. *New England Journal of Medicine* 2006 August 24; 355(8): 756-758. NRCBL: 9.3.1; 9.5.10; 7.1; 9.1.

Blendon, Robert J.; Altman, Drew E. Voters and health care in the 2006 election. *New England Journal of Medicine* 2006 November 2; 355(18): 1928-1933. NRCBL: 9.3.1; 9.1; 21.1; 9.8. SC: em.

Blendon, Robert J.; Brodie, Mollyann; Benson, John M.; Altman, Drew E.; Buhr, Tami. Americans' views of health care costs, access, and quality. *Milbank Quarterly* 2006; 84(4): 623-657. NRCBL: 9.3.1; 9.4; 7.1; 9.8.

Bloche, Gregg. Consumer-directed health care. *New England Journal of Medicine* 2006 October 26; 355(17): 1756-1759. NRCBL: 9.3.1; 9.8.

Blumenthal, David. Employer-sponsored health insurance in the United States — origins and implications. *New*

England Journal of Medicine 2006 July 6; 355(1): 82-88. NRCBL: 9.3.1; 16.3.

Caldwell, Gordon. New guidance on doctors' behaviour from the UK prime minister [letter]. *Lancet* 2006 December 16-22; 368(9553): 2124. NRCBL: 9.3.1; 9.4; 8.1.

Callahan, Daniel. How much medical progress can we afford? Equity and the cost of health care. *Journal of Molecular Biology* 2002 June 14; 319(4): 885-890. NRCBL: 9.3.1; 9.4; 5.2.

Callahan, Daniel. Privatizing the department of defense: a proposal. *Hastings Center Report* 2006 November-December; 36(6): inside back cover. NRCBL: 9.3.1; 21.2.

Callahan, Daniel. Universal health care: from the states to the nation? *Hastings Center Report* 2006 September-October; 36(5): 28-29. NRCBL: 9.3.1; 9.2; 9.4.

Canning, Brenda. Funding, ethics, and assistive technology: should medical necessity be the criterion by which wheeled mobility equipment is justified? *Topics in Stroke Rehabilitation* 2005 Summer; 12(3): 77-81. NRCBL: 9.3.1; 9.2; 4.4.

Capron, Alexander M. Does assessment of medical practices have a future? *Virginia Law Review* 1996 November; 82(8): 1623-1640. NRCBL: 9.3.1; 9.4; 5.2. SC: le.

Carnahan, Sandra J. Law, medicine, and wealth: does concierge medicine promote health care choice, or is it a barrier to access? *Stanford Law and Policy Review* 2006; 17(1): 121-163. NRCBL: 9.3.1; 9.3.2; 8.1; 9.2; 7.1.

Carreyrou, John. How a hospital stumbled across an Rx for Medicaid; Mt. Sinai helps patients avoid the ER, paring state costs and aiding its bottom line; Dr. Chassin goes after salt. *Wall Street Journal* 2006 June 22; p. A1, A14. NRCBL: 9.3.1. SC: po.

Chen, Xiao-Yang. Clinical bioethics in China: the challenge of entering a market economy. *Journal of Medicine and Philosophy* 2006 February; 31(1): 7- 12. NRCBL: 9.3.1; 8.1; 9.7.
Abstract: Over the last quarter-century, China has experienced dramatic changes associated with its development of a market economy. The character of clinical practice is also profoundly influenced by the ways in which reimbursement scales are established in public hospitals. The market distortions that lead to the over-prescription of drugs and the medically unindicated use of more expensive drugs and more costly high-technology diagnostic and therapeutic interventions create the most significant threat to patients. The payment of red packets represents a black-market attempt to circumvent the non-market constraint on physicians' fees for services. These economic and practice pattern changes are taking place as China and many Pacific Rim societies are reconsidering the moral foundations of their professional ethics and their bioethics. The integrity of the medical profession and the trust of patients in physicians can only be restored and protected if the distorting forces of contemporary public policy are altered.

Claxton, K.; Culyer, A.J. Wickedness or folly? The ethics of NICE's decisions. *Journal of Medical Ethics* 2006 July; 32(7): 373-377. NRCBL: 9.3.1; 9.4. SC: an. Identifiers: United Kingdom (Great Britain); National Institute for Health and Clinical Excellence.
Abstract: A rebuttal is provided to each of the arguments adduced by John Harris, an Editor-in-Chief of the Journal of Medical Ethics, in two editorials in the journal in support of the view that National Institute for Health and Clinical Excellence's procedures and methods for making recommendations about healthcare procedures for use in the National Health Service in England and Wales are the product of "wickedness or folly or more likely both", "ethically illiterate as well as socially divisive", responsible for the "perversion of science as well as of morality" and are "contrary to basic morality and contrary to human rights".

Cohen, Joshua; Ubel, Peter. Accounting for fairness and efficiency in health economics. *In:* Davis, John B., ed. The Social Economics of Health Care. New York: Routledge; 2001: 94-109. NRCBL: 9.3.1.

Elhauge, Einer. The limited regulatory potential of medical technology assessment. *Virginia Law Review* 1996 November; 82(8): 1525-1622. NRCBL: 9.3.1; 9.4; 5.2.

Flood, Colleen M. Chaoulli's legacy for the future of Canadian health care policy. *Osgoode Hall Law Journal* 2006 Summer; 44(2): 273-310. NRCBL: 9.3.1; 9.2; 7.1; 21.1. SC: le.

Gaal, Peter; Belli, Paolo Carlo; McKee, Martin; Szócska, Miklós. Informal payments for health care: definitions, distinctions, and dilemmas. *Journal of Health Politics, Policy and Law* 2006 April; 31(2): 251-293. NRCBL: 9.3.1.
Abstract: There is increasing interest in the issue of informal payments for health care in low- and middle-income countries. Emerging evidence suggests that the phenomenon is both diverse, including many variants from cash payments to in-kind contributions and from gift giving to informal charging, and widespread, reported from countries in at least three continents. However, cross-national research is hampered by the lack of consensus among researchers on the definition of informal payments, and the definitions that have been proposed are unable to incorporate all forms of the phenomenon that have been described so far. This article aims to overcome this limitation by proposing a new definition based on the concept of entitlement for services. First, the various forms of informal payment observed in practice are reviewed briefly. Then, some of the proposed definitions are discussed, pointing out that none of the distinctive characteristics implied by these definitions, including illegality, informality, and corruption, is adequate to capture all varieties of the phenomenon. Next, an alternative definition is formulated, which identifies the distinctive feature common to all forms of informal payments as something that is contributed in addition to the terms of entitlement. Then, the boundaries implied by this definition are explored and, finally, the implications for research and policy making are discussed with reference to the lessons developed countries can learn from the experiences of transitional countries.

Gaal, Peter; Evetovits, Tamas; McKee, Martin. Informal payment for health care: evidence from Hungary.

NRCBL: National Reference Center for Bioethics Literature Classification Scheme   See inside front cover for terms.

271

Health Policy 2006 June; 77(1): 86-102. NRCBL: 9.3.1; 9.1; 9.4; 7.1.

Glied, Sherry; Cuellar, Alison. Better behavioral health care coverage for everyone. *New England Journal of Medicine* 2006 March 30; 354(13): 1415-1417. NRCBL: 9.3.1; 9.5.3; 9.5.9; 17.1.

Goold, Susan Dorr; Baum, Nancy M. Define "affordable". *Hastings Center Report* 2006 September-October; 36(5): 22-24. NRCBL: 9.3.1; 9.2; 9.4.

Guillod, Olivier. Recent developments in Swiss health law. *European Journal of Health Law* 2006 June; 13(2): 123-131. NRCBL: 9.3.1; 11.3; 15.3. SC: le.

Gunnar, William P. The fundamental law that shapes the United States health care system: is universal health care realistic within the established paradigm? *Annals of Health Law* 2006 Winter; 15(1): 151-181. NRCBL: 9.3.1; 9.2. SC: le.

Hellinger, Fred J. The impact of financial incentives on physician behavior in managed care plans: a review of the evidence. *Medical Care Research and Review* 1996 September; 53(3): 294-314. NRCBL: 9.3.1; 9.3.2; 7.1.

Hurst, Samia A.; Danis, Marion. Indecent coverage? Protecting the goals of health insurance from the impact of co-payments. *CQ: Cambridge Quarterly of Healthcare Ethics* 2006 Winter; 15(1): 107-113. NRCBL: 9.3.1; 21.1.

Jackman, Martha. "The last line of defence for [which?] citizens": accountability, equality, and the right to health in Chaoulli. *Osgoode Hall Law Journal* 2006 Summer; 44(2): 349-375. NRCBL: 9.3.1; 9.2; 7.1. SC: le.

Jones, James W.; McCullough, Laurence B.; Richman, Bruce W. Ethics and commercial insurance. *Journal of Vascular Surgery* 2004 March; 39(3): 692-693. NRCBL: 9.3.1; 9.2.

Jones, James W.; McCullough, Laurence B.; Richman, Bruce W. Show me the money: the ethics of physicians' income. *Journal of Vascular Surgery* 2005 August; 42(2): 377-379. NRCBL: 9.3.1; 4.1.2; 1.3.1.

Kahn, Charles N. III. Intolerable risk, irreparable harm: the legacy of physician-owned specialty hospitals. *Health Affairs* 2006 January-February; 25(1): 130-133. NRCBL: 9.3.1; 1.3.2; 7.3.

Kolber, Morey J. Stark regulation: a historical and current review of the self-referral laws. *HEC (Healthcare Ethics Committee) Forum* 2006 March; 18(1): 61-84. NRCBL: 9.3.1; 7.3; 1.3.2; 7.4. SC: le.

Krishnan, Suneeta. People's voices on justice, equity and health care in India [review of Health Matters by Shikha Jhingan]. *Indian Journal of Medical Ethics* 2006 July-September; 3(3): 109. NRCBL: 9.3.1; 9.2; 21.1.

Lin, Herng-Ching; Kao, Senyeong; Tang, Chao-Hsuin; Yang, Ming-Chin; Lee, Hong-Shen. Factors contributing to patient dumping in Taiwan. *Health Policy* 2006 June; 77(1): 103-112. NRCBL: 9.3.1; 9.2; 7.1. SC: em.

Linz, Anthony J.; Haas, Paul F.; Fallon, L. Flemming, Jr.; Metz, Richard J. Impact of concierge care on healthcare and clinical practice. *Journal of the American Osteopathic Association* 2005 November; 105(11): 515-520. NRCBL: 9.3.1; 9.8.

Manfredi, Christopher P.; Maioni, Antonia. "The last line of defence for citizens": litigating private health insurance in Chaoulli v. Quebec. *Osgoode Hall Law Journal* 2006 Summer; 44(2): 249-271. NRCBL: 9.3.1; 9.2. SC: le; an.

Marmor, Theodore R. Canada's Supreme Court and its National Health Insurance Program: evaluating the landmark Chaoulli decision from a comparative perspective. *Osgoode Hall Law Journal* 2006 Summer; 44(2): 311-325. NRCBL: 9.3.1; 9.2; 7.1; 21.1. SC: le.

Martinez, Barbara. Health-care consultants reap fees from those they evaluate. *Wall Street Journal* 2006 September 18; p. A1, A14. NRCBL: 9.3.1; 1.3.2. SC: po.

McMillan, Elizabeth. Joint ventures: a risk to the ministry's moral capital? *Health Progress* 1987 April; 68(3): 54-57, 91. NRCBL: 9.3.1; 9.3.2; 1.2.

Milstein, Arnold; Smith, Mark. America's new refugees — seeking affordable surgery offshore. *New England Journal of Medicine* 2006 October 19; 355(16): 1637-1640. NRCBL: 9.3.1; 21.1; 9.8.

Mooney, Gavin. Communitarianism and health economics. *In:* Davis, John B., ed. The Social Economics of Health Care. New York: Routledge; 2001: 40-60. NRCBL: 9.3.1; 1.3.1.

Mooney, Gavin. The inefficiency of medical ethics. *In his:* Economics, Medicine and Health Care. Third edition. New York: Prentice Hall/Financial Times; 2003: 61-72. NRCBL: 9.3.1; 2.1. SC: an.

Mortimer, Duncan. On the relevance of personal characteristics in setting health priorities: a comment on Olsen, Richardson, Dolan and Menzel (2003). *Social Science and Medicine* 2005 April; 60(8): 1661-1664. NRCBL: 9.3.1; 7.1.

Olsen, Jan Abel; Richardson, Jeff; Dolan, Paul; Menzel, Paul. Response to "On the relevance of personal characteristics in setting health care priorities". *Social Science and Medicine* 2005 April; 60(8): 1665-1666. NRCBL: 9.3.1; 7.1.

Pickoff, Robert M. Pay for performance — for whom the bell tolls. *Physician Executive* 2005 November-December; 31(6): 12-14. NRCBL: 9.3.1; 9.5.2; 9.8.

Rai, Saritha. Union disrupts plan to send ailing workers to India for cheaper medical care. *New York Times* 2006 October 11; p. C6. NRCBL: 9.3.1; 9.8; 8.3.1. SC: po. Identifiers: United Steelworkers.

Raine, Rosalind; McIvor, Martin. 9 years on: what progress has been made on achieving UK health-care equity? *Lancet* 2006 October 28-November 3; 368(9546): 1542-1545. NRCBL: 9.3.1; 9.2; 1.1.

Ritz, Sarah. The need for parity in health insurance benefits for the mentally and physically disabled: questioning inconsistency between two leading anti-discrimination laws. *Journal of Law and Health* 2003-2004; 18(2): 263-295. NRCBL: 9.3.1; 9.5.3. SC: le.

Rosenthal, Meredith; Daniels, Norman. Beyond competition: the normative implications of consumer-driven health plans. *Journal of Health Politics, Policy, and Law* 2006 June; 31(3): 671-685. NRCBL: 9.3.1; 9.8.
Abstract: The Federal Trade Commission/Department of Justice 2004 report Improving Health Care: A Dose of Competition appeals to efficiency arguments in promoting a wide range of health care market reforms. But the market-based reforms discussed in Improving Health Care are not simply neutral with regard to equity in access to services; they are likely to have substantial and inequitable distributional effects. We use the case of consumer-driven health plans (CDHPs), the pillar of the Bush administration's private-sector health reform efforts, to illustrate the limitations of viewing health policy reform through the lens of Improving Health Care. We conclude that the speculative efficiency gains from CDHPs need to be balanced against well-documented equity concerns within a normative framework. Moreover, other important ethical issues arise with regard to the risks imposed on the population by the introduction of policies that are based on a faith in markets rather than empirical evidence.

Russano, Jennifer. Is boutique medicine a new threat to American health care or a logical way of revitalizing the doctor-patient relationship? *Washington University Journal of Law and Policy* 2005; 17: 313-340. NRCBL: 9.3.1; 8.1; 7.1.

Secker, Barbara; Goldenberg, Maya J.; Gibson, Barbara E.; Wagner, Frank; Parke, Bob; Breslin, Jonathan; Thompson, Alison; Lear, Jonathan R.; Singer, Peter A. Just regionalization: rehabilitating care for people with disabilities and chronic illnesses. *BMC Medical Ethics [electronic]* 2006; 7: 9. Accessed: http://www.biomedcentral.com/1472-6939/7/9 [nd]. NRCBL: 9.3.1; 9.5.1; 1.1. Identifiers: Ontario.

Silver, Marc T. Primary prevention implantable cardioverter-defibrillators: economics and ethics. *American Heart Hospital Journal* 2005 Summer; 3(3): 205-206. NRCBL: 9.3.1; 9.4; 8.1.

Silverman, Joseph S. A new approach to health system reform: seizing the moral high ground. *Pennsylvania Medicine* 1995 June; 98(6): 28-30. NRCBL: 9.3.1.

Steinbrook, Robert. Health care reform in Massachusetts — a work in progress. *New England Journal of Medicine* 2006 May 18; 354(20): 2095-2098. NRCBL: 9.3.1.

Thompson, Richard E. Is pay for performance ethical? *Physician Executive* 2005 November-December; 31(6): 60-62. NRCBL: 9.3.1; 1.1; 9.8; 9.5.2.

Ward, Andrew. The concept of underinsurance: a general typology. *Journal of Medicine and Philosophy* 2006 October; 31(5): 499-531. NRCBL: 9.3.1. SC: an.
Abstract: In a 2002 speech, Mark McClellan, a member of the Council of Economic Advisors at the White House, said that "[I]n the president's vision, all Americans should have access to high-quality and affordable healthcare." However, many healthcare researchers believe that a growing number of Americans are underinsured. Because any characterization of underinsurance will refer to the value judgments of people about what counts as "adequate" and "inadequate" healthcare, the goal of characterizing and measuring the underinsured is difficult to achieve. In this article, I examine the various dimensions of underinsurance, and propose a typology incorporating those dimensions.

Wax, Amy L. Technology assessment and the doctor-patient relationship. *Virginia Law Review* 1996 November; 82(8): 1641-1662. NRCBL: 9.3.1; 9.4; 5.2; 8.3.1.

Wiggins, Kenneth R. Medicaid and the enforceable right to receive medical assistance: the need for a definition of "medical assistance". *William and Mary Law Review* 2006 February; 47(4): 1487-1512. NRCBL: 9.3.1; 9.5.10; 9.2; 1.3.5.

Zuber, Rebecca Friedman. Compliance with the Medicare conditions of participation: patient rights. *Home Healthcare Nurse* 2005 August; 23(8): 490-494. NRCBL: 9.3.1; 9.5.2; 9.2. SC: le.

HEALTH CARE/. . ./ MANAGED CARE PROGRAMS

Alexander, G. Caleb; Hall, Mark A.; Lantos, John D. Rethinking professional ethics in the cost-sharing era. *American Journal of Bioethics [Online]* 2006 July-August; 6(4): W17-W22. NRCBL: 9.3.2; 8.1.

Banja, John D. Ethics, case management, and the standard of care. *Case Manager* 2006 July-August; 17(4): 20-22. NRCBL: 9.3.2; 9.8. SC: le.

Beidler, Susan M. Ethical considerations for nurse-managed health centers. *Nursing Clinics of North America* 2005 December; 40(4): 759-770. NRCBL: 9.3.2; 4.1.3; 9.1; 9.5.4.

Braun, Sharon A.; Cox, Jane A. Managed mental health care: intentional misdiagnosis of mental disorders. *Journal of Counseling and Development* 2005 Fall; 83(4): 425-433. NRCBL: 9.3.2; 17.1; 8.1; 7.1; 9.3.1.

Brody, Howard. Family medicine, the physician-patient relationship, and patient-centered care. *American Journal*

NRCBL: National Reference Center for Bioethics Literature Classification Scheme   See inside front cover for terms.

273

of Bioethics 2006 January-February; 6(1): 38-39. NRCBL: 9.3.2; 8.1. Comments: G. Caleb Alexander and John D. Lantos. The doctor-patient relationship in the post-managed care era. American Journal of Bioethics 2006 January-February; 6(10): 29-32.

Cross, MargaretAnn. The ethical way in a season of change. *Managed Care* 2005 December; 14(12): 22, 25-27. NRCBL: 9.3.2; 1.3.2.

Doyle, Florence F.; Graunke, Carrie L.; Hildebrandt, Douglas J.; Otto, Robert K.; St. George, Mark C. Act with ethics: Sarbanes-Oxley's role in helping to ensure supply chain integrity. *Materials Management in Health Care* 2005 July; 14(7): 35-40. NRCBL: 9.3.2; 1.3.2; 1.3.5. SC: le.

Gamble, Vanessa Northington. H.R. 5198: The Ethics in Patient Referrals Act: implications for providers. *Journal of Ambulatory Care Management* 1989 May; 12(2): 83-86. NRCBL: 9.3.2; 9.5.2; 7.3. SC: le.

Hunter, Nan D. Managed process, due care: structures of accountability in health care. *Yale Journal of Health Policy, Law and Ethics* 2006 Winter; 6(1): 93-162. NRCBL: 9.3.2; 9.2. SC: le.

Hurt, Mark. Doctors as double agents — conflicting loyalties in the contemporary doctor-patient relationship. *Journal of Medicine and Law* 1997 Fall; 2(1): 25-83. NRCBL: 9.3.2; 7.3; 8.4; 8.5; 8.1. SC: le.

Light, Donald W. Be clear about managed care to get clear about doctor-patient relations. *American Journal of Bioethics* 2006 January-February; 6(1): 35-36. NRCBL: 9.3.2. Comments: G. Caleb Alexander and John D. Lantos. The doctor-patient relationship in the post-managed care era. American Journal of Bioethics 2006 January-February; 6(10): 29-32.

Loud, Kelly M. ERISA preemption and patients' rights in the wake of Aetna Health Inc. v. Davila. *Catholic University Law Review* 2005 Spring; 54(3): 1039-1075. NRCBL: 9.3.2; 9.2; 9.8. SC: le; cs. Identifiers: Employee Retirement Income Security Act.

Lundy, Courtnee. Methods to identify and address the ethical issues associated with managed care. *Penn Bioethics Journal* 2006; 2(2): 3-7. NRCBL: 9.3.2; 1.1.
   Abstract: There are many benefits of managed care, such as its focus on disease prevention and health promotion, its integration of healthcare services to minimize inefficiencies, and its ability to restrict healthcare costs; however, there are also some ethical concerns that arise from managing care. In the context of managed care, ethics is a method for examining conflicts of values and obligations where there are competing interests, each of which presents a reasonably justified position. The principles of procedural, commutative, and general justice are particularly applicable to the ethical issues associated with managed care. Through a review of relevant literature, this paper will examine different methods and principles of justice to consider in establishing an ethical managed care organization and it will offer some examples of plans that have established policies to meet

their ethical goals. By setting common goals, plans and enrollees can minimize ethical conflicts and collaborate to ensure that plans consistently use just procedures to ensure that quality care is available.

Moffic, H. Steven. Managed behavioral healthcare poses multiple ethical challenges for clinicians. *Psychiatric Annals* 2004 February; 34(2): 98-104. NRCBL: 9.3.2; 17.1; 6; 8.4; 7.1.

Price, David M. An ethical perspective. Evaluating managed care. *Journal of Nursing Law* 1998; 5(3): 47-50. NRCBL: 9.3.2; 4.1.3.

Schwab, Abraham P.; Carroll, Kelly A.; Wynia, Matthew K. What is managed care anyway? *American Journal of Bioethics* 2006 January-February; 6(1): 36-37. NRCBL: 9.3.2; 8.1. Comments: G. Caleb Alexander and John D. Lantos. The doctor-patient relationship in the post-managed care era. American Journal of Bioethics 2006 January-February; 6(10): 29-32.

Silva, Mary Cipriano; Williams, Kathleen O. Managed care and the violation of ethical principles: research vignettes. *In:* Cowen, Perle Slavik; Moorhead, Sue, eds. Current Issues in Nursing. 7th ed. St. Louis, MO: Mosby, 2006: 660-667. NRCBL: 9.3.2; 2.1.

Sperry, Len. Ethical dilemmas in the assessment of clinical outcomes. *Psychiatric Annals* 2004 February; 34(2): 107-113. NRCBL: 9.3.2; 1.3.2; 17.1; 9.8; 9.1; 4.1.2.

Thompson, Stephen L.; Salmon, J. Warren. Strikes by physicians: a historical perspective toward an ethical evaluation. *International Journal of Health Services* 2006; 36(2): 331-354. NRCBL: 9.3.2; 1.3.2; 7.1; 2.2.

HEALTH CARE/ HEALTH CARE QUALITY

Full clinical trial disclosure needed: expert [news]. *CMAJ/JAMC: Canadian Medical Association Journal* 2006 July 18; 175(2): 140-141. NRCBL: 9.8; 9.7; 1.3.9. Identifiers: Canadian Expert Drug Advisory Committee (CEDAC).

When doctors hide medical errors [editorial]. *New York Times* 2006 September 9; p. A14. NRCBL: 9.8; 7.1; 8.5. SC: po.

Armitage, Gerry. Drug errors, qualitative research and some reflections on ethics. *Journal of Clinical Nursing* 2005 August; 14(7): 869-875. NRCBL: 9.8; 9.7; 18.5.1; 1.3.9; 18.2.

Baily, Mary Ann; Bottrell, Melissa; Lynn, Joanne; Jennings, Bruce. The ethics of using QI methods to improve health care quality and safety. *Hastings Center Report* 2006 July-August; 36(4): S1-S39. NRCBL: 9.8.

Bakalar, Nicholas. Medical errors? Patients may be the last to know. *New York Times* 2006 August 29; p. F7. NRCBL: 9.8; 8.2. SC: po.

Ballard, Lynette. Putting safety at the core. *Health Progress* 2006 January-February; 87(1): 29-33. NRCBL: 9.8.

Banja, John D. Ethically speaking: the case manager's response to harm-causing error. *Case Manager* 2005 May-June; 16(3): 60-65. NRCBL: 9.8; 8.2; 7.3; 7.1.

Bayley, Carol. Who is responsible? *Hastings Center Report* 2006 May-June; 36(3): 11-12. NRCBL: 9.8; 8.2; 9.7; 9.5.1. SC: cs.

Becker, E. Catherine. The MEDiC Act of 2005: a new approach to safety. *AORN Journal* 2005 December; 82(6): 1055-1058. NRCBL: 9.8; 8.2. SC: le. Identifiers: National Medical Error Disclosure and Compensation Act of 2005.

Berlinger, Nancy. Fair compensation without litigation: addressing patients' financial needs in disclosure. *Journal of Healthcare Risk Management* 2004; 24(1): 7-11. NRCBL: 9.8; 8.2; 8.5; 9.3.1. SC: cs.

Berlinger, Nancy. Who is responsible? *Hastings Center Report* 2006 May-June; 36(3): 12. NRCBL: 9.8; 8.2; 9.7; 9.5.1. SC: cs. Identifiers: medication error.

Brahams, Diana. Should doctors admit their mistakes? [editorial]. *Medico-Legal Journal* 2005; 73(Part 2): 41-44. NRCBL: 9.8; 8.2. Identifiers: United Kingdom (Great Britain).

Brock, Dan W. How much is more life worth? *Hastings Center Report* 2006 May-June; 36(3): 17-19. NRCBL: 9.8; 9.3.1; 9.7; 9.5.1; 4.4; 15.1.

Buetow, S.; Elwyn, G. Are patients morally responsible for their errors? *Journal of Medical Ethics* 2006 May; 32(5): 260-262. NRCBL: 9.8; 8.1; 1.1. SC: an.

Abstract: Amid neglect of patients' contribution to error has been a failure to ask whether patients are morally responsible for their errors. This paper aims to help answer this question and so define a worthy response to the errors. Recent work on medical errors has emphasised system deficiencies and discouraged finding people to blame. We scrutinize this approach from an incompatibilist, agent causation position and draw on Hart's taxonomy of four senses of moral responsibility: role responsibility; capacity responsibility; causal responsibility; and liability responsibility. Each sense is shown to contribute to an overall theoretical judgment as to whether patients are morally responsible for their errors (and success in avoiding them). Though how to weight the senses is unclear, patients appear to be morally responsible for the avoidable errors they make, contribute to or can influence.

Burger, Ingrid; Sugarman, Jeremy; Goodman, Steven N. Ethical issues in evidence-based surgery. *Surgical Clinics of North America* 2006 February; 86(1): 151-168, x. NRCBL: 9.8; 9.4; 18.2; 18.3.

Chan, David K.; Gallagher, Thomas H.; Reznick, Richard; Levinson, Wendy. How surgeons disclose medical errors to patients: a study using standardized patients. *Surgery* 2005 November; 138(5): 851-858. NRCBL: 9.8; 8.2. SC: em.

Chang, Ly-yun. Peer review and medical negligence. *In:* Döring, Ole; Chen, Renbiao, eds. Advances in Chinese Medical Ethics: Chinese and International Perspectives. Hamburg: Institut für Asienkunde; 2002: 337-352. NRCBL: 9.8. Note: Proceedings of the Second Sino-German Interdisciplinary Symposium about Medical Ethics in China, Shanghai, 19-23 October, 1999.

Chen, Donna T.; Worrall, Bradford B. Practice-based clinical research and ethical decision making — Part I: deciding whether to incorporate practice-based research into your clinical practice. *Seminars in Neurology* 2006 February; 26(1): 131-139. NRCBL: 9.8; 1.3.9.

Chen, Donna T.; Worrall, Bradford B. Practice-based clinical research and ethical decision making — Part II: deciding whether to host a particular research study in your practice. *Seminars in Neurology* 2006 February; 26(1): 140-147. NRCBL: 9.8; 18.1; 18.3.

Davies, J.M. Disclosure [editorial]. *Acta Anaesthesiologica Scandinavica* 2005 July; 49(6): 725-727. NRCBL: 9.8; 8.2.

De Young, Paul; Ladenheim, Kala. Hospital-acquired infection disclosure gains momentum. *NCSL Legisbrief* 2005 October; 13(42): 1-2. NRCBL: 9.8; 8.2; 8.4; 1.3.5.

Espin, Sherry; Levinson, Wendy; Regehr, Glenn; Baker, G. Ross; Lingard, Lorelei. Error or "act of God"? A study of patients' and operating room team members' perceptions of error definition, reporting, and disclosure. *Surgery* 2006 January; 139(1): 6-14. NRCBL: 9.8; 8.2; 7.1. SC: em.

Gallagher, Thomas H.; Garbutt, Jane M.; Waterman, Amy D.; Flum, David R.; Larson, Eric B.; Waterman, Brian M.; Dunagan, W. Claiborne; Fraser, Victoria J.; Levinson, Wendy. Choosing your words carefully: how physicians would disclose harmful medical errors to patients. *Archives of Internal Medicine* 2006 August 14-28; 166(15): 1585-1593. NRCBL: 9.8; 8.2. SC: em.

Gallagher, Thomas H.; Waterman, Amy D.; Garbutt, Jane M.; Kapp, Julie M.; Chan, David K.; Dunagan, W. Claiborne; Fraser, Victoria J.; Levinson, Wendy. US and Canadian physicians' attitudes and experiences regarding disclosing errors to patients. *Archives of Internal Medicine* 2006 August 14-28; 166(15): 1605-1611. NRCBL: 9.8; 8.2. SC: em.

Gert, Bernard; Culver, Charles M.; Clouser, K. Danner. What doctors must know about medical practice. *In their:* Bioethics: A Systematic Approach. Second edition. New York: Oxford University Press; 2006: 191-212. NRCBL: 9.8. SC: an.

Groenewegen, Peter P.; Kerssens, Jan J.; Sixma, Herman J.; van der Eijk, Ingrid; Boerma, Wienke G.W. What is important in evaluating health care quality? An international comparison of user views. *BMC Health Ser-*

NRCBL: National Reference Center for Bioethics Literature Classification Scheme   See inside front cover for terms.

275

vices Research 2005 February 21; 5: 9 p. NRCBL: 9.8; 9.1; 21.1. SC: em.

Henry, Linda L. Disclosure of medical errors: ethical considerations for the development of a facility policy and organizational culture change. *Policy, Politics, and Nursing Practice* 2005 May; 6(2): 127-134. NRCBL: 9.8; 8.2; 7.1.

Henry, Stephen G. Recognizing tacit knowledge in medical epistemology. *Theoretical Medicine and Bioethics* 2006; 27(3): 187-213. NRCBL: 9.8; 4.1.2. SC: ph.
   Abstract: The evidence-based medicine movement advocates basing all medical decisions on certain types of quantitative research data and has stimulated protracted controversy and debate since its inception. Evidence-based medicine presupposes an inaccurate and deficient view of medical knowledge. Michael Polanyi's theory of tacit knowledge both explains this deficiency and suggests remedies for it. Polanyi shows how all explicit human knowledge depends on a wealth of tacit knowledge which accrues from experience and is essential for problem solving. Edmund Pellegrino's classic treatment of clinical judgment is examined, and a Polanyian critique of this position demonstrates that tacit knowledge is necessary for understanding how clinical judgment and medical decisions involve persons. An adequate medical epistemology requires much more qualitative research relevant to the clinical encounter and medical decision making than is currently being done. This research is necessary for preventing an uncritical application of evidence-based medicine by health care managers that erodes good clinical practice. Polanyi's epistemology shows the need for this work and provides the structural core for building an adequate and robust medical epistemology that moves beyond evidence-based medicine.

Hobgood, Cherri; Tamayo-Sarver, Joshua H.; Elms, Andrew; Weiner, Bryan. Parental preferences for error disclosure, reporting, and legal action after medical error in the care of their children. *Pediatrics* 2005 December; 116(6): 1276-1286. NRCBL: 9.8; 9.5.7; 8.3.2; 8.5. SC: em.

Jones, James W.; McCullough, Laurence B.; Richman, Bruce W. Whodunit? Ghost surgery and ethical billing. *Journal of Vascular Surgery* 2005 December; 42(6): 1239-1241. NRCBL: 9.8; 9.3.1; 1.3.1; 4.1.2. SC: cs.

Kaldjian, Lauris C.; Jones, Elizabeth W.; Rosenthal, Gary E.; Tripp-Reimer, Toni; Hillis, Stephen L. An empirically derived taxonomy of factors affecting physicians' willingness to disclose medical errors. *JGIM: Journal of General Internal Medicine* 2006 September; 21(9): 942-948. NRCBL: 9.8; 8.2. SC: em.

Leonhardt, David. The choice: a longer life or more stuff. *New York Times* 2006 September 27; p. C1, C7. NRCBL: 9.8; 9.3.1. SC: po.

Lesnewski, Ruth. Mistakes. *JAMA: The Journal of the American Medical Association* 2006 September 20; 269(11): 1327-1328. NRCBL: 9.8; 7.2; 8.2.

Manser, T.; Staender, S. Aftermath of an adverse event: supporting health care professionals to meet patient expectations through open disclosure. *Acta Anaesthesiologica*

Scandinavica 2005 July; 49(6): 728-734. NRCBL: 9.8; 8.2; 8.1.

Marasco, Silvana F.; Ibrahim, Joseph E.; Oakley, Justin. Public disclosure of surgeon-specific report cards: current status of the debate. *ANZ Journal of Surgery* 2005 November; 75(11): 1000-1004. NRCBL: 9.8; 8.2.

Marziali, Elsa; Dergal Serafini, Julie M.; McCleary, Lynn. A systematic review of practice standards and research ethics in technology-based home health care intervention programs for older adults. *Journal of Aging and Health* 2005 December; 17(6): 679-696. NRCBL: 9.8; 1.3.12; 1.3.9; 9.5.2. SC: rv; em.

Mavroudis, Constantine; Mavroudis, Constantine D.; Naunheim, Keith S.; Sade, Robert M. Should surgical errors always be disclosed to the patient? *Annals of Thoracic Surgery* 2005 August; 80(2): 399-408. NRCBL: 9.8; 1.1; 8.2. SC: an.

Mehlman, Maxwell J. Dishonest medical mistakes. *Vanderbilt Law Review* 2006 May; 59(4): 1137-1173. NRCBL: 9.8; 8.2; 8.5; 9.3.2; 7.3. SC: le.

Mills, Ann E.; Rorty, Mary V.; Werhane, Patricia H. Clinical ethics and the managerial revolution in American healthcare. *Journal of Clinical Ethics* 2006 Summer; 17(2): 181-190. NRCBL: 9.8; 9.1; 1.3.2; 9.6.

Moszynski, Peter. Doctors must work in partnership with patients, says GMC [news]. *BMJ: British Medical Journal* 2006 September 9; 333(7567): 513. NRCBL: 9.8; 8.1. Identifiers: United Kingdom (Great Britain); General Medical Council.

Quick, Oliver. Outing medical errors: questions of trust and responsibility. *Medical Law Review* 2006 Spring; 14(1): 22-43. NRCBL: 9.8; 8.1; 7.1.

Rao, Mala; Clarke, Aileen; Sanderson, Colin; Hammersley, Richard. Patients' own assessments of quality of primary care compared with objective records based measures of technical quality of care: cross sectional study. *BMJ: British Medical Journal* 2006 July 1; 333(7557): 19-22. NRCBL: 9.8. SC: em. Identifiers: United Kingdom (Great Britain).

Schwartz, Barry. Apology is integral part of ethics. *Today's FDA* 2005 December; 17(12): 24-26, 28, 30. NRCBL: 9.8; 8.2.

Sparkman, Catherine A. G. Legislating apology in the context of medical mistakes. *AORN Journal* 2005 August; 82(2): 263-264, 266, 269-272. NRCBL: 9.8; 8.2;. SC: le.

Steinbrook, Robert. Public report cards — cardiac surgery and beyond. *New England Journal of Medicine* 2006 November 2; 355(18): 1847-1849. NRCBL: 9.8; 9.5.1.

Tope, Rosie; Koskinen, Marja-Kaarina. Quality assurance — an ethical responsibility? *In:* Tadd, Win, ed. Ethics

---

in Nursing Education, Research and Management. New York: Palgrave Macmillan; 2003: 163-191. NRCBL: 9.8.

Vineis, Paolo. The tension between ethics and evidence-based medicine. *In:* Viafora, Corrado, ed. Clinical Bioethics: A Search for the Foundations. Dordrecht: Springer, 2005: 131-137. NRCBL: 9.8; 1.1. SC: an.

Waring, Justin J. Beyond blame: cultural barriers to medical incident reporting. *Social Science and Medicine* 2005 May; 60(9): 1927-1935. NRCBL: 9.8; 7.1. SC: em.

Woolf, Lord. The medical profession and justice. *Journal of the Royal Society of Medicine* 1997 July; 90(7): 364-367. NRCBL: 9.8; 7.1; 1.3.5; 7.3. SC: le.

HEALTH CARE RATIONING *See* RESOURCE ALLOCATION

HEALTH CARE RIGHTS *See* RIGHT TO HEALTH CARE

HEALTH, CONCEPT OF
See also MENTAL HEALTH, CONCEPT OF

Bambas, Lexi. Integrating equity into health information systems: a human rights approach to health and information. *PLoS Medicine* 2005 April; 2(4): 0299-0301. NRCBL: 4.2; 4.4; 9.1; 21.1; 21.7.

Delkeskamp-Hayes, Corinna. Why patients should give thanks for their disease: traditional Christianity on the joy of suffering. *Christian Bioethics* 2006 August; 12(2): 213-228. NRCBL: 4.2; 1.2; 4.4.
  Abstract: Patristic teaching about sin and disease allows supplementing well-acknowledged conditions for a Christian medicine with further personal challenges, widely disregarded in Western Christianities. A proper appreciation of man's vocation toward (not just achieving forgiveness but) deification reveals the need to cooperate with the Holy Spirit's offer of grace toward restoring man's pre-fallen nature. Ascetical exercises designed at re-establishing the spirit's mastery over the soul distance persons from (even supposedly harmless) passion. They thus inspire the struggle towards emulating Christ's (self-crucifying) kenotic love, and to accept even secularly "undeserved" suffering as spiritually deserved in view of his (forever)lacking fervor in that struggle. Only in the spirit of that love can the evil Adam's sin brought into this world work its therapeutic impact, the eschatological purpose of which explains God's lovingly permitting that evil. This therapeutic impact is physically manifested already in this life through the transforming energies granted the saints of the church.

Eibach, Ulrich. Life history, sin, and disease. *Christian Bioethics* 2006 August; 12(2): 117-131. NRCBL: 4.2; 1.2; 4.4.
  Abstract: On the basis of experiences in pastoral hospital care, the relationship between disease, sin, and guilt in the life of patients is explored. Against the disregard of this subject in medicine, and even in most of pastoral care, it is argued that patients' interest requires that their hidden or manifest questions be addressed, rather than their being exposed to efforts at "helping" through mere attempts at "debt clearance." Only by openly confronting sin and guilt can the patient betaken seriously in his

role as subject of his disease. Theological and anthropological background considerations revealing the essence of sin as a disruption or even destruction of the Divine gift of life in its realization through a lived relationship to God and other humans are offered as evidence for this claim.

Foster, Claire. Disease, suffering, and sin: one Anglican's perspective. *Christian Bioethics* 2006 August; 12(2): 157-163. NRCBL: 4.2; 1.2; 9.5.6; 4.4.
  Abstract: This article explores some of the implications of understanding sin as failure of perception. The theological underpinning of the argument is the choice made in the Garden of Eden to eat the fruit of the tree of knowledge rather than the fruit of the tree of life, or wisdom. This has led to distorted perception, in which all things are seen as having separate, independent existences rather than joined together by their common divine source and their deep interrelatedness in the covenant made with God. The article discusses the fascination with the principle of respect for autonomy in the light of this theology. It also looks at perceptions of the HIV/AIDS crisis in Africa. It finishes with a definition of repentance that makes right perception possible.

Garcia, J.L.A. Sin and suffering in a Catholic understanding of medical ethics. *Christian Bioethics* 2006 August; 12(2): 165-186. NRCBL: 4.2; 1.2; 4.4; 1.1.
  Abstract: Drawing chiefly on recent sources, in Part One I sketch an untraditional way of articulating what I claim to be central elements of traditional Catholic morality, treating it as based in virtues, focused on the recipients("patients") of our attention and concern, and centered in certain person-to-person role-relationships. I show the limited and derivative places of "natural law," and therefore of sin, within that framework. I also sketch out some possible implications for medical ethics of this approach to moral theory, and briefly contrast these with the influential alternative offered by the "principlism" of Beauchamp and Childress. In Part Two, I turn to a Catholic understanding of the nature and meaning of human suffering, drawing especially on writings and addresses of the late Pope John Paul II. He reminds us that physical and mental suffering can provide an opportunity to share in Christ's salvific sacrifice, better to see the nature of our earthly vocation, and to reflect on the dependence that inheres in human existence. At various places, and especially in my conclusion, I suggest a few ways in which this can inform bioethical reflection on morally appropriate responses to those afflicted by physical or mental pain, disability, mental impairment, disease, illness, and poor health prospects. My general point is that mercy must be informed by appreciation of the person's dignity and status. Throughout, my approach is philosophical rather than theological.

Gert, Bernard; Culver, Charles M.; Clouser, K. Danner. Malady. *In their:* Bioethics: A Systematic Approach. Second edition. New York: Oxford University Press; 2006: 129-164. NRCBL: 4.2. SC: an.

Gilbert, Scott F.; Tyler, Anna L.; Zackin, Emily J. New perspectives on old issues: what is "normal"? *In their:* Bioethics and the New Embryology: Springboards for Debate. Sunderland, MA: Sinauer Associates; 2005: 215-225. NRCBL: 4.2; 4.4; 15.2.

Groenhout, Ruth. Not without hope: a reformed analysis of sickness and sin. *Christian Bioethics* 2006 August; 12(2): 133-150. NRCBL: 4.2; 1.2; 4.4.
  Abstract: A Reformed understanding of sickness requires that connections be drawn between the structural effects of sin and

NRCBL: National Reference Center for Bioethics Literature Classification Scheme   See inside front cover for terms.

277

the ways that sickness is experienced in people's lives. Such an understanding can be an important resource for the bioethicist, both the bioethicist who speaks from the Reformed tradition and the bioethicist who speaks to patients and caregivers who may assume that sin and sickness are connected, but may understand that linkage in overly simplistic ways.

Hatfield, Chad. Sin, sickness, and salvation. *Christian Bioethics* 2006 August; 12(2): 199-211. NRCBL: 4.2; 1.2; 4.4.

Abstract: This article seeks to provide commentary and rationale for Orthodox Christian rites and prayers for the sick as found in the Euchologion, or Book of Needs. The reader needs to understand that the prayers of the Orthodox Church prayed at times of sickness and suffering will often strike the non-Orthodox as harsh and even unjust. References to God willing suffering do not sit well with most Western Christians. However, this is the Orthodox Christian belief, and it is expressed in the prayers of the Orthodox Church. Sickness and suffering are understood to be avenues of salvation and a participation in the glory and joys of the resurrection of Christ and life in the Kingdom of God. This is why the Orthodox Church teaches her faithful to accept suffering as something that has the potential to bring them further along in the process of theosis.

Hausman, Daniel M. Valuing health. *Philosophy and Public Affairs* 2006 Summer; 34(3): 246-274. NRCBL: 4.2; 9.3.1; 9.4. SC: an.

Jones, David Albert. Sin, suffering, and the need for theological virtues. *Christian Bioethics* 2006 August; 12(2): 187-198. NRCBL: 4.2.; 1.2; 4.4; 1.1.

Abstract: This article examines the account of the relationship between sin and suffering provided by J. L. A. Garcia in "Sin and Suffering in a Catholic Understanding of Medical Ethics," in this issue. Garcia draws on the (Roman) Catholic tradition and particularly on the thought of Thomas Aquinas, who remains an important resource for Catholic theology. Nevertheless, his interpretation of Thomas is open to criticism, both in terms of omissions and in terms of positive claims. Garcia includes those elements of Thomas that are purely philosophical, such as natural law and acquired virtue, but neglects the theological and infused virtues, the gifts and fruits of the Holy Spirit, and the beatitudes. These omissions distort his account of the Christian life so that he underplays both the radical problem posed by sin (and suffering), and the radical character of the ultimate solution: redemption in Christ through the grace of the Holy Spirit.

Mongoven, Ann. The war on disease and the war on terror: a dangerous metaphorical nexus? *CQ: Cambridge Quarterly of Healthcare Ethics* 2006 Fall; 15(4): 403-416. NRCBL: 4.2; 21.1; 7.1.

Nordby, Halvor. The analytic-synthetic distinction and conceptual analyses of basic health concepts. *Medicine, Health Care and Philosophy* 2006; 9(2): 169-180. NRCBL: 4.2; 1.1. SC: an.

Abstract: Within philosophy of medicine it has been a widespread view that there are important theoretical and practical reasons for clarifying the nature of basic health concepts like disease, illness and sickness. Many theorists have attempted to give definitions that can function as general standards, but as more and more definitions have been rejected as inadequate, pessimism about the possibility of formulating plausible definitions has become increasingly widespread. However, the belief that no definitions will succeed since no definitions have suc-

ceeded is an inductive objection, open to realist responses. The article argues that an influential argument from philosophy of language constitutes a more fundamental objection. I use disease as an example and show that this argument implies that if a common understanding of disease can be analysed into a definition, then this is a non-trivial definition. But any non-trivial analysis must be viciously circular: the analysis must presuppose that disease can be defined, but this is what the analysis is supposed to yield as a result. This means, the article concludes, that disease and other controversial health concepts do not have analyses grounded in a common language. Stipulative and contextual definitions can have local significance, but the normative roles of such definitions are at the same time limited.

Rae, Scott B. On the connection between sickness and sin: a commentary. *Christian Bioethics* 2006 August; 12(2): 151-156. NRCBL: 4.2; 1.2; 4.4.

Abstract: In response to the articles by Eibach and Groenhut in this issue, I argue that there is a general connection between sickness and the entrance of sin into the world. There are times when there is a causal link between more specifics in and sickness, though often the patient is the one who has been sinned against. Illness can also expose sin in a patient's life. Integrating the reality of illness into the life history of a patient is a significant pastoral care issue and can be done with humility and sensitivity if done in accordance with the teaching of Job and Ecclesiastes. These books argue that "under the sun" or this side of eternity, human beings can't grasp the coherence of life, including the "why" of illness. Rather, God provides His loving presence, through His people as a comfort to those suffering from illness.

Räisänen, Ulla; Bekkers, Marie-Jet; Boddington, Paul; Sarangi, Srikant. The causation of disease — the practical and ethical consequences of competing explanations. *Medicine, Health Care and Philosophy* 2006; 9(3): 293-306. NRCBL: 4.2; 1.1.

Richman, Kenneth A. A new theory of health: beneficence and recommendations for treatment. *Advances in Mind-Body Medicine* 2005 Summer; 21(2): 8-18. NRCBL: 4.2; 9.4; 4.4.

Russell, Barbara J. It's not just a wound. *Ostomy Wound Management* 2005 April; 51(4): 82-87. NRCBL: 4.2; 4.4; 8.1; 8.3.1; 8.3.4. SC: cs.

Sisti, Dominic A. Health and disease. *In:* Mitcham, Carl, ed. Encyclopedia of Science, Technology, and Ethics. Farmington Hills, MI: Thomson/Gale, 2005: 902-907. NRCBL: 4.2.

Stempsey, William E. Emerging medical technologies and emerging conceptions of health. *Theoretical Medicine and Bioethics* 2006; 27(3): 227-243. NRCBL: 4.2; 5.1. SC: ph.

Abstract: Using ideas gleaned from the philosophy of technology of Martin Heidegger and Hans Jonas and the philosophy of health of Georges Canguilhem, I argue that one of the characteristics of emerging medical technologies is that these technologies lead to new conceptions of health. When technologies enable the body to respond to more and more challenges of disease, we thus establish new norms of health. Given the continued development of successful technologies, we come to expect more and more that our bodies should be able to respond to ever-new challenges of environment and disease by establish-

---

SC (Subject Captions):   an=analytical   cs=case studies   em=empirical   le=legal   po=popular   rv=review

ing ever-new norms of health. Technologies may aim at the prevention and treatment of disease, but they also bring about modifications of what we consider normal for the human being. Thus, new norms of health arise from technological innovation.

Zatti, Paolo. The right to choose one's health. *In:* Viafora, Corrado, ed. Clinical Bioethics: A Search for the Foundations. Dordrecht: Springer, 2005: 115-129. NRCBL: 4.2; 1.1; 4.1.2.

HISTORY OF BIOETHICS *See* BIOETHICS AND MEDICAL ETHICS/ HISTORY

HOSPICES *See* DEATH AND DYING/ TERMINAL CARE

HOSPITAL ETHICS COMMITTEES *See* ETHICISTS AND ETHICS COMMITTEES

HUMAN EXPERIMENTATION
See also AIDS/ HUMAN EXPERIMENTATION; BEHAVIORAL RESEARCH; BIOMEDICAL RESEARCH

Research agendas: an invitation to readers. *Journal of Empirical Research on Human Research Ethics* 2006 June; 1(2): 3-5. NRCBL: 18.1; 16.3.

Research agendas: an invitation to readers. *Journal of Empirical Research on Human Research Ethics* 2006 March; 1(1): 5-6. NRCBL: 18.1; 1.3.5; 9.8.

The elephant in the room: a biotech trial that went awry [editorial]. *Nature* 2006 December 14; 442(7121): 790. NRCBL: 18.1; 18.2. Identifiers: United Kingdom (Great Britain); TGN1412.

Allmark, P.; Mason, S. Should desperate volunteers be included in randomised controlled trials? *Journal of Medical Ethics* 2006 September; 32(9): 548-553. NRCBL: 18.1; 18.3; 18.5.1. SC: an.
Abstract: Randomised controlled trials (RCTs) sometimes recruit participants who are desperate to receive the experimental treatment. This paper defends the practice against three arguments that suggest it is unethical first, desperate volunteers are not in equipoise. Second clinicians, entering patients onto trials are disavowing their therapeutic obligation to deliver the best treatment; they are following trial protocols rather than delivering individualised care. Research is not treatment; its ethical justification is different. Consent is crucial. Third, desperate volunteers do not give proper consent: effectively, they are coerced. This paper responds by advocating a notion of equipoise based on expert knowledge and widely shared values. Where such collective, expert equipoise exists there is a prima facie case for an RCT. Next the paper argues that trial entry does not involve clinicians disavowing their therapeutic obligation; individualised care based on insufficient evidence is not in patients best interest. Finally, it argues that where equipoise exists it is acceptable to limit access to experimental agents; desperate volunteers are not coerced because their desperation does not translate into a right to receive what they desire.

Barnes, Barbara E.; Friedman, Charles P.; Rosenburg, Jerome L.L.; Russell, Joanne; Beedle, Ari; Levine, Ar-

thur S. Creating an infrastructure for training in the responsible conduct of research: the University of Pittsburgh's experience. *Academic Medicine* 2006 February; 81(2): 119-127. NRCBL: 18.1; 7.2; 2.3. SC: cs.

Baron, Jonathan. Drug research. *In his:* Against Bioethics. Cambridge, MA: MIT Press, 2006: 155-178. NRCBL: 18.1.

Beecher, Henry K. Ethics and clinical research. *New England Journal of Medicine* 1966 June 16; 274(24): 1354-1360. NRCBL: 18.1.

Bhattacharya, Shaoni; Coghlan, Andy. One drug, six men, disaster . . . [news]. *New Scientist* 2006 March 25-31; 189(2544): 10-11. NRCBL: 18.1; 9.7. Identifiers: United Kingdom (Great Britain); TeGenero TGN1412 drug; Parexel.

Borzak, Steven. Funding of clinical trials [letter]. *JAMA: The Journal of the American Medical Association* 2006 October 25; 296(16): 1969. NRCBL: 18.1; 5.3; 9.7.

Budinger, Thomas F.; Budinger, Miriam D. Ethics of human and animal experimentation. *In their:* Ethics of Emerging Technologies: Scientific Facts and Moral Challenges. Hoboken, NJ: John Wiley and Sons; 2006: 277-302. NRCBL: 18.1; 22.2.

Cerinus, Marie. The ethics of research. *Nurse Researcher* 2001; 8(3): 72-89. NRCBL: 18.1; 18.2; 4.1.3; 2.1. SC: em. Identifiers: United Kingdom (Great Britain).

Cleaton-Jones, Peter. Research injury in clinical trials in South Africa. *Lancet* 2006 February 11-17; 367(9509): 458-459. NRCBL: 18.1; 9.3.1; 18.3; 18.5.9. Identifiers: National Institute of Health (NIH); Centers for Disease Control (CDC).

Cooley, Dennis. Responsible Conduct of Research, by Adil E. Shamoo and David B. Resnik [book review]. *Essays in Philosophy* 2003 June; 4(2): 12 p. [Online]. Accessed: http://sorrel.humboldt.edu/%7Eessays/cooley3rev.html [2004 December 16]. NRCBL: 18.1; 1.1; 2.1.

Corrigan, Oonagh; Tutton, Richard. What's in a name? Subjects, volunteers, participants and activists in clinical research. *Clinical Ethics* 2006 June; 1(2): 101-104. NRCBL: 18.1.

Day, Michael. Agency criticises drug trial [news]. *BMJ: British Medical Journal* 2006 June 3; 332(7553): 1290. NRCBL: 18.1.

Day, Michael. US scientists urge overhaul of clinical trials to restore confidence [news]. *BMJ: British Medical Journal* 2006 April 29; 332(7548): 991. NRCBL: 18.1.

DeMarco, Joseph P.; Markman, Maurie. The research misconception. *International Journal of Applied Philoso-*

NRCBL: National Reference Center for Bioethics Literature Classification Scheme   See inside front cover for terms.

279

phy 2004 Fall; 18(2): 241-252. NRCBL: 18.1; 18.2; 1.3.9; 18.3; 18.5.1. Identifiers: therapy in clinical trials.

di Norcia, Vincent. The ethics in human research ethics [editorial]. *Journal of Empirical Research on Human Research Ethics* 2006 June; 1(2): 1-2. NRCBL: 18.1.

Drazen, Jeffrey M. Volunteers at risk [editorial]. *New England Journal of Medicine* 2006 September 7; 355(10): 1060-1061. NRCBL: 18.1.

Dresser, Rebecca. Private-sector research ethics: marketing or good conflicts management? The 2005 John L. Conley Lecture on Medical Ethics. *Theoretical Medicine and Bioethics* 2006; 27(2): 115-139. NRCBL: 18.1; 9.7; 1.3.2; 1.3.9; 5.3.

Dresser, Rebecca; Jansen, Lynn A. Protection of human subjects and scientific progress: can the two be reconciled? [letter and reply]. *Hastings Center Report* 2006 January-February; 36(1): 7, 9. NRCBL: 18.1. Comments: Lynn A. Jansen. A closer look at the bad deal trial. Hastings Center Report 2005 September-October; 35(5): 29- 36.

Faust, Halley S.; Orentlicher, David. Protection of human subjects and scientific progress: can the two be reconciled? [letter and reply]. *Hastings Center Report* 2006 January-February; 36(1): 5-6, 8- 9. NRCBL: 18.1. Comments: David Orentlicher. Making research a requirement of treatment. Hastings Center Report 2005 September-October; 35(5): 20-28.

Frinsina, Michael E. Medical ethics in military biomedical research. *In:* Beam, Thomas E.; Sparacino, Linette R.; Pellegrino, Edmund D.; Hartle, Anthony E.; Howe, Edmund G., eds. Military Medical Ethics. Volume 2. Washington, DC: TMM Publications, Borden Institute, Walter Reed Army Medical Center; 2003: 533-561. NRCBL: 18.1; 18.5.8; 1.3.5; 18.5.3.

Gerrish, Kate. Being a 'marginal native': dilemmas of the participant observer. *Nurse Researcher* 1997 Autumn; 5(1): 25-34. NRCBL: 18.1; 4.1.3; 7.1. SC: em.

Glass, Kathleen Cranley; Orentlicher, David. Protection of human subjects and scientific progress: can the two be reconciled? [letter and reply]. *Hastings Center Report* 2006 January-February; 36(1): 4, 8-9. NRCBL: 18.1; 18.5.1. Comments: David Orentlicher. Making research a requirement of treatment. Hastings Center Report 2005 September- October; 35(5): 20-28.

Goel, Ashish. Ethical issues in international research, Harvard School of Public Health, Boston, USA, 13-17 June 2005. *National Medical Journal of India* 2005 July-August; 18(4): 209. NRCBL: 18.1; 1.3.9; 7.3.

Grady, Christine. Ethical principles in clinical research. *In:* Gallin, John I., ed. Principles and Practice of Clinical Research. San Diego, CA: Academic Press; 2002: 15-26. NRCBL: 18.1.

Grady, Christine. Ethics of vaccine research. *In:* Iltis, Ana Smith, ed. Research Ethics. New York: Routledge, 2006: 22-31. NRCBL: 18.1; 9.7.

Grady, Christine; Dickert, Neal; Jawetz, Tom; Gensler, Gary; Emanuel, Ezekiel. An analysis of U.S. practices of paying research participants. *Contemporary Clinical Trials* 2005 June; 26(3): 365-375. NRCBL: 18.1; 9.3.1. SC: em.

Green, Lawrence W. Ethics and community-based participatory research: commentary on Minkler. *Health Education and Behavior* 2004 December; 31(6): 698-701. NRCBL: 18.1; 18.2; 18.5.1; 18.6.

Griffiths, Pauline. Being a research participant: the nurse's ethical and legal rights. *British Journal of Nursing* 2006 April 13-26; 15(7): 386-390. NRCBL: 18.1; 7.1; 8.4; 18.3. SC: le.

Hochhauser, Mark. Paying for research related injuries in the US [letter]. *BMJ: British Medical Journal* 2006 March 11; 332(7541): 610. NRCBL: 18.1; 9.3.1; 18.3. SC: le. Identifiers: United States.

Hodgson, Helen. Giving the guinea-pigs a voice. *Twentieth Century* 1963 Summer; 172: 110-111. NRCBL: 18.1; 9.7; 8.1. Identifiers: United Kingdom (Great Britain).

Illes, Judy; Kirschen, Matthew P.; Edwards, Emmeline; Stanford, L.R.; Bandettini, Peter; Cho, Mildred K.; Ford, Paul J.; Glover, Gary H.; Kulynych, Jennifer; Macklin, Ruth; Michael, Daniel B.; Wolf, Susan M. Incidental findings in brain imaging research. *Science* 2006 February 10; 311(5762): 783-784. NRCBL: 18.1; 17.1.

Iltis, Ana Smith. Human subjects research: ethics and compliance. *In:* Iltis, Ana Smith, ed. Research Ethics. New York: Routledge, 2006: 1-21. NRCBL: 18.1.

Inglis, Brian. Guinea pig revolution in medical morality. *Twentieth Century* 1962 Winter; 171: 102-109. NRCBL: 18.1; 9.7. Identifiers: United Kingdom (Great Britain).

King, Nancy M.P.; Orentlicher, David. Protection of human subjects and scientific progress: can the two be reconciled? [letter and reply]. *Hastings Center Report* 2006 January-February; 36(1): 6-7, 8- 9. NRCBL: 18.1; 9.5.1; 18.3. Comments: David Orentlicher. Making research a requirement of treatment. Hastings Center Report 2005 September- October; 35(5): 20-28.

Kolata, Gina. Medicare says it will pay, but patients say "no thanks". *New York Times* 2006 March 3; p. C1, C4. NRCBL: 18.1; 8.3.4; 9.3.1; 9.5.2. SC: po.

Laurence, Desmond R. Compensation for non-negligent harm in trials remains shaky [letter]. *BMJ: British Medical Journal* 2006 February 25; 332(7539): 489-490. NRCBL: 18.1; 9.3.1.

Leib, Alden M.; Kowalski, Charles J. Human histological research: is it necessary? Humane? Ethical? *Journal of Periodontology* 2005 July; 76(7): 1207-1210. NRCBL: 18.1; 1.3.9; 9.5.1; 18.2.

Lewens, T. Distinguishing treatment from research: a functional approach. *Journal of Medical Ethics* 2006 July; 32(7): 424-429. NRCBL: 18.1; 8.1. SC: an.
Abstract: The best way to distinguish treatment from research is by their functions. This mode of distinction fits well with the basic ethical work that needs to be carried out. The distinction needs to serve as an ethical flag, highlighting areas in which the goals of doctors and patients are more likely than usual to diverge. The distinction also allows us to illuminate and understand some otherwise puzzling elements of debates on research ethics: it shows the peculiarity of exclusive conceptions of the distinction between research and treatment; it allows us to frame questions about therapeutic obligations in the research context, and it allows us to consider whether there may be research obligations in the therapeutic context.

Lindsay, Ronald A. Role-differentiated morality: the need to consider institutions, not just individuals. *American Journal of Bioethics* 2006 July-August; 6(4): 70-72. NRCBL: 18.1; 7.2; 8.1. Identifiers: comment on Winston Chiong. The real problem with equipoise. American Journal of Bioethics 2006 July-August; 6(4): 37-47.

Long, Jeffrey C. Commentary: an overview of human subjects research in biological anthropology. *In:* Turner, Trudy R. ed. Biological Anthropology and Ethics: From Repatriation to Genetic Identity. Albany, NY: State University of New York Press; 2005: 275-279. NRCBL: 18.1; 15.1.

Macklin, Ruth. The Belmont principle of justice: an idea whose time has come. *APA Newsletters: Newsletter on Philosophy and Medicine* 2006 Spring; 05(2): 4-5. NRCBL: 18.1; 1.1; 9.7; 9.5.6.

Manca, Donna P.; Maher, Peggy; Gallant, Roseanne. Ethical concerns in community practice research. Common concerns encountered by the Alberta family practice research network [editorial]. *Canadian Family Physician* 2006 March; 52: 288-289, 296-298. NRCBL: 18.1; 9.1.

Markman, Maurie. Assuring the ethical conduct of clinical cancer trials in the developing world. *Cancer* 2006 January 1; 106(1): 1-3. NRCBL: 18.1; 21.1.

Marron, Jonathan M.; Siegler, Mark. Ethical issues in innovative colorectal surgery. *Diseases of the Colon and Rectum* 2005 June; 48(6): 1109-1113. NRCBL: 18.1; 9.5.1. SC: cs.

Miller, Franklin G.; Wendler, David. The relevance of empirical research in bioethics. *Schizophrenia Bulletin* 2006 January; 32(1): 37-41. NRCBL: 18.1; 1.1. SC: em.

Miller, P.B.; Weijer, C. Trust based obligations of the state and physician-research to patient subjects. *Journal of Medical Ethics* 2006 September; 32(9): 542-547. NRCBL: 18.1; 8.1. SC: an.

Abstract: When may a physician enroll a patient in clinical research? An adequate answer to this question requires clarification of trust-based obligations of the state and the physician-researcher respectively to the patient-subject. The state relies on the voluntarism of patient-subjects to advance the public interest in science. Accordingly, it is obligated to protect the agent-neutral interests of patient-subjects through promulgating standards that secure these interests. Component analysis is the only comprehensive and systematic specification of regulatory standards for benefit-harm evaluation by research ethics committees (RECs). Clinical equipoise, a standard in component analysis, ensures the treatment arms of a randomised control trial are consistent with competent medical care. It thus serves to protect agent-neutral welfare interests of the patient-subject. But REC review occurs prior to enrolment, highlighting the independent responsibility of the physician-researcher to protect the agent-relative welfare interests of the patient-subject. In a novel interpretation of the duty of care, we argue for a "clinical judgment principle" which requires the physician-researcher to exercise judgment in the interests of the patient-subject taking into account evidence on treatments and the patient-subject's circumstances.

Minkler, Meredith. Ethical challenges for the "outside" researcher in community-based participatory research. *Health Education and Behavior* 2004 December; 31(6): 684-697. NRCBL: 18.1; 18.2; 18.5.1; 18.6.

Montgomery, John H.; Perlis, Roy H.; Nierenberg, Andrew A. Industry funding and author-industry affiliation in clinical trials in psychiatry [letter and reply]. *American Journal of Psychiatry* 2006 June; 163(6): 1110-1111. NRCBL: 18.1; 5.3; 17.1; 9.3.1.

Murff, Harvey J.; Pichert, James W.; Byrne, Daniel W.; Hedstrom, Christa; Black, Margo; Churchill, Larry; Speroff, Ted. IRB: Research participants safety and systems factors in general clinical research centers. *Ethics and Human Research* 2006 November-December; 28(6): 8-14. NRCBL: 18.1; 18.2. SC: em.

Niu, Huei-Chih. Human subject research — ethical and legal approaches for compensation for research induced injury in Taiwan. *In:* Sang-yong, Song; Young-Mo, Koo; Macer, Darryl R.J., eds. Asian Bioethics in the 21st Century. Christchurch, NZ: Eubios Ethics Institute, 2002: 6-15. NRCBL: 18.1; 9.3.1. SC: le. Conference: Proceedings of the Asian Bioethics Conference (ABC4), held 22-25 November 2002 in Seoul, South Korea.

Orton, Colin; Marshall, Christopher; Hendee, William R. Results of publicly-funded scientific research should be immediately available without cost to the public [editorial]. *Medical Physics* 2005 November; 32(11): 3231-3233. NRCBL: 18.1; 1.3.5; 9.3.1; 9.2.

Paradiso, Angelo; Bruno, Michele; Cicoria, Onofrio; Digennaro, Maria; Longo, Salvatore; Rinaldi, Michele; Schittulli, Francesco. Analysis of the reasons for accepting or declining participation in genetic research for breast cancer: a hospital-based population study. *Tumori* 2004 July-August; 90(4): 435-436. NRCBL: 18.1; 15.3. SC: em. Identifiers: Italy.

NRCBL: National Reference Center for Bioethics Literature Classification Scheme   See inside front cover for terms.

281

Pluhar, Evelyn B. Experimentation on humans and nonhumans. *Theoretical Medicine and Bioethics* 2006; 27(4): 333-355. NRCBL: 18.1; 1.1; 22.1. SC: an.

Abstract: In this article, I argue that it is wrong to conduct any experiment on a nonhuman which we would regard as immoral were it to be conducted on a human, because such experimentation violates the basic moral rights of sentient beings. After distinguishing the rights approach from the utilitarian approach, I delineate basic concepts. I then raise the classic "argument from marginal cases" against those who support experimentation on nonhumans but not on humans. After next replying to six important objections against that argument, I contend that moral agents are logically required to accord basic moral rights to every sentient being. I conclude by providing criteria for distinguishing ethical from unethical experimentation.

Rigby, Heather; Fernandez, Conrad V. Providing research results to study participants: support versus practice of researchers presenting at the American Society of Hematology annual meeting. *Blood* 2005 August 15; 106(4): 1199-1202. NRCBL: 18.1; 8.1. SC: em.

Ripley, Elizabeth B.D. A review of paying research participants: it's time to move beyond the ethical debate. *Journal of Empirical Research on Human Research Ethics* 2006 December; 1(4): 9-20. NRCBL: 18.1; 9.3.1; 18.2. SC: rv.

Ripley, Elizabeth B.D.; Macrina, Frank L.; Markowitz, Monika. Paying clinical research participants: one institution's research ethics committees' perspective. *Journal of Empirical Research on Human Research Ethics* 2006 December; 1(4): 37-44. NRCBL: 18.1; 9.3.1. SC: em.

Risch, Neil; Burchard, Esteban; Ziv, Elad; Tang, Hua. Categorization of humans in biomedical research: genes, race and disease. *Genome Biology* 2002 July 1; 3(7): 1-11. NRCBL: 18.1; 15.11; 7.1.

Rollin, Bernard E. Ethics and research on human beings. *In his:* Science and Ethics. New York: Cambridge University Press; 2006: 66-98. NRCBL: 18.1.

Sieber, Joan E. The evolution of best ethical practices in human research [editorial]. *Journal of Empirical Research on Human Research Ethics* 2006 March; 1(1): 1. NRCBL: 18.1; 1.3.7.

Singapore. Bioethics Advisory Committee. Human Genetics Sub-Committee [HGS]. Human Tissue Research. Consultation Paper. Helios, Singapore: Bioethics Advisory Committee, 2002 February 27; 22 p. [Online]. Accessed: http://www.bioethics-singapore.org/resources/pdf/Human%20Tissue%20Research%20Consultation.pdf [2006 May 1]. NRCBL: 18.1; 19.5; 8.3.1; 8.4.

Spence, Des. Research for profit [letter]. *BMJ: British Medical Journal* 2006 May 13; 332(7550): 1155-1156. NRCBL: 18.1; 7.3; 9.3.1. Identifiers: United Kingdom.

Spike, Jeffrey P. Human subjects research. *In:* Mitcham, Carl, ed. Encyclopedia of Science, Technology, and Ethics. Farmington Hills, MI: Thomson/Gale, 2005: 960-963. NRCBL: 18.1; 2.2; 18.2.

Steinbrook, Robert. Compensation for injured research subjects. *New England Journal of Medicine* 2006 May 4; 354(18): 1871-1873. NRCBL: 18.1; 9.3.1; 9.6.

Straus, Stephen E. Unanticipated risk in clinical research. *In:* Gallin, John I., ed. Principles and Practice of Clinical Research. San Diego, CA: Academic Press; 2002: 105-122. NRCBL: 18.1; 5.2.

Sugarman, Jeremy; Levine, Carol; Barnes, Michael R.; Holbrook, Joanna; Feild, John A.; Searls, David B.; Sanseau, Philippe; Ohresser, Marc; Olive, Daniel; Vanhove, Bernard; Watier, Hervé; Focosi, Daniele. Risk in drug trials [correspondence]. *Lancet* 2006 December 23-2007 January 5; 368(9554): 2205-2206. NRCBL: 18.1. Identifiers: TGN1412.

Swerdlow, Paul S. Use of humans in biomedical experimentation. *In:* Macrina, Francis L. Scientific Integrity: Text and Cases in Responsible Conduct of Research. 3rd ed. Washington, DC: ASM Press; 2005: 91-126. NRCBL: 18.1; 18.2.

Thornton, Hazel. "Empowering" patient choice about participation in trials? *In:* Duley, Lelia; Farrell, Barbara, eds. Clinical Trials. London: BMJ Books; 2002: 121-128. NRCBL: 18.1.

Toffoli, Luisa; Rudge, Trudy. Organizational predicaments: ethical conditions for nursing research. *Journal of Advanced Nursing* 2006 December; 56(6): 600-606. NRCBL: 18.1; 4.1.3; 7.1.

Turner, D.D. Just another drug? A philosophical assessment of randomised controlled studies on intercessory prayer. *Journal of Medical Ethics* 2006 August; 32(8): 487-490. NRCBL: 18.1; 1.2; 1.3.9. SC: an.

Abstract: The empirical results from recent randomised controlled studies on remote, intercessory prayer remain mixed. Several studies have, however, appeared in prestigious medical journals, and it is believed by many researchers, including apparent sceptics, that it makes sense to study intercessory prayer as if it were just another experimental drug treatment. This assumption is challenged by (1) discussing problems posed by the need to obtain the informed consent of patients participating in the studies; (2) pointing out that if the intercessors are indeed conscientious religious believers, they should subvert the studies by praying for patients randomised to the control groups; and (3) showing that the studies in questionnaire characterised by an internal philosophical tension because the intercessors and the scientists must take incompatible views of what is going on: the intercessors must take a causation-first view, whereas the scientists must take a correlation-first view. It therefore makes no ethical or methodological sense to study remote, intercessory prayer as if it were just another drug.

United States. Department of Health and Human Services [DHHS]. Office of the Secretary. Protection of Hu-

---

man Subjects; Compensating for Research Injuries; Request for Comments on Report of the President's Commission for the Study of Ethical Problems in Medicine and Biomedical and Behavioral Research. *Federal Register* 1982 November 23; 47(226): 52880-52930. NRCBL: 18.1. Identifiers: compensating research subjects.

Wadman, Meredith. The quiet rise of the clinical contractor. *Nature* 2006 May 4; 441(7089): 22-23. NRCBL: 18.1; 9.3.1; 9.7.

Weijer, Charles. Clinical trials. *In:* Mitcham, Carl, ed. Encyclopedia of Science, Technology, and Ethics. Farmington Hills, MI: Thomson/Gale, 2005: 347-350. NRCBL: 18.1; 2.2.

While, Alison. First steps towards ethical research. *Practice Nurse* 1998 February 20; 15(3): 135-138. NRCBL: 18.1; 9.8; 4.1.3; 2.1. Identifiers: United Kingdom (Great Britain).

Whiteman, David C.; Clutton, Cathy; Hill, David. Australian public's view on privacy and health research [letter]. *BMJ: British Medical Journal* 2006 May 27; 332(7552): 1274. NRCBL: 18.1; 8.4. SC: em.

Williams, Anne. Ethics and action research. *Nurse Researcher* 1995 March; 2(3): 49-59. NRCBL: 18.1; 18.3; 8.4; 4.1.3.

Wood, Alastair J.J.; Darbyshire, Janet. Injury to research volunteer — the clinical-research nightmare. *New England Journal of Medicine* 2006 May 4; 354(18): 1869-1871. NRCBL: 18.1; 18.2.

HUMAN EXPERIMENTATION/ ETHICS COMMITTEES AND POLICY GUIDELINES

Appendix: submission made by FoA to the expert working group studying the TGN1412 incident. *ATLA: Alternatives to Laboratory Animals* 2006 June; 34(3): 354-356. NRCBL: 18.2. Identifiers: Focus on Alternatives.

Drugs tests on trial [news]. *Nature* 2006 April 20; 440(7087): 970. NRCBL: 18.2. Identifiers: United Kingdom (Great Britain).

Editorial. *Bulletin of Medical Ethics* 2005 December-2006 January; (212): 1. NRCBL: 18.2; 18.6. Identifiers: United Kingdom (Great Britain); research ethics committees.

Reconsidering ethics in research. *Protecting Human Subjects* 2006 Spring; (13): 6. NRCBL: 18.2; 21.1.

Research agenda. *Journal of Empirical Research on Human Research Ethics* 2006 September; 1(3): 9-10. NRCBL: 18.2; 18.3; 18.4; 18.6.

Research ethics committees; good clinical practice; advance directives [policy statements]. *Bulletin of Medical Ethics* 2005 June-July; (209): 8-11. NRCBL: 18.2; 20.5.4. Identifiers: United Kingdom (Great Britain).

Research in developing countries. *Protecting Human Subjects* 2006 Spring; (13): 7. NRCBL: 18.2; 21.1.

University's defense against noncompliance charges begin to fail [case study]. *Human Research Report* 2006 June; 21(6): 6-7. NRCBL: 18.2; 1.3.3; 18.5.5; 18.6.

Addison, G. Michael. Ethics committees: we all need research ethics committees [letter]. *BMJ: British Medical Journal* 2006 March 25; 332(7543): 730. NRCBL: 18.2.

Aita, Marilyn; Richer, Marie-Claire. Essentials of research ethics for healthcare professionals. *Nursing and Health Sciences* 2005 June; 7(2): 119-125. NRCBL: 18.2; 1.1; 2.1.

Aksoy, Nurten; Aksoy, Sahin. Research ethics committees in Turkey. *In:* Sang-yong, Song; Young-Mo, Koo; Macer, Darryl R.J., eds. Asian Bioethics in the 21st Century. Christchurch, NZ: Eubios Ethics Institute, 2002: 28-30. NRCBL: 18.2. Conference: Proceedings of the Asian Bioethics Conference (ABC4), held 22-25 November 2002 in Seoul, South Korea.

Alpert, Joseph S.; Shine, Kenneth I.; Adams, Robert J.; Antman, Elliott M.; Kavey, Rae Ellen W.; Friedman, Lawrence; Frye, Robert L.; Harrington, Robert A.; Korn, David; Merz, Jon F.; Ofili, Elizabeth. Task force 1: the ACCF and AHA codes of conduct in human subjects research. *Journal of the American College of Cardiology* 2004 October 19; 44(8): 1724-1728. NRCBL: 18.2; 18.3; 6. Identifiers: American College of Cardiology Foundation; American Heart Association. Conference: ACCF/AHA Consensus Conference Report on Professionalism and Ethics; Heart House, Bethesda, Maryland; 2-3 June 2004.

Al-Shahi, Rustam. Research ethics committees in the UK — the pressure is now on research and development departments. *Journal of the Royal Society of Medicine* 2005 October; 98(10): 444-447. NRCBL: 18.2.

American Society of Clinical Oncology [ASCO]. American Society of Clinical Oncology policy statement: oversight of clinical research. *Journal of Clinical Oncology* 2003 June 15; 21(12): 2377-2386. NRCBL: 18.2; 9.5.1.

American Society of Gene Therapy [ASGT]. American Society of Gene Therapy establishes ethical policy to guide clinical trials [policy statement]. Milwaukee, WI: American Society of Gene Therapy [ASGT], 2000 April 13. 2 p. [Online]. Accessed: http://www.asgt.org/position_statements/ethical_policy.html [27 July 2006]. NRCBL: 18.2; 15.4; 1.3.9.

American Society of Human Genetics [ASHG]; Francke, Uta. Response to National Bioethics Advisory Commission [NBAC] on the ethical issues and policy concerns surrounding research using human biological materials [letter]. Bethesda, MD: American Society of Human Genetics, 1999 January 15. 4 p. [Online]. Accessed:

NRCBL: National Reference Center for Bioethics Literature Classification Scheme   See inside front cover for terms.

283

http://genetics.faseb.org/genetics/ashg/pubs/policy/ pol-33.htm [26 July 2006]. NRCBL: 18.2; 15.1; 2.4. Comments: National Bioethics Advisory Commission draft document "The Use of Human Biological Materials in Research: Ethical Issues and Policy Guidance." The final report is online and accessible at http://bioethics.georgetown.edu/nbac/pubs.html.

Anderson, D.K.; Beattie, M.; Blesch, A.; Bresnahan, J.; Bunge, M.; Dietrich, D.; Dietz, V.; Dobkin, B.; Fawcett, J.; Fehlings, M.; Fischer, I.; Grossman, R.; Guest, J.; Hagg, T.; Hall, E.D.; Houle, J.; Kleitman, N.; McDonald, J.; Murray, M.; Privat, A.; Reier, P.; Steeves, J.; Steward, O.; Tetzlaff, W.; Tuszynski, M.H.; Waxman, S.G.; Whittemore, S.; Wolpaw, J.; Young, W.; Zheng B. Recommended guidelines for studies of human subjects with spinal cord injury. *Spinal Cord* 2005 August; 43(8): 453-458. NRCBL: 18.2.

Anderson, Emily E. A qualitative study of non-affiliated, non-scientist institutional review board members. *Accountability in Research* 2006 April-June; 13(2): 135-155. NRCBL: 18.2; 9.6. SC: em.

Abstract: In addition to outlining criteria for the approval of human subjects research, federal regulations provide guidance regarding local institutional review boards (IRB) membership. IRBs are mandated to include "at least one member whose primary concerns are in nonscientific areas" and "at least one member who is not otherwise affiliated with the institution." Often a single individual serves both of these roles simultaneously. Although there have been calls for increased representation of lay community members in IRBs, little is known regarding their experiences or their perceptions of human subject protections and the IRB process. Using an ethnographic interview approach, this study seeks to gain a perspective from non-affiliated, non-scientist (NA/NS) IRB members about the process in which they participated. Findings suggest a need for clarification regarding whom NA/NS IRB members represent. They also suggest that NA/NS IRB members' experiences could be improved by an increased show of respect from the IRB chair, other members, and staff; efforts to make participation more convenient for these volunteer members; and training tailored specifically to NA/NS members. Further research on this important and understudied topic is needed to determine best practice and policy recommendations.

Anderson, James A. The ethics and science of placebo-controlled trials: assay sensitivity and the Duhem-Quine thesis. *Journal of Medicine and Philosophy* 2006 February; 31(1): 65-81. NRCBL: 18.2. SC: an; em.

Abstract: The principle of clinical equipoise requires that, aside from certain exceptional cases, second generation treatments ought to be tested against standard therapy. In violation of this principle, placebo-controlled trials (PCTs)continue to be used extensively in the development and licensure of second-generation treatments. This practice is typically justified by appeal to methodological arguments that purport to demonstrate that active- controlled trials (ACTs) are methodologically flawed. Foremost among these arguments is the so called assay sensitivity argument. In this paper, I take a closer look at this argument. Following Duhem, I argue that all trials, placebo-controlled or not, rely on external information for their meaningful interpretation. Pending non-circular empirical evidence that we can trust the findings of PCTs to a greater degree than the findings of ACTs, I conclude that the assay sensitivity argument fails to demonstrate that placebo-controlled trials are preferable, methodologically or otherwise, to active-controlled trials. Contrary to the intentions of its authors, the fundamental lesson taught by the assay sensitivity argument is Duhemian: the validity of all clinical trials depends on external information.

Anderson, Warwick P.; Cordner, Christopher D.; Breen, Kerry J. Strengthening Australia's framework for research oversight. All stakeholders should contribute to enhancing Australia's guidelines for ethical research[editorial]. *Medical Journal of Australia* 2006 March 20; 184(6): 261-263. NRCBL: 18.2; 18.6.

Angell, E.; Sutton, A.J.; Windridge, K.; Dixon-Woods, M. Consistency in decision making by research ethics committees: a controlled comparison. *Journal of Medical Ethics* 2006 November; 32(11): 662-664. NRCBL: 18.2. SC: em. Identifiers: United Kingdom (Great Britain).

Abstract: There has been longstanding interest in the consistency of decisions made by research ethics committees (RECs) in the UK, but most of the evidence has come from single studies submitted to multiple committees. A systematic comparison was carried out of the decisions made on 18 purposively selected applications, each of which was reviewed independently by three different RECs in a single strategic health authority. Decisions on 11 applications were consistent, but disparities were found among RECs on decisions on seven applications. An analysis of the agreement between decisions of RECs yielded an overall measure of agreement of kappa = 0.286 (95% confidence interval -0.06 to 0.73), indicating a level of agreement that, although probably better than chance, may be described as "slight". The small sample size limits the robustness of these findings. Further research on reasons for inconsistencies in decision making between RECs, and on the importance of such inconsistencies for a range of arguments, is needed.

Appelbaum, Paul S.; Lidz, Charles W. Clinical ethics versus clinical research. *American Journal of Bioethics* 2006 July-August; 6(4): 53-55. NRCBL: 18.2; 1.3.9; 2.3. Comments: Winston Chiong. The real problem with equipoise. American Journal of Bioethics 2006 July-August; 6(4): 37-47.

Apseloff, Glen. HIV testing in early clinical trials: who should decide whether it is warranted? *Journal of Clinical Pharmacology* 2002 June; 42(6): 601-604. NRCBL: 18.2; 9.5.6; 9.1.

Ar-Rashid, Harun. Regional perspectives in research ethics: a report from Bangladesh. *Eastern Mediterranean Health Journal* 2006; 12(Supplement 1): S66-S72 [Online]. Accessed: http://www.emro.who.int/publications/ EMHJ/12_S/PDF/10.pdf [2007 January 4]. NRCBL: 18.2; 18.6; 21.1. Note: Abstract in French and Arabic.

Ashcroft, Richard E. Ethics of randomised controlled trials—not yet time to give up on equipoise. *Arthritis Research and Therapy* 2004; 6(6): 237-239. NRCBL: 18.2.

Atkinson, Maggie. A response to the parliamentary sub-committee's report and recommendations. *Canadian HIV/AIDS Policy and Law Newsletter* 1997 Spring; 3(2-3): 39-40. NRCBL: 18.2; 9.7; 9.2.

Atkinson, Maggie; Lemmens, Trudo. Compassionate access to investigational therapies: part II. *Canadian HIV/AIDS Policy and Law Newsletter* 1997 Spring; 3(2-3): 38. NRCBL: 18.2; 9.7; 9.2.

Bankowski, Zbigniew; Gutteridge, Frank. Medical ethics and human research. *World Health* 1982 November: 10-13. NRCBL: 18.2; 18.6; 21.1.

Barnes, Graeme; Williamson, Bob. Privacy, safety and community health [letter and reply]. *Journal of Paediatrics and Child Health* 2004 May-June; 40(5- 6): 326-328. NRCBL: 18.2; 18.5.2; 18.3.

Bastian, Hilda. Consumer and researcher collaboration in trials: filling the gaps [editorial]. *Clinical Trials* 2005; 2(1): 3-4. NRCBL: 18.2; 8.1.

Beauchamp, Tom L. Assessing the Belmont Report. *APA Newsletters: Newsletter on Philosophy and Medicine* 2006 Spring; 05(2): 2-3. NRCBL: 18.2.

Beskow, Laura M.; Sandler, Robert S.; Weiberger, Morris. Research recruitment through U.S. central cancer registries: balancing privacy and scientific issues. *American Journal of Public Health* 2006 November; 96(11): 1920-1926. NRCBL: 18.2; 8.4.

Abstract: Cancer registries are a valuable resource for recruiting participants for public health-oriented research, although such recruitment raises potentially competing concerns about patient privacy and participant accrual. We surveyed US central cancer registries about their policies for research contact with patients, and results showed substantial variation. The strategy used most frequently (37.5% of those that allowed patient contact), which was among the least restrictive, was for investigators to notify patients' physicians and then contact patients with an opt-out approach. The most restrictive strategy was for registry staff to obtain physician permission and contact patients with an opt-in approach. Population-based studies enhance cancer control efforts, and registry policies can affect researchers' ability to conduct such studies. Further discussion about balanced recruitment approaches that protect patient privacy and encourage beneficial research is needed.

Bhat, S.B.; Hegde, T.T. Ethical international research on human subjects research in the absence of local institutional review boards. *Journal of Medical Ethics* 2006 September; 32(9): 535-536. NRCBL: 18.2; 18.5.9.

Abstract: International health-related research on human subjects entails unique ethical responsibilities and difficulties. Often, these difficulties are augmented by the lack of a local ethical review infrastructure. In a recent cross-national study conducted by us, three critical components of ethical regulation were identified—external oversight, local oversight and subject involvement—and integrated into the study design. These three concepts are outlined and established as an important aspect of ensuring ethical coherence in the local context, particularly when reviews by the local institutional review boards cannot practically be obtained. The three levels of ethical oversight identified are suggested to be the framework within which future field studies on human subjects are developed and a standard for maintaining ethical rigorousness in research on humans.

Bhogal, Nirmala; Combes, Robert. An update on TGN1412. *ATLA: Alternatives to Laboratory Animals* 2006 June; 34(3): 351-353. NRCBL: 18.2.

Blader, Joseph C. Can keeping clinical trial participants blind to their study treatment adversely affect subsequent care? *Contemporary Clinical Trials* 2005 June; 26(3): 290-299. NRCBL: 18.2; 9.8.

Bland, J. Martin. Untreated controls are wrong when proved treatment exists [letter]. *BMJ: British Medical Journal* 2006 April 1; 332(7544): 796. NRCBL: 18.2.

Bombardier, Claire; Laine, Loren; Burgos-Vargas, Ruben; Davis, Barry; Day, Richard; Ferraz, Marcos Bosi; Hawkey, Christopher J.; Hochberg, Marc C.; Kvien, Tore K.; Schnitzer, Thomas J.; Weaver, Arthur; Reicin, Alise; Shapiro, Deborah. Response to expression of concern regarding VIGOR study [letters]. *New England Journal of Medicine* 2006 March 16; 354(11): 1196-1199. NRCBL: 18.2; 1.3.9; 1.3.7. Identifiers: Vioxx Gastrointestinal Outcome Research(VIGOR).

Bong-Polec, Patrycja; Luków, Pawel. Research ethics committees and personal data protection in Poland. *In:* Beyleveld, D.; Townend, D.; Wright, J., eds. Research Ethics Committees, Data Protection and Medical Research in European Countries. Hants, England; Burlington, VT: Ashgate; 2005: 177-187. NRCBL: 18.2.

Boshier, A.; Shakir, S.A.W.; Telfer, P.; Behr, E.; Pakrashi, T.; Camm, A.J. The negative effect of red tape on research. *Pharmacoepidemiology and Drug Safety* 2005 June; 14(6): 373-376. NRCBL: 18.2; 18.6.

Bower, Peter; King, Michael; Nazareth, Irwin; Lampe, Fiona; Sibbald, Bonnie. Patient preferences in randomised controlled trials: conceptual framework and implications for research. *Social Science and Medicine* 2005 August; 61(3): 685-695. NRCBL: 18.2; 18.3; 8.1. SC: em.

Brainard, Jeffrey. Study finds conflicts of interest on many research-review boards. *Chronicle of Higher Education* 2006 December 8; 53(16): A22. NRCBL: 18.2.

Brasel, Karen J. Research ethics primer. *Journal of Surgical Research* 2005 October; 128(2): 221-225. NRCBL: 18.2; 1.3.9; 18.3; 8.4; 22.2; 18.6.

Braunold, Gillian; Pringle, Mike; Eccles, Simon; Scott, Ian; Osborne, Susan; Stuttle, Barbara. Opting in or out of electronic patient records: national clinical leads of Connecting for Health respond [letter]. *BMJ: British Medical Journal* 2006 July 29; 333(7561): 261-262. NRCBL: 18.2; 1.3.12; 8.4. Identifiers: United Kingdom (Great Britain).

Briggle, Adam. Institutional review boards. *In:* Mitcham, Carl, ed. Encyclopedia of Science, Technology, and Ethics. Farmington Hills, MI: Thomson/Gale, 2005: 1024-1026. NRCBL: 18.2; 2.2.

NRCBL: National Reference Center for Bioethics Literature Classification Scheme   See inside front cover for terms.

285

Brion, Nathalie; Demarez, Jean-Paul.; Belorgey, Chantal. Committee for the protection of persons. *Therapie* 2005 July-August; 60(4): 319-328, 329-337. NRCBL: 18.2. SC: em. Identifiers: France. Note: Full text in English and French.

Brody, Howard. Are there three or four distinct types of medical practice? *American Journal of Bioethics* 2006 July-August; 6(4): 51-53. NRCBL: 18.2; 7.2; 1.3.9. Comments: Winston Chiong. The real problem with equipoise. American Journal of Bioethics 2006 July-August; 6(4): 37-47.

Brown, Joseph S.; Schonfeld, Toby L.; Gordon, Bruce G. "You may have already won. . .": an examination of the use of lottery payments in research [case study]. *IRB: Ethics and Human Research* 2006 January-February; 28(1): 12-16. NRCBL: 18.2; 1.1; 9.3.1; 18.3. SC: cs.

Bryant, John. What is the appropriate role of the trial statistician in preparing and presenting interim findings to an independent data monitoring committee in the U.S. Cancer Cooperative Group setting? *Statistics in Medicine* 2004 May 30; 23(10): 1507-1511. NRCBL: 18.2; 7.3; 9.3.1; 7.1. SC: an.

Bubien, Rosemary S. Practice or research — patient or participant: is there a difference? *Heart Rhythm* 2004 December; 1(6): 757-759. NRCBL: 18.2; 18.6; 9.7; 21.1.

Buchanan, D.R.; Miller, F.G. A public health perspective on research ethics. *Journal of Medical Ethics* 2006 December; 32(12): 729-733. NRCBL: 18.2; 9.1. SC: an.

Burke, Georgine S. Looking into the institutional review board: observations from both sides of the table. *Journal of Nutrition* 2005 April; 135(4): 921-924. NRCBL: 18.2. Conference: Symposium: Bioethics in Scientific Research: Conflicts between Subject's Equitable Access to Participate in Research and Current Regulations; 19 April 2004; Washington, D.C.; American Society for Nutritional Sciences.

Burris, Scott; Moss, Kathryn. U.S. health research review their ethics review boards: a qualitative study. *Journal of Empirical Research on Human Research Ethics* 2006 June; 1(2): 39-58. NRCBL: 18.2; 18.5. SC: em.

Burton, Thomas M. Amid alarm bells, a blood substitute keeps pumping; ten in trial have heart attacks, but data aren't published; FDA allows a new study; doctors' pleas are ignored. *Wall Street Journal* 2006 February 22; p. A1, A12. NRCBL: 18.2; 1.3.9; 19.4. SC: po.

Byrne, Margaret M.; Speckman, Jeanne; Getz, Ken; Sugarman, Jeremy. Variability in the costs of institutional review board oversight. *Academic Medicine* 2006 August; 81(8): 708-712. NRCBL: 18.2; 9.3.1. SC: em.

Califf, Robert M.; Nissen, Steven E.; DeMaria, Anthony N.; Ohman, Erik Magnus; Pitt, Bertram;

Willerson, James T.; Bilheimer, David W.; Cohn, Jay N.; Feigal, David W., Jr.; Hampson, Lindsay; Lorell, Beverly H.; Pepine, Carl J.; Popp, Richard L. Task force 2: investigator participation in clinical research. *Journal of the American College of Cardiology* 2004 October 19; 44(8): 1729-1736. NRCBL: 18.2; 1.3.7; 8.4; 9.3.1. Conference: ACCF/AHA Consensus Conference Report on Professionalism and Ethics; Heart House, Bethesda, Maryland; 2-3 June 2004.

Callen, Jeffrey P.; Robinson, June. Clinical trial registration — a step forward in providing transparency for the positive and negative results of clinical trials. *Archives of Dermatology* 2005 January; 141(1): 75. NRCBL: 18.2; 1.3.7.

Candilis, Philip J.; Lidz, Charles W.; Arnold, Robert M. The need to understand IRB deliberations. *IRB: Ethics and Human Research* 2006 January-February; 28(1): 1-5. NRCBL: 18.2. Identifiers: institutional research board.

Cekanauskaite, Asta; Gefenas, Eugenijus. Research ethics committees in Lithuania. *In:* Beyleveld, D.; Townend, D.; Wright, J., eds. Research Ethics Committees, Data Protection and Medical Research in European Countries. Hants, England; Burlington, VT: Ashgate; 2005: 141-147. NRCBL: 18.2.

Chalmers, Iain. From optimism to disillusion about commitment to transparency in the medico-industrial complex. *Journal of the Royal Society of Medicine* 2006 July; 99(7): 337-341. NRCBL: 18.2; 9.7; 1.3.7. SC: an.

Chan, An-Wen; Upshur, Ross; Singh, Jerome A.; Ghersi, Davina; Chapuis, François; Altman, Douglas G. Research protocols: waiving confidentiality for the greater good. *BMJ: British Medical Journal* 2006 May 6; 332(7549): 1086-1089. NRCBL: 18.2; 8.4; 5.3; 1.3.9; 1.3.7.

Chen, Donna T.; Worrall, B.B.; Brown, R.D., Jr.; Brott, T.G.; Kissela, B.M.; Olson, T.S.; Rich, S.S.; Meschia, J.F. The impact of privacy protections on recruitment in a multicenter stroke genetics study. *Neurology* 2005 February 22; 64(4): 721-724. NRCBL: 18.2; 8.4; 15.1. SC: em.

Chiong, Winston. Response to commentators on "The real problem with equipoise" [letter]. *American Journal of Bioethics [Online]* 2006 July-August; 6(4): W42-W45. NRCBL: 18.2; 8.1; 7.2.

Chiong, Winston. The real problem with equipoise. *American Journal of Bioethics* 2006 July-August; 6(4): 37-47. NRCBL: 18.2; 1.1; 8.1; 9.5.6; 18.5.9; 1.3.9; 7.2. SC: an. Identifiers: Immanuel Kant.

Cipolle, Christina L.; Cipolle, Robert J.; Strand, Linda M. Consistent standards in medication use: the need to care for patients from research to practice. *Journal of the American Pharmacists Association* 2006 March-April; 46(2):

205-212. NRCBL: 18.2; 1.1; 9.7; 9.8. Identifiers: Belmont Report; Food and Drug Administration; United States.

Clemens, Felicity; Elbourne, Diana; Darbyshire, Janet; Pocock, Stuart. Data monitoring in randomized controlled trials: surveys of recent practice and policies. *Clinical Trials* 2005; 2(1): 22-33. NRCBL: 18.2; 18.6. SC: em.

Cleophas, G.C.J.M.; Cleophas T.J. Clinical trials in jeopardy. *International Journal of Clinical Pharmacology and Therapeutics* 2003 February; 41(2): 51-55. NRCBL: 18.2; 9.7; 1.3.9.

Colman, Eric G. The Food and Drug Administration's Osteoporosis Guidance Document: past, present, and future. *Journal of Bone and Mineral Research* 2003 June; 18(6): 1125-1128. NRCBL: 18.2; 9.7; 18.5.1; 18.5.3.

Colt, Joanne S.; Wacholder, Sholom; Schwartz, Kendra; Davis, Faith; Graubard, Barry; Chow, Wong-Ho. Response rates in a case-control study: effect of disclosure of biologic sample collection in the initial contact letter. *Annals of Epidemiology* 2005 October; 15(9): 700-704. NRCBL: 18.2; 18.3; 7.1; 9.5.1. SC: em.

Colwell-Chanthaphonh, Chip. Self-governance, self-representation, self-determination and the questions of research ethics. *Science and Engineering Ethics* 2006 July; 12(3): 508-510. NRCBL: 18.2; 1.1. Comments: Doug Brugge and Mariam Missaghian. Protecting the Navajo people through tribal regulation of research. Science and Engineering Ethics 2006 July; 12(3): 491-507.

Cooper, Jeffrey A. Responsible conduct of radiology research Part III. Exemptions from regulatory requirements for human research. *Radiology* 2005 October; 237(1): 3-7. NRCBL: 18.2; 18.6.

Cottrell, Barbara. Working with research ethics: the role of advisory committees in community-based research. *Atlantis* 2001 Spring; 25(2): 22-30. NRCBL: 18.2; 18.5.1.

Curfman, Gregory D.; Morrissey, Stephen; Drazen, Jeffrey M. Expression of concern reaffirmed [editorial]. *New England Journal of Medicine* 2006 March 16; 354(11): 1193. NRCBL: 18.2; 1.3.9; 1.3.7.

Czarkowski, Marek. The protection of patients' rights in clinical trials. *Science and Engineering Ethics* 2006 January; 12(1): 131-138. NRCBL: 18.2; 6.

de Champlain, J.; Patenaude, J. Review of a mock research protocol in functional neuroimaging by Canadian research ethics boards. *Journal of Medical Ethics* 2006 September; 32(9): 530-534. NRCBL: 18.2; 17.1. SC: em.
  Abstract: To examine how research ethics boards (REBs) review research projects in emerging disciplines such as functional neuroimaging. DESIGN: To compare the criteria applied and the decisions reached by REBs that reviewed the same mock research protocol in functional neuroimaging. PARTICI-PANTS: 44 Canadian biomedical REBs, mostly working in public university or hospital settings. MAIN MEASURE-MENTS: The mock research protocol "The Neurobiology of Social Behavior" included several ethical issues operating at all three levels: personal, institutional and social. Data consisting of responses to closed questions were analysed quantitatively. Qualitative analysis of open-question responses used mixed classification. RESULTS: Similar criteria were used by most participating REBs. Yet the project was unconditionally approved by 3 REBs, approved conditionally by 10 and rejected by 30. CONCLUSIONS: The results point to the difficulty for REBs of reviewing all kinds of research projects, regardless of field, by relying on international and national norms framed in general terms and a possible variation between REBs in the interpretation of their mandate for the protection of research subjects.

DeMets, David L.; Fleming, Thomas R. The independent statistician for data monitoring committees. *Statistics in Medicine* 2004 May 30; 23(10): 1513-1517. NRCBL: 18.2; 7.3; 7.1.

DeMets, David; Califf, Robert; Dixon, Dennis; Ellenberg, Susan; Fleming, Thomas; Held, Peter; Julian, Desmond; Kaplan, Richard; Levine, Robert; Neaton, James; Packer, Milton; Pocock, Stuart; Rockhold, Frank; Seto, Belinda; Siegel, Jay; Snapinn, Steve; Stump, David; Temple, Robert; Whitley, Richard. Issues in regulatory guidelines for data monitoring committees. *Clinical Trials* 2004; 1(2): 162-169. NRCBL: 18.2; 18.6. SC: rv.

Dickson-Swift, Virginia; James, Erica L.; Kippen, Sandra. Do university ethics committees adequately protect public health researchers? *Australian and New Zealand Journal of Public Health* 2005 December; 29(6): 576-579, discussion 580-582. NRCBL: 18.2. SC: em.

Dinnett, Eleanor M.; Mungall, Moira M.B.; Gordon, Claire; Ronald, Elizabeth S.; Gaw, Allan. Offering results to research participants [letter]. *BMJ: British Medical Journal* 2006 March 4; 332(7540): 549-550. NRCBL: 18.2. SC: em. Identifiers: Scotland.

Dixon-Woods, Mary; Jackson, Clare; Windridge, Kate C.; Kenyon, Sara. Receiving a summary of the results of a trial: qualitative study of participants' views. *BMJ: British Medical Journal* 2006 January 28; 332(7535): 206-209. NRCBL: 18.2; 18.5.3. SC: em.

Doaga, Octavian. Bioethical review in Romania. *In:* Beyleveld, D.; Townend, D.; Wright, J., eds. Research Ethics Committees, Data Protection and Medical Research in European Countries. Hants, England; Burlington, VT: Ashgate; 2005: 215-220. NRCBL: 18.2.

Doll, Richard. The role of data monitoring committees. *In:* Duley, Lelia; Farrell, Barbara, eds. Clinical Trials. London: BMJ Books; 2002: 97-104. NRCBL: 18.2.

Douglas, Alison. New role for ethics committees [letter]. *New Zealand Medical Journal* 1993 December 8; 106(969): 528-529. NRCBL: 18.2; 18.3.

NRCBL: National Reference Center for Bioethics Literature Classification Scheme   See inside front cover for terms.

287

Dubler, Nancy Neveloff. Remaining faithful to the promises given: maintaining standards in changing times. *Seton Hall Law Review* 2002; 32(3): 563-572. NRCBL: 18.2; 18.3. Conference: Symposium: New Directions in Human Subject Research: Looking Beyond the Academic Medical Center; Seton Hall Law School; 2001 November; Seton Hall University Graduate School of Medical Education, American Society of Law, Medicine and Ethics.

Eichler, Margrit; Burke, Mary Anne. The BIAS FREE Framework: a new analytical tool for global health research. *Canadian Journal of Public Health* 2006 January-February; 97(1): 63-68. NRCBL: 18.2; 18.5.9; 18.6; 21.1. Identifiers: Africa.

Ellenberg, Susan S.; George, Stephen L. Should statisticians reporting to data monitoring committees be independent of the trial sponsor and leadership? *Statistics in Medicine* 2004 May 30; 23(10): 1503-1505. NRCBL: 18.2; 8.4; 7.1; 1.3.9; 9.7.

Evans, Emily L.; London, Alex John. Equipoise and the criteria for reasonable action. *Journal of Law, Medicine and Ethics* 2006 Summer; 34(2): 441-450. NRCBL: 18.2; 7.1; 8.1. SC: an.

Faulkner, Alison. Inclusive and empowering. *Mental Health Today* 2005 November; 31-33. NRCBL: 18.2; 18.5.9; 18.6.

Feczko, Josephy; Zarin, Deborah A.; Tse, Tony; Ide, Nicholas C.; Drazen, Jeffrey M.; Wood, Alastair J.J.; Haug, Charlotte; Gøtzsche, Peter C.; Schroeder, Torben V. Clinical trials report card [letter and replies]. *New England Journal of Medicine* 2006 March 30; 354(13): 1426-1429. NRCBL: 18.2; 9.7.

Felten, David L.; Vogt, Thomas; Gunsalus, C.K.; Bruner, Edward M.; Burbules, Nicholas C.; Dash, Leon; Finkin, Matthew; Goldberg, Joseph P.; Greenough, William T.; Miller, Gregory A.; Pratt, Michael G. IRBs: going too far or not far enough? [letters]. *Science* 2006 September 8; 313(5792): 1388-1389. NRCBL: 18.2. Identifiers: institutional review board (IRB).

Finn, Peter B. The negotiation and development of a clinical trial agreement. *Journal of Biolaw and Business* 2006; 9(2): 21-27. NRCBL: 18.2; 1.3.9; 8.4; 1.3.2.

Fitzgerald, D.A.; Isaacs, D.; Kemp, A. Scientific ethics committees: a user's guide. *Archives of Disease in Childhood* 2005 December; 90(12): 1249-1250. NRCBL: 18.2.

Fitzgerald, Maureen H.; Phillips, Paul A. Centralized and non-centralized ethics review: a five nation study. *Accountability in Research* 2006 January-March; 13(1): 47-74. NRCBL: 18.2; 18.6; 21.1. SC: em.

Abstract: The research ethics review process is now an inherent part of conducting research and a topic of much discussion. On the negative side it has been presented as cumbersome, expensive, time consuming, and potentially a system that does not adequately deal with the concerns it was set up to address. One common, but often controversial, proposal to address some of these concerns has been the institutionalization of centralized systems of review. This paper uses data on the review systems in place in five countries (Australia, Canada, New Zealand, the USA and the U.K.), some with and some without versions of centralized review, to explore issues related to centralization of the review process. It suggests that there are at least three types of systems (fully centralized, dual, and decentralized or multicommittee) in place; all are made up of two, interrelated components (the administrative and ethics review). We suggest that both components need to be considered in discussions about centralized review. Serious consideration of centralization of the administrative component may address many concerns. Centralization of the ethics review may provide a context that deals with other issues and may encourage reviews that more effectively focus on the ethical issues involved.

Fitzgerald, Maureen H.; Phillips, Paul A.; Yule, Elisa. The research ethics review process and ethics review narrative. *Ethics and Behavior* 2006; 16(4): 377-395. NRCBL: 18.2; 21.1; 7.1. SC: em. Identifiers: Australia; Canada; New Zealand; United Kingdom (Great Britain); United States.

Flum, David R. Interpreting surgical trials with subjective outcomes: avoiding unSPORTsmanlike conduct. *JAMA: The Journal of the American Medical Association* 2006 November 22-29; 296(20): 2483-2485. NRCBL: 18.2.

Frank, Samuel; Kieburtz, Karl; Holloway, Robert; Kim, Scott Y.H. What is the risk of sham surgery in Parkinson disease clinical trials? A review of published reports. *Neurology* 2005 October 11; 65(7): 1101-1103. NRCBL: 18.2; 18.5.1. SC: em.

Freedman, Benjamin. Compassionate access to experimental drugs and catastrophic rights. *Canadian HIV/AIDS Policy and Law Newsletter* 1996 October; 3(1): 44-46. NRCBL: 18.2; 9.7; 2.1.

Gaba, Aline. Face transplants and the difficulties of obtaining research approval. *Journal of Biolaw and Business* 2006; 9(1): 54-55. NRCBL: 18.2; 18.5.1; 19.1.

Garanis-Papadatos, Tina; Boukis, Dimitris. Research ethics committees in Greece. *In:* Beyleveld, D.; Townend, D.; Wright, J., eds. Research Ethics Committees, Data Protection and Medical Research in European Countries. Hants, England; Burlington, VT: Ashgate; 2005: 85-91. NRCBL: 18.2.

Garcia, Jo; Elbourne, Diana; Snowdon, Claire. Equipoise: a case study of the views of clinicians involved in two neonatal trials. *Clinical Trials* 2004; 1(2): 170-188. NRCBL: 18.2; 8.1; 18.5.2. SC: em. Identifiers: United Kingdom (Great Britain).

Gilbert, Donald L.; Buncher, C. Ralph. Assessment of scientific and ethical issues in two randomized clinical trial designs for patients with Tourette's syndrome: a model for studies of multiple neuropsychiatric diagnoses. *Journal of Neuropsychiatry and Clinical Neurosciences* 2005 Summer; 17(3): 324-332. NRCBL: 18.2; 17.1.

Giles, Jim. Warning flag for ethics boards [news]. *Nature* 2006 September 14; 443(7108): 127. NRCBL: 18.2. Identifiers: Canada.

Gilles, Kathy. Uncovering the relationship between IRBs and the HIPAA privacy rule. *Journal of AHIMA* 2004 November-December; 75(10): 48-49, 52, 55-56. NRCBL: 18.2; 8.4; 1.3.5; 18.6. Identifiers: institutional review boards; Health Insurance Portability and Accountability Act.

Glasa, Jozef; Miller, Jane. Research ethics committees in Slovakia. *In:* Beyleveld, D.; Townend, D.; Wright, J., eds. Research Ethics Committees, Data Protection and Medical Research in European Countries. Hants, England; Burlington, VT: Ashgate; 2005: 221-227. NRCBL: 18.2.

Godlee, Fiona. An international standard for disclosure of clinical trial information [editorial]. *BMJ: British Medical Journal* 2006 May 13; 332(7550): 1107-1108 [see correction in BMJ: British Medical Journal 2006 June 17; 332(7555): 1418]. NRCBL: 18.2; 18.1; 1.3.12.

Goldberg, David J. Dermatologic surgical research and the institutional review board. *Dermatologic Surgery* 2005 October; 31(10): 1317-1322. NRCBL: 18.2; 9.5.1.

Goodyear, Michael. Learning from the TGN1412 trial [editorial]. *BMJ: British Medical Journal* 2006 March 25; 332(7543): 677-678. NRCBL: 18.2; 18.5.1.

Goodyear, Michael D.E. A model clinical trials agreement [editorial]. *BMJ: British Medical Journal* 2006 November 25; 333(7578): 1083-1084. NRCBL: 18.2; 9.7. Identifiers: United Kingdom (Great Britain).

Goodyear, Michael D.E. Further lessons from the TGN1412 tragedy: new guidelines call for a change in the culture of research [editorial]. *BMJ: British Medical Journal* 2006 August 5; 333(7562): 270-271. NRCBL: 18.2; 18.5.1; 18.5 18.2. Identifiers: United Kingdom (Great Britain).

Grady, Christine. Payment of clinical research subjects. *Journal of Clinical Investigation* 2005 July; 115(7): 1681-1687. NRCBL: 18.2; 9.3.1; 18.5.1; 18.5.2.

Grady, Christine; Horstmann, Elizabeth; Sussman, Jeffrey S.; Hull, Sara Chandros. The limits of disclosure: what research subjects want to know about investigator financial interests. *Journal of Law, Medicine and Ethics* 2006 Fall; 34(3): 592-599. NRCBL: 18.2; 7.3; 18.3; 1.3.9. SC: em.

Abstract: Research participants' views about investigator financial interests were explored. Reactions ranged from concern to acceptance, indifference, and even encouragement. Although most wanted such information, some said it did not matter, was private, or was burdensome, and other factors were more important to research decisions. Very few said it would affect their research decisions, and many assumed that institutions managed potential conflicts of interest. Although disclosure of investigator financial interest information to research participants is often recommended, its usefulness is limited, especially when participation is desired because of illness.

Green, Lee A.; Lowery, Julie C.; Kowalski, Christine P.; Wyszewianski, Leon. Impact of institutional review board practice variation on observational health services research. *Health Services Research* 2006 February; 41(1): 214-230. NRCBL: 18.2. SC: em.

Grimm, David. A cure for the common trial [news]. *Science* 2006 May 12; 312(5775): 835, 837. NRCBL: 18.2; 1.3.7. SC: em.

Gunsalus, C.K.; Bruner, Edward M.; Burbules, Nicholas C.; Dash, Leon; Finkin, Matthew; Goldberg, Joseph P.; Greenough, William T.; Miller, Gregory A.; Pratt, Michael G. Mission creep in the IRB world [editorial]. *Science* 2006 June 9; 312(5779): 1441. NRCBL: 18.2. Identifiers: Institutional Review Board.

Gurwitz, Jerry H.; Guadagnoli, Edward; Landrum, Mary Beth; Silliman, Rebecca A.; Wolf, Robert; Weeks, Jane C. The treating physician as active gatekeeper in the recruitment of research subjects. *Medical Care* 2001 December; 39(12): 1339-1344. NRCBL: 18.2; 7.1; 18.5.1.

Halpern, Scott D. Evidence-based equipoise and research responsiveness [editorial]. *American Journal of Bioethics* 2006 July-August; 6(4): 1-4. NRCBL: 18.2; 9.7.

Halpern, Scott D.; Karlawish, Jason H.T.; Berlin, Jesse A.; Bacchetti, Peter; Wolf, Leslie E.; Segal, Mark R.; McCulloch, Charles E. Re: "Ethics and sample size" [letter and reply]. *American Journal of Epidemiology* 2005 July 15; 162(2): 195-196. NRCBL: 18.2; 7.1. SC: em.

Hanauer, Stephen B. Institutional review boards: the cost to academic medical centers [editorial]. *Nature Clinical Practice. Gastroenterology and Hepatology* 2005 July; 2(7): 287. NRCBL: 18.2; 9.3.1.

Hanauer, Stephen B. Novel potential perils of volunteering for clinical trials [editorial]. *Nature Clinical Practice Gastroenterology and Hepatology* 2005 August; 2(8): 337. NRCBL: 18.2; 5.2; 8.1.

Hansson, Sven Ove. Uncertainty and the ethics of clinical trials. *Theoretical Medicine and Bioethics* 2006; 27(2): 149-167. NRCBL: 18.2; 1.1.

Harmon, Shawn H.E. Solidarity: a (new) ethic for global health policy. *Health Care Analysis: An International Journal of Health Philosophy and Policy* 2006 December; 14(4): 215-236. NRCBL: 18.2; 1.1; 21.1. Identifiers: CIOMS guidelines; Helsinki Declaration.

Harrison, Jayne E. Orthodontic clinical trials III: reporting of ethical issues associated with clinical trials published in three orthodontic journals between 1989 and 1998. *Journal of Orthodontics* 2005 June; 32(2): 115-121. NRCBL: 18.2; 1.3.7; 4.1.1. SC: em; rv.

NRCBL: National Reference Center for Bioethics Literature Classification Scheme   See inside front cover for terms.

289

Hayes, Gregory J. Institutional review boards: balancing conflicting values in research. *In:* O'Donohue, William; Ferguson, Kyle, eds. Handbook of Professional Ethics for Psychologists: Issues, Questions, and Controversies. Thousand Oaks, Calif.: SAGE Publications; 2003: 101-112. NRCBL: 18.2.

Heaney, Robert P. Ethical issues in the design of osteoporosis clinical trials: the state of the question. *Journal of Bone and Mineral Research* 2003 June; 18(6): 1117- 1120. NRCBL: 18.2; 18.5.1; 9.7; 18.3.

Hedgecoe, A.; Carvalho, F.; Lobmayer, P.; Raka, F. Research ethics committees in Europe: implementing the directive, respecting diversity. *Journal of Medical Ethics* 2006 August; 32(8): 483-486. NRCBL: 18.2; 21.1.
Abstract: With the recent Clinical Trials Directive, a degree of harmonisation into research ethics committees (RECs) across Europe, including the time taken to assess a trial proposal and the kinds of issues a committee should take into account, has been introduced by the European Union (EU). How four different member states-Hungary, Portugal, Sweden and the UK-have chosen to implement the directive is shown. Although this has resulted in four very different ways of structuring RECs, similar themes are present in all four cases, such as centralisation of control over RECs within member states, harmonisation of REC procedures across the EU and increased role of political decision making with regard to such committees.

Hewison, Jenny; Haines, Andy. Confidentiality and consent in medical research: overcoming barriers to recruitment in health research. *BMJ: British Medical Journal* 2006 August 5; 333(7562): 300-302. NRCBL: 18.2; 18.3; 8.4. SC: em. Identifiers: United Kingdom (Great Britain).

Hood, Maureen N.; Gugerty, Brian; Levine, Richard; Ho, Vincent B. Computerized information management for institutional review boards. *Computers, Informatics, Nursing* 2005 July-August; 23(4): 190-200. NRCBL: 18.2; 1.3.12.

Hopkins Tanne, Janice. Researchers funded by NIH are failing to make data available [news]. *BMJ: British Medical Journal* 2006 March 25; 332(7543): 684. NRCBL: 18.2; 18.6.

Howard, Jennifer. Oral history under review. *Chronicle of Higher Education* 2006 November 10; 53(12): A14-A17. NRCBL: 18.2; 1.3.3.

Iltis, Ana Smith. Conducting and terminating randomized clinical trials. *In:* Iltis, Ana Smith, ed. Research Ethics. New York: Routledge, 2006: 86-101. NRCBL: 18.2.

Jansen, Lynn A. The problem with optimism in clinical trials. *IRB: Ethics and Human Research* 2006 July-August; 28(4): 13-19. NRCBL: 18.2; 18.3.

Jaspers, Patricia; van der Arend, Arie; Wanders, Rinus. Inclusion practice in lung cancer trials. *Nursing Ethics* 2006 November; 13(6): 649-660. NRCBL: 18.2; 18.3; 18.5.1. SC: em. Identifiers: Netherlands.

Jayson, Gordon; Harris, John. How participants in cancer trials are chosen: ethics and conflicting interests. *Nature Reviews. Cancer* 2006 April; 6(4): 330-336. NRCBL: 18.2; 18.3; 9.5.1; 18.5.1.

Jeste, Dilip V. Can medication-free research ever be ethical in older people with psychotic disorders? *Schizophrenia Bulletin* 2006 April; 32(2): 303-304. NRCBL: 18.2; 18.5.7; 17.4; 18.5.6.

Johnson, Claire. On the subject of human subjects [editorial]. *Journal of Manipulative and Physiological Therapeutics* 2005 February; 28(2): 79-80. NRCBL: 18.2; 18.3.

Johnson, Matthew S.; Gonzales, Marcia N.; Bizila, Shelley. Responsible conduct of radiology research. Part V. The Health Insurance Portability and Accountability Act and research. *Radiology* 2005 December; 237(3): 757-764. NRCBL: 18.2; 8.4; 18.3; 18.6.

Kanis, J.A.; Alexandre, J.M.; Bone, H.G.; Abadie, E.; Brasseur, D.; Chassany, O.; Durrleman, S.; Lekkerkerker, J.F.F.; Caulin, F. Study design in osteoporosis: a European perspective. *Journal of Bone and Mineral Research* 2003 June; 18(6): 1133- 1138. NRCBL: 18.2; 18.5.1; 18.3; 21.1.

Kean, Sam. Draft research rules are released [news]. *Chronicle of Higher Education* 2006 September 15; 53(4): A27. NRCBL: 18.2; 18.3.

Keith-Spiegel, Patricia; Koocher, Gerald P.; Tabachnick, Barbara. What scientists want from their research ethics committee. *Journal of Empirical Research on Human Research Ethics* 2006 March; 1(1): 67-81. NRCBL: 18.2; 1.1; 1.3.2. SC: em.

Kenter, M.J.H.; Cohen, A.F. Establishing risk of human experimentation with drugs: lessons from TGN1412. *Lancet* 2006 October 14-20; 368(9544): 1387-1391. NRCBL: 18.2; 5.2; 18.6.

Kettner, Matthias. Research ethics committees in Germany. *In:* Beyleveld, D.; Townend, D.; Wright, J., eds. Research Ethics Committees, Data Protection and Medical Research in European Countries. Hants, England; Burlington, VT: Ashgate; 2005: 73-83. NRCBL: 18.2.

Khan, Robyna Irshad. One standard of care for all is not always practical. *Indian Journal of Medical Ethics* 2006 January-March; 3(1): 21-22. NRCBL: 18.2; 21.6.

Khandekar, Jarardan; Khandekar, Melin. Phase 1 clinical trials: not just for safety anymore? *Archives of Internal Medicine* 2006 July 24; 166(14): 1440-1441. NRCBL: 18.2; 9.7.

Khin-Moung-Gyi, Felix A.; Whalen, Matthew. Ethics and human subjects protection. *In:* Fedor, Carol A.; Cola, Philip A.; Pierre, Christine, eds. Responsible Research: A Guide for Coordinators. London; Chicago, IL: Remedics; 2006: 35-48. NRCBL: 18.2.

Kietinun, Somboon. Research ethics review in government and academic institutions in Thailand. *Indian Journal of Medical Ethics* 2006 April-June; 3(2): 67-68. NRCBL: 18.2; 18.6. SC: em.

Killien, Marcia; Bigby, Judy Ann; Champion, Victoria; Fernandez-Repollet, Emma; Jackson, Rebecca D.; Kagawa-Singer, Marjorie; Kidd, Kristin; Naughton, Michele J.; Prout, Marianne. Involving minority and underrepresented women in clinical trials: the National Centers of Excellence in Women's Health. *Journal of Women's Health and Gender-Based Medicine* 2000 December; 9(10): 1061-1070. NRCBL: 18.2; 18.5.3; 18.6.

Kim, Ock-Joo; Park, Byung-Joo; Lee, Seung-Mi; Sohn, Dong-Ryul; Shin, Sang-Goo. Current status of the institutional review boards in Korea: constitution, operation and policy for protection of research participants. *In:* Sang-yong, Song; Young-Mo, Koo; Macer, Darryl R.J., eds. Asian Bioethics in the 21st Century. Christchurch, NZ: Eubios Ethics Institute, 2002: 17-27. NRCBL: 18.2. SC: em. Conference: Proceedings of the Asian Bioethics Conference (ABC4), held 22-25 November 2002 in Seoul, South Korea.

Kim, Ock-Joo; Park, Byung-Joo; Sohn, Dong-Ryul; Lee, Seung-Mi; Shin, Sanfg-Goo. Current status of the institutional review boards in Korea: constitution, operation, and policy for protection of human research participants. *Journal of Korean Medical Science* 2003 February; 18(1): 3-10. NRCBL: 18.2. SC: em.

Kim, Scott Y.H. Evidence-based ethics for neurology and psychiatry research. *NeuroRx* 2004 July; 1(3): 372-377. NRCBL: 18.2; 17.1; 1.3.9; 5.2; 18.3.

Kim, Scott Y.H.; Frank, Samuel; Holloway, Robert; Zimmerman, Carol; Wilson, Renee; Kieburtz, Karl. Science and ethics of sham surgery: a survey of Parkinson disease clinical researchers. *Archives of Neurology* 2005 September; 62(9): 1357-1360. NRCBL: 18.2; 18.5.1; 15.4; 9.5.1. SC: em.

Kipnis, Kenneth; King, Nancy M.P.; Nelson, Robert M. An open letter to institutional review boards considering Northfield Laboratories' PolyHeme trial. *American Journal of Bioethics* 2006 May-June; 6(3): 18-21; discussion W49- W50. NRCBL: 18.2; 19.4; 18.3.1; 18.6.

Kiskaddon, Sarah H. Balancing access to participation in research and protection from risks: applying the principle of justice. *Journal of Nutrition* 2005 April; 135(4): 929-932. NRCBL: 18.2; 1.1. Conference: Symposium: Bioethics in Scientific Research: Conflicts between Subject's Equitable Access to Participate in Research and Current Regulations; 19 April 2004; Washington, D.C.; American Society for Nutritional Sciences.

Kmietowicz, Zosia. Rules for drug trials should be tightened, say experts [news]. *BMJ: British Medical Journal* 2006 August 5; 333(7562): 276. NRCBL: 18.2; 9.7. Identifiers: United Kingdom (Great Britain).

Kondro, Wayne. Dispute over Vioxx study plays out in New England Journal [news]. *CMAJ/JAMC: Canadian Medical Association Journal* 2006 May 9; 174(10): 1397. NRCBL: 18.2; 1.3.9; 1.3.7. Identifiers: New England Journal of Medicine.

Krause-Bachand, Jeanie. Ethical considerations in nursing research. *SCI Nursing* 2002 Fall; 19(3): 136-137. NRCBL: 18.2; 21.1; 18.3; 18.6.

Kvalheim, Vigdis. The Norwegian model for ethical review of medical research. *In:* Beyleveld, D.; Townend, D.; Wright, J., eds. Research Ethics Committees, Data Protection and Medical Research in European Countries. Hants, England; Burlington, VT: Ashgate; 2005: 163-176. NRCBL: 18.2.

Lachin, John M. Conflicts of interest in data monitoring of industry versus publicly financed clinical trials. *Statistics in Medicine* 2004 May 30; 23(10): 1519-1521. NRCBL: 18.2; 5.3; 9.3.1; 7.3; 7.1.

Langston, Anne L.; McCallum, Marilyn; Campbell, Marion K.; Robertson, Clare; Ralston, Stuart H. An integrated approach to consumer representation and involvement in a multicentre randomized controlled trial. *Clinical Trials* 2005; 2(1): 80-87. NRCBL: 18.2; 18.5.1; 7.3.

Lawrence, Dana J.; Johnson, Claire D. On the subject of human subjects [letter and reply]. *Journal of Manipulative and Physiological Therapeutics* 2005 November-December; 28(9): 730-731. NRCBL: 18.2; 9.3.1; 1.3.7.

Lemmens, Trudo. A response to the parliamentary sub-committee's report and recommendations. *Canadian HIV/AIDS Policy and Law Newsletter* 1997 Spring; 3(2-3): 40-43. NRCBL: 18.2; 9.7; 9.2.

Lemmens, Trudo. Compassionate access to experimental drugs: balancing interests and harms. *Canadian HIV/AIDS Policy and Law Newsletter* 1996 October; 3(1): 43-44. NRCBL: 18.2; 9.7; 18.6.

Levine, Robert J. Empirical research to evaluate ethics committees' burdensome and perhaps unproductive policies and practices : a proposal [editorial]. *Journal of Empirical Research on Human Research Ethics* 2006 September; 1(3): 1-3. NRCBL: 18.2; 18.6. SC: an.

Lichterman, Boleslav L. Under the shelter of ethics. *Journal International de Bioéthique = International Journal of Bioethics* 2005 September-December; 16(3-4): 77-79, 172. NRCBL: 18.2; 9.6; 2.4; 18.6. Identifiers: research ethics committees; Russia.

Abstract: Problems of ethics committees in post-communist Russia are briefly discussed. The first ethics committees were established in 1980s upon the initiative of international pharmaceutical companies involved in clinical trials. Generally, such committees exist at hospitals conducting these trials and at re-

---

NRCBL: National Reference Center for Bioethics Literature Classification Scheme   See inside front cover for terms.

291

search institutions dealing with human experimentation. They are bureaucratic structures heavily dependent on hospital or institution administration. Publication of research results in international periodicals is the main reason for their existence. An officially recognized National Ethics Committee is non-existent although there are several competing ethics committees at a national level (at the Ministry of Health, Academy of Sciences, Academy of Medical Sciences, Russian Medical association etc.). There is no federal legislation on the structure and status of ethics committees.

Lilford, Richard J.; Braunholtz, David A. Bayesian perspectives on the ethics of trials. *In:* Duley, Lelia; Farrell, Barbara, eds. Clinical Trials. London: BMJ Books; 2002: 105-120. NRCBL: 18.2.

Lillehammer, Hallvard. Benefit, disability and the non-identity problem. *In:* Gallin, John I., ed. Principles and Practice of Clinical Research. San Diego, CA: Academic Press; 2002: 15-26. NRCBL: 18.2.

Litton, Paul. Defending the distinctions between research and medical care. *American Journal of Bioethics* 2006 July-August; 6(4): 63-66. NRCBL: 18.2; 8.1. Comments: Winston Chiong. The real problem with equipoise. American Journal of Bioethics 2006 July-August; 6(4): 37-47.

London, Alex John. Justice in the Belmont Report and the social division of labor. *APA Newsletters: Newsletter on Philosophy and Medicine* 2006 Spring; 05(2): 5-10. NRCBL: 18.2; 1.1.

Lynn, Mary R.; Nelson, Daniel K. Common (mis)perceptions about IRB review of human subjects research. *Nursing Science Quarterly* 2005 July; 16(3): 264-270. NRCBL: 18.2; 1.3.9. Identifiers: institutional review board.

MacNeil, S. Danielle; Fernandez, Conrad V. Informing research participants of research results: analysis of Canadian university based research ethics board policies. *Journal of Medical Ethics* 2006 January; 32(1): 49-54. NRCBL: 18.2. SC: em.

Abstract: BACKGROUND: Despite potential benefits of the return of research results to research participants, the TriCouncil Policy Statement (TCPS), which reflects Canadian regulatory ethical requirements, does not require this. The policies of Canadian research ethics boards (REBs) are unknown. OBJECTIVES: To examine the policies of Canadian university based REBs regarding returning results to research participants, and to ascertain if the presence/absence of a policy may be influenced by REB member composition. DESIGN: Email survey of the coordinators of Canadian university based REBs to determine the presence/absence of a policy on return of research results to research participants both during an ongoing study and at conclusion. REB coordinators were asked to return a copy of the policy or guidelines and to describe the member composition of their REB. Findings: Of 50 REBs that were contacted 34 (68%) responded and 22 (64.7%) met the inclusion criteria. Two (9.1%) had a policy that governed the return of research results while on a study, and seven (31.8%) following the completion of a study. Presence of an ethicist or a lawyer on the REB did not influence the presence/absence of such policies. No REBs had specific guidelines describing how participants should be informed of results. CONCLUSIONS: Most REBs

did not require researchers to disclose study results to research participants either during or following a study. Thus this study identifies an ethical shortcoming in the conduct of human research in Canada. It has also demonstrated that there are no clear recommendations by REBs to facilitate the return of results to participants following research projects.

MacNeil, S. Danielle; Fernandez, Conrad V. Offering results to research participants [editorial]. *BMJ: British Medical Journal* 2006 January 28; 332(7535): 188-189. NRCBL: 18.2.

Madden, Deirdre; McDonagh, Maeve. Research ethics committees in Ireland. *In:* Beyleveld, D.; Townend, D.; Wright, J., eds. Research Ethics Committees, Data Protection and Medical Research in European Countries. Hants, England; Burlington, VT: Ashgate; 2005: 107-109. NRCBL: 18.2.

Magnus, David. Blood, sweat and tears. *American Journal of Bioethics* 2006 May-June; 6(3): 1-2. NRCBL: 18.2; 19.4; 18.3. Identifiers: PolyHeme.

Malaviya, Prashant; John, Deborah Roedder; Sternthal, Brian; Barnes, James. Human participants — respondents and researchers [discussion]. *Journal of Consumer Psychology* 2001; 10(1-2): 115-121. NRCBL: 18.2; 9.3.1; 18.3; 1.3.9.

Mallia, Pierre. Research ethics committees in Malta. *In:* Beyleveld, D.; Townend, D.; Wright, J., eds. Research Ethics Committees, Data Protection and Medical Research in European Countries. Hants, England; Burlington, VT: Ashgate; 2005: 149-152. NRCBL: 18.2.

Malone, Ruth E.; Yerger, Valerie B.; McGruder, Carol; Froelicher, Erika. "It's like Tuskegee in reverse": a case study of ethical tensions in institutional review board review of community-based participatory research. *American Journal of Public Health* 2006 November; 96(11): 1914-1919. NRCBL: 18.2; 18.6; 9.1. SC: cs; em.

Abstract: Community-based participatory research (CBPR) addresses the social justice dimensions of health disparities by engaging marginalized communities, building capacity for action, and encouraging more egalitarian relationships between researchers and communities. CBPR may challenge institutionalized academic practices and the understandings that inform institutional review board deliberations and, indirectly, prioritize particular kinds of research. We present our attempt to study, as part of a CBPR partnership, cigarette sales practices in an inner-city community. We use critical and communitarian perspectives to examine the implications of the refusal of the university institutional review board (in this case, the University of California, San Francisco) to approve the study. CBPR requires expanding ethical discourse beyond the procedural, principle-based approaches common in biomedical research settings. The current ethics culture of academia may sometimes serve to protect institutional power at the expense of community empowerment.

Maloney, Dennis M. Agency says institutional review board (IRB) did not fulfill duties so agency investigation expands. *Human Research Report* 2006 April; 21(4): 6-7. NRCBL: 18.2; 1.3.3; 18.6.

Maloney, Dennis M. Agency says institutional review board (IRB) failed to warn subjects of significant problems. *Human Research Report* 2006 March; 21(3): 6-7. NRCBL: 18.2; 9.7.

Maloney, Dennis M. Alternatives to local institutional review board (IRB) system debated. *Human Research Report* 2006 April; 21(4): 1-2. NRCBL: 18.2.

Maloney, Dennis M. Better protection for human subjects is outcome of very early clinical trials. *Human Research Report* 2006 May; 21(5): 1-2. NRCBL: 18.2; 9.7.

Maloney, Dennis M. Case study: inadequate university response leads to shutdown of human research projects. *Human Research Report* 2006 July; 21(7): 6-7. NRCBL: 18.2; 1.3.3; 18.6.

Maloney, Dennis M. Case study: institutional review board fails to follow numerous regulations. *Human Research Report* 2006 November; 21(11): 6-7. NRCBL: 18.2; 18.3; 18.5.5; 18.6.

Maloney, Dennis M. How institutional review boards (IRBs) can handle adverse event reports. *Human Research Report* 2006 January; 21(1): 1-3. NRCBL: 18.2.

Maloney, Dennis M. Institutional review board (IRB) did not know about subject problem until after study. *Human Research Report* 2006 May; 21(5): 6-7. NRCBL: 18.2; 1.3.3; 18.6.

Maloney, Dennis M. Institutional review boards (IRBs) and their role in community consultation. *Human Research Report* 2006 November; 21(11): 1-2. NRCBL: 18.2; 18.6.

Maloney, Dennis M. Institutional review boards (IRBs) must be given adequate information. *Human Research Report* 2006 December; 21(12): 1-2. NRCBL: 18.2; 18.6.

Maloney, Dennis M. Research subject says institutional review board (IRB) was no help. *Human Research Report* 2006 January; 21(1): 7. NRCBL: 18.2; 1.3.9; 9.5.6; 9.7.

Maloney, Dennis M. Research subject says institutional review board (IRB) would not answer her questions. *Human Research Report* 2006 February; 21(2): 7. NRCBL: 18.2; 1.3.9; 9.5.6; 9.7.

Maloney, Dennis M. University finally can resume human subjects research again [case study]. *Human Research Report* 2006 August; 21(8): 6-7. NRCBL: 18.2; 1.3.3.

Mangan, Katherine S. Researchers raise concerns about secrecy in company- sponsored clinical trials. *Chronicle of Higher Education* 2006 April 7; 52(31): A39. NRCBL: 18.2; 1.3.9; 18.3; 9.7.

Mann, Howard. How confidential trial negotiations and agreements between the Food and Drug Administration and sponsors marginalize local institutional boards, and what to do about it. *American Journal of Bioethics* 2006 May-June; 6(3): 22-24; discussion W49- W50. NRCBL: 18.2; 1.3.5; 9.7. Comments: Ken Kipnis, Nancy M.P. King, and Robert M. Nelson. An open letter to institutional review boards considering Northfield Laboratories' PolyHeme trial. American Journal of Bioethics 2006 May-June; 6(3): 18-21.

Mann, Howard; Shamoo, Adil E. Introduction to special issue of Accountability in Research on the review and approval of biomedical research proposals. *Accountability in Research* 2006 January-March; 13(1): 1-9. NRCBL: 18.2.

Markman, Maurie. "Therapeutic intent" in phase 1 oncology trials: a justifiable objective. *Archives of Internal Medicine* 2006 July 24; 166(14): 1446-1448. NRCBL: 18.2; 18.3.

Markman, Maurie. Reflections on ethical concerns arising from the incorporation of results of randomized trials of antineoplastic therapy into routine clinical practice. *Cancer Investigation* 2005; 23(8): 735-740. NRCBL: 18.2; 9.8; 9.5.1; 9.1.

Maskens, A.P. Studies on gene-nutrient interactions in the aetiology of colorectal neoplasia ('ECP-genuine' project): ethical and legal aspects. *European Journal of Cancer Prevention* 2002 February; 11(1): 99-100. NRCBL: 18.2; 15.1; 21.1; 18.3.

Masterton, George. Two decades on an ethics committee. *BMJ: British Medical Journal* 2006 March 11; 332(7541): 615. NRCBL: 18.2.

Mattingly, Cheryl. Toward a vulnerable ethics of research practice. *Health (London)* 2005 October; 9(4): 453-471. NRCBL: 18.2; 18.3; 7.1; 1.1; 8.4. SC: an.

Mayor, Susan. Severe adverse reactions prompt call for trial design changes [news]. *BMJ: British Medical Journal* 2006 March 25; 332(7543): 683. NRCBL: 18.2; 18.5.1.

McWilliams, Rita; Hebden, Carl W.; Gilpin, Adele M.K. Concept paper: a virtual centralized IRB system. *Accountability in Research* 2006 January-March; 13(1): 25-45. NRCBL: 18.2; 1.3.12; 7.1; 18.6. Identifiers: institutional review board.

Abstract: Context: As the volume and complexity of research have increased, the amount of time spent on Institutional Review Board (IRB) review has decreased. The complexity of research has expanded, requiring increasingly specialized knowledge to review it. Dilemma: Under the current system, increasing numbers of research studies requiring expertise in ethics, new technologies or diverse study designs place a substantial burden upon local IRBs and often result in substantial variability among their reviews. This lack of uniformity in the review process creates uneven human subjects' protection thus undermining the intent of the Common Rule. Objectives: To outline a scenario for expert centralized IRB review via implementation of a national virtual IRB review system overseen by the Office for Human Research Protections (OHRP). Conclusions: The complicated ethical issues and science involved in much of current research warrant an expert review panel. Centralized review would enable expert review specific to the

NRCBL: National Reference Center for Bioethics Literature Classification Scheme   See inside front cover for terms.

293

research at hand, ensure consistency in human subjects protection, reduce the burden on local IRBs, and may reduce time spent obtaining approval. A centralized virtual system would allow IRB members to remain at their institutions while providing unprecedented expert review through currently available technology, and make information regarding monitoring and adverse event reporting available online in real-time.

Milford, Cecilia; Wassenaar, Douglas; Slack, Catherine. Resources and needs of research ethics committees in Africa: preparations for HIV vaccine trials. *IRB: Ethics and Human Research* 2006 March-April; 28(2): 1-9. NRCBL: 18.2; 18.5.9; 9.5.6. SC: em.

Millat, Bertrand; Borie, Frédéric; Fingerhut, Abe. Patient's preference and randomization: new paradigm of evidence-based clinical research. *World Journal of Surgery* 2005 May; 29(5): 596-600. NRCBL: 18.2; 18.3.

Miller, Franklin G. Equipoise and the ethics of clinical research revisited. *American Journal of Bioethics* 2006 July-August; 6(4): 59-61. NRCBL: 18.2; 7.2. Comments: Winston Chiong. The real problem with equipoise. American Journal of Bioethics 2006 July-August; 6(4): 37-47.

Miller, Franklin G. Revisiting the Belmont Report: the ethical significance of the distinction between clinical research and medical care. *APA Newsletters: Newsletter on Philosophy and Medicine* 2006 Spring; 05(2): 10-14. NRCBL: 18.2; 9.5.1; 1.1; 8.1. SC: an.

Miller, Richard B. How the Belmont Report fails. *Essays in Philosophy* 2003 June; 4(2): 18 p. [Online]. Accessed: http://www.humboldt.edu/~essays/miller.html [2004 December 20]. NRCBL: 18.2.

Mills, Edward J.; Seely, Dugald; Rachlis, Beth; Griffith, Lauren; Wu, Ping; Wilson, Kumanan; Ellis, Peter; Wright, James R. Barriers to participation in clinical trials of cancer: a meta-analysis and systematic review of patient-reported factors. *Lancet Oncology* 2006 February; 7(2): 141-148. NRCBL: 18.2; 18.5.1; 18.3; 9.5.1. SC: rv.

Mitka, Mike. Approval for pesticide toxicity testing in humans draws criticism [news]. *JAMA: The Journal of the American Medical Association* 2006 March 15; 295(11): 1237-1238. NRCBL: 18.2; 16.1. Identifiers: Environmental Protection Agency (EPA).

Mitka, Mike. Guidelines aim to speed drug approval while protecting human subjects [news]. *JAMA: The Journal of the American Medical Association* 2006 March 1; 295(9): 988-989. NRCBL: 18.2. Identifiers: Food and Drug Administration (FDA).

Morreim, E. Haavi; Webb, George E.; Gordon, Harvey L.; Brody, Baruch; Casarett, David; Rosenfield, Ken; Sabin, James; Lantos, John D.; Morenz, Barry; Krouse, Robert; Goodman, Stan. Innovation in human research protection: the AbioCor artificial heart trial. *American Journal of Bioethics [Online]* 2006 September-October; 6(5): W6-W16. NRCBL: 18.2; 19.2; 18.3.

Morris, Norma; Balmer, Brian. Are you sitting comfortably? Perspectives of the researchers and the researched on "being comfortable". *Accountability in Research* 2006 April-June; 13(2): 111-133. NRCBL: 18.2; 18.1; 8.1; 18.4. SC: em.
  Abstract: In a study of volunteers in medical research, we found contrasting readings of "being comfortable" by the volunteer research subjects and the researchers. Although the experimental process (testing a new kind of diagnostic technology) involved some physical discomfort—and the researchers focused on this—the volunteers' concerns centred on feeling socially comfortable and managing feelings of embarrassment or isolation, and they generally made light of the physical aspects. The bias of volunteer concerns, which is understandable in terms of the different situations of researchers and volunteers and the different tensions they create, has potential implications for the engagement of researchers with their research subjects and prevailing standards for the ethical and accountable conduct of research.

Mosconi, Paola; Colombo, Cinzia; Labianca, Roberto; Apolone, Giovanni. Oncologists' opinions about research ethics committees in Italy: an update, 2004. *European Journal of Cancer Prevention* 2006 February; 15(1): 91-94. NRCBL: 18.2. SC: em.

Mosconi, Paola; Poli, Paola; Giolo, Antonio; Apolone, Giovanni. How Italian health consumers feel about clinical research: a questionnaire survey. *European Journal of Public Health* 2005 August; 15(4): 372-379. NRCBL: 18.2; 18.6; 7.1. SC: em. Identifiers: Italy.

Murray, John F.; Rothman, David J. 'The shame of medical research': an exchange [letter and reply]. *New York Review of Books* 2001 May 17; 48(8): 3 p. [Online]. Accessed: http://www.nybooks.com/articles/14239 [2006 October 30]. NRCBL: 18.2; 18.5.9; 9.5.6; 21.1; 9.1.

Muthuswamy, Vasantha. Status of ethical review and challenges in India [editorial]. *Indian Pediatrics* 2005 December; 42(12): 1189-1190. NRCBL: 18.2.

Nowak, Kristin S.; Bankert, Elizabeth A.; Nelson, Robert M. Reforming the oversight of multi-site clinical research: a review of two possible solutions. *Accountability in Research* 2006 January-March; 13(1): 11-24. NRCBL: 18.2; 1.3.12; 7.1; 18.6. SC: rv.
  Abstract: The current system for the ethical oversight of clinical research suffers from structural, procedural, and performance assessment problems. Initially conceived primarily to handle local investigator-initiated single-site studies, the system of institutionally-based committee review has become progressively more inefficient given the increased prevalence of commercially or federally sponsored multi-center trials. To date, proposed solutions do not adequately address these problems. Beginning with a review of these structural, procedural, and performance assessment problems, this article will then consider two proposals for addressing these deficiencies: (a) regional ethics organizations; and (b) IRBNet, a newly developed web-based program for cooperative IRB review. The strengths and weaknesses of these two approaches will be evaluated in light of recent experience with centralized review. The proposal to establish a system of regional ethics organizations presents a comprehensive approach to many of the problems faced by the current system. However, IRBNet offers an immediate and

feasible solution to many of the problems faced by the review of multi-site clinical studies.

Oberle, Kathleen; Allen, Marion. Ethical considerations for nurses in clinical trials. *Nursing Ethics* 2006 March; 13(2): 180-186. NRCBL: 18.2; 4.1.3; 7.1.
Abstract: Ethical issues arise for nurses involved in all phases of clinical trials regardless of whether they are caregivers, research nurses, trial co-ordinators or principal investigators. Potential problem areas centre on nurses' moral obligation related to methodological issues as well as the notions of beneficence/non-maleficence and autonomy. These ethical concerns can be highly upsetting to nurses if they are not addressed, so it is imperative that they are discussed fully prior to the initiation of a trial. Failure to resolve these issues can place both the conduct and the results of research in jeopardy.

Oguz, N. Yasemin. Research ethics committees in developing countries and informed consent: with special reference to Turkey. *Journal of Laboratory and Clinical Medicine* 2003 May; 141(5): 292-296. NRCBL: 18.2; 18.3; 21.1.

Oliver, David. Ethics committees: current research ethics forms are an over-reaction that will stifle research [letter]. *BMJ: British Medical Journal* 2006 March 25; 332(7543): 730. NRCBL: 18.2.

Paradis, Carmen. Equipoise in the real world. *American Journal of Bioethics* 2006 July-August; 6(4): 61-63. NRCBL: 18.2. Comments: Winston Chiong. The real problem with equipoise. American Journal of Bioethics 2006 July-August; 6(4): 37-47.

Patenaude, Johane; Cabanac, Julien; de Champlain, Johane. Pan-Canadian study on variations in research ethics boards' reviews of a research project involving placebo use. *Health Law Review* 2006; 14(3): 32-38. NRCBL: 18.2; 18.3. SC: em.

Patterson, David. New guidelines on ethical considerations in HIV preventive vaccine research. *Canadian HIV/AIDS Policy and Law Newsletter* 2000 Spring-Summer; 5(2-3): 20-22. NRCBL: 18.2; 9.5.6; 9.7.

Pegg, Michael S. Overcoming barriers to recruitment in health research: some research ethics committees believe in facilitating ethical research. *BMJ: British Medical Journal* 2006 August 19; 333(7564): 398. NRCBL: 18.2.

Perneger, T.V. The real ethical problem [editorial]. *International Journal for Quality in Health Care* 2005 October; 17(5): 379. NRCBL: 18.2; 1.3.7.

Peter, Elizabeth. The interplay between the abstract and the particular: research ethics standards and the practice of research as symbolic. *Nursing Science Quarterly* 2006 January; 19(1): 20-24. NRCBL: 18.2; 4.1.3; 1.1.

Prudil, Lukás; Kure, Josef. Research ethics committees in the Czech Republic. *In:* Beyleveld, D.; Townend, D.; Wright, J., eds. Research Ethics Committees, Data Protection and Medical Research in European Countries. Hants, England; Burlington, VT: Ashgate; 2005: 31-34. NRCBL: 18.2.

Qatarneh, Dania; Kashani, Shahram. Local ethics committees and specialised research [letter]. *BMJ: British Medical Journal* 2006 July 29; 333(7561): 261. NRCBL: 18.2.

Rehak, Peter. Research ethics committees in Austria. *In:* Beyleveld, D.; Townend, D.; Wright, J., eds. Research Ethics Committees, Data Protection and Medical Research in European Countries. Hants, England; Burlington, VT: Ashgate; 2005: 3-7. NRCBL: 18.2.

Reidenberg, Marcus M.; Zarin, Deborah A.; Tse, Tony; Ide, Nicholas, C.; Drazen, Jeffrey M.; Wood, Alastair J.J.; Haug, Charlotte; Gøtzsche, Peter C.; Schroeder, Torben V. Clinical trials report card [letter and replies]. *New England Journal of Medicine* 2006 March 30; 354(13): 1428-1429. NRCBL: 18.2.

Resnik, David B.; Sharp, Richard R. Protecting third parties in human subjects research. *IRB: Ethics and Human Research* 2006 July-August; 28(4): 1-7. NRCBL: 18.2; 1.1; 5.3. Note: NHGRI funded publication.

Roginsky, Martin S.; Handley, Albert. Ethical implications of withdrawal of experimental drugs at the conclusion of phase III trials. *Clinical Research* 1978 December; 26(6): 384-388. NRCBL: 18.2; 18.5.1.

Rosenthal, Mark A.; Sarson-Lawrence, M.; Alt, C.; Arkell, K.; Dodds, M. Ethics committee reviews and mutual acceptance: a pilot study. *Internal Medicine Journal* 2005 November; 35(11): 650-654. NRCBL: 18.2. SC: em. Identifiers: Australia.

Rosenzweig, Mary; Knudsen, Lisbeth. Research ethics committees in Denmark. *In:* Beyleveld, D.; Townend, D.; Wright, J., eds. Research Ethics Committees, Data Protection and Medical Research in European Countries. Hants, England; Burlington, VT: Ashgate; 2005: 35-39. NRCBL: 18.2.

Rothman, Kenneth J.; Evans, Stephen. More on JAMA's policy on industry sponsored studies [letter]. *BMJ: British Medical Journal* 2006 February 25; 332(7539): 489. NRCBL: 18.2; 5.3; 1.3.7.

Roy Choudhury, Shormila; Knapp, Leslie A. A review of international and UK-based ethical guidelines for researchers conducting nontherapeutic genetic studies in developing countries. *European Journal of Human Genetics* 2006 January; 14(1): 9-16. NRCBL: 18.2; 15.1; 18.5.9; 18.3; 21.1. SC: rv.

Rubin, Philip; Sieber, Joan E. Empirical research on IRBs and methodologies usually associated with minimal risk [editorial]. *Journal of Empirical Research on Human Research Ethics* 2006 December; 1(4): 1-4. NRCBL: 18.2; 18.6. SC: em.

NRCBL: National Reference Center for Bioethics Literature Classification Scheme   See inside front cover for terms.

295

Rugemalila, J.B.; Kilama, W.L. Proceedings of the seminar on health research ethics in Africa. *Acta Tropica* 2001 January; 78(Supplement 1): S1-S126. NRCBL: 18.2; 18.6; 4.4; 18.3; 21.1; 18.5.9; 21.7. SC: rv.

Santarlasci, Benedetta; Messori, Andrea; Pelagotti, Filippo; Trippoli, Sabrina; Vaiani, Monica. Heterogeneity in the evaluation of observational studies by Italian ethics committees. *Pharmacy World and Science* 2005 February; 27(1): 2-3. NRCBL: 18.2; 18.6. Identifiers: Italy.

Schwab, Abraham P. Splitting the difference position. *American Journal of Bioethics* 2006 July-August; 6(4): 74-76. NRCBL: 18.2; 1.1. Identifiers: comment on Winston Chiong. The real problem with equipoise. American Journal of Bioethics 2006 July-August; 6(4): 37-47.

Schwartz, Myrna F.; Brecher, Adelyn R.; Whyte, John; Klein, Mary G. A patient registry for cognitive rehabilitation research: a strategy for balancing patients' privacy rights with researchers' need for access. *Archives of Physical Medicine and Rehabilitation* 2005 September; 86(9): 1807-1814. NRCBL: 18.2; 8.4. SC: em.

Scott, Timothy. Tricks of the trade. *Ethical Human Psychology and Psychiatry* 2006 Summer; 8(2): 133-146. NRCBL: 18.2; 18.4; 9.7; 18.6.

Sears, Jeanne Marguerite. The payment of research subjects: ethical concerns. *Oncology Nursing Forum* 2001 May; 28(4): 657-663. NRCBL: 18.2; 9.3.1. SC: an.

Shamoo, Adil E.; Resnik, David B. Ethical issues for clinical research managers. *Drug Information Journal* 2006; 40: 371-383. NRCBL: 18.2; 1.3.9; 1.1. SC: cs.

Shamoo, Adil E.; Resnik, David B. Strategies to minimize risks and exploitation in phase one trials on healthy subjects. *American Journal of Bioethics [Online]*. 2006 May-June; 6(3): W1-W13. NRCBL: 18.2; 18.3.

Sharma, Shridhar. Ethical issues in psychiatric research. *Archives of Indian Psychiatry* 1999; 5(1): 7-9. NRCBL: 18.2; 18.4; 18.3; 4.3; 21.1; 15.1.

Sidle, John E.; Were, Edwin; Wools-Kaloustian, Kara; Chuani, Christine; Salmon, Karen; Tierney, William M.; Meslin, Eric M. A needs assessment to build international research ethics capacity. *Journal of Empirical Research on Human Research Ethics* 2006 June; 1(2): 23-28. NRCBL: 18.2; 18.3; 21.7. SC: em.

Siegel, Jay P.; O'Neill, Robert; Temple, Robert; Campbell, Gregory; Foulkes, Mary A. Independence of the statistician who analyses unblinded data. *Statistics in Medicine* 2004 May 30; 23(10): 1527-1529. NRCBL: 18.2; 7.1; 7.3; 5.3. SC: an.

Snapinn, Steven; Cook, Thomas; Shapiro, Deborah; Snavely, Duane. The role of the unblinded sponsor statistician. *Statistics in Medicine* 2004 May 30; 23(10): 1531-1533. NRCBL: 18.2; 9.7; 7.3; 1.3.9; 8.4; 7.1.

Staley, Kristina; Minogue, Virginia. User involvement leads to more ethically sound research. *Clinical Ethics* 2006 June; 1(2): 95-100. NRCBL: 18.2; 18.5.1; 9.3.1; 9.8. Identifiers: United Kingdom (Great Britain); INVOLVE; The Macmillan Listening Study.

Stone, Tracey J. Making the decision about enrolment in a randomised controlled trial. *In:* Smyth, Marie; Williamson, Emma, eds. Researchers and Their 'Subjects': Ethics, Power, Knowledge and Consent. Bristol, UK: Policy Press; 2004: 35-54. NRCBL: 18.2.

Sussman, Michael D. Ethical requirements that must be met before the introduction of new procedures. *Clinical Orthopaedics and Related Research* 2000 September; (378): 15-22. NRCBL: 18.2; 4.1.2; 18.3; 18.6.

Talbot, David; Perou, Joan. Ethical issues. *In:* Di Giovanna, Ignazio; Hayes, Gareth, eds. Principles of Clinical Research. Philadelphia: Wrightson Biomedical Pub.; 2001: 63-83. NRCBL: 18.2.

Teka, Telahun; Lulseged, Sileshi. Living by the code in clinical research [editorial]. *Ethiopian Medical Journal* 2005 April; 43(2): 1 p. NRCBL: 18.2; 18.6.

Thall, Peter F.; Estey, Elihu H. Some ethical issues in phase II trials in acute leukemia. *Clinical Advances in Hematology and Oncology* 2005 December; 3(12): 943-948. NRCBL: 18.2; 18.5.1; 7.1; 9.7. SC: an. Note: Retraction in: Clinical Advances in Hematology and Oncology 2006 February; 4(2): 95.

Thompson, Dan R. What do I tell my patient? *American Journal of Bioethics* 2006 July-August; 6(4): 66-67. NRCBL: 18.2; 8.1. Comments: Winston Chiong. The real problem with equipoise. American Journal of Bioethics 2006 July-August; 6(4): 37-47.

Tierney, Alison. The role of research ethics committees. *Nurse Researcher* 1995 September; 3(1): 43-52. NRCBL: 18.2; 4.1.3. SC: em. Identifiers: United Kingdom (Great Britain); National Health Service.

Tomova, Sylvia. Research ethics committees in Bulgaria. *In:* Beyleveld, D.; Townend, D.; Wright, J., eds. Research Ethics Committees, Data Protection and Medical Research in European Countries. Hants, England; Burlington, VT: Ashgate; 2005: 27-30. NRCBL: 18.2.

Trachtman, Howard. The law of mass action. *American Journal of Bioethics* 2006 July-August; 6(4): 72-74. NRCBL: 18.2. Comments: Winston Chiong. The real problem with equipoise. American Journal of Bioethics 2006 July-August; 6(4): 37-47.

Tremaine, William J.; Carlson, Marilyn R.; Isaacs, Kim L.; Motil, Kathleen J.; Robuck, Patricia R.; Wurzelmann, John I. Ethical issues, safety, and data integrity in clinical trials. *Inflammatory Bowel Diseases* 2005 November; 11(Supplement 1): S17-S21. NRCBL: 18.2; 1.3.9.

Trontelj, Joze. Research ethics committees in Slovenia. *In:* Beyleveld, D.; Townend, D.; Wright, J., eds. Research Ethics Committees, Data Protection and Medical Research in European Countries. Hants, England; Burlington, VT: Ashgate; 2005: 229-232. NRCBL: 18.2.

Trotter, Griffin. Interpreting scientific data ethically: a frontier for research ethics. *In:* Iltis, Ana Smith, ed. Research Ethics. New York: Routledge, 2006: 165-177. NRCBL: 18.2.

Tumber, M.B.; Dickersin, K. Publication of clinical trials: accountability and accessibility. *Journal of Internal Medicine* 2004 October; 256(4): 271-283. NRCBL: 18.2; 1.3.7; 9.7; 1.3.12.

Uys, Leana R. Are ethics committees always ethical? *International Journal of Nursing Practice* 2006 February; 12(1): 1-2. NRCBL: 18.2; 18.6; 21.1.

Valdez-Martinez, Edith; Turnbull, Bernardo; Garduno-Espinosa, Juan; Porter, John D.H. Descriptive ethics: a qualitative study of local research ethics committees in Mexico. *Developing World Bioethics* 2006 May; 6(2): 95-105. NRCBL: 18.2; 18.3. SC: em.

Abstract: Objective: To describe how local research ethics committees (LRECs) consider and apply research ethics in the evaluation of biomedical research proposals. Design: A qualitative study was conducted using purposeful sampling, focus groups and a grounded theory approach to generate data and to analyse the work of the LRECs. Setting and participants: 11 LRECs of the Mexican Institute of Social Security (IMSS). Results: LRECs considered ethics to be implicit in all types of research, but that ethics reviews were only necessary for projects that included the direct participation of human beings. The LRECs appeared to understand the importance of consent, as in the completion of a consent form, but did not emphasise the importance of the process of acquiring 'informed' consent. The committees considered their main roles or functions to be: (a) to improve the methodological quality of research and to verify - if applicable - the ethical aspects; (b) to encourage personnel to undergo research training; (c) to follow-up research to oversee the adherence to norms and compliance with a specified research timetable. Conclusions: This study provides a valuable insight into how these LRECs understand the ethical review process. The emphasis of the committees was on rules, regulations, improving research methodology and research training, rather than a focus on efforts to protect the rights and well being of research subjects. The results encourage further normative and descriptive lines of investigation concerning education and the development of LRECs.

van den Hoonaard, Will C. Trends in Canadian sociology master's theses in relation to research ethics review, 1995-2004. *Journal of Empirical Research on Human Research Ethics* 2006 December; 1(4): 77-88. NRCBL: 18.2; 2.1; 2.2. SC: em.

van der Arend, Arie J.G. Research ethics committees and the nurse's role. *In:* Tadd, Win, ed. Ethics in Nursing Edu-

cation, Research and Management. New York: Palgrave Macmillan; 2003: 116-141. NRCBL: 18.2; 4.1.3.

van Luijn, H.E.M.; Aaronson, N.K.; Keus, R.B.; Musschenga, A.W. The evaluation of the risks and benefits of phase II cancer clinical trials by institutional review boards (IRB) members: a case study. *Journal of Medical Ethics* 2006 March; 32(3): 170-176. NRCBL: 18.2; 18.3. SC: em.

Abstract: There are indications that institutional review board (IRB) members do not find it easy to assess the risks and benefits in medical experiments, although this is their principal duty. This study examined how IRB members assessed the risk/benefit ratio (RBR) of a specific phase II breast cancer clinical trial. Participants and METHODS: The trial was evaluated by means of a questionnaire administered to 43 members of IRBs at six academic hospitals and specialised cancer centres in the Netherlands. The questionnaire addressed: identification and estimation of inconvenience, toxicity, psychosocial distress, and benefits of trial participation to patients; identification and estimation of benefits to future patients and medical science; assessment of the trial's RBR; and assessment of its ethical acceptability. RESULTS: Most IRB members expected trial participation to involve fairly or very serious inconvenience, fairly severe to sometimes life-threatening toxicity, and serious psychological and social consequences. Conversely, the perceived likelihood of benefits to patients was modest. Most regarded the study as important, and the balance between risks and benefits to be favourable, and believed that the protocol should be approved. The IRB members' final judgement on the trial's ethical acceptability was significantly correlated with their RBR assessment of the protocol. CONCLUSIONS: Because most patients who participate in clinical trials hope this will prolong their lives, it is suggested that patient information should better describe the anticipated benefits-for example, the likelihood of prolonging life. This would allow patients to make decisions regarding participation based on realistic expectations.

Vasgird, Daniel R. Resisting power and influence: a case study in virtue ethics. *Journal of Empirical Research on Human Research Ethics* 2006 June; 1(2): 19-22. NRCBL: 18.2; 7.3; 1.1. SC: cs.

Veatch, Robert M. Why researchers cannot establish equipoise. *American Journal of Bioethics* 2006 July-August; 6(4): 55-57. NRCBL: 18.2. Comments: Winston Chiong. The real problem with equipoise. American Journal of Bioethics 2006 July-August; 6(4): 37-47.

Veidebaum, Toomas. Research ethics in Estonia. *In:* Beyleveld, D.; Townend, D.; Wright, J., eds. Research Ethics Committees, Data Protection and Medical Research in European Countries. Hants, England; Burlington, VT: Ashgate; 2005: 41-43. NRCBL: 18.2.

Vick, Catherine C.; Finan, Kelly R.; Kiefe, Catarina; Neumayer, Leigh; Hawn, Mary T. Variation in Institutional Review processes for a multisite observational study. *American Journal of Surgery* 2005 November; 190(5): 805-809. NRCBL: 18.2; 18.5.1. SC: em.

NRCBL: National Reference Center for Bioethics Literature Classification Scheme   See inside front cover for terms.

297

Wadman, Meredith. Drive for drugs leads to baby clinical trials. *Nature* 2006 March 23; 440(7083): 406-407. NRCBL: 18.2; 9.7.

Wadman, Meredith. London's disastrous drug trial has serious side effects for research [news]. *Nature* 2006 March 23; 440(7083): 388-389. NRCBL: 18.2; 5.1. Identifiers: United Kingdom (Great Britain).

Wagner, Andrew L. Vertebroplasty and the randomized study: where science and ethics collide [editorial]. *AJNR: American Journal of Neuroradiology* 2005 August; 26(7): 1610-1611. NRCBL: 18.2; 1.3.9.

Wasserman, David; Hellman, Deborah S.; Wachbroit, Robert. Physicians as researchers: difficulties with the "similarity position". *American Journal of Bioethics* 2006 July-August; 6(4): 57-59. NRCBL: 18.2; 1.3.9; 18.5.9; 9.5.6. Comments: Winston Chiong. The real problem with equipoise. American Journal of Bioethics 2006 July-August; 6(4): 37-47.

Weinfurt, Kevin P.; Dinan, Michaela A.; Allsbrook, Jennifer S.; Friedman, Joëlle Y.; Hall, Mark A.; Schulman, Kevin A.; Sugarman, Jeremy. Policies of academic medical center for disclosing financial conflicts of interest to potential research participants. *Academic Medicine* 2006 February; 81(2): 113-118. NRCBL: 18.2; 18.3; 18.6; 7.2.

Weinfurt, Kevin P.; Friedman, Joëlle Y.; Allsbrook, Jennifer S.; Dinan, Michaela A.; Hall, Mark A.; Sugarman, Jeremy. Views of potential research participants on financial conflicts of interest: barriers and opportunities for effective disclosure. *JGIM: Journal of General Internal Medicine* 2006 September; 21(9): 901-906. NRCBL: 18.2; 1.3.9. SC: em.

Weinfurt, Kevin P.; Friedman, Joëlle Y.; Dinan, Michaela A.; Allsbrook, Jennifer S.; Hall, Mark A.; Dhillon, Jatinder K.; Sugarman, Jeremy. Disclosing conflicts of interest in clinical research: views on institutional review boards, conflict of interest committees, and investigators. *Journal of Law, Medicine and Ethics* 2006 Fall; 34(3): 581-591. NRCBL: 18.2; 7.3; 18.3; 1.3.9. SC: em.

Abstract: Strategies for disclosing investigators' financial interests to potential research participants have been adopted by many research institutions. However, little is known about how decisions are made regarding disclosures of financial interests to potential research participants, including what is disclosed and the rationale for making these determinations. We sought to understand the attitudes, beliefs, and practices of institutional review board chairs, conflict of interest committee chairs, and investigators regarding disclosure of financial interests to potential research participants. Several themes emerged, including general attitudes toward conflicts of interest, circumstances in which financial interests should be disclosed, rationales and benefits of disclosure, what should be disclosed, negative effects of and barriers to disclosure, and timing and presentation of disclosure. Respondents cited several rationales for disclosure, including enabling informed decision making, promoting trust in researchers and research institutions, and reducing legal liability. There was general agreement that disclosure should happen early in the consent process. Respondents disagreed about whether to disclose the amounts of particular financial interests. Clarifying the goals of disclosure and understanding how potential research participants use the information will be critical in efforts to ensure the integrity of clinical research and to protect the rights and interests of participants.

Whittaker, Elvi. Adjudicating entitlements: the emerging discourses of research ethics boards. *Health (London)* 2005 October; 9(4): 513-535. NRCBL: 18.2; 18.3; 8.4; 18.5. SC: an.

Wichman, Alison, Kalyan, Dev N.; Abbott, Lura J.; Wesley, Robert; Sandler, Alan L. Protecting human subjects in the NIH's Intramural Research Program: a draft instrument to evaluate convened meetings of its IRBs. *IRB: Ethics and Human Research* 2006 May-June; 28(3): 7-10. NRCBL: 18.2. Identifiers: National Institutes of Health, institutional review board.

Wilkes, Lesley; Cert, Renal; Beale, Barbara. Role conflict: appropriateness of a nurse researcher's actions in the clinical field. *Nurse Researcher* 2005; 12(4): 57-70. NRCBL: 18.2; 18.1; 4.1.3. SC: em; cs.

Williams, Anne. Pitfalls on the road to ethical approval. *Nurse Researcher* 1997 Autumn; 5(1): 15-22. NRCBL: 18.2; 4.1.3. SC: em. Identifiers: United Kingdom (Great Britain).

Willison, Donald J.; Kapral, Moira K.; Peladeau, Pierrot; Richards, Janice R.A.; Fang, Jiming; Silver, Frank L. Variation in recruitment across sites in a consent-based clinical data registry: lessons from the Canadian Stroke Network. *BMC Medical Ethics* 2006; 7(6): E6 [Online]. Accessed: http://www.biomedcentral.com/1472-6939/7/6 [2006 August 15]. NRCBL: 18.2; 18.3. SC: em.

Abstract: Background : In earlier work, we found important selection biases when we tried to obtain consent for participation in a national stroke registry. Recognizing that not all registries will be exempt from requiring consent for participation, we examine here in greater depth the reasons for the poor accrual of patients from a systems perspective with a view to obtaining as representative sample as possible. Methods : We determined the percent of eligible patients who were approached to participate and, among those approached, the percent who actually consented to participate. In addition we examined the reasons why people were not approached or did not consent and the variation across sites in the percent of patients approached and consented. We also considered site variation in restrictions on the accrual and data collection process imposed by either the local research ethics board or the hospital. Results : Seventy percent of stroke patients were approached, with wide variations in approach rates across sites (from: 41% to 86%), and considerable inter-site variation in hospital policies governing patient accrual. Chief reasons for not approaching were discharge or death before being approached for consent. Seventeen percent of those approached refused to participate (range: 5% to 75%). Finally, 11% of those approached did not participate due to language or communication difficulties. Conclusion : We found wide variation in approach and agree rates across sites that were accounted for, in part, by different approaches to accrual and idiosyncratic policies of the hospitals. This wide variation in approach and agree rates raises important challenges for research ethics boards and data protection authorities in determining when to waive consent requirements, when to press for increased quality control, when to permit local adaptation of the consent process, and when to permit alternatives to individual express consent. We offer several suggestions for those registries that require consent for participation.

Wittes, Janet. Playing safe and preserving integrity: making the FDA model work. *Statistics in Medicine* 2004 May 30; 23(10): 1523-1525. NRCBL: 18.2; 7.1; 1.3.12; 7.3. Identifiers: Food and Drug Administration.

Wolf, Leslie E.; Croughan, Mary; Lo, Bernard. The challenges of IRB review and human subjects protections in practice-based research. *Medical Care* 2002 June; 40(6): 521-529. NRCBL: 18.2; 18.6. Identifiers: institutional review board.

Wolf, Leslie E.; Walden, Janice Ferrara; Lo, Bernard. Human subjects issues and IRB review in practice-based research. *Annals of Family Medicine* 2005 May-June; 3(Supplement 1): S30-S37. NRCBL: 18.2. SC: em.

Wolf, Leslie E.; Zandecki, Jolanta. Sleeping better at night: investigators' experiences with certificates of confidentiality. *IRB: Ethics and Human Research* 2006 November-December; 28(6): 1-7. NRCBL: 18.2; 8.4; 15.1. SC: em.

Wright, Jessica; Gordijn, Bert. Medical research on human subjects and RECs in the Netherlands. *In:* Beyleveld, D.; Townend, D.; Wright, J., eds. Research Ethics Committees, Data Protection and Medical Research in European Countries. Hants, England; Burlington, VT: Ashgate; 2005: 153-161. NRCBL: 18.2.

Yentis, S.M.; Dawson, A.J. Medical studies with 'no material ethical issues' — an unhelpful, confusing and potentially unethical suggestion. *Clinical Ethics* 2006 December; 1(4): 234-236. NRCBL: 18.2; 9.6; 1.3.9.

Zamudio, Stacy. Institutional review boards: the structural and cultural obstacles encountered in human biological research. *In:* Turner, Trudy R. ed. Biological Anthropology and Ethics: From Repatriation to Genetic Identity. Albany, NY: State University of New York Press; 2005: 149-163. NRCBL: 18.2.

HUMAN EXPERIMENTATION/ . . . / LEGAL ASPECTS

Baker, Stephen; Beyleveld, Deryck; Wallace, Susan; Wright, Jessica. Research ethics committees and the law in the UK. *In:* Beyleveld, D.; Townend, D.; Wright, J., eds. Research Ethics Committees, Data Protection and Medical Research in European Countries. Hants, England; Burlington, VT: Ashgate; 2005: 271-289. NRCBL: 18.2. SC: le.

Barnes, Mark; Florencio, Patrik S. Investigator, IRB and institutional financial conflicts of interest in hu-

man-subjects research: past, present and future. *Seton Hall Law Review* 2002; 32(3): 525-561. NRCBL: 18.2; 18.6; 5.3; 1.3.9; 1.3.2; 18.3; 2.2. SC: le. Identifiers: institutional review board. Conference: Symposium: New Directions in Human Subject Research: Looking Beyond the Academic Medical Center; Seton Hall Law School; 2001 November; Seton Hall University Graduate School of Medical Education; American Society of Law, Medicine and Ethics.

Beran, R.G.; Beran, M.E. Ethical misconduct by abuse of conscientious objection laws. *Medicine and Law: The World Association for Medical Law* 2006 September; 25(3): 503-512. NRCBL: 18.2; 9.6; 9.7. SC: em; le.
Abstract: INTRODUCTION: Private clinics and clinicians have been involved in clinical drug trials for approximately two decades. This paper reviews the ethical consideration inherent in this process. METHODS: Involvement of a single community based, private, Australian neurological clinic in the conduct of trials was audited. Changes in ethical considerations were analysed. RESULTS: The clinic previously audited its clinical trial involvement, starting with pharmaceutical company orchestrated trials. These were vetted by hospital based ethics committees (ECs) which then refused to review private research. A private EC accommodating NH and MRC standards was formed to assess private research. Indemnity concerns forced return to institutional ECs with government guaranteed indemnification. Trials evolved to investigator initiated, company sponsored studies thence a company asking the clinic to devise, sponsor and manage a trial. The latter relegated trial co-ordination to the clinic which would control publication thereby creating new ethical standards. DISCUSSION: Private practice trial involvement evolved from reluctant inclusion to a pivotal role in privately sponsored studies. Access to ECs is government endorsed and publication is independent for investigator-sponsored trials. There has been modification of standard operating procedures and enhanced ethical standards.

Bouchie, Aaron. Clinical trial data: to disclose or not to disclose? [news]. *Nature Biotechnology* 2006 September; 24(9): 1058-1060. NRCBL: 18.2; 1.3.9; 18.6. SC: le.

Breen, Kerry J. Maintaining community trust in biomedical research involving humans [forum]. *University of New South Wales Law Journal* 2003; 26(3): 793-798. NRCBL: 18.2; 5.3. SC: le. Identifiers: Australia.

Brewer, Sherry. When things go wrong. . . . *Protecting Human Subjects* 2006 Spring; (13): 13-14. NRCBL: 18.2. SC: le.

Capron, Alexander M. Experimentation with human beings: light or only shadows? *Yale Journal of Health Policy, Law and Ethics* 2006 Summer; 6(2): 431-449. NRCBL: 18.2; 17.2; 2.1. SC: le. Conference: Symposium: A World Less Silent: Celebrating Jay Katz's Contribution to Law, Medicine, and Ethics.

Coleman, Carl H. Duties to subjects in clinical research. *Vanderbilt Law Review* 2005 March; 58(20): 387-449. NRCBL: 18.2; 8.1; 18.5.1; 18.6. SC: le.

Corrao, S.; Arnone, G.; Arnone, S.; Baldari, S. Medical ethics, clinical research, and special aspects in nuclear medicine [editorial]. *Quarterly Journal of Nuclear Medi-*

NRCBL: National Reference Center for Bioethics Literature Classification Scheme   See inside front cover for terms.

299

cine and Molecular Imaging 2004 September; 48(3): 175-180. NRCBL: 18.2; 2.1; 21.1; 16.2. SC: em; le. Identifiers: Italy.

Council of Europe. Additional protocol to the Convention on Human Rights and Biomedicine concerning Biomedical Research, Council of Europe, 2004. *European Journal of Health Law* 2004 September; 11(3): 293-307. NRCBL: 18.2; 18.3. SC: le.

Council of State and Territorial Epidemiologists. Advisory Committee; Hodge, James G., Jr.; Gostin, Lawrence O. Public practice vs. research: a report for public health practitioners including cases and guidance for making distinctions. *Atlanta, Georgia: Council of State and Territorial Epidemiologists* 2004 May 24; 61 pages [Online]. Accessed: http://www.ihs.gov/MedicalPrograms/ Research/pdf_files/CSTEPHResRptHodgeFinal. 5.24.04.pdf [2006 January 25]. NRCBL: 18.2; 9.1; 7.1. SC: le.

Deutsch, Erwin. Limitation of medical research in German law. *Revista de Derecho y Genoma Humano* 2005 July-December; (23): 15-29. NRCBL: 18.2; 18.6. SC: le.

Dhai, A. Research ethics review — protecting participants in research. *South African Medical Journal* 2005 August; 95(8): 595-597. NRCBL: 18.2; 1.3.9; 18.6; 21.1. SC: em; le. Identifiers: United Kingdom (Great Britain).

Faden, Ruth. Response: reflections on Jay Katz's legacy. *Yale Journal of Health Policy, Law and Ethics* 2006 Summer; 6(2): 451-454. NRCBL: 18.2; 2.1. SC: le. Conference: Symposium: A World Less Silent: Celebrating Jay Katz's Contribution to Law, Medicine, and Ethics. Comments: Alexander M. Capron. Experimentation with human beings: light or only shadows? Yale Journal of Health Policy, Law and Ethics 2006 Summer; 6(2): 431-449.

Farrell, Kristen. Human experimentation in developing countries: improving international practices by identifying vulnerable populations and allocating fair benefits. *Journal of Health Care Law and Policy* 2006; 9(1): 136-161. NRCBL: 18.2; 18.3; 18.5.9. SC: le.

Feuillet, Brigitte. The role of ethics committees in relation to French biomedical research: protection of the person and personal data. *In:* Beyleveld, D.; Townend, D.; Wright, J., eds. Research Ethics Committees, Data Protection and Medical Research in European Countries. Hants, England; Burlington, VT: Ashgate; 2005: 55-71. NRCBL: 18.2. SC: le.

Forster, David. Independent institutional review boards. *Seton Hall Law Review* 2002; 32(3): 513-523. NRCBL: 18.2; 2.2; 18.6. SC: le. Conference: Symposium: New Directions in Human Subject Research: Looking Beyond the Academic Medical Center; Seton Hall Law School; 2001 November; Seton Hall University Graduate School of Medical Education; American Society of Law, Medicine and Ethics.

Gatter, Robert. Conflicts of interest in international human drug research and the insufficiency of international protections. *American Journal of Law and Medicine* 2006; 32(2-3): 351-364. NRCBL: 18.2; 9.7; 7.3; 21.1. SC: le.

Goldstein, Nathan. Financial conflict of interest in biomedical human subject research. *Journal of Biolaw and Business* 2006; 9(1): 26-37. NRCBL: 18.2; 1.3.9; 7.3. SC: le.

Goodman, Neville W. Will the new rules for research ethics committees lead to better decisions? *Journal of the Royal Society of Medicine* 2004 April; 97(4): 198-199. NRCBL: 18.2. SC: le. Identifiers: United Kingdom (Great Britain).

Hanning, Christopher D.; Rentowl, Patricia. Harmful impact of EU clinical trials directives: trial of alerting drug in fibromyalgia has had to be abandoned. . . [letter]. *BMJ: British Medical Journal* 2006 March 18; 332(7542): 666. NRCBL: 18.2; 18.6; 21.1. SC: le.

Hutt, Leah E. Protecting the protectors: indemnification agreements for REB members. *CMAJ/JAMC: Canadian Medical Association Journal* 2006 November 7; 175(10): 1229-1230. NRCBL: 18.2; 8.5; 18.3. SC: le. Identifiers: research ethics boards.

Icenogle, Daniel L. IRBs, conflict and liability: will we see IRBs in court? Or is it when? *Clinical Medicine and Research* 2003 January; 1(1): 63-68. NRCBL: 18.2; 18.6. SC: le.

King, Nancy M.P. The line between clinical innovation and human experimentation. *Seton Hall Law Review* 2002; 32(3): 573-582. NRCBL: 18.2; 18.3; 5.2. SC: le; cs. Conference: Symposium: New Directions in Human Subject Research: Looking Beyond the Academic Medical Center; November 2001; Seton Hall Law School, Seton Hall University Graduate School of Medical Education; American Society of Law, Medicine and Ethics.

Kubiak, Cinead R. Conflicting interests and conflicting laws: re-aligning the purpose and practice of research ethics committees. *Brooklyn Journal of International Law* 2005; 30(2): 759-812. NRCBL: 18.2; 1.3.9; 2.2; 7.3; 6. SC: le.

Lattanzi, Roberto. Research ethics committees in Italy's legal system. *In:* Beyleveld, D.; Townend, D.; Wright, J., eds. Research Ethics Committees, Data Protection and Medical Research in European Countries. Hants, England; Burlington, VT: Ashgate; 2005: 111-125. NRCBL: 18.2. SC: le.

Lebeer, Guy; De Boeck, Geneviève. Belgian ethics committees and the protection of personal data. *In:* Beyleveld, D.; Townend, D.; Wright, J., eds. Research Ethics Committees, Data Protection and Medical Research in European Countries. Hants, England; Burlington, VT: Ashgate; 2005: 9-25. NRCBL: 18.2; 8.4. SC: le.

Lehtonen, Lasse A.; Halila, Ritva. The general legal responsibility of research ethics committees in Finland. *In:* Beyleveld, D.; Townend, D.; Wright, J., eds. Research Ethics Committees, Data Protection and Medical Research in European Countries. Hants, England; Burlington, VT: Ashgate; 2005: 45-53. NRCBL: 18.2. SC: le.

Liddell, Kathleen; Bion, Julian; Chamberlain, Douglas; Druml, Christiane; Kompanje, Erwin; Lemaire, Francois; Menon, David; Vrhovac, Bozidar; Wiedermann, Christian J. Medical research involving incapacitated adults: implications of the EU Clinical Trials Directive 2001/20/EC. *Medical Law Review* 2006 Autumn; 14(3): 367-417. NRCBL: 18.2; 18.5.6; 18.3; 8.3.3; 1.1; 2.1. SC: le.

Ludbrook, Philip A.; Clemens, Diane K.; Munson, Ronald; Scannell, Patricia M. Responsible conduct of research. *In:* Schuster, Daniel P.; Powers, William J., eds. Translational and Experimental Clinical Research. Philadelphia, PA: Lippincott Williams and Wilkins; 2005: 163-175. NRCBL: 18.2. SC: le.

Maloney, Dennis M. Research subjects say institutional review boards (IRBs) must change research review procedures. *Human Research Report* 2006 January; 21(1): 8. NRCBL: 18.2; 18.5.3. SC: le. Identifiers: Diaz v. Hillsborough County Hospital Authority d/b/a Tampa General Hospital, et al. (Part 6).

Mathews, Debra J.H.; Donovan, Peter; Harris, John; Lovell-Badge; Robin; Savulescu, Julian; Baden, Ruth. Science and law: integrity in international stem cell research collaborations. *Science* 2006 August 18; 313(5789): 921-922. NRCBL: 18.2; 1.3.9; 18.5.4; 15.1. SC: le; em. Identifiers: Hinxton Group.

Mitchell, Christopher D. Harmful impact of EU clinical trials directives: . . .while paediatric oncology is being scuppered [letter]. *BMJ: British Medical Journal* 2006 March 18; 332(7542): 666. NRCBL: 18.2; 18.6; 21.1. SC: le.

Moniz, Helena; Figalgo, Sónia; Vale e Reis, Rafael; Almeida, Rosalvo. The constitution and operation of health ethics committees in Portugal: rights of patients to personal data protection. *In:* Beyleveld, D.; Townend, D.; Wright, J., eds. Research Ethics Committees, Data Protection and Medical Research in European Countries. Hants, England; Burlington, VT: Ashgate; 2005: 189-213. NRCBL: 18.2. SC: le.

Patterson, David. Resolving legal, ethical, and human rights challenges in HIV vaccine research. *HIV/AIDS Policy and Law Review* 2000; 5(4): 60-66. NRCBL: 18.2; 9.5.6; 21.1. SC: le.

Ploem, M.C. Towards an appropriate privacy regime for medical data research. *European Journal of Health Law*

2006 April; 13(1): 41-64. NRCBL: 18.2; 21.1; 1.1; 18.3. SC: le.

Powell, Daniel J. Using false claims act as a basis for institutional review board liability. *University of Chicago Law Review* 2002 Summer; 69(3): 1399-1426. NRCBL: 18.2. SC: an; le.

Rudze, Laima. Research ethics committees in Latvia. *In:* Beyleveld, D.; Townend, D.; Wright, J., eds. Research Ethics Committees, Data Protection and Medical Research in European Countries. Hants, England; Burlington, VT: Ashgate; 2005: 127-139. NRCBL: 18.2. SC: le.

Ruel, Michael D. Using race in clinical research to develop tailored medications: is the FDA encouraging discrimination or eliminating traditional disparities in health care for African Americans? *Journal of Legal Medicine* 2006 June; 27(2): 225-241. NRCBL: 18.2; 9.7; 9.5.4. SC: le.

Rynning, Elisabeth. The Swedish system for ethics review of biomedical research and processing of sensitive personal data. *In:* Beyleveld, D.; Townend, D.; Wright, J., eds. Research Ethics Committees, Data Protection and Medical Research in European Countries. Hants, England; Burlington, VT: Ashgate; 2005: 245-270. NRCBL: 18.2. SC: le.

Salako, S.E. The declaration of Helsinki 2000: ethical principles and the dignity of difference. *Medicine and Law: The World Association for Medical Law* 2006 June; 25(2): 341-354. NRCBL: 18.2; 21.1. SC: an; le.

Abstract: The first detailed regulations about nontherapeutic research were promulgated by the Prussian Government in 1900. In 1947, the Nuremberg Code was decreed. Since then, the Declaration of Helsinki (DOH) was adopted in 1964 and has been revised five times. The object of this article is to evaluate the 2000 Revision of the DOH and discuss three problems of concern. These problems are: (1) If, unlike its predecessors, the DOH (2000) has recast itself as a minimum set of international standards 'binding' on physicians worldwide, from where does it derive its authority? (2) The wording of the DOH is incongruent with the underlying ethical principles. (3) The projection of the DOH into the realms of social justice raises the issue of human dignity. Finally, the feasibility or desirability of a theory of justice privileging human dignity as one of its guiding principles and the future of the DOH are examined.

Sándor, Judit. Research ethics committees in Hungary. *In:* Beyleveld, D.; Townend, D.; Wright, J., eds. Research Ethics Committees, Data Protection and Medical Research in European Countries. Hants, England; Burlington, VT: Ashgate; 2005: 93-105. NRCBL: 18.2. SC: le.

Saver, Richard S. Medical research oversight from the corporate governance perspective: comparing institutional review boards and corporate boards. *William and Mary Law Review* 2004 November; 46(2): 619-730. NRCBL: 18.2; 1.3.2. SC: le.

Slovenko, Ralph. Milestones in the evolution of standards for experimental treatment or research. *Medicine and Law:*

NRCBL: National Reference Center for Bioethics Literature Classification Scheme   See inside front cover for terms.

301

The World Association for Medical Law 2006 September; 25(3): 523-557. NRCBL: 18.2; 18.3; 2.2. SC: le.

Abstract: The abuses in experimentation that marked the 20th century has resulted in regulations. Standards for experimental treatment or for research involving human subjects has been a major development of the twentieth century, coming about in response to the horrendous experiments carried out by Nazi Germany and also in the United States and elsewhere. How these regulations have fared is discussed herein.

Thomson, Colin J.H. Protecting health information privacy in research: what's an ethics committee like yours doing in a job like this? *Journal of Law and Medicine* 2006 February; 13(3): 304-310. NRCBL: 18.2; 8.4; 18.3; 18.6. SC: le.

Trevena, L.; Irwig, L.; Barratt, A. Impact of privacy legislation on the number and characteristics of people who are recruited for research: a randomised controlled trial. *Journal of Medical Ethics* 2006 August; 32(8): 473-477. NRCBL: 18.2; 8.4. SC: em; le.

Abstract: BACKGROUND: Privacy laws have recently created restrictions on how researchers can approach study participants. Method: In a randomised trial of 152 patients, 50-74 years old, in a family practice, 60 were randomly selected to opt-out and 92 to opt-in methods. Patients were sent an introductory letter by their doctor in two phases, opt-out before and opt-in after introduction of the new Privacy Legislation in December 2001. Opt-out patients were contacted by researchers. Opt-in patients were contacted if patients responded by email, free telephone number or a reply-paid card. RESULTS: Opt-in recruited fewer patients (47%; 43/92) after invitation compared with opt-out (67%; 40/60); (-20%; [-4% to -36%]). No proportional difference in recruitment was found between opt-in and opt-out groups varied by age, sex or socioeconomic status. The opt-in group had significantly more people in active decision-making roles (+30%; [10% to 50%]; p = 0.003). Non-significant trends were observed towards opt-in being less likely to include people with lower education (-11.8%; [-30% to 6.4%]; p = 0.13) and people who were not screened (-19.1%; [-40.1% to 1.9%]; p = 0.08). Opt-in was more likely to recruit people with a family history of colorectal cancer (+12.7%; [-2.8%, 28.2%]; p = 0.12). CONCLUSIONS: The number of participants required to be approached was markedly increased in opt-in recruitment. Existing participants (eg, screening attendees) with a vested interest such as increased risk, and those preferring an active role in health decision making and with less education were likely to be recruited in opt-in. Research costs and generalisability are affected by implementing privacy legislation.

United States. Congress. House. A bill to amend the Public Health Service Act to establish an independent office to be known as the Office for Protection of Human Research Subjects, and to assign to such Office responsibility for administering regulations regarding the protection of human subjects in Federal research projects. Washington, DC: U.S. G.P.O., 2000. 11 p. [Online]. Accessed: http://frwebgate.access.gpo.gov/cgi-bin/getdoc.cgi?dbname=106_cong_bills&docid=f:h3569ih.txt.pdf [2007 March 2]. NRCBL: 18.2. SC: le. Note: H.R. 3569, 106th Congress, 2nd session. Introduced by Rep. Kucinich on February 2, 2000. Referred to the Committee on Commerce.

United States. Congress. House. A bill to amend the Public Health Service Act with respect to the protection of human subjects in research. Washington, DC: U.S. G.P.O., 2000. 35 p. [Online]. Accessed: http://frwebgate.access.gpo.gov/cgi-bin/getdoc.cgi?dbname=106_cong_bills&docid= f:h4605ih.txt.pdf [2007 March 2]. NRCBL: 18.2. SC: le. Note: H.R. 4605, 106th Congress, 2nd session. Introduced by Rep. DeGette on June 8, 2000. Referred to the Committee on Commerce.

United States. Congress. House. A bill to amend the Public Health Service Act with respect to the protection of human subjects in research. Washington, DC: U.S. G.P.O., 2006. 35 p. [Online]. Accessed: http://frwebgate.access.gpo.gov/cgi-bin/useftp.cgi?IPaddress=162.140.64.21&filename=h5578ih.pdf&directory=/diskb/wais/data/109_cong_bills [2006 July 17]. NRCBL: 18.2. SC: le. Identifiers: Protection for Participants in Research Act of 2006. Note: H.R. 5578, 109th Congress, 2d session. Introduced by Rep. DeGette, June 9, 2006. Referred to the Committee on Energy and Commerce.

Watson, Max. Harmful impact of EU clinical trials directives: . . .and so has trial of melatonin in cancer related weight loss. . . [letter]. *BMJ: British Medical Journal* 2006 March 18; 332(7542): 666. NRCBL: 18.2; 18.6; 21.1; 9.7. SC: le.

Wichman, Alison; Sandler, Alan L. Institutional review boards. *In:* Gallin, John I., ed. Principles and Practice of Clinical Research. San Diego, CA: Academic Press; 2002: 51-62. NRCBL: 18.2. SC: le.

HUMAN EXPERIMENTATION/ INFORMED CONSENT
See also INFORMED CONSENT

China: people living with HIV complain about conduct of medical research [news]. *HIV/AIDS Policy and Law Review* 2004 April; 9(1): 31-32. NRCBL: 18.3; 9.5.6; 18.5.7.

The plaintiff as person: cause lawyering, human subject research, and the secret agent problem. *Harvard Law Review* 2006 March; 119(5): 1510-1531. NRCBL: 18.3; 18.1; 1.1; 1.3.8; 1.3.9; 4.4; 8.1. SC: le.

Trialists should tell participants result, but how? [editorial]. *Lancet* 2006 April 1-7; 367(9516): 1030. NRCBL: 18.3; 8.1.

When informed consent is not required for research. *Human Research Report* 2006 June; 21(6): 3. NRCBL: 18.3; 18.6.

Abboud, P-A.; Heard, K.; Al-Marshad, A.A.; Lowenstein, S.R. What determines whether patients are willing to participate in resuscitation studies requiring exception from informed consent? *Journal of Medical Ethics* 2006 August; 32(8): 468-472. NRCBL: 18.3; 9.5.1. SC: em.

Abstract: OBJECTIVES: To examine the willingness of patients to participate in a resuscitation study that requires exception from informed consent and to determine if willingness to participate is associated with demographic and other characteristics. METHODS: Adult patients in an emergency department and in a geriatric outpatient clinic were surveyed. Patients were asked to imagine that they presented to an emergency department with cardiac arrest and asked about their willingness to(1) receive a new drug outside of a study, (2) receive a new drug as part of a study and (3) participate in a randomised controlled trial (RCT) for a new drug. Patients were also asked about participation in studies of invasive procedures. RESULTS: 213 patients from a geriatric clinic and 207 from an emergency department were surveyed. Two thirds of patients from the geriatric clinic and 83% from the emergency department were willing to receive an experimental drug outside of a study. Patients were less willing to participate in a study of the new drug and even less likely to participate in an RCT for the new drug (chi(2) test for trend, p.001 for both settings). Patients were less likely to participate in a study of thoracotomy than in a study that required placement of a femoral catheter (p = 0.008 for the geriatric clinic, p = 0.01 for the emergency department). Willingness to participate was not associated with trust in the doctors. CONCLUSIONS: Study design and invasiveness of the intervention were associated with the willingness of patients to participate in resuscitation studies that require exception from informed consent.

Adam, Dieter; Kasper, S.; Moller, H.J.; Singer, E.A. Placebo-controlled trials in major depression are necessary and ethically justifiable: how to improve the communication between researchers and ethical committees. *European Archives of Psychiatry and Clinical Neuroscience* 2005 August; 255(4): 258-260. NRCBL: 18.3; 17.1; 18.2. SC: em. Identifiers: 3rd European Expert Forum on Ethical Evaluation of Placebo-Controlled Studies in Depression.

Alfano, Bruno; Brunetti, Arturo. Advances in brain imaging: a new ethical challenge. *Annali Dell'Istituto Superiore di Sanità* 1997; 33(4): 483-488. NRCBL: 18.3; 17.1.

Allmark, P.; Mason, S. Improving the quality of consent to randomised controlled trials by using continuous consent and clinician training in the consent process. *Journal of Medical Ethics* 2006 August; 32(8): 439-443. NRCBL: 18.3; 7.2. SC: em.
Abstract: OBJECTIVE: To assess whether continuous consent, a process in which information is given to research participants at different stages in a trial, and clinician training in that process were effective when used by clinicians while gaining consent to the Total Body Hypothermia (TOBY) trial. The TOBY trial is a randomised controlled trial (RCT) investigating the use of whole-body cooling for neonates with evidence of perinatal asphyxia. Obtaining valid informed consent for the TOBY trial is difficult, but is a good test of the effectiveness of continuous consent. METHODS: Semistructured interviews were conducted with 30 sets of parents who consented to the TOBY trial and with 10 clinicians who sought it by the continuous consent process. Analysis was focused on the validity of parental consent based on the consent components of competence, information, understanding and voluntariness. RESULTS: No marked problems with consent validity at the point of signature were observed in 19 of 27 (70%) couples. Problems were found mainly to lie with the competence and understanding of the parents: mothers, particularly, had problems with competence in the early stages of consent. Problems in understanding were primarily to do with side effects. Problems in both competence and understanding were observed to reduce markedly, particularly for mothers, in the post-signature phase, when further discussion took place. Randomisation was generally understood but unpopular. Information was not always given by clinicians in stages during the short period available before parents gave consent. Most clinicians, however, were able to give follow-up information. DISCUSSION: Consent validity was found to compare favourably with similar trials examined in the Euricon study. CONCLUSION: Adopting the elements of the continuous consent process and clinician training in RCTs should be considered by researchers, particularly when they have concerns about the quality of consent they are likely to obtain by using a conventional process.

American Society for Reproductive Medicine [ASRM]. Ethics Committee. Informed consent and the use of gametes and embryos for research. *Fertility and Sterility* 2004 September; 82(Supplement 1): S251-S252. NRCBL: 18.3; 18.5.4; 15.1.

Anderson, Brian; Cranswick, Noel. The placebo (I shall please) — is it so pleasing in children? [editorial]. *Paediatric Anaesthesia* 2005 October; 15(10): 809-813. NRCBL: 18.3; 18.5.2; 1.1.

Angiolillo, Anne L.; Simon, C.; Kodish, E.; Lange, B.; Noll, R.B.; Ruccione, K.; Matloub, Y. Staged informed consent for a randomized clinical trial in childhood leukemia: impact on the consent process. *Pediatric Blood and Cancer* 2004 May; 42(5): 433-437. NRCBL: 18.3; 18.5.2.

Appelbaum, Paul S. Decisional capacity of patients with schizophrenia to consent to research: taking stock. *Schizophrenia Bulletin* 2006 January; 32(1): 22-25. NRCBL: 18.3; 18.5.6.

Appelbaum, Paul S.; Lidz, Charles W. Re-evaluating the therapeutic misconception: response to Miller and Joffe. *Kennedy Institute of Ethics Journal* 2006 December; 16(4): 367-373. NRCBL: 18.3; 5.2. Comments: Franklin G. Miller and Steven Joffe. Evaluating the therapeutic misconception by Miller and Joffe. Kennedy Institute of Ethics Journal 2006 December; 16(4): 353-366.
Abstract: Responding to the paper by Miller and Joffe, we review the development of the concept of therapeutic misconception (TM). Our concerns about TM's impact on informed consent do not derive from the belief that research subjects have poorer outcomes than persons receiving ordinary clinical care. Rather, we believe that subjects with TM cannot give an adequate informed consent to research participation, which harms their dignitary interests and their abilities to make meaningful decisions. Ironically, Miller and Joffe's approach ends up largely embracing the very position that they inaccurately attribute to us: the belief that, with some exceptions, it is only the prospect of poorer outcomes that should motivate efforts to dispel TM. In the absence of empirical studies on the steps required to dispel TM and the impact of such procedures on subject recruitment, it is premature to surrender to the belief that TM must be widely tolerated in clinical research.

Ballard, Hubert O.; Shook, Lori A.; Desai, Nirmala S.; Anand, K.J.S. Neonatal research and the validity of informed consent obtained in the perinatal period. *Journal of*

NRCBL: National Reference Center for Bioethics Literature Classification Scheme See inside front cover for terms.

303

Perinatology 2004 July; 24(7): 409-415. NRCBL: 18.3; 18.5.2; 8.3.2. SC: em.

Barnes, L; Matthews, F. E.; Barber, B.; Davies, L.; Lloyd, D.; Brayne, C.; Parry, B. Brain donation for research: consent and re-consent post Alder Hey. *Bulletin of Medical Ethics* 2005 October-November; (211): 17-21. NRCBL: 18.3; 9.5; 20.1; 17.1. SC: em. Identifiers: United Kingdom (Great Britain).

Baron, Jonathan. A decision analysis consent. *American Journal of Bioethics* 2006 May-June; 6(3): 46-52. NRCBL: 18.3; 1.1; 2.1.

Barrett, Roseann. Quality of informed consent: measuring understanding among participants in oncology clinical trials. *Oncology Nursing Forum* 2005 July 1; 32(4): 751-755. NRCBL: 18.3; 18.2; 9.5.1.

Bell, H.; Busch, N. Bridget; DiNitto, D. Can you ask that over the telephone? Conducting sensitive or controversial research using random-digit dialing. *Medicine and Law: World Association for Medical Law* 2006 March; 25(1): 59-81. NRCBL: 18.3; 8.4; 1.3.12. SC: em.
Abstract: Social science, medical, and legal researchers often study sensitive or controversial topics and behaviors. This research raises methodological and ethical issues. Using examples from the literature and a recent statewide telephone prevalence survey on sexual assault, we focus on the relative merits of various survey methods, especially those employing new technologies; developing instrumentation that includes explicit behavioral questions; obtaining an appropriate sample in a cost efficient way; gaining informed consent and inquiring about sensitive topics while protecting participants from harm or retraumatization; presenting findings in a way that does not further stigmatize participants; and responding to the media.

Bernstein, Mark. Fully informed consent is impossible in surgical clinical trials. *Canadian Journal of Surgery* 2005 August; 48(4): 271-272. NRCBL: 18.3; 18.2; 8.1.

Berto, D.; Peroni, M.; Milleri, S.; Spagnolo, A.G. Evaluation of the readability of information sheets for healthy volunteers in phase-I trials. *European Journal of Clinical Pharmacology* 2000 August; 56(5): 371-374. NRCBL: 18.3. SC: em. Identifiers: Italy.

Booth, Malcolm G.; Lind, A.; Read, E.; Kinsella, J. Public perception of emergency research: a questionnaire. *European Journal of Anaesthesiology* 2005 December; 22(12): 933-937. NRCBL: 18.3; 18.2; 9.5.1. SC: em.

Bosk, Charles L. Obtaining voluntary consent for research in desperately ill patients. *Medical Care* 2002 September; 40(9, Supplement): V64-V68. NRCBL: 18.3.

Braunack-Mayer, Annette J. The ethics of participating in research [editorial]. *Medical Journal of Australia* 2002 November 4; 177(9): 471-472. NRCBL: 18.3; 18.2.

Brauner, Daniel J.; Merel, Susan E. How a model based on linguistic theory can improve the assessment of decision-making capacity for persons with dementia. *Journal*

of Clinical Ethics 2006 Summer; 17(2): 139-148. NRCBL: 18.3; 18.5.7; 8.1; 8.3.3.

Bravo, Gina; Gagnon, Michaël; Wildeman, Sheila; Marshall, David T.; Pâquet, Mariane; Dubois, Marie-France. Comparison of provincial and territorial legislation governing substitute consent for research. *Canadian Journal on Aging* 2005 Fall; 24(3): 237-249. NRCBL: 18.3; 18.6; 8.3.3.

Brody, Baruch A.; Dickey, Nancy; Ellenberg, Susan S.; Heaney, Robert P.; Levine, Robert J.; O'Brien, Richard L.; Purtilo, Ruth B.; Weijer, Charles. Is the use of placebo controls ethically permissible in clinical trials of agents intended to reduce fractures in osteoporosis? *Journal of Bone and Mineral Research* 2003 June; 18(6): 1105-1109. NRCBL: 18.3; 18.5.1; 18.2; 6.

Caron-Flinterman, J. Francisca; Broerse, Jacqueline E.W.; Teerling, Julia; Bunders, Joske F.G. Patients' priorities concerning health research: the case of asthma and COPD research in the Netherlands. *Health Expectations* 2005 September; 8(3): 253-263. NRCBL: 18.3; 18.2. Identifiers: chronic obstructive pulmonary disease.

Casarett, David J.; Karlawish, Jason. Beyond informed consent: the ethical design of pain research. *Pain Medicine* 2001 June; 2(2): 138-146. NRCBL: 18.3; 4.4; 18.2.

Chen, Donna T.; Miller, Franklin G.; Rosenstein, Donald L. Enrolling decisionally impaired adults in clinical research. *Medical Care* 2002 September; 40(9, Supplement): V20-V29. NRCBL: 18.3; 18.5.6.

Clayton, Ellen Wright; Ross, Lainie Friedman; Shalowitz, David I.; Miller, Franklin G. Implications of disclosing individual results of clinical research [letter and reply]. *JAMA: The Journal of the American Medical Association* 2006 January 4; 295(1): 37-38. NRCBL: 18.3.

Coats, T.J.; Shakur, H. Consent in emergency research: new regulations. *Emergency Medicine Journal* 2005 October; 22(10): 683-685. NRCBL: 18.3; 18.5.1; 18.2; 18.6.

Coebergh, Jan Willem W.; van Veen, Evert-Ben; Vandenbroucke, Jan P.; van Diest, Paul; Oosterhuis, Wolter. One-time general consent for research on biological samples: opt out system for patients is optimal and endorsed in many countries [letter]. *BMJ: British Medical Journal* 2006 March 18; 332(7542): 665. NRCBL: 18.3; 19.5; 21.1. SC: le.

Coghlan, Andy. A life and death dilemma. . . . *New Scientist* 2006 October 21-27; 192(2574): 8-9. NRCBL: 18.3; 18.5.1; 18.6. Identifiers: Food and Drug Administration.

Cola, Philip A. The informed consent process. *In:* Fedor, Carol A.; Cola, Philip A.; Pierre, Christine, eds. Responsible Research: A Guide for Coordinators. London; Chicago, IL: Remedics; 2006: 65-76. NRCBL: 18.3.

Cone, David C.; O'Connor, Robert E. Are US informed consent requirements driving resuscitation research overseas? *Resuscitation* 2005 August; 66(2): 141-148. NRCBL: 18.3; 21.1.

Couzin, Jennifer. Proposed guidelines for emergency research aim to quell confusion [news]. *Science* 2006 September 8; 313(5792): 1372-1373. NRCBL: 18.3. Identifiers: Food and Drug Administration (FDA).

Dalton, Rex. Trauma trials leave ethicists uneasy [news]. *Nature* 2006 March 23; 440(7083): 390-391. NRCBL: 18.3; 19.4; 18.5.1.

Davies, Christina; Collins, Rory. Confidentiality and consent in medical research: balancing potential risks and benefits of using confidential data. *BMJ: British Medical Journal* 2006 August 12; 333(7563): 349-351. NRCBL: 18.3; 8.4. Identifiers: United Kingdom (Great Britain).

Davis, Eric A.; Maio, Ronald F. Ethical issues in prehospital research. *Prehospital and Disaster Medicine* 1993 January-March; 8(Supplement 1): S11-S14. NRCBL: 18.3; 18.2; 8.3.3; 9.5.1.

Davis, Terry C.; Holcombe, Randall F.; Berkel, Hans J.; Pramanik, Sumona; Divers, Stephen G. Informed consent for clinical trials: a comparative study of standard versus simplified forms. *Journal of the National Cancer Institute* 1998 May 6; 90(9): 668-674. NRCBL: 18.3; 18.2; 18.5.1. Comments: Journal of the National Cancer Institute 1998 May 6; 90(9): 644-645.

Dawson, Liza; Kass, Nancy E. Views of US researchers about informed consent in international collaborative research. *Social Science and Medicine* 2005 September; 61(6): 1211-1222. NRCBL: 18.3; 18.5.9; 18.6; 21.1. SC: em.

Dein, Simon; Bhui, Kamaldeep. Issues concerning informed consent for medical research among non-westernized ethnic minority patients in the UK. *Journal of the Royal Society of Medicine* 2005 August; 98(8): 354-356. NRCBL: 18.3; 18.5.1; 18.2; 21.7. SC: cs.

Derse, Arthur R. Emergency research and consent: keeping the exception from undermining the rule. *American Journal of Bioethics* 2006 May-June; 6(3): 36-37; discussion W49- W50. NRCBL: 18.3; 19.4; 18.6. Comments: Ken Kipnis, Nancy M.P. King, and Robert M. Nelson. An open letter to institutional review boards considering Northfield Laboratories' PolyHeme trial. American Journal of Bioethics 2006 May-June; 6(3): 18-21.

Diallo, Dapa A.; Doumbo, Ogobara K.; Plowe, Christopher V.; Wellems, Thomas E.; Emanuel, Ezekial J.; Hurst, Samia A. Community permission for medical research in developing countries. *Clinical Infectious Diseases* 2005 July 15; 41(2): 255-259. Erratum in: Clinical Infectious Diseases 2005 September 15; 41(6): 920. NRCBL: 18.3; 18.5.9. Identifiers: Mali.

Dimond, Bridgit. Dermatology: obtaining patient consent in clinical trials. *British Journal of Nursing* 2006 May 11-24; 15(9): 500-501. NRCBL: 18.3. SC: le.

Dreyfuss, Didier. Is it better to consent to an RCT or to care? Muetadeltaepsilonnualphagammaalphanu ("nothing in excess"). *Intensive Care Medicine* 2005 March; 31(3): 345-355. NRCBL: 18.3; 18.2; 5.2. Identifiers: randomized clinical trial.

Dunn, Laura B.; Palmer, Barton W.; Keehan, Monique. Understanding of placebo controls among older people with schizophrenia. *Schizophrenia Bulletin* 2006 January; 32(1): 137-146. NRCBL: 18.3; 18.5.6; 18.5.7.

Ecks, Stefan. Response to Monica Konrad 'Placebo politics: on comparability, interdisciplinarity and international collaborative research'. *Monash Bioethics Review* 2006 October; 25(4): 85-90. NRCBL: 18.3; 18.5.9; 18.4; 21.1. Identifiers: India. Comments: Monica Konrad. Placebo politics: on comparability, interdisciplinarity and international collaborative research. Monash Bioethics Review 2006 October; 25(4): 67-84.

Edward, Sarah J.L.; Stevens, Andrew J.; Braunholtz, David A.; Lilford, Richard J.; Swift, Teresa. The ethics of placebo-controlled trials: a comparison of inert and active placebo controls. *World Journal of Surgery* 2005 May; 29(5): 610-614. NRCBL: 18.3; 18.2; 18.5.1.

Ehni, Hans-Jörg; Wiesing, Urban. Placebos in klinischen Versuchsreihen: eine vergleichende Analyse der internationalen Richtlinien = Placebos in clinical research: a comparative analysis of international guidelines. *Ethik in der Medizin* 2006 September; 18(3): 223-227. NRCBL: 18.3; 6; 9.5.6; 18.2; 21.1.

Ekamm Ladd, Rosalind; Forman, Edwin. Altruistic motives reconsidered. *American Journal of Bioethics* 2006 September-October; 6(5): 55-56. NRCBL: 18.3; 18.5.2. Comments: Christian Simon, Michelle Eder, Eric Kodish and Laura Siminoff. Altruistic discourse in the informed consent process for childhood cancer clinical trials. American Journal of Bioethics 2006 September-October; 6(5): 40-47.

Eldridge, Sandra M.; Ashby, Deborah; Feder, Gene S. Informed patient consent to participation in cluster randomized trials: an empirical exploration of trials in primary care. *Clinical Trials* 2005; 2(2): 91-98. NRCBL: 18.3; 18.2.

Ellenberg, Susan S. Scientific and ethical issues in the use of placebo and active controls in clinical trials. *Journal of Bone and Mineral Research* 2003 June; 18(6): 1121-1124. NRCBL: 18.3; 18.2; 9.7; 18.5.1.

Evans, Barbara J.; Meslin, Eric M. Encouraging translational research through harmonization of FDA and common rule informed consent requirements for research

---

NRCBL: National Reference Center for Bioethics Literature Classification Scheme   See inside front cover for terms.

305

with banked specimens. *Journal of Legal Medicine* 2006 June; 27(2): 119-166. NRCBL: 18.3; 18.2; 18.6. SC: le.

Ferris, Ann M.; Marquis, Grace S. Bioethics in scientific research: conflicts between subject's equitable access to participate in research and current regulations. *Journal of Nutrition* 2005 April; 135(4): 916-917. NRCBL: 18.3; 18.2. Conference: Symposium: Bioethics in Scientific Research: Conflicts between Subject's Equitable Access to Participate in Research and Current Regulations; 19 April 2004; Washington, D.C.; American Society for Nutritional Sciences.

Feussner, John R.; Burris, James F.; McGlynn, Geraldine; Lavori, Philip W. Enhancing protections for human participants in clinical and health services research — a continuing process. *Medical Care* 2002 September; 40(9, Supplement): V4-V11. NRCBL: 18.3; 18.6.

Feussner, John R.; Murray, Thomas H. Making informed consent meaningful — a state-of-the-art conference [editorial]. *Medical Care* 2002 September; 40(9, Supplement): V1-V3. NRCBL: 18.3.

Fisher, Celia B. Goodness-of-fit ethic for informed consent to research involving adults with mental retardation and developmental disabilities. *Mental Retardation and Developmental Disabilities Research Reviews* 2003; 9(1): 27-31. NRCBL: 18.3; 18.5.6; 4.3. SC: rv.

Fisher, Jill A. Procedural misconceptions and informed consent: insights from empirical research on the clinical trials industry. *Kennedy Institute of Ethics Journal* 2006 September; 16(3): 251-268. NRCBL: 18.3; 18.2; 7.1. SC: em.

Fong, Megan; Braun, Kathryn L.; Chang, R. Mei-Ling. Native Hawaiian preferences for informed consent and disclosure of results from research using stored biological specimens. *Pacific Health Dialog* 2004 September; 11(2): 154-159. NRCBL: 18.3; 18.5.1; 15.1; 19.5. SC: em.

Fost, Norman. Ethical issues in clinical research on fracture prevention in patients with osteoporosis [editorial]. *Journal of Bone and Mineral Research* 2003 June; 18(6): 1110- 1115. NRCBL: 18.3; 18.2; 9.7; 18.5.1.

Furness, Peter N. One-time general consent for research on biological samples: good idea, but will it happen? [letter]. *BMJ: British Medical Journal* 2006 March 18; 332(7542): 665. NRCBL: 18.3; 19.5; 15.1. SC: le. Identifiers: United Kingdom (Great Britain).

Geluda, Katia; Bisaglia, Joana Buarque; Moreira, Vivian; Maldonado, Beatriz Motta; Cunha, Antônio J.L.A.; Trajman, Anete. Third-party informed consent in research with adolescents: the good, the bad and the ugly. *Social Science and Medicine* 2005 September; 61(5): 985-988. NRCBL: 18.3; 8.3.2; 18.5.2; 21.1. SC: em. Identifiers: Brazil.

Gibson, Katie. South Africa: book publisher ordered to pay damages for disclosing women's HIV status. *HIV/AIDS Policy and Law Review* 2005 August; 10(2): 53. NRCBL: 18.3; 9.5.6; 8.4. SC: le.

Gilmore, Patricia Davis. An ethical perspective. Waiver of informed consent requirements in certain medical emergencies: ethical dilemmas. *Journal of Nursing Law* 1997; 4(2): 23-39. NRCBL: 18.3; 18.2; 18.6; 8.3.3; 2.1.

Glannon, W. Phase 1 oncology trials: why the therapeutic misconception will not go away. *Journal of Medical Ethics* 2006 May; 32(5): 252-255. NRCBL: 18.3.

Glock, Rosana Soibelmann; Goldim, José Roberto. Informed consent in gerontology. *Eubios Journal of Asian and International Bioethics* 2003 January 13(1): 6-8. NRCBL: 18.3; 18.5.7. SC: em. Identifiers: Brazil.

Gordon, Elisa J.; Prohaska, Thomas R. The ethics of withdrawal from study participation. *Accountability in Research* 2006 October-December; 13(4): 285-309. NRCBL: 18.3; 18.2. SC: em; le.

Gorelick, David A. Health Insurance Portability and Accountability Act privacy rule and research consent documents [letter]. *Annals of Internal Medicine* 2006 November 21; 145(10): 790. NRCBL: 18.3; 8.4.

Gould, Donald. Experimenting on patients. *New Statesman (London, England* 1957) 1966 August 19; 72: 256-257. NRCBL: 18.3.

Gray, Ronald H.; Sewankambo, Nelson K.; Wawer, Maria J.; Serwadda, David; Kiwanuka, Noah; Lutalo, Tom. Disclosure of HIV status on informed consent forms presents an ethical dilemma for protection of human subjects. *Journal of Acquired Immune Deficiency Syndromes* 2006 February 1; 41(2): 246-248. NRCBL: 18.3; 8.4; 9.5.6.

Greco, Dirceu B. Revising the Declaration of Helsinki: ethics vs economics or the fallacy of urgency. *HIV/AIDS Policy and Law Review* 2000; 5(4): 98-101. NRCBL: 18.3; 9.2; 8.2; 9.5.6.

Greenley, Rachel Neff; Drotar, Dennis; Zyzanski, Stephen J.; Kodish, Eric. Stability of parental understanding of random assignment in childhood leukemia trials: an empirical examination of informed consent. *Journal of Clinical Oncology* 2006 February 20; 24(6): 891-897. NRCBL: 18.3; 18.5.2; 18.2. SC: em.

Gu, Shi (Mark). The ethics of placebo-controlled studies on perinatal HIV transmission and its treatment in the developing world. *Penn Bioethics Journal* 2006; 2(2): 21-24. NRCBL: 18.3; 18.5.9; 18.5.2; 18.5.3; 9.7.
Abstract: Perinatal HIV transmission in the United States has been greatly reduced since the 1993 discovery of zidovudine, known as protocol 076. However, a feasible treatment in developing countries has not yet been found due to the high cost and medical standards needed to implement protocol 076. This

presents an ethical question: whether placebo or active control should be used in testing new treatments. Proponents of a placebo control argue that a placebo control is the only method that provides definitive evidence of efficacy and side-effects, especially important given the scarce financial resources present in developing countries. Critics, however, argue that the use of a placebo controlled study when an effective treatment exists would be jeopardizing the health of individuals in developing countries. The key to resolving this debate is realizing that protocol 076 would not necessarily be effective when transplanted to developing countries due to the lack of adequate medical infrastructure, malnutrition, prevalence of disease, and low standard of living—it is not certain protocol 076 would be better than placebo at all. Following this line of reasoning, quite a few placebo-controlled studies on perinatal HIV treatment have already been performed. Upon examination of this accumulated evidence, one finds that protocol 076, and shortened courses of it, are indeed effective in non-breastfeeding participants in developing countries; however, no treatment has been proven effective for breastfeeding populations. Therefore, it would be ethical to conduct placebo-controlled studies on breastfeeding populations, but not on non-breastfeeding populations.

Guterman, Lila. Artificial-blood study has critics seeing red. *Chronicle of Higher Education* 2006 June 16; 52(41): A17. NRCBL: 18.3; 19.4; 18.2.

Guterman, Lila. Guinea pigs in the ER. *Chronicle of Higher Education* 2006 June 16; 52(41): A14-A18. NRCBL: 18.3; 18.2; 9.1.

Haigh, Carol; Neild, Angela; Duncan, Fiona. Balance of power — do patients use researchers to survive hospital? *Nurse Researcher* 2005; 12(4): 71-81. NRCBL: 18.3; 8.1; 9.8. SC: cs; em.

Hampton, Tracy. Are placebos in advanced cancer trials ethically justified? *JAMA: the Journal of the American Medical Association* 2006 July 19; 296(3): 265-266. NRCBL: 18.3; 18.5.7.

Hansson, Mats G.; Dillner, Joakim; Bartram, Claus R.; Carlson, Joyce A.; Helgesson, Gert. Should donors be allowed to give broad consent to future biobank research? *Lancet Oncology* 2006 March; 7(3): 266-269. NRCBL: 18.3; 15.1; 19.5.

Helgason, Höordur Helgi. Informed consent for donating biosamples in medical research — legal requirements in Iceland. *In:* Árnason, Gardar; Nordal, Salvör; Árnason, Vilhjálmur, eds. Blood and Data: Ethical, Legal and Social Aspects of Human Genetic Databases. Reykjavík: University of Iceland Press; 2004: 127-134. NRCBL: 18.3; 15.1; 19.5. SC: le.

Herrera, C.D.; Jansen, Lynn. Protection of human subjects and scientific progress: can the two be reconciled? [letter and reply]. *Hastings Center Report* 2006 January-February; 36(1): 7-8, 9. NRCBL: 18.3; 9.3.1. Comments: Lynn A. Jansen. A closer look at the bad deal trial. Hastings Center Report 2005 September-October; 35(5): 29- 36.

Hester, D. Micah; Hackler, Chris. Improving medicine through research and the constitutive nature of altruism. *American Journal of Bioethics* 2006 September-October; 6(5): 51-52. NRCBL: 18.3; 18.5.2. Comments: Christian Simon, Michelle Eder, Eric Kodish and Laura Siminoff. Altruistic discourse in the informed consent process for childhood cancer clinical trials. American Journal of Bioethics 2006 September-October; 6(5): 40-47.

Holmes-Rovner, Margaret; Wills, Celia E. Improving informed consent — insights from behavioral decision research. *Medical Care* 2002 September; 40(9, Supplement): V30-V38. NRCBL: 18.3; 18.4.

Hunter, David. One-time general consent for research on biological samples: autonomy and majority rules have been misunderstood [letter]. *BMJ: British Medical Journal* 2006 March 18; 332(7542): 665-666. NRCBL: 18.3; 19.5. SC: le. Identifiers: United Kingdom (Great Britain).

Hyder, Adnan A.; Wali, Salman A. Informed consent and collaborative research: perspectives from the developing world. *Developing World Bioethics* 2006 March; 6(1): 33-40. NRCBL: 18.3; 21.1. SC: em.

Abstract: Introduction: Informed consent has been recognized as an important component of research protocols and procedures of disclosure and consent in collaborative research have been criticized, as they may not be in keeping with cultural norms of developing countries. This study, which is part of a larger project funded by the United States National Bioethics Advisory Commission, explores the opinions of developing country researchers regarding informed consent in collaborative research. Methods: A survey of developing country researchers, involved in human subject research, was conducted by distributing a questionnaire with 169 questions, which included questions relating to informed consent. In addition, six focus group discussions, eight in-depth interviews and 78 responses to open-ended questions in the questionnaire provided qualitative data. Results: 203 surveys were considered complete and were included in the analysis. Written consent was not used by nearly 40% of the researchers in their most recent studies. A large proportion of respondents recommended that human subject regulations should allow more flexibility in ways of documenting informed consent. 84% of researchers agreed that a mechanism to measure understanding should be incorporated in research studies as part of the process of informed consent. Discussion: This paper is an empirical step in highlighting the ethical issues concerning disclosure. Health researchers in developing countries are well aware of the importance of consent in health research, and equally value the significance of educating human subjects regarding study protocols and associated risks and benefits. However, respondents emphasize the need for modifying ethical regulations in collaborative research.

Iltis, Ana Smith. Lay concepts in informed consent to biomedical research: the capacity to understand and appreciate risk. *Bioethics* 2006 August; 20(4): 180-190. NRCBL: 18.3.

Abstract: Persons generally must give their informed consent to participate in research. To provide informed consent persons must be given information regarding the study in simple, lay language. Consent must be voluntary, and persons giving consent must be legally competent to consent and possess the capacity to understand and appreciate the information. This paper

NRCBL: National Reference Center for Bioethics Literature Classification Scheme   See inside front cover for terms.

307

examines the relationship between the obligation to disclose information regarding risks and the requirement that persons have the capacity to understand and appreciate the information. There has been insufficient attention to the extent to which persons must be able to understand and appreciate study information in order to have their consent deemed valid when the information is provided in simple, lay language. This paper argues that (1) the capacity to understand and appreciate information that should be deemed necessary to give valid consent should be defined by the capacity of the typical, cognitively normal adult and (2)the capacity of the typical, cognitively normal adult to understand and appreciate the concept of risk is limited. Therefore, (3) all things being equal, potential subjects must possess a limited capacity to understand and appreciate risk to be deemed competent to consent to research participation. (4) In some cases investigators ought to require that persons possess a greater than typical capacity to understand and appreciate risk.

Jacobson, Gloria A. Vulnerable research participants: anyone may qualify. *Nursing Science Quarterly* 2005 October; 18(4): 359-363. NRCBL: 18.3; 18.2; 18.5.1.

Jacoby, Liva. The role of altruism in parental decision-making for childhood cancer clinical trials — further questions to explore. *American Journal of Bioethics* 2006 September-October; 6(5): 52. NRCBL: 18.3; 18.5.2. Comments: Christian Simon, Michelle Eder, Eric Kodish and Laura Siminoff. Altruistic discourse in the informed consent process for childhood cancer clinical trials. American Journal of Bioethics 2006 September- October; 6(5): 40-47.

Jeste, Dilip V.; Depp, Colin A.; Palmer, Barton W. Magnitude of impairment in decisional capacity in people with schizophrenia compared to normal subjects: an overview. *Schizophrenia Bulletin* 2006 January; 32(1): 121-128. NRCBL: 18.3; 18.5.6. SC: em; rv.

Joffe, Steven. Altruistic discourse and therapeutic misconception in research informed consent. *American Journal of Bioethics* 2006 September-October; 6(5): 53-54. NRCBL: 18.3; 18.5.2. Comments: Christian Simon, Michelle Eder, Eric Kodish and Laura Siminoff. Altruistic discourse in the informed consent process for childhood cancer clinical trials. American Journal of Bioethics 2006 September-October; 6(5): 40-47.

Kachuck, Norman J. Challenges and opportunities: what we are learning from the clinical natalizumab experience. *Expert Review of Neurotherapeutics* 2005 September; 5(5): 605-615. NRCBL: 18.3; 9.7; 7.3. Identifiers: Food and Drug Administration; multiple sclerosis.

Kahn, Jeffrey. Informed consent in the context of communities. *Journal of Nutrition* 2005 April; 135(4): 918-920. NRCBL: 18.3. Conference: Symposium: Bioethics in Scientific Research: Conflicts between Subject's Equitable Access to Participate in Research and Current Regulations; 19 April 2004; Washington, D.C.; American Society for Nutritional Sciences.

Kalra, Dipak; Gertz, Renate; Singleton, Peter; Inskip, Hazel M. Confidentiality of personal health information used for research. *BMJ: British Medical Journal* 2006 July 22; 333(7560): 196-198. NRCBL: 18.3; 8.4; 1.3.9; 1.3.12. Identifiers: United Kingdom (Great Britain).

Karlawish, Jason H.T.; Fox, Ellen; Pearlman, Robert. How changes in health care practices, systems, and research challenge the practice of informed consent. *Medical Care* 2002 September; 40(9, Supplement):V12-V19. NRCBL: 18.3; 4.1.2.

Kemmelmeier, Markus; Davis, Deborah; Follette, William C. Seven "sins" of misdirection?: ethical controversies surrounding the use of deception in research. *In:* O'Donohue, William; Ferguson, Kyle, eds. Handbook of Professional Ethics for Psychologists: Issues, Questions, and Controversies. Thousand Oaks, Calif.: SAGE Publications; 2003: 227-256. NRCBL: 18.3.

Kim, Scott Y.H.; Kim, Hyungjin Myra; McCallum, Colleen; Tariot, Pierre N. What do people at risk for Alzheimer disease think about surrogate consent for research? *Neurology* 2005 November 8; 65(9): 1395-1401. NRCBL: 18.3; 8.3.3; 17.1; 9.5.2. SC: em.

Kipnis, Kenneth; King, Nancy M.P.; Nelson, Robert M. Trials and errors: barriers to oversight of research conducted under the emergency research consent waiver. *IRB: Ethics and Human Research* 2006 March-April; 28(2): 16-19. NRCBL: 18.3; 18.2; 9.7; 9.5.1. SC: le. Identifiers: United States Food and Drug Administration [FDA].

Kirschen, Matthew P.; Jaworska, Agnieszka; Illes, Judy. Subjects' expectations in neuroimaging research. *Journal of Magnetic Resonance Imaging* 2006 February; 23(2): 205-209. NRCBL: 18.3; 18.5.1; 7.1. SC: em.

Kompanje, Erwin J.O.; Maas, A.I.R.; Hilhorst, M.T.; Slieker, F.J.A.; Teasdale, G.M. Ethical considerations on consent procedures for emergency research in severe and moderate traumatic brain injury. *Acta Neurochirurgica* 2005 June; 147(6): 633-640. NRCBL: 18.3; 8.3.3; 18.2. Identifiers: European Union.

Konrad, Monica. Placebo politics: on comparability, interdisciplinarity and international collaborative research. *Monash Bioethics Review* 2006 October; 25(4): 67-84. NRCBL: 18.3; 18.5.9; 18.4; 21.1. Identifiers: India.

Kuczewski, Mark G.; Marshall, Patricia. The decision dynamics of clinical research: the context and process of informed consent. *Medical Care* 2002 September; 40(9, Supplement): V45-V54. NRCBL: 18.3; 21.7.

Leavitt, Frank J. Compromised autonomy, and Asian autonomy: commentaries on Glock and Goldim, and Dena Hsin-Chen Hsin. *Eubios Journal of Asian and International Bioethics* 2003 January 13(1): 8. NRCBL: 18.3; 2.1.

Levine, Aran. Clinical trials research: challenges of patient education and informed consent. *Oncology Nursing Forum* 2005 July; 32(4): 737-739. NRCBL: 18.3; 18.2; 18.1; 4.1.3. SC: cs.

Levine, Robert J. Placebo controls in clinical trials of new therapies for osteoporosis. *Journal of Bone and Mineral Research* 2003 June; 18(6): 1154-1159. NRCBL: 18.3; 18.2; 18.5.1; 9.7.

Levine, Robert J. Placebo controls in clinical trials when there are known effective treatments. *In:* Lolas Stepke, Fernando; Agar Corbinos, Lorenzo, eds. Interfaces Between Bioethics and the Empirical Social Sciences. Buenos Aires, Argentina: World Health Organization; 2002: 79-89. NRCBL: 18.3. Identifiers: Declaration of Helsinki.

Lidz, Charles W.; Appelbaum, Paul S. The therapeutic misconception: problems and solutions. *Medical Care* 2002 September; 40(9, Supplement): V55-V63. NRCBL: 18.3; 18.1.

Lipworth, Wendy. Navigating tissue banking regulation: conceptual frameworks for researchers, administrators, regulators and policy-makers. *Journal of Law and Medicine* 2005 November; 13(2): 245-255. NRCBL: 18.3; 19.5; 18.2; 4.4. SC: le.

Littenberg, Benjamin; MacLean, Charles D. Passive consent for clinical research in the age of HIPAA. *JGIM: Journal of General Internal Medicine* 2006 March; 21(3): 207-211. NRCBL: 18.3; 8.4. SC: em; le. Identifiers: Health Insurance Portability and Accountability Act of 1996.

Lucas, Peter. Toward a tiered approach to consent in biomedical research. *In:* Árnason, Gardar; Nordal, Salvör; Árnason, Vilhjálmur, eds. Blood and Data: Ethical, Legal and Social Aspects of Human Genetic Databases. Reykjavík: University of Iceland Press; 2004: 79-83. NRCBL: 18.3; 1.3.9.

Maaroos, Heidi-Ingrid; Tahepold, Heli; Kalda, Ruth. Patient consent rates for video-recording. *Family Practice* 2004 December; 21(6): 706. NRCBL: 18.3; 8.1. Identifiers: Estonia.

Maloney, Dennis M. Defendants claim that research subjects do not quality [sic; qualify] for a class action lawsuit. *Human Research Report* 2006 February; 21(2): 8. NRCBL: 18.3; 18.5.3. SC: le. Identifiers: Diaz v. Hillsborough County Hospital Authority, d/b/a Tampa General Hospital, et al. (Part 7).

Maloney, Dennis M. Federal agency issues new exception to informed consent requirements. *Human Research Report* 2006 July; 21(7): 1-2. NRCBL: 18.3; 18.2; 18.6.

Maloney, Dennis M. In court: court approves settlement between defendants and former research subjects. *Human Research Report* 2006 July; 21(7): 8. NRCBL: 18.3; 18.5.3. SC: le. Identifiers: Diaz v. Hillsborough County Hospital Authority; d/b/a Tampa General Hospital et al. (Part 12).

Maloney, Dennis M. New advice on special duties for institutional review boards (IRBs). *Human Research Report* 2006 October; 21(10): 1-2. NRCBL: 18.3; 18.2; 18.6.

Maloney, Dennis M. No trial needed when financial settlement benefits the former research subjects. *Human Research Report* 2006 April; 21(4): 8. NRCBL: 18.3; 18.5.3. SC: le. Identifiers: Diaz v. Hillsborough County Hospital Authority, d/b/a Tampa General Hospital, et al. (Part 9).

Maloney, Dennis M. Research subjects win battle to obtain class action status. *Human Research Report* 2006 March; 21(3): 8. NRCBL: 18.3; 18.5.3. SC: le. Identifiers: Diaz v. Hillsborough County Hospital Authority, d/b/aTampa General Hospital, et al. (Part 8).

Maloney, Dennis M. The defendants must attempt to find all former research subjects. *Human Research Report* 2006 May; 21(5): 8. NRCBL: 18.3; 18.5.3. SC: le. Identifiers: Diaz v. Hillsborough County Hospital Authority, d/b/aTampa General Hospital, et al. (Part 10).

Markman, Maurie. Providing research participants with findings from completed cancer-related clinical trials: not quite as simple as it sounds. *Cancer* 2006 April 1; 106(7): 1421-1424. NRCBL: 18.3; 18.2.

Marshall, Patricia A. Informed consent in international health research. *Journal of Empirical Research on Human Research Ethics* 2006 March; 1(1): 25-41. NRCBL: 18.3; 18.5.9.

Mason, S.; Barrow, H.; Phillips, A.; Eddison, G.; Nelson, A.; Cullum, N.; Nixon, J. Brief report on the experience of using proxy consent for incapacitated adults. *Journal of Medical Ethics* 2006 January; 32(1): 61-62. NRCBL: 18.3; 8.3.3; 18.5.6. Identifiers: United Kingdom (Great Britain).

Abstract: The Medicines for Human Use (Clinical Trials) Regulations 2004, which came into force in the UK in May 2004, cover the conduct of clinical trials on medicinal products. They allow a legal representative (a person not connected with the conduct of the trial) to consent to the participation of incompetent adults in medical research. Currently, very little is known about how such representatives will make their decisions. We have experience with proxy consent for older adults in a large, national trial. From 2445 potentially eligible but incapacitated patients, proxy, relative assent resulted in actual participation of only 87 (3.6%) patients. The reasons for this were that a large number of incapacitated patients had no relative available for assent (2286), but also a high proportion of relatives approached refused to provide assent (72/159, 45.3%). In comparison, 17.7% of patients declined participation in the trial. Proxy consent allowed only a small increase in trial recruitment of incapacitated patients. The fact that a greater proportion of relatives than patients refused to provide assent implies that they were more cautious than the patients themselves, or perhaps used different criteria, when making their decision. In future research involving incapacitated older patients there is likely to be heavy reliance on proxy consent provision by legal representatives. Our findings imply that consent decisions of legal

NRCBL: National Reference Center for Bioethics Literature Classification Scheme   See inside front cover for terms.

309

representatives will not necessarily reflect those of patients themselves.

Massimo, Luisa M.; Wiley, Thomas J. Randomization, informed consent and physicians' communication skills in pediatric oncology: a delicate balance. *Bulletin du Cancer* 2005 December 1; 92(12): E67-E69. NRCBL: 18.3; 18.5.2; 18.2; 8.1. SC: cs.

McCabe, Melvina; Morgan, Frank; Curley, Helen; Begay, Rick; Gohdes, Dorothy M. The informed consent process in a cross-cultural setting: is the process achieving the intended result? *Ethnicity and Disease* 2005 Spring; 15(2): 300-304. NRCBL: 18.3; 9.5.4; 21.7. Identifiers: Navajo.

McHale, J.V. 'Appropriate consent' and the use of human material for research purposes: the competent adult. *Clinical Ethics* 2006 December; 1(4): 195-199. NRCBL: 18.3; 19.5; 18.6. SC: le.

McQuillan, Geraldine M.; Pan, Qiyuan; Porter, Kathryn S. Consent for genetic research in a general population: an update on the National Health and Nutrition Examination Survey experience. *Genetics in Medicine* 2006 June; 8(6): 354-360. NRCBL: 18.3; 15.1; 21.7. SC: em.

Menon, Girish; Cash, Richard. Research involving medical records review: an Indian perspective. *Indian Journal of Medical Ethics* 2006 April-June; 3(2): 55-57. NRCBL: 18.3; 8.4; 18.6; 21.7.

Meslin, Eric M. Shifting paradigms in health services research ethics: consent, privacy, and the challenges for IRBs. *JGIM: Journal of General Internal Medicine* 2006 March; 21(3): 279-280. NRCBL: 18.3; 8.4; 18.2. Identifiers: institutional review board.

Miller, Franklin G.; Joffe, Steven. Evaluating the therapeutic misconception. *Kennedy Institute of Ethics Journal* 2006 December; 16(4): 353-366. NRCBL: 18.3; 5.2.
Abstract: The "therapeutic misconception," described by Paul Appelbaum and colleagues more than 20 years ago, refers to the tendency of participants in clinical trials to confuse the design and conduct of research with personalized medical care. Although the "therapeutic misconception" has become a term of art in research ethics, little systematic attention has been devoted to the ethical significance of this phenomenon. This article examines critically the way in which Appelbaum and colleagues formulate what is at stake in the therapeutic misconception, paying particular attention to assumptions and implications that clinical trial participation disadvantages research participants as compared with receiving standard medical care. After clarifying the ethical significance of the therapeutic misconception with respect to the decision making of patients, we offer policy recommendations for obtaining informed consent to participation in clinical trials.

Miller, Victoria A.; Nelson, Robert M. A developmental approach to child assent for nontherapeutic research. *Journal of Pediatrics* 2006 July; 149(1, Supplement): S25-S30. NRCBL: 18.3; 18.5.2; 1.1. SC: an.

Mirarchi, Nina M. Clinical research on the subject with dementia: ethical concerns and research regulation. *Penn Bioethics Journal* 2005 April 2; 1(1): 4p. [Online]. Accessed: http://www.bioethicsjournal.com [2005 April 19]. NRCBL: 18.3; 8.3.3; 18.5.6; 18.5.7.

Murff, Harvey J.; Pichert, James W.; Byrne, Daniel W.; Hedstrom, Christa; Black, Margo; Churchill, Larry; Speroff, Ted. General clinical research center staff nurse perceptions and behaviors regarding informed consent: results of a national survey. *IRB: Ethics and Human Research* 2006 July-August; 28(4): 8-12. NRCBL: 18.3; 18.2. SC: em.

Naarden, Allan L.; Cissik, John. Informed consent. *American Journal of Medicine* 2006 March; 119(3): 194-197. NRCBL: 18.3.

Nagasako, Elna M.; Kalauokalani, Donna A. Ethical aspects of placebo groups in pain trials: lessons from psychiatry. *Neurology* 2005 December 29; 65(12 Supplement 4): S59-S65. NRCBL: 18.3; 18.2; 4.4.

Nelson, Robert M.; Merz, Jon F. Voluntariness of consent for research — an empirical and conceptual review. *Medical Care* 2002 September; 40(9, Supplement): V69-V80. NRCBL: 18.3; 1.1.

Nestler, Grit; Steinert, Ralf; Lippert, Hans; Reymond, Marc A. Using human samples in proteomics-based drug development: bioethical aspects. *Expert Review of Proteomics* 2004 June; 1(1): 77-86. NRCBL: 18.3; 15.1; 9.7; 1.3.12; 8.4; 15.8. SC: le.

Nichol, G.; Huszti, E.; Rokosh, J.; Dumbrell, A.; McGowan, J.; Becker, L. Impact of informed consent requirements on cardiac arrest research in the United States: exception from consent or from research? *Resuscitation* 2004 July; 62(1): 3-23. NRCBL: 18.3; 18.1; 18.2. SC: em; rv. Note: Abstract in English, Portuguese and Spanish.

Norman, R.; Sellman, D.; Warner, C. Mental capacity, good practice and the cyclical consent process in research involving vulnerable people. *Clinical Ethics* 2006 December; 1(4): 228-233. NRCBL: 18.3; 8.3.3; 18.5.6.

North American Primary Care Research Group; Society of Teachers of Family Medicine; Hueston, William J.; Mainous, Aarch G., III; Weiss, Barry D.; Macaulay, Aann C.; Hickner, John; Sherwood, Roger A. Protecting participants in family medicine research: a consensus statement on improving research integrity and participants' safety in educational research, community-based participatory research, and practice network research. *Family Medicine* 2006 February; 38(2): 116-120. NRCBL: 18.3; 18.2; 18.5.1; 18.6.

Oberdorfer, Kevin L.J. The lessons of Greenberg: informed consent and the protection of tissue sources' research interests. *Georgetown Law Journal* 2004 November; 93(1): 365-394. NRCBL: 18.3; 4.4; 8.2. SC: le.

Okie, Susan. Health officials debate ethics of placebo use: medical researchers say guidelines would impair some studies. *Washington Post* 2000 November 24; p. A3. NRCBL: 18.3. SC: po. Identifiers: Declaration of Helsinki.

Onder, Robert F. The ethics of placebo-controlled trials: the case of asthma. *Journal of Allergy and Clinical Immunology* 2005 June; 115(6): 1228-1234. NRCBL: 18.3; 18.2; 18.5.1.

Onvomaha Tindana, Paulina; Kass, Nancy; Akweongo, Patricia. The informed consent process in a rural African setting: a case study of the Kassena-Nankana district of Northern Ghana. *IRB: Ethics and Human Research* 2006 May-June; 28(3): 1-6. NRCBL: 18.3; 18.5.9. SC: em. Identifiers: Ghana.

Pandya, Sunil K. Bypassing scientific requirements [response]. *Indian Journal of Medical Ethics* 2006 October-December; 3(4): 135. NRCBL: 18.3; 18.6.

Panno, Joseph. Jesse Gelsinger: down to earth. *In his:* Gene Therapy: Treating Disease by Repairing Genes. New York: Facts on File, 2005: 45-55. NRCBL: 18.3; 18.5.2; 20.1.

Paris, Adeline; Cracowski, Jean-Luc; Maison, Patrick; Radauceanu, Anca; Cornu, Catherine; Hommel, Marc. Impact of French 'Comités de Protection des Personnes' on the readability of informed consent documents (ICD) in biomedical research: more information, but not better information. *Fundamental and Clinical Pharmacology* 2005 June; 19(3): 395-399. NRCBL: 18.3; 18.2; 18.6. SC: em.

Parker, Michael. When is research on patient records without consent ethical? *Journal of Health Services Research and Policy* 2005 July; 10(3): 183-186. NRCBL: 18.3; 8.4; 1.3.9; 1.1.

Parkes, S.E. Legal aspects of records based medical research. *Archives of Disease in Childhood* 2004 October; 89(10): 899-901. NRCBL: 18.3; 18.6; 8.4; 1.3.12. SC: le.

Patel, Vikram. Ethics of placebo-controlled trial in severe mania. *Indian Journal of Medical Ethics* 2006 January-March; 3(1): 11-12. NRCBL: 18.3; 18.5.6; 8.2.

Pearson, Steven D.; Miller, Franklin G.; Emanuel, Ezekiel J. Medicare's requirement for research participation as a condition of coverage: is it ethical? *JAMA: The Journal of the American Medical Association* 2006 August 23-30; 296(8): 988-991. NRCBL: 18.3; 9.8.

Perna, M.A. "Fair's fair argument" and voluntarism in clinical research: but, is it fair? *Journal of Medical Ethics* 2006 August; 32(8): 478-482. NRCBL: 18.3. SC: an.
Abstract: This article sets out to counteract HM Evans's "fair's fair argument" in support of abolishing veto to research participation. Evans's argument attempts to assimilate ordinary clinical practice to clinical research. I shall refer to this attempt as "assimilation claim". I shall attempt to show that this assimilation, as it is carried out in Evans's argument, is misleading and, ultimately, logically undermines the conclusion. I shall then proceed to show that when the fair's fair argument is proposed independently of the assimilation claim, Evans's conclusion is not unavoidable and possible alternatives are equally open within the terms of the argument itself.

Pfeffer, N.; Kent, J. Consent to the use of aborted fetuses in stem cell research and therapies. *Clinical Ethics* 2006 December; 1(4): 216-218. NRCBL: 18.3; 18.5.4; 15.1; 19.5; 12.4.2. SC: cs.

Plomer, Aurora. Protecting the rights of human subjects in emergency research. *European Journal of Health Law* 2001 December; 8(4): 333-352. NRCBL: 18.3; 8.3.3; 2.1; 18.2. SC: le.

Polgar, Stephen; Ng, Joanna. Ethics, methodology and the use of placebo controls in surgical trials. *Brain Research Bulletin* 2005 October 30; 67(4): 290-297. NRCBL: 18.3; 18.2.

Post, Stephen. Full-spectrum proxy consent for research participation when persons with Alzheimer Disease lose decisional capacities: research ethics and the common good. *Alzheimer Disease and Associated Disorders* 2003 April-June; 17(Supplement 1): S3-S11. NRCBL: 18.3; 18.5.6; 8.3.3.

Pucci, Eugenio; Belardinelli, Natascia; Borsetti, Gabriele; Rodriguez, Daniele; Signorino, Mario. Information and competency for consent to pharmacologic clinical trials in Alzheimer disease: an empirical analysis in patients and family caregivers. *Alzheimer Disease and Associated Disorders* 2001 July- September 15(3): 146-154. NRCBL: 18.3; 18.5.6. SC: em.

Ram, Natalie. Regulating consent to human embryo research: a critique of Health Canada's proposal. *Health Law Review* 2006; 14(2): 19-27. NRCBL: 18.3; 18.5.4; 14.4; 14.6; 18.2; 15.1. SC: le.

Rascol, Olivier. Assessing the risk of a necessary harm: placebo surgery in Parkinson disease [editorial]. *Neurology* 2005 October 11; 65(7): 982-983. NRCBL: 18.3; 18.2; 18.5.1.

Resnik, David B. Compensation for research-related injuries: ethical and legal issues. *Journal of Legal Medicine* 2006 September; 27(3): 263-287. NRCBL: 18.3; 18.2; 8.5. SC: le.

Resnik, David B.; Orentlicher, David. Protection of human subjects and scientific progress: can the two be reconciled? [letter and reply]. *Hastings Center Report* 2006 January-February; 36(1): 4-5, 8- 9. NRCBL: 18.3; 9.5.1. Comments: David Orentlicher. Making research a requirement of treatment. Hastings Center Report 2005 September- October; 35(5): 20-28.

Richardson, Lynne D.; Rhodes, Rosamond; Ragin, Deborah Fish; Wilets, Ilene. The role of community con-

NRCBL: National Reference Center for Bioethics Literature Classification Scheme   See inside front cover for terms.

311

sultation in the ethical conduct of research without consent. *American Journal of Bioethics* 2006 May-June; 6(3): 33-35; discussion W46-W50. NRCBL: 18.3; 18.6; 18.2. Comments: Karla F.C. Holloway. Accidental communities: race, emergency medicine, and the problem of PolyHeme. American Journal of Bioethics 2006 May-June; 6(3): 7-17; Ken Kipnis, Nancy M.P. King, and Robert M. Nelson. An open letter to institutional review boards considering Northfield Laboratories' PolyHeme trial. American Journal of Bioethics 2006 May-June; 6(3): 18-21.

Riessman, Catherine Kohler; Mattingly, Cheryl. Introduction: toward a context-based ethics for social research in health. *Health (London)* 2005 October; 9(4): 427-429. NRCBL: 18.3; 7.1.

Roberts, Laura Weiss; Warner, Teddy D.; Hammond, Katherine Green; Hoop, Jinger G. Views of people with schizophrenia regarding aspects of research: study size and funding sources. *Schizophrenia Bulletin* 2006 January; 32(1): 107-115. NRCBL: 18.3; 18.5.6. SC: em.

Rosenblatt, Michael. Is it ethical to conduct placebo-controlled clinical trials in the development of new agents for osteoporosis? An industry perspective. *Journal of Bone and Mineral Research* 2003 June; 18(6): 1142-1145. NRCBL: 18.3; 18.2; 18.5.1; 9.7.

Rosenthal, Joshua P. Politics, culture, and governance in the development of prior informed consent in indigenous communities. *Current Anthropology* 2006 February; 47(1): 119-142. NRCBL: 18.3; 7.1; 9.7; 15.1; 21.7. Identifiers: Mexico; Peru.

Ross, Colin A. The sham ECT literature: implications for consent to ECT. *Ethical Human Psychology and Psychiatry* 2006 Spring; 8(1): 17-28. NRCBL: 18.3; 17.5; 18.2; 7.1. SC: em. Identifiers: electroconvulsive therapy; placebo.

Rothstein, Mark A. Tiered disclosure options promote the autonomy and well-being of research subjects. *American Journal of Bioethics* 2006 November-December; 6(6): 20-21; author reply W10-W13. NRCBL: 18.3; 18.2; 15.1; 15.3; 1.1. Comments: Vardit Ravitsky and Benjamin S. Wilfond. Disclosing individual genetic results to research participants. American Journal of Bioethics 2006 November-December; 6(6): 8-17.

Rubin, Paul. Indian givers: the Havasupai trusted the white man to help with a diabetes epidemic. Instead, ASU tricked them into bleeding for academia. *Phoenix New Times* 2004 May 27; 9 p. [Online]. Accessed: http://www.phoenixnewtimes.com/Issues/2004-05-27/news/feature_print.html [2006 December 28]. NRCBL: 18.3; 15.1; 18.5.1.

Saks, Elyn R.; Dunn, Laura B.; Palmer, Barton W. Meta-consent in research on decisional capacity: a

"Catch-22"? *Schizophrenia Bulletin* 2006 January; 32(1): 42-46. NRCBL: 18.3; 18.5.6. SC: em.

Schrag, Brian. Research with groups: group rights, group consent, and collaborative research. *Science and Engineering Ethics* 2006 July; 12(3): 511-521. NRCBL: 18.3; 18.2. Comments: Doug Brugge and Mariam Missaghian. Protecting the Navajo people through tribal regulation of research. Science and Engineering Ethics 2006 July; 12(3): 491-507.

Schroter, S.; Plowman, R.; Hutchings, A.; Gonzalez, A. Reporting ethics committee approval and patient consent by study design in five general medical journals. *Journal of Medical Ethics* 2006 December; 32(12): 718-723. NRCBL: 18.3; 18.2; 1.3.7. SC: em.

Sevick, Mary Ann; McConnell, Terrance; Muender, Melissa. Conducting research related to treatment of Alzheimer's disease. *Journal of Gerontological Nursing* 2003 February; 29(2): 6-12. NRCBL: 18.3; 18.5.6; 18.6.

Shalowitz, David; Wendler, David. Informed consent for research and authorization under the Health Insurance Portability And Accountability Act privacy rule: an integrated approach. *Annals of Internal Medicine* 2006 May 2; 144(9): 685-688. NRCBL: 18.3; 8.4.

Shamoo, Adil E. Letter to the editor: emergency research consent waiver — a proper way. *American Journal of Bioethics [Online]* 2006 July-August; 6(4): W48-W51. NRCBL: 18.3; 18.2. Identifiers: PolyHeme; Restore Effective Survival in Shock (RESUS) trial.

Shaul, Randi Zlotnik. Potato, potato, proxy consent, permission — just don't call the whole thing off. *Critical Care* 2005 April; 9(2): 123-124. NRCBL: 18.3; 18.2; 8.3.3.

Silbergleit, Robert; Watters, Drew; Sayre, Michael R. What treatments are "satisfactory?" Divining regulatory intent and an ethical basis for exception to informed consent for emergency research. *American Journal of Bioethics* 2006 May-June; 6(3): 24-26; discussion W49-W50. NRCBL: 18.3; 18.2; 19.4; 18.5.1. Comments: Ken Kipnis, Nancy M.P. King, and Robert M. Nelson. An open letter to institutional review boards considering Northfield Laboratories' PolyHeme trial. American Journal of Bioethics 2006 May-June; 6(3): 18-21.

Simon, Christian; Eder, Michelle; Kodish, Eric; Siminoff, Laura. Altruistic discourse in the informed consent process for childhood cancer clinical trials. *American Journal of Bioethics* 2006 September-October; 6(5): 40-47. NRCBL: 18.3; 18.5.2; 18.2. SC: em.

Singleton, Peter; Wadsworth, Michael. Confidentiality and consent in medical research: consent for the use of personal medical data in research. *BMJ: British Medical Journal* 2006 July 29; 333(7561): 255-258. NRCBL: 18.3; 1.3.12; 1.3.9. SC: le. Identifiers: United Kingdom (Great Britain).

Snowdon, Claire; Elbourne, Diana; Garcia, Jo. "It was a snap decision": parental and professional perspectives on the speed of decisions about participation in perinatal randomised controlled trials. *Social Science and Medicine* 2006 May; 62(9): 2279-2290. NRCBL: 18.3; 18.5.2; 9.4.

Sodeke, Stephen O.; Orentlicher, David. Protection of human subjects and scientific progress: can the two be reconciled? [letter and reply]. *Hastings Center Report* 2006 January-February; 36(1): 5, 8-9. NRCBL: 18.3; 9.5.1. Comments: David Orentlicher. Making research a requirement of treatment. Hastings Center Report 2005 September- October; 35(5): 20-28.

Spellecy, Ryan. Unproven or unsatisfactory versus equipoise in emergency research with waived consent. *American Journal of Bioethics* 2006 May-June; 6(3): 44-45. NRCBL: 18.3; 19.4; 18.2; 18.6. Identifiers: PolyHeme. Comments: Ken Kipnis, Nancy M.P. King, and Robert M. Nelson. An open letter to institutional review boards considering Northfield Laboratories' PolyHeme trial. American Journal of Bioethics 2006 May-June; 6(3): 18-21.

Spriggs, Merle. Can children be altruistic research subjects? *American Journal of Bioethics* 2006 September-October; 6(5): 49-50. NRCBL: 18.3; 18.5.2. Comments: Christian Simon, Michelle Eder, Eric Kodish and Laura Siminoff. Altruistic discourse in the informed consent process for childhood cancer clinical trials. American Journal of Bioethics 2006 September-October; 6(5): 40-47.

Stang, Andreas; Hense, Hans-Werner; Jockel, Karl-Heinz; Turner, Erick H.; Tramer, Martin R. Is it always unethical to use a placebo in a clinical trial? *PLoS Medicine* 2005 March; 2(3): 0177-0180. NRCBL: 18.3; 18.2.

Stobbart, Lynne; Murtagh, Madeleine; Louw, Stephen J.; Ford, Gary A. Consent for research in hyperacute stroke [editorial]. *BMJ: British Medical Journal* 2006 June 17; 332(7555): 1405-1406. NRCBL: 18.3; 18.5.6.

Stolt, Ulrica Gustafsson; Helgesson, Gert; Liss, Per-Erik; Svensson, Tommy; Ludvigsson, Johnny. Information and informed consent in a longitudinal screening involving children: a questionnaire survey. *European Journal of Human Genetics* 2005 March; 13(3): 376- 383. NRCBL: 18.3; 15.3; 18.5.2. SC: em. Identifiers: Sweden.

Sudore, Rebecca L.; Landefeld, C. Seth; Williams, Brie A.; Barnes, Deborah E.; Lindquist, Karla; Schillinger, Dean. Use of a modified informed consent process among vulnerable patients: a descriptive study. *Journal of General Internal Medicine* 2006 August; 21(8): 867-873. NRCBL: 18.3; 18.5.1.

Sugarman, Jeremy; Lavori, Philip W.; Boeger, Maryann; Cain, Carole; Edsond, Robert; Morrison, Vicki; Yeh, Shing Shing. Evaluating the quality of in-

formed consent. *Clinical Trials* 2005; 2(1): 34-41. NRCBL: 18.3. SC: em.

Sugarman, Jeremy; Paasche-Orlow, Michael. Confirming comprehension of informed consent as a protection of human subjects. *Journal of General Internal Medicine* 2006 August; 21(8): 898-899. NRCBL: 18.3.

Tharyan, Prathap. Placebo-controlled trials in psychiatry on trial. *Indian Journal of Medical Ethics* 2006 January-March; 3(1): 13-16. NRCBL: 18.3; 18.5.6; 8.2.

Thibeault, Susan L.; Benninger, Michael. Informed consent in otolaryngology research [editorial]. *Otolaryngology — Head and Neck Surgery* 2005 November; 133(5): 651-653. NRCBL: 18.3; 18.2.

Truog, Robert D. Will ethical requirements bring critical care research to a halt? *Intensive Care Medicine* 2005 March; 31(3): 338-344. NRCBL: 18.3; 18.2.

Ungar, David; Joffe, Steven; Kodish, Eric. Children are not small adults: documentation of assent for research involving children. *Journal of Pediatrics* 2006 July; 149(1, Supplement): S31-33. NRCBL: 18.3; 18.5.2; 18.2.

United States. Food and Drug Administration [FDA]. Protection of human subjects; informed consent verification. *Federal Register* 1996 November 5; 61(215): 57278-57280 [Online] Accessed: http://frwebgate.access. gpo.gov/cgi-bin/multidb.cgi [12 December 2005]. NRCBL: 18.3.

United States. Food and Drug Administration [FDA]. Protection of human subjects; informed consent; technical amendment. *Federal Register* 1999 March 8; 64(44): 10942-10943 [Online] Accessed: http://frwebgate.access. gpo.gov/cgi-bin/multidb.cgi [27 December 2005]. NRCBL: 18.3; 18.6. SC: le.

United States. Food and Drug Administration [FDA]. Guidance for institutional review boards, clinical investigations, and sponsors: exception from informed consent requirements for emergency research: draft guidance. Rockville, MD: Food and Drug Administration, 2006 July; 26 p. [Online]. Accessed: http://www.fda.gov/OHRMS/ DOCKETS/98fr/06d-0331-gdl0001.pdf [2006 September 1]. NRCBL: 18.3; 18.2; 18.5.1. SC: le. Note: Date issued for comment is August 29, 2006 as per Federal Register notice of availability. Comments are due by October 29. 2006.

Vargas-Parada, Laura; Kawa, Simon; Salazar, Alberto; Mazon, Juan Jose; Flisser, Ana. Informed consent in clinical research at a general hospital in Mexico: opinions of the investigators. *Developing World Bioethics* 2006 March; 6(1): 41-51. NRCBL: 18.3. SC: em.

Abstract: In Mexico informed consent is a legal requirement that ensures that patients who are invited to participate in clinical trials are provided with all the information needed to decide whether to participate, or not, in a research protocol. To improve our understanding of the problems physicians in develop-

---

NRCBL: National Reference Center for Bioethics Literature Classification Scheme   See inside front cover for terms.

313

ing countries encounter, when obtaining informed consent (IC), we examined their opinion on the importance of IC in clinical research, the quantity and quality of the information provided to the participant, and the conditions in which the IC is obtained. Investigators considered that IC was useful to the patients, providing information that helped the patient to make a decision about his/her participation. Nevertheless, they felt that for some aspects of the research, like drug development in general, the use of placebos, and the randomization process, many of the patients were not capable of fully understanding the information provided, referring to the complexity of the information and illiteracy as the main reasons. Many investigators were not acquainted with some of the guidelines established in the Mexican General Law of Health,(1) 36% of them admitting to not having completed their IC letters. Most investigators gave only minutes to the patient to make a decision and 20% of ICs were obtained while the patient was hospitalized. Except for one investigator, all of them considered that specific training in medical ethics would be useful for the daily clinical work.

Verástegui, Emma L. Consenting of the vulnerable: the informed consent procedure in advanced care patients in Mexico. *BMC Medical Ethics* 2006; 7(13): 12p. NRCBL: 18.3. SC: em.

Vester, A.E.; Christensen, E.F.; Andersen, S.K.; Tonnesen, E. Ethical and practical problems in blood sampling for research purposes during pre-hospital emergencies. *Acta Anaesthesiologica Scandinavica* 2005 November; 49(10): 1540-1543. NRCBL: 18.3; 19.4; 9.5.1. Identifiers: Denmark.

Vieta, Eduard; Carné, Xavier. The use of placebo in clinical trials on bipolar disorder: a new approach for an old debate. *Psychotherapy and Psychosomatics* 2005; 74(1): 10-16. NRCBL: 18.3; 18.2; 18.5.6. Identifiers: Spain.

Waddell, James P. Informed consent [editorial]. *Canadian Journal of Surgery* 2005 August; 48(4): 269. NRCBL: 18.3; 18.2.

Wahn, Eve. An update on Olivieri: what difference did it make? *Health Law in Canada* 2006 June; 26(4): 61-70. NRCBL: 18.3; 18.2; 1.3.9; 8.4. SC: le.

Wasson, Katherine. Altruism and pediatric oncology trials: it does not tip the decision-making scales. *American Journal of Bioethics* 2006 September-October; 6(5): 48. NRCBL: 18.3; 18.5.2. Comments: Christian Simon, Michelle Eder, Eric Kodish and Laura Siminoff. Altruistic discourse in the informed consent process for childhood cancer clinical trials. American Journal of Bioethics 2006 September-October; 6(5): 40-47.

Watts, Nelson B. Is it ethical to use placebos in osteoporosis clinical trials? *Current Osteoporosis Reports* 2004 March; 2(1): 31-36. NRCBL: 18.3; 1.3.9; 18.2.

Weijer, Charles. The ethical analysis of risk in intensive care unit research. *Critical Care* 2004 April; 8(2): 85-86. NRCBL: 18.3; 18.2; 18.1.

Weijer, Charles. The ethics of placebo-controlled trials. *Journal of Bone and Mineral Research* 2003 June; 18(6):

1150-1153. NRCBL: 18.3; 18.2. Identifiers: Declaration of Helsinki; Food and Drug Administration [FDA].

Welie, Sander P.K.; Berghmans, Ron L.P. Inclusion of patients with severe mental illness in clinical trials: issues and recommendations surrounding informed consent. *CNS Drugs* 2006; 20(1): 67-83. NRCBL: 18.3; 18.5.6; 21.1. SC: le.

Wendler, David. Clinical research, clinical tragedies and the assumption of responsibility. *Organizational Ethics: Healthcare, Business, and Policy* 2006 Spring-Summer; 3(1): 46-49. NRCBL: 18.3; 18.5.7; 19.2.

Wendler, David. One-time general consent for research on biological samples: is it compatible with the Health Insurance Portability And Accountability Act? *Archives of Internal Medicine* 2006 July 24; 166(14): 1449-1452. NRCBL: 18.3; 8.4; 15.1; 19.5. SC: le.

Wicher, Camille P.; Michalek, Arthur M. When is informed consent not enough? *Journal of Cancer Education* 2005 Spring; 20(1): 9-10. NRCBL: 18.3; 19.4. SC: cs.

Willis, Gordon. Cognitive interviewing as a tool for improving the informed consent process. *Journal of Empirical Research on Human Research Ethics* 2006 March; 1(1): 9-23. NRCBL: 18.3. SC: cs.

Zhai, Xiaomei. Informed consent in medical research involving human subjects in China. *In:* Sang-yong, Song; Young-Mo, Koo; Macer, Darryl R.J., eds. Asian Bioethics in the 21st Century. Christchurch, NZ: Eubios Ethics Institute, 2002: 4-5. NRCBL: 18.3; 21.7. Conference: Proceedings of the Asian Bioethics Conference (ABC4), held 22-25 November 2002 in Seoul, South Korea.

Zink, Sheldon; Wertlieb, Stacey; Kimberly, Laura. Informed consent. *Progress in Transplantation* 2005 December; 15(4): 371-378. NRCBL: 18.3.

HUMAN EXPERIMENTATION/ REGULATION

NIH and FDA seek to increase oversight of gene therapy research [news]. *Journal of Investigative Medicine* 2000 May; 48(3): 169-171. NRCBL: 18.6; 15.4. Identifiers: National Institutes of Health; Food and Drug Administration.

Phase 1 drug trial disaster [news]. *Bulletin of Medical Ethics* 2006 February-March; (213): 3-5. NRCBL: 18.6; 18.2; 9.7. Identifiers: United Kingdom (Great Britain).

Southall's CNEP trial more than stands up to scrutiny [editorial]. *Lancet* 2006 April 1-7; 367(9516): 1030. NRCBL: 18.6; 18.5.2; 8.3.2. Identifiers: continuous negative extrathoracic-pressure ventilation.

Urgent changes needed for authorisation of phase I trials [editorial]. *Lancet* 2006 April 15-21; 367(9518): 1214. NRCBL: 18.6; 18.2.

Aguiar-Guevara, R. Medicine assisted by information and communication technology: conflicts, responsibility and liability. *Medicine and Law: The World Association for Medical Law* 2006 September; 25(3): 563-571. NRCBL: 18.6; 5.3; 1.3.12; 15.1. SC: le.

Abstract: The term M@TIC, is that which encompasses all Medicine Assisted by Technology on Information and Communication. The development of these techniques brings up many ethical and legal conflicts, mainly because medical science has developed much faster than the law. Justice cannot be properly served if we do not have the regulations to help mankind to avoid aberrant behavior by medical practitioners in this field. M@TIC is still regarded as an experimental research procedure. Not all that is technically feasible is ethically acceptable. There are many potential risks associated with M@TIC and it is largely considered, and so it is understood by doctors, that any damage to the patient would be the fault of the system, never the responsibility of the doctor. It frightens one to think that this fact may be used, in the future, as a shield to protect negligent medical doctors from malpractice suits.

Amstutz, Harlan C. Innovations in design and technology: the story of hip arthroplasty. *Clinical Orthopaedics and Related Research* 2000 September; (378): 23-30. NRCBL: 18.6; 1.3.9; 5.3.

Bates, Benjamin R. Public culture and public understanding of genetics: a focus group study. *Public Understanding of Science* 2005 January; 14(1): 47-65. NRCBL: 18.6; 15.1; 1.3.7. SC: em.

Baylis, Françoise; Robert, Jason Scott. Human embryonic stem cell research: an argument for national research review. *Accountability in Research* 2006 July-September; 13(3): 207-224. NRCBL: 18.6; 18.5.1; 15.1; 18.2; 21.1. SC: an. Identifiers: National Academy of Science (United States).

Abstract: The US National Academy of Sciences (NAS) recently published voluntary guidelines for human embryonic stem (hES) cell research. The NAS guidelines propose two levels of oversight. AT the local level, research institutions are to create Embryonic Stem Cell Research Oversight (ESCRO) committees with a mandate to assess the scientific merit and ethical acceptability of hES cell research. At the national level, a new committee is to be created, not to review specific research proposals, but rather to periodically assess, and as needed revise, the NAS guidelines. In this article, we critically assess this proposal. In particular, we review the benefits and limitations of local research review. On this basis, we argue that local review is insufficient for hES cell research and that while there are obvious pragmatic and political reasons for the NAS to favor local research review, there are more compelling reasons for the NAS to have recommended national review of hES cell research proposals.

Bramstedt, Katrina A. A study of warning letters issued to clinical investigators by the United States Food and Drug Administration. *Clinical and Investigative Medicine* 2004 June; 27(3): 129-134. NRCBL: 18.6; 18.2; 1.3.9; 18.3. SC: em.

Brower, Vicki. The ethics of innovation: should innovative surgery be exempt from clinical trials and regulations? *EMBO Reports* 2003 April; 4(4): 338-339. NRCBL: 18.6; 18.2; 5.1.

Burnet, N.G.; Jefferies, S.J.; Benson, R.J.; Hunt, D.P.; Treasure, F.P. Years of life lost (YLL) from cancer is an important measure of population burden — and should be considered when allocating research funds. *British Journal of Cancer* 2005 January 31; 92(2): 241-245. NRCBL: 18.6; 5.2; 9.5.1. SC: em. Identifiers: United Kingdom (Great Britain).

Cash, Richard A. What is owed to the community before, during and following research: an ethical dialogue. *Eastern Mediterranean Health Journal* 2006; 12(Supplement 1): S37-S41 [Online]. Accessed: http://www.emro.who.int/publications/EMHJ/12_S/PDF/6.pdf [2007 January 3]. NRCBL: 18.6; 18.2; 18.5.9. Note: Abstract in French and Arabic.

Contant, Charles; McCullough, Laurence B.; Mangus, Lorna; Robertson, Claudia; Valadka, Alex; Brody, Baruch. Community consultation in emergency research. *Critical Care Medicine* 2006 August; 34(8): 2049-2052. NRCBL: 18.6; 18.3. SC: em.

Cooper, Jeffrey A. Responsible conduct of radiology research: Part I. The regulatory framework for human research. *Radiology* 2005 August; 236(2): 379-381. NRCBL: 18.6; 18.3; 8.4.

Craft, Alan W.; McIntosh, Neil. Southall and colleagues vindicated once more. *Lancet* 2006 April 1-7; 367(9516): 1035-1037. NRCBL: 18.6.

Day, Michael. Duff's report calls for changes in way drugs are tested [news]. *BMJ: British Medical Journal* 2006 December 16; 333(7581): 1240. NRCBL: 18.6. Identifiers: United Kingdom (Great Britain).

DeAngelis, Catherine D.; Drazen, Jeffrey M.; Frizelle, Frank A.; Haug, Charlotte; Hoey, John; Horton, Richard; Kotzin, Sheldon; Laine, Christine; Marusic, Ana; Overbeke, A. John P.M.; Schroeder, Torben V.; Sox, Hal C.; Van Der Weyden, Martin B. Clinical trial registration — a statement from the International Committee of Medical Journal Editors. *Archives of Dermatology* 2005 January; 141(1): 76-77. NRCBL: 18.6; 1.3.7.

Dickert, Neal W.; Sugarman, Jeremy. Community consultation: not the problem — an important part of the solution. *American Journal of Bioethics* 2006 May-June; 6(3): 26-28; discussion W46- W48. NRCBL: 18.6; 9.5.4; 19.4; 18.5.1. Comments: Karla F.C. Holloway. Accidental communities: race, emergency medicine, and the problem of PolyHeme. American Journal of Bioethics 2006 May-June; 6(3): 7-17.

Downie, Jocelyn. The Canadian agency for the oversight of research involving humans: a reform proposal. *Accountability in Research* 2006 January-March; 13(1): 75-100. NRCBL: 18.6; 18.2; 2.4. SC: an. Identifiers: Canada.

Abstract: In this paper, I propose the creation of a Canadian agency for the oversight of research involving humans. I describe first a series of significant problems with Canada's cur-

NRCBL: National Reference Center for Bioethics Literature Classification Scheme   See inside front cover for terms.

315

rent system of oversight. I then argue for the creation of a national-level agency, covering all research involving humans, with three branches (policy and standards, education, and compliance). Of particular note, the proposed compliance branch consists of a number of independent national and regional Research Ethics Boards (i.e., REBs no longer reside within institutions). There is also an Audit Committee and a Non-compliance Committee (with supporting staff of auditors and compliance officers) to ensure compliance with the policies and standards set by the Policy and Standards Branch. Finally, I answer a series of "frequently asked questions" about the proposed agency design such as "What about 'local context'?" and "Why not have a system of accreditation of institutional REBs instead?" In sum, radical reform is needed and, in this paper, I present a proposal for such reform.

Duff, Gordon. Expert scientific group on phase one clinical trials: interim report. United Kingdom: Expert Scientific Group on Phase One Clinical Trials, 2006 July 20: 71 p. [Online]. Accessed: http://www.dh.gov.uk/assetRoot/ 04/13/75/69/04137569.pdf [2006 September 12]. NRCBL: 18.6; 18.5.1; 9.7. SC: em. Identifiers: TeGenero TGN1412 drug.

Esteve, Rogette; Halpern, Sheri; Kirloss, Mena; Rosenthal, Andrew. Interview with Dr. Ezekiel Emanuel, Chief of the Department of Clinical Bioethics at the National Institute of Health. *Penn Bioethics Journal* 2005 April 2; 1(1): 5p. [Online]. Accessed: http://www. bioethicsjournal.com [2005 April 19]. NRCBL: 18.6.

Evans, Steven; Block, Jerome B. Ethical issues regarding fee-for-service-funded research within a complementary medicine context. *Journal of Alternative and Complementary Medicine* 2001 December; 7(6): 697-702. NRCBL: 18.6; 4.1.1; 9.3.1.

Fontenla, M.; Rycroft-Malone, J. Research governance and ethics: a resource for novice researchers. *Nursing Standard* 2006 February 15-21; 20(23): 41-46. NRCBL: 18.6; 18.2.

Fox, Jeffrey L. US biosecurity advisory board faces delicate balancing act [news]. *Nature Biotechnology* 2005 August; 23(8): 905. NRCBL: 18.6; 5.3; 21.3. SC: le.

Gatter, Ken. Fixing cracks: a discourse norm to repair the crumbling regulatory structure supporting clinical research and protecting human subjects. *University of Missouri Kansas City Law Review (UMKC)* 2005; 73: 581-641. NRCBL: 18.6; 18.2; 18.3; 2.2. SC: le.

Gbadegesin, Segun; Wendler, David. Protecting communities in health research from exploitation. *Bioethics* 2006 September; 20(5): 248-253. NRCBL: 18.6.

Abstract: Guidelines for health research focus on protecting individual research subjects. Yet several commentators have argued that protecting individual subjects, while undoubtedly important, is not sufficient to ensure ethical research. It is also vital to protect the communities involved in health research. In particular, a number of studies have been criticized on the grounds that they exploited host communities. Although these criticisms have received a good deal of attention, there has been no systematic analysis of what constitutes community exploitation in health research, nor an assessment of what safeguards are needed to protect against it. This is a serious deficiency. The absence of an analysis of community exploitation makes it impossible to ensure that host communities are protected against exploitation. The absence of an analysis also raises the possibility that charges of exploitation may block important research, without any way of assessing whether the charges are warranted. The present paper attempts to address these concerns by providing an analysis of community exploitation and, based on this analysis, determining what safeguards are needed to protect communities in health research against exploitation.

Gevers, Sjef. Medical research involving human subjects: towards an international legal framework? [editorial]. *European Journal of Health Law* 2001 December; 8(4): 293-298. NRCBL: 18.6; 21.1. SC: le.

Goodyear, Michael. Closing the gaps: moving closer to a collaborative culture; comments on disclosure timing: balancing increased transparency and competitive advantage; submission to WHO International Clinical Trials Registry Platform [ICTRP]. Geneva: World Health Organization 2006 March 31: [Online]. Accessed: http://www.who.int/ ictrp/007-Michael_Goodyear_31March06.pdf [2006 December 1]. NRCBL: 18.6; 18.2; 21.1. Identifiers: World Health Organization.

Griffiths, Rod. CNEP and research governance. *Lancet* 2006 April 1-7; 367(9516): 1037-1038. NRCBL: 18.6; 1.3.7. Identifiers: continuous negative extrathoracic-pressure ventilation.

Hemminki, Akseli; Kellokumpu-Lehtinen, Pirkko-Liisa. Harmful impact of EU clinical trials directive [editorial]. *BMJ: British Medical Journal* 2006 March 4; 332(7540): 501-502. NRCBL: 18.6; 18.2.

Hey, Edmund; Chalmers, Iain. Are any of the criticisms of the CNEP trial true? *Lancet* 2006 April 1-7; 367(9516): 1032-1033. NRCBL: 18.6; 18.5.2; 8.3.2. Identifiers: continuous negative extrathoracic-pressure ventilation.

Hilgartner, Stephen. Potential effects of a diminishing public domain in biomedical research data. *In:* Esanu, Julie M.; Uhlir, Paul F., eds. The Role of Scientific and Technical Data and Information in the Public Domain: Proceedings of a Symposium. Washington, DC: National Academies Press; 2002: 133-138. NRCBL: 18.6. Note: "The symposium was held on September 5-6, 2002, at the National Academies in Washington, D.C.".

Horton, Richard. Trial registers: protecting patients, advancing trust. *Lancet* 2006 May 20-26; 367(9523): 1633-1635. NRCBL: 18.6; 15.1; 1.3.12; 1.3.7.

Kapp, Marshall B. Protecting human participants in long-term care research: the role of state law and policy. *Journal of Aging and Social Policy* 2004; 16(3): 13-33. NRCBL: 18.6; 18.5.6; 18.3; 18.1. SC: le.

Kennedy, Ian; Grubb, Andrew. Research. *In their:* Medical Law. 3rd ed. London: Butterworths; 2005: 1665-1749. NRCBL: 18.6. SC: le.

Kennedy, S.B.; Harris, A.O.; Oudemans, E.; Young, L.; Kollie, J.; Nelson, E.S.; Nisbett, R.A.; Morris, C.; Bartee, N.; George-Williams, E.; Jones, J. Developing capacity to protect human research subjects in a post-conflict, resource-constrained setting: procedures and prospects. *Journal of Medical Ethics* 2006 October; 32(10): 592-595. NRCBL: 18.6; 21.1.

Kubar, Olga. Ethical aspects in clinical trials in the CIS, in particular the setting up of ethical committees. *Journal International de Bioéthique = International Journal of Bioethics* 2005 September-December; 16(3-4): 81-87,172-173. NRCBL: 18.6; 18.2; 21.1. Identifiers: Commonwealth of Independent States; Armenia; Azerbaijan; Byelorussia; Georgia; Russia; Ukraine.

Abstract: The ethical aspects of clinical trials in the CIS are based on the development of systematic ethical review and ethical insight and responsibility on the part of researchers, sponsors, and government agencies and society. This is the main purpose of the Forum for Ethics Committees in the Commonwealth of Independent States (FECCIS) whose establishment and activities are focused on the integration of the CIS into the world system of biomedical research with regard to safeguarding ethical standards of human rights protection and harmonization of regulative and methodological space to safeguard protection of human rights and the dignity of biomedical research participants in the CIS.

Kvochak, Patricia A. Legal issues. *In:* Gallin, John I., ed. Principles and Practice of Clinical Research. San Diego, CA: Academic Press; 2002: 133-143. NRCBL: 18.6. SC: le.

Lappin, Debra R. Clinical research and the new public partnership — a view from the south. *Journal of Rheumatology* 2005 January; 32(Supplement 72): 27-29. NRCBL: 18.6; 18.2.

Levitt, Mairi; Weiner, Kate; Goodacre, John. Gene week: a novel way of consulting the public. *Public Understanding of Science* 2005 January; 14(1): 67-79. NRCBL: 18.6; 15.1; 1.3.7. SC: em.

Liddell, Kathleen; Wallace, Susan. Emerging regulatory issues for human stem cell medicine. *Genomics, Society and Policy* 2005 February; 1(1): 54-73. NRCBL: 18.6; 18.5.4; 15.1. Identifiers: United Kingdom (Great Britain);European Union.

Lo, Bernard. Strengthening community consultation in critical care and emergency research. *Critical Care Medicine* 2006 August; 34(8): 2236-2238. NRCBL: 18.6; 18.3.

Lo, Bernard; Groman, Michelle. NBAC recommendations on oversight of human subject research. *Seton Hall Law Review* 2002; 32(3): 493-512. NRCBL: 18.6; 18.2; 2.4. Identifiers: National Bioethics Advisory Commission. Conference: Symposium: New Directions in Human Subject Research: Looking Beyond the Academic Medical Center; Seton Hall Law School; 2001 November; Seton Hall University Graduate School of Medical Education; American Society of Law, Medicine and Ethics.

Lunstroth, John. Acting out of ethics: what the open letter asks. *American Journal of Bioethics* 2006 May-June; 6(3): 41-43. NRCBL: 18.6; 19.4; 18.2. Identifiers: PolyHeme. Comments: Ken Kipnis, Nancy M.P. King, and Robert M. Nelson. An open letter to institutional review boards considering Northfield Laboratories' PolyHeme trial. American Journal of Bioethics 2006 May-June; 6(3): 18-21.

Marshall, Eliot. Accident prompts a closer look at antibody trials. *Science* 2006 April 14; 312(5771): 172. NRCBL: 18.6; 18.2.

Marshall, Eliot. Lessons from a failed drug trial. *Science* 2006 August 18; 313(5789): 901. NRCBL: 18.6; 18.5.1; 9.7. Identifiers: TeGenero; TGN1412.

Marshall, Patricia A.; Berg, Jessica W. Protecting communities in biomedical research. *American Journal of Bioethics* 2006 May-June; 6(3): 28-30; discussion W46-W48. NRCBL: 18.6; 9.5.4; 18.3; 18.2; 18.5.1. Comments: Karla F.C. Holloway. Accidental communities: race, emergency medicine, and the problem of PolyHeme. American Journal of Bioethics 2006 May-June; 6(3): 7-17.

Mastroianni, Anna C. Liability, regulation and policy in surgical innovation: the cutting edge of research and therapy. *Health Matrix: The Journal of Law-Medicine* 2006 Summer; 16(2): 351-442. NRCBL: 18.6; 8.5; 18.3; 9.8. SC: le.

Mathews, Anna Wilde. FDA signals it's open to drug trials that shift midcourse. *Wall Street Journal* 2006 July 10; p. B1, B8. NRCBL: 18.6; 9.7. SC: po. Identifiers: Food and Drug Administration.

Mooney, Chris. Stemming research. *In his:* The Republican War on Science. Rev. ed. New York: Basic Books, 2006: 195-216. NRCBL: 18.6.

Morgenstern, Leon. Still imperfect: overseeing clinical research [editorial]. *Nutrition* 2005 July-August; 21(7-8): 887-888. NRCBL: 18.6; 18.3.

Orr, Robert D. Rules is rules. *American Journal of Bioethics* 2006 May-June; 6(3): 40-41. NRCBL: 18.6; 19.4. Identifiers: PolyHeme.

Richmond, David E. The Auckland Hospital ethical committee 1977-1981. *New Zealand Medical Journal* 1983 July 27; 96(736): 569-572. NRCBL: 18.6; 18.2.

Rockhold, Frank W.; Krall, Ronald L. Trial summaries on results databases and journal publication. *Lancet* 2006 May 20-26; 367(9523): 1635-1636. NRCBL: 18.6; 1.3.7; 1.3.12.

Rosenthal, Elisabeth. British rethinking test rules after drug trial nearly kills 6. *New York Times* 2006 April 8; p. A1, A6. NRCBL: 18.6; 18.3; 9.7.

NRCBL: National Reference Center for Bioethics Literature Classification Scheme   See inside front cover for terms.

317

Rosenthal, Elisabeth. Inquiries in Britain uncover loopholes in drug trials. *New York Times* 2006 August 3; p. A3. NRCBL: 18.6; 18.2; 9.7; 9.3.1. SC: po.

Roychowdhury, Viveka. Audits of clinical trials in India: a step in the right direction. *Journal of Biolaw and Business* 2006; 9(3): 26-28. NRCBL: 18.6.

Roychowdhury, Viveka. Good clinical practice (GCP) standards: clinical trials in India. An interview with Dr. Urmila Thatte, Head of Clinical Pharmacology, TN Medical College and BYL Nair Hospital. *Journal of Biolaw and Business* 2006; 9(3): 30-31. NRCBL: 18.6.

Samanta, Ash; Samanta, Jo. Research governance: panacea or problem? *Clinical Medicine* 2005 May-June; 5(3): 235-239. NRCBL: 18.6; 18.2; 21.1.

Schmidt, Terri A.; Delorio, Nicole M.; McClure, Katie B. The meaning of community consultation. *American Journal of Bioethics* 2006 May-June; 6(3): 30-32; discussion W46-W50. NRCBL: 18.6; 18.3; 18.2. Comments: Karla F.C. Holloway. Accidental communities: race, emergency medicine, and the problem of PolyHeme. American Journal of Bioethics 2006 May-June; 6(3): 7-17; Ken Kipnis, Nancy M.P. King, and Robert M. Nelson. An open letter to institutional review boards considering Northfield Laboratories' PolyHeme trial. American Journal of Bioethics 2006 May-June; 6(3): 18-21.

Schneider, Angela J.; Friedman, Theodore. Ethics and oversight in clinical trials: attempts at gene doping would not conform to accepted ethical standards. *In their:* Gene Doping in Sports: The Science and Ethics of Genetically Modified Athletes. Boston: Elsevier Academic Press, 2006: 51-63. NRCBL: 18.6; 4.5; 15.1; 9.5.1.

Schott, Markus. Medical research on humans: regulation in Switzerland, the European Union, and the United States. *Food and Drug Law Journal* 2005; 60(1): 45-77. NRCBL: 18.6; 18.2; 21.1. SC: le.

Shaw, Sara; Boynton, Petra M.; Greenhalgh, Trisha. Research governance: where did it come from, what does it mean? *Journal of the Royal Society of Medicine* 2005 November; 98(11): 496-502. NRCBL: 18.6; 18.2; 21.1. Identifiers: United Kingdom (Great Britain).

Sheehan, Mark. Is the community consultation requirement necessary? *American Journal of Bioethics* 2006 May-June; 6(3): 38-40; discussion W46- W48. NRCBL: 18.6; 18.2; 18.3; 19.4; 18.5.1. Identifiers: PolyHeme. Comments: Karla F.C. Holloway. Accidental communities: race, emergency medicine, and the problem of PolyHeme. American Journal of Bioethics 2006 May-June; 6(3): 7-17.

Siegel-Itzkovich, Judy. Cancer organisation hits out at medical research funded by tobacco companies [news]. *BMJ: British Medical Journal* 2006 January 7; 332(7532): 6. NRCBL: 18.6; 5.3; 9.3.1; 21.1; 9.5.9. Identifiers: Israel Cancer Association; World Health Organization Framework Convention for Tobacco Control.

Sim, Ida; Chan, An-Wen; Gülmezoglu, A. Metin; Evans, Tim; Pang, Tikki. Clinical trial registration: transparency is the watchword. *Lancet* 2006 May 20-26; 367(9523): 1631-1633. NRCBL: 18.6; 5.3.

Slowther, Anne; Boynton, Petra; Shaw, Sara. Research governance: ethical issues. *Journal of the Royal Society of Medicine* 2006 February; 99(2): 65-72. NRCBL: 18.6; 18.2; 18.3; 1.3.9.

Souhami, Robert. Governance of research that uses identifiable personal data: will improve if the public and researchers collaborate to raise standards [editorial]. *BMJ: British Medical Journal* 2006 August 12; 333(7563): 315-316. NRCBL: 18.6; 18.3; 8.4; 1.3.12. Identifiers: United Kingdom (Great Britain).

Steneck, Nicholas H. Office of Research Integrity. *In:* Mitcham, Carl, ed. Encyclopedia of Science, Technology, and Ethics. Farmington Hills, MI: Thomson/Gale, 2005: 1353-1355. NRCBL: 18.6; 1.3.9.

Tolich, Martin; Fitzgerald, Maureen H. If ethics committees were designed for ethnography. *Journal of Empirical Research on Human Research Ethics* 2006 June; 1(2): 71-78. NRCBL: 18.6; 1.3.1; 18.2.

United States. Department of Health and Human Services [DHHS]. Health and Human Services Policy for Protection of Human Subjects Research — HHS Final Rule. *Federal Register* 1994 June 1; 59(104): 28276. NRCBL: 18.6; 18.2; 18.5.4.

United States. Department of Health and Human Services [DHHS]. Protection of human research subjects: delay of effective date. *Federal Register* 2001 May 18; 66(97): 27599 [Online]. Accessed: http://frwebgate.access.gpo.gov/ cgi-bin/multidb.cgi [2005 December 27]. NRCBL: 18.6. SC: le.

United States. Department of Health and Human Services [DHHS] [and] National Science Foundation [NSF] (United States) [and] United States. Department of Transportation [DOT]. Federal policy for the protection of human subjects; final rule; technical amendments. *Federal Register* 2005 June 23; 70(120): 36325-36328 [Online] Accessed: http://frwebgate.access.gov.gpo/ cgi-bin/multidb.cgi [2005 December 28]. NRCBL: 18.6; 18.5.1. SC: le.

United States. Department of Health and Human Services [DHHS]. Office of the Secretary. Exemption of Certain Research and Demonstration Projects From Regulations for Protection of Human Research Subjects: Final Rule. *Federal Register* 1983 March 4; 48(44): 9266-9270. NRCBL: 18.6.

United States. Environmental Protection Agency [EPA]. Human testing; advance notice of proposed rulemaking. *Federal Register* 2003 May 2; 68(88): 24410-24416 [Online]. Accessed: http://frwebgate.access. gpo.gov/cgi-bin/multidb.cgi [2005 December 27]. NRCBL: 18.6; 16.1. SC: le.

United States. Food and Drug Administration [FDA]. Protection of human subjects. *Federal Register* 2000 December 27; 65(249): 81739 [Online]. Accessed: http://frwebgate.access.gpo.gov/cgi-bin/multidb.cgi [2005 December 27]. NRCBL: 18.6; 9.7. SC: le.

United States. Public Health Service [PHS]. Protection of Human Subjects; Reports of the President's Commission for the Study of Ethical Problems in Medicine and Biomedical and Behavioral Research; Notice of availability of reports and request for public comment. *Federal Register* 1983 July 28; 48(146): 34408-34412. NRCBL: 18.6; 18.2; 2.4.

van den Hoonaard, Will C.; Connolly, Anita. Anthropological research in light of research ethics review: Canadian master's theses, 1995-2004. *Journal of Empirical Research on Human Research Ethics* 2006 June; 1(2): 59-69. NRCBL: 18.6; 1.3.1; 18.2; 18.4.

Wadman, Meredith. Earlier drug test on people could be unsafe, critics warn [news]. *Nature Medicine* 2006 February; 12(2): 153. NRCBL: 18.6; 18.2; 9.7.

Walin, Laura. The regulation of genetic research and the commercialisation of its results in Finland. *Medical Law International* 2006; 7(4): 309-328. NRCBL: 18.6; 15.1; 15.10; 1.3.12; 13.1; 14.5; 15.8. SC: an; le.

HUMAN EXPERIMENTATION/ SPECIAL POPULATIONS

Aldhous, Peter. Miracle postponed. *New Scientist* 2006 March 11-17; 189(2542): 38-41. NRCBL: 18.5.1; 1.3.9; 18.5.4; 15.1; 19.1.

Anand, Sonia A. Using ethnicity as a classification variable in health research: perpetuating the myth of biological determinism, serving socio-political agendas, or making valuable contributions to medical sciences? *Ethnicity and Health* 1999 November; 4(4): 241-244. NRCBL: 18.5.1; 15.1.

Anderson, Robert M. Is it ethical to assign medically underserved African Americans to a usual-care control group in community-based intervention research? *Diabetes Care* 2005 July; 28(7): 1817-1820. NRCBL: 18.5.1; 18.6; 9.5.4; 9.3.1.

Baker, Shamim M.; Brawley, Otis W.; Marks, Leonard S. Effects of untreated syphilis in the Negro male, 1932 to 1972: a closure comes to the Tuskegee study, 2004. *Urology* 2005 June; 65(6): 1259-1262. NRCBL: 18.5.1; 18.3; 10.

Becker-Blease, Kathryn A.; Freyd, Jennifer J. Research participants telling the truth about their lives: the ethics of asking and not asking about abuse. *American Psychologist* 2006 April; 61(3): 218-226. NRCBL: 18.5.1; 18.3; 9.1; 9.3.1.

Bloche, M. Gregg. Race, money and medicines. *Journal of Law, Medicine and Ethics* 2006 Fall; 34(3): 555-558. NRCBL: 18.5.1; 9.5.4; 9.7; 15.11.
Abstract: Taking notice of race is both risky and inevitable, in medicine no less than in other endeavors. On the one hand, race can be a useful stand-in for unstudied genetic and environmental factors that yield differences in disease expression and therapeutic response. Attention to race can make a therapeutic difference, to the point of saving lives. On the other hand, racial distinctions have social meanings that are often pejorative or worse, especially when these distinctions are cast as culturally or biologically fixed. I argue in this essay that we should start with a presumption against racial categories in medicine, but permit their use when it might prolong lives or meaningfully improve health. Use of racial categories should be understood as an interim step; follow-up inquiry into the factors that underlie race-correlated clinical differences is important both to improve the efficacy of clinical care and to prevent race in itself from being misunderstood as a biological determinant. If we pursue such inquiry with vigor, the pernicious effects of racial categories on public understanding can be managed. But perverse market and regulatory incentives create the danger that use of race will be "locked-in," once drugs or other therapies are approved. These incentives should be revisited.

Brandon, Dwayne T.; Isaac, Lydia A.; LaVeist, Thomas A. The legacy of Tuskegee and trust in medical care: is Tuskegee responsible for race differences in mistrust of medical care? *Journal of the National Medical Association* 2005 July; 97(7): 951-956. NRCBL: 18.5.1; 18.3; 9.5.4; 21.7. SC: em.

Brugge, Doug; Missaghian, Mariam. Protecting the Navajo people through tribal regulation of research. *Science and Engineering Ethics* 2006 July; 12(3): 491-507. NRCBL: 18.5.1; 18.2.

Buchwald, Dedra; Mendoza-Jenkins, Veronica; Croy, Calvin; McGough, Helen; Bezdek, Marjorie; Spicer, Paul. Attitudes of urban American Indians and Alaskan natives regarding participation in research. *JGIM: Journal of General Internal Medicine* 2006 June; 21(6): 648-651. NRCBL: 18.5.1. SC: em.

Burhansstipanov, Linda; Bemis, Lynne; Kaur, Judith S.; Bemis, Gordon. Sample genetic policy language for research conducted with native communities. *Journal of Cancer Education* 2005 Spring; 20(1, Supplement): 52-57. NRCBL: 18.5.1; 15.1; 21.7; 18.6; 19.1.

Chan, Harry; Moriatry, Kieran. Are ethnic minorities excluded from clinical research? *Bulletin of Medical Ethics* 2005 October-November; (211): 22-24. NRCBL: 18.5.1; 18.2; 18.3. SC: em. Identifiers: United Kingdom(Great Britain).

NRCBL: National Reference Center for Bioethics Literature Classification Scheme   See inside front cover for terms.

319

Check, Erika. Simple recipe gives adult cells embryonic powers [news]. *Nature* 2006 July 6; 442(7098): 11. NRCBL: 18.5.1; 15.1; 18.5.4; 19.1.

Christopher, Suzanne. Recommendations for conducting successful research with Native Americans. *Journal of Cancer Education* 2005 Spring; 20(1, Supplement): 47-51. NRCBL: 18.5.1; 21.7; 18.6.

Cohn, Jay N. The use of race and ethnicity in medicine: lessons from the African-American heart failure trial. *Journal of Law, Medicine and Ethics* 2006 Fall; 34(3): 552-554. NRCBL: 18.5.1; 9.5.4; 18.2; 15.11. SC: cs.
Abstract: Race or ethnic identity, despite its imprecise categorization, is a useful means of identifying population differences in mechanisms of disease and treatment effects. Therefore, race and other arbitrary demographic and physiological variables have appropriately served as a helpful guide to clinical management and to clinical trial participation. The African-American Heart Failure Trial was carried out in African-Americans with heart failure because prior data had demonstrated a uniquely favorable effect in this subpopulation of the drug combination in BiDil. The remarkable effect of the drug in reducing mortality in this study has illuminated an important new mechanism of therapy for heart failure. Application of these findings need not be confined to the population studied, but the observation highlights the need for more precise ways to identify individual responsiveness to therapy.

Cox, Courtney. Only time can tell: unethical research and the passage of time. *Newsletter on Philosophy and Law* 2005 Fall; 05(1): 2-11. NRCBL: 18.5.1; 1.3.9; 1.3.7. SC: le. Identifiers: experimental claim; need claim; use claim.

Cromer, Lisa DeMarni; Freyd, Jennifer J.; Binder, Angela K.; DePrince, Anne P.; Becker-Blease, Kathryn. What's the risk in asking? Participant reaction to trauma history questions compared with reaction to other personal questions. *Ethics and Behavior* 2006; 16(4): 347-362. NRCBL: 18.5.1; 5.2; 17.1; 18.2. SC: em.

Daugherty, Christopher K.; Fitchett, George; Murphy, Patricia E.; Peterman, Amy H.; Banik, Donald M.; Hlubocky, Fay; Tartaro, Jessica. Trusting God and medicine: spirituality in advanced cancer patients volunteering for clinical trials of experimental agents. *Psycho-Oncology* 2005 February; 14(2): 135-146. NRCBL: 18.5.1; 9.1; 1.2; 8.1; 9.5.1. SC: em.

Dein, Simon. Race, culture and ethnicity in minority research: a critical discussion. *Journal of Cultural Diversity* 2006 Summer; 13(2): 68-75. NRCBL: 18.5.1; 7.1; 21.7.

Dennis, Carina. Australia considers changing laws to allow therapeutic cloning [news]. *Nature Medicine* 2006 February; 12(2): 156. NRCBL: 18.5.1; 1.3.5.

DeVita, Michael A.; Wicclair, Mark; Swanson, Dennis; Valenta, Cindy; Schold, Clifford. Research involving the newly dead: an institutional response. *Critical Care Medicine* 2003; 31(Supplement 5): S385-S390. NRCBL: 18.5.1; 18.2; 18.3; 20.1; 20.3.1.

Dixon, Roz. Ethical research with participants who are deaf. *Bulletin of Medical Ethics* 2005 April; (207): 13-19. NRCBL: 18.5.1; 18.2. SC: rv.

DuVal, Gordon; Salmon, Christina. Research note: ethics of drug treatment research with court-supervised subjects. *Journal of Drug Issues* 2004 Fall; 34(4): 991-1005. NRCBL: 18.5.1; 18.3; 9.5.9; 9.7. SC: le.

Foster, Morris W. Analyzing the use of race and ethnicity in biomedical research from a local community perspective. *Journal of Law, Medicine and Ethics* 2006 Fall; 34(3): 508-512. NRCBL: 18.5.1; 9.5.4; 7.1; 18.2; 15.11.
Abstract: Lost in the debate over the use of racial and ethnic categories in biomedical research is community-level analysis of how these categories function and influence health. Such analysis offers a powerful critique of national and transnational categories usually used in biomedical research such as "African-American" and "Native American." Ethnographic research on local African-American and Native American communities in Oklahoma shows the importance of community-level analysis. Local ("intra-community") health practices tend to be shared by members of an everyday interactional community without regard to racial or ethnic identity. Externally created ("extra-community") practices tend to be based on the existence of externally-imposed racial or ethnic identities, but African-American and Native American community members show similar patterns in their use of extra-community practices. Thus, membership in an interactional community seems more important than externally-imposed racial or ethnic identity in determining local health practices, while class may be as or more important in accounting for extra-community practices.

Gamble, Vanessa Northington. The Tuskegee syphilis study and women's health. *Journal of the American Medical Women's Association* 1997 Fall; 52(4): 195-196. NRCBL: 18.5.1; 18.3; 10; 9.5.5; 9.5.4.

Garber, Mandy; Arnold, Robert M. Promoting the participation of minorities in research. *American Journal of Bioethics [Online]*. 2006 May-June; 6(3): W14-W20. NRCBL: 18.5.1.

Gaw, Allan. Beyond consent: the potential for atrocity. *Journal of the Royal Society of Medicine* 2006 April; 99(4): 175-177. NRCBL: 18.5.1; 18.3; 18.5.5; 4.1.2; 2.1; 1.3.5.

Glenn, David. Blood feud. *Chronicle of Higher Education* 2006 March 3; 52(26): A14-A16, A18. NRCBL: 18.5.1; 18.3; 1.3.9; 7.4.

Goldman, Bruce; Coghlan, Andy. Organs on demand, no embryo needed [news]. *New Scientist* 2006 October 7-13; 192(2572): 8-9. NRCBL: 18.5.1; 15.1; 18.5.4; 19.1.

Grady, Christine; Hampson, Lindsay A.; Wallen, Gwenyth R.; Rivera-Goba, Migdalia V.; Carrington, Kelli L.; Mittleman, Barbara B. Exploring the ethics of clinical research in an urban community. *American Journal of Public Health* 2006 November; 96(11): 1996-2001. NRCBL: 18.5.1; 18.6. SC: em.

SC (Subject Captions):   an=analytical   cs=case studies   em=empirical   le=legal   po=popular   rv=review

Abstract: OBJECTIVES: We consulted with representatives of an urban community in Washington, DC, about the ethics of clinical research involving residents of the community with limited access to health care. METHODS: A semistructured community consultation was conducted with core members of the Health Partnership Program of the National Institute of Arthritis and Musculoskeletal and Skin Diseases. Three research case examples were discussed; questions and probes (a predetermined question or series of questions used to further investigate or follow-up a response) guided the discussion. RESULTS: The community representatives who took part in the consultation were supportive of research and appreciated the opportunity to be heard. They noted the importance of respecting the circumstances, values, needs, and welfare of research participants; supported widely representative recruitment strategies; and cited the positive benefits of providing care or treatment to participants. Monitoring participants' welfare and ensuring care at a study's end were emphasized. Trust was a central theme; participants suggested several trust-enhancing strategies, including full disclosure of information and the involvement of advocates, physicians, and trusted church members. CONCLUSIONS: Several important strategies emerged for conducting ethical research in urban communities whose residents have limited access to health care.

Grandison, David. Participation of minorities in research and clinical trials. *In:* Satcher, David; Pamies, Rubens J., eds. Multicultural medicine and health disparities. New York: McGraw-Hill, 2006: 449-458. NRCBL: 18.5.1.

Guevara, Carlos; Cook, Chad; Herback, Natalie; Pietrobon, Ricardo; Jacobs, Danny O.; Vail, Thomas Parker. Gender, racial, and ethical disclosure in NIH K-award funded diabetes and obesity clinical trials. *Accountability in Research* 2006 October-December; 13(4): 311-324. NRCBL: 18.5.1; 18.5.3; 10. SC: em; le. Identifiers: United States Revitalization Act.

Hall, Wayne; Carter, Lucy; Morley, Katherine I. Addiction, ethics and scientific freedom. *Addiction* 2003 July; 98(7): 873-874. NRCBL: 18.5.1; 9.5.9; 18.4.

Hawryluck, Laura. Research ethics in the intensive care unit: current and future challenges [editorial]. *Critical Care* 2004 April; 8(2): 71-72. NRCBL: 18.5.1.

Hoit, Jeannette D. Who goes first? [editorial]. *American Journal of Speech-Language Pathology* 2005 November; 14(4): 259. NRCBL: 18.5.1; 7.3. Identifiers: self-experimentation.

Huber, Sam; Lagay, Faith. Clinical trials in developing countries. *Virtual Mentor* 2001 August; 3(8): 2p. NRCBL: 18.5.1; 21.1; 8.3.1.

Jackson, Fatimah L.C. Tuskegee experiment. *In:* Mitcham, Carl, ed. Encyclopedia of Science, Technology, and Ethics. Farmington Hills, MI: Thomson/Gale, 2005: 1986-1988. NRCBL: 18.5.1; 2.2.

Jenkinson, Crispin; Burton, John S.; Cartwright, Julia; Magee, Helen; Hall, Ian; Alcock, Chris; Burge, Sherwood. Patient attitudes to clinical trials: development of a questionnaire and results from asthma and cancer pa-

tients. *Health Expectations* 2005 September; 8(3): 244-252. NRCBL: 18.5.1; 18.2; 18.3. SC: em.

Kalm, Leah M.; Semba, Richard D. They starved so that others be better fed: remembering Ancel Keys and the Minnesota experiment. *Journal of Nutrition* 2005 June; 135(6): 1347-1352. NRCBL: 18.5.1; 18.4; 21.2.

Kaufert, Joseph; Commanda, Laura; Elias, Brenda; Grey, Rhoda; Young, T. Kue; Masuzumi, Barney. Evolving participation of Aboriginal communities in health research ethics review: the impact of the Inuvik workshop. *International Journal of Circumpolar Health* 1998 April; 58(2): 134-245. NRCBL: 18.5.1; 18.2; 1.3.9; 21.7.

Kaufman, Sharon R. The World War II plutonium experiments: contested stories and their lessons for medical research and informed consent. *Culture, Medicine and Psychiatry* 1997 June; 21(2): 161-197. NRCBL: 18.5.1; 16.2; 18.3; 2.2.

Kishore, R.R. Biomedical research and mining of the poor: the need for their exclusion. *Science and Engineering Ethics* 2006 January; 12(1): 175-183. NRCBL: 18.5.1.

Leavitt, Frank J. Is any medical research population not vulnerable? *CQ: Cambridge Quarterly of Healthcare Ethics* 2006 Winter; 15(1): 81-88. NRCBL: 18.5.1; 18.3; 9.7; 2.3.

Lillquist, Erik; Sullivan, Charles A. Legal regulation of the use of race in medical research. *Journal of Law, Medicine and Ethics* 2006 Fall; 34(3): 535-551. NRCBL: 18.5.1; 9.5.4; 18.2; 15.1; 15.11. SC: le.
Abstract: In this article, we discuss current legal restrictions governing the use of race in medical research. In particular, we focus on whether the use of race in various types of research is presently permitted under federal law and the federal constitution. We also discuss whether federal restrictions on the use of race in research ought to be expanded, and whether federal policies that encourage the use of race ought to be abandoned.

Maloney, Dennis M. Minority groups as human subjects. *Human Research Report* 2006 February; 21(2): 3. NRCBL: 18.5.1.

McDaniel, Patricia A.; Solomon, Gina; Malone, Ruth E. The ethics of industry experimentation using employees: the case of taste-testing pesticide-treated tobacco. *American Journal of Public Health* 2006 January; 96(1): 37-46. NRCBL: 18.5.1; 18.3; 9.5.9.
Abstract: In the United States, companies that use their own funds to test consumer products on their employees are subject to few regulations. Using previously undisclosed tobacco industry documents, we reviewed the history of that industry's efforts to create internal guidelines on the conditions to be met before employee taste testers could evaluate cigarettes made from tobacco treated with experimental pesticides. This history highlights 2 potential ethical issues raised by unregulated industrial research: conflict of interest and lack of informed consent. To ensure compliance with accepted ethical standards, an independent federal office should be established to oversee industrial research involving humans exposed to experimental or

NRCBL: National Reference Center for Bioethics Literature Classification Scheme   See inside front cover for terms.

321

increased quantities of ingested, inhaled, or absorbed chemical agents.

Mitchell, Terry Leigh; Baker, Emerance. Community-building versus career-building research: the challenges, risks, and responsibilities of conducting research with Aboriginal and Native American communities. *Journal of Cancer Education* 2005 Spring; 20(1, Supplement): 41-46. NRCBL: 18.5.1; 21.7; 18.6.

Muroff, Jordana R.; Hoerauf, Sarah L.; Kim, Scott Y.H. Is psychiatric research stigmatized? An experimental survey of the public. *Schizophrenia Bulletin* 2006 January; 32(1): 129-136. NRCBL: 18.5.1; 18.5.6. SC: rv; em.

Nee, P.A.; Griffiths, R.D. Ethical considerations in accident and emergency research. *Emergency Medicine Journal* 2002 September; 19(5): 423-427. NRCBL: 18.5.1; 18.3; 18.2.

Nickel, Philip J. Vulnerable populations in research: the case of the seriously ill. *Theoretical Medicine and Bioethics* 2006; 27(3): 245-264. NRCBL: 18.5.1; 18.3.
Abstract: This paper advances a new criterion of a vulnerable population in research. According to this criterion, there are consent-based and fairness-based reasons for calling a group vulnerable. The criterion is then applied to the case of people with serious illnesses. It is argued that people with serious illnesses meet this criterion for reasons related to consent. Seriously ill people have a susceptibility to "enticing offers" that hold out the prospect of removing or alleviating illness, and this susceptibility reduces their ability to safeguard their own interests. This explains the inclusion of people with serious illnesses in the Belmont Report's list of populations needing special protections, and supports the claim that vulnerability is the rule, rather than the exception, in biomedical research.

Patel, P. A natural stem cell therapy? How novel findings and biotechnology clarify the ethics of stem cell research. *Journal of Medical Ethics* 2006 April; 32(4): 235-239. NRCBL: 18.5.1; 15.1; 19.1.

Resnik, David B.; Portier, Christopher. Pesticide testing on human subjects: weighing benefits and risks. *Environmental Health Perspectives* 2005 July; 113(7): 813-817. NRCBL: 18.5.1; 16.1; 9.7; 18.6.

Roberts, Dorothy E. Legal constraints on the use of race in biomedical research: toward a social justice framework. *Journal of Law, Medicine and Ethics* 2006 Fall; 34(3): 526-534. NRCBL: 18.5.1; 9.5.4; 18.2; 2.1; 1.1.; 18.6; 15.11. SC: le.
Abstract: This article addresses three questions concerning the legal regulation of the use of race as a category in biomedical research: how does the law currently encourage the use of race in biomedical research?; how might the existing legal framework constrain its use?; and what should be the law's approach to race-based biomedical research? It proposes a social justice approach that aims to promote racial equality by discouraging the use of "race" as a biological category while encouraging its use as a socio-political category to understand and investigate ways to eliminate disparities in health status, access to health care, and medical treatment.

Scully, Robert; Glynn, Liam. Researching minority groups [letter]. *Lancet* 2006 August 12-18; 368(9535): 575. NRCBL: 18.5.1.

Shafer, J.K.; Usilton, Lida J.; Gleeson, Geraldine A. Untreated syphilis in the male Negro. *Public Health Reports* 2006; 121(Supplement 1): 235-241; discussion 234. NRCBL: 18.5.1; 9.5.4. SC: em. Identifiers: Tuskegee Study.

Shavers, Vickie L.; Lynch, Charles F.; Burmeister, Leon F. Factors that influence African-Americans' willingness to participate in medical research studies. *Cancer* 2001 January 1; 91(1, Supplement): 233-236. NRCBL: 18.5.1; 18.3. SC: em.

Sterling, Rene; Henderson, Gail E.; Corbie-Smith, Giselle. Public willingness to participate in and public opinions about genetic variation research: a review of literature. *American Journal of Public Health* 2006 November; 96(11): 1971-1978. NRCBL: 18.5.1; 9.5.4; 15.1. SC: em.
Abstract: Scientists are turning to genetic variation research in hopes of addressing persistent racial/ethnic disparities in health. Despite ongoing controversy, the advancement of genetic variation research is likely to produce new knowledge and technologies that will substantially change the ways in which we understand and value health. They also may affect the ways in which individuals and groups organize socially, politically, and economically. Addressing concerns that may exist in different communities is vital to the scientific and ethical advancement of genetic variation research. We review empirical studies of public willingness to participate in and opinions about genetic research with particular attention to differences in consent and opinion by racial/ethnic group membership.

Uhl, George R. Are over-simplified views of addiction neuroscience providing too simplified ethical considerations? *Addiction* 2003 July; 98(7): 872-873. NRCBL: 18.5.1; 9.5.9; 18.4.

United States. Department of Health and Human Services [DHHS]. Indian Health Service [IHS]. Indian Health Service multiple project assurance (mpa) for compliance with DHHS regulations for the protection of human subjects (45 CFR 46) as amended. Rockville, MD: Indian Health Service; 24 pages [Online]. Accessed: http://www.ihs.gov/ medicalprograms/research/pdf%5Ffiles/mpa%2Dihs 2.pdf [2006 January 6]. NRCBL: 18.5.1; 6; 18.2.

Wall, L. Lewis. The medical ethics of Dr. J. Marion Sims: a fresh look at the historical record. *Journal of Medical Ethics* 2006 June; 32(6): 346-350. NRCBL: 18.5.1; 18.5.3; 2.2; 9.5.4. Identifiers: J. Marion Sims.
Abstract: Vesicovaginal fistula was a catastrophic complication of childbirth among 19th century American women. The first consistently successful operation for this condition was developed by Dr J Marion Sims, an Alabama surgeon who carried out a series of experimental operations on black slave women between 1845 and 1849. Numerous modern authors have attacked Sims's medical ethics, arguing that he manipulated the institution of slavery to perform ethically unacceptable human experiments on powerless, unconsenting women. This article reviews

---

these allegations using primary historical source material and concludes that the charges that have been made against Sims are largely without merit. Sims's modern critics have discounted the enormous suffering experienced by fistula victims, have ignored the controversies that surrounded the introduction of anaesthesia into surgical practice in the middle of the 19th century, and have consistently misrepresented the historical record in their attacks on Sims. Although enslaved African American women certainly represented a "vulnerable population" in the 19th century American South, the evidence suggests that Sims's original patients were willing participants in his surgical attempts to cure their affliction — a condition for which no other viable therapy existed at that time.

Weijer, Charles; LeBlanc, Guy J. The balm of Gilead: is the provision of treatment to those who seroconvert in HIV prevention trials a matter of moral obligation or moral negotiation? *Journal of Law, Medicine and Ethics* 2006 Winter; 34(4): 793-808. NRCBL: 18.5.1; 9.5.6; 18.2; 2.1; 21.1. SC: an.
Abstract: Must treatment be provided to subjects who acquire HIV during the course of a prevention study? An analysis of ethical foundation, regulation, and recent argumentation provides no basis for the obligation. We outline an alternative approach to the problem based on moral negotiation.

White, Robert M. Misinformation and misbeliefs in the Tuskegee Study of Untreated Syphilis fuel mistrust in the healthcare system [editorial]. *Journal of the National Medical Association* 2005 November; 97(11): 1566-1573. NRCBL: 18.5.1; 18.3; 10; 2.2; 9.1.

Williams, Charmaine C. Ethical considerations in mental health research with racial and ethnic minority communities. *Community Mental Health Journal* 2005 October; 41(5): 509-520. NRCBL: 18.5.1; 21.7; 18.2; 1.1.

Wilmut, Ian. Recent stem cell research poses several challenges [editorial]. *Cloning and Stem Cells* 2006 Summer; 8(2): 67-68. NRCBL: 18.5.1; 15.1.

Winker, Margaret A. Race and ethnicity in medical research: requirements meet reality. *Journal of Law, Medicine and Ethics* 2006 Fall; 34(3): 520-525. NRCBL: 18.5.1; 9.5.4; 18.2; 1.3.7; 15.11.
Abstract: Race and ethnicity are commonly reported variables in biomedical research, but how they were determined is often not described and the rationale for analyzing them is often not provided. JAMA improved the reporting of these factors by implementing a policy and procedure. However, still lacking are careful consideration of what is actually being measured when race/ethnicity is described, consistent terminology, hypothesis-driven justification for analyzing race/ethnicity, and a consistent and generalizable measurement of socioeconomic status. Furthermore, some studies continue to use race/ethnicity as a proxy for genetics. Research into appropriate measures of race/ethnicity and socioeconomic factors, as well as education of researchers regarding issues of race/ethnicity, is necessary to clarify the meaning of race/ethnicity in the biomedical literature.

Wolf, Susan M. Debating the use of racial and ethnic categories in research. *Journal of Law, Medicine and Ethics* 2006 Fall; 34(3): 483-486. NRCBL: 18.5.1; 9.5.4; 7.1; 18.1; 15.11.

HUMAN EXPERIMENTATION/ . . . / AGED AND TERMINALLY ILL

Dying to live [editorial]. *Nature Medicine* 2006 June; 12(6): 593. NRCBL: 18.5.7; 9.7. SC: le. Identifiers: experimental drugs; Abigail Alliance.

Bharucha, Ashok J.; London, Alex John; Barnard, David; Wactlar, Howard; Dew, Mary Amanda; Reynolds, Charles F., III. Ethical considerations in the conduct of electronic surveillance research. *Journal of Law, Medicine and Ethics* 2006 Fall; 34(3): 611-619. NRCBL: 18.5.7; 18.3; 1.3.12. SC: le.
Abstract: The extant clinical literature indicates profound problems in the assessment, monitoring, and documentation of care in long-term care facilities. The lack of adequate resources to accommodate higher staff-to-resident ratios adds additional urgency to the goal of identifying more cost-effective mechanisms to provide care oversight. The ever expanding array of electronic monitoring technologies in the clinical research arena demands a conceptual and pragmatic framework for the resolution of ethical tensions inherent in the use of such innovative tools. CareMedia is a project that explores the utility of video, audio and sensor technologies as a continuous real-time assessment and outcomes measurement tool. In this paper, the authors describe the seminal ethical challenges encountered during the implementation phase of this project, namely privacy and confidentiality protection, and the strategies employed to resolve the ethical tensions by applying principles of the interest theory of rights.

Bynum, Jack E.; Provonsha, Jack W.; Acuff, F. Gene. Ethics of experimental surgery: the Baby Fae case — an interview and comment. *Pharos* 1986 Fall; 49(4): 23-26. NRCBL: 18.5.7; 19.2.

Cameron, Alisa; Lloyd, Liz; Kent, Naomi; Anderson, Pat. Researching end of life in old age: ethical challenges. *In:* Smyth, Marie; Williamson, Emma, eds. Researchers and Their 'Subjects': Ethics, Power, Knowledge and Consent. Bristol, UK: Policy Press; 2004: 105-117. NRCBL: 18.5.7; 18.4.

Donnelly, J. Can adults with cognitive impairment consent to take part in research? *Journal of Wound Care* 2004 July; 13(7): 257-262. NRCBL: 18.5.7; 18.2; 18.3.

Dresser, Rebecca. Investigational drugs and the Constitution. *Hastings Center Report* 2006 November-December; 36(6): 9-10. NRCBL: 18.5.7; 18.6; 9.5.1. SC: le.

Edwards, Sarah J.L. Restricted treatments, inducements, and research participation. *Bioethics* 2006 April; 20(2): 77-91. NRCBL: 18.5.7; 9.4; 18.6. SC: an.
Abstract: In this paper, I support the claim that placing certain restrictions on public access to possible new treatments is morally problematic under some exceptional circumstances. Very ill patients may find that all available standard treatments are unacceptable, either because they are ineffective or have serious adverse effects, and these patients may understandably be desperate to try something new even if this means stepping into the unknown. Faced with certain death, it is rational to want to try something new and to chance a dire outcome. Restricting possible new treatments to research trials may put these treat-

NRCBL: National Reference Center for Bioethics Literature Classification Scheme   See inside front cover for terms.

323

ments scientifically, geographically or economically out of reach of these patients. For those who can get access, research restrictions could weaken, though not necessarily eliminate, the value of consent participants of such trials are able to give. Some participants may therefore be exploited for scientific purposes in the name of public interest. There are nonetheless compelling reasons for keeping some restrictive regulation in this area.

Groeneveld, Peter W.; Brezis, Mayer; Lehmann, Lisa Soleymani; Pearson, Steven D.; Miller, Franklin G.; Emanuel, Ezekiel J. Medicare requirement for research participation [letters and reply]. *JAMA: The Journal of the American Medical Association* 2006 December 27; 296(24): 2923-2925. NRCBL: 18.5.7; 9.3.1.

Haley, William E. A commentary — institutional review board approval and beyond: proactive steps to improve ethics and quality in end-of-life research. *Gerontologist* 2002 October; 42(Special Issue 3): 109-113. NRCBL: 18.5.7; 18.2.

Kaye, Janet M.; Lawton, Powell; Kaye, Donald. Attitudes of elderly people about clinical research on aging. *Gerontologist* 1990 February; 30(1): 100-106. NRCBL: 18.5.7; 18.3. SC: em.

Locher, Julie L.; Bronstein, Janet; Robinson, Caroline O.; Williams, Charlotte, Ritchie, Christine S. Ethical issues involving research conducted with homebound older adults. *Gerontologist* 2006 April; 46(2): 160-164. NRCBL: 18.5.7; 1.3.9; 4.4; 18.1; 18.3.

Loue, Sana. The participation of cognitively impaired elderly in research. *Care Management Journals* 2004 Winter; 5(4): 245-257. NRCBL: 18.5.7; 18.3.

Mertes, Heidi; Pennings, Guido; Van Steirteghem, André. An ethical analysis of alternative methods to obtain pluripotent stem cells without destroying embryos. *Human Reproduction* 2006 November; 21(11): 2749-2755. NRCBL: 18.5.7; 4.4; 19.1. SC: an.

Morriem, E. Haavi. End-stage heart disease, high-risk research, and competence to consent: the case of the AbioCor artificial heart. *Perspectives on Biology and Medicine* 2006 Winter; 49(1): 19-34. NRCBL: 18.5.7; 18.3; 19.2.

Phipps, Etienne J. What's end of life got to do with it? Research ethics with populations at life's end. *Gerontologist* 2002 October; 42(Special Issue 3): 104-108. NRCBL: 18.5.7; 18.2. SC: em.

Robertson, John A. Controversial medical treatment and the right to health care. *Hastings Center Report* 2006 November-December; 36(6): 15-20. NRCBL: 18.5.7; 18.6; 9.5.1; 18.5; 19.5; 9.3.1. SC: le.

Ross, Daniel S. The two-faced angel: do Phase I clinical trials have a place in modern hospice? *Penn Bioethics Journal* 2006; 2(2): 46-49. NRCBL: 18.5.7; 20.4.1; 2.2; 9.7.

Abstract: Increasingly, bioethicists have been exploring the possibility of making phase I clinical trials available to hospice patients. Phase I clinical trials are designed to test a drug's safety and dosage, not its effectiveness. Participants in these studies generally do not understand that the purpose of the investigation is not to benefit them, thus challenging the notion of informed consent. But furthermore, the idea that patients believe experimental drugs will help them is contrary to the principles of hospice. Also, the very nature of the research in phase I conflicts with hospice's methods. For these reasons, this paper finds that the two models must remain distinct.

Waltz, Emily. US court rules to allow experimental drugs for dying patients [news]. *Nature Medicine* 2006 June; 12(6): 596. NRCBL: 18.5.7; 9.7. SC: le.

Williams, Susan G. How do the elderly and their families feel about research participation? *Geriatric Nursing* 1993 January-February; 14(1): 11-14. NRCBL: 18.5.7; 18.3; 8.3.3; 4.1.3.

HUMAN EXPERIMENTATION/ . . . / EMBRYOS AND FETUSES
See also CLONING

Come veto or high water [editorial]. *Nature* 2006 July 27; 442(7101): 329. NRCBL: 18.5.4; 1.3.9; 15.1; 19.1. Identifiers: stem cell research.

Cow-human chimaera for stem cells faces UK ban [news brief]. *Nature* 2006 December 21-28; 444(7122): 983. NRCBL: 18.5.4; 15.1; 19.1; 22.1. Identifiers: United Kingdom (Great Britain).

Le clonage thérapeutique: mythes et perspectives [Therapeutic cloning: myths and perspectives]. Unpublished Document 2005 May 8; 5 p. NRCBL: 18.5.4; 15.1; 14.5.

One of a kind [editorial]. *New Scientist* 2006 July 1-7; 191(2558): 5. NRCBL: 18.5.4; 15.1; 19.1.

Standing up for stem cell research [editorial]. *New York Times* 2006 July 18; p. A20. NRCBL: 18.5.4; 15.1; 5.3.

Statement on stem cell research issued by the Johns Hopkins University. *South African Medical Journal* 2004 September; 94(9): 739-740. NRCBL: 18.5.4; 15.1; 6.

Who said murder? [editorial]. *New Scientist* 2006 July 29-August 4; 191(2562): 3. NRCBL: 18.5.4; 1.3.9; 15.1; 19.1. Identifiers: stem cell research; George W. Bush.

Abbott, Alison. 'Ethical' stem-cell paper under attack [news]. *Nature* 2006 September 7; 443(7107): 12. NRCBL: 18.5.4; 19.1; 15.1. Identifiers: Robert Lanza; Advanced Cell Technologies, Inc.

American Academy of Neurology [AAN]; American Neurological Association [ANA]. Position statement regarding the use of embryonic and adult human stem cells in biomedical research. *Neurology* 2005 May 24; 64(10): 1679-1680. NRCBL: 18.5.4; 15.1; 18.5.1.

American Society for Reproductive Medicine [ASRM]. Ethics Committee. Disposition of abandoned embryos. *Fertility and Sterility* 2004 September; 82(Supplement 1): S253. NRCBL: 18.5.4; 19.5; 18.3; 14.4; 15.1.

American Society for Reproductive Medicine [ASRM]. Ethics Committee. Embryo splitting for infertility treatment. *Fertility and Sterility* 2004 September; 82(Supplement 1): S256-S257. NRCBL: 18.5.4; 14.1; 14.5; 15.1.

American Society of Human Genetics [ASHG]; Francke, Uta; Worton, Ronald. Re: Draft NIH guidelines for research involving human pluripotent stem cells [letter]. Bethesda, MD: American Society of Human Genetics [ASHG], 2000 January 21: 2 p. [Online]. Accessed: http://www.ashg.org/genetics/ashg/pubs/policy/pol-37.htm [2006 July 25]. NRCBL: 18.5.4; 15.1; 18.2. Note: ASHG Response to NIH Office of Science Policy. Comments: National Institutes of Health [NIH]. Draft National Institutes of Health Guidelines for Research Involving Human Pluripotent Stem Cells. Federal Register 1999 December 2; 64(231): 67576-67579.

Austria. Bioethikkommission beim Bundeskanzleramt = Austria. Bioethics Commission at the Federal Chancellery. Decision of the Bioethics Commission at the Federal Chancellery of 3 April and 8 May 2002. Opinion of the Bioethics Commission on the issue of stem cell research in the context of the EU's Sixth Framework Programme for Research, Technological Development and Demonstration Activities as a contribution towards the realization of the European Research Area (2002-2006). Vienna, Austria: Bioethikkommission beim Bundeskanzleramt; 2002 April 3 [and] 2002 May 8; 6 p. NRCBL: 18.5.4; 15.1; 19.1.

> Abstract: According to the EU's FAQ on the Research Framework Programme (FP), "the FP is the EU's main instrument for research funding in Europe. The FP is proposed by the European Commission and adopted by the Council and the European parliament following a co-decision procedure. FPS cover a period of five years with the last year of one FP and the first year of the following FP overlapping. FPS have been implemented since 1984. The Sixth FP (FP6) will be fully operational as of January 1, 2003. . .FP6 aims to contribute to the creation of a true 'European Research Area' (ERA). ERA is a vision for the future of research in Europe, an internal market for science and technology."

Billings, Paul. Dangerous territory: headline grabbing moves by various US states to fund stem cell and other research could pose serious dangers for public health. *New Scientist* 2006 November 4-10; 192(2576): 22. NRCBL: 18.5.4; 15.1; 19.1; 1.3.5; 1.3.9; 9.1; 18.6.

Birnbacher, Dieter. Forschung an embryonalen Stammzellen — die Rolle der "complicity". *In:* Vollmann, Jochen, ed. Medizin und Ethik: Aktuelle ethische Probleme in Therapie und Forschung. Erlangen: Universitätsbund Erlangen-Nürnberg, 2003: 61-82. NRCBL: 18.5.4; 15.1.

Blumenstyk, Goldie. A tight grip on tech transfer. *Chronicle of Higher Education* 2006 September 15; 53(4): A28-A32. NRCBL: 18.5.4; 15.1; 15.8; 1.3.9; 5.3; 1.3.2.

Bonnicksen, Andrea L. Embryonic stem cells. *In:* Mitcham, Carl, ed. Encyclopedia of Science, Technology, and Ethics. Farmington Hills, MI: Thomson/Gale, 2005: 608-610. NRCBL: 18.5.4; 18.6.

Brock, D.W. Is a consensus possible on stem cell research? Moral and political obstacles. *Journal of Medical Ethics* 2006 January; 32(1): 36-42. NRCBL: 18.5.4; 15.1; 19.1.

Budinger, Thomas F.; Budinger, Miriam D. Ethics of stem cell technologies. *In their:* Ethics of Emerging Technologies: Scientific Facts and Moral Challenges. Hoboken, NJ: John Wiley and Sons; 2006: 342-383. NRCBL: 18.5.4.

Byrnes, W. Malcolm; Berg, Thomas. Inconsistencies in pro ANT-OAR position [letter and reply]. *National Catholic Bioethics Quarterly* 2006 Summer; 6(2): 201-205. NRCBL: 18.5.4; 14.5; 15.1; 14.4; 19.1. Identifiers: altered nuclear transfer-oocyte assisted reprogramming.

Cameron, Nigel M. de S. Research ethics, science policy, and four contexts for the stem cell debate. *Journal of Investigative Medicine* 2006 January; 54(1): 38-42. NRCBL: 18.5.4; 15.1; 18.6; 21.1.

Caulfield, Timothy. From human genes to stem cells: new challenges for patent law? *Trends in Biotechnology* 2003 March; 21(3): 101-103. NRCBL: 18.5.4; 5.3; 15.1; 15.8.

Cedar, S.H. Stem cell and related therapies: nurses and midwives representing all parties. *Nursing Ethics* 2006 May; 13(3): 292-303. NRCBL: 18.5.4; 15.1; 14.5.

Chaplin, C. Ethics of international clinical research collaboration — the experience of AlloStem. *International Journal of Immunogenetics* 2006 February; 33(1): 1-5. NRCBL: 18.5.4; 15.1; 21.1.

Cheng, Linzhao. Ethics: China already has clear stem-cell guidelines. *Nature* 2006 April 20; 440(7087): 992. NRCBL: 18.5.4; 15.1; 19.1.

Cornwell, Glenda. Ethical issues in deriving stem cells from embryos and eggs. *British Journal of Nursing* 2006 June 22-July 12; 15(12): 640-644. NRCBL: 18.5.4; 14.4; 14.6; 15.1; 15.2.

Cyranoski, David; Check, Erika. Koreans admit disguising stem-cell lines [news]. *Nature* 2006 June 15; 441(7095): 790-791. NRCBL: 18.5.4; 19.1; 15.1; 1.3.9.

Davenport, R. John. Drumming up dollars for stem cell research. *Cell* 2005 December 29; 123(7): 1169-1171. NRCBL: 18.5.4; 15.1; 19.1.

Dawkins, Richard. Collateral damage, Part 1. *Free Inquiry* 2006 December-2007 January; 27(1): 12-14.

NRCBL: National Reference Center for Bioethics Literature Classification Scheme   See inside front cover for terms.

325

NRCBL: 18.5.4; 15.1; 21.1. Identifiers: embryonic stem cell research.

de Wert, Guido. The use of human embryonic stem cells for research: an ethical evaluation. *In:* Rees, Dai; Rose, Steven, eds. The New Brain Sciences: Perils and Prospects. New York: Cambridge University Press; 2004: 213-222. NRCBL: 18.5.4; 15.1.

Denker, Hans-Werner. Early human development: new data raise important embryological and ethical questions relevant for stem cell research. *Naturwissenschaften* 2004 January; 91(1): 1-21. NRCBL: 18.5.4; 15.1.

Denker, H.-W. Potentiality of embryonic stem cells: an ethical problem even with alternative stem cell sources. *Journal of Medical Ethics* 2006 November; 32(11): 665-671. NRCBL: 18.5.4; 18.5.1; 19.1; 15.1.

Abstract: The recent discussions about alternative sources of human embryonic stem cells (White Paper of the US President's Council on Bioethics, 2005), while stirring new interest in the developmental potential of the various abnormal embryos or constructs proposed as such sources, also raise questions about the potential of the derived embryonic stem cells. The data on the developmental potential of embryonic stem cells that seem relevant for ethical considerations and aspects of patentability are discussed. Particular attention is paid to the meaning of "totipotency, omnipotency and pluripotency" as illustrated by a comparison of the developmental potential of three-dimensional clusters of blastomeres (morula), embryonic stem cells, somatic or (adult) stem cells or other somatic (non-stem) cells. This paper focuses on embryoid bodies and on direct cloning by tetraploid complementation. Usage and patenting of these cells cannot be considered to be ethically sound as long as totipotency and tetraploid complementability of embryonic stem cells are not excluded for the specific cell line in question. Testing this poses an ethical problem in itself and needs to be discussed in the future.

Devolder, Katrien; Harris, John. Compromise and moral complicity in the embryonic stem cell debate. *In:* Athanassoulis, Nafsika, ed. Philosophical Reflections on Medical Ethics. New York: Palgrave Macmillan; 2005: 88-108. NRCBL: 18.5.4; 19.1; 15.1. SC: an.

Devolder, K. What's in a name? Embryos, entities, and ANTities in the stem cell debate. *Journal of Medical Ethics* 2006 January; 32(1): 43-48. NRCBL: 18.5.4; 15.1; 19.1. Identifiers: altered nuclear transfer.

Abstract: This paper discusses two proposals to the US President's Council on Bioethics that try to overcome the issue of killing embryos in embryonic stem (ES) cell research and argues that neither of them can hold good as a compromise solution. The author argues that (1) the groups of people for which the compromises are intended neither need nor want the two compromises, (2) the US government and other governments of countries with restrictive regulation on ES cell research have not provided a clear and sound justification to take into account minority views on the protection of human life to such a considerable extent as to constrain the freedom of research in the area of stem cell research, and (3) the best way to deal with these issues is to accept that many people and most governments adopt a gradualist and variable viewpoint on the human embryo which implies that embryos can be sacrificed for good reasons and to try to find other, less constraining, ways to take into ac-

count minority views on the embryo. Finally, another more efficient and time and money sparing compromise will be proposed for those who accept IVF, a majority in most societies.

Dillon, Kevin J. Significant developments in stem cell research. *Human Reproduction and Genetic Ethics: An International Journal* 2006; 12(1): 24-28. NRCBL: 18.5.4; 15.1; 18.5.1.

Disilvestro, Russell. Not every cell is sacred: a reply to Charo [response]. *Bioethics* 2006 June; 20(3): 146-157. NRCBL: 18.5.4; 9.5.8; 14.5; 15.1. SC: an.

Abstract: Massimo Reichlin, in an earlier article in this journal, defended a version of the 'argument from potential' (AFP), which concludes that the human embryo should be protected from the moment of conception. But R. Alto Charo, in her essay entitled 'Every Cell is Sacred: Logical Consequences of the Argument from Potential in the Age of Cloning', claims that versions of the AFP like Reichlin's are vulnerable to a rather embarrassing problem: with the advent of human cloning, such versions of the AFP entail that every somatic cell in the human body ought to be protected. Since this entailment is clearly absurd, Charo argues, these versions of AFP should be rejected. I argue that the reasons Charo cites for believing in this entailment are inconclusive. For example, the four reasons she gives for doubting any differences between the nature of skin cells and zygotes are ultimately unconvincing. Against Charo, I maintain that there is a relevant distinction between the sort of potential possessed by the somatic cell and the sort of potential possessed by the early human embryo. Since only the latter sort of potential falls within the scope of the AFP, the alleged absurd entailment Charo invites us to consider is no entailment at all. Hence the AFP cannot be rejected on the grounds Charo advances. Even in an age of cloning, the claim that some cells are 'sacred' because of their potential does not entail the claim that every cell is sacred.

Donohue, John W. The stem cell debate: why is there an irreconcilable division between two groups of thoughtful and sympathetic people? *America* 2006 November 13; 195(15): 25-26. NRCBL: 18.5.4; 15.1.

Drake, Amanda L.; Heilig, Lauren F.; Kozak, Katarzyna Z.; Hester, Eric J.; Dellavalle, Robert P. Researcher opinions on human embryonic stem cell issues. *Journal of Investigative Dermatology* 2004 March; 122(3): 855-856. NRCBL: 18.5.4; 18.1; 15.1.

Eisenstein, Michael. Making ES cells 'ethically sound'. *Nature Methods* 2005 December; 2(12): 891. NRCBL: 18.5.4; 15.1; 19.1; 19.5; 15.1.

Evans, Martin. Ethical sourcing of human embryonic stem cells — rational solutions? *Nature Reviews Molecular Cell Biology* 2005 August; 6(8): 663-667. NRCBL: 18.5.4; 15.1; 18.5.1.

Fields, Helen. What comes next? Scientists are now grappling with a major setback to stem cell research. *U.S. News and World Report* 2006 January 23; 140(3): 56-58. NRCBL: 18.5.4; 15.1; 1.3.9; 19.5; 9.3.1; 18.6. SC: po. Identifiers: Hwang Woo Suk.

Ford, Norman. Human pluripotent stem cell research and ethics. *Monash Bioethics Review* 2006 January; 25(1): 31-41. NRCBL: 18.5.4; 15.1; 19.5.

Franklin, Sarah. Stem cells R us: emergent life forms and the global biological. *In:* Ong, Aihwa; Collier, Stephen J., eds. Global Assemblages: Technology, Politics, and Ethics as Anthropological Problems. Malden, MA: Blackwell Pub.; 2005: 59-78. NRCBL: 18.5.4; 15.1.

Gearhart, John D. The new genetics: stem cell research and cloning. *In:* Miller, Roman J.; Brubaker, Beryl H.; Peterson, James C., eds. Viewing New Creations with Anabaptist Eyes: Ethics of Biotechnology. Telford, PA: Cascadia Pub.; 2005: 21-34. NRCBL: 18.5.4; 14.5; 15.1; 19.1.

Geddes, Linda. 'Virgin birth' stem cells bypass ethical objections. *New Scientist* 2006 July 1-7; 191(2558): 19. NRCBL: 18.5.4; 15.1; 19.1.

Gilbert, Scott F.; Tyler, Anna L.; Zackin, Emily J. Ethical dilemmas in stem cell therapy. *In their:* Bioethics and the New Embryology: Springboards for Debate. Sunderland, MA: Sinauer Associates; 2005: 159-175. NRCBL: 18.5.4; 15.1; 19.1.

Goldman, Steven A. Neurology and the stem cell debate [editorial]. *Neurology* 2005 May 24; 64(10): 1675-1676. NRCBL: 18.5.4; 15.1.

Gottweis, Herbert. Human embryonic stem cells, cloning, and the transformation of biopolitics. *In:* Stehr, Nico, ed. Biotechnology Between Commerce and Civil Society. New Brunswick, NJ: Transaction Publishers; 2004: 239-265. NRCBL: 18.5.4.; 14.5; 15.1.

Great Britain. Parliament. House of Commons. Science and Technology Committee. Human reproductive technologies and the law. *Bulletin of Medical Ethics* 2005 May; (208): 13-21. NRCBL: 18.5.4; 15.1. Identifiers: United Kingdom(Great Britain); Human Fertilization and Embryology Authority.

Greene, Mark. To restore faith and trust: justice and biological access to cellular therapies. *Hastings Center Report* 2006 January-February; 36(1): 57-63. NRCBL: 18.5.4; 15.1; 9.5.4.

Abstract: Stem cell therapies should be available to people of all ethnicities. However, most cells used in the clinic will probably come from lines of cells stored in stem cell banks, which may end up benefitting the majority group most. The solution is to seek additional funding, earmarked for lines that will benefit minorities and offered as a public expression of apology for past discrimination.

Gursahani, Roop. Therapeutic innovation or cynical exploitation [response]. *Indian Journal of Medical Ethics* 2006 October-December; 3(4): 133-134. NRCBL: 18.5.4; 19.1; 21.1; 1.3.12; 12.1; 15.1. SC: cs. Identifiers: research on aborted fetuses.

Guterman, Lila. A silent scientist under fire. *Chronicle of Higher Education* 2006 February 3; 52(22): A15, A18-A19. NRCBL: 18.5.4; 15.1; 1.3.9; 1.3.7. SC: cs.

Haimes, Erica; Luce, Jacquelyne. Studying potential donors' views on embryonic stem cell therapies and preimplantation genetic diagnosis. *Human Fertility (Cambridge, England)* 2006 June; 9(2): 67-71. NRCBL: 18.5.4; 15.1; 15.2; 14.4; 19.5. Identifiers: United Kingdom (Great Britain).

Hamel, Ron. Embryonic stem cell research: perilous pursuit? *Health Progress* 2006 September-October; 87(5): 4-5. NRCBL: 18.5.4.

Hamel, Ron; Panicola, Michael R. Embryonic stem cell research: off limits? *Health Progress* 2006 September-October; 87(5): 23-29. NRCBL: 18.5.4; 15.1. SC: rv.

Hamilton, David P.; Regaldo, Antonio. New questions emerge over stem-cell research claims. *Wall Street Journal* 2006 September 5; p. A15; A19. NRCBL: 18.5.4; 1.3.9; 1.3.7; 15.1. SC: po.

Hampton, Tracy. Scientists, ethicists ponder challenges in moving stem cell research forward. *JAMA: The Journal of the American Medical Association* 2006 December 6; 296(21): 2542-2543. NRCBL: 18.5.4; 15.1; 19.1.

Healy, Lyn; Hunt, Charles; Young, Lesley; Stacey, Glyn. The UK Stem Cell Bank: its role as a public research resource centre providing access to well-characterised seed stocks of human stem cell lines. *Advanced Drug Delivery Reviews* 2005 December 12; 57(13): 1981-1988. NRCBL: 18.5.4; 15.1; 19.5. Identifiers: United Kingdom(Great Britain).

Heng, Boon Chin; Tong, Cao. Refund fertility-treatment costs for donated embryos [letter]. *Nature* 2006 September 7; 443(7107): 26. NRCBL: 18.5.4; 14.4; 19.1; 15.1; 9.3.1.

Heng, Boon Chin; Tong, Guo Qing; Pennings, Guido. Mirror exchange of donor gametes should also accommodate scientific research [letter and reply]. *Human Reproduction* 2006 April; 21(4): 1100-1101. NRCBL: 18.5.4; 19.5; 14.4; 15.1.

Hirsch, Paul J. Stem cell research, politics, and bioethics [editorial]. *New Jersey Medicine* 2004 December; 101(12): 7-9. NRCBL: 18.5.4; 21.1; 15.1.

Holden, Constance. Scientists create human stem cell line from 'dead' embryos [news]. *Science* 2006 September 29; 313(5795): 1869. NRCBL: 18.5.4; 15.1; 19.1.

Holden, Constance. States, foundations lead the way after Bush vetoes stem cell bill. *Science* 2006 July 28; 313(5786): 420-421. NRCBL: 18.5.4; 5.3; 15.1.

Hudson, Kathy L. Embryo biopsy for stem cells: trading old problems for new. *Hastings Center Report* 2006 September-October; 36(5): 50-51. NRCBL: 18.5.4; 15.1.

NRCBL: National Reference Center for Bioethics Literature Classification Scheme   See inside front cover for terms.

327

Hug, Kristina. Sources of human embryos for stem cell research: ethical problems and their possible solutions. *Medicina (Kaunas)* 2005; 41(12): 1002-1010. NRCBL: 18.5.4; 15.1; 19.1.

Hurlbut, William B.; George, Robert P.; Grompe, Markus. Seeking consensus: a clarification and defense of altered nuclear transfer. *Hastings Center Report* 2006 September-October; 36(5): 42-50. NRCBL: 18.5.4; 15.1; 18.5.1.

Hyun, Insoo. Magic eggs and the frontier of stem cell science. *Hastings Center Report* 2006 March-April; 36(2): 16-19. NRCBL: 18.5.4; 15.1; 1.3.9; 19.1; 19.5.

Hyun, Insoo; Jung, Kyu Won. Human research cloning, embryos, and embryo-life artifacts. *Hastings Center Report* 2006 September-October; 36(5): 34-41. NRCBL: 18.5.4; 18.5.1; 15.1.

Hyun, Insoo; Jung, Kyu Won; Hurlbut, William B.; George, Robert P.; Grompe, Markus. ANT vs. SCNT [letter and reply]. *Hastings Center Report* 2006 November-December; 36(6): 6-7. NRCBL: 18.5.4; 15.1. Identifiers: altered nuclear transfer; somatic cell nuclear transfer.

International Stem Cell Forum Ethics Working Party. Ethics issues in stem cell research [letter]. *Science* 2006 April 21; 312(5772): 366-367. NRCBL: 18.5.4; 15.1; 1.3.9; 21.1.

International Stem Cell Initiative. Steering Committee. The International Stem Cell Initiative: toward benchmarks for human embryonic stem cell research. *Nature Biotechnology* 2005 July; 23(7): 795-797. NRCBL: 18.5.4; 5.3; 21.1.

Jaenisch, Rudolph. Making the paper: plotting a course through the ethical minefield of stem cells. *Nature* 2006 January 12; 439(7073): ix. NRCBL: 18.5.4; 15.1. Identifiers: accelerated (alternative) nuclear transfer (ANT).

Jennings, Carole P. From science to politics: the stem cell debate [editorial]. *Policy, Politics and Nursing Practice* 2005 February; 6(1): 3-4. NRCBL: 18.5.4; 15.1; 19.1.

Jung, Kyu Won; Hyun, Insoo. Oocyte and somatic cell procurement for stem cell research: the South Korean experience. *American Journal of Bioethics [Online]*. 2006 January-February; 6(1): W19-W22. NRCBL: 18.5.4; 18.3; 14.4; 15.1.

Kahn, Axel. Clonage thérapeutique, morale et marché [Therapeutic cloning, morality and market]. Unpublished Document 2005 May 8; 3 p. NRCBL: 18.5.4; 15.1; 14.5.

Kahn, Axel. Le clonage humain est-il thérapeutique? [Is human cloning therapeutic?]. Unpublished Document 2005 May 8; 5 p. NRCBL: 18.5.4; 15.1; 14.5.

Kahn, Axel. Le clonage thérapeutique [Therapeutic cloning]. Unpublished Document 2005 May 8; 5 p. NRCBL: 18.5.4; 15.1; 14.5.

Kean, Sam. Bush vetoes bill to loosen policy on stem-cell research. *Chronicle of Higher Education* 2006 July 28; 52(47): A17. NRCBL: 18.5.4; 18.2; 1.3.9; 15.1.

Kischer, C. Ward. The American Association of Anatomists and stem cell research. *Linacre Quarterly* 2006 May; 73(2): 164-171. NRCBL: 18.5.4; 14.5; 15.1.

Kitzinger, Jenny; Williams, Clare. Forecasting science futures: legitimising hope and calming fears in the embryo stem cell debate. *Social Science and Medicine* 2005 August; 61(3): 731-740. NRCBL: 18.5.4; 15.1; 5.1; 1.3.7.

Klinnert, Lars. Die kontroverse um die embryonale stammzellforschung — zurück auf der biopolitischen tagesordnung [The controversy about embryonic stem cell research — back on the biopolitical agenda]. *Ethik in der Medizin* 2006 September; 18(3): 273-275. NRCBL: 18.5.4; 15.1; 21.1. Identifiers: Germany.

Knoepffler, Nikolaus. Konfliktfälle am Lebensanfang. *In his:* Menschenwürde in der Bioethik. New York: Springer; 2004: 95-138. NRCBL: 18.5.4; 12.3; 15.1; 15.2.

Lehrman, Sally. A proposition for stem cells. *Scientific American* 2005 September; 293(3): 40, 42. NRCBL: 18.5.4; 15.1; 18.6.

Levine, Aaron. Trends in the geographical distribution of human embryonic stem-cell research. *Politics and the Life Sciences* 2005 September 14; 23(2): 40-45. NRCBL: 18.5.4; 15.1; 1.3.7; 18.6. SC: em.

Lewis, Ricki. Blastomere blasphemy [editorial]. *American Journal of Bioethics* 2006 November-December; 6(6): 1-3. NRCBL: 18.5.4; 15.1; 1.3.7.

Li, Benfu. The significance of human embryo stem cell research and its ethical disputes. *In:* Sang-yong, Song; Young-Mo, Koo; Macer, Darryl R.J., eds. Asian Bioethics in the 21st Century. Christchurch, NZ: Eubios Ethics Institute, 2002: 58-60. NRCBL: 18.5.4; 15.1. Conference: Proceedings of the Asian Bioethics Conference (ABC4), held 22-25 November 2002 in Seoul, South Korea.

Lo, Bernard; Zettler, Patricia; Cedars, Marcelle I.; Gates, Elena; Kriegstein, Arnold R.; Oberman, Michelle; Reijo Pera, Renee; Wagner, Richard M.; Wuerth, Mary T.; Wolf, Leslie E.; Yamamoto, Keith R. A new era in the ethics of human embryonic stem cell research. *Stem Cells* 2005 November-December; 23(10): 1454-1459. NRCBL: 18.5.4; 15.1; 18.3.

Mackay-Sim, Alan. Stem cells— a beginner's guide. *Social Alternatives* 2003 Summer; 22(1): 27-32. NRCBL: 18.5.4; 15.1; 18.5.1.

Magill, Gerard. An ethical analysis of the policy implications in the United States emerging from the relationship between human genomics and embryonic stem cell research. *In:* Glasa, J. ed. Ethics of Human Genetics: Challenges of the (Post) Genomic Era. Bratislava, Slovak Republic: Charis [and] IMEB Foundation; 2002: 191-2002. NRCBL: 18.5.4; 15.1.

Magill, Gerard. Embryonic stem cell research and human therapeutic cloning: maintaining the ethical tension between respect and research. *In:* Iltis, Ana Smith, ed. Research Ethics. New York: Routledge, 2006: 61-85. NRCBL: 18.5.4; 15.1.

Magnus, David. Stem cell research: the California experience. *Hastings Center Report* 2006 January-February; 36(1): 26-28. NRCBL: 18.5.4; 15.1; 5.3. Identifiers: California Institute for Regenerative Medicine (CIRM).

Magnus, David; Cho, Mildred K. A commentary on oocyte donation for stem cell research in South Korea. *American Journal of Bioethics [Online].* 2006 January-February; 6(1): W23-W24. NRCBL: 18.5.4; 18.3; 15.1.

Maienschein, Jane. The language really matters. *In:* Ruse, Michael; Pynes, Christopher A., eds. The Stem Cell Controversy: Debating the Issues. Amherst, NY: Prometheus Books; 2003: 33-81. NRCBL: 18.5.4; 15.1.

Marchant, Jo. Human eggs supply 'ethical' stem cells [news]. *Nature* 2006 June 29; 441(7097): 1038. NRCBL: 18.5.4; 15.1; 19.1.

Master, Zubin. Embryonic stem-cell gametes: the new frontier in human reproduction. *Human Reproduction* 2006 April; 21(4): 857-863. NRCBL: 18.5.4; 15.1; 19.5.

McLachlan, Hugh V. Harris on Quintavalle and the ethics of stem cell research. *Human Reproduction and Genetic Ethics: An International Journal* 2006; 12(2): 66-69. NRCBL: 18.5.4; 15.1; 18.1. Identifiers: John Harris; Josephine Quintavalle.

Monastersky, Richard. A second life for cloning. *Chronicle of Higher Education* 2006 February 3; 52(22): A14, A16-A17. NRCBL: 18.5.4; 15.1; 14.5; 19.1; 19.5.

Monastersky, Richard. Harvard scientists to start experiments on cloning human stem cells. *Chronicle of Higher Education* 2006 June 23; 52(42): A18. NRCBL: 18.5.4; 15.1; 14.5.

Morain, William D. The stem of our future [editorial]. *Annals of Plastic Surgery* 2005 May; 54(5): 577-578. NRCBL: 18.5.4; 9.5.1; 15.1; 18.6.

Moreno, Jonathan D. The name of the embryo. *Hastings Center Report* 2006 September-October; 36(5): 3. NRCBL: 18.5.4; 15.1.

Moreno, Jonathan D.; Berger, Sam. Taking stem cells seriously. *American Journal of Bioethics* 2006 September-October; 6(5): 6-7. NRCBL: 18.5.4; 15.1.

Morgan, Rose M. Stem-cell research. *In her:* The Genetics Revolution: History, Fears, and Future of a Life-Altering Science. Westport, CT: Greenwood Press; 2006: 131-143. NRCBL: 18.5.4; 15.1.

Murray, Thomas H. Ethical (and political) issues in research with human stem cells. *Novartis Foundation Symposium* 2005; 265: 188-211. NRCBL: 18.5.4; 15.1; 18.6; 21.1.

National Advisory Commission on Biomedical Ethics (Switzerland) [NEK-CNE] = Nationale Ethikkommission im Bereich Humanmedizin = Commission nationale d'éthique pour la médecine humaine = Commissione nazionale d'etica per la medicina. Research Involving Human Embryos and Fetuses. Bern, Switzerland: Swiss National Advisory Commission on Biomedical Ethics, 2006 January; 30 p. NRCBL: 18.5.4; 15.1. Note: Opinion no. 11/2006, adopted 22 September 2005. Abridged version (Sections 1.2; 2.3; 3.3; 4.3; and 5.3 only), translated by Jeff Acheson. Full report available in German and French at http://www.nek-cne.ch. Abridged versions have been published in English and Italian. The German title is Forschung an menschlichen Embryonen und Foten.

National Institutes of Health [NIH] (United States). Draft National Institutes of Health guidelines for research involving human pluripotent stem cells (December 1999). *Cloning* 1999-2000; 1(4): 225-231. NRCBL: 18.5.4; 15.1; 19.1; 19.5; 18.6.

Nisbet, Matthew C. The polls — trends: public opinion about stem cell research and human cloning. *Public Opinion Quarterly* 2004 Spring; 68(1): 131-154. NRCBL: 18.5.4; 15.1; 14.5. SC: em.

Ogbogu, Ubaka. A review of pressing ethical issues relevant to stem cell translational research. *Health Law Review* 2006; 14(3): 39-43. NRCBL: 18.5.4; 15.1; 19.1. SC: em; rv.

Okie, Susan. Single-cell storm. *New England Journal of Medicine* 2006 October 19; 355(16): 1634-1635. NRCBL: 18.5.4; 15.1; 19.5.

Okie, Susan. Stem-cell politics. *New England Journal of Medicine* 2006 October 19; 355(16): 1633-1637. NRCBL: 18.5.4; 15.1; 19.1; 19.5; 21.1; 5.3.

Olson, Sandra F. American Academy of Neurology development of a position on stem cell research [editorial]. *Neurology* 2005 May 24; 64(10): 1674. NRCBL: 18.5.4; 15.1.

Onwu, Martin U. The relevance of the principle of cooperation for the ethical debate on embryonic stem cell re-

NRCBL: National Reference Center for Bioethics Literature Classification Scheme   See inside front cover for terms.

329

search and therapies. *Health Care Ethics USA* 2006; 14(1): E5 [Online]. Accessed: http://chce.slu.edu/Partnerships_HCE_Intro.html [2006 November 17]. NRCBL: 18.5.4; 15.1.

Palaganas, Jamie; Civin, Curt I. Two steps forward: keeping the momentum in stem cell research [editorial]. *Stem Cells* 2004; 22(3): 240-241. NRCBL: 18.5.4; 15.1; 18.6.

Panno, Joseph. Legal issues. *In his:* Stem Cell Research: Medical Applications and Ethical Controversy. New York: Facts on File, 2005: 81-87. NRCBL: 18.5.4; 15.1.

Panno, Joseph. The ethics of stem cell research. *In his:* Stem Cell Research: Medical Applications and Ethical Controversy. New York: Facts on File, 2005: 72-80. NRCBL: 18.5.4; 15.1.

Pattinson, Shaun D. Figo committee for the ethical aspects of human reproduction and women's health. *Medical Law International* 2006; 7(4): 361-367. NRCBL: 18.5.4; 14.5; 9.5.6; 7.2; 15.1.

Pearson, Helen. Early embryos can yield stem cells . . . and survive. *Nature* 2006 August 24; 442(7105): 858. NRCBL: 18.5.4; 19.1; 15.1.

Pearson, Helen; Abbott, Alison. Stem cells derived from "dead" human embryo [news]. *Nature* 2006 September 28; 443(7110): 376-377. NRCBL: 18.5.4; 19.1; 15.1.

Peterson, James C. So who shall we be? A response to John Gearhart. *In:* Miller, Roman J.; Brubaker, Beryl H.; Peterson, James C., eds. Viewing New Creations with Anabaptist Eyes: Ethics of Biotechnology. Telford, PA: Cascadia Pub.; 2005: 35-38. NRCBL: 18.5.4; 15.1.

Programme on Ethical Issues in International Health Research, Department of Population and International Health, Harvard School of Public Health. Innovative therapy or unethical experiment? *Indian Journal of Medical Ethics* 2006 October-December; 3(4): 132. NRCBL: 18.5.4; 19.1; 18.6; 21.1; 12.1; 15.1. Identifiers: research on aborted fetuses.

Resnik, David B. The need for international stem cell agreements. *Nature Biotechnology* 2004 October; 22(10): 1207. NRCBL: 18.5.4; 18.2; 18.6; 15.1.

Resnik, David B.; Shamoo, Adil E.; Krimsky, Sheldon. Fraudulent human embryonic stem cell research in South Korea: lessons learned. *Accountability in Research* 2006 January-March; 13(1): 101- 109. NRCBL: 18.5.4; 18.2; 1.3.9; 15.1; 1.3.7. Identifiers: Woo Suk Hwang; Korea.

Rosenberg, Joshua David. Informed consent and sham surgery as a placebo in fetal cell transplant research for Parkinson's disease. *Einstein Quarterly Journal of Biology and Medicine* 2003; 20(1): 14-18. NRCBL: 18.5.4; 18.3; 15.4; 9.5.1.

Russo, Eugene. Follow the money — the politics of embryonic stem cell research. *PLoS Biology* 2005 July; 3(7): 1167-1171. NRCBL: 18.5.4; 15.1; 1.3.5; 9.3.1; 21.1.

Savulescu, Julian; Saunders, Rhodri. The "Hinxton Group" considers transnational stem cell research. *Hastings Center Report* 2006 May-June; 36(3): inside back cover. NRCBL: 18.5.4; 15.1; 21.1; 1.3.7.

Schwartz, Philip H.; Rae, Scott B. An approach to the ethical donation of human embryos for harvest of stem cells. *Reproductive BioMedicine Online [electronic]* 2006 June; 12(6): 771-775. Accessed: http://www.rbmonline.com/Article/2232 [2006 March 24]. NRCBL: 18.5.4; 15.1; 19.5.

Schwartz, Robert S. The politics and promise of stem cell research. *New England Journal of Medicine* 2006 September 21; 355(12): 1189-1191. NRCBL: 18.5.4; 15.1; 19.1; 19.5; 18.5.1; 9.3.

Scott, Russell. Human embryo research: the Australian experience. *Human Reproduction* 1997 November; 12(11): 2342-2343. NRCBL: 18.5.4; 18.6; 15.1.

Scottish Council on Human Bioethics. Embryonic, fetal and post-natal animal-human mixtures: an ethical discussion. *Human Reproduction and Genetic Ethics: An International Journal* 2006; 12(2): 35-60. NRCBL: 18.5.4; 22.2; 15.1; 19.1; 14.5; 5.3.

Scottish Council on Human Bioethics. Significant developments in stem cell research. *Journal International de Bioéthique = International Journal of Bioethics* 2005 September-December; 16(3-4): 164. NRCBL: 18.5.4; 18.5.1; 15.1. Identifiers: United Kingdom (Great Briton); Donaldson Report; United States.

Siegel, Andrew W. Locating convergence: ethics, public policy, and human stem cell research. *In:* Ruse, Michael; Pynes, Christopher A., eds. The Stem Cell Controversy: Debating the Issues. Amherst, NY: Prometheus Books; 2003: 271-287. NRCBL: 18.5.4; 15.1.

Singapore. Bioethics Advisory Committee. Human Stem Cell Research Consultation Paper. Helios, Singapore: Bioethics Advisory Committee, 2001 November 8; 6 p. [Online]. Accessed: http://www.bioethics-singapore.org/resources/pdf/Human%20Stem%20Cell%20 Consultation.pdf [2006 March 15]. NRCBL: 18.5.4; 18.1; 15.1.

Singer, Peter. Stem cell research: the fallacy in Bush's position. *New Jersey Medicine* 2004 December; 101(12): 14-17. NRCBL: 18.5.4; 15.1; 1.3.5.

Singer, Peter. Why the Korean stem-cell controversy matters. *Free Inquiry* 2006 April-May; 26(3): 25-26. NRCBL: 18.5.4; 15.1; 14.5.

Tuch, Bernard E.; Scott, Hayley; Armati, Patricia J.; Tabiin, Muhammad T.; Wang, Liping P. Use of human fetal tissue for biomedical research in Australia,

1994-2002. *Medical Journal of Australia* 2003 November 17; 179(10): 547- 550. NRCBL: 18.5.4; 18.2; 15.1; 19.5.

United Kingdom. Department of Health. Chief Medical Officer's Expert Group Reviewing the Potential of Developments on Stem Cell Research and Cell Nuclear Replacement to Benefit Human Health. Stem cell research: medical progress with responsibility: executive summary. *Cloning* 2000; 2(2): 91-96. NRCBL: 18.5.4; 15.1; 1.3.9; 19.5.

United Kingdom. Office of the Secretary of State for Health. Government response to the recommendations made in the Chief Medical Officer's Expert Group report: "Stem Cell Research: Medical Progress with Responsibility". *Cloning* 2000; 2(2): 97-100. NRCBL: 18.5.4; 15.1; 18.6; 19.5; 14.5.

Wang, Yanguang. Chinese ethical views on embryo stem (ES) cell research. *In:* Sang-yong, Song; Young-Mo, Koo; Macer, Darryl R.J., eds. Asian Bioethics in the 21st Century. Christchurch, NZ: Eubios Ethics Institute, 2002: 49-55. NRCBL: 18.5.4; 15.1. SC: em. Conference: Proceedings of the Asian Bioethics Conference (ABC4), held 22-25 November 2002 in Seoul, South Korea.

Warnock, Mary. Human fertilization and embryology. *In her:* Nature and Morality: Recollections of a Philosopher in Public Life. New York: Continuum; 2003: 69-110. NRCBL: 18.5.4; 14.1.

Weiss, Rick. The power to divide: stem cells could launch a new era of medicine, curing deadly diseases with custom-made tissues and organs. But science may take a backseat to politics in deciding if — and where — that hope will be realized. *National Geographic* 2005 July; 208(1): 2-7, 15-17, 22-23, 26-27. NRCBL: 18.5.4; 15.1; 19.1; 19.5. SC: po. Note: Photos by Max Aguilera-Hellweg. Other short articles by Jennifer S. Holland on different aspects or issues related to stem cells are on the intervening pages. The entire article runs over pp. 3-27.

Weissman, Irving L. Politic stem cells. *Nature* 2006 January 12; 439(7073): 145, 147-148. NRCBL: 18.5.4; 15.1. Identifiers: alternative nuclear transfer.

Wilmut, Ian; Dominko, Tanja. Government encouragement for therapeutic cloning [editorial]. *Cloning* 2000; 2(2): 53-54. NRCBL: 18.5.4; 15.1; 14.5; 19.5; 18.6.

HUMAN EXPERIMENTATION/ . . . /
EMBRYOS AND FETUSES/ LEGAL ASPECTS
See also CLONING

Australia relaxes ban on stem cell research [news]. *BMJ: British Medical Journal* 2006 December 16; 333(7581): 1236. NRCBL: 18.5.4; 15.1; 14.5. SC: le.

Abbott, Alison. German stem-cell law under fire [news]. *Nature* 2006 November 16; 444(7117): 253. NRCBL: 18.5.4; 19.1; 15.1. SC: le.

Araujo, Robert John. The transnational perspective of the church: the embryonic cloning debate and stem cell research. *Journal of Contemporary Health Law and Policy* 2006 Spring; 22(2): 497-507. NRCBL: 18.5.4; 15.1; 19.5; 21.1. SC: le.

Australia. Parliament. Research Involving Human Embryos Act 2002: An act to regulate certain activities involving the use of human embryos, and for related purposes. Canberra, Australia: Parliament, [No. 145, 2002] 2002 December 19; 36 p. [Online]. Accessed: http://www.comlaw. gov.au/ComLaw/Legislation/Act1.nsf/0/ 86499A7EC1C4AACCA256F72000FA6D8/$file/ 1452002.pdf [2006 August 16]. NRCBL: 18.5.4; 15.1. SC: le. Note: Assented to 19 December 2002.

Blum, Deborah. A pox on stem cell research. *New York Times* 2006 August 1; p. A15. NRCBL: 18.5.4. SC: po; le.

Boudouin, Jean-Louise. Canadian developments on genetic and human embryo research and experimentation = Novedades en Canadá sobre la investigación y experimentación genética y con embriones humanos. *Revista de Derecho Genoma Humano = Law and the Human Genome Review* 1997 January-June; (6): 41-49. NRCBL: 18.5.4; 15.1; 6; 14.1. SC: le.

Clemmens, Emilie W. Creating human embryos for research: a scientist's perspective on managing the legal and ethical issues. *Indiana Health Law Review* 2005; 2(1): 93-115. NRCBL: 18.5.4; 4.4; 18.6; 15.1. SC: le.

Crockin, Susan L. The "embryo" wars: at the epicenter of science, law, religion, and politics. *Family Law Quarterly* 2005 Fall; 39(3): 599-632. NRCBL: 18.5.4; 4.4; 19.5; 18.6; 15.1. SC: le.

Csillag, Claudio. Brazil approves research with embryo stem cells [news]. *European Journal of Cancer* 2005 May; 41(8): 1102. NRCBL: 18.5.4; 15.1; 1.2. SC: le.

Cyranoski, David. Australia lifts ban on cloning [news]. *Nature* 2006 December 14; 442(7121): 799. NRCBL: 18.5.4; 14.5; 15.1. SC: le.

Daar, Abdallah S.; Sheremeta, Lorraine. The science of stem cells: ethical, legal and social issues. *Experimental and Clinical Transplantation* 2003 December; 1(2): 139-146. NRCBL: 18.5.4; 18.5.1; 14.5; 19.5; 19.1; 15.1; 4.4. SC: le.

DeBow, Suzanne; Bubela, Tania; Caulfield, Timothy. Stem cells, politics and the progress paradigm. *Health Law Review* 2006; 15(1): 50-52. NRCBL: 18.5.4; 4.4; 15.1. SC: an; le.

Fujikawa, Ryan. Federal funding of human embryonic stem cell research: an institutional examination. *Southern California Law Review* 2005 May; 78(4): 1075-1124. NRCBL: 18.5.4; 15.1; 9.3.1; 2.2; 18.6. SC: le; rv.

NRCBL: National Reference Center for Bioethics Literature Classification Scheme   See inside front cover for terms.

331

Gould Halme, Dina; Kessler, David A. FDA regulation of stem-cell-based therapies. *New England Journal of Medicine* 2006 October 19; 355(16): 1730-1735. NRCBL: 18.5.4; 15.1; 19.1; 5.2; 5.3. SC: le. Identifiers: Food and Drug Administration.

Hall, Stephen S. Stem cells: a status report. *Hastings Center Report* 2006 January-February; 36(1): 16-22. NRCBL: 18.5.4; 15.1; 5.3; 14.4. SC: le.

Hampton, Tracy. US stem cell research lagging. *JAMA: The Journal of the American Medical Association* 2006 May 17; 295(19): 2233-2234. NRCBL: 18.5.4; 15.1; 19.1; 1.3.9. SC: le.

Health Council (Netherlands) = Gezondheidsraad (Netherlands); Dondrop, Wybo; de Wert, Guido. Embryonic stem cells without moral pain? *Ethics and Health Monitoring Report* 2005 June 29 ; No. 1: 33 p. [Online]. Accessed: http://www.gr.nl/pdf.php?ID=1270&p=1 [12 February 2007]. NRCBL: 18.5.4; 15.1; 4.4. SC: le.

Herrera, Stephan. Leaders and laggards in the stem cell enterprise [news]. *Nature Biotechnology* 2005 July; 23(7): 775-777. NRCBL: 18.5.4; 15.1; 19.5; 21.1. SC: le.

Hinxton Group. An international consortium on stem cells, ethics and law. *Revista de Derecho y Genoma Humano = Law and the Human Genome Review* 2006 January-June; (24): 251-255. NRCBL: 18.5.4; 15.1; 18.6. SC: le.

Holden, Constance. Senate prepares to vote at last on a trio of stem cell bills [news]. *Science* 2006 July 7; 313(5783): 26-27. NRCBL: 18.5.4; 15.1. SC: le.

Hurlbut, William B. Framing the future: embryonic stem cells, ethics and the emerging era of developmental biology. *Pediatric Research* 2006 April; 59(4, Part 2): 4R-12R. NRCBL: 18.5.4; 15.1; 4.4; 5.1; 19.5. SC: le. Identifiers: President's Council on Bioethics; altered nuclear transfer.

Isasi, Rosario M.; Knoppers, Bartha M. Beyond the permissibility of embryonic and stem cell research: substantive requirements and procedural safeguards. *Human Reproduction* 2006 October; 21(10): 2474-2481. NRCBL: 18.5.4; 14.5; 18.6; 18.2; 15.1. SC: le.

Isasi, Rosario; Knoppers, Bartha M. Mind the gap: policy approaches to embryonic stem cell and cloning research in 50 countries. *European Journal of Health Law* 2006 April; 13(1): 9-26. NRCBL: 18.5.4; 15.10; 19.1; 21.1; 18.6. SC: le; rv.

Jain, K.K. Ethical and regulatory aspects of embryonic stem cell research. *Expert Opinion on Biological Therapy* 2005 February; 5(2): 153-162. NRCBL: 18.5.4; 15.1; 21.1. SC: le.

Johnston, Josephine. Is research in Canada limited to "surplus" embryos? *Health Law Review* 2006; 14(3): 3-13. NRCBL: 18.5.4; 15.1; 19.1; 14.4; 14.6. SC: le.

Jones, D.G.; Towns, C.R. Navigating the quagmire: the regulation of human embryonic stem cell research. *Human Reproduction* 2006 May; 21(5): 1113-1116. NRCBL: 18.5.4; 15.1; 19.5; 18.6. SC: le.

Kent, Julie; Pfeffer, Naomi. Regulating the collection and use of fetal stem cells: they currently lie in a regulatory limbo [editorial]. *BMJ: British Medical Journal* 2006 April 15; 332(7546): 866-867. NRCBL: 18.5.4; 15.1; 12.1; 19.5. SC: le. Identifiers: United Kingdom (Great Britain).

Loring, Jeanne F.; Campbell, Cathryn. Intellectual property and human embryonic stem cell research. *Science* 2006 March 24; 311(5768): 1716-1717. NRCBL: 18.5.4; 15.8; 5.3. SC: le.

Lysaght, Michael J. California's Proposition 71 [editorial]. *Tissue Engineering* 2005 March-April; 11(3-4): xi-xiii. NRCBL: 18.5.4; 15.1; 5.3. SC: le.

Magri, Sonia. Research on human embryos and cloning: difficulties of legislating in a changing environment and model approaches to regulation. *Journal of Law and Medicine* 2005 May; 12(4): 483-493. NRCBL: 18.5.4; 14.5; 18.6; 5.3; 15.1. SC: le. Identifiers: Australia.

Magri, Sonia. Research on human embryos, stem cells and cloning — one year since the passing of Australian legislation: Australia, around the world, and back again. *E Law: Murdoch University Electronic Journal of Law* 2003 December; 10(4): 24 p. [Online]. Accessed: http://www.murdoch.edu.au/elaw/issues/v10n4/magri104.html [2006 June 29]. NRCBL: 18.5.4; 15.1; 14.5; 21.1. SC: le. Identifiers: Research Involving Human Embryos Act 2002; Prohibition of Human Cloning Act 2002.

Massachusetts. Department of Public Health. Public Health Council. Biotechnology Regulations [Approved: 29 August 2006]. *Code of Massachusetts Regulations* 2006; 105: 960.000-009. 4p. [Online]. Accessed: http://www.lawlib.state.ma.us/stemcellregs.html [2007 March 9]. NRCBL: 18.5.4; 15.1; 19.1; 14.5. SC: le. Identifiers: Massachusetts Stem Cell Regulations.

Massachusetts. *Laws, statutes, etc.* An act enhancing regenerative medicine in the Commonwealth [Effective: 31 May 2005]. Massachusetts: General Assembly, Acts of 2005 (2005 Session Laws), Chapter 27. Adds Chapter 111L, Biotechnology. 14 p. [Online]. Accessed: http://www.mass.gov/legis/laws/seslaw05/sl050027.htm [2007 March 9]. NRCBL: 18.5.4; 15.1; 14.5; 18.6. SC: le.

Moreno, Jonathan D. Congress's hybrid problem. *Hastings Center Report* 2006 July-August; 36(4): 12-13. NRCBL: 18.5.4; 15.1. SC: le.

Moreno, Jonathan D.; Hynes, Richard O. Guidelines for human embryonic stem cell research. *Nature Biotech-*

nology 2005 July; 23(7): 793-794. NRCBL: 18.5.4; 18.6; 15.1; 18.2; 14.5. SC: le.

Müller, Carola. The status of the extracorporeal embryo in German Law (Part. II). *Revista de Derecho y Genoma Humano* 2005 July-December; (23): 139-165. NRCBL: 18.5.4; 18.2; 18.6; 4.4; 15.1. SC: le. Identifiers: Germany.

New Jersey. *Laws, statutes, etc.* An act concerning human stem cell research and supplementing Title 26 of the Revised Statutes and Title 2C of the New Jersey Statutes [Approved: 2 January 2004]. New Jersey: Public Laws 2003, ch.203. 2 p. [Online]. Accessed: http://www.njleg.state. nj.us/2002/Bills/PL03/203_.PDF [2007 March 9]. NRCBL: 18.5.4; 15.1; 19.5; 4.4. SC: le. Note: Senate Bill 1909, 210th Legislature. Introduced on September 30, 2002. Approved January 2, 2004.

Nguyen, Lauren Thuy. The fate of stem cell research and a proposal for future legislative regulation. *Santa Clara Law Review* 2006; 46(2): 419-449. NRCBL: 18.5.4; 15.1; 1.3.5; 18.6. SC: le.

Prainsack, Barbara. "Negotiating life": the regulation of human cloning and embryonic stem cell research in Israel. *Social Studies of Science* 2006 April; 36(2): 173-205 [Online] Accessed: http://sss.sagepub.com/cgi/reprint/36/ 2/173 [2007 January 23]. NRCBL: 18.5.4; 15.1; 1.2; 14.1; 14.5; 15.1; 21.1. SC: le; rv. Identifiers: Genetic Intervention Law.

Saunders, William L., Jr. Washington insider: national developments. *National Catholic Bioethics Quarterly* 2006 Winter; 6(4): 629-636. NRCBL: 18.5.4; 15.1; 1.3.5; 14.4; 2.4; 10. SC: le.

Sax, Joanna K. The states "race" with the Federal government for stem cell research. *Annals of Health Law* 2006 Winter; 15(1): 1-36. NRCBL: 18.5.4; 15.1; 19.1; 5.3. SC: an; le.

Sheridan, Cormac. Stem cell controversy to stall European tissue and cell therapy rules [news]. *Nature Biotechnology* 2006 May; 24(5): 479-480. NRCBL: 18.5.4; 15.1; 19.1; 18.5; 21.1. SC: le.

Stolberg, Sheryl Gay. First Bush veto maintains limits on stem cell use; override attempt fails; issue divides G.O.P. — Democrats look ahead to fall elections. *New York Times* 2006 July 20; p. A1, A19. NRCBL: 18.5.4; 15.1. SC: po; le.

Tsang, Lincoln. Legal and ethical status of stem cells as medicinal products. *Advanced Drug Delivery Reviews* 2005 December 12; 57(13): 1970-1980. NRCBL: 18.5.4; 15.1; 5.3. SC: le.

Um, Young-Rhan. Dispute over scientific research involving human embryos in South Korea. *In:* Sang-yong, Song; Young-Mo, Koo; Macer, Darryl R.J., eds. Asian Bioethics in the 21st Century. Christchurch, NZ: Eubios

Ethics Institute, 2002: 56-57. NRCBL: 18.5.4; 2.4. SC: le. Conference: Proceedings of the Asian Bioethics Conference (ABC4), held 22-25 November 2002 in Seoul, South Korea.

United States. Congress. House. A bill to amend the Public Health Service Act to prohibit the solicitation or acceptance of tissue from fetuses gestated for research purposes, and for other purposes. Washington, DC: U.S. G.P.O., 2006. 3 p. [Online]. Accessed: http://frwebgate. access.gpo.gov/cgi-bin/useftp.cgi?IPaddress=162.140.64 .21&filename=h5719ih.pdf&directory=/diskb/wais/data/ 109_cong_bills [2006 December 4]. NRCBL: 18.5.4; 15.1. SC: le. Identifiers: Fetus Farming Prohibition Act of 2006; stem cells. Note: H.R. 5719, 109th Congress, 2d session. Introduced by Rep. Weldon, June 29, 2006. Referred to the Committee on Energy and Commerce.

United States. Congress. House. A bill to derive human pluripotent stem cell lines using techniques that do not knowingly harm embryos. Washington, DC: U.S. G.P.O., 2006. 4 p. [Online]. Accessed: http://frwebgate.access. gpo.gov/cgi-bin/useftp.cgi?IPaddress=162.140.64.21& filename=h5526ih.pdf&directory=/diskb/wais/data/ 109_cong_bills [2006 December 14]. NRCBL: 18.5.4; 15.1. SC: le. Identifiers: Alternative Pluripotent Stem Cell Therapies Enhancement Act. Note: H.R. 5526, 109th Congress, 2nd session. Introduced by Rep. Bartlett in the House of Representatives, June 6, 2006. Referred to the Committee on Energy and Commerce.

United States. Congress. House. A bill to amend the Internal Revenue Code of 1986 to allow tax credits to holders of stem cell research bonds. Washington, DC: U.S. G.P.O., 2005. 14 p. [Online]. Accessed: http://frwebgate.access. gpo.gov/cgi-bin/useftp.cgi?IPaddress=162.140.64.21& filename=h1650ih.pdf&directory=/diskb/wais/data/ 109_cong_bills [2006 May 6]. NRCBL: 18.5.4; 9.3.1; 15.1. SC: le. Identifiers: Stem Cell Research Investment Act of 2005. Note: H.R. 1650, 109th Congress, 1st session. Introduced by Rep. Johnson, April 14, 2005. Referred to the Committee on Ways and Means.

United States. Congress. House. A bill to amend the Public Health Service Act to provide for a program at the National Institutes of Health to conduct and support research in the derivation and use of human pluripotent stem cells by means that do not harm human embryos, and for other purposes. Washington, DC: U.S. G.P.O., 2005. 5 p. [Online]. Accessed: http://frwebgate.access.gpo.gov/cgi-bin/ useftp.cgi?IPaddress=162.140.64.21&filename= h3144ih.pdf&directory=/diskb/wais/data/109_cong_bills [2006 May 10]. NRCBL: 18.5.4; 15.1; 4.4. SC: le. Identifiers: Respect for Life Pluripotent Stem Cell Act of 2005. Note: H.R. 3144, 109th Congress, 1st session. Introduced by Rep. Bartlett, June 30, 2005. Referred to the Committee on Energy and Commerce.

NRCBL: National Reference Center for Bioethics Literature Classification Scheme   See inside front cover for terms.

333

United States. Congress. House. A bill to amend the Public Health Service Act to provide for human embryonic stem cell research. Washington, DC: U.S. G.P.O., 2005. 4 p. [Online]. Accessed: http//frwebgate.access.gpo/cgi-bin/useftp.cgi?IPaddress=162.140.64.21&filename=h810ih.pdf&directory=/diskb/wais/data/109_cong_bills [2006 May 10]. NRCBL: 18.5.4; 15.1; 14.4. SC: le. Identifiers: Stem Cell research Enhancement Act of 2005. Note: H.R. 810, 109th Congress, 1st session. Introduced by Rep. Castle, February 15, 2005. Referred to the Committee on Energy and Commerce.

United States. Congress. House. A bill to authorize the use of Federal funds for research on human embryonic stem cells irrespective of the date on which such stem cells were derived, and for other purposes. Washington, DC: U.S. G.P.O., 2005. 4 p. [Online]. Accessed: http://frwebgate.access.gpo.gov/cgi-bin/useftp.cgi?IPaddress=162.140.64.21&filename=h162ih.pdf&directory=/diskb/wais/data/109_cong_bills [2006 June 7]. NRCBL: 18.5.4; 15.1. SC: le. Identifiers: Stem Cell Replenishment Act of 2005. Note: H.R. 162, 109th Congress, 1st session. Introduced by Rep. Millender-McDonald, January 4, 2005. Referred to the Committee on Energy and Commerce.

United States. Congress. Senate. A bill to amend the Public Health Service Act to provide for human embryonic stem cell research. Washington, DC: U.S. G.P.O., 2005. 3 p. [Online]. Accessed: http://frwebgate.access.gpo.gov/cgi-bin/useftp.cgi?IPaddress=162.140.64.88&filename=s471is.pdf&directory=/diskb/wais/data/109_cong_bills [2006 May 10]. NRCBL: 18.5.4; 14.4; 15.1. SC: le. Identifiers: Stem Cell Research Enhancement Act of 2005. Note: S. 471, 109th Congress, 1st session; Introduced by Sen. Specter, February 28, 2005. Referred to the Committee on Health, Education, Labor and Pensions.

United States. Congress. Senate. A bill to derive human pluripotent stem cells using techniques that do not knowingly harm embryos. Washington, DC: U.S. G.P.O., 2006. 4 p. [Online]. Available: http://frwebgate.access.gpo.gov/cgi-bin/useftp.cgi?IPaddress=162.140.64.21&filename=s2754is.pdf&directory=/diskb/wais/data/109_cong_bills [2006 July 17]. NRCBL: 18.5.4; 15.1. SC: le. Identifiers: Alternative Pluripotent Stem Cell Therapies Enhancement Act. Note: S. 2754, 109th Congress, 2d session. Introduced by Sen. Santorum, May 5, 2006. Referred to the Committee on Health, Education, Labor and Pensions.

Vick, Hannah M. Embryonic stem cell research: ethically wrong treatment of the tiniest of humans. *Concerned Women for America* 2000 May 1: 5 pages [Online] Accessed: http://www.cwfa.org/printerfriendly.asp?id=1423&department=cwa&categoryid=life [2005 November 30]. NRCBL: 18.5.4; 18.5.1; 15.1. SC: le.

Vick, Katherine R. Stem cell research debate shifting to the courts. *Journal of Biolaw and Business* 2006; 9(1): 56-57. NRCBL: 18.5.4; 15.1; 19.5. SC: le.

Wadman, Meredith; Abbott, Alison. A long week in stem-cell politics. . . [news]. *Nature* 2006 July 27; 442(7101): 335. NRCBL: 18.5.4; 1.3.9; 15.1; 19.1. SC: le.

Warnock, Mary. Genetics. *In her:* Nature and Mortality: Recollections of a Philosopher in Public Life. New York: Continuum; 2003: 69-110. NRCBL: 18.5.4; 14.1; 15.1. SC: le.

HUMAN EXPERIMENTATION/ . . . / EMBR. & FETUSES/ PHIL. & RELIG. ASPECTS
See also CLONING

Austriaco, Nicanor Pier Giorgio. Science: stem cells. *National Catholic Bioethics Quarterly* 2006 Winter; 6(4): 757-761. NRCBL: 18.5.4; 15.1; 1.2; 20.5.1; 19.1.

Austriaco, Nicanor Pier Giorgio. The moral case for ANT-derived pluripotent stem cell lines. *National Catholic Bioethics Quarterly* 2006 Autumn; 6(3): 517-537. NRCBL: 18.5.4; 15.4; 14.5; 4.4; 1.2. SC: an. Identifiers: altered nuclear transfer.

Bartlett, Thomas. Catholic Cardinal's mention of 'excommunication' for stem-cell researchers provokes uncertainty. *Chronicle of Higher Education* 2006 July 14; 52(45): A10. NRCBL: 18.5.4; 1.2; 15.1.

Baschetti, Riccardo. Evolutionary, biological origins of morality: implications for research with human embryonic stem cells. *Stem Cells and Development* 2005 June; 14(3): 239-247. NRCBL: 18.5.4; 15.1; 1.1; 18.6.

Baschetti, R. Evolutionary ethic and embryonic stem-cell research [letter]. *Internal Medicine Journal* 2004 June; 34(6): 371. NRCBL: 18.5.4; 15.1; 3.2; 1.2.

Baschetti, R.; Cregan, K. Ethics of embryonic stem cell technology: science versus philosophy [letter and reply]. *Internal Medicine Journal* 2005 August; 35(8): 499-500. NRCBL: 18.5.4; 14.5; 1.2; 1.1.

Blackford, R. Stem cell research on other worlds, or why embryos do not have a right to life. *Journal of Medical Ethics* 2006 March; 32(3): 177-180. NRCBL: 18.5.4; 15.1; 19.1; 4.4. SC: an.
Abstract: Anxieties about the creation and destruction of human embryos for the purpose of scientific research on embryonic stem cells have given a new urgency to the question of whether embryos have moral rights. This article uses a thought experiment involving two possible worlds, somewhat removed from our own in the space of possibilities, to shed light on whether early embryos have such rights as a right not to be destroyed or discarded (a "right to life"). It is argued that early embryos do not have meaningful interests or any moral rights. Accordingly, claims about the moral rights of embryos do not justify restrictions on stem cell research.

Blank, Robert. Fetal research. *In:* Mitcham, Carl, ed. Encyclopedia of Science, Technology, and Ethics. Farmington Hills, MI: Thomson/Gale, 2005: 766-768. NRCBL: 18.5.4; 2.2.

Bortolotti, Lisa; Harris, John. Embryos and eagles: symbolic value in research and reproduction. *CQ: Cambridge Quarterly of Healthcare Ethics* 2006 Winter; 15(1): 22-34. NRCBL: 18.5.4; 7.1; 4.4; 1.1; 15.1.

Boyle, Joseph. Tolerating v. supporting research that destroys embryos: a difference that can make a moral difference. *Journal of Contemporary Health Law and Policy* 2006 Spring; 22(2): 448-457. NRCBL: 18.5.4; 4.4; 1.2; 2.2; 15.1.

Brugger, E. Christian. Moral stem cells. *First Things* 2006 May; (163): 14-17. NRCBL: 18.5.4; 15.1; 4.4. Identifiers: Altered Nuclear Transfer-Oocyte Assisted Reprogramming (ANT-OAR).

Burke, William; Pullicino, Patrick; Richard, Edward J. A critique of oocyte-assisted reprogramming [letter]. *National Catholic Bioethics Quarterly* 2006 Spring; 6(1): 12-15. NRCBL: 18.5.4; 14.5; 14.4; 15.4; 1.2.

Clemmens, Emilie W. Creating human embryos for research: a scientist's perspective on managing the legal and ethical issues. *Indiana Health Law Review* 2005; 2(1): 93-115. NRCBL: 18.5.4; 4.4; 18.6; 15.1. SC: le.

Cohen, Cynthia B. Religion, public reason, and embryonic stem cell research. *In:* Guinn, David E., ed. Handbook of Bioethics and Religion. New York: Oxford University Press, 2006: 129-142. NRCBL: 18.5.4; 15.1; 1.2.

Crockin, Susan L. The "embryo" wars: at the epicenter of science, law, religion, and politics. *Family Law Quarterly* 2005 Fall; 39(3): 599-632. NRCBL: 18.5.4; 4.4; 19.5; 18.6; 15.1. SC: le.

Csillag, Claudio. Brazil approves research with embryo stem cells [news]. *European Journal of Cancer* 2005 May; 41(8): 1102. NRCBL: 18.5.4; 15.1; 1.2. SC: le.

Daar, Abdallah S.; Sheremeta, Lorraine. The science of stem cells: ethical, legal and social issues. *Experimental and Clinical Transplantation* 2003 December; 1(2): 139-146. NRCBL: 18.5.4; 18.5.1; 14.5; 19.5; 19.1; 15.1; 4.4. SC: le.

de Lacy, Sheryl. Embryo research: is disclosing commercial intent enough? *Human Reproduction* 2006 July; 21(7): 1662-1667. NRCBL: 18.5.4; 4.4; 18.3; 15.1. SC: rv.

DeBow, Suzanne; Bubela, Tania; Caulfield, Timothy. Stem cells, politics and the progress paradigm. *Health Law Review* 2006; 15(1): 50-52. NRCBL: 18.5.4; 4.4; 15.1. SC: an; le.

Devolder, Katrien; Savulescu, Julian. The moral imperative to conduct embryonic stem cell and cloning research.

CQ: Cambridge Quarterly of Healthcare Ethics 2006 Winter; 15(1): 7-21. NRCBL: 18.5.4; 15.1; 14.5; 1.1; 4.4; 7.1; 5.3; 9.4; 21.1; 9.2.

Doerflinger, Richard M. Human cloning and embryonic stem cell research after Seoul: examining exploitation, fraud, and ethical problems in the research. Testimony of Richard M. Doerflinger. *National Catholic Bioethics Quarterly* 2006 Summer; 6(2): 339-350. NRCBL: 18.5.4; 15.1; 14.5; 7.4; 18.1; 18.2; 4.4.

Doerflinger, Richard M. Washington insider. *National Catholic Bioethics Quarterly* 2006 Autumn; 6(3): 413-420. NRCBL: 18.5.4; 15.1; 18.5.1; 19.4; 2.1. Identifiers: stem-cell research.

Dolan, Timothy; Morlino, Robert; Doyle, Jim. Embryonic stem-cell research. *Origins* 2006 June 15; 36(5): 78-79. NRCBL: 18.5.4; 15.1; 18.5.1; 1.2; 4.4.

Enserink, Martin. A season of generosity. . .and Jeremiads [news]. *Science* 2006 December 8; 314(5805): 1525. NRCBL: 18.5.4; 15.2; 15.5; 1.2.

Evans, Robert W. The promises and perils of human embryonic stem cell research. *In:* Glasa, J. ed. The Ethics of Human Genetics: Challenges of the (Post) Genomic Era. Bratislava, Slovak Republic: Charis [and] IMEB Foundation; 2002: 181-189. NRCBL: 18.5.4; 4.4; 15.1.

Fujikawa, Ryan. Federal funding of human embryonic stem cell research: an institutional examination. *Southern California Law Review* 2005 May; 78(4): 1075-1124. NRCBL: 18.5.4; 15.1; 9.3.1; 2.2; 18.6. SC: le; rv.

Furton, Edward J. Prospects for pluripotent stem cells: a reply to Communio. *National Catholic Bioethics Quarterly* 2006 Summer; 6(2): 223-232. NRCBL: 18.5.4; 18.5.1; 15.1; 14.4; 1.1.

Giles, Jim. Panel clarifies stem-cell rules [news]. *Nature* 2006 March 2; 440(7080): 9. NRCBL: 18.5.4; 15.1; 19.1; 2.4.

Gleeson, Gerald. Why it's wrong to experiment on human embryos. *Social Alternatives* 2003 Summer; 22(1): 33-38. NRCBL: 18.5.4; 15.1; 1.2.

Hanson, Stephen S. "More on respect for embryos and potentiality: does respect for embryos entail respect for in vitro embryos?". *Theoretical Medicine and Bioethics* 2006; 27(3): 215-226. NRCBL: 18.5.4; 12.3; 4.4; 15.1. SC: an.
Abstract: It is commonly assumed that persons who hold abortions to be generally impermissible must, for the same reasons, be opposed to embryonic stem cell research [ESR]. Yet a settled position against abortion does not necessarily direct one to reject that research. The difference in potentiality between the embryos used in ESR and embryos discussed in the abortion debate can make ESR acceptable even if one holds that abortion is impermissible. With regard to their potentiality, in vitro embryos are here argued to be more morally similar to clonable somatic cells than they are to in vivo embryos. This creates an important moral distinction between embryos in vivo and in vi-

NRCBL: National Reference Center for Bioethics Literature Classification Scheme   See inside front cover for terms.

335

tro. Attempts to refute this moral distinction, raised in the recent debate in this journal between Alfonso Gomez-Lobo and Mary Mahowald, are also addressed.

Health Council (Netherlands) = Gezondheidsraad (Netherlands); Dondrop, Wybo; de Wert, Guido. Embryonic stem cells without moral pain? *Ethics and Health Monitoring Report* 2005 June 29 ; No. 1: 33 p. [Online]. Accessed: http://www.gr.nl/pdf.php?ID=1270&p=1 [12 February 2007]. NRCBL: 18.5.4; 15.1; 4.4. SC: le.

Hickman, Larry. Status arguments and genetic research with human embryos. *Southwest Philosophical Review* 1988 January; 4: 45-55. NRCBL: 18.5.4; 4.4; 15.1.

Hinxton Group; Faden, Ruth; Donovan, Peter J.; Harris, John; Lovell-Badge, Robin; Mathews, Debra J.H.; Savulescu, Julian; Azariah, Jayapual; Benvenisty, Nissim; Bok, Hilary; Brunelli, Silvia; Campbell, Philip; Chan, Sarah; Cheng, Linzhao; Coles, David; Devolder, Katrien; Finkel, Julia; Friele, Minou; Heyd, David; Honey, Colin; Hyun, Insoo; Isasi, Rosario M.; Kyu Won, Jung; Liao, S. Matthew; McLaren, Anne; Mori, Maurizio; Munthe, Christian; Murdoch, Alison; Nakatsuji, Norio; O'Toole, Chris; Panicker, Mitradas M.; Patterson, Mark; Pedersen, Roger A.; Pera, Martin Frederick; Purnell, Beverly A.; Regenberg, Alan; Qui, Ren-Zong; Romeo-Casabona, Carlos M.; Salter, Brian; Samuelson, Taylor; Santalo, Josep; Saunders, Rhodri; Sheng, Hui Z.; Skene, Loane; Solter, Davor; Stacey, Glyn; Stubing, William C.; Sugarman, Jeremy; Sugden, Andrew M.; Van Steirteghem, Andre; Wallace, Susan E.; Walters, LeRoy B.; Zambidis, Elias T. Consensus statement: the Hinxton Group: an international consortium on stem cells, ethics and law. Baltimore, MD: Johns Hopkins Medical 2006 February 24; 4p. [Online]. Accessed: http://www.hopkinsmedicine.org/bioethics/finalsc.doc [2006 March 3]. NRCBL: 18.5.4; 6; 2.4.

Holm, Søren. Embryonic stem cell research and the moral status of human embryos. *Reproductive BioMedicine Online [electronic]* 2005 March; 10(Supplement 1): 63-67. NRCBL: 18.5.4; 15.1; 4.4; 14.4; 1.1. SC: an. Identifiers: creation lottery. Conference: Ethics, Law and Moral Philosophy of Reproductive Biomedicine; London, UK; 2004 September 30 - October 1; Royal Society.

Hug, Kristina. Therapeutic perspectives of human embryonic stem cell research versus the moral status of a human embryo—does one have to be compromised for the other? *Medicina (Kaunas)* 2006; 42(2): 107-114. NRCBL: 18.5.4; 15.1; 1.2; 4.4. SC: rv; an.

Hull, Richard. "It's a BA-by!". *Free Inquiry* 2006 December-2007 January; 27(1): 27-31. NRCBL: 18.5.4; 15.1; 1.2; 12.1. Identifiers: embryonic stem cell research.

Hurlbut, William B. Framing the future: embryonic stem cells, ethics and the emerging era of developmental biol-

ogy. *Pediatric Research* 2006 April; 59(4, Part 2): 4R-12R. NRCBL: 18.5.4; 15.1; 4.4; 5.1; 19.5. SC: le. Identifiers: President's Council on Bioethics; altered nuclear transfer.

Kalb, Claudia; Rosenberg, Debra; Mummold, Jonathan. Embryonic war: scientists and ethicists put the latest stem-cell 'breakthrough' under the microscope. *Newsweek* 2006 September 4; 148(10): 42-43. NRCBL: 18.5.4; 15.1; 5.3; 1.2; 7.1; 15.2; 14.4. SC: po.

Kavanaugh, John F. Cloning for Missouri: 'at issue was scientific integrity, not religious fanaticism'. *America* 2006 November 27; 195(17): 8. NRCBL: 18.5.4; 15.1; 1.2.

Kimmelman, Jonathan; Baylis, Françoise; Glass, Kathleen Cranley. Stem cell trials: lessons from gene transfer research. *Hastings Center Report* 2006 January-February; 36(1): 23-26. NRCBL: 18.5.4; 15.1; 15.4; 2.2.

Kintisch, Eli. Scientists look to Missouri to show the way on stem cells [news]. *Science* 2006 November 3; 314(5800): 737, 739. NRCBL: 18.5.4; 15.1; 21.1; 1.2.

Knoepffler, Nikolaus. Konfliktfälle am Lebensanfang. *In his:* Menschenwürde in der Bioethik. New York: Springer; 2004: 95-138. NRCBL: 18.5.4; 12.3; 15.1; 15.2.

Lee, Patrick; George, Robert P. The first fourteen days of human life. *New Atlantis* 2006 Summer; 13: 61-67. NRCBL: 18.5.4; 4.4; 15.1.

Lindsay, Ronald A. Stem cell research: an approach to bioethics based on scientific naturalism. *Free Inquiry* 2006 December-2007 January; 27(1): 23-26. NRCBL: 18.5.4; 15.1; 1.1; 4.4.

Mieth, Dietmar. Stem cells: the ethical problems of using embryos for research. *Journal of Contemporary Health Law and Policy* 2006 Spring; 22(2): 439-447. NRCBL: 18.5.4; 4.4; 1.2; 2.2; 15.1.

Morgan, Lynn M. The rise and demise of a collection of human fetuses at Mount Holyoke College. *Perspectives in Biology and Medicine* 2006 Summer; 49(3): 435-451. NRCBL: 18.5.4; 2.2; 4.4; 15.1.

Morgan, Rose M. A major decision. *In her:* The Genetics Revolution: History, Fears, and Future of a Life-Altering Science. Westport, CT: Greenwood Press; 2006: 145-156. NRCBL: 18.5.4; 15.1; 1.2; 21.1. Identifiers: President George W. Bush.

Müller, Carola. The status of the extracorporeal embryo in German Law (Part. II). *Revista de Derecho y Genoma Humano* 2005 July-December; (23): 139-165. NRCBL: 18.5.4; 18.2; 18.6; 4.4; 15.1. SC: le. Identifiers: Germany.

Neaves, William B. The ends and means of stem cell research. *Practical Bioethics* 2005 Winter; 1(1): 3-5. NRCBL: 18.5.4; 15.1; 1.2; 18.5.1.

New Jersey. *Laws, statutes, etc.* An act concerning human stem cell research and supplementing Title 26 of the Revised Statutes and Title 2C of the New Jersey Statutes [Approved: 2 January 2004]. New Jersey: Public Laws 2003, ch.203. 2 p. [Online]. Accessed: http://www.njleg.state.nj.us/2002/Bills/PL03/203_.PDF [2007 March 9]. NRCBL: 18.5.4; 15.1; 19.5; 4.4. SC: le. Note: Senate Bill 1909, 210th Legislature. Introduced on September 30, 2002. Approved January 2, 2004.

Pasotti, Jacopo; Stafford, Ned. It's legal: Italian researchers defend their work with embryonic stem cells [news]. *Nature* 2006 July 20; 442(7100): 229. NRCBL: 18.5.4; 1.2; 19.1; 15.1.

Pedersen, Roger A. Developments in human embryonic stem cells. *Reproductive BioMedicine Online [electronic]* 2005 March; 10(Supplement 1): 60-62. NRCBL: 18.5.4; 4.4; 9.3.1; 9.4; 15.1. Conference: Ethics, Law and Moral Philosophy of Reproductive Biomedicine; London, UK; 2004 September 30 - October 1; Royal Society.

Pedersen, Roger; Holm, Søren; Bortolotti, Lisa; Savulescu, Julian; Brinsden, Peter; Edwards, Robert; Short, Roger; Robertson, John; Lotz, Mianna; Oglivie, Caroline; Lockwood, Gillian; Onland, Josh; Leather, Suzi. Discussion (day 2 session 1): stem cell outlook. *Reproductive BioMedicine Online [electronic]* 2005 March; 10(Supplement 1): 76-79. NRCBL: 18.5.4; 14.4; 4.4; 15.1. SC: an. Conference: Ethics, Law and Moral Philosophy of Reproductive Biomedicine; London, UK; 2004 September 30 - October 1; Royal Society.

Prainsack, Barbara. "Negotiating life": the regulation of human cloning and embryonic stem cell research in Israel. *Social Studies of Science* 2006 April; 36(2): 173-205 [Online] Accessed: http://sss.sagepub.com/cgi/reprint/36/2/173 [2007 January 23]. NRCBL: 18.5.4; 15.1; 1.2; 14.1; 14.5; 15.1; 21.1. SC: le; rv. Identifiers: Genetic Intervention Law.

Prieur, Michael R.; Atkinson, Joan; Hardingham, Laurie; Hill, David; Kernaghan, Gillian; Miller, Debra; Morton, Sandy; Rowell, Mary; Vallely, John F.; Wilson, Suzanne. Stem cell research in a Catholic institution: yes or no? *Kennedy Institute of Ethics Journal* 2006 March; 16(1): 73-98. NRCBL: 18.5.4; 15.1; 1.2; 1.1; 4.4; 4.1.2.
Abstract: Catholic teaching has no moral difficulties with research on stem cells derived from adult stem cells or fetal cord blood. The ethical problem comes with embryonic stem cells since their genesis involves the destruction of a human embryo. However, there seems to be significant promise of health benefits from such research. Although Catholic teaching does not permit any destruction of human embryos, the question remains whether researchers in a Catholic institution, or any researchers opposed to destruction of human embryos, could participate in research on cultured embryonic stem cells, or whether a Catholic institution could use any therapy that ultimately results from such research. This position paper examines how such research could be conducted legitimately in a Catholic institution by using an ethical analysis involving a narrative context, the nature

of the moral act, and the principle of material cooperation, along with references to significant ethical assessments. It also offers tentative guidelines that could be used by a Catholic institution in implementing such research.

Rosenthal, Elisabeth. Excommunication is sought for stem cell researchers. *New York Times* 2006 July 1; p. A3. NRCBL: 18.5.4; 1.2; 15.1; 1.3.9. SC: po. Identifiers: Roman Catholic Church.

Safranek, Louis; Brugger, E. Christian. Reconsidering ANT-OAR [letter and reply]. *First Things* 2006 October; (166): 5-7. NRCBL: 18.5.4; 15.1; 4.4. Identifiers: altered nuclear transfer-oocyte assisted reprogramming.

Sass, Hans-Martin. Ethical dilemma in stem cell research? *Formosan Journal of Medical Humanities* 2006 June; 7(1-2): 19-38. NRCBL: 18.5.4; 15.1; 1.1.

Saunders, William L., Jr. Washington insider: national developments. *National Catholic Bioethics Quarterly* 2006 Winter; 6(4): 629-636. NRCBL: 18.5.4; 15.1; 1.3.5; 14.4; 2.4; 10. SC: le.

Shannon, Thomas A. Remaking ourselves? The ethics of stem-cell research. *Commonweal* 1998 December 4; 125: 9-10. NRCBL: 18.5.4; 15.1; 4.4.

Shea, John B. Catholic teaching on the human embryo as an object of research. *National Catholic Bioethics Quarterly* 2006 Spring; 6(1): 133-136. NRCBL: 18.5.4; 15.1; 1.2; 14.4; 14.5.

Somfai, Béla. Religious traditions and stem cell research. *In:* Sándor, Judit, ed. Society and Genetic Information: Codes and Laws in the Genetic Era. Budapest, Hungary; New York: CEU Press; 2003: 81-93. NRCBL: 18.5.4; 1.2; 15.1; 19.1.

Steinbock, Bonnie. The morality of killing human embryos. *Journal of Law, Medicine, and Ethics* 2006 Spring; 34(1): 26-34. NRCBL: 18.5.4; 15.1; 4.4; 12.3.

Sujdak Mackiewicz, Birgitta N. Can Catholic facilities justify the use of embryonic stem cell therapies developed from the destruction of human embryos? *Health Care Ethics USA* 2006; 14(2): E3 [Online]. Accessed: http://chce.slu.edu/ Partnerships_HCE_Intro.html [2006 November 17]. NRCBL: 18.5.4; 1.2; 15.1; 19.1.

Um, Young-Rhan. Dispute over scientific research involving human embryos in South Korea. *In:* Sang-yong, Song; Young-Mo, Koo; Macer, Darryl R.J., eds. Asian Bioethics in the 21st Century. Christchurch, NZ: Eubios Ethics Institute, 2002: 56-57. NRCBL: 18.5.4; 2.4. SC: le. Conference: Proceedings of the Asian Bioethics Conference (ABC4), held 22-25 November 2002 in Seoul, South Korea.

United States. Congress. House. A bill to amend the Public Health Service Act to provide for a program at the National Institutes of Health to conduct and support research

---

NRCBL: National Reference Center for Bioethics Literature Classification Scheme   See inside front cover for terms.

337

in the derivation and use of human pluripotent stem cells by means that do not harm human embryos, and for other purposes. Washington, DC: U.S. G.P.O., 2005. 5 p. [Online]. Accessed: http://frwebgate.access.gpo.gov/cgi-bin/useftp.cgi?IPaddress=162.140.64.21&filename=h3144ih.pdf&directory=/diskb/wais/data/109_cong_bills [2006 May 10]. NRCBL: 18.5.4; 15.1; 4.4. SC: le. Identifiers: Respect for Life Pluripotent Stem Cell Act of 2005. Note: H.R. 3144, 109th Congress, 1st session. Introduced by Rep. Bartlett, June 30, 2005. Referred to the Committee on Energy and Commerce.

Walter, James J. A Catholic reflection on embryonic stem cell research. *Linacre Quarterly* 2006 August; 73(3): 255-263. NRCBL: 18.5.4; 15.1; 1.2.

Walters, LeRoy B. Ethical issues in biotechnology: human embryonic stem cell research and the Anabaptist vision. *In:* Miller, Roman J.; Brubaker, Beryl H.; Peterson, James C., eds. Viewing New Creations with Anabaptist Eyes: Ethics of Biotechnology. Telford, PA: Cascadia Pub.; 2005: 122-135. NRCBL: 18.5.4; 1.2; 15.1.

Williamson, Bob. The Walter C. Randall Lecture: embryos, cloning people and stem cell research. *Physiologist* 2005 December; 48(6): 295, 297. NRCBL: 18.5.4; 14.5; 1.2; 15.1.

Wong, Alvin. The ethics of HEK 293. *National Catholic Bioethics Quarterly* 2006 Autumn; 6(3): 473-495. NRCBL: 18.5.4; 19.3; 12.3; 4.4; 1.2; 15.1. SC: an. Identifiers: human embryonic kidney.

HUMAN EXPERIMENTATION/... / FOREIGN NATIONALS

Adams, Vincanne; Miller, Suellen; Craig, Sienna; Nyima; Sonam; Droyoung; Lhakpen; Varner, Michael. The challenge of cross-cultural clinical trials research: case report from the Tibetan Autonomous Region, People's Republic of China. *Medical Anthropology Quarterly* 2005 September; 19(3): 267-289. NRCBL: 18.5.9; 21.7; 18.5.3; 18.2; 18.3.

Berton, Elena. More Chinese get free drugs in clinical trials. *Wall Street Journal* 2006 February 14; p. B1, B8. NRCBL: 18.5.9; 9.7. SC: po.

Cha, Arian Eunjung. AIDS drug trial turned away; protests by prostitutes in Cambodia ended Tenofovir testing. *Washington Post* 2006 May 23; p. A10, A14. NRCBL: 18.5.9; 9.5.6. SC: po.

Cha, Ariana Eunjung. AIDs vaccine testing goes overseas; U.S. funds $120 million trial despite misgivings of some researchers. *Washington Post* 2006 May 22; p. A1, C1. NRCBL: 18.5.9; 9.5.6; 9.7. SC: po.

Chagnon, Napoleon A. Biomedical samples from the Amazon [letter]. *Chronicle of Higher Education* 2006 April 14; 52(32): A55. NRCBL: 18.5.9; 1.3.9; 21.7.

Chen, Christopher P. L.-H. Regulatory issues: an academic viewpoint from Asia (ex-Japan). *International Psychogeriatrics* 2003; 15(Supplement 1): 287-291. NRCBL: 18.5.9; 18.6; 21.1.

Chima, Sylvester C. Regulation of biomedical research in Africa. *BMJ: British Medical Journal* 2006 April 8; 332(7545): 848-851. NRCBL: 18.5.9; 18.6; 18.2; 18.3; 21.1. SC: le.

Chokshi, Dave A.; Kwiatkowski, Dominic P. Ethical challenges of genomic epidemiology in developing countries. *Genomics, Society and Policy* 2005 February; 1(1): 1-15. NRCBL: 18.5.9; 15.3; 18.3; 15.8; 18.6.

Abstract: Ethical challenges in genomic epidemiology are the direct result of novel tools used to confront scientific challenges in the field. An orders-of-magnitude increase in scale of genetic data collection has created the need for establishing diffuse international partnerships, sometimes across developed- and developing-world countries, with ramifications for assigning research ownership, distributing intellectual property rights, and encouraging capacity-building. Meanwhile, the fact that genomic epidemiological research is so far upstream in the pipeline of therapy development has implications for the privacy rights of research participants and for a rigorous definition of valid informed consent, particularly in resource-poor settings. From these scientific underpinnings, we distill out two main categories of ethical issues: (1) How should researchers ensure that the subjects of research are appropriately protected? and (2) What is the structure of an equitable and fair system for distributing the financial and scientific rewards of research? We attempt to delineate the contours of specific problems in each category and propose steps toward solutions with reference to a particular project, known as gMap.net, that focuses on genomic epidemiological studies of malaria.

Corneli, Amy L.; Bentley, Margaret E.; Sorenson, James R.; Henderson, Gail E.; van der Horst, Charles; Moses, Agnes; Nkhoma, Jacqueline; Tenthani, Lyson; Ahmed, Yusuf; Heilig, Charles M.; Jamieson, Denise J. Using formative research to develop a context-specific approach to informed consent for clinical trials. *Journal of Empirical Research on Human Research Ethics* 2006 December; 1(4): 45-60. NRCBL: 18.5.9; 21.1; 9.5.6; 21.7; 18.3. SC: em; rv. Identifiers: Malawi.

Creed-Kanashiro, Hilary; Ore, Beatriz; Scurrah, Maria; Gil, Ana; Penny, Mary. Conducting research in developing countries: experiences of the informed consent process from community studies in Peru. *Journal of Nutrition* 2005 April; 135(4): 925-928. NRCBL: 18.5.9; 18.3. Conference: Symposium: Bioethics in Scientific Research: Conflicts between Subject's Equitable Access to Participate in Research and Current Regulations; 19 April 2004; Washington, D.C.; American Society for Nutritional Sciences.

Dowdy, D.W. Partnership as an ethical model for medical research in developing countries: the example of the "implementation trial". *Journal of Medical Ethics* 2006 June; 32(6): 357-360. NRCBL: 18.5.9; 21.1. SC: an.

Abstract: The existing model for ethical review of medical research consists primarily of regulations designed to prevent exploitation of participants. This model may fail when reviewing other ethical obligations, particularly the responsibility to provide valuable knowledge to society. Such failure is most apparent in developing countries, in which many stakeholders lack incentives or power to uphold society's interests. An alternative ethical model is that of partnership, which actively involves all partners during ethical review and aims to secure partners' best interests through compromise. Unlike the existing "regulatory" model, the partnership model effectively addresses ethical obligations to provide positive benefits to society. For the partnership model to be effective, power must be shared among partners; thus, the partnership model can be harmonised with the "regulatory" model through explicit consideration of power structures. One opportunity for crafting power balance in developing countries is apparent in "implementation trials"- randomised trials motivated by and integrated into the implementation of long term public health interventions. Given the failings of the existing ethical review model, alternative models - for example, partnership-and means to balance power-for example, implementation trials-must be explored to ensure that medical research provides knowledge of value to societies in the developing world.

Ehni, Hans-Jörg. The definition of adequate care in externally sponsored clinical trials: the terminological controversy about the concept "standard of care". *Science and Engineering Ethics* 2006 January; 12(1): 123-130. NRCBL: 18.5.9; 18.3; 9.2; 9.8.

Gregor, Thomas A.; Gross, Daniel R. Guilt by association: the culture of accusation and the American Anthropological Association's investigation of Darkness in El Dorado. *American Anthropologist* 2004 December; 106(4): 687-698. NRCBL: 18.5.9; 18.4; 1.3.1; 1.3.8.

Hawkins, Jennifer S. Justice and placebo controls. *Social Theory and Practice* 2006 July; 32(3): 467-496. NRCBL: 18.5.9; 18.3; 9.5.6; 4.1.2; 1.1; 18.6. SC: cs.

Ibanga, Hannah B.; Brookes, Roger H.; Hill, Philip C.; Owiafe, Patrick K.; Fletcher, Helen A.; Lienhardt, Christian; Hill, Adrian V.; Adegbola, Richard A.; McShane, Helen. Early clinical trials with a new tuberculosis vaccine, MVA85A, in tuberculosis-endemic countries: issues in study design. *Lancet Infectious Diseases* 2006 August; 6(8): 522-528. NRCBL: 18.5.9; 18.3. Identifiers: Republic of the Gambia.

Kilama, W.L. Ethical perspective on malaria research for Africa. *Acta Tropica* 2005 September; 95(3): 276-284. NRCBL: 18.5.9; 18.2; 18.3; 18.6.

Lienhardt, Christian; Cook, Sharlette V. Conducting clinical trials on tuberculosis in resource-poor countries: imposed science or equally-shared efforts? [editorial]. *International Journal of Tuberculosis and Lung Disease* 2005 September; 9(9): 943. NRCBL: 18.5.9; 18.2; 9.5.1.

London, Alex John. The moral foundations of equipoise and its role in international research. *American Journal of Bioethics* 2006 July-August; 6(4): 48-51. NRCBL: 18.5.9; 18.2; 9.5.6. Comments: Winston Chiong. The real problem with equipoise. American Journal of Bioethics 2006 July-August; 6(4): 37-47.

Mann, Howard. Extensions and refinements of the equipoise concept in international clinical research: would Benjamin Freedman approve? *American Journal of Bioethics* 2006 July-August; 6(4): 67-69. NRCBL: 18.5.9; 18.2. Identifiers: comment on Winston Chiong. The real problem with equipoise. American Journal of Bioethics 2006 July-August; 6(4): 37-47.

Medical Research Council (Great Britain) [MRC]. MRC ethics guide. Research involving human participants in developing societies. London: Medical Research Council 2004: 1-8. NRCBL: 18.5.9; 18.2.

Medical Research Council (Great Britain) [MRC]. Research in developing countries [position statement]. *Bulletin of Medical Ethics* 2005 May; (208): 7-11. NRCBL: 18.5.9; 18.2. SC: rv; le.

Moazam, Farhat. Research and developing countries: hopes and hypes. *Eastern Mediterranean Health Journal/La Revue de Santé de la Méditerranée orientale* 2006; 12(Supplement 1): S30-S36 [Online]. Accessed: http://www.emro.who.int/publications/EMHJ/12_S/PDF/5.pdf [2007 January 3]. NRCBL: 18.5.9; 18.2; 18.6; 8.1; 9.7; 21.7. Note: Abstract in French and Arabic.

Molyneux, C.S.; Peshu, N.; Marsh, K. Trust and informed consent: insights from community members on the Kenyan coast. *Social Science and Medicine* 2005 October; 61(7): 1463-1473. NRCBL: 18.5.9; 18.3; 8.1; 21.1. SC: em.

Molyneux, C.S.; Wassenaar, D.R.; Peshu, N.; Marsh, K. 'Even if they ask you to stand by a tree all day, you will have to do it (laughter). . .!': community voices on the notion and practice of informed consent for biomedical research in developing countries. *Social Science and Medicine* 2005 July; 61(2): 443-454. NRCBL: 18.5.9; 18.3; 18.5.2; 9.5.6. SC: cs. Identifiers: Kenya.

Nama, Nosisana; Swartz, Leslie. Ethical and social dilemmas in community-based controlled trials in situations of poverty: a view from a South African project. *Journal of Community and Applied Social Psychology* 2002 July-August; 12(4): 286-297. NRCBL: 18.5.9; 18.4; 18.5.3; 17.1; 21.7.

Nuffield Council on Bioethics. The ethics of research related to healthcare in developing countries: a follow-up discussion paper. London: Nuffield Council on Bioethics 2005 March 17; 128p. [Online] Accessed: http://www.nuffieldbioethics.org/fileLibrary/pdf/HRRDC_Follow-up_Discussion_Paper001.pdf [2006 September 14]. NRCBL: 18.5.9; 18.3.

Petryna, Adriana. Globalizing human subjects research. *In:* Petryna, Adriana; Lakoff, Andrew; Kleinman, Arthur, eds. Global Pharmaceuticals: Ethics, Markets, Practices. Durham: Duke University Press; 2006: 33-60. NRCBL: 18.5.9; 21.1.

NRCBL: National Reference Center for Bioethics Literature Classification Scheme   See inside front cover for terms.

339

Resnik, David B.; Jones, Caitlin W. Research subjects with limited English proficiency: ethical and legal issues. *Accountability in Research* 2006 April-June; 13(2): 157-177. NRCBL: 18.5.9; 18.6; 21.1; 18.2. SC: em; le.

Abstract: In this article, we examine Institutional Review Board (IRB) policies, international guidelines, and federal regulations and guidance for dealing with Limited English Proficiency (LEP) research subjects. We show that federal and international guidance concerning this topic is insufficient, and there is considerable variation in IRB policies. While some IRBs have thorough and useful policies, others do not. Many IRBs do not provide researchers and IRB member with answers to several important questions relating to language barriers in research. We recommend that federal agencies, international organizations, IRBs, and researchers take steps to fill in the gaps in guidance and policy to help insure that LEP populations will receive equitable and ethical treatment in research.

Riessman, Catherine Kohler. Exporting ethics: a narrative about narrative research in South India. *Health (London)* 2005 October; 9(4): 473-490. NRCBL: 18.5.9; 21.7; 18.3.

Shah, Sonia. Drug trial double standards: why don't people who volunteer for clinical trials in the developing world get the same safeguards as those in the West. *New Scientist* 2006 November 18-24; 192(2578): 22. NRCBL: 18.5.9.

Sheikh, Abdul Latif. Pharmaceutical research: paradox, challenge or dilemma? *Eastern Mediterranean Health Journal* 2006; 12(Supplement 1): S42-S49 [Online]. Accessed: http://www.emro.who.int/publications/EMHJ/12_S/PDF/7.pdf [2007 January 3]. NRCBL: 18.5.9; 9.7; 18.6. Note: Abstract in French and Arabic.

Srinivasan, Sandhya; Loff, Bebe. Medical research in India. *Lancet* 2006 June 17-23; 367(9527): 1962-1964. NRCBL: 18.5.9; 18.6.

Tharyan, Prathap. Whose trial is it anyway? Reflections on morality, double standards, uncertainty and criticism in international collaborative health research. *Monash Bioethics Review* 2006 October; 25(4): 51-66. NRCBL: 18.5.9; 18.4; 18.3; 18.2. Identifiers: India.

Turner, Trudy R.; Nelson, Jeffrey D. Darkness in El Dorado: claims, counter-claims, and the obligations of researchers. *In:* Turner, Trudy R. ed. Biological Anthropology and Ethics: From Repatriation to Genetic Identity. Albany, NY: State University of New York Press; 2005: 165-183. NRCBL: 18.5.9; 15.1; 18.3; 18.4.

United States. Congress. House. A bill to promote safe and ethical clinical trials of drugs and other test articles on people overseas. Washington, DC: U.S. G.P.O., 2006. 11 p. [Online]. Accessed: http://frwebgate.access.gpo.gov/cgi-bin/useftp.cgi?IPaddress=162.140.64.21&filename=h5641ih.pdf&directory=/diskb/wais/data/109_cong_bills [2006 July 17]. NRCBL: 18.5.9; 9.7; 5.3. SC: le. Identifiers: Safe Overseas Human Testing Act. Note: H.R. 5641, 109th Congress, 2d session. Introduced by Rep. Lantos,

June 20, 2006. Referred to the Committee on International Relations.

Upvall, Michele; Hashwani, S. Negotiating the informed-consent process in developing countries: a comparison of Swaziland and Pakistan. *International Nursing Review* 2001 September; 48(3): 188-192. NRCBL: 18.5.9; 18.3.

Zion, Deborah. Clinical research, vulnerability and exploitation [editorial]. *Monash Bioethics Review* 2006 October; 25(4): 1-2. NRCBL: 18.5.9; 18.4; 18.5.1.

HUMAN EXPERIMENTATION/ . . . / MENTALLY DISABLED

Alpert, Jonathan E.; Biggs, Melanie M.; Davis, Lori; Shores-Wilson, Kathy; Harlan, William R.; Schneider, Gregory W.; Ford, Amy L.; Farabaugh, Amy; Stegman, Diane; Ritz, A. Louise; Husain, Mustafa M.; Macleod, Laurie; Wisniewski, Stephen R.; Rush, A. John. Enrolling research subjects from clinical practice: ethical and procedural issues in the Sequenced Treatment Alternatives to Relieve Depression (STAR*D) trial. *Psychiatry Research* 2006 February 28; 141(2): 193-200. NRCBL: 18.5.6; 18.2; 18.3; 8.1.

American Psychiatric Association. Task Force on Research Ethics. Ethical principles and practices for research involving human participants with mental illness. *Psychiatric Services* 2006 April; 57(4): 552-557. NRCBL: 18.5.6.

Appelbaum, Paul S.; Weiss Roberts, Laura. Introduction: report of the APA's Task Force on Research Ethics. *Psychiatric Services* 2006 April; 57(4): 550-551. NRCBL: 18.5.6. Identifiers: American Psychiatric Association.

Boothroyd, Roger A. The impact of research participation on adults with severe mental illness. *Mental Health Services Research* 2000; 2(4): 213-221. NRCBL: 18.5.6; 8.4; 9.3.2; 18.3; 18.4. SC: em.

Candilis, Philip J.; Geppert, Cynthia M.A.; Fletcher, Kenneth E.; Lidz, Charles W.; Appelbaum, Paul S. Willingness of subjects with thought disorder to participate in research. *Schizophrenia Bulletin* 2006 January; 32(1): 159-165. NRCBL: 18.5.6; 18.3. SC: em.

Chen, Donna T.; Miller, Franklin G.; Rosenstein, Donald L. Ethical aspects of research into the etiology of autism. *Mental Retardation and Developmental Disabilities Research Reviews* 2003; 9(1): 48-53. NRCBL: 18.5.6; 8.1; 15.6; 18.3; 18.5.2.

Chen, Donna T.; Moreno, Jonathan D. Ethics of medication-free research in schizophrenia. *Schizophrenia Bulletin* 2006 April; 32(2): 307-309. NRCBL: 18.5.6; 18.2; 17.4.

Connell, Cathleen M.; Shaw, Benjamin A.; Holmes, Sara B.; Foster, Norman L. Caregivers' attitudes toward their family members' participation in Alzheimer disease research: implications for recruitment and retention. *Alzheimer Disease and Associated Disorders* 2001 July-September; 15(3): 137-145. NRCBL: 18.5.6; 18.3.

Dresser, Rebecca. Research participants with mental disabilities: the more things change. . . . *In:* Frost, Lynda E.; Bonnie, Richard J., eds. The Evolution of Mental Health Law. Washington, DC: American Psychological Association; 2001: 57-74. NRCBL: 18.5.6.

Dunn, Laura B.; Candilis, Philip J.; Roberts, Laura Weiss. Emerging empirical evidence on the ethics of schizophrenia research. *Schizophrenia Bulletin* 2006 January; 32(1): 47-68. NRCBL: 18.5.6; 18.2; 18.3.

Dunn, Laura B.; Palmer, Barton W.; Keehan, Monique; Jeste, Dilip V.; Appelbaum, Paul S. Assessment of therapeutic misconception in older schizophrenia patients with a brief instrument. *American Journal of Psychiatry* 2006 March; 163(3): 500-506. NRCBL: 18.5.6; 18.3. SC: em.

Fisher, Celia B.; Cea, Christine D.; Davidson, Philip W.; Fried, Adam L. Capacity of persons with mental retardation to consent to participate in randomized clinical trials. *American Journal of Psychiatry* 2006 October; 163(10): 1813-1820. NRCBL: 18.5.6; 18.3. SC: em.

Haroun, Nasra; Dunn, Laura; Haroun, Ansar; Cadenhead, Kristin S. Risk and protection in prodromal schizophrenia: ethical implications for clinical practice and future research. *Schizophrenia Bulletin* 2006 January; 32(1): 166-178. NRCBL: 18.5.6; 18.3. SC: em.

Khanna, Sumant. Response to Dr. Vikram Patel. *Indian Journal of Medical Ethics* 2006 January-March; 3(1): 17-18. NRCBL: 18.5.6; 8.2.

Kim, Scott Y.H. When does decisional impairment become decisional incompetence? Ethical and methodological issues in capacity research in schizophrenia. *Schizophrenia Bulletin* 2006 January; 32(1): 92-97. NRCBL: 18.5.6; 4.3; 18.3. SC: em.

Marson, Daniel C.; Savage, Robert; Phillips, Jacqueline. Financial capacity in persons with schizophrenia and serious mental illness: clinical and research ethics aspects. *Schizophrenia Bulletin* 2006 January; 32(1): 81-91. NRCBL: 18.5.6; 18.2; 9.3.1. SC: em.

Meldolesi, Anna. Italians scuttle embryo law [news brief]. *Nature Biotechnology* 2005 July; 23(7): 771. NRCBL: 18.5.6. SC: le.

Minkler, Meredith; Fadem, Pamela; Perry, Martha; Blum, Klaus; Moore, Leroy; Rogers, Judith. Ethical dilemmas in participatory action research: a case study from the disability community. *Health Education and Behavior*

2002 February; 29(1): 14-29. NRCBL: 18.5.6; 20.5.1; 7.2. SC: cs; em.

Molinuevo, José L.; Blesa, Rafael. Regulatory issues. *International Psychogeriatrics* 2003; 15(Supplement 1): 283-286. NRCBL: 18.5.6; 18.3; 8.3.3.

Moser, David J.; Reese, Rebecca L.; Hey, Clare T.; Schultz, Susan K.; Arndt, Stephan; Beglinger, Leigh J.; Duff, Kevin M.; Andreasen, Nancy C. Using a brief intervention to improve decisional capacity in schizophrenia research. *Schizophrenia Bulletin* 2006 January; 32(1): 116-120. NRCBL: 18.5.6; 18.3. SC: em.

Mudur, Ganapati. Indian study sparks debate on the use of placebo in psychiatry trials [news]. *BMJ: British Medical Journal* 2006 March 11; 332(7541): 566. NRCBL: 18.5.6; 18.3.

Nelson, Sarah. Research with psychiatric patients: knowing their own minds? *In:* Smyth, Marie; Williamson, Emma, eds. Researchers and Their 'Subjects': Ethics, Power, Knowledge and Consent. Bristol, UK: Policy Press; 2004: 91-103. NRCBL: 18.5.6; 18.4.

Palmer, Barton W.; Jeste, Dilip V. Relationship of individual cognitive abilities to specific components of decisional capacity among middle-aged and older patients with schizophrenia. *Schizophrenia Bulletin* 2006 January; 32(1): 98-106. NRCBL: 18.5.6; 18.3. SC: em.

Roberts, Laura Weiss. Advancing our understanding of the ethics of schizophrenia research: the contribution of conceptual analyses and empirical evidence. *Schizophrenia Bulletin* 2006 January; 32(1): 20-21. NRCBL: 18.5.6. SC: em.

Roberts, Laura Weiss. Ethics and mental illness research. *Psychiatric Clinics of North America* 2002 September; 25(3): 525-545. NRCBL: 18.5.6; 18.3. SC: em.

Roberts, Laura Weiss; Dunn, Laura B.; Green Hammond, Katherine A.; Warner, Teddy D. Do research procedures pose relatively greater risk for healthy persons than for persons with schizophrenia? *Schizophrenia Bulletin* 2006 January; 32(1): 153-158. NRCBL: 18.5.6; 18.3; 18.5.1; 18.2. SC: em.

Roberts, Laura Weiss; Hammond, Katherine Green; Hoop, Jinger. An inverse relationship between perceived harm and participation willingness in schizophrenia research protocols. *American Journal of Psychiatry* 2006 November; 163(11): 2002-2004. NRCBL: 18.5.6. SC: em.

Roberts, Laura Weiss; Warner, Teddy D.; Hammond, Katherine Green; Dunn, Laura B. Assessment by patients with schizophrenia and psychiatrists of relative risk of research procedures. *Psychiatric Services* 2006 November; 57(11): 1629-1635. NRCBL: 18.5.6; 5.2. SC: em.

Roelcke, Volker; Hohendorf, Gerrit; Rotzoll, Maike. Psychiatrische Forschung, "Euthanasie" und der "Neue

NRCBL: National Reference Center for Bioethics Literature Classification Scheme   See inside front cover for terms.

341

Mensch": Zur Debatte um Menschenbild und Wersetzungen im Nationalsozialismus. *In:* Frewer, Andreas; Eickhoff, Clemens, eds. "Euthanasie" und die aktuelle Sterbehilfe-Debatte: Die historischen Hintergründe medizinischer Ethik. Frankfurt; New York: Campus; 2000: 193-217. NRCBL: 18.5.6; 1.3.5; 2.2; 15.5; 20.5.1; 21.4.

Shore, David. Ethical issues in schizophrenia research: a commentary on some current concerns. *Schizophrenia Bulletin* 2006 January; 32(1): 26-29. NRCBL: 18.5.6.

Stroup, T. Scott; Appelbaum, Paul S. Evaluation of "subject advocate" procedures in the clinical antipsychotic trials of intervention effectiveness (CATIE) schizophrenia study. *Schizophrenia Bulletin* 2006 January; 32(1): 147-152. NRCBL: 18.5.6; 18.3. SC: em.

Tarleton, Beth; Williams, Val; Palmer, Neil; Gramlich, Stacey. 'An equal relationship'?: people with learning difficulties getting involved in research. *In:* Smyth, Marie; Williamson, Emma, eds. Researchers and Their 'Subjects': Ethics, Power, Knowledge and Consent. Bristol, UK: Policy Press; 2004: 73-88. NRCBL: 18.5.6; 18.4.

Wilson, Scott T.; Stanley, Barbara. Ethical concerns in schizophrenia research: looking back and moving forward. *Schizophrenia Bulletin* 2006 January; 32(1): 30-36. NRCBL: 18.5.6.

Wright, Sarah; Waters, Rachel; Nicholls, Vicky. Ethical considerations in service-user-led research: strategies for Living Project. *In:* Smyth, Marie; Williamson, Emma, eds. Researchers and Their 'Subjects': Ethics, Power, Knowledge and Consent. Bristol, UK: Policy Press; 2004: 19-34. NRCBL: 18.5.6; 18.4.

HUMAN EXPERIMENTATION/ . . . / MILITARY PERSONNEL

Amoroso, Paul J.; Wenger, Lynn L. The human volunteer in military biomedical research. *In:* Beam, Thomas E.; Sparacino, Linette R.; Pellegrino, Edmund D.; Hartle, Anthony E.; Howe, Edmund G., eds. Military Medical Ethics. Volume 2. Washington, DC: TMM Publications, Borden Institute, Walter Reed Army Medical Center; 2003: 563-660. NRCBL: 18.5.8; 1.3.9.

Andrews, Jason. Research in the ranks: vulnerable subjects, coercible collaboration, and the Hepatitis E vaccine trial in Nepal. *Perspectives on Biology and Medicine* 2006 Winter; 49(1): 35-51. NRCBL: 18.5.8; 18.59; 21.1.

Brown, Keri D. An ethical obligation to our service members: meaningful benefits for informed consent violations. *South Texas Law Review* 2006 Summer; 47(4): 919-947. NRCBL: 18.5.8; 18.3; 18.2; 18.6.

Dyer, Owen. British soldiers are "guinea pigs" for new use of blood clotting agent [news]. *BMJ: British Medical Jour-*

nal 2006 September 23; 333(7569): 618. NRCBL: 18.5.8; 9.7.

Lederer, Susan E. The Cold War and beyond: covert and deceptive American medical experimentation. *In:* Beam, Thomas E.; Sparacino, Linette R.; Pellegrino, Edmund D.; Hartle, Anthony E.; Howe, Edmund G., eds. Military Medical Ethics. Volume 2. Washington, DC: TMM Publications, Borden Institute, Walter Reed Army Medical Center; 2003: 507-531. NRCBL: 18.5.8; 1.3.5; 21.3.

Moreno, Jonathan D. The role of brain research in national defense. *Chronicle of Higher Education* 2006 November 10; 53(12): B6-B7. NRCBL: 18.5.8; 18.2; 18.4; 1.3.5; 18.6.

Sharp, David. Ethics at Porton Down. *Lancet* 2006 August 19-15; 368(9536): 631-632. NRCBL: 18.5.8; 21.3; 18.3.

HUMAN EXPERIMENTATION/ . . . / MINORS

Agency proposes safeguards for children in clinical trials. *Human Research Report* 2006 June; 21(6): 1-2. NRCBL: 18.5.2; 18.2.

Clinical trials in children, for children [editorial]. *Lancet* 2006 June 17-23; 367(9527): 1953. NRCBL: 18.5.2.

Abramovitch, Rona; Freedman, Jonathan L.; Thoden, Kirby; Nikolich, Crystal. Children's capacity to consent to participation in psychological research: empirical findings. *Child Development* 1991; 62: 1100-1109. NRCBL: 18.5.2; 18.3; 18.4. SC: em. Identifiers: Canada.

Beardsmore, C.S. Ethical issues in lung function testing in children. *Paediatric Respiratory Review* 2000 December; 1(4): 342-346. NRCBL: 18.5.2; 8.3.2; 1.1.

Bernard, Jean-Louis. Professional skills and shared consent in paediatric research. *Lancet Oncology* 2004 October; 5(10): 592. NRCBL: 18.5.2; 18.2.

Bernard, J.-L.; Aubert-Fourmy, C. La publicité des travaux et la publication des résultats des recherches en pédiatrie, une question d'éthique = The publicity of works and publication of the results in pediatric research, a question of ethics [editorial]. *Archives de Pediatrie* 2005 April; 12(4): 377-379. NRCBL: 18.5.2; 1.3.7.

Borzekowski, Dina L.G.; Rickert, Vaughn I.; Ipp, Lisa; Fortenberry, J. Dennis. At what price? The current state of subject payment in adolescent research. *Journal of Adolescent Health* 2003 November; 33(5): 378-384. NRCBL: 18.5.2; 9.3.1; 18.2; 7.1.

Brody, Janet L.; Annett, Robert D.; Scherer, David G.; Perryman, Mandy L.; Cofrin, Keely M.W. Comparisons of adolescent and parent willingness to participate in minimal and above-minimal risk pediatric asthma research protocols. *Journal of Adolescent Health* 2005 September; 37(3): 229-235. NRCBL: 18.5.2. SC: em.

Buchanan, David R.; Miller, Franklin G. Justice and fairness in the Kennedy Krieger Institute lead paint study: the ethics of public health research on less expensive, less effective interventions. *American Journal of Public Health* 2006 May; 96(5): 781-787. NRCBL: 18.5.2; 9.1; 18.1.

Abstract: The Kennedy Krieger lead paint study stirred controversial questions about whether research designed to develop less expensive interventions that are not as effective as existing treatments can be ethically warranted. Critics questioned the social value of such research and alleged that it sanctions a double standard, exploits participants, and is complicit in perpetuating the social injustice. In response, we demonstrate the propriety of conducting research on interventions that can be extended to the population in need by stipulating the limited conditions in which it is ethically warranted and providing fair terms of participation. We contend that the failure to conduct such research causes greater harm, because it deprives disadvantaged populations of the benefits of imminent incremental improvements in their health conditions.

Burgess, E.; Singhal, N.; Amin, H.; McMillan, D.D.; Devrome, H.; Fenton, A.C. Consent for clinical research in the neonatal intensive care unit: a retrospective survey and a prospective study. *Archives of Disease in Childhood Fetal and Neonatal Edition* 2003 July; 88(4): F280-F286. NRCBL: 18.5.2; 18.3.3. SC: em. Identifiers: Canada.

Cetin, Irene; Gill, Robin. Ethical issues in perinatal nutrition research. *Advances in Experimental Medicine and Biology* 2005; 569: 132-138. NRCBL: 18.5.2; 18.3; 18.2.

Chappuy, H.; Doz, F.; Blanche, S.; Gentet, J.C.; Pons, G.; Tréluyer, J.M. Parental consent in paediatric clinical research. *Archives of Disease in Childhood* 2006 February; 91(2): 112-116. NRCBL: 18.5.2; 18.3; 8.3.2. SC: em. Identifiers: France.

Conrad, Barbara; Horner, Sharon. Issues in pediatric research: safeguarding the children. *Journal of the Society of Pediatric Nurses* 1997 October-December; 2(4): 163-171. NRCBL: 18.5.2; 18.2; 18.6.

Daly, Barbara J. Pediatric informed consent and assent. *In:* Fedor, Carol A.; Cola, Philip A.; Pierre, Christine, eds. Responsible Research: A Guide for Coordinators. London; Chicago, IL: Remedics; 2006: 79-92. NRCBL: 18.5.2; 18.3.

de Meyrick, Julian. Approval procedures and passive consent considerations in research among young people. *Health Education* 2005; 105(4): 249-258. NRCBL: 18.5.2; 18.3. SC: em. Identifiers: Australia.

Diekema, Douglas S. Conducting ethical research in pediatrics: a brief historical overview and review of pediatric regulations. *Journal of Pediatrics* 2006 July; 149(1, Supplement): S3-S11. NRCBL: 18.5.2; 18.2; 2.2; 18.3; 9.3.1. SC: le.

Eiser, C.; Davies, H.; Jenney, M.; Glaser, A. Mothers' attitudes to the randomized controlled trial (RCT): the case of acute lymphoblastic leukaemia (ALL) in children.

Child: Care, Health and Development 2005 September; 31(5): 517-523. NRCBL: 18.5.2. SC: em. Identifiers: United Kingdom (Great Britain).

Fox, Anthony W.; Pothmann, Raymund. Clinical trials ethics [letter and reply]. *Headache* 2005 September; 45(8): 1090-1091. NRCBL: 18.5.2; 18.3. Identifiers: Germany.

Gattuso, Jami; Hinds, Pamela; Tong, Xin; Srivastava, Kumar. Monitoring child and parent refusals to enrol [sic; enroll] in clinical research protocols. *Journal of Advanced Nursing* 2006 February; 53(3): 319-326. NRCBL: 18.5.2; 18.3. SC: em.

Gordon, Elisa J.; Harris Yamokoski, Amy; Kodish, Eric. Children, research, and guinea pigs: reflections on a metaphor. *IRB: Ethics and Human Research* 2006 September-October; 28(5): 12-19. NRCBL: 18.5.2; 18.3.

Henderson, John. Conducting longitudinal epidemiological research in children. *In:* Smyth, Marie; Williamson, Emma, eds. Researchers and Their 'Subjects': Ethics, Power, Knowledge and Consent. Bristol, UK: Policy Press; 2004: 157-174. NRCBL: 18.5.2; 15.1.

Hulst, Jessie M.; Peters, Jeroen W.B.; van den Bos, Ada; Joosten, Koen F.M.; van Goudoever, Johannes B.; Zimmermann, Luc J.I.; Tibboel, Dick. Illness severity and parental permission for clinical research in a pediatric ICU population. *Intensive Care Medicine* 2005 June; 31(6): 880-884. NRCBL: 18.5.2; 18.3. SC: em.

Jonsen, Albert R. Nontherapeutic research with children: the Ramsey versus McCormick debate. *Journal of Pediatrics* 2006 July; 149(1, Supplement): S12-S14. NRCBL: 18.5.2; 18.2; 18.3; 2.2. Identifiers: Paul Ramsey; Richard McCormick; Willowbrook.

Kopelman, Loretta M. When should research with infants, children, or adolescents be permitted? *In:* Iltis, Ana Smith, ed. Research Ethics. New York: Routledge, 2006: 121-131. NRCBL: 18.5.2.

Kuther, Tara L.; Posada, Margarita. Children and adolescents' capacity to provide informed consent for participation in research. *In:* Shohov, Serge, P., ed. Advances in Psychology Research, Volume 32. Huntington, N.Y.: Nova Science Publishers; 2004: 163-173. NRCBL: 18.5.2; 18.3; 17.1. SC: rv.

Litt, Iris F. Research with, not on, adolescents: community-based participatory research. *Journal of Adolescent Health* 2003 November; 33(5): 315-316. NRCBL: 18.5.2; 18.2.

Luu, Arlene D. Research examines the minimal risk standard for pediatric research. *Journal of Biolaw and Business* 2006; 9(1): 52-53. NRCBL: 18.5.2; 18.2.

Maloney, Dennis M. In court: court says children may have been used like canaries in a mine. *Human Research Report* 2006 December; 21(12): 8. NRCBL: 18.5.2; 16.1;

NRCBL: National Reference Center for Bioethics Literature Classification Scheme   See inside front cover for terms.

343

18.2. SC: le. Identifiers: Grimes v. Kennedy Krieger Institute (KKI) (associate with John Hopkins University [part 2]).

Maloney, Dennis M. In court: court says researchers have duty to inform about risks. *Human Research Report* 2006 November; 21(11): 8. NRCBL: 18.5.2; 18.3. SC: le. Identifiers: Grimes v. Kennedy Krieger Institute (KKI).

McClure, Cori A.; Gray, Glenda; Rybczyk, G. Kyle; Wright, Peter F. Challenges to conducting HIV preventative vaccine trials with adolescents. *Journal of Acquired Immune Deficiency Syndrome* 2004 June 1; 36(2): 726-733. NRCBL: 18.5.2; 9.5.6; 18.2.

Miller, Victoria A.; Drotar, Dennis; Burant, Christopher; Kodish, Eric. Clinician-parent communication during informed consent for pediatric leukemia trials. *Journal of Pediatric Psychology* 2005 April-May; 30(3): 219-229. NRCBL: 18.5.2; 18.3; 8.3.2; 8.1. SC: em.

Nelson, Robert M.; Ross, Lainie Friedman. In defense of a single standard of research risk for all children [editorial]. *Journal of Pediatrics* 2005 November; 147(5): 565-566. NRCBL: 18.5.2; 18.2.

Niebrój, L. Genetic medicine: Polish deontological guidelines and the ethical practice of research studies with children. *Human Reproduction and Genetic Ethics: An International Journal* 2006; 12(1): 3-12. NRCBL: 18.5.2; 18.2; 15.1; 21.1.

O'Lonergan, Theresa; Zodrow, John J. Pediatric assent: subject protection issues among adolescent females enrolled in research. *Journal of Law, Medicine and Ethics* 2006 Summer; 34(2): 451-459. NRCBL: 18.5.2; 18.3; 18.5.3. SC: le.

Oppenheim, D.; Geoerger, B.; Hartmann, O. Ethical issues in pediatric oncology phase I-II trials based on a mother's point of view. *Bulletin du Cancer* 2005 November; 92(11): E57-E60. NRCBL: 18.5.2; 8.1. SC: cs.

Prescott, Heather Munro. Using the student body: college and university students as research subjects in the United States during the twentieth century. *Journal of the History of Medicine* 2002 January; 57: 3-38. NRCBL: 18.5.2; 18.2; 18.5.1; 18.3; 18.6; 2.2.

Ramsey, Bonnie W. Appropriate compensation of pediatric research participants: thoughts from an Institute of Medicine committee report. *Journal of Pediatrics* 2006 July; 149(1, Supplement): S15-S19. NRCBL: 18.5.2; 9.3.1; 18.2. SC: le.

Rew, Lynn; Taylor-Seehafer, Margaret; Thomas, Nancy. Without parental consent: conducting research with homeless adolescents. *Journal of the Society of Pediatric Nurses* 2000 July-September; 5(3): 131-139. NRCBL: 18.5.2; 18.3; 18.2. SC: le.

Richards, David F. The central role of informed consent in ethical treatment and research with children. *In:* O'Donohue, William; Ferguson, Kyle, eds. Handbook of Professional Ethics for Psychologists: Issues, Questions, and Controversies. Thousand Oaks, Calif.: SAGE Publications; 2003: 377-359. NRCBL: 18.5.2; 18.3.

Rodriguez, Alina; Tuvemo, Torsten; Hansson, Mats G. Parents' perspectives on research involving children. *Upsala Journal of Medical Sciences* 2006; 111(1): 73-86. NRCBL: 18.5.2; 18.3. SC: em. Identifiers: Sweden.

Ross, Lainie Friedman. Phase I research and the meaning of direct benefit. *Journal of Pediatrics* 2006 July; 149(1, Supplement): S20-S24. NRCBL: 18.5.2; 18.2; 18.3. SC: an; le.

Ross, Lainie Friedman; Nelson, Robert M.; Wendler, David; Belsky, Leah; Thompson, Kimberly M.; Emanuel, Ezekiel J. Pediatric research and the federal minimal risk standard [letter and reply]. *JAMA: The Journal of the American Medical Association* 2006 February 15; 295(7): 759-760. NRCBL: 18.5.2. SC: le.

Sanci, Lena A.; Sawyer, Susan M.; Weller, Penny J.; Bond, Lyndal M.; Patton, George C. Youth health research ethics: time for a mature-minor clause? *Medical Journal of Australia* 2004 April 5; 180(7): 336-338. NRCBL: 18.5.2; 18.2; 18.6.

Shochet, Ian M.; O'Gorman, J.G. Ethical issues in research on adolescent depression and suicidal behaviour. *Australian Psychologist* 1995 November; 30(3): 183-186. NRCBL: 18.5.2; 17.1; 20.7; 18.2.

Slack, Catherine; Strode, Ann; Grant, Catherine; Milford, Cecilia. Implications of the ethical-legal framework for adolescent HIV vaccine trials — report of a consultative forum. *South African Medical Journal* 2005 September; 95(9): 682-684. NRCBL: 18.5.2; 9.5.6; 9.7; 18.2. SC: le. Identifiers: South Africa.

Society for Adolescent Medicine. Guidelines for adolescent health research. *Journal of Adolescent Health* 1995 November; 17(5): 264-269. NRCBL: 18.5.2; 18.2; 18.3; 8.3.2; 5.2. Comments: Conference on Guidelines for Adolescent Health Research; Alexandria, VA; 19-20 May 1994.

Society for Adolescent Medicine; Santelli, John S.; Rosenfeld, Walter D.; DuRant, Robert H.; Dubler, Nancy; Morreale, Madlyn; English, Abigail; Rogers, Audrey Smith. Guidelines for adolescent health research: a position paper of the society for adolescent medicine. *Journal of Adolescent Health* 1995 November; 17(5): 270-276. NRCBL: 18.5.2; 18.2; 18.3; 8.3.2; 8.4; 18.4.

Stobie, Melissa; Strode, Ann; Slack, Cathy. The dilemma of enrolling children in HIV vaccine research in South Africa: what is in 'the child's best interest'? *In:* van Niekerk, Anton A.; Kopelman, Loretta M., eds. Ethics and

AIDS in Africa: The Challenge to Our Thinking. Walnut Creek, CA: Left Coast Press; 2006: 190-207. NRCBL: 18.5.2; 9.5.6; 9.7. SC: le.

Stolberg, Sheryl Gay. Preschool meds: the first clinical trial examining the effects of generic Ritalin on 3- to 5-year-old subjects raises questions not only about the safety of the drug but also about the ethics of testing on ever younger brains. *New York Times Magazine* 2002 November 17; p. 58-61. NRCBL: 18.5.2; 17.4.

Truog, Robert D. Increasing the participation of children in clinical research [editorial]. *Intensive Care Medicine* 2005 June; 31(6): 760-761. NRCBL: 18.5.2; 18.2; 18.3.

United States. Congress. Senate. An act to amend the Federal Food, Drug, and Cosmetics Act to authorize the Food and Drug Administration to require certain research into drugs used in pediatric patients. Washington, DC: U.S. G.P.O., 2003. 22 p. [Online]. Accessed: http://frwebgate.access.gpo.gov/cgi-bin/useftp.cgi? IPaddress=162.140.64.21&file name=s650es.pdf& directory=/disk2/wais/data/108_cong_bills [2006 December 15]. NRCBL: 18.5.2; 9.7. SC: le. Identifiers: Pediatric Research Equity Act of 2003. Note: S. 650, 108th Congress, 1st session. Passed the Senate July 23, 2003.

United States. Department of Education. Protection of human subjects; final regulations. *Federal Register* 1997 November 26; 62(228): 63219-63222 [Online] Accessed: http://frwebgate.access.gpo.gov/cgi-bin/multidb.cgi [2005 December 27]. NRCBL: 18.5.2; 18.6. SC: le.

Waterhouse, Tessa; Pollard, Andrew. Clinical trials: consent in children [editorial]. *Expert Review of Vaccines* 2005 February; 4(1): 1-3. NRCBL: 18.5.2; 18.2; 18.3.

Weithorn, Lois A.; Scherer, David G. Children's involvement in research participation decisions: psychological considerations. *In:* Gordin, M.; Glantz, L., eds. Children as Research Subjects. Oxford University Press; 1994: 133-179. NRCBL: 18.5.2; 18.3; 17.1. SC: le.

Wendler, David. Assent in paediatric research: theoretical and practical considerations. *Journal of Medical Ethics* 2006 April; 32(4): 229-234. NRCBL: 18.5.2; 18.3. SC: an.

Wendler, David; Emanuel, Ezekiel J. What is a "minor" increase over minimal risk? *Journal of Pediatrics* 2005 November; 147(5): 575-578. NRCBL: 18.5.2; 18.2. SC: em.

Wiesemann, Claudia; Dahl, Matthias. Forschung mit Kindern und Jugendlichen: Ist eine neue rechtliche Regelung notwendig? *In:* Vollmann, Jochen, ed. Medizin und Ethik: Aktuelle ethische Probleme in Therapie und Forschung. Erlangen: Universitätsbund Erlangen-Nürnberg, 2003: 83-106. NRCBL: 18.5.2. SC: le.

Wolthers, O.D. A questionnaire on factors influencing children's assent and dissent to non-therapeutic research.

Journal of Medical Ethics 2006 May; 32(5): 292-297. NRCBL: 18.5.2; 8.3.2; 18.3. SC: em.

Abstract: BACKGROUND: Knowledge about assent or dissent of children to non-therapeutic research is poor. OBJECTIVES: To assess sociodemographic characteristics in healthy children and adolescents who were invited to participate in non-therapeutic research, to evaluate their motives for assent or dissent and their understanding of the information given. METHODS: A total of 1281 healthy children and adolescents six to sixteen years of age were invited to participate in a non-therapeutic study and a questionnaire. RESULTS: Assenting children were motivated by a desire to help sick children (n = 638, 98%) and to gain experience with participating in a research study (n = 503, 82%). Dissenting children made their decision because of worries about having a blood (n = 193, 46%) or a urine sample (n = 94, 26%) taken or because of worries about a doctor's examination (n = 136, 33%). Fewer children in the assent group (n = 166, 25%) than in the dissent group (136, 33%) worried about the doctor's examination (p = 0.01). In the assent and dissent group, 568 (86%) and 343 (85%) children, respectively, said they were able to understand some or all of the written information (p = 0.42), and 650 (97%) and 330 (98%), respectively, were able to understand some or all of the verbal information (p = 0.07). CONCLUSIONS: Sociodemographic characteristics may not influence healthy children's decision to volunteer for non-therapeutic research. Assenting children have altruistic and educational motives, whereas worries about procedures may cause children to dissent. A great majority of school children and adolescents feel capable of understanding and giving assent or dissent to non-therapeutic research.

Woodring, Barbara C. The role of the staff nurse in protecting children and families involved in research. *Journal of Pediatric Nursing* 2004 August; 19(4): 311-313. NRCBL: 18.5.2; 18.2; 18.3; 4.1.3.

HUMAN EXPERIMENTATION/ . . . / PRISONERS

Safe drug testing in prisons [editorial]. *New York Times* 2006 August 23; p. A22. NRCBL: 18.5.5; 9.7. SC: po.

Bastian, Till. Medizinische Experimente. *In his:* Furchtbare Ärzte: medizinische Verbrechen im Dritten Reich. München: Verlag C.H. Beck; 1995: 72-87. NRCBL: 18.5.5; 1.3.5; 2.2; 15.5; 21.4.

Brainard, Jeffrey. Report calls for easing rules on research involving prisoners. *Chronicle of Higher Education* 2006 July 28; 52(47): A16. NRCBL: 18.5.5; 18.2.

Georges, Jane M.; Benedict, Susan. An ethics of testimony: prisoner nurses at Auschwitz. *Advances in Nursing Science* 2006 April-June; 29(2): 161-169. NRCBL: 18.5.5; 4.1.3. SC: an.

Gordon, Richard F. Nazi medical data obtained from concentration camp victims: should it be used? *Delaware Medical Journal* 2005 April; 77(4): 143-150. NRCBL: 18.5.5; 21.4; 1.3.9.

Gostin, Lawrence O.; Hamden, Michael S. Prisoners and medical research. *Chronicle of Higher Education* 2006 November 3; 53(11): B20. NRCBL: 18.5.5; 18.2.

NRCBL: National Reference Center for Bioethics Literature Classification Scheme   See inside front cover for terms.

345

Harris, Sheldon H. Japanese biomedical experimentation during the World-War-II era. *In:* Beam, Thomas E.; Sparacino, Linette R.; Pellegrino, Edmund D.; Hartle, Anthony E.; Howe, Edmund G., eds. Military Medical Ethics. Volume 2. Washington, DC: TMM Publications, Borden Institute, Walter Reed Army Medical Center; 2003: 463-506. NRCBL: 18.5.5; 21.1.

Loewenberg, Samuel. U.S. advisory panel revisits prison research rules. *Lancet* 2006 September 30- October 6; 368(9542): 1143-1144. NRCBL: 18.5.5; 18.6.

Maloney, Dennis M. Case study: the more a federal office digs, the more problems it finds with the institutional review board (IRB). *Human Research Report* 2006 October; 21(10): 6-7. NRCBL: 18.5.5; 18.2; 18.6.

Maloney, Dennis M. Case study: university tries to explain regulatory noncompliance in research. *Human Research Report* 2006 December; 21(12): 6-7. NRCBL: 18.5.5; 18.2; 18.3; 18.6. SC: cs.

Maloney, Dennis M. Human subject protection rules may apply later, even if they don't at first. *Human Research Report* 2006 September; 21(9): 1-2. NRCBL: 18.5.5; 18.2.

Maloney, Dennis M. University's medical center ordered to suspend research with prisoners — for starters [case study]. *Human Research Report* 2006 September; 21(9): 6-7. NRCBL: 18.5.5; 1.3.3; 18.6.

Pozos, Robert S. Nazi hypothermia research: should the data be used? *In:* Beam, Thomas E.; Sparacino, Linette R.; Pellegrino, Edmund D.; Hartle, Anthony E.; Howe, Edmund G., eds. Military Medical Ethics. Volume 2. Washington, DC: TMM Publications, Borden Institute, Walter Reed Army Medical Center; 2003: 437-461. NRCBL: 18.5.5; 21.4.

Sheard, L.; Tompkins, C.N.E.; Wright, N.M.J.; Adams, C.E. Non-commercial clinical trials of a medicinal product: can they survive the current process of research approvals in the UK? *Journal of Medical Ethics* 2006 July; 32(7): 430-434. NRCBL: 18.5.5; 18.2; 18.6. Identifiers: United Kingdom (Great Britain).

Abstract: Over recent years, considerable attention has been paid to the National Health Service (NHS) research governance and ethics approvals process in the UK. New regulations mean that approval from the Medicines and Healthcare Products Regulatory Agency (MHRA) is now also needed for conducting all clinical trials. Practical experience of gaining MHRA and sponsorship approval has yet to be described and critically explored in the literature. Our experience, from start to finish, of applying for these four approvals for a multicentre randomised controlled trial of two licensed drugs for opiate detoxification in the prison setting is described here. In addition, the implications of the approvals process for research projects, particularly clinical trials, in terms of time and funding, and also indirect implications for NHS patients are discussed. Inconsistencies are discussed and suggestions that could improve and streamline the overall process are made. The current approvals process could now be hindering non-commercial clinical trials, leading to a loss of important evidence-based medical information

Tierney, E. The Nazi hypothermia experiments: forbidden data? [letter]. *Anaesthesia* 2005 April; 60(4): 413. NRCBL: 18.5.5; 21.4; 1.3.9.

Urbina, Ian. Panel suggests using inmates in drug trials. *New York Times* 2006 August 13; p. A1, A21. NRCBL: 18.5.5. SC: po.

HUMAN EXPERIMENTATION/ . . . / WOMEN

Blake, Mary Beth; Ince, Melissa; Dean, Cathy J. Inclusion of women in cardiac research: current trends and need for reassessment. *Gender Medicine* 2005 June; 2(2): 71-75. NRCBL: 18.5.3; 10; 18.6. SC: le.

Epstein, Steven. Bodily differences and collective identities: the politics of gender and race in biomedical research in the United States. *Body and Society* 2004 June-September; 10(2-3): 183-204 [Online] Accessed: http://bod.sagepub.com/cgi/reprint/10/2-3/183 [2007 February 6]. NRCBL: 18.5.3; 18.5.1; 15.1.

Hayunga, Eugene G.; Pinn, Vivian W. NIH policy on the inclusion of women and minorities as subjects in clinical research. *In:* Gallin, John I., ed. Principles and Practice of Clinical Research. San Diego, CA: Academic Press; 2002: 145-160. NRCBL: 18.5.3; 18.2; 18.5.1; 18.6.

Maloney, Dennis M. Defendants agree to multimillion dollar settlement for research subjects. *Human Research Report* 2006 August; 21(8): 8. NRCBL: 18.5.3; 9.3.1. SC: le. Identifiers: Diaz v. Hillsborough County Hospital Authority, d/b/a Tampa General Hospital, et al. (Part 13).

Marshall, Mary Faith; Menikoff, Jerry; Paltrow, Lynn M. Perinatal substance abuse and human subjects research: are privacy protections adequate? *Mental Retardation and Developmental Disabilities Research Reviews* 2003; 9(1): 54-59. NRCBL: 18.5.3; 18.2; 8.4; 18.5.2; 9.5.9. SC: le.

McCormick, Janice; Kirkham, Sheryl Reimer; Hayes, Virginia. Abstracting women: essentialism in women's health research. *Health Care for Women International* 1998 November-December; 19(6): 495-504. NRCBL: 18.5.3; 1.1; 10.

McCullough, Laurence B.; Coverdale, John H.; Chervenak, Frank A. A comprehensive ethical framework for responsibly designing and conducting pharmacologic research that involves pregnant women. *American Journal of Obstetrics and Gynecology* 2005 September; 193(3, Part 2): 901-907. NRCBL: 18.5.3; 18.2; 18.5.4; 18.3; 9.7. SC: em.

Melisko, Michelle E.; Hassin, Fern; Metzroth, Lauren; Moore, Dan H.; Brown, Beth; Patel, Kiran; Rugo, Hope S.; Tripathy, Debu. Patient and physician attitudes toward breast cancer clinical trials: developing interventions based on understanding barriers. *Clinical Breast*

Cancer 2005 April; 6(1): 45-54. NRCBL: 18.5.3; 18.3; 4.1.1; 8.1. SC: em.

Palmlund, Ingar. Loyalties in clinical research on drugs: the case of hormone replacement therapy. *Social Science and Medicine* 2006 July; 63(2): 540-551. NRCBL: 18.5.3; 7.3; 8.1; 9.7. Identifiers: Pierre Bourdien.

Ramasubbu, K.; Gurm, H.; Litaker, D. Gender bias in clinical trials: do double standards still apply? *Journal of Women's Health and Gender-Based Medicine* 2001 October; 10(8): 757-764. NRCBL: 18.5.3; 18.2; 10; 18.6.

Selby, Peter; Kapur, Bhushan M.; Hackman, Richard; Koren, Gideon. "No one asked the baby" — an ethical issue in placebo-controlled trials in pregnant smokers. *Canadian Journal of Clinical Pharmacology* 2005 Summer; 12(2): e180-e181. NRCBL: 18.5.3.

Thorne, Sally; Varcoe, Colleen. The tyranny of feminist methodology in women's health research. *Health Care for Women International* 1998 November-December; 19(6): 481-493. NRCBL: 18.5.3; 1.1; 10.

United States. District Court, Middle District of Tennessee. Craft v. Vanderbilt University [Date of Decision: 19 August 1998]. *Federal Supplement*, 2d Series, 1998; 18: 786-798. NRCBL: 18.5.3 18.5.4 16.2 18.3. SC: le.
Abstract: Court Decision: 18 Federal Supplement, 2d Series 786; 1998 Aug 19 (date of decision). In a memorandum opinion, the U.S. District Court for the Middle District of Tennessee detailed the reasoning behind an earlier decision to allow the research subjects of radiation experiments to continue their case against a private university, a private foundation, and the state. The subjects were pregnant women who were not informed of the risks of ingesting radioactive iron isotopes in a series of experiments at Vanderbilt University between 1945-1947. Nor were they informed in a later follow-up study about the involuntary exposure, nor contacted later when another follow-up study showed a disproportionately high incidence of cancer among the subjects. Because actions by both Vanderbilt and the Rockefeller Foundation in this joint project were so entwined with those of Tennessee, they could be found liable under federal civil rights law. The claims were not time-barred under Tennessee's medical malpractice statutes, because "the experiments did not constitute medical care." Instead the court concluded that the statute of limitations may be tolled because of fraudulent concealment, noting that "[w]here a confidential relationship exists, as between a physician and a patient, there is an affirmative duty to disclose, and that duty renders silence or failure to disclose known facts fraudulent.

University of Bristol, Domestic Violence Research Group. Domestic violence and research ethics. *In:* Smyth, Marie; Williamson, Emma, eds. Researchers and Their 'Subjects': Ethics, Power, Knowledge and Consent. Bristol, UK: Policy Press; 2004: 195-210. NRCBL: 18.5.3; 18.4; 18.5.2.

van Niekerk, Anton A. Mother-to-child transmission of HIV/AIDS in Africa: ethical problems and perspectives. *In:* van Niekerk, Anton A.; Kopelman, Loretta M., eds. Ethics and AIDS in Africa: The Challenge to Our Think-ing. Walnut Creek, CA: Left Coast Press; 2006: 141-159. NRCBL: 18.5.3; 9.5.6; 18.2; 18.3.

Woodsong, Cynthia; MacQueen, Kathleen; Namey, Emily; Sahay, Seema; Morrar, Neetha; Mlingo, Margaret; Meheldale, Sanjay. Women's autonomy and informed consent in microbicides clinical trials. *Journal of Empirical Research on Human Research Ethics* 2006 September; 1(3): 11-26. NRCBL: 18.5.3; 9.5.6; 18.1; 21.1; 18.6. SC: cs.

HUMAN RIGHTS *See* INTERNATIONAL HUMAN RIGHTS

IMMUNIZATION *See* CARE FOR SPECIFIC GROUPS; DRUG INDUSTRY; HUMAN EXPERIMENTATION/ SPECIAL POPULATIONS/ MILITARY PERSONNEL; PUBLIC HEALTH

IN VITRO FERTILIZATION
See also REPRODUCTIVE TECHNOLOGIES

Assisted reproductive technologies hit all time high [editorial]. *Lancet* 2006 July 1-7; 368(9529): 2. NRCBL: 14.4; 21.1; 7.1.

Safeguards for donors [editorial]. *Nature* 2006 August 10; 442(7103): 601. NRCBL: 14.4; 14.6; 18.5.1; 18.5.4; 9.3.1; 19.5.

Adamson, David. Regulation of assisted reproductive technologies in the United States. *Family Law Quarterly* 2005 Fall; 39(3): 727-744. NRCBL: 14.4; 14.5; 9.8. SC: le.

Adsuar, Natalie; Zweifel, Julianne E.; Pritts, Elizabeth A.; Davidson, Marie A.; Olive, David L.; Lindheim, Steven R. Assessment of wishes regarding disposition of oocytes and embryo management among ovum donors in an anonymous egg donation program. *Fertility and Sterility* 2005 November; 84(5): 1513-1516. NRCBL: 14.4; 14.6. SC: em.

American Society for Reproductive Medicine [ASRM]. Ethics Committee. Financial incentives in recruitment of oocyte donors. *Fertility and Sterility* 2004 September; 82(Supplement 1): S240-S244. NRCBL: 14.4; 9.3.1; 19.5.

American Society for Reproductive Medicine [ASRM]. Ethics Committee. Shared-risk or refund programs in assisted reproduction. *Fertility and Sterility* 2004 September; 82(Supplement 1): S249-S250. NRCBL: 14.4; 5.2; 9.3.1.

Bellieni, Carlo V.; Buonocore, Giuseppe. Assisted procreation: too little consideration for the babies. *Ethics and Medicine* 2006 Summer; 22(2): 93-98. NRCBL: 14.4; 5.2; 9.5.7; 4.4.

Benagiano, Giuseppe. The four referendums attempting to modify the restrictive Italian IVF legislation failed to reach the required quorum [editorial]. *Reproductive*

NRCBL: National Reference Center for Bioethics Literature Classification Scheme   See inside front cover for terms.

347

BioMedicine Online [electronic] 2005 September; 11(3): 279-281. NRCBL: 14.4; 5.3; 1.2.

Bender, Leslie. "To err is human" ART mix-ups: a labor-based, relational proposal. *Journal of Gender, Race and Justice* 2006 Spring; 9(3): 443-508. NRCBL: 14.4; 8.5; 14.2; 15.1; 9.8. SC: le.

Blank, Robert H. Embryos, stem cell research, and the promise of health. *Politics and the Life Sciences* 2003 September; 22(2): 9-11. NRCBL: 14.4; 18.5.4; 15.1. Comments: Andrea D. Gurmankin; Dominic, Sisti; Arthur L. Caplan, Embryo disposal practices in IVF clinics in the United States. Politics and the Life Sciences 2003 September; 22(2): 4-8.

Blyth, Eric; Speirs, Jennifer. Meeting the rights and needs of donor-conceived people: the contribution of a voluntary contact register. *Nordisk Sosialt Arbeid* 2004; 24(4): 318-330. NRCBL: 14.4; 14.2; 19.5; 8.4.

Bonnicksen, Andrea L. In vitro fertilization and genetic screening. *In:* Mitcham, Carl, ed. Encyclopedia of Science, Technology, and Ethics. Farmington Hills, MI: Thomson/Gale, 2005: 1054-1057. NRCBL: 14.4; 15.2; 15.3.

Cameron, Nigel M. de S. Pandora's progeny: ethical issues in assisted human reproduction. *Family Law Quarterly* 2005 Fall; 39(3): 745-779. NRCBL: 14.4; 15.2; 18.5.4; 4.4; 14.5; 15.1. SC: le.

Chang, Wendy Y.; DeCherney, Alan H. History of regulation of assisted reproductive technology (ART) in the USA: a work in progress. *Human Fertility* 2003 May; 6(2): 64-70. NRCBL: 14.4; 2.2; 5.3. SC: le.

Cotton, Sara, et al. Model Assisted Reproductive Technology Act. *Journal of Gender, Race and Justice* 2005 Fall; 9(1): 55-107. NRCBL: 14.4; 14.2; 8.4; 14.6; 4.4; 15.3; 18.5.4. SC: le.

Debrock, Sophie; Spiessens, Carl; Meuleman, Christel; Segal, Luc; De Loecker, Peter; Meeuwis, Luc; D'Hooghe, Thomas M. New Belgian legislation regarding the limitation of transferable embryos in in vitro fertilization cycles does not significantly influence the pregnancy rate but reduces the multiple pregnancy rate in a threefold way in the Leuven University Fertility Center. *Fertility and Sterility* 2005 May; 83(5): 1572-1574. NRCBL: 14.4. SC: le; em. Identifiers: Belgium.

Dolgin, Janet L. Method, mediations, and the moral dimensions of preimplantation genetic diagnosis. *Cumberland Law Review* 2004-2005; 35(3): 519-542. NRCBL: 14.4; 15.2; 4.4; 2.1; 1.1.

Edwards, R.G. Ethics and moral philosophy in the initiation of IVF, preimplantation diagnosis and stem cells. *Reproductive BioMedicine Online [electronic]* 2005 March; 10(Supplement 1): 1-8. NRCBL: 14.4; 2.2; 18.5.4; 15.2.

Conference: Ethics, Law and Moral Philosophy of Reproductive Biomedicine; London, UK; 2004 September 30 - October 1; Royal Society.

Edwards, R.G.; Ahuja, K.K. Legal cases spell big trouble and great opportunities for IVF embryologists. *Reproductive BioMedicine Online [electronic]* 2001 July 2; 2(1): 1 p. Accessed: http://www.rbmonline.com/index.html [2005 June 3]. NRCBL: 14.4; 8.5; 21.1. SC: le. Identifiers: in vitro fertilization; United Kingdom (Great Britain).

Elford, Kimberly; Lawrence, Carole; Leader, Arthur. Research implications of embryo cryopreservation choices made by patients undergoing in vitro fertilization. *Fertility and Sterility* 2004 April; 81(4): 1154-1155. NRCBL: 14.4; 14.6. SC: em.

English, Veronica. Autonomy versus protection — who benefits from the regulation of IVF? *Human Reproduction* 2006 December; 21(12): 3044-3049. NRCBL: 14.4; 5.3; 1.1. Identifiers: in vitro fertilization.

Erwin, Cheryl. Utopian dreams and harsh realities: who is in control of assisted reproductive technologies in a high-tech world? *Journal of Gender, Race and Justice* 2006 Spring; 9(3): 621-635. NRCBL: 14.4; 15.2; 5.3.

Fenton, Rachel Anne. Catholic doctrine versus women's rights: the new Italian law on assisted reproduction. *Medical Law Review* 2006 Spring; 14(1): 73-107. NRCBL: 14.4; 1.2; 9.5.5; 14.6; 4.4; 14.3. SC: le.

Franco, J.G.; Baruff, R.L.R.; Mauri, A.L.; Petersen, C.G.; Carillo, S.V.; Silva, P.; Martinhago, C.D.; Oliveira, J.B.A. Concerns regarding the follow-up on children conceived after assisted reproduction in Latin America. *Reproductive BioMedicine Online [electronic]* 2004 August; 9(2): 127-128. NRCBL: 14.4; 9.5.7. SC: em.

Garcia-Velasco, Juan A.; Garrido, Nicolas. How would revealing the identity of gamete donors affect current practice? *Reproductive BioMedicine Online [electronic]* 2005 May; 10(5): 564-566. Accessed: http://www.rbmonline.com/Article/1755 [2005 November 17]. NRCBL: 14.4; 8.4; 8.2; 14.1. Identifiers: Spain.

Gleicher, Norbert; Barad, David. The relative myth of elective single embryo transfer. *Human Reproduction* 2006 June; 21(6): 1337-1344. NRCBL: 14.4; 9.8; 1.1.

Goodwin, Michele. Assisted reproductive technology and the double bind: the illusory choice of motherhood. *Journal of Gender, Race and Justice* 2005 Fall; 9(1): 1-54. NRCBL: 14.4; 9.5.5; 10. SC: le.

Grazi, Richard V. Halachic dilemmas of the process of IVF. *In:* Rosner, Fred, ed. Medicine and Jewish Law. Volume III. Brooklyn, NY: Yashar Books, Inc.; 2005: 25-39. NRCBL: 14.4; 1.2.

Grothaus-Day, Cyrene. Criminal conception: behind the white coat. *Family Law Quarterly* 2005 Fall; 39(3): 707-725. NRCBL: 14.4; 15.1; 4.4; 1.3.5. SC: le.

Gurmankin, Andrea D.; Sisti, Dominic; Caplan, Arthur L. Embryo disposal practices in IVF clinics in the United States. *Politics and the Life Sciences* 2003 September; 22(2): 4-8. NRCBL: 14.4; 14.6; 18.5.4; 15.1. SC: em.

Heng, Boon Chin. Ethical issues in paying for long-distance travel and accommodation expenses of oocyte donors. *Reproductive BioMedicine Online [electronic]* 2005 November; 11(5): 552-553. NRCBL: 14.4; 14.2; 19.5; 7.3; 9.3.1; 21.1.

Human Fertilisation and Embryology Authority [HFEA] (Great Britain). Egg donation. London: Human Fertilisation and Embryology Authority, 1995 January; 7 p. NRCBL: 14.4.

Human Fertilisation and Embryology Authority [HFEA] (Great Britain). Recent deliberations on the case of human fetal oocytes and on pregnancies in post-menopausal women by the British Human Fertilisation and Embryology Authority. *Human Reproduction* 1995 January; 9(12): 239-244. NRCBL: 14.4.; 19.1; 4.4; 18.5.4; 14.6.

Hyun, Insoo. Fair payment or undue inducement? *Nature* 2006 August 10; 442(7103): 629-630. NRCBL: 14.4; 9.3.1; 14.6; 18.3; 18.5.1; 18.5.4; 19.5.

Inhorn, Marcia C. "He won't be my son" Middle Eastern Muslim men's discourses of adoption and gamete donation. *Medical Anthropology Quarterly* 2006 March; 20(1): 94-120. NRCBL: 14.4; 1.2; 14.1.

Johnson, Martin H. Escaping the tyranny of the embryo? A new approach to ART regulation based on UK and Australian experiences. *Human Reproduction* 2006 November; 21(11): 2756-2765. NRCBL: 14.4; 4.4. SC: le.

Johnston, Josephine. Paying egg donors: exploring the arguments. *Hastings Center Report* 2006 January-February; 36(1): 28-31. NRCBL: 14.4; 9.3.1; 19.5.

Jones, Caroline. The Department of Health Review of the Human Fertilisation and Embryology Act 1990. *Clinical Ethics* 2006 December; 1(4): 200-204. NRCBL: 14.4; 5.3; 18.6; 14.2; 14.6; 15.2. SC: le.

Kahraman, S.; Findikli, N. Effect of Italian referendum on global IVF: a comment from Turkey. *Reproductive BioMedicine Online [electronic]* 2005 December; 11(6): 662-663. Accessed: http://www.rbmonline.com/Article/2052 [2006 July 25]. NRCBL: 14.4; 21.1; 1.2. SC: le.

Klein, Renate. Women as body parts in the era of reproductive and genetic engineering. *Health Care for Women International* 1991 October-December; 12(4): 393-405. NRCBL: 14.4; 15.1; 4.4; 10.

Kleinfeld, Joshua. Tort law and in vitro fertilization: the need for legal recognition of "procreative injury". *Yale Law Journal* 2005 October; 115(1): 237-245. NRCBL: 14.4; 9.8. SC: le.

Kriari-Catranis, Ismini. Human assisted procreation and human rights — the Greek response to the felt necessities of the time. *European Journal of Health Law* 2003 September; 10(3): 271-280. NRCBL: 14.4; 14.5; 18.5.4; 14.2; 14.6; 15.1. SC: le.

Krones, Tanja; Neuwonhner, Elke; El Ansari, Susan; Wissner, Thomas; Richter, Gerd. Kinderwunsch und Wunschkinder: Möglichkeiten und Grenzen der in-vitro-fertilisations-Behandlung = Desire for a child and desired children —possibilities and limits of reproductive biomedicine. *Ethik in der Medizin* 2006 March; 18(1): 51-62. NRCBL: 14.4; 9.3.1. SC: em.

Malinowski, Michael J. A law-policy proposal to know where babies come from during the reproductive revolution. *Journal of Gender, Race and Justice* 2006 Spring; 9(3): 549-568. NRCBL: 14.4; 2.4; 5.3. SC: le.

Masek, Lawrence. A contralife argument against altered nuclear transfer. *National Catholic Bioethics Quarterly* 2006 Summer; 6(2): 235-240. NRCBL: 14.4; 18.5.4; 15.1; 4.4; 1.2. SC: an.

McLean, Sheila A.M. De-regulating assisted reproduction: some reflections. *Medical Law International* 2006; 7(3): 233-247. NRCBL: 14.4; 18.5.4; 18.6; 5.3; 2.4. SC: le.

Mills, Peter; Whittall, Hugh. "Legal cases spell big trouble and great opportunities for IVF embryologists": a comment from the perspective of the HFEA. *Reproductive BioMedicine Online [electronic]* 2001; 2(3): 1 p. Accessed: http://www.rbmonline.com/index.html [2005 June 3]. NRCBL: 14.4; 21.1; 6. Identifiers: in vitro fertilization; Human Fertilisation and Embryology Act 1990.

Mitchell, C. Ben. Human egg "donation" [editorial]. *Ethics and Medicine* 2006 Fall; 22(3): 133-134. NRCBL: 14.4; 14.6; 18.5.4; 5.2; 7.1.

Mori, Maurizio. The morality of assisted reproduction of genetic manipulation. *Cadernos de Saúde Pública* 1999; 15(suppl. 1): 65-72. NRCBL: 14.4; 15.1; 4.5. SC: an.

Murray, Clare; Golombok, Susan. To tell or not to tell: the decision-making process of egg-donation parents. *Human Fertility* 2003 May; 6(2): 89-95. NRCBL: 14.4; 8.4; 9.5.7; 8.3.1; 8.2. SC: em. Identifiers: United Kingdom(Great Britain).

Nowak, Rachel. Methuselah moms. *New Scientist* 2006 October 21-27; 192(2574): 46-51. NRCBL: 14.4; 14.6.

O'Dowd, Adrian. Society issues guidance on IVF [news]. *BMJ: British Medical Journal* 2006 September 9; 333(7567): 517. NRCBL: 14.4; 9.8. Identifiers: United Kingdom (Great Britain); in vitro fertilization.

NRCBL: National Reference Center for Bioethics Literature Classification Scheme   See inside front cover for terms.

349

Olivennes, Francois. Do children born after assisted reproductive technology have a higher incidence of birth defects? *Fertility and Sterility* 2005 November; 84(5): 1325-1326. NRCBL: 14.4; 9.5.7; 8.1.

Orobitg, Gemma; Salazar, Carles. The gift of motherhood: egg donation in a Barcelona infertility clinic. *Ethnos* 2005 March; 70(1): 31-52. NRCBL: 14.4; 9.5.5; 8.1; 19.5; 21.7. SC: em.

Parker, Michael. The welfare of the child. *Human Fertility* 2005 March; 8(1): 13-17. NRCBL: 14.4; 9.5.7. SC: le; cs. Identifiers: United Kingdom (Great Britain).

Paxson, Heather. With or against nature? IVF, gender and reproductive agency in Athens, Greece. *Social Science and Medicine* 2003 May; 56(9): 1853-1866. NRCBL: 14.4; 21.7; 14.1. SC: an. Identifiers: in vitro fertilization.

Pearson, Helen. Ethicists and biologists ponder the price of eggs. *Nature* 2006 August 10; 442(7103): 606-608. NRCBL: 14.4; 9.3.1; 14.6; 18.5.1; 18.5.4; 19.5.

Pilcher, Helen. The egg and sperm race. *New Scientist* 2006 October 21-27; 192(2574): 52-54. NRCBL: 14.4; 14.6; 18.5.4; 15.1; 19.1.

Pinto, Maria Cristina Rosamond. Medically assisted procreation: legal framework in Portugal. *Eubios Journal of Asian and International Bioethics* 2006 September; 16(5): 158-160. NRCBL: 14.4; 15.2; 18.5.1. SC: le.

Porter, Deborah. The regulation of in-vitro fertilisation: social norms and discrimination. *E Law: Murdoch University Electronic Journal of Law* 1997 September; 4(3): 7 p. [Online]. Accessed: http://www.murdoch.edu.au/elaw/issues/v4n3/port43.html [2006 June 29]. NRCBL: 14.4. SC: le. Identifiers: Western Australia; Human Reproductive Technology Act.

Samuels, Alec. Donor anonymity. *Medico-Legal Journal* 2005; 73(Part 2): 71-72. NRCBL: 14.4; 14.6; 8.4; 21.1.

Sauer, Mark V. Further HFEA restrictions on egg donation in the UK: two strikes and you're out! *Reproductive BioMedicine Online [electronic]* 2005; 10(4): 431-433. NRCBL: 14.4; 5.3; 9.3.1; 8.4; 19.5. Identifiers: Human Fertilisation and Embryology Authority; United Kingdom (Great Britain).

Schenker, Joseph G. Assisted reproductive practice: religious perspectives. *Reproductive BioMedicine Online [electronic]* 2005 March; 10(3): 310-319. Accessed: http://www.rbmonline.com/Article/1539 [2005 September 30]. NRCBL: 14.4; 14.1; 14.2; 14.3.; 14.5; 14.6; 1.2; 10; 12.1; 18.1. SC: rv.

Schenker, Joseph G. Ethical, religious and legal debate on IVF and alternate assisted reproduction. *In:* Masiach, S.; Ben-Rafael, Z.; Laufer, N.; Schenker, J.G., eds. Advances in Assisted Reproductive Technologies. New York: Plenum Press, 1990: 1041-1052. NRCBL: 14.4; 14.2; 14.6; 18.5.4; 1.2.

Schieve, Laura A. The promise of single-embryo transfer [editorial]. *New England Journal of Medicine* 2006 March 16; 354(11): 1190-1193. NRCBL: 14.4.

Shea, John B. The immorality of in vitro fertilization: conception and Catholic moral teaching. *Ethics and Medics* 2006 October; 31(10): 1-2. NRCBL: 14.4; 1.2.

Society for Assisted Reproductive Technology [SART]. Practice Committee; American Society for Reproductive Medicine [ASRM]. Guidelines on the number of embryos transferred. *Fertility and Sterility* 2004 September; 82(Supplement 1): S1-S2. NRCBL: 14.4.

Spar, Debora. Buying our children. Selling our souls?: the commodification of children. *Conscience* 2006 Autumn; 27(3): 14-16. NRCBL: 14.4; 4.4.

Sureau, C.; Shenfield, F. Oocyte donation by a daughter. *Human Reproduction* 1995 June; 10(6): 1334. NRCBL: 14.4; 14.6.

van den Akker, Olga. A review of family donor constructs: current research and future directions. *Human Reproduction Update* 2006 March; 12(2): 91-101. NRCBL: 14.4; 19.5; 8.4.

Varone, Frédéric; Rothmayr, Christine; Montpetit, Eric. Regulating biomedicine in Europe and North America: a qualitative comparative analysis. *European Journal of Political Research* 2006 March; 45(2): 317-343. NRCBL: 14.4; 14.2; 21.1.

Wahrman, Miryam Z. Fruit of the womb: artificial reproductive technologies and Jewish law. *Journal of Gender, Race and Justice* 2005 Fall; 9(1): 109-136. NRCBL: 14.4; 14.2; 14.6; 18.5.4; 1.2. SC: le.

Wechter, David; Masek, Lawrence. ANT and the contralife argument [letter and reply]. *National Catholic Bioethics Quarterly* 2006 Winter; 6(4): 617-618. NRCBL: 14.4; 15.4; 4.4; 1.1. Identifiers: altered nuclear transfer.

Whelan, Jo. Sex is for fun: IVF is for children. *New Scientist* 2006 October 21-27; 192(2574): 42-45. NRCBL: 14.4. Identifiers: in vitro fertilization.

White, Caroline. Fertility treatment regulator steps up warning about multiple births [news]. *BMJ: British Medical Journal* 2006 June 10; 332(7554): 1353. NRCBL: 14.4. SC: em; le. Identifiers: United Kingdom (Great Britain).

Zutlevics, Tamara. Should ART be offered to HIV-serodiscordant and HIV-serocordant couples: an ethical discussion? *Human Reproduction* 2006 August; 21(8): 1956-1960. NRCBL: 14.4; 9.5.6; 9.5.5. Identifiers: assisted reproductive technology.

INCOMPETENTS *See* INFORMED CONSENT/ INCOMPETENTS

INDIGENTS *See* CARE FOR SPECIFIC GROUPS/ INDIGENTS

INFANTICIDE *See* EUTHANASIA AND ALLOWING TO DIE/ MINORS

INFANTS *See* CARE FOR SPECIFIC GROUPS/ MINORS; EUTHANASIA AND ALLOWING TO DIE/ MINORS; HUMAN EXPERIMENTATION/ SPECIAL POPULATIONS/ MINORS

INFORMATICS *See* TELEMEDICINE AND INFORMATICS

INFORMED CONSENT

See also HUMAN EXPERIMENTATION/ INFORMED CONSENT; TREATMENT REFUSAL

Ågård, Anders. Informed consent: theory versus practice. *Nature Clinical Practice Cardiovascular Medicine* 2005 June; 2(6): 270-271. NRCBL: 8.3.1.

Ahmed, Shenaz; Green, Josephine; Hewison, Jenny. Antenatal thalassaemia carrier testing: women's perceptions of 'information' and 'consent'. *Journal of Medical Screening* 2005; 12(2): 69-77. NRCBL: 8.3.1; 15.2; 9.5.5. SC: em.

Akkad, Andrea; Jackson, Clare; Kenyon, Sara; Dixon-Woods, Mary; Taub, Nick; Habiba, Marwan. Patients' perceptions of written consent: questionnaire. *BMJ: British Medical Journal* 2006 September 9; 333(7567): 528-529. NRCBL: 8.3.1; 9.1; 9.5.5. SC: em. Identifiers: United Kingdom (Great Britain).

American Academy of Pediatric Dentistry. Council on Clinical Affairs. Guideline on informed consent. *Pediatric Dentistry* 2005-2006; 27(7 Reference Manual): 182-183. NRCBL: 8.3.1; 4.1.1. Identifiers: American Academy of Pediatric Dentistry (AAPD).

Appelbaum, Paul S.; Roth, Loren H.; Lidz, Charles. The therapeutic misconception: informed consent in psychiatric research. *International Journal of Law and Psychiatry* 1982; 5(3-4): 319-329. NRCBL: 8.3.1; 17.1; 18.2; 18.3; 18.5.6.

Arora, Neeraj K.; McHorney, Colleen A. Patient preferences for medical decision making: who really wants to participate? *Medical Care* 2000 March; 38(3): 335-341. NRCBL: 8.3.1; 9.4; 8.1.

Ataç, Adnan; Guven, Tolga; Uçar, Muharrem; Kir, Tayfun. A study of the opinions and behaviors of physicians with regard to informed consent and refusing treatment. *Military Medicine* 2005 July; 170(7): 566-571. NRCBL: 8.3.1; 8.3.4; 8.2. SC: em.

Babic-Bosanac, Sanja; Dzakula, Aleksandar. Patients' rights in the Republic of Croatia. *European Journal of Health Law* 2006 December; 13(4): 399-411. NRCBL: 8.3.1; 8.4; 18.3; 8.5. SC: le.

Baron, Jonathan. Coercion and consent. *In his:* Against Bioethics. Cambridge, MA: MIT Press, 2006: 97-130. NRCBL: 8.3.1; 18.3.

Baum, Neil. A new look at informed consent. *Healthcare Financial Management* 2006 February; 60(2): 106-110, 112. NRCBL: 8.3.1.

Bekker, H.; Thornton, J.; Airey, M., Connelly, J.B.; Hewison, J.; Robinson, M.B.; Lileyman, J.; MacIntosh, M.; Maule, A.J.; Michie, S.; Pearman, A.D. Informed decision-making: an annotated bibliography and systematic review. *Health Technology Assessment* 1999; 3(1): 1-156. NRCBL: 8.3.1; 5.2. SC: rv.

Bernat, James L.; Peterson, Lynn M. Patient-centered informed consent in surgical practice. *Archives of Surgery* 2006 January; 141(1): 86-92. NRCBL: 8.3.1; 8.1; 9.5.1; 8.3.3.

Bhurgri, H.; Qidwai, W. Awareness of the process of informed consent among family practice patients in Karachi. *Journal of the Pakistan Medical Association* 2004 July; 54(7): 398-401. NRCBL: 8.3.1; 21.7. SC: em.

Bobrow, Martin. The Patient's Consent. Helios, Singapore: Bioethics Advisory Committee, 2004 August 4; 8 p. [Online]. Accessed: http://www.bioethics-singapore.org/ resources/pdf/Patient%27s%20Consent_MB%20 040804.pdf [2006 March 2]. NRCBL: 8.3.1; 18.5; 18.1.

Brady Wagner, Lynne C. Clinical ethics in the context of language and cognitive impairment: rights and protections. *Seminars in Speech and Language* 2003 November; 24(4): 275- 284. NRCBL: 8.3.1; 4.3; 9.5.1; 1.1; 20.5.4. SC: cs.

Breier-Mackie, Sarah. Ethics and endoscopy. *Gastroenterology Nursing* 2005 November-December; 28(6): 514-515. NRCBL: 8.3.1.

British Committee for Standards in Haematology; Treleaven, J.; Cullis, J.O.; Maynard, R.; Bishop, E.; Ainsworth-Smith, I.; Roques, A.; Webb, A.; Favre, J.; Milligan, D. Obtaining consent for chemotherapy. *British Journal of Haematology* 2006 March; 132(5): 552-559. NRCBL: 8.3.1; 9.5.1.

Brown, Jeremy. The spectrum of informed consent in emergency psychiatric research. *Annals of Emergency Medicine* 2006 January; 47(1): 68-74. NRCBL: 8.3.1; 8.3.3; 17.1; 18.5.6; 18.6.

Bunch, Wilton H. Informed consent. *Clinical Orthopaedics and Related Research* 2000 September; (378): 71-77. NRCBL: 8.3.1.

NRCBL: National Reference Center for Bioethics Literature Classification Scheme   See inside front cover for terms.

351

Bunch, Wilton H.; Dvonch, Victoria M. Informed consent in sports medicine. *Clinics in Sports Medicine* 2004 April; 23(2): 183-193. NRCBL: 8.3.1; 1.1; 8.1.

Burkell, Jacquelyn; Campbell, D. Grant. "What does this mean?" How Web-based consumer health information fails to support information seeking in the pursuit of informed consent for screening test decisions. *Journal of the Medical Library Association* 2005 July; 93(3): 363-373. NRCBL: 8.3.1; 9.1; 15.2; 5.2.

Burns, Paul; Keogh, Ivan; Timon, Conrad. Informed consent: a patients' perspective. *Journal of Laryngology and Otology* 2005 January; 119(1): 19-22. NRCBL: 8.3.1; 8.1; 8.3.2. SC: em. Identifiers: Ireland.

Callens, S. Informed consent. *Acta Chirurgica Belgica* 2000 August; 100(4): 169-174. NRCBL: 8.3.1; 8.5. SC: le. Identifiers: Belgium.

Campbell, Bruce. Informed consent: special section [editorial]. *Annals of the Royal College of Surgeons of England* 2004 November; 86(6): 457-458. NRCBL: 8.3.1.

Caspi, Opher; Holexa, Joshua. Lack of standards in informed consent in complementary and alternative medicine. *Complementary Therapies in Medicine* 2005 June; 13(2): 123-130. NRCBL: 8.3.1; 4.1.1. SC: em.

Casteel, J. Keenan. The ethics of informed consent among storyteller cultures. *International Journal of Circumpolar Health* 1998; 57(Supplement 1): 41-42. NRCBL: 8.3.1; 21.7.

Chervenak, Frank A.; McCullough, Laurence B. Ethical and legal aspects. *In:* Kurjak, A., ed. Ultrasound and the Ovary: Progress in Obstetric and Gynecological Sonography Series, volume 1. New York: Parthenon Publishing Group, 1994: 255-261. NRCBL: 8.3.1; 1.1. SC: le. Identifiers: ovarian cancer.

Chervenak, Frank A.; McCullough, Laurence B.; Chasen, Stephen T. Clinical implications of the ethics of informed consent for first-trimester risk assessment for trisomy 21. *Seminars in Perinatology* 2005 August; 29(4): 277-279. NRCBL: 8.3.1; 9.5.5; 15.2.

Cheung, D.; Sandramouli, S. The consent and counselling of patients for cataract surgery: a prospective audit. *Eye* 2005 September; 19(9): 963-971. NRCBL: 8.3.1. SC: em.

Corbeel, L. Informed consent: ethical point of view. *Acta Chirurgica Belgica* 2000 August; 100(4): 156-159. NRCBL: 8.3.1; 6; 18.2. Identifiers: National Council of Europe; Declaration of Lisbon, 1981; Declaration of Amsterdam, 1994.

Coulson, Karen M.; Glasser, Brandy L.; Liang, Bryan A. Informed consent: issues for providers. *Hematology/Oncology Clinics of North America* 2002 December; 16(6): 1365-1380. NRCBL: 8.3.1. SC: le.

Cundy, Paul R.; Hassey, Alan. To opt in or out of electronic patient records?: Isle of Wight and Scottish projects are not opt out schemes [letter]. *BMJ: British Medical Journal* 2006 July 15; 333(7559): 146. NRCBL: 8.3.1; 1.3.12; 8.4. Identifiers: United Kingdom (Great Britain).

Dawes, P.J.D.; O'Keefe, L.; Adcock, S. Informed consent: the assessment of two structured interview approaches compared to the current approach. *Journal of Laryngology and Otology* 1992 May; 106(5): 420-424. NRCBL: 8.3.1; 9.5.1. SC: em.

de Mol, B.A.J.M. New surgical techniques and informed consent — safety first. *Acta Chirurgica Belgica* 2000 August; 100(4): 177-182. NRCBL: 8.3.1; 5.2; 9.8.

Degen, Peter A. Reflections of a Protestant Christian on the history of informed consent in Germany. *In:* Döring, Ole; Chen, Renbiao, eds. Advances in Chinese Medical Ethics: Chinese and International Perspectives. Hamburg: Institut für Asienkunde; 2002: 73-84. NRCBL: 8.3.1; 18.3. Note: Proceedings of the Second Sino-German Interdisciplinary Symposium about Medical Ethics in China, Shanghai, 19-23 October, 1999.

del Carmen, Marcella G.; Joffe, Steven. Informed consent for medical treatment and research: a review. *Oncologist* 2005 September; 10(8): 636-641. NRCBL: 8.3.1; 18.3. SC: rv.

Denton, Jane; Traub, Tony. A summary of the workshop: handling ART consent. *Human Fertility (Cambridge)* 2005 September; 8(3): 167-168. NRCBL: 8.3.1; 14.6; 14.4. Identifiers: United Kingdom (Great Britain).

Dimond, Bridgit. Colostomy: getting patient consent to treatment for surgery. *British Journal of Nursing* 2006 March 23-April 12; 15(6): 334-335. NRCBL: 8.3.1. SC: cs. Identifiers: United Kingdom (Great Britain).

Dimond, Bridgit. Consent to use complementary therapies on critical care wards. *British Journal of Nursing* 2006 September 14-27; 15(16): 893-894. NRCBL: 8.3.1; 4.1.1.

Dolgin, Janet L. The evolution of the "patient": shifts in attitudes about consent, genetic information, and commercialization in health care. *Hofstra Law Review* 2005 Fall; 34(1): 137-183. NRCBL: 8.3.1; 1.1; 14.1; 15.1. SC: an; le.

Druart, M.L.; Squifflet, J.-P. Informed consent: principles and recent developments. *Acta Chirurgica Belgica* 2000 August; 100(4): 175-176. NRCBL: 8.3.1. SC: le. Identifiers: Belgium.

Dunn, Laura B.; Nowrangi, Milap A.; Palmer, Barton W.; Jeste, Dilip V.; Saks, Elyn R. Assessing decisional capacity for clinical research or treatment: a review of instructions. *American Journal of Psychiatry* 2006 August; 163(8): 1323-1334. NRCBL: 8.3.1; 18.3; 4.3. SC: em.

Edwards, T.J.; Finlay, I.; Wilkins, D.C.; Lambert, A.W. Improving risk disclosure during the consent process. *Annals of the Royal College of Surgeons of England* 2004 November; 86(6): 458-462. NRCBL: 8.3.1.

Ek, Eugene T.; Yu, Emma P.; Chan, Jason T.; Love, Bruce R. Nerve injuries in orthopaedics: is there anything more we need to tell our patients? *ANZ Journal of Surgery* 2005 March; 75(3): 132-135. NRCBL: 8.3.1; 8.2. SC: em. Identifiers: Australia.

El-Wakeel, H.; Taylor, G.J.; Tate, J.J.T. What do patients really want to know in an informed consent procedure? A questionnaire-based survey of patients in the Bath area, UK. *Journal of Medical Ethics* 2006 October; 32(10): 612-616. NRCBL: 8.3.1. SC: em. Identifiers: United Kingdom (Great Britain).

Epstein, M. Why effective consent presupposes autonomous authorisation: a counter orthodox argument. *Journal of Medical Ethics* 2006 June; 32(6): 342-345. NRCBL: 8.3.1. SC: an.

Fallberg, Lars. Consequences of the Amsterdam Declaration—a rights revolution in Europe? [editorial]. *European Journal of Health Law* 2003 March; 10(1): 5-10. NRCBL: 8.3.1; 2.2; 21.1. SC: le.

Fine, Adrian; Fontaine, Bunny; Kraushar, Maryann M.; Rich, Beverly R. Nephrologists should voluntarily divulge survival data to potential dialysis patients: a questionnaire study. *Peritoneal Dialysis International* 2005 May-June; 25(3): 269-273. NRCBL: 8.3.1; 19.3; 8.2. SC: em.

Foley, Michael. To opt in or out of electronic patient records?: electronic patient record is incompatible with confidentiality [letter]. *BMJ: British Medical Journal* 2006 July 15; 333(7559): 146-147. NRCBL: 8.3.1; 1.3.12; 8.4. Identifiers: United Kingdom (Great Britain).

Follette, William C.; Davis, Deborah; Kemmelmeier, Markus. Ideals and realities in the development and practice of informed consent. *In:* O'Donohue, William; Ferguson, Kyle, eds. Handbook of Professional Ethics for Psychologists: Issues, Questions, and Controversies. Thousand Oaks, Calif.: SAGE Publications; 2003: 195-226. NRCBL: 8.3.1; 17.1.

Ford, Helen L. The effect of consent guidelines on a multiple sclerosis register. *Multiple Sclerosis* 2006 February; 12(1): 104-107. NRCBL: 8.3.1; 8.3.4; 7.1; 9.5.1. SC: em. Identifiers: United Kingdom (Great Britain).

Franklin, Deborah. "Come again?" Good medicine requires clarity. *New York Times* 2006 January 24; p. F5. NRCBL: 8.3.1. SC: po.

Geppert, Cynthia M.A.; Dettmer, Elizabeth; Jakiche, Antonie. Ethical challenges in the care of persons with hepatitis C infection: a pilot study to enhance informed consent with veterans. *Psychosomatics* 2005 Septem-

ber-October; 46(5): 392-401. NRCBL: 8.3.1; 17.1; 9.5.1. SC: em.

Gert, Bernard; Culver, Charles M.; Clouser, K. Danner. Adequate information, competence, and coercion. *In their:* Bioethics: A Systematic Approach. Second edition. New York: Oxford University Press; 2006: 213-236. NRCBL: 8.3.1; 8.3.4. SC: an.

Ghulam, Amina T.; Kessler, Margrit; Bachmann, Lucas M.; Haller, Urs; Kessler, Thomas M. Patients' satisfaction with the preoperative informed consent procedure: a multicenter questionnaire survey in Switzerland. *Mayo Clinic Proceedings* 2006 March; 81(3): 307-312. NRCBL: 8.3.1; 9.5.5. SC: em.

Haller, Dagmar M.; Sanci, Lena A.; Patton, George C.; Sawyer, Susan M. Practical evidence in favour of mature-minor consent in primary care research [letter]. *Medical Journal of Australia* 2005 October 17; 183(8): 439. NRCBL: 8.3.1; 9.5.7; 18.3; 18.5.2.

Haroun, Ansar M. Ethical discussion of informed consent. *Journal of Clinical Psychopharmacology* 2005 October; 25(5): 405-406. NRCBL: 8.3.1; 17.4.

Hattori, Kenji. East Asian family and biomedical ethics. *In:* Sang-yong, Song; Young-Mo, Koo; Macer, Darryl R.J., eds. Asian Bioethics in the 21st Century. Christchurch, NZ: Eubios Ethics Institute, 2002: 229-231. NRCBL: 8.3.1; 8.1; 20.5.1; 21.7. Conference: Proceedings of the Asian Bioethics Conference (ABC4), held 22-25 November 2002 in Seoul, South Korea.

Hedgecoe, Adam. 'At the point at which you can do something about it, then it becomes more relevant': informed consent in the pharmacogenetic clinic. *Social Science and Medicine* 2005 September; 61(6): 1201-1210. NRCBL: 8.3.1; 15.1; 9.7. SC: em. Identifiers: United Kingdom (Great Britain).

Heilig, Lauren F.; D'Ambrosia, Renee; Drake, Amanda L.; Dellavalle, Robert P.; Hester, Eric J. A case for informed consent? Indoor UV tanning facility operator's provision of health risks information (United States). *Cancer Causes and Control* 2005 June; 16(5): 557-560. NRCBL: 8.3.1; 5.3. SC: em.

Hindley, Carol; Thomson, Ann M. The rhetoric of informed choice: perspectives from midwives on intrapartum fetal heart rate monitoring. *Health Expectations* 2005 December; 8(4): 306-314. NRCBL: 8.3.1; 9.5.5; 9.5.8; 4.1.3; 8.1. SC: em.

Ho, Anita. Family and informed consent in multicultural setting. *American Journal of Bioethics* 2006 January-February; 6(1): 26-28; discussion W27-W28. NRCBL: 8.3.1; 8.2; 21.1; 9.5.2; 8.1. Comments: Akira Akabayashi and Brian Taylor Slingsby. Informed consent revisited: Japan and the U.S. American Journal of Bioethics 2006 January-February; 6(1): 9-14.

NRCBL: National Reference Center for Bioethics Literature Classification Scheme   See inside front cover for terms.

353

Hoffmann, Diane. Choosing paternalism? *Medical Ethics Newsletter* 2006 Spring; 13(2): 4, 12. NRCBL: 8.3.1; 8.3.3; 1.1. SC: le.

Howsepian, A.A. Must physicians always act in their patient's best interests? *Ethics and Medicine* 2006 Fall; 22(3): 151-161. NRCBL: 8.3.1; 1.1; 4.1.2. SC: an. Identifiers: virtue ethics; Robert Veatch.

Human Fertilisation and Embryology Authority [HFEA] (Great Britain). Consent to the use and storage of gametes and embryos. London: Human Fertilisation and Embryology Authority, 1996 May; 6 p. NRCBL: 8.3.1; 14.6.

Hurst, Irene. The legal landscape at the threshold of viability for extremely premature infants: a nursing perspective, Part II. *Journal of Perinatal and Neonatal Nursing* 2005 July-September; 19(3): 253-262. NRCBL: 8.3.1; 8.1; 4.1.2; 8.3.2.

Ivarsson, Bodil; Larsson, Sylvia; Luhrs, Carsten; Sjoberg, Trygve. Extended written pre-operative information about possible complications at cardiac surgery — do the patients want to know? *European Journal of Cardio-thoracic Surgery* 2005 September; 28(3): 407-414. NRCBL: 8.3.1. SC: em.

Jacob, R.; Clare, I.C.; Holland, A.; Watson, P.C.; Maimaris, C.; Gunn, M. Self-harm, capacity, and refusal of treatment: implications for emergency medical practice. A prospective observational study. *Emergency Medicine Journal* 2005 November; 22(11): 799-802. NRCBL: 8.3.1; 8.3.4; 9.5.1; 8.1. SC: em.

Jafarey, Aamir. Informed consent: views from Karachi. *Eastern Mediterranean Health Journal/La Revue de Santé de la Méditerranée orientale* 2006; 12(Supplement 1): S50-S55 [Online]. Accessed: http://www.emro.who.int/ Publications/EMHJ/12_S/PDF/8.pdf [2007 January 3]. NRCBL: 8.3.1; 18.3; 18.5.3; 21.7; 18.5.9. Note: Abstract in French and Arabic.

Janssen, A.J.G.M. Informing patients about small risks: a comparative approach. *European Journal of Health Law* 2006 June; 13(2): 159-172. NRCBL: 8.3.1; 2.1; 21.1. SC: le. Identifiers: Netherlands; Germany; United Kingdom (Great Britain).

Johnston, Carolyn; Holt, Genevieve. The legal and ethical implications of therapeutic privilege — is it ever justified to withhold treatment information from a competent patient? *Clinical Ethics* 2006 September; 1(3): 146-151. NRCBL: 8.3.1; 8.2; 2.1. SC: le.

Jones, James W.; McCullough, Laurence B.; Richman, Bruce W. Ethics of surgical innovation to treat rare diseases. *Journal of Vascular Surgery* 2004 April; 39(4): 918-919. NRCBL: 8.3.1.

Jones, Paul M.; Appelbaum, Paul S.; Siegel, David M. Law enforcement interviews of hospital patients: a conundrum for clinicians. *JAMA: The Journal of the American Medical Association* 2006 February 15; 295(7): 822-825. NRCBL: 8.3.1; 1.3.5; 8.4. SC: le. Identifiers: Massachusetts Work Group on Law Enforcement Access to Hospital Patients.

Jones, Sian; Davies, Kevin; Jones, Bridie. The adult patient, informed consent and the emergency care setting. *Accident and Emergency Nursing* 2005 July; 13(3): 167-170. NRCBL: 8.3.1; 9.5.1. SC: le.

Kashani, S.; Kinnear, P.; Porter, B. Consent for anaesthesia in cataract surgery [letter]. *Journal of Medical Ethics* 2006 September; 32(9): 555. NRCBL: 8.3.1. Identifiers: United Kingdom (Great Britain).

Kennedy, Ian; Grubb, Andrew. Consent. *In their:* Medical Law. 3rd ed. London: Butterworths; 2005: 575-773. NRCBL: 8.3.1. SC: le.

Khot, U.P.; Vellacott, K.D.; Swarnkar, K.J. Islamic practices: informed consent for stoma [letter]. *Colorectal Disease* 2005 September; 7(5): 529-530. NRCBL: 8.3.1; 1.2; 9.5.1.

King, Jaime Staples; Moulton, Benjamin W. Rethinking informed consent: the case for shared medical decision-making. *American Journal of Law and Medicine* 2006; 32(4): 429-501. NRCBL: 8.3.1; 8.1; 8.5. SC: le; rv.

Kitamura, Toshinori. Stress-reductive effects of information disclosure to medical and psychiatric patients. *Psychiatry and Clinical Neurosciences* 2005 December; 59(6): 627-633. NRCBL: 8.3.1; 8.2.

Klove, Carole A.; DiBoise, Sarah J.; Pang, Betty; Yarbrough, William C. Informed consent: ethical and legal aspects. *Thoracic Surgery Clinics* 2005 May; 15(2): 213-219. NRCBL: 8.3.1; 8.5. SC: le.

Kluge, Eike-Henner W. Competence, capacity, and informed consent: beyond the cognitive-competence model. *Canadian Journal of Aging* 2005 Fall; 24(3): 295-304. NRCBL: 8.3.1; 8.3.3.

Koch, Douglas D. Refractive lens exchange: ethical considerations in the informed consent process. *Journal of Cataract and Refractive Surgery* 2005 May; 31(5): 863. NRCBL: 8.3.1; 9.5.1.

LaFleur, William R. More information, broader dissent on informed consent. *American Journal of Bioethics* 2006 January-February; 6(1): 15-16. NRCBL: 8.3.1; 9.1; 8.2; 8.1. Identifiers: Japan. Comments: Akira Akabayashi and Brian Taylor Slingsby. Informed consent revisited: Japan and the U.S. American Journal of Bioethics 2006 January-February; 6(1): 9-14.

Lagay, Faith. Physicians' responsibility in the face of patients' irrational decisions. *Virtual Mentor* 2001 September; 3(9): 2p. NRCBL: 8.3.1.

Lal, Seema. Consent in dentistry. *Pacific Health Dialog* 2003 March; 10(1): 102-105. NRCBL: 8.3.1; 8.3.2; 4.1.1.

Langdon, I.J.; Hardin, R.; Learmonth, I.D. Informed consent for total hip arthroplasty: does a written information sheet improve recall by patients? *Annals of the Royal College of Surgeons of England* 2002 November; 84(6): 404-408. NRCBL: 8.3.1; 18.5.1. SC: em.

Leigh, B. Consent — an event or a memory?: A judicial view. *Journal of Bone and Joint Surgery (British volume)* 2006 January; 88(1): 16-18. NRCBL: 8.3.1. SC: le. Identifiers: Sidaway v. the Bethlem and Maudsley Hospitals; Chester v. Afshar; United Kingdom(Great Britain).

Lemaire, R. Informed consent — a contemporary myth? *Journal of Bone and Joint Surgery (British volume)* 2006 January; 88(1): 2-7. NRCBL: 8.3.1.

Lewin, Matthew R.; Montauk, Lance; Shalit, Marc; Nobay, Flavia. An unusual case of subterfuge in the emergency department: covert administration of antipsychotic and anxiolytic medications to control an agitated patient. *Annals of Emergency Medicine* 2006 January; 47(1): 75-78. NRCBL: 8.3.1; 9.7; 7.1.

Maclean, Alisdair. Autonomy, consent and persuasion. *European Journal of Health Law* 2006 December; 13(4): 321-338. NRCBL: 8.3.1; 1.1. SC: le.

Malek, Janet. Informed consent. *In:* Mitcham, Carl, ed. Encyclopedia of Science, Technology, and Ethics. Farmington Hills, MI: Thomson/Gale, 2005: 1016-1019. NRCBL: 8.3.1; 2.2; 18.3.

Marshall, Tom. Informed consent for mammography screening: modelling the risks and benefits for American women. *Health Expectations* 2005 December; 8(4): 295-305. NRCBL: 8.3.1; 9.5.5. SC: em.

Marteau, Theresa M.; Dormandy, Elizabeth; Michie, Susan. A measure of informed choice. *Health Expectations* 2001 June; 4(2): 99-108. NRCBL: 8.3.1; 15.2; 15.3; 7.1; 9.5.3. SC: em. Identifiers: United Kingdom(Great Britain).

Matta, A.M. Informed consent in medical treatment: conflict or consensus. *Medicine and Law: The World Association for Medical Law* 2006 June; 25(2): 319-339. NRCBL: 8.3.1; 21.1; 2.2; 8.3.4. SC: le.
  Abstract: The author reviews the legal theory and practice of the requirements for informed consent. He uses a discussion of relevant cases and judgements from courts in the UK, USA, Australia and Malaysia to illustrate apparently conflicting attitudes exemplified by these cases. From this he aims to form some consensus in their application to everyday practice.

Mavis, Brian E.; Henry, Rebecca C. Being uninformed on informed consent: a pilot survey of medical education

faculty. *BMC Medical Education* 2005 April 25; 5(1): 12; 7 p. NRCBL: 8.3.1; 7.2. SC: em.

Mazur, Dennis J.; Hickam, David H. Patients' preferences for risk disclosure and role in decision making for invasive medical procedures. *Journal of General Internal Medicine* 1997 February; 12(2): 114-117. NRCBL: 8.3.1. SC: em.

McQuillen, Michael P.; Tariot, Pierre. Who can say yes (or no) to a physician—and how does the physician know they can? [editorial]. *Neurology* 2005 May 10; 64(9): 1494-1495. NRCBL: 8.3.1; 8.3.3.

Meisel, Alan. Response: from tragedy to catastrophe: lawyers and the bureaucratization of informed consent. *Yale Journal of Health Policy, Law and Ethics* 2006 Summer; 6(2): 479-483. NRCBL: 8.3.1; 7.1. Conference: Symposium: A World Less Silent: Celebrating Jay Katz's Contribution to Law, Medicine, and Ethics. Comments: Ellen Wright Clayton. The web of relations: thinking about physicians and patients. Yale Journal of Health Policy, Law and Ethics 2006 Summer; 6(2): 465-477.

Mezza, E.; Consiglio, V.; Soragna, G.; Putaggio, S.; Burdese, M.; Perrotta, L.; Jeantet, A.; Segoloni, G.P.; Piccoli, G.B. CKD patients and erythropoietin: do we need evidence-based informed consent? *International Journal of Artificial Organs* 2005 June; 28(6): 591-599. NRCBL: 8.3.1; 9.5.1. SC: em. Identifiers: Italy; chronic kidney disease.

Michel, Donna M.; Moss, Alvin H. Communicating prognosis in the dialysis consent process: a patient-centered, guideline-supported approach. *Advances in Chronic Kidney Disease* 2005 April; 12(2): 196-201. NRCBL: 8.3.1; 8.1; 19.3.

Miller, Robert D. Decision-making concerning individuals. *In his:* Problems in Health Care Law. Ninth edition. Sudbury, MA: Jones and Bartlett Publishers; 2006: 315-425. NRCBL: 8.3.1; 8.3.2; 8.3.3; 8.3.4; 20.5.4.

Miola, José. The need for informed consent: lessons from the ancient Greeks. *CQ: Cambridge Quarterly of Healthcare Ethics* 2006 Spring; 15(2): 152-160. NRCBL: 8.3.1; 2.2; 1.1; 7.1; 4.4.

Moreno, Jonathan D.; Zuckerman, Connie; London, Alex John. Ethical considerations in the care of patients with neurosurgical disease. *In:* Cottrell, J. and Smith, D., eds. Anesthesia and Neurosurgery, fourth edition. St. Louis: Mosby; 2001: 749-763. NRCBL: 8.3.1; 8.3.3; 9.5.1; 8.1; 20.5.4; 20.5.1; 2.2.

Morris, Grant H. Informed consent in psychopharmacology: legal discussion of informed consent [editorial]. *Journal of Clinical Psychopharmacology* 2005 October; 25(5): 403-404. NRCBL: 8.3.1; 8.3.3; 17.4; 8.3.4. SC: le.

NRCBL: National Reference Center for Bioethics Literature Classification Scheme   See inside front cover for terms.

355

Mulley, Albert G., Jr. Developing skills for evidence-based surgery: ensuring that patients make informed decisions. *Surgical Clinics of North America* 2006 February; 86(1): 181-192, xi. NRCBL: 8.3.1; 9.4; 9.5.1; 9.8; 8.1.

Muylaert, P. The patient's informed consent. Recent evolution of the Case Law. The physician's point of view. *Acta Chirurgica Belgica* 2000 August; 100(4): 151-155. NRCBL: 8.3.1. SC: le. Identifiers: Belgium.

Naimark, David. Clinical discussion of informed consent [editorial]. *Journal of Clinical Psychopharmacology* 2005 October; 25(5): 404-405. NRCBL: 8.3.1; 17.1.

Nelson, John C.; Schwartzberg, Joanne G.; Vergara, Katherine C. The public's and the patient's right to know: AMA commentary on "Public health literacy in America: an ethical imperative". *American Journal of Preventive Medicine* 2005 April; 28(3): 325-326. NRCBL: 8.3.1; 9.1. Identifiers: American Medical Association.

Norheim, Ole Frithjof. Soft paternalism and the ethics of shared electronic patient records [editorial]. *BMJ: British Medical Journal* 2006 July 1; 333(7557): 2-3. NRCBL: 8.3.1; 1.3.12. Identifiers: United Kingdom (Great Britain).

Northoff, Georg. Neuroscience of decision making and informed consent: an investigation in neuroethics. *Journal of Medical Ethics* 2006 February; 32(2): 70-73. NRCBL: 8.3.1; 17.1.

Abstract: Progress in neuroscience will allow us to reveal the neuronal correlates of psychological processes involved in ethically relevant notions such as informed consent. Informed consent involves decision making, the psychological and neural processes of which have been investigated extensively in neuroscience. The neuroscience of decision making may be able to contribute to an ethics of informed consent by providing empirical and thus descriptive criteria. Since, however, descriptive criteria must be distinguished from normative criteria, the neuroscience of decision making cannot replace the ethics of informed consent. Instead, the neuroscience of decision making could complement the current ethics, resulting in what can be called neuroethics of informed consent. It is concluded that current progress in the neurosciences could complement and change the way in which we approach ethical problems in neuropsychiatry.

O'Neill, Onora. Accountability, trust and informed consent in medical practice and research. *Clinical Medicine* 2004 May-June; 4(3): 269-276. NRCBL: 8.3.1; 9.1; 9.8. Identifiers: United Kingdom (Great Britain).

O'Rourke, Joanne Mcfarland; Roehrig, Stephen; Heeringa, Steven G.; Reed, Beth Glover; Birdsall, William C.; Overcashier, Margaret; Zidar, Kelly. Solving problems of disclosure risk while retaining key analytical uses of publicly released microdata. *Journal of Empirical Research on Human Research Ethics* 2006 September; 1(3): 63-84. NRCBL: 8.3.1; 1.3.12; 8.4; 9.5.9.

Olbourne, Norman A. The influence of Rogers v. Whitaker on the practice of cosmetic plastic surgery. *Journal of Law and Medicine* 1998 May; 5(4): 334-347. NRCBL: 8.3.1; 9.5.1. SC: le.

Orr, Daniel L., II; Curtis, William J. Obtaining written informed consent for the administration of local anesthetic in dentistry. *JADA: Journal of the American Dental Association* 2005 November; 136(11): 1568-1571. NRCBL: 8.3.1; 4.1.1; 8.5. SC: le; em.

Orrell, Jon M. To opt in or out of electronic patient records?: integration technology is key to success [letter]. *BMJ: British Medical Journal* 2006 July 15; 333(7559): 146. NRCBL: 8.3.1; 1.3.12; 8.4. Identifiers: United Kingdom (Great Britain).

Panting, Gerard. The theory of consent. *East African Medical Journal* 2005 July; 82(7 Supplement): S131-S132. NRCBL: 8.3.1. SC: le.

Paradis, Carmen. Informing consent: analogies to history-taking. *American Journal of Bioethics* 2006 January-February; 6(1): 24-26; discussion W27-W28. NRCBL: 8.3.1; 8.2; 8.1. Comments: Akira Akabayashi and Brian Taylor Slingsby. Informed consent revisited: Japan and the U.S. American Journal of Bioethics 2006 January-February; 6(1): 9-14.

Parmar, Vinay N.; Mayberry, John F. An audit of informed consent in gastroscopy: investigation of a hospital's informed consent procedure in endoscopy by assessing current practice. *European Journal of Gastroenterology and Hepatology* 2005 July; 17(7): 721-724. NRCBL: 8.3.1. SC: em. Identifiers: United Kingdom (Great Britain).

Pearson, Yvette E. Reconfiguring informed consent (with a little help from the capability approach). *American Journal of Bioethics* 2006 January-February; 6(1): 22-24; discussion W27-W28. NRCBL: 8.3.1; 8.2; 1.1; 8.1. Comments: Akira Akabayashi and Brian Taylor Slingsby. Informed consent revisited: Japan and the U.S. American Journal of Bioethics 2006 January-February; 6(1): 9-14.

Proot, L; Vanderheyden, L. Informed consent [editorial]. *Acta Chirurgica Belgica* 2000 August; 100(4): 149-150. NRCBL: 8.3.1.

Richardson-Tench, Marilyn; Brookes, Alison; Hardley, Andrew. Nursing ethics in practice: issues for perioperative nursing. *Journal of Perioperative Practice* 2006 March; 16(3): 138, 140-143. NRCBL: 8.3.1; 4.1.3; 8.1.

Robertson, Gerald B. Informed consent in Canada: an empirical study. *Osgoode Hall Law Review* 1984 Spring; 22(1): 139-161. NRCBL: 8.3.1.

Rodgers, Willard; Nolte, Michael. Solving problems of disclosure risk in an academic setting: using a combination of restricted data and restricted access methods. *Journal of*

Empirical Research on Human Research Ethics 2006 September; 1(3): 85-97. NRCBL: 8.3.1; 1.3.12; 8.4; 9.5.2.

Rothschild, Barbra Bluestone; Estroff, Sue E.; Churchill, Larry R. The cultural calculus of consent. *Clinical Obstetrics and Gynecology* 2005 September; 48(3): 574-594. NRCBL: 8.3.1; 8.3.2; 4.2; 7.1.

Royal College of Physicians of London; Royal College of Pathologists [RCPath]; British Society for Human Genetics [BSHG]; Farndon, Peter; Douglas, Fiona. Consent and confidentiality in genetic practice: guidance on genetic testing and sharing genetic information. A report of the Joint Committee on Medical Genetics. London: Royal College of Physicians [RCP]; Royal College of Pathologists [RCPath]; British Society of Human Genetics [BSHG], 2006 April; 30 p. NRCBL: 15.3; 8.3.1; 8.3.2; 8.3.3; 8.4; 15.1. Note: This report on Consent and Confidentiality in Genetic Practice was prepared, compiled and edited by Peter Farndon and Fiona Douglas. The report appendices contain sample forms for consent to genetic testing and sharing of information and for photographic record.

Rudge, David. Do unknown risks preclude informed consent? *Essays in Philosophy* 2003 June; 4(2): 10 p. [Online]. Accessed: http://www.humboldt.edu/~essays/rudge.html [2004 December 24]. NRCBL: 8.3.1; 18.3.

Sabin, James; Fanelli, Robert; Flaherty, Helen; Istfan, Nawfal; Mariner, Wendy; Barnes, Janet Nally; Pratt, Janey S.A.; Rossi, Laura; Samour, Patricia. Best practice guidelines on informed consent for weight loss surgery patients. *Obesity Research* 2005 February; 13(2): 250-253. NRCBL: 8.3.1; 4.5; 9.5.1. SC: em.

Samuels, Alec. The duty to warn the patient. *British Journal of Neurosurgery* 2005 April; 19(2): 117-119. NRCBL: 8.3.1; 8.5. SC: le.

Saw, K. Chee; Wood, Alison M.; Murphy, Karen; Parry, John R.W.; Hartfall, W. Guy. Informed consent: an evaluation of patients' understanding and opinion (with respect to the operation of transurethral resection of prostate). *Journal of the Royal Society of Medicine* 1994 March; 87(3): 143-144. NRCBL: 8.3.1; 9.5.1.

Schäfer, Christof; Herbst, Manfred. Ethical aspects of patient information in radiation oncology: an introduction and a review of the literature. *Strahlentherapie und Onkologie* 2003 July; 179(7): 431-440. NRCBL: 8.3.1; 9.5.1. SC: rv. Note: Abstract available in English and German.

Schildmann, Jan; Cushing, Annie; Doyal, Len; Vollmann, Jochen. Informed consent in clinical practice: pre-registration house officers' knowledge, difficulties and the need for postgraduate training. *Medical Teacher* 2005 November; 27(7): 649-651. NRCBL: 8.3.1; 7.2. SC: em.

Schmitz, Dagmar; Reinacher, Peter. C. Informed consent in neurology — translating ethical theory into action. *Journal of Medical Ethics* 2006 September; 32(9): 497-498. NRCBL: 8.3.1.

Abstract: Although a main principle of medical ethics and law since the 1970s, standards of informed consent are regarded with great scepticism by many clinicians. METHODS: By reviewing the reactions to and adoption of this principle of medical ethics in neurosurgery, the characteristic conflicts that emerge between theory and everyday clinical experience are emphasised and a modified conception of informed consent is proposed. RESULTS: The adoption and debate of informed consent in neurosurgery took place in two steps. Firstly, respect for patient autonomy was included into the ethical codes of the professional organisations. Secondly, the legal demands of the principle were questioned by clinicians. Informed consent is mainly interpreted in terms of freedom from interference and absolute autonomy. It lacks a constructive notion of physician-patient interaction in its effort to promote the best interest of the patient, which, however, potentially emerges from are consideration of the principle of beneficence. CONCLUSION: To avoid insufficient legal interpretations, informed consent should be understood in terms of autonomy and beneficence. A continuous interaction between the patient and the given physician is considered as an essential prerequisite for the realisation of the standards of informed consent.

Schniederjan, Stephanie; Donovan, G. Kevin. Ethics versus education: pelvic exams on anesthetized women. *Journal of the Oklahoma State Medical Association* 2005 August; 98(8): 386-388. NRCBL: 8.3.1; 9.5.5; 7.2.

Schwab, A.P. Formal and effective autonomy in healthcare. *Journal of Medical Ethics* 2006 October; 32(10): 575-579. NRCBL: 8.3.1; 1.1.

Sillender, M. Can patients be sure they are fully informed when representatives of surgical equipment manufacturers attend their operations? *Journal of Medical Ethics* 2006 July; 32(7): 395-397. NRCBL: 8.3.1; 9.3.1; 9.7; 7.3. SC: em.

Abstract: OBJECTIVE: To determine the practice in UK hospitals regarding the level of patient involvement and consent when representatives of commercial surgical device manufacturers attend and advise during operations. METHODS: An anonymous postal questionnaire was sent to the senior nurse in charge in all 236 UK gynaecology theatres in 2004. 79/236 (33%) replies were received. RESULTS: Operating departments were visited every 2 weeks on average by a representative of the surgical device manufacturer. Actual operations were attended every 10 weeks, although there was much variation. 33/79 (42%) units consistently obtained patient consent for visits, usually orally, whereas 40/79 (51%) units did not. 65/79 (82%) units had no guidelines for surgical device representative visits. 91% of nurses in charge believed that there should be guidelines to protect both patients and staff. 6/79 (8%) units were preparing local guidelines at the time of the survey. CONCLUSIONS: Currently, patient safety, confidentiality and autonomy are being protected by a minority of NHS operating theatres when surgical device representatives attend surgery. National guidelines would hopefully ensure that fully informed patient consent is obtained and that representatives are fully trained and supervised.

Singh, Sameer; Mayahi, Rez. Consent in orthopaedic surgery. *Annals of the Royal College of Surgeons of Eng-*

NRCBL: National Reference Center for Bioethics Literature Classification Scheme   See inside front cover for terms.

357

land 2004 September; 86(5): 339-341. NRCBL: 8.3.1; 9.5.1.

Skjennald, Arnulf. How much should we inform our patients? [editorial]. *Acta Radiologica* 2005 November; 46(7): 662. NRCBL: 8.3.1; 8.1; 7.1.

Slovenko, Ralph. Informed consent. *In his:* Psychiatry in Law/Law in Psychiatry. Volume 2. New York: Brunner-Routledge; 2002: 711-738. NRCBL: 8.3.1; 17.1. SC: le.

Sones, Ben. A tale of two countries: parallel visions for informed consent in the United States and the United Kingdom. *Vanderbilt Journal of Transnational Law* 2006 January; 39(1): 253-290. NRCBL: 8.3.1; 9.3.1; 1.1; 21.1. SC: le.

Stuart, Kate. Informed consent and the advanced nurse practitioner. *In:* Bartter, Karen, ed. Ethical Issues in Advanced Nursing Practice. Boston: Butterworth-Heinemann; 2001: 80-100. NRCBL: 8.3.1. SC: le.

Tait, D.M.; Hardy, J. Consent for investigating and treating adults with cancer. *Clinical Oncology (Royal College of Radiology)* 2006 February; 18(1): 23-29. NRCBL: 8.3.1; 8.3.4; 18.3. Identifiers: United Kingdom (Great Britain).

Tamura, Chieko. The family-facilitated approach could be dangerous if there is pressure by family dynamics. *American Journal of Bioethics* 2006 January-February; 6(1): 16-18; discussion W27-W28. NRCBL: 8.3.1; 8.2; 15.2; 21.1; 8.1. Identifiers: Japan. Comments: Akira Akabayashi and Brian Taylor Slingsby. Informed consent revisited: Japan and the U.S. American Journal of Bioethics 2006 January-February; 6(1): 9-14.

Taylor, E.M.; Ramsay, M.P.; Bunton, L. Do our patients understand? A comparison of understanding in adult inpatients and schoolchildren. *New Zealand Medical Journal* 1998 November 27; 111(1078): 449-451. NRCBL: 8.3.1; 9.5.1; 9.5.7; 8.1.

Tsolova, Svetla. Patients' rights in Bulgaria. *European Journal of Health Law* 2003 September; 10(3): 281-293. NRCBL: 8.3.1; 8.4; 19.5; 8.5. SC: le.

Tsotsi, N.M.; Rudolph, M.J. Informed consent in oral health care. *East African Medical Journal* 2005 April; 82(4): 216-220. NRCBL: 8.3.1; 9.5.1. SC: em.

Ubel, Peter A. Is information always a good thing? Helping patients make "good" decisions. *Medical Care* 2002 September; 40(9, Supplement): V39-V44. NRCBL: 8.3.1; 9.8.

Ueki, Satoshi. Informed consent eine rechtsvergleichende betrachtung des arzthaftungsrechts. *Kansai University Review of Law and Politics* 1996 March; (17): 1-9. NRCBL: 8.3.1. SC: le.

Valmassoi, G.; Mazzon, D. Informed consent to proposed course of medical treatment: recent case law stances. *Minerva Anestesiologica* 2005 November; 71(11): 659-669. NRCBL: 8.3.1; 8.1. SC: le.

Van den Hof, Michiel; Wilson, R. Douglas. Obstetric ultrasound: is it time for informed consent? = Echographie obstetricale: le temps est-il venu d'avoir recours au consentement eclaire? [editorial]. *Journal of Obstetrics and Gynaecology Canada* 2005 June; 27(6): 569-571. NRCBL: 8.3.1; 9.5.5; 14.1. Note: Full text in English and French.

Vernon, Martin J. Informed consent. *In:* Rai, Gurcharan S, ed. Medical Ethics and the Elderly. 2nd ed. San Francisco: Radcliffe Medical Press; 2004: 19-31. NRCBL: 8.3.1; 8.3.3.

Watson, Nigel; Halamka, John. Patients should have to opt out of national electronic care records. *BMJ: British Medical Journal* 2006 July 1; 333(7557): 39-42. NRCBL: 8.3.1; 1.3.12. Identifiers: United Kingdom (Great Britain).

Weinstein, James N. Partnership: doctor and patient: advocacy for informed choice vs. informed consent. *Spine* 2005 February 1; 30(3): 269-271. NRCBL: 8.3.1; 8.1.

Wendler, David. One-time general consent for research on biological samples. *BMJ: British Medical Journal* 2006 March 4; 332(7540): 544-547. NRCBL: 8.3.1; 5.1; 18.1; 18.2. SC: em.

Wenger, Neil S.; Lieberman, Jay R. Achieving informed consent when patients appear to lack capacity and surrogates. *Clinical Orthopaedics and Related Research* 2000 September; (378): 78-82. NRCBL: 8.3.1; 8.3.3. SC: cs.

Wilansky, Daniel P. Civil rights: prisoners' right to treatment information under Pabon v. Wright. *Journal of Law, Medicine and Ethics* 2006 Winter; 34(4): 831-832. NRCBL: 8.3.1; 8.3.4. SC: le.

Wilkinson, Jan. Commentary: what's all the fuss about? *BMJ: British Medical Journal* 2006 July 1; 333(7557): 42-43. NRCBL: 8.3.1; 1.3.12. Identifiers: United Kingdom (Great Britain).

Willems, S.; De Maesschalck, S.; Devuegele, M.; Derese, A.; De Maeseneer, J. Socio-economic status of the patient and doctor-patient communication: does it make a difference? *Patient Education and Counseling* 2005 February; 56(2): 139-146. NRCBL: 8.3.1; 8.1; 7.1; 9.5.10. SC: rv.

Williams, M.R.; Hegde, S.; Norton, M.R. Informed consent and surgeons in training: do patients consent to allow surgical trainees to operate on them? *Annals of the Royal College of Surgeons of England* 2004 November; 86(6): 465. NRCBL: 8.3.1; 7.2.

Wiseman, Oliver J.; Wijewardena, M.; Calleary, J.; Masood, J.; Hill, J.T. 'Will you be doing my operation, doctor?' Patient attitudes to informed consent. *Annals of the Royal College of Surgeons of England* 2004 November; 86(6): 462-464. NRCBL: 8.3.1.

Wolf, Susan M. Response: doctor and patient: an unfinished revolution. *Yale Journal of Health Policy, Law and Ethics* 2006 Summer; 6(2): 485-500. NRCBL: 8.3.1; 8.1. Conference: Symposium: A World Less Silent: Celebrating Jay Katz's Contribution to Law, Medicine, and Ethics. Comments: Ellen Wright Clayton. The web of relations: thinking about physicians and patients. Yale Journal of Health Policy, Law and Ethics 2006 Summer; 6(2): 465-477.

Yadwad, B.S.; Gouda, H. Consent — its medico legal aspects. *Journal of the Association of Physicians in India* 2005 October; 53: 891-894. NRCBL: 8.3.1; 8.3.2; 8.3.3; 18.3. SC: le.

Yamalik, Nermin. Dentist-patient relationship and quality care 4. Professional information and informed consent. *International Dental Journal* 2005 October; 55(5): 342-344. NRCBL: 8.3.1; 8.1; 4.1.1.

Yentis, S.M. When lecturers need patient consent. *BMJ: British Medical Journal* 2006 May 6; 332(7549): 1100. NRCBL: 8.3.1; 1.3.7.

Yeoman, A.D.; Dew, M.J.; Das, L.; Rajapaksa, S. Role of cognitive function in assessing informed consent for endoscopy. *Postgraduate Medical Journal* 2006; 82(963): 65-69 [Online]. Accessed: http://pmj.bmjjournals.com/cgi/reprint/82/963/65 [2006 March 7]. NRCBL: 8.3.1; 8.3.3; 17.1. SC: em. Identifiers: United Kingdom (Great Britain).

Yucel, Aylin; Gecici, O.; Emul, M.; Oyar, O.; Gulsoy, U.K.; Dayanir, Y.O.; Acar, M.; Degirmenci B.; Haktanir, A. Effect of informed consent for intravascular contrast material on the level of anxiety: how much information should be given? *Acta Radiologica* 2005 November; 46(7): 701-707. NRCBL: 8.3.1; 8.1; 17.1.

Zarate, Alvan O.; Zayatz, Laura. Essentials of the disclosure review process: a federal perspective. *Journal of Empirical Research on Human Research Ethics* 2006 September; 1(3): 51-62. NRCBL: 8.3.1; 1.3.12; 8.4; 18.6; 18.2.

INFORMED CONSENT/ INCOMPETENTS

Bay, Michael. Making the law match the reality; making the reality match the law. *Journal of Ethics in Mental Health* 2006 November; 1(1): E12, 4 p. NRCBL: 8.3.3; 17.7. SC: le. Identifiers: Canada.

Chandramohan, Daniel; Soleman, Nadia; Shibuya, Kenji; Porter, John. Ethical issues in the application of verbal autopsies in mortality surveillance systems [editorial]. *Tropical Medicine and International Health* 2005

November; 10(11): 1087-1089. NRCBL: 8.3.3; 20.1; 1.3.12.

Cohen-Mansfield, J. Consent and refusal in dementia research: conceptual and practical considerations. *Alzheimer Disease and Associated Disorders* 2003 April-June; 17(Supplement 1): S17-S25. NRCBL: 8.3.3; 18.3; 18.5.6.

Dimond, Bridgit. Mental capacity and professional advice in a patient with dysphagia. *British Journal of Nursing* 2006 May 25-June 7; 15(10): 574-575. NRCBL: 8.3.3; 4.3; 8.3.4. SC: le.

Dreher, George K. Is this patient really incompetent? *American Family Physician* 2005 January 1; 71(1): 198-199. NRCBL: 8.3.3. SC: cs.

Ferres, Beverley J. Usual medical practice in the process of obtaining consent to medical procedures for the elderly person. *Journal of Law and Medicine* 1998 May; 5(4): 355-363. NRCBL: 8.3.3; 9.5.2. SC: le.

Ganzini, Linda; Goy, Elizabeth R. Influence of mental illness on decision making at the end of life. *In:* Jansen, Lynn A., ed. Death in the Clinic. Lanham, MD: Rowman and Littlefield; 2006: 81-96. NRCBL: 8.3.3; 8.3.4.

Ganzini, Linda; Volicer, Ladislav; Nelson, William A.; Fox, Ellen; Derse, Arthur R. Ten myths about decision-making capacity. *Journal of the American Medical Directors Association* 2005 May-June; 6(3 Supplement): S100-S104. NRCBL: 8.3.3; 8.1.

Goldblatt, David. Must physicians respect an incompetent patient's refusal of treatment? *Medical Ethics Newsletter* 2006 Spring; 13(2): 3. NRCBL: 8.3.3. SC: cs.

Griffith, Richard. Making decisions for incapable adults 1: capacity and best interest. *British Journal of Community Nursing* 2006 March; 11(3): 119-125. NRCBL: 8.3.3; 1.3.5. SC: le.

Gyamfi, Cynthia; Berkowitz, Richard L. Responses by pregnant Jehovah's witnesses on health care proxies [reply]. *Obstetrics and Gynecology* 2005 February; 105(2): 442-443. NRCBL: 8.3.3; 8.3.4; 9.5.5; 19.4; 1.2.

Henwood, S.; Wilson, M.A.; Edwards, I. The role of competence and capacity in relation to consent for treatment in adult patients. *British Dental Journal* 2006 January 14; 200(1): 18-21. NRCBL: 8.3.3; 8.3.1. SC: le.

Hirschman, Karen B.; Joyce, Colette M.; James, Bryan D.; Xie, Sharon X.; Karlawish, Jason H.T. Do Alzheimer's disease patients want to participate in a treatment decision, and would their caregivers let them? *Gerontologist* 2005 June; 45(3): 381-388. NRCBL: 8.3.3; 17.1; 9.5.2. SC: em.

Howe, Edmund G. Patients may benefit from postponing assessment of mental capacity. *Journal of Clinical Ethics*

NRCBL: National Reference Center for Bioethics Literature Classification Scheme   See inside front cover for terms.

359

2006 Summer; 17(2): 99-109. NRCBL: 8.3.3; 8.1; 9.5.2; 20.4.1; 4.3.

Hyun, Insoo; Griggins, Cynthia; Weiss, Margaret; Robbins, Dorothy; Robichaud, Allyson; Daly, Barbara. When patients do not have a proxy: a procedure for medical decision making when there is no one to speak for the patient. *Journal of Clinical Ethics* 2006 Winter; 17(4): 323-330. NRCBL: 8.3.3; 20.5.4.

Jennings, Bruce. The ordeal of reminding: traumatic brain injury and the goals of care. *Hastings Center Report* 2006 March-April; 36(2): 29-37. NRCBL: 8.3.3; 9.5.4; 17.1.

Kapp, Marshall B. Informed consent implications of diagnostic evaluations for dementia. *American Journal of Alzheimer's Disease and Other Dementias* 2006 January-February; 21(1): 24-27. NRCBL: 8.3.3; 9.5.2; 17.1. SC: le.

Kennedy, Ian; Grubb, Andrew. Consent by others. *In their:* Medical Law. 3rd ed. London: Butterworths; 2005: 774-989. NRCBL: 8.3.3; 8.3.2; 8.3.4. SC: le.

Kon, Alexander A.; Klug, Michael. Methods and practices of investigators for determining participants' decisional capacity and comprehension of protocols. *Journal of Empirical Research on Human Research Ethics* 2006 December; 1(4): 61-68. NRCBL: 8.3.3; 18.5.2; 18.3; 8.3.2. SC: em.

Kothari, Sunil; Kirschner, Kristi. Beyond consent: assent and empowerment in brain injury rehabilitation. *Journal of Head Trauma Rehabilitation* 2003 July-August; 18(4): 379-382. NRCBL: 8.3.3; 8.3.1. SC: cs.

Lagay, Faith. Consent needed to perform procedures on the newly deceased for training purposes. *Virtual Mentor* 2001 August; 3(8): 2p. NRCBL: 8.3.3; 7.2.

Lidz, Charles W.; Arnold, Robert M. Rethinking autonomy in long term care. *University of Miami Law Review* 1993 January; 47(3): 603-623. NRCBL: 8.3.3; 1.1; 9.5.2. SC: le.

Lutrell, Steven. Mental incapacity and best interests. *In:* Rai, Gurcharan S, ed. Medical Ethics and the Elderly. 2nd ed. San Francisco: Radcliffe Medical Press; 2004: 71-79. NRCBL: 8.3.3. SC: le.

Mitrevski, Julia P.; Chamberlain, John R. Competence to stand trial and application of Sell standards. Involuntary medication allowed in a nondangerous defendant, to restore competence at trial. *Journal of the American Academy of Psychiatry and the Law* 2006; 34(2): 250-252. NRCBL: 8.3.3; 17.4. SC: le.

Parker, M. Competence by consequence: ambiguity and incoherence in the law. *Medicine and Law: World Association for Medical Law* 2006 March; 25(1): 1-12. NRCBL: 8.3.3; 1.1. SC: le.

Abstract: There is an ambiguity of principle delivered by those legal judgements which have considered the issue of whether the level of patients' decision-making capacity should vary in accordance with the seriousness of risks associated with the procedure subject to decision, particularly in decisions to refuse life-saving treatment. There appears to be support for (1) a risk-related standard of capacity, although some judgements could also be interpreted as (2) a procedural standard, subject to a rigorous standard of evidence of capacity. I argue that a risk-related standard of capacity itself is incoherent. This would lend weight to the second interpretation. However, I argue that the wording of the judgements belies an allegiance to the first interpretation, which is also consistent with how medical practitioners generally view capacity in these situations. I consider the implications of the dissonance between the two ways of interpreting the judgments, and make suggestions aimed at clarifying the issue of risk-related competence for clinicians.

Pruchno, Rachel A.; Lemay, Edward P., Jr.; Feild, Lucy; Levinsky, Norman G. Spouse as health care proxy for dialysis patients: whose preferences matter? *Gerontologist* 2005 December; 45(6): 812-819. NRCBL: 8.3.3; 19.3. SC: em.

Quill, Timothy E.; McCann, Robert. Decision making for the cognitively impaired. *In:* Morrison, R. Sean; Meier, Diane E.; Capello, Carol, eds. Geriatric Palliative Care. New York: Oxford University Press; 2003: 332-341. NRCBL: 8.3.3; 20.4.1.

Ramsey, Sara. The Adults with Incapacity (Scotland) Act — Who knows? Who cares? *Scottish Medical Journal* 2005 February; 50(1): 20-22. NRCBL: 8.3.3; 8.1. SC: le.

Royal College of Physicians of London. Mental Capacity Bill: Briefing from the Royal College of Physicians. London: Royal College of Physicians of London 2004 July 22; 6 p. [Online]. Accessed: http://www.rcplondon.ac.uk/college/statements/response_mcb.htm [2006 August 18]. NRCBL: 8.3.3; 4.3; 20.5.4; 18.5.6; 18.3. Identifiers: United Kingdom (Great Britain).

Saks, Elyn R. Competency to refuse psychotropic medication: three alternatives to the law's cognitive standard. *University of Miami Law Review* 1993 January; 47(3): 689-761. NRCBL: 8.3.3; 17.4; 8.3.4; 1.3.5; 4.3. SC: le.

Shah, Ajit; Dickenson, Donna. The Bournewood case and its implications for health and social services. *Journal of the Royal Society of Medicine* 1998 July; 91(7): 349-351. NRCBL: 8.3.3; 17.7; 7.1. SC: cs.

Shalowitz, David I.; Garrett-Mayer, Elizabeth; Wendler, David. The accuracy of surrogate decision makers: a systematic review. *Archives of Internal Medicine* 2006 March 13; 166(5): 493-497. NRCBL: 8.3.3. SC: em.
Abstract: BACKGROUND: Clinicians currently rely on patient-designated and next-of-kin surrogates to make end-of-life treatment decisions for incapacitated patients. Surrogates are instructed to use the substituted judgment standard, which directs them to make the treatment decision that the patient would have made if he or she were capacitated. However, commentators have questioned the accuracy with which surrogates predict patients' treatment preferences. METHODS: A systematic

literature search was conducted using PubMed, the Cochrane Library, and manuscript references, to identify published studies that provide empirical data on how accurately surrogates predict patients' treatment preferences and on the efficacy of commonly proposed methods to improve surrogate accuracy. Two of us (D.I.S. and D.W.) reviewed all articles and extracted data on the hypothetical scenarios used to assess surrogate accuracy and the percentage of agreement between patients and surrogates. RESULTS: The search identified 16 eligible studies, involving 151 hypothetical scenarios and 2595 surrogate-patient pairs, which collectively analyzed 19 526 patient-surrogate paired responses. Overall, surrogates predicted patients' treatment preferences with 68% accuracy. Neither patient designation of surrogates nor prior discussion of patients' treatment preferences improved surrogates' predictive accuracy. CONCLUSIONS: Patient-designated and next-of-kin surrogates incorrectly predict patients' end-of-life treatment preferences in one third of cases. These data undermine the claim that reliance on surrogates is justified by their ability to predict incapacitated patients' treatment preferences. Future studies should assess whether other mechanisms might predict patients' end-of-life treatment preferences more accurately. Also, they should assess whether reliance on patient-designated and next-of-kin surrogates offers patients and/or their families benefits that are independent of the accuracy of surrogates' decisions.

Shen, Xiaoling; Wang, Zucheng. Cases of informed consent for mental health patients. *In:* Döring, Ole; Chen, Renbiao, eds. Advances in Chinese Medical Ethics: Chinese and International Perspectives. Hamburg: Institut für Asienkunde; 2002: 444-449. NRCBL: 8.3.3. Note: Proceedings of the Second Sino-German Interdisciplinary Symposium about Medical Ethics in China, Shanghai, 19-23 October, 1999.

Shukunami, Ken-ichi.; Nishijima, Koji; Yoshida, Yoshio; Kotsuji, Fumikazu. Responses by pregnant Jehovah's witnesses on health care proxies [letter]. *Obstetrics and Gynecology* 2005 February; 105(2): 442. NRCBL: 8.3.3; 8.3.4; 9.5.5; 19.4; 1.2.

Thomas, J. Mervyn. Responses by pregnant Jehovah's witnesses on health care proxies [letter]. *Obstetrics and Gynecology* 2005 February; 105(2): 441. NRCBL: 8.3.3; 8.3.4; 9.5.5; 19.4; 1.2.

Van Der Weyden, Martin B. Ethics committees and guardianship legislation [letter]. *Medical Journal of Australia* 2003 October 6; 179(7): 390. NRCBL: 8.3.3; 9.6.

Vig, Elizabeth K.; Taylor, Janelle S.; Starks, Helene; Hopley, Elizabeth K.; Fryer-Edwards, Kelly. Beyond substituted judgment: how surrogates navigate end-of-life decision-making. *Journal of American Geriatrics Society* 2006 November; 54(11): 1688-1693. NRCBL: 8.3.3; 20.5.4. SC: em.

White, S.M.; Baldwin, T.J. The Mental Capacity Act 2005 — implications for anaesthesia and critical care. *Anaesthesia* 2006 April; 61(4): 381-389. NRCBL: 8.3.3. SC: le.

Winick, Bruce J. Competency to consent to treatment: the distinction between assent and objection. *In:* Wexler, David B.; Winick, Bruce J. Essays in Therapeutic Jurisprudence. Durham, NC: Carolina Academic Press, 1991: 41-81. NRCBL: 8.3.3.

Winick, Bruce J. Competency to consent to voluntary hospitalization: a therapeutic jurisprudence analysis of Zinermon v. Burch. *In:* Wexler, David B.; Winick, Bruce J. Essays in Therapeutic Jurisprudence. Durham, NC: Carolina Academic Press, 1991: 83-132. NRCBL: 8.3.3.

INFORMED CONSENT/ MINORS

Foolish vaccine exemptions [editorial]. *New York Times* 2006 October 12; p. A28. NRCBL: 8.3.2; 9.7; 9.1. SC: po.

Alderson, Priscilla. Who should decide and how? *In:* Parens, Erik, ed. Surgically Shaping Children: Technology, Ethics, and the Pursuit of Normality. Baltimore, MD: Johns Hopkins University Press; 2006: 157-176. NRCBL: 8.3.2.

Alderson, Priscilla; Hawthorne, Joanna; Killen, Margaret. Parents' experiences of sharing neonatal information and decisions: consent, cost and risk. *Social Science and Medicine* 2006 March; 62(6): 1319-1329. NRCBL: 8.3.2; 8.1; 9.5.7. SC: em.

Alderson, Priscilla; Sutcliffe, Katy; Curtis, Katherine. Children's competence to consent to medical treatment. *Hastings Center Report* 2006 November-December; 36(6): 25-34. NRCBL: 8.3.2; 18.5.2. SC: em; cs.

Arshagouni, Paul. "But I'm an adult now. . . sort of". Adolescent consent in health care decision making and the adolescent brain. *Journal of Health Care Law and Policy* 2006; 9(2): 315-364. NRCBL: 8.3.2; 4.4; 20.5.2; 11.2; 12.4.2. SC: le.

Aspinall, Cassandra. Children and parents and medical decisions. *Hastings Center Report* 2006 November-December; 36(6): 3. NRCBL: 8.3.2; 9.5.7; 4.5.

Bartholome, William G. A new understanding of consent in pediatric practice: consent, parental permission, and child assent. *Pediatric Annals* 1989 April; 18(4): 262-265. NRCBL: 8.3.2; 9.5.7.

Byrne, Paul J.; Murphy, Aisling. Informed consent and hypoplastic left heart syndrome. *Acta Paediatrica* 2005 September; 94(9): 1171-1175. NRCBL: 8.3.2. Identifiers: Canada; University of Alberta.

Campbell, Amy T. Consent, competence, and confidentiality related to psychiatric conditions in adolescent medicine practice. *Adolescent Medicine Clinics* 2006 February; 17(1): 25-47. NRCBL: 8.3.2; 9.5.7; 8.3.3; 8.4.

Coates, Jonathan. When do parents have the right to refuse medical treatment on behalf of their children? *New*

NRCBL: National Reference Center for Bioethics Literature Classification Scheme   See inside front cover for terms.

361

Zealand Medical Journal 2000 July 14; 113(1113): 297. NRCBL: 8.3.2; 8.3.4; 9.5.7.

Cohan, John Alan. Judicial enforcement of lifesaving treatment for unwilling patients. *Creighton Law Review* 2006 June; 39(4): 849-913. NRCBL: 8.3.2; 8.3.1; 9.5.7; 8.3.4; 9.5.5; 9.5.8. SC: le.

Dickens, Bernard M.; Cook, R.J. Adolescents and consent to treatment. *International Journal of Gynecology and Obstetrics* 2005 May; 89(2): 179-184. NRCBL: 8.3.2; 11.2; 8.4. SC: le. Identifiers: Canada.

Evans, Audrey E. Medical research: why trouble the patient for informed consent? Commentary. *Medical and Pediatric Oncology* 2002 September; 39(3): 210- 211. NRCBL: 8.3.2; 9.5.1; 18.2; 18.3; 18.5.2.

Farnell, Sheila M. Medical research: why trouble the patient for informed consent? *Medical and Pediatric Oncology* 2002 September; 39(3): 207- 209. NRCBL: 8.3.2; 9.5.7; 18.2; 18.3; 18.5.2.

French, Kathy. In strictest confidence. *Nursing Management* 2005 December; 12(8): 26-29. NRCBL: 8.3.2; 8.4; 10. SC: le. Identifiers: United Kingdom (Great Britain).

Glass, Kathleen Cranley, Carnevale, Franco A. Decisional challenges for children requiring assisted ventilation at home. *HEC (Healthcare Ethics Committee) Forum* 2006 September; 18(3): 207-221. NRCBL: 8.3.2; 20.5.2.

Grisso, Thomas, Vierling, Linda. Minor's consent to treatment: a developmental perspective. *Professional Psychology* 1978 August; 9(3): 412-427. NRCBL: 8.3.2; 17.1; 9.5.7. SC: le.

Jackson, Grace E. Mental health screening in schools: essentials of informed consent. *Ethical Human Psychology and Psychiatry* 2006 Fall-Winter; 8(3): 217-224. NRCBL: 8.3.2; 17.4; 1.3.3; 9.7. SC: le.

Kaser-Boyd, Nancy; Adelman, Howard S.; Taylor, Linda; Nelson, Perry. Children's understanding of risks and benefits of psychotherapy. *Journal of Clinical Child Psychology* 1986; 15(2): 165-171. NRCBL: 8.3.2; 17.2; 9.5.7. SC: em.

Keenan, Heather T.; Doron, Mia W.; Seyda, Beth A. Comparison of mothers' and counselors' perceptions of predelivery counseling for extremely premature infants. *Pediatrics* 2005 July; 116(1): 104-111. NRCBL: 8.3.2; 8.1; 20.5.2.

Kon, Alexander A. When parents refuse treatment for their child. *JONA's Healthcare Law, Ethics, and Regulation* 2006 January-March; 8(1): 5-11. NRCBL: 8.3.2; 8.3.4; 7.2. SC: cs.

Lindseth, Richard E. Ethical issues in pediatric orthopaedics. *Clinical Orthopaedics and Related Research* 2000 September; (378): 61-65. NRCBL: 8.3.2. SC: cs.

Luxembourg. Commission Consultative Nationale d'Éthique pour les Sciences de la Vie et de la Santé [CNE]. Avis concernant les articles 7, alinéas 3 et 4, et 43 du projet de loi No 2557 relatif à la protection de la jeunesse: Avis 3/1990 [Opinion 3/1990: Opinion concerning articles 7, line nos. 3 and 4 and 43 of Bill 2557 concerning the protection of youth]. Luxembourg: Commission Nationale d'Éthique, 1990; 18 p. [Online]. Accessed: http://www.cne.public.lu/publications/avis/1990_3.PDF [2006 April 7]. NRCBL: 8.3.2; 9.5.7. Note: Loi No. 2557 relatif à la protection de la jeunesse ayant l'intention de régler la situation où des parents voire des tuteurs s'opposent à des interventions médicales urgentes et indispensables selon l'avis d'un médecin [Law No. 2557 concerning the protection of youth intended to regulate the situation where parents or guardians refuse urgent and essential medical interventions advised by physicians].

Markon, Jerry. Fight intensifies over who acts for children; judge lets teen waive usual cancer care; trial set for August. *Washington Post* 2006 July 26; p. B8. NRCBL: 8.3.2; 8.3.4. SC: po.

Markon, Jerry. Who decides child medical care in dispute. *Washington Post* 2006 July 26; p. B1, B8. NRCBL: 8.3.2; 8.3.4. SC: po; le.

McDade, William. A racist parent [case study]. *Virtual Mentor* 2001 November; 3(11): 2p. NRCBL: 8.3.2. SC: cs.

McDonald, Patrick. There's a bug in your head. *Hastings Center Report* 2006 May-June; 36(3): 7. NRCBL: 8.3.2; 9.5.4; 9.5.7; 17.1.

Mohebbi, Mohammad Reza; Weisleder, Pedro. The right of minors to confidentiality and informed consent [letter and reply]. *Journal of Child Neurology* 2005 May; 20(5): 460-461. NRCBL: 8.3.2; 8.4; 21.7.

Mulholland, Maureen. Re W (A Minor): autonomy, consent and the anorexic teenager. *Professional Negligence* 1993; 9(1): 21-24. NRCBL: 8.3.2; 8.3.4; 1.1. SC: le.

Nwomeh, Benedict C.; Waller, Andrea L.; Caniano, Donna A.; Kelleher, Kelly J. Informed consent for emergency surgery in infants and children. *Journal of Pediatric Surgery* 2005 August; 40(8): 1320-1325. NRCBL: 8.3.2.

Pang, Alfred H.T.; Lai, K.Y.C.; Bailey, V. Children's consent to psychiatric treatment: all or nothing? *International Journal of Clinical Practice* 1997 September; 51(6): 412-413. NRCBL: 8.3.2; 17.1. SC: cs. Identifiers: United Kingdom (Great Britain).

Paris, John J.; Graham, Neil; Schreiber, Michael D.; Goodwin, Michele. Has the emphasis on autonomy gone too far? Insights from Dostoevsky and parental decisionmaking in NICU. *CQ: Cambridge Quarterly of Healthcare Ethics* 2006 Spring; 15(2): 147-151. NRCBL: 8.3.2; 20.5.2; 1.1; 1.2; 7.1. Identifiers: neonatal intensive care unit.

Sanders, Alan. Assent in medical decision-making with children. *Health Care Ethics USA* 2006; 14(1): E4 [Online]. Accessed: http://chce.slu.edu/Partnerships_HCE_Intro.html [2006 November 17]. NRCBL: 8.3.2.

Sankoorikal, Teena-Ann V. Using scientific advances to conceive the "perfect" donor: the Pandora's box of creating child donors for the purpose of saving ailing family members. *Seton Hall Law Review* 2002; 32(3): 583-616. NRCBL: 8.3.2; 14.4; 19.5; 15.2. SC: le.

Talmadge, Stephen A. Who should determine what is best for children in state custody who object to psychotropic medication? *Annals of Health Law* 2006 Summer; 15(2): 183-211. NRCBL: 8.3.2; 17.4; 17.7; 8.3.4. SC: le; rv.

Taylor, Bridget. Parental autonomy and consent to treatment. *Journal of Advanced Nursing* 1999 March; 29(3): 570-576. NRCBL: 8.3.2; 1.1.

Ward, Frances R. Parents and professionals in the NICU: communication within the context of ethical decision making — an integrative review. *Neonatal Network* 2005 May-June; 24(3): 25-33. NRCBL: 8.3.2; 9.5.7; 8.1; 4.1.3. SC: rv. Identifiers: neonatal intensive care unit.

Waterston, T. A general paediatrician's practice in children's rights. *Archives of Disease in Childhood* 2005 February; 90(2): 178-181. NRCBL: 8.3.2; 9.5.7; 8.4. Identifiers: United Kingdom (Great Britain).

Watson, Katie. A conversation with Mary Stainton: power dynamics and informed consent [interview]. *Atrium* 2006 Fall; 3: 16-17. NRCBL: 8.3.2; 9.5.5; 11.3.

Watts, Cara D. Asking adolescents: does a mature minor have a right to participate in health care decisions? *Hastings Women's Law Journal* 2005 Summer; 16(2): 221-249. NRCBL: 8.3.2; 8.3.4; 9.5.7. SC: le; cs.

Will, Jonathan F. My God, my choice: the mature minor doctrine and adolescent refusal of live-saving or sustaining medical treatment based upon religious beliefs. *Journal of Contemporary Health Law and Policy* 2006 Spring; 22(2): 233-300. NRCBL: 8.3.2; 8.3.4; 1.2. SC: le.

Wray, Julie. Confidentiality and teenage pregnancy — the affinity gap. *RCM Midwives* 2005 December; 8(12): 493. NRCBL: 8.3.2; 8.4; 9.5.7.

INSTITUTIONAL REVIEW BOARDS *See* HUMAN EXPERIMENTATION/ ETHICS COMMITTEES

INTERNATIONAL HUMAN RIGHTS
See also TORTURE, GENOCIDE AND WAR CRIMES; WAR AND TERRORISM

Editorial. *Bulletin of Medical Ethics* 2005 April; (207): 1. NRCBL: 21.1; 9.1; 9.3.1. Identifiers: healthcare; Organization of Economic Cooperation and Development.

Annas, George J. The statue of security: human rights and post-9/11 epidemics. *Journal of Health Law* 2005 Spring; 38(2): 319-351. NRCBL: 21.1; 9.1; 21.3; 21.4. SC: le.

Bates, Benjamin R. Care of the self and American physicians' place in the "war on terror": a Foucauldian reading of Senator Bill Frist, M.D. *Journal of Medicine and Philosophy* 2006 August; 31(4): 385-400. NRCBL: 21.1; 7.1; 1.3.5; 4.1.1; 1.1.
Abstract: American physicians are increasingly concerned that they are losing professional control. Other analysts of medical power argue that physicians have too much power. This essay argues that current analyses are grounded in a structuralist reading of power. Deploying Michel Foucault's "care of the self" and rhetorician Raymie McKerrow's "critical rhetoric," this essay claims that medical power is better understood as a way that medical actors take on power through rhetoric rather than a force that has power over medical actors. Through a close reading of an essay by Senator Bill Frist, this paper argues that physicians experience a process of "subjection" wherein they are both agents of and objects of medical power as it is combined with state and corporate power in the American "war on terror." This alternative mode of analyzing medical power has implications for our collective understanding of its operations and the means by which we propose alternative enactments of medical power.

Benatar, S.R. Ethics and tropical diseases: some global considerations. *In:* Cook, Gordon C.; Zumla, Alimuddin I. eds. Manson's Tropical Diseases, 21st Edition. Philadelphia: W.B. Saunders; 2003: 85-93. NRCBL: 21.1; 9.1; 9.5.1; 7.1; 4.4.

Berlinguer, Giovanni. Bioethics, human security, and global health. *In:* Chen, Lincoln; Leaning, Jennifer; Narasimhan, Vasant, eds. Global Health Challenges for Human Security. Cambridge, MA.: Global Equity Initiative; Asia Center, Harvard University; 2003: 53-65. NRCBL: 21.1; 2.1; 9.1.

Chapman, Audrey R. Human rights. *In:* Mitcham, Carl, ed. Encyclopedia of Science, Technology, and Ethics. Farmington Hills, MI: Thomson/Gale, 2005: 957-960. NRCBL: 21.1; 5.1.

Chapman, Audrey R. The human rights implications of intellectual property protection. *Journal of International Economic Law* 2002 December; 5(4): 861-882. NRCBL: 21.1; 9.2. SC: le.

Fernandez de Casadevante Romani, Carlos. The Convention on the Protection of Human Rights and the Dignity of the Human Being in regard to Applications of Biology and Medicine: Convention on Human Rights and Biomedicine = El Conveniopara la Protección de los Derechos Humanos y la Dignidad del Ser Humano con respeto a la aplicación de la Biología y la Medicina: Convención sobre Derechos Humanos y Biomedicina. *Revista de Derecho Genoma Humano = Law and the Human Genome Review* 1997 July-December; (7): 99-112. NRCBL: 21.1; 18.3; 19.5; 15.1; 4.4; 2.4; 9.3.1. SC: le.

NRCBL: National Reference Center for Bioethics Literature Classification Scheme   See inside front cover for terms.

363

Furedy, John J. The decline of the "Euppur si muove" spirit in North American science: professional organizations and PC pressures. *Mankind Quarterly* 1997 Fall-Winter; 38(1-2): 55-66. NRCBL: 21.1; 1.3.9; 5.1; 15.11; 7.3.

Hall, Amy Laura. Whose progress? The language of global health. *Journal of Medicine and Philosophy* 2006 June; 31(3): 285-304. NRCBL: 21.1; 2.1. SC: an.

Kershaw, Josephine M. Human rights and undergraduate healthcare management education. *Journal of Health Administration Education* 2005 Fall; 22(4): 459-470. NRCBL: 21.1; 7.2; 9.3.2.

Koch, T. Weaponizing medicine: "tutti fratelli," no more. *Journal of Medical Ethics* 2006 May; 32(5): 249-252. NRCBL: 21.2; 4.1.2.

Melvin, Louise. Health needs of immigrants: rights to treatment and confidentiality. *Journal of Family Planning and Reproductive Health Care* 2005 October; 31(4): 331-332. NRCBL: 21.1; 9.2; 8.4. SC: cs. Identifiers: National Health Service; United Kingdom (Great Britain).

Morioka, Masahiro. Cross-cultural approaches to the philosophy of life in the contemporary world: from bioethics to life studies. *In:* Sleeboom, Margaret, ed. Genomics in Asia: A Clash of Bioethical Interests? New York: Kegan Paul; 2004: 179-199. NRCBL: 21.1; 21.7.

Nyanzi, Stella; Nyanzi, Barbara; Bessie, Kalina. "Abortion? That's for women!" Narratives and experiences of commercial motorbike riders in south-western Uganda. *African Journal of Reproductive Health* 2005 April; 9(1): 142-161. NRCBL: 21.1; 12.5.2. SC: em.

Rubenstein, Leonard S. A new medical ethic: physicians and the fight for human rights. *Harvard International Review* 1998 Summer; 20(3): 54-57. NRCBL: 21.1; 4.1.2.

Sreenivasan, Gopal; Benatar, Soloman R. Challenges for global health in the 21st century: some upstream considerations. *Theoretical Medicine and Bioethics* 2006; 27(1): 3-11. NRCBL: 21.1; 9.3.1; 9.1; 9.2; 21.2.

United Nations. Office of the High Commissioner for Human Rights. Principles of medical ethics relevant to the role of health personnel, particularly physicians, in the protection of prisoners and detainees against torture and other cruel, inhuman or degrading treatment or punishment. Geneva: United Nations Office of the High Commissioner for Human Rights, 1982 December 18: 2 p. [Online]. Accessed: http://www.ohchr.org/english/law/medicalethics.htm [2007 January 31]. NRCBL: 21.1; 21.4; 9.5.1; 6. Note: Adopted by General Assembly resolution 37/194 of 18 December 1982.

INTERNATIONAL MIGRATION OF HEALTH CARE PROFESSIONALS

Poaching nurses from the developing world [editorial]. *Lancet* 2006 June 3-9; 367(9525): 1791. NRCBL: 21.6; 9.4; 7.1.

Dugger, Celia W. U.S. plan to lure nurses may hurt poor nations. *New York Times* 2006 May 24; p. A1, A12. NRCBL: 21.6.

Kapur, Devesh; McHale, John. Should a cosmopolitan worry about the "brain drain"? *Ethics and International Affairs* 2006; 20(3): 305-320. NRCBL: 21.6; 21.1.

McElmurry, Beverly J.; Solheim, Karen; Kishi, Rieko; Coffia, Marcia A.; Woith, Wendy; Janepanish, Poolsuk. Ethical concerns in nurse migration. *Journal of Professional Nursing* 2006 July-August; 22(4): 226-235. NRCBL: 21.6.

McLean, Thomas R. The offshoring of American medicine: scope, economic issues and legal liabilities. *Annals of Health Law* 2005 Summer; 14(2): 205-265. NRCBL: 21.6; 1.3.12; 9.1; 8.5; 9.3.1. SC: le.

Watkins, Sylvia. Migration of healthcare professionals: practical and ethical considerations. *Clinical Medicine* 2005 May-June; 5(3): 240-243. NRCBL: 21.6; 21.1. Identifiers: United Kingdom (Great Britain).

INVOLUNTARY COMMITMENT

Abma, Tineke A.; Widdershoven, Guy A.M. Moral deliberation in psychiatric nursing practice. *Nursing Ethics* 2006 September; 13(5): 546-557. NRCBL: 17.7; 4.1.3. SC: em. Identifiers: Netherlands.
  Abstract: Moral deliberation has been receiving more attention in nursing ethics. Several ethical conversation models have been developed. This article explores the feasibility of the so-called CARE (Considerations, Actions, Reasons, Experiences) model as a framework for moral deliberation in psychiatric nursing practice. This model was used in combination with narrative and dialogical approaches to foster discourse between various stakeholders about coercion in a closed admission clinic in a mental hospital in the Netherlands. The findings demonstrate that the CARE model provides a substantial framework for structuring moral deliberations. Narratives and dialogue are useful tools for broadening issues in conversations, to engage various stakeholders (including patients), and to gain shared understandings.

Acquaviva, Gregory L. Mental health courts: no longer experimental. *Seton Hall Law Review* 2006; 36(3): 971-1013. NRCBL: 17.7; 1.3.5; 4.3. SC: le.

Bauer, A.; Rosca, P.; Grinshpoon, A.; Khawalled, R.; Mester, R. Monitoring long-term court order psychiatric hospitalization: a pilot project in Israel. *Medicine and Law: World Association for Medical Law* 2006 March; 25(1): 83-99. NRCBL: 17.7; 9.5.3; 9.2. SC: le; em.
  Abstract: BACKGROUND: In Israel, the rules of compulsory psychiatric hospitalization, including hospitalization under a

court order, are set out in the Israel Mental Health Act, 1991 (MHA). The MHA does not specifically define the time limits of hospitalization by Court Order, though every patient, by law has to be brought before the Regional Psychiatric Board (RPB) once every six months for reevaluation. The Supreme Court recently addressed this issue and suggested that by having no specific time span, the way lies open for infringement of individual rights (Criminal Appeals 3854\02). Consequently the Supreme Court suggested that some court committed patients should be moved from the criminal to the civil track which inflicts less severe infringement of the mentally ill patient's rights. This ruling generated rethinking at the ministerial level aimed at improving the monitoring of the care of long-term psychiatric hospitalization in criminal cases. The Ministry of Health initiated a project designed to study this issue. OBJECTIVES: The main objective of this project, which is described below, is to monitor the type and incidence of forensic mental patients hospitalized in Israel for more than 10 years, and to propose alternatives to replace this untenable situation. METHODS: All the 12 psychiatric hospitals in Israel which hospitalize forensic patients were sent written requests for data on criminal patients hospitalized under court orders, including demographic data, diagnosis and type of offense. We identified in all 65 such patients. The data received were compared with the National Psychiatric Register databank of the Ministry of Health and divided in subgroups according to diagnosis, type of offence, demographic variables and length of hospitalization. RESULTS: Most of the subjects of the sample (89%) suffered from psychotic disorder mainly schizophrenia of the paranoid type. 95.5% were male. The most prominent type of offense was assault against family members (37%),which is in keeping with statistics reported in the relevant literature. The profile of the typical patient of this sample is: male, aged 45-65, unmarried, with 8 years of education and suffering from paranoid schizophrenia. DISCUSSION: No correlation between type and severity of offense and length of involuntary forensic hospitalization was found. We suggest some possible alternatives to improve the current handling of the group of long term hospitalized forensic patients. We also feel that a further study should be carried out on forensic patients hospitalized for a period of five to ten years.

Bloom, Joseph D. Civil commitment is disappearing in Oregon. *Journal of the American Academy of Psychiatry and the Law* 2006; 34(4): 534-537. NRCBL: 17.7. SC: em.

Brooks, Robert A. U.S. psychiatrists' beliefs and wants about involuntary civil commitment grounds. *International Journal of Law and Psychiatry* 2006 January-February; 29(1): 13-21. NRCBL: 17.7; 1.3.8. SC: em; le.

Collins, Gary. Court-mandated psychiatric outpatient treatment in New York: doesn't this process invoke more care than controversy? [editorial]. *Criminal Behaviour and Mental Health* 2005; 15(4): 214-220. NRCBL: 17.7. SC: le.

Cornwell, John Kip; Deeney, Raymond. Exposing the myths surrounding preventive outpatient commitment for individuals with chronic mental illness. *Psychology, Public Policy, and Law* 2003 March-June; 9(1-2): 209-232. NRCBL: 17.7; 17.4; 1.3.5. SC: le.

Dyer, Clare. Third time lucky? [news]. *BMJ: British Medical Journal* 2006 November 25; 333(7578): 1090. NRCBL: 17.7; 17.1. SC: le. Identifiers: United Kingdom (Great Britain).

Finn, Peter. In Russia, psychiatry is again a tool against dissent. *Washington Post* 2006 September 30; p. A1, A14. NRCBL: 17.7; 21.1. SC: po.

Gable, Lance; Vásquez, Javier; Gostin, Lawrence O.; Jiménez, Heidi V. Mental health and due process in the Americas: protecting the human rights of persons involuntarily admitted to and detained in psychiatric institutions. *Revista panamericana de salud pública/Pan American Journal of Public Health* 2005 October-November; 18(4-5): 366-373. NRCBL: 17.7; 21.1. Identifiers: Latin America.

Geller, Jeffrey L. The evolution of outpatient commitment in the USA: from conundrum to quagmire. *International Journal of Law and Psychiatry* 2006 May-June; 29(3): 234-248. NRCBL: 17.7; 1.3.5. SC: le; an.

Geller, Jeffrey L.; Fisher, William H.; Grudzinskas, Albert J., Jr.; Clayfield, Jonathan C.; Lawlor, Ted. Involuntary outpatient treatment as "desinstitutionalized coercion": the net-widening concerns. *International Journal of Law and Psychiatry* 2006 November-December; 29(6): 551-562. NRCBL: 17.7; 8.3.3. SC: em.

Hewit, David W. Incapable patients and the law [letter]. *BMJ: British Medical Journal* 2006 January 28; 332(7535): 237. NRCBL: 17.7. SC: le. Identifiers: United Kingdom (Great Britain). Comments: R. Stewart. Mental health legislation and decision making capacity. BMJ: British Medical Journal 2006 January 14; 332(7533): 118-119.

Hiday, Virginia Aldige. Outpatient commitment: the state of empirical research on its outcomes. *Psychology, Public Policy, and Law* 2003 March-June; 9(1-2): 8-32. NRCBL: 17.7. SC: le; em.

Hillman, Alison A. Human rights and deinstitutionalization: a success story in the Americas. *Revista panamericana de salud pública/Pan American Journal of Public Health* 2005 October-November; 18(4-5): 374-379. NRCBL: 17.7; 21.1. Identifiers: Paraguay.

Jukic, Vlado; Goreta, Miroslav; Kozumplik, Oliver; Herceg, Miroslav; Majdancic, Željko; Mužinic, Lana. Implementation of first Croatian Law on Protection of Persons with Mental Disorders. *Collegium Antropologicum* 2005 December; 29(2): 543-549. NRCBL: 17.7; 1.3.5. SC: em; le.

Kaltiala-Heino, Riittakerttu; Välimäki, Maritta. Involuntary commitment in health care: an analysis of the status and rights of involuntarily treated psychiatric patients in comparison with patients treated involuntarily under other acts. *European Journal of Health Law* 2001 December; 8(4): 299-316. NRCBL: 17.7; 8.3.4; 9.5.3. SC: le; an.

Linford, Steven. Mental health law: compulsory treatment in a general medical setting. *British Journal of Hospi-*

NRCBL: National Reference Center for Bioethics Literature Classification Scheme   See inside front cover for terms.

365

tal Medicine (London, England) 2005 October; 66(10): 569-571. NRCBL: 17.7; 8.3.4; 8.3.3; 1.3.5. SC: le.

Luchins, Daniel J.; Cooper, Amy E.; Hanrahan, Patricia; Heyrman, Mark J. Lawyers' attitudes towards involuntary treatment. *Journal of the American Academy of Psychiatry and the Law* 2006; 34(4): 492-500. NRCBL: 17.7; 17.4. SC: em.

Nahon, Daniella; Pugachova, Inna; Yoffe, Rinat; Levav, Itzhak. The impact of human rights advocacy, mental health legislation and psychiatric reform on the epidemiology of involuntary psychiatric hospitalizations. *Medicine and Law: The World Association for Medical Law* 2006 June; 25(2): 283-295. NRCBL: 17.7. SC: em.
  Abstract: Several years ago, the Ministry of Health published a report on the epidemiology of involuntary psychiatric hospitalizations. Many developments (advances in human rights advocacy, mental health legislation and the nascent Psychiatric Reform) have occurred in the mental health field in Israel since 1990 when the earlier report was released. Those favorable developments in mental health care were thought to have the capacity to modify the admission rates. We explored several parameters to check the hospitalization patterns (eg, by demographic factors, diagnosis) and found no substantial modifications. The case for an analytic study was clearly established.

Noll, Steven. The public face of Southern institutions for the "feeble-minded". *Public Historian* 2005 Spring; 27(2): 25-41. NRCBL: 17.7; 4.3; 9.5.3.

O'Reilly, R.L.; Gray, J.E. Most important lesson from Starson ignored in article. *Health Law in Canada* 2006 November; 27(2): 36-40. NRCBL: 17.7; 17.8. SC: le.

Perlin, Michael L. Therapeutic jurisprudence and outpatient commitment law: Kendra's law as case study. *Psychology, Public Policy, and Law* 2003 March-June; 9(1-2): 183-208. NRCBL: 17.7; 1.3.5. SC: le.

Saks, Elyn R. Involuntary outpatient commitment. *Psychology, Public Policy, and Law* 2003 March-June; 9(1-2): 94-106. NRCBL: 17.7.

Schopp, Robert F. Outpatient civil commitment: a dangerous charade or a component of a comprehensive institution of civil commitment? *Psychology, Public Policy, and Law* 2003 March-June; 9(1-2): 33-69. NRCBL: 17.7; 8.3.4; 1.3.5. SC: le.

Segal, Steven P.; Burgess, Philip M. The utility of extended outpatient civil commitment. *International Journal of Law and Psychiatry* 2006 November-December; 29(6): 525-534. NRCBL: 17.7.

Slovenko, Ralph. Civil commitment (involuntary hospitalization). *In his:* Psychiatry in Law/Law in Psychiatry. Volume 2. New York: Brunner-Routledge; 2002: 555-583. NRCBL: 17.7. SC: le.

Steinert, Tilman; Lepping, Peter; Baranyai, Reka; Hoffmann, Markus; Leherr, Herbert. Compulsory admission and treatment in schizophrenia: a study of ethical attitudes in four European countries. *Social Psychiatry and Psychiatric Epidemiology* 2005 August; 40(8): 635-641. NRCBL: 17.7; 21.1; 7.1. SC: em.

Swartz, Marvin S.; Swanson, Jeffrey W.; Monahan, John. Endorsement of personal benefit of outpatient commitment among persons with severe mental illness. *Psychology, Public Policy, and Law* 2003 March-June; 9(1-2): 70-93. NRCBL: 17.7. SC: em.

Truscott, Derek; Goodkey, Lori. Ethical principles of the psychology profession and involuntary commitment. *In:* O'Donohue, William; Ferguson, Kyle, eds. Handbook of Professional Ethics for Psychologists: Issues, Questions, and Controversies. Thousand Oaks, Calif.: SAGE Publications; 2003: 167-180. NRCBL: 17.7.

Wagner, H. Ryan; Swartz, Marvin S.; Swanson, Jeffrey W.; Burns, Barbara J. Does involuntary outpatient commitment lead to more intensive treatment? *Psychology, Public Policy, and Law* 2003 March-June; 9(1-2): 145-158. NRCBL: 17.7. SC: em.

Welsh, Johnathan R. In whose 'best interests'? Ethical issues involved in the moral dilemmas surrounding the removal of sexually abused adolescents from a community-based residential treatment unit to a locked, forensic adult psychiatric unit. *Journal of Advanced Nursing* 1998 January; 27(1): 45-51. NRCBL: 17.7.; 9.5.7; 9.1; 10; 1.1; 4.1.3. Identifiers: Ireland.

Winick, Bruce J. Outpatient commitment: a therapeutic jurisprudence analysis. *Psychology, Public Policy, and Law* 2003 March-June; 9(1-2): 107-144. NRCBL: 17.7; 1.3.5. SC: le.

JOURNALISM AND PUBLISHING
See also BIOMEDICAL RESEARCH

Cash-per-publication. . . [editorial]. *Nature* 2006 June 15; 441(7095): 786. NRCBL: 1.3.7; 1.3.9.

How does PLoS medicine manage competing interests? [editorial]. *PLoS Medicine* 2005 March; 2(3): 0171-0172. NRCBL: 1.3.7.

Our conflicted medical journals [editorial]. *New York Times* 2006 July 23; p. WK11. NRCBL: 1.3.7. SC: po.

Peer review and fraud [editorial]. *Nature* 2006 December 21-28; 444(7122): 971-972. NRCBL: 1.3.7; 1.3.9; 7.3.

Sacking of CMAJ editors is deeply troubling [editorial]. *Lancet* 2006 March 4-10; 367(9512): 704. NRCBL: 1.3.7; 9.7; 11.1. Identifiers: Canadian Medical Association Journal.

Standards for papers on cloning [editorial]. *Nature* 2006 January 19; 439(7074): 243. NRCBL: 1.3.7; 1.3.9; 14.5.

The power of the media [interviews]. *Atrium* 2006 Fall; 3: 8-11. NRCBL: 1.3.7; 9.6. Identifiers: Glenn McGee;

Edmund D. Pellegrino; Carl Elliot; Laurie Zoloth; Arthur Caplan; David Magnus.

Armstrong, David. How the New England Journal missed warning signs on Vioxx: medical weekly waited years to report flaws in article that praised pain drug; Merck seen as "punching bag". *Wall Street Journal* 2006 May 15; p. A1, A10. NRCBL: 1.3.7; 9.7. SC: po.

Armstrong, David. JAMA to toughen rules on author disclosure. *Wall Street Journal* 2006 July 12; p. D2. NRCBL: 1.3.7. SC: po.

Armstrong, David. Medical journal spikes article on industry ties of kidney group. *Wall Street Journal* 2006 December 26; p. B1, B4. NRCBL: 1.3.7; 9.5.1; 9.3.1; 19.3. SC: po. Identifiers: National Kidney Foundation.

Armstrong, David. Medical reviews face criticism over lapses. *Wall Street Journal* 2006 July 19; p. B1, B2. NRCBL: 1.3.7. SC: po.

Austen, Ian. Canadian medical group fires top editors of journal. *New York Times* 2006 February 22; p. C9. NRCBL: 1.3.7; 12.1; 9.7. SC: po.

Begley, Sharon. New journals bet "negative results" save time, money. *Wall Street Journal* 2006 September 15; p. B1. NRCBL: 1.3.7. SC: po.

Begley, Sharon. Science journals artfully try to boost their rankings. *Wall Street Journal* 2006 June 5; p. B1, B8. NRCBL: 1.3.7; 1.3.9. SC: po.

Bennett, Susanne. Clinical writing of a therapy in progress: ethical questions and therapeutic challenges. *Clinical Social Work Journal* 2006 Summer; 34(2): 215-226. NRCBL: 1.3.7; 17.2; 8.1; 8.3.1.

Benninger, Michael S.; Jackler, Robert K.; Johnson, Jonas T.; Johns, Michael M.; Kennedy, David W.; Ruben, Robert J.; Sataloff, Robert T.; Smith, Richard J.H.; Weber, Peter C.; Weber, Randal S.; Young, Eric D. Consortium of otolaryngology — head and neck surgery journals to collaborate in maintenance of high ethical standards [editorial]. *Otology and Neurotology* 2005 May; 26(3): 331-332. NRCBL: 1.3.7; 1.3.9; 8.4.

Benos, Dale J.; Fabres, Jorge; Gutierrez, Jessica P.; Hennessy, Kristin; Kosek, David; Lee, Joo Hyoung; Olteanu, Dragos; Russell, Tara; Shaikh, Faheem; Wang, Kai. Ethics and scientific publication. *Advances in Physiology Education* 2005; 29(2): 59-74 [Online] Accessed: http://advan.physiology.org/cgi/reprint/29/2/59 [25 September 2006]. NRCBL: 1.3.7; 1.3.9.

Bosman, Julie. Reporters find science journals harder to trust, but not easy to verify. *New York Times* 2006 February 13; p. C1, C3. NRCBL: 1.3.7; 1.3.9. SC: po.

Brockway, Laura M.; Furcht, Leo T.; DeAngelis, Catherine D. Financial disclosure policies of scientific publications [letter and reply]. *JAMA: The Journal of the American Medical Association* 2006 December 27; 296(24): 2925-2926. NRCBL: 1.3.7; 1.3.9.

Broome, Marion E. Self-plagiarism: oxymoron, fair use, or scientific misconduct? [editorial]. *Nursing Outlook* 2004 November-December; 52(6): 273-274. NRCBL: 1.3.7; 1.3.9; 4.1.3.

Calame, Byron. Truth, justice, abortion and The Times Magazine [op-ed]. *New York Times* 2006 December 31; p. WK8. NRCBL: 1.3.7; 12.5.1. Identifiers: The public editor; El Salvador.

Canadian Medical Association Journal. The editorial autonomy of CMAJ [editorial]. *CMAJ/JAMC: Canadian Medical Association Journal* 2006 January 3; 174(1): 9. NRCBL: 1.3.7; 1.3.9.

Carey, Benedict. Correcting the errors of disclosure. *New York Times* 2006 July 25; p. F5. NRCBL: 1.3.7; 1.3.9. SC: po.

Charatan, Fred. US journal in row over sponsored supplement [news]. *BMJ: British Medical Journal* 2006 August 5; 333(7562): 277. NRCBL: 1.3.7; 9.7; 9.3.1; 1.3.9.

Christakis, Dimitri A.; Rivara, Frederick P. Publication ethics: editors' perspectives. *Journal of Pediatrics* 2006 July; 149(1, Supplement): S39-S42. NRCBL: 1.3.7; 1.3.9; 18.5.2; 18.6.

Chubin, Daryl E.; Hackett, Edward J. Peer review. *In:* Mitcham, Carl, ed. Encyclopedia of Science, Technology, and Ethics. Farmington Hills, MI: Thomson/Gale, 2005: 1390-1394. NRCBL: 1.3.7; 5.3; 18.6.

Daskalopoulou, Stella S.; Mikhailidis, Dimitri P.; Jacobs, Adam. Exorcising ghosts and unwelcome guests [letters]. *Annals of Internal Medicine* 2006 January 17; 144(2): 149. NRCBL: 1.3.7; 1.3.9.

Davis, Philip M. The ethics of republishing: a case study of Emerald/MCB University Press journals. *Library Resources and Technical Services* 2005 April; 49(2): 72-78. NRCBL: 1.3.7; 1.3.9. SC: cs.

DeMaria, Anthony N. Publication bias and journals as policemen. *Journal of the American College of Cardiology* 2004 October 19; 44(8): 1707-1708. NRCBL: 1.3.7; 1.3.9.

Dowd, M. Denise. Breaching the contract: the ethics of nonpublication of research studies [editorial]. *Archives of Pediatrics and Adolescent Medicine* 2004 October; 158(10): 1014-1015. NRCBL: 1.3.7; 1.3.9; 7.4; 18.2.

El-Deiry, Wafik S. Plagiarism is not acceptable in science or for cancer biology and therapy. *Cancer Biology and Therapy* 2005 June; 4(6): 619-620. NRCBL: 1.3.7; 1.3.9.

Fernandez, Conrad V. Publication of ethically suspect research: should it occur? [editorial]. *International Journal*

NRCBL: National Reference Center for Bioethics Literature Classification Scheme   See inside front cover for terms.

367

for Quality in Health Care 2005 October; 17(5): 377-378. NRCBL: 1.3.7; 18.6; 1.3.9; 18.3.

Finucane, Thomas E.; Ancoli-Israel, Sonia; Folks, David G.; Krystal, Andrew D.; McCall, W. Vaughn. Advertising the new hypnotics [letter and reply]. *Journal of the American Geriatrics Society* 2006 January; 54(1): 170-172. NRCBL: 1.3.7; 1.3.9; 9.7.

Flanagin, Annette; Fontanarosa, Phil B.; DeAngelis, Catherine D. Update on JAMA's conflict of interest policy. *JAMA: the Journal of the American Medical Association* 2006 July 12; 296(2): 220-221. NRCBL: 1.3.7; 1.3.9; 7.3.

Fontanarosa, Phil B.; DeAngelis, Catherine D. JAMA's policy on industry sponsored studies [letter]. *BMJ: British Medical Journal* 2006 January 21; 332(7534): 177. NRCBL: 1.3.7; 5.3; 1.3.9.

Fraser, J.; Alexander, C. Publish and perish: a case study of publication ethics in a rural community. *Journal of Medical Ethics* 2006 September; 32(9): 526-529. NRCBL: 1.3.7; 1.3.9; 9.1. SC: em.

Abstract: Health researchers must weigh the benefits and risks of publishing their findings. OBJECTIVE: To explore differences in decision making between rural health researchers and managers on the publication of research from small identifiable populations. METHOD: A survey that investigated the attitudes of Australian rural general practitioners (GPs) to nurse practitioners was explored. Decisions on the study's publication were analysed with bioethical principles and health service management ethical decision-making models. RESULTS: Response rate was 78.5% (62/79 GPs). 84-94% of GP responders considered it to be undesirable for nurse practitioners to initiate referrals to medical specialists (n=58), to initiate diagnostic imaging (n=56) and to prescribe medication (n=52). BIOETHICAL ANALYSIS: It was concluded that the principle of beneficence outweighed the principle of non-maleficence and that a valid justification for the publication of these results existed. DECISION-MAKING MODELS OF HEALTH SERVICE MANAGERS: On the basis of models of ethical decision making in health service management, the decisions of the area's health managers resulted in approval to publish this project's results being denied. This was because the perceived risks to the health service outweighed benefits. Confidentiality could not be ensured by publication under a regional nom de plume. CONCLUSIONS: A conflict of interests between rural researchers and health managers on publication of results is shown by this case study. Researchers and managers at times owe competing duties to key stakeholders. Both weigh the estimated risks and benefits of the effect of research findings. This is particularly true in a rural area, where identification of the subjects becomes more likely.

Freda, Margaret Comerford; Kearney, Margaret H. Ethical issues faced by nursing editors. *Western Journal of Nursing Research* 2005 June; 27(4): 487-499. NRCBL: 1.3.7; 4.1.3. SC: em.

Freedman, Robert; Lewis, David A.; Michels, Robert; Pine, Daniel S.; Schultz, Susan K.; Tamminga, Carol T.; Patterson, Sandra L.; McIntyre, John S.; Goldman, Howard H.; Yudofsky, Stuart C.; Hales, Robert E.; Rapaport, Mark H.; Hales, Deborah; Krajeski, James;

Kupfer, David J.; Badaracco, Mary Anne; Scully, James H. Jr. Conflict of interest, round 2 [editorial]. *American Journal of Psychiatry* 2006 September; 163(9): 1481-1483. NRCBL: 1.3.7; 1.3.9.

Freeman, Paul B. To err is human . . . sometimes [editorial]. *Optometry* 2006 February; 77(2): 59. NRCBL: 1.3.7; 1.3.9.

Freshwater, Dawn. Editors and publishing: integrity, trust and faith [editorial]. *Journal of Psychiatric and Mental Health Nursing* 2006 February; 13(1): 1-2. NRCBL: 1.3.7; 1.3.9.

Fulda, Joseph S. Academics: multiple publications reconsidered II. *Journal of Information Ethics* 2006 Spring; 15(1): 5-7. NRCBL: 1.3.7. SC: an.

Fulda, Joseph S. Multiple publication reconsidered. *Journal of Information Ethics* 1998 Fall; 7(2): 47-53. NRCBL: 1.3.7.

Fuyuno, Ichiko; Cyranoski, David. Cash for papers: putting a premium on publication [news]. *Nature* 2006 June 15; 441(7095): 792. NRCBL: 1.3.7; 1.3.9.

Giles, Jim. Stacking the deck [news]. *Nature* 2006 March 16; 440(7082): 270-272. NRCBL: 1.3.7; 1.3.9; 18.1.

Glover, D. A suggested code of conduct for editors of peer-reviewed journals. *Journal of Wound Care* 2006 February; 15(2): 85-86. NRCBL: 1.3.7; 1.3.9; 6.

Godlee, Fiona; Dickersin, Kay. Bias, subjectivity, chance, and conflict of interest in editorial decisions. *In:* Godlee, Fiona; Jefferson, Tom, eds. Peer Review in Health Sciences. 2nd ed. London: BMJ Books; 2003: 91-117. NRCBL: 1.3.7; 1.3.9.

Goldstein, Irwin. The silver lining of a crisis: the Journal of Sexual Medicine establishes the ethics committee [editorial]. *Journal of Sexual Medicine* 2005 March; 2(2): 161-162. NRCBL: 1.3.7; 9.6.

Gøtzsche, Peter C.; Hrobjartsson, Asbjorn; Johansen, Helle Krogh; Haahr, Mette T.; Altman, Douglas G.; Chan, An-Wen. Constraints on publication rights in industry-initiated clinical trials [letter]. *JAMA: The Journal of the American Medical Association* 2006 April 12; 295(14): 1645-1646. NRCBL: 1.3.7; 1.3.9; 18.6. SC: em.

Gould, Donald. When doctors should tell. *New Statesman (London, England:* 1957) 1968 November 29; 76: 741-742. NRCBL: 1.3.7; 8.2; 8.5.

Griffith, Ezra E. H. Correction and disclosure. Regarding: Lewis DO, Yeager CA, Blake P, Bard B, Sternziok M: ethics questions raised by the neuropsychiatric, neuropsychological, educational, developmental, and family characteristics of 18 juveniles awaiting execution in Texas. *Journal of the American Academy of Psychiatry and the Law* 2006; 34(2): 142-144. NRCBL: 1.3.7; 18.2.

Haller, Daniel G. JCO and the public trust [editorial]. *Journal of Clinical Oncology* 2006 January 20; 24(3): 323-324. NRCBL: 1.3.7; 1.3.9; 7.3.

Hickey, Steve. Censorship of medical journals [letter]. *BMJ: British Medical Journal* 2006 July 1; 333(7557): 45. NRCBL: 1.3.7; 1.3.12.

Hoey, John. Editorial independence and the Canadian Medical Association Journal. *New England Journal of Medicine* 2006 May 11; 354(19): 1982-1983. NRCBL: 1.3.7; 9.7; 11.1.

Jones, James W.; McCullough, Laurence B.; Richman, Bruce W. The ethics of bylines: would the real authors please stand up? *Journal of Vascular Surgery* 2005 October; 42(4): 816-818. NRCBL: 1.3.7; 7.3.

Kaiser, Jocelyn. MEDLINE supplements must list corporate ties [news]. *Science* 2006 October 20; 314(5798): 405. NRCBL: 1.3.7; 1.3.9; 9.3.1; 1.3.12.

Kassirer, Jerome P.; Davidoff, Frank; O'Hara, Kathryn; Redelmeier, Donald A. Editorial autonomy of CMAJ. *CMAJ/JAMC: Canadian Medical Association Journal* 2006 March 28; 174(7): 945-950. NRCBL: 1.3.7; 11.1.

King, Tekoa L.; Murphy, Patricia Aikins. Editorial policies and publication ethics [editorial]. *Journal of Midwifery and Women's Health* 2006 March-April; 51(2): 69-70. NRCBL: 1.3.7; 9.8.

Kurth, Timothy; Cook, Nancy R.; Logroscino, Giancarlo; Diener, Hans-Christoph; Buring, Julie E.; DeAngelis, Catherine D. Unreported financial disclosures in a study of migraine and cardiovascular disease (letters). *JAMA: the Journal of the American Medical Association* 2006 August 9; 296(6): 653-654. NRCBL: 1.3.7; 1.3.9; 9.7. SC: cs.

Laflin, Molly T.; Glover, Elbert D.; McDermott, Robert J. Publication ethics: an examination of authorship practices. *American Journal of Health Behavior* 2005 November-December; 29(6): 579-587. NRCBL: 1.3.7.

Lanzafame, Raymond J. Ethics in reporting: truth and the scientific literature [editorial]. *Photomedicine and Laser Surgery* 2004 August; 22(4): 5-6. NRCBL: 1.3.7; 1.3.9; 18.2. SC: cs.

Lewis, David A.; Michels, Robert; Pine, Daniel S.; Schultz, Susan K.; Tamminga, Carol A.; Freedman, Robert. Conflict of interest [editorial]. *American Journal of Psychiatry* 2006 April; 163(4): 571-573. NRCBL: 1.3.7; 1.3.9; 9.7; 9.3.1.

Lexchin, Joel; Light, Donald W. Commercial influence and the consent of medical journals. *BMJ: British Medical Journal* 2006 June 17; 332(7555): 1444-1447. NRCBL: 1.3.7; 1.3.9; 9.3.1; 1.3.2.

Lim, Byungmook; Schmidt, Katja; White, Adrian; Ernst, Edzard. Reporting of ethical standards: differences between complementary and orthodox medicine journals? *Wiener Klinische Wochenschrift* 2004 July 31; 116(14): 500-503. NRCBL: 1.3.7; 18.1; 18.3; 18.2. SC: em.

Lush, Mary. Who wrote this? [letter]. *New Scientist* 2006 August 19-25; 191(2565): 20. NRCBL: 1.3.7; 1.3.9. Identifiers: authorship; collaboration in science.

Marcus, Emilie. Retraction controversy [editorial]. *Cell* 2005 October 21; 123(2): 173-175. NRCBL: 1.3.7; 1.3.9.

Marris, Emma. PS I want all the rights [news]. *Nature* 2006 July 13; 442(7099): 118-119. NRCBL: 1.3.7; 1.3.9. Identifiers: open-access debate.

Marris, Emma. Sackings put editorial freedom on the spot [news]. *Nature* 2006 March 2; 440(7080): 10-11. NRCBL: 1.3.7; 1.3.9; 9.7; 11.1. Identifiers: Canadian Medical Association Journal.

Marris, Emma. Should journals police scientific fraud? *Nature* 2006 February 2; 439(7076): 520-521. NRCBL: 1.3.7; 1.3.9.

Matteson, Eric L.; Bongartz, Tim. Investigation, explanation, and apology for incomplete and erroneous disclosures [letter]. *JAMA: The Journal of the American Medical Association* 2006 November 8; 296(18): 2205. NRCBL: 1.3.7; 1.3.9.

Mayer, S. Declaration of patent applications as financial interests: a survey of practice among authors of papers on molecular biology in Nature. *Journal of Medical Ethics* 2006 November; 32(11): 658-661. NRCBL: 1.3.7; 1.3.9; 8.2. SC: em.

Mayor, Susan. Surgery journal bans authors who hide conflicts of interest [news]. *BMJ: British Medical Journal* 2006 January 21; 332(7534): 135. NRCBL: 1.3.7; 1.3.9.

McLellan, Faith; Riis, Povl. Ethical conduct for reviewers of grant applications and manuscripts. *In:* Godlee, Fiona; Jefferson, Tom, eds. Peer Review in Health Sciences. 2nd ed. London: BMJ Books; 2003: 236-247. NRCBL: 1.3.7; 1.3.9.

McNeil, Donald G., Jr. Tough-talking journal editor faces accusations of leniency. *New York Times* 2006 August 1; p. F1, F3. NRCBL: 1.3.7. SC: po.

Nayak, Barun K. Editorial duty and misconduct — keeping an eye. *Indian Journal of Ophthalmology* 2006 March; 54(1): 1-2. NRCBL: 1.3.7.

Neale, Anne Victoria; Schwartz, Kendra L.; Bowman, Marjorie A. Conflict of interest: can we minimize its influence in the biomedical literature? [editorial]. *Journal of the American Board of Family Practice* 2005 September-October; 18(5): 411-413. NRCBL: 1.3.7; 1.3.9; 7.3; 9.7.

NRCBL: National Reference Center for Bioethics Literature Classification Scheme   See inside front cover for terms.

369

Newman, A.; Jones, R. Authorship for research papers: ethical and professional issues for short-term researchers. *Journal of Medical Ethics* 2006 July; 32(7): 420-423. NRCBL: 1.3.7; 1.3.9.

Abstract: Although the International Committee of Medical Journal Editors has published clear guidance on the authorship of scientific papers, short-term contract research workers, who perform much of the research that is reported in the biomedical literature, are often at a disadvantage in terms of recognition, reward and career progression. This article identifies several professional, ethical and operational issues associated with the assignment of authorship, describes how a university department of primary care set about identifying and responding to the concerns of its contract research staff on authorship and describes a set of guidelines that were produced to deal with the ethical and professional issues raised. These guidelines include directions on how authorship should be negotiated and allocated and how short-term researchers can begin to develop as authors. They also deal with the structures required to support an equitable system, which deals with the needs of short-term researchers in ways that are realistic in the increasingly competitive world of research funding and publication, and may offer a model for more formal guidelines that could form part of institutional research policy.

Niparko, John K.; Levine, Paul A.; Johns, Michael M.E. Our approach to addressing potential conflicts of interest [editorial]. *Archives of Otolaryngology—Head and Neck Surgery* 2005 November; 131(11): 943-944. NRCBL: 1.3.7.

Oberlander, Sarah E.; Spencer, Robert J. Graduate students and the culture of authorship. *Ethics and Behavior* 2006; 16(3): 217-232. NRCBL: 1.3.7; 17.1; 1.3.3; 6.

Phaosavasdi, Sukhit; Taneepanichskul, Surasak; Tannirandorn, Yuen; Thamkhantho, Manopchai; Prugsapong, Chumsak; Phupong, Vorapong; Karnjanapitak, Aurchart. What is your opinion on the "medical ethics of medical journal editors"? *Journal of the Medical Association of Thailand* 2005 August; 88(8): 1163-1164. NRCBL: 1.3.7; 1.3.9.

Rennie, Drummond. Misconduct and journal peer review. *In:* Godlee, Fiona; Jefferson, Tom, eds. Peer Review in Health Sciences. 2nd ed. London: BMJ Books; 2003: 118-129. NRCBL: 1.3.7; 1.3.9.

Ridker, Paul M. Incomplete financial disclosure for study of funding and outcomes in major cardiovascular trials [letter]. *JAMA: The Journal of the American Medical Association* 2006 June 21; 295(23): 2725-2726. NRCBL: 1.3.7; 1.3.9; 7.3.

Rivara, Frederick P.; Christakis, Dimitri A.; Cummings, Peter. Duplicate publication [editorial]. *Archives of Pediatrics and Adolescent Medicine* 2004 September; 158(9): 926. NRCBL: 1.3.7; 1.3.9.

Roth, Kevin A. Journal of Histochemistry and Cytochemistry editorial policies and ethical guidelines [editorial]. *Journal of Histochemistry and Cytochemistry* 2006 February; 54(2): 129-130. NRCBL: 1.3.7; 1.3.9.

Senn, Stephen J. JAMA's policy does not go far enough [letter]. *BMJ: British Medical Journal* 2006 February 4; 332(7536): 305. NRCBL: 1.3.7; 1.3.9. Identifiers: Journal of the American Medical Association.

Shimada, Yasuhiro. Conflict of interest in scientific medical journal [editorial]. *Japanese Journal of Clinical Oncology* 2005 June; 35(6): 363. NRCBL: 1.3.7; 1.3.9.

Shuchman, Miriam; Redelmeier, Donald A. Politics and independence — the collapse of the Canadian Medical Association Journal. *New England Journal of Medicine* 2006 March 30; 354(13): 1337-1339. NRCBL: 1.3.7.

Smart, Andrew. Reporting the dawn of the post-genomic era: who wants to live forever? *Sociology of Health and Illness* 2003 January; 25(1): 24-49. NRCBL: 1.3.7; 5.3; 15.10. Identifiers: Human Genome Project; United Kingdom(Great Britain).

Smith, Richard. Medical journals are an extension of the marketing arm of pharmaceutical companies. *PLoS Medicine* 2005 May; 2(5): 0364-0366. NRCBL: 1.3.7; 1.3.2; 9.7.

Smith, Richard. The trouble with medical journals. *Journal of the Royal Society of Medicine* 2006 March; 99(3): 115-119. NRCBL: 1.3.7; 1.3.9.

Tanne, Janice Hopkins. Science will tighten standards after retracting stem cell papers [news]. *BMJ: British Medical Journal* 2006 December 9; 333(7580): 1189. NRCBL: 1.3.7; 1.3.9.

Tyrer, Peter. Combating editorial racism in psychiatric publications [editorial]. *British Journal of Psychiatry* 2005 January; 186: 1-3. NRCBL: 1.3.7; 1.3.9; 21.1; 17.1. Identifiers: United Kingdom (Great Britain).

Wager, Elizabeth; Herxheimer, Andrew. Peer review and the pharmaceutical industry. *In:* Godlee, Fiona; Jefferson, Tom, eds. Peer Review in Health Sciences. 2nd ed. London: BMJ Books; 2003: 130-139. NRCBL: 1.3.7; 1.3.9; 9.7.

Watson, Roger. Editorial: should studies without ethical permission be published in JCN? *Journal of Clinical Nursing* 2006 March; 15(3): 251. NRCBL: 1.3.7; 1.3.9.

Webster, Paul. Canadian researchers respond to CMAJ crisis. *Lancet* 2006 April 8-14; 367(9517): 1133-1134. NRCBL: 1.3.7; 1.3.2; 7.3; 11.1. Identifiers: Canadian Medical Association Journal.

Webster, Paul. CMAJ editors dismissed amid calls for more editorial freedom. *Lancet* 2006 March 4-10; 367(9512): 720. NRCBL: 1.3.7; 9.7. Identifiers: Canadian Medical Association Journal.

Wilson, Mark H. The CMA's legitimation crisis [letter]. *BMJ: British Medical Journal* 2006 April 8; 332(7545):

854. NRCBL: 1.3.7. Identifiers: Canadian Medical Association.

Woolley, Karen L.; Ely, Julie A.; Woolley, Mark J.; Findlay, Leigh; Lynch, Felicity A.; Choi, Yoonah; Mc-Donald, Jane M. Declaration of medical writing assistance in international peer-reviewed publications [letter]. *JAMA: The Journal of the American Medical Association* 2006 August 23-30; 296(8): 932-934. NRCBL: 1.3.7; 1.3.9. SC: em.

Youngs, Robin; Kenyon, Guy. Maintaining ethical standards in medical publishing [editorial]. *Journal of Laryngology and Otology* 2006 January; 120(1): 1-2. NRCBL: 1.3.7.

JUSTICE *See* RESOURCE ALLOCATION; RIGHT TO HEALTH CARE

LEGAL ASPECTS *See* ABORTION/ LEGAL ASPECTS; AIDS/ LEGAL ASPECTS; BIOETHICS AND MEDICAL ETHICS/ LEGAL ASPECTS; CLONING/ LEGAL ASPECTS; EUTHANASIA AND ALLOWING TO DIE/ LEGAL ASPECTS; GENETIC SCREENING/ LEGAL ASPECTS; GENETICS/ LEGAL ASPECTS; HUMAN EXPERIMENTATION/ ETHICS COMMITTEES AND POLICY GUIDELINES/ LEGAL ASPECTS; HUMAN EXPERIMENTATION/ SPECIAL POPULATIONS/ EMBRYOS AND FETUSES/ LEGAL ASPECTS; ORGAN AND TISSUE TRANSPLANTATION/ DONATION AND PROCUREMENT/ LEGAL ASPECTS

LIVING WILLS *See* ADVANCE DIRECTIVES

MALPRACTICE AND PROFESSIONAL MISCONDUCT
See also BIOMEDICAL RESEARCH/ RESEARCH ETHICS AND SCIENTIFIC MISCONDUCT

Fraud and the role of the NHS nurse. *British Journal of Nursing* 2006 June 22-July 12; 15(12): 655. NRCBL: 7.4; 7.1; 9.8. SC: cs. Identifiers: National Health Service; United Kingdom(Great Britain).

Adrian, Cheri. Therapist sexual feelings in hypnotherapy: managing therapeutic boundaries in hypnotic work. *International Journal of Clinical and Experimental Hypnosis* 1996 January; 44(1): 20-32. NRCBL: 7.4; 17.2; 8.1; 10. SC: cs.

Beller, George A. Fraud in medicine. *Journal of Nuclear Cardiology* 2005 May-June; 12(3): 253-254. NRCBL: 7.4; 9.3.1.

Bonetta, Laura. The aftermath of scientific fraud. *Cell* 2006 March 10; 124(5): 873-875. NRCBL: 7.4; 1.3.9.

Campbell, R. Joan. Intimacy boundaries: between mental health nurses and psychiatric patients. *Journal of Psychosocial Nursing and Mental Health Services* 2005 May; 43(5): 32-39. NRCBL: 7.4; 17.1; 10; 4.1.3; 8.1. SC: cs; em. Identifiers: Canada.

Dimond, Bridgit. Duty to report: legal implications of nurses stealing from patients. *British Journal of Nursing* 2006 November 23-December 13; 15(21): 1196-1197. NRCBL: 7.4; 8.4. SC: le.

Dobash, Tanya J. Physician-patient sexual contact: the battle between the state and the medical profession. *Washington and Lee Law Review* 1993 Fall; 50(4): 1725-1759. NRCBL: 7.4; 1.3.5; 8.1; 10. SC: le.

Donohoe, Martin T. Problem doctors: is there a system-level solution? [letter]. *Annals of Internal Medicine* 2006 June 6; 144(11): 862. NRCBL: 7.4; 9.5.9.

Drew, Christopher; Dewan, Shaila. Accused doctor said to have faced chaos at New Orleans Hospital. *New York Times* 2006 July 20; p. A18. NRCBL: 7.4; 20.4.1; 20.5.1. SC: po; le. Identifiers: Hurricane Katrina 2005.

Dusesoi, J. A basic understanding of the judicial procedure. *Acta Chirurgica Belgica* 2000 August; 100(4): 165-168. NRCBL: 8.5; 8.3.1. SC: le.

Foehl, John C. "How could this happen to me?": sexual misconduct and us. *Journal of the American Psychoanalytic Association* 2005 Summer; 53(3): 957-970. NRCBL: 7.4; 8.1; 17.2; 10.

Genovese, Elizabeth. Workers' compensation fraud and the physician. *Clinics in Occupational and Environmental Medicine* 2004 May; 4(2): 361-372. NRCBL: 7.4; 16.3.

Gifford, David R; Crausman, Robert S.; Mcintyre, Bruce W. Problem doctors: is there a system-level solution? [letter]. *Annals of Internal Medicine* 2006 June 6; 144(11): 862-863. NRCBL: 7.4; 9.5.9.

Glass, Allan R.; Papadakis, Maxine A.; Rattner, Susan L.; Stern, David T. Unprofessional behavior among medical students [letter and reply]. *New England Journal of Medicine* 2006 April 27; 354(17): 1851-1853. NRCBL: 7.4; 7.2.

Gold, Mark S. Problem doctors: is there a system-level solution? [letter]. *Annals of Internal Medicine* 2006 June 6; 144(11): 861-862. NRCBL: 7.4; 9.5.9.

Hanauer, Stephen B. Conflicts of interest. *Nature Clinical Practice. Gastroenterology and Hepatology* 2005 January; 2(1): 1. NRCBL: 7.4.

Healy, Gerald B. Unprofessional behavior: enough is enough. *Laryngoscope* 2006 March; 116(3): 357-358. NRCBL: 7.4; 7.3; 9.8.

Kessler, Daniel P.; Summerton, Nicholas; Graham, John R. Effects of the medical liability system in Austra-

NRCBL: National Reference Center for Bioethics Literature Classification Scheme   See inside front cover for terms.

371

lia, the UK, and the USA. *Lancet* 2006 July 15-21; 368(9531): 240-246. NRCBL: 8.5; 21.1. SC: le; rv.

Kuhn, Duncan M. Problem doctors: is there a system-level solution? [letter]. *Annals of Internal Medicine* 2006 June 6; 144(11): 861. NRCBL: 7.4; 9.5.9.

Lowenfels, Albert B.; Papadakis, Maxine A.; Rattner, Susan L.; Stern, David T. Unprofessional behavior among medical students [letter and reply]. *New England Journal of Medicine* 2006 April 27; 354(17): 1852-1853. NRCBL: 7.4; 7.2.

Lust, A. Some practical advice concerning a medical lawsuit. *Acta Chirurgica Belgica* 2000 August; 100(4): 160-164. NRCBL: 8.5; 9.3.1. SC: le. Identifiers: Belgium.

Nichols, Polly S.; Winslow, Gerald. The dating dentist. *General Dentistry* 2005 September-October; 53(5): 324-326. NRCBL: 7.4; 10. SC: cs.

Nilstun, Tore; Westerholm, Peter. Whistleblowing. *In:* Westerholm, Peter; Nilstun, Tore; Øvretveit, John, eds. Practical Ethics in Occupational Health. San Francisco: Radcliffe Medical Press; 2004: 283-290. NRCBL: 7.4; 16.3.

Odom, Lamar; Garcia, Anthony; Milburn, Pamela. The ethics of capping non-economic damages to control rising healthcare costs: panacea or false and misleading practice? *Leadership in Health Services* 2005; 18(3): i-xi. NRCBL: 8.5; 9.3.1. SC: rv.

Papadimos, T.J. Nietzsche's morality: a genealogy of medical malpractice. *Medical Humanities* 2006 December; 32(2): 107-110. NRCBL: 8.5; 1.1; 8.1.

Povar, Gail. Are we our brothers' (and sisters') keepers? *Maryland Medicine* 2005 Summer; 6(3): 44, 46. NRCBL: 7.4; 9.8; 9.5.9; 1.1. SC: cs.

Rackoff, Wayne R.; Papadakis, Maxine A.; Rattner, Susan L.; Stern, David T. Unprofessional behavior among medical students [letter and reply]. *New England Journal of Medicine* 2006 April 27; 354(17): 1852-1853. NRCBL: 7.4; 7.2.

Rockey, Don C.; Papadakis, Maxine A.; Rattner, Susan L.; Stern, David T. Unprofessional behavior among medical students [letter and reply]. *New England Journal of Medicine* 2006 April 27; 354(17): 1852-1853. NRCBL: 7.4; 7.2.

Samuels, Alec. Serious professional misconduct. *Medico-Legal Journal* 2005; 73(Part 4): 166-168. NRCBL: 7.4.

Sheather, Julian. Sexual relationships between doctors and former patients [editorial]. *BMJ: British Medical Journal* 2006 December 2; 333(7579): 1132. NRCBL: 7.4; 8.1; 10. Identifiers: United Kingdom (Great Britain).

Sherman, Nancy. Holding doctors responsible at Guantánamo. *Kennedy Institute of Ethics Journal* 2006 June; 16(2): 199-203. NRCBL: 7.4; 21.4; 21.2; 17.1; 8.1; 1.1.

Slovenko, Ralph. Patient and non-patient spouse lawsuits for undue familiarity. *Journal of Psychiatry and Law* 2006 Winter; 34(4): 567-578. NRCBL: 7.4; 10; 8.1; 8.5. SC: le.

Slovenko, Ralph. The boundary violation of undue familiarity. *In his:* Psychiatry in Law/Law in Psychiatry. Volume 2. New York: Brunner-Routledge; 2002: 739-763. NRCBL: 7.4; 8.1; 10.

Thomson, Alexander N.; White, Gillian Eyres. Attitudes toward sexual contact between general practitioners and their patients. *New Zealand Medical Journal* 1995 June 28; 108(1002): 247-249. NRCBL: 7.4; 8.1; 10.

West, John C. Medical malpractice/battery. Various causes of action available in 'ghost surgery' case. *Journal of Healthcare Risk Management* 2004; 24(1): 31-32. NRCBL: 8.5; 9.8. SC: cs; le. Identifiers: Meyers v. Epstein, 282 F. Supp. 2d 151 (S. D. N. Y. 2003).

Woteki, Catherine E. Ethics opinion: conflicts of interest in presentations and publications and dietetics research. *Journal of the American Dietetic Association* 2006 January; 106(1): 27-31. NRCBL: 7.4; 7.3; 1.3.9.

MANAGED CARE PROGRAMS *See* HEALTH CARE/ HEALTH CARE ECONOMICS/ MANAGED CARE PROGRAMS

MASS SCREENING *See* PUBLIC HEALTH

MEDICAL EDUCATION
See also BIOETHICS AND MEDICAL ETHICS/ EDUCATION

What should the dean do? [case study and commentaries]. *Hastings Center Report* 2006 July-August; 36(4): 14. NRCBL: 7.2; 8.1; 7.1.

Abbo, Elmer D.; Volandes, Angelo E. Teaching residents to consider costs in medical decision making. *American Journal of Bioethics* 2006 July-August; 6(4): 33-34. NRCBL: 7.2; 2.3; 9.3.1. Comments: Susan Dorr Goold and David T. Stern. Ethics and professionalism: what does a resident need to learn? American Journal of Bioethics 2006 July-August; 6(4): 9-17.

Acharya, Shashidhar. The ethical climate in academic dentistry in India: faculty and student perceptions. *Journal of Dental Education* 2005 June; 69(6): 671-680. NRCBL: 7.2; 4.1.1; 2.1. SC: em.

Arnold, Robert M. Focusing on education rather than clinical ethics. *American Journal of Bioethics* 2006 July-August; 6(4): 18-19. NRCBL: 7.2; 2.3. Comments: Susan Dorr Goold and David T. Stern. Ethics and professionalism: what does a resident need to learn? *American Journal of Bioethics* 2006 July-August; 6(4): 9-17.

Austin, Zubin; Simpson, Stephanie; Reynen, Emily. 'The fault lies not in our students, but in ourselves': academic honesty and moral development in health professions education — results of a pilot study in Canadian pharmacy. *Teaching in Higher Education* 2005 April; 10(2): 143-156. NRCBL: 7.2; 9.7; 1.1. SC: em.

Baldwin, DeWitt C.; Self, Donnie J. The assessment of moral reasoning and professionalism in medical education and practice. *In:* Stern, David Thomas, ed. Measuring Medical Professionalism. New York: Oxford University Press; 2006: 75-93. NRCBL: 7.2.

Barnbaum, Deborah R. Teaching empathy in medical ethics: the use of "lottery assignments". *Teaching Philosophy* 2001 March; 24(1): 63-75. NRCBL: 7.2; 2.3.

Barnett, Katherine Gergen; Fortin, Auguste H., VI. Spirituality and medicine: a workshop for medical students and residents. *JGIM: Journal of General Internal Medicine* 2006 May; 21(5): 481-485. NRCBL: 7.2; 1.2.

Begley, Ann M. Facilitating the development of moral insight in practice: teaching ethics and teaching virtue. *Nursing Philosophy* 2006 October; 7(4): 257-265. NRCBL: 7.2; 1.1; 1.3.1; 4.1.

Bertolami, Charles N. Why our ethics curricula don't work. *Journal of the American College of Dentists* 2006 Summer; 73(2): 35-46. NRCBL: 7.2; 2.3; 4.1.1.

Bolin, Jane Nelson. Strategies for incorporating professional ethics education in graduate medical programs. *American Journal of Bioethics* 2006 July-August; 6(4): 35-36. NRCBL: 7.2; 2.3. Comments: Susan Dorr Goold and David T. Stern. Ethics and professionalism: what does a resident need to learn? American Journal of Bioethics 2006 July-August; 6(4): 9-17.

Boutain, Doris M. Social justice as a framework for professional nursing. *Journal of Nursing Education* 2005 September; 44(9): 404-408. NRCBL: 7.2; 4.1.3; 1.1.

Bowman, Marjorie A.; Pearle, David L. Changes in drug prescribing patterns related to commercial company funding of continuing medical education. *Journal of Continuing Education in the Health Professions* 1988; 8(1): 13-20. NRCBL: 7.2; 9.7; 7.3; 9.3.1.

Brecher, B. Why the Kantian ideal survives medical learning curves, and why it matters. *Journal of Medical Ethics* 2006 September; 32(9): 511-512. NRCBL: 7.2; 8.1; 1.1.
Abstract: The "Kantian ideal" is often misunderstood as invoking individual autonomy rather than rational self legislation. Le Morvan and Stock's otherwise insightful discussion of "Medical learning curves and the Kantian ideal"— for example — draws the mistaken inference that that [sic; the] ideal is inconsistent with the realities of medical practice. But it is not. Rationally to be a patient entails accepting its necessary conditions.

Brorsson, Annika; Hellquist, Gunilla; Björkelund, Cecilia; Råstam, Lennart. Serious, frightening and interesting conditions: differences in values and attitudes between first-year and final-year medical students. *Medical Education* 2002 June; 36(6): 555-560. NRCBL: 7.2.

Bucci, Kathryn K.; Frey, Keith A. Involvement of pharmacy faculty in the development of policies for pharmaceutical sales representatives. *Journal of Family Practice* 1992 January; 34(1): 49-52. NRCBL: 7.2; 9.7; 7.3. SC: em.

Buchanan, David; Khoshnood, Kaveh; Stopka, Tom; Shaw, Susan; Santelices, Claudia; Singer, Merrill. Ethical dilemmas created by the criminalization of status behaviors: case examples from ethnographic field research with injection drug users. *Health Education and Behavior* 2002 February; 29(1): 30-42. NRCBL: 7.2; 9.5.9; 8.4; 8.3.1. SC: cs; em.

Byrne, Michelle M. Uncovering racial bias in nursing fundamentals textbooks. *Nursing and Health Care Perspectives* 2001 November-December; 22(6): 299-303. NRCBL: 7.2; 4.1.3; 21.1. SC: em. Identifiers: African Americans.

Carpenter, Robert O.; Austin, Mary T.; Tarpley, John L.; Griffin, Marie R.; Lomis, Kimberly D. Work-hour restrictions as an ethical dilemma for residents. *American Journal of Surgery* 2006 April; 191(4): 527-532. NRCBL: 7.2; 7.1. SC: em. Identifiers: New York.

Caves, N.D.; Irwin, M.G. Attitudes to basic life support among medical students following the 2003 SARS outbreak in Hong Kong. *Resuscitation* 2006 January; 68(1): 93-100. NRCBL: 7.2; 20.5.1; 20.3.2.

Cohn, Jennifer M. Bioethics curriculum for paediatrics residents: implementation and evaluation. *Medical Education* 2005 May; 39(5): 530. NRCBL: 7.2; 2.3.

Cowley, C. Polemic: five proposals for a medical school admission policy. *Journal of Medical Ethics* 2006 August; 32(8): 491-494. NRCBL: 7.2; 4.1.2; 7.1.
Abstract: Five proposals for admitting better applicants into medical school are discussed in this article: (1) An A level in a humanity or social science would be required, to supplement—not replace—the stringent science requirement. This would ensure that successful candidates would be better "primed" for the medical curriculum. (2) Extra points in the applicant's initial screening would be awarded for an A level in English literature. (3) There would be a minimum age of 23 for applicants, although a prior degree would not be required. This is to ensure that the applicants are mature enough to know themselves and the world better, to make a more informed and motivated choice of career, and to get more out of the humanities components of the curriculum. (4) A year's full-time experience in a healthcare or charity environment would be desirable. (5) Applicants would be given two lists of interview discussion topics to prepare: works of literature and topics in healthcare politics.

Craig, Jana M.; May, Thomas. Ethics consultation as a tool for teaching residents. *American Journal of Bioethics*

NRCBL: National Reference Center for Bioethics Literature Classification Scheme   See inside front cover for terms.

373

2006 July-August; 6(4): 25-27. NRCBL: 7.2; 2.3. Comments: Susan Dorr Goold and David T. Stern. Ethics and professionalism: what does a resident need to learn? American Journal of Bioethics 2006 July-August; 6(4): 9-17.

Daniels, A.U. Dan. Ethics Education at the engineering/medicine interface. *Journal of Investigative Surgery* 1992 July-September; 5(3): 209-218. NRCBL: 7.2; 1.3.4.

Darmoni, S.J.; Le Duff, F.; Joubert, M.; Le Beux, P.; Fieschi, M.; Weber, J.; Benichou, J. A preliminary study to assess a French code of ethics for health teaching resources on the Internet. *Studies in Health Technology and Informatics* 2002; 90: 621- 626. NRCBL: 7.2; 1.3.12; 6.

de Freitas, Sérgio Fernando Torres; Kovaleski, Douglas Francisco; Boing, Antonio Fernando; de Oliveira, Walter Ferreira. Stages of moral development among Brazilian dental students. *Journal of Dental Education* 2006 March; 70(3): 296-306. NRCBL: 7.2; 1.3.1; 7.1. SC: em.

DelSignore, Jeanne L. Current guidelines regarding industry-sponsored continuing medical education. *Clinical Orthopaedics and Related Research* 2003 July; (412): 21-27. NRCBL: 7.2; 9.7; 1.3.2; 6; 9.3.1.

DeRenzo, Evan G. Individuals, systems, and professional behavior. *Journal of Clinical Ethics* 2006 Fall; 17(3): 275-288. NRCBL: 7.2; 8.1; 9.8; 4.1.1; 9.6.

Detorie, Nicholas. All medical physicists entering the field should have a specific course on research and practice ethics in their educational background: against the proposition. *Medical Physics* 2003 December; 30(12): 3050-3051. NRCBL: 7.2; 1.1; 2.3.

Dowling, Claudia. The visible man: the execution and electronic afterlife of Joseph Paul Jernigan. *Life* 1997 February 20: 41, 44. NRCBL: 7.2; 1.3.12.

Dwyer, James. What should the dean do? [case study and commentaries]. *Hastings Center Report* 2006 July-August; 36(4): 16. NRCBL: 7.2; 8.1; 7.1.

Eastwood, Gregory L. What should the dean do? [case study and commentaries]. *Hastings Center Report* 2006 July-August; 36(4): 14-15. NRCBL: 7.2; 8.1; 7.1.

Escobar, Mauricio A.; McCullough, Laurence B. Responsibly managing ethical challenges of residency training: a guide for surgery residents, educators, and residency program leaders. *Journal of the American College of Surgeons* 2006 March; 202(3): 531-535. NRCBL: 7.2.

Evans, Martyn. Reflections on the humanities in medical education. *Medical Education* 2002 June; 36(6): 508-513. NRCBL: 7.2; 7.1.

Faunce, Thomas A.; Gatenby, Paul. Flexner's ethical oversight reprised? Contemporary medical education and the health impacts of corporate globalisation. *Medical Ed-* ucation 2005 October; 39(10): 1066-1074. NRCBL: 7.2; 21.1; 9.3.1; 2.2.

Ferguson, Robert P.; Rhim, Eugene; Belizaire, Waindel; Egede, Leonard; Carter, Kennita; Langsdale, Thomas. Encounters with pharmaceutical sales representatives among practicing internists. *American Journal of Medicine* 1999 August; 107(2): 149-152. NRCBL: 7.2; 9.7; 7.3. SC: em.

Forster, Jean L.; Kahn, Jeffrey P. Ethical challenges in public health education research and practice: introduction. *Health Education and Behavior* 2002 February; 29(1): 12-13. NRCBL: 7.2; 9.1; 18.1.

Frank, Erica; Carrera, Jennifer S.; Stratton, Terry; Bickel, Janet; Nora, Lois Margaret. Experiences of belittlement and harassment and their correlates among medical students in the United States: longitudinal survey. *BMJ: British Medical Journal* 2006 September 30; 333(7570): 682-684. NRCBL: 7.2; 7.1. SC: em.

Friedland, Allen R.; Farber, Neil J.; Collier, Virginia U. Brief report: health care provided by program directors to their resident physicians and families. *JGIM: Journal of General Internal Medicine* 2006 December; 21(12): 1310-1312. NRCBL: 7.2; 7.3; 8.1. SC: em.

Fryer-Edwards, Kelly; Wilkins, M. Davis; Baernstein, Amy; Braddock, Clarence H., III. Bringing ethics education to the clinical years: ward ethics sessions at the University of Washington. *Academic Medicine* 2006 July; 81(7): 626-631. NRCBL: 7.2; 2.3. SC: em.

Goldberg, Aviva. Are dead bodies necessary? Dissecting prosections in anatomy lab. *Atrium* 2005 Spring; 1: 6-7. NRCBL: 7.2; 20.3.2.

Goldie, John; Schwartz, Lisa; McConnachie, Alex; Jolly, Brian; Morrison, Jillian. Can students' reasons for choosing set answers to ethical vignettes be reliably rated? Development and testing of a method. *Medical Teacher* 2004 December; 26(8): 713-718. NRCBL: 7.2; 2.3.

Goold, Susan Dorr; Stern, David T. Ethics and professionalism: what does a resident need to learn? *American Journal of Bioethics* 2006 July-August; 6(4): 9-17. NRCBL: 7.2; 2.3; 2.1. SC: em.

Hafferty, Frederic W. Professionalism — the next wave [editorial]. *New England Journal of Medicine* 2006 November 16; 355(20): 2151-2152. NRCBL: 7.2; 4.1.2.

Haidet, Paul; Dains, Joyce E.; Paterniti, Debora A.; Hechtel, Laura; Chang, Tai; Tseng, Ellen; Rogers, John C. Medical student attitudes toward the doctor-patient relationship. *Medical Education* 2002 June; 36(6): 568-574. NRCBL: 7.2; 8.1.

Handelsman, Mitchell M.; Gottlieb, Michael C.; Knapp, Samuel. Training ethical psychologists: an acculturation model. *Professional Psychology: Research and*

Practice 2005 February; 36(1): 59-65. NRCBL: 7.2; 17.1; 4.1.2.

Hren, Darko; Vujaklija, Ana; Ivanisevic, Ranka; Knezevic, Josip; Marusic, Matko; Marusic, Ana. Students' moral reasoning, Machiavellianism and socially desirable responding: implications for teaching ethics and research integrity. *Medical Education* 2006 March; 40(3): 269-277. NRCBL: 7.2; 2.3. SC: em.

Jotkowitz, Alan; Glick, Shimon. Education in professionalism should never end. *American Journal of Bioethics* 2006 July-August; 6(4): 27-28. NRCBL: 7.2; 2.3. Comments: Susan Dorr Goold and David T. Stern. Ethics and professionalism: what does a resident need to learn? American Journal of Bioethics 2006 July-August; 6(4): 9-17.

Kerridge, Ian H.; Ankeny, Rachel A.X.; Jordens, Christopher F.C.; Lipworth, Wendy L. Increasing diversity at the cost of decreasing equity? Issues raised by the establishment of Australia's first religiously affiliated medical school. *Medical Journal of Australia* 2005 July 4; 183(1): 28-30. NRCBL: 7.2; 1.2.

Kinzie, Susan. Med school owes its existence to many bodies of knowledge. *Washington Post* 2006 December 3; p. A1, A10. NRCBL: 7.2; 19.5. Identifiers: University of Maryland Medical School.

Kirklin, Deborah. Humanities in medical training and education. *Clinical Medicine* 2001 January-February; 1(1): 25-27. NRCBL: 7.2; 7.1; 8.1. Identifiers: United Kingdom (Great Britain).

La Marne, Paula. Reflexion ethique et formation medicale: soins palliatifs et accompagnement = Ethical reflections and medical education: palliative care and terminal care. *ADSP* 1999 September; (28): 54-56. NRCBL: 7.2; 20.4.1.

Larkin, Gregory Luke; McKay, Mary Pat; Angelos, Peter. Six core competencies and seven deadly sins: a virtues-based approach to the new guidelines for graduate medical education. *Surgery* 2005 September; 138(3): 490-497. NRCBL: 7.2. Identifiers: Accreditation Council for Graduate Medical Education (ACGME).

Lawler, P.G. Assessment of doctors in training: should patients give consent? *BMJ: British Medical Journal* 2006 February 18; 332(7538): 431. NRCBL: 7.2; 9.8; 8.3.1.

Lazarus, Arthur. Pharmaceutical policy issues for medical schools. *Psychiatric Services* 2006 February; 57(2): 167. NRCBL: 7.2; 1.3.9; 7.3.

Lindberg, Michael; Vergara, Cunegundo; Wild-Wesley, Rebecca; Gruman, Cynthia. Physicians-in-training attitudes toward caring for and working with patients with alcohol and drug abuse diagnoses. *Southern Medical Journal* 2006 January; 99(1): 28-35. NRCBL: 7.2; 9.5.9; 8.1.

Mahood, S.; Zagozeski, C.; Bradel, T.; Lawrence, K. Pharmaceutical policies in Canadian family medicine training: survey of residency programs. *Canadian Family Physician* 1997 November; 43: 1947-1951. NRCBL: 7.2; 9.7; 7.3. SC: em.

Mangan, Katherine. Acting sick. *Chronicle of Higher Education* 2006 September 15; 53(4): A10-A12. NRCBL: 7.2; 7.4; 8.2.

Mattick, Karen; Bligh, John. Undergraduate ethics teaching: revisiting the consensus statement. *Medical Education* 2006 April; 40(4): 329-332. NRCBL: 7.2; 2.3. SC: em. Identifiers: United Kingdom (Great Britain).

McComb, Peter. Negotiating consent = Consentement de négociation [editorial]. *Journal of Obstetrics and Gynaecology Canada* 2005 April; 27(4): 317-320. NRCBL: 7.2; 8.3.1; 9.5.5. Identifiers: Canada. Note: Full text in English and French.

Meier, Barry. Growing debate as doctors train on new devices. *New York Times* 2006 August 1; p. A1, C6. NRCBL: 7.2; 9.7. SC: po.

Modell, Stephen M.; Citrin, Toby. Ethics instruction in an issues-oriented course on public health genetics. *Health Education and Behavior* 2002 February; 29(1): 43-60. NRCBL: 7.2; 9.1; 15.1.

Mohamed, Mahmoud; Punwani, Manisha; Clay, Marjorie; Appelbaum, Paul. Protecting the residency training environment: a resident's perspective on the ethical boundaries in the faculty-resident relationship. *Academic Psychiatry* 2005 September-October; 29(4): 368-373. NRCBL: 7.2; 7.3.

Mohl, Paul C. Psychiatric training program engagement with the pharmaceutical industry: an educational issue, not strictly an ethical one. *Academic Psychiatry* 2005 May-June; 29(2): 215-221. NRCBL: 7.2; 17.1; 9.7; 1.3.3.

Morton, Kelly R.; Worthley, Joanna S.; Testerman, John K.; Mahoney, Marita L. Defining features of moral sensitivity and moral motivation: pathways to moral reasoning in medical students. *Journal of Moral Education* 2006 September; 35(3): 387-406. NRCBL: 7.2; 1.3.1; 1.2; 1.1; 7.1. SC: em. Identifiers: James Rest.

Mueller, Paul S.; Koenig, Barbara A. Systematic review of ethics consultation: a route to curriculum development in post-graduate medical education. *American Journal of Bioethics* 2006 July-August; 6(4): 21-23. NRCBL: 7.2; 2.3. Comments: Susan Dorr Goold and David T. Stern. Ethics and professionalism: what does a resident need to learn? American Journal of Bioethics 2006 July-August; 6(4): 9-17.

Nagata-Kobayashi, Shizuko; Sekimoto, Miho; Koyama, Hiroshi; Yamamoto, Wari; Goto, Eiji; Fukushima, Osamu; Ino, Teruo; Shimada, Tomoe;

NRCBL: National Reference Center for Bioethics Literature Classification Scheme   See inside front cover for terms.

375

Shimbo, Takuro; Asai, Atsushi; Koizumi, Shunzo; Fukui, Tsuguya. Medical student abuse during clinical clerkships in Japan. *JGIM: Journal of General Internal Medicine* 2006 March; 21(3): 212-218. NRCBL: 7.2; 7.3; 7.4. SC: em.

Nauta, Noks. Education in ethics. *In:* Westerholm, Peter; Nilstun, Tore; Øvretveit, John, eds. Practical Ethics in Occupational Health. San Francisco: Radcliffe Medical Press; 2004: 291-306. NRCBL: 7.2; 16.3; 2.3.

Nnodim, J.O.; Osuji, C.U. Comparison of medical and non-medical student attitudes to social issues in medicine. *Medical Education* 1995 July; 29(4): 273-277. NRCBL: 7.2; 4.1.2; 4.1.1; 9.1.

O'Brien, Richard L. Moral priorities in a teaching hospital: commentary. *Hastings Center Report* 2006 November-December; 36(6): 13, 14. NRCBL: 7.2; 8.1; 1.3.2. SC: cs.

O'Carroll, R.E.; Whiten, S.; Jackson, D.; Sinclair, D.W. Assessing the emotional impact of cadaver dissection on medical students. *Medical Education* 2002 June; 36(6): 550-554. NRCBL: 7.2; 20.3.

Otto, Sheila. Getting from here to there. *American Journal of Bioethics* 2006 July-August; 6(4): 19-21. NRCBL: 7.2; 2.3. Comments: Susan Dorr Goold and David T. Stern. Ethics and professionalism: what does a resident need to learn? American Journal of Bioethics 2006 July-August; 6(4): 9-17.

Page, Gayle Giboney. The importance of animal research to nursing science. *Nursing Outlook* 2004 March-April; 52(2): 102-107. NRCBL: 7.2; 4.1.3; 22.2.

Park, Park Bae. Teaching medical ethics in the future [discussion]. *Yonsei Medical Journal* 1985 December; 26(2): 139-141. NRCBL: 7.2; 2.3. Identifiers: Korea.

Parks, R.; Warren, P.M.; Boyd, K.M.; Cameron, H.; Cumming, A.; Lloyd-Jones, G. The objective structured clinical examination and student collusion: marks do not tell the whole truth. *Journal of Medical Ethics* 2006 December; 32(12): 734-738. NRCBL: 7.2; 7.4. SC: em.

Patel, Cynthia Joan; Shikongo, Armas E.E. Handling spirituality / religion in professional training: experiences of a sample of Muslim psychology students. *Journal of Religion and Health* 2006 Spring: 45(1): 93-112. NRCBL: 7.2; 1.2; 17.1; 7.1. SC: em.

Perez, Thomas E. Enhancing access to health care and eliminating racial and ethnic disparities in health status: a compelling case for health professions schools to implement race-conscious admissions policies. *Journal of Health Care Law and Policy* 2006; 9(1): 77-104. NRCBL: 7.2; 9.5.4. Conference: Symposium; Bridging the racial divide in health care: eliminating racial and ethnic disparities in health status; Baltimore, Maryland; 2005 March 11;

University of Maryland School of Law's Law and Health Care Program.

Pilon, Susan. Learning on the job — the case for mandatory research ethics education for research teams. *Clinical and Investigative Medicine* 2005 April; 28(2): 46-47. NRCBL: 7.2; 18.2. Identifiers: Canada.

Rancich, Ana María; Pérez, Marta Lucia; Morales, Celina; Gelpi, Ricardo Jorge. Beneficence, justice, and lifelong learning expressed in medical oaths. *Journal of Continuing Education in the Health Professions* 2005 Summer; 25(3): 211-220. NRCBL: 7.2; 6; 1.1. SC: em.

Rautio, Arja; Sunnari, Vappu; Nuutinen, Matti; Laitala, Marja. Mistreatment of university students most common during medical studies. *BMC Medical Education* 2005 October 18; 5(36): 12 p. NRCBL: 7.2; 10; 7.3. SC: em. Identifiers: Finland.

Reiheld, Alison. An unexpected opening to teach the impact of interactions between healthcare personnel. *American Journal of Bioethics* 2006 July-August; 6(4): 29-30. NRCBL: 7.2; 7.3; 2.3. Comments: Susan Dorr Goold and David T. Stern. Ethics and professionalism: what does a resident need to learn? American Journal of Bioethics 2006 July-August; 6(4): 9-17.

Rentmeester, Christy A. Moral priorities in a teaching hospital: commentary. *Hastings Center Report* 2006 November-December; 36(6): 13-14. NRCBL: 7.2; 8.1; 1.3.2. SC: cs.

Rentmeester, Christy A. What's legal? What's moral? What's the difference? A guide for teaching residents. *American Journal of Bioethics* 2006 July-August; 6(4): 31-33. NRCBL: 7.2; 2.3. Comments: Susan Dorr Goold and David T. Stern. Ethics and professionalism: what does a resident need to learn? American Journal of Bioethics 2006 July-August; 6(4): 9-17.

Richter, Lisa. Corporate sponsorships in dental education: solution or sellout? *CDS Review* 2005 September-October; 98(5): 12-17. NRCBL: 7.2; 4.1.1; 1.3.2; 9.3.1; 7.3.

Roberts, Laura Weiss; Geppert, Cynthia M.A.; Warner, Teddy D.; Green Hammond, Katherine A.; Lamberton, Leandrea Prosen. Bioethics principles, informed consent, and ethical care for special populations: curricular needs expressed by men and women physicians-in-training. *Psychosomatics* 2005 September-October; 46(5): 440-450. NRCBL: 7.2; 7.1; 2.2. SC: em.

Roberts, Laura Weiss; Warner, Teddy D.; Hammond, Katherine Green; Geppert, Cynthia M.A.; Heinrich, Thomas. Becoming a good doctor: perceived need for ethics training focused on practical and professional development topics. *Academic Psychiatry* 2005 July-August; 29(3): 301-309. NRCBL: 7.2; 2.1; 4.1.2; 1.3.1. SC: em.

Rosner, Fred. Research and/or training on the newly dead: the Jewish perspective. *Mount Sinai Journal of Medicine* 1997 March; 64(2): 120-124. NRCBL: 7.2; 20.2.1; 18.2; 18.3; 1.2.

Rowley, Beverley D.; Baldwin, DeWitt C., Jr.; Bay, R. Curtis; Cannula, Marco. Can professional values be taught? A look at residency training. *Clinical Orthopaedics and Related Research* 2000 September; (378): 110-114. NRCBL: 7.2; 4.1.2. SC: em.

Rowley, Beverley D.; Baldwin, DeWitt C., Jr.; Bay, R. Curtis; Karpman, Robert R. Professionalism and professional values in orthopaedics. *Clinical Orthopaedics and Related Research* 2000 September; (378): 90-96. NRCBL: 7.2; 7.3. SC: em.

Scanlan, Judith M.; Care, W. Dean; Gessler, Sandra. Dealing with the unsafe student in clinical practice. *Nurse Educator* 2001 January-February; 26(1): 23-27. NRCBL: 7.2; 4.1.3; 1.1; 9.8. SC: em.

Schiller, M. Rosita. E-cheating: electronic plagiarism. *Journal of the American Dietetic Association* 2005 July; 105(7): 1058, 1060-1062. NRCBL: 7.2; 1.3.12.

Schmidt, Sally D. Cheating: an ethical concern for nursing educators. *Kansas Nurse* 2006 January; 81(1): 1-2. NRCBL: 7.2; 4.1.3; 7.4.

Schneider, John A.; Arora, Vineet; Kasza, Kristen; Van Harrison, R., Humphrey, Holly. Residents' perceptions over time of pharmaceutical industry interactions and gifts and the effect of an educational intervention. *Academic Medicine* 2006 July; 81(7): 595-602. NRCBL: 7.2; 9.7; 1.3.2; 9.3.1. SC: em.

Self, Donnie J.; Baldwin, DeWitt C., Jr. Should moral reasoning serve as a criterion for student and resident selection? *Clinical Orthopaedics and Related Research* 2000 September; (378): 115-123. NRCBL: 7.2; 2.1.

Silva, Mary Cipriano; Ludwick, Ruth. Is the doctor of nursing practice ethical? *Online Journal of Issues in Nursing* 2006; 11(2): 8 p. NRCBL: 7.2; 4.1.3.

Spalding, Peter M.; Bradley, Richard E. Commercialization of dental education: have we gone too far? *Journal of the American College of Dentists* 2006 Fall; 73(3): 30-35. NRCBL: 7.2; 4.1.1; 9.3.1.

Spencer, John. Decline in empathy in medical education: how can we stop the rot? [editorial]. *Medical Education* 2004 September; 38(9): 916-920. NRCBL: 7.2; 8.1.

Spike, Jeffrey P. Residency education in clinical ethics and professionalism: not just what, but when, where, and how ought residents be taught? *American Journal of Bioethics* 2006 July-August; 6(4): 23-35. NRCBL: 7.2; 2.3. Comments: Susan Dorr Goold and David T. Stern. Ethics and professionalism: what does a resident need to

learn? American Journal of Bioethics 2006 July-August; 6(4): 9-17.

Stern, David T.; Papadakis, Maxine. The developing physician — becoming a professional. *New England Journal of Medicine* 2006 October 26; 355(17): 1794-1799. NRCBL: 7.2; 2.1; 1.3.1.

Tai, Michael Cheng-tek. A survey on the effectiveness of bioethics teaching in medical institutes. *Formosan Journal of Medical Humanities* 2006 June; 7(1-2): 133-157. NRCBL: 7.2; 2.3. SC: em.

ter Braak, Edith. Patients need not give consent in all clinical education [letter]. *BMJ: British Medical Journal* 2006 March 4; 332(7540): 549. NRCBL: 7.2; 8.3.1.

Tsai, Daniel Fu-Chang; Chen, Ding-Shinn. What should the dean do? [case study and commentaries]. *Hastings Center Report* 2006 July-August; 36(4): 15. NRCBL: 7.2; 8.1; 7.1.

Walsh, Kieran. Diva [case study]. *Advances in Health Sciences Education: Theory and Practice* 2005; 10(1): 81-84. NRCBL: 7.2; 8.4; 8.3.1. SC: cs. Identifiers: informed consent.

Weiting, Mark W.; Mevis, Howard; Zuckerman, Joseph D. The role of industry in Internet education. *Clinical Orthopaedics and Related Research* 2003 July; (412): 28-32. NRCBL: 7.2; 9.7; 1.3.12; 7.3.

Wendler, David; Shah, Seema. How can medical training and informed consent by reconciled with volume-outcome data? *Journal of Clinical Ethics* 2006 Summer; 17(2): 149-157. NRCBL: 7.2; 8.2; 8.3.1; 9.8.

Wicclair, Mark R. Training on newly deceased patients: an ethical analysis. *In:* Jansen, Lynn A., ed. Death in the Clinic. Lanham, MD: Rowman and Littlefield; 2006: 135-154. NRCBL: 7.2; 8.3.1; 8.3.3; 20.1.

Wilson, Elizabeth. End-of-life decisions by GPs. *Family Medicine* 2005 March; 37(3): 221. NRCBL: 7.2; 21.1; 20.5.1. Identifiers: general practitioners.

Wilson, Frederic S. Continuing medical education: ethical collaboration between sponsor and industry. *Clinical Orthopaedics and Related Research* 2003 July; (412): 33-37. NRCBL: 7.2; 9.7; 7.3; 8.1; 1.3.12.

Witek-Janusek, Linda. Commentary on the importance of animal research to nursing science. *Nursing Outlook* 2004 March-April; 52(2): 108-110. NRCBL: 7.2; 4.1.3; 22.2.

Wofford, James L.; Ohl, Christopher A. Teaching appropriate interactions with pharmaceutical company representatives: the impact of an innovative workshop on student attitudes. *BMC Medical Education [electronic]* 2005 February 8; 5(1): 5; 7 p. Accessed: http://www.

NRCBL: National Reference Center for Bioethics Literature Classification Scheme   See inside front cover for terms.

377

biomedcentral.com/1472-6920/5/5 [2006 February 22]. NRCBL: 7.2; 9.7; 7.3; 9.3.1. SC: em.

Wolf, G. Portrayal of negative qualities in a doctor as a potential teaching tool in medical ethics and humanism: Journey to the End of Night by Louis-Ferdinand Céline. *Postgraduate Medical Journal* 2006 February; 82(964): 154-156. NRCBL: 7.2; 7.1.

Wood, Diana F. Bullying and harassment in medical schools [editorial]. *BMJ: British Medical Journal* 2006 September 30; 333(7570): 664-665. NRCBL: 7.2; 7.3; 7.4. Identifiers: United Kingdom (Great Britain); United States.

MEDICAL ERRORS *See* HEALTH CARE/ HEALTH CARE QUALITY

MEDICAL ETHICS *See* BIOETHICS AND MEDICAL ETHICS

MENTAL HEALTH, CONCEPT OF
See also MENTAL HEALTH THERAPIES

Beresford, Peter; Wilson, Anne. Genes spell danger: mental health service users/survivors, bioethics and control. *Disability and Society* 2002 August; 17(5): 541-553. NRCBL: 4.3; 9.5.1; 9.5.3; 15.1; 17.1; 21.1. Identifiers: United Kingdom(Great Britain).

Breeding, John. Human rights progress in psychiatry: more apparent than real (observations and reflections on life in the Texas mental health courts). *Ethical Human Psychology and Psychiatry* 2006 Fall-Winter; 8(3): 241-254. NRCBL: 4.3; 4.4; 17.8. SC: cs.

Eastman, N.; Starling, B. Mental disorder ethics: theory and empirical investigation. *Journal of Medical Ethics* 2006 February; 32(2): 94-99. NRCBL: 4.3; 9.5.3. SC: em.
Abstract: Mental disorders and their care present unusual problems within biomedical ethics. The disorders themselves invite an ethical critique, as does society's attitude to them; researching the diagnosis and treatment of mental disorders also presents special ethical issues. The current high profile of mental disorder ethics, emphasised by recent political and legal developments, makes this a field of research that is not only important but also highly topical. For these reasons, the Wellcome Trust's biomedical ethics programme convened a meeting, "Investigating Ethics and Mental Disorders", in order to review some current research, and to stimulate topics and methods of future research in the field. The meeting was attended by policy makers, regulators, research funders, and researchers, including social scientists, psychiatrists, psychologists, lawyers, philosophers, criminologists, and others. As well as aiming to inspire a stronger research endeavour, the meeting also sought to stimulate an improved understanding of the methods and interactions that can contribute to "empirical ethics" generally. This paper reports on the meeting by describing contributions from individual speakers and discussion sections of the meeting. At the end we describe and discuss the conclusions of the meeting. As a result, the text is referenced less than would normally be expected in a review. Also, in summarising contributions from named presenters at the meeting it is possible that we have created inaccuracies; however, the definitive version of

each paper, as provided directly by the presenter, is available at http://www.wellcome.ac.uk/doc. WTX025116.html.

Gert, Bernard; Culver, Charles M.; Clouser, K. Danner. Mental maladies. *APA Newsletters: Newsletter on Philosophy and Medicine* 2006 Spring; 05(2): 20-22. NRCBL: 4.3; 7.1. SC: an.

Gert, Bernard; Culver, Charles M.; Clouser, K. Danner. Mental maladies. *In their:* Bioethics: A Systematic Approach. Second edition. New York: Oxford University Press; 2006: 165-190. NRCBL: 4.3. SC: an.

Maloney, Michelle. Polishing the mirror: mental health from a Bahá'i perspective. *Journal of Religion and Health* 2006 Fall; 45(3): 405-418. NRCBL: 4.3; 1.2.

Nichols, Alan. Foucault: power, madness and the symbol of the asylum. *Southwest Philosophy Review* 2000 January; 16(1): 133-140. NRCBL: 4.3; 17.1; 2.2.

Nys, Thomas R.V.; Nys, Maurits G. Psychiatry under pressure: reflections on psychiatry's drift towards a reductionist biomedical conception of mental illness. *Medicine, Health Care and Philosophy* 2006; 9(1): 107-115. NRCBL: 4.3; 1.1.
Abstract: We argue that contemporary psychiatry adopts a defensive strategy vis-a-vis various external sources of pressure. We will identify two of these sources—the plea for individual autonomy and the idea of Managed Care—and explain how they have promoted a strict biomedical conception of disease. The demand for objectivity, however, does not take into account the complexity of mental illness. It ignores that the psychiatrist's profession is essentially characterized by fragility: fluctuating between scientific reduction and the irreducible complexity of reality. Therefore, the psychiatrist is not in need of hard and fast rules, but of judgment. At the end, we suggest that philosophy could inject some healthy uncertainty within psychiatry in order to restore its fragile identity. Our examples are drawn from the Dutch situation but we are confident that they apply to other countries as well.

Pearson, Megan. The effect of clinical judgment in decision-making: the Mental Health Act 1986 (Vic.) and the Mental Health Review Board. *Ethical Human Psychology and Psychiatry* 2006 Spring; 8(1): 43-53. NRCBL: 4.3; 17.1; 8.3.1; 8.3.4; 8.4; 7.3. SC: le.

Pomerantz, Andrew M.; Segrist, Dan J. The influence of payment method on psychologists' diagnostic decisions regarding minimally impaired clients. *Ethics and Behavior* 2006; 16(3): 253-263. NRCBL: 4.3; 9.3.1; 17.1; 9.3.2; 7.1.

Sheather, Julian. The Mental Capacity Act 2005. *Clinical Ethics* 2006 March; 1(1): 33-36. NRCBL: 4.3; 8.3.1; 20.5.4; 8.3.4; 8.3.3. SC: le.

Single, Gregg. United States v. Sell: involuntary administration of antipsychotic medication. Are you dangerous or not? *Journal of Law and Health* 2003-2004; 18(2): 297-321. NRCBL: 4.3; 17.7; 8.3.4. SC: le.

Stefan, Susan. Silencing the different voice: competence, feminist theory and law. *University of Miami Law Review*

1993 January; 47(3): 763-815. NRCBL: 4.3; 10; 9.5.1; 8.3.3. SC: le.

Tomasini, Floris. Exploring ethical justification for self-demand amputation. *Ethics and Medicine* 2006 Summer; 22(2): 99-115. NRCBL: 4.3; 4.4; 1.1.

Winick, Bruce J. Psychotropic medication in the criminal trial process: the constitutional and therapeutic implications of Riggins v. Nevada. *New York Law School Journal of Human Rights* 1993 Symposium; 10(Part 3): 637-709. NRCBL: 4.3; 17.3; 7.1; 17.4; 8.3.4. SC: le.

MENTAL HEALTH THERAPIES

See also BEHAVIOR CONTROL; CARE FOR SPECIFIC GROUPS/ MENTALLY DISABLED; ELECTROCONVULSIVE THERAPY; HUMAN EXPERIMENTATION/ SPECIAL POPULATIONS/ MENTALLY DISABLED; INVOLUNTARY COMMITMENT; MENTAL HEALTH, CONCEPT OF; PSYCHOPHARMACOLOGY; PSYCHOTHERAPY

Ethics and ICT implants in humans [news]. *Bulletin of Medical Ethics* 2005 March; (206): 3-4. NRCBL: 17.1; 1.3.12; 1.1; 22.2. Identifiers: United Kingdom (Great Britain); information and communication technology.

Memory enhancement — a neuroethical dilemma [editorial]. *Lancet* 2006 August 19-15; 368(9536): 620. NRCBL: 17.1; 4.5.

Morals and the mind [review of The Ethical Brain, by Michael Gazzaniga]. *New Atlantis* 2006 Winter; 11: 121-125. NRCBL: 17.1; 4.4.

Neuroethics needed [editorial]. *Nature* 2006 June 22; 441(7096): 907. NRCBL: 17.1; 4.4.

The ethics of brain science: open your mind. *Economist* 2002 May 25; 363(8274): 5 p. [Online]. Accessed: http://web.ebscohost.com/ehost/delivery?vid=8&hid=5&sid=c902ab2a-0616-456 [2006 November 27]. NRCBL: 17.1; 5.2; 4.4; 8.4.

Adshead, Gwen; Sarkar, Sameer P. Justice and welfare: two ethical paradigms in forensic psychiatry. *Australian and New Zealand Journal of Psychiatry* 2005 November-December; 39(11-12): 1011-1017. NRCBL: 17.1; 1.1; 2.1; 1.3.5.

Allott, Piers. Mental disorder, diagnosis, treatment and ethics. *Journal of Ethics in Mental Health* 2006 November; 1(1): E11, 2 p. NRCBL: 17.1; 17.4.

Allphin, Claire. An ethical attitude in the analytic relationship. *Journal of Analytical Psychology* 2005 September; 50(4): 451-468. NRCBL: 17.2; 1.3.1.

Austin, Wendy; Bergum, Vangie; Nuttgens, Simon; Peternelj-Taylor, Cindy. A re-visioning of boundaries in

professional helping relationships: exploring other metaphors. *Ethics and Behavior* 2006; 16(2): 77-94. NRCBL: 17.1; 8.1; 7.1; 10. SC: an.

Ballantyne, Ron. Mental health ethics: the new reality [editorial]. *Journal of Ethics in Mental Health* 2006 November; 1(1): E1, 1 p. NRCBL: 17.1; 1.3.7.

Behr, G.M.; Ruddock, J.P.; Benn, P.; Crawford, M.J. Zero tolerance of violence by users of mental health services: the need for an ethical framework [editorial]. *British Journal of Psychiatry* 2005 July; 187: 7-8. NRCBL: 17.1; 8.1; 2.1; 6. Identifiers: National Health Service; United Kingdom (Great Britain).

Bird, Stephanie J. Neuroethics. *In:* Mitcham, Carl, ed. Encyclopedia of Science, Technology, and Ethics. Farmington Hills, MI: Thomson/Gale, 2005: 1310-1316. NRCBL: 17.1; 18.1.

Blass, David M.; Rye, Rebecca M.; Robbins, Beatrice M.; Miner, Mary M.; Handel, Sharon; Carroll, John L. Jr.; Rabins, Peter V. Ethical issues in mobile psychiatric treatment with homebound elderly patients: the psychogeriatric assessment and treatment in city housing experience. *Journal of the American Geriatrics Society* 2006 May; 54(5): 843-848. NRCBL: 17.1; 9.5.2; 8.3.4; 8.4.

Bloch, Sidney; Green, Stephen A. An ethical framework for psychiatry. *British Journal of Psychiatry* 2006 January; 188: 7-12. NRCBL: 17.1; 4.1.2; 1.1; 2.1.

Bloch, Sidney; Pargiter, Russell. A history of psychiatric ethics. *Psychiatric Clinics of North America* 2002 September; 25(3): 509-524. NRCBL: 17.1; 2.2; 6.

Bolmsjö, Ingrid Ågren; Edberg, Anna-Karin; Sandman, Lars. Everyday ethical problems in dementia care: a teleological model. *Nursing Ethics* 2006 July; 13(4): 340-359. NRCBL: 17.1; 1.1; 9.5.2.

Abstract: In this article, a teleological model for analysis of everyday ethical situations in dementia care is used to analyse and clarify perennial ethical problems in nursing home care for persons with dementia. This is done with the aim of describing how such a model could be useful in a concrete care context. The model was developed by Sandman and is based on four aspects: the goal; ethical side-constraints to what can be done to realize such a goal; structural constraints; and nurses' ethical competency. The model contains the following main steps: identifying and describing the normative situation; identifying and describing the different possible alternatives; assessing and evaluating the different alternatives; and deciding on, implementing and evaluating the chosen alternative. Three ethically difficult situations from dementia care were used for the application of the model. The model proved useful for the analysis of nurses' everyday ethical dilemmas and will be further explored to evaluate how well it can serve as a tool to identify and handle problems that arise in nursing care.

Brown, Jeffrey L.; Cogan, Karen D. Ethical clinical practice and sport psychology: when two worlds collide.

NRCBL: National Reference Center for Bioethics Literature Classification Scheme   See inside front cover for terms.

379

Ethics and Behavior 2006; 16(1): 15-23. NRCBL: 17.1; 1.3.1; 8.4; 4.3; 9.3.1.

Abstract: From their own practices, the authors offer insight into potential ethical dilemmas that may frequently develop in an applied psychology setting in which sport psychology is also being practiced. Specific ethical situations offered for the reader's consideration include confidentiality with coaches, administration, parents, and athlete-clients; accountability in ethical billing practices and accurate diagnosing; identification of ethical boundaries in nontraditional practice settings (locker room, field, rink, etc.); and establishment of professional competence as it relates to professional practice and marketing.

Buller, T. What can neuroscience contribute to ethics? *Journal of Medical Ethics* 2006 February; 32(2): 63-64. NRCBL: 17.1.

Cantegreil-Kallen, Inge; Turbelin, Clement; Olaya, Emile; Blanchon, Thierry; Moulin, Florence; Rigaud, Anne-Sophie; Flahault, Antoine. Disclosure of diagnosis of Alzheimer's disease in French general practice. *American Journal of Alzheimer's Disease and Other Dementias* 2005 July-August; 20(4): 228-232. NRCBL: 17.1; 8.2; 9.5.2. SC: em.

Cheshire, William P., Jr. Neuroscience, nuance, and neuroethics. *Ethics and Medicine* 2006 Summer; 22(2): 71-73. NRCBL: 17.1; 4.2; 4.3; 4.5; 7.1.

Cowen, Tyler. Enter the neuro-economists: why do investors do what they do? *New York Times* 2006 April 20; p. C3. NRCBL: 17.1; 1.3.2.

Dawson, John. Fault-lines in community treatment order legislation. *International Journal of Law and Psychiatry* 2006 November-December; 29(6): 482-492. NRCBL: 17.1; 17.7; 8.3.3. SC: em; le.

Debiec, Jacek; Altemus, Margaret. Toward a new treatment for traumatic memories. *Cerebrum: The DANA Forum on Brain Science* 2006 September: 2-11. NRCBL: 17.1; 17.4; 5.1.

Dickens, Bernard. The ethics of "ethics": black and white or shades of grey. *Journal of Ethics in Mental Health* 2006 November; 1(1): E3, 3 p. NRCBL: 17.1; 2.1.

Drescher, Jack. Ethical issues in treating gay and lesbian patients. *Psychiatric Clinics of North America* 2002 September; 25(3): 605-621. NRCBL: 17.1; 10.

Elbogen, Eric B.; Swartz, Marvin S.; Van Dorn, Richard; Swanson, Jeffrey W.; Kim, Mimi; Scheyett, Anna. Clinical decision making and views about psychiatric advance directives. *Psychiatric Services* 2006 March; 57(3): 350-355. NRCBL: 17.1; 8.3.3; 8.3.4. SC: em.

Farah, Martha J. Emerging ethical issues in neuroscience. *Nature Neuroscience* 2002 November; 5(11): 1123-1129. NRCBL: 17.1; 4.3; 4.4; 17.4.

Farah, Martha J. Reply to Jedlicka: neuroethics, reductionism and dualism. *Trends in Cognitive Sciences* 2005 April; 9(4): 173. NRCBL: 17.1; 1.1.

Fins, Joseph J. Clinical pragmatism and the care of brain damaged patients: toward a palliative neuroethics for disorders of consciousness. *Progress in Brain Research* 2005; 150: 565-582. NRCBL: 17.1; 20.4.1; 1.1. SC: em.

Fins, Joseph J. Neuromodulation, free will and determinism: lessons from the psychosurgery debate. *Clinical Neuroscience Research* 2004 July; 4(1-2): 113-118 [Online]. Accessed: http://www.sciencedirect.com [2007 February 26]. NRCBL: 17.6; 17.5. SC: rv.

Gabbard, Glen O. Post-termination sexual boundary violations. *Psychiatric Clinics of North America* 2002 September; 25(3): 593-603. NRCBL: 17.1; 6; 8.1; 10; 7.4. SC: cs.

Garside, Sarah; Maher, John. Assertive Community Treatment (ACT): 23 cases. *Journal of Ethics in Mental Health* 2006 November; 1(1): E6, 4 p. NRCBL: 17.1. SC: cs.

Gevers, Sjef. Dementia and the law. *European Journal of Health Law* 2006 September; 13(3): 209-217. NRCBL: 17.1; 9.5.2; 20.5.4; 18.5.6. SC: le.

Gillett, G. Cyborgs and moral identity. *Journal of Medical Ethics* 2006 February; 32(2): 79-83. NRCBL: 17.1; 4.4; 5.1; 15.1. SC: an.

Abstract: Neuroscience and technological medicine in general increasingly faces us with the imminent reality of cyborgs-integrated part human and part machine complexes. If my brain functions in a way that is supported by and exploits intelligent technology both external and implantable, then how should I be treated and what is my moral status-am I a machine or am I a person? I explore a number of scenarios where the balance between human and humanoid machine shifts, and ask questions about the moral status of the individuals concerned. The position taken is very much in accordance with the Aristotelian idea that our moral behaviour is of a piece with our social and personal skills and forms a reactive and reflective component of those skills.

Gindro, Sandro; Mordini, Emilio. Ethical, legal and social issues in brain research. *Current Opinion in Psychiatry* 1998 September; 11(5): 10 p. [Online]. Accessed: http://gateway.ut.ovid.com [2007 February 26]. NRCBL: 17.1; 17.2; 18.4. SC: rv. Identifiers: Europe.

Glannon, Walter. Neuroethics. *Bioethics* 2006 February; 20(1): 37-52. NRCBL: 17.1; 2.1; 17.4; 4.5; 17.5; 17.6.

Abstract: Neuroimaging, psychosurgery, deep-brain stimulation, and psychopharmacology hold considerable promise for more accurate prediction and diagnosis and more effective treatment of neurological and psychiatric disorders. Some forms of psychopharmacology may even be able to enhance normal cognitive and affective capacities. But the brain remains the most complex and least understood of all the organs in the human body. Mapping the neural correlates of the mind through brain scans, and altering these correlates through surgery, stimulation, or pharmacological interventions can affect us in both positive and negative ways. We need to carefully weigh the potential benefit against the potential harm of such techniques. This paper examines some of these techniques and explores the emerging ethical issues in clinical neuroscience.

Gould, Donald. Is it too easy to be put away? *New Statesman (London, England:* 1957) 1969 June 27; 77: 906-907. NRCBL: 17.1; 8.1; 8.2. SC: cs. Identifiers: United Kingdom (Great Britain).

Greely, Henry T. Knowing sin: making sure good science doesn't go bad. *Cerebrum: The Dana Forum on Brain Science* 2006 June: 1-8. NRCBL: 17.1; 5.3; 18.4.

Green, Joshua; Cohen, Jonathan. For the law, neuroscience changes nothing and everything. *Royal Society of London - Series B: Biological Sciences* 2004 November 29; 359(1451): 1775-1785 [Online]. Accessed: http://www.journals.royalsoc.ac.uk/media/dltehetrrr5vtwmlpt6y/contributions/p/f/8/u/pf8u1kjk14u871yu.pdf [2007 February 26]. NRCBL: 17.1; 1.3.5; 1.1; 20.6. SC: le; an.

Groves, Kashina. Justified paternalism: the nature of beneficence in the care of dementia patients. *Penn Bioethics Journal* 2006; 2(2): 17-20. NRCBL: 17.1; 9.5.2; 8.3.1; 20.5.4; 1.1.

Abstract: The issue of patient autonomy in cases of permanent dementia has recently received a great deal of philosophical attention. Specifically, many have worried about ethical issues surrounding advance directives in which people specify how they shall be treated when they are no longer competent to make their own medical decisions. Ronald Dworkin has been a staunch defender of what he calls precedent autonomy in these cases, believing persons have a right to control, to some degree, how their lives will end, despite the common intuition that the principle of beneficence requires us to improve the experiential quality of patients' lives. Objections have been brought against Dworkin on a number of fronts, including worries about personal identity theory and informed consent. Here, I offer an objection to Dworkin's assessment of the nature of paternalism as it relates to cases of permanent dementia.

Gutheil, Thomas G.; Simon, Robert I. Non-sexual boundary crossings and boundary violations: the ethical dimension. *Psychiatric Clinics of North America* 2002 September; 25(3): 585-592. NRCBL: 17.1; 8.1. SC: cs.

Hegde, R.; Bell, D.; Cole, P. The Jehovah's Witness and dementia: who or what defines 'best interests'? *Anaesthesia* 2006 August; 61(8): 802-806. NRCBL: 17.1; 9.5.2; 1.2; 8.3.3. SC: em; cs. Identifiers: United Kingdom(Great Britain).

Helmchen, Hanfried. Forthcoming ethical issues in biological psychiatry. *World Journal of Biological Psychiatry* 2005; 6(Supplement 2): 56-64. NRCBL: 17.1; 18.1; 15.3; 4.5; 7.1; 17.4; 18.5.6.

Henig, Robin Marantz. Looking for the lie: Scientists are using brain imaging and other tools as new kinds of lie detectors. But trickier even than finding the source of deception might be navigating a world without it. *New York Times Magazine* 2006 February 5; p. 47-53, 76, 80. NRCBL: 17.1; 1.3.5. SC: po.

Hinton, Veronica J. Ethics of neuroimaging in pediatric development. *Brain and Cognition* 2002 December; 50(3): 455-468. NRCBL: 17.1; 18.5.2; 18.4; 18.3.

Hughes, Julian C. Patterns of practice: a useful notion in medical ethics? *Journal of Ethics in Mental Health* 2006 November; 1(1): E2, 5 p. NRCBL: 17.1; 1.1; 17.7.

Hughes, Julian C.; Fulford, K.W.M. (Bill). Hurly-burly of psychiatric ethics. *Australian and New Zealand Journal of Psychiatry* 2005 November-December; 39(11-12): 1001-1007. NRCBL: 17.1; 4.3; 4.4; 7.1.

Illes, Judy; De Vries, Raymond; Cho, Mildred K.; Schraedley-Desmond, Pam. ELSI priorities for brain imaging. *American Journal of Bioethics [Online]*. 2006 March-April; 6(2): W24-W31. NRCBL: 17.1; 5.2. SC: em.

Illes, Judy; Kirschen, Matthew P.; Gabrieli, John D.E. From neuroimaging to neuroethics. *Nature Neuroscience* 2003 March; 6(3): 205. NRCBL: 17.1; 1.3.7. SC: em.

Illes, Judy; Raffin, Thomas A. Neuroethics: an emerging new discipline in the study of brain and cognition. *Brain and Cognition* 2002 December; 50(3): 341-344. NRCBL: 17.1; 18.2; 18.3.

Jackson, Grace E. A curious consensus: "brain scans prove disease"? *Ethical Human Psychology and Psychiatry* 2006 Spring; 8(1): 55-60. NRCBL: 17.1; 5.2.

Jedlicka, Peter. Neuroethics, reductionism and dualism. *Trends in Cognitive Sciences* 2005 April; 9(4): 172-173. NRCBL: 17.1; 1.1.

Jenkins, David; Price, Bob. Dementia and personhood: a focus for care? *Journal of Advanced Nursing* 1996 July; 24(1): 84-90. NRCBL: 17.1; 4.4; 4.1.3.

Kalian, Moshe; Mester, Roberto. Forensic psychiatry corner 3: the issue of anonymity in lay referrals [case study]. *Israel Journal of Psychiatry and Related Sciences* 2004; 41(4): 306-307. NRCBL: 17.1; 8.4. SC: cs; le.

Kaplan, Dana L. Can legislation alone solve America's mental health dilemma? Current state legislative schemes cannot achieve mental health parity. *Quinnipac Health Law* 2004-2005; 8: 325-361. NRCBL: 17.1; 9.3.1. SC: le.

Kitamura, Toshinori; Kitamura, Fusako. Competency testing in medical and psychiatric practice: legal and psychological concepts and dilemmas. *In:* Takahashi, Takao, ed. Taking Life and Death Seriously: Bioethics from Japan. Amsterdam; Boston: Elsevier JAI; 2005: 113-138. NRCBL: 17.1; 8.3.1.

Koller, Regine. Mind metaphors, neurosciences and ethics. *In:* Rees, Dai; Rose, Steven, eds. The New Brain Sciences: Perils and Prospects. New York: Cambridge University Press; 2004: 71-87. NRCBL: 17.1.

NRCBL: National Reference Center for Bioethics Literature Classification Scheme   See inside front cover for terms.

381

Lomax, James W., II; Karff, Samuel; McKenny, Gerald P. Ethical considerations in the integration of religion and psychotherapy: three perspectives. *Psychiatric Clinics of North America* 2002 September; 25(3): 547-559. NRCBL: 17.1; 1.2; 4.1.1.

Martone, Marilyn. Traumatic brain injury and the goals of care. *Hastings Center Report* 2006 March-April; 36(2): 3. NRCBL: 17.1; 8.1.

McGlashan, Thomas H. Early detection and intervention in psychosis: an ethical paradigm shift. *British Journal of Psychiatry* 2005 August; 187 (Supplement 48): s113-s115. NRCBL: 17.1; 4.1.2; 4.3.

McKenna, Brian G.; Simpson, Alexander I. F.; Coverdale, John H. Outpatient commitment and coercion in New Zealand: a matched comparison study. *International Journal of Law and Psychiatry* 2006 March-April; 29(2): 145-158. NRCBL: 17.1; 17.7; 8.3.1; 8.3.3; 8.3.4. SC: em.

Mullen, Richard; Dawson, John; Gibbs, Anita. Dilemmas for clinicians in use of community treatment orders. *International Journal of Law and Psychiatry* 2006 November-December; 29(6): 535-550. NRCBL: 17.1; 17.7; 8.1; 8.3.3. SC: em.

Norbergh, Karl-Gustaf; Helin, Yvonne; Dahl, Annika; Hellzén, Ove; Asplund, Kenneth. Nurses' attitudes towards people with dementia: the semantic differential technique. *Nursing Ethics* 2006 May; 13(3): 264-274. NRCBL: 17.1; 9.5.2; 7.1. Identifiers: Sweden.

O'Reilly, Richard L.; Keegan, David L.; Corring, Deborah; Shrikhande, Satish; Natarajan, Dhanapal. A qualitative analysis of the use of community treatment orders in Saskatchewan. *International Journal of Law and Psychiatry* 2006 November-December; 29(6): 516-524. NRCBL: 17.1; 17.7; 8.3.4. SC: em.

Oliver, Jeffrey. The myth of Thomas Szasz. *New Atlantis* 2006 Summer; 13: 68-84. NRCBL: 17.1; 4.3.

Paladin, A. Vanzan. Ethics and neurology in the Islamic world. Continuity and change. *Italian Journal of Neurological Sciences* 1998 August: 19(4): 255-258. NRCBL: 17.1; 9.5.1; 8.1; 19.5; 1.2.

Pardes, Herbert; Lieber, Constance E. Philanthropy for psychiatry [editorial]. *American Journal of Psychiatry* 2006 May; 163(5): 766-767. NRCBL: 17.1; 9.3.1; 5.3.

Pauline, Jeffrey S.; Pauline, Gina A.; Johnson, Scott R.; Gamble, Kelly M. Ethical issues in exercise psychology. *Ethics and Behavior* 2006; 16(1): 61-76. NRCBL: 17.1; 1.3.1; 6; 21.7; 7.3; 8.4; 1.3.2.

Abstract: Exercise psychology encompasses the disciplines of psychiatry, clinical and counseling psychology, health promotion, and the movement sciences. This emerging field involves diverse mental health issues, theories, and general information related to physical activity and exercise. Numerous research investigations across the past 20 years have shown both physical and psychological benefits from physical activity and exercise. Exercise psychology offers many opportunities for growth while positively influencing the mental and physical health of individuals, communities, and society. However, the exercise psychology literature has not addressed ethical issues or dilemmas faced by mental health professionals providing exercise psychology services. This initial discussion of ethical issues in exercise psychology is an important step in continuing to move the field forward. Specifically, this article will address the emergence of exercise psychology and current health behaviors and offer an overview of ethics and ethical issues, education/training and professional competency, cultural and ethnic diversity, multiple-role relationships and conflicts of interest, dependency issues, confidentiality and recording keeping, and advertisement and self-promotion.

Pearson, Helen. Lure of lie detectors spooks ethicists [news]. *Nature* 2006 June 22; 441(7096): 918-919. NRCBL: 17.1.

Perkinson, Margaret A.; Berg-Weger, Marla L.; Carr, David B.; Meuser, Thomas M.; Palmer, Janice L.; Buckles, Virginia D.; Powlishta, Kimberly K.; Foley, Daniel J.; Morris, John C. Driving and dementia of the Alzheimer type: beliefs and cessation strategies among stakeholders. *Gerontologist* 2005 October; 45(5): 676-685. NRCBL: 17.1; 9.5.2. SC: em.

Phillips, Helen. Who is messing with your head? [news]. *New Scientist* 2006 January 21-27; 189(2535): 11. NRCBL: 17.1; 18.4.

Pollack, David A. Ethical health policy work at the governmental level. *Psychiatric Annals* 2004 February; 34(2): 157, 160-161, 164-166. NRCBL: 17.1; 1.3.5; 9.1; 9.2; 9.3.2; 2.1.

Popovsky, Mark. Dementia and the ethics of decision-making. *Conservative Judaism* 2005 Fall; 58(1): 18-35. NRCBL: 17.1; 9.5.2; 8.3.3.

Post, Jerrold M. Ethical considerations in psychiatric profiling of political figures. *Psychiatric Clinics of North America* 2002 September; 25(3): 635-646. NRCBL: 17.1; 1.3.5; 6; 21.1.

Pratt, Bridget. "Soft" science in the courtroom?: the effects of admitting neuroimaging evidence into legal proceedings. *Penn Bioethics Journal* 2005 April 2; 1(1): 3p. [Online]. Accessed: http://www.bioethicsjournal.com [2005 April 19]. NRCBL: 17.1; 9.7; 5.1. SC: le.

Rai, Gurcharan S.; Blackman, Iva. Ethical issues in dementia. *In:* Rai, Gurcharan S, ed. Medical Ethics and the Elderly. 2nd ed. San Francisco: Radcliffe Medical Press; 2004: 125-137. NRCBL: 17.1; 9.5.2.

Read, Cynthia A. Neuroethics society launched. *Cerebrum: The Dana Forum on Brain Science* 2006 July: 1-2. NRCBL: 17.1.

Robinson, David; O'Neill, Desmond. Ethics of driving assessment in dementia: care, competence and communication. *In:* Rai, Gurcharan S, ed. Medical Ethics and the Elderly. 2nd ed. San Francisco: Radcliffe Medical Press; 2004: 103-111. NRCBL: 17.1; 9.5.2.

Roskies, Adina. Neuroethics for the new millenium. *Neuron* 2002 July 3; 35(1): 21-23. NRCBL: 17.1; 8.3.1; 1.1.

Schneider, P.L.; Branstedt, K.A. When psychiatry and bioethics disagree about patient decision making capacity (DMC). *Journal of Medical Ethics* 2006 February; 32(2): 90-93. NRCBL: 17.1; 2.1; 8.5.1. SC: an.

> Abstract: The terms "competency" and "decision making capacity" (DMC) are often used interchangeably in the medical setting. Although competency is a legal determination made by judges, "competency" assessments are frequently requested of psychiatrists who are called to consult on hospitalised patients who refuse medical treatment. In these situations, the bioethicist is called to consult frequently as well, sometimes as a second opinion or "tie breaker". The psychiatric determination of competence, while a clinical phenomenon, is based primarily in legalism and can be quite different from the bioethics approach. This discrepancy highlights the difficulties that arise when a patient is found to be "competent" by psychiatry but lacking in DMC by bioethics. Using a case, this dilemma is explored and guidance for reconciling the opinions of two distinct clinical specialties is offered.

Sententia, Wrye. Neuroethical considerations: cognitive liberty and converging technologies for improving human cognition. *Annals of the New York Academy of Sciences* 2004 May; 1013: 221-228. NRCBL: 17.1; 17.4; 4.5; 5.4. Identifiers: NBIC (Nano-Bio-Info-Cogno).

Simon, Laurence. Abnormal psychology textbooks: valid science or political propaganda. *Ethical Human Psychology and Psychiatry* 2006 Summer; 8(2): 101-110. NRCBL: 17.1; 7.2; 4.3. SC: an. Identifiers: Thomas Szasz.

Sinaiko, Anna D.; McGuire, Thomas G. Patient inducement, provider priorities, and resource allocation in public mental health systems. *Journal of Health Politics, Policy and Law* 2006 December; 31(6): 1075-1106. NRCBL: 17.1; 1.3.5; 9.4.

Skultans, Vieda. Varieties of deception and distrust: moral dilemmas in the ethnography of psychiatry. *Health (London)* 2005 October; 9(4): 491-512. NRCBL: 17.1; 2.1; 7.1; 8.1. Identifiers: Latvia.

Society of Nuclear Brain Imaging Council. Ethical clinical practice of functional brain imaging. *Journal of Nuclear Medicine* 1996 July; 37(7): 1256-1259. NRCBL: 17.1; 9.5.1; 6.

Solomon, Andrew. Our great depression. *New York Times* 2006 November 17; p. A31. NRCBL: 17.1; 5.3; 9.3.1. SC: po.

Srebnik, Debra; Appelbaum, Paul S.; Russo, Joan. Assessing competence to complete psychiatric advance directives with the competence assessment tool for psychiatric advance directives. *Comprehensive Psychiatry*

2004 July-August; 45(4): 239-245. NRCBL: 17.1; 8.3.3; 8.3.4. SC: em.

Srebnik, Debra; Kim, Scott Y. Competency for creation, use, and revocation of psychiatric advance directives. *Journal of the American Academy of Psychiatry and the Law* 2006; 34(4): 501-510. NRCBL: 17.1; 8.3.3; 8.3.4. SC: le.

Stone, Alan A. Mental health and the law: the facts and the future. *In:* Deschill, S.; Lebovici, S., eds. The Challenge for Psychoanalysis and Psychotherapy Solutions for the Future. London: Jessica Kingsley Publishers Ltd., 1999: 320-335. NRCBL: 17.1; 2.2; 4.3. SC: le.

Swanson, Jeffrey W.; Swartz, Marvin; Ferron, Joelle; Elbogen, Eric; Van Dorn, Richard. Psychiatric advance directives among public mental health consumers in five U.S. cities: prevalence, demand, and correlates. *Journal of the American Academy of Psychiatry and the Law* 2006; 34(1): 43-57. NRCBL: 17.1; 9.5.3; 20.5.4; 8.3.3. SC: le; em.

Tarvydas, Vilia M.; Leahy, Michael J.; Saunders, Jodi L. A comparison of the ethical beliefs of certified rehabilitation counselors and national certified counselors. *Rehabilitation Counseling Bulletin* 2004 Summer; 47(4): 234-246. NRCBL: 17.1; 2.1; 4.1.1. SC: em.

Taylor, Mary Lou. Ethical issues for psychologists in pain management. *Pain Medicine* 2001 June; 2(2): 147-154. NRCBL: 17.1; 4.4; 8.3.1; 8.4. SC: cs.

United States. Department of Health and Human Services [DHHS]. Center for Mental Health Service, Substance Abuse and Mental Health Services Administration. Substance Abuse and Mental Health Services Administration; requirements applicable to protection and advocacy of individuals with mental illness; final rule. *Federal Register* 1997 October 15; 62(199): 53548-53571. [Online]. Accessed: http://frwebgate.access.gpo.gov/cgi-bin/ multidb.cgi [2005 December 28]. NRCBL: 17.1. SC: le.

Van Dorn, Richard A.; Elbogen, Eric B.; Redlich, Allison D.; Swanson, Jeffrey W.; Swartz, Marvin S.; Mustillo, Sarah. The relationship between mandated community treatment and perceived barriers to care in persons with severe mental illness. *International Journal of Law and Psychiatry* 2006 November-December; 29(6): 495-506. NRCBL: 17.1; 8.3.3. SC: em.

Wales, Heathcote W.; Hiday, Virginia Aldigé. PLC or TLC: is outpatient commitment the/an answer? *International Journal of Law and Psychiatry* 2006 November-December; 29(6): 451-468. NRCBL: 17.1; 17.7; 8.3.3. SC: le.

Wasley, Paula. Psychologists debate ethics of their involvement in interrogations. *Chronicle of Higher Education* 2006 September 1; 53(2): 28. NRCBL: 17.1; 21.4;

NRCBL: National Reference Center for Bioethics Literature Classification Scheme   See inside front cover for terms.

21.2; 7.4.6. Identifiers: American Psychological Association.

Weiss Roberts, Laura. Ethical philanthropy in academic psychiatry. *American Journal of Psychiatry* 2006 May; 163(5): 772-778. NRCBL: 17.1; 9.3.1; 5.3.

Weiss Roberts, Laura; Geppert, Cynthia M.A.; Coverdale, John; Louie, Alan; Edenharder, Kristin. Ethical and regulatory considerations in educational research [editorial]. *Academic Psychiatry* 2005 Spring; 29(1): 1-5. NRCBL: 17.1; 7.2; 18.4; 1.3.3.

Wettstein, Robert M. Ethics and forensic psychiatry. *Psychiatric Clinics of North America* 2002 September; 25(3): 623-633. NRCBL: 17.1; 1.3.5; 6.

Woods, Bob; Pratt, Rebekah. Awareness in dementia: ethical and legal issues in relation to people with dementia. *Aging and Mental Health* 2005 September; 9(5): 423-429. NRCBL: 17.1; 9.5.2; 1.1; 20.5.4; 8.3.3; 8.2.

Wynne, Louis. Dr. Szasz's gauntlet: a critical review of the work of American psychiatry's most vocal gadfly. *Ethical Human Psychology and Psychiatry* 2006 Summer; 8(2): 111-122. NRCBL: 17.1; 4.3. SC: an.

Yarhouse, Mark A. Ethical issues in considering "religious impairment" in diagnosis. *Mental Health, Religion and Culture* 2003 July; 6(2): 131-147. NRCBL: 17.1; 1.2; 6; 10. SC: cs; em. Identifiers: mental health assessment models.

Zerby, Stephen A.; Thomas, Christopher R. Legal issues, rights, and ethics for mental health in juvenile justice. *Child and Adolescent Psychiatric Clinics of North America* 2006 April; 15(2): 373-390. NRCBL: 17.1; 1.1; 1.3.5; 9.5.2. SC: le; rv.

MENTALLY DISABLED *See* CARE FOR SPECIFIC GROUPS/ MENTALLY DISABLED; HUMAN EXPERIMENTATION/ SPECIAL POPULATIONS/ MENTALLY DISABLED; INFORMED CONSENT/ INCOMPETENTS

MENTALLY HANDICAPPED *See* CARE FOR SPECIFIC GROUPS/ MENTALLY DISABLED; HUMAN EXPERIMENTATION/ SPECIAL POPULATIONS/ MENTALLY DISABLED; INFORMED CONSENT/ INCOMPETENTS

MENTALLY ILL *See* CARE FOR SPECIFIC GROUPS/ MENTALLY DISABLED; HUMAN EXPERIMENTATION/ SPECIAL POPULATIONS/ MENTALLY DISABLED; INFORMED CONSENT/ INCOMPETENTS; TREATMENT REFUSAL/ MENTALLY ILL

MERCY KILLING *See* EUTHANASIA AND ALLOWING TO DIE

MIGRATION OF HEALTH CARE PROFESSIONALS *See* INTERNATIONAL MIGRATION OF HEALTH CARE PROFESSIONALS

MILITARY PERSONNEL *See* HUMAN EXPERIMENTATION/ SPECIAL POPULATIONS/ MILITARY PERSONNEL

MINORITIES *See* CARE FOR SPECIFIC GROUPS/ MINORITIES

MINORS *See* CARE FOR SPECIFIC GROUPS/ MINORS; DEATH AND DYING/ TERMINAL CARE FOR MINORS; EUTHANASIA AND ALLOWING TO DIE/ MINORS; HUMAN EXPERIMENTATION/ SPECIAL POPULATIONS/ MINORS; INFORMED CONSENT/ MINORS

MISCONDUCT *See* BIOMEDICAL RESEARCH/ RESEARCH ETHICS AND SCIENTIFIC MISCONDUCT; MALPRACTICE AND PROFESSIONAL MISCONDUCT

MORAL AND RELIGIOUS ASPECTS *See* ABORTION/ MORAL AND RELIGIOUS ASPECTS; HUMAN EXPERIMENTATION/ SPECIAL POPULATIONS/ EMBRYOS AND FETUSES/ PHILOSOPHICAL AND RELIGIOUS ASPECTS

NANOTECHNOLOGY

Berne, Rosalyn W. Nanoethics. *In:* Mitcham, Carl, ed. Encyclopedia of Science, Technology, and Ethics. Farmington Hills, MI: Thomson/Gale, 2005: 1259-1262. NRCBL: 5.4.

Best, Robert; Khushf, George. The social conditions for nanomedicine: disruption, systems, and lock-in. *Journal of Law, Medicine and Ethics* 2006 Winter; 34(4): 733-740. NRCBL: 5.4; 7.1.

> Abstract: Here we consider two ways that nanomedicine might be disruptive. First, low-end disruptions that are intrinsically unpredictable but limited in scope, and second, high end disruptions that involve broader societal issues but can be anticipated, allowing opportunity for ethical reflection.

Best, Robert; Khushf, George; Wilson, Robin. A sympathetic but critical assessment of nanotechnology initiatives. *Journal of Law, Medicine and Ethics* 2006 Winter; 34(4): 655-657. NRCBL: 5.4; 5.3.

Gaskell, George; Ten Eyck, Toby; Jackson, Jonathan; Veltri, Giuseppi. Imagining nanotechnology: cultural support for technological innovation in Europe and the United States. *Public Understanding of Science* 2005 January; 14(1): 81-90. NRCBL: 5.4; 15.7; 5.3; 5.1; 4.4. SC: em.

Grinbaum, Alexei. Cognitive barriers in perception of nanotechnology. *Journal of Law, Medicine and Ethics* 2006 Winter; 34(4): 689-694. NRCBL: 5.4. SC: an.

Abstract: This article is concerned with predictions of future events, such as technological achievements and changes in the human condition that they will bring about. Cognitive barriers arise when human agents are either asked or forced to make judgments and decisions with respect to unknown singular events. This article argues that barriers such as an aversion to not knowing and the impossibility to believe trump expert and ordinary human reasoning. These barriers apply to nanotechnology. To avoid undesired societal effects arising from them, this essay proposes a set of steps designed to foster responsible public dialogue.

Grunwald, Armin. Nanotechnology — a new field of ethical inquiry? *Science and Engineering Ethics* 2005 April; 11(2): 187-201. NRCBL: 5.4; 4.4; 1.1.

Jotterand, Fabrice. The politicization of science and technology: its implications for nanotechnology. *Journal of Law, Medicine and Ethics* 2006 Winter; 34(4): 658-666. NRCBL: 5.4; 5.3. SC: an.

Abstract: The development of nanotechnology intensifies challenges to the traditional understanding of how to pursue scientific and technological knowledge. Science can no longer be construed simply as the ideal of the quest for truth (i.e., "pure science"). Science has become the source of economic power and political power. In this paper, I argue that nanotechnology is a cardinal exemplar of "this politicization." At the same time, I assert that this new scientific ethos offers the possibility of a better integration of ethical and philosophical reflections at the core of scientific and technological development.

Kaiser, Mario. Drawing the boundaries of nanoscience — rationalizing the concerns? *Journal of Law, Medicine and Ethics* 2006 Winter; 34(4): 667-674. NRCBL: 5.4; 1.1. SC: an.

Abstract: Nanotechnology as an emerging field is strongly related to visionary prospects which are disposed to reappear as dystopian concerns. As long as nanotechnology does not provide reliable criteria for assessing these worries as rational or as irrational they remain a challenge for ethical reflection. Given this underdetermination, many nanovisions and their corresponding concerns should therefore be considered as "a rational." For that reason, a "constructivist" stance is endorsed which does not seek to take part in discussions as to how ethicists should cope with controversial worries, but tries to observe how concerns are managed by different social actors. This perspective allows us to remodel some concerns such as "grey goo" not solely as a societal reaction, but also as challenging and irritating factors. As such they potentially initiate two different processes simultaneously: a differentiation in terms of demarcating science from non-science on the one hand, and a rationalization of concerns on the other. Analyzing these processes empirically allows to reconstruct how "a rational" concerns are socially made rational or, on the contrary, irrational.

Kurzweil, Ray. Nanoscience, nanotechnology, and ethics: promise and peril. *In:* Mitcham, Carl, ed. Encyclopedia of Science, Technology, and Ethics. Farmington Hills, MI: Thomson/Gale, 2005: xli-xlviii. NRCBL: 5.4.

Meaney, Mark E. Lessons from the sustainability movement: toward an integrative decision-making framework for nanotechnology. *Journal of Law, Medicine and Ethics* 2006 Winter; 34(4): 682-688. NRCBL: 5.4; 5.3; 16.1. SC: an.

Abstract: The author argues that bioethicists must develop alternative approaches to facilitate the study of the conditions for the responsible development of nanotechnologies. Proponents of "sustainability" have developed a useful model to integrate multiple perspectives into the evaluation of the impact of technologies on global ecological integrity under conditions of uncertainty.

Parr, Douglas. Will nanotechnology make the world a better place? *Trends in Biotechnology* 2005 August; 23(8): 395-398. NRCBL: 5.4; 5.1; 5.3; 15.7; 1.3.11.

Sandler, Ronald; Kay, W.D. The national nanotechnology initiative and the social good. *Journal of Law, Medicine and Ethics* 2006 Winter; 34(4): 675-681. NRCBL: 5.4; 5.3; 1.1. SC: an.

Abstract: The purpose of the National Nanotechnology Initiative (NNI) is to promote nanotechnology in a way that benefits the citizens of the United States. It involves a commitment to support responsible development of nanotechnology. The NNI's enactment of this commitment is critically assessed. It is concluded that there are not adequate avenues within the NNI by which social and ethical issues can be raised, considered, and, when appropriate, addressed.

Stang, Charma; Sheremata, Lorraine. Nanotechnology — a lot of hype over almost nothing? *Health Law Review* 2006; 15(1): 53-55. NRCBL: 5.4.

Tennant, Agnieszka. Define 'better': an interview with bioethicist C. Ben Mitchell. *Christianity Today* 2004 January; 48(1): 42-44. NRCBL: 5.4; 4.5; 1.2. Identifiers: human enhancement; nanotechnology.

Wardak, Ahson; Gorman, Michael E. Using trading zones and life cycle analysis to understand nanotechnology regulation. *Journal of Law, Medicine and Ethics* 2006 Winter; 34(4): 695-703. NRCBL: 5.4; 5.3. SC: rv.

Abstract: This article reviews the public health and environmental regulations applicable to nanotechnology using a life cycle model from basic research through end-of-life for products. Given nanotechnology's immense promise and public investment, regulations are important, balancing risk with the public good. Trading zones and earth systems engineering management assist in explaining potential solutions to gaps in an otherwise complex, overlapping regulatory system.

Weckert, John. The control of scientific research: the case of nanotechnology. *In:* Tavani, Herman T., ed. Ethics, Computing, and Genomics. Sudbury, MA: Jones and Bartlett; 2006: 323-339. NRCBL: 5.4.

Wilson, Robin Fretwell. Nanotechnology: the challenge of regulating known unknowns. *Journal of Law, Medicine and Ethics* 2006 Winter; 34(4): 704-713. NRCBL: 5.4; 5.3. SC: an.

Abstract: Media reports of the health hazards posed by nano-sized particles (NSPs) have turned a white hot spotlight on the risks of nanotechnology. Worried about the risks posed to workers producing nano-materials, the Washington Post has labeled nanotechnology a "seat-of-the-pants occupational health

NRCBL: National Reference Center for Bioethics Literature Classification Scheme   See inside front cover for terms.

385

experiment." This article examines our emerging knowledge base about the hazards of two types of exposure: inhalation of NSPs and topical application of products containing NSPs. It argues that a clear-eyed evaluation of the benefits and risks of nanotechnology is made extremely difficult by the marriage of a complex science with a venture capitalist-like hype. It then suggests that, absent additional statutory authority, governmental regulators cannot readily address the risks posed by these products. This regulatory inaction leaves a significant role for the private insurance market, a role that regulators should support in tangible ways outlined in the article.

Zebrowski, Robin L. Altering the body: nanotechnology and human nature. *International Journal of Applied Philosophy* 2006 Fall; 20(2): 229-246. NRCBL: 5.4; 4.4; 2.1. SC: an.

NATIVE AMERICANS AS RESEARCH SUBJECTS *See* HUMAN EXPERIMENTATION/ SPECIAL POPULATIONS

NONTHERAPEUTIC HUMAN EXPERIMENTATION *See* HUMAN EXPERIMENTATION

NURSE PATIENT RELATIONSHIP *See* NURSING ETHICS AND PHILOSOPHY; PATIENT RELATIONSHIPS

NURSING CARE *See* CARE FOR SPECIFIC GROUPS; DEATH AND DYING/ TERMINAL CARE; NURSING ETHICS AND PHILOSOPHY

NURSING ETHICS AND PHILOSOPHY
See also BIOETHICS AND MEDICAL ETHICS; CODES OF ETHICS; PROFESSIONAL ETHICS

Armstrong, Alan E. Towards a strong virtue ethics for nursing practice. *Nursing Philosophy* 2006 July; 7(3): 110-124. NRCBL: 4.1.3; 1.1.

Arndt, Marianne. Teaching ethics in nursing. *In:* Tadd, Win, ed. Ethics in Nursing Education, Research and Management. New York: Palgrave Macmillan; 2003: 39-67. NRCBL: 4.1.3; 2.3; 7.2.

Arries, E. Virtue ethics: an approach to moral dilemmas in nursing. *Curationis* 2005 August; 28(3): 64-72. NRCBL: 4.1.3; 1.1.

Bégat, Ingrid; Ikeda, Noriko; Amemiya, Takiko; Emiko, Konishi; Iwasaki, Akiko; Severinsson, Elisabeth. Comparative study of perceptions of work environment and moral sensitivity among Japanese and Norwegian nurses. *Nursing and Health Sciences* 2004 September; 6(3): 193-200. NRCBL: 4.1.3; 7.1. SC: em. Identifiers: Norway; Japan.

Berghs, M.; Dierckx de Casterlé, B.; Gastmans, C. Nursing, obedience, and complicity with eugenics: a contextual interpretation of nursing morality at the turn of the twentieth century. *Journal of Medical Ethics* 2006 February; 32(2): 117-122. NRCBL: 4.1.3; 15.5. SC: em. Identifiers: United Kingdom (Great Britain).
Abstract: This paper uses Margaret Urban Walker's "expressive collaborative" method of moral inquiry to examine and illustrate the morality of nurses in Great Britain from around 1860 to 1915, as well as nursing complicity in one of the first eugenic policies. The authors aim to focus on how context shapes and limits morality and agency in nurses and contributes to a better understanding of debates in nursing ethics both in the past and present.

Bin Saeed, Khalid S. Attitudes of nurses towards ethical issues and their attributes in Saudi hospitals. *Saudi Medical Journal* 1999 February; 20(2): 189-196. NRCBL: 4.1.3; 8.1; 8.4; 9.8; 21.1. SC: em. Identifiers: Saudi Arabia.

Bjorklund, Pamela. Taking responsibility: toward an understanding of morality in practice: a critical review of the empirical and selected philosophical literature on the social organization of responsibility. *Advances in Nursing Science [electronic]* 2006 April-June; 29(2): E56-E73. NRCBL: 4.1.3; 7.1. SC: an.

Butz, Arlene M.; Redman, Barbara K.; Fry, Sara T.; Kolodner, Ken. Ethical conflicts experienced by certified pediatric nurse practitioners in ambulatory settings. *Journal of Pediatric Health Care* 1998 July-August; 12(4): 183-190. NRCBL: 4.1.3; 9.5.7; 9.1; 9.3.1; 9.3.2; 8.1.

Capella, Elena A.; Aumman, Gretchen. Ethical theory and the practice of the legal nurse consultant. *In:* Iyer, Patricia W., ed. Legal Nurse Consulting: Principles and Practice. 2nd ed. Boca Raton: CRC Press; 2003: 221-238. NRCBL: 4.1.3; 1.1. SC: le.

Cloyes, Kristin Gates. An ethic of analysis: an argument for critical analysis of research interviews as an ethical practice. *Advances in Nursing Science* 2006 April-June; 29(2): 84-97. NRCBL: 4.1.3. SC: an.

Curtin, Leah L.; Arnold, Lauren. A framework for analysis, Part II. *Nursing Administration Quarterly* 2005 July-September; 29(3): 288-291. NRCBL: 4.1.3.

Cusveller, Bart. Cut from the right wood: spiritual and ethical pluralism in professional nursing practice. *Journal of Advanced Nursing* 1998 August; 28(2): 266-273. NRCBL: 4.1.3; 21.7; 1.2. Identifiers: Netherlands.

Dinc, Leyla; Ulusoy, Mehlika Filiz. How nurses approach ethical problems in Turkey. *International Nursing Review* 1998 September-October; 45(5): 137-139. NRCBL: 4.1.3. SC: em.

Erlen, Judith A. Wanted-nurses: ethical issues and the nursing shortage. *Orthopaedic Nursing* 2004 July-August; 23(4): 289-292. NRCBL: 4.1.3; 9.3.1.

Esterhuizen, Philip. Is the professional code still the cornerstone of clinical nursing practice? *Journal of Advanced Nursing* 2006 January; 53(1): 104-110. NRCBL: 4.1.3; 6.

Falk-Rafael, Adeline. Speaking truth to power: nursing's legacy and moral imperative. *ANS: Advances in Nursing Science* 2005 July-September; 28(3): 212-223. NRCBL: 4.1.3; 9.4; 9.2.

Forsberg, Ralph P. Teaching virtue theory using a model from nursing. *Teaching Philosophy* 2001 June; 24(2): 155-166. NRCBL: 4.1.3; 1.1.

Fry, Sara T. Protecting patients from incompetent or un-ethical colleagues: an important dimension of the nurse's advocacy role. *Journal of Nursing Law* 1997; 4(4): 15-22. NRCBL: 4.1.3; 9.1; 9.8; 7.3.

Gallagher, Ann; Wainwright, Paul. The ethical divide. *Nursing Standard* 2005 October 26-November 1; 20(7): 22-25. NRCBL: 4.1.3; 1.3.1; 8.1.

Gastmans, Chris. Editorial comment. *Nursing Ethics* 2006 May; 13(3): 217-218. NRCBL: 4.1.3; 6; 21.1. Identifiers: Do we need a European society for nursing ethics?

Gastmans, Chris; Verpeet, Ellen. 30th anniversary commentary on Esterhuizen P. (1996) Is the professional code still the cornerstone of clinical nursing practice? Journal of Advanced Nursing 23, 25-31. *Journal of Advanced Nursing* 2006 January; 53(1): 111-112. NRCBL: 4.1.3; 6.

Glasberg, Ann-Louise; Eriksson, Sture; Dahlqvist, Vera; Lindahl, Elisabeth; Strandberg, Gunilla; Söderberg, Anna; Sørlie, Venke; Norberg, Astrid. Development and initial validation of the stress of conscience questionnaire. *Nursing Ethics* 2006 November; 13(6): 633-648. NRCBL: 4.1.3; 4.1.1; 16.3. SC: em. Identifiers: Sweden.

Heikkinen, Anne; Lemonidou, Chryssoula; Petsios, Konstantinos; Sala, Roberta; Barazzetti, Gaia; Radaelli, Stefania; Leino-Kilpi, Helena. Ethical codes in nursing practice: the viewpoint of Finnish, Greek and Italian nurses. *Journal of Advanced Nursing* 2006 August; 55(3): 310-319. NRCBL: 4.1.3; 6; 21.1. SC: em.

Hewlett, Bonnie L.; Hewlett, Barry S. Providing care and facing death: nursing during Ebola outbreaks in central Africa. *Journal of Transcultural Nursing* 2005 October; 16(4): 289-297. NRCBL: 4.1.3; 8.1; 7.1. SC: em.

Holm, Søren. What should other healthcare professions learn from nursing ethics. *Nursing Philosophy* 2006 July; 7(3): 165-174. NRCBL: 4.1.3; 2.1.

Izumi, Shigeko. Bridging western ethics and Japanese local ethics by listening to nurses' concerns. *Nursing Ethics* 2006 May; 13(3): 275-283. NRCBL: 4.1.3; 8.1; 21.1. SC: em.

Izumi, Shigeko; Konishi, Emiko; Yahiro, Michiko; Kodama, Maki. Japanese patients' descriptions of "The Good Nurse": personal involvement and professionalism. *Advances in Nursing Science [electronic]* 2006 April-June; 29(2):E14-E26. NRCBL: 4.1.3; 1.1. SC: an. Identifiers: virtue ethics.

Jairath, Nalini; Donley, Rosemary; Shelton, Deborah; McMullen, Patricia; Grandjean, Cynthia. Nursing and the common good: a clearer definition of the concept could be helpful to all the healing professions. *Health Progress* 2006 November-December; 87(6): 59-63. NRCBL: 4.1.3; 9.1; 1.3.2; 1.1.

Kikuchi, June F. Cultural theories of nursing responsive to human needs and values. *Journal of Nursing Scholarship* 2005; 37(4): 302-307. NRCBL: 4.1.3; 1.1; 21.7.

Koh, Younsuck; Ku, Eun Yong; Koo, Young-Mo; Kim, Ock-Joo; Lee, Soon Haeng; Lee, Sang Il; Han, Oh Su. Ethical issues identified in intensive care units of a university hospital. *In:* Sang-yong, Song; Young-Mo, Koo; Macer, Darryl R.J., eds. Asian Bioethics in the 21st Century. Christchurch, NZ: Eubios Ethics Institute, 2002: 108-109. NRCBL: 4.1.3; 9.5.1. SC: em. Conference: Proceedings of the Asian Bioethics Conference (ABC4), held 22-25 November 2002 in Seoul, South Korea.

Kopala, Beverly; Burkhart, Lisa. Ethical dilemma and moral distress: proposed new NANDA diagnoses. *International Journal of Nursing Terminologies and Classifications* 2005 January-March; 16(1): 3-13. NRCBL: 4.1.3; 8.1. SC: cs. Identifiers: North American Nursing Diagnoses Association.

Lange, Bernadette. Mutual moral caring actions: a framework for community nursing practice. *Advances in Nursing Science [electronic]* 2006 April-June; 29(2): E45-E55. NRCBL: 4.1.3; 9.5.9. SC: an.

Law Harrison, Lynda. Maintaining the ethic of caring in nursing. *Journal of Advanced Nursing* 2006 May; 54(3): 255-257. NRCBL: 4.1.3; 4.1.1. Note: Reprinted from Lynda Law Harrison. Maintaining the ethic of caring in nursing. Journal of Advanced Nursing 1990: 15, 125-127.

Leino-Kilpi, Helena. 30th anniversary commentary on Esterhuizen P. (1996) Is the professional code still the cornerstone of clinical nursing practice? Journal of Advanced Nursing 23, 25-31. *Journal of Advanced Nursing* 2006 January; 53(1): 112-113. NRCBL: 4.1.3; 6.

Lunardi, Valeria Lerch; Peter, Elizabeth; Gastaldo, Denise. Are submissive nurses ethical?: Reflecting on power anorexia. *Revista Brasileira* 2002 March-April; 55(2): 183-188. NRCBL: 4.1.3; 7.1; 7.3. Note: Abstract in English, Portuguese and Spanish.

Markus, Karen. The nurse as patient advocate: is there a conflict of interest? *In:* Cowen, Perle Slavik; Moorhead, Sue, eds. Current Issues in Nursing. 7th ed. St. Louis, MO: Mosby, 2006: 620-625. NRCBL: 4.1.3.

Maze, Claire D. Martino. Registered nurses' personal rights vs. professional responsibility in caring for members

NRCBL: National Reference Center for Bioethics Literature Classification Scheme   See inside front cover for terms.

387

of underserved and disenfranchised populations. *Journal of Clinical Nursing* 2005 May; 14(5): 546-554. NRCBL: 4.1.3; 9.5.4; 9.5.10; 9.5.9; 21.7.

McCarthy, Joan. A pluralist view of nursing ethics. *Nursing Philosophy* 2006 July; 7(3): 157-164. NRCBL: 4.1.3; 10.

McKinley, Shirley; Rodney, Paddy; Storch, Jan; McAlpine, Heather. The role of ethics in nursing. *Nursing BC* 2004 February; 36(1): 12-16. NRCBL: 4.1.3; 6; 18.2. Identifiers: Canada.

Milton, Constance L. Breaking the rules of the game: ethical implications for nursing practice and education. *Nursing Science Quarterly* 2006 July; 19(3): 207-210. NRCBL: 4.1.3.

Milton, Constance L. Symbols and ethics: integrity and the discipline of nursing. *Nursing Science Quarterly* 2005 July; 18(3): 211-214. NRCBL: 4.1.3; 2.1.

Milton, Constance L. The metaphor of nurse as guest with ethical implications for nursing and healthcare. *Nursing Science Quarterly* 2005 October; 18(4): 301-303. NRCBL: 4.1.3; 8.1; 9.1.

Mohammed, Selina A. Moving beyond the "exotic": applying postcolonial theory in health research. *Advances in Nursing Science* 2006 April-June; 29(2): 98-109. NRCBL: 4.1.3; 18.5.9. SC: an.

Monsen, Rita Black; Lessick, Mira; MacDonald, Deborah; Jenkins, Jean. International Society of Nurses in Genetics (ISONG) testimony for the Secretary's Advisory Committee on Genetic Testing. *Nursing Outlook* 2000 July-August; 48(4): 185-188. NRCBL: 4.1.3; 9.5.2; 7.1.

Naef, Rahel. Bearing witness: a moral way of engaging in the nurse-person relationship. *Nursing Philosophy* 2006 July; 7(3): 146-156. NRCBL: 4.1.3; 8.1.

O'Sullivan Burchard, Dorothee J.H. Ethos, ethics, and endeavors: new horizons in family nursing. *Journal of Family Nursing* 2005 November; 11(4): 354-370. NRCBL: 4.1.3. SC: ph.

Salladay, Susan A. Putting your life on the line. *Nursing* 2006 February; 36(2): 24. NRCBL: 4.1.3; 16.3; 8.4.

Salvage, Jane. More than a makeover is needed to improve nursing's image. *Journal of Advanced Nursing* 2006 May; 54(3): 259-260. NRCBL: 4.1.3; 4.1.1. Comments: Lynda Law Harrison. Maintaining the ethics of caring in nursing. Journal of Advanced Nursing 1990; 15: 125-127.

Scott, P. Anne. Perceiving the moral dimension of practice: insights from Murdoch, Vetlesen, and Aristotle. *Nursing Philosophy* 2006 July; 7(3): 137-145. NRCBL: 4.1.3; 1.1.

Shields, Linda. The nursing shortage and developing countries: an ethical dilemma [editorial]. *Journal of Clinical Nursing* 2005 August; 14(7): 787-788. NRCBL: 4.1.3; 7.2; 21.1; 21.7.

Sibbald, Barbara. Ethics in action: for more than 30 years, Dr. Janet Storch has endeavoured to move ethics out of the textbooks and into nursing practice. *Canadian Nurse* 2005 May; 101(5): 44, 43. NRCBL: 4.1.3; 2.1; 7.2.

Sibbald, Barbara. Practising to code. *Canadian Nurse* 2006 February; 102(2): 40, 39. NRCBL: 4.1.3.

Southby, Janet R. Nursing ethics and the military. *In:* Beam, Thomas E.; Sparacino, Linette R.; Pellegrino, Edmund D.; Hartle, Anthony E.; Howe, Edmund G., eds. Military Medical Ethics. Volume 2. Washington, DC: TMM Publications, Borden Institute, Walter Reed Army Medical Center; 2003: 661-686. NRCBL: 4.1.3; 1.3.5.

Storch, Janet L. Casualization of nurses and unregulated workers impair ethical practice. *International Nursing Review* 1998 September-October; 45(5): 140-141. NRCBL: 4.1.3; 9.8.

Strachan-Bennett, Seonaid. Campaigning nurses — the ethical dilemma. *Nursing Times* 2006 March 14-20; 102(11): 18-19. NRCBL: 4.1.3.

Suziedelis, Ann. Nurses: the Rodney Dangerfields of health care? *Health Care Ethics USA* 2006; 14(2): E4 [Online]. Accessed: http://chce.slu.edu/Partnerships_HCE_Intro.html [2006 November 17]. NRCBL: 4.1.3; 1.3.2; 9.6.

Tadd, Win; Clarke, Angela; Lloyd, Llynos; Leino-Kilpi, Helena; Strandell, Camilla; Lemonidou, Chryssoula; Petsios, Konstantinos; Sala, Roberta; Barazzetti, Gaia; Radaelli, Stefania; Zalewski, Zbigniew; Bialecka, Anna; van der Arend, Arie; Heymans, Regien. The value of nurses' codes: European nurses' views. *Nursing Ethics* 2006 July; 13(4): 376-393. NRCBL: 4.1.3; 6. SC: em. Identifiers: United Kingdom (Great Britain); Finland; Italy; Greece; Poland; Netherlands.

Abstract: Nurses are responsible for the well-being and quality of life of many people, and therefore must meet high standards of technical and ethical competence. The most common form of ethical guidance is a code of ethics/professional practice; however, little research on how codes are viewed or used in practice has been undertaken. This study, carried out in six European countries, explored nurses' opinions of the content and function of codes and their use in nursing practice. A total of 49 focus groups involving 311 nurses were held. Purposive sampling ensured a mix of participants from a range of specialisms. Qualitative analysis enabled emerging themes to be identified on both national and comparative bases. Most participants had a poor understanding of their codes. They were unfamiliar with the content and believed they have little practical value because of extensive barriers to their effective use. In many countries nursing codes appear to be 'paper tigers' with little or no impact; changes are needed in the way they are developed and written, introduced in nurse education, and reinforced/implemented in clinical practice.

Taylor, Carol R. Ethics in nursing. *Australian Nursing Journal* 2004 December-2005 January; 12(6): 11. NRCBL: 4.1.3; 1.3.1; 20.5.1.

Tschudin, Verena. Cultural and historical perspectives on nursing and ethics: listening to each other — report of the conference in Taipei, Taiwan, 19 May 2005, organized by ICNE and Nursing Ethics. *Nursing Ethics* 2006 May; 13(3): 304-322. NRCBL: 4.1.3; 21.7.

Tschudin, Verena. How nursing ethics as a subject changes: an analysis of the first 11 years of publication of the journal Nursing Ethics. *Nursing Ethics* 2006 January; 13(1): 65-85. NRCBL: 4.1.3.

Abstract: By analysing the first, second, 10th and 11th years of publication (i.e. volumes 1, 2, 10, 11) of Nursing Ethics, I will show the significant visible trends in the articles and draw some conclusions. The trends are visible at various levels: from simple analysis of an issue, or a comment on a situation in the early years, to in-depth philosophical and research studies; and from short statements to much longer articles. The ethical approaches used go from either none or unquestioned assumptions to several approaches used in any one study. This corresponds to the general postmodern trend in society. The interpretation made of these trends is of a kind of protest at nurses and nursing being devalued. Although this is expressed negatively, the positive message conveyed is that nurses are now taking their professional life into their own hands, vigorously and more daringly than a decade ago.

Tschudin, Verena. 30th anniversary commentary on Esterhuizen P. (1996) Is the professional code still the cornerstone of clinical nursing practice? Journal of Advanced Nursing 23, 25-31. *Journal of Advanced Nursing* 2006 January; 53(1): 113. NRCBL: 4.1.3; 6.

Turkoski, Beatrice B. Home care and hospice ethics: using the code for nurses as a guide. *Home Healthcare Nurse* 2000 May; 18(5): 308-317. NRCBL: 4.1.3; 2.1; 6.

van der Arend, Arie J.G.; Smits, Marie-Josee. Ethics education: does it make for practice? *In:* Tadd, Win, ed. Ethics in Nursing Education, Research and Management. New York: Palgrave Macmillan; 2003: 86-100. NRCBL: 4.1.3; 2.3; 7.2.

Verpeet, Ellen; Dierckx de Casterlé, Bernadette; Lemiengre, Joke; Gastmans, Chris. Belgian nurses' views on codes of ethics: development, dissemination, implementation. *Nursing Ethics* 2006 September; 13(5): 531-545. NRCBL: 4.1.3; 6. SC: em. Identifiers: Belgium.

Abstract: The aim of this study was to explore how Belgian nurses view issues related to the development, dissemination and implementation of a code of ethics for nurses. Fifty nurses took part in eight focus groups. The participants stated that, on the whole, a code of ethics for nurses would be useful. They stressed that a code should be a practical and useful instrument developed by nurses for nurses, and that it should be formulated and presented in a practical way, just as educational courses dealing specifically with codes of ethics require a practical approach to be effective. They emphasized that the development of a code should be an ongoing process, enabling nurses to provide input as they reflect on the ethical issues dealt within the code and apply the code in their practice. Finally, they stressed

the need for support at institutional level for the effective implementation of a code.

Vivat, Bella. Situated ethics and feminist ethnography in a west of Scotland hospice. *In:* Bondi, Liz et al., eds. Subjectivities, Knowledges, and Feminist Geographies: The Subjects and Ethics of Social Research. Lanham, MD: Rowman and Littlefield, 2002: 236-252. NRCBL: 4.1.3; 20.4.1; 7.3; 10. SC: cs.

Watson, Jean. Can an ethic of caring be maintained? *Journal of Advanced Nursing* 2006 May; 54(3): 257-259. NRCBL: 4.1.3; 4.1.1. Comments: Lynda Law Harrison. Maintaining the ethics of caring in nursing. Journal of Advanced Nursing 1990; 15: 125-127.

Watson, Jean. Caring science: belonging before being as ethical cosmology. *Nursing Science Quarterly* 2005 October; 18(4): 304-305. NRCBL: 4.1.3; 1.1.

Wiens, Arlene G. Biotechnology through a nursing ethics lens. *In:* Miller, Roman J.; Brubaker, Beryl H.; Peterson, James C., eds. Viewing New Creations with Anabaptist Eyes: Ethics of Biotechnology. Telford, PA: Cascadia Pub.; 2005: 187-192. NRCBL: 4.1.3; 15.1.

Woods, Simon; Sandman, Lars. Continental philosophy and nursing ethics. *In:* Tadd, Win, ed. Ethics in Nursing Education, Research and Management. New York: Palgrave Macmillan; 2003: 14-34. NRCBL: 4.1.3; 1.1.

Zink, Margo R.; Potter, Jeanne; Chirlin, Kristi. Ethical issues and resources for nurses across the continuum. *In:* Cowen, Perle Slavik; Moorhead, Sue, eds. Current Issues in Nursing. 7th ed. St. Louis, MO: Mosby, 2006: 626-632. NRCBL: 4.1.3.

Zoloth, Laurie. Learning a practice of uncertainty: clinical ethics and the nurse. *In:* Cowen, Perle Slavik; Moorhead, Sue, eds. Current Issues in Nursing. 7th ed. St. Louis, MO: Mosby, 2006: 668-678. NRCBL: 4.1.3.

OCCUPATIONAL HEALTH

Alklint, Tommy. Alcohol abuse in the workplace: some ethical considerations. *In:* Westerholm, Peter; Nilstun, Tore; Øvretveit, John, eds. Practical Ethics in Occupational Health. San Francisco: Radcliffe Medical Press; 2004: 167-176. NRCBL: 16.3; 9.5.9.

Andersen, Knut Erik. Workplace rehabilitation. *In:* Westerholm, Peter; Nilstun, Tore; Øvretveit, John, eds. Practical Ethics in Occupational Health. San Francisco: Radcliffe Medical Press; 2004: 189-198. NRCBL: 16.3.

Carlton, Olivia. A case of workplace drug and alcohol testing in a UK transport company. *In:* Westerholm, Peter; Nilstun, Tore; Øvretveit, John, eds. Practical Ethics in Occupational Health. San Francisco: Radcliffe Medical Press; 2004: 151-165. NRCBL: 16.3; 9.5.9.

NRCBL: National Reference Center for Bioethics Literature Classification Scheme   See inside front cover for terms.

389

Coggon, David. Occupational health research. *In:* Westerholm, Peter; Nilstun, Tore; Øvretveit, John, eds. Practical Ethics in Occupational Health. San Francisco: Radcliffe Medical Press; 2004: 241-251. NRCBL: 16.3; 18.5.1.

Ellis, Niki. Employer attitudes to ethics in occupational health. *In:* Westerholm, Peter; Nilstun, Tore; Øvretveit, John, eds. Practical Ethics in Occupational Health. San Francisco: Radcliffe Medical Press; 2004: 263-282. NRCBL: 16.3.

Grytten, Stein E. Reducing sick leave: swimming upstream — positioning and multiple loyalties. *In:* Westerholm, Peter; Nilstun, Tore; Øvretveit, John, eds. Practical Ethics in Occupational Health. San Francisco: Radcliffe Medical Press; 2004: 133-150. NRCBL: 16.3.

Harling, Kit. The ethics of risk assessment. *In:* Westerholm, Peter; Nilstun, Tore; Øvretveit, John, eds. Practical Ethics in Occupational Health. San Francisco: Radcliffe Medical Press; 2004: 49-60. NRCBL: 16.3.

Harling, Kit; Westerholm, Peter; Nilstun, Tore. Professional codes of ethics. *In:* Westerholm, Peter; Nilstun, Tore; Øvretveit, John, eds. Practical Ethics in Occupational Health. San Francisco: Radcliffe Medical Press; 2004: 321-329. NRCBL: 16.3; 6.

Hasle, Peter; Limborg, Hans Jorgen. The ethics of workplace interventions. *In:* Westerholm, Peter; Nilstun, Tore; Øvretveit, John, eds. Practical Ethics in Occupational Health. San Francisco: Radcliffe Medical Press; 2004: 61-76. NRCBL: 16.3.

Heikkinen, Anne; Launis, V.; Wainwright, P.; Leino-Kilpi, H. Privacy and occupational health services. *Journal of Medical Ethics* 2006 September; 32(9): 522-525. NRCBL: 16.3; 8.4.
Abstract: Privacy is a key ethical principle in occupational health services. Its importance is emphasised in several laws, in ethical codes of conduct as well as in the literature, yet there is only very limited empirical research on privacy in the occupational health context. Conceptual questions on privacy in the occupational health context are discussed. The baseline assumption is that, in this context, privacy cannot be approached and examined only from the employee's (an individual)vantage point but the employer's (a group) point of view must also be taken into account, and that the concept has several dimensions (physical, social, informational and psychological). Even though privacy is a basic human need, there is no universally accepted definition of the concept and no consensus on whether an organisation can have privacy in the same way as people do. Many of the challenges surrounding privacy in the context of occupational health seem to be associated with the dual loyalties of occupational health professionals towards the employee and employer and with their simultaneous duties of disseminating and protecting information (informational privacy). Privacy is thus not an absolute value, but more research is needed to understand its multidimensional nature in the context of occupational health.

Johnson, Kirk. In old mining town, new charges over asbestos; clinic sees pressure to close — company faults diagnoses. *New York Times* 2006 April 22; p. A1, A11. NRCBL: 16.3; 16.1. SC: le.

Juntunen, Juhani. Insurance medicine and work-related diseases: some ethical and legal aspects. *In:* Westerholm, Peter; Nilstun, Tore; Øvretveit, John, eds. Practical Ethics in Occupational Health. San Francisco: Radcliffe Medical Press; 2004: 199-215. NRCBL: 16.3.

Kanhere, Vijay. The Clemenceau debate and occupational health. *Indian Journal of Medical Ethics* 2006 April-June; 3(2): 46-47. NRCBL: 16.3; 16.1; 7.2.

Martimo, Kari-Pekka. Workplace health surveillance. *In:* Westerholm, Peter; Nilstun, Tore; Øvretveit, John, eds. Practical Ethics in Occupational Health. San Francisco: Radcliffe Medical Press; 2004: 77-90. NRCBL: 16.3.

Nilstun, Tore; Øvretveit, John. Ethical analysis. *In:* Westerholm, Peter; Nilstun, Tore; Øvretveit, John, eds. Practical Ethics in Occupational Health. San Francisco: Radcliffe Medical Press; 2004: 37-47. NRCBL: 16.3.

Øvretveit, John. Ethical occupational health management and organisation. *In:* Westerholm, Peter; Nilstun, Tore; Øvretveit, John, eds. Practical Ethics in Occupational Health. San Francisco: Radcliffe Medical Press; 2004: 307-319. NRCBL: 16.3.

Øvretveit, John. Ethics, research-informed practice and quality improvement. *In:* Westerholm, Peter; Nilstun, Tore; Øvretveit, John, eds. Practical Ethics in Occupational Health. San Francisco: Radcliffe Medical Press; 2004: 23-36. NRCBL: 16.3; 9.8.

Symington, Ian S. Blood-borne viruses as workplace hazards. *In:* Westerholm, Peter; Nilstun, Tore; Øvretveit, John, eds. Practical Ethics in Occupational Health. San Francisco: Radcliffe Medical Press; 2004: 177-187. NRCBL: 16.3.

Verbeek, Jos; Hulshof, Carel. Work disability assessment in the Netherlands. *In:* Westerholm, Peter; Nilstun, Tore; Øvretveit, John, eds. Practical Ethics in Occupational Health. San Francisco: Radcliffe Medical Press; 2004: 105-114. NRCBL: 16.3.

Vogel, Laurent. The ethics of health and safety services: a trade union perspectives. *In:* Westerholm, Peter; Nilstun, Tore; Øvretveit, John, eds. Practical Ethics in Occupational Health. San Francisco: Radcliffe Medical Press; 2004: 253-261. NRCBL: 16.3.

Weel, Andre N.H.; Kelder, Marja J. Sickness absence management. *In:* Westerholm, Peter; Nilstun, Tore; Øvretveit, John, eds. Practical Ethics in Occupational Health. San Francisco: Radcliffe Medical Press; 2004: 115-131. NRCBL: 16.3.

Whitaker, Stuart. Health examinations on new employment: ethical issues. *In:* Westerholm, Peter; Nilstun, Tore; Øvretveit, John, eds. Practical Ethics in Occupational

Health. San Francisco: Radcliffe Medical Press; 2004: 91-104. NRCBL: 16.3.

ORGAN AND TISSUE TRANSPLANTATION
See also BLOOD DONATION AND TRANSFUSION

Stem cells without embryo loss [editorial]. *New York Times* 2006 August 26; p. A14. NRCBL: 19.1; 18.5.4; 15.1. SC: po.

Ackerman, P.D.; Thistlethwaite, J.R., Jr.; Ross, L.F. Attitudes of minority patients with end-stage renal disease regarding ABO-incompatible list-paired exchanges. *American Journal of Transplantation* 2006 January; 6(1): 83-88. NRCBL: 19.3; 9.5.4; 17.1.

Aghanwa, H.S.; Akinsola, A.; Akinola, D.O.; Makanjuola, R.O.A. Attitudes toward kidney donation. *Journal of the National Medical Association* 2003 August; 95(8): 725-731. NRCBL: 19.3; 19.5; 17.1.

Al Qattan, S.M.B.K. Islamic jurisprudential judgement on human organ transplantation. *Saudi Medical Journal* 1992 November; 13(6): 483-487. NRCBL: 19.1; 1.2.

Albar, M.A. Organ transplantation — an Islamic perspective. *Saudi Medical Journal* 1991 July; 12(4): 280-284. NRCBL: 19.1; 1.2. SC: em. Identifiers: Saudi Arabia.

Anand, Kuldip P.; Kashyap, Ajit; Kashyap, Surekha. Thinking the unthinkable: selling kidneys [letter]. *BMJ: British Medical Journal* 2006 July 15; 333(7559): 149. NRCBL: 19.3; 19.5; 9.3.1.

Ashby, Michael; op't Hoog, Corinne; Kellehear, Aallan; Kerr, Peter G.; Brooks, Denise; Nicholls, Kathy; Forrest, Marian. Renal dialysis abatement: lessons from a social study. *Palliative Medicine* 2005 July; 19(5): 389-396. NRCBL: 19.3; 8.3.4. SC: em.

Bagheri, Alireza. Compensated kidney donation: an ethical review of the Iranian model. *Kennedy Institute of Ethics Journal* 2006 September; 16(3): 269-282. NRCBL: 19.3; 9.3.1; 21.1.

Barnett, William, II; Saliba, Michael; Walka, Deborah. A flea market in kidneys: efficient and equitable. *Independent Review* 2001 Winter; 5(3): 373-385. NRCBL: 19.3; 19.6; 4.4.

Bollinger, R. Randal; Heneghan, Michael A. Procurement and allocation of donor livers. *In:* Killenberg, P.G.; Clavien, P.A, eds. Medical Care of the Liver Transplant Patient. Massachusetts: Blackwell Science, 1997: 124-136. NRCBL: 19.1; 19.5.

Brook, Nicholas R.; Nicholson, Michael L. Non-directed live kidney donation. *Lancet* 2006 July 29-August 4; 368(9533): 346-347. NRCBL: 19.3; 19.6.

Brook, N.R.; Nicholson, M.L. Kidney transplantation from non heart-beating donors. *Surgeon Journal of the Royal Colleges of Surgeons of Edinburgh and Ireland* 2003 December; 1(6): 323-322. NRCBL: 19.3; 19.5; 20.1. SC: em.

Bruzzone, Paolo; Pretagostini, R.; Poli, L.; Rossi, M.; Berloco, P.B. Ethical considerations on kidney transplantation from living donors. *Transplantation Proceedings* 2005 July-August; 37(6): 2436-2438. NRCBL: 19.3; 19.5; 9.3.1. SC: em. Identifiers: Italy.

Carosella, Edgardo; Pradeu, Thomas. Transplantation and identity: a dangerous split? *Lancet* 2006 July 15-21; 368(9531): 183-184. NRCBL: 19.1; 4.4.

Clement, Renaud; Chevalet, Pascal; Rodat, Olivier; Ould-Aoudia, Vincent; Berger, Michel. Withholding or withdrawing dialysis in the elderly: the perspective of a western region of France. *Nephrology Dialysis Transplantation* 2005 November; 20(11): 2446-2452. NRCBL: 19.3; 9.5.2; 20.5.1.

Cohen, Lawrence. Operability, bioavailability, and exception. *In:* Ong, Aihwa; Collier, Stephen J., eds. Global Assemblages: Technology, Politics, and Ethics as Anthropological Problems. Malden, MA: Blackwell Pub.; 2005: 79-90. NRCBL: 19.1; 21.1. SC: le. Identifiers: India.

Cohen, Lawrence. The other kidney: biopolitics beyond recognition. *In:* Scheper-Hughes, Nancy; Wacquant, Loïc, eds. Commodifying Bodies. Thousand Oaks, CA: SAGE Publications; 2002: 9-29. NRCBL: 19.3; 7.1; 9.3.1; 19.5; 21.1. Identifiers: India.

Danino, Alain Michel; Danino, Isabelle Weber; Moutel, Gregoire; Hervé, Christian; Malka, Gabriel. Non-life-saving human composite allograft: ethical considerations [letter]. *Plastic and Reconstructive Surgery* 2005 January; 115(1): 342- 343. NRCBL: 19.1; 8.3.1.

Delmonico, Francis L.; Burdick, James F. Maximizing the success of transplantation with kidneys from older donors [editorial]. *New England Journal of Medicine* 2006 January 26; 354(4): 411-413. NRCBL: 19.3; 19.5; 9.5.2.

Dyer, Clare. Paired kidney transplants to start in the United Kingdom [news]. *BMJ: British Medical Journal* 2006 April 29; 332(7548): 989. NRCBL: 19.3. SC: le.

Fischman, Josh. Mix, match, and switch: kidney exchanges between strangers are helping to ease the organ shortage and could save thousands of lives. *U.S. News and World Report* 2006 October 16; 141(14): 74-76. NRCBL: 19.3; 19.5. SC: po.

Friedlaender, Michael M. The role of commercial non-related living kidney transplants. *Journal of Nephrology* 2003 November-December; 16(Supplement 7): S10-S15. NRCBL: 19.3; 19.5; 9.3.1; 21.1; 1.1. Identifiers: Israel.

NRCBL: National Reference Center for Bioethics Literature Classification Scheme   See inside front cover for terms.

391

Ghods, Ahad J.; Nasrollahzadeh, Dariush. Transplant tourism and the Iranian model of renal transplantation program: ethical considerations. *Experimental and Clinical Transplantation* 2005 December; 3(2): 351-354. NRCBL: 19.3; 9.3.1; 21.1.

Gould, Donald. Doctors and the public. *New Statesman (London, England:* 1957) 1969 June 6; 77: 793-794. NRCBL: 19.2; 5.3; 19.5. Identifiers: United Kingdom (Great Britain).

Gould, Donald. Surgical morals. *New Statesman (London, England:* 1957) 1968 March 1; 75: 266. NRCBL: 19.1; 9.5.1; 5.3. Identifiers: United Kingdom (Great Britain).

Gould, Donald. Truth about transplants. *New Statesman (London, England:* 1957) 1968 May 10: 610. NRCBL: 19.2; 19.3; 18.1; 4.4. Identifiers: United Kingdom (Great Britain).

Hippen, Benjamin. The commerce of the body: the case for kidney markets. *New Atlantis* 2006 Fall; 14: 47-61. NRCBL: 19.3; 4.4; 9.3.1.

Huxtable, R.; Woodley, J. (When) will they have faces? A response to Agich and Siemionov. *Journal of Medical Ethics* 2006 July; 32(7): 403-404. NRCBL: 19.1; 9.5.1. SC: an.

Iyer, T.K.K. Kidney donations — Singapore's legislative proposals. *Malayan Law Journal* 1987 July: liii-lxi. NRCBL: 19.3; 19.5. SC: le.

Jiang, Changmin. Ethical considerations on organ transplantation in China. *Penn Bioethics Journal* 2006; 2(1): 3p. [Online]. Accessed: http://www.bioethicsjournal.com [2006 February 21]. NRCBL: 19.1.

Johannes, Laura. New kidney-transplant rules to benefit blacks. *Wall Street Journal* 2004 February 5; p. D4. NRCBL: 19.3; 19.6; 9.5.4. SC: po.

Kelly, Matthew. Critical objections to Michael Steinberg's opt-in system for kidney transplantation. *Penn Bioethics Journal* 2006; 2(1): 3p. [Online]. Accessed: http://www.bioethicsjournal.com [2006 February 21]. NRCBL: 19.3; 19.6.

Klarenbach, Scott; Garg, Amit X.; Vlaicu, Sorina. Living organ donors face financial barriers: a national reimbursement policy is needed. *CMAJ/JAMC: Canadian Medical Association Journal* 2006 March 14; 174(6): 797-798. NRCBL: 19.3; 9.3.1; 19.5.

McKenna, Phil. Are uterus transplants on the horizon [news]. *New Scientist* 2006 November 11-17; 192(2577): 12. NRCBL: 19.1; 14.1; 18.5.3.

Mitka, Mike. Efforts under way to increase number of potential kidney transplant donors. *JAMA: the Journal of the American Medical Association* 2006 June 14; 295(22): 2588-2589. NRCBL: 19.3; 19.5; 19.6.

Montgomery, Robert A.; Gentry, Sommer E.; Marks, William H.; Warren, Daniel S.; Hiller, Janet; Houp, Julie; Zachary, Andrea A.; Melancon, J. Keith; Maley, Warren R.; Rabb, Hamid; Simpkins, Christopher; Segev, Dorry L. Domino paired kidney donation: a strategy to make best use of live non-directed donation. *Lancet* 2006 July 29-August 4; 368(9533): 419-421. NRCBL: 19.3; 19.6.

Morreim, E. Haavi. When research ethics meets business ethics: the AbioCor artificial heart trial. *Organizational Ethics: Healthcare, Business, and Policy* 2006 Spring-Summer; 3(1): 40-45. NRCBL: 19.2; 1.3.2; 1.3.7; 18.2. SC: le. Comments: Elizabeth A. Powell and Rebecca Goldberg Oliver. Abiomed and the AbioCore clinical trials, Part 1. and Part 2. Organizational Ethics: Healthcare, Business, and Policy 2006 Spring-Summer; 3(1): 19-32, 33-39.

Muggeridge, Malcolm. My true love hath my heart. *New Statesman (London, England:* 1957) 1968 October 4: 423. NRCBL: 19.2; 18.1; 9.5.1; 19.5. Identifiers: South Africa.

Murphy, Timothy F. Would my story get me a kidney? *Hastings Center Report* 2006 March-April; 36(2): inside back cover. NRCBL: 19.3; 1.3.12.

Nakasone, Ronald Y. Ethics of ambiguity: a Buddhist reflection on the Japanese organ transplant law. *In:* Guinn, David E., ed. Handbook of Bioethics and Religion. New York: Oxford University Press, 2006: 291-303. NRCBL: 19.1; 1.2. SC: le.

Norman, Douglas J. The kidney transplant wait-list: allocation of patients to a limited supply of organs. *Seminars in Dialysis* 2005 November-December; 18(6): 456-459. NRCBL: 19.3; 19.6.

Okie, Susan. Brave new face. *New England Journal of Medicine* 2006 March 2; 354(9): 889-894. NRCBL: 19.1; 18.5.1.

Ponticelli, Claudio. Altruistic living renal transplantation. *Journal of Nephrology* 2003 November-December; 16(Supplement 7): S6-S9. NRCBL: 19.3; 19.5.

Powell, Elizabeth A.; Goldberg Oliver, Rebecca. Abiomed and the AbioCor clinical trials, Part 2. *Organizational Ethics: Healthcare, Business, and Policy* 2006 Spring-Summer; 3(1): 33-39. NRCBL: 19.2; 1.3.2; 18.3. SC: le.

Powell, Elizabeth A.; Goldberg Oliver, Rebecca. Abiomed and the AbioCore clinical trials, Part 1. *Organizational Ethics: Healthcare, Business, and Policy* 2006 Spring-Summer; 3(1): 19-32. NRCBL: 19.2; 1.3.2; 1.3.7; 5.2; 18.2.

Powell, Tia. Face transplant: real and imagined ethical challenges. *Journal of Law, Medicine, and Ethics* 2006 Spring; 34(1): 111-115. NRCBL: 19.1; 4.4; 5.2; 5.1.

Ralph, Cheryl. Pregnancy in a hemodialysis patient with an ethical/cultural challenge. *CANNT Journal* 2000 January-March; 10(1): 35-38. NRCBL: 19.3; 9.5.5; 14.1; 8.3.1; 1.2. SC: cs.

Rice, Mary. 'Inappropriate' regulation proposed for tissue engineering. *European Journal of Cancer* 2005 September; 41(14): 2035. NRCBL: 19.1; 5.1.

Roff, Sue Rabbitt. Thinking the unthinkable: selling kidneys. *BMJ: British Medical Journal* 2006 July 1; 333(7557): 51. NRCBL: 19.3; 9.3.1.

Ross, Lainie Friedman. Ethical considerations related to pregnancy in transplant recipients. *New England Journal of Medicine* 2006 March 23; 354(12): 1313-1316. NRCBL: 19.1; 14.1.

Rotarius, Timothy; Oetjen, Dawn. The comprehensive organizational plan revisited: building in an ethical component. *Dialysis and Transplantation* 2005 March; 34(3): 150, 152, 157-158,185. NRCBL: 19.3; 1.3.2; 9.1.

Sato, Hajime; Akabayashi, Akira; Kai, Ichiro. Public, experts, and acceptance of advanced medical technologies: the case of organ transplant and gene therapy in Japan. *Health Care Analysis: An International Journal of Health Philosophy and Policy* 2006 December; 14(4): 203-214. NRCBL: 19.1; 15.4; 18.2; 20.2.1. SC: em.

Scheper-Hughes, Nancy. The global trade in human organs. *Current Anthropology* 2000 April; 41(2): 191-224. NRCBL: 19.1; 21.1; 8.3.1; 19.5; 9.3.1.

Shapiro, Carla. Emerging ethical issues in nephrology nursing — Part II. *CANNT Journal* 2000 January-March; 10(1): 23-25. NRCBL: 19.3; 9.2; 9.4; 8.1. SC: cs.

Smetanka, Stella L. Who will protect the "disruptive" dialysis patient? *American Journal of Law and Medicine* 2006; 32(1): 53-91. NRCBL: 19.3; 9.3.1; 9.2; 8.1. SC: le.

Spital, Aaron. Increasing the pool of transplantable kidneys through unrelated living donors and living donor paired exchanges. *Seminars in Dialysis* 2005 November-December; 18(6): 469-473. NRCBL: 19.3; 19.5.

Stack, Austin G.; Martin, David R. Association of patient autonomy with increased transplantation and survival among new dialysis patients in the United States. *American Journal of Kidney Diseases* 2005 April; 45(4): 730-742. NRCBL: 19.3; 8.1; 1.1.

Stanton, Jennifer. Renal dialysis: counting the cost versus counting the need. *Clio Medica* 2005; 75: 217-241. NRCBL: 19.3; 9.4; 2.2; 7.1. Identifiers: United Kingdom (Great Britain).

Starzomski, Rosalie. Ethical issues: to dialyze or not? Is that the question? *CANNT Journal* 2000 October-December; 10(4): 45-46. NRCBL: 19.3; 19.6; 9.2; 8.3.4.

Steiner, Robert. How should we ethically select living kidney donors when they all are at risk? [letter]. *American Journal of Transplantation* 2005 May; 5(5): 1172-1173. NRCBL: 19.3; 19.5.

Swartz, Richard D.; Perry, Erica. Medical family: a new view of the relationship between chronic dialysis patients and staff arising from discussions about advance directives. *Journal of Women's Health and Gender-Based Medicine* 1999 November; 8(9): 1147-1153. NRCBL: 19.3; 8.1; 20.5.4.

Taylor, James Stacey. Personal autonomy, posthumous harm, and presumed consent policies for organ procurement. *Public Affairs Quarterly* 2006 October; 20(4): 381-404. NRCBL: 19.1; 19.5; 8.3.1; 1.1. SC: an.

Union of American Hebrew Congregations. Committee on Bio-Ethics; United States. Health Resources and Services Administration (HRSA). Organ Donation and Transplantation: Bioethics Program/Case Study: Program Guide IX. New York, NY: Union of American Hebrew Congregations, 1997 Spring; 111 p. NRCBL: 19.1; 1.2; 19.5; 19.6.

Vogel, Gretchen. Scientists derive line from single embryo cell. *Science* 2006 August 25; 313(5790): 1031. NRCBL: 19.1; 18.5.4; 15.1.

Warnke, Patrick H. Repair of a human face by allotransplantation. *Lancet* 2006 July 15-21; 368(9531): 181-183. NRCBL: 19.1; 4.4.

White, S.A.; Prasad, K.R. Liver transplantation from non-heart beating donors: a promising way to increase the supply of organs. *BMJ: British Medical Journal* 2006 February 18; 332(7538): 376-377. NRCBL: 19.1; 20.2.1.

Williams, Mark E.; Kitsen, Jenny. The involuntarily discharged dialysis patient: conflict (of interest) with providers. *Advances in Chronic Kidney Disease* 2005 January; 12(1): 107-112. NRCBL: 19.3; 9.5.9; 17.1; 9.5.10; 8.3.4. SC: cs.

Zhu, Yongming. Ethical issues of blood transfusion and bone marrow transplantation in China. *In:* Döring, Ole; Chen, Renbiao, eds. Advances in Chinese Medical Ethics: Chinese and International Perspectives. Hamburg: Institut für Asienkunde; 2002: 367-377. NRCBL: 19.1; 19.4. Note: Proceedings of the Second Sino-German Interdisciplinary Symposium about Medical Ethics in China, Shanghai, 19-23 October, 1999.

NRCBL: National Reference Center for Bioethics Literature Classification Scheme   See inside front cover for terms.

393

ORGAN AND TISSUE TRANSPLANTATION/ ALLOCATION

Alberta Kidney Disease Network; Tonelli, Marcello; Klarenbach, Scott; Manns, Braden; Culleton, Bruce; Hemmelgarn, Brenda; Betazzon, Stefania; Wiebe, Natasha; Gill, John S. Residence location and likelihood of kidney transplantation. *CMAJ/JAMC: Canadian Medical Association Journal* 2006 August 29; 175(5): 478-482. NRCBL: 19.6; 19.3. SC: em. Identifiers: Canada.

Barshes, Neal R.; Lee, Timothy C.; Udell, Ian W.; O'Mahoney, Christine A.; Carter, Bet A.; Karpen, Saul J.; Goss, John A. Adult liver transplant candidate attitudes toward graft sharing are not obstacles to split liver transplantation. *American Journal of Transplantation* 2005 August; 5(8): 2047-2051. NRCBL: 19.6; 19.1. SC: em.

Bramstedt, Katrina A. Supporting organ transplantation in non-resident aliens within limits. *Ethics and Medicine* 2006 Summer; 22(2): 75-81. NRCBL: 19.6; 21.1; 9.2; 7.1.

Bramstedt, Katrina A. Supporting organ transplantation in non-resident aliens within limits. *Ethics and Medicine* 2006 Spring; 22(1): 39-45. NRCBL: 19.6; 9.4; 17.1; 21.1.

Bramstedt, Katrina A.; Jabbour, N. When alcohol abstinence criteria create ethical dilemmas for the liver transplant team. *Journal of Medical Ethics* 2006 May; 32(5): 263-265. NRCBL: 19.6; 9.4; 9.5.9.

Dietrich, Frank. Causal responsibility and rationing in medicine. *Ethical Theory and Moral Practice* 2002 March; 5(1): 113-131. NRCBL: 19.6; 9.4; 9.3.1. Identifiers: Germany; United Kingdom (Great Britain).

Egan, Thomas M.; Kotloff, Robert M. Pro/con debate: lung allocation should be based on medical urgency and transplant survival and not on waiting time. *Chest* 2005 July; 128(1): 407-415. NRCBL: 19.6; 19.1; 4.4. SC: an.

Furth, Susan L.; Garg, Pushkal P.; Neu, Alicia M.; Hwang, Wenke; Fivush, Barbara A.; Powe, Neil R. Racial differences in access to the kidney transplant waiting list for children and adolescents with end-stage renal disease. *Pediatrics* 2000 October; 106(4): 756-761. NRCBL: 19.6; 19.3; 9.5.7; 9.5.4. SC: em.

Geddes, Colin C.; Rodger, R. Stuart C. Kidneys for transplant [editorial]. *BMJ: British Medical Journal* 2006 May 13; 332(7550): 1105-1106. NRCBL: 19.6; 19.5; 19.3. Identifiers: United Kingdom (Great Britain).

Geddes, Colin C.; Rodger, R. Stuart C.; Smith, Christopher; Ganai, Anita. Allocation of deceased donor kidneys for transplantation: opinions of patients with CKD. *American Journal of Kidney Diseases* 2005 November; 46(5): 949-956. NRCBL: 19.6; 19.3. SC: em. Identifiers: chronic kidney disease.

Gould, Donald. Deciding who shall die. *New Statesman (London, England:* 1957) 1969 January 24; 77: 112. NRCBL: 19.6; 19.5. Identifiers: United Kingdom (Great Britain).

Grady, Denise. Lung patients see a new era of transplants. *New York Times* 2006 September 24; p. A1, A30. NRCBL: 19.6. SC: po.

Heitz, Theresa L.; Kayira, Eric F. Worth its weight in gold: organ transplantation and the new UNOS policies for allocation of hearts and livers. *Journal of Health and Hospital Law* 1997 Fall; 30(3): 195-200. NRCBL: 19.6; 19.2; 19.1. SC: le. Identifiers: United Network for Organ Sharing.

Meier-Kriesche, Herwig-Ulf; Schold, Jesse D.; Gaston, Robert S.; Wadstrom, Jonas; Kaplan, Bruce. Kidneys from deceased donors: maximizing the value of a scarce resource. *American Journal of Transplantation* 2005 July; 5(7): 1725-1730. NRCBL: 19.6; 9.5.2; 19.3; 19.5. SC: em.

Ohio Solid Organ Transplantation Consortium. Substance abuse addendum to patient selection criteria. Worthington, Ohio: Ohio Solid Organ Transplantation Consortium, n.d. [2005?]: 2 p. [Online]. Accessed: http://www.osotc.org/1saa.htm [2006 August 15]. NRCBL: 19.6.

Peters, Thomas G. Racial disparities and transplantation [editorial]. *American Journal of Kidney Diseases* 2005 October; 46(4): 760-762. NRCBL: 19.6; 19.3; 9.5.4.

Ross, Lainie Friedman; Zenios, Stefanos; Thistlethwaite, J. Richard, Jr. Shared decision making in deceased-donor transplant. *Lancet* 2006 July 22-28; 368(9532): 333-337. NRCBL: 19.6; 8.1; 8.3.1; 5.2; 8.3.4.

Schaffer, Randolph L., III; Kulkarni, Sanjay; Harper, Ann; Millis, J. Michael; Cronin, David C., II. The sickest first? Disparities with model for end-stage lever disease-based organ allocation: one region's experience. *Liver Transplantation* 2003 November; 9(11): 1211-1215. NRCBL: 19.6; 19.1; 9.2; 9.4.

Steinburg, David. The allocation of organs donated by altruistic strangers. *Annals of Internal Medicine* 2006 August 1; 145(3): 197-203. NRCBL: 19.6; 19.5.

Zaltzman, Jeffrey S. Kidney transplantation in Canada: unequal access. *CMAJ/JAMC: Canadian Medical Association Journal* 2006 August 29; 175(5): 489-490. NRCBL: 19.6; 19.3.

ORGAN AND TISSUE TRANSPLANTATION/ DONATION AND PROCUREMENT

Chinese Embassy's Statement on the Issue of Falun Gong. Beijing: Ministry of Foreign Affairs, 2006 July 26; 2 p. [Online]. Accessed: http://www.chinaembassycanada.org/eng/xwdt/t265055.htm [2006 July 27]. NRCBL: 19.5;

21.1; 21.4; 1.3.5. Note: This statement addresses the "Report into Allegations of Organ Harvesting of Falun Gong Practitioners in China," an independent report issued by David Matas and David Kilgour on July 6, 2006.

Effective implementation of the Human Tissue Act [editorial]. *Lancet* 2006 September 9-15; 368(9539): 891. NRCBL: 19.5; 8.3.1; 8.3.3; 18.3; 18.2.

Medicine: organ donation. *National Catholic Bioethics Quarterly* 2006 Winter; 6(4): 769-775. NRCBL: 19.5; 12.5.2; 11.1; 9.7; 4.4; 8.3.1; 20.6; 15.2.

Response to the so called "China's organ harvesting report". Beijing: Ministry of Foreign Affairs, 2006 July 6; 1 p. [Online]. Accessed: http://www.chinaembassycanada.org/eng/xwdt/t261810.htm [2006 July 31]. NRCBL: 19.5; 21.1; 21.4; 1.3.5. Note: This is the original response from the Chinese Embassy with regard to the "Report into Allegations of Organ Harvesting of Falun Gong Practitioners in China," an independent report issued by David Matas, an international human rights lawyer, and David Kilgour, former Secretary of State (Asia-Pacific) for Canada and former member of Parliament (from May 1979 until January 2006), on July 6, 2006. The Embassy of China issued a revised response on July 26, 2007, which is online at http://www.chinaembassycanada.org/eng/xwdt/t265055.htm.

Akgün, H.S.; Bilgin, N.; Tokalak, I.; Kut, A.; Haberal, Mehmet. Organ donation: a cross-sectional survey of the knowledge and personal views of Turkish health care professionals. *Transplantation Proceedings* 2003 June; 35(4): 1273-1275. NRCBL: 19.5; 7.1. SC: em.

Albright, C.L.; Glanz, K.; Wong, L.; Dela Cruz, M.R.; Abe, L.; Sagayadoro, T.L. Knowledge and attitudes about deceased donor organ donation in Filipinos: a qualitative assessment. *Transplantation Proceedings* 2005 December; 37(10): 4153-4158. NRCBL: 19.5. SC: em.

Aldhous, Peter. Scandal grows over suspect body parts. *New Scientist* 2006 September 2-8; 191(2567): 10. NRCBL: 19.5; 9.8.

Alkhawari, Fawzi S.; Stimson, Gerry V.; Warrens, Anthony N. Attitudes toward transplantation in U.K. Muslim Indo-Asians in West London. *American Journal of Transplantation* 2005 June; 5(6): 1326-1331. NRCBL: 19.5; 20.1; 1.2. SC: em; cs.

Al-Khader, Abdullah; Jondeby, Mohamed; Ghamdi, Ghormullah; Flaiw, Ahmed; Hejaili, Fayez; Querishi, Junaid. Assessment of the willingness of potential live related kidney donors. *Annals of Transplantation* 2005; 10(1): 35-37. NRCBL: 19.5; 19.3; 8.2; 8.1.

Al-Khader, A.A.; Shaheen, F.A.M.; Al-Jondeby, M.S. Important social factors that affect organ transplantation in Islamic countries. *Experimental and Clinical Transplanta-*

tion 2003 December; 1(2): 96-101. NRCBL: 19.5; 1.2; 20.3.3; 21.7.

American Society for Reproductive Medicine [ASRM]. Guidelines for cryopreserved embryo donation. *Fertility and Sterility* 2004 September; 82(Supplement 1): S16-S17. NRCBL: 19.5; 14.6. Note: Released June 2002 as part of 2002 Guideline Supplement.

American Society for Reproductive Medicine [ASRM]. Guidelines for oocyte donation. *Fertility and Sterility* 2004 September; 82(Supplement 1): S13-S15. NRCBL: 19.5; 14.6. Note: Released June 2002 as part of 2002 Guideline Supplement.

American Society for Reproductive Medicine [ASRM]. Guidelines for sperm donation. *Fertility and Sterility* 2004 September; 82(Supplement 1): S9-S12. NRCBL: 19.5; 14.1; 14.6. Note: Released June 2002 as part of 2002 Guideline Supplement.

American Society for Reproductive Medicine [ASRM]. Ethics Committee. Donating spare embryos for embryonic stem-cell research. *Fertility and Sterility* 2004 September; 82(Supplement 1): S224-S227. NRCBL: 19.5; 14.6; 18.3; 18.5.4; 15.1.

American Society for Reproductive Medicine [ASRM]. Ethics Committee. Family members as gamete donors and surrogates. *Fertility and Sterility* 2004 September; 82(Supplement 1): S217-S223. NRCBL: 19.5; 14.1; 8.1.

Anderson-Shaw, Lisa; Orfali, Kristina. Child-to-parents bone marrow donation for treatment of sickle cell disease. *Journal of Clinical Ethics* 2006 Spring; 17(1): 53-61. NRCBL: 19.5; 19.1; 8.3.2; 9.6; 9.5.1. SC: cs.

Applequist, Hilary; Giedt, Elizabeth M. Organ donation: autonomy and beneficence: the case of Mr. P. *JONA's Healthcare Law, Ethics, and Regulation* 2006 April-June; 8(2): 37-41. NRCBL: 19.5; 1.1. SC: cs.

Ashraf, Omar; Ali, Saad; Ali, Sumbul A.; Ali, Hina; Alam, Mehrulnisa; Ali, Arshad; Ali, Talaha M. Attitude toward organ donation: a survey in Pakistan. *Artificial Organs* 2005 November; 29(11): 899-905. NRCBL: 19.5; 7.1. SC: em.

Avard, Denise; Vallance, Hilary; Greenberg, Cheryl; Laberge, Claude; Kharaboyan, Linda; Plant, Margo. Variability in the storage and use of newborn dried bloodspots in Canada: is it time for national standards? *Genomics, Society and Policy* 2006 December; 2(3): 80-95. NRCBL: 19.5; 9.5.7; 15.3; 18.3; 18.5.2. SC: em.
Abstract: Storage and secondary use of bloodspots collected for newborn screening raises controversies because of the particularly sensitive nature of the information that can be derived from them and the lack of national standards and consistent provincial policies that can serve to guide storage facilities. This report, derived through a review of Canadian and provincial policy statements, a survey of provincial newborn screening laboratory directors and program directors, as well as through a

NRCBL: National Reference Center for Bioethics Literature Classification Scheme   See inside front cover for terms.

395

consultative workshop, illustrates the social, ethical and legal issues regarding the storage, access and further uses of newborn bloodspots. The report indicates that there is a need for heightened transparency and clear recommendations concerning the criteria for storage, the duration of storage, and permissible secondary uses of dried bloodspots in Canada.

Bagheri, Alireza. Can the "Japan organ transplantation law" promote organ procurement from the brain dead? *In:* Sang-yong, Song; Young-Mo, Koo; Macer, Darryl R.J., eds. Asian Bioethics in the 21st Century. Christchurch, NZ: Eubios Ethics Institute, 2002: 133-137. NRCBL: 19.5; 20.2.1. Conference: Proceedings of the Asian Bioethics Conference (ABC4), held 22-25 November 2002 in Seoul, South Korea.

Bagheri, Alireza; Tanaka, Takamasa; Takahashi, Hideto; Shoji, Shin'ichi. Brain death and organ transplantation: knowledge, attitudes, and practice among Japanese students. *Eubios Journal of Asian and International Bioethics* 2003 January 13(1): 3-5. NRCBL: 19.5; 20.2.1. SC: em.

Barber, Kerri; Falvey, Sue; Hamilton, Claire; Collett, Dave; Rudge, Chris. Potential for organ donation in the United Kingdom: audit of intensive care records. *BMJ: British Medical Journal* 2006 May 13; 332(7550): 1124-1126. NRCBL: 19.5. SC: em.
    Abstract: OBJECTIVES: To determine the true potential for solid organ donation from deceased heartbeating donors and the reasons for non-donation from potential donors. DESIGN: An audit of all deaths in intensive care units, 1 April 2003 to 31 March 2005. The study was hierarchic, in that information was sought on whether or not brain stem testing was carried out; if so, whether or not organ donation was considered; if so whether or not the next of kin were approached; if so, whether or not consent was given; if so, whether or not organ donation took place. SETTING: 341 intensive care units in 284 hospitals in the United Kingdom. PARTICIPANTS: 46,801 dead patients, leading to 2740 potential heartbeating solid organ donors and 1244 actual donors. MAIN OUTCOME MEASURES: Proportion of potential deceased heartbeating donors considered for organ donation, proportion of families who denied consent, and proportion of potential donors who became organ donors. RESULTS: Over the two years of the study, 41% of the families of potential donors denied consent. The refusal rate for families of potential donors from ethnic minorities was twice that for white potential donors, but the age and sex of the potential donor did not affect the refusal rate. In 15% of families of potential donors there was no record of the next of kin being approached for permission for organ donation. CONCLUSIONS: Intensive care units are extremely good in considering possible organ donation from suitable patients. The biggest obstacle to improving the organ donation rate is the high proportion of relatives who deny consent.

Bardale, Rajesh V. Birth after death: questions about posthumous sperm retrieval. *Indian Journal of Medical Ethics* 2006 October-December; 3(4): 122-123. NRCBL: 19.5; 14.6; 20.1.

Barlow, Benjamin G. Religious views vary on organ donation. *Nephrology News and Issues* 2006 February; 20(2): 37-39. NRCBL: 19.5; 1.2.

Baruch, Jay. Prisoners and organ donation. *Medicine and Health Rhode Island* 2005 December; 88(12): 437-438. NRCBL: 19.5; 9.5.1; 1.3.5; 8.3.1.

Bernat, J.L.; D'Alessandro, A.M.; Port, F.K.; Bleck, T.P.; Heard, S.O.; Medina, J.; Rosenbaum, S.H.; Devita, M.A.; Gaston, R.S.; Merion, R.M.; Barr, M.L.; Marks, W.H.; Nathan, H.; O'Connor, K.; Rudow, D.L.; Leichtman, A.B.; Schwab, P.; Ascher, N.L.; Metzger, R.A.; Mc Bride, V.; Graham, W; Wagner, D.; Warren, J.; Delmonico, F.L. Report of a national Conference on donation after cardiac death. *American Journal of Transplantation* 2006 February; 6(2): 281-291. NRCBL: 19.5; 20.1; 8.3.1; 19.6.

Boden, J.; Williams, D.I. Donor anonymity: rights and meanings. *Human Fertility* 2004 March; 7(1): 19-21. NRCBL: 19.5; 8.4; 14.6; 14.2; 14.4.

Bøgh, L.; Madsen, M. Attitudes, knowledge, and proficiency in relation to organ donation: a questionnaire-based analysis in donor hospitals in northern Denmark. *Transplantation Proceedings* 2005 October; 37(8): 3256-3257. NRCBL: 19.5; 7.1. SC: em.

Boissy, Adrienne R.; Provencio, J. Javier; Smith, Cheryl A.; Diringer, Michael N. Neurointensivists' opinions about death by neurological criteria and organ donation. *Neurocritical Care* 2005; 3(2): 115-121. NRCBL: 19.5; 20.2.1; 17.1. SC: em.

Boulware, L. Ebony; Ratner, Lloyd E.; Troll, Misty U.; Chaudron, Alexis; Yeung, Edwina; Chen, Shirley; Klein, Andrew S.; Hiller, Janet; Powe, Neil R. Attitudes, psychology, and risk taking of potential live kidney donors: strangers, relatives, and the general public. *American Journal of Transplantation* 2005 July; 5(7): 1671-1680. NRCBL: 19.5; 19.3. SC: em.

Burns, Lawrence. Banking on the value of analogies in bioethics. *American Journal of Bioethics* 2006 November-December; 6(6): 63-65; author reply W13-W14. NRCBL: 19.5; 19.4; 1.3.12. Comments: Bjørn Hofmann, Jan Helge Solbakk, and Søren Holm. Analogical reasoning in handling emerging technologies: the case of umbilical cord blood biobanking. American Journal of Bioethics 2006 November-December; 6(6): 49-57.

Check, Erika. Tissue-sample payments anger lawmakers [news]. *Nature* 2006 June 22; 441(7096): 912-913. NRCBL: 19.5; 15.1.

Childress, James F. How can we ethically increase the supply of transplantable organs? *Annals of Internal Medicine* 2006 August 1; 145(3): 224-225. NRCBL: 19.5.

Christensen, Angi M. Moral considerations in body donation for scientific research: a unique look at the University of Tennessee's anthropological research facility. *Bioethics* 2006 June; 20(3): 136-145. NRCBL: 19.5; 8.3.1; 1.1; 7.2; 1.3.5. SC: an.

Abstract: This paper discusses keys to the moral procurement, treatment and disposition of remains used for scientific research, specifically those donated to the University of Tennessee's Anthropological Research Facility (ARF). The ARF is an outdoor laboratory dedicated to better understanding the fate of human remains in forensic contexts, and focuses its research on decomposition, time since death estimates, body location and recovery techniques, and skeletal analysis. Historically, many donations were unclaimed bodies received from medical examiners (although it will be shown that this trend is changing), and it has been argued that the use of the unclaimed bodies for medical or scientific purposes is a violation of autonomy since no consent was given by the individual. It is argued here, however, that the domain of autonomous choice extends to one's own corpse only insofar as expressed wishes are made known prior to one's death, and that in the absence of expressed intent toward final disposition, it is acceptable for institutions to receive donations from medical examiners or family members. This paper also discusses other philosophical issues related to donation, consent and autonomy, and the forensic benefits of research conducted at the Anthropological Research Facility.

Cohen, Bernard; Smits, Jacqueline M.; Haase, Bernadette; Persijn, Guido; Vanrenterghem, Yves; Frei, Ulrich. Expanding the donor pool to increase renal transplantation. *Nephrology Dialysis Transplantation* 2005 January; 20(1): 34-41. NRCBL: 19.5; 19.6; 19.3. SC: em.

Coppen, Remco; Friele, Roland D.; Marquet, Richard L.; Gevers, Sjef K.M. Opting-out systems: no guarantee for higher donation rates. *Transplant International* 2005 November; 18(11): 1275-1279. NRCBL: 19.5; 8.3.1. SC: em.

de Ortúzar, M.G.; Soratti, C.; Velez, I. Bioethics and organ transplantation. *Transplantation Proceedings* 1997 December; 29(8): 3627-3630. NRCBL: 19.5; 1.1; 2.1. Conference: Fourth International Congress of The Society for Organ Sharing; Washington, DC; 1997 July 10-12.

Delmonico, Francis L.; Graham, W.K. Direction of the Organ Procurement and Transplantation Network and United Network for Organ Sharing regarding the oversight of live donor transplantation and solicitation for organs. *American Journal of Transplantation* 2006 January; 6(1): 37-40. NRCBL: 19.5; 19.1.

DeVeaux, Theresa E. Non-heart-beating organ donation: issues and ethics for the critical care nurse. *Journal of Vascular Nursing* 2006 March; 24(1): 17-21. NRCBL: 19.5; 20.1; 21.7.

Domen, Ronald E. Ethical issues in transfusion medicine: the safety of blood and hematopoietic stem cell donation. *Current Hematology Reports* 2005 November; 4(6): 465-469. NRCBL: 19.5; 19.4; 9.8.

Draper, Heather; MacDiarmaid-Gordon, Adam; Strumidlo, Laura; Teuten, Bea; Updale, Eleanor. Virtual ethics committee, case 4: why can't a dead mother donate a kidney to her son? *Clinical Ethics* 2006 December; 1(4): 183-190. NRCBL: 19.5; 9.4; 8.3.3; 20.3.1. SC: cs.

Elding, Christine; Scholes, Julie. Organ and tissue donation: a trustwide perspective or critical care concern? *Nursing in Critical Care* 2005 May-June; 10(3): 129-135. NRCBL: 19.5; 20.3.3. Identifiers: United Kingdom (Great Britain).

El-Shoubaki, H.; Bener, Abdulbari. Public knowledge and attitudes toward organ donation and transplantation: a cross-cultural study. *Transplantation Proceedings* 2005 June; 37(5): 1993-1997. NRCBL: 19.5. SC: em. Identifiers: Qatar.

Evans, David W. Living organ donation needs debate on harm to donors [letter]. *BMJ: British Medical Journal* 2006 October 28; 333(7574): 919. NRCBL: 19.5; 19.3; 8.3.1.

Evans, H.M. What's wrong with "retained organs"? Some personal reflections in the afterglow of "Alder Hey". *Journal of Clinical Pathology* 2001 November; 54(11): 824-826. NRCBL: 19.5; 20.1; 8.3.1; 4.4.

Fahrenwald, Nancy L.; Stabnow, Wendy. Sociocultural perspective on organ and tissue donation among reservation-dwelling American Indian adults. *Ethnicity and Health* 2005 November; 10(4): 341-354. NRCBL: 19.5; 21.7. SC: em.

Feeley, Thomas Hugh; Servoss, Timothy J. Examining college students' intentions to become organ donors. *Journal of Health Communication* 2005 April-May; 10(3): 237-249. NRCBL: 19.5; 8.1. SC: em.

Fitzgibbons, Sean R. Cadaveric organ donation and consent: a comparative analysis of the United States, Japan, Singapore, and China. *ILSA Journal of International and Comparative Law* 1999 Fall; 6(1): 73-105. NRCBL: 19.5; 20.1; 8.3.1; 21.1.

Flaum, Tzvi. Living donor organ transplants. *In:* Rosner, Fred, ed. Medicine and Jewish Law. Volume III. Brooklyn, NY: Yashar Books, Inc.; 2005: 131-140. NRCBL: 19.5.

Gimbel, Ronald W.; Strosberg, Martin A.; Lehrman, Susan E.; Gefenas, Eugenijus; Taft, Frank. Presumed consent and other predictors of cadaveric organ donation in Europe. *Progress in Transplantation* 2003 March; 13(1): 17-23. NRCBL: 19.5; 8.3.1. SC: em.

Godin, Gaston; Sheeran, P.; Conner, M.; Germain, M.; Blondeau, D.; Gagné, C.; Beaulieu, D.; Naccache, H. Factors explaining the intention to give blood among the general population. *Vox Sanguinis* 2005 October; 89(3): 140-149. NRCBL: 19.5; 19.4. SC: em.

Haddow, Gillian. The phenomenology of death, embodiment and organ transplantation. *Sociology of Health and Illness* 2005 January; 27(1): 92-113. NRCBL: 19.5; 20.1; 8.1. SC: cs. Identifiers: United Kingdom (Great Britain).

Heinonen, Maarit; Oila, Outi; Nordström, Katrina. Current issues in the regulation of human tissue-engineer-

---

NRCBL: National Reference Center for Bioethics Literature Classification Scheme See inside front cover for terms.

397

ing products in the European Union. *Tissue Engineering* 2005 November-December; 11(11-12): 1905-1911. NRCBL: 19.5; 15.1; 5.3; 21.1.

Hester, D. Micah. Why we must leave our organs to others. *American Journal of Bioethics [Online]* 2006 July-August; 6(4): W23-W28. NRCBL: 19.5.

Institute of Medicine (United States) [IOM]. Committee on Increasing Rates of Organ Donation. Presumed consent. *In:* Childress, James F.; Liverman, Catharyn T., eds. Organ Donation: Opportunities for Action. Washington, DC: National Academies Press; 2006: 205-228. NRCBL: 19.5; 8.3.1.

Institute of Medicine (United States) [IOM]. Committee on Increasing Use of Organ Donation. Ethical considerations in living donation. *In:* Childress, James F.; Liverman, Catharyn T., eds. Organ Donation: Opportunities for Action. Washington, DC: National Academies Press; 2006: 263-279. NRCBL: 19.5.

Jacob, Marie-Andrée. Another look at the presumed-versus-informed consent dichotomy in postmortem organ procurement. *Bioethics* 2006 November; 20(6): 293-300. NRCBL: 19.5; 8.3.1; 9.5.1. SC: an.

Jendrisak, Martin D.; Hong, B.; Shenoy, S.; Lowell, J.; Desai, N.; Chapman, W.; Vijayan, A.; Wetzel, R.D.; Smith, M.; Wagner, J.; Brennan, S.; Brockmeier, D.; Kappel, D. Altruistic living donors: evaluation for nondirected kidney or liver donation. *American Journal of Transplantation* 2006 January; 6(1): 115-120. NRCBL: 19.5; 19.3; 19.1.

Kaiser, Jocelyn. House panel finds fault with how NIH handles tissue samples. *Science* 2006 June 23; 312(5781): 1733. NRCBL: 19.5; 1.3.9; 15.1; 8.4; 5.1. Identifiers: National Institutes of Health; Trey Sunderland; Karen Putnam.

Kilgour, David; Matas, David. Response of David Kilgour and David Matas to the Chinese government statement. Ottawa, Ontario, Canada: David Kilgour and David Matas, 2006 July 7; 4 p. [Online]. Accessed: http://investigation.redirectme.net [2006 July 27]. NRCBL: 19.5; 21.1; 21.4; 1.3.5. Identifiers: illegal acquisition of organs from Falun Gong practitioners. Note: This document is a response to the Chinese Embassy's Statement on the independent "Report into Allegations of Organ Harvesting of Falun Gong Practitioners in China" issued by David Matas and David Kilgour on July 6, 2006.

Kim, Dean Y.; Cauduro, Silvania P.; Bohorquez, Humberto E.; Ishitani, Michael B.; Nyberg, Scott L.; Rosen, Charles B. Routine use of livers from deceased donors older than 70: is it justified? *Transplant International* 2005 January; 18(1): 73-77. NRCBL: 19.5; 20.1. SC: em.

Luxembourg. Commission Consultative Nationale d'Éthique pour les Sciences de la Vie et de la Santé

[CNE]. Bref Avis sur le project de loi no. 5448 relatif aux tissus et cellules humains utilisés à des fins thérapeutiques: Avis No 19 [Opinion No. 19: Short opinion on Bill no. 5448 concerning human tissues and cells used for therapeutic ends]. Luxembourg: Commission Nationale d'Éthique, 2005 December 22; 6 p. [Online]. Accessed: http://www.cne.public.lu/publications/avis/Avis_19.pdf [2006 April 7]. NRCBL: 19.5; 18.1.

MacLeod, Kendra D.; Whitsett, Stan F.; Mash, Eric J.; Pelletier, Wendy. Pediatric sibling donors of successful and unsuccessful hematopoietic stem cell transplants (HSCT): a qualitative study of their psychosocial experience. *Journal of Pediatric Psychology* 2003 June; 28(4): 223-231. NRCBL: 19.5; 9.5.7; 8.3.1. SC: em.

Manno, Edward M. Nonheart-beating donation in the neurologically devastated patient. *Neurocritical Care* 2005; 3(2): 111-114. NRCBL: 19.5; 20.2.1.

Marcus, Amy Dockser. Patients with rare diseases work to jump-start research; advocacy groups create their own tissue banks to aid in drug development. *Wall Street Journal* 2006 July 11; p. D1, D2. NRCBL: 19.5. SC: po.

Meilaender, Gilbert. Gifts of the body. *New Atlantis* 2006 Summer; 13: 25-35. NRCBL: 19.5; 19.1; 4.4.

Misje, Aksel H.; Bosnes, V.; Gasdal, O.; Heier, H.E. Motivation, recruitment and retention of voluntary non-remunerated blood donors: a survey-based questionnaire study. *Vox Sanguinis* 2005 November; 89(4): 236-244. NRCBL: 19.5; 19.4. SC: em.

Miyagi, Shigehito; Kawagishi, Naoki; Fujimori, Keisei; Sekiguchi, Satoru; Fukumori, Tatsuya; Akamatsu, Yorihiro; Satomi, Susumu. Risks of donation and quality of donors' life after living donor liver transplantation. *Transplant International* 2005 January; 18(1): 47-51. NRCBL: 19.5; 5.2; 4.4. SC: em. Identifiers: Japan.

Morioka, Masahiro. Commentary on Bagheri et al. *Eubios Journal of Asian and International Bioethics* 2003 January 13(1): 6. NRCBL: 19.5; 20.2.1.

Morrissey, Paul E.; Dube, Catherine; Gohh, Reginald; Yango, Angelito; Gautam, Amitabh; Monaco, Anthony P. Good Samaritan kidney donation. *Transplantation* 2005 November 27; 80(10): 1369-1373. NRCBL: 19.5; 19.3.

Murphy, Timothy F.; Veatch, Robert M. Members first: the ethics of donating organs and tissues to groups. *CQ: Cambridge Quarterly of Healthcare Ethics* 2006 Winter; 15(1): 50-59. NRCBL: 19.5; 19.6; 7.1; 1.1. Identifiers: LifeSharers.

Nicholas, Richard. Ethical considerations in allograft tissue transplantation: a surgeon's perspective. *Clinical Orthopaedics and Related Research* 2005 June; (435): 11-16. NRCBL: 19.5; 8.3.1; 8.1.

Nowak, Rachel. Not brain-dead, but ripe for transplant. *New Scientist* 2006 August 5-11; 191(2563): 6-7. NRCBL: 19.5; 20.2.1.

O'Connor, Mat; Hulatt, Ian; Drake, Linda; Brown, Jane. Means of consent. *Nursing Standard* 2004 May 5; 18(34): 20. NRCBL: 19.5; 8.3.1.

Palmeri, Debera. Directed donation: what is a transplant center to do? *Nephrology Nursing Journal* 2005 November-December; 32(6): 701-702. NRCBL: 19.5.

Parry, Bronwyn; Gere, Cathy. Contested bodies: property models and the commodification of human biological artefacts. *Science as Culture* 2006 June; 15(2): 139-158. NRCBL: 19.5; 5.3; 15.1; 4.4; 7.1. Identifiers: Addenbrooke Hospital Brain Bank.

Parry, Jane. Chinese rules on transplantation do not go far enough [news]. *BMJ: British Medical Journal* 2006 April 8; 332(7545): 810. NRCBL: 19.5; 20.2.1; 20.6.

Parturkar, D. Legal and ethical issues in human organ transplantation. *Medicine and Law: The World Association for Medical Law* 2006 June; 25(2): 389-398. NRCBL: 19.5; 20.2.1; 4.4; 8.5.

Abstract: The Indian Law on Human Organ and Tissue transplantation protects the interests and preserves the lives of both the donor as well as the recipient patient. An issue arises as to the relationship of others with one's body or parts thereof especially one's cadaver. The posessory rights of the cadaver, property rights in the human corpse will be discussed in this paper. The ethical issues involved in altruism give rise to number of contradictions on which this paper focuses. The removal of organs would constitute an "injury" in ethical and legal terms if the intended use of an organ or tissue is not legally and ethically acceptable. How one determines the existence of the 'injury' in this context, where application of the concept of non-malfeasance is itself a good defense, is discussed in the paper. Consent in case of a cadaver has always been a matter of debate. The application of the doctrine of consent will be referred to in the course of this article.

Pentz, Rebecca. Duty and altruism: alternative analyses of the ethics of sibling bone marrow donation. *Journal of Clinical Ethics* 2006 Fall; 17(3): 227-230. NRCBL: 19.5; 19.1; 9.5.7; 1.3.5; 8.3.2. SC: cs.

Popp, F.C.; Eggert, N.; Hoy, L.; Lang, S.A.; Obed, A.; Piso, P.; Schlitt, H.J.; Dahlke, M.H. Who is willing to take the risk? Assessing the readiness for living liver donation in the general German population. *Journal of Medical Ethics* 2006 July; 32(7): 389-394. NRCBL: 19.5. SC: em.

Abstract: BACKGROUND: Shortage of donor organs is one of the major problems for liver transplant programmes. Living liver donation is a possible alternative, which could increase the amount of donor organs available in the short term. OBJECTIVE: To assess the attitude towards living organ donation in the general population to have an overview of the overall attitude within Germany. METHODS: A representative quota of people was evaluated by a mail questionnaire (n = 250). This questionnaire had 24 questions assessing the willingness to be a living liver donor for different potential recipients. Factors for and against living liver donation were assessed. RESULTS: Donating a part of the liver was almost as accepted as donating a kidney. The readiness to donate was highest when participants were asked to donate for children. In an urgent life-threatening situation the will to donate was especially high, whereas it was lower in the case of recipient substance misuse. More women than men expressed a higher disposition to donate for their children. Sex, religion, state of health and age of the donor, however, did not influence other questions on the readiness to consider living organ donation. The will for postmortem organ donation positively correlated with the will to be a living organ donor. CONCLUSIONS: The motivation in different demographic subgroups to participate in living liver transplantation is described. Differences in donation readiness resulting from the situation of every donor and recipient are thoroughly outlined. The acceptance for a living liver donation was found to be high - and comparable to that of living kidney donation.

Prottas, Jeffrey M. Altruism, motivation, and allocation: giving and using human organs. *Journal of Social Issues* 1993 Summer; 49(2): 137-150. NRCBL: 19.5; 19.6. SC: an; em.

Ramirez, Anthony. Medicine meets religion in organ donation debate. *New York Times* 2006 November 18; p. B2. NRCBL: 19.5; 1.2; 20.2.1. Identifiers: Judaism.

Reding, Raymond. Is it right to promote living donor liver transplantation for fulminant hepatic failure in pediatric recipients? *American Journal of Transplantation* 2005 July; 5(7): 1587-1591. NRCBL: 19.5; 19.1; 9.5.7.

Richardson, Ruth. Narratives of compound loss: parents' stories from the organ retention scandal. *In:* Hurwitz, Brian; Greenhalgh, Trisha; Skultans, Vieda, eds. Narrative Research in Health and Illness. Malden MA: BMJ Books; 2004: 239-256. NRCBL: 19.5; 8.3.2; 20.3.3.

Robley, Lois R. Increasing the availability of organs for transplantation: an ethical analysis. *Journal of the Medical Association of Georgia* 1998 April; 87(2): 113-116. NRCBL: 19.5; 19.1; 22.2.

Rosell, Tarris D. An ethics conflict and culture: should this kidney be used? *Pediatric Nursing* 2006 January-February; 32(1): 68-70. NRCBL: 19.5; 19.3; 9.5.7; 8.3.1; 21.7; 8.1. SC: cs.

Ross, Lainie Friedman. Should a PVS patient be a live organ donor? *Medical Ethics Newsletter [Lahey Clinic]* 2006 Winter; 13(1): 3. NRCBL: 19.5; 20.5.1; 8.3.3; 4.4. SC: cs. Identifiers: permanent vegetative state.

Ross, Lainie Friedman. The ethical limits in expanding living donor transplantation. *Kennedy Institute of Ethics Journal* 2006 June; 16(2): 151-172. NRCBL: 19.5; 19.6; 1.1.

Abstract: The past decade has witnessed the emergence of novel methods to increase the number of living donors. Although such programs are not likely to yield high volumes of organs, some transplant centers have gone to great lengths to establish one or more of them. I discuss some of the ethical and policy issues raised by five such programs: (1) living-paired and cascade exchanges; (2) unbalanced living-paired exchanges; (3) list-paired exchanges; (4) nondirected donors; and (5)nondirected donors catalyzing cascade exchanges. I argue that living-paired and cascade exchanges are ethically sound,

NRCBL: National Reference Center for Bioethics Literature Classification Scheme   See inside front cover for terms.

399

but will lead to only a few additional transplants. Unbalanced exchanges and list-paired exchanges raise ethical issues that should limit their permissibility. Nondirected donations can be ethically sound with adherence to strict eligibility criteria and fair allocation procedures. Nondirected donors catalyzing cascade exchanges can be ethically sound provided that individuals with blood types O and B are not made worse off.

Ross, Lainie Friedman; Glannon, Walter. A compounding of errors: the case of bone marrow donation between non-intimate siblings. *Journal of Clinical Ethics* 2006 Fall; 17(3): 220-226. NRCBL: 19.5; 19.1; 9.5.7; 1.3.5; 8.3.2. SC: cs.

Royal College of Physicians of London. Human Tissue Bill. Response from the Royal College of Physicians. London: Royal College of Physicians of London 2004 June 16; 4 p. [Online]. Accessed: http://www.rcplondon.ac.uk/college/statements/response_htb.htm [2006 August 18]. NRCBL: 19.5; 8.3.1; 6. Identifiers: United Kingdom (Great Britain). Note: The Human Tissue Bill grew out of the work of the Retained Organs Commission after events at Alder Hey Hospital and locations.

Sanner, Margareta A. Living with a stranger's organ — views of the public and transplant recipients. *Annals of Transplantation* 2005; 10(1): 9-12. NRCBL: 19.5; 4.4. Identifiers: Sweden.

Satel, Sally. Death's waiting list. *New York Times* 2006 May 15; p. A21. NRCBL: 19.5; 19.6; 19.3.

Satyapal, K.S. Ethics, transplantation, and the changing role of anatomists. *Clinical Anatomy* 2005 March; 18(2): 150-153. NRCBL: 19.5; 20.1; 4.1.1.

Shaheen, F.A.M.; Kurpad, R.; Al-Attar, B.A.; Al-Khader, A.A. A proposed Saudi approach to the ethical utilization of living unrelated kidney donation. *Transplantation Proceedings* 2005 June; 37(5): 2004-2006. NRCBL: 19.5; 19.3.

Shemie, Sam D.; Baker, Andrew J.; Knoll, Greg; Wall, William; Rocker, Graeme; Howes, Daniel; Davidson, Janet; Pagliarello, Joe; Chambers-Evans, Jane; Cockfield, Sandra; Farrell, Catherine; Glannon, Walter; Gourlay, William; Grant, David; Langevin, Stéphan; Wheelock, Brian; Young, Kimberly; Dossetor, John. Donation after cardiocirculatory death in Canada. *CMAJ/JAMC: Canadian Medical Association Journal* 2006 October 10; 175(8, Supplement): S1-S24. NRCBL: 19.5; 21.1. SC: em.

Siminoff, Laura A.; Burant, Christopher J.; Ibrahim, Said A. Racial disparities in preferences and perceptions regarding organ donation. *JGIM: Journal of General Internal Medicine* 2006 September; 21(9): 995-1000. NRCBL: 19.5; 9.5.4. SC: em.

Simpson, Bob. Impossible gifts: bodies, Buddhism and bioethics in contemporary Sri Lanka. *Journal of the Royal Anthropological Institute* 2004 December; 10(4): 839-859. NRCBL: 19.5; 1.1; 2.1; 14.6; 19.4. Identifiers: Buddhism.

Skloot, Rebecca. Taking the least of you: Most of us have tissue or blood samples on file somewhere, whether we know it or not. What we don't typically know is what research they are being used for and how much money is being made from them. And science may want to keep things that way. *New York Times Magazine* 2006 April 16; p. 38-45, 75, 79, 81. NRCBL: 19.5; 18.3; 19.4.

Sokalska, Maria. Recent developments in health law in Poland: new law on the removal, storage, and transplantation of cells, tissues, and organs. *European Journal of Health Law* 2006 June; 13(2): 115-122. NRCBL: 19.5; 8.3.1; 18.5.4.

Spital, Aaron. More on directed kidney donation by altruistic living strangers: a response to Dr. Hilhorst and his colleagues. *Transplantation* 2005 October 27; 80(8): 1001-1002. NRCBL: 19.5; 19.3; 1.1.

Spital, Aaron. More on parental living liver donation for children with fulminant hepatic failure: addressing concerns about competing interests, coercion, consent and balancing acts. *American Journal of Transplantation* 2005 November; 5(11): 2619-2622. NRCBL: 19.5; 19.1; 9.5.7; 8.3.2.

Streat, Stephen. Clinical review: moral assumptions and the process of organ donation in the intensive care unit. *Critical Care* 2004 October; 8(5): 382-388. NRCBL: 19.5; 1.1; 8.1. SC: rv.

Suarez, Isabel Maria Belda; Fernandez-Montoya, Antorio; Fernandez, Andres Rodriguez; Lopez-Berrio, Antorio; Cillero- Penuela, Manuel. How regular blood donors explain their behavior. *Transfusion* 2004 October; 44(10): 1441-1446. NRCBL: 19.5; 19.4. SC: em.

Tabarrok, Alexander; Undis, David J. Response to "Members First: the Ethics of Donating Organs and Tissues to Groups" by Timothy F. Murphy and Robert M. Veatch (CQ Vol 15, No 1). *CQ: Cambridge Quarterly of Healthcare Ethics* 2006 Fall; 15(4): 450-456. NRCBL: 19.5; 19.6; 7.1; 1.1.

Thasler, Wolfgang E.; Schlott, Thilo; Kalkuhl, Arno; Plän, Thomas; Irrgang, Bernhard; Juach, Karl-Walter; Weiss, Thomas S. Human tissue for in vitro research as an alternative to animal experiments: a charitable "honest broker"model to fulfil ethical and legal regulations and to protect research participants. *ATLA: Alternatives to Laboratory Animals* 2006 August; 34(4): 387-392. NRCBL: 19.5; 18.2; 22.2.

Tonti-Filippini, Nicholas. New issues in organ donation. *Linacre Quarterly* 2006 November; 73(4): 326-343. NRCBL: 19.5; 20.2.1; 1.2; 8.3.1.

Topbas, Murat; Çan, G.; Can, M.A.; Özgün, S. Outmoded attitudes toward organ donation among Turkish health care professionals. *Transplantation Proceedings* 2005 June; 37(5): 1998-2000. NRCBL: 19.5; 7.1; 2.1. SC: em.

Townell, Nick. Quality of life after donor nephrectomy: is better after laparoscopy than the mini incision technique [editorial]. *BMJ: British Medical Journal* 2006 July 29; 333(7561): 209-210. NRCBL: 19.5; 19.3; 4.4.

Truog, Robert D.; Cochrane, Thomas I. The truth about "donation after cardiac death". *Journal of Clinical Ethics* 2006 Summer; 17(2): 133-136. NRCBL: 19.5; 20.2.1; 20.5.1.

Valapour, Maryam. Donation after cardiac death: consent is the issue, not death. *Journal of Clinical Ethics* 2006 Summer; 17(2): 137-138. NRCBL: 19.5; 8.3.1; 20.2.1.

Vandenbroucke, Amy. HIV and organ donation: Illinois' solution to organ donation shortages. *DePaul Journal of Health Care Law* 2006 Spring; 9(3): 1285-1316. NRCBL: 19.5; 9.5.6.

Veatch, Robert M. Organ exchanges: fairness to the O-blood group [editorial]. *American Journal of Transplantation* 2006 January; 6(1): 1-2. NRCBL: 19.5; 8.3.1; 1.1.

Weimar, Willem; Zuidema, Willij; de Klerk, Marry; Haase-Kromwijk, Bernadette; Ijzermans, Jan. Altruistic kidney donation. *Lancet* 2006 September 16-22; 368(9540): 987. NRCBL: 19.5; 19.3; 1.1.

Weisz, Victoria; Robbennolt, Jennifer K. Risks and benefits of pediatric bone marrow donation: a critical need for research. *Behavioral Sciences and the Law* 1996 Autumn; 14(4): 375-391. NRCBL: 19.5; 4.4; 8.3.2.

Williams, Mark E. Internet organ solicitation, explained. *Advances in Chronic Kidney Disease* 2006 January; 13(1): 70-75. NRCBL: 19.5; 1.3.12.

Wing, A.J. Organs for transplantation: should the UK follow Belgium? [editorial]. *Journal of the Royal Society of Medicine* 1996 December; 89(12): 661-662. NRCBL: 19.5; 8.3.1; 20.1. Identifiers: United Kingdom.

Woien, Sandra; Rady, Mohamed Y.; Verheijde, Joseph L.; McGregor, Joan. Organ procurement organizations internet enrollment for organ donation: abandoning informed consent. *BMC Medical Ethics* 2006; 7(14): 9p. NRCBL: 19.5; 8.3.1.

Yew, Y.W.; Saw, Seang-Mei; Pan, J.C.-H.; Shen, H.M.; Lwin, M.; Yew, M.-S.; Heng, W.-J. Knowledge and beliefs on corneal donation in Singapore adults. *British Journal of Ophthalmology* 2005 July; 89(7): 835-840. NRCBL: 19.5; 21.7; 1.2. SC: em.

ORGAN AND TISSUE TRANSPLANTATION/ . . . / ECONOMIC ASPECTS

Not for sale at any price [editorial]. *Lancet* 2006 April 8-14; 367(9517): 1118. NRCBL: 19.5; 9.3.1; 21.1. SC: le.

Abouna, George M. Ethical issues in organ and tissue transplantation. *Experimental and Clinical Transplantation* 2003 December; 1(2): 125-138. NRCBL: 19.5; 19.6; 19.3; 9.3.1; 20.1; 22.2; 1.3.5.

Audi, Robert. The morality and utility of organ transplantation. *Utilitas* 1996 July; 8(2): 141-158. NRCBL: 19.5; 19.6; 19.1; 9.3.1; 8.3.1; 4.4.

Benes, Francine M. Ethical issues in brain banking [editorial]. *Current Opinion in Psychiatry* 2005 May; 18(3): 277-283. NRCBL: 19.5; 15.1; 17.1; 8.3.1; 9.3.1.

Bjorkman, Barbro. Why we are not allowed to sell that which we are encouraged to donate. *CQ: Cambridge Quarterly of Healthcare Ethics* 2006 Winter; 15(1): 60-70. NRCBL: 19.5; 9.3.1; 1.1. Identifiers: virtue ethics.

Bryce, C.L.; Siminoff, L.A.; Ubel, P.A.; Nathan, H.; Caplan, A.; Arnold, R.M. Do incentives matter? Providing benefits to families of organ donors. *American Journal of Transplantation* 2005 December; 5(12): 2999-3008. NRCBL: 19.5; 9.3.1.

Cantarovich, Felix. Public opinion and organ donation suggestions for overcoming barriers. *Annals of Transplantation* 2005; 10(1): 22-25. NRCBL: 19.5; 9.3.1; 1.2; 20.1.

Cohen, Alfred. Sale or donation of human organs. *Journal of Halacha and Contemporary Society* 2006 Fall; (52): 37-64. NRCBL: 19.5; 9.3.1; 1.2.

Dickenson, Donna. Human tissue and global ethics. *Genomics, Society and Policy* 2005 February; 1(1): 41-53. NRCBL: 19.5; 9.3.1; 5.3; 21.7. Identifiers: Tonga; Maori; Australia; New Zealand.

Dubner, Stephen; Levitt, Steven. Freakonomics. Flesh trade: why not let people sell their organs? *New York Times Magazine* 2006 July 9; p. 20, 21. NRCBL: 19.5; 9.3.1. SC: po.

Frati, Paola. Organ transplantation from living donors, between bioethics and the law. *Transplantation Proceedings* 2005 July-August; 37(6): 2433-2435. NRCBL: 19.5; 9.3.1; 19.1; 22.2; 18.5.4; 21.1. SC: le. Identifiers: Italy.

Friedman, Amy L. Payment for living organ donation should be legalised. *BMJ: British Medical Journal* 2006 October 7; 333(7571): 746-748. NRCBL: 19.5; 19.3; 9.3.1.

Ghods, Ahad J. Governed financial incentives as an alternative to altruistic organ donation. *Experimental and Clinical Transplantation* 2004 December; 2(2): 221-228. NRCBL: 19.5; 9.3.1; 19.3. Identifiers: Iran.

NRCBL: National Reference Center for Bioethics Literature Classification Scheme See inside front cover for terms.

401

Grigoriu, Bogdan-Dragos. Ethical flaws in Romania's health reform [letter]. *Lancet* 2006 June 24-30; 367(9528): 2059. NRCBL: 19.5; 9.3.1.

Haddow, G. "Because you're worth it?" The taking and selling of transplantable organs. *Journal of Medical Ethics* 2006 June; 32(6): 324-328. NRCBL: 19.5; 9.3.1. SC: em. Identifiers: United Kingdom (Great Britain).

Abstract: In the UK, the legal processes underpinning the procurement system for cadaveric organs for transplantation and research after death are under review. The review originated after media reports of hospitals, such as Alder Hey and Bristol, retaining organs after death without the full, informed consent of relatives. The organ procurement systems for research and transplantation are separate and distinct, but given that legal change will be applicable to both, some have argued now is the time to introduce alternative organ transplant procurement systems such as presumed consent or incentive based schemes (despite inconclusive British and American research on the status of public attitudes). Findings are reported in this paper from qualitative and quantitative research undertaken in Scotland in order to ascertain the public acceptability of different procurement systems. Nineteen in depth interviews carried out with donor families about their experiences of donating the organs of the deceased covered their views of organ retention, presumed consent, and financial incentives. This led onto a representative interview survey of 1009 members of the Scottish public. The originality of the triangulated qualitative and quantitative study offers exploration of alternative organ procurement systems from different "sides of the fence". The findings suggest that the legal changes taking place are appropriate in clarifying the role of the family but can go further in strengthening the choice of the individual to donate.

Heng, Boon Chin. Alternative solutions to the current situation of oocyte donation in Singapore. *Reproductive BioMedicine Online [electronic]* 2006 March; 12(3): 286-291. NRCBL: 19.5; 9.3.1; 14.6; 21.1.

Institute of Medicine (United States) [IOM]. Committee on Increasing Rates of Organ Donation. Incentives for deceased donation. *In:* Childress, James F.; Liverman, Catharyn T., eds. Organ Donation: Opportunities for Action. Washington, DC: National Academies Press; 2006: 229-262. NRCBL: 19.5; 9.3.1; 19.6.

Jan, Stephen; Thompson, Mardi. Proposal: two part payment scheme for live kidney donors [letter]. *BMJ: British Medical Journal* 2006 July 29; 333(7561): 262. NRCBL: 19.5; 19.3; 9.3.1. Identifiers: United Kingdom (Great Britain).

Joseph, Julia. Selling with dignity: organ selling and the safeguarding of human dignity. *Penn Bioethics Journal* 2006; 2(1): 3p. [Online]. Accessed: http://www.bioethicsjournal.com [2006 February 21]. NRCBL: 19.5; 9.3.1; 4.4.

Lawler, Peter Augustine. The commerce of the body: is the body property? *New Atlantis* 2006 Fall; 14: 62-72. NRCBL: 19.5; 4.4; 9.3.1.

Mayrhofer-Reinhartshuber, David; Fitzgerald, Annelies; Fitzgerald, Robert D. Money for consent —

Mor, Eytan; Boas, Hagao. Organ trafficking: scope and ethical dilemma. *Current Diabetes Reports* 2005 August; 5(4): 294-299. NRCBL: 19.5; 9.3.1; 19.3. Identifiers: Israel.

National Advisory Commission on Biomedical Ethics (Switzerland) [NEK-CNE] = Nationale Ethikkommission im Bereich Humanmedizin = Commission nationale d'éthique pour la médecine humaine = Commissione nazionale d'etica per la medicina. Living-Donor Partial Liver Transplantation: The Question of Financing. Bern, Switzerland: Swiss National Advisory Commission on Biomedical Ethics, 2003 October 22; 3 p. NRCBL: 19.5; 9.3.1. Note: Opinion no. 5/2003, unanimously adopted by the Commission [2003 October 22]. Also available in German and French at the NEK website, http://www.nek-cne.ch.

Parry, Bronwyn. The new Human Tissue Bill: categorization and definitional issues and their implications. *Genomics, Society and Policy* 2005 February; 1(1): 74-85. NRCBL: 19.5; 5.3; 9.3.1. SC: le.

Pennings, Guido. Commentary on Craft and Thornhill: new ethical strategies to recruit gamete donors. *Reproductive BioMedicine Online [electronic]* 2005; 10(3): 307-309. NRCBL: 19.5; 14.4; 8.4; 9.3.1; 14.6.

Rivera-Lopez, Eduardo. Organ sales and moral distress. *Journal of Applied Philosophy* 2006; 23(1): 41-52. NRCBL: 19.5; 9.3.1; 1.1. SC: an; le.

Abstract: The possibility that organ sales by living adults might be made legal is morally distressing to many of us. However, powerful arguments have been provided recently supporting legalisation (I consider two of those arguments: the Consequentialist Argument and the Autonomy Argument). Is our instinctive reaction against a market of organs irrational then? The aim of this paper is not to prove that legalization would be immoral, all things considered, but rather to show, first, that there are some kinds of arguments, offered in favour of legalisation, that are, in an important sense, illegitimate, and second, that even if legalisation might not be wrong all things considered, there are good reasons for our negative moral intuitions. Moreover, identifying these reasons will help highlight some features of moral decisions in non-ideal situations, which in turn might be relevant to some other moral or policy choices.

Robinson, Shelby E. Organs for sale? An analysis of proposed systems for compensating organ providers. *University of Colorado Law Review* 1999 Summer; 70(3): 1019-1050. NRCBL: 19.5; 9.3.1; 19.1; 20.1.

Roels, Leo; Kalo, Zoltán; Boesebeck, Detlef; Whiting, James; Wight, Celia. Cost-benefit approach in evaluating investment into donor action: the German case. *Transplant International* 2003 May; 16(5): 321-326. NRCBL: 19.5; 19.3; 9.3.1. SC: em. Identifiers: Germany.

Scheper-Hughes, Nancy. Commodity fetishism in organs trafficking. *In:* Scheper-Hughes, Nancy; Wacquant, Loïc, eds. Commodifying Bodies. Thousand Oaks, CA: SAGE Publications; 2002: 31-62. NRCBL: 19.5; 19.3; 9.3.1; 4.4.

Scheper-Hughes, Nancy. The last commodity: post-human ethics and the global traffic in "fresh" organs. *In:* Ong, Aihwa; Collier, Stephen J., eds. Global Assemblages: Technology, Politics, and Ethics as Anthropological Problems. Malden, MA: Blackwell Pub.; 2005: 145-167. NRCBL: 19.5; 9.3.1; 21.1.

Shenfield, F. Too late for change, too early to judge, but an oxymoron will not solve the problem. *Reproductive BioMedicine Online [electronic]* 2005; 10(4): 433-435. NRCBL: 19.5; 14.4; 8.4; 9.3.1; 14.6.

Steinbrook, Robert. Egg donation and human embryonic stem-cell research. *New England Journal of Medicine* 2006 January 26; 354(4): 324-326. NRCBL: 19.5; 14.5; 1.3.9; 18.5.4; 15.1; 18.5.3; 9.3.1.

Taylor, James Stacey. Autonomy, inducements and organ sales. *In:* Athanassoulis, Nafsika, ed. Philosophical Reflections on Medical Ethics. New York: Palgrave Macmillan; 2005: 109-134. NRCBL: 19.5; 9.3.1; 1.1. SC: an.

Taylor, James Stacey. Black markets, transplant kidneys and interpersonal coercion. *Journal of Medical Ethics* 2006 December; 32(12): 698-701. NRCBL: 19.5; 9.3.1; 19.3. SC: an.

Wilkinson, Stephen. Biomedical research and the commercial exploitation of human tissue. *Genomics, Society and Policy* 2005 February; 1(1): 27-40. NRCBL: 19.5; 9.3.1; 4.4; 18.5.1. SC: an.

Zarocostas, John. UN questions China over organ harvesting [news]. *BMJ: British Medical Journal* 2006 October 14; 333(7572): 770. NRCBL: 19.5; 9.3.1; 20.6.

Zwillich, Todd. USA confronts looming organ-shortage crisis. *Lancet* 2006 August 12-18; 368(9535): 567-568. NRCBL: 19.5; 9.3.1; 20.2.1; 8.3.1; 19.6; 1.3.12; 7.1.

ORGAN AND TISSUE TRANSPLANTATION/ . . . / LEGAL ASPECTS

Not for sale at any price [editorial]. *Lancet* 2006 April 8-14; 367(9517): 1118. NRCBL: 19.5; 9.3.1; 21.1. SC: le.

Spanish Constitutional Court. Ruling of 19 of December 1996. The challenge on the grounds of inconstitutionality against Law 42/1988, of 28 December, regulating the donation and use of human embryos and foetuses or the cells, tissues or organs there from. *Revista de Derecho y Genoma Humano = Law and the Human Genome Review* 1998 January-June; (8): 119-133. NRCBL: 19.5; 18.5.4; 14.6; 15.1. SC: le.

Alston, Bruce. Blood rights: the body and information privacy. *Journal of Law and Medicine* 2005 May; 12(4):

426-440. NRCBL: 19.5; 8.4; 1.3.12; 4.4; 8.3.1. SC: le. Identifiers: Australia.

Bagheri, Alireza. Organ transplantation laws in Asian countries: a comparative study. *Transplantation Proceedings* 2005 December; 37(10): 4159-4162. NRCBL: 19.5. SC: le.

Bell, M.D.D. The UK Human Tissue Act and consent: surrendering a fundamental principle to transplantation needs? *Journal of Medical Ethics* 2006 May; 32(5): 283-286. NRCBL: 19.5; 8.3.1. SC: le. Identifiers: United Kingdom (Great Britain).

Bernat, James L. Are organ donors after cardiac death really dead? *Journal of Clinical Ethics* 2006 Summer; 17(2): 122-132. NRCBL: 19.5; 20.2.1; 20.3.4. SC: le.

Brazier, M.; Fovargue, S. A brief guide to the Human Tissue Act 2004. *Clinical Ethics* 2006 March; 1(1): 26-32. NRCBL: 19.5; 8.3.1; 8.3.2; 4.3. SC: le.

Burghignoli, Massimo. European Directive 2004/23/EC of 31 March 2004 on tissue banks, and Italian law. *International Journal of Biological Markers* 2005 January-March; 20(1): 1-4. NRCBL: 19.5; 5.3. SC: le.

Carlson, Patrick D. The 2004 Organ Donation Recovery and Improvement Act: how Congress missed an opportunity to say "yes" to financial incentives for organ donation. *Journal of Contemporary Health Law and Policy* 2006 Fall; 23(1): 136-167. NRCBL: 19.5; 4.4. SC: le.

Frati, Paola. Organ transplantation from living donors, between bioethics and the law. *Transplantation Proceedings* 2005 July-August; 37(6): 2433-2435. NRCBL: 19.5; 9.3.1; 19.1; 22.2; 18.5.4; 21.1. SC: le. Identifiers: Italy.

Furness, Peter N. The Human Tissue Act [editorial]. *BMJ: British Medical Journal* 2006 September 9; 333(7567): 512. NRCBL: 19.5; 8.3.1; 18.1. SC: le. Identifiers: United Kingdom (Great Britain).

Glazier, Alexandra K. Donor rights and registries. *Medical Ethics Newsletter [Lahey Clinic]* 2006 Winter; 13(1): 4. NRCBL: 19.5. SC: le.

Goold, Imogen. Tissue donation: ethical guidance and legal enforceability. *Journal of Law and Medicine* 2004 February; 11(3): 331-340. NRCBL: 19.5; 18.2; 18.6. SC: le.

Great Britain. Human Tissue Authority. Human tissue codes of practice. *Bulletin of Medical Ethics* 2005 June-July; (209): 18-24. NRCBL: 19.5; 18.3; 18.2. SC: le.

Hirtle, Marie; Knoppers, Bartha M.; Lormeau, Sébastien. Banking of human materials, intellectual property rights and ownership issues; emerging trends in the literature and international policy positions (part II) = Bancos demateriales humanos, derechos de propiedad intelectual y cuestiones relatives a la titularidad: nuevas tendencias en la literatura científica y posiciones en la

NRCBL: National Reference Center for Bioethics Literature Classification Scheme   See inside front cover for terms.

403

normativa internacional (Parte II). *Revista de Derecho Genoma Humano = Law and the Human Genome Review* 1997 January-June; (6): 63-83. NRCBL: 19.5; 15.8; 21.1. SC: le.

Jayaprakash, Azza. Sum of your parts: are there adequate remedies for victims of fraudulent tissue and organ acquisition? *DePaul Journal of Health Care Law* 2006 Spring; 9(3): 1235-1259. NRCBL: 19.5; 4.4; 18.6. SC: le.

Kennedy, Ian; Grubb, Andrew. Donation and transplant of human tissue and fluids. *In their:* Medical Law. 3rd ed. London: Butterworths; 2005: 1750-1904. NRCBL: 19.5; 19.1. SC: le.

Mavroforou, A.; Giannoukas, A.; Michalodimitrakis, Emmanuel. Consent for organ and tissue retention in British law in the light of the Human Tissue Act 2004. *Medicine and Law: The World Association for Medical Law* 2006 September; 25(3): 427-434. NRCBL: 19.5; 8.3.1. SC: le.

Abstract: The experience from the scandals in hospitals at Liverpool and Bristol in the UK where retention of tissue and organs was undertaken without the consent of the parents and relatives raised serious concerns regarding the efficacy of the existing Human Tissue Act 1961, in England and the operation of the law by medical practitioners. In the aftermath of these damaging scandals a combination of public distrust and government overreaction has led to the enactment of new legislation, the Human Tissue Act 2004, which is aiming to prevent any further instances of the retention of organs and tissue from dead children or adults without their next of kin's consent or knowledge. However, scientists have expressed concerns that such changes might seriously endanger several medical research programmes, and also tissue and organ donation for transplantation. The aim of this article is to highlight important issues raised by existing practice in the post-mortem examinations in the UK and the lessons learnt from this and to discuss the benefits and the potential problems arising from the new Act.

Musson, Ruth; Burnapp, Lisa. Human Tissue Act 2004 comes into force. *British Journal of Nursing* 2006 August 10-September 13; 15(15): 804. NRCBL: 19.5; 8.3.1. SC: le.

Nygren, Sara Lind. Organ donation by incompetent patients: a hybrid approach. *University of Chicago Legal Forum* 2006: 471-502. NRCBL: 19.5; 8.3.3; 1.1. SC: le.

Opel, Douglas J.; Diekema, Douglas S. The case of A.R.: the ethics of sibling donor bone marrow transplantation revisited. *Journal of Clinical Ethics* 2006 Fall; 17(3): 207-219. NRCBL: 19.5; 19.1; 9.5.7; 8.3.2. SC: le; cs.

Parry, Bronwyn. The new Human Tissue Bill: categorization and definitional issues and their implications. *Genomics, Society and Policy* 2005 February; 1(1): 74-85. NRCBL: 19.5; 5.3; 9.3.1. SC: le.

Rivera-Lopez, Eduardo. Organ sales and moral distress. *Journal of Applied Philosophy* 2006; 23(1): 41-52. NRCBL: 19.5; 9.3.1; 1.1. SC: an; le.

Abstract: The possibility that organ sales by living adults might be made legal is morally distressing to many of us. However, powerful arguments have been provided recently supporting legalisation (I consider two of those arguments: the Consequentialist Argument and the Autonomy Argument). Is our instinctive reaction against a market of organs irrational then? The aim of this paper is not to prove that legalization would be immoral, all things considered, but rather to show, first, that there are some kinds of arguments, offered in favour of legalisation, that are, in an important sense, illegitimate, and second, that even if legalisation might not be wrong all things considered, there are good reasons for our negative moral intuitions. Moreover, identifying these reasons will help highlight some features of moral decisions in non-ideal situations, which in turn might be relevant to some other moral or policy choices.

Siegal, Gil; Bonnie, Richard J. Closing the organ gap: a reciprocity-based social contract approach. *Journal of Law, Medicine and Ethics* 2006 Summer; 34(2): 415-423. NRCBL: 19.5; 19.6; 8.3.1; 9.4. SC: le.

United States. Department of Health and Human Services [DHHS]. Food and Drug Administration [FDA]. Human cells, tissues, and cellular and tissue-based products; establishment registration and listing. *Federal Register* 2001 January 19; 66(13): 5447-5469 [Online] Accessed: http://frwebgate.access.gpo.gov/cgi-bin/getdoc.cgi?dbname=2001_register&docid=01-1126-filed.pdf [2006 September 6]. NRCBL: 19.5; 5.3. SC: le.

van Veen, Ben-Evert. Human tissue bank regulations [letter]. *Nature Biotechnology* 2006 May; 24(5): 496-498. NRCBL: 19.5; 15.1; 18.2. SC: le.

ORGAN AND TISSUE TRANSPLANTATION/ XENOTRANSPLANTATION

Anderson, M. Xenotransplantation: a bioethical evaluation. *Journal of Medical Ethics* 2006 April; 32(4): 205-208. NRCBL: 19.1; 22.2. SC: an.

Cooper, D.K.C. Draft reports for public comment from the US Secretary's Advisory Committee on Xenotransplantation. *Xenotransplantation* 2005 July; 12(4): 255-257. NRCBL: 19.1; 22.2; 18.3; 5.3.

Council of Europe. Recommendation Rec (2003) 10 of the committee of ministers to member states on xenotransplantation. *European Journal of Health Law* 2003 September; 10(3): 305-315. NRCBL: 19.1; 22.2; 18.3. SC: le.

Eidgenössische Ethikkommission für die Gentechnik im ausserhumanen Bereich = Commission fédérale d'éthique pour le génie génétique dans le domaine non humain = Commissione federale d'etica per l'ingegneria genetica nei settore nonumano = Swiss Ethics Committee on Non-Human Gene Technology [ECNH]. Statement on the draft bill of the Federal Law relating to the transplantation of organs, tissues and cells (Transplantation Law, TxG). Bern, Switzerland: Swiss Ethics Committee on Non-Human Gene Technology, 2000 February 28; 11 p. [Online]. Accessed: http://www.

umwelt-schweiz.ch/imperia/md/content/ekah/20.pdf
[2006 April 6]. NRCBL: 19.1; 22.2.

Einsiedel, Edna F. Assessing a controversial medical technology: Canadian public consultations on xenotransplantation. *Public Understanding of Science* 2002 October; 11(4): 315-331. NRCBL: 19.1; 22.2; 5.3; 18.2; 7.1. SC: em.

Gould, Donald. Cool it with a baboon's blood. *New Statesman (London, England:* 1957) 1968 September 27; 76: 390. NRCBL: 19.1; 18.1; 22.2; 9.5.1. Identifiers: South Africa.

Incorvati, Giovanni. Xenotransplantation, public responsibility and law. *European Journal of Health Law* 2003 September; 10(3): 295-304. NRCBL: 19.1; 22.2; 18.3; 5.2; 18.6. SC: le.

Lundin, Susanne. Creating identity with biotechnology: the xenotransplanted body as the norm. *Public Understanding of Science* 2002 October; 11(4): 333-345. NRCBL: 19.1; 22.2.

Macer, Darryl; Inaba, Masakazu; Maekawa, Fumi; Ng, Maryann Chen; Obata, Hiroko. Japanese attitudes toward xenotransplantation. *Public Understanding of Science* 2002 October; 11(4): 347-362. NRCBL: 19.1; 22.2; 5.3; 7.1; 5.2. SC: em.

Nolan, Carmel. Xenotransplantation — Law and Ethics, by Sheila McLean and Laura Williamson [book review]. *Genomics, Society and Policy* 2006 December; 2(3): 142-144. NRCBL: 19.1; 22.2.

Olakanmi, Ololade. Xenotransplantation: a rational choice? *Penn Bioethics Journal* 2006; 2(2): 38-41. NRCBL: 19.1; 22.2; 5.2.

Abstract: There are many potential benefits that xenotransplantation (cross-species transplantation) might afford us, but there are also many weighty biological hurdles which must be surmounted if this procedure is ever to become a clinical reality. Many of these biological concerns are being addressed by specific and novel therapies; however, we must still determine the point at which xenotransplantation could be considered safe enough for clinical implementation. Many members of the scientific community believe that we should strive to make xenotransplantation products as safe and effective as possible, whereas others argue that we should not need to optimize the safety and efficaciousness of xenotransplantation products for them to be deemed acceptable for human use. In this paper I take the latter position, I argue that "the scientific community should move from the paradigm of. . .trying to indicate to society optimal solutions to that of. . .trying to help society in finding 'satisficing' solutions" which, although not necessarily optimal, are, nevertheless, good enough (Giampietro, 2002, p. 466).

Rios, A.R.; Conesa, C.C.; Ramírez, P.; Rodríguez, M.M.; Parrilla, P. Public attitude toward xenotransplantation: opinion survey. *Transplantation Proceedings* 2004 December; 36(10): 2901-2905. NRCBL: 19.1; 22.2. SC: em. Identifiers: Spain.

Rosner, Fred. Pig organs for transplantation: a Jewish view. *In:* Rosner, Fred, ed. Medicine and Jewish Law. Volume III. Brooklyn, NY: Yashar Books, Inc.; 2005: 149-160. NRCBL: 19.1; 22.2; 1.2.

Ruipeng, Lei. Is cross-species infection morally irrelevant in xenotransplantation? *In:* Sang-yong, Song; Young-Mo, Koo; Macer, Darryl R.J., eds. Asian Bioethics in the 21st Century. Christchurch, NZ: Eubios Ethics Institute, 2002: 139-140. NRCBL: 19.1; 22.2. Conference: Proceedings of the Asian Bioethics Conference (ABC4), held 22-25 November 2002 in Seoul, South Korea.

Smetanka, C.; Cooper, D.K.C. The ethics debate in relation to xenotransplantation. *Revue Scientifique et Technique* 2005 April; 24(1): 335-342. NRCBL: 19.1; 22.2.

Tonti-Filippini, Nicholas; Fleming, John I.; Pike, Gregory K.; Campbell, Ray. Ethics and human-animal transgenesis. *National Catholic Bioethics Quarterly* 2006 Winter; 6(4): 689-704. NRCBL: 19.1; 22.2; 1.2; 15.4; 14.4.

Zink, Sheldon. Organ transplants. *In:* Mitcham, Carl, ed. Encyclopedia of Science, Technology, and Ethics. Farmington Hills, MI: Thomson/Gale, 2005: 1371-1373. NRCBL: 19.1; 22.2.

ORGAN DONATION *See* ORGAN AND TISSUE TRANSPLANTATION/ DONATION AND PROCUREMENT

OVA *See* CRYOBANKING OF SPERM, OVA AND EMBRYOS

OVUM DONORS *See* REPRODUCTIVE TECHNOLOGIES

PALLIATIVE CARE *See* DEATH AND DYING/ TERMINAL CARE

PARENTAL CONSENT *See* EUTHANASIA AND ALLOWING TO DIE/ MINORS; CARE FOR SPECIFIC GROUPS/ MINORS; HUMAN EXPERIMENTATION/ SPECIAL POPULATIONS/ MINORS; INFORMED CONSENT/ MINORS

PATENTS

Recommendations of the Danish Council of Ethics on the patentability of human genes = Recomendaciones del Consejo Danés de Etica sobre la patentabilidad de los genes humanos. *Law and the Human Genome Review = Revista de Derecho y Genoma Humano* 1995 July-December; (3): 297-298. NRCBL: 15.8; 5.3. SC: le. Identifiers: Etiske Rad (Denmark).

The patentability of human genes: a necessary debate (with imagination) = La patentabilidad de genes humanos: un

---

NRCBL: National Reference Center for Bioethics Literature Classification Scheme   See inside front cover for terms.

405

debate necesario (con imaginación) [editorial]. *Law and the Human Genome Review = Revista de Derecho y Genoma Humano* 1995 July-December; (3): 15-19. NRCBL: 15.8. SC: le. Identifiers: Europe.

Abbott, Alison. Stem-cell technique 'contrary to public order' [news]. *Nature* 2006 December 14; 442(7121): 799. NRCBL: 15.8; 18.5.4; 14.5; 15.1. SC: le. Identifiers: Germany.

Åkesson, Lynn. Bioeconomics — between persons and things. *In:* Lundin, Susanne; Åkesson, Lynn, eds. Gene Technology and Economy. Lund: Nordic Academic Press; 2002: 72-79. NRCBL: 15.8.

American Society of Human Genetics [ASHG]. Board of Directors; Worton, Ronald. Re: Revised interim utilities examination guidelines and revised interim guidelines for examination of patent applications [letter]. Bethesda, MD: American Society of Human Genetics, 2000 March 22: 3 p. [Online]. Accessed: http://genetics.faseb.org/genetics/ashg/pubs/policy/pol-39.htm [2006 July 26]. NRCBL: 15.8. Comments: Department of Commerce. Patent and Trademark Office. Revised Utility Examination Guidelines; Request for Comments [notice and request for public comments]. Federal Register 1999 December 21; 64(244): 71440-71442.

American Society of Human Genetics [ASHG]. Human Genome Committee. American Society of Human Genetics. Board of Directors. American Society of Human Genetics Position Paper on Patenting of Expressed Sequence Tags [ESTs] [position statement]. Bethesda, MD: American Society of Human Genetics, 1991 November: 3 p. [Online]. Accessed: http://www.ashg.org/genetics/pubs/policy/pol-08.htm [2006 July 25]. NRCBL: 15.8.

Angrist, Misha; Cook-Deegan, Robert M. Who owns the genome? *New Atlantis* 2006 Winter; 11: 87-96. NRCBL: 15.8; 15.10; 4.4; 5.3.

Austria. Bioethikkommission beim Bundeskanzleramt = Austria. Bioethics Commission at the Federal Chancellery. Decision of the Bioethics Commission at the Federal Chancellery of 6 March 2002. Opinion of the Bioethics Commission on the issue of national implementation of the Council Directive 98/44/EC on the legal protection of biotechnological inventions. Vienna, Austria: Bioethikkommission beim Bundeskanzleramt, 2002 March 6: 5 p. NRCBL: 15.8.

Bertomeu, Maria Julia; Sommer, Susana E. Patents on genetic material: a new originary accumulation. *In:* Tong, Rosemarie; Donchin, Anne; Dodds, Susan, eds. Linking Visions: Feminist Bioethics, Human Rights, and the Developing World. Lanham, MD: Rowman and Littlefield Publishers; 2004: 183-201. NRCBL: 15.8. SC: le.

Beyleveld, Deryck; Brownsword, Roger; Llewelyn, Margaret. The morality clauses of the Directive on the Le-

gal Protection of Biotechnological Inventions: compromise and the patent community. *In:* Goldberg, Richard; Lonbay, Julian, eds. Pharmaceutical Medicine, Biotechnology, and European Law. New York: Cambridge University Press; 2000: 157-181. NRCBL: 15.8; 21.1.

Brody, Baruch. Intellectual property and biotechnology: the U.S. internal experience — Part I. *Kennedy Institute of Ethics Journal* 2006 March; 16(1): 1-37. NRCBL: 15.8; 5.3; 4.4. SC: le.
Abstract: In the development of biotechnology in the United States, many questions were raised about the appropriateness of applying to this area a traditional robust system of intellectual property rights. Despite these hesitations, the U.S. rejected suggested modifications. This was a mistake, and there is a need to develop a modified system that promotes more of the relevant ethical values.

Brody, Baruch. Intellectual property and biotechnology: the U.S. internal experience — Part II. *Kennedy Institute of Ethics Journal* 2006 June; 16(2): 105-128. NRCBL: 15.8; 5.3; 2.2; 9.2. SC: le.
Abstract: Continuing the discussion begun in the March 2006 issue of the Kennedy Institute of Ethics Journal, this paper further documents the failure of the United States to adequately consider possible modifications in the traditional robust system of intellectual property rights as applied to biotechnology. It discusses concrete suggestions for alternative disclosure requirements, for exemptions for research tools, and for improved access to clinical advances. In each of these cases, the modifications might be more responsive to the full set of relevant values.

Bulterman, Mielle. Court of Justice of the European Communities (CJEC) 2001/4 Case C-377/98, Netherlands/Parliament and Council. *European Journal of Health Law* 2001 December; 8(4): 373-374. NRCBL: 15.8; 18.3. SC: le.

Byk, Christian. Biotechnology: from refound law to manipulated law? = La Biotecnología: ¿de un Derecho refundido a un Derecho manipulado? *Law and the Human Genome Review = Revista de Derecho y Genoma Humano* 1996 July-December; (5): 35-46. NRCBL: 15.8. SC: le.

Cardoso, Augusto Lopes. Brief review notes on the Opinion of the Portuguese National Council of Ethics for Life Sciences regarding the legal protection of biotechnological inventions = Breves notas sobre el Dictamen del Consejo Nacional de Etica para las Ciencias de la Vida de Portugal en relación con la protección jurídica de las invenciones biotecnológicas. *Law and the Human Genome Review = Revista de Derecho y Genoma Humano* 1995 July-December; (3): 253-260. NRCBL: 15.8; 15.4; 2.4. SC: le.

Caulfield, Timothy. Stem cell patents and social controversy: a speculative view from Canada. *Medical Law International* 2006; 7(3): 219-232. NRCBL: 15.8; 18.5.4; 15.1; 19.1; 4.4.

Caulfield, Timothy; Cook-Deegan, Robert M.; Kieff, F. Scott; Walsh, John P. Evidence and anecdotes: an analysis of human gene patenting controversies. *Nature Bio-*

technology 2006 September; 24(9): 1091-1094. NRCBL: 15.8; 5.3. SC: rv.

Caulfield, Timothy; Einsiedel, Edna; Merz, Jon F.; Nicol, Dianne. Trust, patents and public perceptions: the governance of controversial biotechnology research. *Nature Biotechnology* 2006 November; 24(11): 1352-1354. NRCBL: 15.8; 1.3.9; 7.3; 5.1.

Caulfield, Timothy; von Tigerstrom, Barbara. Gene patents, health care policy and licensing schemes. *Trends in Biotechnology* 2006 June; 24(6): 251-254. NRCBL: 15.8; 5.3; 21.1. Identifiers: Doha Declaration; argument on Trade Related Intellectual Property Rights (TRIPS).

Cela Conde, Camilo José. Genes, causes and patents: the tortuous path of the Human Genome Project = Genes, causas, y patentes. El callejón tortuoso del Proyecto Genoma Humano. *Revista de Derecho Genoma Humano = Law and the Human Genome Review* 1997 January-June; (6): 155-169. NRCBL: 15.8; 15.10.

Council of Europe. Recommendation 1240 (1994), on the protection and patentability of materials of human origin = Consejo de Europa: Recomendación 1240 (1994), relativa a la protección y patentabilidad de los productos de origen humano. *Law and the Human Genome Review = Revista de Derecho y Genoma Humano* 1995 July-December; (3): 293-295. NRCBL: 15.8; 5.3; 21.1. SC: le.

Cüer, Pierre. Can usable sequences extracted from the human genome be patented? = ¿Pueden patentarse secuencias utilizables extraídas del genoma humano? *Law and the Human Genome Review = Revista de Derecho y Genoma Humano* 1995 July-December; (3): 199-209. NRCBL: 15.8; 15.10. SC: le.

Curley, Duncan; Sharples, Andrew. Ethical questions to ponder in the European stem cell patent debate. *Journal of Biolaw and Business* 2006; 9(3): 12-16. NRCBL: 15.8; 18.5.4; 18.6; 5.3. SC: le.

da Silva, Paula Martinho. Genes and patents: will traditional law become outdated? = Genes y patentes: ¿estará desfasado el derecho tradicional? *Law and the Human Genome Review = Revista de Derecho y Genoma Humano* 1995 July-December; (3): 143-152. NRCBL: 15.8. SC: le.

Eidgenössische Ethikkommission für die Gentechnik im ausserhumanen Bereich = Commission fédérale d'éthique pour le génie génétique dans le domaine non humain = Commissione federale d'etica per l'ingegneria genetica nei settore nonumano = Swiss Ethics Committee on Non-Human Gene Technology [ECNH]. Patents on animals and plants: A contribution to discussion. Bern, Switzerland: Swiss Ethics Committee on Non-Human Gene Technology, 2001; 15 p. [Online]. Accessed: http://www.umwelt-schweiz.ch/imperia/md/content/ekah/14.pdf [2006 April 6]. NRCBL: 15.8; 22.1; 1.3.11. Identifiers: Switzerland.

Eisenberg, Rebecca S. Biotech patents: looking backward while moving forward. *Nature Biotechnology* 2006 March; 24(3): 317-319. NRCBL: 15.8; 1.3.9. SC: le.

Franchitto, N.; Gavarri, L; Telmon, N.; Rougé, D. Comment on the provisions of the French laws of 6 August 2004 and 8 December 2004 relative to the protection of genetic inventions. *Medicine and Law: The World Association for Medical Law* 2006 June; 25(2): 379-387. NRCBL: 15.8; 2.2. SC: le.
Abstract: The question of gene patentability has raised some opposition in France. Too broad a definition of the rights conferred by patent would hamper the development of research. The French legislature strictly defined genetic inventions in the Laws of 6 August 2004 and 8 December 2004. Exclusivity of use applies only to the function or functions precisely described in the patent application. Potential abusive use of rights by the holder of the patent has also been addressed through reinforcement of the provisions of the Code of Intellectual Property to combat such abuse. The Laws we discuss smooth the way to the granting of dependency licenses and broaden the field of application of ex officio licenses. The French legislature has achieved satisfactory balance between the legal protection of genetic inventions necessary to finance research, and the free circulation of scientific knowledge indispensable for medical progress.

Friend, William B. An introduction to genes and patents = Una introducción a los genes y a las patentes. *Law and the Human Genome Review = Revista de Derecho y Genoma Humano* 1995 July-December; (3): 245-252. NRCBL: 15.8; 1.2.

García-Miján, Manuel Lobato. European Patent Office: Decision of 18 January 1995 (Subject Relaxina) = Oficina Europea de Patentes: Decisión de 18 de enero de 1995 (Asunto Relaxina). *Law and the Human Genome Review = Revista de Derecho y Genoma Humano* 1995 July-December; (3): 169-180. NRCBL: 15.8; 21.1. SC: le.

Gold, E. Richard. Gene patents and medical access. *Intellectual Property Forum* 2002 June; 49: 20-27. NRCBL: 15.8; 21.1. SC: le.

Greenfield, Debra L. Greenberg v. Miami Children's Hospital: unjust enrichment and the patenting of human genetic material. *Annals of Health Law* 2006 Summer; 15(2): 213-249. NRCBL: 15.8; 18.6. SC: le.

Hakki, Murat Metin. European Directive on the Legal Protection of Biotechnological Inventions: scope, status and controversies in a nutshell. *E Law: Murdoch University Electronic Journal of Law* 2004 March; 11(1): 31 p.[Online]. Accessed: http://www.murdoch.edu.au/elaw/issues/v11n1/hakki_text111.html [2006 August 2]. NRCBL: 15.8; 15.3. SC: le.

Hamilton, Chris. Biodiversity, biopiracy and benefits: what allegations of biopiracy tell us about intellectual property. *Developing World Bioethics* 2006 December; 6(3): 158-173. NRCBL: 15.8; 1.1; 9.4; 16.1. SC: an.
Abstract: This paper examines the concept of biopiracy, which initially emerged to challenge various aspects of the regime for

NRCBL: National Reference Center for Bioethics Literature Classification Scheme   See inside front cover for terms.

407

intellectual property rights (IPR) in living organisms, as well as related aspects pertaining to the ownership and apportioning of benefits from 'genetic resources' derived from the world's biodiversity. This paper proposes that we take the allegation of biopiracy seriously due to the impact it has as an intervention which indexes a number of different, yet interrelated, problematizations of biodiversity, biotechnology and IPR. Using the neem tree case as an example, it describes activists' use of the term as one that involves a deliberate simplification of science and IPR. Additionally, it argues that in so doing, biopiracy is positioned as a touchstone that mobilizes actors and problems, and ultimately generates 'solutions' to the very challenges it creates. The paper will also encourage a view of biopiracy claims that does not always treat them simply as claims of theft, or as a misallocation of benefits, but rather as claims that are designed to raise broader questions about the IPR system itself. It concludes by advocating that, in order to properly understand how to address biopiracy, we must be prepared to move beyond the current narrow readings to develop a more complete picture of the term's influence in challenging how, and by whom, the decisions about what is natural and what is invented come to be made.

Heathcotte, Brock; Robert, Jason Scott. The strange case of the humanzee patent quest. *National Catholic Bioethics Quarterly* 2006 Spring; 6(1): 51-59. NRCBL: 15.8; 15.1; 18.1; 22.1; 14.4; 4.4; 5.3; 1.1. SC: le.

Hilyard, Nicholas; Sexton, Sarah. No patents on life. *Forum for Applied Research and Public Policy* 2000 Spring; 15(1): 69-74. NRCBL: 15.8. SC: an. Identifiers: European Union.

Kahn, Jonathan. Patenting race. *Nature Biotechnology* 2006 November; 24(11): 1349-1357. NRCBL: 15.8; 15.1; 3.1; 9.5.4; 15.11. SC: le.

Kirby, Michael. Playing God? Owning God? — Patenting and the human genome [forum]. *University of New South Wales Law Journal* 2003; 26(3): 770- 781. NRCBL: 15.8; 21.1; 5.3. SC: le. Identifiers: Australia.

Kishore, R.R. Human Genome: the promises, concerns and controversies (part II) = El Genoma Humano: promesas, preocupaciones y controversias (Parte II). *Revista de Derecho Genoma Humano = Law and the Human Genome Review* 1997 July-December; (7): 189-197. NRCBL: 15.8; 15.4.

Lawson, Charles. Patenting genes and gene sequences in Australia. *Journal of Law and Medicine* 1998 May; 5(4): 364-371. NRCBL: 15.8; 1.3.9; 5.3. SC: le.

Lee, Peter. Patents, paradigm shifts, and progress in biomedical science. *Yale Law Journal* 2004 December; 114(3): 659-695. NRCBL: 15.8; 1.1. SC: an.

Lock, Margaret. The alienation of body tissue and the biopolitics of immortalized cell lines. *Body and Society* 2001 June-September; 7(2-3): 63-91 [Online] Accessed: http://bod.sagepub.com/cgi/reprint/7/2-3/63 [2007 January 29]. NRCBL: 15.8; 19.1; 4.4; 15.11; 1.3.1; 221.1. Identifiers: Human Genome Diversity Project.

Mortimer, Debra. Proprietary rights in body parts: the relevance of Moore's case in Australia. *Monash University Law Review* 1993; 19(1): 217-255. NRCBL: 15.8; 8.3; 4.4; 8.2. SC: le.

Nunnally, Allen C. Intellectual property perspectives in pharmacogenomics. *Jurimetrics* 2006 Spring; 46(3): 249-262. NRCBL: 15.8; 15.1; 9.7. SC: le.

Oldham, Paul; Cutter, Anthony Mark. Mapping global status and trends in patent activity for biological and genetic material. *Genomics, Society and Policy* 2006 August; 2(2): 62-91. NRCBL: 15.8; 21.1. SC: em; rv.
Abstract: The extension of intellectual property rights into the realm of biology has emerged as an increasing focus of controversy in relation to science, biodiversity, agriculture, health, development, human rights and trade. This paper presents the results of a review of international trends in activity for patent protection between 1990-2000 and provisional data to 2004 and 2005 from over 70 national patent offices, four regional patent offices and the World Intellectual Property Organisation (WIPO) using the European Patent Office esp@cenet worldwide database. The review employed patent publication counts as an indicator of activity for traditional medicines, pharmaceuticals, agriculture, and biotechnology. The research provides insights into the internationalisation of patent activity in multiple areas of biology. The review emphasises the need to combine the further development of quantitative methods with qualitative analysis of the implications of international patent activity in relation to biological and genetic material for science, society and policy.

Olsson, Håkan. The commercialization of genes: a patent on breast cancer genes as pilot case. *In:* Lundin, Susanne; Åkesson, Lynn, eds. Gene Technology and Economy. Lund: Nordic Academic Press; 2002: 42-51. NRCBL: 15.8; 15.3.

Palma, Enrique Marín. The status of biotechnological inventions in Europe: proposal for a Directive (Part I) = La situación de las invenciones biotecnológicas en Europa: la propuesta de Directiva (Parte I). *Law and the Human Genome Review = Revista de Derecho y Genoma Humano* 1995 July-December; (3): 261-276. NRCBL: 15.8; 5.3; 21.1. SC: le.

Palma, Enrique Marín. The status of biotechnological inventions in Europe: Proposal for Directives (Part II) = La situación de las invenciones biotecnológicas en Europa: la propuesta de Directiva (Parte II). *Law and the Human Genome Review = Revista de Derecho y Genoma Humano* 1996 January-June; (4): 165-199. NRCBL: 15.8; 21.1. SC: le.

Palombi, Luigi. Patentable subject matter, TRIPS and the European Biotechnology Directive: Australia and patenting human genes [forum]. *University of New South Wales Law Journal* 2003; 26(3): 782- 792. NRCBL: 15.8; 5.3; 21.1. SC: le. Identifiers: Agreement on Trade-Related Aspects of Intellectual Property Rights, 1994.

Plomer, Aurora. European patent law and ethics [editorial]. *Drug Discovery Today* 2005 July 15; 10(14):

947-948. NRCBL: 15.8; 18.5.4. SC: le. Identifiers: European Union.

Porter, Gerard; Denning, Chris; Plomer, Aurora; Sinden, John; Torremans, Paul. The patentability of human embryonic stem cells in Europe. *Nature Biotechnology* 2006 June; 24(6): 653-655. NRCBL: 15.8; 18.5.4; 15.1; 19.5. SC: le.

Prada, Juan Luis Iglesias. The patentability of human genes = La patentabilidad de los genes humanos. *Law and the Human Genome Review = Revista de Derecho y Genoma Humano* 1995 July-December; (3): 103-121. NRCBL: 15.8; 4.4; 21.1. SC: le.

Rabin, Sander. The human use of humanoid beings: chimeras and patent law. *Nature Biotechnology* 2006 May; 24(5): 517-519. NRCBL: 15.8; 15.1; 18.1; 22.1. SC: le.

Reed, Esther D. Property rights, genes, and common good. *Journal of Religious Ethics* 2006 March; 34(1): 41-67. NRCBL: 15.8; 1.1; 1.2; 2.4.

Regalado, Antonio. The great gene grab. *Technology Review* 2000 September-October; 103(5): 48-51, 53, 55. NRCBL: 15.8; 5.1; 15.10.

Shrader-Frechette, Kristin. Gene patents and Lockean constraints. *Public Affairs Quarterly* 2006 April; 20(2): 135-161. NRCBL: 15.8; 1.1.

Spinello, Richard A. Property rights in genetic information. *Ethics and Information Technology* 2004; 6(1): 29-42. NRCBL: 15.8; 4.4.

Spinello, Richard A. Property rights in genetic information. *In:* Tavani, Herman T., ed. Ethics, Computing, and Genomics. Sudbury, MA: Jones and Bartlett; 2006: 213-233. NRCBL: 15.8; 4.4.

Stix, Gary. Owning the stuff of life. *Scientific American* 2006 February; 294(2): 76-83. NRCBL: 15.8.

Sturges, Melissa L. Who should hold property rights to the human genome? An application of the common heritage of humankind. *American University of International Law Review* 1997; 13(1): 219-261. NRCBL: 15.8; 15.10; 21.1. SC: le.

Taymor, Kenneth S.; Scott, Christopher Thomas; Greely, Henry T. The paths around stem cell intellectual property. *Nature Biotechnology* 2006 April; 24(4): 411-413. NRCBL: 15.8; 18.5.4; 15.1; 19.5. SC: le.

Weeden, Jeffrey Lawrence. Genetic liberty, genetic property: protecting genetic information. *Ave Maria Law Review* 2006 Summer; 4(2): 611-664. NRCBL: 15.8; 15.10; 8.4. SC: le.

Williamson, Alan R. Gene patents: socially acceptable monopolies or an unnecessary hindrance to research? *Trends in Genetics* 2001 November; 17(11): 670-673. NRCBL: 15.8; 5.1; 21.1. SC: le; em.

PATERNALISM *See* PATIENT RELATION-SHIPS

PATIENT ACCESS TO RECORDS *See* CONFIDENTIALITY; TRUTH DISCLOSURE

PATIENT CARE *See* CARE FOR SPECIFIC GROUPS; DEATH AND DYING/ TERMINAL CARE; PATIENT RELATIONSHIPS

PATIENT RELATIONSHIPS

See also CARE FOR SPECIFIC GROUPS; PROFESSIONAL ETHICS

Adamson, T. Elaine; Bunch, Wilton H.; Baldwin, DeWitt C., Jr.; Oppenberg, Andrew. The virtuous orthopaedist has fewer malpractice suits. *Clinical Orthopaedics and Related Research* 2000 September; (378): 104-109. NRCBL: 8.1; 9.8; 8.5. SC: em.

Alexander, G. Caleb; Lantos, John D. Commentary: physicians as public servants in the setting of bioterrorism. *CQ: Cambridge Quarterly of Healthcare Ethics* 2006 Fall; 15(4): 422-423. NRCBL: 8.1; 5.2; 4.1.2; 1.3.1.

Alexander, G. Caleb; Lantos, John D. The doctor-patient relationship in the post-managed care era. *American Journal of Bioethics* 2006 January-February; 6(1): 29-32. NRCBL: 8.1; 9.3.2.

American Medical Association [AMA]. Council on Ethical and Judicial Affairs; Moren, Karine; Higginson, Daniel; Goldrich, Michael. Physician obligation in disaster preparedness and response. *CQ: Cambridge Quarterly of Healthcare Ethics* 2006 Fall; 15(4): 417-431. NRCBL: 8.1; 5.2; 4.1.2; 1.3.1; 6.

Antommaria, Armand H. Matheny; Srivastava, Rajendu. If cardiologists take care of patients with heart disease, what do hospitals treat?: hospitalists and the doctor-patient relationship. *American Journal of Bioethics* 2006 January-February; 6(1): 47-49. NRCBL: 8.1; 9.3.2. Comments: G. Caleb Alexander and John D. Lantos. The doctor-patient relationship in the post-managed care era. American Journal of Bioethics 2006 January-February; 6(10): 29-32.

Appel, Jacob M. May doctors refuse infertility treatments to gay patients? *Hastings Center Report* 2006 July-August; 36(4): 20-21. NRCBL: 8.1; 10; 14.4. SC: le.

Ashcroft, Richard; Hope, Tony; Parker, Michael. Ethical issues and evidence-based patient choice. *In:* Edwards, Adrian; Elwyn, Glyn, eds. Evidence-Based Patient Choice: Inevitable or Impossible? Oxford; New York: Oxford University Press; 2001: 53-65. NRCBL: 8.1.

Asher, Joy Bickley. Keeping boundaries clear with patients. *Nursing New Zealand* 2005 May; 11(4): 24. NRCBL: 8.1; 7.4; 4.1.3; 10.

NRCBL: National Reference Center for Bioethics Literature Classification Scheme   See inside front cover for terms.

409

Atkins, Kim. Autonomy and autonomy competencies: a practical and relational approach. *Nursing Philosophy* 2006 October; 7(4): 205-215. NRCBL: 8.1; 1.1.

Aultman, Julie M. Finding meaning in the doctor-patient relationship. *American Journal of Bioethics* 2006 January-February; 6(1): 39-41. NRCBL: 8.1; 9.3.2. Comments: G. Caleb Alexander and John D. Lantos. The doctor-patient relationship in the post-managed care era. American Journal of Bioethics 2006 January-February; 6(10): 29-32.

Barr, Donald. Reinvesting in the doctor-patient relationship in the coming era of scarcity. *American Journal of Bioethics* 2006 January-February; 6(1): 33-34. NRCBL: 8.1; 9.3.2. Comments: G. Caleb Alexander and John D. Lantos. The doctor-patient relationship in the post-managed care era. American Journal of Bioethics 2006 January-February; 6(10): 29-32.

Bartlow, Bruce. Who has rights, anyway? An ethical approach to dealing with difficult patients and staff. *Nephrology News and Issues* 2005 April; 19(5): 45-46, 48. NRCBL: 8.1; 9.2; 8.3.1; 9.5.1.

Berlin, Leonard. Communicating radiology results. *Lancet* 2006 February 4-10; 367(9508): 373-375. NRCBL: 8.1; 7.3; 9.8. SC: le.

Bernat, James L. Ethical aspects of determining and communicating prognosis in critical care. *Neurocritical Care* 2004; 1(1): 107-117. NRCBL: 8.1; 8.3.1; 8.3.3; 9.4.

Berney, Lee; Kelly, Moira; Doyal, Len; Feder, Gene; Griffiths, Chris; Jones, Ian Rees. Ethical principles and the rationing of health care: a qualitative study in general practice. *British Journal of General Practice* 2005 August; 55(517): 620-625. NRCBL: 8.1; 9.4. SC: em. Identifiers: United Kingdom (Great Britain).

Bliton, Mark J. Parental hope confronting scientific uncertainty: a test of ethics in maternal-fetal surgery for spina bifida. *Clinical Obstetrics and Gynecology* 2005 September; 48(3): 595-607. NRCBL: 8.1; 9.5.5; 9.5.8; 4.4; 1.2.

Brown, Ian. Nurses' attitudes towards adult patients who are obese: literature review. *Journal of Advanced Nursing* 2006 January; 53(2): 221-232. NRCBL: 8.1; 9.5.1. SC: em; rv.

Bruhn, John G. Equal partners: doctors and patients explore the limits of autonomy. *Journal of the Oklahoma State Medical Association* 2001 February; 94(2): 46-54. NRCBL: 8.1; 1.1; 7.1; 9.4; 8.3.1.

Bryan, Charles S. Aequanimitas redux: William Osler on detached concern versus humanistic empathy. *Perspectives in Biology and Medicine* 2006 Summer; 49(3): 384-392. NRCBL: 8.1; 7.1.

Carr, Vincent F. Dual agency and fiduciary responsibilities in modern medicine. *Physician Executive* 2005 November-December; 31(6): 56-58. NRCBL: 8.1; 9.3.1; 9.7; 9.5.7.

Cheng, Guang-Shing. Prejudice. *Hastings Center Report* 2006 September-October; 36(5): 8-9. NRCBL: 8.1; 9.8. SC: cs.

Clayton, Ellen Wright. The web of relations: thinking about physicians and patients. *Yale Journal of Health Policy, Law and Ethics* 2006 Summer; 6(2): 465-477. NRCBL: 8.1; 2.1. Conference: Symposium: A World Less Silent: Celebrating Jay Katz's Contribution to Law, Medicine, and Ethics.

Cummiskey, David. Confucian ethics: responsibilities, rights, and relationships. *Eubios Journal of Asian and International Bioethics* 2006 January; 16(1): 9-21. NRCBL: 8.1; 1.2.

Dauterive, Robin. Was my patient fortunate or forsaken? *Journal of Clinical Ethics* 2006 Spring; 17(1): 90-93. NRCBL: 8.1; 8.3.4; 9.5.9; 20.4.1. SC: cs.

Davidhizar, Ruth. Benevolent power. *Journal of Practical Nursing* 2005 Winter; 55(4): 5-9. NRCBL: 8.1; 7.3; 4.1.3. Identifiers: nurses.

Deber, Raisa B.; Kraetschmer, Nancy; Urowitz, Sara; Sharpe, Natasha. Patient, consumer, client, or customer: what do people want to be called? *Health Expectations* 2005 December; 8(4): 345-351. NRCBL: 8.1; 9.1. SC: em.

Deverell, A.S. The patient-physician relationship — a return to paternalism? *South African Medical Journal = Suid Afrikaanse Tydskrif Vir Geneeskunde* 2001 January; 91(1): 42-44. NRCBL: 8.1; 9.1.

Dickens, Bernard M. Ethical misconduct by abuse of conscientious objection laws. *Medicine and Law: The World Association for Medical Law* 2006 September; 25(3): 513-522. NRCBL: 8.1; 7.4. SC: le.

Abstract: This paper addresses laws and practices urged by conservative religious organizations that invoke conscientious objection in order to deny patients access to lawful procedures. Many are reproductive health services, such as contraception, sterilization and abortion, on which women's health depends. Religious institutions that historically served a mission to provide healthcare are now perverting this commitment in order to deny care. Physicians who followed their calling honourably in a spirit of self-sacrifice are being urged to sacrifice patients' interests to promote their own, compromising their professional ethics by conflict of interest. The shield tolerant societies allowed to protect religious conscience is abused by religiously-influenced agencies that beat it into a sword to compel patients, particularly women, to comply with religious values they do not share. This is unethical unless accompanied by objectors' duty of referral to non-objecting practitioners, and governmental responsibility to ensure supply of and patients' access to such practitioners.

Dimond, Bridgit. Rights, resources and health care [editorial]. *Nursing Ethics* 2006 July; 13(4): 335-336. NRCBL: 8.1; 9.2; 9.4. SC: le. Identifiers: United Kingdom (Great Britain).

Eldh, Ann Catrine; Ekman, Inger; Ehnfors, Margareta. Conditions for patient participation and non-participation in health care. *Nursing Ethics* 2006 September; 13(5): 503-514. NRCBL: 8.1. SC: em. Identifiers: Sweden.

Abstract: This study explored patients' experiences of participation and non-participation in their health care. A questionnaire-based survey method was used. Content analysis showed that conditions for patient participation occurred when information was provided not by using standard procedures but based on individual needs and accompanied by explanations, when the patient was regarded as an individual, when the patient's knowledge was recognized by staff, and when the patient made decisions based on knowledge and needs, or performed self-care. Thus, to provide conditions for true patient participation, professionals need to recognize each patient's unique knowledge and respect the individual's description of his or her situation rather than just inviting the person to participate in decision making.

Escarce, José J. How does race matter, anyway? [editorial]. *Health Services Research* 2005 February; 40(1): 1-7. NRCBL: 8.1; 9.5.4.

Fagerström, Lisbeth. The dialectic tension between 'being' and 'not being' a good nurse. *Nursing Ethics* 2006 November; 13(6): 622-632. NRCBL: 8.1; 4.1.3. SC: em. Identifiers: Finland.

Fan, Minsheng. Patients are not ordinary consumers. *In:* Döring, Ole; Chen, Renbiao, eds. Advances in Chinese Medical Ethics: Chinese and International Perspectives. Hamburg: Institut für Asienkunde; 2002: 353-357. NRCBL: 8.1. Note: Proceedings of the Second Sino-German Interdisciplinary Symposium about Medical Ethics in China, Shanghai, 19-23 October, 1999.

Ferguson, Warren J.; Candib, Lucy M. Culture, language, and the doctor-patient relationship. *Family Medicine* 2002 May; 34(5): 353-361. NRCBL: 8.1; 21.7.

French, Kathy. Young people and sexuality: consent and confidentiality. *Nursing Times* 2006 January 31-February 6; 102(5): 50-51. NRCBL: 8.1; 8.3.2; 8.4.

Gallagher, Janet. Religious freedom, reproductive health care, and hospital mergers. *Journal of the American Medical Women's Association* 1997 Spring; 52(2): 65-68. NRCBL: 8.1; 9.1; 1.3.2; 11.1; 12.1.

Gampel, Eric. Does professional autonomy protect medical futility judgments? *Bioethics* 2006 April; 20(2): 92-104. NRCBL: 8.1; 1.1; 4.1.2; 20.5.1; 9.4. SC: an.

Abstract: Despite substantial controversy, the use of futility judgments in medicine is quite common, and has been backed by the implementation of hospital policies and professional guidelines on medical futility. The controversy arises when health care professionals (HCPs) consider a treatment futile which patients or families believe to be worthwhile: should HCPs be free to refuse treatments in such a case, or be required to provide them? Most physicians seem convinced that professional autonomy protects them from being forced to provide treatments they judge mentally futile, given the lack of patient benefit as well as the waste of medical resources involved. The argument from professional autonomy has been presented in a number of articles, but it has not been subjected to much critical scrutiny. In this paper I distinguish three versions of the argument: 1) that each physician should be free to exercise his or her own medical judgment; 2) that the medical profession as a whole may provide futility standards to govern the practice of its members; and 3) that the moral integrity of each physician serves as a limit to treatment demands. I maintain that none of these versions succeeds in overcoming the standard objection that futility determinations involve value judgments best left to the patients, their designated surrogates, or their families. Nor do resource considerations change this fact, since they should not influence the properly patient-centered judgment about futility.

Garay, Alain. El paciente, el médico y el abogado [The patient, the doctor and the lawyer]. *Persona y Bioética* 1999 February-May; 2(6): 113-122. NRCBL: 8.1; 7.3. SC: le.

George, Lloyd. Ethical moment: is it ethical for a dentist to date a patient? *Journal of the American Dental Association* 2005 September; 136(9): 1312-1313. NRCBL: 8.1; 7.1; 4.1.1.

Gert, Bernard; Culver, Charles M.; Clouser, K. Danner. Paternalism and its justification. *In their:* Bioethics: A Systematic Approach. Second edition. New York: Oxford University Press; 2006: 237-282. NRCBL: 8.1. SC: an.

Gold, Rachel Benson; Sonfield, Adam. Refusing to participate in health care: a continuing debate. *Guttmacher Report* 2000 February; 3(1): 8-11. [Online]. Accessed: http://www.guttmacher.org/pubs/tgr/03/1/gr030108.pdf [2006 November 1]. NRCBL: 8.1; 1.3.2; 9.3.2; 9.1; 12.1; 11.1. SC: le; rv.

Guyatt, Gordon H.; Mitchell, Alba; Molloy, D. William; Capretta, Rosalie; Horsman, John; Griffith, Lauren. Measuring patient and relative satisfaction with level or aggressiveness of care and involvement in care decisions in the context of life threatening illness. *Journal of Clinical Epidemiology* 1995 October; 48(10): 1215-1224. NRCBL: 8.1; 9.8. SC: em.

Haddad, Amy. Where do you draw the line between protecting your personal safety and caring for a potentially violent patient? *RN* 2005 May; 68(5): 30. NRCBL: 8.1; 8.3.4; 4.1.3.

Hallström, Inger; Elander, Gunnel. Decision-making during hospitalization: parents' and children's involvement. *Journal of Clinical Nursing* 2004 March; 13(3): 367-375. NRCBL: 8.1; 9.5.7. SC: em. Identifiers: Sweden.

Hasegawa, Thomas K.; Matthews, Merrill; Frederiksen, Neil. Pregnancy, x-rays, and risks — the radiology dilemma. Response to ethical dilemma #41. *Texas Dental Journal* 2002 October; 119(10): 1049-1051. NRCBL: 8.1; 8.3.4; 9.5.5; 14.1.

Helft, Paul R. An intimate collaboration: prognostic communication with advanced cancer patients. *Journal of*

NRCBL: National Reference Center for Bioethics Literature Classification Scheme   See inside front cover for terms.

411

Clinical Ethics 2006 Summer; 17(2): 110-121. NRCBL: 8.1; 8.2; 20.4.1; 20.3.2.

Henry, M.S. Uncertainty, responsibility, and the evolution of the physician/patient relationship. *Journal of Medical Ethics* 2006 June; 32(6): 321-323. NRCBL: 8.1; 9.8.

Abstract: The practice of evidence based medicine has changed the role of the physician from information dispenser to gatherer and analyser. Studies and controlled trials that may contain unknown errors, or uncertainties, are the primary sources for evidence based decisions in medicine. These sources may be corrupted by a number of means, such as inaccurate statistical analysis, statistical manipulation, population bias, or relevance to the patient in question. Regardless of whether any of these inaccuracies are apparent, the uncertainty of their presence in physician information should be disclosed to the patient. These uncertainties are not, however, shared by physicians with patients, and have caused a direct increase in patient responsibilities and mistrust. Only when disclosure of uncertainty becomes commonplace in medical practice will the physician/patient relationship evolve to a level of greater understanding and satisfaction for both the physician and patient.

Hoffmaster, Barry. What does vulnerability mean? *Hastings Center Report* 2006 March-April; 36(2): 38-45. NRCBL: 8.1; 1.1; 20.4.1; 4.4.

Hook, Mary L. Partnering with patients — a concept ready for action. *Journal of Advanced Nursing* 2006 October; 56(2): 133-143. NRCBL: 8.1; 4.1.3.

Howe, Edmund G. Beyond respect for autonomy. *Journal of Clinical Ethics* 2006 Fall; 17(3): 195-206. NRCBL: 8.1; 1.1; 8.3.1; 8.3.2; 8.3.4; 21.7.

Howe, Edmund G. Do we undervalue feelings in patients who are cognitively impaired? *Journal of Clinical Ethics* 2006 Winter; 17(4): 291-301. NRCBL: 8.1; 9.5.3; 9.5.2; 8.3.3.

Howe, Edmund G. Throwing Jello: a primer on helping patients. *Journal of Clinical Ethics* 2006 Spring; 17(1): 3-14. NRCBL: 8.1; 9.5.3; 17.1; 17.2. SC: cs.

Huber, Lara. Patientenautonomie als nichtidealisierte "natürliche Autonomie" [Patient autonomy as non-idealized "natural autonomy". *Ethik in der Medizin* 2006 June; 18(2): 133-147. NRCBL: 8.1; 1.1.

Hui, E.C. The centrality of patient-physician relationship to medical professionalism: an ethical evaluation of some contemporary models. *Hong Kong Medical Journal* 2005 June; 11(3): 222-223. NRCBL: 8.1; 4.1.1; 21.7. Identifiers: China.

Hunter, Robert; Cameron, Rosie. Patient involvement in health care will improve quality [letter]. *BMJ: British Medical Journal* 2006 July 15; 333(7559): 147-148. NRCBL: 8.1; 9.1; 9.8. Identifiers: United Kingdom (Great Britain).

Johns, Jeanine L. A concept analysis of trust. *Journal of Advanced Nursing* 1996 July; 24(1): 76-83. NRCBL: 8.1; 4.1.3. SC: rv.

Jones, James W.; McCullough, Laurence B.; Richman, Bruce W. The ethics of operating on a family member. *Journal of Vascular Surgery* 2005 November; 42(5): 1033-1035. NRCBL: 8.1; 4.1.2; 7.1.

Jotkowitz, Alan. Medical education, managed care and the doctor-patient relationship. *American Journal of Bioethics* 2006 January-February; 6(1): 46-47. NRCBL: 8.1; 9.3.2; 7.2. Comments: G. Caleb Alexander and John D. Lantos. The doctor-patient relationship in the post-managed care era. American Journal of Bioethics 2006 January-February; 6(10): 29-32.

Kao, Audiey. A physician by any other name. *Virtual Mentor* 2001 October; 3(10): 1p. NRCBL: 8.1.

Keller, F.; Allert, G.; Baitsch, H.; Sponholz, G. Discourse ethics in practical medicine. *Medical Humanities* 2006 December; 32(2): 99-103. NRCBL: 8.1; 2.1; 4.1.2. SC: an.

Kerridge, I.H.; McGrath, C.; White, K. One woman's journey is a journey we all may share. *Internal Medicine Journal* 2006 May; 36(5): 323-324. NRCBL: 8.1; 20.3.2; 20.3.3.

Knupp, Jackie. Kant's assessment of motivation in the fulfillment of social obligations. *Penn Bioethics Journal* 2006; 2(2): 29-32. NRCBL: 8.1; 7.1; 1.1.

Abstract: This paper explores the motivations of physicians who promote the health of their communities through the fulfillment of social obligations beyond the boundaries of their own patients. Based on the assumption that physicians do not have social obligations, this paper looks at the normative, motivational question, namely "How should physicians be motivated to fulfill social obligations?" The paper traces the Kantian view of morality and motivation. The distinctions between required, merely permissible, and forbidden actions is drawn. Furthermore, Kant's view that required actions done in accordance with duty are of no moral worth is critiqued from three stand points. First, it is argued that just because motivations outside of Kantian-based duty are not as good, it does not follow that these motivations are of no moral worth. Second, it is argued that there are some motivations behind required actions that are clearly better than other motivations. Third, it is argued that required actions done in accordance with duty are clearly better than those actions done without relevance to duty. The paper concludes that many required actions done in accordance with duty are performed from motivations that do have moral worth.

Koocher, Gerald P. Ethics and the advertising of professional services: blame Canada. *Canadian Psychology/Psychologie Canadienne* 2004 May; 45(2): 137-138. NRCBL: 8.1; 1.3.2; 17.1.

Lagay, Faith. Right to choose patients and duty not to neglect. *Virtual Mentor* 2001 September; 3(9): 2p. NRCBL: 8.1; 9.2.

Lazare, Aaron. Apology in medical practice: an emerging clinical skill. *JAMA: The Journal of the American Medical Association* 2006 September 20; 269(11): 1401-1404. NRCBL: 8.1; 8.2; 9.8.

Lewis, Carmen E. My computer, my doctor: a constitutional call for federal regulation of cybermedicine. *American Journal of Law and Medicine* 2006; 32(4): 585-609. NRCBL: 8.1; 1.3.12; 9.8. SC: le.

Little, M. 'On being both professional and human': a response. *Internal Medicine Journal* 2006 May; 36(5): 319-322. NRCBL: 8.1; 7.2; 20.3.3; 20.3.4.

Mayer, Dan. A commentary on Maya J. Goldenberg's "The Doctor-Patient Relationship in the Age of Evidence-Based Health Care (and Not the 'Post-Managed Care Era')" [letter]. *American Journal of Bioethics [Online]*. 2006 May-June; 6(3): W45. NRCBL: 8.1; 9.8. Comments: American Journal of Bioethics 2006: 6(1): W32.

McCabe, Catherine. Nurse-patient communication: an exploration of patients' experiences. *Journal of Clinical Nursing* 2004 January; 13(1): 41-49. NRCBL: 8.1; 4.1.3. SC: em. Identifiers: Ireland.

McDade, William. The racist parent. *Virtual Mentor* 2001 September; 3(9): 2p. NRCBL: 8.1; 9.5.4; 7.2.

Meador, Helen E.; Zazove, Philip. Health care interactions with deaf culture. *Journal of the American Board of Family Practice* 2005 May-June; 18(3): 218-222. NRCBL: 8.1; 9.5.1.

Mellon, Suzanne; Berry-Bobovski, Lisa; Gold, Robin; Levin, Nancy; Tainsky, Michael A. Communication and decision-making about seeking inherited cancer risk information: findings from female survivor-relative focus groups. *Psycho-Oncology* 2006 March; 15(3): 193-208. NRCBL: 8.1; 9.5.1; 10; 15.1. SC: em.

Millard, Lynda; Hallett, Christine; Luker, Karen. Nurse-patient interaction and decision-making in care: patient involvement in community nursing. *Journal of Advanced Nursing* 2006 July; 55(2): 142-150. NRCBL: 8.1; 4.1.3.

Miller, Courtney. Reflections on protecting conscience for health care providers: a call for more inclusive statutory protection in light of constitutional considerations. *Southern California Review of Law and Social Justice* 2006 Spring; 15(2): 327-362. NRCBL: 8.1; 9.5.1; 1.2; 1.1. SC: le.

Miller, Patrice Marie; Commons, Michael Lamport; Gutheil, Thomas G. Clinicians' perceptions of boundaries in Brazil and the United States. *Journal of the American Academy of Psychiatry and the Law* 2006; 34(1): 33-42. NRCBL: 8.1; 17.1; 17.2; 7.4; 21.1; 1.3.1. SC: em.

Miller, Paul B.; Weijer, Charles. Fiduciary obligation in clinical research. *Journal of Law, Medicine and Ethics* 2006 Summer; 34(2): 424-440. NRCBL: 8.1; 18.1; 7.1; 2.1. SC: le.

Miller, Robert D. Relationship of patient and provider. *In his:* Problems in Health Care Law. Ninth edition. Sudbury,

MA: Jones and Bartlett Publishers; 2006: 279-314. NRCBL: 8.1; 9.1; 9.2. SC: le.

Mishler, Elliot G. Patient stories, narratives of resistance and the ethics of humane care: a la recherche du temps perdu. *Health (London)* 2005 October; 9(4): 431-451. NRCBL: 8.1; 8.3.4.

Monterosso, Leanne; Kristjanson, Linda; Sly, Peter D.; Mulcahy, Mary; Holland, Beng Gee; Grimwood, Sarah; White, Kate. The role of the neonatal intensive care nurse in decision-making: advocacy, involvement in ethical decisions and communication. *International Journal of Nursing Practice* 2005 June; 11(3): 108-117. NRCBL: 8.1; 9.1; 4.1.3. SC: em. Identifiers: Australia.

Murray, Elizabeth; de Zulueta, Paquita. Conscientious objection in medicine: the ethics of responding to bird flu [letter]. *BMJ: British Medical Journal* 2006 February 18; 332(7538): 425. NRCBL: 8.1.

Murtagh, F.E.M.; Thorns, A. Evaluation and ethical review of a tool to explore patient preferences for information and involvement in decision making. *Journal of Medical Ethics* 2006 June; 32(6): 311-315. NRCBL: 8.1; 8.2; 8.4.1; 20.4.1. SC: em. Identifiers: United Kingdom (Great Britain).

Abstract: AIM: To improve clinical and ethical understanding of patient preferences for information and involvement in decision making. OBJECTIVES: To develop and evaluate a clinical tool to elicit these preferences and to consider the ethical issues raised. DESIGN: A before and after study. SETTING: Three UK hospices. PARTICIPANTS: Patients with advanced life-threatening illnesses and their doctors. INTERVENTION: Questionnaire on information and decision-making preferences. MAIN OUTCOME MEASURES: Patient-based outcome measures were satisfaction with the amount of information given, with the way information was given, with family or carer information, and confidence about future decision making. Doctor-based outcome measures were confidence in matching information to patient preference, matching family or carer communication to patient preference, knowing patient preferences and matching future decision making with patient preference. RESULTS: Of 336 admissions, 101 patients(mean age 67.3 years, 47.5% men) completed the study (control, n = 40; intervention, n = 61). Patient satisfaction with the way information was given (chi2 = 6.38, df = 2, p = 0.041) and family communication (chi2 = 14.65, df = 2, p 0.001) improved after introduction of the tool. Doctor confidence improved across all outcome measures (all p values 0.001). CONCLUSIONS: Patient satisfaction and doctor confidence were improved by administering the questionnaire, but complex ethical issues were raised by implementing and applying this research. The balance of ethical considerations were changed by advanced life-threatening illness, because there is increased risk of harm through delivery of information discordant with the patient's own preferences. The importance of truly understanding patient preferences towards the end of life is highlighted by this study.

Nåden, Dagfinn; Sæteren, Berit. Cancer patients' perception of being or not being confirmed. *Nursing Ethics* 2006 May; 13(3): 222-235. NRCBL: 8.1; 9.5.1. SC: em. Identifiers: Norway.

NRCBL: National Reference Center for Bioethics Literature Classification Scheme   See inside front cover for terms.

413

Naik, Gautam. Surgeons weighty dilemma; wary of extra risk, work, some doctors won't replace knees, hips of obese patients. *Wall Street Journal* 2006 February 28; p. B1, B8. NRCBL: 8.1; 9.5.1. SC: po.

Nelken, Melissa L. The limits of privilege: the developing scope of federal psychotherapist-patient privilege law. *Review of Litigation* 2000 Winter; 20(1): 1-43 [Online]. Accessed: http://jaffee-redmond.org/articles/nelken.htm [2001 October 17]. NRCBL: 8.1; 17.2; 1.3.5. SC: le.

Nicoletti, Toni A. Quality of care in evaluating the doctor-patient relationship. *American Journal of Bioethics* 2006 January-February; 6(1): 44-45. NRCBL: 8.1; 9.8; 9.3.2. Comments: G. Caleb Alexander and John D. Lantos. The doctor-patient relationship in the post-managed care era. American Journal of Bioethics 2006 January-February; 6(10): 29-32.

O'Neill, Jill Brace. Professional boundaries in pediatric nursing practice. *Journal of Pediatric Health Care* 1998 July-August; 12(4): 225-227. NRCBL: 8.1; 4.1.3; 9.5.7.

Oeseburg, Barth; Abma, Tineke A. Care as a mutual endeavour: experiences of a multiple sclerosis patient and her healthcare professionals. *Medicine, Health Care and Philosophy* 2006; 9(3): 349-357. NRCBL: 8.1; 9.5.1. SC: cs. Identifiers: Netherlands.

Olson, L.G.; Terry, W. The missing future tense in medical narrative. *Medical Humanities* 2006 December; 32(2): 88-91. NRCBL: 8.1; 7.1; 7.2. SC: an.

Özdemir, M. Hakan; Ergönen, Akça T.; Sönmez, Ersel; Can, I. Özgür, Salacin, Serpil. The approach taken by the physicians working at educational hospitals in Ismir towards patient rights. *Patient Education and Counseling* 2006 April; 61(1): 87-91. NRCBL: 8.1; 8.3.1; 8.3.2; 9.2. SC: em. Identifiers: Turkey.

Parker, Michael. The ethics of communication. *In:* Macdonald, Elisbeth, ed. Difficult Conversations in Medicine. New York: Oxford University Press; 2004: 20-31. NRCBL: 8.1.

Parker, Michael. The ethics of evidence-based patient choice. *Health Expectations* 2001 June; 4(2): 87-91. NRCBL: 8.1; 1.3.1; 7.1; 9.4. SC: an.

Parsi, Kayhan. Conversation with a famous patient. *Virtual Mentor* 2001 September; 3(9): 2p. NRCBL: 8.1; 1.1. Identifiers: Dax Cowart.

Pellegrino, Edmund D. The moral foundations of the patient-physician relationship: the essence of medical ethics. *In:* Beam, Thomas E.; Sparacino, Linette R.; Pellegrino, Edmund D.; Hartle, Anthony E.; Howe, Edmund G., eds. Military Medical Ethics. Volume 1. Washington, DC: TMM Publications, Borden Institute, Walter Reed Army Medical Center; 2003: 3-21. NRCBL: 8.1; 1.1; 2.1.

Pérez, S.G.; Gelpi, R.J.; Rancich, A.M. Doctor-patient sexual relationships in medical oaths. *Journal of Medical Ethics* 2006 December; 32(12): 702-705. NRCBL: 8.1; 6; 10. SC: em.

Pirakitikulr, Darlyn; Bursztajn, Harold J. The grand inquisitor's choice: comment on the CEJA report on withholding information from patients. *Journal of Clinical Ethics* 2006 Winter; 17(4): 307-311. NRCBL: 8.1; 8.2; 8.3.1; 9.7; 6. Identifiers: American Medical Association Council on Ethical and Judicial Affairs.

Popp, Richard L.; Smith, Sidney C., Jr. Cardiovascular professionalism and ethics in the modern era. *Journal of the American College of Cardiology* 2004 October 19; 44(8): 1722-1723. NRCBL: 8.1; 7.3.

Repper-DeLisi, Jennifer; Kilroy, Susan M. "We need to meet". *Journal of Clinical Ethics* 2006 Spring; 17(1): 85-89. NRCBL: 8.1; 8.3.4; 9.5.3; 20.4.1. SC: cs.

Rhodes, Rosamond. Commentary: the professional obligation of physicians in times of hazard and need. *CQ: Cambridge Quarterly of Healthcare Ethics* 2006 Fall; 15(4): 424-428. NRCBL: 8.1; 5.2; 4.1.2; 1.3.1.

Rice, Natalie; Follette, Victoria M. The termination and referral of clients. *In:* O'Donohue, William; Ferguson, Kyle, eds. Handbook of Professional Ethics for Psychologists: Issues, Questions, and Controversies. Thousand Oaks, Calif.: SAGE Publications; 2003: 147-166. NRCBL: 8.1; 17.1.

Roman, Kathleen M. Risk management assessment: dentists' ethical duty to provide emergency after-hours care. *Dental Assistant* 2005 March-April; 74(2): 30-31, 36. NRCBL: 8.1.

Rudermand, Carly; Tracy, C. Shawn; Benismon, Cécile M.; Bernstein, Mark; Hawryluck, Laura; Zlotnik Shaul, Randi; Upshur, Ross E.G. On pandemics and the duty to care: whose duty? who cares? *BMC Medical Ethics [electronic]* 2006; 7: 5. Accessed: http://www.biomedcentral.com/1472-6939/7/5 [nd]. NRCBL: 8.1; 9.1; 9.5.1; 2.1. Identifiers: Canadian Medical Association [CMA]; American Medical Association [AMA].

Savulescu, Julian. Conscientious objection in medicine. *BMJ: British Medical Journal* 2006 February 4; 332(7536): 294-297. NRCBL: 8.1; 1.2; 7.1; 4.1.2; 1.3.1.

Savulescu, Julian; Foddy, Bennett; Rogers, J. What should we say? *Journal of Medical Ethics* 2006 January; 32(1): 7-12. NRCBL: 8.1.

Abstract: Abstract ethics mostly focuses on what we do. One form of action is a speech act. What we say can have profound effects. We can and should choose our words and how we speak wisely. When someone close to us suffers an injury or serious illness, a duty of beneficence requires that we support that person through beneficial words or actions. Though our intentions are most often benign, by what we say we often make the unfortunate person feel worse. Beginning with two personal accounts, this article explains what can go wrong in the compassionate speech of well wishers, and uncovers some of the reasons why people say things that are hurtful or harmful. Despite a large body of clinical evidence, there is no perfect strategy for comforting a friend or relative who is ill, and sometimes even the best thing to say can still be perceived as insensitive and hurtful. In some cases, we may have good reason to knowingly say a hurtful or insensitive thing. Saying these 'wrong' things can sometimes be the best way to help a person in the long term. To complicate matters, there can be moral reasons for overriding what is good for the patient. What kind of admonishments should we make to a badly behaved patient? What is the value of authenticity in our communication with the people we love? These questions demand an ethical defence of those speech acts which are painful to hear but which need to be said, and of those which go wrong despite the best efforts of the wellwisher. We offer an ethical account, identifying permissible and impermissible justifications for the things we say to a person with a serious injury or illness.

Schank, Janet; Slater, Rachel; Banerjee-Stevens, Devjani; Skovholt, Thomas M. Ethics of multiple overlapping relationships. *In:* O'Donohue, William; Ferguson, Kyle, eds. Handbook of Professional Ethics for Psychologists: Issues, Questions, and Controversies. Thousand Oaks, Calif.: SAGE Publications; 2003: 181-193. NRCBL: 8.1; 7.3; 17.1.

Schei, Edvin. Doctoring as leadership: the power to heal. *Perspectives in Biology and Medicine* 2006 Summer; 49(3): 393-406. NRCBL: 8.1; 7.1.

Schnittker, Jason; Liang, Ke. The promise and limits of racial/ethnic concordance in physician-patient interaction. *Journal of Health Politics, Policy and Law* 2006 August; 31(4): 811-838. NRCBL: 8.1; 9.5.4.
Abstract: Although some scholars suggest that racial/ethnic concordance between physicians and patients will do much to eliminate disparities in medical care, the evidence for concordance effects is mixed. Using nationally representative data with an over sample of blacks and Latinos, this study examines a variety of topics, including beliefs about and preferences for concordance, the effects of concordance on patient experiences, and interactions between expectations and experiences. The results point to the limited effects of concordance in general but illuminate for whom concordance matters most. The results encourage more nuanced and contingent theories. They suggest that racial/ethnic concordance holds little salience in the minds of most black and Latino patients and that discordance has little effect. Nevertheless, there is some evidence that concordance has a positive effect among those who prefer concordance-thus the apparent effects of concordance might reflect the effects of patient choice more than concordance per se. The conclusion sketches policy implications, including the merits of promoting concordance among targeted groups of patients, even in the absence of overall effects on disparities.

Schoot, Tineke; Proot, Ireen; ter Meulen, Ruud; de Witte, Luc. Recognition of client values as a basis for tailored care: the view of Dutch expert patients and family caregivers. *Scandinavian Journal of Caring Sciences* 2005 June; 19(2): 169-176. NRCBL: 8.1; 8.3.1; 9.8; 4.1.3. SC: em. Identifiers: Netherlands.

Schüklenk, Udo. Medical professionalism and ideological symbols in doctors' rooms. *Journal of Medical Ethics* 2006 January; 32(1): 1-2. NRCBL: 8.1.

Sellman, Derek. The importance of being trustworthy. *Nursing Ethics* 2006 March; 13(2): 105-115. NRCBL: 8.1.
Abstract: The idea that nurses should be trustworthy seems to be accepted as generally unproblematic. However, being trustworthy as a nurse is complicated because of the diverse range of expectations from patients, relatives, colleagues, managers, peers, professional bodies and the institutions within which nursing takes place. Nurses are often faced with competing demands and an action perceived by some as trustworthy can be seen by others as untrustworthy. In this article some of the reasons for the importance of being trustworthy are offered together with a preliminary discussion about how being a trustworthy nurse is far from straightforward.

Shead, N. Will; Dobson, Keith S. Psychology for sale: the ethics of advertising professional services. *Canadian Psychology/Psychologie Canadienne* 2004 May; 45(2): 125-136. NRCBL: 8.1; 1.3.2; 17.1.

Shead, N. Will; Dobson, Keith S. Towards more assertive advertising practices: an evolutionary, not revolutionary, step forward. *Canadian Psychology/Psychologie Canadienne* 2004 May; 45(2): 139-140. NRCBL: 8.1; 1.3.2; 17.1.

Shiloh, Shoshana; Gerad, Liora; Goldman, Boleslav. Patients' information needs and decision-making processes: what can be learned from genetic counselees? *Health Psychology* 2006 March; 25(2): 211-219. NRCBL: 8.1; 15.2. SC: em. Identifiers: Israel.

Sieber, Joan E. Introduction: data sharing and disclosure limitation techniques. *Journal of Empirical Research on Human Research Ethics* 2006 September; 1(3): 47-49. NRCBL: 8.1; 1.3.12; 8.4; 18.6; 18.2.

Slowther, Anne-Marie. Patient requests for specific-treatments. *Clinical Ethics* 2006 September; 1(3): 135-137. NRCBL: 8.1; 1.1; 9.4.

Slowther, Anne-Marie. The role of the family in patient care. *Clinical Ethics* 2006 December; 1(4): 191-193. NRCBL: 8.1; 8.3.3; 8.3.2.

Smith, Henry F. Invisible racism. *Psychoanalytic Quarterly* 2006 January; 75(1): 3-19. NRCBL: 8.1; 9.5.4.

Smith, Vaughan P. Conscientious objection in medicine: doctors' freedom of conscience [letter]. *BMJ: British Medical Journal* 2006 February 18; 332(7538): 425. NRCBL: 8.1; 4.1.2; 1.2.

Spence, Sean A. Patients bearing gifts: are there strings attached? *BMJ: British Medical Journal* 2005 December 24-31; 331(7531): 1527-1529. NRCBL: 8.1.

Spigel, Nadine. Euthanasia and physician assisted suicide: effect on the doctor patient relationship. *Penn Bioethics Journal* 2005 April 2; 1(1): 3p. [Online]. Accessed:

NRCBL: National Reference Center for Bioethics Literature Classification Scheme   See inside front cover for terms.

415

http://www.bioethicsjournal.com [2005 April 19]. NRCBL: 8.1; 20.5.1; 20.7.

Stabell, Aase; Nådan, Dagfinn. Patients' dignity in a rehabilitation ward: ethical challenges for nursing staff. *Nursing Ethics* 2006 May; 13(3): 236-248. NRCBL: 8.1; 9.5.1. SC: em. Identifiers: Norway.

Stagno, Susan J.; Zhukovsky, Donna S.; Walsh, Declan. Bioethics: communication and decision-making in advanced disease. *Seminars in Oncology* 2000 February; 27(1): 94-100. NRCBL: 8.1; 20.4.1; 20.5.1.

Stein, Rob. Health workers' choice debated; proposals back right not to treat. *Washington Post* 2006 January 30; p. A1, A9. NRCBL: 8.1; 11.1; 11.2. SC: po.

Stein, Rob. Medical practices blend health and faith; doctors, patients distance themselves from care they consider immoral. *Washington Post* 2006 August 31; p. A1, A10. NRCBL: 8.1; 1.2. SC: po.

Stewart, Moira. Reflections on the doctor-patient relationship: from evidence and experience. *British Journal of General Practice* 2005 October; 55(519): 793-801. NRCBL: 8.1; 7.1; 4.1.2.

Szer, J. Democracy or dictatorship at the bedside? [editorial]. *Internal Medicine Journal* 2006 May; 36(5): 275. NRCBL: 8.1; 8.3.1.

Taft, Lee. Apology and medical mistake: opportunity or foil? *Annals of Health Law* 2005 Winter; 14(1): 55-94. NRCBL: 8.1; 8.2; 8.5. SC: le.

Tännsjö, Torbjörn. Negotiating ethics in anaesthesia [editorial]. *European Journal of Anaesthesiology* 2005 October; 22(10): 737-740. NRCBL: 8.1; 1.1; 20.5.1.

Tarn, Derjung M.; Meredith, Lisa S.; Kagawa-Singer, Marjorie; Matsumura, Shinji; Bito, Seiji; Oye, Robert K.; Liu, Honghu; Kahn, Katherine L.; Fukuhara, Shunichi; Wenger, Neil S. Trust in one's physician: the role of ethnic match, autonomy, acculturation, and religiosity among Japanese and Japanese Americans. *Annals of Family Medicine* 2005 July-August; 3(4): 339-347. NRCBL: 8.1; 1.1; 1.2; 21.7. SC: em.

Taub, Sara; Parsi, Kayhan. The trend toward casual dress and address in the medical profession. *Virtual Mentor* 2001 October; 3(10): 2p. NRCBL: 8.1.

Tauber, Alfred I. In search of medicine's moral guide. *American Journal of Bioethics* 2006 January-February; 6(1): 41-44. NRCBL: 8.1; 9.3.2. Comments: G. Caleb Alexander and John D. Lantos. The doctor-patient relationship in the post-managed care era. American Journal of Bioethics 2006 January-February; 6(10): 29-32.

Tauber, Alfred I. The moral domain of the medical record: the routine ethics evaluation. *American Journal of*

Bioethics [Online] 2006 July-August; 6(4): W1-W16. NRCBL: 8.1; 2.3; 7.2.

Thorne, Sally; Hislop, T. Gregory; Kuo, Margot; Armstrong, Elizabeth-Anne. Hope and probability: patient perspectives of the meaning of numerical information in cancer communication. *Qualitative Health Research* 2006 March; 16(3): 318-336. NRCBL: 8.1; 8.3.1; 9.5.1. SC: em.

Tomycz, N.D. A profession selling out: lamenting the paradigm shift in physician advertising. *Journal of Medical Ethics* 2006 January; 32(1): 26-28. NRCBL: 8.1; 1.3.2.

Torda, A. How far does a doctor's 'duty of care' go? *Internal Medicine Journal* 2005 May; 35(5): 295-296. NRCBL: 8.1; 4.1.2; 7.1.

Torjuul, Kirsti; Sorlie, Venke. Nursing is different than medicine: ethical difficulties in the process of care in surgical units. *Journal of Advanced Nursing* 2006 November; 56(4): 404-413. NRCBL: 8.1; 4.1.3. SC: em. Identifiers: Norway.

Tsai, Daniel F.C. The two-dimensional concept of Confucian personhood in biomedical practice. *In:* Döring, Ole; Chen, Renbiao, eds. Advances in Chinese Medical Ethics: Chinese and International Perspectives. Hamburg: Institut für Asienkunde; 2002: 195-213. NRCBL: 8.1; 4.4; 1.1. Note: Proceedings of the Second Sino-German Interdisciplinary Symposium about Medical Ethics in China, Shanghai, 19-23 October, 1999.

Tucker, Philip. Good faith: in search of a unifying principle for the doctor-patient relationship. *Journal of Law and Medicine* 1998 May; 5(4): 372-391. NRCBL: 8.1; 8.2; 8.5. SC: le.

Tzeng, Huey-Ming; Yin, Chang-Yi. Comment. *Nursing Ethics* 2006 May; 13(3): 219-221. NRCBL: 8.1; 9.1; 9.5.1. Identifiers: avian H5N1 flu.

Tzeng, Huey-Ming; Yin, Chang-Yi. Demands for religious care in the Taiwanese health system. *Nursing Ethics* 2006 March; 13(2): 163-179. NRCBL: 8.1; 1.2; 20.4.1. SC: em. Identifiers: Taiwan.

Abstract: In order to care ethically nurses need to care holistically; holistic care includes religious/spiritual care. This research attempted to answer the question: Do nurses have the resources to offer religious care? This article discusses only one aspect—the provision of religious care within the Taiwanese health care system. It is assumed that, if hospitals do not provide enough religious services, nurses working in these hospitals cannot be fully ethical beings or cannot respect patients' religious needs. The relevant literature was reviewed, followed by a survey study on the provision of religious facilities and services. Aspects considered are: the religions influences in and on Taiwanese society; the religious needs of patients and their families; strategies that patients use to enable them to cope with their health care problems; professional motives for attuning to patients' religious needs; and hospital provision for meeting the religious and spiritual needs of patients. A survey of nursing executives showed differences between religious service provision in hospitals with and without a hospice ward. The practical implications for hospital management and nursing practice are discussed.

Tzeng, Huey-Ming; Yin, Chang-Yi. Nurses' fears and professional obligations concerning possible human-to-human avian flu. *Nursing Ethics* 2006 September; 13(5): 455-470. NRCBL: 8.1; 9.5.1. SC: em. Identifiers: Taiwan.

Abstract: This survey aimed to illustrate factors that contribute to nurses' fear when faced with a possible human-to-human avian flu pandemic and their willingness to care for patients with avian flu in Taiwan. The participants were nursing students with a lesser nursing credential who were currently enrolled in a bachelor degree program in a private university in southern Taiwan. Nearly 42% of the nurses did not think that, if there were an outbreak of avian flu, their working hospitals would have sufficient infection control measures and equipment to prevent nosocomial infection in their working environment. About 57% of the nurse participants indicated that they were willing to care for patients infected with avian influenza. Nurses' fear about an unknown infectious disease, such as the H5N1 influenza virus, could easily be heightened to levels above those occurring during the 2003 severe acute respiratory syndrome outbreak in Taiwan.

Waller-Wise, Renece. Conscientious objection: do nurses have the right to refuse to provide care? *AWHONN Lifelines* 2005 August-September; 9(4): 283-286. NRCBL: 8.1; 4.1.3; 12.4.3; 12.3.

Weinstein, James N. The missing piece: embracing shared decision making to reform health care [editorial]. *Spine* 2000 January; 25(1): 1-4. NRCBL: 8.1; 9.4; 9.3.1.

Williams, John R. The physician's role in the protection of human research subjects. *Science and Engineering Ethics* 2006 January; 12(1): 5-12. NRCBL: 8.1; 18.2.

Winch, Sarah. Constructing a morality of caring: codes and values in Australian carer discourse. *Nursing Ethics* 2006 January; 13(1): 5-16. NRCBL: 8.1; 1.1; 7.1; 9.5.2.

Abstract: In this analysis I apply a Foucauldian approach to ethics to examine the politically prescribed moral and ethical character required of carers of aged persons at home in Australia and the role of nurses in shaping these behaviours. The work that spousal carers provide, although often founded on love and/or obligation, has been formalized through a variety of policy initiatives and technologies that serve to construct the moral approach they must adopt. This shaping of conduct at the most personal level takes place through the application of codes of behaviour policed largely by nurses. These codes redefine the mode of coexistence between an aged husband and wife and propose a new form of relationship that is derived from and supports policies of the deinstitutionalization of care services for elderly persons. In this way modern carer policy has drawn on knowledge and governance of the self to produce a morality of caring that is both authoritative and scientific.

Wright, LaTonia Denise. Violating professional boundaries. *Nursing* 2006 March; 36(3): 52-54. NRCBL: 8.1; 4.1.3; 7.4.

Zikmund-Fisher, Brian J.; Sarr, Brianna; Fagerlin, Angela; Ubel, Peter A. A matter of perspective: choosing for others differs from choosing for yourself in making treatment decisions. *JGIM: Journal of General Internal Medicine* 2006 June; 21(6): 618-622. NRCBL: 8.1; 8.3.1. SC: em.

Zutlevics, T.L.; Henning, P.H. Obligation of clinicians to treat unwilling children and young people: an ethical discussion. *Journal of Paediatrics and Child Health* 2005 December; 41(12): 677-681. NRCBL: 8.1; 8.3.2; 8.3.4. SC: cs.

Zwi, Anthony B.; McNeill, Paul M.; Grove, Natalie J. Commentary: responding more broadly and ethically. *CQ: Cambridge Quarterly of Healthcare Ethics* 2006 Fall; 15(4): 428-431. NRCBL: 8.1; 5.2; 4.1.2; 1.3.1; 1.1.

PATIENTS' RIGHTS *See* CARE FOR SPECIFIC GROUPS; CONFIDENTIALITY; INFORMED CONSENT; RIGHT TO HEALTH CARE; TREATMENT REFUSAL; TRUTH DISCLOSURE

PERSONHOOD *See* QUALITY AND VALUE OF LIFE

PHILOSOPHICAL ASPECTS *See* BIOETHICS AND MEDICAL ETHICS/ PHILOSOPHICAL ASPECTS

PHILOSOPHY *See* BIOETHICS AND MEDICAL ETHICS/ PHILOSOPHICAL PERSPECTIVES; EUTHANASIA AND ALLOWING TO DIE/ PHILOSOPHICAL ASPECTS; NURSING ETHICS AND PHILOSOPHY; PHILOSOPHY OF MEDICINE

PHILOSOPHY OF MEDICINE

Angelini, Fiorenzo. The responsibility of Catholic health workers: humanity in medicine and service to life. *Dolentium Hominum* 1994; 9(3): 56-59. NRCBL: 4.1.2; 1.2; 2.1; 4.4; 15.1.

Baxter, Lawrence. Doctors on trial: Steve Biko, medical ethics on the courts. *South African Journal on Human Rights* 1985; 1: 137-151. NRCBL: 4.1.2; 9.5.1. SC: le.

Benson, M.K.D.; Bourne, R.; Hanley, E., Jr.; Harrison, J.; Jodoin, A.; Nicol, R.; van Wyk, L.; Weinstein, S. Ethics in orthopaedic surgery [editorial]. *Journal of Bone and Joint Surgery. British volume* 2005 November; 87-B(11): 1449-1451. NRCBL: 4.1.2; 1.3.1; 7.3.

Brody, Howard. Physician integrity, enhancement technologies, and consumer autonomy. *Newsletter on Philosophy and Medicine* 2005 Fall; 05(1): 14-15. NRCBL: 4.1.2; 1.3.7; 4.4; 9.5.1; 1.1. SC: an.

Bryan, Charles S.; Saunders, Donald E., Jr. Medicine as business, learned profession, and moral enterprise: an evolution of emphasis, 1905-2005. *Journal of the South*

NRCBL: National Reference Center for Bioethics Literature Classification Scheme   See inside front cover for terms.

417

Carolina Medical Association 2005 June; 101(5): 163-168. NRCBL: 4.1.2; 1.3.2; 9.3.1.

Bryan, C.S. Medicine and the seven basic virtues [editorial]. *Journal of the South Carolina Medical Association* 2005 October; 101(9): 327-328. NRCBL: 4.1.2; 1.1.

Bryan, C.S. The seven basic virtues in medicine. I. Prudence (practical wisdom) [editorial]. *Journal of the South Carolina Medical Association* 2005 October; 101(9): 329-331. NRCBL: 4.1.2.

Chee, Y.C. Do no harm: do thyself no harm. *Singapore Medical Journal* 2005 December; 46(12): 667-674. NRCBL: 4.1.2; 7.1; 9.1; 9.8.

Chervenak, Frank A.; McCullough, Laurence B. Ethics and growing legal crisis in medicine. *Croatian Medical Journal* 2005 October; 46(5): 724-727. NRCBL: 4.1.2; 1.3.1; 8.1; 8.5; 7.3. Identifiers: John Gregory.

Ellsbury, Kathleen; Carline, Jan D.; Wenrich, Marjorie D. Competing professionalism values among community-based family physicians. *Academic Medicine* 2006 October; 81(10, Supplement): S25-S29. NRCBL: 4.1.2; 1.3.1; 9.1; 1.3.2. SC: em.

Fischer, Johannes. Güter, Tugenden, Pflichten: zum sittlichen Fundament der Medizinethik = Goods, virtues, duties: on the moral foundation of medical ethics. *Ethik in der Medizin* 2006 June; 18(2): 148-163. NRCBL: 4.1.2; 1.1; 20.5.1; 20.7.

Fischer, Josef E. Surgeons: employees or professionals? [editorial]. *American Journal of Surgery* 2005 July; 190(1): 1-3. NRCBL: 4.1.2; 9.3.1; 1.3.1. SC: an.

Freedman, Alfred M.; Halpern, Abraham L. The erosion of ethics and morality in medicine: physician participation in legal executions in the United States. *Law School Review* 1996-1997; 41: 169-188. NRCBL: 4.1.2; 17.2.

Freeman, J.M. Ethical theory and medical ethics: a personal perspective. *Journal of Medical Ethics* 2006 October; 32(10): 617-618. NRCBL: 4.1.2; 1.1; 2.1.

Geraghty, Karen. Guarding the art: Edmund D. Pellegrino, MD. [photos]. *In:* American Medical Association. Professing Medicine: strengthening the ethics and professionalism of tomorrow's physicians. Chicago: American Medical Association; 2001: 96-101. NRCBL: 4.1.2. Note: Commemorative issue of Virtual Mentor, AMA's online ethics journal.

Hadfield, S.J. Conscience of the doctor. *Twentieth Century* 1969; 177(1041): 14-17. NRCBL: 4.1.2; 6. SC: po.

Hanford, Jack. Normative ethics in health care. *Ethics and Medicine* 2006 Spring; 22(1): 31-38. NRCBL: 4.1.2; 1.3.1; 2.2; 1.1; 8.3.3. SC: cs; an. Identifiers: narrative ethics; Stanley Hauerwas; David Burrell; David Thomusma; Edmund Pellegrino; Robert Veatch.

Hilton, Sean R.; Slotnick, Henry B. Proto-professionalism: how professionalisation occurs across the continuum of medical education. *Medical Education* 2005 January; 39(1): 58-65. NRCBL: 4.1.2; 7.2.

Hojaij, Carlos Roberto. Ethics for psychiatrists [editorial]. *World Journal of Biological Psychiatry* 2005; 6(2): 66-68. NRCBL: 4.1.2; 7.3; 9.7; 17.1.

Horton, Richard; Gilmore, Ian. The evolving doctor. *Lancet* 2006 November 18-24; 368(9549): 1750-1751. NRCBL: 4.1.2; 1.3.1; 8.1; 7.3.

Hsin, Dena Hsin-Chen; Macer, Darryl R.J. Heroes of SARS: professional roles and ethics of health care workers. *Journal of Infection* 2004 October; 49(3): 210-215. NRCBL: 4.1.2; 4.1.3. Identifiers: China; Taiwan; severe acute respiratory syndrome.

Janofsky, Jeffrey S. Lies and coercion: why psychiatrists should not participate in police and intelligence interrogations. *Journal of the American Academy of Psychiatry and the Law* 2006; 34(4): 472-478. NRCBL: 4.1.2; 1.3.5; 6; 17.1; 21.4.

Kamal, R.S. Ethics in medical practice. *Journal of the Pakistan Medical Association* 2004 June; 54(6): 325-327. NRCBL: 4.1.2; 4.4; 2.1.

Kang, Shinik. Professional medical ethics in Korean context: towards and moral contract. *In:* Sang-yong, Song; Young-Mo, Koo; Macer, Darryl R.J., eds. Asian Bioethics in the 21st Century. Christchurch, NZ: Eubios Ethics Institute, 2002: 294-297. NRCBL: 4.1.2; 7.1; 8.1. Conference: Proceedings of the Asian Bioethics Conference (ABC4), held 22-25 November 2002 in Seoul, South Korea.

Kao, Audiey. Ethics, law, and professionalism: what physicians need to know. *In:* Stern, David Thomas, ed. Measuring Medical Professionalism. New York: Oxford University Press; 2006: 39-52. NRCBL: 4.1.2; 7.2.

Kenny, Nuala. Uncharted territory: Hippocratic ethics and health systems [editorial]. *CMAJ/JAMC: Canadian Medical Association Journal* 2006 May 9; 174(10): 1385. NRCBL: 4.1.2; 8.1.

Kolchinsky, Alexander. Evaded bioethics [letter]. *Surgical Neurology* 2000 August; 54(2): 199. NRCBL: 4.1.2; 9.3.1; 7.3; 1.1. Comments: M. Velasco-Suarez. Evaded bioethics and the vocation of medicine — the future at stake. Surgical Neurology 2000; 53: 193-196.

Krupp, Brandon H. Ethical issues in forensic medicine in Rhode Island. *Medicine and Health Rhode Island* 2005 December; 88(12): 418-420. NRCBL: 4.1.2; 1.3.5; 8.1; 8.4. SC: cs.

Lantos, John. The sociobiology of humanism. *Hastings Center Report* 2006 November-December; 36(6): 20-22. NRCBL: 4.1.2; 1.1; 7.1; 15.9. SC: cs.

Luglié, P.F.; Campus, G.; Lai, V. Ethics: problems of clinical conduct. *Minerva Stomatologica* 2005 September; 54(9): 473-480. NRCBL: 4.1.2; 9.8; 9.2; 7.1; 8.1. SC: le.

Marcus, Gilbert. The abdication of responsibility: the role of doctors in the Uitenhage unrest. *South African Journal on Human Rights* 1985; 1: 151-154. NRCBL: 4.1.2; 9.5.1. SC: le. Identifiers: Steve Biko; South Africa.

Moreno, Jonathan D. Conscience, professionalism and corporate obligation. *Conscience* 2006 Autumn; 27(3): 36-37. NRCBL: 4.1.2; 1.3.1; 1.1; 7.1; 11.1; 9.7; 1.3.2.

Phaosavasdi, Sukhit; Taneepanichskul, Surasak; Tannirandorn, Yuen; Thamkhantho, Manopchai; Pruksapong, Chumsak; Kanjanapitak, Aurchart. Medical ethics and the survival of medical profession. *Journal of the Medical Association of Thailand* 2005 April; 88(4): 563-566. NRCBL: 4.1.2; 1.3.1; 8.5; 2.1.

Phaosavasdi, Sukhit; Taneepanichskul, Surasak; Tannirandorn, Yuen; Thamkhantho, Manopchai; Pruksapong, Chumsak; Kanjanapitak, Aurchart. Medical ethics for senior medical doctors (episode I). *Journal of the Medical Association of Thailand* 2005 May; 88(5): 708-709. NRCBL: 4.1.2; 1.3.1.

Phaosavasdi, Sukhit; Taneepanichskul, Surasak; Tannirandorn, Yuen; Thamkhantho, Manopchai; Pruksapong, Chumsak; Kanjanapitak, Aurchart. Medical ethics for senior medical doctors (episode II). *Journal of the Medical Association of Thailand* 2005 June; 88(6): 867-868. NRCBL: 4.1.2; 1.3.1.

Prather, Erin. Rx for trouble: prescribing for family, friends discouraged. *Texas Medicine* 2005 July; 101(7): 65-67. NRCBL: 4.1.2; 9.7; 8.1.

Reisman, Anna B. Outing the hidden curriculum. *Hastings Center Report* 2006 July-August; 36(4): 9. NRCBL: 4.1.2; 7.3.

Rodriguez, Raoul P. Ethics in orthopedic practice [editorial]. *American Journal of Orthopedics* 2002 December; 31(12): 669-670. NRCBL: 4.1.2; 9.5.1; 8.1.

Ross, Lainie Friedman. What is wrong with the Physician Charter on Professionalism. *Hastings Center Report* 2006 July-August; 36(4): 17-19. NRCBL: 4.1.2; 1.3.1; 1.1; 8.1.

Santa Barbara, Joanna. Working for peace through health — ethical values and principles. *Croatian Medical Journal* 2005 December; 46(6): 1007-1009. NRCBL: 4.1.2; 21.2.

Seifert, Josef. The nature and seven goals of medicine. *Aletheia* 1995-2001; 7: 321-416. NRCBL: 4.1.2; 2.2; 4.2.

Silove, Derrick. The psychiatrist as a political leader in war: does the medical profession have a monitoring role? [editorial]. *Journal of Nervous and Mental Disease* 1995 March; 183(3): 125-126. NRCBL: 4.1.2; 1.3.1; 21.1; 1.3.5. Identifiers: Bosnia.

Sodano, Angelo. The physician and the new evangelization. *Dolentium Hominum* 1994; 9(3): 22-24. NRCBL: 4.1.2; 1.2.

Thomas, George. Junior doctors, strikes and patient care in public hospitals. *Indian Journal of Medical Ethics* 2006 April-June; 3(2): 44-45. NRCBL: 4.1.2; 1.3.1; 7.1; 9.3.1; 9.4. SC: le.

Toledo-Pereyra, Luis H. Integrity [editorial]. *Journal of Investigative Surgery* 2006 January-February; 19(1): 1-3. NRCBL: 4.1.2; 8.1.

Tongan, Anthony; Adam, Mary B. Ethics involved in simulation-based medical planning. *Ethics and Medicine* 2006 Spring; 22(1): 23-29. NRCBL: 4.1.2; 1.3.1; 3.1; 9.7; 9.8; 5.3; 1.3.12.

Vollmar, Lewis C., Jr. Development of the laws of war as they pertain to medical units and their personnel. *Military Medicine* 1992 May; 157(5): 231-236. NRCBL: 4.1.2; 2.2; 21.2. SC: rv.

Walter, Robert J. Medicine's goals and the prophetic tradition. *Health Progress* 2006 September-October; 87(5): 40-45. NRCBL: 4.1.2; 1.2.

Wynen, A. The physician and torture. *World Medical Journal* 1982 March-April; 28(2): 18-19. NRCBL: 4.1.2; 1.3.1; 21.4; 21.1.

Young, John L. Commentary: it's all about the fundamentals. *Journal of the American Academy of Psychiatry and the Law* 2006; 34(4): 479-481. NRCBL: 4.1.2; 1.3.5; 6; 17.1; 21.4. Comments: Jeffrey S. Janofsky. Lies and coercion: why psychiatrists should not participate in police and intelligence interrogations. Journal of the American Academy of Psychiatry and the Law 2006; 34(4): 472-478.

PHILOSOPHY OF NURSING *See* NURSING ETHICS AND PHILOSOPHY

PHYSICIAN PATIENT RELATIONSHIP *See* BIOETHICS AND MEDICAL ETHICS; PATIENT RELATIONSHIPS

POPULATION POLICY
See also CONTRACEPTION; STERILIZATION

Gao, Xiangdong; Xu, Yan. Ethical issues in the regulation of population growth and reproduction. *In:* Döring, Ole; Chen, Renbiao, eds. Advances in Chinese Medical Ethics: Chinese and International Perspectives. Hamburg: Institut für Asienkunde; 2002: 327-334. NRCBL: 13.1; 11.1; 12.1. Note: Proceedings of the Second Sino-German Interdisciplinary Symposium about Medical Ethics in China, Shanghai, 19-23 October, 1999.

NRCBL: National Reference Center for Bioethics Literature Classification Scheme   See inside front cover for terms.

419

Jackson, Thomas R.; Hesketh, Therese; Xing, Zhu Wei. China's one-child family policy [letter and reply]. *New England Journal of Medicine* 2006 February 23; 354(8): 877. NRCBL: 13.3; 21.1.

Mamdani, Bashir; Mamdani, Meenal. The impact of China's one-child policy. *Indian Journal of Medical Ethics* 2006 July-September; 3(3): 106-108. NRCBL: 13.3; 13.2; 12.5.1; 21.1.

Mosher, Steven W. China's one-child policy: twenty-five years later. *Human Life Review* 2006 Winter; 32(1): 76-101. NRCBL: 13.3.

Qian, Wang; Qian, Qian. Population policy in China. *In:* Mitcham, Carl, ed. Encyclopedia of Science, Technology, and Ethics. Farmington Hills, MI: Thomson/Gale, 2005: 1456-1458. NRCBL: 13.3; 13.2.

Russo, Nancy Felipe; Denious, Jean E. Controlling birth: science, politics, and public policy. *Journal of Social Issues* 2005 March; 61(1): 181-191. NRCBL: 13.3; 11.1.

PRENATAL DIAGNOSIS *See* GENETIC COUNSELING; GENETIC SCREENING; SEX DETERMINATION

PRIORITIES IN HEALTH CARE *See* RESOURCE ALLOCATION

PRISONERS *See* FORCE FEEDING OF PRISONERS; HUMAN EXPERIMENTATION/ SPECIAL POPULATIONS/ PRISONERS

PRIVACY *See* CONFIDENTIALITY; GENETIC PRIVACY

PRIVILEGED COMMUNICATION *See* CONFIDENTIALITY

PROCUREMENT *See* ORGAN AND TISSUE TRANSPLANTATION/ DONATION AND PROCUREMENT

PROFESSIONAL ETHICS
See also BIOETHICS AND MEDICAL ETHICS; CODES OF ETHICS; NURSING ETHICS AND PHILOSOPHY

American Academy of Pediatric Dentistry. Council on Clinical Affairs. Policy on the ethics of failure to treat or refer. *Pediatric Dentistry* 2005-2006; 27(7 Reference Manual): 61. NRCBL: 4.1.1; 1.3.1. Identifiers: American Academy of Pediatric Dentistry (AAPD).

American Board of Orthodontics; Moffitt, Allen H.; Greco, Peter M.; Fleisher, Lynn D. Appropriate use of the designation of ABO certification: a statement by the American Board of Orthodontics. *American Journal of Orthodontics and Dentofacial Orthopedics* 2006 April; 129(4): 571-573. NRCBL: 4.1.1; 6; 7.4; 9.8.

Balmer, Lynsey. Royal Pharmaceutical Society and conscientious objectors. *Lancet* 2006 June 17-23; 367(9527): 1980. NRCBL: 4.1.1; 1.3.1; 9.7.

Black, Roxie M. Intersections of care: an analysis of culturally competent care, client centered care, and the feminist ethic of care. *Work* 2005; 24(4): 409-422. NRCBL: 4.1.1; 8.1; 10; 4.1.3; 9.8.

Bramstedt, Katrina A. When pharmacists refuse to dispense prescriptions. *Lancet* 2006 April 15-21; 367(9518): 1219-1220. NRCBL: 4.1.1; 9.7; 1.2; 8.1; 11.1.

Brubaker, Beryl H. An ethic of caring. *In:* Miller, Roman J.; Brubaker, Beryl H.; Peterson, James C., eds. Viewing New Creations with Anabaptist Eyes: Ethics of Biotechnology. Telford, PA: Cascadia Pub.; 2005: 136-148. NRCBL: 4.1.1; 4.1.3; 14.5.

Chakraborti, Chhanda. Ethics of care and HIV: a case for rural women in India. *Developing World Bioethics* 2006 May; 6(2): 89-94. NRCBL: 4.1.1; 9.5.6; 9.5.5; 9.5.10; 21.1.
Abstract: Recent literature shows that ethics of care can be used as a theoretical basis to add a new, important dimension to social issues. This paper argues for a similar extension of the theoretical support from ethics of care to an area in bioethics. Specifically, it contends that a justification based ethics of care can be constructed to argue for a moral obligation to give some priority in the HIV-related initiatives to one of most vulnerable groups; namely, the rural women in India. In an epidemic situation this care-based approach has certain advantages as a moral justification over the usual traditional approaches.

Chalfin, Henry. Ethics and professionalism: the past, present, and future. *Journal of the American College of Dentists* 2006 Spring; 73(1): 42-47. NRCBL: 4.1.1; 9.3.1.

Churchill, Jack L. What's a dentist to do? Values, Part three. *Northwest Dentistry* 2005 March-April; 84(2): 53, 72. NRCBL: 4.1.1; 1.3.1. SC: cs.

Davis, Michael. Profession and professionalism. *In:* Mitcham, Carl, ed. Encyclopedia of Science, Technology, and Ethics. Farmington Hills, MI: Thomson/Gale, 2005: 1515-1519. NRCBL: 1.3.1.

Dickenson, Donna L. The case for international ethics education. *In:* Tadd, Win, ed. Ethics in Nursing Education, Research and Management. New York: Palgrave Macmillan; 2003: 68-85. NRCBL: 4.1.1; 2.3; 7.2.

George, Lloyd. Is it ethical for a dentist to date a patient? *Journal of the American Dental Association* 2005 September; 136(9): 1312-1313. NRCBL: 4.1.1; 1.3.1; 8.1; 6.

Greenfield, Bruce H. Reflections of moral dilemmas and patterns of ethical decision making in five clinical physical therapists. *In:* Dinkins, Christine Sorrell; Sorrell, Jeanne Merkle, eds. Listening to the Whispers: Re-Thinking Ethics in Healthcare. Madison, WI: University of Wisconsin Press; 2006: 190-247. NRCBL: 4.1.1; 1.3.1.

Hamel, Oliver; Marchal, Christine; Hervé, Christian. Ethical reflection in dentistry: first steps at the faculty of dental surgery of Toulouse. *Journal of the American College of Dentists* 2006 Fall; 73(3): 36-39. NRCBL: 4.1.1; 1.3.1; 7.2; 8.1. SC: em. Identifiers: France.

Hasegawa, Thomas K.; Matthews, Merrill; Peltier, Bruce. Ethical dilemma #52: transferring records of the demanding patient. *Texas Dental Journal* 2005 July; 122(7): 683-685. NRCBL: 4.1.1; 1.3.1; 8.4; 7.3; 8.1.

Hess, David. Complementary and alternative medicine. *In:* Mitcham, Carl, ed. Encyclopedia of Science, Technology, and Ethics. Farmington Hills, MI: Thomson/Gale, 2005: 384-387. NRCBL: 4.1.1; 1.1; 2.1.

Institute of Medicine (United States) [IOM]. Committee on the Use of Complementary and Alternative Medicine by the American Public. An ethical framework for CAM research, practice, and policy. *In its:* Complementary and Alternative Medicine in the United States. Washington, DC: National Academies Press; 2005: 168-195. NRCBL: 4.1.1.

Jenson, Larry. Restoration and enhancement: is cosmetic dentistry ethical? *Journal of the American College of Dentists* 2005 Winter; 72(4): 48-53. NRCBL: 4.1.1; 1.3.1; 9.5.1.

Kleinman, Carol S. Ethical drift: when good people do bad things. *JONA's Healthcare Law, Ethics, and Regulation* 2006 July-September; 8(3): 72-76. NRCBL: 4.1.1; 1.1; 4.1.3. SC: cs.
Abstract: There are many factors in today's healthcare environment which challenge nurses and nursing administration in adhering to ethical values. This article discusses the phenomenon of ethical drift, a gradual erosion of ethical behavior that occurs in individuals below their level of awareness. It is imperative for nurse managers and executives to be aware of the danger that workplace pressures pose in encouraging ethical drift at all levels of nursing, and to take steps to prevent this phenomena from occurring in their facilities.

Koper, Megan; Bubela, Tania; Caulfield, Timothy; Boon, Heather. Media portrayal of conflicts of interest in herbal remedy clinical trials. *Health Law Review* 2006; 15(1): 9-11. NRCBL: 4.1.1; 7.3; 1.3.7.

Krizova, Eva. Alternative medicine: a dispute on truth, power, or money? *In:* Rehmann-Sutter, Christoph; Düwell, Marcus; Mieth, Dietmar, eds. Bioethics in Cultural Contexts: Reflections on Methods and Finitude. Dordrecht: Springer, 2006: 197-210. NRCBL: 4.1.1.

Kubsch, Sylvia M.; Hankerson, Christine; Ghoorahoo, Raschid. Content analysis of holistic ethics. *Complementary Therapies in Clinical Practice* 2005 February; 11(1): 51-57. NRCBL: 4.1.1; 4.1.3; 1.1.

Lavoie, Mireille; De Koninck, Thomas; Blondeau, Danielle. The nature of care in light of Emmanuel Levinas. *Nursing Philosophy* 2006 October; 7(4): 225-234. NRCBL: 4.1.1; 1.1; 4.1.3.

Lutzen, Kim; Dahlqvist, Vera; Eriksson, Sture; Norberg, Astrid. Developing the concept of moral sensitivity in health care practice. *Nursing Ethics* 2006 March; 13(2): 187-196. NRCBL: 4.1.1; 1.3.1. SC: em.
Abstract: The aim of this Swedish study was to develop the concept of moral sensitivity in health care practice. This process began with an overview of relevant theories and perspectives on ethics with a focus on moral sensitivity and related concepts, in order to generate a theoretical framework. The second step was to construct a questionnaire based on this framework by generating a list of items from the theoretical framework. Nine items were finally selected as most appropriate and consistent with the research team's understanding of the concept of moral sensitivity. The items were worded as assumptions related to patient care. The questionnaire was distributed to two groups of health care personnel on two separate occasions and a total of 278 completed questionnaires were returned. A factor analysis identified three factors: sense of moral burden, moral strength and moral responsibility. These seem to be conceptually interrelated yet indicate that moral sensitivity may involve more dimensions than simply a cognitive capacity, particularly, feelings, sentiments, moral knowledge and skills.

McMinn, Mark R.; Buchanan, Trey; Ellens, Brent M.; Ryan, Molly K. Technology, professional practice, and ethics: survey findings and implications. *Professional Psychology: Research and Practice* 1999 April; 30(2): 165-172. NRCBL: 4.1.1; 5.1; 1.3.12; 8.4; 17.1. SC: em.

Myhrvold, Trine. The different other — towards an including ethics of care. *Nursing Philosophy* 2006 July; 7(3): 125-136. NRCBL: 4.1.1; 4.1.3; 8.1.

Nair, Indira. Ethics of care. *In:* Mitcham, Carl, ed. Encyclopedia of Science, Technology, and Ethics. Farmington Hills, MI: Thomson/Gale, 2005: 695-700. NRCBL: 4.1.1; 5.1.

Nichols, Polly S.; Winslow, Gerald. If dentists lack virtue. *General Dentistry* 2005 July-August; 53(4): 254-256. NRCBL: 4.1.1; 1.3.1.

Nosse, Larry J.; Sagiv, Lilach. Theory-based study of the basic values of 565 physical therapists. *Physical Therapy* 2005 September; 85(9): 834-850. NRCBL: 4.1.1; 7.1; 1.3.1; 9.8. SC: em.

Oguamanam, Chidi. From rivalry to rapproachment: biomedicine, complementary alternative medicine (CAM) at ethical crossroads. *HEC (Healthcare Ethics Committee) Forum* 2006 September; 18(3): 245-264. NRCBL: 4.1.1; 5.1; 5.2.

Parker, C. "Misconstructions of self": a response. *Medical Humanities* 2006 December; 32(2): 104-106. NRCBL: 4.1.1; 1.1; 8.1.

Peltier, Bruce; Dower, James S. Jr. The ethics of adopting a new drug: articaine as an example. *Journal of the*

NRCBL: National Reference Center for Bioethics Literature Classification Scheme   See inside front cover for terms.

421

American College of Dentists 2006 Fall; 73(3): 11-19. NRCBL: 4.1.1; 1.3.1; 9.5.1; 9.7.

Pembroke, Neil. Marcelian charm in nursing practice: the unity of agape and eros as the foundation of an ethic of care. *Nursing Philosophy* 2006 October; 7(4): 266-274. NRCBL: 4.1.1; 1.1; 4.1.3.

Quinn, Carol. On learning how to care appropriately: a case for developing a model of support for those in need. *In:* Tong, Rosemarie; Donchin, Anne; Dodds, Susan, eds. Linking Visions: Feminist Bioethics, Human Rights, and the Developing World. Lanham, MD: Rowman and Littlefield Publishers; 2004: 105-118. NRCBL: 4.1.1; 9.1; 10; 21.1.

Reamer, Frederic G. Nontraditional and unorthodox interventions in social work: ethical and legal implications. *Families in Society* 2006 April-June; 87(2): 191-197. NRCBL: 1.3.1; 1.3.10; 8.1.

Schiller, M. Rosita. Ethics in the practice of dietetics. *Topics in Clinical Nutrition* 1997 March; 12(2): 1-11. NRCBL: 4.1.1; 2.1; 1.3.2.

Scully, Jackie Leach. Disabled embodiment and an ethic of care. *In:* Rehmann-Sutter, Christoph; Düwell, Marcus; Mieth, Dietmar, eds. Bioethics in Cultural Contexts: Reflections on Methods and Finitude. Dordrecht: Springer, 2006: 247-261. NRCBL: 4.1.1; 9.5.3; 4.4.

Sharp, Helen M.; Kuthy, Raymond A.; Heller, Keith E. Ethical dilemmas reported by fourth-year dental students. *Journal of Dental Education* 2005 October; 69(10): 1116-1122. NRCBL: 4.1.1; 1.3.1; 7.2. SC: em.

Sheldon, Tony. Dutch doctors suspended for use of complementary medicine [news]. *BMJ: British Medical Journal* 2006 April 22; 332(7547): 929. NRCBL: 4.1.1; 7.4.

Sporrong, Sofia Kävemark; Höglund, Anna T.; Arnetz, Bergt. Measuring moral distress in pharmacy and clinical practice. *Nursing Ethics* 2006 July; 13(4): 416-427. NRCBL: 4.1.1; 9.7. SC: em. Identifiers: Sweden.
Abstract: This article presents the development, validation and application of an instrument to measure everyday moral distress in different health care settings. The concept of moral distress has been discussed and developed over 20 years. A few instruments have been developed to measure it, predominantly in nursing. The instrument presented here consists of two factors: level of moral distress, and tolerance/openness towards moral dilemmas. It was tested in four medical departments and three pharmacies, where 259 staff members completed a questionnaire. The two factors were found to be reliable. Differences in levels of moral distress were found between pharmacies and clinical departments, and between the youngest and oldest age groups; departmental staff and the youngest group experienced higher levels of moral distress. Departments reported less tolerance/openness towards moral dilemmas than pharmacies. The instrument needs to be tested further, but its strengths are the focus on everyday ethical dilemmas and its usefulness in different health care settings.

Strand, Edythe A. Clinical and professional ethics in the management of motor speech disorders. *Seminars in Speech and Language* 2003 November; 24(4): 301- 311. NRCBL: 4.1.1; 2.1; 1.3.1; 1.1; 6; 9.5.7. SC: cs.

Sullivan, William M. Confronting moral ambiguity: the struggle for professional ethics. *In his:* Work and Integrity: The Crisis and Promise of Professionalism in America. Second ed. San Francisco, CA: Jossey-Bass; 2005: 257-282, 312-316. NRCBL: 1.3.1; 4.1.1; 6.

Watson, Jean. Caring theory as an ethical guide to administrative and clinical practices. *JONA's Healthcare Law, Ethics, and Regulation* 2006 July-September; 8(3): 87-93. NRCBL: 4.1.1; 1.1; 4.1.3. SC: em.
Abstract: This article explores the conventional relationship between caring, economics, and administrative practices that no longer serve patients, practitioners, or systems. A shift toward human caring values and an ethic of authentic healing relationships is required as systems now have to value human resources and life purposes, inner meanings, and processes for workers and patients alike, not just economics alone. This shift requires a professional ethos with renewed attention to practice that is ethics/values-based and theory-guided, alongside evidence and economics. Emergent professional, caring-theory-guided practice options are presented, which are grounded on this deeper ethical moral and theoretical foundation for transforming the practitioners and the system.

Welie, Jos V.M. Is dentistry a profession? Part 1. Professionalism defined. *Journal of the Canadian Dental Association* 2004 September; 70(8): 529-532. NRCBL: 4.1.1; 1.3.1.

Welie, Jos V.M. Is dentistry a profession? Part 2. The hallmarks of professionalism. *Journal of the Canadian Dental Association* 2004 October; 70(9): 599-602. NRCBL: 4.1.1; 1.3.1.

Welie, Jos V.M. Is dentistry a profession? Part 3. Future challenges. *Journal of the Canadian Dental Association* 2004 November; 70(10): 675-678. NRCBL: 4.1.1; 1.3.1.

PROFESSIONAL MISCONDUCT *See* BIOMEDICAL RESEARCH/ RESEARCH ETHICS AND SCIENTIFIC MISCONDUCT; MALPRACTICE AND PROFESSIONAL MISCONDUCT

PROFESSIONAL PATIENT RELATIONSHIP *See* CARE FOR SPECIFIC GROUPS; NURSING ETHICS AND PHILOSOPHY; PATIENT RELATIONSHIPS; PROFESSIONAL ETHICS

PROFESSIONAL PROFESSIONAL RELATIONSHIP

Avoiding conflict of interest: a challenge for leaders in all professions. *Health Care Food and Nutrition Focus* 2005 November; 22(11): 9-12. NRCBL: 7.3; 1.3.2; 7.2.

Don't shoot the messenger [editorial]. *New Scientist* 2006 June 17-23; 190(2556): 5. NRCBL: 7.3; 1.3.9; 9.5.7; 9.8. Identifiers: Andrew Wakefield.

Ackerman, A. Bernard. An antidote for prevaricating physicians in matters medicolegal: Coalition and Center for Ethical Medical Testimony [editorial]. *Cutis* 2004 May; 73(5): 295-298. NRCBL: 7.3; 1.3.5. SC: le.

American Academy of Neurology [AAN]; Sagsveen, Murray G. American Academy of Neurology policy on expert medical testimony [editorial]. *Neurology* 2004 November 9; 63(9): 1555-1556. NRCBL: 7.3; 1.3.5. SC: le.

American College of Surgeons [ACS]. Statement on the physician acting as an expert witness. *Journal of the American College of Surgeons* 2004 November; 199(5): 746-747. NRCBL: 7.3; 1.3.5.

Andersen, Nina Vinther. Dispute over conflicts of interests leads to changes for medical society [news]. *BMJ: British Medical Journal* 2006 December 16; 333(7581): 1240. NRCBL: 7.3; 9.7; 9.3.1; 21.1.

Angell, Marcia; Brennan, Troyen A.; Rothman, David J.; Naughton, James; Cohen, Jordan; Kimball, Harry; Blumenthal, David; Smelser, Neil; Kassirer, Jerome P.; Goldman, JanLori. Academic medical centers and conflicts of interest [letter and reply]. *JAMA: The Journal of the American Medical Association* 2006 June 28; 295(24): 2848, 2848-2849. NRCBL: 7.3; 9.7.

Banks, David. Pharmacists, pharmaceutical manufacturers, and conflicts of interest. *American Journal of Health-System Pharmacy* 2005 September 1; 62(17): 1827-1832. NRCBL: 7.3; 9.7; 1.3.2.

Baron, Jonathan. Conflict of interest. *In his:* Against Bioethics. Cambridge, MA: MIT Press, 2006: 131-154. NRCBL: 7.3; 1.3.9.

Billi, John E.; Eigel, Brian; Montgomery, William H.; Nadkarni, Vinay M.; Hazinski, Mary Fran. Management of conflict of interest issues in the activities of the American Heart Association Emergency Cardiovascular Care Committee, 2000-2005 [editorial]. *Circulation* 2005 December 13; 112(24 Supplement): IV204-IV205. NRCBL: 7.3.

Billi, John E.; Zideman, David A.; Eigel, Brian; Nolan, Jerry P.; Montgomery, William H.; Nadkarni, Vinay M. Conflict of interest management before, during, and after the 2005 International Consensus Conference on cardiopulmonary resuscitation and emergency cardiovascular care science with treatment recommendations [editorial]. *Resuscitation* 2005 November-December; 67(2-3): 171-173. NRCBL: 7.3.

Bleakley, Alan. A common body of care: the ethics and politics of teamwork in the operating theater are insepara-ble. *Journal of Medicine and Philosophy* 2006 June; 31(3): 305-322. NRCBL: 7.3; 2.1; 1.1. SC: an.

Abstract: In the operating theater, the micro-politics of practice, such as interpersonal communications, are central to patient safety and are intimately tied with values as well as knowledge and skills. Team communication is a shared and distributed work activity. In an era of "professionalism," that must now encompass "interprofessionalism," a virtue ethics framework is often invoked to inform practice choices, with reference to phronesis or practical wisdom. However, such a framework is typically cast in individualistic terms as a character trait, rather than in terms of a distributed quality that may be constituted through intentionally collaborative practice, or is an emerging property of a complex, adaptive system. A virtue ethics approach is a necessary but not sufficient condition for a collaborative bioethics within the operating theater. There is also an ecological imperative-the patient's entry into the household (oikos) of the operating theater invokes the need for "hospitality" as a form of ethical practice.

Bonow, Robert O.; Zipes, Douglas P.; Anderson, Jeffrey L.; Cheitlin, Melvin D.; Goldstein, Larry B.; Grant, Augustus O.; Faxon, David; Lima, Joao A.C.; Robertson, Rose Marie. Task force 5: expert testimony and opinions. *Journal of the American College of Cardiology* 2004 October 19; 44(8): 1747-1749. NRCBL: 7.3; 1.3.5; 8.5; 9.7. SC: le. Conference: ACCF/AHA Consensus Conference Report on Professionalism and Ethics; Heart House, Bethesda, Maryland; 2-3 June 2004.

Brassington, I. Teaching to the converted: religious belief in the seminar room. *Journal of Medical Ethics* 2006 November; 32(11): 678-681. NRCBL: 7.3; 1.2; 2.3.

Abstract: It is not unknown for participants in discussions of ethics to prefix their claims with a profession of their religious faith — to say, for instance, "Well, I'm a Christian/Muslim/whatever, so I think that . . .". Other participants in the debate may well worry about how to respond without the risk of giving offence or appearing ad hominem. Within a teaching environment, the worry may be even more acute. Nevertheless, it is suggested in this paper that such worries should not be allowed to impede debate; moreover, a teacher who let such prefixes pass without critique would be considered a poor teacher. In fact, a kind of duty for a teacher of ethics is to be contrary and to play the apostate.

Brennan, Troyen A.; Rothman, David J.; Blank, Linda; Blumenthal, David; Chimonas, Susan C.; Cohen, Jordan J.; Goldman, JanLori; Kassirer, Jerome P.; Kimball, Harry; Naughton, James; Smelser, Neil. Health industry practices that create conflicts of interest: a policy proposal for academic medical centers. *JAMA: The Journal of the American Medical Association* 2006 January 25; 295(4): 429-433. NRCBL: 7.3; 9.7.

Abstract: Conflicts of interest between physicians' commitment to patient care and the desire of pharmaceutical companies and their representatives to sell their products pose challenges to the principles of medical professionalism. These conflicts occur when physicians have motives or are in situations for which reasonable observers could conclude that the moral requirements of the physician's roles are or will be compromised. Although physician groups, the manufacturers, and the federal government have instituted self-regulation of marketing, research in the psychology and social science of gift receipt and giving indicates that current controls will not satisfactorily pro-

NRCBL: National Reference Center for Bioethics Literature Classification Scheme   See inside front cover for terms.

423

tect the interests of patients. More stringent regulation is necessary, including the elimination or modification of common practices related to small gifts, pharmaceutical samples, continuing medical education, funds for physician travel, speakers bureaus, ghostwriting, and consulting and research contracts. We propose a policy under which academic medical centers would take the lead in eliminating the conflicts of interest that still characterize the relationship between physicians and the health care industry.

Brody, Howard. Confronting a colleague who covers up a medical error. *American Family Physician* 2006 April 1; 73(7): 1272, 1274. NRCBL: 7.3; 9.8.

Brody, Howard; Brennan, Troyen A.; Rothman, David J.; Naughton, James; Cohen, Jordan; Kimball, Harry; Blumenthal, David; Smelser, Neil; Kassirer, Jerome P.; Goldman, JanLori. Academic medical centers and conflicts of interest [letter and reply]. *JAMA: The Journal of the American Medical Association* 2006 June 28; 295(24): 2848, 2848-2849. NRCBL: 7.3; 9.7.

Busey, J. Craig. Recognizing and addressing conflicts of interest. *Journal of the American Dietetic Association* 2006 March; 106(3): 351-355. NRCBL: 7.3; 6.

Campbell, Margaret L. Teaching medical ethics in critical care. *New Horizons* 1998 August; 6(3): 289-292. NRCBL: 7.3; 2.3; 2.1; 9.5.1.

Dan, N.G. Professional responsibility: the ethical argument for expert evidence. *Journal of Clinical Neuroscience* 1996 July; 3(3): 216-219. NRCBL: 7.3; 1.3.5; 2.2; 2.1. Identifiers: Australia.

Degos, L. Conflicts of interest [editorial]. *Hematology Journal* 2001; 2(2): 69. NRCBL: 7.3; 9.3.1; 9.4.

Doran, E.; Kerridge, I.; McNeil, P.; Henry, David. Empirical uncertainty and moral contest: a qualitative analysis of the relationship between medical specialists and the pharmaceutical industry in Australia. *Social Science and Medicine* 2006 March; 62(6): 1510-1519. NRCBL: 7.3; 1.3.2; 9.3.1; 9.7. SC: em.

Eisman, Michael; Sierles, Frederick S. Medical student exposure to drug company interactions [letter and reply]. *JAMA: The Journal of the American Medical Association* 2006 January 18; 295(3): 281-282. NRCBL: 7.3; 7.2; 9.7.

Farber, Neil J.; Gilibert, Stephanie G.; Aboff, Brian M.; Collier, Virginia U.; Weiner, Joan; Boyer, E. Gil. Physicians' willingness to report impaired colleagues. *Social Science and Medicine* 2005 October; 61(8): 1772-1775. NRCBL: 7.3; 9.8; 8.4; 9.5.9. SC: em.

Firtko, Angela; Jackson, Debra. Do the ends justify the means? Nursing and the dilemma of whistleblowing. *Australian Journal of Advanced Nursing* 2005 September-November; 23(1): 51-56. NRCBL: 7.3; 4.1.3; 9.8.

Geraghty, Karen. The code as expert witness. *In:* American Medical Association. Professing Medicine: strength-

ening the ethics and professionalism of tomorrow's physicians. Chicago: American Medical Association; 2001: 111-113. NRCBL: 7.3; 1.3.5; 6. Note: Commemorative issue of Virtual Mentor, AMA's online ethics journal.

Goldblum, Orin M.; Franzblau, Michael J.; Brennan, Troyen A.; Rothman, David J.; Naughton, James; Cohen, Jordan; Kimball, Harry; Blumenthal, David; Smelser, Neil; Kassirer, Jerome P.; Goldman, JanLori. Academic medical centers and conflicts of interest [letter and reply]. *JAMA: The Journal of the American Medical Association* 2006 June 28; 295(24): 2845-2846, 2848-2849. NRCBL: 7.3; 9.7.

Gottlieb, Michael C. A template for peer ethics consultation. *Ethics and Behavior* 2006; 16(2): 151-162. NRCBL: 7.3; 17.1; 17.2.

Gozum, Marvin E.; Brennan, Troyen A.; Rothman, David J.; Naughton, James; Cohen, Jordan; Kimball, Harry; Blumenthal, David; Smelser, Neil; Kassirer, Jerome P.; Goldman, JanLori. Academic medical centers and conflicts of interest [letter and reply]. *JAMA: The Journal of the American Medical Association* 2006 June 28; 295(24): 2845, 2848-2849. NRCBL: 7.3; 9.7.

Gunning, Thomas G.; Coleman, Terry S. Harmonizing legal and ethical standards for interactions between health care providers and industry. *Fertility and Sterility* 2005 October; 84(4): 861-866. NRCBL: 7.3; 1.3.9; 9.7; 9.3.1; 1.3.5; 9.8. SC: le.

Hammond, Charles B.; Schwartz, Peter A. Ethical issues related to medical expert testimony. *Obstetrics and Gynecology* 2005 November; 106(5 Part 1): 1055-1058. NRCBL: 7.3; 1.3.5; 8.5. SC: le.

Hasegawa, Thomas K.; Matthews, Merrill; Peltier, Bruce; Witherspoon, David. The endodontist's painful dilemma. Response to ethical dilemma #36. *Texas Dental Journal* 2001 July; 118(7): 559-562. NRCBL: 7.3; 7.1; 9.8.

Healy, Gerald B.; Healy, Lisa H. Honesty is the ONLY policy: physician expert witnesses in the 21st century. *Journal of the American College of Surgeons* 2004 November; 199(5): 741-745. NRCBL: 7.3; 1.3.5.

Hilliard, Tom; Chambers, Timothy. The relationship between paediatricians and commerce. *Paediatric Respiratory Reviews* 2006 March; 7(1): 54-59. NRCBL: 7.3; 1.3.2; 9.3.1; 9.5.7; 9.7.

Hughes, Henrietta. What is your duty of care? *Journal of Family Planning and Reproductive Health Care* 2005 July; 31(3): 245-246. NRCBL: 7.3; 8.1. SC: cs.

Jacobs, Alice K.; Lindsay, Bruce D.; Bellande, Bruce J.; Fonarow, Gregg C.; Nishimura, Rick A.; Shah, Pravin M.; Annex, Brian H.; Fuster, Valentin; Gibbons, Raymond J.; Jackson, Marcia J.; Rahimtoola,

Shahbudin H. Task force 3: disclosure of relationships with commercial interests: policy for educational activities and publications. *Journal of the American College of Cardiology* 2004 October 19; 44(8): 1736-1740. NRCBL: 7.3; 7.2; 1.3.2; 9.3.1. Conference: ACCF/AHA Consensus Conference Report on Professionalism and Ethics; Heart House, Bethesda, Maryland; 2-3 June 2004.

Johnston, K. Wayne; Hertzer, Norman R.; Rutherford, Robert B.; Smith, Robert B., III; Yao, James S.T. Joint council guidelines for disclosure of conflict of interest [editorial]. *Journal of Vascular Surgery* 2000 July; 32(1): 213-215. NRCBL: 7.3; 9.3.1.

Jones, Jackie; Hoffman, Toni. 'I had to act': in conversation with a whistleblower [editorial]. *Australian Journal of Advanced Nursing* 2005 September-November; 23(1): 4-6. NRCBL: 7.3; 9.8.

Jones, James W.; McCullough, Laurence B.; Richman, Bruce W. Consultation or corruption? The ethics of signing on to the medical-industrial complex. *Journal of Vascular Surgery* 2006 January; 43(1): 192-195. NRCBL: 7.3; 9.7; 1.3.2; 9.3.1; 4.1.2; 1.3.1.

Jones, James W.; McCullough, Laurence B.; Richman, Bruce W. Ethics of professional courtesy. *Journal of Vascular Surgery* 2004 May; 39(5): 1140-1141. NRCBL: 7.3; 7.1; 9.3.1.

Jones, James W.; McCullough, Laurence B.; Richman, Bruce W. Turf wars: the ethics of professional territorialism. *Journal of Vascular Surgery* 2005 September; 42(3): 587-589. NRCBL: 7.3; 9.4; 9.8. SC: cs.

Klitzman, Robert. "Post-residency disease" and the medical self: identity, work, and health care among doctors who become patients. *Perspectives in Biology and Medicine* 2006 Autumn; 49(4): 542-552. NRCBL: 7.3; 8.1. SC: em.

Komesaroff, Paul A. Ethical issues in the relationships with industry: an ongoing challenge. New guidelines open for public comment. *Journal of Paediatrics and Child Health* 2005 November; 41(11): 558-560. NRCBL: 7.3; 1.3.2; 9.3.1; 9.7; 1.3.9. Identifiers: Principles of Biomedical Ethics.

Leather, David A.; Davis, Sarah C. Paediatricians and the pharmaceutical industry: an industry perspective of the challenges ahead. *Paediatric Respiratory Reviews* 2006 March; 7(1): 60-66. NRCBL: 7.3; 1.3.9; 9.7; 9.3.1; 9.5.7.

Levin, Peter J.; McGee, Glenn. Physician, divest thyself [editorial]. *American Journal of Bioethics* 2006 March-April; 6(2): 1-2 [see correction in American Journal of Bioethics 2006 May-June; 6(3): 78]. NRCBL: 7.3; 9.7; 1.3.2.

Lex, Joseph Rohan Jr. The physician-pharmaceutical industry relationship. *Journal of Law and Health* 2003-2004; 18(2): 323-342. NRCBL: 7.3; 9.7; 1.3.2.

MacFarlane, Phil; Campbell, Norm; McAlister, Finlay A.; Hoey, John. Not all guidelines are created equal [letters and reply]. *CMAJ/JAMC: Canadian Medical Association Journal* 2006 March 14; 174(6): 814-815. NRCBL: 7.3; 9.7.

Mather, Charles. The pipeline and the porcupine: alternate metaphors of the physician-industry relationship. *Social Science and Medicine* 2005 March; 60(6): 1323-1334. NRCBL: 7.3; 1.3.2; 9.7; 9.3.1. Identifiers: Canada.

McCullough, Laurence B. Practicing preventive ethics — the keys to avoiding ethical conflicts in health care. *Physician Executive* 2005 March-April; 31(2): 18-21. NRCBL: 7.3; 9.3.1.

McGrath, Pam; Holewa, Hamish. Ethical decision making in an acute medical ward: Australian findings on dealing with conflict and tension. *Ethics and Behavior* 2006; 16(3): 233-252. NRCBL: 7.3; 8.1; 7.1; 20.5.1. SC: em.

Meador, Kimford J.; Brennan, Troyen A.; Rothman, David J.; Naughton, James; Cohen, Jordan; Kimball, Harry; Blumenthal, David; Smelser, Neil; Kassirer, Jerome P.; Goldman, JanLori. Academic medical centers and conflicts of interest [letter and reply]. *JAMA: The Journal of the American Medical Association* 2006 June 28; 295(24): 2845, 2848-2849. NRCBL: 7.3; 9.7.

Morgan, M.A.; Dana, J.; Loewenstein, G.; Zinberg, S.; Schulkin, J. Interactions of doctors with the pharmaceutical industry. *Journal of Medical Ethics* 2006 October; 32(10): 559-563. NRCBL: 7.3; 9.7. SC: em.

Nagele, Robin Locke. Model conflict-of-interest policies. *Journal of Health Law* 2005 Spring; 38(2): 353-366. NRCBL: 7.3. SC: le.

Oriola, Taiwo A. The propriety of expert ethics testimony in the courtroom: a disclosure. *Journal of Philosophy, Science and Law* 2006 December 11; 6: 1-25. NRCBL: 7.3; 1.3.5. SC: le.

Palmer, N.; Braunack-Mayer, A.; Rogers, W.; Provis, C.; Cullity, G. Conflicts of interest in divisions of general practice. *Journal of Medical Ethics* 2006 December; 32(12): 715-717. NRCBL: 7.3; 9.1. Identifiers: Australia.

Pearson, Steven D.; Kleinman, Ken; Rusinak, Donna; Levinson, Wendy. A trial of disclosing physicians' financial incentives to patients. *Archives of Internal Medicine* 2006 March 27; 166(6): 623-628. NRCBL: 7.3; 8.1; 9.3.1. SC: em.

Abstract: BACKGROUND: Concern regarding financial conflict of interest for physicians has led to calls for disclosure of financial incentives to patients. However, limited data on the outcomes of disclosure exist to guide policy. METHODS: This randomized trial was conducted among 8000 adult patients at 2

NRCBL: National Reference Center for Bioethics Literature Classification Scheme   See inside front cover for terms.

425

multispecialty group practices based in the Boston, Mass, and Los Angeles, Calif, areas. Intervention patients were mailed a compensation disclosure letter written by the chief medical officer of their physician group, and all patients were surveyed approximately 3 months later. RESULTS: Disclosure patients were significantly more able to identify correctly the compensation model of their primary care physician, in Boston (adjusted odds ratio, 2.30; 95% confidence interval, 1.92-2.75) and in Los Angeles (adjusted odds ratio, 1.37; 95% confidence interval, 1.03-1.82). Disclosure patients also had more confidence in their ability to judge the possible influence of incentives on their health care: in Boston, 32.5% vs 17.8% (P001); and in Los Angeles, 31.8% vs 26.4% (P = .20). The disclosure intervention did not change trust in primary care physicians overall. However, of patients who remembered receiving the disclosure, 21.4% in Boston and 24.4% in Los Angeles responded that the disclosure had increased trust either greatly or somewhat, while in both cities less than 5% of patients responded that the information decreased trust. Patients' loyalty to their physician group was higher among disclosure patients in Boston (73.4% vs 70.2%; P = .03) and Los Angeles (74.1% vs 66.9%; P = .08). CONCLUSIONS: Among diverse patient populations, a single mailed disclosure letter from physician groups was associated with improved knowledge of physicians' compensation models. Patients' trust in their physicians was unharmed, and their loyalty to their physician group was strengthened. For physician groups with similar compensation programs, disclosure to patients should be considered an effective method to enhance the patient-physician relationship.

Poses, Roy M.; Silverstein, Scot; Smith, Wally R.; Brennan, Troyen A.; Rothman, David J.; Naughton, James; Cohen, Jordan; Kimball, Harry; Blumenthal, David; Smelser, Neil; Kassirer, Jerome P.; Goldman, JanLori. Academic medical centers and conflicts of interest [letter and reply]. *JAMA: The Journal of the American Medical Association* 2006 June 28; 295(24): 2846-2847, 2848-2849. NRCBL: 7.3; 9.7.

Ray, Susan L. Whistleblowing and organizational ethics. *Nursing Ethics* 2006 July; 13(4): 438-445. NRCBL: 7.3; 9.8; 1.3.2; 9.1.

Abstract: The purpose of this article is to discuss an external whistleblowing event that occurred after all internal whistleblowing through the hierarchy of the organization had failed. It is argued that an organization that does not support those that whistle blow because of violation of professional standards is indicative of a failure of organizational ethics. Several ways to build an ethics infrastructure that could reduce the need to resort to external whistleblowing are discussed. A relational ethics approach is presented as a way to eliminate the negative consequences of whistleblowing by fostering an interdependent moral community to address ethical concerns.

Ritchie, James L.; Wolk, Michael J.; Hirshfeld, John W., Jr.; Messer, Joseph V.; Peterson, Eric D.; Prystowsky, Eric N.; Gardner, Timothy J.; Kimball, Harry R.; Popp, Richard L.; Smaha, Lynn; Smith, Sidney C., Jr.; Wann, L. Samuel. Task force 4: appropriate clinical care and issues of "self-referral". *Journal of the American College of Cardiology* 2004 October 19; 44(8): 1740-1746. NRCBL: 7.3; 9.3.1; 1.3.2; 9.1. SC: le. Conference: ACCF/AHA Consensus Conference Report on Professionalism and Ethics; Heart House, Bethesda, Maryland; 2-3 June 2004.

Savage, Teresa A. Physician-nurse relationships and their effect on ethical nursing practice. *Journal of Clinical Ethics* 2006 Fall; 17(3): 260-265. NRCBL: 7.3; 9.6; 4.1.3; 7.2.

Scardino, Peter T.; Farley, Suzanne J. The physician and conflict of interest [editorial]. *Nature Clinical Practice. Urology* 2005 March; 2(3): 113. NRCBL: 7.3; 1.3.2; 9.3.1.

Schwartz, Barry. Receiving gifts: a conflict of interest discussion. *Journal of the Canadian Dental Association* 2005 September; 71(8): 561-562. NRCBL: 7.3; 9.7; 1.3.2; 4.1.1.

Schwartz, Robert. When doing the right things means breaking the law — what is the role of the health lawyer? *Journal of Law, Medicine and Ethics* 2006 Fall; 34(3): 624-628. NRCBL: 7.3; 8.1; 1.3.8. SC: cs; le.

Squire, Charles F.; Asai, Rickland G.; Largent, Beverly A. Is it ethical to criticize other dentists' work? *Journal of the American Dental Association* 2005 June; 136(6): 812-813. NRCBL: 7.3; 4.1.1.

Stevenson, Keith; Randle, Jacqueline; Grayling, Ian. Inter-group conflict in health care: UK students' experiences of bullying and the need for organisational solutions. *Online Journal of Issues in Nursing* 2006; 11(2): 17p. NRCBL: 7.3; 4.1.3; 7.2.

Sutton, A.G. Reasoned and reasonable approaches to ethics in undergraduate medical courses [letter]. *Journal of Medical Ethics* 2006 November; 32(11): 682. NRCBL: 7.3; 2.3.

Taeusch, C.F. Should the doctor testify? *International Journal of Ethics* 1928 July; (38): 401-415. NRCBL: 7.3; 8.4; 1.3.5; 4.1.2; 8.1. SC: le.

Tattersall, Martin; Kerridge, Ian. The drug industry and medical professionalism [letter]. *Lancet* 2006 January 7-13; 367(9504): 28. NRCBL: 7.3; 1.3.9; 9.7.

Thomas, P.S.; Tan, K.-S.; Yates, D.H. Ethical issues in the relationships involving medicine and industry [letter]. *Internal Medicine Journal* 2005 December; 35(12): 732. NRCBL: 7.3; 9.7; 1.3.2; 9.3.1.

Thompson, Richard E. Lantern of Diogenes: is "honest physician" a 21st century oxymoron? *Physician Executive* 2005 March-April; 31(2): 36-38. NRCBL: 7.3.

Ting, Joseph Yuk Sang; Brennan, Troyen A.; Rothman, David J.; Naughton, James; Cohen, Jordan; Kimball, Harry; Blumenthal, David; Smelser, Neil; Kassirer, Jerome P.; Goldman, JanLori. Academic medical centers and conflicts of interest [letter and reply]. *JAMA: The Journal of the American Medical Association* 2006 June 28; 295(24): 2846, 2848-2849. NRCBL: 7.3; 9.7.

Tuech, Jean-Jacques; Moutel, Gregoire; Pessaux, Patrick; Thoma, Veronique; Schraub, Simon; Herve,

Christian. Disclosure of competing financial interests and role of sponsors in phase III cancer trials. *European Journal of Cancer* 2005 October; 41(15): 2237-2240. NRCBL: 7.3; 1.3.9; 18.2; 5.3. SC: em.

United States. *Laws, statutes, etc.* Health insurance for aged and disabled. Limitation on certain physician referrals. United States Code 2003; Title 42: Section 1395nn. [Online]. Accessed: http://frwebgate1.access.gpo.gov/cgi-bin/waisgate.cgi?WAISdocID=862834393531+0+0+0&WAISaction=retrieve [2007 March 2]. NRCBL: 7.3. SC: le. Identifiers: Ethics in Patient Referrals Act; Stark Act.

Wakley, Gill. The conduct of colleagues. *Journal of Family Planning and Reproductive Health Care* 2005 April; 31(2): 156-157. NRCBL: 7.3; 9.8; 11.1; 7.4. SC: cs.

Watson, Peter Y.; Musial, Joseph L.; Khandewal, Akshay K.; Buckley, John D.; Brennan, Troyen A.; Rothman, David J.; Naughton, James; Cohen, Jordan; Kimball, Harry; Blumenthal, David; Smelser, Neil; Kassirer, Jerome P.; Goldman, JanLori. Academic medical centers and conflicts of interest [letter and reply]. *JAMA: The Journal of the American Medical Association* 2006 June 28; 295(24): 2847-2848, 2848-2849. NRCBL: 7.3; 9.7.

Wolk, Michael J.; Popp, Richard L.; Smith, Sidney C., Jr.; DeMaria, Anthony N. President's page: the trust imperative: ethical choice always puts patient first. *Journal of the American College of Cardiology* 2004 October 19; 44(8): 1709-1711. NRCBL: 7.3; 18.2.

Wyse, D. George. Conflict of interest — draining the swamp means confronting alligators [editorial]. *Journal of Interventional Cardiac Electrophysiology* 2005 June; 13(1): 5-7. NRCBL: 7.3; 9.3.1; 1.3.9.

PROLONGATION OF LIFE *See* EUTHANASIA AND ALLOWING TO DIE

PROXY DECISION MAKING *See* ADVANCE DIRECTIVES; EUTHANASIA AND ALLOWING TO DIE; INFORMED CONSENT/ INCOMPETENTS; INFORMED CONSENT/ MINORS

PSYCHOPHARMACOLOGY
See also BEHAVIOR CONTROL; CARE FOR SPECIFIC GROUPS/ MENTALLY DISABLED; MENTAL HEALTH THERAPIES

Ethical issues in prescribing an antipsychotic medication following neuroleptic malignant syndrome. *Psychiatric Annals* 2005 March; 35(3): 201-202. NRCBL: 17.4. SC: cs.

Anderson, Brian. Psychedelic psychotherapy: the ethics of medicine for the soul. *Penn Bioethics Journal* 2006;

2(1): 4p. [Online]. Accessed: http://www.bioethicsjournal.com [2006 February 21]. NRCBL: 17.4; 17.2; 1.2; 9.5.9.

Block, Jerald J.; McGlashan, Thomas H. Ethical concerns regarding Olanzapine versus placebo in patients prodromally symptomatic for psychosis [letter and reply]. *American Journal of Psychiatry* 2006 October; 163(10): 1838. NRCBL: 17.4; 18.5.1.

Cahill, Molly. The ethical consequences of Modafinil use. *Penn Bioethics Journal* 2005 April 2; 1(1): 3p. [Online]. Accessed: http://www.bioethicsjournal.com [2005 April 19]. NRCBL: 17.4; 4.5; 4.2; 4.3; 4.4.

Charlton, Bruce G. If 'atypical' neuroleptics did not exist, it wouldn't be necessary to invent them: perverse incentives in drug development, research, marketing and clinical practice [editorial]. *Medical Hypotheses* 2005; 65(6): 1005-1009. NRCBL: 17.4; 9.7.

Cooper, Paul. Education in the age of Ritalin. *In:* Rees, Dai; Rose, Steven, eds. The New Brain Sciences: Perils and Prospects. New York: Cambridge University Press; 2004: 249-262. NRCBL: 17.4; 9.5.7.

Esposito, Michael F. Ethical implications of pharmacological enhancement of mood and cognition. *Penn Bioethics Journal* 2005 April 2; 1(1): 4p. [Online]. Accessed: http://www.bioethicsjournal.com [2005 April 19]. NRCBL: 17.4; 4.5; 4.3.

Fitzpatrick, Erin Elizabeth. Lessons from Starson on consent and capacity. *Health Law in Canada* 2006 June; 26(4): 74-88. NRCBL: 17.4; 8.3.3; 8.3.4. SC: le.

Glannon, W. Psychopharmacology and memory. *Journal of Medical Ethics* 2006 February; 32(2): 74-78. NRCBL: 17.4; 4.5; 17.1.
Abstract: Psychotropic and other drugs can alter brain mechanisms regulating the formation, storage, and retrieval of different types of memory. These include "off label" uses of existing drugs and new drugs designed specifically to target the neural bases of memory. This paper discusses the use of beta-adrenergic antagonists to prevent or erase non-conscious pathological emotional memories in the amygdala. It also discusses the use of novel psychopharmacological agents to enhance long term semantic and short term working memory by altering storage and retrieval mechanisms in the hippocampus and prefrontal cortex. Although intervention in the brain to alter memory as therapy or enhancement holds considerable promise, the long term effects of experimental drugs on the brain and memory are not known. More studies are needed to adequately assess the potential benefits and risks of these interventions.

Gray, Jeremy R.; Thompson, Paul M. Neurobiology of intelligence: science and ethics. *Nature Reviews Neuroscience* 2004 June; 5(6): 471-482. NRCBL: 17.4; 4.5; 15.6. SC: rv.

Greenfield, Susan A. Biotechnology, the brain and the future. *TRENDS in Biotechnology* 2005 January; 23(1): 34-41. NRCBL: 17.4; 15.10; 5.4.

NRCBL: National Reference Center for Bioethics Literature Classification Scheme   See inside front cover for terms.

427

Healy, David. Psychopharmacology at the interface between the market and the new biology. *In:* Rees, Dai; Rose, Steven, eds. The New Brain Sciences: Perils and Prospects. New York: Cambridge University Press; 2004: 232-248. NRCBL: 17.4; 9.3.1.

Hyman, Steven E. Improving our brains? *Biosciences* 2006 March; 1(1): 103-111. NRCBL: 17.4; 4.5; 9.5.7; 5.2.

Lenz, Connie. Prescribing a legislative response: educators, physicians, and psychotropic medication for children. *Journal of Contemporary Health Law and Policy* 2005 Fall; 22(1): 72-106. NRCBL: 17.4; 9.5.7; 8.3.2. SC: le.

Manninen, B.A. Medicating the mind: a Kantian analysis of overprescribing psychoactive drugs. *Journal of Medical Ethics* 2006 February; 32(2): 100-105. NRCBL: 17.4. SC: an.

Abstract: Psychoactive drugs are being prescribed to millions of Americans at an increasing rate. In many cases these drugs are necessary in order to overcome debilitating emotional problems. Yet in other instances, these drugs are used to supplant, not supplement, interpersonal therapy. The process of overcoming emotional obstacles by introspection and the attainment of self knowledge is gradually being eroded via the gratuitous use of psychoactive medication in order to rapidly attain are lease from the common problems that life inevitably presents us with. In this paper, I argue that Kant's formula of humanity, which maintains that persons ought never to treat others or themselves solely as a means to an end, proscribes this. Moreover, Kant argues that we have an imperfect duty of self development, and I argue that we fail to adhere to such a duty whenever we seek to evade the process of introspection and self knowledge in favour of the expedient results that drugs may provide us with as we attempt to overcome the emotional hurdles in our lives.

McHenry, L. Ethical issues in psychopharmacology. *Journal of Medical Ethics* 2006 July; 32(7): 405-410. NRCBL: 17.4; 9.7; 7.3.

Abstract: The marketing of selective serotonin reuptake inhibitors in the psychopharmacological industry presents a serious moral problem for the corporate model of medicine. In this paper I examine ethical issues relating to the efficacy and safety of these drugs. Pharmaceutical companies have a moral obligation to disclose all information in their possession bearing on the true risks and benefits of their drugs. Only then can patients make fully informed decisions about their treatment.

Mulligan, Elizabeth J.; Claus, Eric D. Psychopharmacology. *In:* Mitcham, Carl, ed. Encyclopedia of Science, Technology, and Ethics. Farmington Hills, MI: Thomson/Gale, 2005: 1542-1545. NRCBL: 17.4.

Olsen, J. Mark. Depression, SSRIs and the supposed obligation to suffer mentally. *Kennedy Institute of Ethics Journal* 2006 September; 16(3): 283-303. NRCBL: 17.4; 4.3; 4.5; 1.1; 7.1; 2.4.

Rabin, Cara. The medicated self: implications of Prozac on selfhood, embodiment, and identity. *Penn Bioethics Journal* 2006; 2(1): 4p. [Online]. Accessed: http://www.bioethicsjournal.com [2006 February 21]. NRCBL: 17.4; 4.4; 4.5.

Roberts, Laura Weiss; Geppert, Cynthia M.A. Ethical use of long-acting medications in the treatment of severe and persistent mental illnesses. *Comprehensive Psychiatry* 2004 May-June; 45(3): 161-167. NRCBL: 17.4; 17.8; 8.3.4. SC: an.

Rose, Nikolas. Becoming neurochemical selves. *In:* Stehr, Nico, ed. Biotechnology Between Commerce and Civil Society. New Brunswick, NJ: Transaction Publishers; 2004: 89-126. NRCBL: 17.4.

Scheurich, Neil. The prescriber as moralist: values in the antidepressant debate. *Perspectives in Biology and Medicine* 2006 Spring; 49(2): 199-208. NRCBL: 17.4; 1.3.1. SC: an.

Stein, Dan J. Cosmetic psychopharmacology of anxiety: bioethical considerations. *Current Psychiatry Reports* 2005 August; 7(4): 237-238. NRCBL: 17.4; 2.1.

Turner, Danielle C.; Sahakian, Barbara J. Neuroethics of cognitive enhancement. *BioSocieties* 2006 March; 1(1): 113-123. NRCBL: 17.4; 4.5.

Vedantam, Shankar. Comparison of schizophrenia drugs often favors firm funding study. *Washington Post* 2006 April 12; p. A1, A6. NRCBL: 17.4; 9.7. SC: po.

PSYCHOTHERAPY
See also CARE FOR SPECIFIC GROUPS/ MENTALLY DISABLED; INVOLUNTARY COMMITMENT; MENTAL HEALTH THERAPIES

Bader, Ellyn. Dual relationships: legal and ethical trends. *Transactional Analysis Journal* 1994 January; 24(1): 64-66. NRCBL: 17.2; 8.5. SC: le.

Bingley, Amanda. Research ethics in practice. *In:* Bondi, Liz et al., eds. Subjectivities, Knowledges, and Feminist Geographies: The Subjects and Ethics of Social Research. Lanham, MD: Rowman and Littlefield, 2002: 208-222. NRCBL: 17.2; 18.1; 7.3.

Birrell, Pamela J. An ethic of possibility: relationship, risk, and presence. *Ethics and Behavior* 2006; 16(2): 95-115. NRCBL: 17.2; 6; 1.1; 1.3.1. SC: an; cs. Identifiers: Levinas.

Björn, Gunilla Jarkman. Ethics and interpreting in psychotherapy with refugee children and families. *Nordic Journal of Psychiatry* 2005 December; 59(6): 516-521. NRCBL: 17.2; 9.5.7; 2.1.

Cottone, R. Rocco. Detrimental therapist-client relationships — beyond thinking of "dual" or "multiple" roles: reflections on the 2001 AAMFT code of ethics. *American Journal of Family Therapy* 2005 January-February; 33(1): 1-17. NRCBL: 17.2; 8.1; 10; 6. Identifiers: American Association for Marriage and Family Therapy.

Kaslow, Florence. Ethical problems in mental health practice. *Journal of Family Psychotherapy* 1998; 9(2): 41-54. NRCBL: 17.2; 8.4.

Kessler, Laura E.; Waehler, Charles A. Addressing multiple relationships between clients and therapists in lesbian, gay, bisexual, transgender communities. *Professional Psychology: Research and Practice* 2005 February; 36(1): 66-72. NRCBL: 17.2; 10; 6.

Klontz, Bradley T. Ethical practice of group experiential psychotherapy. *Psychotherapy* 2004 Summer; 41(2): 172-179. NRCBL: 17.2.

Kochiras, Hylarie. Freud said — or Simon says? Informed consent and the advancement of psychoanalysis as a science. *Medicine, Health Care and Philosophy* 2006; 9(2): 227-241. NRCBL: 17.2; 8.4; 18.3; 18.4. SC: an.
Abstract: Is it ever permissible to publish a patient's confidences without permission? I investigate this question for the field of psychoanalysis. Whereas most medical fields adopted a 1995 recommendation for consent requirements, psychoanalysis continues to defend the traditional practice of nonconsensual publication. Both the hermeneutic and the scientific branches of the field justify the practice, arguing that it provides data needed to help future patients, and both branches advance generalizations and causal claims. However the hermeneutic branch embraces methods tending to undermine the reliability of such claims, while the scientific branch aims to improve the field's empirical base - in their words, to advance psychoanalysis as a science. The scientific branch therefore has the stronger claim to the traditional practice, and it their claim that I consider. An immediate concern arises. We seem unable to answer the applied ethical question without first determining which ethical theory is correct; for defenders of the practice appeal variously to therapeutic privilege, principlism, and utilitarianism, while opponents wage autonomy-based arguments. The concern turns out to be unfounded, however, because all of these ethical approaches fail to justify the traditional practice. The more promising defenses fail partly because even the scientific branch of the field lacks empirically sound methods for establishing its causal claims and generalizations, often appealing to authority instead. I conclude that it is currently unethical for analysts to continue publishing their patients' confidences without permission, and I suggest that the field help future patients by attending to its methodological problems.

Sebek, Michael. Some critical notes on Solomon's paper 'The ethical attitude — a bridge between psychoanalysis and analytical psychology'. *Journal of Analytical Psychology* 2002 April; 47(2): 195-201. NRCBL: 17.2; 1.1. SC: cs.

Tribbensee, Nancy E.; Claiborn, Charles D. Confidentiality in psychotherapy and related contexts. *In:* O'Donohue, William; Ferguson, Kyle, eds. Handbook of Professional Ethics for Psychologists: Issues, Questions, and Controversies. Thousand Oaks, Calif.: SAGE Publications; 2003: 287-300. NRCBL: 17.2; 8.4.

Widiger, Thomas A.; Rorer, Leonard. The Responsible psychotherapist. *American Psychologist* 1984 May; 39(5): 503-515. NRCBL: 17.2.

PUBLIC HEALTH
See also AIDS; HEALTH CARE

Allmark, P.; Tod, A. How should public health professionals engage with lay epidemiology? *Journal of Medical Ethics* 2006 August; 32(8): 460-463. NRCBL: 9.1; 7.1. SC: an.
Abstract: "Lay epidemiology" is a term used to describe the processes through which health risks are understood and interpreted by lay people. It is seen as a barrier to public health when the public disbelieves or fails to act on public health messages. Two elements to lay epidemiology are proposed: (a) empirical beliefs about the nature of illness and (b) values about the place of health and risks to health in a good life. Both elements have to be dealt with by effective public health schemes or programmes, which would attempt to change the public's empirical beliefs and values. This is of concern, particularly in a context in which the lay voice is increasingly respected. Empirically, the scientific voice of standard epidemiology should be deferred to by the lay voice, provided a clear distinction exists between the measurement of risk, which is empirical, and its weighting, which is based on values. Turning to engagement with values, health is viewed to be an important value and is discussed and reflected on by most people. Public health professionals are therefore entitled and advised to participate in that process. This view is defended against some potential criticisms.

Blendon, Robert J.; DesRoches, Catherine M.; Cetron, Martin S.; Benson, John M.; Meinhardt, Theodore; Pollard, William. Attitudes toward the use of quarantine in a public health emergency in four countries. *Health Affairs* 2006 January-June; Web Exclusives: W15-W25. NRCBL: 9.1; 21.1. SC: em. Identifiers: Hong Kong; Singapore; Taiwan; United States.

Blum, John D.; Talib, Norchaya. Balancing individual rights versus collective good in public health enforcement. *Medicine and Law: The World Association for Medical Law* 2006 June; 25(2): 273-281. NRCBL: 9.1; 9.7; 8.3.4. SC: le.
Abstract: This paper explores the balance between common good and individual liberty in the context of public health regulation. The issues are explored in reference to two areas of regulation, isolation and quarantine in the case of SARS, and the rights of parents to refuse mandatory childhood immunizations. In the case of SARS, the analysis explores the age old practice of isolation and quarantine, an important preventive measure with clear civil liberty implications. In reference to childhood immunization the paper considers the American controversy involving the refusal of parents to have their children vaccinated, fearing that mercury in vaccines will lead to autism. The analysis explores the US Supreme Court case of Jacobson v. Massachusetts which 100 years ago established a four part test for evaluating claims of individuals that government public health authorities were infringing on their liberty interests. The paper endorses the four elements of necessity, reasonableness, proportionality, and harm avoidance identified in Jacobson, but calls for a more rigorous scientific evaluation to accompany this traditional test.

Burke, Taylor; Rosenbaum, Sara. Molloy v Meier and the expanding standard of medical care: implications for public health policy and practice. *Public Health Reports*

NRCBL: National Reference Center for Bioethics Literature Classification Scheme   See inside front cover for terms.

429

2005 March-April; 120(2): 209-210. NRCBL: 9.1; 15.3; 9.5.7; 15.2. SC: le.

Dawson, A.; Paul, Y. Mass public health programmes and the obligation of sponsoring and participating organisations. *Journal of Medical Ethics* 2006 October; 32(10): 580-583. NRCBL: 9.1; 1.3.2. SC: an.

Dorfman, Lori; Wallack, Lawrence; Woodruff, Katie. More than a message: framing public health advocacy to change corporate practices. *Health Education and Behavior* 2005 June; 32(3): 320-336. NRCBL: 9.1; 1.1; 1.3.7; 1.3.2.

Fidler, David P. Caught between paradise and power: public health, pathogenic threats, and the axis of illness. *McGeorge Law Review* 2004; 35(1): 45-104. NRCBL: 9.1; 21.1; 21.3.

Fidler, David P.; Gostin, Lawrence O. The new international health regulations: an historic development for international law and public health. *Journal of Law, Medicine, and Ethics* 2006 Spring; 34(1): 85-94. NRCBL: 9.1; 21.1. SC: le.

Freudenberg, Nicholas. Public health advocacy to change corporate practices: implications for health education practice and research. *Health Education and Behavior* 2005 June; 32(3): 298-319. NRCBL: 9.1; 1.1; 1.3.3; 1.3.2.

Gammon, Keri. Pandemics and pandemonium: constitutional jurisdiction over public health. *Dalhousie Journal of Legal Studies* 2006; 15: 1-38. NRCBL: 9.1; 1.3.5; 9.2. SC: le.

Gazmararian, Julie A.; Curran, James W.; Parker, Ruth M.; Bernhardt, Jay M.; DeBuono, Barbara A. Public health literacy in America: an ethical imperative. *American Journal of Preventive Medicine* 2005 April; 28(3): 317-322. NRCBL: 9.1; 8.1.

Gostin, Lawrence O. Public health strategies for pandemic influenza: ethics and the law. *JAMA: The Journal of the American Medical Association* 2006 April 12; 295(14): 1700-1704. NRCBL: 9.1; 9.5.1. SC: em; rv.

Gostin, Lawrence O.; Powers, Madison. What does social justice require for the public's health? Public health ethics and policy imperatives. *Health Affairs* 2006 July-August; 25(4): 1053-1060. NRCBL: 9.1; 1.1; 9.4.

Gruskin, Sofia; Dickens, Bernard. Human rights and ethics in public health [editorial]. *American Journal of Public Health* 2006 November; 96(11): 1903-1905. NRCBL: 9.1; 21.1; 9.3.1; 9.4.

Häyry, Matti. Public health and human values. *Journal of Medical Ethics* 2006 September; 32(9): 519-521. NRCBL: 9.1. SC: an.
  Abstract: The ends and means of public health activities are suggested to be at odds with the values held by human individuals and communities. Although promoting longer lives in better

health for all seems like an endeavour that is obviously acceptable, it can be challenged by equally self-evident appeals to autonomy, happiness, integrity and liberty, among other values. The result is that people's actual concerns are not always adequately dealt with by public health measures and assurances.

Hodge, James G. Jr.; Gostin, Lawrence O.; Gebbie, Kristine; Erickson, Deborah L. Transforming public health law: the Turning Point Model State Public Health Act. *Journal of Law, Medicine, and Ethics* 2006 Spring; 34(1): 77-84. NRCBL: 9.1. SC: le.

John, T. Jacob. Human rights and public health during pandemic influenza [editorial]. *Indian Journal of Medical Ethics* 2006 January-March; 3(1): 2-3. NRCBL: 9.1.

May, Thomas. Bioterror and public health infrastructure: a response to commentators [letter]. *American Journal of Bioethics [Online]*. 2006 January-February; 6(1): W29-W31. NRCBL: 9.1; 21.1.

Mello, Michelle M.; Studdert, David M.; Brennan, Troyen A. Obesity — the new frontier of public health law. *New England Journal of Medicine* 2006 June 15; 354(24): 2601-2610. NRCBL: 9.1; 7.1.

Nixon, Stephanie A. Critical public health ethics and Canada's role in global health. *Canadian Journal of Public Health* 2006 January-February; 97(1): 32-34. NRCBL: 9.1; 9.5.6.

Puzio, Dorothy. An overview of public health in the new millenium: individual liberty vs. public safety. *Journal of Law and Health* 2003-2004; 18(2): 173-198. NRCBL: 9.1. SC: le.

Rogers, Wendy A. Feminism and public health ethics. *Journal of Medical Ethics* 2006 June; 32(6): 351-354. NRCBL: 9.1; 10. SC: an.
  Abstract: This paper sketches an account of public health ethics drawing upon established scholarship in feminist ethics. Health inequities are one of the central problems in public health ethics; a feminist approach leads us to examine not only the connections between gender, disadvantage, and health, but also the distribution of power in the processes of public health, from policy making through to programme delivery. The complexity of public health demands investigation using multiple perspectives and an attention to detail that is capable of identifying the health issues that are important to women, and investigating ways to address these issues. Finally, a feminist account of public health ethics embraces rather than avoids the inescapable political dimensions of public health.

Shelley, Jacob. Deference in the public health context. *Health Law Review* 2006; 15(1): 33-36. NRCBL: 9.1; 8.3.4.

Wynia, Matthew K. Markets and public health: pushing and pulling vaccines into production. *American Journal of Bioethics* 2006 May-June; 6(3): 3-6. NRCBL: 9.1; 9.5.1; 9.7; 9.5.6; 9.5.7.

Wynia, Matthew K. Risk and trust in public health: a cautionary tale. *American Journal of Bioethics* 2006 March-April; 6(2): 3-6. NRCBL: 9.1; 9.7; 9.5.1. Identifiers: Center for Disease Control.

PUBLISHING *See* JOURNALISM AND PUBLISHING

QUALITY AND VALUE OF LIFE

Andrews, Lori. Who owns your body? A patient's perspective on Washington University v. Catalona. *Journal of Law, Medicine and Ethics* 2006 Summer; 34(2): 398-407. NRCBL: 4.4; 9.3.1; 8.3. SC: le.

Austriaco, Nicanor Pier Giorgio. How to navigate species boundaries: a reply to The American Journal of Bioethics. *National Catholic Bioethics Quarterly* 2006 Spring; 6(1): 61-71. NRCBL: 4.4; 3.1; 15.1; 22.1; 18.1; 1.1.

Awaya, Tsuyoshi. Gene-enhanced animals and high-efficiency humanoid robots: changing the notion of "human" and "us". *In:* Sang-yong, Song; Young-Mo, Koo; Macer, Darryl R.J., eds. Asian Bioethics in the 21st Century. Christchurch, NZ: Eubios Ethics Institute, 2002: 172-176. NRCBL: 4.4; 5.1; 15.1. Conference: Proceedings of the Asian Bioethics Conference (ABC4), held 2002 November 22-25 in Seoul, South Korea.

Belde, David. Human dignity in patient care: keeping persons at the center of moral disclosure. *Health Care Ethics USA* 2006; 14(3): E3. NRCBL: 4.4; 8.1.

Björkman, B.; Hansson, S.O. Bodily rights and property rights. *Journal of Medical Ethics* 2006 April; 32(4): 209-214. NRCBL: 4.4; 19.5; 1.1. SC: an.

Blacksher, Erika. Hearing from pain: using ethics to reframe, prevent, and resolve the problem of unrelieved pain. *Pain Medicine* 2001 June; 2(2): 169-175. NRCBL: 4.4; 2.1; 7.1.

Bowen, Leslie Maria. Reconfigured bodies: the problem of ownership. *Communication Theory* 2005 February; 15(1): 23-38. NRCBL: 4.4; 7.2; 20.1; 19.5; 14.6; 15.1. SC: le. Identifiers: Diamond v. Chakrabarty; Moore v. Regents of the University of California.

Bowens, Krietta Kai. The legal status of embryos and implications for reproductive technologies and biotechnology research. *Journal of Biolaw and Business* 2006; 9(1): 17-25. NRCBL: 4.4; 18.5.4; 15.4. SC: le.

Brouwer, Werner B.F.; van Exel, N. Job A.; Stolk, Elly A. Acceptability of less than perfect health states. *Social Science and Medicine* 2005 January; 60(2): 237-246. NRCBL: 4.4; 9.4; 9.2; 7.1. SC: em.

Brown, Harold O.J.; Colson, Charles; George, Timothy; Hill, Kent; James, Frank; Johns, Cheryl Bridges; Moore, T.M.; Oden, Thomas; Packer, James; Sumner, Sarah; Vanhoozer, Kevin J.; Woodbridge, John; Buckley, James J.; Casarella, Peter; Culpepper, Gary; Dulles, Avery Cardinal; Guarino, Thomas; Kennedy, Arthur; Levering, Matthew; Martin, Francis; Neuhaus, Richard John; Oakes, Edward T.; Weigel, George; Wilken, Robert Louis. That they may have life. A statement of Evangelicals and Catholics together. *First Things* 2006 October; (166): 18-25. NRCBL: 4.4; 12.3; 12.2; 20.5.1.

Calder, Gideon. Ownership rights and the body. *CQ: Cambridge Quarterly of Healthcare Ethics* 2006 Winter; 15(1): 89-100. NRCBL: 4.4; 1.1.

Casarett, David; Karlawish, Jason; Sankar, Pamela; Hirschman, Karen B.; Asch, David A. Obtaining informed consent for pain research: patients' information needs and concerns. *Pain* 2001 May; 92(1-2): 71-79. NRCBL: 4.4; 18.2; 18.3; 18.5.1.

Caulfield, Timothy; Brownsword, Roger. Human dignity: a guide to policy making in the biotechnology era? *Nature Reviews Genetics* 2006 January; 7(1): 72-76. NRCBL: 4.4; 15.1; 1.3.12; 8.3.1; 15.8; 14.5; 18.5.4.

Caulfield, Timothy; Chapman, Audrey. Human dignity as a criterion for science policy. *PLoS Medicine* 2005 August; 2(8): 736-738. NRCBL: 4.4; 5.3; 18.6.

Chadwick, Ruth. Right to life. *In:* Mitcham, Carl, ed. Encyclopedia of Science, Technology, and Ethics. Farmington Hills, MI: Thomson/Gale, 2005: 1636-1637. NRCBL: 4.4; 1.1.

Charo, R. Alta. Body of research — ownership and use of human tissue. *New England Journal of Medicine* 2006 October 12; 355(15): 1517-1519. NRCBL: 4.4; 19.5; 9.3.1. SC: le.

Chico, Victoria. Saviour siblings: trauma and tort law. *Medical Law Review* 2006 Summer; 14(2): 180-218. NRCBL: 4.4; 14.4; 11.4; 15.2. SC: le.

Cochran, Clarke E.; Cochran, David Carroll. Consistently defending the sanctity of human life. *In their:* Catholics, Politics, and Public Policy: Beyond Left and Right. Maryknoll: Orbis Books; 2003: 182-205. NRCBL: 4.4; 1.2; 12.3; 14.1; 20.6; 21.2; 20.5.1.

Copp, Laurel Archer. An ethical responsibility for pain management [editorial]. *Journal of Advanced Nursing* 2006 July; 55(1): 1-3. NRCBL: 4.4.

Copp, Laurel Archer. Pain and suffering: responsiveness, progress and perserverence [editorial]. *Journal of Advanced Nursing* 2006 July; 55(1): 3-4. NRCBL: 4.4.

Damschen, Gregor; Gómez-Lobo, Alfonso; Schönecker, Dieter. Sixteen days? A reply to B. Smith and B. Brogaard on the beginning of human individuals [response]. *Journal of Medicine and Philosophy* 2006 April; 31(2): 165-175. NRCBL: 4.4; 1.1.

NRCBL: National Reference Center for Bioethics Literature Classification Scheme   See inside front cover for terms.

431

Abstract: When does a human being begin to exist? Barry Smith and Berit Brogaard have argued that it is possible, through a combination of biological fact and philosophical analysis, to provide a definitive answer to this question. In their view, a human individual begins to exist at gastrulation, i. e. at about sixteen days after fertilization. In this paper we argue that even granting Smith and Brogaard's ontological commitments and biological assumptions, the existence of a human being can be shown to begin much earlier, viz., with fertilization. Their interpretative claim that a zygote divides immediately into two substances and therefore ceases to exist is highly implausible by their own standards, and their factual claim that there is no communication between the blastomeres has to be abandoned in light of recent embryological research.

Dennis, William J.; Furton, Edward J. Personhood and the impaired infant. *Ethics and Medics* 2006 November; 31(11): 1-2. NRCBL: 4.4; 20.5.2; 1.2.

Derbyshire, Stuart W.G. Can fetuses feel pain? *BMJ: British Medical Journal* 2006 April 15; 332(7546): 909-912. NRCBL: 4.4; 12.1.

Dickenson, Donna. Ownership, property and women's bodies. *In:* Widdows, Heather; Idiakez, Itziar Alkorta; Cirión, Aitziber Emaldi, eds. Women's Reproductive Rights. New York: Palgrave Macmillan; 2006: 17-32. NRCBL: 4.4; 9.5.5.

Dolgin, Janet L. Surrounding embryos: biology, ideology, and politics. *Health Matrix: The Journal of Law-Medicine* 2006 Winter; 16(1): 27-64. NRCBL: 4.4; 12.3; 14.6; 18.5.4; 15.1.

Emanuel, Linda. Ethics and pain management: an introductory overview. *Pain Medicine* 2001 June; 2(2): 112-116. NRCBL: 4.4; 1.1; 9.5.1; 7.3; 20.4.1; 20.7. SC: cs.

Eppinette, Matthew; Fergusson, Andrew. Human dignity: still defying devaluation. *Ethics and Medicine* 2006 Spring; 22(1): 5-7. NRCBL: 4.4; 1.1.

Ferrell, Betty. Ethical perspectives on pain and suffering. *Pain Management Nursing* 2005 September; 6(3): 83-90. NRCBL: 4.4; 1.1; 10.

Fishman, Scott M. The politics of pain and its impact on pain medicine [editorial]. *Pain Medicine* 2005 May-June; 6(3): 199-200. NRCBL: 4.4; 5.3; 9.7.

Flamigni, Carlo. The embryo question. *Annals of the New York Academy of Sciences* 2001 September; 943: 352-359. NRCBL: 4.4; 9.5.8; 1.2. Identifiers: Italy; Roman Catholics.

Forschner, Maximilian. Menschenwürde, Lebensschutz und biomedizinischer Fortschritt. *In:* Vollmann, Jochen, ed. Medizin und Ethik: Aktuelle ethische Probleme in Therapie und Forschung. Erlangen: Universitätsbund Erlangen-Nürnberg, 2003: 153-180. NRCBL: 4.4.

Foster, C.; Hope, T.; McMillan, J. Submissions from non-existent claimants: the non-identity problem and the law. *Medicine and Law: World Association for Medical Law* 2006 March; 25(1): 159-173. NRCBL: 4.4; 1.1; 15.2; 11.4. SC: le.

Abstract: Some medical interventions (or indeed omissions) determine the identity of a person. Those interventions or omissions may themselves cause harm, for which a child subsequently sues. Even if they do not themselves cause harm they may result in the birth of a child who subsequently brings a claim for being allowed to exist in the state caused by the intervention. The obvious objection to a claim of either class is that in the absence of the medical intervention or omission of which the claimant complains, the claimant would never have existed at all. This objection arises from what philosophers have called the "non-identity problem". This article examines the attitude that the English courts would be likely to have to such a claim. It concludes that the English law has so far failed to appreciate the significance of the non-identity problem, but will have to grapple with it soon.

Gallagher, Rollin M. Ethics in pain medicine: good for our health, good for the public health [editorial]. *Pain Medicine* 2001 June; 2(2): 87-89. NRCBL: 4.4; 9.1; 7.1; 4.1.2.

George, Robert P. Ethics, politics, and genetic knowledge. *Social Research* 2006 Fall; 73(3): 1029-1032. NRCBL: 4.4; 15.5.

Gethmann, Carl Friedrich. The special status of the human being as a topic of practical philosophy. *In:* Duncker, H.-R.; Prieß, K., eds. On the Uniqueness of Humankind. Berlin; New York: Springer; 2005: 95-105. NRCBL: 4.4.

Gilbert, Scott F.; Howes-Mischel, Rebecca. 'Show me your original face before you were born': the convergence of public fetuses and sacred DNA. *History and Philosophy of the Life Sciences* 2004; 26(3-4): 377-394. NRCBL: 4.4; 1.3.12; 1.3.7; 15.1; 12.5.2.

Gilbert, Scott F.; Tyler, Anna L.; Zackin, Emily J. Philosophical, theological, and scientific arguments. *In their:* Bioethics and the New Embryology: Springboards for Debate. Sunderland, MA: Sinauer Associates; 2005: 31-45. NRCBL: 4.4.

Gitter, Donna M. Ownership of human tissue: a proposal for federal recognition of human research participants' property rights in their biological material. *Washington and Lee Law Review* 2004 Winter; 61(1): 257-345. NRCBL: 4.4; 15.8; 5.3; 18.3; 19.1. SC: le.

Gloth, F. Michael III. The politics of pain: legislative and public policy issues. *In:* Gloth, F.M., ed. Handbook of Pain Relief in Older Adults: An Evidence-Based Approach. Totowa: Humana Press Inc., 2003: 185-205. NRCBL: 4.4; 1.3.5.

Goodwin, Michele. Formalism and the legal status of body parts. *University of Chicago Legal Forum* 2006: 317-388. NRCBL: 4.4; 19.5; 8.3.1. SC: le.

Greaves, David. Conceptions of persons and dementia. *In his:* The Healing Tradition: Reviving the Soul of Western

Medicine. Oxford; San Francisco: Radcliffe Publishing.; 2004: 55-65. NRCBL: 4.4; 4.3.

Hamaty, Daniel. Pain medicine's role in the restoration and reformation of medical ethics. *Pain Medicine* 2001 June; 2(2): 117-120. NRCBL: 4.4; 2.1.

Harmon, Shawn H.E. A penny for your thoughts, a pound for your flesh: implications of recognizing property rights in our own excised body parts. *Medical Law International* 2006; 7(4): 329-353. NRCBL: 4.4; 2.1. SC: le.

Heath, Iona. In defence of ambiguity. *Monash Bioethics Review* 2006 July; 25(3): 26-27. NRCBL: 4.4; 10; 1.2; 1.3.5. Comments: Annemarie Jutel. Conflicted encounters: theoretical considerations in the understanding of disease-mongering. Monash Bioethics Review 2006 July; 25(3): 7-23.

Hershenov, David; Koch-Hershenov, Rose J. Fission and confusion. *Christian Bioethics* 2006 December; 12(3): 237-254. NRCBL: 4.4; 1.2.
Abstract: Catholic opponents of abortion and embryonic stem cell research usually base their position on a hylomorphic account of ensoulment at fertilization. They maintain that we each started out as one-cell ensouled organisms. Critics of this position argue that it is plagued by a number of intractable problems due to fission (twinning) and fusion. We're unconvinced that such objections to early ensoulment provide any reason to doubt the coherence of the hylomorphic account. However, we do maintain that a defense of ensoulment at fertilization must deny that we're essentially organisms.

Ihde, Don. Body. *In:* Mitcham, Carl, ed. Encyclopedia of Science, Technology, and Ethics. Farmington Hills, MI: Thomson/Gale, 2005: 239-242. NRCBL: 4.4; 2.2.

Jones, D. Gareth. The emergence of persons. *In:* Jeeves, Michael, ed. From Cells to Souls — and Beyond: Changing Portraits of Human Nature. Grand Rapids, MI: W.B. Eerdmans; 2004: 11-30. NRCBL: 4.4.

Jureidini, Jon. Disease-mongering: a response. *Monash Bioethics Review* 2006 July; 25(3): 24-25. NRCBL: 4.4; 10; 1.2; 1.3.5. Comments: Annemarie Jutel. Conflicted encounters: theoretical considerations in the understanding of disease-mongering. Monash Bioethics Review 2006 July; 25(3): 7-23.

Kaiser, Jocelyn. Court decides tissue samples belong to university, not patients [news]. *Science* 2006 April 21; 312(5772): 346. NRCBL: 4.4; 19.5; 18.4. SC: le.

Karlsen, J.R.; de Faria, P.L.; Solbakk, J.H. To know the value of everything— a critical commentary on B. Björkman and S.O. Hansson's "Bodily rights and property rights". *Journal of Medical Ethics* 2006 April; 32(4): 215-219. NRCBL: 4.4; 19.5; 1.1. SC: an.

Khushf, George. Owning up to our agendas: on the role and limits of science in debates about embryos and brain death. *Journal of Law, Medicine, and Ethics* 2006 Spring; 34(1): 58-76. NRCBL: 4.4; 2.4; 2.1; 21.7.

Koch, Rose. Conjoined twins and the biological account of personal identity. Unpublished Document, University at Buffalo 2004 November 14: 18 p. NRCBL: 4.4; 1.1. SC: an. Conference: Conference on Medicine and Metaphysics; SUNY at Buffalo; 14 November 2004; SUNY Buffalo.

Koch-Hershenov, Rose. Totipotency, twinning, and ensoulment at fertilization. *Journal of Medicine and Philosophy* 2006 April; 31(2): 139-164. NRCBL: 4.4; 1.1.
Abstract: From fertilization to approximately the sixteenth day of development, human embryonic cells are said to have the capacities of totipotency and monozygotic twinning, both of which are problematic to a theory of ensoulment at fertilization. In this article I will address the problems which these capacities pose to such a theory and present an interpretation of the biological data which renders ensoulment at fertilization more plausible. I will then argue that not only is an ensoulment theory consistent with current biological data on the human embryo, but it may offer an explanation for the phenomenon of monozygotic twinning.

Krentel, John Bologna. The Louisiana "human embryo" statute revisited: reasonable recognition and protection for the in vitro fertilized ovum. *Loyola Law Review* 1999 Summer; 45(2): 239-246. NRCBL: 4.4; 14.4; 14.6. SC: le.

Lazarev, Nikolai. The intrinsic value of human life: a critique of Life's Dominion. *E Law: Murdoch University Electronic Journal of Law* 2005 July; 12(1-2): 17 p. [Online]. Accessed: http://www.murdoch.edu.au/elaw/issues/v12n1_2/Lavarev12_1.html [2006 August 2]. NRCBL: 4.4.

Lebovits, Allen. Ethics and pain: why and for whom? [editorial]. *Pain Medicine* 2001 June; 2(2): 92-96. NRCBL: 4.4; 7.1; 9.5.1.

Lee, Patrick. Embryonic human beings. *Journal of Contemporary Health Law and Policy* 2006 Spring; 22(2): 424-438. NRCBL: 4.4; 18.5.4; 15.1.

Lee, Pil Ryul. Is the 'pre-embryo' not equivalent to a human being? *In:* Sang-yong, Song; Young-Mo, Koo; Macer, Darryl R.J., eds. Asian Bioethics in the 21st Century. Christchurch, NZ: Eubios Ethics Institute, 2002: 76-78. NRCBL: 4.4; 18.5.4. Conference: Proceedings of the Asian Bioethics Conference (ABC4), held 22-25 November 2002 in Seoul, South Korea.

Lee, Shui Chuen. A Confucian concept of personhood and its implication for medical ethics. *In:* Döring, Ole; Chen, Renbiao, eds. Advances in Chinese Medical Ethics: Chinese and International Perspectives. Hamburg: Institut für Asienkunde; 2002: 167-177. NRCBL: 4.4; 1.2. Note: Proceedings of the Second Sino-German Interdisciplinary Symposium about Medical Ethics in China, Shanghai, 1999 October, 19-23.

Lesage, Pauline; Portenoy, Russell K. Ethical challenges in the care of patients with serious illness. *Pain Medicine* 2001 June; 2(2): 121-130. NRCBL: 4.4; 20.5.1; 8.3.1.

NRCBL: National Reference Center for Bioethics Literature Classification Scheme   See inside front cover for terms.

433

Liao, S. Matthew. The embryo rescue case. *Theoretical Medicine and Bioethics* 2006; 27(2): 141-147. NRCBL: 4.4; 1.1. SC: an; cs.

Libby, Ronald T. Treating doctors as drug dealers: the DEA's war on prescription painkillers. *CATO Institute Policy Analysis* 2005 June 16; (545): 27 p. [Online]. Accessed: http://www.cato.org/pubs/pas/pa545.pdf [2006 November 29]. NRCBL: 4.4; 7.1; 8.1; 9.7. SC: rv.

Livovich, Jeffrey. Ethics in managed care and pain medicine. *Pain Medicine* 2001 June; 2(2): 155-161. NRCBL: 4.4; 9.3.2; 7.1.

Lock, Margaret. The alienation of body tissue and the biopolitics of immortalized cell lines. *In:* Scheper-Hughes, Nancy; Wacquant, Loïc, eds. Commodifying Bodies. Thousand Oaks, CA: SAGE Publications; 2002: 63-91. NRCBL: 4.4; 2.2; 15.1.

Lockwook, Michael. The moral status of the human embryo: implications for IVF. *Reproductive BioMedicine Online [electronic]* 2005 March; 10(Supplement 1): 17-20. NRCBL: 4.4; 9.5.8; 12.4.1; 20.5.2; 14.4. Conference: Ethics, Law and Moral Philosophy of Reproductive Biomedicine; London, UK; 2004 September 30 - October 1; Royal Society.

Lugosi, Charles I. Conforming to the rule of law: when person and human being finally mean the same thing in Fourteenth Amendment jurisprudence. *Issues in Law and Medicine* 2006 Fall-2007 Spring; 22(2-3): 119-303. NRCBL: 4.4; 12.4.1; 1.1; 1.3.8; 2.2; 12.3. SC: le.

Lyman, Bobbi J.; Lee, Susan J.; Ralston, Henry J. Peter, III; Drey, Eleanor A.; Partridge, John Colin; Rosen, Mark A. Fetal pain [letter and reply]. *JAMA: The Journal of the American Medical Association* 2006 January 11; 295(2): 159, 160-161. NRCBL: 4.4; 9.5.8; 9.5.7.

May, William E. The misinterpretation of John Paul II's teaching in Evangelium vitae n. 73. *National Catholic Bioethics Quarterly* 2006 Winter; 6(4): 705-717. NRCBL: 4.4; 12.3; 1.2; 12.4.4.

McClellan, Frank. Medical malpractice law, morality and the culture wars: a critical assessment of the tort reform movement. *Journal of Legal Medicine* 2006 March; 27(1): 33-53. NRCBL: 4.4; 8.5. SC: le.

McLeod, Carolyn; Baylis, Françoise. Feminists on the inalienability of human embryos. *Hypatia: A Journal of Feminist Philosophy* 2006 Winter; 21(1): 1-14. NRCBL: 4.4; 10; 18.5.4. SC: an.

Meulenbergs, Tom; Schotsmans, Paul. The sanctity of autonomy?: Transcending the opposition between a quality of life and a sanctity of life ethic. *In their:* Euthanasia and Palliative Care in the Low Countries. Dudley, MA: Peeters, 2005: 121-146. NRCBL: 4.4; 1.2.

Mitcham, Carl; Briggle, Adam. Life. *In:* Mitcham, Carl, ed. Encyclopedia of Science, Technology, and Ethics. Farmington Hills, MI: Thomson/Gale, 2005: 1128-1131. NRCBL: 4.4; 3.1; 15.1.

Montgomery, Kathryn. The moral status of the (preserved) fetus. *Atrium* 2005 Spring; 1: 3. NRCBL: 4.4.

Mordacci, Roberto. Recognition and respect for persons: a personalistic interpretation of Kant's categorical imperative. *In:* Rehmann-Sutter, Christoph; Düwell, Marcus; Mieth, Dietmar, eds. Bioethics in Cultural Contexts: Reflections on Methods and Finitude. Dordrecht: Springer, 2006: 129-143. NRCBL: 4.4; 1.1; 20.5.1.

Morgan, Lynn M. "Life begins when they steal your bicycle": cross-cultural practices of personhood at the beginnings and ends of life. *Journal of Law, Medicine, and Ethics* 2006 Spring; 34(1): 8-15. NRCBL: 4.4; 21.7; 7.1. SC: an.

Müller-Terpitz, Ralf. The "uniqueness" of the human being in constitutional law. *In:* Duncker, H.-R.; Prieß, K., eds. On the Uniqueness of Humankind. Berlin; New York: Springer; 2005: 107-122. NRCBL: 4.4. SC: le.

Mundy, Liz. Souls on ice: America's human embryo glut and the unbearable lightness of almost being. *Mother Jones* 2006 July/August; 31(4): 39-45. NRCBL: 4.4; 14.4.

Myers, Laura B.; Bulich, Linda A.; Mizrahi, Arielle; Santangelo, Stephen; Lee, Susan J.; Ralston, Henry J. Peter, III; Drey, Eleanor A.; Partridge, John Colin; Rosen, Mark A. Fetal pain [letter and reply]. *JAMA: The Journal of the American Medical Association* 2006 January 11; 295(2): 159, 160-161. NRCBL: 4.4; 9.5.8; 9.5.7.

Nakayama, Susumu. On human dignity: Japan and the west. *In:* Takahashi, Takao, ed. Taking Life and Death Seriously: Bioethics from Japan. Amsterdam; Boston: Elsevier JAI; 2005: 47-64. NRCBL: 4.4; 21.1.

Neame, Alexandra. "What is man?" The politics of representing genetics. *Social Alternatives* 2003 Summer; 22(1): 53-57. NRCBL: 4.4; 15.2; 14.4.

Nguyen, Marisa; Ugarte, Carlos; Fuller, Ivonne; Haas, Gregory; Portenoy, Russell K. Access to care for chronic pain: racial and ethnic differences. *Journal of Pain* 2005 May; 6(5): 301-314. NRCBL: 4.4; 9.2; 9.5.4.

Nord, Erik. Concerns for the worse off: fair innings versus severity. *Social Science and Medicine* 2005 January; 60(2): 257-263. NRCBL: 4.4; 9.4. SC: an. Identifiers: Norway; Sweden.

O'Donovan, Katherine. Taking a neutral stance on the legal protection of the fetus: Vo v. France. *Medical Law Review* 2006 Spring; 14(1): 115-123. NRCBL: 4.4; 8.5. SC: le.

O'Malley, Patricia. The undertreatment of pain: ethical and legal implications for the Clinical Nurse Specialist. *Clinical Nurse Specialist* 2005 September-October; 19(5): 236-237. NRCBL: 4.4; 4.1.3.

O'Rourke, Kevin D. The embryo as person. *National Catholic Bioethics Quarterly* 2006 Summer; 6(2): 241-251. NRCBL: 4.4; 18.5.4; 15.1; 14.4; 1.1; 1.2.

Parks, Brian D. The natural-artificial distinction and conjoined twins: a response to Judith Thomson's argument for abortion rights. *National Catholic Bioethics Quarterly* 2006 Winter; 6(4): 671-680. NRCBL: 4.4; 12.3; 14.1; 1.1.

Perrett, Roy W. Taking life and the argument from potentiality. *Midwest Studies in Philosophy* 2000 August; 24: 186-198. NRCBL: 4.4; 1.1. SC: an.

Persson, Ingmar. Peter Singer on why persons are irreplaceable. *Utilitas* 1995 May; 7(1): 55-66. NRCBL: 4.4; 1.1. SC: an.

Peters, Ted. Dignity. *In:* Mitcham, Carl, ed. Encyclopedia of Science, Technology, and Ethics. Farmington Hills, MI: Thomson/Gale, 2005: 528-530. NRCBL: 4.4.

Post, Stephen G. Posthumanism. *In:* Mitcham, Carl, ed. Encyclopedia of Science, Technology, and Ethics. Farmington Hills, MI: Thomson/Gale, 2005: 1458-1462. NRCBL: 4.4; 4.5.

Quante, Michael. The indispensability of quality of life. *Human Reproduction and Genetic Ethics: An International Journal* 2006; 12(1): 13-15. NRCBL: 4.4.

Quill, Timothy E.; Kimsma, G.K. How much suffering is enough? *Medical Ethics Newsletter* 2006 Spring; 13(2): 10-11. NRCBL: 4.4; 20.7; 20.5.1; 8.1.

Ranson, David. The "born alive" rule. *Journal of Law and Medicine* 2006 February; 13(3): 285-288. NRCBL: 4.4. SC: le.

Reddy, Bhavani S. The epidemic of unrelieved chronic pain: the ethical, societal, and regulatory barriers facing opioid prescribing physicians. *Journal of Legal Medicine* 2006 December; 27(4): 427-442. NRCBL: 4.4; 9.5.9.

Roberts, Melinda A. Supernumerary pregnancy, collective harm, and two forms of the nonidentity problem. *Journal of Law, Medicine and Ethics* 2006 Winter; 34(4): 776-792. NRCBL: 4.4; 9.5.8; 14.1; 1.1. SC: an.

Abstract: An interesting question, in both the moral and the legal context, is whether babies born of an infertility treatment-induced supernumerary pregnancy (or ITISP) are properly considered to have been harmed. One might wonder how such a question could even arise in the face of data that clearly demonstrate that ITISP leaves an unduly large number of babies blind, deaf, and palsied, and facing lifelong disabilities. In fact, however, a number of arguments, based on the problem of collective form and two forms of the so-called "nonidentity problem," challenge the claim of harm in the ITISP context. The purpose of the present paper is to establish, as

against these arguments, that harm has been imposed on the ITISP-damaged offspring.

Robertson, John A. Embryo culture and the "culture of life": Constitutional issues in the embryonic stem cell debate. *University of Chicago Legal Forum* 2006: 1-40. NRCBL: 4.4; 18.5.4; 15.1. SC: le.

Robichaud, Philip. Metaphysics and the morality at the boundaries of life. *Journal of Medicine and Philosophy* 2006 April; 31(2): 97-105. NRCBL: 4.4; 1.1; 12.3; 20.2.1; 20.5.1; 20.7.

Rodriguez, Eva; Pinto, Jose Luis. The social value of health programmes: is age a relevant factor? *Health Economics* 2000 October; 9(7): 611-621. NRCBL: 4.4; 9.4; 7.1.

Rollin, Bernard E. Pain and ethics. *In his:* Science and Ethics. New York: Cambridge University Press; 2006: 215-246. NRCBL: 4.4.

Scheper-Hughes, Nancy. Bodies for sale — whole or in parts. *In:* Scheper-Hughes, Nancy; Wacquant, Loïc, eds. Commodifying Bodies. Thousand Oaks, CA: SAGE Publications; 2002: 1-8. NRCBL: 4.4; 9.3.1.

Scott, Anne. "Like editing bits of ourselves": geneticisation and human fate. *New Genetics and Society* 2006 April; 25(1): 109-124. NRCBL: 4.4; 15.10; 3.1. SC: em.

Seers, Kate; Watt-Watson, Judy; Bucknall, Tracey. Challenges of pain management for the 21st century [editorial]. *Journal of Advanced Nursing* 2006 July; 55(1): 4-6. NRCBL: 4.4.

Sgreccia, Elio. Bioética y rehabilitación [Bioethics and rehabilitation]. *Persona y Bioética* 1999 February-May; 2(6): 24-42. NRCBL: 4.4; 9.5.1; 4.2; 2.1.

Shepherd, Lois. Terri Schiavo and the disability rights community: a cause for concern. *University of Chicago Legal Forum* 2006: 253-273. NRCBL: 4.4; 20.2.1; 8.3.4. SC: le.

Sites, Brian D.; Lee, Susan J.; Ralston, Henry J. Peter, III; Drey, Eleanor A.; Partridge, John Colin; Rosen, Mark A. Fetal pain [letter and reply]. *JAMA: The Journal of the American Medical Association* 2006 January 11; 295(2): 160-161. NRCBL: 4.4; 9.5.8; 9.5.7; 12.1.

Smolensky, Kirsten Rabe. Defining life from the perspective of death: an introduction to the Force Symmetry Approach. *University of Chicago Legal Forum* 2006: 41-85. NRCBL: 4.4; 20.2.1; 12.1. SC: le.

Snyder, Evan Y.; Hinman, Lawrence M.; Kalichman, Michael W. Can science resolve the ethical impasse in stem cell research? *Nature Biotechnology* 2006 April; 24(4): 397-400. NRCBL: 4.4; 18.5.4; 14.5; 15.1.

NRCBL: National Reference Center for Bioethics Literature Classification Scheme   See inside front cover for terms.

435

Statman, Daniel. Human dignity and technology. *In:* Árnason, Gardar; Nordal, Salvör; Árnason, Vilhjálmur, eds. Blood and Data: Ethical, Legal and Social Aspects of Human Genetic Databases. Reykjavík: University of Iceland Press; 2004: 223-228. NRCBL: 4.4; 1.1; 5.1.

Stern, Megan. Dystopian anxieties versus utopian ideals: medicine from Frankenstein to The Visible Human Project and Body Worlds. *Science as Culture* 2006 March; 15(1): 61-84. NRCBL: 4.4; 5.1; 7.1; 20.1.

Stones, William. Women, doctors and pain. *In:* Unnithan-Kumar, Maya, ed. Reproductive Agency, Medicine and the State: Cultural Transformations in Childbearing. New York: Berghahn Books; 2004: 103-112. NRCBL: 4.4; 8.1; 9.5.5; 10. SC: em.

Strong, Carson. Preembryo personhood: an assessment of the President's Council arguments. *Theoretical Medicine and Bioethics* 2006; 27(5): 433-453. NRCBL: 4.4; 18.5.4; 15.1; 19.5; 14.5.

Sullivan, Mark. Ethical principles in pain management. *Pain Medicine* 2001 June; 2(2): 106-111. NRCBL: 4.4; 1.1; 2.1.

Sulmasy, Daniel P. Dignity, vulnerability, and medical error. *Health Progress* 2006 January-February; 87(1): 12-14. NRCBL: 4.4; 9.8.

Tauer, Carol A. The tradition of probabilism and the moral status of the early embryo. *Theological Studies* 1984 March; 45(1): 3-33. NRCBL: 4.4. SC: an.

Taylor, Richard. Human property: threat or saviour? *E Law: Murdoch University Electronic Journal of Law* 2002 December; 9(4): 14 p. [Online]. Accessed: http://www.murdoch.edu.au/elaw/issues/v9n4/taylor94.html [2006 June 29]. NRCBL: 4.4; 5.3; 15.8; 19.5. SC: le.

Tengland, Per-Anders. The goals of health work: quality of life, health and welfare. *Medicine, Health Care and Philosophy* 2006; 9(2): 155-167. NRCBL: 4.4; 9.1; 4.2. SC: an.
Abstract: Health-related quality of life is the ultimate general goal for medicine, health care and public health, including health promotion and health education. The other important general goal is health-related welfare. The aim of the paper is to explain what this means and what the consequences of these assumptions are for health work. This involves defining the central terms "health", "quality of life" and "welfare" and showing what their conceptual relations are. Health-related quality of life has two central meanings: health-related well-being, which constitutes quality of life, and health as ability, which contributes causally to quality of life. Four meanings of health-related welfare are put forward: general well-being, health as ability, other inner properties of the individual, and external factors. States and processes covered by these categories contribute causally to health-related quality of life. Finally, using these distinctions, some more specific goals for medicine and health care, on the one hand, and for public health and health promotion, on the other, are outlined. In the former fields work is primarily directed towards changing the health-related quality of life of the individual through direct measures, "manipulating" the individual, whereas public health work and health promotion primarily use indirect measures and further health through various sorts of health-related welfare changes, e.g. through changing the environment.

Tiefer, Leonore. Sex and disease-mongering: a special case? *Monash Bioethics Review* 2006 July; 25(3): 28-35. NRCBL: 4.4; 10; 1.2; 1.3.5.

Tollefsen, Christopher. Fission, fusion, and the simple view. *Christian Bioethics* 2006 December; 12(3): 255-263. NRCBL: 4.4; 1.2.
Abstract: In this essay, I defend three Simple Views concerning human beings. First, that the human embryo is, from the one-cell stage onwards, a single unitary organism. Second, that when an embryo twins, it ceases to exist and two new embryos come into existence. And third, that you and I are essentially human organisms. This cluster of views shows that it is not necessary to rely on co-location, or other obscure claims, in understanding human embryo genesis.

Trías, Encarna Roca. The perplexities of law: mysteries of embryos = El derecho perplejo: los misterios de los embriones. *Law and the Human Genome = Revista de Derecho y Genoma Humano* 1994 July-December; (1): 119-148. NRCBL: 4.4; 2.4; 21.1; 15.4; 15.2. SC: le.

Union of American Hebrew Congregations. Committee on Bio-Ethics. The Role of Pain and Suffering in Decision Making: Bioethics Program/Case Study: Program Guide VIII. New York, NY: Union of American Hebrew Congregations, 1996 Winter; 38 p. NRCBL: 4.4; 8.1; 1.2; 9.4; 7.1.

United States. Congress. House. A bill to amend title 18, United States Code, and the Uniform Code of Military Justice to protect unborn children from assault and murder, and for other purposes. Washington, DC: U.S. G.P.O., 2001. 7p. [Online]. Accessed: http://frwebgate.access.gpo.gov/cgi-bin/getdoc.cgi?dbname=107_cong_bills&docid=f:h503ih.txt.pdf [2007 March 2]. NRCBL: 4.4; 9.1; 9.5.8. SC: le. Note: H.R. 503, 107th Congress, 1st session. Introduced by Rep. Graham on February 7, 2001. Referred to the Committee on the Judiciary and the Committee on Armed Services.

United States. Congress. House. A bill to provide that human life shall be deemed to exist from conception. Washington, DC: U.S. G.P.O., 2005. 4 p. [Online]. Accessed: http://frwebgate.access.gpo.gov/cgi-bin/useftp.cgi?IPaddress=162.140.64.21&filename=h776ih.pdf&directory=/diskb/wais/data/109_cong_bills [2006 November 27]. NRCBL: 4.4. SC: le. Identifiers: Sanctity of Life Act of 2005. Note: H.R. 776, 109th Congress, 1st session. Introduced by Rep. Paul, February 10, 2005. Referred to the Committee on the Judiciary.

United States. Congress. Senate. A bill to amend titles 10 and 18, United States Code, to protect unborn victims of violence. Washington, DC: U.S. G.P.O., 2001. 7 p. [Online]. Accessed: http://frwebgate.access.gpo.gov/cgi-bin/getdoc.cgi?dbname=107_cong_bills&docid=

f:s480is.txt.pdf [2007 March 2]. NRCBL: 4.4; 9.1; 9.5.8. SC: le. Note: S. 480, 107th Congress, 1st session. Introduced by Sen. DeWine on March 7, 2001. Referred to the Committee on the Judiciary.

United States. Congress. Senate. A bill to amend the Public Health Service Act to prohibit the solicitation or acceptance of tissue from fetuses gestated for research purposes, and for other purposes. Washington, DC: U.S. G.P.O., 2006. 3 p. [Online]. Available http://frwebgate. access.gpo.gov/cgi-bin/useftp.cgi?IPaddress=162.140.64 .21&filename=s3504is.pdf&directory=/diskb/wais/data/ 109_cong_bills [2006 July 17]. NRCBL: 4.4; 18.5.4; 15.1. SC: le. Identifiers: Fetus Farming Prohibition Act of 2006. Note: S. 3504, 109th Congress, 2d Session. Introduced by Sen. Santorum, June 13, 2006. Referred to the Committee on Health, Education, Labor and Pensions.

Virt, Günter. Unity and variety of ethical principles: human dignity endangered. *Human Reproduction and Genetic Ethics: An International Journal* 2006; 12(2): 61-65. NRCBL: 4.4; 2.1; 21.1.

Volkov, Ilia. A part of life, a part of me, and "the quality of life". *Journal of Clinical Ethics* 2006 Summer; 17(2): 191-192. NRCBL: 4.4; 7.2.

Wall, L. Lewis; Brown, Douglas. Regarding zygotes as persons: implications for public policy. *Perspectives in Biology and Medicine* 2006 Autumn; 49(4): 602-610. NRCBL: 4.4; 1.3.5.

Wancata, Andrew. No value for a pound of flesh: extending market-inalienability of the human body. *Journal of Law and Health* 2003-2004; 18(2): 199-228. NRCBL: 4.4; 19.5; 9.3.1. SC: le.

Watson, Katie. Jarred and jarring: the unfolding history of a museum of anatomy. *Atrium* 2005 Spring; 1: 1-3. NRCBL: 4.4; 19.5.

Wehlte, Christian. Über die "Heiligkeit des Lebens" — Zur Vernachlässigung soziokultureller Dimensionen in der Euthanasie-Diskussion. *In:* Frewer, Andreas; Eickhoff, Clemens, eds. "Euthanasie" und die aktuelle Sterbehilfe-Debatte: Die historischen Hintergründe medizinischer Ethik. Frankfurt; New York: Campus; 2000: 336-355. NRCBL: 4.4; 20.5.1.

Wils, Jean-Pierre. Body, perception and identity. *In:* Rehmann-Sutter, Christoph; Düwell, Marcus; Mieth, Dietmar, eds. Bioethics in Cultural Contexts: Reflections on Methods and Finitude. Dordrecht: Springer, 2006: 231-245. NRCBL: 4.4.

Yahata, Hideyuki. Moral thinking about the embryo-fetus period: reconsidering the problems of identity and existence. *In:* Takahashi, Takao, ed. Taking Life and Death Seriously: Bioethics from Japan. Amsterdam; Boston: Elsevier JAI; 2005: 65-84. NRCBL: 4.4.

Zoloth, Laurie. The gaze toward the beautiful dead: considering ethical issues raised by the Body Worlds exhibit. *Atrium* 2005 Spring; 1: 5-6. NRCBL: 4.4; 19.5; 20.1.

RATIONING OF HEALTH CARE *See* RESOURCE ALLOCATION

RECOMBINANT DNA RESEARCH
See also GENETIC RESEARCH; GENOME MAPPING

Birrer, Frans; Paula, Lino. Including public perspectives in industrial biotechnology and the biobased economy. *Journal of Agricultural and Environmental Ethics* 2006; 19(3): 253-267. NRCBL: 15.7; 15.1; 1.3.11; 16.1.

Briggle, Adam. Asilomar Conference. *In:* Mitcham, Carl, ed. Encyclopedia of Science, Technology, and Ethics. Farmington Hills, MI: Thomson/Gale, 2005: 118-121. NRCBL: 15.7; 2.2.

Briggle, Adam. Institutional biosafety committees. *In:* Mitcham, Carl, ed. Encyclopedia of Science, Technology, and Ethics. Farmington Hills, MI: Thomson/Gale, 2005: 1022-1024. NRCBL: 15.7; 2.2; 18.2.

Kawar, Amal; Sherlock, Richard. Theoretical issues in the regulation of genetically engineered organisms: the case of deliberate release. *Politics and the Life Sciences* 1989 February; 7(2): 129-134. NRCBL: 15.7; 1.3.11; 5.3. SC: le; an.

Krimsky, Sheldon. Science, biopolitics, and risk: margins of uncertainty. *Politics and the Life Sciences* 1989 February; 7(2): 140-142. NRCBL: 15.7; 5.3.

Miller, Judith. Environmental protection and uncertainty: the case of deliberate release of genetically engineered organisms. *Politics and the Life Sciences* 1989 February; 7(2): 142-145. NRCBL: 15.7; 1.3.11; 16.1.

Ravetz, Jerome R. Taming the technological imperative: a comment. *Politics and the Life Sciences* 1989 February; 7(2): 145-147. NRCBL: 15.7; 5.3.

Taverne, Dick. The new fundamentalism. *Nature Biotechnology* 2005 April; 23(4): 415-416. NRCBL: 15.7; 3.1.

Welsh, Rick; Ervin, David. Precaution as an approach to technology development: the case of transgenic crops. *Science, Technology, and Human Values* 2006 March; 31(2): 153-172. NRCBL: 15.7; 5.2; 16.1; 1.3.11. SC: cs; an.

Witkowski, Jan A.; Miller, Henry I.; Conko, Gregory. Should we make a fuss? [letters]. *Nature Biotechnology* 2006 August; 24(8): 899-900. NRCBL: 15.7; 15.5; 2.2.

Zimmerman, Burke K. Commentary on Kawar and Sherlock. *Politics and the Life Sciences* 1989 February; 7(2): 148-153. NRCBL: 15.7; 21.1; 1.3.11.

NRCBL: National Reference Center for Bioethics Literature Classification Scheme   See inside front cover for terms.

437

REGULATION *See* ABORTION/ LEGAL ASPECTS; BIOETHICS AND MEDICAL ETHICS/ LEGAL ASPECTS; CLONING/ LEGAL ASPECTS; EUTHANASIA AND ALLOWING TO DIE/ LEGAL ASPECTS; GENETIC SCREENING/ LEGAL ASPECTS; GENETICS/ LEGAL ASPECTS; HUMAN EXPERIMENTATION/ ETHICS COMMITTEES AND POLICY GUIDELINES/ LEGAL ASPECTS; HUMAN EXPERIMENTATION/ REGULATION; ORGAN AND TISSUE TRANSPLANTATION/ DONATION AND PROCUREMENT/ LEGAL ASPECTS

RELIGIOUS ASPECTS *See* ABORTION/ MORAL AND RELIGIOUS ASPECTS; BIOETHICS AND MEDICAL ETHICS/ RELIGIOUS PERSPECTIVES; EUTHANASIA AND ALLOWING TO DIE/ RELIGIOUS ASPECTS; HUMAN EXPERIMENTATION/ SPECIAL POPULATIONS/ EMBRYOS AND FETUSES/ PHILOSOPHICAL AND RELIGIOUS ASPECTS

REPRODUCTION *See* REPRODUCTIVE TECHNOLOGIES

REPRODUCTIVE TECHNOLOGIES
See also ARTIFICIAL INSEMINATION/ SURROGATE MOTHERS; CLONING; CRYOBANKING OF SPERM, OVA, AND EMBRYOS; IN VITRO FERTILIZATION; SEX DETERMINATION

Beyond IVF: should parents be free to decide what is acceptable? [editorial]. *New Scientist* 2006 October 21-27; 192(2574): 5. NRCBL: 14.1; 15.2; 14.4. Identifiers: in-vitro fertilization.

Guiding regulatory reform in reproduction and genetics. *Harvard Law Review* 2006 December; 2: 574-596. NRCBL: 14.1; 14.5; 15.1. SC: le.

National Committee on Assisted Human Reproduction: a promising first step = Comisión Nacional de Reproducción Asistida: un primer paso prometedor [editorial]. *Revista de Derecho Genoma Humano = Law and the Human Genome Review* 1999 January-June; (10): 15-18. NRCBL: 14.1; 2.4. Identifiers: Spain.

Spain's Constitutional Court and assisted reproduction techniques = El Tribunal Constitucional español y las técnicas de reproducción asistada. *Revista de Derecho Genoma Humano = Law and the Human Genome Review* 1999 July-December; (11): 15-17. NRCBL: 14.1. SC: le.

Abraham, Abraham S. Infertility and halachah. *In:* Rosner, Fred, ed. Medicine and Jewish Law. Volume III. Brooklyn, NY: Yashar Books, Inc.; 2005: 15-23. NRCBL: 14.1; 1.2.

Ahmad, Norhayati Haji. Assisted reproduction — Islamic views on the science of procreation. *Eubios Journal of Asian and International Bioethics* 2003 March 13(2): 59-61. NRCBL: 14.1; 1.2.

Alkorta, Itziar. Women's rights in European fertility medicine regulation. *In:* Widdows, Heather; Idiakez, Itziar Alkorta; Cirión, Aitziber Emaldi, eds. Women's Reproductive Rights. New York: Palgrave Macmillan; 2006: 111-123. NRCBL: 14.1; 21.1. SC: le.

American Society for Reproductive Medicine [ASRM]. Ethics Committee. Child-rearing ability and the provision of fertility services. *Fertility and Sterility* 2004 September; 82(Supplement 1): S208-S211. NRCBL: 14.1; 17.1.

American Society for Reproductive Medicine [ASRM]. Ethics Committee. Use of fetal oocytes in assisted reproduction. *Fertility and Sterility* 2004 September; 82(Supplement 1): S258-S259. NRCBL: 14.1; 18.5.4; 15.1.

American Society for Reproductive Medicine [ASRM]. Practice Committee. Elements to be considered in obtaining informed consent for ART. *Fertility and Sterility* 2004 September; 82(Supplement 1): S202-S203. NRCBL: 14.1; 8.3.1. Identifiers: assisted reproductive technology. Note: Committee Opinion January 1998. Approved by the Board of Directors June 1997.

Andrews, Lori B. Assisted reproductive technology and the challenge for paternity laws. *In:* Rothstein, Mark A.; Murray, Thomas H.; Kaebnick, Gregory E.; Majumder, Mary Anderlik, eds. Genetic Ties and the Family: The Impact of Paternity Testing on Parents and Children. Baltimore: Johns Hopkins University Press; 2005: 187-212. NRCBL: 14.1; 15.1. SC: le.

Andrews, Lori B. How is technology changing the meaning of motherhood for western women. *In:* Widdows, Heather; Idiakez, Itziar Alkorta; Cirión, Aitziber Emaldi, eds. Women's Reproductive Rights. New York: Palgrave Macmillan; 2006: 124-139. NRCBL: 14.1.

Bahadur, Gulam. Parliamentary proposals for liberal approaches to assisted conception. *Reproductive BioMedicine Online [electronic]* 2005 August; 11(2): 177-182. Accessed: http://www.rbmonline.com/Article/1884 [2006 January 22]. NRCBL: 14.1; 5.3; 4.4; 15.2. SC: le.

Barri, Pedro N. Procreatics and honesty. *Human Reproduction* 1996 July; 11(7): 1368-1369. NRCBL: 14.1; 5.3.

Bartel, Sarah Smith. Welcoming the child at birth. *National Catholic Bioethics Quarterly* 2006 Summer; 6(2): 273-294. NRCBL: 14.1; 9.5.5; 9.5.7; 4.4; 5.3; 1.2.

Beckman, Linda J.; Harvey, S. Marie. Current reproductive technologies: increased access and choice? *Journal of Social Issues* 2005 March; 61(1): 1-20. NRCBL: 14.1; 9.2.

Bellis, Mark A.; Hughes, Karen; Hughes, Sara; Ashton, John R. Measuring paternal discrepancy and its public health consequences. *Journal of Epidemiology and Community Health* 2005 September; 59: 749-754. NRCBL: 14.1; 15.3; 9.1. SC: em.

Benatar, David. Reproductive freedom and risk. *Human Reproduction* 2006 October; 21(10): 2491-2493. NRCBL: 14.1; 1.1.

Bharadwaj, Aditya. Why adoption is not an option in India: the visibility of infertility, the secrecy of donor insemination, and other cultural complexities. *Social Science and Medicine* 2003 May; 56(9): 1867-1880. NRCBL: 14.1; 14.2; 21.7; 8.4.

Blackford, R. Sinning against nature: the theory of background conditions. *Journal of Medical Ethics* 2006 November; 32(11): 629-634. NRCBL: 14.1; 1.1; 5.1; 15.1.
Abstract: Debates about the moral and political acceptability of particular sexual practices and new technologies often include appeals to a supposed imperative to follow nature. If nature is understood as the totality of all phenomena or as those things that are not artificial, there is little prospect of developing a successful argument to impugn interference with it or sinning against it. At the same time, there are serious difficulties with approaches that seek to identify "proper" human functioning. An alternative approach is to understand interference with nature as acting in a manner that threatens basic background conditions to human choice. Arguably, the theory of background conditions helps explain much of the hostility to practices and technologies that allegedly sin against nature. The theory does not, however, entail that appeals to nature are relevant or rational. Such appeals should be subjected to sceptical scrutiny. Indeed, the theory suggests that arguments against practices and technologies that can be seen as contrary to nature sometimes exercise a psychological attraction that is disproportional to their actual cogency.

Blustein, Jeffrey. Ethical issues in DNA-based paternity testing. *In:* Rothstein, Mark A.; Murray, Thomas H.; Kaebnick, Gregory E.; Majumder, Mary Anderlik, eds. Genetic Ties and the Family: The Impact of Paternity Testing on Parents and Children. Baltimore: Johns Hopkins University Press; 2005: 34-49. NRCBL: 14.1; 15.1.

Blyth, Eric. Assisted reproduction: what's in it for children? *Children and Society* 1990; 4(2): 167-182. NRCBL: 14.1; 9.5.7.

Blyth, Eric. What do donor offspring want to know about their genetic origins? *Journal of Fertility Counselling* 1998 Summer; 5(2): 15-17. NRCBL: 14.1; 8.4; 14.2; 14.4.

Boivin, J.; Pennings, G. Parenthood should be regarded as a right. *Archives of Disease in Childhood* 2005 August; 90(8): 784-785. NRCBL: 14.1; 9.5.7; 1.3.5. SC: le. Identifiers: United Kingdom (Great Britain).

Budinger, Thomas F.; Budinger, Miriam D. Ethics of assisted reproductive technologies. *In their:* Ethics of Emerging Technologies: Scientific Facts and Moral Challenges. Hoboken, NJ: John Wiley and Sons; 2006: 303-341. NRCBL: 14.1.

Cameron, Nigel M. de S. Selecting our embryonic children [editorial]. *Ethics and Medicine* 2006 Spring; 22(1): 3-4. NRCBL: 14.1; 15.2; 4.5; 15.5; 5.3.

Chadwick, Ruth. Rights and reproduction. *In:* Mitcham, Carl, ed. Encyclopedia of Science, Technology, and Ethics. Farmington Hills, MI: Thomson/Gale, 2005: 1629-1630. NRCBL: 14.1; 1.1.

Charo, R. Alta. And baby makes three — or four, or five, or six: redefining the family after the reprotech revolution. *Wisconsin Women's Law Journal* 1992-1993; 7-8: 1-23. NRCBL: 14.1; 8.3.2 15.1. SC: le.

Chwalisz, Bart; McVeigh, Edna; Hope, Tony; Kennedy, Stephen. Prioritizing IVF patients according to the number of existing children — a proposed refinement to the current guideline. *Human Reproduction* 2006 May; 21(5): 1110-1112. NRCBL: 14.4; 9.4; 9.3.1.

Cole, Andrew. Assisted conception business should be better regulated [news]. *BMJ: British Medical Journal* 2006 April 1; 332(7544): 748. NRCBL: 14.1; 9.3.1; 1.3.2; 5.3. Identifiers: United Kingdom (Great Britain).

Cussac, José Luis González. Genetic manipulation and assisted reproduction in Spain's penal reform = Manipulación genética y reproducción asistida en la reforma penal española. *Law and the Human Genome Review = Revista de Derecho y Genoma Humano* 1995 July-December; (3): 67-97. NRCBL: 14.1; 15.1; 1.3.5. SC: le.

Daniels, Ken. Ethical considerations in professionals' contribution to policy development in assisted human reproduction. *In:* Sang-yong, Song; Young-Mo, Koo; Macer, Darryl R.J., eds. Asian Bioethics in the 21st Century. Christchurch, NZ: Eubios Ethics Institute, 2002: 358-362. NRCBL: 14.1; 1.3.10; 4.1.2; 6; 9.1. Identifiers: New Zealand. Conference: Proceedings of the Asian Bioethics Conference (ABC4), held 22-25 November 2002 in Seoul, South Korea.

Daniels, Ken. Genetics and artificial procreation in New Zealand. *In:* Meulders-Klein, Marie-Thérèse; Deech, Ruth; Vlaardingerbroek, Paul, eds. Biomedicine, the Family and Human Rights. New York: Kluwer Law International, 2002: 123-132. NRCBL: 14.1; 15.1.

de Melo-Martín, Inmaculada. Assisted reproduction technology. *In:* Mitcham, Carl, ed. Encyclopedia of Science, Technology, and Ethics. Farmington Hills, MI: Thomson/Gale, 2005: 123-125. NRCBL: 14.1.

Desai, Ravi V.; Krishnamurthy, Mahesh; Patel, Harish; Hoffman, David N. Postmortem sperm retrieval: an ethical dilemma [letter]. *American Journal of Medicine* 2004 June 15; 116(12): 858. NRCBL: 14.1.

NRCBL: National Reference Center for Bioethics Literature Classification Scheme   See inside front cover for terms.

Djerassi, Carl. Technology and human reproduction: 1950-2050. *Journal of Molecular Biology* 2002 June 14; 319(4): 979-984. NRCBL: 14.1; 1.2; 2.2. SC: an.

Draper, Heather. Why there is no right to know one's genetic origin? *In:* Athanassoulis, Nafsika, ed. Philosophical Reflections on Medical Ethics. New York: Palgrave Macmillan; 2005: 70-87. NRCBL: 14.1; 8.4. SC: an.

Dreifus, Claudia. An economist examines the business of fertility: a conversation with Debora Spar. *New York Times* 2006 February 28; p. F5, F8. NRCBL: 14.1; 1.3.2; 14.6; 19.5; 10. SC: po.

Dyer, Owen. GMC hears complaints about UK fertility specialist [news]. *BMJ: British Medical Journal* 2006 March 11; 332(7541): 567. NRCBL: 14.1; 7.4. Identifiers: General Medical Council; United Kingdom (Great Britain).

Edwards, Jeanette. Incorporating incest: gamete, body and relation in assisted conception. *Journal of the Royal Anthropological Institute* 2004 December; 10(4): 755-774. NRCBL: 14.1; 10; 8.1. SC: cs. Identifiers: United Kingdom (Great Britain).

Edwards, Jeanette. Taking "public understanding" seriously. *New Genetics and Society* 2002 December; 21(3): 315-325. NRCBL: 14.1; 15.2. SC: em. Identifiers: new reproductive and genetic technologies.

Elster, Nanette R. Assisted reproductive technologies: contracts, consents, and controversies. *American Journal of Family Law* 2005 Winter; 18(4): 193-199. NRCBL: 14.1; 1.3.5.

Ertman, Martha M. What's wrong with a parenthood market? A new and improved theory of commodification. *North Carolina Law Review* 2003 December; 82(1): 1-59. NRCBL: 14.1; 9.3.1; 14.2; 14.4. SC: le.

Evans, John H. Religious belief, perceptions of human suffering, and support for reproductive genetic technology. *Journal of Health Politics, Policy and Law* 2006 December; 31(6): 1047-1074. NRCBL: 14.1; 15.1; 4.5; 4.4; 1.2. SC: em.

Feinman, Michael; Sher, Geoffrey. Comparing the British and American approaches to regulating ART programmes. *Human Reproduction* 1996 July; 11(7): 1366-1367. NRCBL: 14.1; 5.3. Identifiers: assisted reproductive technology.

Fuscaldo, Giuliana. Genetic ties: are they morally binding? *Bioethics* 2006 April; 20(2): 64-76. NRCBL: 14.1; 19.5; 1.1. SC: an.

Abstract: Does genetic relatedness define who is a mother or father and who incurs obligations towards or entitlements over children? While once the answer to this question may have been obvious, advances in reproductive technologies have complicated our understanding of what makes a parent. In a recent publication Bayne and Kolers argue for a pluralistic account of parenthood on the basis that genetic derivation, gestation, extended custody and sometimes intention to parent are sufficient (but not necessary) grounds for parenthood. Bayne and Kolers further suggest that definitions of parenthood are underpinned by the assumption that 'being causally implicated in the creation of a child is the key basis for being its parent'. This paper examines the claim that genetic relatedness is sufficient grounds for parenthood based on a causal connection between genetic parents and their offspring. I argue that parental obligations are about moral responsibility and not causal responsibility because we are not morally accountable for every consequence to which we causally contribute. My account includes the conditions generally held to apply to moral responsibility, i.e. freedom and foreseeability. I argue that parental responsibilities are generated whenever the birth of a child is a reasonably foreseeable consequence of voluntary actions. I consider the implications of this account for third parties involved in reproductive technologies. I argue that under some conditions the obligations generated by freely and foreseeably causing a child to exist can be justifiably transferred to others.

Gibson, Mark. Outcomes with assisted reproductive technology: shooting first, asking questions later [editorial]. *Obstetrics and Gynecology* 2004 June; 103(6): 1142-1143. NRCBL: 14.1; 9.5.7; 9.8.

Gilbert, Scott F.; Tyler, Anna L.; Zackin, Emily J. Assisted reproductive technologies: safety and ethical issues. *In their:* Bioethics and the New Embryology: Springboards for Debate. Sunderland, MA: Sinauer Associates; 2005: 71-79. NRCBL: 14.1.

Greene, Richard A.; Jenkins, Thomas M.; Wapner, Ronald J. The new genetic era in reproductive medicine: possibilities, probabilities, and problems. *International Journal of Fertility and Women's Medicine* 2001 May-June; 46(3): 169-183. NRCBL: 14.1; 15.2; 15.3; 14.5; 14.4; 15.4; 15.1. SC: rv.

Haderka, Jirí F. Assisted Reproduction Law in East European countries = La regulación jurídica de la reproducción asistida humana en los países de Europa oriental. *Law and the Human Genome = Revista de Derecho y Genoma Humano* 1994 July-December; (1): 31-47. NRCBL: 14.1; 21.1. SC: le.

Haker, Hille. Reproductive rights in the twenty-first century. *In:* Widdows, Heather; Idiakez, Itziar Alkorta; Cirión, Aitziber Emaldi, eds. Women's Reproductive Rights. New York: Palgrave Macmillan; 2006: 167-187. NRCBL: 14.1.

Hamdan, Aisha. Assisted reproductive technology. *Al Jumuah* 2005 December; 17(11): 24-32. NRCBL: 14.1; 1.2.

Hanson, Clare. Reproductive futures. *In her:* A Cultural History of Pregnancy: Pregnancy, Medicine and Culture, 1750-2000. New York: Palgrave Macmillan; 2004: 146-175. NRCBL: 14.1.

Harris, Evan. Reproductive freedom and the state. *Reproductive BioMedicine Online [electronic]* 2005 March; 10(Supplement 1): 140-143. NRCBL: 14.1; 1.3.5; 1.3.7;

1.2. SC: le. Conference: Ethics, Law and Moral Philosophy of Reproductive Biomedicine; London, UK; 2004 September 30 - October 1; Royal Society.

Harris, John. Reproductive liberty, disease and disability. *Reproductive BioMedicine Online [electronic]* 2005 March; 10(Supplement 1): 13-16. NRCBL: 14.1; 4.4; 1.3.5; 15.1. SC: an. Conference: Ethics, Law and Moral Philosophy of Reproductive Biomedicine; London, UK; 2004 September 30 - October 1; Royal Society.

Hellsten, Sirkku K. Beyond Europe: rhetoric of reproductive rights in global population policies. *In:* Widdows, Heather; Idiakez, Itziar Alkorta; Cirión, Aitziber Emaldi, eds. Women's Reproductive Rights. New York: Palgrave Macmillan; 2006: 199-213. NRCBL: 14.1; 13.3; 21.1.

Heng, Boon Chin. "Reproductive tourism": should locally registered fertility doctors be held accountable for channelling patients to foreign medical establishments? [letter]. *Human Reproduction* 2006 March; 21(3): 840-842. NRCBL: 14.1; 21.6; 7.3.

Heng, Boon Chin. Handing out free travel and accommodation to oocyte donors in lieu of monetary payment: is this ethically justifiable? [letter]. *Medical Hypotheses* 2005; 66(1): 212-213. NRCBL: 14.1; 9.3.1.

Henifin, Mary S. New reproductive technologies: equity and access to reproductive health care. *Journal of Social Issues* 1993 Summer; 49(2): 61-74. NRCBL: 14.1; 9.4; 9.2.

Howard, Agnes R. In moral labor. *First Things* 2006 March; (161): 9-12. NRCBL: 14.1; 1.2; 9.5.5; 5.3.

Hui, Edwin C.; Zhiwei, Xu. Freedom, autonomy, reproductive rights and contextualism. *In:* Döring, Ole; Chen, Renbiao, eds. Advances in Chinese Medical Ethics: Chinese and International Perspectives. Hamburg: Institut für Asienkunde; 2002: 98-115. NRCBL: 14.1. SC: an. Note: Proceedings of the Second Sino-German Interdisciplinary Symposium about Medical Ethics in China, Shanghai, 19-23 October, 1999.

Human Fertilisation and Embryology Authority [HFEA] (Great Britain). The role of the HFEA. London: Human Fertilisation and Embryology Authority, 1995 January: 5 p. NRCBL: 14.1. SC: le. Identifiers: Human Fertilisation and Embryology Authority.

Human Fertilisation and Embryology Authority [HFEA] (Great Britain). Treatment clinic: questions to ask. London: Human Fertilisation and Embryology Authority, 1995 January: 10 p. NRCBL: 14.1; 14.6.

Inhorn, Marcia C. Global infertility and the globalization of new reproductive technologies: illustrations from Egypt. *Social Science and Medicine* 2003 May; 56(9): 1837-1851. NRCBL: 14.1; 21.1; 7.1; 14.4; 10; 1.2. Identifiers: in vitro fertilization (IVF).

Kaplan, B.; Orvieto, R.; Yogev, Y.; Simon, Y. Social aspects of the new assisted reproduction technologies: attitudes of Israeli gynecologists. *Clinical and Experimental Obstetrics and Gynecology* 2004; 31(4): 285-286. NRCBL: 14.1; 14.4; 14.2; 7.1. SC: em.

Kemelmajer de Carlucci, Aida Rosa. Genetic material and assisted reproduction. Case law reaction (Part I) = Material genético y reproducción asistida. Reacción jurisprudencial (Parte I). *Revista de Derecho Genoma Humano = Law and the Human Genome Review* 1997 January-June; (6): 131-152. NRCBL: 14.1; 15.1; 14.4; 14.2; 21.1. SC: le.

Kennedy, Ian; Grubb, Andrew. Medically assisted reproduction. *In their:* Medical Law. 3rd ed. London: Butterworths; 2005: 1211-1404. NRCBL: 14.1; 15.2. SC: le.

Kissling, Frances. The Vatican and reproductive freedom. *Conscience* 2006-2007; 27(Special European Supplement): 20-22. NRCBL: 14.1; 13.3; 1.2.

Kreß, Hartmut. Gesundheitsschutz und Embryonenschutz in ethisch-rechtlicher Abwägung. Bericht der Bioethik-Kommission Rheinland-Pfalz zum revisionsbedarf von Embryonenschutz und Stammzellgesetz = Health protection and embryo protection from an ethical-legal perspective. Report of the Bioethics Committee of Rheinland-Pfalz on the need to revise the embryo protection and stem cell laws. *Ethik in der Medizin* 2006 March; 18(1): 92-99. NRCBL: 14.1; 15.1; 18.5.4. SC: le.

Langdridge, Darren; Blyth, Eric. Regulation of assisted conception services in Europe: implications of the new reproductive technologies for 'the family'. *Journal of Social Welfare and Family Law* 2001 February 1; 23(1): 45-64. NRCBL: 14.1; 21.1; 1.3.5.

Lillehammer, Hallvard. Benefit, disability, and the non-identity problem. *In:* Athanassoulis, Nafsika, ed. Philosophical Reflections on Medical Ethics. New York: Palgrave Macmillan; 2005: 24-43. NRCBL: 14.1; 1.1.

Liu, Chi-Hong. Impact of assisted reproductive technology on modern medicine. *Journal of the Formosan Medical Association* 2000 February; 99(2): 100-106. NRCBL: 14.1; 12.1; 14.4; 15.2. Identifiers: Taiwan.

Lobo, Rogerio A. ART reporting: the American view. *Human Reproduction* 1996 July; 11(7): 1369-1370. NRCBL: 14.1; 5.3. Identifiers: assisted reproductive technologies.

Lorio, Kathryn Venturatos. The process of regulating assisted reproductive technologies: what we can learn from our neighbors — what translates and what does not. *Loyola Law Review* 1999 Summer; 45(2): 247-268. NRCBL: 14.1; 21.1; 18.6; 5.3. SC: an; le.

Maclean, M. Parenthood should not be regarded as a right [debate]. *Archives of Disease in Childhood* 2005 August;

NRCBL: National Reference Center for Bioethics Literature Classification Scheme   See inside front cover for terms.

441

90(8): 782-783. NRCBL: 14.1; 9.5.7; 1.3.5. SC: le. Identifiers: United Kingdom (Great Britain).

Malek, Janet. Identity, harm, and the ethics of reproductive technology. *Journal of Medicine and Philosophy* 2006 February; 31(1): 83- 95. NRCBL: 14.1; 1.1; 4.4. SC: an.

Manna, Claudio; Nardo, Luciano G. Italian law on assisted conception: clinical and research implications. *Reproductive BioMedicine Online [electronic]* 2005 November; 11(5): 532-534. NRCBL: 14.1; 19.5. SC: le.

Matthews, Colin D. ART regulation: the Australian viewpoint. *Human Reproduction* 1996 July; 11(7): 1365-1366. NRCBL: 14.1; 5.3. Identifiers: assisted reproductive technology.

Maunder, Judith. The Human Rights Act 1998 — legal implications for those engaged in infertility services. *Human Fertility* 2004 March; 7(1): 5-9. NRCBL: 14.1; 14.4; 14.6; 1.3.5; 21.1. SC: le. Identifiers: United Kingdom(Great Britain).

Mayeda, Mayumi. Present state of reproductive medicine in Japan — ethical issues with a focus on those seen in court cases. *BMC Medical Ethics [electronic]* 2006; 7(3): 16 p. Accessed: http://www.biomedcentral.com/1472-6939/7/3 [2006 September 12]. NRCBL: 14.1. SC: le.
Abstract: BACKGROUND : Against a background of on the one hand, a declining demography and a conservative family register system that emphasizes the importance of the blood line, and on the other hand, an increase in the number of people undergoing fertility treatment, the absence of a legal regulatory framework concerning ART matters is likely to result in an increasing number of contradictory situations. It is against this background that the paper sets out to examine the judgements of court cases related to ART, with a particular focus on the legal determination of parental status, and to link these to aspects of the legal and socio-ethical environment within which the courts make their judgements. METHODS : The methods used were thorough investigation of all the court cases concerning ART in the public domain in Japan, including the arguments of the concerned parties and the judgements so far delivered. With the court cases as a central focal point, trends in Japan, including deliberations by government and academic societies, are reviewed, and the findings of surveys on the degree of understanding and attitudes among the people toward ART are summarized. RESULTS : In terms of the judgements to date, the central criteria used by the courts in determining parental status were the act of parturition and the consent of the husband of the concerned couple. The government and academic societies have displayed a cautious attitude toward ART, but the findings of attitude surveys among the people at large show a generally positive attitude toward ART. Attitudes toward the overwhelming importance hitherto attached to the bloodline are also seen to be changing. CONCLUSION : The main conclusion is that in the absence of a legal regulatory framework for ART, there is likely to be an increase in the contradictions between the use of outdated legal precedents and the technical development of ART. Since much of the specialist discussion necessary for the formulation of a legal framework has already been carried out, the speedy enactment of comprehensive and at the same time flexible legislation would be highly desirable, but further wide-ranging discussion involving the general public is likely to be needed first.

McCormick, Richard A. Reproductive technologies: where are we headed? *Loyola Law Review* 1999 Summer; 45(2): 269-285. NRCBL: 14.1; 1.2; 4.4.

McSherry, Bernadette. Posthumous reproduction. *Journal of Law and Medicine* 2005 August; 13(1): 15-18. NRCBL: 14.1; 20.1. SC: le. Identifiers: Australia.

Mepham, Ben. A time to be born? *In his:* Bioethics: An Introduction for the Biosciences. Oxford; New York: Oxford University Press; 2005: 96-123. NRCBL: 14.1; 11.1.

Miller, Robert D. Reproductive issues. *In his:* Problems in Health Care Law. Ninth edition. Sudbury, MA: Jones and Bartlett Publishers; 2006: 737-764. NRCBL: 14.1; 11.2; 11.3; 11.4; 12.4.1.

Minkoff, Howard L.; Berkowitz, Richard. The myth of the precious baby. *Obstetrics and Gynecology* 2005 September; 106(3): 607-609. NRCBL: 14.1; 9.5.5.

Morgan, Rose M. Laboratory babies: new biology, old medicine. *In her:* The Genetics Revolution: History, Fears, and Future of a Life-Altering Science. Westport, CT: Greenwood Press; 2006: 55-69. NRCBL: 14.1; 4.4.

Morgan, Rose M. The Warnock report. *In her:* The Genetics Revolution: History, Fears, and Future of a Life-Altering Science. Westport, CT: Greenwood Press; 2006: 55-69. NRCBL: 14.1; 2.4; 4.4; 18.5.4. SC: le.

Murtagh, Ged M. The limits of reproductive decisions. *Human Studies* 2004; 27(4): 417-427. NRCBL: 14.1; 1.1. SC: an.

New, John G. "Aren't you lucky you have two mamas?": redefining parenthood in light of evolving reproductive technologies and social change. *Chicago-Kent Law Review* 2006; 81(2): 773-808. NRCBL: 14.1; 14.4. SC: le.

Park, Soo-Mi; Mathur, Raj; Smith, Gordon C.S. Congenital anomalies after treatment for infertility [editorial]. *BMJ: British Medical Journal* 2006 September 30; 333(7570): 665-666. NRCBL: 14.1; 15.1.

Pelias, Mary Z.; DeAngelis, Margaret M. The new genetic technologies: new options, new hope, and new challenges. *Loyola Law Review* 1999 Summer; 45(2): 287-306. NRCBL: 14.1; 15.2. SC: le.

Pellicer, Antonio. The Italian law on assisted reproduction: a view from Spain. *Reproductive BioMedicine Online [electronic]* 2005 December; 11(6): 660-661. Accessed: http://www.rbmonline.com/Article/2060 [2006 July 25]. NRCBL: 14.1; 14.4; 1.3.5; 1.2. SC: le.

Rivera-López, Eduardo. The claim from adoption revisited. *Bioethics* 2006 November; 20(6): 319-325. NRCBL: 14.1; 21.1; 1.1. SC: an.

Rogers, Alix. Transplantation of ovarian tissue. *Penn Bioethics Journal* 2006; 2(1): 4p. [Online]. Accessed:

http://www.bioethicsjournal.com [2006 February 21]. NRCBL: 14.1; 19.1.

Romano, L.; de Conciliis, B.; Liguori, M.; Roseto, V. Technical procedure and ethical behaviour in biotechnologies of reproduction = Fare tecnico ed agire etico nelle biotecnologie della riproduzione. *Minerva Ginecologica* 2002 October; 54(5): 403-415. NRCBL: 14.1; 14.2; 14.4. Note: complete text in English and Italian.

Rowland, Debran. The reproductive rights of "new medicine.". *In her:* The Boundaries of Her Body: The Troubling History of Women's Rights in America. Naperville, IL: Sphinx Pub.; 2004: 397-460. NRCBL: 14.1.

Ryan, Maura A. The delivery of controversial services: reproductive health and ethical and religious directives. *In:* Guinn, David E., ed. Handbook of Bioethics and Religion. New York: Oxford University Press, 2006: 385-401. NRCBL: 14.1; 9.5.5.

Schieve, Laura A.; Rasmussen, Sonja A.; Buck, Germaine M.; Schendel, Diana E.; Reynolds, Meredith A.; Wright, Victoria C. Are children born after assisted reproductive technology at increased risk for adverse health outcomes? *Obstetrics and Gynecology* 2004 June; 103(6): 1154-1163. NRCBL: 14.1; 9.5.7; 9.8. SC: em; rv.

Schulman, Joseph D. Further comment on the House of Commons' report Human Reproductive Technologies and the Law. *Reproductive BioMedicine Online [electronic]* 2005 August; 11(2): 158-160. Accessed: http://www.rbmonline.com/Article/1877 [2006 January 22]. NRCBL: 14.1; 5.3; 14.3; 1.3.5.

Shanthi, K. Feminist bioethics and reproductive rights of women in India: myth and reality. *In:* Tong, Rosemarie; Donchin, Anne; Dodds, Susan, eds. Linking Visions: Feminist Bioethics, Human Rights, and the Developing World. Lanham, MD: Rowman and Littlefield Publishers; 2004: 119-132. NRCBL: 14.1; 10.

Sheriff, D.S.; Sheriff, S. Omer. Interventions in reproduction. *Indian Journal of Medical Ethics* 2006 July-September; 3(3): 97-98. NRCBL: 14.1.

Abstract: Assisted reproductive technology has helped many childless couples. It has also raised questions about how appropriate the technology might be in different situations. How we understand parenthood is crucial in taking a stand on such scientific intervention. It is suggested that physicians should decide on offering artificial insemination, surrogacy and in-vitro fertilisation only after considering if the child will have good parents and if there will be legal complications from the use of the technology.

Shultz, Marjorie M. Taking account of ARTs in determining parenthood: a troubling dispute in California. *Washington University Journal of Law and Policy* 2005; 19: 77-128. NRCBL: 14.1; 14.2; 14.4; 1.3.5.

Simonstein, Frida. Artificial reproduction technologies (RTs) — all the way to the artificial womb? *Medicine, Health Care and Philosophy* 2006; 9(3): 359-365. NRCBL: 14.1; 19.1; 15.1.

Simpson, Bob. Localising a brave new world: new reproductive technologies and the politics of fertility in contemporary Sri Lanka. *In:* Unnithan-Kumar, Maya, ed. Reproductive Agency, Medicine and the State: Cultural Transformations in Childbearing. New York: Berghahn Books; 2004: 43-57. NRCBL: 14.1; 21.1; 21.7.

Skene, Loane. Genetics and artificial procreation in Australia. *In:* Meulders-Klein, Marie-Thérèse; Deech, Ruth; Vlaardingerbroek, Paul, eds. Biomedicine, the Family and Human Rights. New York: Kluwer Law International, 2002: 107-121. NRCBL: 14.1; 15.1.

Society for Assisted Reproductive Technology [SART]. Practice Committee; American Society for Reproductive Medicine [ASRM]. Guidelines for advertising by ART programs. *Fertility and Sterility* 2004 September; 82(Supplement 1): S3. NRCBL: 14.1; 9.3.1; 1.3.2. Identifiers: assisted reproductive technology.

Society for Assisted Reproductive Technology [SART]. Practice Committee; American Society for Reproductive Medicine [ASRM]. Revised minimum standards for practices offering assisted reproductive technologies. *Fertility and Sterility* 2004 September; 82(Supplement 1): S4-S7. NRCBL: 14.1; 18.2; 18.5.4; 15.1.

Spar, Debora L. Designing babies: fixing flaws and pursuing perfection. *In her:* The Baby Business: How Money, Science, and Politics Drive the Commerce of Conception. Boston: Harvard Business School Press; 2006: 97-127. NRCBL: 14.1; 4.4.

Spar, Debora L. Where babies come from: supply and demand in an infant marketplace. *Harvard Business Review* 2006 February; 84(2): 133-140, 142-143. NRCBL: 14.1; 1.3.2; 9.3.1; 1.3.5; 21.1; 14.3.

St. Peter, Christine. Feminist discourse, infertility, and reproductive technologies. *NWSA Journal* 1989 Spring; 1(3): 353-367. NRCBL: 14.1; 10; 1.1. SC: an.

Stormann, Michael. Genetics and artificial procreation in Austria. *In:* Meulders-Klein, Marie-Thérèse; Deech, Ruth; Vlaardingerbroek, Paul, eds. Biomedicine, the Family and Human Rights. New York: Kluwer Law International, 2002: 367-376. NRCBL: 14.1; 15.1.

Storrow, Richard F. Quests for conceptions: fertility tourists, globalization and feminist legal theory. *Hastings Law Review* 2005; 57(2): 295-330. NRCBL: 14.1; 14.4; 21.1; 9.5.5. SC: le.

Sureau, Claude. From transgression to pragmatism in reproductive medicine. *Reproduction, Nutrition, Development* 2005 May-June; 45(3): 307-319. NRCBL: 14.1; 11.1; 12.3; 14.5; 1.2; 15.1. SC: le; rv.

NRCBL: National Reference Center for Bioethics Literature Classification Scheme   See inside front cover for terms.

443

Taylor, Bridget. Whose baby is it? The impact of reproductive technologies on kinship. *Human Fertility (Cambridge)* 2005 September; 8(3): 189-195. NRCBL: 14.1; 1.3.1.

Tesarik, Jan; Greco, Ermanno. A zygote is not an embryo: ethical and legal considerations. *Reproductive BioMedicine Online [electronic]* 2004 July; 9(1): 4 p. Accessed: http://www.rbmonline.com/index.html [2005 June 3]. NRCBL: 14.1; 4.4; 21.1. SC: le.

Turner, William B. Putting the contract into contractions: reproductive rights and the founding of the republic. *Wisconsin Law Review* 2005; 2005(6): 1535-1610. NRCBL: 14.1; 11.1; 9.3.1; 1.3.5; 5.3. SC: le.

Turney, Lyn. Paternity secrets: why women don't tell. *Journal of Family Studies* 2005 October; 11(2): 227-248. NRCBL: 14.1; 15.1. SC: em.

Union of American Hebrew Congregations. Committee on Bio-Ethics. A Time to Be Born: Bioethics Program/Case Study: Program Guide I. New York, NY: Union of American Hebrew Congregations, 1998 Fall: 35 p. NRCBL: 14.1; 1.2; 14.2; 14.4; 9.5.7. SC: cs.

Union of American Hebrew Congregations. Committee on Bio-Ethics. Infertility and Assisted Reproduction: Bioethics Program/Case Study: Study Guide XI. New York, NY: Union of American Hebrew Congregations, 1999 Autumn; 95p. NRCBL: 14.1; 1.2; 14.2; 14.4.

van Wijmen, Frans C.B.; de Wert, Guido M.W.R. Genetics and artificial procreation in the Netherlands. *In:* Meulders-Klein, Marie-Thérèse; Deech, Ruth; Vlaardingerbroek, Paul, eds. Biomedicine, the Family and Human Rights. New York: Kluwer Law International, 2002: 275-300. NRCBL: 14.1; 15.1.

Vandervort, Lucinda. Reproductive choice: screening policy and access to the means of reproduction. *Human Rights Quarterly* 2006 May; 28(2): 438-464. NRCBL: 14.1; 9.2; 21.1.

Verlinsky, Yury. Designing babies: what the future holds. *Reproductive BioMedicine Online [electronic]* 2005 March; 10(Supplement 1): 24-26. NRCBL: 14.1; 15.2; 18.5.4. Conference: Ethics, Law and Moral Philosophy of Reproductive Biomedicine; London, UK; 2004 September 30 - October 1; Royal Society.

Weil, Elizabeth. Breeder reaction: does everybody have the right to have a baby? And who should pay when nature alone doesn't work? *Mother Jones* 2006 July/August; 31(4): 33-37. NRCBL: 14.1; 10; 14.4.

Widdows, Heather. The impact of new reproductive technologies on concepts of genetic relatedness and non-relatedness. *In:* Widdows, Heather; Idiakez, Itziar Alkorta; Cirión, Aitziber Emaldi, eds. Women's Reproductive Rights. New York: Palgrave Macmillan; 2006: 151-164. NRCBL: 14.1; 15.1.

Wilkinson, Stephen. 'Designer babies', instrumentalisation and the child's right to an open future. *In:* Athanassoulis, Nafsika, ed. Philosophical Reflections on Medical Ethics. New York: Palgrave Macmillan; 2005: 44-69. NRCBL: 14.1; 14.4. SC: an.

Woliver, Laura R. Adoption and surrogacy: children as commodities, wombs for rent. *In her:* The Political Geographies of Pregnancy. Urbana: University of Illinois Press; 2002: 115-135. NRCBL: 14.1; 4.4.

Woliver, Laura R. New reproductive technologies: medicalization of pregnancy, birth, reproduction, and infertility. *In her:* The Political Geographies of Pregnancy. Urbana: University of Illinois; 2002: 27-44. NRCBL: 14.1.

Zorn, Jean-René. About the HFEA patients' guide to donor insemination and in-vitro fertilization (IVF) clinics — are we crossing the Rubicon? *Human Reproduction* 1996 July; 11(7): 1367-1368. NRCBL: 14.1; 14.4; 14.2; 5.3. Identifiers: Human Fertilisation and Embryology Authority.

RESEARCH *See* BEHAVIORAL RESEARCH; BIOMEDICAL RESEARCH; GENETIC RESEARCH; HUMAN EXPERIMENTATION

RESEARCH ETHICS *See* ANIMAL EXPERIMENTATION; BIOMEDICAL RESEARCH/ RESEARCH ETHICS AND SCIENTIFIC MISCONDUCT; HUMAN EXPERIMENTATION

RESEARCH ETHICS COMMITTEES *See* HUMAN EXPERIMENTATION/ ETHICS COMMITTEES AND POLICY GUIDELINES

RESOURCE ALLOCATION
See also HEALTH CARE ECONOMICS

Anand, Paul. Social choice as the synthesis of incommensurable claims: the case of health care rationing. *In:* Davis, John B., ed. The Social Economics of Health Care. New York: Routledge; 2001: 61-93. NRCBL: 9.4.

Anand, Paul; Dolan, Paul. Equity, capabilities and health: introduction. *Social Science and Medicine* 2005 January; 60(2): 219-222. NRCBL: 9.4.

Ashcroft, Richard E. Fair rationing is essentially local: an argument for postcode prescribing. *Health Care Analysis: An International Journal of Health Philosophy and Policy* 2006 September; 14(3): 135-144. NRCBL: 9.4; 1.1; 9.3.1; 14.4. Identifiers: National Health Service; United Kingdom(Great Britain).
  Abstract: In this paper I argue that resource allocation in publicly funded medical systems cannot be done using a purely substantive theory of justice, but must also involve procedural justice. I argue further that procedural justice requires institu-

tions and that these must be "local" in a specific sense which I define. The argument rests on the informational constraints on any non-market method for allocating scarce resources among competing claims of need. However, I resist the identification of this normative account of local justice with the actual approach to local decision-making taken within the UK National Health Service. I illustrate my argument with reference to the case of provision of In Vitro Fertilisation within the UK NHS.

Baron, Jonathan. Allocation. *In his:* Against Bioethics. Cambridge, MA: MIT Press, 2006: 179-203. NRCBL: 9.4.

Barrett, Ann; Roques, Tom; Small, Matthew; Smith, Richard D. How much will Herceptin really cost? *BMJ: British Medical Journal* 2006 November 25; 333(7578): 1118-1120. NRCBL: 9.4; 9.5.5; 9.1. Identifiers: United Kingdom(Great Britain).

Begley, Sharon. If we must ration vaccines for a flu, who calls the shots? *Wall Street Journal* 2006 October 6; p. B1. NRCBL: 9.4; 9.7; 9.1. SC: po.

Bell, Jennifer A.H.; Hyland, Sylvia; DePellegrin, Tania; Upshur, Ross E.G.; Bernstein, Mark; Martin, Douglas K. SARS and hospital priority setting: a qualitative case study and evaluation. *BMC Health Services Research[electronic]* 2004 December 19; 4(1): 36; 7 p. Accessed: http://www.biomedcentral.com/1472-6963/4/36 [21 November 2005]. NRCBL: 9.4; 9.1; 1.3.2; 9.8. Identifiers: Canada.

Bowen, Deborah J.; Urban, Nicole; Carrell, David; Kinne, Susan. Comparisons of strategies to prevent breast cancer mortality. *Journal of Social Issues* 1993 Summer; 49(2): 35-60. NRCBL: 9.4; 5.2; 9.5.5.

Brennan, F. James. Ethical issues with implantable defibrillators. *Pacing and Clinical Electrophysiology* 2004 July; 27(7): 897-898. NRCBL: 9.4; 9.7; 18.1. Identifiers: Canada.

Callahan, Daniel. Setting policy: the need for full participation. *Frontiers of Health Services Management* 1991 Fall; 8(1): 34- 36. NRCBL: 9.4; 9.3.1; 9.1.

Callahan, Daniel; Topinkovà. Age, rationing, and palliative care. *In:* Morrison, R. Sean; Meier, Diane E.; Capello, Carol, eds. Geriatric Palliative Care. New York: Oxford University Press; 2003: 46-54. NRCBL: 9.4; 9.5.2; 20.4.1.

Carlsen, Benedicte; Norheim, Ole Frithjof. "Saying no is no easy matter" a qualitative study of competing concerns in rationing decisions in general practice. *BMC Health Services Research [electronic]* 2005 November 9; 5: 11p. NRCBL: 9.4; 8.1; 9.8; 7.1; 1.1. SC: em. Identifiers: Norway.

Christian, Michael D.; Hawryluck, Laura; Wax, Randy S.; Cook, Tim; Lazar, Neil M.; Herridge, Margaret S.; Muller, Matthew P.; Gowans, Douglas R.; Fortier, Wendy; Burkle, Frederick M., Jr. Development of a triage protocol for critical care during an influenza pandemic. *CMAJ/JAMC: Canadian Medical Association Journal* 2006 November 21; 175(11): 1377-1381. NRCBL: 9.4; 9.5.1; 9.1; 21.1.

Coates, Jonathan. Patient requests for unwarranted treatment. *New Zealand Medical Journal* 2002 January 25; 115(1146): 23. NRCBL: 9.4; 8.1; 9.2; 9.8.

Cummings, Nicholas A. Ethics and the allocation of healthcare. *In:* O'Donohue, William; Ferguson, Kyle, eds. Handbook of Professional Ethics for Psychologists: Issues, Questions, and Controversies. Thousand Oaks, Calif.: SAGE Publications; 2003: 115-133. NRCBL: 9.4.

Daniels, Norman. Equity and population health: toward a broader bioethics agenda. *Hastings Center Report* 2006 July-August; 36(4): 22-35. NRCBL: 9.4; 13.1; 21.7; 1.1.

Dawes, Robyn M. The ethical implications of Paul Meehl's work on comparing clinical versus actuarial prediction methods. *Journal of Clinical Psychology* 2005 October; 61(10): 1245-1255. NRCBL: 9.4; 17.1; 1.1. SC: an.

DeCoster, Barry. Avian influenza and the failure of public rationing discussions. *Journal of Law, Medicine and Ethics* 2006 Fall; 34(3): 620-623. NRCBL: 9.4; 9.7.

Dillon, Andrew; Littlejohns, Peter; Minhas, Rubin; Twisselmann, Birte. How much will Herceptin really cost? [letters]. *BMJ: British Medical Journal* 2006 December 9; 333(7580): 1219-1220. NRCBL: 9.4; 9.3.1. Identifiers: United Kingdom (Great Britain).

Emanuel, Ezekiel J.; Wertheimer, Alan. Who should get influenza vaccine when not all can? *Science* 2006 May 12; 312(5775): 854-855. NRCBL: 9.4; 9.1; 9.7.

Evans, Daryl. Cultural lag, economic scarcity, and the technological quagmire of "Infant Doe". *Journal of Social Issues* 1993 Summer; 49(2): 89-113. NRCBL: 9.4; 20.5.2; 9.5.3. SC: em.

Field, Charles K.; Kerstein, Morris D. Cost benefit analysis of lower-extremity amputation: ethical considerations. *Wounds* 1993 January-February; 5(1): 10-13. NRCBL: 9.4; 9.8.

Fleck, Leonard M. The costs of caring: who pays? Who profits? Who panders? *Hastings Center Report* 2006 May-June; 36(3): 13-17. NRCBL: 9.4; 9.3.1; 19.3; 9.7; 4.4; 9.5.1; 15.1.

Frank, Robert H. Weighing the true costs and benefits in a matter of life and death (opinion). *New York Times* 2006 January 19; p. C3. NRCBL: 9.4; 20.5.1; 9.5.10. SC: po.

Gamble, Vanessa Northington; Stone, Deborah. U.S. policy on health inequities: the interplay of politics and research. *Journal of Health Politics, Policy and Law* 2006 February; 31(1): 93-126. NRCBL: 9.4; 9.1. Identifiers: United States.
  Abstract: What is the relationship between scientific research and government action in addressing health inequalities in the United States? What factors increase the impact of scientific re-

NRCBL: National Reference Center for Bioethics Literature Classification Scheme   See inside front cover for terms.

445

search on public policy? To answer these questions, we focus on racial and ethnic disparities in health status and health care in the United States. We first review the history of the disparities issue to elucidate how the continual and persistent interplay between political action and scientific research drives government policy. We then analyze two recent government-sponsored reports about racial and ethnic disparities to understand the strategic consequences of issue framing. We draw lessons about how disparities research can have a greater impact on public policy.

Gibson, Jennifer L.; Martin, Douglas K.; Singer, Peter A. Priority setting in hospitals: fairness, inclusiveness, and the problem of institutional power differences. *Social Science and Medicine* 2005 December; 61(11): 2355-2362. NRCBL: 9.4; 1.3.2. SC: cs. Identifiers: Canada.

Gibson, Jennifer; Mitton, Craig; Martin, Douglas; Donaldson, Cam; Singer, Peter. Ethics and economics: does programme budgeting and marginal analysis contribute to fair priority setting? *Journal of Health Services Research and Policy* 2006 January; 11(1): 32-37. NRCBL: 9.4. SC: em. Identifiers: Canada.

Goel, Ashish; Aggarwal, Praveen. Making choices in an emergency room. *Indian Journal of Medical Ethics* 2006 July-September; 3(3): 105. NRCBL: 9.4; 7.3.

González-Pier, Eduardo; Gutiérrez-Delgado, Cristina; Stevens, Gretchen; Barraza-Lloréns, Mariana; Porras-Condey, Raúl; Carvalho, Natalie; Loncich, Kristen; Dias, Rodrigo H.; Kulkarni, Sandeep; Casey, Anna; Murakami, Yuki; Ezzati, Majid; Salomon, Joshua A. Priority setting for health interventions in Mexico's System of Social Protection in Health. *Lancet* 2006 November 4-10; 368(9547): 1608-1618. NRCBL: 9.4; 9.8.

Hasman, Andreas; Hope, Tony; Østerdal, Lars Peter. Health care need: three interpretations. *Journal of Applied Philosophy* 2006; 23(2): 145-156. NRCBL: 9.4; 4.4. SC: an.

> Abstract: The argument that scarce health care resources should be distributed so that patients in 'need' are given priority for treatment is rarely contested. In this paper, we argue that if need is to play a significant role in distributive decisions it is crucial that what is meant by need can be precisely articulated. Following a discussion of the general features of health care need, we propose three principal interpretations of need, each of which focuses on separate intuitions. Although this account may not be a completely exhaustive reflection of what people mean when they refer to need, the three interpretations provide a starting-point for further debate of what the concept means in its specific application. We discuss combined interpretations, the meaning of grading needs, and compare needs-based priority setting to social welfare maximisation.

Hitt, David H. Ethical roles can exist only in an ethical system. *Frontiers of Health Services Management* 1991 Fall; 8(1): 37- 42. NRCBL: 9.4; 9.3.1; 9.1.

Hofmann, Paul B. Ethical decision making requires collaboration between administrators and clinicians. *Frontiers of Health Services Management* 1991 Fall; 8(1): 31-33. NRCBL: 9.4; 9.3.1; 9.1. Identifiers: Hippocratic Oath.

Holm, S. Self inflicted harm — NICE in ethical self destruct mode? [editorial]. *Journal of Medical Ethics* 2006 March; 32(3): 125-126. NRCBL: 9.4; 9.5.1. Identifiers: United Kingdom (Great Britain); National Institute for Health and Clinical Excellence.

Holmberg, Martin; Emanuel, Ezekiel J.; Wertheimer, Alan. Deciding who should get the flu vaccine [letter and reply]. *Science* 2006 December 8; 314(5805): 1539-1540. NRCBL: 9.4; 9.7; 9.1.

Hurst, Samia; Slowther, Anne-Marie; Forde, Reidun; Pegoraro, Renzo; Reiter-Theil, Stella; Perrier, Arnaud; Garrett-Mayer, Elizabeth; Danis, Marion. Prevalence and determinants of physician bedside rationing: data from Europe. *JGIM: Journal of General Internal Medicine* 2006 November; 21(11): 1138-1143. NRCBL: 9.4; 21.1; 9.5.2; 9.5.10; 20.3.2. SC: em. Identifiers: Italy; Norway; Switzerland; United Kingdom (Great Britain). Note: Appendix. Values at the Bedside. A Survey of Physicians Regarding Ethical Dilemmas in Clinical Practice.

Jennings, Bruce. Health policy in a new key: setting democratic priorities. *Journal of Social Issues* 1993 Summer; 49(2): 169-184. NRCBL: 9.4; 1.3.5; 9.1.

Kirsner, Robert S.; Federman, Daniel G. The ethical dilemma of population-based medical decision making. *American Journal of Managed Care* 1998 November; 4(11): 1571-1576. NRCBL: 9.4; 8.1; 9.3.1; 9.3.2. SC: cs.

Kukla, Rebecca. The limits of lines: negotiating hard medicine choices. *Newsletter on Philosophy and Medicine* 2005 Fall; 05(1): 15-19. NRCBL: 9.4; 8.1; 9.8; 1.1. SC: an.

Lamm, Richard D. The moral imperative of limiting elderly health entitlements. *In:* Altman, Stuart H.; Shactman, David I., eds. Policies for an Aging Society. Baltimore: Johns Hopkins University Press; 2002: 199-216. NRCBL: 9.4; 9.5.2.

Lerner, Barron H. Choosing a "God Squad," when the mind has faded. *New York Times* 2006 August; 29; p. F5. NRCBL: 9.4; 9.3.1; 9.5.1; 8.3.4. SC: po.

Lesch, Walter. Coping with limits: two strategies and their anthropological and ethical implications. *In:* Rehmann-Sutter, Christoph; Düwell, Marcus; Mieth, Dietmar, eds. Bioethics in Cultural Contexts: Reflections on Methods and Finitude. Dordrecht: Springer, 2006: 263-273. NRCBL: 9.4.

Lilford, Richard; Girling, Alan; Stevens, Andrew; Almasri, Abdullah; Mohammed, Mohammed A.; Braunholtz, David. Adjusting for treatment refusal in rationing decisions. *BMJ: British Medical Journal* 2006 March 4; 332(7540): 542-544. NRCBL: 9.4; 8.3.4. Identifiers: United Kingdom (Great Britain).

Lopez, Karen Dunn. Ethics of health care reform: should health care be rationed? *In:* Cowen, Perle Slavik; Moorhead, Sue, eds. Current Issues in Nursing. 7th ed. St. Louis, MO: Mosby, 2006: 611-619. NRCBL: 9.4.

Luttrell, Steven. Ethical issues and expenditure on health and social care. *In:* Rai, Gurcharan S, ed. Medical Ethics and the Elderly. 2nd ed. San Francisco: Radcliffe Medical Press; 2004: 51-57. NRCBL: 9.4; 9.3.1; 9.5.2.

Lyall, Sarah. British clinic is allowed to deny medicine; decision on cost has broad impact. *New York Times* 2006 February 16; p. A10. NRCBL: 9.4; 9.3.1. SC: po.

Lyall, Sarah. Court backs Briton's right to a costly drug. *New York Times* 2006 April 13; p. A3. NRCBL: 9.4; 9.7; 9.3.1; 9.5.1. SC: le.

Marsh, Richard. Hard decisions will have to be made: view from intensive care. *BMJ: British Medical Journal* 2006 April 1; 332(7544): 790-791. NRCBL: 9.4; 9.5.1. Identifiers: England.

McConnaha, Scott. Catholic teaching and disparities in care. *Health Progress* 2006 January-February; 87(1): 46-50. NRCBL: 9.4; 1.1; 1.2.

McHale, Jean V. Law, patient's rights and NHS resource allocation: is Eurostar the answer? *Health Care Analysis: An International Journal of Health Philosophy and Policy* 2006 September; 14(3): 169-183. NRCBL: 9.4; 9.2; 9.3.1. SC: le. Identifiers: National Health Service (Great Britain); European Union.
　　Abstract: Historically attempts to use the courts as a means of challenging decisions to refuse NHS resources have met with little success. However two recent developments, that of the Human Rights Act 1998 and the development of European Union law through the application of Article 49 of the EC Treaty have provided the prospect for a challenge to this position. This article examines the impact of a recent case that of Watts v Bedford PCT in which a woman sought to by-pass NHS waiting lists by seeking treatment in France and then claimed reimbursement of the cost of the operation and the possible impact of this case in the context of patients's rights and resource allocation.

McMillan, J.; Sheehan, M.; Austin, D.; Howell, J. Ethics and opportunity costs: have NICE grasped the ethics of priority setting? *Journal of Medical Ethics* 2006 March; 32(3): 127-128. NRCBL: 9.4. Identifiers: United Kingdom (Great Britain); National Institute for Health and Clinical Excellence.

Melnychuk, Ryan M.; Kenny, Nuala P. Pandemic triage: the ethical challenge. *CMAJ/JAMC: Canadian Medical Association Journal* 2006 November 21; 175(11): 1393-1394. NRCBL: 9.4; 9.5.1; 9.1; 21.1. Comments: Michael D. Christian, Laura Hawryluck, Randy S. Wax, Tim Cook, Neil M. Lazar, Margaret S. Herridge, Matthew P. Muller, Douglas R. Gowans, Wendy Fortier, Frederick M. Burkle, Jr. Development of a triage protocol for critical care during an influenza pandemic. CMAJ/JAMC: Cana-

dian Medical Association Journal 2006 November 21; 175(11): 1377-1381.

Mohindra, Raj K.; Hall, Jim A. Desmond's non-NICE choice: dilemmas from drug-eluting stents in the affordability gap. *Clinical Ethics* 2006 June; 1(2): 105-108. NRCBL: 9.4; 5.2; 9.3.1. Identifiers: National Institute for Clinical Evidence (NICE).

Mooney, Gavin. Communitarian claims and community capabilities: furthering priority setting? *Social Science and Medicine* 2005 January; 60(2): 247-255. NRCBL: 9.4; 1.3.1.

Moss, Arthur J. Comments on Ethical Issues with Implantable Defibrillators by F. James Brennan. *Pacing and Clinical Electrophysiology* 2004 July; 27(7): 900. NRCBL: 9.4; 9.7; 18.1.

Nakata, Yoshinori; Okuno-Fujiwara, Masahiro; Goto, Takahisa; Morita, Shigeho. Risk attitudes of anesthesiologists and surgeons in clinical decision making with expected years of life. *Journal of Clinical Anesthesia* 2000 March; 12(2): 146-150. NRCBL: 9.4; 7.1. SC: em. Identifiers: Japan.

Olick, Robert S. Rationing the flu vaccine. *Journal of Public Health Management and Practice* 2005 July-August; 11(4): 373-374. NRCBL: 9.4; 9.7; 9.1; 9.5.1.

Peacock, Stuart; Ruta, Danny; Mitton, Craig; Donaldson, Cam; Bate, Angela; Murtagh, Madeleine. Using economics to set pragmatic and ethical priorities. *BMJ: British Medical Journal* 2006 February 25; 332(7539): 482-485. NRCBL: 9.4; 9.3.1.

Povar, Gail. The bellicose back patient. *Maryland Medicine* 2004 Winter; 5(1): 34, 37. NRCBL: 9.4; 8.1.

Rahmoeller, Glenn. Comments on Ethical Issues with Implantable Defibrillators by F. James Brennan. *Pacing and Clinical Electrophysiology* 2004 July; 27(7): 899. NRCBL: 9.4; 9.7; 18.1. Identifiers: Canada.

Reeleder, David; Martin, Douglas K.; Keresztes, Christian; Singer, Peter A. What do hospital decision-makers in Ontario, Canada, have to say about the fairness of priority setting in their institutions? *BMC Health Services Research [electronic]* 2005 January 21; 5(1): 8; 6 p. Accessed: http://www.biomedcentral.com/1472-6963/5/8 [22 February 2006]. NRCBL: 9.4; 9.2; 7.1. SC: em.

Repine, Thomas B.; Lisagor, Philip; Cohen, David J. The dynamics and ethics of triage: rationing care in hard times. *Military Medicine* 2005 June; 170(6): 505-509. NRCBL: 9.4; 21.2.

Richardson, Jeff; McKie, John. Empiricism, ethics and orthodox economic theory: what is the appropriate basis for decision-making in the health sector? *Social Science and Medicine* 2005 January; 60(2): 265-275. NRCBL: 9.4; 7.1.

NRCBL: National Reference Center for Bioethics Literature Classification Scheme   See inside front cover for terms.

447

Ries, N.M. Legal rights, constitutional controversies, and access to health care: lessons from Canada. *Medicine and Law: World Association for Medical Law* 2006 March; 25(1): 45-57. NRCBL: 9.4; 9.3.1. SC: le.

Abstract: This paper provides a critical analysis of the use of legal claims to assert rights to access health care. Using Canada's system of public health insurance as an example, the paper discusses two significant Supreme Court of Canada cases in which claimants use legal mechanisms to influence health care reform. While one case seeks to expand the range of services covered by public health insurance, the other challenges the government "monopoly" over health care and advocates an expanded role for private health care. These legal claims play out in an adversarial setting where the focus is on the rights claims advanced by individual litigants. Yet, the outcomes of these cases involve broad implications regarding allocation of scarce health care resources and the very structure of the health care system. This paper discusses the benefits and limits of using legal claims in this context and also considers the role of courts in making decisions that may have the effect of constraining policy options available to government decision-makers.

Rivlin, Michael M. Can age-based rationing of health care be morally justified? *Mount Sinai Journal of Medicine* 1997 March; 64(2): 113-119. NRCBL: 9.4; 9.5.2; 4.4.

Scott, P. Anne. Allocation of resources: issues for nurses. *In:* Tadd, Win, ed. Ethics in Nursing Education, Research and Management. New York: Palgrave Macmillan; 2003: 145-162. NRCBL: 9.4.

Seelman, Katherine D. Assistive technology policy: a road to independence for individuals with disabilities. *Journal of Social Issues* 1993 Summer; 49(2): 115-136. NRCBL: 9.4; 5.3; 9.5.1; 9.5.3.

Seidman, Guy I. Regulating life and death: the case of Israel's "health basket" committee. *Journal of Contemporary Health Law and Policy* 2006 Fall; 23(1): 9-63. NRCBL: 9.4; 9.3.1; 9.2; 14.4. SC: le.

Sexton, Sarah. Deceptive promises of cures for diseases. *World Watch* 2002 July-August; 15(4): 18-20. NRCBL: 9.4; 15.1; 9.2. SC: po.

Sheather, Julian. Ethics in the face of uncertainty: preparing for pandemic flu. *Clinical Ethics* 2006 December; 1(4): 224-227. NRCBL: 9.4; 9.7; 9.1.

Sheldon, Tony. Dutch consider excluding costly treatments from health insurance [news]. *BMJ: British Medical Journal* 2006 July 15; 333(7559): 113. NRCBL: 9.4; 9.3.1; 4.4.

Silverstein, Gerry. Preparing for pandemic influenza. *Lancet* 2006 April 15-21; 367(9518): 1239-1240. NRCBL: 9.4; 9.5.1; 7.1. SC: em.

Simpson, Christopher S.; Hoffmaster, Barry; Dorian, Paul. Downward delegation of implantable cardioverter defibrillator decision-making in a restricted-resource environment: the pitfalls of bedside rationing. *Canadian Journal of Cardiology* 2005 May 15; 21(7): 595-599. NRCBL: 9.4; 8.1; 9.8.

Smith, George Davey; Frankel, Stephen; Ebrahim, Shah. Rationing for health equity: is it necessary? *Health Economics* 2000 October; 9(7): 575-579. NRCBL: 9.4; 9.3.1; 9.1; 9.7; 7.1. SC: an.

Smith, Peter C. User charges and priority setting in health care: balancing equity and efficiency. *Journal of Health Economics* 2005 September; 24(5): 1018-1029. NRCBL: 9.4; 9.3.1.

Stanton-Ife, John. Resource allocation and the duty to give reasons. *Health Care Analysis: An International Journal of Health Philosophy and Policy* 2006 September; 14(3): 145-156. NRCBL: 9.4; 1.1; 9.3.1; 9.5.7. SC: an; le. Identifiers: Jaymee Bowen; Child B.

Abstract: In a much cited phrase in the famous English 'Child B' case, Mr Justice Laws intimated that in life and death cases of scarce resources it is not sufficient for health care decision-makers to 'toll the bell of tight resources': they must also explain the system of priorities they are using. Although overturned in the Court of Appeal, the important question remains of the extent to which health-care decision-makers have a duty to give reasons for their decisions. In this paper, I examine the philosophical foundations of the legal obligation to give reasons in English law. Why are judges sometimes supportive of the imposition of a duty to give reasons and sometimes not? What is it about the context of life and death health care allocation problems that makes it unsuitable in their view for such a duty; and is this stance justified? What is it to give a reason for a decision? I examine Frederick Schauer's account of reason-giving in terms of generalisation and commitment and I suggest that it provides an overstated account of what giving a reason commits one to. I go on to examine an idea of judicial creation: that where value judgements are "inexpressible" there is a strong reason not to impose a duty to give reasons on to public bodies. The strongest case for a duty to give reasons is in terms of the value of respect for citizens. I argue that there is nothing in the very nature of reason-giving that ought to preclude the imposition of such a duty in this context, but concede that there is a serious danger of legalism that could result in a hamstringing of health care decision-making. It is up to judges and lawyers to seek to avoid this danger.

Syrett, Keith. Priority-setting and public law: potential realised or unfulfilled? *Medical Law International* 2006; 7(3): 265-279. NRCBL: 9.4; 7.1. SC: le.

Tallgren, M.; Klepstad, P.; Petersson, J.; Skram, U.; Hynninen, M. Ethical issues in intensive care — a survey among Scandinavian intensivists. *Acta Anaesthesiologica Scandinavica* 2005 September; 49(8): 1092-1100. NRCBL: 9.4; 20.5.1; 8.1. SC: em.

Tsuchiya, Aki; Williams, Alan. A "fair innings" between the sexes: are men being treated inequitably? *Social Science and Medicine* 2005 January; 60(2): 277-286. NRCBL: 9.4; 10; 4.4.

Turiel, Judith Steinberg. Health-care rationing: taking it personally. *In her:* Our Parents, Ourselves: How American Health Care Imperils Middle Age and Beyond. Berkeley: University of California Press; 2005: 143-178. NRCBL: 9.4.

Ubel, Peter A. Tough questions, even harder answers [editorial]. *JGIM: Journal of General Internal Medicine* 2006 November; 21(11): 1209-1210. NRCBL: 9.4; 8.1.

Union of American Hebrew Congregations. Committee on Bio-Ethics. Allocation of Scarce Medical Resources: Program Guide VII. New York, NY: Union of American Hebrew Congregations, 1994 Autumn; 61 p. NRCBL: 9.4; 1.2; 9.2; 9.3.1; 7.1.

van der Steen, Jenny T.; Ooms, Marcel E.; Ribbe, Miel W.; van der Wal, Gerrit. Decisions to treat or not to treat pneumonia in demented psychogeriatric nursing home patients: evaluation of a guideline. *Alzheimer Disease and Associated Disorders* 2001 July-September; 15(3): 119-128. NRCBL: 9.4; 8.1; 9.5.3.

Vancouver Coastal Health Corporate Ethics Committee. How to make allocation decisions: a theory and test questions. *Healthcare Management Forum* 2005 Spring; 18(1): 32-33. NRCBL: 9.4; 9.6; 9.8. Identifiers: Canada.

Veatch, Robert M. Allocating health resources ethically: new roles for administrators and clinicians. *Frontiers of Health Services Management* 1991 Fall; 8(1): 3-29. NRCBL: 9.4; 9.3.1; 1.1; 9.1. Identifiers: Hippocratic Oath.

Veatch, Robert M. Reply. *Frontiers of Health Services Management* 1991 Fall; 8(1): 43-44. NRCBL: 9.4; 9.3.1; 9.1. Comments: articles by Paul B. Hofmann, Daniel Callahan, and David H. Hitt, Frontiers of Health Services Management 1991 Fall; 8(1): 31-33, 34-36, 37-42.

Wailoo, Allan; Anand, Paul. The nature of procedural preferences for health-care rationing decisions. *Social Science and Medicine* 2005 January; 60(2): 223-236. NRCBL: 9.4; 7.1. SC: em.

Wechsler, Harlan J. Religious perspectives on access to health care: a Jewish perspective. *Mount Sinai Journal of Medicine* 1997 March; 64(2): 84-89. NRCBL: 9.4; 1.2; 4.4; 9.2.

Wegener, Stephen T. The rehabilitation ethic and ethics. *Rehabilitation Psychology* 1996; 41(1): 5-17. NRCBL: 9.4; 8.3.4; 9.5.1; 8.1. SC: em.

Werntoft, Elisabet; Hallberg, Ingalill Rahn; Elmståhl, Sölve; Edberg, Anna-Karin. Older people's views of prioritization in health care. *Aging Clinical and Experimental Research* 2005 October; 17(5): 402-411. NRCBL: 9.4; 9.5.2; 10; 4.4. SC: em.

Whitehouse, Peter J. The end of Alzheimer disease II: commentary on "Decisions to treat or not to treat pneumonia in demented psychogeriatric nursing home patients". *Alzheimer Disease and Associated Disorders* 2001 July-September; 15(3): 118. NRCBL: 9.4; 8.1; 9.5.3.

Whitney, Simon N.; Ethier, Angela M.; Frugé, Ernest; Berg, Stacey; McCullough, Laurence B.; Hockenberry, Marilyn. Decision making in pediatric oncology: who should take the lead? The decisional priority in pediatric oncology model. *Journal of Clinical Oncology* 2006 January 1; 24(1): 160-165. NRCBL: 9.4; 8.1; 8.3.2; 9.5.7; 9.5.1.

Wikler, Daniel. Polls and focus groups in bioethics: the case of resource allocation. *In:* Lolas Stepke, Fernando; Agar Corbinos, Lorenzo, eds. Interfaces Between Bioethics and the Empirical Social Sciences. Buenos Aires: World Health Organization; 2002: 91-98. NRCBL: 9.4. SC: em.

Williams, Alan. Thinking about equity in health care. *Journal of Nursing Management* 2005 September; 13(5): 397-402. NRCBL: 9.4; 9.2; 9.3.1.

Wiseman, David. Medical resource allocation as a function of selected patient characteristics. *Journal of Applied Social Psychology* 2006 March; 36(3): 683-689. NRCBL: 9.4; 19.3; 9.2; 9.8. SC: em.

Wynia, Matthew K. Ethics and public health emergencies: rationing vaccines. *American Journal of Bioethics* 2006 November-December; 6(6): 4-7. NRCBL: 9.4; 9.5.1; 9.7.

RESUSCITATION ORDERS *See* EUTHANASIA AND ALLOWING TO DIE

RIGHT TO DIE *See* ASSISTED SUICIDE; EUTHANASIA AND ALLOWING TO DIE

RIGHT TO HEALTH CARE

US judge: inadequate medical care for HIV-positive prisoners is a violation of rights. *HIV/AIDS Policy and Law Review* 2004 August; 9(2): 48-49. NRCBL: 9.2; 9.5.6. SC: le.

Abbing, Henriette Roscam. Recent developments in health law in the Netherlands. *European Journal of Health Law* 2006 June; 13(2): 133-142. NRCBL: 9.2; 17.7; 20.5.1. SC: le.

Beach, Mary Catherine; Meredith, Lisa S.; Halpern, Jodi; Wells, Kenneth B.; Ford, Daniel E. Physician conceptions of responsibility to individual patients and distributive justice in health care. *Annals of Family Medicine* 2005 January-February; 3(1): 53-59. NRCBL: 9.2; 8.1; 9.3.2; 7.1. SC: em.

Buchanan, Allen. Philosophic perspectives on access to health care: distributive justice in health care. *Mount Sinai Journal of Medicine* 1997 March; 64(2): 90-95. NRCBL: 9.2; 1.1.

Callahan, Daniel. Equity, quality, and patient rights: can they be reconciled? *In:* Lolas Stepke, Fernando; Agar Corbinos, Lorenzo, eds. Interfaces Between Bioethics and the Empirical Social Sciences. Buenos Aires, Argentina:

NRCBL: National Reference Center for Bioethics Literature Classification Scheme　　　　　See inside front cover for terms.

449

World Health Organization; 2002: 33-36. NRCBL: 9.2; 9.8.

Carrasco, Edgar. Access to treatment as a right to life and health. *HIV/AIDS Policy and Law Review* 2000; 5(4): 102-103. NRCBL: 9.2; 9.5.6. SC: le.

Chassin, Mark R. The health care juggling act: balancing universal access, cost containment, and quality improvement. *Mount Sinai Journal of Medicine* 1997 March; 64(2): 101-104. NRCBL: 9.2; 9.3.1; 9.8; 7.1. SC: an.

Clark, Brietta. When free exercise exemptions undermine religious liberty and the liberty of conscience: a case study of the Catholic hospital conflict. *Oregon Law Review* 2003 Fall; 82(3): 625-694. NRCBL: 9.2; 1.2; 9.8; 9.1. SC: le.

Cochran, Clarke E.; Cochran, David Carroll. Rethinking healthcare policy. *In their:* Catholics, Politics, and Public Policy: Beyond Left and Right. Maryknoll: Orbis Books; 2003: 48-69. NRCBL: 9.2; 1.2; 9.1; 5.1.

Cohen, Frederick H. An unfulfilled promise of the Medicaid Act: enforcing Medicaid recipients' right to health care. *Loyola Consumer Law Review* 2005; 17(4): 375-393. NRCBL: 9.2; 9.3.1; 9.5.10; 9.5.7. SC: le.

Contandriopoulos, Damien; Denis, Jean-Louis; Langley, Ann. Defining the 'public' in a public healthcare system. *Human Relations* 2004 December; 57(12): 1573-1596. NRCBL: 9.2; 9.4; 7.1; 9.1. Identifiers: Canada.

Daniels, Norman. Decisions about access to health care and accountability for reasonableness. *Journal of Urban Health* 1999 June; 76(2): 176-191. NRCBL: 9.2; 9.3.1; 9.4.

Davidson, Rosemary; Kitzinger, Jenny; Hunt, Kate. The wealthy get healthy, the poor get poorly? Lay perceptions of health inequalities. *Social Science and Medicine* 2006 May; 62(9): 2171-2182. NRCBL: 9.2; 9.5.1; 9.5.10; 9.8.

Day, Lisa. Distributive justice and personal responsibility for choices about health. *American Journal of Critical Care* 2006 January; 15(1): 96-98. NRCBL: 9.2; 1.1. SC: an.

den Exter, André P. The European Court of Justice and the Keller case: a bridge too far? *Medicine and Law: The World Association for Medical Law* 2006 June; 25(2): 267-271. NRCBL: 9.2; 21.1. SC: le.

Dow, William H.; Harris, Dean M.; Liu, Zhimei. Differential effectiveness in what are the causes? An example from the drive-through delivery laws. *Journal of Health Politics, Policy and Law* 2006 December; 31(6): 1107-1127. NRCBL: 9.2; 9.3.1; 9.5.5. SC: le.

Fahey, Charles J. Religious perspectives on access to health care: a Catholic perspective. *Mount Sinai Journal of Medicine* 1997 March; 64(2): 80-83. NRCBL: 9.2; 1.2; 4.4; 9.1.

Faria, Miguel A., Jr. Is there a natural right to medical care? [editorial]. *Surgical Neurology* 2005 November; 64(5): 471-473. NRCBL: 9.2; 1.1.

Feldman, Eric A. Patients, rights, and protest in contemporary Japan. *In his:* The Ritual of Rights in Japan: Law, Society, and Health Policy. New York: Cambridge University Press, 2000: 38-52. NRCBL: 9.2.

Fowler, Kenneth P.; Elpern, David J. Perceptions of a patients' bill of rights: a comparison of Massachusetts and South Carolina. *Journal of the South Carolina Medical Association* 1997 January; 93(1): 21-25. NRCBL: 9.2; 7.1. SC: em.

France. Comité consultatif national d'éthique pour les sciences de la vie et de la santé. Inégalités d'accès aux soins et dans la participation à la recherche à l'échelle mondiale: problèmes éthiques. *Journal International de Bioéthique = International Journal of Bioethics* 2005 September-December; 16(3-4): 152-153. NRCBL: 9.2; 18.5.9. Identifiers: France.

Garforth, Kathryn. Canadian "medical necessity" and the right to health. *HIV/AIDS Policy and Law Review* 2003 December; 8(3): 63-69. NRCBL: 9.2; 9.3.1. SC: le.

Gordimer, Nadine. A new racism. *World Watch* 2002 July-August; 15(4): 17. NRCBL: 9.2; 15.1. SC: po. Identifiers: South Africa.

Greaves, David. Contrasting perspectives of inequalities in health and in medical care. *In his:* The Healing Tradition: Reviving the Soul of Western Medicine. Oxford; San Francisco: Radcliffe Publishing.; 2004: 99-112. NRCBL: 9.2.

Gruber, Jonathan. The Massachusetts health care revolution: a local start for universal access. *Hastings Center Report* 2006 September-October; 36(5): 14-19. NRCBL: 9.2; 9.3.1; 9.4.

Haber, Joram Graf. Philosophic perspectives on access to health care: putting the care into health care. *Mount Sinai Journal of Medicine* 1997 March; 64(2): 96-100. NRCBL: 9.2; 1.1; 9.4.

Hagen, Gregory R. Personal inviolability and public health care: Chaoulli v. Quebec. *Health Law Review* 2006; 14(2): 34-37. NRCBL: 9.2; 9.3.1. SC: le.

Hardcastle, Lorian. Comment: Cilinger C. Centre Hospitalier de Chicoutimi. *Health Law Review* 2006; 14(3): 44-50. NRCBL: 9.2; 9.4. SC: le.

Hirschhorn, Kurt. A doctor's perspective. *Mount Sinai Journal of Medicine* 1997 March; 64(2): 105-107.

NRCBL: 9.2; 9.8; 9.3.2. Identifiers: Issues in Medical Ethics — Public Policy.

Hogerzeil, Hans; Samson, Melanie; Casanovas, Jaume Vidal; Rahmani-Ocora, Ladan. Is access to essential medicines as part of the fulfilment of the right to health enforceable through the courts? *Lancet* 2006 July 22-28; 368(9532): 305-311. NRCBL: 9.2; 9.7; 21.1. SC: le.

Joolaee, Soodabeh; Nikbakht-Nasrabadi, Alireza; Parsa-Yekta, Zohreh; Tschudin, Verena; Mansouri, Iman. An Iranian perspective on patients' rights. *Nursing Ethics* 2006 September; 13(5): 488-502. NRCBL: 9.2. SC: em.

Abstract: The aim of this phenomenological research study carried out in Iran was to capture the meaning of patients' rights from the lived experiences of patients and their companions. To achieve this, 12 semistructured interviews were conducted during 2005 in a teaching hospital in Tehran with patients and/or their companions. In addition, extensive field notes were compiled during the interviews. The data were analyzed using Benner's thematic analysis. The themes captured were classified into three main categories, with certain themes identified within each category. The categories were: (1) the concept of patients' rights; (2) barriers to patients' rights; and (3) facilitators of patients' rights. The distinctive themes within each of the categories were identified as: (1a) receiving real care, (1b) focus on the patient, and (1c) equality and accessibility; (2a) dissatisfaction with caregivers, and (2b) specific work environment limitations; (3a) the patient's companion, (3b) a responsible system, and (3c) the public's awareness of rights. Although certain themes identified closely resemble those identified in international patients' bills of rights, the current study focused on themes that are particularly relevant to the Iranian sociocultural context.

Kapilashrami, M.C. Universal access to health — a rights based approach. *Indian Journal of Public Health* 2005 April-June; 49(2): 48-52. NRCBL: 9.2; 9.3.1; 9.1. Identifiers: India.

Keehan, Carol. Those who don't receive medical care. *Origins* 2006 June 22; 36(6): 81-85. NRCBL: 9.2; 9.5.10; 1.2; 9.3.1.

Kinney, Eleanor D.; Clark, Brian Alexander. Provisions for health and health care in the constitutions of the countries of the world. *Cornell International Law Journal* 2004; 37(2): 285-355. NRCBL: 9.2; 21.1; 9.1; 1.3.5.

Kuzu, N.; Ergin, A.; Zencir, M. Patients' awareness of their rights in a developing country. *Public Health* 2006 April; 120(4): 290-296. NRCBL: 9.2; 7.1; 8.1. SC: em. Identifiers: Turkey.

McCarrick, Theodore. Securing decent health care for all. *Origins* 2006 June 15; 36(5): 65-68. NRCBL: 9.2; 9.8; 9.3.1; 1.2.

McDonnell, William M. Will EMTALA changes leave emergency patients dying on the hospital doorstep? *Journal of Health Law* 2005 Winter; 38(1): 77-93. NRCBL: 9.2; 9.5.1. SC: le. Identifiers: Emergency Medical Treatment and Labor Act.

McSherry, Bernadette. The government's duty of care to provide adequate health care to immigration detainees. *Journal of Law and Medicine* 2006 February; 13(3): 281-284. NRCBL: 9.2; 17.7. SC: le.

Menzel, Paul; Light, Donald W. A conservative case for universal access to healthcare. *Hastings Center Report* 2006 July-August; 36(4): 36-45. NRCBL: 9.2; 9.3.1; 21.1; 1.1.

Newdick, Chris; Derrett, Sarah. Access, equity and the roles of rights in health care. *Health Care Analysis: An International Journal of Health Philosophy and Policy* 2006 September; 14(3): 157-168. NRCBL: 9.2; 1.1; 9.3.1; 9.4. Identifiers: National Health Service (Great Britain); New Zealand.

Abstract: Modern health care rhetoric promotes choice and individual patient rights as dominant values. Yet we also accept that in any regime constrained by finite resources, difficult choices between patients are inevitable. How can we balance rights to liberty, on the one hand, with equity in the allocation of scarce resources on the other? For example, the duty of health authorities to allocate resources is a duty owed to the community as a whole, rather than to specific individuals. Macro-duties of this nature are founded on the notion of equity and fairness amongst individuals rather than personal liberty. They presume that if hard choices have to be made, they will be resolved according to fair and consistent principles which treat equal cases equally, and unequal cases unequally. In this paper, we argue for greater clarity and candour in the health care rights debate. With this in mind, we discuss (1) private and public rights, (2) negative and positive rights, (3)procedural and substantive rights, (4) sustainable health care rights and (5) the New Zealand booking system for prioritising access to elective services. This system aims to consider: individual need and ability to benefit alongside the resources made available to elective health services in an attempt to give the principles of equity practical effect. We describe a continuum on which the merits of those, sometimes competing, values—liberty and equity—can be evaluated and assessed.

Newdick, Christopher. 'Exceptional circumstances' — access to low priority treatments after the Herceptin case. *Clinical Ethics* 2006 December; 1(4): 205-208. NRCBL: 9.2; 9.4.

Nussbaum, Martha C. Long-term care and social justice: a challenge to conventional ideas of the social contract. *In:* Ethical Choices in Long-Term Care. What Does Justice Require? Geneva: World Health Organization, 2002. pp. 31-65 [Online]. Accessed: http://www.who.int/mediacentre/news/notes/ethical_choices.pdf [2006 September 25]. NRCBL: 9.2; 9.5.1; 9.5.3; 1.1; 4.4.

Nys, Herman. Comparative health law and the harmonization of patients' rights in Europe. *European Journal of Health Law* 2001 December; 8(4): 317-331. NRCBL: 9.2; 21.7. SC: le.

Piette, John D.; Bibbins-Domingo, Kirsten; Schillinger, Dean. Health care discrimination, processes of care, and diabetes patients' health status. *Patient Education and Counseling* 2006 January; 60(1): 41-48. NRCBL: 9.2; 8.1; 9.5.1. SC: em.

NRCBL: National Reference Center for Bioethics Literature Classification Scheme   See inside front cover for terms.

451

Rolfsen, Michael L.; Bartlett, John G.; Hayden, Frederick G. The ethics of personal stockpiles [letter and reply]. *Annals of Internal Medicine* 2006 February 21; 144(4): 304-305. NRCBL: 9.2; 9.7. Comments: John G. Bartlett and Frederick G. Hayden. Influenza A (HFN1): will it be the next pandemic influenza? Are we ready? Annals of Internal Medicine 2005; 143: 460-462.

Romero-Ortuño, Román. Access to health care for illegal immigrants in the EU: should we be concerned? *European Journal of Health Law* 2004 September; 11(3): 245-272. NRCBL: 9.2; 9.5.10; 21.1. SC: le.

Sabin, James. "Disappointing but fair": the connector's challenge. *Hastings Center Report* 2006 September-October; 36(5): 26-28. NRCBL: 9.2; 9.3.5; 9.4.

Satel, Sally; Klick, Jonathan. Are doctors biased? *Policy Review* 2006 April-May; 136: 41-54. NRCBL: 9.2; 7.1; 9.5.1; 9.5.4; 9.8.

Stoate, Howard. Parliament, ethics and NHS resources [editorial]. *Clinical Ethics* 2006 December; 1(4): 180-182. NRCBL: 9.2.

Suy, R. Governmental proposals concerning the tights [sic; rights] of the patient. Pandora's box? *Acta Chirurgica Belgica* 2000 August; 100(4): 183-184. NRCBL: 9.2. SC: le. Identifiers: The Netherlands.

Tanner, Michael. The wrong road to reform. *Hastings Center Report* 2006 September-October; 36(5): 24-26. NRCBL: 9.2; 9.3.1; 9.4.

Teitelbaum, Joel B. Health care and civil rights: an introduction. *Ethnicity and Disease* 2005 Spring; 15(2 supplement 2): S2- 27-S2-30. NRCBL: 9.2; 9.5.4; 2.2.

Trotochaud, Karen. Ethical issues and access to healthcare. *Journal of Infusion Nursing* 2006 May-June; 29(3): 165-170. NRCBL: 9.2; 9.3.1; 9.4; 1.1.

Tsyboulsky, Vadim B. Patients' rights in Russia. *European Journal of Health Law* 2001 September; 8(3): 257-263. NRCBL: 9.2; 8.3.1; 8.4. SC: le.

Tuckett, Anthony G. Residents' rights and nurses' ethics in the Australian nursing home. *International Nursing Review* 2005 September; 52(3): 219-224. NRCBL: 9.2; 9.5.2; 8.1; 4.1.3. SC: rv. Identifiers: Australia.

White, Katherine A. Crisis of conscience: reconciling religious health care providers' beliefs and patients' rights. *Stanford Law Review* 1999 July; 51(6): 1703-1749. NRCBL: 9.2; 1.2; 1.3.5.

Woolhandler, Steffie; Himmelstein, David U. The new Massachusetts health reform: half a step forward and three steps back. *Hastings Center Report* 2006 September-October; 36(5): 19-21. NRCBL: 9.2; 9.3.1; 9.4.

RIGHTS *See* INTERNATIONAL HUMAN RIGHTS; RIGHT TO HEALTH CARE

SCIENCE AND TECHNOLOGY *See* BIOMEDICAL RESEARCH/ SOCIAL CONTROL OF SCIENCE AND TECHNOLOGY; NANOTECHNOLOGY

SCIENTIFIC MISCONDUCT *See* BIOMEDICAL RESEARCH/ RESEARCH ETHICS AND SCIENTIFIC MISCONDUCT

SEX DETERMINATION
See also GENETIC COUNSELING; GENETIC SCREENING

Allen, Charlotte. Politically incorrect abortion. Boys only. *New Republic* 1992 March 9: 16-18. NRCBL: 14.3; 15.2; 12.1. SC: po.

American Society for Reproductive Medicine [ASRM]. Ethics Committee. Preconception gender selection for nonmedical reasons. *Fertility and Sterility* 2004 September; 82(Supplement 1): S232-S235. NRCBL: 14.3.

Bahadur, G. Concerns of sex selection and regulation in the report on Human Reproductive Technologies and the Law. *Reproductive BioMedicine Online [electronic]* 2005 July; 11(1): 13-14. Accessed: http://www.rbmonline.com/ Article/1839 [2005 December 16]. NRCBL: 14.3; 21.1. SC: le.

Banks, Sarah; Scully, Jackie Leach; Shakespeare, Tom. Ordinary ethics: lay people's deliberations on social sex selection. *New Genetics and Society* 2006 December; 25(3): 289-303. NRCBL: 14.3; 15.2; 1.1.

Bhargava, Pushpa M. Response to 'No country is an island: comment on the House of Commons report Human Reproductive Technologies and the Law'. *Reproductive BioMedicine Online [electronic]* 2005 July; 11(1): 12. Accessed: http://www.rbmonline.com/Article/1863 [2005 December 16]. NRCBL: 14.3; 21.1. SC: le. Identifiers: United Kingdom (Great Britain); India. Comments: Edgar Dahl. No country is an island. Reproductive BioMedicine Online 2005 July; 11(1): 10-11.

Dahl, Edgar. No country is an island: comment on the House of Commons report Human Reproductive Technologies and the Law. *Reproductive BioMedicine Online [electronic]* 2005 July; 11(1): 10-11. Accessed: http://www.rbmonline.com/Article/1830 [2005 December 16]. NRCBL: 14.3; 15.2; 14.4; 21.1. SC: le. Identifiers: United Kingdom (Great Britain); India.

Dahl, Edgar. Preconception gender selection: a threat to the sex ratio? *Reproductive BioMedicine Online [electronic]* 2005 March; 10(Supplement 1): 116-118. NRCBL: 14.3; 10; 15.2; 7.1. SC: em. Conference: Ethics, Law and

Moral Philosophy of Reproductive Biomedicine; London, UK; 2004 September 30 - October 1; Royal Society.

Dahl, Edgar; Hinsch, K.D.; Brosig, B.; Beutel, M. Attitudes towards preconception sex selection: a representative survey from Germany. *Reproductive BioMedicine Online [electronic]* 2004 December; 9(6): 600-603. NRCBL: 14.3. SC: em.

Darnovsky, Marcy; Jesudason, Sujatha. Sex selection. *In:* Mitcham, Carl, ed. Encyclopedia of Science, Technology, and Ethics. Farmington Hills, MI: Thomson/Gale, 2005: 1758-1761. NRCBL: 14.3; 15.2; 14.4.

Dawson, Karen; Trounson, Alan. Ethics of sex selection for family balancing. Why balance families? *Human Reproduction* 1996 December; 11(12): 2577-2578. NRCBL: 14.3.

Dickens, Bernard M.; Serour, G.I.; Cook, R.J.; Qiu, R.Z. Sex selection: treating different cases differently. *International Journal of Gynecology and Obstetrics* 2005 August; 90(2): 171-177. NRCBL: 14.3; 12.1. SC: le. Identifiers: Canada; China; India.

Gentleman, Amelia. Doctor in India jailed for telling sex of a fetus. *New York Times* 2006 March 30; p. A15. NRCBL: 14.3; 8.1; 12.5.1. SC: po.

George, Sabu M.; Bhat, Mari; Grover, Anil; Vijayvergiya, Rajesh; Jha, Prabhat; Kumar, Rajesh; Dhingra, Neeraj; Bardia, Aditya; Anand, Krishnan; Bhopal, Raj; Somerville, Margaret. Sex ratio in India [letters and reply]. *Lancet* 2006 May 27-June 2; 367(9524): 1725-1729. NRCBL: 14.3.

Gilbert, Scott F.; Tyler, Anna L.; Zackin, Emily J. Should we select the sex of our children?: arguments for and against sex selection. *In their:* Bioethics and the New Embryology: Springboards for Debate. Sunderland, MA: Sinauer Associates; 2005: 95-108. NRCBL: 14.3; 14.4; 15.2.

Golombok, Susan; Schulman, Joe; Dahl, Edgar; McLean, Sheila; Doyal, Len; Lotts, Jim; Lockwood, Gillian; Bhargava, Pushpa; McMahan, Jeff; Alikani, Mina; Lotz, Mianna; Te Velde, Egbert; Savulescu, Julian. Discussion (day 2 session 3):ethics of choosing the sex of our offspring. *Reproductive BioMedicine Online [electronic]* 2005 March; 10(Supplement 1): 125-128. NRCBL: 14.3; 10; 13.1; 9.3.1; 15.1. Conference: Ethics, Law and Moral Philosophy of Reproductive Biomedicine; London, UK; 2004 September 30 - October 1; Royal Society.

Grant, V.J. Sex predetermination and the ethics of sex selection. *Human Reproduction* 2006 July; 21(7): 1659-1661. NRCBL: 14.3.

Habgood, John. A Christian approach to bioethics. *Human Fertility* 2003 August; 6(3): 137-141. NRCBL: 14.3; 15.1; 1.2.

Herissone-Kelly, Peter. The prohibition of sex selection for social reasons in the United Kingdom: public opinion trumps reproductive liberty? *CQ: Cambridge Quarterly of Healthcare Ethics* 2006 Summer; 15(3): 261-272. NRCBL: 14.3; 7.1. SC: le.

Kahraman, Semra. Are we talking about the butterflies or a butterfly effect? *Reproductive BioMedicine Online [electronic]* 2005 July; 11(1): 14-15. Accessed: http://www.rbmonline.com/Article/1864 [2005 December 16]. NRCBL: 14.3; 21.1. SC: le. Identifiers: United Kingdom (Great Britain). Comments: E. Dahl. No country is an island. Reproductive BioMedicine Online 2005 July; 11(1): 10-11.

Kumar, T.C. Anand. Legislation on reproductive technologies in India [editorial]. *Human Reproduction* 1996 April; 11(4): 685. NRCBL: 14.3; 1.3.5; 13.3.

Mudur, Ganapati. Doctors in India prosecuted for sex determination, but few convicted [news]. *BMJ: British Medical Journal* 2006 February 4; 332(7536): 257. NRCBL: 14.3; 12.1; 7.4. SC: le.

Pandit, Santishree. Hindu bioethics, the concept of dharma and female infanticide in India. *In:* Sleeboom, Margaret, ed. Genomics in Asia: A Clash of Bioethical Interests? New York: Kegan Paul; 2004: 67-84. NRCBL: 14.3; 1.2; 20.5.1.

Pennings, Guido. Questioning the assumptions in the debate on assisted reproduction: comment on the House of Commons report Human Reproductive Technologies and the Law. *Reproductive BioMedicine Online [electronic]* 2005 August; 11(2): 152-154. Accessed: http://www.rbmonline.com/Article/1852 [2006 January 22]. NRCBL: 14.3; 15.2; 14.4; 5.3.

Puigpelat Marti, Francesca. Sex selection: legal aspects and critical appraisal = La selección de sexo: aspectos jurídicos y valoración crítica. *Revista de Derecho Genoma Humano = Law and the Human Genome Review* 1997 January-June; (6): 85-100. NRCBL: 14.3; 12.4.2. SC: le. Identifiers: Spain.

Rothman, Barbara Katz. The consequences of sex selection. *Chronicle of Higher Education* 2006 February 24; 52(25): B16. NRCBL: 14.3; 15.3; 13.1.

Shenfield, Françoise. Procreative liberty, or collective responsibility? Comment on the House of Commons report Human Reproductive Technologies and the Law, and on Dahl's response. *Reproductive BioMedicine Online [electronic]* 2005 August; 11(2): 155-157. Accessed: http://www.rbmonline.com/Article/1861 [2006 January 22]. NRCBL: 14.3; 15.2; 14.4; 5.3; 21.1.

NRCBL: National Reference Center for Bioethics Literature Classification Scheme   See inside front cover for terms.

453

Sheth, Shirish S. Missing female births in India. *Lancet* 2006 January 21-27; 367(9506): 185-186. NRCBL: 14.3; 15.2; 9.5.5; 12.5.1; 7.1. SC: em; le.

Shinagawa, Shinryo N. Bioethical issues in prenatal sex selection in Japan. *In:* Sang-yong, Song; Young-Mo, Koo; Macer, Darryl R.J., eds. Asian Bioethics in the 21st Century. Christchurch, NZ: Eubios Ethics Institute, 2002: 344-346. NRCBL: 14.3. Conference: Proceedings of the Asian Bioethics Conference (ABC4), held 22-25 November 2002 in Seoul, South Korea.

Wiegle, Thomas C. The biotechnology of sex preselection: social issues in a public policy context. *Policy Studies Review* 1985 February; 4(3): 445-460. NRCBL: 14.3; 15.1; 5.3; 2.2.

Zilberberg, Julie M. A boy or a girl: is any choice moral?: The ethics of sex selection and sex preselection in context. *In:* Tong, Rosemarie; Donchin, Anne; Dodds, Susan, eds. Linking Visions: Feminist Bioethics, Human Rights, and the Developing World. Lanham, MD: Rowman and Littlefield Publishers; 2004: 147-156. NRCBL: 14.3; 15.2.

SEX PRESELECTION *See* SEX DETERMINATION

SEXUALITY
See also MALPRACTICE AND PROFESSIONAL MISCONDUCT

Ahmed, S.F.; Morrison, S.; Hughes, I.A. Intersex and gender assignment; the third way? *Archives of Disease in Childhood* 2004 September; 89(9): 847-850. NRCBL: 10; 9.5.7.

Blustein, Jeffrey; Charuvastra, Anthony. Infertility treatments for gay parents? [letters]. *Hastings Center Report* 2006 September-October; 36(5): 6-7. NRCBL: 10; 14.1; 8.1.

Brookey, Robert Alan. Homosexuality debate. *In:* Mitcham, Carl, ed. Encyclopedia of Science, Technology, and Ethics. Farmington Hills, MI: Thomson/Gale, 2005: 934-935. NRCBL: 10.

Comité Consultatif de Bioéthique de Belgique. Avis no. 24 du 13 mars 2006 sur la proposition de loi relative à ka transsexualité déposée par Mmes Hilde Vautmans, Valérie Déom, Marie-Christine Marghem et M. Guy Swennen [Opinion no. 34 of Mar. 13, 2006 concerning the bill on transsexuality brought forward by Mmes Hilde Vautmans, Valérie Déom, Marie-Christine Marghem, and M. Guy Swennen]. *Bioethica Belgica* 2006 March; (25): 38-40. NRCBL: 10. SC: le. Identifiers: Belgium.

Diamond, Milton; Beh, Hazel Glenn. The right to be wrong: sex and gender decisions. *In:* Sytsma, Sharon E., ed. Ethics and Intersex. Dordrecht: Springer, 2006: 103-113. NRCBL: 10.

Dreger, Alice Domurat. Intersex and human rights. *In:* Sytsma, Sharon E., ed. Ethics and Intersex. Dordrecht: Springer, 2006: 73-86. NRCBL: 10.

Drescher, Jack. Ethical concerns raised when patients seek to change same-sex attraction. *In:* Shidlo, Ariel; Schroeder, Michael; Drescher, Jack, eds. Sexual Conversion Therapy: Ethical, Clinical, and Research Perspectives. New York: Haworth Medical Press; 2001: 181-208. NRCBL: 10; 17.2.

Dyer, Owen. Sex change expert accused of rushing patients into surgery [news]. *BMJ: British Medical Journal* 2006 November 4; 333(7575): 935. NRCBL: 10; 7.4. Identifiers: United Kingdom (Great Britain).

Feder, Ellen K. Doctor's orders: parents and intersexed children. *In:* Kittay, Eva Feder; Feder, Ellen K., eds. The Subject of Care: Feminist Perspectives on Dependency. Lanham, MD: Rowman and Littlefield Publishers; 2002: 294-320. NRCBL: 10; 9.5.7.

Forstein, Marshall. Overview of ethical and research issues in sexual orientation therapy. *In:* Shidlo, Ariel; Schroeder, Michael; Drescher, Jack, eds. Sexual Conversion Therapy: Ethical, Clinical, and Research Perspectives. New York: Haworth Medical Press; 2001: 167-179. NRCBL: 10; 17.2.

Gabard, Donald L. Homosexuality and the Human Genome Project: private and public choices. *Journal of Homosexuality* 1999; 37(1): 25-51. NRCBL: 10; 15.3; 15.10.

Greenberg, Julie A. International legal developments protecting the autonomy rights of sexual minorities. *In:* Sytsma, Sharon E., ed. Ethics and Intersex. Dordrecht: Springer, 2006: 87-101. NRCBL: 10; 21.1. SC: le.

Hester, J. David. Intersex and the rhetorics of healing. *In:* Sytsma, Sharon E., ed. Ethics and Intersex. Dordrecht: Springer, 2006: 47-71. NRCBL: 10.

Howe, Edmund G. Advances in treating (or not treating) intersexed persons: understanding resistance to change. *In:* Sytsma, Sharon E., ed. Ethics and Intersex. Dordrecht: Springer, 2006: 115-137. NRCBL: 10.

Jenkins, David; Johnston, Lon B. Unethical treatment of gay and lesbian people with conversion therapy. *Families In Society* 2004 October-December; 85(4): 557-561. NRCBL: 10; 1.3.10; 17.3.

Ligon, B. Lee. Albert Ludwig Sigesmund Neisser: discoverer of the cause of gonorrhea. *Seminars in Pediatric Infectious Diseases* 2005 October; 16(4): 336-341. NRCBL: 10; 9.5.1; 18.2; 18.3; 18.6.

Månsdotter, Anna; Lindholm, Lars; Lundberg, Michael. Health, wealth and fairness based on gender: the support for ethical principles. *Social Science and Medicine* 2006 May; 62(9): 2327-2335. NRCBL: 10; 9.2; 9.5.1; 9.5.5.

Morland, Iain. Postmodern intersex. *In:* Sytsma, Sharon E., ed. Ethics and Intersex. Dordrecht: Springer, 2006: 319-332. NRCBL: 10.

Murphy, Timothy F. Experiments in gender: ethics at the boundaries of clinical practice and research. *In:* Sytsma, Sharon E., ed. Ethics and Intersex. Dordrecht: Springer, 2006: 139-151. NRCBL: 10.

Murphy, Timothy F. Gay science: assisted reproductive technologies and the sexual orientation of children. *Reproductive BioMedicine Online [electronic]* 2005 March; 10(Supplement 1): 102-106. NRCBL: 10; 15.6; 15.2. SC: le. Conference: Ethics, Law and Moral Philosophy of Reproductive Biomedicine; London, UK; 2004 September 30-October 1; Royal Society.

Ozar, David T. Towards a more inclusive conception of gender-diversity for intersex advocacy and ethics. *In:* Sytsma, Sharon E., ed. Ethics and Intersex. Dordrecht: Springer, 2006: 17-46. NRCBL: 10.

Richters, Juliet. Understanding sexual orientation: a plea for clarity. *Reproductive Health Matters* 1998 November; 6(12): 144-149 [Online] Accessed: http://www.sciencedirect.com [2007 January 31]. NRCBL: 10; 15.1. SC: an.

Schober, Justine. Ethics and futuristic scientific developments concerning genitoplasty. *In:* Sytsma, Sharon E., ed. Ethics and Intersex. Dordrecht: Springer, 2006: 311-317. NRCBL: 10; 9.5.1.

Schroeder, Michael; Shidlo, Ariel. Ethical issues in sexual orientation conversion therapies: an empirical study of consumers. *In:* Shidlo, Ariel; Schroeder, Michael; Drescher, Jack, eds. Sexual Conversion Therapy: Ethical, Clinical, and Research Perspectives. New York: Haworth Medical Press; 2001: 131-166. NRCBL: 10; 17.2. SC: em.

Shaffer, Nancy. Transgender patients: implications for emergency department policy and practice. *Journal of Emergency Nursing* 2005 August; 31(4): 405-407. NRCBL: 10; 9.5.1; 4.1.3.

Sytsma, Sharon E. Intersexuality, cultural influences, and cultural relativism. *In:* Sytsma, Sharon E., ed. Ethics and Intersex. Dordrecht: Springer, 2006: 259-270. NRCBL: 10; 21.7.

Ude-Koeller, Susanne; Müller, Luise; Wiesemann, Claudia. Junge oder Mädchen? Elternwunsch, Geschlechtswahl und geschlechtskorrigierende Operationen bei Kindern mit Störungen der Geschlechtsentwicklung = Girl or boy? — Parents' preferences, choice of sex, and sex reassignment surgery for children with disorders of sex development. *Ethik in der Medizin* 2006 March; 18(1): 63-70. NRCBL: 10; 9.5.7.

Wagner, Gorm; Bondil, Pierre; Dabees, Khalid; Dean, John; Fourcroy, Jean; Gingell, Clive; Kingsberg,

Sheryl; Kothari, Prakash; Rubio-Aurioles, Eusebio; Ugarte, Fernando; Navarrete, R. Vela. Ethical aspects of sexual medicine. *Journal of Sexual Medicine* 2005 March; 2(2): 163-168. NRCBL: 10; 8.1; 2.1; 21.7.

Warne, Garry; Bhatia, Vijayalakshmi. Intersex, east and west. *In:* Sytsma, Sharon E., ed. Ethics and Intersex. Dordrecht: Springer, 2006: 183-205. NRCBL: 10; 21.1; 21.7. SC: em.

Weil, Elizabeth. What if it's (sort of) a boy and (sort of) a girl? *New York Times Magazine* 2006 September 24; p. 48-53. NRCBL: 10; 8.3.2; 8.3.4; 9.5.7. SC: po.

Yarhouse, Mark A.; Throckmorton, Warren. Ethical issues in attempts to ban reorientation therapies. *Psychotherapy: Theory/Research/Practice/Training* 2002 Spring; 39(1): 66-75. NRCBL: 10; 17.3.

Zhai, Xiaomei. How should the issue of homosexuality be regarded in Chinese medical ethics? *In:* Döring, Ole; Chen, Renbiao, eds. Advances in Chinese Medical Ethics: Chinese and International Perspectives. Hamburg: Institut für Asienkunde; 2002: 290-297. NRCBL: 10. Note: Proceedings of the Second Sino-German Interdisciplinary Symposium about Medical Ethics in China, Shanghai, 19-23 October, 1999.

Zucker, Kenneth J.; Spitzer, Robert L. Was the gender identity disorder of childhood diagnosis introduced into DSM-III as a backdoor maneuver to replace homosexuality? A historical note. *Journal of Sex and Marital Therapy* 2005 January-February; 31(1): 31-42. NRCBL: 10; 17.1.

SOCIAL ASPECTS *See* ABORTION/ SOCIAL ASPECTS

SOCIAL CONTROL OF SCIENCE AND TECHNOLOGY *See* BIOMEDICAL RESEARCH/ SOCIAL CONTROL OF SCIENCE AND TECHNOLOGY

SOCIAL JUSTICE *See* RESOURCE ALLOCATION; RIGHT TO HEALTH CARE

SOCIOBIOLOGY

Arnhart, Larry. Aristotle's biopolitics: a defense of biological teleology against biological nihilism. *Politics and the Life Sciences* 1988 February; 6(2): 173-191. NRCBL: 15.9; 1.1; 3.1; 17.1; 3.2.

Abstract: Modern Darwinian biology seems to promote nihilism, for it seems to teach that there is no rationally discoverable standard in nature for giving meaning to life. The purpose of this article is to argue for a revival of Aristotle's biological teleology as a reasonable alternative to biological nihilism. The article begins with Edward Wilson's vain struggle against nihilism. Then it is argued that a teleological understanding of nature is assumed in the practice of medicine, as illustrated by one case from Oliver Sacks' neurological practice. The article then considers the importance of biological teleology for Aristotle's moral and political philosophy, and attention is given to

NRCBL: National Reference Center for Bioethics Literature Classification Scheme   See inside front cover for terms.

455

some points of agreement and disagreement with contemporary sociobiologists. The main part of the article is then devoted to a defense of Aristotle's biology against the five objections that might be made by a Darwinian biologist. Finally, the article illustrates the practical implications of this issue for bioethics by considering the recent work of Engelhardt.

Bluhm, William T. Aristotelian teleology and Aristotelian reason: a commentary. *Politics and the Life Sciences* 1988 February; 6(2): 192-195; author's reply 223-225. NRCBL: 15.9; 1.1; 3.1. Comments: Larry Arnhart. Aristotle's biopolitics: a defense of biological teleology against biological nihilism. Politics and the Life Sciences 1988 February; 6(2): 173-191.

Bokina, John. History and biological teleology. *Politics and the Life Sciences* 1988 February; 6(2): 195-198; author's reply 223-225. NRCBL: 15.9; 1.1; 3.1. Comments: Larry Arnhart. Aristotle's biopolitics: a defense of biological teleology against biological nihilism. Politics and the Life Sciences 1988 February; 6(2): 173-191.

Cornell, John F. On the relevance of Aristotle's bioethics. *Politics and the Life Sciences* 1988 February; 6(2): 199-201; author's reply 223-225. NRCBL: 15.9; 1.1; 2.1; 3.2. Comments: Larry Arnhart. Aristotle's biopolitics: a defense of biological teleology against biological nihilism. Politics and the Life Sciences 1988 February; 6(2): 173-191.

Engelhardt, H. Tristram, Jr. Biological nihilism and modern moral and political theory. *Politics and the Life Sciences* 1988 February; 6(2): 202-205; author's reply 223-225. NRCBL: 15.9; 1.1. Comments: Larry Arnhart. Aristotle's biopolitics: a defense of biological teleology against biological nihilism. Politics and the Life Sciences 1988 February; 6(2): 173-191.

Fortin, Ernest L. Aristotle and the sociobiologists: an old controversy revived. *Politics and the Life Sciences* 1988 February; 6(2): 205-208; author's reply 223-225. NRCBL: 15.9; 1.1; 3.2. Comments: Larry Arnhart. Aristotle's biopolitics: a defense of biological teleology against biological nihilism. Politics and the Life Sciences 1988 February; 6(2): 173-191.

Lopreato, Joseph. Human nature and morality: a sociobiological perspective. *Politics and the Life Sciences* 1988 February; 6(2): 208-213; author's reply 223-225. NRCBL: 15.9; 1.1. Comments: Larry Arnhart. Aristotle's biopolitics: a defense of biological teleology against biological nihilism. Politics and the Life Sciences 1988 February; 6(2): 173-191.

Ruse, Michael. Sociobiology. *In:* Mitcham, Carl, ed. Encyclopedia of Science, Technology, and Ethics. Farmington Hills, MI: Thomson/Gale, 2005: 1820-1823. NRCBL: 15.9; 2.2.

Salkever, Stephen G. Final causes and instant cases: a comment. *Politics and the Life Sciences* 1988 February; 6(2): 213-215; author's reply 223-225. NRCBL: 15.9; 1.1.

Comments: Larry Arnhart. Aristotle's biopolitics: a defense of biological teleology against biological nihilism. Politics and the Life Sciences 1988 February; 6(2): 173-191.

Segerstråle, Ullica. Politics by scientific means and science by political means: Trojan horses in the sociobiology debate. *Science Studies* 2000 June; 13(1): 3-18. NRCBL: 15.9. SC: an.

Sorenson, Leonard R. On the problematic dimensions of bioethics and the pre-conditions of natural right. *Politics and the Life Sciences* 1988 February; 6(2): 215-220; author's reply 223-225. NRCBL: 15.9; 1.1; 2.1. Comments: Larry Arnhart. Aristotle's biopolitics: a defense of biological teleology against biological nihilism. Politics and the Life Sciences 1988 February; 6(2): 173-191.

Wiser, James L. The good life and the life sciences. *Politics and the Life Sciences* 1988 February; 6(2): 220-222; author's reply 223-225. NRCBL: 15.9; 1.1. Comments: Larry Arnhart. Aristotle's biopolitics: a defense of biological teleology against biological nihilism. Politics and the Life Sciences 1988 February; 6(2): 173-191.

SOCIOLOGY OF MEDICINE

Armstrong, David. U.S. seeks to more tightly restrict doctors' billings for medical tests. *Wall Street Journal* 2006 October 23; p. A1, A10. NRCBL: 7.1; 9.3.1; 5.3. SC: po. Identifiers: Medicare.

Cao, Kaibin. Approaches to health in ancient China. *In:* Döring, Ole; Chen, Renbiao, eds. Advances in Chinese Medical Ethics: Chinese and International Perspectives. Hamburg: Institut für Asienkunde; 2002: 223-232. NRCBL: 7.1; 4.1.2; 4.2. Note: Proceedings of the Second Sino-German Interdisciplinary Symposium about Medical Ethics in China, Shanghai, 19-23 October, 1999.

Chaffee, Mary W. Making the decision to report to work in a disaster: nurses may have conflicting obligations. *AJN: American Journal of Nursing* 2006 September; 106(9): 54-57. NRCBL: 7.1; 16.3.

Custers, Bart. The risks of epidemiological data mining. *In:* Tavani, Herman T., ed. Ethics, Computing, and Genomics. Sudbury, MA: Jones and Bartlett; 2006: 153-165. NRCBL: 7.1; 1.3.12.

de Costa, Caroline M. James Marion Sims: some speculations and a new position. *Medical Journal of Australia* 2003 June 16; 178(12): 660-663. NRCBL: 7.1; 9.5.5; 9.5.4; 8.3.1.

Dewey, Marc; Schagen, Udo; Eckart, Wolfgang U.; Schönenberger, Eva. Ernst Ferdinand Sauerbruch and his ambiguous role in the period of National Socialism. *Annals of Surgery* 2006 August; 244(2): 315-321. NRCBL: 7.1; 1.3.5; 15.5; 21.4.

Fuller, Lisa. Justified commitments? Considering resource allocation and fairness in Medecins sans Frontieres-Holland. *Developing World Bioethics* 2006 May; 6(2): 59-70. NRCBL: 7.1; 9.4; 21.1. Identifiers: Doctors Without Borders.

Abstract: Non-governmental aid programs are an important source of health care for many people in the developing world. Despite the central role non-governmental organizations (NGOs) play in the delivery of these vital services, for the most part they either lack formal systems of accountability to their recipients altogether, or have only very weak requirements in this regard. This is because most NGOs are both self-mandating and self-regulating. What is needed in terms of accountability is some means by which all the relevant stakeholders can have their interests represented and considered. An ideally accountable decision-making process for NGOs should identify acceptable justifications and rule out unacceptable ones. Thus, the point of this paper is to evaluate three prominent types of justification given for decisions taken at the Dutch headquarters of Medecins sans Frontieres. They are: population health justifications, mandate-based justifications and advocacy-based justifications. The central question at issue is whether these justifications are sufficiently robust to answer the concerns and objections that various stakeholders may have. I am particularly concerned with the legitimacy these justifications have in the eyes of project beneficiaries. I argue that special responsibilities to certain communities can arise out of long-term engagement with them, but that this type of priority needs to be constrained such that it does not exclude other potential beneficiaries to an undesirable extent. Finally, I suggest several new institutional mechanisms that would enhance the overall equity of decisions and so would ultimately contribute to the legitimacy of the organization as a whole.

Geraghty, Karen. Guarding the art: Edmund D. Pellegrino. *Virtual Mentor* 2001 October; 3(10): 2 p. NRCBL: 7.1. Identifiers: Edmund D. Pellegrino.

Guinan, Patrick. Who is my patient? *Linacre Quarterly* 2006 August; 73(3): 290-292. NRCBL: 7.1; 8.1. Identifiers: Declaration of Professional Responsibility: Medicine's Social Contract with Humanity.

Kagu, M.B.; Abjah, U.A.M.; Ahmed, S.G. Awareness and acceptability of prenatal diagnosis of sickle cell anaemia among health professionals and students in North Eastern Nigeria. *Nigerian Journal of Medicine* 2004 January-March; 13(1): 48-51. NRCBL: 7.1; 15.2; 9.5.1; 1.2. SC: em.

Kaiser, Irwin H. Reappraisals of J. Marion Sims. *American Journal of Obstetrics and Gynecology* 1978 December 15; 132(8): 878-884. NRCBL: 7.1; 9.5.5; 8.1.

Kassirer, Jerome P. Excerpts from: On the Take. *Physician Executive* 2005 March-April; 31(2): 28-32. NRCBL: 7.1; 1.3.2; 9.3.1.

Keith, Stephen N. Collective bargaining and strikes among physicians. *Journal of the National Medical Association* 1984 November; 76(11): 1117-1121. NRCBL: 7.1.

Landman, Willem A.; Schüklenk, Udo. Medecins sans Frontieres under the spotlight [editorial]. *Developing World Bioethics* 2006 May; 6(2): iii-iv. NRCBL: 7.1; 9.4; 21.1. Identifiers: Doctors Without Borders.

Lane, Harlan. Ethnicity, ethics, and the deaf-world. *Journal of Deaf Studies and Deaf Education* 2005 Summer; 10(3): 291-310. NRCBL: 7.1; 21.7; 9.5.1; 15.5. SC: rv.

Mason, Diana J. In their shoes [editorial]. *AJN: American Journal of Nursing* 2006 October; 106(10): 11. NRCBL: 7.1; 20.5.1. SC: le.

Mavroudis, Constantine. Ethical forces that shape a career in surgery. *American Journal of Surgery* 2005 August; 190(2): 319-323. NRCBL: 7.1; 4.1.2; 2.1; 9.8; 8.3.1; 8.2.

Miller, Joan F. Opportunities and obstacles for good work in nursing. *Nursing Ethics* 2006 September; 13(5): 471-487. NRCBL: 7.1; 4.1.3; 8.1. SC: em.

Abstract: Good work in nursing is work that is scientifically effective as well as morally and socially responsible. The purpose of this study was to examine variables that sustain good work among entering nurses (with one to five years of experience) and experienced professional nurses despite the obstacles they encounter. In addition to role models and mentors, entering and experienced nurses identified team work, cohesiveness and shared values as levers for good work. These nurses used prioritization, team building and contemplative practices to overcome obstacles. Entering professional nurses tended to avoid conflict in the work setting. Experienced nurses reported forming teams of decision makers who share similar values to resolve conflict. These findings have implications for nurse education and nursing practice. Reflection on the importance of values and virtue in sustaining good work is important. Entering professional nurses should be encouraged to seek positive role models and reflect on the lessons that can be learned from experienced exemplary nurses.

Nakayama, Takeo; Sakai, Michi; Slingsby, Brian Taylor. Japan's ethical guidelines for epidemiologic research: a history of their development. *Journal of Epidemiology* 2005 July; 15(4): 107-112. NRCBL: 7.1; 1.3.12; 8.4.

Olson, Michael M.; Sandor, M. Kay; Sierpina, Victor S.; Vanderpool, Harold Y.; Dayao, Patricia. Mind, body, and spirit: family physicians' beliefs, attitudes, and practices regarding the integration of patient spirituality into medical care. *Journal of Religion and Health* 2006 Summer; 45(2): 234-247. NRCBL: 7.1; 1.2; 8.1. SC: em.

Pollard, Irina. Bioscience-bioethics and life factors affecting reproduction with special reference to the indigenous Australian population. *Reproduction* 2005 April; 129(4): 391-402. NRCBL: 7.1; 9.5.7; 9.5.4; 9.5.9; 9.5.10.

Prentky, Robert. A sex offender as a patient. *American Family Physician* 2005 October 1; 72(7): 1386, 1389. NRCBL: 7.1; 10; 9.5.7; 8.4; 7.3.

Rennie, Stuart. Is it ethical to study what ought not to happen? *Developing World Bioethics* 2006 May; 6(2): 71-77. NRCBL: 7.1; 9.4; 9.5.6; 21.1. Identifiers: Medecins Sans Frontieres-Belgium; Doctors Without Borders; Democratic Republic of Congo.

NRCBL: National Reference Center for Bioethics Literature Classification Scheme   See inside front cover for terms.

457

Abstract: In the Democratic Republic of Congo, only an estimated 2% of all AIDS patients have access to treatment. As AIDS treatment access is scaled-up in the coming years, difficult rationing decisions will have to be made concerning who will come to gain access to this scarce medical resource. This article focuses on the position, expressed by representatives of Medecins sans Frontieres (MSF), that the practice of AIDS treatment access rationing is fundamentally unethical because it conflicts with the ideal of universal treatment access and the human right to health. The conclusion is that MSF's position lacks coherence, has negative practical implications, and is unfair to governments struggling to increase patient's access to AIDS treatment in unfavorable circumstances.

Rich, Ben A. The doctor as double agent. *Pain Medicine* 2005 September-October; 6(5): 393-395. NRCBL: 7.1; 9.3.1; 4.1.2.

Shalev, Moshe. NIH announces final rules on ethics. *Lab Animal* 2005 October; 34(9): 17. NRCBL: 7.1; 9.3.1; 1.3.2; 1.3.9. Identifiers: National Institutes of Health.

Solbakk, Jan Helge. Cartharsis and moral therapy II: an Aristotelian account. *Medicine, Health Care and Philosophy* 2006; 9(2): 141-153. NRCBL: 7.1; 7.2; 2.3. 1.1.
Abstract: This article aims at analysing Aristotle's poetic conception of catharsis to assess whether it may be of help in enlightening the particular didactic challenges involved when training medical students to cope morally with complex or tragic situations of medical decision-making. A further aim of this investigation is to show that Aristotle's criteria for distinguishing between history and tragedy may be employed to reshape authentic stories of sickness into tragic stories of sickness. Furthermore, the didactic potentials of tragic stories of sickness will be tried out. The ultimate aim is to investigate whether the possibilities of developing a therapeutic conception of medical ethics researched in a previous article on catharsis and moral therapy in Plato may be strengthened through the hermeneutics of the Aristotelian conception of tragic catharsis.

Sypher, Blake; Hall, Robert T.; Rosencrance, Gregory. Autonomy, informed consent and advance directives: a study of physician attitudes. *West Virginia Medical Journal* 2005 May-June; 101(3): 131-133. NRCBL: 7.1; 8.1; 8.3.1; 20.5.4.

Watkins, Peter. On the use of human tissue after death [editorial]. *Clinical Medicine* 2004 September-October; 4(5): 393-394. NRCBL: 7.1; 20.3.2; 19.5.

Zachariah, Rony; Janssens, Vincent; Ford, Nathan. Do aid agencies have an ethical duty to comply with researchers? A response to Rennie. *Developing World Bioethics* 2006 May; 6(2): 78-80. NRCBL: 7.1; 9.4; 21.1; 7.3. Identifiers: Medecins Sans Frontieres; Doctors Without Borders.
Abstract: Medical AID organisations such as Medecins Sans Frontieres receive several requests from individuals and international academic institutions to conduct research at their implementation sites in Africa. Do AID agencies have an ethical duty to comply with research requests? In this paper we respond to the views and constructed theories (albeit unfounded) of one such researcher, whose request to conduct research at one of our sites in the Democratic Republic of Congo was turned down.

SPECIAL POPULATIONS *See* CARE FOR SPECIFIC GROUPS; HUMAN EXPERIMENTATION/ SPECIAL POPULATIONS

SPERM *See* CRYOBANKING OF SPERM, OVA AND EMBRYOS

STEM CELL RESEARCH *See* HUMAN EXPERIMENTATION/ SPECIAL POPULATIONS/ EMBRYOS AND FETUSES

STERILIZATION
See also CONTRACEPTION; POPULATION POLICY

Bastian, Till. Sterilisation zur "Verhütung erbkranken Nachwuchses.". *In his:* Furchtbare Ärzte: medizinische Verbrechen im Dritten Reich. München: Verlag C.H. Beck; 1995: 45-48. NRCBL: 11.3; 1.3.5; 2.2; 15.5; 21.4.

Caetano, André J.; Potter, Joseph E. Politics and female sterilization in northeast Brazil. *Population and Development Review* 2004 March; 30(1): 79-108. NRCBL: 11.3; 9.5.5; 9.3.1; 21.1. SC: an; le.

Czech Republic. Public Defender of Rights / Verejný Ochránce Práv. Final Statement of the Public Defender of Rights in the Matter of Sterilisations Performed in Contravention of the Law and Proposed Remedial Measures. Brno,Czech Republic: Public Defender of Rights, 2005 December 23; 79 p. [Online]. Accessed: http://www.ochrance.cz/documents/doc1142289721.pdf [2006 September 7]. NRCBL: 11.3; 8.3.1; 9.5.4; 9.5.5; 21.4.
Abstract: This statement responds to a complaint that the Czech Public Defender of Rights received via IQ Roma servis on September 9, 2004 relating to "the sterilisation of Romani women." IQ Roma Servis is a non-governmental, non-profit organization based in the South Moravian city of Brno in the Czech Republic. For more information see http://www.iqrs.cz/en/.

Diekema, Douglas S. Involuntary sterilization of persons with mental retardation: an ethical analysis. *Mental Retardation and Developmental Disabilities Research Reviews* 2003; 9(1): 21-26. NRCBL: 11.3; 9.5.3; 2.2; 15.5; 8.3.3; 4.3. SC: rv.

George, Asha. In search of closure for quinacrine: science and politics in contexts of uncertainty and inequality. *In:* Unnithan-Kumar, Maya, ed. Reproductive Agency, Medicine and the State: Cultural Transformations in Childbearing. New York: Berghahn Books; 2004: 137-160. NRCBL: 11.3; 18.5.3; 10; 18.6.

Kaseta, Suzanne. The ethics of population policy: emphasizing female sterilization in the third world. *Einstein Quarterly Journal of Biology and Medicine* 1994; 12(1): 15-20. NRCBL: 11.3; 11.1; 13.3; 21.1.

Krosnar, Katka. Women forced into sterilisation protest to UN [news]. *BMJ: British Medical Journal* 2006 August

26; 333(7565): 410. NRCBL: 11.3; 8.3.4; 10. Identifiers: Roma; Czech Republic.

Lawrence, Jane. The Indian Health Service and the sterilization of Native American women. *American Indian Quarterly* 2000 Summer; 24(3): 400-419 [Online]. http://muse.jhu.edu/journals/american_indian_quarterly/vo24/24.3lawrence.pdf [2007 February 5]. NRCBL: 11.3; 9.5.4; 9.5.5; 8.3.1. SC: le.

Rutkiewicz, Malgorzata. Towards a human rights-based contraceptive policy; a critique of anti-sterilisation law in Poland. *European Journal of Health Law* 2001 September; 8(3): 225-242. NRCBL: 11.3; 21.1. SC: le.

Tännsjö, Torbjörn. Non-voluntary sterilization. *Journal of Medicine and Philosophy* 2006 August; 31(4): 401-415. NRCBL: 11.3; 8.3.1. SC: an.

Abstract: We cannot easily condemn in principle a policy where people are non-voluntarily sterilized with their informed consent (where they accept sterilization, if they do, in order to avoid punishment). There are conceivable circumstances where such a policy would be morally acceptable. One such conceivable circumstance is the one (incorrectly, as it were) believed by most decent advocates of eugenics in the late nineteenth and early twentieth century to exist: to wit, a situation where the human race as such is facing a threat. Perhaps today's Chinese experience with a threat of over-population is a more realistic example? Finally, there is some room for a kind of non-voluntary (and coercive) sterilization without informed consent. I think of people who are severely mentally retarded, and who cannot understand how sexual intercourse relates to conception. If some of these persons are fertile and sexually active, it may very well be the morally right thing to do to sterilize these persons, in their own best interest, but without their consent—if necessary even through coercive means.

Trehan, Nidhi; Crowhurst, Isabel. Minority groups and reproductive rights: coerced sterilisation and female genital mutilation in Europe. *In:* Widdows, Heather; Idiakez, Itziar Alkorta; Cirión, Aitziber Emaldi, eds. Women's Reproductive Rights. New York: Palgrave Macmillan; 2006: 88-108. NRCBL: 11.3; 9.5.5; 9.5.7; 21.1.

Watson, Katie. Sterilization of people with disabilities today. *Atrium* 2006 Fall; 3: 17, 21. NRCBL: 11.3; 9.5.1. SC: le.

SUBSTANCE ABUSERS *See* CARE FOR SPECIFIC GROUPS/ SUBSTANCE ABUSERS

SUICIDE *See* ASSISTED SUICIDE

SURROGATE DECISION MAKING *See* EUTHANASIA AND ALLOWING TO DIE; INFORMED CONSENT

SURROGATE MOTHERS *See* ARTIFICIAL INSEMINATION AND SURROGATE MOTHERS

TECHNOLOGIES, BIOMEDICAL *See* ORGAN AND TISSUE TRANSPLANTATION; REPRODUCTIVE TECHNOLOGIES

TELEMEDICINE AND INFORMATICS

Brent, Nancy J. The use and misuse of electronic patient data. *Journal of Infusion Nursing* 2005 July-August; 28(4): 251-257. NRCBL: 1.3.12; 8.4; 4.1.3; 9.1. SC: le.

Curtin, Leah L. Ethics in informatics: the intersection of nursing, ethics, and information technology. *Nursing Administration Quarterly* 2005 October-December; 29(4): 349-352. NRCBL: 1.3.12; 8.4.

Denton, David R. Ethical and legal issues related to telepractice. *Seminars in Speech and Language* 2003 November; 24(4): 313- 322. NRCBL: 1.3.12; 9.1; 8.4; 8.3.1; 9.8. SC: le; rv.

Dyer, Owen. Patients can't stop their data being put on to NHS "spine" [news]. *BMJ: British Medical Journal* 2006 December 9; 333(7580): 1188. NRCBL: 1.3.12; 8.3.1. SC: em. Identifiers: United Kingdom (Great Britain);National Health Service.

Foster, Andrea L. The bionic CIO. *Chronicle of Higher Education* 2006 June 16; 52(41): A30-A32. NRCBL: 1.3.12; 9.1; 5.1. Identifiers: chief information officer.

Gurwitz, David; Lunshof, Jeantine E.; Altman, Russ B. A call for the creation of personalized medicine databases. *Nature Reviews Drug Discovery* 2006 January; 5(1): 23-26. NRCBL: 1.3.12; 15.1; 15.10; 21.1; 9.7.

Houkin, Kiyohiro; Nonaka, Tadashi; Oka, Shinnichi; Koyanagi, Izumi. Inadequate website disclosure of surgical outcome of intracranial aneurysms. *Neurologia Medico-Chirurgica* 2005 September; 45(9): 448-453. NRCBL: 1.3.12. SC: em.

Hudson, James M.; Bruckman, Amy. "Go away": participant objections to being studied and the ethics of chatroom research. *Information Society* 2004 April-June; 20(2): 127-139. NRCBL: 1.3.12; 18.1; 18.3; 18.6. SC: em.

Kassaw, Kristin; Gabbard, Glen O. The ethics of e-mail communication in psychiatry. *Psychiatric Clinics of North America* 2002 September; 25(3): 665-674. NRCBL: 1.3.12; 17.1; 8.4.

Pezier, Thomas F. Opting in or out of electronic patient records: debate has missed the boat [letter]. *BMJ: British Medical Journal* 2006 July 29; 333(7561): 261-262. NRCBL: 1.3.12; 8.4. Identifiers: United Kingdom (Great Britain).

Pimple, Kenneth D. Ethics at the interface: a successful online seminar. *Science and Engineering Ethics* 2005 July; 11(3): 495-499. NRCBL: 1.3.12; 2.3. Comments: Toby L. Schonfeld. Reflections on teaching healthcare ethics on the web. Science and Engineering Ethics 2005 July; 11(3): 481-494.

Prachusilpa, Sukunya; Oumtanee, Areewan. Internet health ethics. *Journal of the Medical Association of Thai-*

NRCBL: National Reference Center for Bioethics Literature Classification Scheme   See inside front cover for terms.

459

land 2005 January; 88(1): 124-125. NRCBL: 1.3.12; 8.4; 9.8.

TERMINAL CARE *See* DEATH AND DYING/ TERMINAL CARE

TERMINALLY ILL *See* DEATH AND DYING/ TERMINAL CARE; HUMAN EXPERIMENTA-TION/ SPECIAL POPULATIONS/ AGED AND TERMINALLY ILL

TERRORISM *See* WAR AND TERRORISM

TEST TUBE FERTILIZATION *See* IN VITRO FERTILIZATION

THERAPEUTIC RESEARCH *See* HUMAN EX-PERIMENTATION

THIRD PARTY CONSENT *See* HUMAN EX-PERIMENTATION/ INFORMED CONSENT; IN-FORMED CONSENT

TISSUE DONATION *See* ORGAN AND TISSUE TRANSPLANTATION/ DONATION AND PRO-CUREMENT

TORTURE, GENOCIDE, AND WAR CRIMES

Burns-Cox, Christopher J.; Rouse, Andrew; Halpin, David; Mayor, Vidhu; Marshall, Tom. Guantanamo: a call for action: would GMC dismiss a complaint against Guantanamo doctor? [letter]. *BMJ: British Medical Journal* 2006 April 8; 332(7545): 854-855. NRCBL: 21.4; 7.4; 21.5; 7.1. Identifiers: United Kingdom (Great Britain).

Cappell, Mitchell S. The effect of Nazism on medical progress in gastroenterology: the inefficiency of evil. *Digestive Diseases and Sciences* 2006 June; 51(6): 1137-1158. NRCBL: 21.4; 1.3.5; 7.1; 15.5. SC: em; cs; rv.

Clark, Peter A. Medical ethics at Guantanamo Bay and Abu Ghraib: the problem of dual loyalty. *Journal of Law, Medicine and Ethics* 2006 Fall; 34(3): 570-580. NRCBL: 21.4; 18.5.5; 18.5.8; 8.1; 4.1.2.

Abstract: Although knowledge of torture and physical and psy-chological abuse was widespread at both the Guantanamo Bay detention facility and Abu Ghraib prison in Iraq, and known to medical personnel, there was no official report before the Janu-ary 2004 Army investigation of military health personnel re-porting abuse, degradation or signs of torture. Military medical personnel are placed in a position of a "dual loyalty" conflict. They have to balance the medical needs of their patients, who happen to be detainees, with their military duty to their em-ployer. The United States military medical system failed to pro-tect detainee's human rights, violated the basic principles of medical ethics and ignored the basic tenets of medical profes-sionalism.

Green, David A.; Nierhoff, Sabine. When doctors partic-ipate in torture. *Indian Journal of Medical Ethics* 2006 Oc-tober-December; 3(4): 128-129. NRCBL: 21.4.

Jeffcoate, William J. Should eponyms be actively de-tached from diseases? [editorial]. *Lancet* 2006 April 22-28; 367(9519): 1296-1297. NRCBL: 21.4; 7.1. Identi-fiers: Hans Reiter; Friedrich Wegener.

Jesani, Amar. Medical professionals and interrogation: lies about finding the "truth" [editorial]. *Indian Journal of Medical Ethics* 2006 October-December; 3(4): 116-117. NRCBL: 21.4; 17.1; 17.4; 21.1; 4.4.

Justo, Luis. Doctors, interrogation, and torture [editorial]. *BMJ: British Medical Journal* 2006 June 24; 332(7556): 1462. NRCBL: 21.4; 22.1; 7.4.

Keller, Allen S. Torture in Abu Ghraib. *Perspectives in Bi-ology and Medicine* 2006 Autumn; 49(4): 553-569. NRCBL: 21.4; 1.3.5. SC: cs.

Kottow, Michael H. Letter to the editor: a commentary on M.K. Wynia's "Consequentialism and Harsh Interroga-tions". *American Journal of Bioethics [Online]*. 2006 March-April; 6(2): W36. NRCBL: 21.4; 21.2; 9.1. Com-ments: M.K. Wynia. Consequentialism and harsh interro-gations. American Journal of Bioethics 2005; 5(1): 4-6.

Lagerwey, Mary D. The Third Reich in the pages of the American Journal of Nursing, 1932-1950. *Nursing History Review* 2006; 14: 59-87. NRCBL: 21.4; 2.2; 4.1.3; 1.3.7.

Langbein, Hermann. Dr. Wirths. *In his:* People in Auschwitz. Chapel Hill: The University of North Carolina Press; 2004: 365-385. NRCBL: 21.4; 7.4.

Langbein, Hermann. Physicians in the SS. *In his:* People in Auschwitz. Chapel Hill: The University of North Carolina Press; 2004: 333-364. NRCBL: 21.4; 7.4; 18.5.5.

Lee, Philip R.; Conant, Marcus; Jonsen, Albert R.; Heilig, Steve. Participation in torture and interrogation: an inexcusable breach of medical ethics. *CQ: Cambridge Quarterly of Healthcare Ethics* 2006 Spring; 15(2): 202-203. NRCBL: 21.4; 4.1.2; 1.3.1. SC: le.

Matthews, Richard S. Indecent medicine: in defense of the absolute prohibition against physician participation in torture. *American Journal of Bioethics [Online]*. 2006 May-June; 6(3): W34-W44. NRCBL: 21.4; 1.1; 4.1.2.

Miles, Steven H. A battle for the soul of medicine: medical complicity in torture. *Atrium* 2006 Fall; 3: 7. NRCBL: 21.4; 4.1.2.

Miles, Steven H. Medical investigations of homicides of prisoners of war in Iraq and Afghanistan. *Newsletter on Philosophy and Medicine* 2005 Fall; 05(1): 5-14. NRCBL: 21.4; 1.3.5; 20.1; 21.2.

Nicosia, Francis R. Nazi medicine. *In:* Mitcham, Carl, ed. Encyclopedia of Science, Technology, and Ethics. Farmington Hills, MI: Thomson/Gale, 2005: 1301-1303. NRCBL: 21.4; 15.5; 2.2.

Nie, Jing-Bao. The United States cover-up of Japanese wartime medical atrocities: complicity committed in the national interest and two proposals for contemporary action. *American Journal of Bioethics [Online].* 2006 May-June; 6(3): W21-W33. NRCBL: 21.4; 21.3; 18.5.8; 18.5.9.

Nötzoldt, Peter; Walther, Peter Th. The Prussian Academy of Sciences during the Third Reich. *Minerva: A Review of Science, Learning and Policy* 2004; 42(4): 421-444. NRCBL: 21.4; 5.1; 1.3.3.

O'Mathúna, Dónal P. Human dignity in the Nazi era: implications for contemporary bioethics [debate]. *BMC Medical Ethics* 2006; 7(2): 12 p. [Online]. Accessed: http://www.biomedcentral.com/bmcmedethics/ [2006 September 7]. NRCBL: 21.4; 4.4; 2.1; 15.5; 15.9.

Abstract: BACKGROUND : The justification for Nazi programs involving involuntary euthanasia, forced sterilisation, eugenics and human experimentation were strongly influenced by views about human dignity. The historical development of these views should be examined today because discussions of human worth and value are integral to medical ethics and bioethics. We should learn lessons from how human dignity came to be so distorted to avoid repetition of similar distortions. DISCUSSION: Social Darwinism was foremost amongst the philosophies impacting views of human dignity in the decades leading up to Nazi power in Germany. Charles Darwin's evolutionary theory was quickly applied to human beings and social structure. The term 'survival of the fittest' was coined and seen to be applicable to humans. Belief in the inherent dignity of all humans was rejected by social Darwinists. Influential authors of the day proclaimed that an individual's worth and value were to be determined functionally and materialistically. The popularity of such views ideologically prepared German doctors and nurses to accept Nazi social policies promoting survival of only the fittest humans. A historical survey reveals five general presuppositions that strongly impacted medical ethics in the Nazi era. These same five beliefs are being promoted in different ways in contemporary bioethical discourse. Ethical controversies surrounding human embryos revolve around determinations of their moral status. Economic pressures force individuals and societies to examine whether some people's lives are no longer worth living. Human dignity is again being seen as a relative trait found in certain humans, not something inherent. These views strongly impact what is taken to be acceptable within medical ethics. SUMMARY : Five beliefs central to social Darwinism will be examined in light of their influence on current discussions in medical ethics and bioethics. Acceptance of these during the Nazi era proved destructive to many humans. Their widespread acceptance today would similarly lead to much human death and suffering. A different ethic is needed which views human dignity as inherent to all human individuals.

Proctor, Robert N. Nazi medical ethics: ordinary doctors? *In:* Beam, Thomas E.; Sparacino, Linette R.; Pellegrino, Edmund D.; Hartle, Anthony E.; Howe, Edmund G., eds. Military Medical Ethics. Volume 2. Washington, DC: TMM Publications, Borden Institute, Walter Reed Army Medical Center; 2003: 403-436. NRCBL: 21.4; 15.5; 1.3.5.

Redies, Christoph; Viebig, Michael; Zimmermann, Susanne; Fröber, Rosemarie. Origin of corpses received

by the anatomical institute at the University of Jena during the Nazi regime. *Anatomical Record (Part B, New Anatomy)* 2005 July; 285B(1): 6-10. NRCBL: 21.4; 7.2; 20.3.2. SC: em.

Reuben, Adrian. First do no harm. *Hepatology* 2006 February; 43(2, Supplement 1): S243-S249. NRCBL: 21.4; 18.5.1; 18.3. Identifiers: Hans Eppinger; Germany.

Roelcke, Volker; Hohendorf, Gerrit; Rotzoll, Maike. Psychiatric research and 'euthanasia': the case of the psychiatric department at the University of Heidelberg, 1941-1945. *History of Psychiatry* 1994 December; 5(4: 20): 517-532. NRCBL: 21.4; 20.5.1; 20.5.2; 17.1; 2.2.

Schroeder, Doris. A child's life or a "little bit of torture"? State-sanctioned violence and dignity. *CQ: Cambridge Quarterly of Healthcare Ethics* 2006 Spring; 15(2): 188-201. NRCBL: 21.4; 4.4; 1.3.5; 1.1. SC: le; cs.

Schröter, Sonja. Die Heil- und Pflegeanstalt Waldheim in Sachsen 1939-1945. *In her:* Psychiatrie in Waldheim/ Sachsen (1716-1946): ein Beitrag zur Geschichte der forensischen Psychiatrie in Deutschland. Frankfurt am Main: Mabuse; 2003: 121-192. NRCBL: 21.4; 20.5.1; 1.3.5; 2.2; 15.5.

Sharfstein, Steven S. American Psychiatric Association clarifies its position on human rights [letter]. *BMJ: British Medical Journal* 2006 July 8; 333(7558): 97-98. NRCBL: 21.4; 7.4; 17.1; 21.1.

Stein, Ben. When scarcity leads to madness. *New York Times* 2006 September 17; p. BU4. NRCBL: 21.4; 1.3.5. SC: po.

Strous, Rael D. Nazi euthanasia of the mentally ill at Hadamar. *American Journal of Psychiatry* 2006 January; 163(1): 27. NRCBL: 21.4; 20.5.1; 17.1; 15.5.

Wasti, Sabahat A.; Bhatti, Sajid Z. Guantanamo: a call for action: doctors should not treat detainees only to render them fit to further abuse [letter]. *BMJ: British Medical Journal* 2006 April 8; 332(7545): 855. NRCBL: 21.4; 21.5; 7.1.

Weiss, Sheila. "Essay Review: Racial Science and Genetics at the Kaiser Wilhelm Society". *Journal of the History of Biology* 2005 Summer; 38(2): 367-379. NRCBL: 21.4; 15.11; 15.5; 2.2.

Wilks, Michael. Guantanamo: a call for action [editorial]. *BMJ: British Medical Journal* 2006 March 11; 332(7541): 560-561. NRCBL: 21.4; 21.5; 7.4; 8.3.4.

Woywodt, Alexander; Haubitz, Marion; Haller, Hermann; Matteson, Eric L. Wegener's granulomatosis. *Lancet* 2006 April 22-28; 367(9519): 1362-1366. NRCBL: 21.4; 7.1. Identifiers: National Socialist Party.

Wynia, Matthew K. Consequentialism and outrageous options: response to commentary on "Consequentialism

NRCBL: National Reference Center for Bioethics Literature Classification Scheme　　　See inside front cover for terms.

461

and Harsh Interrogations". *American Journal of Bioethics [Online]*. 2006 March-April; 6(2): W37. NRCBL: 21.4; 21.3; 9.1; 2.1. Comments: Michael H. Kottow. Letter to the Editor: A Commentary on M.K. Wynia's "Consequentialism and Harsh Interrogations". American Journal of Bioethics [Online]. 2006 March- April; 6(2): W36.

Zonana, Howard. Torture and interrogation by psychiatrists. *American Academy of Psychiatry and the Law* 2006 September; 31(3): 5-9. NRCBL: 21.4; 17.1; 8.

TRANSPLANTATION *See* ORGAN AND TISSUE TRANSPLANTATION

TREATMENT REFUSAL
See also ADVANCE DIRECTIVES; EUTHANASIA AND ALLOWING TO DIE; INFORMED CONSENT

Archibold, Randal C. Killings loom over debate on treating mentally ill; New Mexico considers commitment law. *New York Times* 2006 February 8; p. A16. NRCBL: 8.3.4; 17.1. SC: po; le.

Beezhold, Julian; Foëx, B.A. Jehovah's Witnesses in A&E [editorial]. *Emergency Medicine Journal* 2005 December; 22(12): 838. NRCBL: 8.3.4; 19.4; 1.2; 8.3.2.

Bernheim, Susannah M.; Ross, Joseph S.; Bradley, Elizabeth H.; Quigley, Catherine; Atherton, Janet; Rylands, Alison; Spiess, Jeffrey L.; Tomm, Lisa; Brummel-Smith, Kenneth; Spike, Jeffrey; Carrese, Joseph. Refusal of care by patients [letters and reply]. *JAMA: The Journal of the American Medical Association* 2006 December 27; 296(24): 2921-2923. NRCBL: 8.3.4.

Brewster, William D. In re E.G., a Minor: death over life: a judicial trend continues as the Illinois Supreme Court grants minors the right to refuse life-saving medical treatment. *John Marshall Law Review* 1990 Summer; 23(4): 771-786. NRCBL: 8.3.4; 8.3.2; 19.4; 1.2. SC: le.

Cantor, Julie D. Of pills and needles: involuntarily medicating the psychotic inmate when execution looms. *Indiana Health Law Review* 2005; 2(1): 117-170. NRCBL: 8.3.4; 7.1; 1.3.5; 4.3; 17.4. SC: le; an.

Caplan, Arthur. The ethics of forced drug treatment for addicts. *Free Inquiry* 2006 December-2007 January; 27(1): 21-22. NRCBL: 8.3.4; 9.5.9; 9.7.

Carey, Ruth. Ontario: people can now apply for forced HIV testing in certain situations [news]. *HIV/AIDS Policy and Law Review* 2003 December; 8(3): 25-27. NRCBL: 8.3.4; 19.4. SC: le.

Carrese, Joseph A. Refusal of care: patients' well-being and physicians' ethical obligations. *JAMA: the Journal of the American Medical Association* 2006 August 9; 296(6): 691-695. NRCBL: 8.3.4; 8.1; 9.6.

Dagg, Paul. Actual case outcome. *Journal of Ethics in Mental Health* 2006 November; 1(1): E10, 1 p. NRCBL: 8.3.4; 9.7; 17.1.

Dagg, Paul. John has hepatitis and schizophrenia. *Journal of Ethics in Mental Health* 2006 November; 1(1): E7, 1 p. NRCBL: 8.3.4; 17.1; 9.7. SC: cs.

Dimond, Bridgit. What is the law if a patient refuses treatment based on the nurse's race? *British Journal of Nursing* 2006 October 26-November 8; 15(19): 1077-1078. NRCBL: 8.3.4; 21.1; 7.1. SC: le.

Dudzinski, Denise M.; Shannon, Sarah E. Competent patients' refusal of nursing care. *Nursing Ethics* 2006 November; 13(6): 608-621. NRCBL: 8.3.4; 20.5.1. SC: cs.

Elliott, Richard. Reform MP proposes compulsory testing. *Canadian HIV/AIDS Policy and Law Newsletter* 2000 Spring-Summer; 5(2-3): 25-27. NRCBL: 8.3.4; 9.5.6; 9.5.1; 8.4. SC: le.

Fischer, Jennifer. Comparative look at the right to refuse treatment for involuntarily hospitalized persons with a mental illness. *Hastings International and Comparative Law Review* 2006 Winter; 29(2): 153-186. NRCBL: 8.3.4; 17.7; 8.3.3; 4.3. SC: le.

Glannon, Walter. 2. Commentary on "John". *Journal of Ethics in Mental Health* 2006 November; 1(1): E9, 1 p. NRCBL: 8.3.4; 17.4; 17.1. Comments: Paul Dagg. John has hepatitis and schizophrenia. Journal of Ethics in Mental Health 2006 November; 1(1): E7.

Green, Stephen A.; Bloch, Sidney. 1. Joint commentary on "John". *Journal of Ethics in Mental Health* 2006 November; 1(1): E8, 1 p. NRCBL: 8.3.4; 17.7; 17.4. Comments: Paul Dagg. John has hepatitis and schizophrenia. Journal of Ethics in Mental Health 2006 November; 1(1): E7.

Griffith, Richard. Immunisation and the law: compulsion or parental choice? *Nursing Standard* 2003 November 19; 18(10): 39-41. NRCBL: 8.3.4; 8.3.2; 1.3.5; 9.5.1; 9.5.7; 9.7. SC: le. Identifiers: United Kingdom (Great Britain).

Herczeg, L.; Szokol, J.; Horvath, G.; Vaszily, M.; Peterffy, A. Open-heart surgery and Jehovah's Witnesses. *Medicine and Law: The World Association for Medical Law* 2006 June; 25(2): 233-239. NRCBL: 8.3.4; 1.2; 19.4. SC: em.
Abstract: The religious community of Jehovah's Witnesses holds that blood transfusion is against God's law. Therefore, surgical treatment of Jehovah's Witnesses is a great challenge for every surgeon, especially for cardiac surgeons because blood transfusion is frequently needed during such operations. In this study we summarize the experience with Jehovah's Witnesses who have undergone open-heart surgery in Debrecen from 1989 to 1999 due to various cardiac diseases. Applying a complex surgical procedure developed by the authors to minimize blood loss during operation, preserved blood products were omitted. Three patients out of twenty-four died during the postoperative period. The twenty-one longtime survivors

showed significant improvement in their clinical stage during the mean follow up of 37.6 months. More and more operations are done successfully without blood or preserved blood products worldwide, so it could be said that nowadays surgical treatment of Jehovah's Witnesses has a lower risk than before.

Huggins, Eily S. Assisted outpatient treatment: an unconstitutional invasion of protected rights or a necessary government safeguard? *Journal of Legislation* 2004; 30: 305-325. NRCBL: 8.3.4; 8.3.3; 17.1. SC: an; le.

Hung, T.; Tong, M.; van Hasselt, C.A. Jehovah's Witnesses and surgery. *Hong Kong Medical Journal* 2005 August; 11(4): 311-312. NRCBL: 8.3.4; 19.4; 1.2.

Kee, Pei-Teing. Refusal to consent to treatment on religious grounds. *E Law: Murdoch University Electronic Journal of Law* 1995 July; 2(2): 16 p. [Online]. Accessed: http://www.murdoch.edu.au/elaw/issues/v2n2/kee221.html [2006 June 29]. NRCBL: 8.3.4; 1.2. SC: le.

Malecha, Wayne. Faith healing exemptions to child protection laws. *Journal of Legislation* 1985; 12: 243-263. NRCBL: 8.3.4; 1.2; 8.3.2. SC: le.

Markon, Jerry. Fight over a child's care ends in compromise; Va. judge's order could have forced teen to get chemotherapy. *Washington Post* 2006 August 17; p. A1, A13. NRCBL: 8.3.4; 8.3.2. SC: po. Identifiers: Virginia; Starchild Abraham Cherrix.

Martins, David S. Compliance rhetoric and the impoverishment of context. *Communication Theory* 2005 February; 15(1): 59-77. NRCBL: 8.3.4; 15.1; 4.4.

Nenner, F. A patient's choice [letter]. *Journal of Medical Ethics* 2006 September; 32(9): 554-555. NRCBL: 8.3.4; 20.5.4.

Olsen, Douglas P. Should RNs be forced to get the flu vaccine? *AJN: American Journal of Nursing* 2006 October; 106(10): 76-80. NRCBL: 8.3.4; 16.3; 9.1.

Sedgwick, Emma. Patients' right to refuse treatment [editorial]. *Hospital Medicine* 2002 April; 63(4): 196-197. NRCBL: 8.3.4; 20.5.4. SC: le.

Seelig, Michelle D.; Gelberg, Lillian; Tavrow, Paula; Lee, Martin; Rubenstein, Lisa V. Determinants of physician unwillingness to offer medical abortion using mifepristone. *Women's Health Issues* 2006 January-February; 16(1): 14-21. NRCBL: 8.3.4; 12.4.3; 9.7; 9.2; 7.2. SC: em.

Abstract: PURPOSE: We sought to identify factors associated with contemplating versus not contemplating offering medical abortion with mifepristone among physicians not opposed to it. METHODS: We analyzed data from a Kaiser Family Foundation survey of a nationally representative sample of 790 American obstetrician/gynecologists and primary care physicians. Our study sample consisted of 419 physicians who were not personally opposed to medical abortion and could be classified as not actively considering (precontemplation) or actively considering (contemplation) offering mifepristone. We conducted multivariate logistic regression to predict being unlikely to offer mifepristone (i.e., in the precontemplation stage of change). PRINCIPAL FINDINGS: In 2001, 1 year after U.S. Food and Drug Administration (FDA) approval, 5% of physicians surveyed were offering mifepristone. Among the 750 physicians not offering mifepristone, 57% were not opposed. Of those not opposed, 74% reported that they were unlikely to offer mifepristone in the next year (precontemplation) as compared to 23% who might offer it (contemplation). Independent predictors of being in the precontemplation stage were being a primary care versus OB/GYN physician (odds ratio[OR] 3.29, p = .02), being in private versus hospital-based practice (OR 2.40, p = .03), and lacking concerns about FDA regulations (OR 2.06, p = .01) or violence and protests (OR 1.93, p = .03) as barriers to offering mifepristone. CONCLUSIONS: For precontemplation-stage physicians, the most efficient strategy for increasing the availability of medical abortion may be to design programs that emphasize clinical benefits and feasibility to stimulate interest in the procedure. For contemplation-stage physicians, the optimum approach may be one that helps to overcome barriers associated with FDA regulations and concerns about violence and protests.

Sharp, Helen M.; Bryant, Karen N. Ethical issues in dysphagia: when patients refuse assessment or treatment. *Seminars in Speech and Language* 2003 November; 24(4): 285-299. NRCBL: 8.3.4; 8.3.1; 4.3; 20.5.4; 8.3.3; 20.5.1.

Stein, Rob. A medical crisis of conscience: faith drives some to refuse patients medication or care. *Washington Post* 2006 July 16; p. A1, A6. NRCBL: 8.3.4; 1.2. SC: po.

Strauss, Ronald P. Ethical and social concerns in facial surgical decision making. *Plastic and Reconstructive Surgery* 1983 November; 72(5): 727-730. NRCBL: 8.3.4; 9.4. Conference: Annual Meeting of the American Cleft Palate Association: Denver, Colorado: April 21, 1982.

van Bogaert, Louis-Jacques. Rights of and duties to non-consenting patients — informed refusal in the developing world. *Developing World Bioethics* 2006 March; 6(1): 13-22. NRCBL: 8.3.4; 21.1.

Abstract: The principle of informed refusal poses a specific problem when it is invoked by a pregnant woman who, in spite of having accepted her pregnancy, refuses the diagnostic and/or therapeutic measures that would ensure the well-being of her endangered fetus. Guidelines issued by professional bodies in the developed world are conflicting: either they allow autonomy and informed consent to be overruled to the benefit of the fetus, or they recommend the full respect of these principles. A number of medical ethicists advocate the overruling of alleged irrational or unreasonable refusal for the benefit of the fetus. The present essay supports the view of fetal rights to health and to life based on the principle that an 'accepted' fetus is a 'third person'. In developing countries, however, the implementation of the latter principle is likely to be in conflict with a 'communitarian' perception of the individual - in this case, the pregnant woman. Within the scope of the limitations to the right to autonomy of J.S. Mill's 'harm principle', the South African Patients' Charter makes provision for informed refusal. The fact that, in practice, it is not implemented illustrates the well- known difficulty of applying Western bioethical principles in real life in the developing world.

Varelius, Jukka. Autonomy, wellbeing, and the case of the refusing patient. *Medicine, Health Care and Philosophy* 2006; 9(1): 117-125. NRCBL: 8.3.4; 1.1. SC: an.

NRCBL: National Reference Center for Bioethics Literature Classification Scheme   See inside front cover for terms.

463

Abstract: A moral problem arises when a patient refuses a treatment that would save her life. Should the patient be treated against her will? According to an influential approach to questions of biomedical ethics, certain considerations pertaining to individual autonomy provide a solution to this problem. According to this approach, we should respect the patient's autonomy and, since she has made an autonomous decision accepting the treatment, she should not be treated. This article argues against the view that our answer to the question of whether or not the refusing patient ought to be treated should be based on these kinds of considerations pertaining to individual autonomy and maintains that finding a plausible answer to this question presupposes that we resolve questions concerning subjectivity and objectivity of individual wellbeing.

Woolley, S. Children of Jehovah's Witnesses and adolescent Jehovah's Witnesses: what are their rights? *Archives of Disease in Childhood* 2005 July; 90(7): 715-719. NRCBL: 8.3.4; 8.3.2; 19.4; 1.2. Identifiers: United Kingdom(Great Britain); Australia; Canada.

Woolley, S. Jehovah's Witnesses in the emergency department: what are their rights? *Emergency Medicine Journal* 2005 December; 22(12): 869-871. NRCBL: 8.3.4; 19.4; 1.2; 8.3.2.

TREATMENT REFUSAL/ MENTALLY ILL

Bartlett, Peter. Psychiatric treatment: in the absence of law? R (on the application of B) v. Ashworth Hospital Authority and another. *Medical Law Review* 2006 Spring; 14(1): 124-131. NRCBL: 17.8; 8.3.4; 9.5.3. SC: le.

Goodnough, Abby. Officials clash over mentally ill in Florida jails. *New York Times* 2006 November 15; p. A1, A20. NRCBL: 17.8; 1.3.5. SC: po; le.

Gross, David E. Presumed dangerous: California's selective policy of forcibly medicating state prisoners with antipsychotic drugs. *University of California Davis Law Review* 2002 January; 35: 483-517. NRCBL: 17.8; 8.3.4; 17.4. SC: le.

Irvin, Tracey L. Legal, ethical and clinical implications of prescribing involuntary, life-threatening treatment: the case of the sunshine kid. *Journal of Forensic Sciences* 2003 July; 48(4): 856-860. NRCBL: 17.8; 1.3.5; 8.1; 1.1. SC: cs.

Mossman, Douglas. Is persecution "medically appropriate?": New law, policy and medicine of involuntary treatment: a comprehensive case problem approach to criminal and civil aspects. *New England Journal on Criminal and Civil Confinement* 2005 Winter; 31(1): 15-80. NRCBL: 17.8; 17.4; 1.3.5; 20.4; 1.1. SC: le.

Perez-Pena, Richard. State still confines mentally ill in nursing homes, suit says. *New York Times* 2006 March 8; p. A1, B6. NRCBL: 17.8. SC: po; le.

Slovenko, Ralph. Right to treatment and right to refuse treatment. *In his:* Psychiatry in Law/Law in Psychiatry.

Volume 2. New York: Brunner-Routledge; 2002: 585-618. NRCBL: 17.8; 8.3.4. SC: le.

TRUTH DISCLOSURE

Did nurses have duty to tell pt. what happened? *Nursing Law's Regan Report* 2005 November; 46(6): 1. NRCBL: 8.2; 8.5; 4.1.3. SC: le.

Akabayashi, Akira; Slingsby, Brian Taylor. Informed consent revisited: Japan and the U.S. *American Journal of Bioethics* 2006 January-February; 6(1): 9-14. NRCBL: 8.2; 8.3.1; 21.1; 9.1; 8.1. Identifiers: Japan Medical Association.

Ardalan, Kaveh. Hope and autonomy in the context of heart transplantation. *Penn Bioethics Journal* 2005 April 2; 1(1): 3p. [Online]. Accessed: http://www.bioethicsjournal.com [2005 April 19]. NRCBL: 8.2; 1.1. SC: em.

Arnold, Robert L.; Egan, Kathleen. Breaking the "bad" news to patients and families: preparing to have the conversation about end-of-life and hospice care. *American Journal of Geriatric Cardiology* 2004 November-December; 13(6): 307-312. NRCBL: 8.2; 20.5.1; 20.4.1; 9.8.

Back, Michael F.; Huak, Chan Yiong. Family centred decision making and non-disclosure of diagnosis in a South East Asian oncology practice. *Psycho-Oncology* 2005 December; 14(12): 1052-1059. NRCBL: 8.2; 9.5.1; 8.1; 9.4.

Barnett, Mandy M. Does it hurt to know the worst? — psychological morbidity, information preferences and understanding of prognosis in patients with advanced cancer. *Psycho-Oncology* 2006 January; 15(1): 44-55. NRCBL: 8.2; 9.5.1. SC: em.

Bennett, Michael; Alison, Dawn. Discussing the diagnosis and prognosis with cancer patients. *Postgraduate Medical Journal* 1996 January; 72(843): 25-29. NRCBL: 8.2; 8.1; 9.5.1.

Bird, Sheryl Thorburn; Bogart, Laura M. Conspiracy beliefs about HIV/AIDS and birth control among African Americans: implications for the prevention of HIV, other STIs, and unintended pregnancy. *Journal of Social Issues* 2005 March; 61(1): 109-126. NRCBL: 8.2; 9.5.6; 9.5.4; 10; 11; 1.9.1.

Bostick, Nathan A.; Sade, Robert; McMahon, John W.; Benjamin, Regina. Report of the American Medical Association Council on Ethical and Judicial Affairs: withholding information from patients: rethinking the propriety of "therapeutic privilege". *Journal of Clinical Ethics* 2006 Winter; 17(4): 302-306. NRCBL: 8.2; 8.1; 6.

Colgan, Terence J. Disclosure of diagnostic errors: the death knell of retrospective pathology reviews? *Journal of*

Lower Genital Tract Disease 2005 October; 9(4): 216-218. NRCBL: 8.2; 9.8; 7.1.

Collis, S.P. The importance of truth-telling in health care. *Nursing Standard* 2006 January 4-10; 20(17): 41-45. NRCBL: 8.2; 4.1.3.

Crow, Karine; Mathson, Lou; Steed, Alicia. Informed consent and truth-telling: cultural directions for healthcare providers. *Journal of Nursing Administration* 2000 March; 30(3): 148-152. NRCBL: 8.2; 8.3.1; 8.1; 21.7. SC: cs; em.

Faunce, Thomas A.; Bolsin, S.N. Fiduciary disclosure of medical mistakes: the duty to promptly notify patients of adverse health care events. *Journal of Law and Medicine* 2005 May; 12(4): 478-482. NRCBL: 8.2; 8.1. SC: an; le.

Fowler, Esther. An ethical dilemma: is it ever acceptable to lie to a patient? *British Journal of Perioperative Nursing* 2004 October; 14(10): 448-451. NRCBL: 8.2; 8.1.

Fugh-Berman, Adriane. Carcinogen diagnosis. *Hastings Center Report* 2006 September-October; 36(5): [53]. NRCBL: 8.2; 5.2; 9.8; 8.3.1.

Godkin, D. Should children's autonomy be respected by telling them of their imminent death? *Journal of Medical Ethics* 2006 January; 32(1): 24-25. NRCBL: 8.2; 20.4.2. Comments: T. Vince and A. Petros. Should children's autonomy be respected by telling them of their imminent death? Journal of Medical Ethics 2006 January; 32(1): 21-23.

Goldstein, Nathan E.; Concato, John; Bradley, Elizabeth H.; O'Leary, John R.; Fried, Terri R. Doctor-patient communication about prognosis: the influence of race and financial status. *Journal of Palliative Medicine* 2005 October; 8(5): 998-1004. NRCBL: 8.2; 8.1; 9.5.4; 9.5.10.

Gonçalves, Ferraz; Marques, Ágata; Rocha, Sónia; Leitão, Pedro; Mesquita, Teresa; Moutinho, Susana. Breaking bad news: experiences and preferences of advanced cancer patients at a Portuguese oncology centre. *Palliative Medicine* 2005 October; 19(7): 526-531. NRCBL: 8.2; 9.5.1; 8.1. SC: em.

Grace, Pamela J. The clinical use of placebos: is it ethical? Not when it involves deceiving patients. *AJN: American Journal of Nursing* 2006 February; 106(2): 58-61. NRCBL: 8.2; 7.2. SC: cs.

Hofmann, Paul B. Telling patients of mistakes [letter]. *Hastings Center Report* 2006 September-October; 36(5): 7. NRCBL: 8.2; 9.8.

Howe, Edmund G. Comment on the CEJA guidelines: treating patients who deny reality. *Journal of Clinical Ethics* 2006 Winter; 17(4): 317-322. NRCBL: 8.2; 8.1; 6. Identifiers: American Medical Association Council on Ethical and Judicial Affairs.

Johnstone, Megan-Jane; Kanitsaki, Olga. The ethics and practical importance of defining, distinguishing and disclosing nursing errors: a discussion paper. *International Journal of Nursing Studies* 2006 March; 43(3): 367-376. NRCBL: 8.2; 9.8; 7.1.

Keating, Dominic T.; Nayeem, Kayser; Gilmartin, J.J.; O'Keeffe, Shaun T. Advance directives for truth disclosure. *Chest* 2005 August; 128(2): 1037-1039. NRCBL: 8.2; 8.3.1; 20.5.4; 9.5.2; 17.1; 9.5.1. SC: em.

Kipnis, Kenneth. Taking families seriously enough. *American Journal of Bioethics* 2006 January-February; 6(1): 21-22; discussion W27-W28. NRCBL: 8.2; 8.4; 8.1. Comments: Akira Akabayashi and Brian Taylor Slingsby. Informed consent revisited: Japan and the U.S. American Journal of Bioethics 2006 January-February; 6(1): 9-14.

Klitzman, Robert. Complications of culture in obtaining informed consent. *American Journal of Bioethics* 2006 January-February; 6(1): 20-21; discussion W27-W28. NRCBL: 8.2; 21.1; 8.3.3; 8.1. Comments: Akira Akabayashi and Brian Taylor Slingsby. Informed consent revisited: Japan and the U.S. American Journal of Bioethics 2006 January-February; 6(1): 9-14.

Kostopoulou, V.; Katsouyanni, K. The truth-telling issue and changes in lifestyle in patients with cancer. *Journal of Medical Ethics* 2006 December; 32(12): 693-697. NRCBL: 8.2; 9.1. SC: em.

Lazcano-Ponce, Eduardo; Angeles-Llerenas, Angélica; Alvarez-del Río, Asunción; Salazar-Martínez, Eduardo; Allen, Betania; Hernández-Avila, Mauricio; Kraus, Arnoldo. Ethics and communication between physicians and their patients with cancer, HIV/AIDS, and rheumatoid arthritis in Mexico. *Archives of Medical Research* 2004 January-February; 35(1): 66-75. NRCBL: 8.2; 9.5.1; 8.3.1. SC: em; cs.

Lerner, Barron H. Beyond informed consent: did cancer patients challenge their physicians in the post-World War II era? *Journal of the History of Medicine and Allied Sciences* 2004 October; 59(4): 507-521. NRCBL: 8.2; 8.3.1; 9.5.1; 8.1. SC: rv; em.

Lin, Chia-Chin; Tsay, Hsiu-Fen. Relationships among perceived diagnostic disclosure, health locus of control, and levels of hope in Taiwanese cancer patients. *Psycho-Oncology* 2005 May; 14(5): 376-385. NRCBL: 8.2; 9.5.1; 4.4. SC: em.

Lin, Ker-Neng; Liao, Yi-Chu; Wang, Pei-Ning; Liu, Hsiu-Chih. Family members favor disclosing the diagnosis of Alzheimer's disease. *International Psychogeriatrics* 2005 December; 17(4): 679-688. NRCBL: 8.2; 9.5.2. SC: em.

Mamdani, Bashir. Placebos: can you get something for nothing? *Indian Journal of Medical Ethics* 2006 October-December; 3(4): 136-138. NRCBL: 8.2. Comments:

NRCBL: National Reference Center for Bioethics Literature Classification Scheme   See inside front cover for terms.

Daniel E. Moerman. Cultural variations in the placebo effect: ulcers, anxiety, and blood pressure. *Medical Anthropology Quarterly* 2000; 14: 51-72.

McCaffery, Margo; Arnstein, Paul. The debate over placebos in pain management: the ASPMN disagrees with a recent placebo position statement. *AJN: American Journal of Nursing* 2006 February; 106(2): 62-65. NRCBL: 8.2; 7.2. SC: cs. Identifiers: American Society for Pain Management Nursing.

Mendelssohn, David C. Both sides now: disclosure of prognosis on dialysis. *Peritoneal Dialysis International* 2005 May-June; 25(3): 238-239. NRCBL: 8.2; 8.3.1; 19.3.

Miller, Ronald B. Morbidity and mortality data associated with ESRD and dialysis: should patients be informed? The "truth," the whole truth, and nothing but the truth. . .informing ESRD patients of their prognoses. *Nephrology Nursing Journal* 2005 July-August; 32(4): 441-442. NRCBL: 8.2; 8.1. Identifiers: end stage renal disease.

Mystakidou, Kyriaki; Tsilika, E.; Parpa, E.; Katsouda, E.; Vlahos, L. Patterns and barriers in information disclosure between health care professionals and relatives with cancer patients in Greek society. *European Journal of Cancer Care* 2005 May; 14(2): 175-181. NRCBL: 8.2; 8.4; 8.1; 9.5.1. SC: rv.

Nelson, Michelle. Morbidity and mortality data associated with ESRD and dialysis: should patients be informed? Giving hope through information. *Nephrology Nursing Journal* 2005 July-August; 32(4): 440-441. NRCBL: 8.2; 19.3.

Papathanasopoulos, P.G.; Nikolakopoulou, A.; Scolding, N.J. Disclosing the diagnosis of multiple sclerosis. *Journal of Neurology* 2005 November; 252(11): 1307-1309. NRCBL: 8.2; 8.1. SC: em.

Philpott, Shona. The truth, the whole truth and nothing but the truth? *Nursing New Zealand* 2005 May; 11(4): 16-18. NRCBL: 8.2; 4.1.3; 8.1; 6.

Pleat, J.M.; Dunkin, C.S.J.; Davies, C.E.; Ripley, R.M.; Tyler, M.P.H. Prospective survey of factors affecting risk discussion during consent in a surgical specialty. *British Journal of Surgery* 2004 October; 91(10): 1377-1380. NRCBL: 8.2; 8.3.1; 5.2. SC: le.

Powell, Tia. Culture and communication: medical disclosure in Japan and the USA Akabayashi and B.T. Slingsby. *American Journal of Bioethics* 2006 January-February; 6(1): 18-20; discussion W27-W28. NRCBL: 8.2; 21.1; 8.1. Comments: Akira Akabayashi and Brian Taylor Slingsby. Informed consent revisited: Japan and the U.S. American Journal of Bioethics 2006 January-February; 6(1): 9-14.

Purtilo, Ruth B. Beyond disclosure: seeking forgiveness [editorial]. *Physical Therapy* 2005 November; 85(11):

1124-1126. NRCBL: 8.2; 8.1. Identifiers: medical error; apology.

Ross, Karen. When volunteers are not healthy. *EMBO Reports* 2005 December; 6(12): 1116-1119. NRCBL: 8.2; 18.1; 17.1.

Sirotin, Nicole; Lo, Bernard. The end of therapeutic privilege? *Journal of Clinical Ethics* 2006 Winter; 17(4): 312-316. NRCBL: 8.2; 8.1. SC: cs. Identifiers: American Medical Association Council on Ethical and Judicial Affairs.

Sokol, Daniel K. Dissecting "deception". *CQ: Cambridge Quarterly of Healthcare Ethics* 2006 Fall; 15(4): 457-464. NRCBL: 8.2.

Sokol, Daniel K. Truth-telling in the doctor-patient relationship: a case analysis. *Clinical Ethics* 2006 September; 1(3): 130-134. NRCBL: 8.2; 15.3; 8.3.1. SC: cs.

Sonnenberg, Amnon. Exploring how to tell the truth and preserve hope: can a balance between communication and empathy be calculated? *Clinical Gastroenterology and Hepatology* 2004 June; 2(6): 518-522. NRCBL: 8.2; 8.3.1; 20.4.1. SC: em.

Springer, Rachelle. Disclosing unanticipated events. *Plastic Surgical Nursing* 2005 October-December; 25(4): 199-201. NRCBL: 8.2.

Tanasiewicz, Marta; Bednarski, Jacek; Galazka, Alicja. The truth, misunderstanding or lie? Different forms of doctor-patient relations. *Bulletin of Medical Ethics* 2005 June-July; (209): 13-17. NRCBL: 8.2; 9.8; 8.1. SC: rv.

Tanida, Noritoshi. Breach of information ethics and medical professional ethics during the SARS epidemic in Japan. *Formosan Journal of Medical Humanities* 2006 June; 7(1-2): 57-65. NRCBL: 8.2; 1.3.7; 1.3.5; 9.1.

Thompson, W. Grant. The ethics of using placebos. *In his:* The Placebo Effect and Health: Combining Science and Compassionate Care. Amherst, NY: Prometheus Books; 2005: 203-214. NRCBL: 8.2.

Toscani, Franco; Farsides, Calliope. Deception, Catholicism, and hope: understanding problems in the communication of unfavorable prognoses in traditionally-Catholic countries. *American Journal of Bioethics [Online]*. 2006 January-February; 6(1): W6-W18. NRCBL: 8.2; 1.2; 8.3.1; 21.1; 20.4.1.

Veatch, Robert M. Benevolent lies: fallible universalism and the quest for an international standard. *Formosan Journal of Medical Humanities* 2006 June; 7(1-2): 3-18. NRCBL: 8.2; 1.1.

Vince, T.; Petros, A. Should children's autonomy be respected by telling them of their imminent death? *Journal of Medical Ethics* 2006 January; 32(1): 21-23. NRCBL: 8.2; 20.4.2.

Abstract: Respect for an individual's autonomy determines that doctors should inform patients if their illness is terminal. This becomes complicated when the terminal diagnosis is recent and death is imminent. The authors examine the admission to paediatric intensive care of an adolescent with terminal respiratory failure. While fully ventilated, the patient was kept sedated and comfortable but when breathing spontaneously he was capable of non-verbal communication and understanding. Once resedated and reintubated, intense debate ensued over whether to wake the patient to tell him he was going to die. The authors discuss the ethical arguments that surrounded their decision.

Winslade, William; McKinney, E. Bernadette. The ethical health lawyer. *Journal of Law, Medicine and Ethics* 2006 Winter; 34(4): 813-816. NRCBL: 8.2; 8.5. SC: le.

VALUE OF LIFE *See* QUALITY AND VALUE OF LIFE

WAR AND TERRORISM
See also TORTURE, GENOCIDE, AND WAR CRIMES

Declaration of Gijón: against the use of biological weapons. *Eubios Journal of Asian and International Bioethics* 2006 January; 16(1): 2-3. NRCBL: 21.3; 6.

DoD issues guidance for medical personnel dealing with detainees. *Military Medicine* 2005 Summer; (Supplement): 10-11. NRCBL: 21.2; 9.5.1; 1.3.5; 8.4. Identifiers: Department of Defense.

Proceed with caution [editorial]. *New Scientist* 2006 October 14-20; 192(2573): 5. NRCBL: 21.3; 1.3.9. Identifiers: dual-use biotech.

Towards better biosecurity [editorial]. *Nature* 2006 April 6; 440(7085): 715. NRCBL: 21.3; 1.3.9.

Aldhous, Peter. Bioterror: friend or foe? *New Scientist* 2006 October 14-20; 192(2573): 20-23. NRCBL: 21.3; 1.3.9.

Aldhous, Peter. The accidental terrorists. *New Scientist* 2006 June 10-16; 190(2555): 24. NRCBL: 21.3; 1.3.9; 1.3.7. Identifiers: bioterrorism.

Allhoff, Fritz. Physician involvement in hostile interrogations. *CQ: Cambridge Quarterly of Healthcare Ethics* 2006 Fall; 15(4): 392-402. NRCBL: 21.2; 8.1; 21.4; 1.1.

Annas, George J. Bioterror and "bioart" — a plague o' both your houses. *New England Journal of Medicine* 2006 June 22; 354(25): 2715-2720. NRCBL: 21.3; 5.1. SC: le.

Atlas, Ronald M. Biodefense research: an emerging conundrum. *Current Opinion in Biotechnology* 2005 June; 16(3): 239-242. NRCBL: 21.3; 5.1.

Atlas, Ronald M. Securing life sciences research in an age of terrorism. *Issues in Science and Technology* 2006 Fall; 23(1): 41-49. NRCBL: 21.3; 1.3.9; 5.3; 15.1.

Bennahum, David A. Historical reflections on the ethics of military medicine. *CQ: Cambridge Quarterly of Healthcare Ethics* 2006 Fall; 15(4): 345-355. NRCBL: 21.2; 7.1; 8.1.

Duckler, Lawrence. Moral conduct of an infantry medic [letter]. *Military Medicine* 1999 August; 164(8): R7. NRCBL: 21.2; 1.3.5; 4.1.1.

Enemark, Christian. United States biodefense, international law, and the problem of intent. *Politics and the Life Sciences* 2005 March-September; 24(1-2): 32-42. NRCBL: 21.3; 21.1; 5.1; 15.7.

Gould, Donald. Conscience of a doctor. *New Statesman (London, England: 1957)* 1967 May 26; 73: 716-717. NRCBL: 21.2; 8.1; 4.1.2.

Green, Shane K. E^{3}LSI research: an essential element of biodefense. *Biosecurity and Bioterrorism* 2005; 3(2): 128-137. NRCBL: 21.3; 1.3.5. Identifiers: ethical, economic, environmental, legal, and social implications.

Grönvall, Gigi Kwik. A new role for scientists in the Biological Weapons Convention. *Nature Biotechnology* 2005 October; 23(10): 1213-1216. NRCBL: 21.3; 1.3.9.

Gross, Michael L. Author's reply to review of Bioethics and Armed Conflict [letter]. *BMJ: British Medical Journal* 2006 December 16; 333(7581): 1272. NRCBL: 21.2; 21.4.

Hirsch, Jules. An anniversary for cancer chemotherapy. *JAMA: The Journal of the American Medical Association* 2006 September 27; 296(12): 1518-1520. NRCBL: 21.3; 18.5.8; 2.2. Identifiers: Chemical war-time study.

Holdstock, Douglas. Chemical and biological warfare: some ethical dilemmas. *CQ: Cambridge Quarterly of Healthcare Ethics* 2006 Fall; 15(4): 356-365. NRCBL: 21.3; 5.3; 7.1; 1.3.9.

Keram, Emily A. Will medical ethics be a casualty of the war on terror? [editorial]. *Journal of the American Academy of Psychiatry and the Law* 2006; 34(1): 6-8. NRCBL: 21.2; 21.4; 9.2.6.

Kottow, Michael H. Should medical ethics justify violence? *Journal of Medical Ethics* 2006 August; 32(8): 464-467. NRCBL: 21.2; 21.4; 4.1.2. SC: an.

London, Leslie; Rubenstein, Leonard S.; Baldwin-Ragaven, Laurel; Van Es, Adriaan. Dual loyalty among military health professionals: human rights and ethics in times of armed conflict. *CQ: Cambridge Quarterly of Healthcare Ethics* 2006 Fall; 15(4): 381-391. NRCBL: 21.2; 8.1; 1.1; 21.4; 21.1; 9.8.

May, Thomas. Isolation is not the answer. International scientific collaboration is the best defence against bioterror. *Nature* 2004 June 10; 429(6992): 603. NRCBL: 21.3; 1.3.9; 9.1; 21.1.

NRCBL: National Reference Center for Bioethics Literature Classification Scheme   See inside front cover for terms.

467

Miles, Steven H. Medical oaths betrayed. *Washington Post* 2006 July 9; p. B1, B4. NRCBL: 21.2. SC: po. Identifiers: Abu Ghraib prison.

Poteliakhoff, Alex. A commitment to peace: a doctor's tale. *Medicine, Conflict and Survival* 2006 January-March; 22(1, Supplement): S3-S55. NRCBL: 21.2; 6; 4.1.1.

Schmidt, Ulf. Cold War at Porton Down: informed consent in Britain's biological and chemical warfare experiments. *CQ: Cambridge Quarterly of Healthcare Ethics* 2006 Fall; 15(4): 366-380. NRCBL: 21.3; 7.1; 18.3; 18.5.8.

Stambolovic, V.; Đuric, M.; Đonic, D.; Kelecevic, J.; Rakocevic, Z. Patient-physician relationship in the aftermath of war. *Journal of Medical Ethics* 2006 December; 32(12): 739-742. NRCBL: 21.2; 8.1. SC: em. Identifiers: Serbia.

Steinbruner, John. In the name of defence: bioweapons research in the U.S. could trigger just the sort of arms race it is meant to forestall. But that's not the worst of it. *New Scientist* 2006 November 25-December 1; 192(2579): 20. NRCBL: 21.3; 1.3.9.

United States. *Laws, statutes, etc.* Chemical and biological warfare program. Reports to Congress. United States Code 1994; Title 50: Section 1511. [Online]. Accessed: http://frwebgate4.access.gpo.gov/cgi-bin/waisgate.cgi? WAISdocID=8628003093+0+0+0&WAISaction= retrieve [2007 March 2]. NRCBL: 21.3; 18.6. SC: le. Note: Repealed by Public Law 104-106, Title X, Section 1061(k), February 10, 1996. (110 Statutes at Large 443).

United States. *Laws, statutes, etc.* Chemical and biological warfare program. Use of human subjects for testing of chemical or biological agents by Department of Defense; accounting to Congressional committees with respect to experiments and studies; notification of local civilian officials. United States Code 1994; Title 50: Section 1520. [Online]. Accessed: http://frwebgate1.access.gpo.gov/ cgi-bin/waisgate.cgi?WAISdocID=862184395128+0+ 0+0&WAISaction=retrieve [2007 March 2]. NRCBL: 21.3; 18.6. SC: le. Note: Repealed by Public Law 105-85, Title X, Section 1078(g), 18 November 1997.

WITHHOLDING TREATMENT *See* EUTHA-NASIA AND ALLOWING TO DIE

WOMEN *See* CARE FOR SPECIFIC GROUPS/ WOMEN; HUMAN EXPERIMENTATION/ SPE-CIAL POPULATIONS/ WOMEN

WRONGFUL BIRTH *See* CONTRACEPTION

XENOTRANSPLANTATION *See* ORGAN AND TISSUE TRANSPLANTATION/ XENOTRANSPLANTATION

SECTION II:
PERIODICAL LITERATURE
AND ESSAYS

AUTHOR INDEX

Section II: Periodical Literature and Essays
Author Index

A

Abbing, Henriette Roscam. Recent developments in health law in the Netherlands. *European Journal of Health Law* 2006 June; 13(2): 133-142. Subject: 9.2

Abbo, Elmer D.; Volandes, Angelo E. Rare but routine: the physician's obligation to protect third parties. *American Journal of Bioethics* 2006 March-April; 6(2): 34-36. Subject: 8.4

Abbo, Elmer D.; Volandes, Angelo E. Teaching residents to consider costs in medical decision making. *American Journal of Bioethics* 2006 July-August; 6(4): 33-34. Subject: 7.2

Abbott, Alison. A defining moment for bioethics [review of Biblioethics: A User's Dictionary, directed by Luca Ronconi]. *Nature* 2006 March 2; 440(7080): 30. Subject: 2.1

Abbott, Alison. 'Ethical' stem-cell paper under attack [news]. *Nature* 2006 September 7; 443(7107): 12. Subject: 18.5.4

Abbott, Alison. German stem-cell law under fire [news]. *Nature* 2006 November 16; 444(7117): 253. Subject: 18.5.4

Abbott, Alison. Questions linger about unexplained gene-therapy trial death [news]. *Nature Medicine* 2006 June; 12(6): 597. Subject: 15.4

Abbott, Alison. Stem-cell technique 'contrary to public order' [news]. *Nature* 2006 December 14; 442(7121): 799. Subject: 15.8

Abboud, P-A.; Heard, K.; Al-Marshad, A.A.; Lowenstein, S.R. What determines whether patients are willing to participate in resuscitation studies requiring exception from informed consent? *Journal of Medical Ethics* 2006 August; 32(8): 468-472. Subject: 18.3

Abdel-Khalek, Ahmed; Lester, David; Schaller, Sylvia. Attitudes toward physician-assisted suicide and death anxiety among Kuwaiti students. *Psychological Reports* 2005 June; 96(3, Part 1): 625-626. Subject: 20.7

Abdur Rab, M.; Khayat, M.H. Human cloning: Eastern Mediterranean region perspective. *Eastern Mediterranean*

Health Journal 2006; 12(Supplement 2): S29-S37 [On-line]. Accessed: http://www.emro.who.int/publications/EMHJ/12_S2/PDF/4.pdf [2007 January 4]. Subject: 14.5

Abel, Elizabeth; Horner, Sharon D.; Tyler, Diane; Innerarity, Sheryl A. The impact of genetic information on policy and clinical practice. *Policy, Politics, and Nursing Practice* 2005 February; 6(1): 5-14. Subject: 15.3

Abelson, Reed. Charities tied to doctors get drug industry gifts. *New York Times* 2006 June 28; p. A1, C4. Subject: 9.7

Abelson, Reed. Heart procedure is off the charts in an Ohio city. *New York Times* 2006 August 18; p. A1, C4. Subject: 9.3.1

Abelson, Reed. New nerve test, a moneymaker, divides doctors. *New York Times* 2006 October 20; p. A1, C6. Subject: 9.7

Abma, Tineke A.; Widdershoven, Guy A.M. Moral deliberation in psychiatric nursing practice. *Nursing Ethics* 2006 September; 13(5): 546-557. Subject: 17.7

Abouna, George M. Ethical issues in organ and tissue transplantation. *Experimental and Clinical Transplantation* 2003 December; 1(2): 125-138. Subject: 19.5

Abraham, Abraham S. Genetic engineering and cloning. *In:* Rosner, Fred, ed. Medicine and Jewish Law. Volume III. Brooklyn, NY: Yashar Books, Inc.; 2005: 83-88. Subject: 15.1

Abraham, Abraham S. Infertility and halachah. *In:* Rosner, Fred, ed. Medicine and Jewish Law. Volume III. Brooklyn, NY: Yashar Books, Inc.; 2005: 15-23. Subject: 14.1

Abramovitch, Rona; Freedman, Jonathan L.; Thoden, Kirby; Nikolich, Crystal. Children's capacity to consent to participation in psychological research: empirical findings. *Child Development* 1991; 62: 1100-1109. Subject: 18.5.2

Abrams, Jerold J. Pragmatism, artificial intelligence, and posthuman bioethics: Shusterman, Rorty, Foucault. *Human Studies* 2004 September; 27(3): 241-258. Subject: 15.1

See SUBJECT HEADING KEY FOR SECTION II on inside back cover.

471

Abramson, John; Starfield, Barbara. The effect of conflict of interest on biomedical research and clinical practice guidelines: can we trust the evidence in evidence-based medicine? *Journal of the American Board of Family Practice* 2005 September-October; 18(5): 414-418. Subject: 1.3.9

Ach, Johann S.; Gaidt, Andreas. Wehret den Anfängen? Anmerkungen zum Argument der "schiefen Ebene" in der gegenwätigen Euthanasie-Debatte. *In:* Frewer, Andreas; Eickhoff, Clemens, eds. "Euthanasie" und die aktuelle Sterbehilfe-Debatte: Die historischen Hintergründe medizinischer Ethik. Frankfurt; New York: Campus; 2000: 424-447. Subject: 20.5.1

Acharya, Shashidhar. The ethical climate in academic dentistry in India: faculty and student perceptions. *Journal of Dental Education* 2005 June; 69(6): 671-680. Subject: 7.2

Achter, Paul; Parrott, Roxanne; Silk, Kami. African Americans' opinions about human-genetics research. *Politics and the Life Sciences* 2004 March; 23(1): 60-66. Subject: 15.1

Ackerman, A. Bernard. An antidote for prevaricating physicians in matters medicolegal: Coalition and Center for Ethical Medical Testimony [editorial]. *Cutis* 2004 May; 73(5): 295-298. Subject: 7.3

Ackerman, Felicia. "For now have I my death": the "duty to die" versus the duty to help the ill stay alive. *Midwest Studies in Philosophy* 2000 August; 24: 172-185. Subject: 20.5.1

Ackerman, P.D.; Thistlethwaite, J.R., Jr.; Ross, L.F. Attitudes of minority patients with end-stage renal disease regarding ABO-incompatible list-paired exchanges. *American Journal of Transplantation* 2006 January; 6(1): 83-88. Subject: 19.3

Ackerman, Terrence F. Ethical issues in genetic testing for cancer susceptibility. *In:* Ellis, C.N., ed. Inherited Cancer Syndromes: Current Clinical Management. New York: Springer-Verlag, 2004: 61-82. Subject: 15.3

Ackmann, Elizabeth A. Prenatal testing gone awry: the birth of a conflict of ethics and liability. *Indiana Health Law Review* 2005; 2(1): 199-224. Subject: 15.2

Acquaviva, Gregory L. Mental health courts: no longer experimental. *Seton Hall Law Review* 2006; 36(3): 971-1013. Subject: 17.7

Adalsteinsson, Ragnar. The constitutionality of the Icelandic Act on a health sector database. *In:* Sándor, Judit, ed. Society and Genetic Information: Codes and Laws in the Genetic Era. Budapest, Hungary; New York: CEU Press; 2003: 203-211. Subject: 15.1

Adam, Dieter; Kasper, S.; Moller, H.J.; Singer, E.A. Placebo-controlled trials in major depression are necessary and ethically justifiable: how to improve the communication between researchers and ethical committees. *Euro-pean Archives of Psychiatry and Clinical Neuroscience* 2005 August; 255(4): 258-260. Subject: 18.3

Adams, Maurice; Nys, Herman. Euthanasia in the low countries: comparative reflections on the Belgian and Dutch Euthanasia Act. *In:* Schotsmans, Paul; Meulenbergs, Tom, eds. Euthanasia and Palliative Care in the Low Countries. Dudley, MA: Peeters, 2005: 5-33. Subject: 20.5.1

Adams, Vincanne; Miller, Suellen; Craig, Sienna; Nyima; Sonam; Droyoung; Lhakpen; Varner, Michael. The challenge of cross-cultural clinical trials research: case report from the Tibetan Autonomous Region, People's Republic of China. *Medical Anthropology Quarterly* 2005 September; 19(3): 267-289. Subject: 18.5.9

Adamson, David. Regulation of assisted reproductive technologies in the United States. *Family Law Quarterly* 2005 Fall; 39(3): 727-744. Subject: 14.4

Adamson, T. Elaine; Bunch, Wilton H.; Baldwin, DeWitt C., Jr.; Oppenberg, Andrew. The virtuous orthopaedist has fewer malpractice suits. *Clinical Orthopaedics and Related Research* 2000 September; (378): 104-109. Subject: 8.1

Adchalingam, K.; Kong, W.H.; Zakiah, M.A.; Zaini, M.; Wong, Y.L.; Lang, C.C. Attitudes of medical students towards euthanasia in a multicultural setting. *Medical Journal of Malaysia* 2005 March; 60(1): 46-49. Subject: 20.5.1

Addison, G. Michael. Ethics committees: we all need research ethics committees [letter]. *BMJ: British Medical Journal* 2006 March 25; 332(7543): 730. Subject: 18.2

Adenipekun, A.; Onibokun, A.; Elumelu, T.N.; Soyannwo, O.A. Knowledge and attitudes of terminally ill patients and their family to palliative care and hospice services in Nigeria. *Nigerian Journal of Clinical Practice* 2005 June; 8(1): 19-22. Subject: 20.4.1

Adeyemo, W.L. Sigmund Freud: smoking habit, oral cancer and euthanasia. *Nigerian Journal of Medicine* 2004 April-June; 13(2): 189-195. Subject: 20.5.1

Adhikary, Sanjib Das; Raviraj, R. Do not resuscitate orders [case study]. *Indian Journal of Medical Ethics* 2006 July-September; 3(3): 100-101. Subject: 20.5.1

Adrian, Cheri. Therapist sexual feelings in hypnotherapy: managing therapeutic boundaries in hypnotic work. *International Journal of Clinical and Experimental Hypnosis* 1996 January; 44(1): 20-32. Subject: 7.4

Adshead, Gwen; Sarkar, Sameer P. Justice and welfare: two ethical paradigms in forensic psychiatry. *Australian and New Zealand Journal of Psychiatry* 2005 November-December; 39(11-12): 1011-1017. Subject: 17.1

Adsuar, Natalie; Zweifel, Julianne E.; Pritts, Elizabeth A.; Davidson, Marie A.; Olive, David L.; Lindheim, Steven R. Assessment of wishes regarding disposition of oocytes and embryo management among ovum donors in an anonymous egg donation program. *Fertility and Sterility* 2005 November; 84(5): 1513-1516. Subject: 14.4

Agar, Nicholas; Prusak, Bernard G. The debate over liberal eugenics [letter and reply]. *Hastings Center Report* 2006 March-April; 36(2): 4-5, 6-7. Subject: 15.5

Ågård, Anders. Informed consent: theory versus practice. *Nature Clinical Practice Cardiovascular Medicine* 2005 June; 2(6): 270-271. Subject: 8.3.1

Ågård, Anders; Bolmsjö, Ingrid Ågren; Hermerén, Göran; Wahlstöm, Jan. Familial hypercholesterolemia: ethical, practical and psychological problems from the perspective of patients. *Patient Education and Counseling* 2005 May; 57(2): 162-167. Subject: 15.3

Aghanwa, H.S.; Akinsola, A.; Akinola, D.O.; Makanjuola, R.O.A. Attitudes toward kidney donation. *Journal of the National Medical Association* 2003 August; 95(8): 725-731. Subject: 19.3

Agich, George. A phenomenological approach to bioethics. *In:* Ashcroft, Richard; Lucassen, Anneke; Parker, Michael; Verkerk, Marian; Widderhoven, Guy, eds. Case Analysis in Clinical Ethics. New York: Cambridge University Press; 2005: 187-200. Subject: 15.3

Aguiar-Guevara, R. Medicine assisted by information and communication technology: conflicts, responsibility and liability. *Medicine and Law: The World Association for Medical Law* 2006 September; 25(3): 563-571. Subject: 18.6

Ahmad, Khabir. Ethics of AIDS drug trials on foster children questioned [news]. *Lancet Infectious Diseases* 2005 June; 5(6): 333-334. Subject: 9.5.6

Ahmad, Norhayati Haji. Assisted reproduction — Islamic views on the science of procreation. *Eubios Journal of Asian and International Bioethics* 2003 March 13(2): 59-61. Subject: 14.1

Ahmed, A.M.; Kheir, M.M. Attitudes towards euthanasia among final-year Khartoum University medical students. *Eastern Mediterranean Health Journal* 2006; 12(3 and 4): 391-397 [Online]. Accessed: http://www.emro.who.int/publications/emhj/1203_4/PDF/16.pdf [2007 January 4]. Subject: 20.5.1

Ahmed, Amer S. The last twist of the knife: encouraging the regulation of innovative surgical procedures. *Columbia Law Review* 2005 June; 105(5): 1529-1562. Subject: 5.3

Ahmed, Shenaz; Green, Josephine; Hewison, Jenny. Antenatal thalassaemia carrier testing: women's perceptions of 'information' and 'consent'. *Journal of Medical Screening* 2005; 12(2): 69-77. Subject: 8.3.1

Ahmed, S.F.; Morrison, S.; Hughes, I.A. Intersex and gender assignment; the third way? *Archives of Disease in Childhood* 2004 September; 89(9): 847-850. Subject: 10

Ahuja, Kamal K.; Mamiso, Julian; Emmerson, Geraldine; Bowen-Simpkins, Peter; Seaton, Angela; Simons, Eric G. Pregnancy following intracytoplasmic sperm injection treatment with dead husband's spermatozoa: ethical and policy considerations. *Human Reproduction* 1997 June; 12(6): 1360-1363. Subject: 14.2

Ahuja, K.K.; Simons, E.G. Advanced oocyte cryopreservation will not undermine the practice of ethical egg sharing. *Reproductive BioMedicine Online [electronic]* 2006 March; 12(3): 282-283. Subject: 14.6

Aiello, Allison E.; King, Nicholas B.; Foxman, B. Ethical conflicts in public health research and practice: antimicrobial resistance and the ethics of drug development. *American Journal of Public Health* 2006 November; 96(11): 1910-1914. Subject: 9.7

Aita, Kaoruko; Kai, Ichiro. Withdrawal of care in Japan. *Lancet* 2006 July 1-7; 368(9529): 12-14. Subject: 20.5.1

Aita, Marilyn; Richer, Marie-Claire. Essentials of research ethics for healthcare professionals. *Nursing and Health Sciences* 2005 June; 7(2): 119-125. Subject: 18.2

Aitkenhead, Decca. Nip/tuck nation. *In:* Miller, Paul; Wilsdon, James, eds. Better Humans?: The Politics of Human Enhancement and Life Extension. London: Demos, 2006: 103-113. Subject: 9.5.1

Aizenman, N.C. Nicaragua's total ban on abortion spurs critics. *Washington Post* 2006 November 28; p. A1, A13. Subject: 12.4.1

Akabayashi, Akira; Slingsby, Brian Taylor. Informed consent revisited: Japan and the U.S. *American Journal of Bioethics* 2006 January-February; 6(1): 9-14. Subject: 8.2

Åkesson, Lynn. Bioeconomics — between persons and things. *In:* Lundin, Susanne; Åkesson, Lynn, eds. Gene Technology and Economy. Lund: Nordic Academic Press; 2002: 72-79. Subject: 15.8

Akgün, H.S.; Bilgin, N.; Tokalak, I.; Kut, A.; Haberal, Mehmet. Organ donation: a cross-sectional survey of the knowledge and personal views of Turkish health care professionals. *Transplantation Proceedings* 2003 June; 35(4): 1273-1275. Subject: 19.5

Akkad, Andrea; Jackson, Clare; Kenyon, Sara; Dixon-Woods, Mary; Taub, Nick; Habiba, Marwan. Patients' perceptions of written consent: questionnaire. *BMJ: British Medical Journal* 2006 September 9; 333(7567): 528-529. Subject: 8.3.1

Aksoy, Nurten; Aksoy, Sahin. Research ethics committees in Turkey. *In:* Sang-yong, Song; Young-Mo, Koo; Macer, Darryl R.J., eds. Asian Bioethics in the 21st Century. Christchurch, NZ: Eubios Ethics Institute, 2002: 28-30. Subject: 18.2

Aksoy, Sahin. Ethical considerations on the end of life issues in Turkey. *In:* Sang-yong, Song; Young-Mo, Koo; Macer, Darryl R.J., eds. Asian Bioethics in the 21st Century. Christchurch, NZ: Eubios Ethics Institute, 2002: 79-83. Subject: 20.4.1

See SUBJECT HEADING KEY FOR SECTION II on inside back cover.

Akufo-Tetteh, Mary. Advance directives — considerations for advanced nurse practitioners. *In:* Bartter, Karen, ed. Ethical Issues in Advanced Nursing Practice. Boston: Butterworth-Heinemann; 2001: 118-133. Subject: 20.5.4

Al-Khader, Abdullah; Jondeby, Mohamed; Ghamdi, Ghormullah; Flaiw, Ahmed; Hejaili, Fayez; Querishi, Junaid. Assessment of the willingness of potential live related kidney donors. *Annals of Transplantation* 2005; 10(1): 35-37. Subject: 19.5

Al-Khader, A.A.; Shaheen, F.A.M.; Al-Jondeby, M.S. Important social factors that affect organ transplantation in Islamic countries. *Experimental and Clinical Transplantation* 2003 December; 1(2): 96-101. Subject: 19.5

Al-Marzouki, Sanaa; Roberts, Ian; Marshall, Tom; Evans, Stephen. The effect of scientific misconduct on the results of clinical trials: a Delphi survey. *Contemporary Clinical Trials* 2005 June; 26(3): 331-337. Subject: 1.3.9

Al Qattan, S.M.B.K. Islamic jurisprudential judgement on human organ transplantation. *Saudi Medical Journal* 1992 November; 13(6): 483-487. Subject: 19.1

Al-Shahi, Rustam. Research ethics committees in the UK — the pressure is now on research and development departments. *Journal of the Royal Society of Medicine* 2005 October; 98(10): 444-447. Subject: 18.2

Alan Guttmacher Institute. Minors' access to contraceptive services. *State Policies in Brief* 2006 February 1: 3 pages [Online]. Accessed: http://www.guttmacher.org/statecenter/spibs/spib_MACS.pdf [21 February 2006]. Subject: 11.2

Alan Guttmacher Institute. An overview of abortion laws. *State Policies in Brief* 2006 February 1: 3 page [Online]. Accessed: http://www.guttmacher.org/statecenter/spibs/spib_OAL.pdf [21 February 2006]. Subject: 12.4.1

Alan Guttmacher Institute. Refusing to provide health services. *State Policies in Brief* 2006 February 1: 3 page [Online]. Accessed: http://www.guttmacher.org/statecenter/spibs/spib_RPHS.pdf [21 February 2006]. Subject: 12.4.3

Alan Guttmacher Institute. Restricting insurance coverage of abortion. *State Policies in Brief* 2006 February 1: 2 page [Online]. Accessed: http://guttmacher.org/statecenter/spibs/spib_RICA.pdf [21 February 2006]. Subject: 12.4.1

Alan Guttmacher Institute. State policies on late-term abortions. *State Policies in Brief* 2006 February 1: 2 page [Online]. Accessed: http://www.guttmacher.org/statecenter/spibs/spib_PLTA.pdf [21 February 2006]. Subject: 12.4.1

Albar, M.A. Counselling about genetic disease: an Islamic perspective. *Eastern Mediterranean Health Journal* 1999; 5(6): 1129-1133. Subject: 15.2

Albar, M.A. Organ transplantation — an Islamic perspective. *Saudi Medical Journal* 1991 July; 12(4): 280-284. Subject: 19.1

Albert, S.M.; Rabkin, J.G.; Del Bene, M.L.; Tider, T.; O'Sullivan, I.; Rowland, L.P.; Mitsumoto, H. Wish to die in end-stage ALS. *Neurology* 2005 July 12; 65(1): 68-74. Subject: 20.3.1

Alberta Kidney Disease Network; Tonelli, Marcello; Klarenbach, Scott; Manns, Braden; Culleton, Bruce; Hemmelgarn, Brenda; Betazzon, Stefania; Wiebe, Natasha; Gill, John S. Residence location and likelihood of kidney transplantation. *CMAJ/JAMC: Canadian Medical Association Journal* 2006 August 29; 175(5): 478-482. Subject: 19.6

Albiston, Catherine. The social meaning of the Norplant condition: constitutional considerations of race, class, and gender. *Berkeley Women's Law Journal* 1994; 9: 9-57. Subject: 11.1

Albright, C.L.; Glanz, K.; Wong, L.; Dela Cruz, M.R.; Abe, L.; Sagayadoro, T.L. Knowledge and attitudes about deceased donor organ donation in Filipinos: a qualitative assessment. *Transplantation Proceedings* 2005 December; 37(10): 4153-4158. Subject: 19.5

Alderson, Priscilla. Who should decide and how? *In:* Parens, Erik, ed. Surgically Shaping Children: Technology, Ethics, and the Pursuit of Normality. Baltimore, MD: Johns Hopkins University Press; 2006: 157-176. Subject: 8.3.2

Alderson, Priscilla; Hawthorne, Joanna; Killen, Margaret. Parents' experiences of sharing neonatal information and decisions: consent, cost and risk. *Social Science and Medicine* 2006 March; 62(6): 1319-1329. Subject: 8.3.2

Alderson, Priscilla; Sutcliffe, Katy; Curtis, Katherine. Children's competence to consent to medical treatment. *Hastings Center Report* 2006 November-December; 36(6): 25-34. Subject: 8.3.2

Aldhous, Peter. The accidental terrorists. *New Scientist* 2006 June 10-16; 190(2555): 24. Subject: 21.3

Aldhous, Peter. Bioterror: friend or foe? *New Scientist* 2006 October 14-20; 192(2573): 20-23. Subject: 21.3

Aldhous, Peter. Do drug firm links sway psychiatry? *New Scientist* 2006 April 29-May 5; 190(2549): 14. Subject: 9.7

Aldhous, Peter. Hwang's forgotten crime: the exploitation of women is a far worse offence than data fabrication. *New Scientist* 2006 February 4-10; 189(2537): 22. Subject: 1.3.9

Aldhous, Peter. Miracle postponed. *New Scientist* 2006 March 11-17; 189(2542): 38-41. Subject: 18.5.1

Aldhous, Peter. Scandal grows over suspect body parts. *New Scientist* 2006 September 2-8; 191(2567): 10. Subject: 19.5

Subject = NRCBL Primary Classification Number; see inside front cover.

Aldhous, Peter. Tailored medicines for rich and poor alike. *New Scientist* 2006 September 9-15; 191(2568): 13. Subject: 15.1

Aldhous, Peter; Coghlan, Andy. Ten years on, has the cloning dream died? *New Scientist* 2006 July 1-7; 191(2558): 8-10. Subject: 14.5

Aldhous, Peter; Coghlan, Andy. Therapeutic cloning set back by hype and fraud. *New Scientist* 2006 July 1-7; 191(2558): 11. Subject: 14.5

Alexander, G. Caleb; Hall, Mark A.; Lantos, John D. Rethinking professional ethics in the cost-sharing era. *American Journal of Bioethics [Online]* 2006 July-August; 6(4): W17-W22. Subject: 9.3.2

Alexander, G. Caleb; Lantos, John D. Commentary: physicians as public servants in the setting of bioterrorism. *CQ: Cambridge Quarterly of Healthcare Ethics* 2006 Fall; 15(4): 422-423. Subject: 8.1

Alexander, G. Caleb; Lantos, John D. The doctor-patient relationship in the post-managed care era. *American Journal of Bioethics* 2006 January-February; 6(1): 29-32. Subject: 8.1

Alexandrova, Anna. Legal and ethical issues in microbicides research and development in Canada. *HIV/AIDS Policy and Law Review* 2004 August; 9(2): 39-42. Subject: 9.5.6

Alfano, Bruno; Brunetti, Arturo. Advances in brain imaging: a new ethical challenge. *Annali Dell'Istituto Superiore di Sanità* 1997; 33(4): 483-488. Subject: 18.3

Alkhawari, Fawzi S.; Stimson, Gerry V.; Warrens, Anthony N. Attitudes toward transplantation in U.K. Muslim Indo-Asians in West London. *American Journal of Transplantation* 2005 June; 5(6): 1326-1331. Subject: 19.5

Alklint, Tommy. Alcohol abuse in the workplace: some ethical considerations. *In:* Westerholm, Peter; Nilstun, Tore; Øvretveit, John, eds. Practical Ethics in Occupational Health. San Francisco: Radcliffe Medical Press; 2004: 167-176. Subject: 16.3

Alkorta, Itziar. Women's rights in European fertility medicine regulation. *In:* Widdows, Heather; Idiakez, Itziar Alkorta; Cirión, Aitziber Emaldi, eds. Women's Reproductive Rights. New York: Palgrave Macmillan; 2006: 111-123. Subject: 14.1

Allen, Ben L. Ethical Issues at the Interface Between Orthopedics and Bioengineering. *Journal of Investigative Surgery* 1992 July-September; 5(3): 191-199. Subject: 5.2

Allen, Charlotte. Politically incorrect abortion. Boys only. *New Republic* 1992 March 9: 16-18. Subject: 14.3

Allen, Colin. Ethics and the science of animal minds. *Theoretical Medicine and Bioethics* 2006; 27(4): 375-394. Subject: 22.1

Allen, David B.; Fost, Norman. hGH for short stature: ethical issues raised by expanded access. *Journal of Pediatrics* 2004 May; 144(5): 648-652. Subject: 9.5.7

Allen, Garland E. Genetics, eugenics and the medicalization of social behavior: lessons from the past. *Endeavour* 1999; 23(1): 10-19. Subject: 15.5

Allen, Michael P. Congress and Terri Schiavo: a primer on the American Constitutional order? *West Virginia Law Review* 2005 Winter; 108(2): 309-360. Subject: 20.5.1

Allen, Michael P. Terri's law and democracy. *Stetson Law Review* 2005 Fall; 35(1): 179-193. Subject: 20.5.1

Allen, William. Erring too far on the side of life: déjà vu all over again in the Schiavo saga. *Stetson Law Review* 2005 Fall; 35(1): 123-145. Subject: 20.5.1

Allhoff, Fritz. Physician involvement in hostile interrogations. *CQ: Cambridge Quarterly of Healthcare Ethics* 2006 Fall; 15(4): 392-402. Subject: 21.2

Allmark, P. Choosing Health and the inner citadel. *Journal of Medical Ethics* 2006 January; 32(1): 3-6. Subject: 9.1

Allmark, P.; Mason, S. Improving the quality of consent to randomised controlled trials by using continuous consent and clinician training in the consent process. *Journal of Medical Ethics* 2006 August; 32(8): 439-443. Subject: 18.3

Allmark, P.; Mason, S. Should desperate volunteers be included in randomised controlled trials? *Journal of Medical Ethics* 2006 September; 32(9): 548-553. Subject: 18.1

Allmark, P.; Tod, A. How should public health professionals engage with lay epidemiology? *Journal of Medical Ethics* 2006 August; 32(8): 460-463. Subject: 9.1

Allmark, Peter. An argument for the use of Aristotelian method in bioethics. *Medicine, Health Care and Philosophy* 2006; 9(1): 69-79. Subject: 2.1

Allott, Piers. Mental disorder, diagnosis, treatment and ethics. *Journal of Ethics in Mental Health* 2006 November; 1(1): E11, 2 p. Subject: 17.1

Allphin, Claire. An ethical attitude in the analytic relationship. *Journal of Analytical Psychology* 2005 September; 50(4): 451-468. Subject: 17.1

Almarsdóttir, Anna Birna; Traulsen, Janine Morgall; Björnsdóttir, Ingunn. "We don't have that many secrets" — the lay perspective on privacy and genetic data. *In:* Árnason, Gardar; Nordal, Salvör; Árnason, Vilhjálmur, eds. Blood and Data: Ethical, Legal and Social Aspects of Human Genetic Databases. Reykjavík: University of Iceland Press; 2004: 193-200. Subject: 15.1

Almeling, Rene. "Why do you want to be a donor?": gender and the production of altruism in egg and sperm donation. *New Genetics and Society* 2006 August; 25(2): 143-157. Subject: 14.2

See SUBJECT HEADING KEY FOR SECTION II on inside back cover.

475

Almond, Brenda. Genetic profiling of newborns: ethical and social issues. *Nature Reviews Genetics* 2006 January; 7(1): 67-71. Subject: 15.3

Alonso Bedate, Carlos. Ethical and legal implications of the use of molecular biology in the clinic. *Journal of Pediatric Endocrinology and Metabolism* 2005 December; 18(Supplement 1): 1137-1143. Subject: 15.2

Alpert, Jonathan E.; Biggs, Melanie M.; Davis, Lori; Shores-Wilson, Kathy; Harlan, William R.; Schneider, Gregory W.; Ford, Amy L.; Farabaugh, Amy; Stegman, Diane; Ritz, A. Louise; Husain, Mustafa M.; Macleod, Laurie; Wisniewski, Stephen R.; Rush, A. John. Enrolling research subjects from clinical practice: ethical and procedural issues in the Sequenced Treatment Alternatives to Relieve Depression (STAR*D) trial. *Psychiatry Research* 2006 February 28; 141(2): 193-200. Subject: 18.5.6

Alpert, Joseph S.; Shine, Kenneth I.; Adams, Robert J.; Antman, Elliott M.; Kavey, Rae Ellen W.; Friedman, Lawrence; Frye, Robert L.; Harrington, Robert A.; Korn, David; Merz, Jon F.; Ofili, Elizabeth. Task force 1: the ACCF and AHA codes of conduct in human subjects research. *Journal of the American College of Cardiology* 2004 October 19; 44(8): 1724-1728. Subject: 18.2

Alpert, Sheri A. Protecting medical privacy: challenges in the age of genetic information. *Journal of Social Issues* 2003; 59(2): 301-322. Subject: 8.4

Alsever, Jennifer. Basking on the beach, or maybe on the operating table. *New York Times* 2006 October 15; p. BU5. Subject: 9.3.1

Alston, Bruce. Blood rights: the body and information privacy. *Journal of Law and Medicine* 2005 May; 12(4): 426-440. Subject: 19.5

Althanasiou, Tom; Darnovsky, Marcy. The genome as a commons. *World Watch* 2002 July-August; 15(4:) 33-36. Subject: 15.10

Altman, Dennis. Rights matter: structural interventions and vulnerable communities. *Health and Human Rights: An International Journal* 2005; 8(2): 203-213. Subject: 9.5.6

Altman, Stuart H.; Doonan, Michael. Can Massachusetts lead the way in health care reform? *New England Journal of Medicine* 2006 May 18; 354(20): 2093-2095. Subject: 9.3.1

Alvarez-Castillo, Fatima; Feinholz, Dafna. Women in developing countries and benefit sharing. *Developing World Bioethics* 2006 December; 6(3): 113-121. Subject: 15.1

American Academy of Neurology [AAN]; American Neurological Association [ANA]. Position statement regarding the use of embryonic and adult human stem cells in biomedical research. *Neurology* 2005 May 24; 64(10): 1679-1680. Subject: 18.5.4

American Academy of Neurology [AAN]; Sagsveen, Murray G. American Academy of Neurology policy on expert medical testimony [editorial]. *Neurology* 2004 November 9; 63(9): 1555-1556. Subject: 7.3

American Academy of Neurology [AAN]; Williams, M.A.; Mackin, G.A.; Beresford, H.R.; Gordon, J.; Jacobson, P.L.; McQuillen, M.P.; Reimschisel, T.E.; Taylor, R.M.; Bernat, J.L.; Rizzo, M.; Snyder, R.D.; Sagsveen, M.G.; Amery, M.; Brannon, W.L., Jr. American Academy of Neurology qualifications and guidelines for the physician expert witness. *Neurology* 2006 January 10; 66(1): 13-14. Subject: 6

American Academy of Pain Medicine [AAPM]. Council on Ethics. Ethics charter from American Academy of Pain Medicine. *Pain Medicine* 2005 May-June; 6(3): 203-212. Subject: 6

American Academy of Pediatric Dentistry. Council on Clinical Affairs. Guideline on informed consent. *Pediatric Dentistry* 2005-2006; 27(7 Reference Manual): 182-183. Subject: 8.3.1

American Academy of Pediatric Dentistry. Council on Clinical Affairs. Policy on the ethics of failure to treat or refer. *Pediatric Dentistry* 2005-2006; 27(7 Reference Manual): 61. Subject: 4.1.1

American Academy of Psychiatry and the Law [AAPL]. American Academy of Psychiatry and the Law ethical guidelines for the practice of forensic psychiatry. *Bloomfield, CT: American Academy of Psychiatry and the Law,* 1995: 5 p. [Online]. Accessed: http://www.aapl.org/ethics.htm [14 December 2005]. Subject: 6

American Association for Hospice and Palliative Medicine. Position statement on sedation at the end-of-life. *In:* Tännsjö, Torbjörn, ed. Terminal Sedation: Euthanasia in Disguise? Boston: Kluwer Academic Publishers; 2004: 129-131. Subject: 20.4.1

American Association for Hospice and Palliative Medicine. Position statement on sedation at the end-of-life. *In:* Tännsjö, Torbjörn, ed. Terminal Sedation: Euthanasia in Disguise? Boston: Kluwer Academic Publishers; 2004: 127-128. Subject: 20.4.1

American Board of Orthodontics; Moffitt, Allen H.; Greco, Peter M.; Fleisher, Lynn D. Appropriate use of the designation of ABO certification: a statement by the American Board of Orthodontics. *American Journal of Orthodontics and Dentofacial Orthopedics* 2006 April; 129(4): 571-573. Subject: 4.1.1

American College of Obstetricians and Gynecologists [ACOG]. Committee on Ethics. ACOG Committee Opinion #321: maternal decision making, ethics, and the law. *Obstetrics and Gynecology* 2005 November; 106(5 Part 1): 1127-1137. Subject: 9.5.5

American College of Surgeons [ACS]. Statement on the physician acting as an expert witness. *Journal of the Amer-*

ican College of Surgeons 2004 November; 199(5): 746-747. Subject: 7.3

American College of Surgeons [ACS]. Task Force on Professionalism. Code of professional conduct. *Journal of the American College of Surgeons* 2004 November; 199(5): 734-735. Subject: 6

American College of Surgeons [ACS]. Task Force on Professionalism; Barry, Linda; Blair, Patrice Gabler; Cosgrove, Ellen M.; Cruess, Richard L.; Cruess, Sylvia R.; Eastman, A. Brent; Fabri, P. Jeffrey; Kirksey, Thomas D.; Liscum, Kathleen R.; Morrison, Rosemary; Sachdeva, Ajit K.; Svahn, David S.; Russell, Thomas R.; Dickey, Jamie; Ungerleider, Ross M.; Harken, Alden H. One year, and counting, after publication of our ACS "Code of Professional Conduct". *Journal of the American College of Surgeons* 2004 November; 199(5): 736-740. Subject: 6

American Health Information Management Association. Professional Ethics Committee. American Health Information Management Association code of ethics. *Journal of AHIMA* 2004 November-December; 75(10): 80A-80D. Subject: 6

American Medical Association. Council on Ethical and Judicial Affairs; Green, Shane K.; Taub, Sara; Morin, Karine; Higginson, Daniel. Guidelines to prevent malevolent use of biomedical research. *CQ: Cambridge Quarterly of Healthcare Ethics* 2006 Fall; 15(4): 432-447. Subject: 1.3.9

American Medical Association. Council on Ethical and Judicial Affairs; Moren, Karine; Higginson, Daniel; Goldrich, Michael. Physician obligation in disaster preparedness and response. *CQ: Cambridge Quarterly of Healthcare Ethics* 2006 Fall; 15(4): 417-431. Subject: 8.1

American Occupational Therapy Association [AOTA]. Enforcement procedures for the Occupational Therapy Code of Ethics. *American Journal of Occupational Therapy* 2005 November-December; 59(6): 643-652. Subject: 6

American Osteopathic Association; End-of-Life Care Committee. American Osteopathic Association's policy statement on end-of-life care. *Journal of the American Osteopathic Association* 2005 November; 105(11, Supplement 5): S32-S34. Subject: 20.5.1

American Pharmacists Association [APhA]. APhA Statement on FDA's Recent Approval of Plan B for OTC Status. Washington, DC: American Pharmacists Association, 2006 August 24: 1 p. [Online]. Accessed: http://www.aphanet.org/AM/Template.cfm?Template= CM/ContentDisplay.cfm&ContentID=6569 [2006 September 26]. Subject: 11.1

American Pharmacists Association [APhA]; MacLean, Linda Garrelts. Freedom of Conscience for Small Pharmacies. Submitted to the House Small Business Committee. Testimony of the American Pharmacists Association.

Washington, DC: The Association [APhA] 2005 July 25; 10 p. [Online]. Accessed: http://www.aphanet.org/AM/Template.cfm?Section= Home&CONTENTID=3565& Template=/cm/CONTENTDisplay.cfm [2006 September 18]. Subject: 9.7

American Psychiatric Association. Task Force on Research Ethics. Ethical principles and practices for research involving human participants with mental illness. *Psychiatric Services* 2006 April; 57(4): 552-557. Subject: 18.5.6

American Society for Reproductive Medicine [ASRM]. Guidelines for cryopreserved embryo donation. *Fertility and Sterility* 2004 September; 82(Supplement 1): S16-S17. Subject: 19.5

American Society for Reproductive Medicine [ASRM]. Guidelines for oocyte donation. *Fertility and Sterility* 2004 September; 82(Supplement 1): S13-S15. Subject: 19.5

American Society for Reproductive Medicine [ASRM]. Guidelines for sperm donation. *Fertility and Sterility* 2004 September; 82(Supplement 1): S9-S12. Subject: 19.5

American Society for Reproductive Medicine [ASRM]. Ethics Committee. Child-rearing ability and the provision of fertility services. *Fertility and Sterility* 2004 September; 82(Supplement 1): S208-S211. Subject: 14.1

American Society for Reproductive Medicine [ASRM]. Ethics Committee. Disposition of abandoned embryos. *Fertility and Sterility* 2004 September; 82(Supplement 1): S253. Subject: 18.5.4

American Society for Reproductive Medicine [ASRM]. Ethics Committee. Donating spare embryos for embryonic stem-cell research. *Fertility and Sterility* 2004 September; 82(Supplement 1): S224-S227. Subject: 19.5

American Society for Reproductive Medicine [ASRM]. Ethics Committee. Embryo splitting for infertility treatment. *Fertility and Sterility* 2004 September; 82(Supplement 1): S256-S257. Subject: 18.5.4

American Society for Reproductive Medicine [ASRM]. Ethics Committee. Family members as gamete donors and surrogates. *Fertility and Sterility* 2004 September; 82(Supplement 1): S217-S223. Subject: 19.5

American Society for Reproductive Medicine [ASRM]. Ethics Committee. Financial incentives in recruitment of oocyte donors. *Fertility and Sterility* 2004 September; 82(Supplement 1): S240-S244. Subject: 14.4

American Society for Reproductive Medicine [ASRM]. Ethics Committee. Human immunodeficiency virus and infertility treatment. *Fertility and Sterility* 2004 September; 82(Supplement 1): S228-S231. Subject: 9.5.6

American Society for Reproductive Medicine [ASRM]. Ethics Committee. Human somatic cell nuclear transfer (cloning). *Fertility and Sterility* 2004 September; 82(Supplement 1): S236-S239. Subject: 14.5

See SUBJECT HEADING KEY FOR SECTION II on inside back cover.

477

American Society for Reproductive Medicine [ASRM]. Ethics Committee. Informed consent and the use of gametes and embryos for research. *Fertility and Sterility* 2004 September; 82(Supplement 1): S251-S252. Subject: 18.3

American Society for Reproductive Medicine [ASRM]. Ethics Committee. Informing offspring of their conception by gamete donation. *Fertility and Sterility* 2004 September; 82(Supplement 1): S212-S216. Subject: 14.2

American Society for Reproductive Medicine [ASRM]. Ethics Committee. Oocyte donation to postmenopausal women. *Fertility and Sterility* 2004 September; 82(Supplement 1): S254-S255. Subject: 14.6

American Society for Reproductive Medicine [ASRM]. Ethics Committee. Posthumous reproduction. *Fertility and Sterility* 2004 September; 82(Supplement 1): S260-S262. Subject: 14.6

American Society for Reproductive Medicine [ASRM]. Ethics Committee. Preconception gender selection for nonmedical reasons. *Fertility and Sterility* 2004 September; 82(Supplement 1): S232-S235. Subject: 14.3

American Society for Reproductive Medicine [ASRM]. Ethics Committee. Sex selection and preimplantation genetic diagnosis. *Fertility and Sterility* 2004 September; 82(Supplement 1): S245-S248. Subject: 15.2

American Society for Reproductive Medicine [ASRM]. Ethics Committee. Shared-risk or refund programs in assisted reproduction. *Fertility and Sterility* 2004 September; 82(Supplement 1): S249-S250. Subject: 14.4

American Society for Reproductive Medicine [ASRM]. Ethics Committee. Use of fetal oocytes in assisted reproduction. *Fertility and Sterility* 2004 September; 82(Supplement 1): S258-S259. Subject: 14.1

American Society for Reproductive Medicine [ASRM]. Practice Committee. Elements to be considered in obtaining informed consent for ART. *Fertility and Sterility* 2004 September; 82(Supplement 1): S202-S203. Subject: 14.1

American Society for Reproductive Medicine [ASRM]. Practice Committee Society for Assisted Reproductive Technology. Revised minimum standards for practices offering assisted reproductive technologies. *Fertility and Sterility* 2004 September; 82(Supplement 1): S4-S7. Subject: 14.1

American Society of Clinical Oncology [ASCO]. American Society of Clinical Oncology policy statement: oversight of clinical research. *Journal of Clinical Oncology* 2003 June 15; 21(12): 2377-2386. Subject: 18.2

American Society of Clinical Oncology [ASCO]. American Society Of Clinical Oncology: revised conflict of interest policy. *Journal of Clinical Oncology* 2006 January 20; 24(3): 519-521. Subject: 1.3.9

American Society of Clinical Oncology [ASCO]. Revisions of and clarifications to the ASCO conflict of interest policy. *Journal of Clinical Oncology* 2006 January 20; 24(3): 517-518. Subject: 1.3.9

American Society of Gene Therapy [ASGT]. American Society of Gene Therapy establishes ethical policy to guide clinical trials [policy statement]. Milwaukee, WI: American Society of Gene Therapy [ASGT], 2000 April 13. 2 p. [Online]. Accessed: http://www.asgt.org/position_statements/ethical_policy.html [27 July 2006]. Subject: 18.2

American Society of Human Genetics [ASHG]. Code of ethics. Bethesda, MD: American Society of Human Genetics, 2006 March; 2 p. [Online]. Accessed: http://genetics.faseb.org/genetics/ashg/pubs/policy/pol-49.pdf [2007 February 7]. Subject: 6

American Society of Human Genetics [ASHG]. Should family members about whom you collect only medical history information for your research be considered 'human subjects'? [policy statement]. Bethesda, MD: American Society of Human Genetics, 2000 March: 3 p. [Online]. Accessed: http://www.ashg.org/genetics/ashg/pubs/policy/pol-38.htm [2006 July 25]. Subject: 15.1

American Society of Human Genetics [ASHG]; Francke, Uta. Response to National Bioethics Advisory Commission [NBAC] on the ethical issues and policy concerns surrounding research using human biological materials [letter]. Bethesda, MD: American Society of Human Genetics, 1999 January 15. 4 p. [Online]. Accessed: http://genetics.faseb.org/genetics/ashg/pubs/policy/pol-33.htm [26 July 2006]. Subject: 18.2

American Society of Human Genetics [ASHG]; Francke, Uta; Worton, Ronald. Re: Draft NIH guidelines for research involving human pluripotent stem cells [letter]. Bethesda, MD: American Society of Human Genetics [ASHG], 2000 January 21: 2 p. [Online]. Accessed: http://www.ashg.org/genetics/ashg/pubs/policy/pol-37.htm [2006 July 25]. Subject: 18.5.4

American Society of Human Genetics [ASHG]. Ad Hoc Committee on Consumer Issues. Genetic lay advocacy groups: significant others in the conduct of human genetics research. Committee Report. Bethesda, MD: American Society of Human Genetics, 2001 October 18. 9 p. [Online]. Accessed: http://genetics.faseb.org/genetics/ashg/pubs/policy/pol_46.pdf [2006 July 24]. Subject: 15.1

American Society of Human Genetics [ASHG]. Board of Directors; Worton, Ronald. Re: Revised interim utilities examination guidelines and revised interim guidelines for examination of patent applications [letter]. Bethesda, MD: American Society of Human Genetics, 2000 March 22: 3 p. [Online]. Accessed: http://genetics.faseb.org/genetics/ashg/pubs/policy/pol-39.htm [2006 July 26]. Subject: 15.8

American Society of Human Genetics [ASHG]. Human Genome Committee American Society of Human Genetics. Board of Directors. American Society of Human

---

Genetics Position Paper on Patenting of Expressed Sequence Tags [ESTs] [position statement]. Bethesda, MD: American Society of Human Genetics, 1991 November: 3 p. [Online]. Accessed: http://www.ashg.org/genetics/pubs/policy/pol-08.htm [2006 July 25]. Subject: 15.8

Ames, David A. Ethical dilemmas in clinical medicine: although ethical principles are normative statements and theoretical constructs can be applied to many situations, each case is unique. *Rhode Island Medical Journal* 1986 March; 69(3): 117-120. Subject: 2.1

Aminoff, Bechor Zvi. Overprotection phenomenon with dying dementia patients [editorial]. *American Journal of Hospice and Palliative Medicine* 2005 July-August; 22(4): 247-248. Subject: 20.5.1

Amoroso, Kimberly. Frozen embryo adoption and the United States government. *Newsletter on Philosophy and Medicine* 2005 Fall; 05(1): 3-5. Subject: 14.6

Amoroso, Paul J.; Wenger, Lynn L. The human volunteer in military biomedical research. *In:* Beam, Thomas E.; Sparacino, Linette R.; Pellegrino, Edmund D.; Hartle, Anthony E.; Howe, Edmund G., eds. Military Medical Ethics. Volume 2. Washington, DC: TMM Publications, Borden Institute, Walter Reed Army Medical Center; 2003: 563-660. Subject: 18.5.8

Amstutz, Harlan C. Innovations in design and technology: the story of hip arthroplasty. *Clinical Orthopaedics and Related Research* 2000 September; (378): 23-30. Subject: 18.6

Anand, Kuldip P.; Kashyap, Ajit; Kashyap, Surekha. Thinking the unthinkable: selling kidneys [letter]. *BMJ: British Medical Journal* 2006 July 15; 333(7559): 149. Subject: 19.3

Anand, Paul. Social choice as the synthesis of incommensurable claims: the case of health care rationing. *In:* Davis, John B., ed. The Social Economics of Health Care. New York: Routledge; 2001: 61-93. Subject: 9.4

Anand, Paul; Dolan, Paul. Equity, capabilities and health: introduction. *Social Science and Medicine* 2005 January; 60(2): 219-222. Subject: 9.4

Anand, Sonia A. Using ethnicity as a classification variable in health research: perpetuating the myth of biological determinism, serving socio-political agendas, or making valuable contributions to medical sciences? *Ethnicity and Health* 1999 November; 4(4): 241-244. Subject: 18.5.1

Anderman, Jonathan. Right to access experimental drugs. *American Journal of Law and Medicine* 2006; 32(4): 611-614. Subject: 20.4.1

Andersen, Knut Erik. Workplace rehabilitation. *In:* Westerholm, Peter; Nilstun, Tore; Øvretveit, John, eds. Practical Ethics in Occupational Health. San Francisco: Radcliffe Medical Press; 2004: 189-198. Subject: 16.3

Andersen, Morten; Kragstrup, Jakob; Søndergaard, Jens. How conducting a clinical trial affects physicians' guideline adherence and drug preferences. *JAMA: The Journal of the American Medical Association* 2006 June 21; 295(23): 2759-2764. Subject: 9.7

Andersen, Nina Vinther. Dispute over conflicts of interests leads to changes for medical society [news]. *BMJ: British Medical Journal* 2006 December 16; 333(7581): 1240. Subject: 7.3

Anderson, Brian. Psychedelic psychotherapy: the ethics of medicine for the soul. *Penn Bioethics Journal* 2006; 2(1): 4p. [Online]. Accessed: http://www.bioethicsjournal.com [2006 February 21]. Subject: 17.4

Anderson, Brian; Cranswick, Noel. The placebo (I shall please) — is it so pleasing in children? [editorial]. *Paediatric Anaesthesia* 2005 October; 15(10): 809-813. Subject: 18.3

Anderson, D.K.; Beattie, M.; Blesch, A.; Bresnahan, J.; Bunge, M.; Dietrich, D.; Dietz, V.; Dobkin, B.; Fawcett, J.; Fehlings, M.; Fischer, I.; Grossman, R.; Guest, J.; Hagg, T.; Hall, E.D.; Houle, J.; Kleitman, N.; McDonald, J.; Murray, M.; Privat, A.; Reier, P.; Steeves, J.; Steward, O.; Tetzlaff, W.; Tuszynski, M.H.; Waxman, S.G.; Whittemore, S.; Wolpaw, J.; Young, W.; Zheng B. Recommended guidelines for studies of human subjects with spinal cord injury. *Spinal Cord* 2005 August; 43(8): 453-458. Subject: 18.2

Anderson, Emily E. A qualitative study of non-affiliated, non-scientist institutional review board members. *Accountability in Research* 2006 April-June; 13(2): 135-155. Subject: 18.2

Anderson, James A. The ethics and science of placebo-controlled trials: assay sensitivity and the Duhem-Quine thesis. *Journal of Medicine and Philosophy* 2006 February; 31(1): 65-81. Subject: 18.2

Anderson, Maria. Bush dismisses council members: scientific group angry at loss of Elizabeth Blackburn from group considering stem cells. *Scientist* 2004 March 3; 5(1): 6 p. [Online]. Accessed: http://www.the-scientist.com/news/20040303/04/ [12 October 2006]. Subject: 2.4

Anderson, M. Xenotransplantation: a bioethical evaluation. *Journal of Medical Ethics* 2006 April; 32(4): 205-208. Subject: 19.1

Anderson, Rebecca. The singular moral compass of Otto Krayer. *Molecular Interventions* 2005 December; 5(6): 324-329. Subject: 1.3.9

Anderson, Robert M. Is it ethical to assign medically underserved African Americans to a usual-care control group in community-based intervention research? *Diabetes Care* 2005 July; 28(7): 1817-1820. Subject: 18.5.1

Anderson, Warwick P.; Cordner, Christopher D.; Breen, Kerry J. Strengthening Australia's framework for research oversight. All stakeholders should contribute to enhancing Australia's guidelines for ethical research [edi-

See SUBJECT HEADING KEY FOR SECTION II on inside back cover.

479

torial]. *Medical Journal of Australia* 2006 March 20; 184(6): 261-263. Subject: 18.2

Anderson-Shaw; Lisa. Rural health care ethics: networking and resources can lead to original research. *American Journal of Bioethics* 2006 March-April; 6(2): 61-62. Subject: 9.5.1

Anderson-Shaw, Lisa; Orfali, Kristina. Child-to-parents bone marrow donation for treatment of sickle cell disease. *Journal of Clinical Ethics* 2006 Spring; 17(1): 53-61. Subject: 19.5

Andorno, Roberto. Seeking common ground on genetic issues: the UNESCO Declaration on the Human Genome. *In:* Sándor, Judit, ed. Society and Genetic Information: Codes and Laws in the Genetic Era. Budapest, Hungary; New York: CEU Press; 2003: 105-123. Subject: 15.1

Andraghetti, R.; Foran, S.; Colebunders, R.; Tomlinson, D.; Vyras, P.; Borleffs, C.J.; Fleerackers, Y.; Schrooten, W.; Borchert, M. Euthanasia: from the perspective of HIV infected persons in Europe. *HIV Medicine* 2001 January; 2(1): 3-10. Subject: 20.7

Andrews, Jason. Research in the ranks: vulnerable subjects, coercible collaboration, and the Hepatitis E vaccine trial in Nepal. *Perspectives on Biology and Medicine* 2006 Winter; 49(1): 35-51. Subject: 18.5.8

Andrews, Lesley; Mireskandari, Shab; Jessen, Jaime; Thewes, Belinda; Solomon, Michael; Macrae, Finlay; Meiser, Bettina. Impact of familial adenomatous polyposis on young adults: attitudes toward genetic testing, support, and information needs. *Genetics in Medicine* 2006 November; 8(11): 697-703. Subject: 15.3

Andrews, Lori. Who owns your body? A patient's perspective on Washington University v. Catalona. *Journal of Law, Medicine and Ethics* 2006 Summer; 34(2): 398-407. Subject: 4.4

Andrews, Lori B. Assisted reproductive technology and the challenge for paternity laws. *In:* Rothstein, Mark A.; Murray, Thomas H.; Kaebnick, Gregory E.; Majumder, Mary Anderlik, eds. Genetic Ties and the Family: The Impact of Paternity Testing on Parents and Children. Baltimore: Johns Hopkins University Press; 2005: 187-212. Subject: 14.1

Andrews, Lori B. How is technology changing the meaning of motherhood for western women. *In:* Widdows, Heather; Idiakez, Itziar Alkorta; Cirión, Aitziber Emaldi, eds. Women's Reproductive Rights. New York: Palgrave Macmillan; 2006: 124-139. Subject: 14.1

Andrews, Maria; Marian, Mary. Ethical framework for the registered dietitian in decisions regarding withholding/withdrawing medically assisted nutrition and hydration. *Journal of the American Dietetic Association* 2006 February; 106(2): 206-208. Subject: 20.5.1

Angelini, Fiorenzo. The responsibility of Catholic health workers: humanity in medicine and service to life. *Dolentium Hominum* 1994; 9(3): 56-59. Subject: 4.1.2

Angell, E.; Sutton, A.J.; Windridge, K.; Dixon-Woods, M. Consistency in decision making by research ethics committees: a controlled comparison. *Journal of Medical Ethics* 2006 November; 32(11): 662-664. Subject: 18.2

Angell, Marcia; Brennan, Troyen A.; Rothman, David J.; Naughton, James; Cohen, Jordan; Kimball, Harry; Blumenthal, David; Smelser, Neil; Kassirer, Jerome P.; Goldman, JanLori. Academic medical centers and conflicts of interest [letter and reply]. *JAMA: The Journal of the American Medical Association* 2006 June 28; 295(24): 2848, 2848-2849. Subject: 7.3

Angelucci, Patricia A. Grasping the concept of medical futility. *Nursing Management* 2006 February; 37(2): 12, 14. Subject: 20.5.1

Angiolillo, Anne L.; Simon, C.; Kodish, E.; Lange, B.; Noll, R.B.; Ruccione, K.; Matloub, Y. Staged informed consent for a randomized clinical trial in childhood leukemia: impact on the consent process. *Pediatric Blood and Cancer* 2004 May; 42(5): 433-437. Subject: 18.3

Angrist, Misha; Cook-Deegan, Robert M. Who owns the genome? *New Atlantis* 2006 Winter; 11: 87-96. Subject: 15.8

Angrosino, Michael V. Catholic social policy and U.S. health care reform: a relationship revisited. *Medical Anthropology Quarterly* 2001 September; 15(3): 312-328. Subject: 9.3.1

Ankeny, Rachel A.; Clifford, Ross; Jordens, Christopher F.C.; Kerridge, Ian H.; Benson, Rod. Religious perspectives on withdrawal of treatment from patients with multiple organ failure. *Medical Journal of Australia* 2005 December 5-19; 183(11-12): 616-621. Subject: 20.5.1

Annas, George J. Bioterror and "bioart" — a plague o' both your houses. *New England Journal of Medicine* 2006 June 22; 354(25): 2715-2720. Subject: 21.3

Annas, George J. Congress, controlled substances, and physician-assisted suicide — elephants in mouseholes. *New England Journal of Medicine* 2006 March 9; 354(10): 1079-1084. Subject: 20.7

Annas, George J. Fathers anonymous: beyond the best interests of the sperm donor. *Child Welfare* 1981 March; 60(3): 161-174. Subject: 14.2

Annas, George J. Hunger strikes at Guantanamo — medical ethics and human rights in a "legal black hole". *New England Journal of Medicine* 2006 September 28; 355(13): 1377-1382. Subject: 21.5

Annas, George J. "I want to live": medicine betrayed by ideology in the political debate over Terri Schiavo. *Stetson Law Review* 2005 Fall; 35(1): 49-80. Subject: 20.5.1

Subject = NRCBL Primary Classification Number; see inside front cover.

Annas, George J. The statue of security: human rights and post-9/11 epidemics. *Journal of Health Law* 2005 Spring; 38(2): 319-351. Subject: 21.1

Annett, Tim. Balancing competing interests over frozen embryos: the judgment of Solomon? Evans v. United Kingdom. *Medical Law Review* 2006 Autumn; 14(3): 425-433. Subject: 14.6

Anstey, Kyle W. Prenatal testing and disability: the need for a participatory approach to research. *In:* Sang-yong, Song; Young-Mo, Koo; Macer, Darryl R.J., eds. Asian Bioethics in the 21st Century. Christchurch, NZ: Eubios Ethics Institute, 2002: 347-356. Subject: 15.2

Antommaria, Armand H. Matheny. "Who Should Survive?: One of the Choices on our Conscience": Mental retardation and the history of contemporary bioethics. *Kennedy Institute of Ethics Journal* 2006 September; 16(3): 205-224. Subject: 20.5.2

Antommaria, Armand H. Matheny; Srivastava, Rajendu. If cardiologists take care of patients with heart disease, what do hospitals treat?: hospitalists and the doctor-patient relationship. *American Journal of Bioethics* 2006 January-February; 6(1): 47-49. Subject: 8.1

Apel, Susan B. Cryopreserved embryos: a response to "forced parenthood" and the role of intent. *Family Law Quarterly* 2005 Fall; 39(3): 663-681. Subject: 14.6

Appel, Jacob M. A duty to kill? A duty to die? Rethinking the euthanasia controversy of 1906. *Bulletin of the History of Medicine* 2004 Fall; 78(3): 610-634. Subject: 20.5.1

Appel, Jacob M. Judicial diagnosis 'conscience' vs. care how refusal clauses are reshaping the rights revolution. *Medicine and Health, Rhode Island* 2005 August; 88(8): 279-281. Subject: 12.4.3

Appel, Jacob M. May doctors refuse infertility treatments to gay patients? *Hastings Center Report* 2006 July-August; 36(4): 20-21. Subject: 8.1

Appel, Jacob M. The monster's laws: a legal history of chimera research. *GeneWatch* 2006 March-April; 19(2): 12-16. Subject: 15.1

Appelbaum, Paul S. Commentary: psychiatric advance directives at a crossroads—when can PADs be overridden? *Journal of the American Academy of Psychiatry and the Law* 2006; 34(3): 395-397. Subject: 20.5.4

Appelbaum, Paul S. Decisional capacity of patients with schizophrenia to consent to research: taking stock. *Schizophrenia Bulletin* 2006 January; 32(1): 22-25. Subject: 18.3

Appelbaum, Paul S.; Lidz, Charles W. Clinical ethics versus clinical research. *American Journal of Bioethics* 2006 July-August; 6(4): 53-55. Subject: 18.2

Appelbaum, Paul S.; Lidz, Charles W. Re-evaluating the therapeutic misconception: response to Miller and Joffe. *Kennedy Institute of Ethics Journal* 2006 December; 16(4): 367-373. Subject: 18.3

Appelbaum, Paul S.; Roth, Loren H.; Lidz, Charles. The therapeutic misconception: informed consent in psychiatric research. *International Journal of Law and Psychiatry* 1982; 5(3-4): 319-329. Subject: 8.3.1

Appelbaum, Paul S.; Weiss Roberts, Laura. Introduction: report of the APA's Task Force on Research Ethics. *Psychiatric Services* 2006 April; 57(4): 550-551. Subject: 18.5.6

Applbaum, Kalman. Educating for global mental health: the adoption of SSRIs in Japan. *In:* Petryna, Adriana; Lakoff, Andrew; Kleinman, Arthur, eds. Global Pharmaceuticals: Ethics, Markets, Practices. Durham: Duke University Press; 2006: 85-110. Subject: 9.7

Applebaum, David. Judges' voices in the French abortion debate of the 1970s. *E Law: Murdoch University Electronic Journal of Law* 1995 December; 2(3): 25 p. [Online]. Accessed: http://www.murdoch.edu.au/elaw/issues/v2n3/applebaum23.html [2006 June 29]. Subject: 12.4.1

Applequist, Hilary; Giedt, Elizabeth M. Organ donation: autonomy and beneficence: the case of Mr. P. *JONA's Healthcare Law, Ethics, and Regulation* 2006 April-June; 8(2): 37-41. Subject: 19.5

Apseloff, Glen. HIV testing in early clinical trials: who should decide whether it is warranted? *Journal of Clinical Pharmacology* 2002 June; 42(6): 601-604. Subject: 18.2

Aquilina, Carmelo; Greaves, Suki; Al-Saadi, Mohammed; Parmentier, Henk; Tarrant, Joyce; Wantoch, Elaine. Please do not resuscitate: automatic refusal is as harmful as offering resuscitation to all [letter]. *BMJ: British Medical Journal* 2006 March 11; 332(7541): 608-609. Subject: 20.5.1

Ar-Rashid, Harun. Regional perspectives in research ethics: a report from Bangladesh. *Eastern Mediterranean Health Journal* 2006; 12(Supplement 1): S66-S72 [Online]. Accessed: http://www.emro.who.int/publications/EMHJ/12_S/PDF/10.pdf [2007 January 4]. Subject: 18.2

Arar, Nedal H.; Hazuda, Helen; Steinbach, Rebecca; Arar, Mazen Y.; Abboud, Hanna E. Ethical issues associated with conducting genetic family studies of complex disease. *Annals of Epidemiology* 2005 October; 15(9): 712-719. Subject: 15.3

Araujo, Robert John. The transnational perspective of the church: the embryonic cloning debate and stem cell research. *Journal of Contemporary Health Law and Policy* 2006 Spring; 22(2): 497-507. Subject: 18.5.4

Aravind, K.; Kannappan, J.G. Hippocratic oath in the modern times. *Indian Journal of Dental Research* 2005 April-June; 16(2): 37-41. Subject: 6

Archibald, Kathy. No need for monkeys [letter]. *New Scientist* 2006 July 1-7; 191(2558): 26. Subject: 22.2

Archibold, Randal C. Killings loom over debate on treating mentally ill; New Mexico considers commitment law. *New York Times* 2006 February 8; p. A16. Subject: 8.3.4

See SUBJECT HEADING KEY FOR SECTION II on inside back cover.

481

Ardalan, Kaveh. Hope and autonomy in the context of heart transplantation. *Penn Bioethics Journal* 2005 April 2; 1(1): 3p. [Online]. Accessed: http://www. bioethicsjournal.com [2005 April 19]. Subject: 8.2

Arlettaz, Romaine; Mieth, Dieto; Bucher, Hans-Ulrich; Duc, Gabriel; Fauchère, Jean-Claude. End-of-life decisions in delivery room and neonatal intensive care unit. *Acta Paediatrica* 2005 November; 94(11): 1626-1631. Subject: 20.5.2

Armitage, Gerry. Drug errors, qualitative research and some reflections on ethics. *Journal of Clinical Nursing* 2005 August; 14(7): 869-875. Subject: 9.8

Armstrong, Alan E. Towards a strong virtue ethics for nursing practice. *Nursing Philosophy* 2006 July; 7(3): 110-124. Subject: 4.1.3

Armstrong, David. Baby talk: Drug firm's cash sways debate over test for pregnant women; Glaxo funds lectures urging herpes screening — an idea widely rejected by experts; at issue: virus's risk to infants. *Wall Street Journal* 2006 December 13; p. A1, A12. Subject: 9.5.5

Armstrong, David. Financial ties to industry cloud major depression study; at issue: whether it's safe for pregnant women to stay on medication; JAMA asks authors to explain. *Wall Street Journal* 2006 July 11; p. A1, A9. Subject: 1.3.9

Armstrong, David. How the New England Journal missed warning signs on Vioxx: medical weekly waited years to report flaws in article that praised pain drug; Merck seen as "punching bag". *Wall Street Journal* 2006 May 15; p. A1, A10. Subject: 1.3.7

Armstrong, David. JAMA to toughen rules on author disclosure. *Wall Street Journal* 2006 July 12; p. D2. Subject: 1.3.7

Armstrong, David. Medical journal spikes article on industry ties of kidney group. *Wall Street Journal* 2006 December 26; p. B1, B4. Subject: 1.3.7

Armstrong, David. Medical reviews face criticism over lapses. *Wall Street Journal* 2006 July 19; p. B1, B2. Subject: 1.3.7

Armstrong, David. U.S. seeks to more tightly restrict doctors' billings for medical tests. *Wall Street Journal* 2006 October 23; p. A1, A10. Subject: 7.1

Arndt, Marianne. Teaching ethics in nursing. *In:* Tadd, Win, ed. Ethics in Nursing Education, Research and Management. New York: Palgrave Macmillan; 2003: 39-67. Subject: 4.1.3

Arnhart, Larry. Aristotle's biopolitics: a defense of biological teleology against biological nihilism. *Politics and the Life Sciences* 1988 February; 6(2): 173-191. Subject: 15.9

Arnhart, Larry. Biotech ethics. *In:* Mitcham, Carl, ed. Encyclopedia of Science, Technology, and Ethics.

Farmington Hills, MI: Thomson/Gale, 2005: 227-232. Subject: 5.1

Arnhart, Larry. President's Council on Bioethics. *In:* Mitcham, Carl, ed. Encyclopedia of Science, Technology, and Ethics. Farmington Hills, MI: Thomson/Gale, 2005: 1482-1486. Subject: 2.4

Arnold, Elizabeth Mayfield. Factors that influence consideration of hastening death among people with life-threatening illnesses. *Health and Social Work* 2004 February; 29(1): 17-26. Subject: 20.5.1

Arnold, L. Eugene. Turn-of-the-century ethical issues in child psychiatric research. *Current Psychiatry Reports* 2001 April; 3(2): 109-114. Subject: 9.5.7

Arnold, Robert L.; Egan, Kathleen. Breaking the "bad" news to patients and families: preparing to have the conversation about end-of-life and hospice care. *American Journal of Geriatric Cardiology* 2004 November- December; 13(6): 307-312. Subject: 8.2

Arnold, Robert M. Focusing on education rather than clinical ethics. *American Journal of Bioethics* 2006 July-August; 6(4): 18-19. Subject: 7.2

Arnold, Robert M.; Han, Paul K.J.; Seltzer, Deborah. Opioid contracts in chronic nonmalignant pain management: objectives and uncertainties. *American Journal of Medicine* 2006 April; 119(4): 292-296. Subject: 9.7

Aronson, Jane. Silenced complaints, suppressed expectations: the cumulative effects of home care rationing. *International Journal of Health Services* 2006; 36(3): 535-556. Subject: 9.5.3

Arora, Neeraj K.; McHorney, Colleen A. Patient preferences for medical decision making: who really wants to participate? *Medical Care* 2000 March; 38(3): 335-341. Subject: 8.3.1

Aroskar, Mila Ann. Healthcare organizations as moral communities. *Journal of Clinical Ethics* 2006 Fall; 17(3): 255-256. Subject: 9.6

Arries, E. Virtue ethics: an approach to moral dilemmas in nursing. *Curationis* 2005 August; 28(3): 64-72. Subject: 4.1.3

Arshagouni, Paul. "But I'm an adult now. . . sort of". Adolescent consent in health care decision making and the adolescent brain. *Journal of Health Care Law and Policy* 2006; 9(2): 315-364. Subject: 8.3.2

Arzamendi, José Luis de la Cuesta. The so called 'genetic manipulation' offences in the new Spanish Criminal Code of 1995 = Los llamados delitos de <manipulación genética> en el nuevo Código Penal español de 1995. *Law and the Human Genome Review = Revista de Derecho y Genoma Humano* 1996 July-December; (5): 47-72. Subject: 15.1

Asada, Yukiko. Is health inequality across individuals of moral concern? *Health Care Analysis: An International*

Subject = NRCBL Primary Classification Number; see inside front cover.

Journal of Health Philosophy and Policy 2006 March; 14(1): 25-36. Subject: 9.1

Asch, Adrienne. Two cheers for conscience exceptions. *Hastings Center Report* 2006 November-December; 36(6): 11-12. Subject: 11.1

Ashby, Michael A.; Kellehear, Allan; Stoffell, Brian F. Resolving conflict in end-of-life care: we need to acknowledge the inevitability of death to have some choice in the manner of our dying [editorial]. *Medical Journal of Australia* 2005 September 5; 183(5): 230-231. Subject: 20.5.1

Ashby, Michael; op't Hoog, Corinne; Kellehear, Aallan; Kerr, Peter G.; Brooks, Denise; Nicholls, Kathy; Forrest, Marian. Renal dialysis abatement: lessons from a social study. *Palliative Medicine* 2005 July; 19(5): 389-396. Subject: 19.3

Ashcroft, Richard. 'Power, corruption and lies': ethics and power. *In:* Ashcroft, Richard; Lucassen, Anneke; Parker, Michael; Verkerk, Marian; Widderhoven, Guy, eds. Case Analysis in Clinical Ethics. New York: Cambridge University Press; 2005: 77-94. Subject: 15.3

Ashcroft, Richard E. Ethics of randomised controlled trials—not yet time to give up on equipoise. *Arthritis Research and Therapy* 2004; 6(6): 237-239. Subject: 18.2

Ashcroft, Richard E. Fair rationing is essentially local: an argument for postcode prescribing. *Health Care Analysis: An International Journal of Health Philosophy and Policy* 2006 September; 14(3): 135-144. Subject: 9.4

Ashcroft, Richard; Hope, Tony; Parker, Michael. Ethical issues and evidence-based patient choice. *In:* Edwards, Adrian; Elwyn, Glyn, eds. Evidence-Based Patient Choice: Inevitable or Impossible? Oxford; New York: Oxford University Press; 2001: 53-65. Subject: 8.1

Asher, Joy Bickley. Keeping boundaries clear with patients. *Nursing New Zealand* 2005 May; 11(4): 24. Subject: 8.1

Ashraf, Omar; Ali, Saad; Ali, Sumbul A.; Ali, Hina; Alam, Mehrulnisa; Ali, Arshad; Ali, Talaha M. Attitude toward organ donation: a survey in Pakistan. *Artificial Organs* 2005 November; 29(11): 899-905. Subject: 19.5

Asian Community AIDS Services [ACAS]. Legal, ethical, and human rights issues facing East and Southeast Asian-Canadians. *Canadian HIV/AIDS Policy and Law Newsletter* 1999 Fall-Winter; 5(1): 27-29. Subject: 9.5.6

Aspinall, Cassandra. Children and parents and medical decisions. *Hastings Center Report* 2006 November-December; 36(6): 3. Subject: 8.3.2

Assael, Leon A. Lies: the cruelty of scientific and clinical dishonesty [editorial]. *Journal of Oral and Maxillofacial Surgery* 2006 April; 64(4): 569-570. Subject: 1.3.9

Ataç, Adnan; Guven, Tolga; Uçar, Muharrem; Kir, Tayfun. A study of the opinions and behaviors of physicians with regard to informed consent and refusing treatment. *Military Medicine* 2005 July; 170(7): 566-571. Subject: 8.3.1

Athanassoulis, Nafsika. The treatment that leaves something to luck. *In:* Athanassoulis, Nafsika, ed. Philosophical Reflections on Medical Ethics. New York: Palgrave Macmillan; 2005: 180-197. Subject: 20.5.1

Atkins, Kim. Autonomy and autonomy competencies: a practical and relational approach. *Nursing Philosophy* 2006 October; 7(4): 205-215. Subject: 8.1

Atkinson, Leigh. Ethics and conjoined twins. *Child's Nervous System* 2004 August; 20(8-9): 504-507. Subject: 20.5.2

Atkinson, Maggie. A response to the parliamentary sub-committee's report and recommendations. *Canadian HIV/AIDS Policy and Law Newsletter* 1997 Spring; 3(2-3): 39-40. Subject: 18.2

Atkinson, Maggie; Lemmens, Trudo. Compassionate access to investigational therapies: part II. *Canadian HIV/AIDS Policy and Law Newsletter* 1997 Spring; 3(2-3): 38. Subject: 18.2

Atlas, Ronald M. Biodefense research: an emerging conundrum. *Current Opinion in Biotechnology* 2005 June; 16(3): 239-242. Subject: 21.3

Atlas, Ronald M. Securing life sciences research in an age of terrorism. *Issues in Science and Technology* 2006 Fall; 23(1): 41-49. Subject: 21.3

Atwill, Nicole. Human cloning: French legislation and European initiatives. *International Journal of Legal Information* 2000 Winter; 28(3): 500-504. Subject: 14.5

Au, Derrick K.S. A case of terminal metastic carcinoma of the lung: who makes the decision for terminal sedation? *In:* Döring, Ole; Chen, Renbiao, eds. Advances in Chinese Medical Ethics: Chinese and International Perspectives. Hamburg: Institut für Asienkunde; 2002: 417-420. Subject: 20.4.1

Audi, Robert. The morality and utility of organ transplantation. *Utilitas* 1996 July; 8(2): 141-158. Subject: 19.5

Aulisio, Mark. Bioethics in a global village [editorial]. *American Journal of Bioethics* 2006 January-February; 6(1): 1-4. Subject: 2.1

Aultman, Julie M. Eugenomics: eugenics and ethics in the 21st century. *Genomics, Society and Policy* 2006 August; 2(2): 28-49. Subject: 15.5

Aultman, Julie M. Finding meaning in the doctor-patient relationship. *American Journal of Bioethics* 2006 January-February; 6(1): 39-41. Subject: 8.1

Aultman, Julie M. A foreigner in my own country: forgetting the heterogeneity of our national community. *American Journal of Bioethics* 2006 March-April; 6(2): 56-59. Subject: 9.5.1

Auray-Blais, Christiane; Patenaude Johane. A biobank management model applicable to biomedical research.

See SUBJECT HEADING KEY FOR SECTION II on inside back cover.

483

BMC Medical Ethics [Online]. 2006; 7(4): 9 p. Accessed: http://www.biomedcentral.com/bmcmedethics/ [15 June 2006]. Subject: 15.1

Ausman, James I. Corruption in medicine. *Surgical Neurology* 2005 October; 64(4): 375-376. Subject: 1.3.9

Austen, Ian. Canadian medical group fires top editors of journal. *New York Times* 2006 February 22; p. C9. Subject: 1.3.7

Austin, Wendy; Bergum, Vangie; Nuttgens, Simon; Peternelj-Taylor, Cindy. A re-visioning of boundaries in professional helping relationships: exploring other metaphors. *Ethics and Behavior* 2006; 16(2): 77-94. Subject: 17.1

Austin, Zubin; Simpson, Stephanie; Reynen, Emily. 'The fault lies not in our students, but in ourselves': academic honesty and moral development in health professions education — results of a pilot study in Canadian pharmacy. *Teaching in Higher Education* 2005 April; 10(2): 143-156. Subject: 7.2

Australia. Parliament. Research Involving Human Embryos Act 2002: An act to regulate certain activities involving the use of human embryos, and for related purposes. Canberra, Australia: Parliament, [No. 145, 2002] 2002 December 19; 36 p. [Online]. Accessed: http://www.comlaw.gov.au/ComLaw/Legislation/Act1.nsf/0/86499A7EC1C4AACCA256F72000FA6D8/$file/1452002.pdf [2006 August 16]. Subject: 18.5.4

Austriaco, Nicanor Pier Giorgio. How to navigate species boundaries: a reply to The American Journal of Bioethics. *National Catholic Bioethics Quarterly* 2006 Spring; 6(1): 61-71. Subject: 4.4

Austriaco, Nicanor Pier Giorgio. The moral case for ANT-derived pluripotent stem cell lines. *National Catholic Bioethics Quarterly* 2006 Autumn; 6(3): 517-537. Subject: 18.5.4

Austriaco, Nicanor Pier Giorgio. Science: stem cells. *National Catholic Bioethics Quarterly* 2006 Winter; 6(4): 757-761. Subject: 18.5.4

Austria. Bioethikkommission beim Bundeskanzleramt = Austria. Bioethics Commission at the Federal Chancellery. Decision of the Bioethics Commission at the Federal Chancellery of 11 February 2002 concerning the recommendation for Austria's accession to the Biomedicine Convention of the Council of Europe. Vienna, Austria: Bioethikkommission beim Bundeskanzleramt, 2002 February 11: 6 p. Subject: 5.3

Austria. Bioethikkommission beim Bundeskanzleramt = Austria. Bioethics Commission at the Federal Chancellery. Decision of the Bioethics Commission at the Federal Chancellery of 6 March 2002. Opinion of the Bioethics Commission on the issue of national implementation of the Council Directive 98/44/EC on the legal protection of biotechnological inventions. Vienna, Austria:

Bioethikkommission beim Bundeskanzleramt, 2002 March 6: 5 p. Subject: 15.8

Austria. Bioethikkommission beim Bundeskanzleramt = Austria. Bioethics Commission at the Federal Chancellery. Decision of the Bioethics Commission at the Federal Chancellery of 3 April and 8 May 2002. Opinion of the Bioethics Commission on the issue of stem cell research in the context of the EU's Sixth Framework Programme for Research, Technological Development and Demonstration Activities as a contribution towards the realization of the European Research Area (2002-2006). Vienna, Austria: Bioethikkommission beim Bundeskanzleramt; 2002 April 3 [and] 2002 May 8; 6 p. Subject: 18.5.4

Austria. Bioethikkommission beim Bundeskanzleramt = Austria. Bioethics Commission at the Federal Chancellery. Erster Tätigkeitsbericht der Bioethikkommission an den Bundeskanzler 2001/2002 [First activity report of the Bioethics Commission at the Federal Chancellery 2001/2002]. Vienna, Austria: Bioethikkommission beim Bundeskanzleramt, 2002: 31 p. Subject: 2.4

Austria. Bioethikkommission beim Bundeskanzleramt = Austria. Bioethics Commission at the Federal Chancellery. Interim report on so-called reproductive cloning with regard to a detailed opinion on the application of human cloning, embryo protection and embryo research, preimplantation diagnosis as well as additional issues concerning reproductive medicine. Vienna, Austria: Bioethikkommission beim Bundeskanzleramt, 2003 February 12: 3 p. Subject: 14.5

Austria. Bioethikkommission beim Bundeskanzleramt = Austria. Bioethics Commission at the Federal Chancellery. Resolution of the Bioethics Commission at the Federal Chancellery, dated 10 March 2004. Statement by the Bioethics Commission on the draft Federal Legislation to Amend the Law Regulating Reproductive Medicine (FMedG) (Amendment to FMedG2004). Vienna, Austria: Bioethikkommission beim Bundeskanzleramt; 2004 March 10, 3 p. Subject: 14.2

Austria. Bioethikkommission beim Bundeskanzleramt = Austria. Bioethics Commission at the Federal Chancellery. Tätigkeitsbericht der Bioethikkommission an den Bundeskanzler Juli 2001 - Juli 2003 [Activity report of the Bioethics Commission at the Federal Chancellery July 2001 - July 2003]. Vienna, Austria: Bioethikkommission beim Bundeskanzleramt, 2003: 35 p. Subject: 2.4

Austria. Bioethikkommission beim Bundeskanzleramt = Austria. Bioethics Commission at the Federal Chancellery. Tätigkeitsbericht der Bioethikkommission an den Bundeskanzler Juli 2003 - Juli 2005 [Activity report of the Bioethics Commission at the Federal Chancellery July 2003 - July 2005]. Vienna, Austria: Bioethikkommission beim Bundeskanzleramt, 2005: 15 p. Subject: 2.4

Austria. Bioethikkommission beim Bundeskanzleramt = Austria. Bioethics Commission at the Federal Chancellery. Tätigkeitsbericht der Juli 2003 - Juli 2004 [Activ-

---

Subject = NRCBL Primary Classification Number; see inside front cover.

ity report of the Bioethics Commission at the Federal Chancellery July 2003 - July 2004]. Vienna, Austria: Bioethikkommission beim Bundeskanzleramt, 2004: 13 p. Subject: 2.4

Avard, Denise; Vallance, Hilary; Greenberg, Cheryl; Laberge, Claude; Kharaboyan, Linda; Plant, Margo. Variability in the storage and use of newborn dried bloodspots in Canada: is it time for national standards? *Genomics, Society and Policy* 2006 December; 2(3): 80-95. Subject: 19.5

Averill, Marilyn. HIV/AIDS. *In:* Mitcham, Carl, ed. Encyclopedia of Science, Technology, and Ethics. Farmington Hills, MI: Thomson/Gale, 2005: 924-927. Subject: 9.5.6

Averill, Marilyn. Unintended consequences. *In:* Mitcham, Carl, ed. Encyclopedia of Science, Technology, and Ethics. Farmington Hills, MI: Thomson/Gale, 2005: 1995-1999. Subject: 5.1

Avorn, Jerry. Dangerous deception — hiding the evidence of adverse drug effects. *New England Journal of Medicine* 2006 November 23; 355(21): 2169-2171. Subject: 1.3.9

Avrett, Sam; Collins, Chris. HIV vaccines: current challenges and future directions. *HIV/AIDS Policy and Law Review* 2002 July; 7(1): 1, 20-25. Subject: 9.5.6

Awaya, Tsuyoshi. Gene-enhanced animals and high-efficiency humanoid robots: changing the notion of "human" and "us". *In:* Sang-yong, Song; Young-Mo, Koo; Macer, Darryl R.J., eds. Asian Bioethics in the 21st Century. Christchurch, NZ: Eubios Ethics Institute, 2002: 172-176. Subject: 4.4

Axon, A.T.R.; Beilenhoff, U.; James, T.; Ladas, S.D.; Larsen, E.; Neumann, C.S.; Nowak, A.; Schofl, R.; Tveit, K.M. Legal and ethical considerations: group 4 report. *Endoscopy* 2004 April; 36(4): 362-365. Subject: 9.1

Ayres, Ed. A landmark issue. *World Watch* 2002 July-August; 15(4): 3. Subject: 15.1

Azariah, Jayapaul. Asian bioethics in global society. *In:* Sang-yong, Song; Young-Mo, Koo; Macer, Darryl R.J., eds. Asian Bioethics in the 21st Century. Christchurch, NZ: Eubios Ethics Institute, 2002: 219-223. Subject: 2.1

Azevêdo, Eliane S.; Tavares-Neto, José. Black identity and registries in Brazil: a question of rights and justice. *Eubios Journal of Asian and International Bioethics* 2006 January; 16(1): 22-24. Subject: 15.11

Aziz, Tipu. Essential Animals [letter]. *New Scientist* 2006 August 5-11; 191(2563): 20. Subject: 22.2

Azmi, K.A. Shafqat; Siddiqui, M.K. Islamic medical ethics with special reference to Moalejat-e-Buqratiya. *Bulletin of the Indian Institute of History of Medicine* 1999 January; 29(1): 15-27. Subject: 2.2

B

Babay, Z.A. Attitudes of a high-risk group of pregnant Saudi Arabian women to prenatal screening for chromosomal anomalies. *Eastern Mediterranean Health Journal* 2004 July-September; 10(4-5): 522-527. Subject: 15.2

Babic-Bosanac, Sanja; Dzakula, Aleksandar. Patients' rights in the Republic of Croatia. *European Journal of Health Law* 2006 December; 13(4): 399-411. Subject: 8.3.1

Babu, M.N. Human cloning: an ethically negative feat in genetic engineering. *Philosophy and Social Action* 1998 April-June; 24(2): 46-55. Subject: 14.5

Baccarini, Elvio. A liberal argument on the topic of genetic engineering. *Acta Analytica* 2001; 16(27): 49-66. Subject: 15.1

Bacchetta, Matthew; Richter, Gerd. Contemporary ethical analysis: a shortfall in scientific knowledge. *Politics and the Life Sciences* 1998 March; 17(1): 11-12. Subject: 15.4

Back, Michael F.; Huak, Chan Yiong. Family centred decision making and non-disclosure of diagnosis in a South East Asian oncology practice. *Psycho-Oncology* 2005 December; 14(12): 1052-1059. Subject: 8.2

Badagliacco, Joanna M.; Ruiz, Carey D. Impoverished Appalachia and Kentucky genomes: what is at stake? How to do feminists reply? *New Genetics and Society* 2006 August; 25(2): 209-226. Subject: 15.10

Bader, Ellyn. Dual relationships: legal and ethical trends. *Transactional Analysis Journal* 1994 January; 24(1): 64-66. Subject: 17.2

Bagaric, Mirko. The Kuhse-Singer euthanasia survey: why it fails to undermine the slippery slope argument comparing apples and apples. *European Journal of Health Law* 2002 September; 9(3): 229-241. Subject: 20.5.1

Bagaric, Mirko; Amarasekara, Kumar. Euthanasia: why does it matter (much) what the doctor thinks and why there is no suggestion that doctors should have a duty to kill. *Journal of Law and Medicine* 2002 November; 10(2): 221-231. Subject: 20.5.1

Bagheri, Alireza. Can the "Japan organ transplantation law" promote organ procurement from the brain dead? *In:* Sang-yong, Song; Young-Mo, Koo; Macer, Darryl R.J., eds. Asian Bioethics in the 21st Century. Christchurch, NZ: Eubios Ethics Institute, 2002: 133-137. Subject: 19.5

Bagheri, Alireza. Compensated kidney donation: an ethical review of the Iranian model. *Kennedy Institute of Ethics Journal* 2006 September; 16(3): 269-282. Subject: 19.3

Bagheri, Alireza. Organ transplantation laws in Asian countries: a comparative study. *Transplantation Proceedings* 2005 December; 37(10): 4159-4162. Subject: 19.5

Bagheri, Alireza; Asai, Atsushi; Ida, Ryuichi. Experts' attitudes towards medical futility: an empirical survey

See SUBJECT HEADING KEY FOR SECTION II on inside back cover.

485

from Japan. *BMC Medical Ethics [electronic]* 2006; 7:8. Accessed: http://www.biomedcentral.com/1472-6939/7/8 [nd]. Subject: 20.5.1

Bagheri, Alireza; Tanaka, Takamasa; Takahashi, Hideto; Shoji, Shin'ichi. Brain death and organ transplantation: knowledge, attitudes, and practice among Japanese students. *Eubios Journal of Asian and International Bioethics* 2003 January 13(1): 3-5. Subject: 19.5

Bahadur, Gulam. Parliamentary proposals for liberal approaches to assisted conception. *Reproductive BioMedicine Online [electronic]* 2005 August; 11(2): 177-182. Accessed: http://www.rbmonline.com/Article/1884 [2006 January 22]. Subject: 14.1

Bahadur, G. Concerns of sex selection and regulation in the report on Human Reproductive Technologies and the Law. *Reproductive BioMedicine Online [electronic]* 2005 July; 11(1): 13-14. Accessed: http://www.rbmonline.com/Article/1839 [2005 December 16]. Subject: 14.3

Bailes, Marion J.; Minas, I. Harry; Klimidis, Steven. Mental health research, ethics and multiculturalism. *Monash Bioethics Review* 2006 January; 25(1): 53-63. Subject: 21.7

Bailey, Barbara Jean. Congress ignores the parameters of the health exception: judicial responses to congressional evidence and partial-birth abortion in the wake of Stenberg v. Carhart. *Journal of Legal Medicine* 2006 March; 27(1): 71-85. Subject: 12.4.2

Bailey, Susan. Decision making in acute care: a practical framework supporting the 'best interests' principle. *Nursing Ethics* 2006 May; 13(3): 284-291. Subject: 20.5.1

Baily, Mary Ann. How do we avoid compounding the damage? *American Journal of Bioethics* 2006 September-October; 6(5): 36-38; discussion W30-W32. Subject: 20.5.1

Baily, Mary Ann; Bottrell, Melissa; Lynn, Joanne; Jennings, Bruce. The ethics of using QI methods to improve health care quality and safety. *Hastings Center Report* 2006 July-August; 36(4): S1-S39. Subject: 9.8

Baily, Mary Ann; Menzel, Paul; Light, Donald W. Talking to each other about universal health care: do values belong in the discussion? [letter and reply]. *Hastings Center Report* 2006 November-December; 36(6): 4-5. Subject: 9.3.1

Baird, Barbara. Abortion, questions, ethics, embodiment. *History Workshop Journal* 2001 Autumn; (52): 197-216. Subject: 12.5.1

Baird, Karen L. Globalizing reproductive control: consequences of the "global gag rule.". *In:* Tong, Rosemarie; Donchin, Anne; Dodds, Susan, eds. Linking Visions: Feminist Bioethics, Human Rights, and the Developing World. Lanham, MD: Rowman and Littlefield Publishers; 2004: 133-145. Subject: 12.4.1

Bakalar, Nicholas. Medical errors? Patients may be the last to know. *New York Times* 2006 August 29; p. F7. Subject: 9.8

Baker, Robert. Confidentiality in professional medical ethics. *American Journal of Bioethics* 2006 March-April; 6(2): 39-41. Subject: 8.4

Baker, Shamim M.; Brawley, Otis W.; Marks, Leonard S. Effects of untreated syphilis in the Negro male, 1932 to 1972: a closure comes to the Tuskegee study, 2004. *Urology* 2005 June; 65(6): 1259-1262. Subject: 18.5.1

Baker, Stephen; Beyleveld, Deryck; Wallace, Susan; Wright, Jessica. Research ethics committees and the law in the UK. *In:* Beyleveld, D.; Townend, D.; Wright, J., eds. Research Ethics Committees, Data Protection and Medical Research in European Countries. Hants, England; Burlington, VT: Ashgate; 2005: 271-289. Subject: 18.2

Bakitas, Marie A. Self-determination: analysis of the concept and implications for research in palliative care. *Canadian Journal of Nursing Research* 2005 June; 37(2): 22-49. Subject: 20.4.1

Baldwin, Clive. Narrative, ethics and people with severe mental illness. *Australian and New Zealand Journal of Psychiatry* 2005 November-December; 39(11-12): 1022-1029. Subject: 9.5.3

Baldwin, DeWitt C., Jr.; Bunch, Wilton H. Moral reasoning, professionalism, and the teaching of ethics to orthopaedic surgeons. *Clinical Orthopaedics and Related Research* 2000 September; (378): 97-103. Subject: 2.1

Baldwin, DeWitt C.; Self, Donnie J. The assessment of moral reasoning and professionalism in medical education and practice. *In:* Stern, David Thomas, ed. Measuring Medical Professionalism. New York: Oxford University Press; 2006: 75-93. Subject: 7.2

Baldwin, Thomas. Behavioural genetics: prospects and challenges. *Human Fertility* 2004 March; 7(1): 11-18. Subject: 15.6

Balint, John. Should confidentiality in medicine be absolute? *American Journal of Bioethics* 2006 March-April; 6(2): 19-20. Subject: 8.4

Ballantyne, Ron. Mental health ethics: the new reality [editorial]. *Journal of Ethics in Mental Health* 2006 November; 1(1): E1, 1 p. Subject: 17.1

Ballard, Dustin W.; Derlet, Robert W.; Rich, Ben A.; Lowe, Robert A. EMTALA, two decades later: a descriptive review of fiscal year 2000 violations. *American Journal of Emergency Medicine* 2006 March; 24(2): 197-205. Subject: 9.3.1

Ballard, Hubert O.; Shook, Lori A.; Desai, Nirmala S.; Anand, K.J.S. Neonatal research and the validity of informed consent obtained in the perinatal period. *Journal of Perinatology* 2004 July; 24(7): 409-415. Subject: 18.3

Ballard, Lynette. Putting safety at the core. *Health Progress* 2006 January-February; 87(1): 29-33. Subject: 9.8

Ballard, Megan J. A practical analysis of the constitutional and legal infirmities of Norplant as a condition of probation. *Wisconsin Women's Law Journal* 1992-1993; 7-8: 85-106. Subject: 11.1

Balls, Michael. Animal experimentation: should the three Rs be abandoned? [editorial]. *ATLA: Alternatives to Laboratory Animals* 2006 May; 34(2): 139-141. Subject: 22.2

Balls, Michael. Future improvements: replacement in vitro methods. *ILAR Journal* 2002; 43(supplement): S69-S73. Subject: 22.2

Balls, Michael. On facing up to risk and uncertainty in relation to animal and non-animal safety testing [editorial]. *ATLA: Alternatives to Laboratory Animals* 2006 December; 34(6): 547-549. Subject: 22.2

Balls, Michael. Primates in medical research: the plot thickens [editorial]. *ATLA: Alternatives to Laboratory Animals* 2006 June; 34(3): 271-272. Subject: 22.2

Balmaseda, María Angeles Egusquiza. The legal role of biological proof and refusal to undergo testing in investigations of paternity (Part II) = El papel jurídico de las pruebas biológicas y la negativa a su sometimiento en la investigación de la paternidad (y II). *Law and the Human Genome Review = Revista de Derecho y Genoma Humano* 1995 July-December; (3): 43-66. Subject: 15.1

Balmer, Lynsey. Royal Pharmaceutical Society and conscientious objectors. *Lancet* 2006 June 17-23; 367(9527): 1980. Subject: 4.1.1

Bambas, Lexi. Integrating equity into health information systems: a human rights approach to health and information. *PLoS Medicine* 2005 April; 2(4): 0299-0301. Subject: 4.2

Bane, Audra; Brown, Lesli; Carter, Joy; Cote, Chris; Crider, Karin; de la Forest, Suzanne; Livingston, Michelle; Montero, Darrel. Life and death decisions: America's changing attitudes towards genetic engineering, genetic testing and abortion, 1972-98. *International Social Work* 2003 April; 46(2): 209-219. Subject: 15.1

Banja, John D. Ethically speaking: the case manager's response to harm-causing error. *Case Manager* 2005 May-June; 16(3): 60-65. Subject: 9.8

Banja, John D. Ethics, case management, and the standard of care. *Case Manager* 2006 July-August; 17(4): 20-22. Subject: 9.3.2

Banja, John D. Qualifying confidentiality obligations. *American Journal of Bioethics* 2006 March-April; 6(2): 28-29. Subject: 8.4

Bankauskaite, V.; Jakusovaite, I. Dealing with ethical problems in the healthcare system in Lithuania: achievements and challenges. *Journal of Medical Ethics* 2006 October; 32(10): 584-587. Subject: 2.1

Bankowski, Brandon J.; Lyerly, Anne D.; Faden, Ruth R.; Wallach, Edward E. The social implications of embryo cryopreservation. *Fertility and Sterility* 2005 October; 84(4): 823-832. Subject: 14.6

Bankowski, Zbigniew; Gutteridge, Frank. Medical ethics and human research. *World Health* 1982 November: 10-13. Subject: 18.2

Banks, Angela D.; Malone, Ruth E. Accustomed to enduring: experiences of African-American women seeking care for cardiac symptoms. *Heart and Lung* 2005 January-February; 34(1): 13-21. Subject: 9.5.4

Banks, Daniel; Crow, Sue. Helping residents in nursing homes find peace. *Linacre Quarterly* 2006 November; 73(4): 302-317. Subject: 9.5.2

Banks, David. Pharmacists, pharmaceutical manufacturers, and conflicts of interest. *American Journal of Health-System Pharmacy* 2005 September 1; 62(17): 1827-1832. Subject: 7.3

Banks, Sarah; Scully, Jackie Leach; Shakespeare, Tom. Ordinary ethics: lay people's deliberations on social sex selection. *New Genetics and Society* 2006 December; 25(3): 289-303. Subject: 14.3

Banner, Michael; Suk, Jonathan E. Genomics in the UK: mapping the social science landscape. *Genomics, Society and Policy* 2006 August; 2(2): 1-27. Subject: 15.1

Barbaro, Michael. In reversal, Wal-Mart will sell contraceptive. *New York Times* 2006 March 4; p. C4. Subject: 11.1

Barber, Kerri; Falvey, Sue; Hamilton, Claire; Collett, Dave; Rudge, Chris. Potential for organ donation in the United Kingdom: audit of intensive care records. *BMJ: British Medical Journal* 2006 May 13; 332(7550): 1124-1126. Subject: 19.5

Barclay, Linda. Rights, intrinsic values and the politics of abortion. *Utilitas* 1999 July; 11(2): 215-229. Subject: 12.3

Bardale, Rajesh V. Birth after death: questions about posthumous sperm retrieval. *Indian Journal of Medical Ethics* 2006 October-December; 3(4): 122-123. Subject: 19.5

Barie, Philip S. The arrogance of power unchecked — the terrible, grotesque tragedy of the case of Terri Schiavo [editorial]. *Surgical Infections* 2005 Spring; 6(1): 1-5. Subject: 20.5.1

Barie, Philip S. Temporary insanity? [editorial]. *Surgical Infections* 2005; 6(2): 181-184. Subject: 5.3

Barilan, Y. Michael. Bodyworlds and the ethics of using human remains: a preliminary discussion. *Bioethics* 2006 September; 20(5): 233-247. Subject: 20.1

Barilan, Y. Michael. Speciesism as a precondition to justice. *Politics and the Life Sciences* 2004 March; 23(1): 22-33. Subject: 22.1

Barker, Joanne. The Human Genome Diversity Project: "peoples", "populations" and the cultural politics of identi-

See SUBJECT HEADING KEY FOR SECTION II on inside back cover.

487

fication. *Cultural Studies* 2004 July; 18(4): 571-606. Subject: 15.10

Barlow, Benjamin G. Religious views vary on organ donation. *Nephrology News and Issues* 2006 February; 20(2): 37-39. Subject: 19.5

Barlow-Stewart, Kristine. New genetics: benefits and burdens for families. *Reform* 2001 Spring; 79: 14-18, 74. Subject: 15.3

Barnard, David. The skull at the banquet. *In:* Jansen, Lynn A., ed. Death in the Clinic. Lanham, MD: Rowman and Littlefield; 2006: 66-80. Subject: 20.4.1

Barnbaum, Deborah R. Teaching empathy in medical ethics: the use of "lottery assignments". *Teaching Philosophy* 2001 March; 24(1): 63-75. Subject: 7.2

Barnes, Barbara E.; Friedman, Charles P.; Rosenburg, Jerome L.l; Russell, Joanne; Beedle, Ari; Levine, Arthur S. Creating an infrastructure for training in the responsible conduct of research: the University of Pittsburgh's experience. *Academic Medicine* 2006 February; 81(2): 119-127. Subject: 18.1

Barnes, Graeme; Williamson, Bob. Privacy, safety and community health [letter and reply]. *Journal of Paediatrics and Child Health* 2004 May-June; 40(5- 6): 326-328. Subject: 18.2

Barnes, L; Matthews, F. E.; Barber, B.; Davies, L.; Lloyd, D.; Brayne, C.; Parry, B. Brain donation for research: consent and re-consent post Alder Hey. *Bulletin of Medical Ethics* 2005 October-November; (211): 17-21. Subject: 18.3

Barnes, Mark; Florencio, Patrik S. Investigator, IRB and institutional financial conflicts of interest in human-subjects research: past, present and future. *Seton Hall Law Review* 2002; 32(3): 525-561. Subject: 18.2

Barnett, Katherine Gergen; Fortin, Auguste H., VI. Spirituality and medicine: a workshop for medical students and residents. *JGIM: Journal of General Internal Medicine* 2006 May; 21(5): 481-485. Subject: 7.2

Barnett, Mandy M. Does it hurt to know the worst? — psychological morbidity, information preferences and understanding of prognosis in patients with advanced cancer. *Psycho-Oncology* 2006 January; 15(1): 44-55. Subject: 8.2

Barnett, William, II; Saliba, Michael; Walka, Deborah. A flea market in kidneys: efficient and equitable. *Independent Review* 2001 Winter; 5(3): 373-385. Subject: 19.3

Barnoy, Sivia; Ehrenfeld, Malka; Sharon, Rina; Tabak, Nili. Knowledge and attitudes toward human cloning in Israel. *New Genetics and Society* 2006 April; 25(1): 21-31. Subject: 14.5

Baron, Carol; Blicker, Ilena J.; Levy, Michael H.; Moss, Steven; Kozberg, Cary; Hill, C. Stratton, Jr.; Quill, Timothy E.; Tendler, Moshe; Rosner, Fred; Jacob, Walter; Freehof, Solomon B. The role of pain and

suffering in decision making: case no. 3. *Journal of Psychology and Judaism* 1996 Spring; 20(1): 59-97. Subject: 20.4.1

Baron, Charles H. Not DEA'd yet: Gonzales v. Oregon. *Hastings Center Report* 2006 March-April; 36(2): 8. Subject: 20.7

Baron, Jonathan. Allocation. *In his:* Against Bioethics. Cambridge, MA: MIT Press, 2006: 179-203. Subject: 9.4

Baron, Jonathan. The bigger picture. *In his:* Against Bioethics. Cambridge, MA: MIT Press, 2006: 205-213. Subject: 2.1

Baron, Jonathan. Coercion and consent. *In his:* Against Bioethics. Cambridge, MA: MIT Press, 2006: 97-130. Subject: 8.3.1

Baron, Jonathan. Conflict of interest. *In his:* Against Bioethics. Cambridge, MA: MIT Press, 2006: 131-154. Subject: 7.3

Baron, Jonathan. Death and the value of life. *In his:* Against Bioethics. Cambridge, MA: MIT Press, 2006: 83-96. Subject: 20.1

Baron, Jonathan. A decision analysis consent. *American Journal of Bioethics* 2006 May-June; 6(3): 46-52. Subject: 18.3

Baron, Jonathan. Drug research. *In his:* Against Bioethics. Cambridge, MA: MIT Press, 2006: 155-178. Subject: 18.1

Baron, Jonathan. Going against nature. *In his:* Against Bioethics. Cambridge, MA: MIT Press, 2006: 51-82. Subject: 2.1

Barr, Donald. Reinvesting in the doctor-patient relationship in the coming era of scarcity. *American Journal of Bioethics* 2006 January-February; 6(1): 33-34. Subject: 8.1

Barrett, Ann; Roques, Tom; Small, Matthew; Smith, Richard D. How much will Herceptin really cost? *BMJ: British Medical Journal* 2006 November 25; 333(7578): 1118-1120. Subject: 9.4

Barrett, Geraldine; Cassell, Jackie A.; Peacock, Janet L.; Coleman, Michel P. National survey of British public's views on use of identifiable medical data by the National Cancer Registry. *BMJ: British Medical Journal* 2006 May 6; 332(7549): 1068-1070. Subject: 8.4

Barrett, Ronald Keith. Dialogues in diversity: an invited series of papers, advance directives, DNRs, and end-of-life care for African Americans. *Omega* 2005-2006; 52(3): 249-261. Subject: 20.5.4

Barrett, Ronald Keith. Recommendations for culturally competent end-of-life care giving. *Virtual Mentor* 2001 December; 3(12): 4p. Subject: 20.5.1

Barrett, Roseann. Quality of informed consent: measuring understanding among participants in oncology clinical

---

Subject = NRCBL Primary Classification Number; see inside front cover.

trials. *Oncology Nursing Forum* 2005 July 1; 32(4): 751-755. Subject: 18.3

Barri, Pedro N. Procreatics and honesty. *Human Reproduction* 1996 July; 11(7): 1368-1369. Subject: 14.1

Barron, Jeremy S.; Duffey, Patricia L.; Byrd, Linda Jo; Campbell, Robin; Ferrucci, Luigi. Informed consent for research participation in frail older persons. *Aging Clinical and Experimental Research* 2004 February; 16(1): 79-85. Subject: 9.5.2

Barry, Ursula. Abortion in the republic of Ireland. *Feminist Review* 1988 Spring; (29): 57-63. Subject: 12.4.2

Barshes, Neal R.; Lee, Timothy C.; Udell, Ian W.; O'Mahoney, Christine A.; Carter, Bet A.; Karpen, Saul J.; Goss, John A. Adult liver transplant candidate attitudes toward graft sharing are not obstacles to split liver transplantation. *American Journal of Transplantation* 2005 August; 5(8): 2047-2051. Subject: 19.6

Bartel, Sarah Smith. Welcoming the child at birth. *National Catholic Bioethics Quarterly* 2006 Summer; 6(2): 273-294. Subject: 14.1

Bartholome, William G. A new understanding of consent in pediatric practice: consent, parental permission, and child assent. *Pediatric Annals* 1989 April; 18(4): 262-265. Subject: 8.3.2

Bartholomew, Terence P.; Carvalho, Tatiana. General practitioners' competence and confidentiality determinations with a minor who requests the oral contraceptive pill. *Journal of Law and Medicine* 2005 November; 13(2): 191-203. Subject: 11.2

Bartlett, Peter. Psychiatric treatment: in the absence of law? R (on the application of B) v. Ashworth Hospital Authority and another. *Medical Law Review* 2006 Spring; 14(1): 124-131. Subject: 17.8

Bartlett, Thomas. Catholic Cardinal's mention of 'excommunication' for stem-cell researchers provokes uncertainty. *Chronicle of Higher Education* 2006 July 14; 52(45): A10. Subject: 18.5.4

Bartlow, Bruce. End of life: lessons learned from Terri Schiavo. *Nephrology News and Issues* 2005 June; 19(7): 55, 57-58. Subject: 20.5.1

Bartlow, Bruce. Who has rights, anyway? An ethical approach to dealing with difficult patients and staff. *Nephrology News and Issues* 2005 April; 19(5): 45-46, 48. Subject: 8.1

Barton, Lorayne; Hodgman, Joan E. The contribution of withholding or withdrawing care to newborn mortality. *Pediatrics* 2005 December; 116(6): 1487-1491. Subject: 20.5.2

Baruch, Jay. Prisoners and organ donation. *Medicine and Health Rhode Island* 2005 December; 88(12): 437-438. Subject: 19.5

Baruch, Jay M. What is the Ocean State Ethics Network? *Medicine and Health Rhode Island* 2005 April; 88(4): 123-126. Subject: 2.4

Barula, Archana. Designing humans. *Eubios Journal of Asian and International Bioethics* 2006 September; 16(5): 154-158. Subject: 15.1

Basak, Jyotish C. Cloning: social or scientific priority? *Indian philosophical quarterly* 2002 October; 29(4): 517-528. Subject: 14.5

Basanta, W. Eugene. Advance directives and life-sustaining treatment: a legal primer. *Hematology/Oncology Clinics of North America* 2002 December; 16(6): 1381-1396. Subject: 20.5.4

Baschetti, Riccardo. Evolutionary, biological origins of morality: implications for research with human embryonic stem cells. *Stem Cells and Development* 2005 June; 14(3): 239-247. Subject: 18.5.4

Baschetti, R. Evolutionary ethic and embryonic stem-cell research [letter]. *Internal Medicine Journal* 2004 June; 34(6): 371. Subject: 18.5.4

Baschetti, R.; Cregan, K. Ethics of embryonic stem cell technology: science versus philosophy [letter and reply]. *Internal Medicine Journal* 2005 August; 35(8): 499-500. Subject: 18.5.4

Baskett, Peter J.F.; Steen, Petter A.; Bossaert, Leo. European Resuscitation Council guidelines for resuscitation 2005. Section 8. The ethics of resuscitation and end-of-life decisions. *Resuscitation* 2005 December; 67(Supplement 1): S171-S180. Subject: 20.5.1

Basta, Lofty L. End-of-life medical treatment of older cardiac patients. *American Journal of Geriatric Cardiology* 2004 November- December; 13(6): 313-315. Subject: 20.5.1

Basta, Lofty L. Ethical issues in the management of geriatric cardiac patients: a hospital's ethics committee decides to not give analgesics to a terminally ill patient to relieve her pain. *American Journal of Geriatric Cardiology* 2005 May-June; 14(3): 150-151. Subject: 20.4.1

Basta, Lofty L. Ethical issues in the management of geriatric cardiac patients: an 89-year-old terminally ill cardiac patient asks you to undertake every possible intervention to keep him alive. *American Journal of Geriatric Cardiology* 2004 November-December; 13(6): 327-328. Subject: 20.5.1

Basta, Lofty L. Ethical issues in the management of geriatric cardiac patients: the cardiologist acted in good faith, which resulted in losing the legal battle, the support of the hospital administration, and the friendship of the pulmonologist. *American Journal of Geriatric Cardiology* 2005 November-December; 14(6): 331-332. Subject: 20.4.1

Bastable, Ruth; Bateman, Hilarie; Hibble, Arthur; Wells, Christina. Developing an educational curriculum

See SUBJECT HEADING KEY FOR SECTION II on inside back cover.

489

in primary care with practitioner and manager involvement: the governance shackle. *Medical Teacher* 2005 March; 27(2): 127-129. Subject: 1.3.9

Bastek, Tara K.; Richardson, Douglas K.; Zupancic, John A.F.; Burns, Jeffrey P. Prenatal consultation practices at the border of viability: a regional survey. *Pediatrics* 2005 August; 116(2): 407-413. Subject: 20.5.2

Bastian, Hilda. Consumer and researcher collaboration in trials: filling the gaps [editorial]. *Clinical Trials* 2005; 2(1): 3-4. Subject: 18.2

Bastian, Hilda. Non-peer review: consumer involvement in research review. *In:* Godlee, Fiona; Jefferson, Tom, eds. Peer Review in Health Sciences. 2nd ed. London: BMJ Books; 2003: 248-262. Subject: 1.3.9

Bastian, Till. Die "wilde" Euthanasie. *In his:* Furchtbare Ärzte: medizinische Verbrechen im Dritten Reich. München: Verlag C.H. Beck; 1995: 58-63. Subject: 20.5.1

Bastian, Till. Die Aktion "T4.". *In his:* Furchtbare Ärzte: medizinische Verbrechen im Dritten Reich. München: Verlag C.H. Beck; 1995: 49-57. Subject: 20.5.1

Bastian, Till. Medizinische Experimente. *In his:* Furchtbare Ärzte: medizinische Verbrechen im Dritten Reich. München: Verlag C.H. Beck; 1995: 72-87. Subject: 18.5.5

Bastian, Till. Selektion und andere Verbrechen in den Konzentrationslagern. *In his:* Furchtbare Ärzte: medizinische Verbrechen im Dritten Reich. München: Verlag C.H. Beck; 1995: 64-71. Subject: 20.5.1

Bastian, Till. Sterilisation zur "Verhütung erbkranken Nachwuchses." *In his:* Furchtbare Ärzte: medizinische Verbrechen im Dritten Reich. München: Verlag C.H. Beck; 1995: 45-48. Subject: 11.3

Basu, Maitraye. Are the present day "designer babies" a threat to humankind? *Eubios Journal of Asian and International Bioethics* 2006 September; 16(5): 151-152. Subject: 15.2

Bates, Benjamin R. Care of the self and American physicians' place in the "war on terror": a Foucauldian reading of Senator Bill Frist, M.D. *Journal of Medicine and Philosophy* 2006 August; 31(4): 385-400. Subject: 21.1

Bates, Benjamin R. Public culture and public understanding of genetics: a focus group study. *Public Understanding of Science* 2005 January; 14(1): 47-65. Subject: 18.6

Bates, Benjamin R.; Lynch, John A.; Bevan, Jennifer L.; Condit, Celeste M. Warranted concerns, warranted outlooks: a focus group study of public understandings of genetic research. *Social Science and Medicine* 2005 January; 60(2): 331-344. Subject: 15.1

Battin, Margaret P.; Spellecy, Ryan. What kind of freedom? Szasz's misleading perception of physician-assisted suicide. *In:* Schaler, Jeffrey A., ed. Szasz Under Fire: The Psychiatric Abolitionist Faces His Critics. Chicago: Open Court; 2004: 277-290. Subject: 20.7

Bauer, A.; Rosca, P.; Grinshpoon, A.; Khawalled, R.; Mester, R. Monitoring long-term court order psychiatric hospitalization: a pilot project in Israel. *Medicine and Law: World Association for Medical Law* 2006 March; 25(1): 83-99. Subject: 17.7

Bauer, Martin W. Long-term trends in public sensitivities about genetic identification: 1973-2002. *In:* Árnason, Gardar; Nordal, Salvör; Árnason, Vilhjálmur, eds. Blood and Data: Ethical, Legal and Social Aspects of Human Genetic Databases. Reykjavík: University of Iceland Press; 2004: 143-159. Subject: 15.1

Baum, Neil. A new look at informed consent. *Healthcare Financial Management* 2006 February; 60(2): 106-110, 112. Subject: 8.3.1

Baumann-Hölzle, Ruth. Das menschliche Genom, eine zu bewahrende Ressource oder manipulierbares Material? *In:* Rehmann-Sutter, Christoph; Müller, Hansjakob, eds. Ethik und Gentherapie: Zum praktischen Diskurs um die molekulare Medizin. Tübingen: Attempto Verlag; 1995: 188-194. Subject: 15.1

Baumann-Hölzle, Ruth; Maffezzoni, Marco; Bucher, Hans Ulrich. A framework for ethical decision making in neonatal intensive care. *Acta Paediatrica* 2005 December; 94(12): 1777-1783. Subject: 20.5.2

Baumans, V. Science-based assessment of animal welfare: laboratory animals. *Revue Scientifique et Technique* 2005 August; 24(2): 503-513. Subject: 22.2

Baume, Peter; O'Malley, Emma. Euthanasia: attitudes and practices of medical practitioners. *Medical Journal of Australia* 1994 July 18; 161: 137-144. Subject: 20.5.1

Baumer, David; Earp, Julia Brande; Payton, Fay Cobb. Privacy of medical records: IT implications of HIPAA. *In:* Tavani, Herman T., ed. Ethics, Computing, and Genomics. Sudbury, MA: Jones and Bartlett; 2006: 137-152. Subject: 8.4

Baumgartner, Fritz; Cochrane, Thomas I.; Truog, Robert D. The ethical requirement to provide hydration and nutrition [letter and reply]. *Archives of Internal Medicine* 2006 June 26; 166(12): 1324-1325. Subject: 20.5.1

Baumrucker, Steven J. Case study: honoring the patient's wishes or passive euthanasia? *American Journal of Hospice and Palliative Medicine* 2004 May-June; 21(3): 233-236. Subject: 20.5.1

Baumrucker, Steven J.; Carter, Greg; Morris, Gerald M.; VandeKieft, Gregg K.; Owens, Darrell. Case study: advisability of partial-code orders. *American Journal of Hospice and Palliative Medicine* 2006 January-February; 23(1): 59-64. Subject: 20.5.1

Baumrucker, Steven J.; Carter, Greg; Morris, Gerald M.; VandeKieft, Gregg K.; Wallace, Jo-Anne R. Case study — living wills vs. the will of loved ones. *American Journal of Hospice and Palliative Medicine* 2005 July-August; 22(4): 310-314. Subject: 20.5.4

Subject = NRCBL Primary Classification Number; see inside front cover.

Baumrucker, Steven J.; Craig, Gillian; Stolick, Matt; Morris, Gerald M.; Sheldon, Joanne. Sedation for palliation of terminal symptoms (SPTS), and nutrition and hydration at end of life [case study and commentaries]. *American Journal of Hospice and Palliative Medicine* 2005 March-April; 22(2): 153-157. Subject: 20.5.1

Baumrucker, Steven J.; Davis, Mellar P.; Paganini, Emil; Morris, Gerald M.; Stolick, Matt; Sheldon, Joanne E. Case study: dementia, quality of life, and appropriate treatment. *American Journal of Hospice and Palliative Medicine* 2005 September-October; 22(5): 385-391. Subject: 20.5.1

Baumrucker, Steven J.; Longenecker, Paul D.; Carter, Greg; Morris, Gerald M.; Stolick, Matt; Sheldon, Joanne E. SPTS — how soon is too soon? [case study and commentaries]. *American Journal of Hospice and Palliative Medicine* 2005 May-June; 22(3): 233-236. Subject: 20.4.1

Baxter, Lawrence. Doctors on trial: Steve Biko, medical ethics on the courts. *South African Journal on Human Rights* 1985; 1: 137-151. Subject: 4.1.2

Bay, Michael. Making the law match the reality; making the reality match the law. *Journal of Ethics in Mental Health* 2006 November; 1(1): E12, 4 p. Subject: 8.3.3

Bayer, Ronald; Fairchild, Amy L. Changing the paradigm for HIV testing — the end of exceptionalism. *New England Journal of Medicine* 2006 August 17; 355(7): 647-649. Subject: 9.5.6

Bayley, Carol. Ethics Committee DX: failure to thrive. *HEC (Healthcare Ethics Committee) Forum* 2006 December; 18(4): 357-367. Subject: 9.6

Bayley, Carol. Pay for performance: the next best thing. *Hastings Center Report* 2006 January-February; 36(1): inside back cover. Subject: 9.3.1

Bayley, Carol. Who is responsible? *Hastings Center Report* 2006 May-June; 36(3): 11-12. Subject: 9.8

Bayley, Carol; Boyle, Philip; Heller, Jan C.; McCruden, Patrick J.; O'Brien, Dan. Shedding light on organizational ethics: five ethicists help define and contextualize an elusive topic. *Health Progress* 2006 November-December; 87(6): 28-33. Subject: 9.1

Baylis, Françoise; Ginn, Diana. Expanding access to post-exposure prophylaxis: ethical and legal issues. *Canadian HIV/AIDS Policy and Law Newsletter* 1999 Summer; 4(4): 29-38. Subject: 9.5.6

Baylis, Françoise; Robert, Jason Scott. Gene therapy. *In:* Mitcham, Carl, ed. Encyclopedia of Science, Technology, and Ethics. Farmington Hills, MI: Thomson/Gale, 2005: 829-831. Subject: 15.4

Baylis, Françoise; Robert, Jason Scott. Human embryonic stem cell research: an argument for national research review. *Accountability in Research* 2006 July-September; 13(3): 207-224. Subject: 18.6

Bayvel, A.C.D. The use of animals in agriculture and science: historical context, international considerations and future direction. *Revue Scientifique et Technique* 2005 August; 24(2): 791-813. Subject: 22.2

Beach, Judith E. The new RAC: restructuring of the National Institutes of Health Recombinant DNA Advisory Committee. *Food and Drug Law Journal* 1999; 54(1): 49-53. Subject: 15.4

Beach, Mary Catherine; Meredith, Lisa S.; Halpern, Jodi; Wells, Kenneth B.; Ford, Daniel E. Physician conceptions of responsibility to individual patients and distributive justice in health care. *Annals of Family Medicine* 2005 January-February; 3(1): 53-59. Subject: 9.2

Beach, Mary Catherine; Sugarman, Jeremy; Johnson, Rachel L.; Arbelaez, Jose J.; Duggan, Patrick S.; Cooper, Lisa A. Do patients treated with dignity report higher satisfaction, adherence, and receipt of preventive care? *Annals of Family Medicine* 2005 July-August; 3(4): 331-338. Subject: 9.5.1

Beals, Katharine P. The ethics of autism: what's wrong with the dominant paradigms and how to fix them. *Mental Retardation and Developmental Disabilities Research Reviews* 2003; 9(1): 32-39. Subject: 9.5.7

Beam, Thomas E. Medical ethics on the battlefield: the crucible of military medical ethics. *In:* Beam, Thomas E.; Sparacino, Linette R.; Pellegrino, Edmund D.; Hartle, Anthony E.; Howe, Edmund G., eds. Military Medical Ethics. Volume 2. Washington, DC: TMM Publications, Borden Institute, Walter Reed Army Medical Center; 2003: 369-402. Subject: 2.1

Beam, Thomas E. A proposed ethic for military medicine. *In:* Beam, Thomas E.; Sparacino, Linette R.; Pellegrino, Edmund D.; Hartle, Anthony E.; Howe, Edmund G., eds. Military Medical Ethics. Volume 2. Washington, DC: TMM Publications, Borden Institute, Walter Reed Army Medical Center; 2003: 851-868. Subject: 2.1

Beam, Thomas E.; Howe, Edmund G. A look toward the future. *In:* Beam, Thomas E.; Sparacino, Linette R.; Pellegrino, Edmund D.; Hartle, Anthony E.; Howe, Edmund G., eds. Military Medical Ethics. Volume 2. Washington, DC: TMM Publications, Borden Institute, Walter Reed Army Medical Center; 2003: 831-850. Subject: 5.1

Beardsmore, C.S. Ethical issues in lung function testing in children. *Paediatric Respiratory Review* 2000 December; 1(4): 342-346. Subject: 18.5.2

Bearison, David J. Withholding and withdrawing curative treatments. *In his:* When Treatment Fails: How Medicine Cares for Dying Children. New York: Oxford University Press; 2006: 109-145. Subject: 20.5.2

Beauchamp, Tom L. Assessing the Belmont Report. *APA Newsletters: Newsletter on Philosophy and Medicine* 2006 Spring; 05(2): 2-3. Subject: 18.2

See SUBJECT HEADING KEY FOR SECTION II on inside back cover.

491

Beauchamp, Tom L. The right to die as the triumph of autonomy. *Journal of Medicine and Philosophy* 2006 December; 31(6): 643-654. Subject: 20.5.1

Becker, E. Catherine. The MEDiC Act of 2005: a new approach to safety. *AORN Journal* 2005 December; 82(6): 1055-1058. Subject: 9.8

Becker, Janet E. Oncology social workers' attitudes toward hospice care and referral behavior. *Health and Social Work* 2004 February; 29(1): 36-45. Subject: 20.3.2

Becker-Blease, Kathryn A.; Freyd, Jennifer J. Research participants telling the truth about their lives: the ethics of asking and not asking about abuse. *American Psychologist* 2006 April; 61(3): 218-226. Subject: 18.5.1

Beckman, Linda J.; Harvey, S. Marie. Current reproductive technologies: increased access and choice? *Journal of Social Issues* 2005 March; 61(1): 1-20. Subject: 14.1

Beckman, Linda J.; Harvey, S. Marie; Sherman, Christy A.; Petitti, Diana B. Changes in providers' views and practices about emergency contraception: an HMO based intervention. *Obstetrics and Gynecology* 2001 June; 97(6): 942-946. Subject: 11.1

Beckman, Ludvig. Genetic privacy from Locke's point of view. *Journal of Value Inquiry* 2004; 38(2): 241-251. Subject: 15.3

Beckstrand, Renea L.; Callister, Lynn Clark; Kirchhoff, Karin T. Providing a "good death": critical care nurses' suggestions for improving end-of-life care. *American Journal of Critical Care* 2006 January; 15(1): 38-46. Subject: 20.4.1

Beckwith, Francis J. Defending abortion philosophically: a review of David Boonin's A Defense of Abortion [book review]. *Journal of Medicine and Philosophy* 2006 April; 31(2): 177-203. Subject: 12.3

Beckwith, Jon. A historical view of social responsibility in genetics. *Bioscience* 1993 May; 43(5): 187-193. Subject: 15.1

Bedward, Julie; Davison, Ian; Field, Stephen; Thomas, Hywel. Audit, educational development and research: what counts for ethics and research governance? *Medical Teacher* 2005 March; 27(2): 99-101. Subject: 1.3.9

Beecher, Henry K. Ethics and clinical research. *New England Journal of Medicine* 1966 June 16; 274(24): 1354-1360. Subject: 18.1

Beezhold, Julian; Foëx, B.A. Jehovah's Witnesses in A&E [editorial]. *Emergency Medicine Journal* 2005 December; 22(12): 838. Subject: 8.3.4

Bégat, Ingrid; Ikeda, Noriko; Amemiya, Takiko; Emiko, Konishi; Iwasaki, Akiko; Severinsson, Elisabeth. Comparative study of perceptions of work environment and moral sensitivity among Japanese and Norwegian nurses. *Nursing and Health Sciences* 2004 September; 6(3): 193-200. Subject: 4.1.3

Begley, Ann M. Facilitating the development of moral insight in practice: teaching ethics and teaching virtue. *Nursing Philosophy* 2006 October; 7(4): 257-265. Subject: 7.2

Begley, Sharon. If we must ration vaccines for a flu, who calls the shots? *Wall Street Journal* 2006 October 6; p. B1. Subject: 9.4

Begley, Sharon. New journals bet "negative results" save time, money. *Wall Street Journal* 2006 September 15; p. B1. Subject: 1.3.7

Begley, Sharon. Science journals artfully try to boost their rankings. *Wall Street Journal* 2006 June 5; p. B1, B8. Subject: 1.3.7

Behr, G.M.; Ruddock, J.P.; Benn, P.; Crawford, M.J. Zero tolerance of violence by users of mental health services: the need for an ethical framework [editorial]. *British Journal of Psychiatry* 2005 July; 187: 7-8. Subject: 17.1

Beider, Shay. An ethical argument for integrated palliative care. *Evidence-Based Complementary and Alternative Medicine* 2005; 2(2): 227-231. Subject: 20.4.1

Beidler, Susan M. Ethical considerations for nurse-managed health centers. *Nursing Clinics of North America* 2005 December; 40(4): 759-770. Subject: 9.3.2

Beisel, Nicola; Kay, Tamara. Abortion, race, and gender in nineteenth-century America. *American Sociological Review* 2004 August; 69(4): 498-518. Subject: 12.1

Bekker, H.; Thornton, J.; Airey, M., Connelly, J.B.; Hewison, J.; Robinson, M.B.; Lileyman, J.; MacIntosh, M.; Maule, A.J.; Michie, S.; Pearman, A.D. Informed decision-making: an annotated bibliography and systematic review. *Health Technology Assessment* 1999; 3(1): 1-156. Subject: 8.3.1

Bekker, Linda-Gail; Wood, Robin. Blood safety — at what cost? [editorial]. *JAMA: The Journal of the American Medical Association* 2006 February 1; 295(5): 557-558. Subject: 19.4

Belde, David. Human dignity in patient care: keeping persons at the center of moral disclosure. *Health Care Ethics USA* 2006; 14(3): E3. Subject: 4.4

Belgium. National Medical Council. Bulletin of the National Council, 9th December 2001: euthanasia. *Acta Chirurgica Belgica* 2002 November-December; 102(6): 369- 370. Subject: 20.7

Belgium. National Medical Council. Opinion of the National Council on euthanasia. *Acta Chirurgica Belgica* 2002 November-December; 102(6): 368. Subject: 20.7

Belicza, Biserka. Teaching about ethical aspects in human genetics to medical professionals: experience in Croatia. *In:* Glasa, J., ed. Ethics of Human Genetics: Challenges of the (Post) Genomic Era. Bratislava, Slovak Republic: Charis [and] IMEB Foundation; 2002: 41-52. Subject: 15.1

Subject = NRCBL Primary Classification Number; see inside front cover.

Bélisle, Jean-Pierre; Binder, Louise. Newly infected people and clinical trials: ethical issues. *Canadian HIV/AIDS Policy and Law Newsletter* 1999 Summer; 4(4): 1, 19-20. Subject: 9.5.6

Belkin, Gary S. Misconceived bioethics?: the misconception of the "therapeutic misconception". *International Journal of Law and Psychiatry* 2006 March-April; 29(2): 75-85. Subject: 2.1

Bell, Brian. Legal, ethical, and human rights issues raised by HIV/AIDS: a plan for 1999-2003. *Canadian HIV/AIDS Policy and Law Newsletter* 1999 Spring; 4(2-3): 5-8. Subject: 9.5.6

Bell, H.; Busch, N. Bridget; DiNitto, D. Can you ask that over the telephone? Conducting sensitive or controversial research using random-digit dialing. *Medicine and Law: World Association for Medical Law* 2006 March; 25(1): 59-81. Subject: 18.3

Bell, Jennifer A.H.; Hyland, Sylvia; DePellegrin, Tania; Upshur, Ross E.G.; Bernstein, Mark; Martin, Douglas K. SARS and hospital priority setting: a qualitative case study and evaluation. *BMC Health Services Research [electronic]* 2004 December 19; 4(1): 36; 7 p. Accessed: http://www.biomedcentral.com/1472-6963/4/36 [21 November 2005]. Subject: 9.4

Bell, M.D.D. The UK Human Tissue Act and consent: surrendering a fundamental principle to transplantation needs? *Journal of Medical Ethics* 2006 May; 32(5): 283-286. Subject: 19.5

Bellamy, Stephen. Lives to save lives — the ethics of tissue typing. *Human Fertility* 2005 March; 8(1): 5-11. Subject: 15.2

Beller, George A. Disparities in health care in racial and ethnic minorities. *Journal of Nuclear Cardiology* 2005 November-December; 12(6): 617-619. Subject: 9.5.4

Beller, George A. Fraud in medicine. *Journal of Nuclear Cardiology* 2005 May-June; 12(3): 253-254. Subject: 7.4

Bellieni, Carlo V.; Buonocore, Giuseppe. Assisted procreation: too little consideration for the babies. *Ethics and Medicine* 2006 Summer; 22(2): 93-98. Subject: 14.4

Bellis, Mark A.; Hughes, Karen; Hughes, Sara; Ashton, John R. Measuring paternal discrepancy and its public health consequences. *Journal of Epidemiology and Community Health* 2005 September; 59: 749-754. Subject: 14.1

Belmont, Elisabeth; Felt, J. Kay; Foley, Elizabeth M.; Gadberry, Gavin J.; Miltenberger, Barbara L.; Puri, Christopher C.; Vandecaveye, Lisa Diehl. A guide to legal issues in life-limiting conditions. *Journal of Health Law* 2005 Spring; 38(2): 145-202. Subject: 20.5.4

Benagiano, Giuseppe. The four referendums attempting to modify the restrictive Italian IVF legislation failed to reach the required quorum [editorial]. *Reproductive*

BioMedicine Online [electronic] 2005 September; 11(3): 279-281. Subject: 14.4

Benatar, D. Bioethics and health and human rights: a critical view. *Journal of Medical Ethics* 2006 January; 32(1): 17-20. Subject: 2.1

Benatar, David. Reproductive freedom and risk. *Human Reproduction* 2006 October; 21(10): 2491-2493. Subject: 14.1

Benatar, S.R. Ethics and tropical diseases: some global considerations. *In:* Cook, Gordon C.; Zumla, Alimuddin I. eds. Manson's Tropical Diseases, 21st Edition. Philadelphia: W.B. Saunders; 2003: 85-93. Subject: 21.1

Benatar, Solomon. Facing ethical challenges in rolling out antiretroviral treatment in resource-poor countries: comment on "they call it 'patient selection' in Khayelitsha". *CQ: Cambridge Quarterly of Healthcare Ethics* 2006 Summer; 15(3): 322-330. Subject: 9.5.6

Benatar, Solomon; Fleischer, Theodore; Macklin, Ruth. Bioethics with blinders [letter and reply]. *Hastings Center Report* 2006 September-October; 36(5): 4-5. Subject: 2.1

Benatar, Solomon R.; Berwick, Donald M.; Bisognano, Maureen; Dalton, James; Davidoff, Frank; Frenk, Julio; Hiatt, Howard; Hurwitz, Brian; Janeway, Penny; Marshall, Margaret H.; Norling, Richard; Rocklage, Mary Roch; Scott, Hilary; Sen, Amartya; Smith, Richard; Sommerville, Ann. A shared statement of ethical principles. *Nursing Standard* 1999 January 27-February 2; 13(19): 34-36. Subject: 6

Benatar, Solomon R.; Landman, Willem A. Bioethics in South Africa. *CQ: Cambridge Quarterly of Healthcare Ethics* 2006 Summer; 15(3): 239-247. Subject: 2.1

Bender, Leslie. "To err is human" ART mix-ups: a labor-based, relational proposal. *Journal of Gender, Race and Justice* 2006 Spring; 9(3): 443-508. Subject: 14.4

Bendiksen, Robert. Death, dying and bioethics: current issues in the USA. *In:* Charmaz, Kathy; Howarth, Glennys; Kellehear, Allan, eds. The Unknown Country: Death in Australia, Britain and the USA. New York: St. Martin's Press; 1997: 198-212. Subject: 20.4.1

Benedict, James. "Goses, Terefah, and Kiddush Ha-Shem" exceptions in Jewish bioethics regarding the preservation of life. *Brethren Life and Thought* 1998 Winter-Spring; 43(1 and 2): 43-53. Subject: 20.4.1

Benes, Francine M. Ethical issues in brain banking [editorial]. *Current Opinion in Psychiatry* 2005 May; 18(3): 277-283. Subject: 19.5

Bengtsson, Karin Erika. Policy for human genetic resources as compared to environmental genetic resources. *In:* Árnason, Gardar; Nordal, Salvör; Árnason, Vilhjálmur, eds. Blood and Data: Ethical, Legal and Social Aspects of Human Genetic Databases. Reykjavík: University of Iceland Press; 2004: 339-346. Subject: 15.1

See SUBJECT HEADING KEY FOR SECTION II on inside back cover.

493

Benjamin, Martin. Determining death. *In his:* Philosophy and This Actual World: An Introduction to Practical Philosophical Inquiry. Lanham, MD: Rowman and Littlefield Publishers; 2003: 149-169. Subject: 20.2.1

Benn, Piers. The role of conscience in medical ethics. *In:* Athanassoulis, Nafsika, ed. Philosophical Reflections on Medical Ethics. New York: Palgrave Macmillan; 2005: 160-179. Subject: 2.1

Bennahum, David A. Historical reflections on the ethics of military medicine. *CQ: Cambridge Quarterly of Healthcare Ethics* 2006 Fall; 15(4): 345-355. Subject: 21.2

Bennett, Belinda. Rewriting the future? Biomedical advances and legal dilemmas. *Journal of Law and Medicine* 2006 February; 13(3): 295-303. Subject: 5.2

Bennett, Michael; Alison, Dawn. Discussing the diagnosis and prognosis with cancer patients. *Postgraduate Medical Journal* 1996 January; 72(843): 25-29. Subject: 8.2

Bennett, Sara; Chanfreau, Catherine. Approaches to rationing antiretroviral treatment: ethical and equity implications. *Bulletin of the World Health Organization* 2005 July; 83(7): 541-547. Subject: 9.5.6

Bennett, Susanne. Clinical writing of a therapy in progress: ethical questions and therapeutic challenges. *Clinical Social Work Journal* 2006 Summer; 34(2): 215-226. Subject: 1.3.7

Bennett-Woods, Deb. Healthcare ethics: a pedagogical goldmine. *Journal of Health Administration Education* 2005 Spring; 22(2): 159-169. Subject: 2.3

Benninger, Michael S.; Jackler, Robert K.; Johnson, Jonas T.; Johns, Michael M.; Kennedy, David W.; Ruben, Robert J.; Sataloff, Robert T.; Smith, Richard J.H.; Weber, Peter C.; Weber, Randal S.; Young, Eric D. Consortium of otolaryngology — head and neck surgery journals to collaborate in maintenance of high ethical standards [editorial]. *Otology and Neurotology* 2005 May; 26(3): 331-332. Subject: 1.3.7

Benos, Dale J.; Fabres, Jorge; Gutierrez, Jessica P.; Hennessy, Kristin; Kosek, David; Lee, Joo Hyoung; Olteanu, Dragos; Russell, Tara; Shaikh, Faheem; Wang, Kai. Ethics and scientific publication. *Advances in Physiology Education* 2005; 29(2): 59-74 [Online] Accessed: http://advan.physiology.org/cgi/reprint/29/2/59 [25 September 2006]. Subject: 1.3.7

Benson, M.K.D.; Bourne, R.; Hanley, E., Jr.; Harrison, J.; Jodoin, A.; Nicol, R.; van Wyk, L.; Weinstein, S. Ethics in orthopaedic surgery [editorial]. *Journal of Bone and Joint Surgery. British volume* 2005 November; 87-B(11): 1449-1451. Subject: 4.1.2

Benzenhöfer, Udo. Geschichte im Recht: NS-Euthanasie in neueren Gerichtsbeschlüssen zum Thema "Behandlungsbegrenzung" (AG Hanau 1995, OLG Frankfurt 1998). *In:* Frewer, Andreas; Eickhoff, Clemens, eds. "Euthanasie" und die aktuelle Sterbehilfe-Debatte: Die historischen Hintergründe medizinischer Ethik. Frankfurt; New York: Campus; 2000: 356-369. Subject: 20.5.1

Beran, R.G.; Beran, M.E. Ethical misconduct by abuse of conscientious objection laws. *Medicine and Law: The World Association for Medical Law* 2006 September; 25(3): 503-512. Subject: 18.2

Berdes, Celia; Emanuel, Linda. Creative adaptation in aging and dying: ethical imperative or impossible dream? *In:* Jansen, Lynn A., ed. Death in the Clinic. Lanham, MD: Rowman and Littlefield; 2006: 97-117. Subject: 9.5.2

Berenson, Alex. A cancer drug shows promise, at a price that many can't pay. *New York Times* 2006 February 15; p. A1, C2. Subject: 9.3.1

Berenson, Alex. Disparity emerges in Lilly data on schizophrenia drug. *New York Times* 2006 December 21; p. C1, C5. Subject: 1.3.9

Berenson, Alex. Drug files show maker promoted unapproved use; Lilly's marketing effort; company denies aiming schizophrenia pills at dementia patients. *New York Times* 2006 December 18; p. A1, A26. Subject: 9.7

Berer, Marge. Abortion: unfinished business. *Reproductive Health Matters* 1997 May; (9): 6-9. Subject: 12.5.1

Berer, Marge. Whatever happened to 'a woman's right to choose'? *Feminist Review* 1988 Spring; (29): 24-37. Subject: 12.5.1

Beresford, Peter; Wilson, Anne. Genes spell danger: mental health service users/survivors, bioethics and control. *Disability and Society* 2002 August; 17(5): 541-553. Subject: 4.3

Berg, Jessica. A qualified defense of legal disclosure requirements. *American Journal of Bioethics* 2006 March-April; 6(2): 25-26. Subject: 8.4

Berg, Jessica; King, Nicholas. Strange bedfellows? Reflections on bioethics' role in disaster response planning. *American Journal of Bioethics* 2006 September-October; 6(5): 3-5. Subject: 2.1

Berg, Kare. Ethical aspects of early diagnosis of genetic disease. *World Health* 1996 September-October; 49(5): 20-21. Subject: 15.3

Berg, Thomas. Human brain cells in animal brains: philosophical and moral considerations. *National Catholic Bioethics Quarterly* 2006 Spring; 6(1): 89-107. Subject: 15.1

Bergel, Salvador Darío. UNESCO Declaration on the Protection of the Human Genome = El Proyecto de Declaración de la UNESCO sobre Protección del Genoma Humano. *Revista de Derecho Genoma Humano = Law and the Human Genome Review* 1997 July-December; (7): 31-57. Subject: 15.10

Berger, Edward M. IVONT and the trojan horse. *Politics and the Life Sciences* 1998 March; 17(1):13-14. Subject: 15.4

Berger, Jeffrey T. Suffering in advanced dementia: diagnostic and treatment challenges and questions about palliative sedation. *Journal of Clinical Ethics* 2006 Winter; 17(4): 364-366. Subject: 20.4.1

Berger, Jeffrey T.; Gorski, Matthew; Cohen, Todd. Advance health planning and treatment preferences among recipients of implantable cardioverter defibrillators: an exploratory study. *Journal of Clinical Ethics* 2006 Spring; 17(1): 72-78. Subject: 9.5.1

Berger, Jeffrey T.; Gunderson, Martin. Say what you mean and mean what you say: a patient's conflicting preferences for care [case study]. *Hastings Center Report* 2006 January-February; 36(1): 14-15. Subject: 20.5.4

Berghs, M.; Dierckx de Casterlé, B.; Gastmans, C. Nursing, obedience, and complicity with eugenics: a contextual interpretation of nursing morality at the turn of the twentieth century. *Journal of Medical Ethics* 2006 February; 32(2): 117-122. Subject: 4.1.3

Bergquist, Amy. Pharmacist refusals: dispensing (with) religious accommodation under Title VII. *Minnesota Law Review* 2006 April; 90(4): 1073-1105. Subject: 9.7

Bergues, Ulrike; Sèle, Bernard. Destruction of cryopreserved embryos: what fate lies in store for the cryopreserved human embryos in France? The French law leaves uncertainties. *Human Reproduction* 1997 February; 12(2): 207-208. Subject: 14.6

Berlin, Leonard. Communicating radiology results. *Lancet* 2006 February 4-10; 367(9508): 373-375. Subject: 8.1

Berlinger, Nancy. Fair compensation without litigation: addressing patients' financial needs in disclosure. *Journal of Healthcare Risk Management* 2004; 24(1): 7-11. Subject: 9.8

Berlinger, Nancy. Who is responsible? *Hastings Center Report* 2006 May-June; 36(3): 12. Subject: 9.8

Berlinguer, Giovanni. Bioethics, human security, and global health. *In:* Chen, Lincoln; Leaning, Jennifer; Narasimhan, Vasant, eds. Global Health Challenges for Human Security. Cambridge, MA.: Global Equity Initiative; Asia Center, Harvard University; 2003: 53-65. Subject: 21.1

Bernal, Ellen W. What we do not know about racial/ethnic discrimination in end-of-life treatment decisions. *American Journal of Bioethics* 2006 September-October; 6(5): 21-23; discussion W30-W32. Subject: 20.5.1

Bernal, Susan Kerr. The intelligent couch potato. *Journal of Andrology* 2006 March-April; 27(2): 151-152. Subject: 14.2

Bernal, Susan Kerr. Trite but true, better safe than sorry. *Journal of Andrology* 2005 September-October; 26(5): 559-562. Subject: 14.6

Bernal Villegas, Jaime Eduardo. Retos de la manipulación genética a los países del tercer mundo / Challenges of genetic manipulation for third-world countries.

Revista Latinoamericana de Bioética 2003 January; (4): 80-99. Subject: 15.1

Bernard, Jean-Louis. Professional skills and shared consent in paediatric research. *Lancet Oncology* 2004 October; 5(10): 592. Subject: 18.5.2

Bernard, J.-L.; Aubert-Fourmy, C. La publicité des travaux et la publication des résultats des recherches en pédiatrie, une question d'éthique = The publicity of works and publication of the results in pediatric research, a question of ethics [editorial]. *Archives de Pediatrie* 2005 April; 12(4): 377-379. Subject: 18.5.2

Bernat, Erwin. Legal aspects of developments in human genetics: an Austrian viewpoint = Aspectos legales de los avances en genética humana. Un punto de vista austriaco. *Law and the Human Genome Review = Revista de Derecho y Genoma Humano* 1995 July-December; (3): 35-42. Subject: 15.3

Bernat, James L. Are organ donors after cardiac death really dead? *Journal of Clinical Ethics* 2006 Summer; 17(2): 122-132. Subject: 19.5

Bernat, James L. Chronic disorders of consciousness. *Lancet* 2006 April 8-14; 367(9517): 1181-1192. Subject: 20.5.1

Bernat, James L. The concept and practice of brain death. *Progress in Brain Research* 2005; 150: 369-379. Subject: 20.2.1

Bernat, James L. Defining death. *In:* Jansen, Lynn A., ed. Death in the Clinic. Lanham, MD: Rowman and Littlefield; 2006: 27-46. Subject: 20.2.1

Bernat, James L. Ethical aspects of determining and communicating prognosis in critical care. *Neurocritical Care* 2004; 1(1): 107-117. Subject: 8.1

Bernat, James L. Medical futility: definition, determination, and disputes in critical care. *Neurocritical Care* 2005; 2(2): 198-205. Subject: 20.5.1

Bernat, James L.; Peterson, Lynn M. Patient-centered informed consent in surgical practice. *Archives of Surgery* 2006 January; 141(1): 86-92. Subject: 8.3.1

Bernat, J.L.; D'Alessandro, A.M.; Port, F.K.; Bleck, T.P.; Heard, S.O.; Medina, J.; Rosenbaum, S.H.; Devita, M.A.; Gaston, R.S.; Merion, R.M.; Barr, M.L.; Marks, W.H.; Nathan, H.; O'Connor, K.; Rudow, D.L.; Leichtman, A.B.; Schwab, P.; Ascher, N.L.; Metzger, R.A.; Mc Bride, V.; Graham, W; Wagner, D.; Warren, J.; Delmonico, F.L. Report of a national Conference on donation after cardiac death. *American Journal of Transplantation* 2006 February; 6(2): 281-291. Subject: 19.5

Berne, Rosalyn W. Nanoethics. *In:* Mitcham, Carl, ed. Encyclopedia of Science, Technology, and Ethics. Farmington Hills, MI: Thomson/Gale, 2005: 1259-1262. Subject: 5.4

Berney, Lee; Kelly, Moira; Doyal, Len; Feder, Gene; Griffiths, Chris; Jones, Ian Rees. Ethical principles and

See SUBJECT HEADING KEY FOR SECTION II on inside back cover.

495

the rationing of health care: a qualitative study in general practice. *British Journal of General Practice* 2005 August; 55(517): 620-625. Subject: 8.1

Bernhardt, Barbara A.; Tambor, Ellen S.; Fraser, Gertrude; Wissow, Lawrence S.; Geller, Gail. Parents' and children's attitudes toward the enrollment of minors in genetic susceptibility research: implications for informed consent. *American Journal of Medical Genetics* 2003 February 1; 116A(4): 315-323. Subject: 15.3

Bernheim, Susannah M.; Ross, Joseph S.; Bradley, Elizabeth H.; Quigley, Catherine; Atherton, Janet; Rylands, Alison; Spiess, Jeffrey L.; Tomm, Lisa; Brummel-Smith, Kenneth; Spike, Jeffrey; Carrese, Joseph. Refusal of care by patients [letters and reply]. *JAMA: The Journal of the American Medical Association* 2006 December 27; 296(24): 2921-2923. Subject: 8.3.4

Bernstein, Joseph; Perlis, Clifford; Bartolozzi, Arthur R. Ethics in sports medicine. *Clinical Orthopaedics and Related Research* 2000 September; (378): 50-60. Subject: 9.5.1

Bernstein, Mark. Fully informed consent is impossible in surgical clinical trials. *Canadian Journal of Surgery* 2005 August; 48(4): 271-272. Subject: 18.3

Bernstein, Robert. Commentary: the climate for physician adherence to psychiatric advance directives. *Journal of the American Academy of Psychiatry and the Law* 2006; 34(3): 402-405. Subject: 20.5.4

Bernt, Francis; Clark, Peter; Starrs, Josita; Talone Patricia. Ethics committees in Catholic hospitals. *Health Progress* 2006 March-April; 87(2): 18-25. Subject: 9.6

Bern-Klug, Mercedes. The ambiguous dying syndrome. *Health and Social Work* 2004 February; 29(1): 55-65. Subject: 20.4.1

Berry, Roberta M. Beyond therapy, beyond the beltway: an opening argument for a public debate on enhancement biotechnologies. *HEC (Healthcare Ethics Committee) Forum* 2006 June; 18(2): 131-155. Subject: 4.5

Berto, D.; Peroni, M.; Milleri, S.; Spagnolo, A.G. Evaluation of the readability of information sheets for healthy volunteers in phase-I trials. *European Journal of Clinical Pharmacology* 2000 August; 56(5): 371-374. Subject: 18.3

Bertolami, Charles N. Why our ethics curricula don't work. *Journal of the American College of Dentists* 2006 Summer; 73(2): 35-46. Subject: 7.2

Bertomeu, Maria Julia; Sommer, Susana E. Patents on genetic material: a new originary accumulation. *In:* Tong, Rosemarie; Donchin, Anne; Dodds, Susan, eds. Linking Visions: Feminist Bioethics, Human Rights, and the Developing World. Lanham, MD: Rowman and Littlefield Publishers; 2004: 183-201. Subject: 15.8

Berton, Elena. More Chinese get free drugs in clinical trials. *Wall Street Journal* 2006 February 14; p. B1, B8. Subject: 18.5.9

Berys, Flavia. Interpreting a rent-a-womb contract: how California courts should proceed when gestational surrogacy arrangements go sour. *California Western Law Review* 2006 Spring; 42(2): 321-352. Subject: 14.2

Beskow, Laura M. Considering the nature of individual research results. *American Journal of Bioethics* 2006 November-December; 6(6): 38-40; author reply W10-W12. Subject: 15.1

Beskow, Laura M.; Sandler, Robert S.; Weiberger, Morris. Research recruitment through U.S. central cancer registries: balancing privacy and scientific issues. *American Journal of Public Health* 2006 November; 96(11): 1920-1926. Subject: 18.2

Bessinger, C.D. Life-Systems Ethics and Physician-Engineer Interactions. *Journal of Investigative Surgery* 1992 July-September; 5(3): 185-190. Subject: 5.2

Best, Robert; Khushf, George. The social conditions for nanomedicine: disruption, systems, and lock-in. *Journal of Law, Medicine and Ethics* 2006 Winter; 34(4): 733-740. Subject: 5.4

Best, Robert; Khushf, George; Wilson, Robin. A sympathetic but critical assessment of nanotechnology initiatives. *Journal of Law, Medicine and Ethics* 2006 Winter; 34(4): 655-657. Subject: 5.4

Best, Steven; Kellner, Douglas. Biotechnology, ethics and the politics of cloning. *Democracy and Nature* 2002 November; 8(3): 439-465. Subject: 14.5

Best, Steven; Kellner, Douglas. Biotechnology, ethics, and the politics of cloning. *In:* Stehr, Nico, ed. Biotechnology Between Commerce and Civil Society. New Brunswick, NJ: Transaction Publishers; 2004: 53-88. Subject: 14.5

Bevan, David. The changing face of scientific misconduct. *Clinical and Investigative Medicine* 2004 June; 27(3): 117-119. Subject: 1.3.9

Beyleveld, Deryck. Rationality in bioethics: reasonable adjudication in a life and death case of the separation of conjoined twins. *In:* Rehmann-Sutter, Christoph; Düwell, Marcus; Mieth, Dietmar, eds. Bioethics in Cultural Contexts: Reflections on Methods and Finitude. Dordrecht: Springer, 2006: 145-162. Subject: 20.5.2

Beyleveld, Deryck; Brownsword, Roger; Llewelyn, Margaret. The morality clauses of the Directive on the Legal Protection of Biotechnological Inventions: compromise and the patent community. *In:* Goldberg, Richard; Lonbay, Julian, eds. Pharmaceutical Medicine, Biotechnology, and European Law. New York: Cambridge University Press; 2000: 157-181. Subject: 15.8

Bhan, Anant. Killing for the state: death penalty and the medical profession: a call for action in India. *National*

Medical Journal of India 2005 July-August; 18(4): 205-208. Subject: 20.6

Bharadwaj, Aditya. Why adoption is not an option in India: the visibility of infertility, the secrecy of donor insemination, and other cultural complexities. *Social Science and Medicine* 2003 May; 56(9): 1867-1880. Subject: 14.1

Bhardwaj, Minakshi. Developing countries participation in the global governance of biotechnology. *In:* Sang-yong, Song; Young-Mo, Koo; Macer, Darryl R.J., eds. Asian Bioethics in the 21st Century. Christchurch, NZ: Eubios Ethics Institute, 2002: 197-205. Subject: 5.1

Bhargava, Pushpa M. Response to 'No country is an island: comment on the House of Commons report Human Reproductive Technologies and the Law'. *Reproductive BioMedicine Online [electronic]* 2005 July; 11(1): 12. Accessed: http://www.rbmonline.com/Article/1863 [2005 December 16]. Subject: 14.3

Bharucha, Ashok J.; London, Alex John; Barnard, David; Wactlar, Howard; Dew, Mary Amanda; Reynolds, Charles F., III. Ethical considerations in the conduct of electronic surveillance research. *Journal of Law, Medicine and Ethics* 2006 Fall; 34(3): 611-619. Subject: 18.5.7

Bhat, S.B.; Hegde, T.T. Ethical international research on human subjects research in the absence of local institutional review boards. *Journal of Medical Ethics* 2006 September; 32(9): 535-536. Subject: 18.2

Bhattacharya, Shaoni; Coghlan, Andy. One drug, six men, disaster . . . [news]. *New Scientist* 2006 March 25-31; 189(2544): 10-11. Subject: 18.1

Bhogal, Nirmala; Combes, Robert. An update on TGN1412. *ATLA: Alternatives to Laboratory Animals* 2006 June; 34(3): 351-353. Subject: 18.2

Bhopal, Raj. Race and ethnicity: responsible use from epidemiological and public health perspectives. *Journal of Law, Medicine and Ethics* 2006 Fall; 34(3): 500-507. Subject: 9.5.4

Bhurgri, H.; Qidwai, W. Awareness of the process of informed consent among family practice patients in Karachi. *Journal of the Pakistan Medical Association* 2004 July; 54(7): 398-401. Subject: 8.3.1

Bibeau, Gilles. Quel humanism pour un âge post-génomique?/ What kind of humanism in the post-genomique era? *Anthropologie et Sociétés* 2003; 27(3): 93-113 [Online]. Accessed: http://www.erudit.org/revue/as/2003/v27/n3/007926ar.pdf [25 January 2007]. Subject: 15.1

Biedrzycki, Barbara A. Artificial nutrition and hydration at the end of life: whose decision is it? *ONS News* 2005 November; 20(12): 8, 10. Subject: 20.5.1

Biedrzycki, Barbara A. Genetic discrimination: it could happen to you. *ONS News* 2005 December; 20(13): 8-9. Subject: 15.1

Biesecker, Leslie G. Human genetics therapies and manipulations. *In:* Miller, Roman J.; Brubaker, Beryl H.; Peterson, James C., eds. Viewing New Creations with Anabaptist Eyes: Ethics of Biotechnology. Telford, PA: Cascadia Pub.; 2005: 39-57. Subject: 15.1

Biggs, Hazel. In whose best interests: who knows? *Clinical Ethics* 2006 June; 1(2): 90-93. Subject: 20.5.1

Biggs, Hazel; Mackenzie, Robin. End of life decision-making, policy and the criminal justice system: untrained carers assuming responsibility [UCARes] and their uncertain legal liabilities. *Genomics, Society and Policy* 2006 May; 2(1): 118-128. Subject: 20.4.1

Billi, John E.; Eigel, Brian; Montgomery, William H.; Nadkarni, Vinay M.; Hazinski, Mary Fran. Management of conflict of interest issues in the activities of the American Heart Association Emergency Cardiovascular Care Committee, 2000-2005 [editorial]. *Circulation* 2005 December 13; 112(24 Supplement): IV204-IV205. Subject: 7.3

Billi, John E.; Zideman, David A.; Eigel, Brian; Nolan, Jerry P.; Montgomery, William H.; Nadkarni, Vinay M. Conflict of interest management before, during, and after the 2005 International Consensus Conference on cardiopulmonary resuscitation and emergency cardiovascular care science with treatment recommendations [editorial]. *Resuscitation* 2005 November-December; 67(2-3): 171-173. Subject: 7.3

Billings, Paul. Dangerous territory: headline grabbing moves by various US states to fund stem cell and other research could pose serious dangers for public health. *New Scientist* 2006 November 4-10; 192(2576): 22. Subject: 18.5.4

Billings, Paul R. A medical geneticist's view. *World Watch* 2002 July-August; 15(4): 16. Subject: 5.3

Bin Saeed, Khalid S. Attitudes of nurses towards ethical issues and their attributes in Saudi hospitals. *Saudi Medical Journal* 1999 February; 20(2): 189-196. Subject: 4.1.3

Bingley, Amanda. Research ethics in practice. *In:* Bondi, Liz et al., eds. Subjectivities, Knowledges, and Feminist Geographies: The Subjects and Ethics of Social Research. Lanham, MD: Rowman and Littlefield, 2002: 208-222. Subject: 17.2

Birch, Kean. Introduction: biofutures / biopresents. *Science as Culture* 2006 September; 15(3): 173-181. Subject: 5.1

Birch, Kean. The neoliberal underpinnings of the bioeconomy: the ideological discourses and practices of economic competitiveness. *Genomics, Society and Policy* 2006 December; 2(3): 1-15. Subject: 15.1

Birchall, Melissa. Decision-making in palliative care: a reflective case study. *Contemporary Nurse* 2005 July-August; 19(1-2): 253-263. Subject: 20.4.1

See SUBJECT HEADING KEY FOR SECTION II on inside back cover.

497

Bird, Sara. Epilepsy, driving and confidentiality. *Australian Family Physician* 2005 December; 34(12): 1057-1058. Subject: 8.4

Bird, Sara. A GP's duty of confidentiality. *Australian Family Physician* 2005 October; 34(10): 881. Subject: 8.4

Bird, Sheryl Thorburn; Bogart, Laura M. Conspiracy beliefs about HIV/AIDS and birth control among African Americans: implications for the prevention of HIV, other STIs, and unintended pregnancy. *Journal of Social Issues* 2005 March; 61(1): 109-126. Subject: 8.2

Bird, Sheryl Thorburn; Bogart, Laura M. Perceived race-based and socio-economic status (SES)-based discrimination in interactions with health care providers. *Ethnicity and Disease* 2001 Autumn; 11(3): 554-563. Subject: 9.5.4

Bird, Sheryl Thorburn; Harvey, S. Marie; Beckman, Linda J. Emergency contraceptive pills: an exploratory study of knowledge and perceptions among Mexican women from both sides of the border. *Journal of American Medical Women's Association* 1998 Fall; 53(5, Supplement 2): 262-265. Subject: 11.1

Bird, Stephanie. Misconduct in science. *In:* Mitcham, Carl, ed. Encyclopedia of Science, Technology, and Ethics. Farmington Hills, MI: Thomson/Gale, 2005: 1205-1207. Subject: 1.3.9

Bird, Stephanie J. Neuroethics. *In:* Mitcham, Carl, ed. Encyclopedia of Science, Technology, and Ethics. Farmington Hills, MI: Thomson/Gale, 2005: 1310-1316. Subject: 17.1

Bird, Stephanie J. Research ethics, research integrity and the responsible conduct of research [editorial]. *Science and Engineering Ethics* 2006 July; 12(3): 411-412. Subject: 1.3.9

Bird, Stephanie J. Responsible conduct of research. *In:* Mitcham, Carl, ed. Encyclopedia of Science, Technology, and Ethics. Farmington Hills, MI: Thomson/Gale, 2005: 1624-1625. Subject: 1.3.9

Bird, Stephanie J.; Briggle, Adam. Research ethics: an overview. *In:* Mitcham, Carl, ed. Encyclopedia of Science, Technology, and Ethics. Farmington Hills, MI: Thomson/Gale, 2005: 1599-1607. Subject: 1.3.9

Birenbaum-Carmeli, D. On the prevalence of population groups in the human-genetics research literature. *Politics and the Life Sciences* 2004 March; 23(1): 34-41. Subject: 15.11

Birke, Lynda; Whitworth, Rosalind. Seeking knowledge: women, science, and Islam. *Women's Studies International Forum* 1998 March-April; 21(2): 147-159. Subject: 5.1

Birmingham, Luke; Wilson, Simon; Adshead, Gwen. Prison medicine: ethics and equivalence [editorial]. *British Journal of Psychiatry* 2006 January; 188: 4-6. Subject: 9.5.1

Birnbacher, Dieter. Eine ethische Bewertung der Unterschiede in der Praxis der Sterbehilfe in den Niederlanden und in Deutschland. *In:* Gordijn, Bert; ten Have, Henk, eds. Medizinethik und Kultur: Grenzen medizinischen Handelns in Deutschland und den Niederlanden. Stuttgart: Frommann-Holzboog; 2000: 419-432. Subject: 20.5.1

Birnbacher, Dieter. Forschung an embryonalen Stammzellen — die Rolle der "complicity". *In:* Vollmann, Jochen, ed. Medizin und Ethik: Aktuelle ethische Probleme in Therapie und Forschung. Erlangen: Universitätsbund Erlangen-Nürnberg, 2003: 61-82. Subject: 18.5.4

Birnbacher, Dieter. Human cloning and human dignity. *Reproductive BioMedicine Online [electronic]* 2005 March; 10(Supplement 1): 50-55. Subject: 14.5

Birnbacher, Dieter. Predictive medicine — the right to know and the right not to know. *Acta Analytica* 2001; 16(27): 35-47. Subject: 15.3

Birnbacher, Dieter. Zentrale Ethikkommission der Bundesärztekammer veröffentlicht Stellungnahme zum Forschungsklonen mit dem Ziel therapeutischer Anwendungen [Central Ethics Committee of the German Medical Association publishes statement on research cloning with the goal of therapeutic applications]. *Ethik in der Medizin* 2006 June; 18(2): 189-191. Subject: 14.5

Birrell, J.; Thomas, D.; Jones, C.A. Promoting privacy and dignity for older patients in hospital. *Nursing Standard* 2006 January 11-17; 20(18): 41-46. Subject: 9.5.2

Birrell, Pamela J. An ethic of possibility: relationship, risk, and presence. *Ethics and Behavior* 2006; 16(2): 95-115. Subject: 17.2

Birrer, Frans; Paula, Lino. Including public perspectives in industrial biotechnology and the biobased economy. *Journal of Agricultural and Environmental Ethics* 2006; 19(3): 253-267. Subject: 15.7

Bishop, Gene; Brodkey, Amy C. Personal responsibility and physician responsibility — West Virginia's Medicaid plan. *New England Journal of Medicine* 2006 August 24; 355(8): 756-758. Subject: 9.3.1

Bishop, Jeffrey P.; Jotterand, Fabrice. Bioethics as biopolitics. *Journal of Medicine and Philosophy* 2006 June; 31(3): 205-212. Subject: 2.1

Bishop, J.P. Euthanasia, efficiency, and the historical distinction between killing a patient and allowing a patient to die. *Journal of Medical Ethics* 2006 April; 32(4): 220-224. Subject: 20.5.1

Bishop, J.P. Framing euthanasia. *Journal of Medical Ethics* 2006 April; 32(4): 225-228. Subject: 20.5.1

Bix, Amy Sue. Experiences and voices of eugenics fieldworkers: "women's work" in biology. *Social Studies of Science* 1997 August; 27(4): 625-668. Subject: 15.5

Bjorklund, Pamela. Taking responsibility: toward an understanding of morality in practice: a critical review of the empirical and selected philosophical literature on the social organization of responsibility. *Advances in Nursing Science [electronic]* 2006 April-June; 29(2): E56-E73. Subject: 4.1.3

Bjorkman, Barbro. Why we are not allowed to sell that which we are encouraged to donate. *CQ: Cambridge Quarterly of Healthcare Ethics* 2006 Winter; 15(1): 60-70. Subject: 19.5

Björkman, B.; Hansson, S.O. Bodily rights and property rights. *Journal of Medical Ethics* 2006 April; 32(4): 209-214. Subject: 4.4

Björn, Gunilla Jarkman. Ethics and interpreting in psychotherapy with refugee children and families. *Nordic Journal of Psychiatry* 2005 December; 59(6): 516-521. Subject: 17.2

Björn, Gunilla Jarkman; Björn, Åke. Ethical aspects when treating traumatized refugee children and their families. *Nordic Journal of Psychiatry* 2004; 58(3): 193-198. Subject: 9.5.7

Black, Michael. Genetics in the courtroom [forum]. *University of New South Wales Law Journal* 2003; 26(3): 755-763. Subject: 15.1

Black, Roxie M. Intersections of care: an analysis of culturally competent care, client centered care, and the feminist ethic of care. *Work* 2005; 24(4): 409-422. Subject: 4.1.1

Blackburn, Laura. Genetic testing: U.K. embryos may be screened for cancer risk [news]. *Science* 2006 May 19; 312(5776): 984. Subject: 15.3

Blackford, R. Sinning against nature: the theory of background conditions. *Journal of Medical Ethics* 2006 November; 32(11): 629-634. Subject: 14.1

Blackford, R. Stem cell research on other worlds, or why embryos do not have a right to life. *Journal of Medical Ethics* 2006 March; 32(3): 177-180. Subject: 18.5.4

Blacksher, Erika. Hearing from pain: using ethics to reframe, prevent, and resolve the problem of unrelieved pain. *Pain Medicine* 2001 June; 2(2): 169-175. Subject: 4.4

Blader, Joseph C. Can keeping clinical trial participants blind to their study treatment adversely affect subsequent care? *Contemporary Clinical Trials* 2005 June; 26(3): 290-299. Subject: 18.2

Blake, Mary Beth; Ince, Melissa; Dean, Cathy J. Inclusion of women in cardiac research: current trends and need for reassessment. *Gender Medicine* 2005 June; 2(2): 71-75. Subject: 18.5.3

Blanck, Peter David; Marti, Mollie Weighner. Genetic discrimination and the employment provisions of the Americans with Disabilities Act: emerging legal, empiri-cal and policy implications. *Behavioral Sciences and the Law* 1996 Autumn; 14(4): 411-432. Subject: 15.10

Bland, J. Martin. Untreated controls are wrong when proved treatment exists [letter]. *BMJ: British Medical Journal* 2006 April 1; 332(7544): 796. Subject: 18.2

Blank, Robert. Fetal research. *In:* Mitcham, Carl, ed. Encyclopedia of Science, Technology, and Ethics. Farmington Hills, MI: Thomson/Gale, 2005: 766-768. Subject: 18.5.4

Blank, Robert H. The brain, aggression, and public policy. *Politics and the Life Sciences* 2005 March-September; 24(1-2): 12-21. Subject: 18.4

Blank, Robert H. Embryos, stem cell research, and the promise of health. *Politics and the Life Sciences* 2003 September; 22(2): 9-11. Subject: 14.4

Blank, Robert H. Genethics. *In:* Mitcham, Carl, ed. Encyclopedia of Science, Technology, and Ethics. Farmington Hills, MI: Thomson/Gale, 2005: 831-836. Subject: 15.1

Blank, Robert H. Teaching biomedical policy to undergraduates. *Politics and the Life Sciences* 1986 August; 5(1): 67-74. Subject: 2.3

Blass, David M.; Rye, Rebecca M.; Robbins, Beatrice M.; Miner, Mary M.; Handel, Sharon; Carroll, John L. Jr.; Rabins, Peter V. Ethical issues in mobile psychiatric treatment with homebound elderly patients: the psychogeriatric assessment and treatment in city housing experience. *Journal of the American Geriatrics Society* 2006 May; 54(5): 843-848. Subject: 17.1

Bleakley, Alan. A common body of care: the ethics and politics of teamwork in the operating theater are inseparable. *Journal of Medicine and Philosophy* 2006 June; 31(3): 305-322. Subject: 7.3

Blech, Jörg. The illness industry. *New Scientist* 2006 July 22-28; 191(2561): 24. Subject: 9.7

Bleich, J. David. Genetic screening. *In:* Rosner, Fred, ed. Medicine and Jewish Law. Volume III. Brooklyn, NY: Yashar Books, Inc.; 2005: 55-82. Subject: 15.3

Blendon, Robert J.; Altman, Drew E. Voters and health care in the 2006 election. *New England Journal of Medicine* 2006 November 2; 355(18): 1928-1933. Subject: 9.3.1

Blendon, Robert J.; Brodie, Mollyann; Benson, John M.; Altman, Drew E.; Buhr, Tami. Americans' views of health care costs, access, and quality. *Milbank Quarterly* 2006; 84(4): 623-657. Subject: 9.3.1

Blendon, Robert J.; DesRoches, Catherine M.; Cetron, Martin S.; Benson, John M.; Meinhardt, Theodore; Pollard, William. Attitudes toward the use of quarantine in a public health emergency in four countries. *Health Affairs* 2006 January-June; Web Exclusives: W15-W25. Subject: 9.1

See SUBJECT HEADING KEY FOR SECTION II on inside back cover.

499

Blevins, Dean; Preston, Thomas A.; Werth, James L. Characteristics of persons approving of physician-assisted death. *Death Studies* 2005 September; 29(7): 601-623. Subject: 20.7

Blickle, Gerhard. Professional ethics needs a theoretical background. *European Psychologist* 2004 December; 9(4): 273-274. Subject: 6

Bliton, Mark J. Parental hope confronting scientific uncertainty: a test of ethics in maternal-fetal surgery for spina bifida. *Clinical Obstetrics and Gynecology* 2005 September; 48(3): 595-607. Subject: 8.1

Bloch, Sidney; Green, Stephen A. An ethical framework for psychiatry. *British Journal of Psychiatry* 2006 January; 188: 7-12. Subject: 17.1

Bloch, Sidney; Pargiter, Russell. A history of psychiatric ethics. *Psychiatric Clinics of North America* 2002 September; 25(3): 509-524. Subject: 17.1

Bloche, Gregg. Consumer-directed health care. *New England Journal of Medicine* 2006 October 26; 355(17): 1756-1759. Subject: 9.3.1

Bloche, M. Gregg. Race, money and medicines. *Journal of Law, Medicine and Ethics* 2006 Fall; 34(3): 555-558. Subject: 18.5.1

Bloche, M. Gregg. The Supreme Court and the purposes of medicine. *New England Journal of Medicine* 2006 March 9; 354(10): 993- 995. Subject: 2.1

Bloche, M. Gregg. WTO deference to national health policy: toward an interpretive principle. *Journal of International Economic Law* 2002 December; 5(4): 825-848. Subject: 9.1

Block, Jerald J.; McGlashan, Thomas H. Ethical concerns regarding Olanzapine versus placebo in patients prodromally symptomatic for psychosis [letter and reply]. *American Journal of Psychiatry* 2006 October; 163(10): 1838. Subject: 17.4

Bloom, Barry R.; Rothman, David J. Medical morals: an exchange [letter and reply]. *New York Review of Books* 2001 March 8; 48(4): 5 p. [Online] Accessed: http://www.nybooks.com/articles/14108 [2006 October 30]. Subject: 9.5.6

Bloom, Joseph D. Civil commitment is disappearing in Oregon. *Journal of the American Academy of Psychiatry and the Law* 2006; 34(4): 534-537. Subject: 17.7

Bluhm, William T. Aristotelian teleology and Aristotelian reason: a commentary. *Politics and the Life Sciences* 1988 February; 6(2): 192-195; author's reply 223-225. Subject: 15.9

Blukis, Uldis. Diversity is protection against our ignorance. *World Watch* 2002 September-October; 15(5): 6. Subject: 15.1

Blum, Deborah. A pox on stem cell research. *New York Times* 2006 August 1; p. A15. Subject: 18.5.4

Blum, John D.; Talib, Norchaya. Balancing individual rights versus collective good in public health enforcement. *Medicine and Law: The World Association for Medical Law* 2006 June; 25(2): 273-281. Subject: 9.1

Blumenstyk, Goldie. A tight grip on tech transfer. *Chronicle of Higher Education* 2006 September 15; 53(4): A28-A32. Subject: 18.5.4

Blumenthal, David. Employer-sponsored health insurance in the United States — origins and implications. *New England Journal of Medicine* 2006 July 6; 355(1): 82-88. Subject: 9.3.1

Blumenthal, David; Campbell, Eric G.; Gokhale, Manjusha; Yucel, Recai; Clarridge, Brian; Hilgartner, Stephen; Holtzman, Neil A. Data withholding in genetics and other life sciences: prevalences and predictors. *Academic Medicine* 2006 February; 81(2): 137-145. Subject: 15.1

Blumsohn, Aubrey; Mansfield, Peter R.; Pimazoni, Augusto. Doctors as lapdogs to drug firms [letters]. *BMJ: British Medical Journal* 2006 November 25; 333(7578): 1121-1122. Subject: 9.7

Blustein, Jeffrey. Ethical issues in DNA-based paternity testing. *In:* Rothstein, Mark A.; Murray, Thomas H.; Kaebnick, Gregory E.; Majumder, Mary Anderlik, eds. Genetic Ties and the Family: The Impact of Paternity Testing on Parents and Children. Baltimore: Johns Hopkins University Press; 2005: 34-49. Subject: 14.1

Blustein, Jeffrey; Charuvastra, Anthony. Infertility treatments for gay parents? [letters]. *Hastings Center Report* 2006 September-October; 36(5): 6-7. Subject: 10

Blyth, Eric. Access to information about gamete and embryo donors in the UK [editorial]. *Obstetrics and Gynaecology Today* 2003 March; 8(3): 109-112. Subject: 14.6

Blyth, Eric. Assisted reproduction: what's in it for children? *Children and Society* 1990; 4(2): 167-182. Subject: 14.1

Blyth, Eric. "I wanted to be interesting. I wanted to be able to say 'I've done something interesting with my life'": interviews with surrogate mothers in Britain. *Journal of Reproductive and Infant Psychology* 1994; 12: 189- 198. Subject: 14.2

Blyth, Eric. 'Not a primrose path': commissioning parents' experiences of surrogacy arrangements in Britain. *Journal of Reproductive and Infant Psychology* 1995; 13: 185-196. Subject: 14.2

Blyth, Eric. Secrets and lies: barriers to the exchange of genetic origins information following donor assisted conception. *Adoption and Fostering* 1999; 23(1): 49-58. Subject: 14.6

Blyth, Eric. Sharing genetic origins information in third party assisted conception: a case for Victorian family values? *Children and Society* 2000; 14(1): 11-22. Subject: 14.2

Blyth, Eric. What do donor offspring want to know about their genetic origins? *Journal of Fertility Counselling* 1998 Summer; 5(2): 15-17. Subject: 14.1

Blyth, Eric; Speirs, Jennifer. Meeting the rights and needs of donor-conceived people: the contribution of a voluntary contact register. *Nordisk Sosialt Arbeid* 2004; 24(4): 318-330. Subject: 14.4

Bobrow, Martin. The Patient's Consent. Helios, Singapore: Bioethics Advisory Committee, 2004 August 4; 8 p. [Online]. Accessed: http://www.bioethics-singapore.org/resources/pdf/Patient%27s%20Consent_MB%20040804.pdf [2006 March 2]. Subject: 8.3.1

Boddington, Paula; Hogben, Susan. Working up policy: the use of specific disease exemplars in formulating general principles governing childhood genetic testing. *Health Care Analysis: An International Journal of Health Philosophy and Policy* 2006 March; 14(1): 1-13. Subject: 15.3

Boden, J.; Williams, D.I. Donor anonymity: rights and meanings. *Human Fertility* 2004 March; 7(1): 19-21. Subject: 19.5

Boggio, Andrea. Charitable trusts and human research genetic databases: the way forward? *Genetics, Society, and Policy* 2005 August; 1(2): 41-49. Subject: 15.1

Bøgh, L.; Madsen, M. Attitudes, knowledge, and proficiency in relation to organ donation: a questionnaire-based analysis in donor hospitals in northern Denmark. *Transplantation Proceedings* 2005 October; 37(8): 3256-3257. Subject: 19.5

Bohannon, John. Fighting words from WHO's new malaria chief [news]. *Science* 2006 February 3; 311(5761): 599. Subject: 9.1

Boire, Richard Glen. Neurocops: the politics of prohibition and the future of enforcing social policy from inside the body. *Journal of Law and Health* 2004-2005; 19(2): 215-257. Subject: 17.3

Boissy, Adrienne R.; Provencio, J. Javier; Smith, Cheryl A.; Diringer, Michael N. Neurointensivists' opinions about death by neurological criteria and organ donation. *Neurocritical Care* 2005; 3(2): 115-121. Subject: 19.5

Boitte, Pierre. For an ethical function in hospitals. *In:* Viafora, Corrado, ed. Clinical Bioethics: A Search for the Foundations. Dordrecht: Springer, 2005: 169-180. Subject: 9.6

Boivin, J.; Pennings, G. Parenthood should be regarded as a right. *Archives of Disease in Childhood* 2005 August; 90(8): 784-785. Subject: 14.1

Bokina, John. History and biological teleology. *Politics and the Life Sciences* 1988 February; 6(2): 195-198; author's reply 223-225. Subject: 15.9

Bolin, Jane N. Pernicious encroachment into end-of-life decision making: federal intervention in palliative pain treatment. *American Journal of Bioethics* 2006 September-October; 6(5): 34-36; discussion W30-W32. Subject: 20.5.1

Bolin, Jane Nelson. Strategies for incorporating professional ethics education in graduate medical programs. *American Journal of Bioethics* 2006 July-August; 6(4): 35-36. Subject: 7.2

Bollinger, R. Randal; Heneghan, Michael A. Procurement and allocation of donor livers. *In:* Killenberg, P.G.; Clavien, P.A, eds. Medical Care of the Liver Transplant Patient. Massachusetts: Blackwell Science, 1997: 124-136. Subject: 19.1

Bolmsjö, Ingrid Ågren; Edberg, Anna-Karin; Sandman, Lars. Everyday ethical problems in dementia care: a teleological model. *Nursing Ethics* 2006 July; 13(4): 340-359. Subject: 17.1

Bolmsjö, Ingrid Ågren; Sandman, Lars; Andersson, Edith. Everyday ethics in the care of elderly people. *Nursing Ethics* 2006 May; 13(3): 249-263. Subject: 9.5.2

Bolognesi, Natasha. Bad Medicine [news]. *Nature Medicine* 2006 July; 12(7): 723-724. Subject: 9.5.6

Bolognesi, Natasha. University shuts down virologist's work on questionable AIDS drug [news]. *Nature Medicine* 2006 September; 12(9): 982. Subject: 1.3.9

Bombardier, Claire; Laine, Loren; Burgos-Vargas, Ruben; Davis, Barry; Day, Richard; Ferraz, Marcos Bosi; Hawkey, Christopher J.; Hochberg, Marc C.; Kvien, Tore K.; Schnitzer, Thomas J.; Weaver, Arthur; Reicin, Alise; Shapiro, Deborah. Response to expression of concern regarding VIGOR study [letters]. *New England Journal of Medicine* 2006 March 16; 354(11): 1196-1199. Subject: 18.2

Bompiani, Andriano. Genetic data and regulations on protection of personal data in Italy. *European Journal of Health Law* 2001 March; 8(1): 41-50. Subject: 8.4

Bonaccorso, Monica M. E. Programmes of gamete donation: strategies in (private) clinics of assisted conception. *In:* Unnithan-Kumar, Maya, ed. Reproductive Agency, Medicine and the State: Cultural Transformations in Childbearing. New York: Berghahn Books; 2004: 83-101. Subject: 14.6

Bonchek, Lawrence I.; Gawande, Atul. Why physicians participate in executions [letter and reply]. *New England Journal of Medicine* 2006 July 6; 355(1): 99-100. Subject: 20.6

Boncz, Imre; Sebestyén, Andor. Compensation for vaccine injury in Hungary. *Lancet* 2006 April 8-14; 367(9517): 1144. Subject: 9.5.1

Bond, Alex. Where nowhere can lead you. *Hastings Center Report* 2006 November-December; 36(6): 22-24. Subject: 20.5.1

Bonetta, Laura. The aftermath of scientific fraud. *Cell* 2006 March 10; 124(5): 873-875. Subject: 7.4

See SUBJECT HEADING KEY FOR SECTION II on inside back cover.

Bong-Polec, Patrycja; Luków, Pawel. Research ethics committees and personal data protection in Poland. *In:* Beyleveld, D.; Townend, D.; Wright, J., eds. Research Ethics Committees, Data Protection and Medical Research in European Countries. Hants, England; Burlington, VT: Ashgate; 2005: 177-187. Subject: 18.2

Bonito, V.; Caraceni, A.; Borghi, L.; Marcello, N.; Mori, M.; Porteri, C.; Casella, G.; Causarano, R.; Gasparini, M.; Colombi, L.; Defanti, C.A. The clinical and ethical appropriateness of sedation in palliative neurological treatments = La sedazione nelle cure palliative neurologiche: appropriatezza clinica ed etica. *Neurological Sciences* 2005 December; 26(5): 370-385. Subject: 20.4.1

Bonito, Virginio; Spada, Maria Simonetta; Locati, Francesco; Marchesi, Gianmariano; Salmoiraghi, Marco; Spinsanti, Sandro; di Bergamo, Ospedali Riuniti; Halpern, Scott D. Consent and HIV testing in critically ill patients [letter and reply]. *JAMA: The Journal of the American Medical Association* 2006 January 4; 295(1): 38. Subject: 9.5.6

Bonner, Raymond. Debate on abortion pill in Australia becomes personal. *New York Times* 2006 February 10; p. A3. Subject: 12.5.1

Bonnicksen, Andrea. Egg cell nuclear transfer continued: infertility treatment [response]. *Politics and the Life Sciences* 1998 March; 17(1): 36-38. Subject: 15.4

Bonnicksen, Andrea L. Embryonic stem cells. *In:* Mitcham, Carl, ed. Encyclopedia of Science, Technology, and Ethics. Farmington Hills, MI: Thomson/Gale, 2005: 608-610. Subject: 18.5.4

Bonnicksen, Andrea L. In vitro fertilization and genetic screening. *In:* Mitcham, Carl, ed. Encyclopedia of Science, Technology, and Ethics. Farmington Hills, MI: Thomson/Gale, 2005: 1054-1057. Subject: 14.4

Bonnicksen, Andrea L. Transplanting nuclei between human eggs: implications for germ-line genetics. *Politics and the Life Sciences* 1998 March; 17(1): 3-10. Subject: 15.4

Bonow, Robert O.; Zipes, Douglas P.; Anderson, Jeffrey L.; Cheitlin, Melvin D.; Goldstein, Larry B.; Grant, Augustus O.; Faxon, David; Lima, Joao A.C.; Robertson, Rose Marie. Task force 5: expert testimony and opinions. *Journal of the American College of Cardiology* 2004 October 19; 44(8): 1747-1749. Subject: 7.3

Bookman, Terry A.; Gordon, Harvey L.; Address, Richard F.; Reines, Alvin J.; Zlotowitz, Bernard; Seltzer, Sanford; Edelheit, Joseph A.; Borowitz, Eugene B.; Kahn, Yoel H.; Sinclair, David; Dorff, Elliot; Arlas, Samuel; Quill, Timothy E.; Frehof, Solomon B. Voluntary active euthanasia assisted suicide: Case No. 2. *Journal of Psychology and Judaism* 1996 Spring; 20(1): 23-57. Subject: 20.7

Booth, Malcolm G.; Lind, A.; Read, E.; Kinsella, J. Public perception of emergency research: a questionnaire. *Eu-*

ropean Journal of Anaesthesiology 2005 December; 22(12): 933-937. Subject: 18.3

Boothroyd, Roger A. The impact of research participation on adults with severe mental illness. *Mental Health Services Research* 2000; 2(4): 213-221. Subject: 18.5.6

Borgmann, Caitlin E. Winter count: taking stock of abortion rights after Casey and Carhart. *Fordham Urban Law Journal* 2004 March; 31(3): 675-716. Subject: 12.4.1

Borovecki, Ana; ten Have, Hank; Orešković, Stjepan. Ethics and the European countries in transition — the past and the future. *Bulletin of Medical Ethics* 2006 April-May; (214): 15-20. Subject: 2.2

Borovecki, Ana; ten Have, Henk; Orešković, Stjepan. Ethics committees in Croatia in the healthcare institutions: the first study about their structure and functions, and some reflections on the major issues and problems. *HEC (Healthcare Ethics Committee) Forum* 2006 March; 18(1): 49-60. Subject: 9.6

Borovecki, A.; ten Have, H.; Orešković, S. Education of ethics committee members: experience from Croatia. *Journal of Medical Ethics* 2006 March; 32(3): 138-142. Subject: 9.6

Borrego, Matthew E.; Short, Jennifer; House, Naomi; Gupchup, Gireesh; Naik, Rupali; Cuellar, Denise. New Mexico pharmacists' knowledge, attitudes, and beliefs toward prescribing oral emergency contraception. *Journal of the American Pharmacists Association* 2006 January-February; 46(1): 33-43. Subject: 9.7

Borry, Pascal; Schotsmans, Paul; Dierickx, Kris. Author, contributor or just a signer? A quantitative analysis of authorship trends in the field of bioethics. *Bioethics* 2006 August; 20(4): 213-220. Subject: 2.1

Borry, Pascal; Schotsmans, Paul; Dierickx, Kris. Empirical research in bioethical journals. A quantitative analysis. *Journal of Medical Ethics* 2006 April; 32(4): 240-245. Subject: 2.1

Borry, Pascal; Schotsmans, Paul; Dierickx, Kris. How international is bioethics? A quantitative retrospective study. *BMC Medical Ethics* 2006; 7(1): 6 p. [Online]. Accessed: http://www.biomedcentral.com/bmcmedethics/ [2006 February 21]. Subject: 2.1

Borthwick, Chris. Ethics and the vegetative state. *Neuropsychological Rehabilitation* 2005 July-September; 15(3-4): 257-263. Subject: 20.5.1

Borthwick, Jane. Something for every body. *Lancet* 2006 June 17-23; 367(9527): 1971-1972. Subject: 20.1

Bortolotti, Lisa; Harris, John. Embryos and eagles: symbolic value in research and reproduction. *CQ: Cambridge Quarterly of Healthcare Ethics* 2006 Winter; 15(1): 22-34. Subject: 18.5.4

Bortolotti, Lisa; Mameli, Matteo. Deception in psychology: moral costs and benefits of unsought self-knowledge.

Subject = NRCBL Primary Classification Number; see inside front cover.

Accountability in Research 2006 July-September; 13(3): 259-275. Subject: 18.4

Borzak, Steven. Funding of clinical trials [letter]. *JAMA:The Journal of the American Medical Association* 2006 October 25; 296(16): 1969. Subject: 18.1

Borzekowski, Dina L.G.; Rickert, Vaughn I.; Ipp, Lisa; Fortenberry, J. Dennis. At what price? The current state of subject payment in adolescent research. *Journal of Adolescent Health* 2003 November; 33(5): 378-384. Subject: 18.5.2

Bosch, Xavier. Concerns over new EU ethics panel. *Scientist* 2005 November 21; 19(22): 3 p. [Online]. Accessed: http://www.the-scientist.com/article/display/15886 [2006 December 3]. Subject: 2.3

Bosch, Xavier. Group ponders genomics and public health. *JAMA: The Journal of the American Medical Association* 2006 April 19; 295(15): 1762. Subject: 15.1

Boshier, A.; Shakir, S.A.W.; Telfer, P.; Behr, E.; Pakrashi, T.; Camm, A.J. The negative effect of red tape on research. *Pharmacoepidemiology and Drug Safety* 2005 June; 14(6): 373-376. Subject: 18.2

Bosk, Charles L. Obtaining voluntary consent for research in desperately ill patients. *Medical Care* 2002 September; 40(9, Supplement): V64-V68. Subject: 18.3

Bosman, Julie. Reporters find science journals harder to trust, but not easy to verify. *New York Times* 2006 February 13; p. C1, C3. Subject: 1.3.7

Bosshard, Georg; de Stoutz, Noémi; Bär, Walter. Eine gesetzliche Regulierung des Umgangs mit Opiaten und Sedativa bei medizinischen Entscheidungen am Lebensende? [Legal regulation of opiate and sedative use in medical end-of-life decisions]. *Ethik in der Medizin* 2006 June; 18(2): 120-132. Subject: 20.4.1

Bossi, Jeanne. European Directive of October 24, 1995 and protection of medical data: the consequences of the law governing data processing and freedoms. *European Journal of Health Law* 2002 September; 9(3): 201-206. Subject: 8.4

Bostanci, Adam. Two drafts, one genome? Human diversity and human genome research. *Science as Culture* 2006 September; 15(3): 183-198. Subject: 15.10

Bostick, Nathan A.; Sade, Robert; McMahon, John W.; Benjamin, Regina. Report of the American Medical Association Council on Ethical and Judicial Affairs: withholding information from patients: rethinking the propriety of "therapeutic privilege". *Journal of Clinical Ethics* 2006 Winter; 17(4): 302-306. Subject: 8.2

Bostrom, Barry A. Gonzales v. Oregon. *Issues in Law and Medicine* 2006 Spring; 21(3): 203-210. Subject: 20.7

Bostrom, Nick. Human genetic enhancements: a transhumanist perspective. *Journal of Value Inquiry* 2003; 37(4): 493-506. Subject: 15.4

Bostrom, Nick. Welcome to a world of exponential change. *In:* Miller, Paul; Wilsdon, James, eds. Better Humans?: The Politics of Human Enhancement and Life Extension. London: Demos, 2006: 40-50. Subject: 4.5

Bostrom, Nick; Ord, Toby. The reversal test: eliminating status quo bias in applied ethics. *Ethics* 2006 July; 116(4): 656-679. Subject: 15.1

Botkin, Jeffrey R. Research for newborn screening: developing a national framework. *Pediatrics* 2005 October; 116(4): 862-871. Subject: 15.3

Bouchie, Aaron. Clinical trial data: to disclose or not to disclose? [news]. *Nature Biotechnology* 2006 September; 24(9): 1058-1060. Subject: 18.2

Boudouin, Jean-Louise. Canadian developments on genetic and human embryo research and experimentation = Novedades en Canadá sobre la investigación y experimentación genética y con embriones humanos. *Revista de Derecho Genoma Humano = Law and the Human Genome Review* 1997 January-June; (6): 41-49. Subject: 18.5.4

Boulware, L. Ebony; Ratner, Lloyd E.; Troll, Misty U.; Chaudron, Alexis; Yeung, Edwina; Chen, Shirley; Klein, Andrew S.; Hiller, Janet; Powe, Neil R. Attitudes, psychology, and risk taking of potential live kidney donors: strangers, relatives, and the general public. *American Journal of Transplantation* 2005 July; 5(7): 1671-1680. Subject: 19.5

Boutain, Doris M. Social justice as a framework for professional nursing. *Journal of Nursing Education* 2005 September; 44(9): 404-408. Subject: 7.2

Bovenberg, Jasper. Whose tissue is it anyway? *Nature Biotechnology* 2005 August; 23(8): 929-933. Subject: 15.1

Bovenberg, Jasper A. Blood, sweat, and grants—'honest Jim' and the European database-right. *Genetics, Society, and Policy* 2005 August; 1(2): 1-28. Subject: 15.1

Bovenberg, Jasper A. Towards an international system of ethics and governance of biobanks: a "special status" for genetic data? *Critical Public Health* 2005 December; 15(4): 369-383. Subject: 15.1

Bovens, L. The rhythm method and embryonic death. *Journal of Medical Ethics* 2006 June; 32(6): 355-356. Subject: 11.1

Bowen, Deborah J.; Battuello, Kathryn M.; Raats, Monique. Marketing genetic tests: empowerment or snake oil? *Health Education and Behavior* 2005 October; 32(5): 676-685. Subject: 15.3

Bowen, Deborah J.; Urban, Nicole; Carrell, David; Kinne, Susan. Comparisons of strategies to prevent breast cancer mortality. *Journal of Social Issues* 1993 Summer; 49(2): 35-60. Subject: 9.4

See SUBJECT HEADING KEY FOR SECTION II on inside back cover.

503

Bowen, Leslie Maria. Reconfigured bodies: the problem of ownership. *Communication Theory* 2005 February; 15(1): 23-38. Subject: 4.4

Bowens, Krietta Kai. The legal status of embryos and implications for reproductive technologies and biotechnology research. *Journal of Biolaw and Business* 2006; 9(1): 17-25. Subject: 4.4

Bower, Peter; King, Michael; Nazareth, Irwin; Lampe, Fiona; Sibbald, Bonnie. Patient preferences in randomised controlled trials: conceptual framework and implications for research. *Social Science and Medicine* 2005 August; 61(3): 685-695. Subject: 18.2

Bowling, Ann. Quality of life in healthcare decisions. *In:* Rai, Gurcharan S, ed. Medical Ethics and the Elderly. 2nd ed. San Francisco: Radcliffe Medical Press; 2004: 147-154. Subject: 9.5.2

Bowman, James E. Genetic screening programs and public policy. *Phylon* 1977 June; 38(2): 117-142. Subject: 15.3

Bowman, Marjorie A.; Pearle, David L. Changes in drug prescribing patterns related to commercial company funding of continuing medical education. *Journal of Continuing Education in the Health Professions* 1988; 8(1): 13-20. Subject: 7.2

Boylan, Michael. The duty to rescue and the limits of confidentiality. *American Journal of Bioethics* 2006 March-April; 6(2): 32-34. Subject: 8.4

Boyle, Joseph. Tolerating v. supporting research that destroys embryos: a difference that can make a moral difference. *Journal of Contemporary Health Law and Policy* 2006 Spring; 22(2): 448-457. Subject: 18.5.4

Bradley, A.N. Utility and limitations of genetic testing and information. *Nursing Standard* 2005 October 12-18; 20(5): 52-55. Subject: 15.3

Bradley, S. Gaylen. Managing competing interests. *In:* Macrina, Francis L., ed. Scientific Integrity: Text and Cases in Responsible Conduct of Research. 3rd ed. Washington, DC: ASM Press; 2005: 159-185. Subject: 1.3.9

Brady Wagner, Lynne C. Clinical ethics in the context of language and cognitive impairment: rights and protections. *Seminars in Speech and Language* 2003 November; 24(4): 275-284. Subject: 8.3.1

Brahams, Diana. Should doctors admit their mistakes? [editorial]. *Medico-Legal Journal* 2005; 73(Part 2): 41-44. Subject: 9.8

Brainard, Jeffrey. An activist group's hidden-camera investigation at Chapel Hill raises issues about colleges' oversight of animal welfare. *Chronicle of Higher Education* 2006 March 3; 52(26): A21-A23. Subject: 22.2

Brainard, Jeffrey. Animal-rights groups fight colleges over access to research records. *Chronicle of Higher Education* 2006 March 31; 52(30): A29. Subject: 22.1

Brainard, Jeffrey. Report calls for easing rules on research involving prisoners. *Chronicle of Higher Education* 2006 July 28; 52(47): A16. Subject: 18.5.5

Brainard, Jeffrey. Study finds conflicts of interest on many research-review boards. *Chronicle of Higher Education* 2006 December 8; 53(16): A22. Subject: 18.2

Brainard, Jeffrey. Universities experiment with classes in scientific ethics. *Chronicle of Higher Education* 2006 November 10; 53(12): A22-A23. Subject: 1.3.9

Brakman, Sarah-Vaughn; Scholz, Sally J. Adoption, ART, and a re-conception of the maternal body: toward embodied maternity. *Hypatia: A Journal of Feminist Philosophy* 2006 Winter; 21(1): 54-73. Subject: 9.5.5

Bramstedt, Katrina A. A study of warning letters issued to clinical investigators by the United States Food and Drug Administration. *Clinical and Investigative Medicine* 2004 June; 27(3): 129-134. Subject: 18.6

Bramstedt, Katrina A. Supporting organ transplantation in non-resident aliens within limits. *Ethics and Medicine* 2006 Spring; 22(1): 39-45. Subject: 19.6

Bramstedt, Katrina A. Supporting organ transplantation in non-resident aliens within limits. *Ethics and Medicine* 2006 Summer; 22(2): 75-81. Subject: 19.6

Bramstedt, Katrina A. Transfusion contracts for Jehovah's Witnesses receiving organ transplants: ethical necessity or coercive pact? *Journal of Medical Ethics* 2006 April; 32(4): 193-195. Subject: 19.4

Bramstedt, Katrina A. When pharmacists refuse to dispense prescriptions. *Lancet* 2006 April 15-21; 367(9518): 1219-1220. Subject: 4.1.1

Bramstedt, Katrina A.; Jabbour, N. When alcohol abstinence criteria create ethical dilemmas for the liver transplant team. *Journal of Medical Ethics* 2006 May; 32(5): 263-265. Subject: 19.6

Bramwell, R.; Weindling, M. Families' views on ward rounds in neonatal units. *Archives of Disease in Childhood Fetal and Neonatal Edition* 2005 September; 90(5): F429-F431. Subject: 9.5.7

Brand, Angela. Public health and genetics — a dangerous combination? *European Journal of Public Health* 2005 April; 15(2): 114-116. Subject: 15.10

Brandon, Dwayne T.; Isaac, Lydia A.; LaVeist, Thomas A. The legacy of Tuskegee and trust in medical care: is Tuskegee responsible for race differences in mistrust of medical care? *Journal of the National Medical Association* 2005 July; 97(7): 951-956. Subject: 18.5.1

Brandt-Rauf, Sherry I.; Raveis, Victoria H.; Drummond, Nathan F.; Conte, Jill A.; Rothman, Sheila M. Ashkenazi Jews and breast cancer: the consequences of linking ethnic identity to genetic disease. *American Journal of Public Health* 2006 November; 96(11): 1979-1988. Subject: 15.1

Subject = NRCBL Primary Classification Number; see inside front cover.

Branthwaite, Margaret. Should patients be able to choose physician-assisted suicide at the end of their lives? *Lancet Oncology* 2006 July; 7(7): 602-604. Subject: 20.7

Brasel, Karen J. Research ethics primer. *Journal of Surgical Research* 2005 October; 128(2): 221-225. Subject: 18.2

Brassington, I. Body art and medical need. *Journal of Medical Ethics* 2006 January; 32(1): 13-16. Subject: 9.5.1

Brassington, I. Killing people: what Kant could have said about suicide and euthanasia but did not. *Journal of Medical Ethics* 2006 October; 32(10): 571-574. Subject: 20.7

Brassington, I. Teaching to the converted: religious belief in the seminar room. *Journal of Medical Ethics* 2006 November; 32(11): 678-681. Subject: 7.3

Braude, Peter. Preimplantation diagnosis for genetic susceptibility. *New England Journal of Medicine* 2006 August 10; 355(6): 541-543. Subject: 15.2

Braun, Lundy. Reifying human difference: the debate on genetics, race, and health. *International Journal of Health Services* 2006; 36(3): 557-573. Subject: 9.5.1

Braun, Sharon A.; Cox, Jane A. Managed mental health care: intentional misdiagnosis of mental disorders. *Journal of Counseling and Development* 2005 Fall; 83(4): 425-433. Subject: 9.3.2

Braunack-Mayer, Annette J. The ethics of participating in research [editorial]. *Medical Journal of Australia* 2002 November 4; 177(9): 471-472. Subject: 18.3

Brauner, Daniel J.; Merel, Susan E. How a model based on linguistic theory can improve the assessment of decision-making capacity for persons with dementia. *Journal of Clinical Ethics* 2006 Summer; 17(2): 139-148. Subject: 18.3

Braunold, Gillian; Pringle, Mike; Eccles, Simon; Scott, Ian; Osborne, Susan; Stuttle, Barbara. Opting in or out of electronic patient records: national clinical leads of Connecting for Health respond [letter]. *BMJ: British Medical Journal* 2006 July 29; 333(7561): 261-262. Subject: 18.2

Bravo, Gina; Gagnon, Michaël; Wildeman, Sheila; Marshall, David T.; Pâquet, Mariane; Dubois, Marie-France. Comparison of provincial and territorial legislation governing substitute consent for research. *Canadian Journal on Aging* 2005 Fall; 24(3): 237-249. Subject: 18.3

Brazier, M.; Fovargue, S. A brief guide to the Human Tissue Act 2004. *Clinical Ethics* 2006 March; 1(1): 26-32. Subject: 19.5

Brecher, B. Why the Kantian ideal survives medical learning curves, and why it matters. *Journal of Medical Ethics* 2006 September; 32(9): 511-512. Subject: 7.2

Breeding, John. Human rights progress in psychiatry: more apparent than real (observations and reflections on life in the Texas mental health courts). *Ethical Human Psy-*

chology and Psychiatry 2006 Fall-Winter; 8(3): 241-254. Subject: 4.3

Breen, Kerry J. Maintaining community trust in biomedical research involving humans [forum]. *University of New South Wales Law Journal* 2003; 26(3): 793- 798. Subject: 18.2

Breen, Kerry J. The medical profession and the pharmaceutical industry: when will we open our eyes? *Medical Journal of Australia* 2004 April 19; 180(8): 409-410. Subject: 9.7

Breeze, Jayne. Can paternalism be justified in mental health care? *Journal of Advanced Nursing* 1998 August; 28(2): 260-265. Subject: 9.1

Breggin, Peter R. Court filing makes public my previously suppressed analysis of Paxil's effects. *Ethical Human Psychology and Psychiatry* 2006 Spring; 8(1): 77-84. Subject: 9.7

Breggin, Peter R. How GlaxoSmithKline suppressed data on Paxil-Induced Akathisia: implications for suicidality and violence. *Ethical Human Psychology and Psychiatry* 2006 Summer; 8(2): 91-100. Subject: 9.7

Brehany, John F. Ethics in vaccine development and production: transforming health care. *Health Care Ethics USA* 2006; 14(3): E2. Subject: 9.7

Breheny, Nikki; Geelhoed, Elizabeth; Goldblatt, Jack; O'Leary, Peter. Cost-effectiveness of predictive genetic tests for familial breast and ovarian cancer. *Genetics, Society, and Policy* 2005 August; 1(2): 67-79. Subject: 15.3

Breier-Mackie, Sarah. Ethics and endoscopy. *Gastroenterology Nursing* 2005 November-December; 28(6): 514-515. Subject: 8.3.1

Breier-Mackie, Sarah. Ethics, artificial nutrition, and anorexia nervosa. *Practical Bioethics* 2006 Spring-Summer; 2(2-3): 3-5. Subject: 20.5.1

Breier-Mackie, Sarah. Why ethics and gastroenterology nursing? *Gastroenterology Nursing* 2005 May-June; 28(3): 248-249. Subject: 2.1

Breier-Mackie, Sarah J. PEGs and ethics revisited: a timely reflection in the wake of the Terri Schiavo case. *Gastroenterology Nursing* 2005 July-August; 28(4): 292-297. Subject: 20.5.1

Breitbart, William. "Unintended consequences": can legalizing physician-assisted suicide actually result in improved palliative care practices? [editorial]. *Palliative and Supportive Care* 2003 September; 1(3): 213-214. Subject: 20.7

Breivik, Gunnar. Sport, gene doping and ethics. *In:* Tamburrini, Claudio; Tännsjö, Torbjörn, eds. Genetic Technology and Sport: Ethical Questions. London; New York: Routledge; 2005: 165-177. Subject: 15.4

Bremberg, Stefan; Nilstun, Tore. Justifications of physicians' choice of action: attitudes among the general public,

See SUBJECT HEADING KEY FOR SECTION II on inside back cover.

505

GPs, and oncologists in Sweden. *Scandinavian Journal of Primary Health Care* 2005 June; 23(2): 102-108. Subject: 9.5.9

Brender, Alan. A nation's pride turns to shame. *Chronicle of Higher Education* 2006 January 6; 52(18): A27-A29. Subject: 1.3.9

Brennan, F. James. Ethical issues with implantable defibrillators. *Pacing and Clinical Electrophysiology* 2004 July; 27(7): 897-898. Subject: 9.4

Brennan, Troyen A.; Rothman, David J.; Blank, Linda; Blumenthal, David; Chimonas, Susan C.; Cohen, Jordan J.; Goldman, JanLori; Kassirer, Jerome P.; Kimball, Harry; Naughton, James; Smelser, Neil. Health industry practices that create conflicts of interest: a policy proposal for academic medical centers. *JAMA: The Journal of the American Medical Association* 2006 January 25; 295(4): 429-433. Subject: 7.3

Brent, Nancy J. The use and misuse of electronic patient data. *Journal of Infusion Nursing* 2005 July-August; 28(4): 251-257. Subject: 1.3.12

Brentlinger, Paula E. Health, human rights, and malaria control: historical background and current challenges. *Health and Human Rights: An International Journal* 2006; 9(2): 11-38. Subject: 9.5.1

Brentnall, Vicki. Directing your own end-of-life care. *Medical Economics* 2005 September 16; 82(18): 54-55. Subject: 20.5.4

Brettingham, Madeleine. Roche denies claims it sacked employee for "whistle blowing" [news]. *BMJ: British Medical Journal* 2006 May 20; 332(7551): 1175. Subject: 1.3.9

Bretzke, James T. A burden of means: interpreting recent Catholic magisterial teaching on end-of-life issues. *Journal of the Society of Christian Ethics* 2006 Fall-Winter; 26(2): 183-200. Subject: 20.5.1

Brewaeys, A.; Golombok, S.; Naaktgeboren, N.; de Bruyn, J.K.; van Hall, E.V. Donor insemination: Dutch parents' opinions about confidentiality and donor anonymity and the emotional adjustment of their children. *Human Reproduction* 1997 July; 12(7): 1591-1597. Subject: 14.2

Brewer, Janet K. Individual boundaries and the impact of genetic databases upon collectivist cultures: molecular, cognitive and philosophical views. *In:* Árnason, Gardar; Nordal, Salvör; Árnason, Vilhjálmur, eds. Blood and Data: Ethical, Legal and Social Aspects of Human Genetic Databases. Reykjavík: University of Iceland Press; 2004: 291-296. Subject: 15.1

Brewer, Rose M. Thinking critically about race and genetics. *Journal of Law, Medicine and Ethics* 2006 Fall; 34(3): 513-519. Subject: 15.11

Brewer, Sherry. When things go wrong. . . . *Protecting Human Subjects* 2006 Spring; (13): 13-14. Subject: 18.2

Brewster, William D. In re E.G., a Minor: death over life: a judicial trend continues as the Illinois Supreme Court grants minors the right to refuse life-saving medical treatment. *John Marshall Law Review* 1990 Summer; 23(4): 771-786. Subject: 8.3.4

Brey, Philip. Prosthetics. *In:* Mitcham, Carl, ed. Encyclopedia of Science, Technology, and Ethics. Farmington Hills, MI: Thomson/Gale, 2005: 1527-1532. Subject: 9.7

Bridges, Khiara M. A judicial bypass procedure for an adolescent's abortion. *California Law Review* 2006 January; 94(1): 215-242. Subject: 12.4.2

Briggle, Adam. Asilomar Conference. *In:* Mitcham, Carl, ed. Encyclopedia of Science, Technology, and Ethics. Farmington Hills, MI: Thomson/Gale, 2005: 118-121. Subject: 15.7

Briggle, Adam. Double effect and dual use. *In:* Mitcham, Carl, ed. Encyclopedia of Science, Technology, and Ethics. Farmington Hills, MI: Thomson/Gale, 2005: 543-546. Subject: 2.1

Briggle, Adam. Institutional biosafety committees. *In:* Mitcham, Carl, ed. Encyclopedia of Science, Technology, and Ethics. Farmington Hills, MI: Thomson/Gale, 2005: 1022-1024. Subject: 15.7

Briggle, Adam. Institutional review boards. *In:* Mitcham, Carl, ed. Encyclopedia of Science, Technology, and Ethics. Farmington Hills, MI: Thomson/Gale, 2005: 1024-1026. Subject: 18.2

Briggle, Adam; Mitcham, Carl. Bioethics committees and commissions. *In:* Mitcham, Carl, ed. Encyclopedia of Science, Technology, and Ethics. Farmington Hills, MI: Thomson/Gale, 2005: 202-207. Subject: 2.4

Briggs, Gerald G. Comment: pharmacist critique was ill-informed. *Annals of Pharmacotherapy* 2006 July-August; 40: 1474-1475. Subject: 11.1

Brinchmann, Berit Støre; Torstein, Vik. Parents' involvement in life-and-death decisions in neonatal intensive care: Norwegian attitudes. *Newborn and Infant Nursing Reviews* 2005 June; 5(2): 77-81. Subject: 20.5.2

Brinkmann, Bill; Maines, T. Dean; Naughton, Michael J.; Stebbins, J. Michael; Weimerskirch, Arnold. Bridging the gap: Catholic health care organizations need concrete ways to connect social principles to practice. *Health Progress* 2006 November-December; 87(6): 43-50. Subject: 9.1

Brion, Nathalie; Demarez, Jean-Paul.; Belorgey, Chantal. Committee for the protection of persons. *Therapie* 2005 July-August; 60(4): 319-328, 329-337. Subject: 18.2

British Association of Critical Care Nurses; Bray, Kate; Hill, Karen; Robson, Wayne; Leaver, Gill; Walker, Nikki; O'Leary, Mary; Delaney, Trish; Walsh, Dominic; Gager, Melanie; Waterhouse, Catheryne. British Association of Critical Care Nurses position statement on the use of restraint in adult critical care units. *Nursing in Critical Care* 2004 September-October; 9(5): 199-212. Subject: 17.3

British Columbia Persons with AIDS Society. Position statement on euthanasia released [news]. *Canadian HIV/AIDS Policy and Law Newsletter* 1994 October; 1(1): 15. Subject: 20.5.1

British Committee for Standards in Haematology; Treleaven, J.; Cullis, J.O.; Maynard, R.; Bishop, E.; Ainsworth-Smith, I.; Roques, A.; Webb, A.; Favre, J.; Milligan, D. Obtaining consent for chemotherapy. *British Journal of Haematology* 2006 March; 132(5): 552-559. Subject: 8.3.1

Brock, D.W. Is a consensus possible on stem cell research? Moral and political obstacles. *Journal of Medical Ethics* 2006 January; 32(1): 36-42. Subject: 18.5.4

Brock, Dan W. Behavioral genetics and equality. *In:* Parens, Erik; Chapman, Audrey R.; Press, Nancy, eds. Wrestling with Behavioral Genetics: Science, Ethics, and Public Conversion. Baltimore, MD: Johns Hopkins University Press; 2006: 199-219. Subject: 15.6

Brock, Dan W. How much is more life worth? *Hastings Center Report* 2006 May-June; 36(3): 17-19. Subject: 9.8

Brock, Dan W. Terminal sedation from the moral rights' perspective. *In:* Tännsjö, Torbjörn, ed. Terminal Sedation: Euthanasia in Disguise? Boston: Kluwer Academic Publishers; 2004: 71-79. Subject: 20.4.1

Brock, Dan W.; Ho, William; Robinson, Walter. In the line of duty: SARS and physician responsibility in epidemics [forum]. *Medical Ethics Newsletter* 2006 Spring; 13(2): 5-8. Subject: 9.1

Brock, Dan W.; Prusak, Bernard G. The debate over liberal eugenics [letter and reply]. *Hastings Center Report* 2006 March-April; 36(2): 5-6, 6-7. Subject: 15.5

Brockway, Laura M.; Furcht, Leo T.; DeAngelis, Catherine D. Financial disclosure policies of scientific publications [letter and reply]. *JAMA: The Journal of the American Medical Association* 2006 December 27; 296(24): 2925-2926. Subject: 1.3.7

Broder, John M. Questions over method lead to delay of execution. *New York Times* 2006 February 22; p. A11. Subject: 20.6

Broderick, Pia; Walker, Iain. Donor gametes and embryos: who wants to know what about whom, and why? *Politics and the Life Sciences* 2001 March; 20(1): 29-42. Subject: 8.4

Brodkey, Amy C. The role of the pharmaceutical industry in teaching psychopharmacology: a growing problem. *Academic Psychiatry* 2005 May-June; 29(2): 222-229. Subject: 9.7

Brodwin, Paul. "Bioethics in action" and human population genetics research. *Culture, Medicine and Psychiatry* 2005 June; 29(2): 145-178. Subject: 15.11

Brody, Baruch. Intellectual property and biotechnology: the U.S. internal experience — Part I. *Kennedy Institute of Ethics Journal* 2006 March; 16(1): 1-37. Subject: 15.8

Brody, Baruch. Intellectual property and biotechnology: the U.S. internal experience — Part II. *Kennedy Institute of Ethics Journal* 2006 June; 16(2): 105-128. Subject: 15.8

Brody, Baruch A.; Dickey, Nancy; Ellenberg, Susan S.; Heaney, Robert P.; Levine, Robert J.; O'Brien, Richard L.; Purtilo, Ruth B.; Weijer, Charles. Is the use of placebo controls ethically permissible in clinical trials of agents intended to reduce fractures in osteoporosis? *Journal of Bone and Mineral Research* 2003 June; 18(6): 1105-1109. Subject: 18.3

Brody, Howard. Are there three or four distinct types of medical practice? *American Journal of Bioethics* 2006 July-August; 6(4): 51-53. Subject: 18.2

Brody, Howard. The company we keep: why physicians should refuse to see pharmaceutical representatives. *Annals of Family Medicine* 2005 January-February; 3(1): 82-85. Subject: 9.7

Brody, Howard. Confronting a colleague who covers up a medical error. *American Family Physician* 2006 April 1; 73(7): 1272, 1274. Subject: 7.3

Brody, Howard. Family medicine, the physician-patient relationship, and patient-centered care. *American Journal of Bioethics* 2006 January-February; 6(1): 38-39. Subject: 9.3.2

Brody, Howard. Physician integrity, enhancement technologies, and consumer autonomy. *Newsletter on Philosophy and Medicine* 2005 Fall; 05(1): 14-15. Subject: 4.1.2

Brody, Howard; Brennan, Troyen A.; Rothman, David J.; Naughton, James; Cohen, Jordan; Kimball, Harry; Blumenthal, David; Smelser, Neil; Kassirer, Jerome P.; Goldman, JanLori. Academic medical centers and conflicts of interest [letter and reply]. *JAMA: The Journal of the American Medical Association* 2006 June 28; 295(24): 2848, 2848-2849. Subject: 7.3

Brody, Jane E. Medical due diligence: a living will should spell out the specifics. *New York Times* 2006 November 28; p. F7. Subject: 20.5.4

Brody, Janet L.; Annett, Robert D.; Scherer, David G.; Perryman, Mandy L.; Cofrin, Keely M.W. Comparisons of adolescent and parent willingness to participate in minimal and above-minimal risk pediatric asthma research protocols. *Journal of Adolescent Health* 2005 September; 37(3): 229-235. Subject: 18.5.2

Broeckaert, Bert; Janssens, Rien. Palliative care and euthanasia: Belgian and Dutch perspectives. *In:* Schotsmans, Paul; Meulenbergs, Tom, eds. Euthanasia and Palliative Care in the Low Countries. Dudley, MA: Peeters, 2005: 35-69. Subject: 20.4.1

See SUBJECT HEADING KEY FOR SECTION II on inside back cover.

507

Broggi, Marc Antoni. Historia del <Comité de Bioética de Cataluña>. *Bioetica and Debat* 2006 April-June; 12(44): 8-10. Subject: 2.2

Bromage, D.I. Prenatal diagnosis and selective abortion: a result of the cultural turn? *Medical Humanities* 2006 June; 32(1): 38-42. Subject: 15.2

Bronx Health REACH Coalition. Action Committee; Calman, Neil S.; Golub, Maxine; Ruddock, Charmaine; Le, Lan; Hauser, Diane. Separate and unequal care in New York City. *Journal of Health Care Law and Policy* 2006; 9(1): 105-120. Subject: 9.5.4

Brook, Nicholas R.; Nicholson, Michael L. Non-directed live kidney donation. *Lancet* 2006 July 29-August 4; 368(9533): 346-347. Subject: 19.3

Brook, N.R.; Nicholson, M.L. Kidney transplantation from non heart-beating donors. *Surgeon Journal of the Royal Colleges of Surgeons of Edinburgh and Ireland* 2003 December; 1(6): 323-322. Subject: 19.3

Brookey, Robert Alan. Homosexuality debate. *In:* Mitcham, Carl, ed. Encyclopedia of Science, Technology, and Ethics. Farmington Hills, MI: Thomson/Gale, 2005: 934-935. Subject: 10

Brooks, Robert A. U.S. psychiatrists' beliefs and wants about involuntary civil commitment grounds. *International Journal of Law and Psychiatry* 2006 January-February; 29(1): 13-21. Subject: 17.7

Broome, Marion E. Self-plagiarism: oxymoron, fair use, or scientific misconduct? [editorial]. *Nursing Outlook* 2004 November-December; 52(6): 273-274. Subject: 1.3.7

Brorsson, Annika; Hellquist, Gunilla; Björkelund, Cecilia; Råstam, Lennart. Serious, frightening and interesting conditions: differences in values and attitudes between first-year and final-year medical students. *Medical Education* 2002 June; 36(6): 555-560. Subject: 7.2

Brotzman, Gregory L.; Mark, David H. Policies regulating the activities of pharmaceutical representatives in residency programs. *Journal of Family Practice* 1992 January; 34(1): 54-57. Subject: 9.7

Brouwer, Werner B.F.; van Exel, N. Job A.; Stolk, Elly A. Acceptability of less than perfect health states. *Social Science and Medicine* 2005 January; 60(2): 237-246. Subject: 4.4

Brower, Vicki. The ethics of innovation: should innovative surgery be exempt from clinical trials and regulations? *EMBO Reports* 2003 April; 4(4): 338-339. Subject: 18.6

Brown, David. Johns Hopkins scales down its deal with cosmetics firm after criticism [news]. *BMJ: British Medical Journal* 2006 April 22; 332(7547): 929. Subject: 5.3

Brown, Harold O.J. The victory of the abstract over the real. *Human Life Review* 2006 Spring; 32(2): 64-70. Subject: 12.1

Brown, Harold O.J.; Colson, Charles; George, Timothy; Hill, Kent; James, Frank; Johns, Cheryl Bridges; Moore, T.M.; Oden, Thomas; Packer, James; Sumner, Sarah; Vanhoozer, Kevin J.; Woodbridge, John; Buckley, James J.; Casarella, Peter; Culpepper, Gary; Dulles, Avery Cardinal; Guarino, Thomas; Kennedy, Arthur; Levering, Matthew; Martin, Francis; Neuhaus, Richard John; Oakes, Edward T.; Weigel, George; Wilken, Robert Louis. That they may have life. A statement of Evangelicals and Catholics together. *First Things* 2006 October; (166): 18-25. Subject: 4.4

Brown, Ian. Nurses' attitudes towards adult patients who are obese: literature review. *Journal of Advanced Nursing* 2006 January; 53(2): 221-232. Subject: 8.1

Brown, James Henderson; Hentelheff, Paul; Barakat, Samia; Rowe, Cheryl June. Is it normal for terminally ill patients to desire death? *American Journal of Psychiatry* 1986 February; 143(2): 208-211. Subject: 20.5.1

Brown, Jeffrey L.; Cogan, Karen D. Ethical clinical practice and sport psychology: when two worlds collide. *Ethics and Behavior* 2006; 16(1): 15-23. Subject: 17.1

Brown, Jeremy. The spectrum of informed consent in emergency psychiatric research. *Annals of Emergency Medicine* 2006 January; 47(1): 68-74. Subject: 8.3.1

Brown, Joseph S.; Schonfeld, Toby L.; Gordon, Bruce G. "You may have already won. . .": an examination of the use of lottery payments in research [case study]. *IRB: Ethics and Human Research* 2006 January-February; 28(1): 12-16. Subject: 18.2

Brown, Keri D. An ethical obligation to our service members: meaningful benefits for informed consent violations. *South Texas Law Review* 2006 Summer; 47(4): 919-947. Subject: 18.5.8

Brown, Margaret; Fisher, John W.; Brumley, David J.; Ashby, Michael A.; Milliken, Jan. Advance directives in action in a regional palliative care service: "road testing" the provisions of the Medical Treatment Act 1988 (VIC). *Journal of Law and Medicine* 2005 November; 13(2): 186-190. Subject: 20.5.4

Brownback, Sam. Bioethics and the future of humanity. *National Catholic Bioethics Quarterly* 2006 Autumn; 6(3): 423-430. Subject: 2.1

Browne, Alister. Causation, intention, and active euthanasia. *CQ: Cambridge Quarterly of Healthcare Ethics* 2006 Winter; 15(1): 71-80. Subject: 20.5.1

Browne, Alister; Sullivan, Bill. Advance directives in Canada. *CQ: Cambridge Quarterly of Healthcare Ethics* 2006 Summer; 15(3): 256-260. Subject: 20.5.4

Browner, C.H.; Preloran, H. Mabel. Interpreting low-income Latinas' amniocentesis refusals. *Hispanic Journal of Behavioral Sciences* 2000 August 1; 22(3): 346-368. Subject: 15.2

Subject = NRCBL Primary Classification Number; see inside front cover.

Browner, C.H.; Preloran, H. Mabel; Casado, Maria Christina; Bass, Harold N.; Walker, Ann P. Genetic counseling gone awry: miscommunication between prenatal genetic service providers and Mexican-origin clients. *Social Science and Medicine* 2003 May; 56(9): 1933-1946. Subject: 15.2

Brownstein, John S.; Cassa, Christopher A.; Mandl, Kenneth D. No place to hide — reverse identification of patients from published maps [letter]. *New England Journal of Medicine* 2006 October 19; 355(16): 1741-1742. Subject: 8.4

Brubaker, Beryl H. An ethic of caring. *In:* Miller, Roman J.; Brubaker, Beryl H.; Peterson, James C., eds. Viewing New Creations with Anabaptist Eyes: Ethics of Biotechnology. Telford, PA: Cascadia Pub.; 2005: 136-148. Subject: 4.1.1

Bruce, Ann; Tait, Joyce. Interests, values, and genetic databases. *In:* Árnason, Gardar; Nordal, Salvör; Árnason, Vilhjálmur, eds. Blood and Data: Ethical, Legal and Social Aspects of Human Genetic Databases. Reykjavík: University of Iceland Press; 2004: 211-216. Subject: 15.1

Bruce, Donald. Categorizing genes: commodifying people? *In:* Árnason, Gardar; Nordal, Salvör; Árnason, Vilhjálmur, eds. Blood and Data: Ethical, Legal and Social Aspects of Human Genetic Databases. Reykjavík: University of Iceland Press; 2004: 269-273. Subject: 15.1

Bruce, Donald. To everything there is a season? Time, eternity and the promise of extending human life. *EMBO Reports* 2005 July; 6(Special Issue): S63-S66. Subject: 20.5.1

Bruce, Donald M. Moral and ethical issues in gene therapy. *Human Reproduction and Genetic Ethics: An International Journal* 2006; 12(1): 16-23. Subject: 15.4

Bruce, J.C. Trauma patients' rights during resuscitation. *Curationis: South African Journal of Nursing* 2000 March; 23(1): 53-56. Subject: 20.5.1

Brugada, Ramon. Genetics, ethics and ethnicity [editorial]. *Heart Rhythm* 2004 November; 1(5): 608-609. Subject: 15.11

Brugge, Doug; Missaghian, Mariam. Protecting the Navajo people through tribal regulation of research. *Science and Engineering Ethics* 2006 July; 12(3): 491-507. Subject: 18.5.1

Brugger, E. Christian. Moral stem cells. *First Things* 2006 May; (163): 14-17. Subject: 18.5.4

Bruhn, John G. Equal partners: doctors and patients explore the limits of autonomy. *Journal of the Oklahoma State Medical Association* 2001 February; 94(2): 46-54. Subject: 8.1

Bruhn, John G. Looking good, but behaving badly: leader accountability and ethics failure. *Health Care Manager* 2005 July-September; 24(3): 191-199. Subject: 9.1

Brulliard, Karin. In competitive marketplace, Asian egg donors in demand. *Washington Post* 2006 November 19; p. A1, A7. Subject: 14.6

Brunk, Conrad G. Biotechnology and the future. *In:* Miller, Roman J.; Brubaker, Beryl H.; Peterson, James C., eds. Viewing New Creations with Anabaptist Eyes: Ethics of Biotechnology. Telford, PA: Cascadia Pub.; 2005: 257-260. Subject: 15.1

Brunk, Conrad G. The biotechnology vision: insight from Anabaptist values. *In:* Miller, Roman J.; Brubaker, Beryl H.; Peterson, James C., eds. Viewing New Creations with Anabaptist Eyes: Ethics of Biotechnology. Telford, PA: Cascadia Pub.; 2005: 106-121. Subject: 15.1

Bruzzone, Paolo; Pretagostini, R.; Poli, L.; Rossi, M.; Berloco, P.B. Ethical considerations on kidney transplantation from living donors. *Transplantation Proceedings* 2005 July-August; 37(6): 2436-2438. Subject: 19.3

Bryan, C.S. Medicine and the seven basic virtues [editorial]. *Journal of the South Carolina Medical Association* 2005 October; 101(9): 327-328. Subject: 4.1.2

Bryan, C.S. The seven basic virtues in medicine. I. Prudence (practical wisdom) [editorial]. *Journal of the South Carolina Medical Association* 2005 October; 101(9): 329-331. Subject: 4.1.2

Bryan, Charles S. Aequanimitas redux: William Osler on detached concern versus humanistic empathy. *Perspectives in Biology and Medicine* 2006 Summer; 49(3): 384-392. Subject: 8.1

Bryan, Charles S.; Saunders, Donald E., Jr. Medicine as business, learned profession, and moral enterprise: an evolution of emphasis, 1905-2005. *Journal of the South Carolina Medical Association* 2005 June; 101(5): 163-168. Subject: 4.1.2

Bryant, John. What is the appropriate role of the trial statistician in preparing and presenting interim findings to an independent data monitoring committee in the U.S. Cancer Cooperative Group setting? *Statistics in Medicine* 2004 May 30; 23(10): 1507-1511. Subject: 18.2

Bryant, Taimie L. Animals unmodified: defining animals/defining human obligations to animals. *University of Chicago Legal Forum* 2006: 137-194. Subject: 22.1

Bryce, C.L.; Siminoff, L.A.; Ubel, P.A.; Nathan, H.; Caplan, A.; Arnold, R.M. Do incentives matter? Providing benefits to families of organ donors. *American Journal of Transplantation* 2005 December; 5(12): 2999-3008. Subject: 19.5

Bubien, Rosemary S. Practice or research — patient or participant: is there a difference? *Heart Rhythm* 2004 December; 1(6): 757-759. Subject: 18.2

Bucci, Kathryn K.; Frey, Keith A. Involvement of pharmacy faculty in the development of policies for pharmaceutical sales representatives. *Journal of Family Practice* 1992 January; 34(1): 49-52. Subject: 7.2

See SUBJECT HEADING KEY FOR SECTION II on inside back cover.

509

dics and Related Research 2000 September; (378): 44-49. Subject: 2.1

Bunge, Mario. Bioethics. *In his:* Philosophical Dictionary. Enlarged edition. Amherst, NY: Prometheus Books; 2003: 32. Subject: 2.1

Bunge, Mario. Principlism. *In his:* Philosophical Dictionary. Enlarged edition. Amherst, NY: Prometheus Books; 2003: 224. Subject: 2.1

Burack, Jeffrey H. Jewish reflections on genetic enhancement. *Journal of Society of Christian Ethics* 2006 Spring-Summer; 26(1): 137-161. Subject: 15.1

Burchardi, Nicole; Rauprich, Oliver; Hecht, Martin; Beck, Marcus; Vollmann, Jochen. Discussing living wills. A qualitative study of a German sample of neurologists and ALS patients. *Journal of the Neurological Sciences* 2005 October 15; 237(1-2): 67-74. Subject: 20.5.4

Burck, Russell; Anderson-Shaw, Lisa; Sheldon, Mark; Egan, Erin A. The clinical response to brain death: a policy proposal. *JONA's Healthcare Law, Ethics, and Regulation* 2006 April-June; 8(2): 53-59. Subject: 20.2.1

Burger, Ingrid; Sugarman, Jeremy; Goodman, Steven N. Ethical issues in evidence-based surgery. *Surgical Clinics of North America* 2006 February; 86(1): 151-168, x. Subject: 9.8

Burgess, E.; Singhal, N.; Amin, H.; McMillan, D.D.; Devrome, H.; Fenton, A.C. Consent for clinical research in the neonatal intensive care unit: a retrospective survey and a prospective study. *Archives of Disease in Childhood Fetal and Neonatal Edition* 2003 July; 88(4): F280-F286. Subject: 18.5.2

Burgess, Sally; Hawton, Keith. Suicide, euthanasia, and the psychiatrist. *Philosophy, Psychiatry, and Psychology* 1998 June; 5(2): 113-126. Subject: 20.7

Burggraeve, Roger. You shall not let anyone die alone: responsible care for suffering and dying people. *In:* Schotsmans, Paul; Meulenbergs, Tom, eds. Euthanasia and Palliative Care in the Low Countries. Dudley, MA: Peeters, 2005: 147-173. Subject: 20.4.1

Burghignoli, Massimo. European Directive 2004/23/EC of 31 March 2004 on tissue banks, and Italian law. *International Journal of Biological Markers* 2005 January-March; 20(1): 1-4. Subject: 19.5

Burgin, Eileen. Dollars, disease, and democracy: has the Director's Council of Public Representatives improved the National Institutes of Health? *Politics and the Life Sciences* 2005 March-September; 24(1-2): 43-63. Subject: 1.3.9

Burhansstipanov, Linda; Bemis, Lynne; Kaur, Judith S.; Bemis, Gordon. Sample genetic policy language for research conducted with native communities. *Journal of Cancer Education* 2005 Spring; 20(1, Supplement): 52-57. Subject: 18.5.1

Burk, Dan L. Bioinformatics lessons from the open source movement. *In:* Tavani, Herman T., ed. Ethics, Computing, and Genomics. Sudbury, MA: Jones and Bartlett; 2006: 247-254. Subject: 15.1

Burke, Georgine S. Looking into the institutional review board: observations from both sides of the table. *Journal of Nutrition* 2005 April; 135(4): 921-924. Subject: 18.2

Burke, Suzanne M. The case manager's view. *Journal of Clinical Ethics* 2006 Spring; 17(1): 83-84. Subject: 9.5.1

Burke, Taylor; Rosenbaum, Sara. Molloy v Meier and the expanding standard of medical care: implications for public health policy and practice. *Public Health Reports* 2005 March-April; 120(2): 209-210. Subject: 9.1

Burke, William; Pullicino, Patrick; Richard, Edward J. A critique of oocyte-assisted reprogramming [letter]. *National Catholic Bioethics Quarterly* 2006 Spring; 6(1): 12-15. Subject: 18.5.4

Burke, Wylie; Diekema, Douglas S. Ethical issues arising from the participation of children in genetic research. *Journal of Pediatrics* 2006 July; 149(1, Supplement): S34-S38. Subject: 15.1

Burke, Wylie; Khoury, Muin J.; Stewart, Alison; Zimmern, Ronald L. The path from genome-based research to population health: development of an international public health genomics network. *Genetics in Medicine* 2006 July; 8(7): 451-458. Subject: 15.1

Burkell, Jacquelyn; Campbell, D. Grant. "What does this mean?" How Web-based consumer health information fails to support information seeking in the pursuit of informed consent for screening test decisions. *Journal of the Medical Library Association* 2005 July; 93(3): 363-373. Subject: 8.3.1

Burleigh, Michael. Die Nazi-Analogie und die Debatten zur Euthanasie. *In:* Frewer, Andreas; Eickhoff, Clemens, eds. "Euthanasie" und die aktuelle Sterbehilfe-Debatte: Die historischen Hintergründe medizinischer Ethik. Frankfurt; New York: Campus; 2000: 408-423. Subject: 20.5.1

Burley, Justine; Colman, Alan. Science and philosophy: bridging the two cultures divide. *Journal of Molecular Biology* 2002 June 14; 319(4): 907-915. Subject: 2.1

Burnet, N.G.; Jefferies, S.J.; Benson, R.J.; Hunt, D.P.; Treasure, F.P. Years of life lost (YLL) from cancer is an important measure of population burden — and should be considered when allocating research funds. *British Journal of Cancer* 2005 January 31; 92(2): 241-245. Subject: 18.6

Burns, Jeffrey P. Is there any consensus about end-of-life care in pediatrics? *Archives of Pediatrics and Adolescent Medicine* 2005 September; 159(9): 889-891. Subject: 20.4.2

Burns, Lawrence. Banking on the value of analogies in bioethics. *American Journal of Bioethics* 2006 Novem-

See SUBJECT HEADING KEY FOR SECTION II on inside back cover.

511

ber-December; 6(6): 63-65; author reply W13-W14. Subject: 19.5

Burns, Paul; Keogh, Ivan; Timon, Conrad. Informed consent: a patients' perspective. *Journal of Laryngology and Otology* 2005 January; 119(1): 19-22. Subject: 8.3.1

Burns-Cox, Christopher J.; Rouse, Andrew; Halpin, David; Mayor, Vidhu; Marshall, Tom. Guantanamo: a call for action: would GMC dismiss a complaint against Guantanamo doctor? [letter]. *BMJ: British Medical Journal* 2006 April 8; 332(7545): 854-855. Subject: 21.4

Burr, Jennifer. "Repellent to proper ideas about the procreation of children": procreation and motherhood in the legal and ethical treatment of the surrogate mother. *Psychology, Evolution and Gender* 2000 August; 2(2): 105-117. Subject: 14.2

Burris, Scott; Moss, Kathryn. U.S. health research review their ethics review boards: a qualitative study. *Journal of Empirical Research on Human Research Ethics* 2006 June; 1(2): 39-58. Subject: 18.2

Burton, J.L.; Underwood, J.C.E. Necropsy practice after the "organ retention scandal": requests, performance, and tissue retention. *Journal of Clinical Pathology* 2003 July; 56(7): 537-541. Subject: 20.1

Burton, Sarah K.; Withrow, Kara; Arnos, Kathleen S.; Kalfoglou, Andrea L.; Pandya, Arti. A focus group study of consumer attitudes toward genetic testing and newborn screening for deafness. *Genetics in Medicine* 2006 December; 8(12): 779-783. Subject: 15.3

Burton, Thomas M. Amid alarm bells, a blood substitute keeps pumping; ten in trial have heart attacks, but data aren't published; FDA allows a new study; doctors' pleas are ignored. *Wall Street Journal* 2006 February 22; p. A1, A12. Subject: 18.2

Burton, Thomas M. Biopure moves to sell blood substitute in Europe. *Wall Street Journal* 2006 July 12; p. D2. Subject: 19.4

Burton, Thomas M. Blood-substitute study is criticized by U.S. agency. *Wall Street Journal* 2006 March 10; p. A3. Subject: 19.4

Burton, Thomas M. FDA to weigh test of blood substitute out of public view. *Wall Street Journal* 2006 July 11; p. D3. Subject: 19.4

Burton, Thomas M. FDA to weigh using fake blood in trauma trial. *Wall Street Journal* 2006 July 6; p. B1, B2. Subject: 19.4

Burton, Thomas M. Use of substitution for blood draws ethics challenge. *Wall Street Journal* 2006 March 20; p. A2. Subject: 19.4

Busby, Helen. Consent, trust and ethics: reflections on the findings of an interview based study with people donating blood for genetic research for research within the NHS. *Clinical Ethics* 2006 December; 1(4): 211-215. Subject: 19.4

Busby, Helen. UK biobank: social and political landscapes. *In:* Árnason, Gardar; Nordal, Salvör; Árnason, Vilhjálmur, eds. Blood and Data: Ethical, Legal and Social Aspects of Human Genetic Databases. Reykjavík: University of Iceland Press; 2004: 307-311. Subject: 15.1

Busby, Helen; Martin, Paul. Biobanks, national identity and imagined communities: the case of UK biobank. *Science as Culture* 2006 September; 15(3): 237-251. Subject: 15.1

Busey, J. Craig. Recognizing and addressing conflicts of interest. *Journal of the American Dietetic Association* 2006 March; 106(3): 351-355. Subject: 7.3

Busfield, Joan. Pills, power, people: sociological understandings of the pharmaceutical industry. *Sociology* 2006 April; 40(2): 297-314. Subject: 9.7

Buttel, Frederick H. Theoretical issues in the regulation of genetically engineered organisms: a commentary. *Politics and the Life Sciences* 1989 February; 7(2): 135-139. Subject: 5.7

Butter, Irene H. Premature adoption and routinization of medical technology: illustrations from childbirth technology. *Journal of Social Issues* 1993 Summer; 49(2): 11-34. Subject: 5.2

Butz, Arlene M.; Redman, Barbara K.; Fry, Sara T.; Kolodner, Ken. Ethical conflicts experienced by certified pediatric nurse practitioners in ambulatory settings. *Journal of Pediatric Health Care* 1998 July-August; 12(4): 183-190. Subject: 4.1.3

Butzel, Henry M. Teaching at the interface between genetics and law. *Politics and the Life Sciences* 1986 August; 5(1): 54-58. Subject: 15.1

Buyx, Alena M. Jenseits der Therapie [Beyond therapy]. *Ethik in der Medizin* 2006 September; 18(3): 267-272. Subject: 4.5

Byers, Peter H. 2005 ASHG Presidential Address. If only we spoke the same language—we would have so much to discuss. *American Journal of Human Genetics* 2006 March; 78(3): 368-372. Subject: 15.1

Byk, Christian. Biotechnology: from refound law to manipulated law? = La Biotecnología: ¿de un Derecho refundido a un Derecho manipulado? *Law and the Human Genome Review = Revista de Derecho y Genoma Humano* 1996 July-December; (5): 35-46. Subject: 15.8

Bynum, Jack E.; Provonsha, Jack W.; Acuff, F. Gene. Ethics of experimental surgery: the Baby Fae case — an interview and comment. *Pharos* 1986 Fall; 49(4): 23-26. Subject: 18.5.7

Byrne, Margaret M.; Speckman, Jeanne; Getz, Ken; Sugarman, Jeremy. Variability in the costs of institutional review board oversight. *Academic Medicine* 2006 August; 81(8): 708-712. Subject: 18.2

Subject = NRCBL Primary Classification Number; see inside front cover.

Byrne, Mary. Ethics, assisted reproductive technologies and cloning. *Reform* 2001 Spring; 79: 22-26, 71. Subject: 14.5

Byrne, Michelle M. Uncovering racial bias in nursing fundamentals textbooks. *Nursing and Health Care Perspectives* 2001 November-December; 22(6): 299-303. Subject: 7.2

Byrne, Paul J.; Murphy, Aisling. Informed consent and hypoplastic left heart syndrome. *Acta Paediatrica* 2005 September; 94(9): 1171-1175. Subject: 8.3.2

Byrne, Peter; Cassidy, Brendan; Higgins, Patrick. Knowledge and attitudes toward electroconvulsive therapy among health care professionals and students. *Journal of ECT* 2006 June; 22(2): 133-138. Subject: 17.5

Byrne, Steven; Goldsmith, Jay P. Non-initiation and discontinuation of resuscitation. *Clinics in Perinatology* 2006 March; 33(1): 197-218. Subject: 20.5.2

Byrnes, W. Malcolm; Berg, Thomas. Inconsistencies in pro ANT-OAR position [letter and reply]. *National Catholic Bioethics Quarterly* 2006 Summer; 6(2): 201-205. Subject: 18.5.4

Byron, Margaret; Cockshott, Zoë; Brownett, Hilary; Ramkalawan, Tina. What does 'disability' mean for medical students? An exploration of the words medical students associate with the term 'disability'. *Medical Education* 2005 February; 39(2): 176-183. Subject: 9.5.1

C

Caddell, David P.; Newton, Rae R. Euthanasia: American attitudes toward the physician's role. *Social Science and Medicine* 1995 June; 40(12): 1671-1681. Subject: 20.5.1

Cadge, Wendy; Catlin, Elizabeth A. Making sense of suffering and death: how health care providers' construct meanings in a neonatal intensive care unit. *Journal of Religion and Health* 2006 Summer; 45(2): 248-263. Subject: 20.5.2

Cadoré, Bruno. A hermeneutical approach to clinical bioethics. *In:* Viafora, Corrado, ed. Clinical Bioethics: A Search for the Foundations. Dordrecht: Springer, 2005: 53-59. Subject: 2.1

Caenepeel, Didier; Jobin, Guy. Discursivité et co-autorité en éthique clinique: regard critique sur le rôle et les fonctions de la délibération éthique en comité = Discursiveness and co-authority in clinical ethics: A critical look at the role and functions of ethics committee deliberations. *Journal International de Bioéthique = International Journal of Bioethics* 2005 September-December; 16(3-4): 107-133, 174-175. Subject: 9.6

Caetano, André J.; Potter, Joseph E. Politics and female sterilization in northeast Brazil. *Population and Development Review* 2004 March; 30(1): 79-108. Subject: 11.3

Cahill, Judith A.; Maddux, Michael S.; Gans, John A.; Manasse, Henri R. Pharmacist critique woefully outdated and uninformed [letter]. Washington, DC: American Pharmacists Association 2006: 2 p. Subject: 11.1

Cahill, Lisa Sowle. Bioethics. *Theological Studies* 2006 March; 67(1): 120-142. Subject: 20.5.1

Cahill, Lisa Sowle. Biotechnology, genes, and justice. *In her:* Theological Bioethics: Participation, Justice, and Change. Washington, DC: Georgetown University Press; 2005: 211-251. Subject: 15.1

Cahill, Lisa Sowle. Decline and dying: cultural and theological interpretations. *In her:* Theological Bioethics: Participation, Justice, and Change. Washington, DC: Georgetown University Press; 2005: 70-101. Subject: 20.3.1

Cahill, Lisa Sowle. Decline and dying: principles of analysis and practices of solidarity. *In her:* Theological Bioethics: Participation, Justice, and Change. Washington, DC: Georgetown University Press; 2005: 102-130. Subject: 20.5.1

Cahill, Lisa Sowle. Genetics in context: beyond anatomy and the market. *Politics and the Life Sciences* 1998 March; 17(1): 14-16. Subject: 15.4

Cahill, Lisa Sowle. National and international health access reform. *In her:* Theological Bioethics: Participation, Justice, and Change. Washington, DC: Georgetown University Press; 2005: 131-168. Subject: 9.1

Cahill, Lisa Sowle. Reproduction and early life. *In her:* Theological Bioethics: Participation, Justice, and Change. Washington, DC: Georgetown University Press; 2005: 169-210. Subject: 12.3

Cahill, Lisa Sowle. Theology's role in public bioethics. *In:* Guinn, David E., ed. Handbook of Bioethics and Religion. New York: Oxford University Press, 2006: 37-57. Subject: 2.1

Cahill, Molly. The ethical consequences of Modafinil use. *Penn Bioethics Journal* 2005 April 2; 1(1): 3p. [Online]. Accessed: http://www.bioethicsjournal.com [2005 April 19]. Subject: 17.4

Cahn, Ellen. Dementia and the nursing home decision. *Conservative Judaism* 2006 Summer; 58(4): 32-50. Subject: 9.5.2

Calame, Byron. Truth, justice, abortion and The Times Magazine [op-ed]. *New York Times* 2006 December 31; p.WK8. Subject: 1.3.7

Calder, Gideon. Ownership rights and the body. *CQ: Cambridge Quarterly of Healthcare Ethics* 2006 Winter; 15(1): 89-100. Subject: 4.4

Calderón, Rosario. The Human Genome Diversity Project: ethical aspects = El Proyecto Genoma Humano sobre Diversidad: aspectors éticos. *Law and the Human Genome Review = Revista de Derecho y Genoma Humano* 1996 January-June; (4): 107-123. Subject: 15.11

See SUBJECT HEADING KEY FOR SECTION II on inside back cover.

513

Caldwell, Gordon. New guidance on doctors' behaviour from the UK prime minister [letter]. *Lancet* 2006 December 16-22; 368(9553): 2124. Subject: 9.3.1

Califf, Robert M.; Nissen, Steven E.; DeMaria, Anthony N.; Ohman, Erik Magnus; Pitt, Bertram; Willerson, James T.; Bilheimer, David W.; Cohn, Jay N.; Feigal, David W., Jr.; Hampson, Lindsay; Lorell, Beverly H.; Pepine, Carl J.; Popp, Richard L. Task force 2: investigator participation in clinical research. *Journal of the American College of Cardiology* 2004 October 19; 44(8): 1729-1736. Subject: 18.2

California. Court of Appeal, Second District. Johnson v. Superior Court [Date of Decision: 2000 May 18]. *California Reporter*, 2d Series 2000; 95: 864-879. Subject: 14.2

California. Supreme Court. Catholic Charities of Sacramento County v. Superior Court of Sacramento County [Date of Decision: 2004 March 1]. *Pacific Reporter*, 3d Series, 2004; 85: 67-108. Subject: 11.1

California Dental Association. California Dental Association: Code of Ethics. *Journal of the California Dental Association* 2006 January; 34(1): 57-62. Subject: 6

Callahan, Daniel. Bioethics and ideology. *Hastings Center Report* 2006 January-February; 36(1): 3. Subject: 2.1

Callahan, Daniel. A commentary — putting autonomy in its place: developing effective guidelines. *Gerontologist* 2002 October; 42(Special Issue 3): 129-131. Subject: 20.4.1

Callahan, Daniel. Equity, quality, and patient rights: can they be reconciled? *In:* Lolas Stepke, Fernando; Agar Corbinos, Lorenzo, eds. Interfaces Between Bioethics and the Empirical Social Sciences. Buenos Aires, Argentina: World Health Organization; 2002: 33-36. Subject: 9.2

Callahan, Daniel. How much medical progress can we afford? Equity and the cost of health care. *Journal of Molecular Biology* 2002 June 14; 319(4): 885-890. Subject: 9.3.1

Callahan, Daniel. Living and dying with medical technology. *Critical Care Medicine* 2003 May; 31(5 Supplement): S344-S346. Subject: 20.5.1

Callahan, Daniel. Privatizing the department of defense: a proposal. *Hastings Center Report* 2006 November-December; 36(6): inside back cover. Subject: 9.3.1

Callahan, Daniel. Rejecting the gambler's principle [review of Rights and Liberties in the Biotech Age: Why We Need a Genetic Bill of Rights, edited by Sheldon Kimberly and Peter Shorett]. *Nature Biotechnology* 2005 October; 23(10): 1220. Subject: 2.4

Callahan, Daniel. Setting policy: the need for full participation. *Frontiers of Health Services Management* 1991 Fall; 8(1): 34- 36. Subject: 9.4

Callahan, Daniel. Terminal sedation and the artefactual fallacy. *In:* Tännsjö, Torbjörn, ed. Terminal Sedation: Eu-

thanasia in Disguise? Boston: Kluwer Academic Publishers; 2004: 93-102. Subject: 20.4.1

Callahan, Daniel. Universal health care: from the states to the nation? *Hastings Center Report* 2006 September-October; 36(5): 28-29. Subject: 9.3.1

Callahan, Daniel; Topinkovà. Age, rationing, and palliative care. *In:* Morrison, R. Sean; Meier, Diane E.; Capello, Carol, eds. Geriatric Palliative Care. New York: Oxford University Press; 2003: 46-54. Subject: 9.4

Callen, Jeffrey P.; Robinson, June. Clinical trial registration — a step forward in providing transparency for the positive and negative results of clinical trials. *Archives of Dermatology* 2005 January; 141(1): 75. Subject: 18.2

Callens, S. Informed consent. *Acta Chirurgica Belgica* 2000 August; 100(4): 169-174. Subject: 8.3.1

Callister, Lynn Clark. Perinatal ethics: state of the science. *Journal of Perinatal and Neonatal Nursing* 2006 January-March; 20(1): 37-39. Subject: 9.5.5

Calnan, Michael; Montaner, David; Horne, Rob. How acceptable are innovative health-care technologies? A survey of public beliefs and attitudes in England and Wales. *Social Science and Medicine* 2005 May; 60(9): 1937-1948. Subject: 5.1

Calnan, Michael; Wainwright, David; Glasner, Peter; Newbury-Ecob, Ruth; Ferlie, Ewan. 'Medicine's next goldmine?' The implications of new genetic health technologies for the health service. *Medicine, Health Care, and Philosophy* 2006; 9(1): 33-41. Subject: 15.1

Cameron, Alisa; Lloyd, Liz; Kent, Naomi; Anderson, Pat. Researching end of life in old age: ethical challenges. *In:* Smyth, Marie; Williamson, Emma, eds. Researchers and Their 'Subjects': Ethics, Power, Knowledge and Consent. Bristol, UK: Policy Press; 2004: 105-117. Subject: 18.5.7

Cameron, Edwin. Human rights, racism and AIDS: the new discrimination. *South African Journal on Human Rights* 1993; 9: 22-29. Subject: 9.5.6

Cameron, Edwin; Gupta, Alok. Global access to treatment: achievements and challenges. *HIV/AIDS Policy and Law Review* 2002 July; 7(1): 59-71. Subject: 9.5.6

Cameron, Nigel M. de S. Biotechnology and the future of humanity. *Journal of Contemporary Health Law and Policy* 2006 Spring; 22(2): 413-423. Subject: 2.1

Cameron, Nigel M. de S. "On one path or the other": cloning, religion, and the making of U.S. biopolicy. *In:* Guinn, David E., ed. Handbook of Bioethics and Religion. New York: Oxford University Press, 2006: 305-327. Subject: 14.5

Cameron, Nigel M. de S. Pandora's progeny: ethical issues in assisted human reproduction. *Family Law Quarterly* 2005 Fall; 39(3): 745-779. Subject: 14.4

Subject = NRCBL Primary Classification Number; see inside front cover.

Cameron, Nigel M. de S. Research ethics, science policy, and four contexts for the stem cell debate. *Journal of Investigative Medicine* 2006 January; 54(1): 38-42. Subject: 18.5.4

Cameron, Nigel M. de S. Selecting our embryonic children [editorial]. *Ethics and Medicine* 2006 Spring; 22(1): 3-4. Subject: 14.1

Camilleri, Michael; Gamble, Gail L.; Kopecky, Stephen L.; Wood, Michael B.; Hockema, Marianne L. Principles and process in the development of the Mayo Clinic's individual and institutional conflict of interest policy. *Mayo Clinic Proceedings* 2005 October; 80(10): 1340-1346. Subject: 5.3

Campbell, Alastair. A virtue-ethics approach. *In:* Ashcroft, Richard; Lucassen, Anneke; Parker, Michael; Verkerk, Marian; Widderhoven, Guy, eds. Case Analysis in Clinical Ethics. New York: Cambridge University Press; 2005: 45-56. Subject: 15.3

Campbell, Alastair V. Public policy and the future of bioethics. *Genomics, Society and Policy* 2005 February; 1(1): 86-91. Subject: 2.1

Campbell, Amy T. Consent, competence, and confidentiality related to psychiatric conditions in adolescent medicine practice. *Adolescent Medicine Clinics* 2006 February; 17(1): 25-47. Subject: 8.3.2

Campbell, Bruce. Informed consent: special section [editorial]. *Annals of the Royal College of Surgeons of England* 2004 November; 86(6): 457-458. Subject: 8.3.1

Campbell, Courtney. Prophecy and citizenry: the case of human cloning. *Sunstone* 1998 June; 21: 11-15. Subject: 14.5

Campbell, Eric G.; Blumenthal, David. Academic industry relationships in biotechnology: a primer on policy and practice. *Cloning* 2000; 2(3): 129-136. Subject: 5.3

Campbell, Eric G.; Weissman, Joel S.; Vogeli, Christine; Clarridge, Brian R.; Abraham, Melissa; Marder, Jessica E.; Koski, Greg. Financial relationships between institutional review board members and industry. *New England Journal of Medicine* 2006 November 30; 355(22): 2321-2329. Subject: 1.3.9

Campbell, Margaret L. Teaching medical ethics in critical care. *New Horizons* 1998 August; 6(3): 289-292. Subject: 7.3

Campbell, Matthew. Holland to allow 'baby euthanasia'. *Sunday Times* 2006 March 5: 3 p. [Online]. Accessed: http://infoweb.newsbank.com/iw-search/we/InfoWeb/ ?p_action=print&p_docid=1. . . [2006 November 27]. Subject: 20.5.2

Campbell, Nancy D. Drugs. *In:* Mitcham, Carl, ed. Encyclopedia of Science, Technology, and Ethics. Farmington Hills, MI: Thomson/Gale, 2005: 546-549. Subject: 9.7

Campbell, Pamela. Raising awareness of the ethical issues surrounding termination of pregnancy for fetal abnor- malities. *In:* Bartter, Karen, ed. Ethical Issues in Advanced Nursing Practice. Boston: Butterworth-Heinemann; 2001: 51-65. Subject: 12.3

Campbell, R. Joan. Intimacy boundaries: between mental health nurses and psychiatric patients. *Journal of Psychosocial Nursing and Mental Health Services* 2005 May; 43(5): 32-39. Subject: 7.4

Canada. House of Commons. Bill C-6: an act respecting assisted reproduction and related research = Project de loi C-6: loi concernant la procréation assistée et la recherche connexe. House of Commons of Canada 2004 February 11, 3rd session, 37 Parliament, 52-53 Elizabeth 11, 2004: 37 p. [Online]. Accessed: http://www2.parl.gc.ca/content/ hoc/Bills/373/Government/C-6/c-6_3/c-6_3.pdf [2007 March 6]. Subject: 14.2

Canadian College of Health Service Executives. Code of ethics. *Healthcare Management Forum* 2005 Winter; 18(4): 22-25. Subject: 6

Canadian Council on Animal Care [CCAC]; Olfert, Ernest; Bhasin, Jag; Latt, Richard; Macallum; McCutcheon, Kathie, Rainnie, Don; Schunk, Michael. CCAC guidelines on: choosing an appropriate endpoint in experiments using animals for research, teaching and testing. Ottawa: Canadian Council on Animal Care 1998: 24 p. [Online]. Accessed: http://www.ccac.ca/en/CCAC_ Programs/Guidelines_Policies/PDFs/APPOPEN.pdf [2006 October 4]. Subject: 22.2

Canadian Medical Association Journal. The editorial autonomy of CMAJ [editorial]. *CMAJ/JAMC: Canadian Medical Association Journal* 2006 January 3; 174(1): 9. Subject: 1.3.7

Canadian Paediatric Society. Ethics Committee; Arbour, Laura. Guidelines for genetic testing of healthy children [policy statement]. Ottawa, Ontario, Canada: Canadian Society of Medical Geneticists, 2002 October 28. 11 p. [Online]. Accessed: http://ccmg.medical.org/pdf/ cps_gentestchild.pdf [2006 July 26]. Subject: 15.3

Candilis, Philip J.; Geppert, Cynthia M.A.; Fletcher, Kenneth E.; Lidz, Charles W.; Appelbaum, Paul S. Willingness of subjects with thought disorder to participate in research. *Schizophrenia Bulletin* 2006 January; 32(1): 159-165. Subject: 18.5.6

Candilis, Philip J.; Lidz, Charles W.; Arnold, Robert M. The need to understand IRB deliberations. *IRB: Ethics and Human Research* 2006 January-February; 28(1): 1-5. Subject: 18.2

Canellopoulou-Bottis, Maria. The implementation of European Directive 95/46/EC in Greece and medical/genetic data. *European Journal of Health Law* 2002 September; 9(3): 207-218. Subject: 8.4

Canelloupou-Bottis, Maria. Recent developments in health law in Greece. *European Journal of Health Law* 2006 June; 13(2): 107-113. Subject: 6

See SUBJECT HEADING KEY FOR SECTION II on inside back cover.

Canning, Brenda. Funding, ethics, and assistive technology: should medical necessity be the criterion by which wheeled mobility equipment is justified? *Topics in Stroke Rehabilitation* 2005 Summer; 12(3): 77-81. Subject: 9.3.1

Cantarovich, Felix. Public opinion and organ donation suggestions for overcoming barriers. *Annals of Transplantation* 2005; 10(1): 22-25. Subject: 19.5

Cantegreil-Kallen, Inge; Turbelin, Clement; Olaya, Emile; Blanchon, Thierry; Moulin, Florence; Rigaud, Anne-Sophie; Flahault, Antoine. Disclosure of diagnosis of Alzheimer's disease in French general practice. *American Journal of Alzheimer's Disease and Other Dementias* 2005 July-August; 20(4): 228-232. Subject: 17.1

Cantor, Julie. Cosmetic dermatology and physicians' ethical obligations: more than just hope in a jar. *Seminars in Cutaneous Medicine and Surgery* 2005 September; 24(3): 155-160. Subject: 4.5

Cantor, Julie D. Of pills and needles: involuntarily medicating the psychotic inmate when execution looms. *Indiana Health Law Review* 2005; 2(1): 117-170. Subject: 8.3.4

Cantor, Julie D.; Reisman, Neal R. When an adult female seeks ritual genital alteration: ethics, law, and the parameters of participation. *Plastic and Reconstructive Surgery* 2006 April; 117(4): 1158-1166. Subject: 9.5.5

Cantor, Norman L. Déjà vu all over again: the false dichotomy between sanctity of life and quality of life. *Stetson Law Review* 2005 Fall; 35(1): 81-100. Subject: 20.5.1

Cao, Kaibin. Approaches to health in ancient China. *In:* Döring, Ole; Chen, Renbiao, eds. Advances in Chinese Medical Ethics: Chinese and International Perspectives. Hamburg: Institut für Asienkunde; 2002: 223-232. Subject: 7.1

Capella, Elena A.; Aumman, Gretchen. Ethical theory and the practice of the legal nurse consultant. *In:* Iyer, Patricia W., ed. Legal Nurse Consulting: Principles and Practice. 2nd ed. Boca Raton: CRC Press; 2003: 221-238. Subject: 4.1.3

Caplan, Arthur. Bioengineering and self-improvement. *Free Inquiry* 2006 April-May; 26(3): 20-21. Subject: 4.5

Caplan, Arthur. Commentary: improving quality of life is a morally important goal for gene therapy. *Human Gene Therapy* 2006 December; 17(2): 1164. Subject: 15.4

Caplan, Arthur. The ethics of forced drug treatment for addicts. *Free Inquiry* 2006 December-2007 January; 27(1): 21-22. Subject: 8.3.4

Caplan, Arthur. Is it wrong to try to improve human nature? *In:* Miller, Paul; Wilsdon, James, eds. Better Humans?: The Politics of Human Enhancement and Life Extension. London: Demos, 2006: 31-39. Subject: 4.5

Caplan, Arthur. Lies in embryo [op-ed]. *Free Inquiry* 2006 June-July; 26(4): 15-16. Subject: 14.6

Caplan, Arthur L. Death as an unnatural process: why is it wrong to seek a cure for ageing? *EMBO Reports* 2005 July; 6(Special Issue): S72-S75. Subject: 20.5.1

Caplan, Arthur L. Engineering plants, microbes, and animals. *In his:* Smart Mice, Not-So-Smart People: An Interesting and Amusing Guide to Bioethics. Lanham, MD: Rowman & Littlefield, 2007: 47-58. Subject: 15.1

Caplan, Arthur L. Human cloning and stem cell research. *In his:* Smart Mice, Not-So-Smart People: An Interesting and Amusing Guide to Bioethics. Lanham, MD: Rowman & Littlefield, 2007: 95-118. Subject: 14.5

Caplan, Arthur L. Mapping ourselves. *In his:* Smart Mice, Not-So-Smart People: An Interesting and Amusing Guide to Bioethics. Lanham, MD: Rowman & Littlefield, 2007: 119-138. Subject: 15.10

Caplan, Arthur L. No method, thus madness? *Hastings Center Report* 2006 March-April; 36(2): 12-13. Subject: 1.3.9

Caplan, Arthur; Elliott, Carl. Is it ethical to use enhancement technologies to make us better than well? *PLoS Medicine* 2004 December; 1(3): 172-175. Subject: 15.4

Caplan, Arthur; Fiester, Autumn. Bioethics centers. *In:* Mitcham, Carl, ed. Encyclopedia of Science, Technology, and Ethics. Farmington Hills, MI: Thomson/Gale, 2005: 200-201. Subject: 2.3

Cappell, Mitchell S. The effect of Nazism on medical progress in gastroenterology: the inefficiency of evil. *Digestive Diseases and Sciences* 2006 June; 51(6): 1137-1158. Subject: 21.4

Capron, Alexander M. Addressing an ethical dilemma dialogically rather than (merely) logically. *American Journal of Bioethics* 2006 March-April; 6(2): 36-39. Subject: 8.4

Capron, Alexander M. Does assessment of medical practices have a future? *Virginia Law Review* 1996 November; 82(8): 1623-1640. Subject: 9.3.1

Capron, Alexander M. Experimentation with human beings: light or only shadows? *Yale Journal of Health Policy, Law and Ethics* 2006 Summer; 6(2): 431-449. Subject: 18.2

Carassiti, M.; Tambone, V.; Agrò, F.E. Blood transfusion and the principle of the double effect act: proposal of a new ethical view for Jehovah's Witnesses. *Clinica Terapeutica* 2003 November-December; 154(6): 447. Subject: 19.4

Carbone, June; Gottheim, Paige. Markets, subsidies, regulation, and trust: building ethical understandings into the market for fertility services. *Journal of Gender, Race and Justice* 2006 Spring; 9(3): 509-547. Subject: 14.2

Card, Robert F. Two puzzles for Marquis's conservative view on abortion. *Bioethics* 2006 September; 20(5): 264-277. Subject: 12.3

Subject = NRCBL Primary Classification Number; see inside front cover.

Cardoso, Augusto Lopes. Brief review notes on the Opinion of the Portuguese National Council of Ethics for Life Sciences regarding the legal protection of biotechnological inventions = Breves notas sobre el Dictamen del Consejo Nacional de Etica para las Ciencias de la Vida de Portugal en relación con la protección jurídica de las invenciones biotecnológicas. *Law and the Human Genome Review = Revista de Derecho y Genoma Humano* 1995 July-December; (3): 253-260. Subject: 15.8

Carey, Benedict. Correcting the errors of disclosure. *New York Times* 2006 July 25; p. F5. Subject: 1.3.7

Carey, Benedict. Doctors say electric pulses aided brain-damaged man. *New York Times* 2006 October 16; p. A14. Subject: 9.5.1

Carey, Benedict. Mental activity seen in a brain gravely injured. *New York Times* 2006 September 8; p. A1, A6. Subject: 20.5.1

Carey, Benedict. Study cites links to firms by psychiatrists. *New York Times* 2006 April 20; p. A23. Subject: 9.7

Carey, Gregory; Gottesman, Irving I. Genes and antisocial behavior: perceived versus real threats to jurisprudence. *Journal of Law, Medicine and Ethics* 2006 Summer; 34(2): 342-351. Subject: 15.6

Carey, Kristen N. Wrongful life and wrongful birth: legal aspects of failed genetic testing in oocyte donation. *Penn Bioethics Journal* 2005 April 2; 1(1): 4p. [Online]. Accessed: http://www.bioethicsjournal.com [2005 April 19]. Subject: 15.2

Carey, Ruth. Ontario: people can now apply for forced HIV testing in certain situations [news]. *HIV/AIDS Policy and Law Review* 2003 December; 8(3): 25-27. Subject: 8.3.4

Carey, Ruth. Recent developments in privacy legislation. *HIV/AIDS Policy and Law Review* 2003 August; 8(2): 1, 11-17. Subject: 8.4

Carlin, Farr A.; Caplan, Arthur L. Talking through your epistemological hat [letter and reply]. *Hastings Center Report* 2006 July-August; 36(4): 7-8. Subject: 1.3.9

Carlisle, J.; Shickle, D.; Cork, M.; McDonagh, A. Concerns over confidentiality may deter adolescents from consulting their doctors. A qualitative exploration. *Journal of Medical Ethics* 2006 March; 32(3): 133-137. Subject: 8.4

Carlsen, Benedicte; Norheim, Ole Frithjof. "Saying no is no easy matter" a qualitative study of competing concerns in rationing decisions in general practice. *BMC Health Services Research [electronic]* 2005 November 9; 5: 11 p. Subject: 9.4

Carlson, Bryant; Simopolous, Nicole; Goy, Elizabeth R.; Jackson, Ann; Ganzini, Linda. Oregon hospice chaplains' experiences with patients requesting physician-assisted suicide. *Journal of Palliative Medicine* 2005 December; 8(6): 1160-1166. Subject: 20.5.1

Carlson, Patrick D. The 2004 Organ Donation Recovery and Improvement Act: how Congress missed an opportunity to say "yes" to financial incentives for organ donation. *Journal of Contemporary Health Law and Policy* 2006 Fall; 23(1): 136-167. Subject: 19.5

Carlton, Olivia. A case of workplace drug and alcohol testing in a UK transport company. *In:* Westerholm, Peter; Nilstun, Tore; Øvretveit, John, eds. Practical Ethics in Occupational Health. San Francisco: Radcliffe Medical Press; 2004: 151-165. Subject: 16.3

Carmen, Ira H. A death in the laboratory: the politics of the Gelsinger aftermath. *Molecular Therapy* 2001 April; 3(4): 425-428. Subject: 15.4

Carnahan, Sandra J. Law, medicine, and wealth: does concierge medicine promote health care choice, or is it a barrier to access? *Stanford Law and Policy Review* 2006; 17(1): 121-163. Subject: 9.3.1

Carnevale, Franco A.; Canouï, Pierre; Hubert, Philippe; Farrell, Catherine; Leclerc, Francis; Doussau, Amélie; Seguin, Marie-Josée; Lacroix, Jacques. The moral experience of parents regarding life-support decisions for their critically-ill children: a preliminary study in France. *Journal of Child Health Care* 2006 March; 10(1): 69-82. Subject: 20.5.2

Carney, Marie. Positive and negative outcomes from values and beliefs held by healthcare clinician and non-clinician managers. *Journal of Advanced Nursing* 2006 April; 54(1): 111-119. Subject: 9.1

Caron, Lorraine; Karkazis, Katrina; Raffin, Thomas A.; Swan, Gary; Koenig, Barbara A. Nicotine addiction through a neurogenomic prism: ethics, public health, and smoking. *Nicotine and Tobacco Research* 2005 April; 7(2): 181-197. Subject: 15.10

Caron-Flinterman, J. Francisca; Broerse, Jacqueline E.W.; Teerling, Julia; Bunders, Joske F.G. Patients' priorities concerning health research: the case of asthma and COPD research in the Netherlands. *Health Expectations* 2005 September; 8(3): 253-263. Subject: 18.3

Carosella, Edgardo; Pradeu, Thomas. Transplantation and identity: a dangerous split? *Lancet* 2006 July 15-21; 368(9531): 183-184. Subject: 19.1

Carpenter, Robert O.; Austin, Mary T.; Tarpley, John L.; Griffin, Marie R.; Lomis, Kimberly D. Work-hour restrictions as an ethical dilemma for residents. *American Journal of Surgery* 2006 April; 191(4): 527-532. Subject: 7.2

Carr, A.J. Which research is to be believed? The ethics of industrial funding of orthopaedic research [editorial]. *Journal of Bone and Joint Surgery. British Volume* 2005 November; 87-B(11): 1452-1453. Subject: 1.3.9

Carr, Vincent F. Dual agency and fiduciary responsibilities in modern medicine. *Physician Executive* 2005 November-December; 31(6): 56-58. Subject: 8.1

See SUBJECT HEADING KEY FOR SECTION II on inside back cover.

517

Carrasco, Edgar. Access to treatment as a right to life and health. *HIV/AIDS Policy and Law Review* 2000; 5(4): 102-103. Subject: 9.2

Carrese, Joseph A. Refusal of care: patients' well-being and physicians' ethical obligations. *JAMA: the Journal of the American Medical Association* 2006 August 9; 296(6): 691-695. Subject: 8.3.4

Carreyrou, John. Cephalon used improper tactics to sell drug, probe finds. *Wall Street Journal* 2006 November 21; p. B1, B2. Subject: 9.7

Carreyrou, John. How a hospital stumbled across an Rx for Medicaid; Mt. Sinai helps patients avoid the ER, paring state costs and aiding its bottom line; Dr. Chassin goes after salt. *Wall Street Journal* 2006 June 22; p. A1, A14. Subject: 9.3.1

Carreyrou, John. Seizures of Canadian drugs rise as Congress, Customs spar. *Wall Street Journal* 2006 July 24; p. B1, B8. Subject: 9.7

Carroll, Robert G. Using animals in teaching: APS position statement and rationale. *Physiologist* 2005 August; 48(4): 206-208. Subject: 22.2

Carter, Gregory T.; VandeKieft, Gregg K.; Barron, David W. Whose life is it, anyway? The federal government vs. the state of Oregon on the legality of physician-assisted suicide. *American Journal of Hospice and Palliative Care* 2005 July-August; 22(4): 249-251. Subject: 20.7

Carter, Ross E. Psychological evaluation a consideration in the ethics of genetic testing for breast cancer. *Psychiatric Annals* 2004 February; 34(2): 119-124. Subject: 15.3

Carter, Sarah; Taylor, David; Bates, Ian. Institutionalized paternalism? Stakeholders' views on public access to genetic testing. *Journal of Health Services Research and Policy.* 2006 July; 11(3): 155-161. Subject: 15.3

Carulla, Santiago Ripol. The protection of medical and genetic data in the Council of Europe's normative texts (Part I) = La protección de los datos médicos y genéticos en la normativa del Consejo de Europa (Parte I). *Law and the Human Genome Review = Revista de Derecho y Genoma Humano* 1996 July-December; (5): 109-120. Subject: 8.4

Carvalho, Ana Sofia; Machado, Pedro; Malcata, Francisco Xavier. Public perception of science: cloning in the Portuguese press. *In:* Glasa, J., ed. Ethics of Human Genetics: Challenges of the (Post) Genomic Era. Bratislava, Slovak Republic: Charis [and] IMEB Foundation; 2002: 203-208. Subject: 14.5

Casabona, Carlos María Romeo. Legal aspects of genetic counselling = Aspectos jurídicos del consejo genético. *Law and the Human Genome = Revista de Derecho y Genoma Humano* 1994 July-December; (1): 149-172. Subject: 15.2

Casabona, Carlos María Romeo. The UNESCO Outline of a Declaration on the Protection of the Human Genome: comments on a necessary initiative = El Proyecto de Declaración de la UNESCO sobre la Protección del Genoma Humano: observaciones a una iniciativa necesaria. *Law and the Human Genome Review = Revista de Derecho y Genoma Humano* 1995 July-December; (3): 153-165. Subject: 15.10

Casado, María. The conflict between legal interests in clinical genetics: public health requirements and the safeguarding of human dignity = El conflicto entre bienes jurídicos en el campo de la genética clínica: exigencias de salud pública y salvaguarda de la dignidad humana. *Law and the Human Genome Review = Revista de Derecho y Genoma Humano* 1996 January-June; (4): 23-37. Subject: 15.1

Casarett, David; Karlawish, Jason; Sankar, Pamela; Hirschman, Karen B.; Asch, David A. Obtaining informed consent for pain research: patients' information needs and concerns. *Pain* 2001 May; 92(1-2): 71-79. Subject: 4.4

Casarett, David; Van Ness, Peter H.; O'Leary, John R.; Fried, Terri R. Are patient preferences for life-sustaining treatment really a barrier to hospice enrollment for older adults with serious illness? *Journal of the American Geriatrics Society* 2006 March; 54(3): 472-478. Subject: 20.4.1

Casarett, David J.; Karlawish, Jason. Beyond informed consent: the ethical design of pain research. *Pain Medicine* 2001 June; 2(2): 138-146. Subject: 18.3

Casarett, David J.; Teno, Joan; Higginson, Irene. How should nations measure the quality of end-of-life care for older adults? Recommendations for an international minimum data set. *Journal of American Geriatrics Society* 2006 November; 54(11): 1765-1771. Subject: 20.4.1

Cash, Richard A. What is owed to the community before, during and following research: an ethical dialogue. *Eastern Mediterranean Health Journal* 2006; 12(Supplement 1): S37-S41 [Online]. Accessed: http://www.emro.who.int/publications/EMHJ/12_S/PDF/6.pdf [2007 January 3]. Subject: 18.6

Caspi, Opher; Holexa, Joshua. Lack of standards in informed consent in complementary and alternative medicine. *Complementary Therapies in Medicine* 2005 June; 13(2): 123-130. Subject: 8.3.1

Cassels, Alan. Canada may be forced to allow direct to consumer advertising [news]. *BMJ: British Medical Journal* 2006 June 24; 332(7556): 1469. Subject: 9.7

Casteel, J. Keenan. The ethics of informed consent among storyteller cultures. *International Journal of Circumpolar Health* 1998; 57(Supplement 1): 41-42. Subject: 8.3.1

Castignone, Silvana. The problem of limits of law in bioethical issues. *In:* Rehmann-Sutter, Christoph; Düwell, Marcus; Mieth, Dietmar, eds. Bioethics in Cultural Contexts: Reflections on Methods and Finitude. Dordrecht: Springer, 2006: 81-90. Subject: 2.1

Subject = NRCBL Primary Classification Number; see inside front cover.

Castledine, George. Are nurses concerned over legalizing euthanasia? *British Journal of Nursing* 2006 May 25-June 7; 15(10): 587. Subject: 20.5.1

Catholic Church. National Conference of Catholic Bishops [NCCB]. Committee on Science and Human Values. The Promise and Peril of Genetic Screening. Washington, DC: United States Catholic Conference, 1997. Subject: 15.3

Catholic Church. National Conference of Catholic Bishops [NCCB]. Committee on Science and Human Values. Dialogue Group of Scientists and Catholic Bishops. The Manner of Our Dying. Washington, DC: United States Catholic Conference, 1998. Subject: 20.1

Catholic Church. United States Conference of Catholic Bishops [USCCB]. Brief supports partial-birth abortion ban. *Origins* 2006 June 8; 36(4): 58-63. Subject: 12.4.4

Catt, Susan; Blanchard, Martin; Addington-Hall, Julia; Zis, Maria; Blizard, Bob; King, Michael. The development of a questionnaire to assess the attitudes of older people to end-of-life issues (AEOLI). *Palliative Medicine* 2005; 19(5): 397-401. Subject: 20.3.1

Catt, Susan; Blanchard, Martin; Addington-Hall, Julia; Zis, Maria; Blizard, Robert; King, Michael. Older adults' attitudes to death, palliative treatment and hospice care. *Palliative Medicine* 2005 July; 19(5): 402-410. Subject: 20.3.1

Caulfield, Timothy. From human genes to stem cells: new challenges for patent law? *Trends in Biotechnology* 2003 March; 21(3): 101-103. Subject: 18.5.4

Caulfield, Timothy. Perceptions of risk and human genetic databases: consent and confidentiality policies. *In:* Árnason, Gardar; Nordal, Salvör; Árnason, Vilhjálmur, eds. Blood and Data: Ethical, Legal and Social Aspects of Human Genetic Databases. Reykjavík: University of Iceland Press; 2004: 283-289. Subject: 15.1

Caulfield, Timothy. Stem cell patents and social controversy: a speculative view from Canada. *Medical Law International* 2006; 7(3): 219-232. Subject: 15.8

Caulfield, Timothy; Brownsword, Roger. Human dignity: a guide to policy making in the biotechnology era? *Nature Reviews Genetics* 2006 January; 7(1): 72-76. Subject: 4.4

Caulfield, Timothy; Chapman, Audrey. Human dignity as a criterion for science policy. *PLoS Medicine* 2005 August; 2(8): 736-738. Subject: 4.4

Caulfield, Timothy; Cook-Deegan, Robert M.; Kieff, F. Scott; Walsh, John P. Evidence and anecdotes: an analysis of human gene patenting controversies. *Nature Biotechnology* 2006 September; 24(9): 1091-1094. Subject: 15.8

Caulfield, Timothy; Einsiedel, Edna; Merz, Jon F.; Nicol, Dianne. Trust, patents and public perceptions: the governance of controversial biotechnology research. *Na-*

ture Biotechnology 2006 November; 24(11): 1352-1354. Subject: 15.8

Caulfield, Timothy; von Tigerstrom, Barbara. Gene patents, health care policy and licensing schemes. *Trends in Biotechnology* 2006 June; 24(6): 251-254. Subject: 15.8

Cavalieri, Paola. The animal debate: a reexamination. *In:* Singer, Peter, ed. In Defense of Animals: The Second Wave. Malden, MA: Blackwell Pub.; 2006: 54-68. Subject: 22.1

Caves, N.D.; Irwin, M.G. Attitudes to basic life support among medical students following the 2003 SARS outbreak in Hong Kong. *Resuscitation* 2006 January; 68(1): 93-100. Subject: 7.2

Ceasar, Mike. Court ends Colombia's abortion ban. *Lancet* 2006 May 20-26; 367(9523): 1645-1646. Subject: 12.4.1

Cedar, S.H. Stem cell and related therapies: nurses and midwives representing all parties. *Nursing Ethics* 2006 May; 13(3): 292-303. Subject: 18.5.4

Cekanauskaite, Asta; Gefenas, Eugenijus. Research ethics committees in Lithuania. *In:* Beyleveld, D.; Townend, D.; Wright, J., eds. Research Ethics Committees, Data Protection and Medical Research in European Countries. Hants, England; Burlington, VT: Ashgate; 2005: 141-147. Subject: 18.2

Cela Conde, Camilo José. Genes, causes and patents: the tortuous path of the Human Genome Project = Genes, causas, y patentes. El callejón tortuoso del Proyecto Genoma Humano. *Revista de Derecho Genoma Humano = Law and the Human Genome Review* 1997 January-June; (6): 155-169. Subject: 15.8

Centers for Disease Control and Prevention [CDC] (United States). CDC Releases Revised HIV Testing Recommendations in Health-Care Settings. Atlanta, GA: Centers for Disease Control and Prevention [CDC] (United States) 2006 September; 3 p. [Online]. Accessed: http://www.cdc.gov/hiv/topics/testing/resources/factsheets/pdf/healthcare.pdf [2006 September 25]. Subject: 9.5.6

Centers for Disease Control and Prevention [CDC] (United States). Revised recommendations for HIV testing of adults, adolescents, and pregnant women in health-care settings. *MMWR: Morbidity and Mortality Weekly Report [electronic]* 2006 September 22; 55(RR-14): 17 p. Accessed: http://www.cdc.gov/hiv/topics/testing/resources/reports/pdf/rr5514.pdf [2006 September 25]. Subject: 9.5.6

Cerinus, Marie. The ethics of research. *Nurse Researcher* 2001; 8(3): 72-89. Subject: 18.1

Cerminara, Kathy. 2005-2006 National Health Law Moot Court competition: problem. *Journal of Legal Medicine* 2006 December; 27(4): 377-394. Subject: 20.5.1

See SUBJECT HEADING KEY FOR SECTION II on inside back cover.

519

Cerminara, Kathy L. Tracking the storm: the far-reaching power of the forces propelling the Schiavo cases. *Stetson Law Review* 2005 Fall; 35(1): 147-178. Subject: 20.5.1

Cerullo, Michael A. Cosmetic pyschopharmacology and the President's Council on Bioethics. *Perspectives in Biology and Medicine* 2006 Autumn; 49(4): 515-523. Subject: 4.5

Cessario, Romanus. Catholic considerations on palliative care. *National Catholic Bioethics Quarterly* 2006 Winter; 6(4): 639-650. Subject: 20.4.1

Cetin, Irene; Gill, Robin. Ethical issues in perinatal nutrition research. *Advances in Experimental Medicine and Biology* 2005; 569: 132-138. Subject: 18.5.2

Cetina, Karin Knorr. The rise of a culture of life: the biological sciences are encouraging the move away from the ideals of the Enlightenment towards an idea of individual perfectibility and enhancement. *EMBO Reports* 2005 July; 6(Special Issue): S76-S80. Subject: 4.5

Cha, Arian Eunjung. AIDS drug trial turned away; protests by prostitutes in Cambodia ended Tenofovir testing. *Washington Post* 2006 May 23; p. A10, A14. Subject: 18.5.9

Cha, Ariana Eunjung. AIDs vaccine testing goes overseas; U.S. funds $120 million trial despite misgivings of some researchers. *Washington Post* 2006 May 22; p. A1, C1. Subject: 18.5.9

Chacko, Ninan. Autonomy or economy? A paper written more to provoke re-thinking, than to enlighten or educate! *Humane Health Care International* 2006; 6(1): 1-6 [Online]. Accessed: http://www.humanehealthcare.com/volume_page.asp?id=164 [2006 July 18]. Subject: 21.7

Chadwick, David; Privitera, Michael. How skeptical should we be about industry-sponsored studies? [editorial]. *Neurology* 2006 August 8; 67(3): 378-379. Subject: 18.4

Chadwick, Ruth. Euthanasia. *In:* Mitcham, Carl, ed. Encyclopedia of Science, Technology, and Ethics. Farmington Hills, MI: Thomson/Gale, 2005: 710-713. Subject: 20.5.1

Chadwick, Ruth. Nutrigenomics, individualism and sports. *In:* Tamburrini, Claudio; Tännsjö, Torbjörn, eds. Genetic Technology and Sport: Ethical Questions. London; New York: Routledge; 2005: 126-135. Subject: 15.4

Chadwick, Ruth. Right to die. *In:* Mitcham, Carl, ed. Encyclopedia of Science, Technology, and Ethics. Farmington Hills, MI: Thomson/Gale, 2005: 1634-1635. Subject: 20.5.1

Chadwick, Ruth. Right to life. *In:* Mitcham, Carl, ed. Encyclopedia of Science, Technology, and Ethics. Farmington Hills, MI: Thomson/Gale, 2005: 1636-1637. Subject: 4.4

Chadwick, Ruth. Rights and reproduction. *In:* Mitcham, Carl, ed. Encyclopedia of Science, Technology, and Ethics.

Farmington Hills, MI: Thomson/Gale, 2005: 1629-1630. Subject: 14.1

Chadwick, Ruth; Marturano, Antonio. Computing, genetics, and policy: theoretical and practical considerations. *In:* Tavani, Herman T., ed. Ethics, Computing, and Genomics. Sudbury, MA: Jones and Bartlett; 2006: 75-83. Subject: 15.1

Chadwick, Ruth; Wilson, Sarah. Bio-Amazons — a comment. *In:* Tamburrini, Claudio; Tännsjö, Torbjörn, eds. Genetic Technology and Sport: Ethical Questions. London; New York: Routledge; 2005: 205-208. Subject: 15.4

Chaffee, Mary W. Making the decision to report to work in a disaster: nurses may have conflicting obligations. *AJN: American Journal of Nursing* 2006 September; 106(9): 54-57. Subject: 7.1

Chagnon, Napoleon A. Biomedical samples from the Amazon [letter]. *Chronicle of Higher Education* 2006 April 14; 52(32): A55. Subject: 18.5.9

Chai, Jianhua. Human genetic resources, genetic information and medical ethics. *In:* Döring, Ole; Chen, Renbiao, eds. Advances in Chinese Medical Ethics: Chinese and International Perspectives. Hamburg: Institut für Asienkunde; 2002: 159-163. Subject: 15.1

Chakraborti, Chhanda. Ethics of care and HIV: a case for rural women in India. *Developing World Bioethics* 2006 May; 6(2): 89-94. Subject: 4.1.1

Chalfin, Henry. Ethics and professionalism: the past, present, and future. *Journal of the American College of Dentists* 2006 Spring; 73(1): 42-47. Subject: 4.1.1

Chalmers, D.; Otlowski, M.; Nicol, D.; Skene, Loane. Legal and ethical implications of human genetic research: Australian perspectives = Implicaciones legales y éticas de la investigación genética humana: perspectivas australianas. *Law and the Human Genome Review = Revista de Derecho y Genoma Humano* 1995 July-December; (3): 211-220. Subject: 15.1

Chalmers, Iain. From optimism to disillusion about commitment to transparency in the medico-industrial complex. *Journal of the Royal Society of Medicine* 2006 July; 99(7): 337-341. Subject: 18.2

Chalmers, Iain. Preventing scientific misconduct. *Lancet* 2006 August 5-11; 368(9534): 450. Subject: 1.3.9

Chalmers, Iain. Role of systematic reviews in detecting plagiarism: case of Asim Kurjak. *BMJ: British Medical Journal* 2006 September 16; 333(7568): 594-596. Subject: 1.3.9

Chambers, John C. Please do not resuscitate: do we perform cardiopulmonary resuscitation on living or dead people? [letter]. *BMJ: British Medical Journal* 2006 March 11; 332(7541): 608. Subject: 20.5.1

Chambers, Tod. Bioethics, religion, and linguistic capital. *In:* Guinn, David E., ed. Handbook of Bioethics and Reli-

---

Subject = NRCBL Primary Classification Number; see inside front cover.

gion. New York: Oxford University Press, 2006: 81-91. Subject: 2.1

Chan, An-Wen; Upshur, Ross; Singh, Jerome A.; Ghersi, Davina; Chapuis, François; Altman, Douglas G. Research protocols: waiving confidentiality for the greater good. *BMJ: British Medical Journal* 2006 May 6; 332(7549): 1086-1089. Subject: 18.2

Chan, David K.; Gallagher, Thomas H.; Reznick, Richard; Levinson, Wendy. How surgeons disclose medical errors to patients: a study using standardized patients. *Surgery* 2005 November; 138(5): 851-858. Subject: 9.8

Chan, Harry; Moriatry, Kieran. Are ethnic minorities excluded from clinical research? *Bulletin of Medical Ethics* 2005 October-November; (211): 22-24. Subject: 18.5.1

Chan, S. Cord blood banking: what are the real issues? [editorial]. *Journal of Medical Ethics* 2006 November; 32(11): 621-622. Subject: 19.4

Chan, Sarah; Harris, John. The ethics of gene therapy. *Current Opinion in Molecular Therapeutics* 2006 October; 8(5): 377-383. Subject: 15.4

Chandis, V.; Williams, T. The patient, the doctor, the fetus, and the court-compelled cesarean: why courts should address the question through a bioethical lens. *Medicine and Law: The World Association for Medical Law* 2006 December; 25(4): 729-746. Subject: 9.5.5

Chandramohan, Daniel; Soleman, Nadia; Shibuya, Kenji; Porter, John. Ethical issues in the application of verbal autopsies in mortality surveillance systems [editorial]. *Tropical Medicine and International Health* 2005 November; 10(11): 1087-1089. Subject: 8.3.3

Chang, Cindy. Health care for undocumented immigrant children: special members of an underclass. *Washington University Law Quarterly* 2005; 83(4): 1271-1294. Subject: 9.5.7

Chang, Ly-yun. Peer review and medical negligence. *In:* Döring, Ole; Chen, Renbiao, eds. Advances in Chinese Medical Ethics: Chinese and International Perspectives. Hamburg: Institut für Asienkunde; 2002: 337-352. Subject: 9.8

Chang, Pepe Lee. Who's in the business of saving lives? *Journal of Medicine and Philosophy* 2006 October; 31(5): 465-482. Subject: 9.7

Chang, Wendy Y.; DeCherney, Alan H. History of regulation of assisted reproductive technology (ART) in the USA: a work in progress. *Human Fertility* 2003 May; 6(2): 64-70. Subject: 14.4

Chaplin, C. Ethics of international clinical research collaboration — the experience of AlloStem. *International Journal of Immunogenetics* 2006 February; 33(1): 1-5. Subject: 18.5.4

Chapman, Audrey R. Human rights. *In:* Mitcham, Carl, ed. Encyclopedia of Science, Technology, and Ethics.

Farmington Hills, MI: Thomson/Gale, 2005: 957-960. Subject: 21.1

Chapman, Audrey R. The human rights implications of intellectual property protection. *Journal of International Economic Law* 2002 December; 5(4): 861-882. Subject: 21.1

Chapman, Charlotte. Dual relationships in substance abuse treatment: ethical implications. *Alcoholism Treatment Quarterly* 1997; 15(2): 73-79. Subject: 9.5.9

Chapman, Clare. Swiss hospital lets terminally ill patients commit suicide in its beds [news]. *BMJ: British Medical Journal* 2006 January 7; 332(7532): 7. Subject: 20.7

Chapman, Simon. Research from tobacco industry affiliated authors: need for particular vigilance [editorial]. *Tobacco Control* 2005 August; 14(4): 217-219. Subject: 1.3.9

Chapple, A.; Ziebland, S.; McPherson, A.; Herxheimer, A. What people close to death say about euthanasia and assisted suicide: a qualitative study. *Journal of Medical Ethics* 2006 December; 32(12): 706-710. Subject: 20.7

Chappuy, H.; Doz, F.; Blanche, S.; Gentet, J.C.; Pons, G.; Tréluyer, J.M. Parental consent in paediatric clinical research. *Archives of Disease in Childhood* 2006 February; 91(2): 112-116. Subject: 18.5.2

Charatan, Fred. US journal in row over sponsored supplement [news]. *BMJ: British Medical Journal* 2006 August 5; 333(7562): 277. Subject: 1.3.7

Charatan, Fred. US Supreme Court upholds Oregon's Death with Dignity Act [news]. *BMJ: British Medical Journal* 2006 January 28; 332(7535): 195. Subject: 20.7

Charlebois, Edwin D.; Maiorana, Andre; McLaughlin, Marisa; Koester, Kim; Gaffney, Stuart; Rutherford, George W.; Morin, Stephen F. Potential deterrent effect of name-based HIV infection surveillance. *Journal of Acquired Immune Deficiency Syndromes* 2005 June 1; 39(2): 219-227. Subject: 9.5.6

Charles-Edwards, Imelda; Brotchie, Jane. Privacy: what does it mean for children's nurses? *Paediatric Nursing* 2005 June; 17(5): 38-43. Subject: 8.4

Charlesworth, Max. Bioethics in ethically pluralist societies. *Internal Medicine Journal* 2006 January; 36(1): 51-53. Subject: 2.1

Charlton, Bruce G. If 'atypical' neuroleptics did not exist, it wouldn't be necessary to invent them: perverse incentives in drug development, research, marketing and clinical practice [editorial]. *Medical Hypotheses* 2005; 65(6): 1005-1009. Subject: 17.4

Charo, R. Alta. And baby makes three — or four, or five, or six: redefining the family after the reprotech revolution. *Wisconsin Women's Law Journal* 1992-1993; 7-8: 1-23. Subject: 14.1

See SUBJECT HEADING KEY FOR SECTION II on inside back cover.

521

Charo, R. Alta. Body of research — ownership and use of human tissue. *New England Journal of Medicine* 2006 October 12; 355(15): 1517-1519. Subject: 4.4

Charo, R. Alta. Fear and the First Amendment. *Hastings Center Report* 2006 September-October; 36(5): 12-13. Subject: 1.3.9

Charon, Rita. The ethicality of narrative medicine. *In:* Hurwitz, Brian; Greenhalgh, Trisha; Skultans, Vieda, eds. Narrative Research in Health and Illness. Malden MA: BMJ Books; 2004: 23-36. Subject: 2.1

Charuvastra, Anthony; Friedmann, Peter D.; Stein, Michael D. Physician attitudes regarding the prescription of medical marijuana. *Journal of Addictive Diseases* 2005; 24(3): 87-93. Subject: 9.5.1

Chase, Marilyn. Gates won't fund AIDS researchers unless they pool data. *Wall Street Journal* 2006 July 20; p. B1, B4. Subject: 9.5.6

Chassin, Mark R. The health care juggling act: balancing universal access, cost containment, and quality improvement. *Mount Sinai Journal of Medicine* 1997 March; 64(2): 101-104. Subject: 9.2

Chatterjee, A. The promise and predicament of cosmetic neurology. *Journal of Medical Ethics* 2006 February; 32(2): 110-113. Subject: 17.5

Chatterjee, J.S. From compliance to concordance in diabetes. *Journal of Medical Ethics* 2006 September; 32(9): 507-510. Subject: 9.5.1

Check, Erika. Gene therapists hopeful as trials resume with childhood disease [news]. *Nature* 2004 June 10; 429(6992): 587. Subject: 15.4

Check, Erika. The rocky road to success [news]. *Nature* 2005 September 8; 437(7056): 185-186. Subject: 14.5

Check, Erika. Simple recipe gives adult cells embryonic powers [news]. *Nature* 2006 July 6; 442(7098): 11. Subject: 18.5.1

Check, Erika. Synthetic biologists try to calm fears [news]. *Nature* 2006 May 25; 441(7092): 388-389. Subject: 15.1

Check, Erika. Tissue-sample payments anger lawmakers [news]. *Nature* 2006 June 22; 441(7096): 912-913. Subject: 19.5

Check, Erika. Universities urged to do more for poor nations [news]. *Nature* 2006 November 23; 444(7118): 412-413. Subject: 9.7

Chee, Y.C. Do no harm: do thyself no harm. *Singapore Medical Journal* 2005 December; 46(12): 667-674. Subject: 4.1.2

Cheek, Dennis W. Ramsey, Paul. *In:* Mitcham, Carl, ed. Encyclopedia of Science, Technology, and Ethics. Farmington Hills, MI: Thomson/Gale, 2005: 1580-1581. Subject: 2.2

Chen, Christopher P. L.-H. Regulatory issues: an academic viewpoint from Asia (ex-Japan). *International Psychogeriatrics* 2003; 15(Supplement 1): 287-291. Subject: 18.5.9

Chen, Donna T.; Miller, Franklin G.; Rosenstein, Donald L. Enrolling decisionally impaired adults in clinical research. *Medical Care* 2002 September; 40(9, Supplement): V20-V29. Subject: 18.3

Chen, Donna T.; Miller, Franklin G.; Rosenstein, Donald L. Ethical aspects of research into the etiology of autism. *Mental Retardation and Developmental Disabilities Research Reviews* 2003; 9(1): 48-53. Subject: 18.5.6

Chen, Donna T.; Moreno, Jonathan D. Ethics of medication-free research in schizophrenia. *Schizophrenia Bulletin* 2006 April; 32(2): 307-309. Subject: 18.5.6

Chen, Donna T.; Worrall, Bradford B. Practice-based clinical research and ethical decision making — Part I: deciding whether to incorporate practice-based research into your clinical practice. *Seminars in Neurology* 2006 February; 26(1): 131-139. Subject: 9.8

Chen, Donna T.; Worrall, Bradford B. Practice-based clinical research and ethical decision making — Part II: deciding whether to host a particular research study in your practice. *Seminars in Neurology* 2006 February; 26(1): 140-147. Subject: 9.8

Chen, Donna T.; Worrall, Bradford B.; Brown, R.D., Jr.; Brott, T.G.; Kissela, B.M.; Olson, T.S.; Rich, S.S.; Meschia, J.F. The impact of privacy protections on recruitment in a multicenter stroke genetics study. *Neurology* 2005 February 22; 64(4): 721-724. Subject: 18.2

Chen, Renbiao; Qui, Xiangxing; Gao, Zhiyan; Shen, Mingxian. The development of biomedical ethics in China. *In:* Döring, Ole; Chen, Renbiao, eds. Advances in Chinese Medical Ethics: Chinese and International Perspectives. Hamburg: Institut für Asienkunde; 2002: 12-25. Subject: 2.1

Chen, Rongxia. Religious emotions and bioethics. *In:* Döring, Ole; Chen, Renbiao, eds. Advances in Chinese Medical Ethics: Chinese and International Perspectives. Hamburg: Institut für Asienkunde; 2002: 214-222. Subject: 2.1

Chen, Xiao-Yang. Clinical bioethics in China: the challenge of entering a market economy. *Journal of Medicine and Philosophy* 2006 February; 31(1): 7- 12. Subject: 9.3.1

Cheng, Anthony M. The real death of vitalism: implications of the Wöhler myth. *Penn Bioethics Journal* 2005 April 2; 1(1): 3p. [Online]. Accessed: http://www.bioethicsjournal.com [2005 April 19]. Subject: 2.1

Cheng, Guang-Shing. Prejudice. *Hastings Center Report* 2006 September-October; 36(5): 8-9. Subject: 8.1

Subject = NRCBL Primary Classification Number; see inside front cover.

Cheng, Linzhao. Ethics: China already has clear stem-cell guidelines. *Nature* 2006 April 20; 440(7087): 992. Subject: 18.5.4

Cheng, Wan-Chiung; Li, Wan-Ping. A study on the ethical, legal, and social aspects of the Chinese genetic database in Taiwan. *In:* Árnason, Gardar; Nordal, Salvör; Árnason, Vilhjálmur, eds. Blood and Data: Ethical, Legal and Social Aspects of Human Genetic Databases. Reykjavík: University of Iceland Press; 2004: 45-49. Subject: 15.1

Cherry, Mark J. Financial conflicts of interest and the human passion to innovate. *In:* Iltis, Ana Smith, ed. Research Ethics. New York: Routledge, 2006: 147-164. Subject: 1.3.9

Cherry, Mark J. How should Christians make judgments at the edge of life and death? *Christian Bioethics* 2006 April; 12(1): 1-10. Subject: 20.5.1

Chervenak, Frank A.; McCullough, Laurence B. Conscientious objection in medicine: author did not meet standards of argument based ethics [letter]. *BMJ: British Medical Journal* 2006 February 18; 332(7538): 425. Subject: 12.4.3

Chervenak, Frank A.; McCullough, Laurence B. Ethical and legal aspects. *In:* Kurjak, A., ed. Ultrasound and the Ovary: Progress in Obstetric and Gynecological Sonography Series, volume 1. New York: Parthenon Publishing Group, 1994: 255-261. Subject: 8.3.1

Chervenak, Frank A.; McCullough, Laurence B. Ethics and growing legal crisis in medicine. *Croatian Medical Journal* 2005 October; 46(5): 724-727. Subject: 4.1.2

Chervenak, Frank A.; McCullough, Laurence B.; Arabin, Birgit. Why the Groningen Protocol should be rejected. *Hastings Center Report* 2006 September-October; 36(5): 30-33. Subject: 20.5.2

Chervenak, Frank A.; McCullough, Laurence B.; Chasen, Stephen T. Clinical implications of the ethics of informed consent for first-trimester risk assessment for trisomy 21. *Seminars in Perinatology* 2005 August; 29(4): 277-279. Subject: 8.3.1

Chervenak, Frank A.; McCullough, Laurence B.; Skupski, Daniel; Chasen, Stephen T. Ethical issues in the management of pregnancies complicated by fetal anomalies. *Obstetrical and Gynecological Survey* 2003 July; 58(7): 473-483. Subject: 9.5.8

Cheshire, William P., Jr. Neuroscience, nuance, and neuroethics. *Ethics and Medicine* 2006 Summer; 22(2): 71-73. Subject: 17.1

Cheshire, William P., Jr. When eloquence is inarticulate. *Ethics and Medicine* 2006 Fall; 22(3): 135-138. Subject: 2.1

Cheung, D.; Sandramouli, S. The consent and counselling of patients for cataract surgery: a prospective audit. *Eye* 2005 September; 19(9): 963-971. Subject: 8.3.1

Chiang, Chun. The social capital theory research of the public medical service about relations of caring for patients. *Formosan Journal of Medical Humanities* 2006 June; 7(1-2): 159-177. Subject: 9.1

Chiang, H-H; Chao, Y-M (Yu); Yuh, Y-S. Informed choice of pregnant women in prenatal screening tests for Down's syndrome. *Journal of Medical Ethics* 2006 May; 32(5): 273-277. Subject: 15.2

Chico, Victoria. Saviour siblings: trauma and tort law. *Medical Law Review* 2006 Summer; 14(2): 180-218. Subject: 4.4

Childress, Herb. The anthropologist and the crayons: changing our focus from avoiding harm to doing good. *Journal of Empirical Research on Human Research Ethics* 2006 June; 1(2): 79-87. Subject: 18.4

Childress, James F. How can we ethically increase the supply of transplantable organs? *Annals of Internal Medicine* 2006 August 1; 145(3): 224-225. Subject: 19.5

Chilton, Mariana. Developing a measure of dignity for stress-related health outcomes. *Health and Human Rights: An International Journal* 2006; 9(2): 209-233. Subject: 9.1

Chima, Sylvester C. Regulation of biomedical research in Africa. *BMJ: British Medical Journal* 2006 April 8; 332(7545): 848-851. Subject: 18.5.9

Chiong, Winston. The real problem with equipoise. *American Journal of Bioethics* 2006 July-August; 6(4): 37-47. Subject: 18.2

Chiong, Winston. Response to commentators on "The real problem with equipoise" [letter]. *American Journal of Bioethics [Online]* 2006 July-August; 6(4): W42-W45. Subject: 18.2

Chipman, Peter. The moral implications of prenatal genetic testing. *Penn Bioethics Journal* 2006; 2(2): 13-16. Subject: 15.2

Cho, Mildred K. Racial and ethnic categories in biomedical research: there is no baby in the bathwater. *Journal of Law, Medicine and Ethics* 2006 Fall; 34(3): 497-499. Subject: 9.5.4

Cho, Mildred K.; McGee, Glenn; Magnus, David. Lessons of the stem cell scandal. *Science* 2006 February 3; 311(5761): 614-615. Subject: 1.3.9

Chokshi, Dave A.; Kwiatkowski, Dominic P. Ethical challenges of genomic epidemiology in developing countries. *Genomics, Society and Policy* 2005 February; 1(1): 1-15. Subject: 18.5.9

Chong, Sei. Investigations document still more problems for stem cell researchers [news]. *Science* 2006 February 10; 311(5762): 754-755. Subject: 1.3.9

Chong, Sei; Normile, Dennis. How young Korean researchers helped unearth a scandal. . . [news]. *Science* 2006 January 6; 311(5757): 22-23, 25. Subject: 1.3.9

See SUBJECT HEADING KEY FOR SECTION II on inside back cover.

523

Choo, Dong-Ryul. Two master arguments in the ethics of human cloning: the procreative right of couples vs. autonomy of the future clones. *In:* Sang-yong, Song; Young-Mo, Koo; Macer, Darryl R.J., eds. Asian Bioethics in the 21st Century. Christchurch, NZ: Eubios Ethics Institute, 2002: 402-417. Subject: 14.5

Christakis, Dimitri A.; Rivara, Frederick P. Publication ethics: editors' perspectives. *Journal of Pediatrics* 2006 July; 149(1, Supplement): S39-S42. Subject: 1.3.7

Christensen, Angi M. Moral considerations in body donation for scientific research: a unique look at the University of Tennessee's anthropological research facility. *Bioethics* 2006 June; 20(3): 136-145. Subject: 19.5

Christian, Michael D.; Hawryluck, Laura; Wax, Randy S.; Cook, Tim; Lazar, Neil M.; Herridge, Margaret S.; Muller, Matthew P.; Gowans, Douglas R.; Fortier, Wendy; Burkle, Frederick M., Jr. Development of a triage protocol for critical care during an influenza pandemic. *CMAJ/JAMC: Canadian Medical Association Journal* 2006 November 21; 175(11): 1377-1381. Subject: 9.4

Christmas, Colleen; Finucane, Tom. Artificial nutrition and hydration. *In his:* Is Human Life Special?: Religious and Philosophical Perspectives on the Principle of Human Dignity. New York: P. Lang; 2002: 175-187. Subject: 20.5.1

Christmas, Colleen; Finucane, Tom. Artificial nutrition and hydration. *In:* Morrison, R. Sean; Meier, Diane E.; Capello, Carol, eds. Geriatric Palliative Care. New York: Oxford University Press; 2003: 36-45. Subject: 20.4.1

Christopher, Myra. Role of ethics committees, ethics networks, and ethics centers in improving end-of-life care. *Pain Medicine* 2001 June; 2(2): 162-168. Subject: 9.6

Christopher, Suzanne. Recommendations for conducting successful research with Native Americans. *Journal of Cancer Education* 2005 Spring; 20(1, Supplement): 47-51. Subject: 18.5.1

Chubin, Daryl E.; Hackett, Edward J. Peer review. *In:* Mitcham, Carl, ed. Encyclopedia of Science, Technology, and Ethics. Farmington Hills, MI: Thomson/Gale, 2005: 1390-1394. Subject: 1.3.7

Church, Jonathan T.; Shopes, Linda; Blanchard, Margaret A. For the record: should all disciplines be subject to the Common Rule? Human subjects in social science research. *Academe* 2002 May-June; 88(3): 11 p. [Online]. Accessed: http://plinks.ebscohost.com/ehost/delivery?id=12&hid=102&sid=8c8f3742-ec0b. . . [2006 October 16]. Subject: 18.4

Churchill, Jack L. What's a dentist to do? To say or not to say. *Northwest Dentistry* 2006 January-February; 85(1): 39-40. Subject: 8.4

Churchill, Jack L. What's a dentist to do? Values, Part three. *Northwest Dentistry* 2005 March-April; 84(2): 53, 72. Subject: 4.1.1

Chur-Hansen, Anna; Zion, Deborah. 'Let's fix the chemical imbalance first, and then we can work on the problems second': an exploration of ethical implications of prescribing an SSRI for 'depression'. *Monash Bioethics Review* 2006 January; 25(1): 15-30. Subject: 9.5.3

Chwalisz, Bart; McVeigh, Edna; Hope, Tony; Kennedy, Stephen. Prioritizing IVF patients according to the number of existing children — a proposed refinement to the current guideline. *Human Reproduction* 2006 May; 21(5): 1110-1112. Subject: 14.1

Ciccarelli, Janice C.; Beckman, Linda J. Navigating rough waters: an overview of psychological aspects of surrogacy. *Journal of Social Issues* 2005 March; 61(1): 21-43. Subject: 14.2

Ciccarelli, John K.; Ciccarelli, Janice C. The legal aspects of parental rights in assisted reproductive technology. *Journal of Social Issues* 2005 March; 61(1): 127-137. Subject: 14.2

Cipolle, Christina L.; Cipolle, Robert J.; Strand, Linda M. Consistent standards in medication use: the need to care for patients from research to practice. *Journal of the American Pharmacists Association* 2006 March-April; 46(2): 205-212. Subject: 18.2

Cirión, Aitziber Emaldi. Genetics and the current eugenic trends: the new law in the People's Republic of China = La genética y las actuales corrientes eugenésicas: la nueva Ley de la República Popular China. *Law and the Human Genome Review = Revista de Derecho y Genoma Humano* 1996 July-December; (5): 147-156. Subject: 15.5

Cirion, Aitziber Emaldi. Preimplantation diagnosis: problems and future perspectives. *In:* Widdows, Heather; Idiakez, Itziar Alkorta; Cirión, Aitziber Emaldi, eds. Women's Reproductive Rights. New York: Palgrave Macmillan; 2006: 140-150. Subject: 15.2

Clafflin, Carol J.; Barbarin, Oscar A. Does "telling" less protect more? Relationships among age, information disclosure, and what children with cancer see and feel. *Journal of Pediatric Psychology* 1991 April; 16(2): 169-191. Subject: 9.5.7

Clancy, Carolyn M. Closing the health care disparities gap: turning evidence into action. *Journal of Health Care Law and Policy* 2006; 9(1): 121-135. Subject: 9.5.4

Clarfield, A. Mark. Enteral feeding tubes in end-stage dementia patients: to insert or not to insert? Administrative and financial aspects [editorial]. *Israel Medical Association Journal* 2005 July; 7(7): 467-469. Subject: 20.5.1

Clark, Alexander M.; Findlay, Iain N. Attaining adequate consent for the use of electronic patient records: an opt-out strategy to reconcile individuals' rights and public benefit. *Public Health* 2005 November; 119(11): 1003-1010. Subject: 8.4

Clark, Annette E. Ethics [ethics squared]: the ethics of bioethics in the biotechnology industry. *Seattle Journal for Social Justice* 2004 Fall-Winter; 3(1): 311-344. Subject: 5.1

Clark, Brietta. When free exercise exemptions undermine religious liberty and the liberty of conscience: a case study of the Catholic hospital conflict. *Oregon Law Review* 2003 Fall; 82(3): 625-694. Subject: 9.2

Clark, Brietta R. Hospital flight from minority communities: how our existing civil rights framework fosters racial inequality in healthcare. *DePaul Journal of Health Care Law* 2005; 9(2): 1023-1100. Subject: 9.5.4

Clark, David. Cradle to the grave? Terminal care in the United Kingdom, 1948-67. *Mortality* 1999; 4(3): 225-247. Subject: 20.4.1

Clark, Graeme. Socioeconomics and ethics. *In:* Clark, Graeme, ed. Cochlear Implants: Fundamentals and Applications. New York: Springer; 2003: 767-786. Subject: 5.2

Clark, Katrina. Who's your daddy? Mine was an anonymous sperm donor. That made me mad. So I decided to find him. *Washington Post* 2006 December 17; p. B1, B5. Subject: 14.2

Clark, Masharia A. Involuntary admission and the medical inpatient: judicious use of physical restraint. *Medsurg Nursing* 2005 August; 14(4): 213-219. Subject: 17.3

Clark, Peter. Tube feedings and persistent vegetative state patients: ordinary and extraordinary means? *Christian Bioethics* 2006 April; 12(1): 43-64. Subject: 20.5.1

Clark, Peter A. Medical ethics at Guantanamo Bay and Abu Ghraib: the problem of dual loyalty. *Journal of Law, Medicine and Ethics* 2006 Fall; 34(3): 570-580. Subject: 21.4

Clark, Peter A. Mother-to-child transmission of HIV in Botswana: an ethical perspective on mandatory testing. *Developing World Bioethics* 2006 March; 6(1): 1-12. Subject: 9.5.6

Clark, Peter A. Physician participation in executions: care giver or executioner? *Journal of Law, Medicine, and Ethics* 2006 Spring; 34(1): 95-104. Subject: 20.6

Clark, Peter A. To circumcise or not to circumcise? *Health Progress* 2006 September-October; 87(5): 30-39. Subject: 9.5.7

Clarke, Angus; Richards, Martin; Kerzin-Storrar, Lauren; Halliday, Jane; Young, Mary Anne; Simpson, Sheila A.; Featherstone, Katie; Forrest, Karen; Lucassen, Anneke; Morrison, Patrick J.; Quarrell, Oliver W.J.; Stewart, Helen. Genetic professionals' reports of nondisclosure of genetic risk information within families. *European Journal of Human Genetics* 2005 May; 13(5): 556-562. Subject: 8.4

Clarke, Mickey; McCartney, Denise A.; Siegel, Barry A. Regulatory oversight. *In:* Schuster, Daniel P.; Powers, William J., eds. Translational and Experimental Clinical Research. Philadelphia, PA: Lippincott Williams and Wilkins; 2005: 176-188. Subject: 1.3.9

Claxton, John; Sachez, Elena; Matthiessen-Guyader, Line. Ethical, legal, and social aspects of farm animal cloning in the 6th Framework Programme for Research. *Cloning and Stem Cells* 2004; 6(2): 178-181. Subject: 14.5

Claxton, K.; Culyer, A.J. Wickedness or folly? The ethics of NICE's decisions. *Journal of Medical Ethics* 2006 July; 32(7): 373-377. Subject: 9.3.1

Clayton, Ellen. Ethical concerns in HapMap project. *Protecting Human Subjects* 2006 Spring; (13): 9-11. Subject: 15.10

Clayton, Ellen Wright. Talking with parents before newborn screening. *Journal of Pediatrics* 2005 September; 147(3, Supplement): S26-S29. Subject: 9.5.7

Clayton, Ellen Wright. The web of relations: thinking about physicians and patients. *Yale Journal of Health Policy, Law and Ethics* 2006 Summer; 6(2): 465-477. Subject: 8.1

Clayton, Ellen Wright; Ross, Lainie Friedman; Shalowitz, David I.; Miller, Franklin G. Implications of disclosing individual results of clinical research [letter and reply]. *JAMA: The Journal of the American Medical Association* 2006 January 4; 295(1): 37-38. Subject: 18.3

Clayton, Josephine M.; Butow, Phyllis N.; Arnold, Robert M.; Tattersall, Martin H.N. Discussing end-of-life issues with terminally ill cancer patients and their carers: a qualitative study. *Supportive Care in Cancer* 2005 August; 13(8): 589-599. Subject: 20.4.1

Cleaton-Jones, Peter. Research injury in clinical trials in South Africa. *Lancet* 2006 February 11-17; 367(9509): 458-459. Subject: 18.1

Clemens, Felicity; Elbourne, Diana; Darbyshire, Janet; Pocock, Stuart. Data monitoring in randomized controlled trials: surveys of recent practice and policies. *Clinical Trials* 2005; 2(1): 22-33. Subject: 18.2

Clement, Renaud; Chevalet, Pascal; Rodat, Olivier; Ould-Aoudia, Vincent; Berger, Michel. Withholding or withdrawing dialysis in the elderly: the perspective of a western region of France. *Nephrology Dialysis Transplantation* 2005 November; 20(11): 2446-2452. Subject: 19.3

Clemmens, Emilie W. Creating human embryos for research: a scientist's perspective on managing the legal and ethical issues. *Indiana Health Law Review* 2005; 2(1): 93-115. Subject: 18.5.4

Cleophas, G.C.J.M.; Cleophas T.J. Clinical trials in jeopardy. *International Journal of Clinical Pharmacology and Therapeutics* 2003 February; 41(2): 51-55. Subject: 18.2

See SUBJECT HEADING KEY FOR SECTION II on inside back cover.

525

Cline, Rebecca J. Welch; Young, Henry N. Direct-to-consumer print ads for drugs: do they undermine the physician-patient relationship? *Journal of Family Practice* 2005 December; 54(12): 1049-1057. Subject: 9.7

Cloud, David S. Perfect vision, via surgery, is helping and hurting Navy. *New York Times* 2006 June 20; p. A1, A15. Subject: 4.5

Clowes, Brian. The mathematics of applied scientific racism. *Human Life Review* 2006 Spring; 32(2): 52-63. Subject: 12.1

Cloyes, Kristin Gates. An ethic of analysis: an argument for critical analysis of research interviews as an ethical practice. *Advances in Nursing Science* 2006 April-June; 29(2): 84-97. Subject: 4.1.3

Coates, Jonathan. Patient requests for unwarranted treatment. *New Zealand Medical Journal* 2002 January 25; 115(1146): 23. Subject: 9.4

Coates, Jonathan. When do parents have the right to refuse medical treatment on behalf of their children? *New Zealand Medical Journal* 2000 July 14; 113(1113): 297. Subject: 8.3.2

Coats, T.J.; Shakur, H. Consent in emergency research: new regulations. *Emergency Medicine Journal* 2005 October; 22(10): 683-685. Subject: 18.3

Cobanoglu, Nesrin; Kayhan, Zeynep. Research note: an assessment of medical ethics education. *Nursing Ethics* 2006 September; 13(5): 558-561. Subject: 2.3

Cobbe, N. Why the apparent haste to clone humans? *Journal of Medical Ethics* 2006 May; 32(5): 298-302. Subject: 14.5

Cochran, Clarke E. Catholic health care in the public square: tension on the frontier. *In:* Guinn, David E., ed. Handbook of Bioethics and Religion. New York: Oxford University Press, 2006: 403-425. Subject: 9.1

Cochran, Clarke E.; Cochran, David Carroll. Consistently defending the sanctity of human life. *In their:* Catholics, Politics, and Public Policy: Beyond Left and Right. Maryknoll: Orbis Books; 2003: 182-205. Subject: 4.4

Cochran, Clarke E.; Cochran, David Carroll. Rethinking healthcare policy. *In their:* Catholics, Politics, and Public Policy: Beyond Left and Right. Maryknoll: Orbis Books;2003: 48-69. Subject: 9.2

Cochrane, Thomas I.; Perry, Joshua E.; Kirshner, Howard S.; Churchill, Larry R. Relevance of patient diagnosis to analysis of the Terri Schiavo case [letter and reply]. *Annals of Internal Medicine* 2006 February 21; 144(4): 305- 306. Subject: 20.5.1

Cochrane, Thomas I.; Truog, Robert D.; Casarett, David; Kapo, Jennifer; Caplan, Arthur. Appropriate use of artificial nutrition and hydration [letter and reply]. *New England Journal of Medicine* 2006 March 23; 354(12): 1320-1321. Subject: 20.5.1

Cocon Group; Moreau, Caroline; Bajos, Nathalie; Bouyer, Jean. Access to health care for induced abortions. Analysis by means of a French national survey. *European Journal of Public Health* 2004 December; 14(4): 369- 374. Subject: 12.4.2

Codd, Helen. Policing procreation: prisoners, artificial insemination and the law. *Genomics, Society and Policy* 2006 May; 2(1): 110-117. Subject: 14.2

Cody, Jannine D. Creating partnerships and improving health care: the role of genetic advocacy groups. *Genetics in Medicine* 2006 December; 8(12): 797-799. Subject: 15.1

Coebergh, Jan Willem W.; van Veen, Evert-Ben; Vandenbroucke, Jan P.; van Diest, Paul; Oosterhuis, Wolter. One-time general consent for research on biological samples: opt out system for patients is optimal and endorsed in many countries [letter]. *BMJ: British Medical Journal* 2006 March 18; 332(7542): 665. Subject: 18.3

Coggon, David. Occupational health research. *In:* Westerholm, Peter; Nilstun, Tore; Øvretveit, John, eds. Practical Ethics in Occupational Health. San Francisco: Radcliffe Medical Press; 2004: 241-251. Subject: 16.3

Coggon, J. Arguing about physician-assisted suicide: a response to Steinbock. *Journal of Medical Ethics* 2006 June; 32(6): 339-341. Subject: 20.7

Coggon, John. Could the right to die with dignity represent a new right to die in English law? *Medical Law Review* 2006 Summer; 14(2): 219-237. Subject: 20.5.1

Coghlan, Andy. A contentious cut: unethical mutilation in the name of medicine or a procedure that might save millions of lives in Africa? [news]. *New Scientist* 2006 November 25-December 1; 192(2579): 8-9. Subject: 9.5.1

Coghlan, Andy. A life and death dilemma. . . . *New Scientist* 2006 October 21-27; 192(2574): 8-9. Subject: 18.3

Coghlan, Andy. One million people, one medical gamble [news]. *New Scientist* 2006 January 21-27; 189(2535): 8-9. Subject: 15.1

Cohan, John Alan. Judicial enforcement of lifesaving treatment for unwilling patients. *Creighton Law Review* 2006 June; 39(4): 849-913. Subject: 8.3.2

Cohen, Alfred. Sale or donation of human organs. *Journal of Halacha and Contemporary Society* 2006 Fall; (52): 37-64. Subject: 19.5

Cohen, Bernard; Smits, Jacqueline M.; Haase, Bernadette; Persijn, Guido; Vanrenterghem, Yves; Frei, Ulrich. Expanding the donor pool to increase renal transplantation. *Nephrology Dialysis Transplantation* 2005 January; 20(1): 34-41. Subject: 19.5

Cohen, Cynthia B. Religion, public reason, and embryonic stem cell research. *In:* Guinn, David E., ed. Handbook of Bioethics and Religion. New York: Oxford University Press, 2006: 129-142. Subject: 18.5.4

Subject = NRCBL Primary Classification Number; see inside front cover.

Cohen, Eric. Biotechnology and the spirit of capitalism. *New Atlantis* 2006 Spring; 12: 9-23. Subject: 5.3

Cohen, Eric. Conservative bioethics and the search for wisdom. *Hastings Center Report* 2006 January-February; 36(1): 44-56. Subject: 2.1

Cohen, Frederick H. An unfulfilled promise of the Medicaid Act: enforcing Medicaid recipients' right to health care. *Loyola Consumer Law Review* 2005; 17(4): 375-393. Subject: 9.2

Cohen, Joshua; Ubel, Peter. Accounting for fairness and efficiency in health economics. *In:* Davis, John B., ed. The Social Economics of Health Care. New York: Routledge; 2001: 94-109. Subject: 9.3.1

Cohen, Lawrence. Operability, bioavailability, and exception. *In:* Ong, Aihwa; Collier, Stephen J., eds. Global Assemblages: Technology, Politics, and Ethics as Anthropological Problems. Malden, MA: Blackwell Pub.; 2005: 79-90. Subject: 19.1

Cohen, Lawrence. The other kidney: biopolitics beyond recognition. *In:* Scheper-Hughes, Nancy; Wacquant, Loïc, eds. Commodifying Bodies. Thousand Oaks, CA: SAGE Publications; 2002: 9-29. Subject: 19.3

Cohen, Leonard A.; Romberg, Elaine; Grace, Edward G.; Barnes, Douglas M. Attitudes of advanced dental education students toward individuals with AIDS. *Journal of Dental Education* 2005 August; 69(8): 896-900. Subject: 9.5.6

Cohen, Lewis; Ganzini, Linda; Mitchell, Christine; Arons, Stephen; Goy, Elizabeth; Cleary, James. Accusations of murder and euthanasia in end-of-life care [editorial]. *Journal of Palliative Medicine* 2005 December; 8(6): 1096-1104. Subject: 20.5.1

Cohen, Lewis M. A medical revolution in death-hastening decisions. *Palliative and Supportive Care* 2003 December; 1(4): 377-379. Subject: 20.5.1

Cohen, Lewis M. Pulling the plug. *Palliative and Supportive Care* 2003 September; 1(3): 279-283. Subject: 20.5.1

Cohen, Peter J. Medical marijuana, compassionate use, and public policy: expert opinion or vox populi? *Hastings Center Report* 2006 May-June; 36(3): 19-22. Subject: 9.5.1

Cohen, Simon; Sprung, Charles; Sjokvist, Peter; Lippert, Anne; Ricou, Bara; Baras, Mario; Hovilehto, Seppo; Maia, Paulo; Phelan, Dermot; Reinhart, Konrad; Werdan, Karl; Bulow, Hans-Henrik; Woodcock, Tom. Communication of end-of-life decisions in European intensive care units. *Intensive Care Medicine* 2005 September; 31(9): 1215-1221. Subject: 20.5.1

Cohen-Mansfield, J. Consent and refusal in dementia research: conceptual and practical considerations. *Alzheimer Disease and Associated Disorders* 2003 April-June; 17(Supplement 1): S17-S25. Subject: 8.3.3

Cohn, Jay N. The use of race and ethnicity in medicine: lessons from the African-American heart failure trial. *Journal of Law, Medicine and Ethics* 2006 Fall; 34(3):552-554. Subject: 18.5.1

Cohn, Jennifer M. Bioethics curriculum for paediatrics residents: implementation and evaluation. *Medical Education* 2005 May; 39(5): 530. Subject: 7.2

Cola, Philip A. The informed consent process. *In:* Fedor, Carol A.; Cola, Philip A.; Pierre, Christine, eds. Responsible Research: A Guide for Coordinators. London; Chicago, IL: Remedics; 2006: 65-76. Subject: 18.3

Cola, Philip A.; Cottington, Eric M. Responsible conduct of research. *In:* Fedor, Carol A.; Cola, Philip A.; Pierre, Christine, eds. Responsible Research: A Guide for Coordinators. London; Chicago, IL: Remedics; 2006: 49-64. Subject: 1.3.9

Colah, Roshan; Surve, Reema; Nadkarni, Anita; Gorakshakar, Ajit; Phanasgaonkar, Supriya; Satoskar, Poornima; Mohanty, Dipika. Prenatal diagnosis of sickle syndromes in India: dilemmas in counselling. *Prenatal Diagnosis* 2005 May; 25(5): 345-349. Subject: 15.2

Colby, Jacqueline L. Consent: moral rightness versus non-moral goodness. *American Journal of Bioethics* 2006 May-June; 6(3): 69-71; discussion W51- W53. Subject: 2.1

Cole, Andrew. Assisted conception business should be better regulated [news]. *BMJ: British Medical Journal* 2006 April 1; 332(7544): 748. Subject: 14.1

Cole, Andrew. Genetic tests and staff are cut to save money [news]. *BMJ: British Medical Journal* 2006 December 16; 333(7581): 1238. Subject: 15.3

Cole, Andrew. UK launches panel to tackle research misconduct [news]. *BMJ: British Medical Journal* 2006 April 15; 332(7546): 871. Subject: 1.3.9

Cole, Simon A. The myth of fingerprints: the legacy of forensic fingerprinting and arrestee. *GeneWatch* 2006 November-December; 19(6): 3-6. Subject: 15.1

Coleman, Carl H. Duties to subjects in clinical research. *Vanderbilt Law Review* 2005 March; 58(20): 387-449. Subject: 18.2

Coleman, Carl H.; Menikoff, Jerry A.; Goldner, Jesse A.; Dubler, Nancy Neveloff. Genetics research. *In their:* The Ethics and Regulation of Research with Human Subjects: Teacher's Manual. Newark, NJ: LexisNexis, 2005: 209-219. Subject: 15.1

Coleman, Carl H.; Menikoff, Jerry A.; Goldner, Jesse A.; Dubler, Nancy Neveloff. Genetics research. *In their:* The Ethics and Regulation of Research with Human Subjects. Newark, NJ: LexisNexis, 2005: 697-746. Subject: 15.1

See SUBJECT HEADING KEY FOR SECTION II on inside back cover.

527

Coleman, David L. Who's guarding medical privacy? *Business and Health* 1999 March; 17(3): 29-30, 32, 37-8. Subject: 8.4

Coleman, David L.; Kazdin, Alan E.; Miller, Lee Ann; Morrow, Jon S.; Udelsman, Robert. Guidelines for interactions between clinical faculty and the pharmaceutical industry: one medical school's approach. *Academic Medicine* 2006 February; 81(2): 154-160. Subject: 9.7

Coleman, Karen. The politics of abortion in Australia: freedom, church, and state. *Feminist Review* 1988 Spring; (29): 75-97. Subject: 12.4.2

Coleman, P.K.; Reardon, D.C.; Lee, M.B. Women's preferences for information and complication seriousness ratings related to elective medical procedures. *Journal of Medical Ethics* 2006 August; 32(8): 435-438. Subject: 9.5.5

Colgan, Terence J. Disclosure of diagnostic errors: the death knell of retrospective pathology reviews? *Journal of Lower Genital Tract Disease* 2005 October; 9(4): 216-218. Subject: 8.2

Colgrove, James. The ethics and politics of compulsory HPV vaccination. *New England Journal of Medicine* 2006 December 7; 355(23): 2389-2391. Subject: 9.5.1

Collett, Teresa Stanton. Transporting minors for immoral purposes: the case of the Child Custody Protection Act and the Child Interstate Abortions Notification Act. *Health Matrix: The Journal of Law-Medicine* 2006 Winter; 16(1): 107-150. Subject: 12.4.2

Collier, Joe. Big pharma and the U.K. government. *Lancet* 2006 January 14-20; 367(9505): 97-98. Subject: 9.7

Collier, Julie; Rorty, Mary; Sandborg, Christy. Rafting the ethical rapids. *HEC (Healthcare Ethics Committee) Forum* 2006 December; 18(4): 332-341. Subject: 9.6

Collins, Francis S.; Mansoura, Monique K. The Human Genome Project: revealing the shared inheritance of all humankind. *Cancer* 2001 January 1; 91(1, Supplement): 221-225. Subject: 15.10

Collins, Gary. Court-mandated psychiatric outpatient treatment in New York: doesn't this process invoke more care than controversy? [editorial]. *Criminal Behaviour and Mental Health* 2005; 15(4): 214-220. Subject: 17.7

Collins, Mary K. Conscience clauses and oral contraceptives: conscientious objection or calculated obstruction? *Annals of Health Law* 2006 Winter; 15(1): 37-60. Subject: 11.1

Collins, Nerida; Knowles, Ann D. Adolescents' attitudes towards confidentiality between the school counsellor and the adolescent client. *Australian Psychologist* 1995 November; 30(3): 179-182. Subject: 8.4

Collins, Timothy P. Human technology manufacturing platforms. *National Catholic Bioethics Quarterly* 2006 Autumn; 6(3): 497-515. Subject: 9.5.1

Collins-Nakai, Ruth. "Patient information — sacred trust". *Health Law in Canada* 2006 March; 26(3): 36-39. Subject: 8.4

Collis, S.P. The importance of truth-telling in health care. *Nursing Standard* 2006 January 4-10; 20(17): 41-45. Subject: 8.2

Collste, Göran. Infanticide and the principle of human dignity. *In his:* Is Human Life Special?: Religious and Philosophical Perspectives on the Principle of Human Dignity. New York: P. Lang; 2002: 175-187. Subject: 20.5.2

Colman, Alan. Everyone listed on Dolly paper met established criteria for authorship. *Nature* 2006 April 27; 440(7088): 1112. Subject: 1.3.9

Colman, Eric G. The Food and Drug Administration's Osteoporosis Guidance Document: past, present, and future. *Journal of Bone and Mineral Research* 2003 June; 18(6): 1125-1128. Subject: 18.2

Colorado. *Laws, statutes, etc.* An act concerning genetic privacy [Approved: 1 June 2002]. Colorado: General Assembly, 2002. 2 p. [Online]. Accessed: http://www.state.co.us/gov_dir/leg_dir/olls/sl2002a/sl.262.pdf 2007 March 8]. Subject: 15.3

Colt, Joanne S.; Wacholder, Sholom; Schwartz, Kendra; Davis, Faith; Graubard, Barry; Chow, Wong-Ho. Response rates in a case-control study: effect of disclosure of biologic sample collection in the initial contact letter. *Annals of Epidemiology* 2005 October; 15(9): 700-704. Subject: 18.2

Colwell-Chanthaphonh, Chip. Self-governance, self-representation, self-determination and the questions of research ethics. *Science and Engineering Ethics* 2006 July; 12(3): 508-510. Subject: 18.2

Combes, Robert. SPEAK v. pro-test — the Newsnight animal experimentation debate — round 1 [editorial]. *ATLA: Alternatives to Laboratory Animals* 2006 October; 34(5): 463-465. Subject: 22.2

Comby, M.C.; Filbet, M. The demand for euthanasia in palliative care units: a prospective study in seven units of the 'Rhône-Alpes' region. *Palliative Medicine* 2005 December; 19(8): 587-593. Subject: 20.5.1

Comeau, Pauline. Conscription fears accompany threat of pandemic [news]. *CMAJ/JAMC: Canadian Medical Association Journal* 2006 April 25; 174(9): 1245-1246. Subject: 9.1

Comité Consultatif de Bioéthique de Belgique. Avis no. 1 du 12 mai 1997 concernant l'opportunité d'un règlement légal de l'euthanasie / Notice no. 1 of 12th May, 1997 concerning the chance of legal regulation of euthanasia. *In:* Les Avis du Comité Consultatif de Bioéthique de Belgique 1996-2000. Brussels: De Boeck University; 2001: 11-15. Subject: 20.5.1

Comité Consultatif de Bioéthique de Belgique. Avis no. 9 du 22 fevrier 1999 concernant l'arrêt actif de la vie des personnes incapables d'exprimer leur volonté / Notice no. 9 of 22 February 1999 concerning active termination of life of persons unable to express their will. *In:* Les Avis du Comité Consultatif de Bioéthique de Belgique 1996-2000. Brussels: De Boeck University; 2001:93-116. Subject: 20.7

Comité consultatif de Bioéthique de Belgique. Avis no. 24 du 13 mars 2006 sur la proposition de loi relative à ka transsexualité déposée par Mmes Hilde Vautmans, Valérie Déom, Marie-Christine Marghem et M. Guy Swennen [Opinion no. 34 of Mar. 13, 2006 concerning the bill on transsexuality brought forward by Mmes Hilde Vautmans, Valérie Déom, Marie-Christine Marghem, and M. Guy Swennen]. *Bioethica Belgica* 2006 March; (25): 38-40. Subject: 10

Comité Consultatif de Bioéthique de Belgique. Avis no. 33 du 7 novembre 2005 relatif aux modifications géniques somatiques et germinales à visées thérapeutiques et/ ou mélioratives [Opinion no. 33 of Nov. 7, 2005 concerning somatic and germ cell gene therapy for therapeutic or enhancement purposes]. *Bioethica Belgica* 2006 March; (25): 3-37. Subject: 15.4

La commission de l'éthique de la science et de la technologie [Québec]. Pour une gestion éthique des OGM: mises en garde. *Journal International de Bioéthique = International Journal of Bioethics* 2005 September-December; 16(3-4): 137-140. Subject: 15.1

Comparetto, C.; Giudici, S.; Coccia, M.E.; Scarselli, G.; Borruto, F. Clinical, ethical, and medical legal considerations on emergency contraception. *Clinical and Experimental Obstetrics and Gynecology* 2005; 32(2): 107-110. Subject: 11.1

Condit, Celeste Michelle; Parrott, Roxanne; Harris, Tina M. Lay understandings of the relationship between race and genetics: development of a collectivized knowledge through shared discourse. *Public Understanding of Science* 2002 October; 11(4): 373-387. Subject: 15.11

Cone, David C.; O'Connor, Robert E. Are US informed consent requirements driving resuscitation research overseas? *Resuscitation* 2005 August; 66(2): 141-148. Subject: 18.3

Cong, Yali. Consideration of medical ethics education in China from the comparison between China and the United States. *In:* Sang-yong, Song; Young-Mo, Koo; Macer, Darryl R.J., eds. Asian Bioethics in the 21st Century. Christchurch, NZ: Eubios Ethics Institute, 2002: 251-254. Subject: 2.3

Coni, Nick; McAdam, Catherine. Achieving and good death. *In:* Rai, Gurcharan S, ed. Medical Ethics and the Elderly. 2nd ed. San Francisco: Radcliffe Medical Press; 2004: 113-123. Subject: 20.4.1

Coni, Nick; Rai, Gurcharan S. The use of restraints. *In:* Rai, Gurcharan S, ed. Medical Ethics and the Elderly. 2nd

ed. San Francisco: Radcliffe Medical Press; 2004: 139-145. Subject: 17.3

Conlee, Kathleen M.; Boysen, Sarah T. Chimpanzees in research: past, present, and future. *In:* Salem, Deborah J.; Rowan, Andrew N., eds. The State of the Animals III, 2005. Washington, DC: Humane Society Press, 2005: 119-133. Subject: 22.2

Connell, Cathleen M.; Shaw, Benjamin A.; Holmes, Sara B.; Foster, Norman L. Caregivers' attitudes toward their family members' participation in Alzheimer disease research: implications for recruitment and retention. *Alzheimer Disease and Associated Disorders* 2001 July-September; 15(3): 137-145. Subject: 18.5.6

Connolly, June. Contraception and the under 16s — legal and ethical implications for the advanced nurse practitioner. *In:* Bartter, Karen, ed. Ethical Issues in Advanced Nursing Practice. Boston: Butterworth-Heinemann; 2001: 16-30. Subject: 11.2

Connor, Kenneth. Connor on Schiavo. *Stetson Law Review* 2005 Fall; 35(1): 31-38. Subject: 20.5.1

Connors, Rachel. Y v Austin Health and the Royal Women's Hospital. *Journal of Law and Medicine* 2006 February; 13(3): 292-294. Subject: 14.6

Connors, Rachel. Yz v Infertility Treatment Authority. *Journal of Law and Medicine* 2006 February; 13(3): 289-291. Subject: 14.6

Conrad, Barbara; Horner, Sharon. Issues in pediatric research: safeguarding the children. *Journal of the Society of Pediatric Nurses* 1997 October-December; 2(4): 163-171. Subject: 18.5.2

Conrad, Ellison. Terminal success. *HEC (Healthcare Ethics Committee) Forum* 2006 December; 18(4): 287-290. Subject: 9.6

Conrad, Peter. Public eyes and private genes: historic frames, news constructions and social problems. *Social Problems* 1997; 44: 139-154. Subject: 15.6

Conrad, Peter. Use of expertise: sources, quotes, and voice in the reporting of genetics in the news. *Public Understanding of Science* 1999; 8: 285-302. Subject: 15.1

Conroy, Ronán M. Female genital mutilation: whose problem, whose solution? [editorial]. *BMJ: British Medical Journal* 2006 July 15; 333(7559): 106-107. Subject: 9.5.5

Conroy, Simon P.; Luxton, Tony; Dingwall, Robert; Harwood, Rowan H.; Gladman, John R. F. Cardiopulmonary resuscitation in continuing care settings: time for a rethink? *BMJ: British Medical Journal* 2006 February 25; 332(7539): 479-482. Subject: 20.5.1

Consoli, Luca. Scientific misconduct and science ethics: a case study based approach. *Science and Engineering Ethics* 2006 July; 12(3): 533-541. Subject: 1.3.9

See SUBJECT HEADING KEY FOR SECTION II on inside back cover.

529

Contandriopoulos, Damien; Denis, Jean-Louis; Langley, Ann. Defining the 'public' in a public healthcare system. *Human Relations* 2004 December; 57(12): 1573-1596. Subject: 9.2

Contant, Charles; McCullough, Laurence B.; Mangus, Lorna; Robertson, Claudia; Valadka, Alex; Brody, Baruch. Community consultation in emergency research. *Critical Care Medicine* 2006 August; 34(8): 2049-2052. Subject: 18.6

Conti, A. The recent Italian consolidation act on privacy: new measures for data protection. *Medicine and Law: World Association for Medical Law* 2006 March; 25(1): 127-138. Subject: 8.4

Cook, Ann Freeman; Hoas, Helena. Re-framing the question: what do we really want to know about rural health care ethics? *American Journal of Bioethics* 2006 March-April; 6(2): 51-53. Subject: 9.5.1

Cook, R.J.; Dickens, B.M.; Horga, M. Safe abortion: WHO technical and policy guidance. *International Journal of Gynecology and Obstetrics* 2004 July; 86(1): 79-84. Subject: 12.1

Cook-Deegan, Robert. The urge to commercialize: interactions between public and private research development. *In:* Esanu, Julie M.; Uhlir, Paul F., eds. The Role of Scientific and Technical Data and Information in the Public Domain: Proceedings of a Symposium. Washington, DC: National Academies Press; 2002: 87-94. Subject: 5.3

Cooley, Dennis. Responsible Conduct of Research, by Adil E. Shamoo and David B. Resnik [book review]. *Essays in Philosophy* 2003 June; 4(2): 12 p. [Online]. Accessed: http://sorrel.humboldt.edu/%7Eessays/cooley3rev.html [2004 December 16]. Subject: 18.1

Cooper, D.K.C. Draft reports for public comment from the US Secretary's Advisory Committee on Xenotransplantation. *Xenotransplantation* 2005 July; 12(4): 255-257. Subject: 19.1

Cooper, Jeffrey A. Responsible conduct of radiology research: Part I. The regulatory framework for human research. *Radiology* 2005 August; 236(2): 379-381. Subject: 18.6

Cooper, Jeffrey A. Responsible conduct of radiology research Part III. Exemptions from regulatory requirements for human research. *Radiology* 2005 October; 237(1): 3-7. Subject: 18.2

Cooper, Paul. Education in the age of Ritalin. *In:* Rees, Dai; Rose, Steven, eds. The New Brain Sciences: Perils and Prospects. New York: Cambridge University Press; 2004: 249-262. Subject: 17.4

Cooper, Peter; Collins, John; Leveaux, Viviane; Isaacs, David; Kilham, Henry; Tobin, Bernadette. Rebecca's story. *Journal of Paediatrics and Child Health* 2005 August; 41(8): 453-455. Subject: 20.5.2

Cooper, Richelle J.; Gupta, Malkeet; Wilkes, Michael S.; Hoffman, Jerome R. Conflict of interest disclosure policies and practices in peer-reviewed biomedical journals. *JGIM: Journal of General Internal Medicine* 2006 December; 21(12): 1248-1252. Subject: 1.3.9

Cooper, Zachary N.; Nelson, Robert M.; Ross, Lainie F. Informed consent for genetic research involving pleiotropic genes: an empirical study of ApoE research. *IRB: Ethics and Human Research* 2006 September-October; 28(5): 1-11. Subject: 15.1

Coors, Marilyn E. Considering chimeras: the confluence of genetic engineering and ethics. *National Catholic Bioethics Quarterly* 2006 Spring; 6(1): 75-87. Subject: 15.1

Coors, Marilyn E.; Townsend, Susan F. Supporting pregnant women through difficult decisions: a case of prenatal diagnosis of osteogenesis imperfecta. *Journal of Clinical Ethics* 2006 Fall; 17(3): 266-274. Subject: 9.5.5

Copp, Laurel Archer. An ethical responsibility for pain management [editorial]. *Journal of Advanced Nursing* 2006 July; 55(1): 1-3. Subject: 4.4

Copp, Laurel Archer. Pain and suffering: responsiveness, progress and perserverence [editorial]. *Journal of Advanced Nursing* 2006 July; 55(1): 3-4. Subject: 4.4

Coppen, Remco; Friele, Roland D.; Marquet, Richard L.; Gevers, Sjef K.M. Opting-out systems: no guarantee for higher donation rates. *Transplant International* 2005 November; 18(11): 1275-1279. Subject: 19.5

Corbeel, L. Informed consent: ethical point of view. *Acta Chirurgica Belgica* 2000 August; 100(4): 156-159. Subject: 8.3.1

Corneli, Amy L.; Bentley, Margaret E.; Sorenson, James R.; Henderson, Gail E.; van der Horst, Charles; Moses, Agnes; Nkhoma, Jacqueline; Tenthani, Lyson; Ahmed, Yusuf; Heilig, Charles M.; Jamieson, Denise J. Using formative research to develop a context-specific approach to informed consent for clinical trials. *Journal of Empirical Research on Human Research Ethics* 2006 December; 1(4): 45-60. Subject: 18.5.9

Cornell, John F. On the relevance of Aristotle's bioethics. *Politics and the Life Sciences* 1988 February; 6(2): 199-201; author's reply 223-225. Subject: 15.9

Cornwell, Glenda. Ethical issues in deriving stem cells from embryos and eggs. *British Journal of Nursing* 2006 June 22-July 12; 15(12): 640-644. Subject: 18.5.4

Cornwell, John Kip; Deeney, Raymond. Exposing the myths surrounding preventive outpatient commitment for individuals with chronic mental illness. *Psychology, Public Policy, and Law* 2003 March-June; 9(1-2): 209-232. Subject: 17.7

Corrao, S.; Arnone, G.; Arnone, S.; Baldari, S. Medical ethics, clinical research, and special aspects in nuclear medicine [editorial]. *Quarterly Journal of Nuclear Medi-*

cine and Molecular Imaging 2004 September; 48(3): 175-180. Subject: 18.2

Correa, Francisco Javier Léon. Bioética de la atención de enfermería al enfermo terminal [Bioethics of nursing care for the terminally ill]. *Persona y Bioética* 1999 February-May; 2(6): 123-142. Subject: 20.4.1

Corrigan, Oonagh; Tutton, Richard. What's in a name? Subjects, volunteers, participants and activists in clinical research. *Clinical Ethics* 2006 June; 1(2): 101-104. Subject: 18.1

Cortina, Adela. The public role of bioethics and the role of the public. *In:* Rehmann-Sutter, Christoph; Düwell, Marcus; Mieth, Dietmar, eds. Bioethics in Cultural Contexts: Reflections on Methods and Finitude. Dordrecht: Springer, 2006: 165-174. Subject: 2.1

Cosman, Madeleine Pelner. Frogs, crabs, and the culture of death: lessons from the Schiavo case. *Journal of American Physicians and Surgeons* 2005 Summer; 10(2): 55-57. Subject: 20.5.1

Costich, Julia Field. The Perruche case and the issue of compensation for the consequences of medical error. *Health Policy* 2006 August 22; 78(1): 8-16. Subject: 15.2

Cot, Annie L. "Breed out the unfit and breed in the fit": Irving Fisher, economics, and the science of heredity. *American Journal of Economics and Sociology* 2005 July; 64(3): 793-826. Subject: 15.5

Cotton, Sara, et al. Model Assisted Reproductive Technology Act. *Journal of Gender, Race and Justice* 2005 Fall; 9(1): 55-107. Subject: 14.4

Cottone, R. Rocco. Detrimental therapist-client relationships — beyond thinking of "dual" or "multiple" roles: reflections on the 2001 AAMFT code of ethics. *American Journal of Family Therapy* 2005 January-February; 33(1): 1-17. Subject: 17.2

Cottrell, Barbara. Working with research ethics: the role of advisory committees in community-based research. *Atlantis* 2001 Spring; 25(2): 22-30. Subject: 18.2

Coulehan, Jack. "They wouldn't pay attention": death without dignity. *American Journal of Hospice and Palliative Medicine* 2005 September-October; 22(5): 339-343. Subject: 20.5.1

Coulson, Karen M.; Glasser, Brandy L.; Liang, Bryan A. Informed consent: issues for providers. *Hematology/Oncology Clinics of North America* 2002 December; 16(6): 1365-1380. Subject: 8.3.1

Council for Responsible Genetics. Genetic testing: preliminary policy guidelines [guideline]. *GeneWatch* 2006 July-August; 19(4): 15-18. Subject: 15.3

Council for Responsible Genetics. Intelligence and genetic determinism. *GeneWatch* 2006 November-December; 19(6): 9-12. Subject: 15.1

Council for Responsible Genetics. Sexual orientation and genetic discrimination. *GeneWatch* 2006 July-August; 19(4): i-iv. Subject: 15.1

Council of Europe. Additional protocol to the Convention on Human Rights and Biomedicine concerning Biomedical Research, Council of Europe, 2004. *European Journal of Health Law* 2004 September; 11(3): 293-307. Subject: 18.2

Council of Europe. Recommendation Rec (2003) 10 of the committee of ministers to member states on xenotransplantation. *European Journal of Health Law* 2003 September; 10(3): 305-315. Subject: 19.1

Council of Europe. Recommendation 1240 (1994), on the protection and patentability of materials of human origin = Consejo de Europa: Recomendación 1240 (1994), relativa a la protección y patentabilidad de los productos de origen humano. *Law and the Human Genome Review = Revista de Derecho y Genoma Humano* 1995 July-December; (3): 293-295. Subject: 15.8

Council of Europe. Committee of Ministers. Recommendation Rec(2006)4 of the Committee of Ministers to member states on research on biological materials of human origin. *Genetics in Medicine* 2006 September; 13(3): 302-310. Subject: 15.1

Council of Europe. Directorate General I - Legal Affairs. Bioethics Department. Steering Committee on Bioethics (CDBI): Information document concerning the CDBI. Strasbourg: Council of Europe, 2006 June 20: 27 p. [Online]. Accessed: http://www.coe.int/t/e/legal_affairs/legal_co-operation/bioethics/cdbi/INF(2006)2%20e%20CDBI%20info%20doc1.asp#TopOfPage [2007 March 5]. Subject: 2.4

Council of Europe. Parliamentary Assembly. Social, Health and Family Affairs Committee; Marty, Dick. Euthanasia: report [draft resolution]. Strasbourg, France: Council of Europe, 2003 September 10; 16 p. [Online]. Accessed: http://assembly.coe.int/Documents/WorkingDocs/Doc03/EDOC9898.htm [2006 June 13]. Subject: 20.5.1

Council of Europe. Steering Committee on Bioethics [CDBI]. Replies to the questionnaire for member states relating to euthanasia. Strasbourg, France: Council of Europe, 2003 January 20; 66 p. [Online]. Accessed: http://www.coe.int/t/e/legal_affairs/legal_co-operation/bioethics/activities/ euthanasia/INF(2003)8e_replies_euthanasia.pdf [2006 September 21]. Subject: 20.5.1

Council of State and Territorial Epidemiologists. Advisory Committee; Hodge, James G., Jr.; Gostin, Lawrence O. Public practice vs. research: a report for public health practitioners including cases and guidance for making distinctions. *Atlanta, Georgia: Council of State and Territorial Epidemiologists* 2004 May 24; 61 pages [Online]. Accessed: http://www.ihs.gov/MedicalPrograms/

See SUBJECT HEADING KEY FOR SECTION II on inside back cover.

531

Research/pdf_files/CSTEPHResRptHodgeFinal.
5.24.04.pdf [2006 January 25]. Subject: 18.2

Couzin, Jennifer. Breakdown of the year: scientific fraud. *Science* 2006 December 22; 314(5807): 1853. Subject: 1.3.9

Couzin, Jennifer. Desperate measures. *Science* 2006 August 18; 313(5789): 904-907. Subject: 9.5.8

Couzin, Jennifer. Fake data, but could the idea still be right? *Science* 2006 July 14; 313(5784): 154. Subject: 1.3.9

Couzin, Jennifer. Proposed guidelines for emergency research aim to quell confusion [news]. *Science* 2006 September 8; 313(5792): 1372-1373. Subject: 18.3

Couzin, Jennifer. Truth and consequences. *Science* 2006 September 1; 313(5791): 1222-1226. Subject: 1.3.9

Couzin, Jennifer. . . .And how the problems eluded peer reviewers and editors [news]. *Science* 2006 January 6; 311(5757): 23-24. Subject: 1.3.9

Couzin, Jennifer; Schirber, Michael. Fraud upends oral cancer field, casting doubt on prevention trial [news]. *Science* 2006 January 27; 311(5760): 448-449. Subject: 1.3.9

Couzin, Jennifer; Unger, Katherine. Cleaning up the paper trail [news]. *Science* 2006 April 7; 312(5770): 38-43. Subject: 1.3.9

Cowan, Ruth Schwartz. Eugenics, genetic screening, and the slippery slope. *In:* Miller, Roman J.; Brubaker, Beryl H.; Peterson, James C., eds. Viewing New Creations with Anabaptist Eyes: Ethics of Biotechnology. Telford, PA: Cascadia Pub.; 2005: 149-167. Subject: 15.3

Cowell, Henry R. Ethical responsibilities of editors, reviewers, and authors. *Clinical Orthopaedics and Related Research* 2000 September; (378): 83-89. Subject: 1.3.9

Cowen, Tyler. Enter the neuro-economists: why do investors do what they do? *New York Times* 2006 April 20; p. C3. Subject: 17.1

Cowley, C. Polemic: five proposals for a medical school admission policy. *Journal of Medical Ethics* 2006 August; 32(8): 491-494. Subject: 7.2

Cox, Courtney. Only time can tell: unethical research and the passage of time. *Newsletter on Philosophy and Law* 2005 Fall; 05(1): 2-11. Subject: 18.5.1

Craft, Alan W.; McIntosh, Neil. Southall and colleagues vindicated once more. *Lancet* 2006 April 1-7; 367(9516): 1035-1037. Subject: 18.6

Craig, Amber. North Carolina Medicaid and the funding of routine non- therapeutic circumcisions. *In:* Denniston, George C.; Hodges, Frederick Mansfield; Milos, Marilyn Fayre, eds. Flesh and Blood: Perspectives on the Problems of Circumcision in Contemporary Society. New York: Kluwer Academic/Plenum Publishers; 2004: 207-216. Subject: 9.5.7

Craig, Gillian; Janssens, Rien M.J.P.A.; Olthuis, Gert; Dekkers, Wim; Harvath, Theresa A.; Smyth, Dion. Sedation without hydration can seriously damage your health [debate]. *International Journal of Palliative Nursing* 2005 July; 11(7): 333-337. Subject: 20.5.1

Craig, Jana M.; May, Thomas. Ethics consultation as a tool for teaching residents. *American Journal of Bioethics* 2006 July-August; 6(4): 25-27. Subject: 7.2

Craig, Jana .M.; May, Thomas. Evaluating the outcomes of ethics consultation. *Journal of Clinical Ethics* 2006 Summer; 17(2): 168-180. Subject: 9.6

Crane, Monica K.; Wittink, Marsha; Doukas, David J. Respecting end-of-life treatment preferences. *American Family Physician* 2005 October 1; 72(7): 1263-1268. Subject: 20.5.4

Craven, Christa. Claiming respectable American motherhood: homebirth mothers, medical officials, and the state. *Medical Anthropology Quarterly* 2005 June; 19(2): 194-215. Subject: 9.5.5

Crawford, Amy E. Under siege: freedom of choice and the statutory ban on abortions on military bases. *University of Chicago Law Review* 2004 Fall; 71(4): 1549-1582. Subject: 12.4.1

Creed-Kanashiro, Hilary; Ore, Beatriz; Scurrah, Maria; Gil, Ana; Penny, Mary. Conducting research in developing countries: experiences of the informed consent process from community studies in Peru. *Journal of Nutrition* 2005 April; 135(4): 925-928. Subject: 18.5.9

Creinin, Mitchell D. Medical abortion regiments: historical context and overview. *American Journal of Obstetrics and Gynecology* 2000 August; 183(Supplement 2): S3-S9. Subject: 12.1

Crews, Heather A. Women be warned, egg donation isn't all it's cracked up to be: the copulation of science and the courts makes multiple mommies. *North Carolina Journal of Law and Technology* 2005 Fall; 7(1): 141-156. Subject: 14.2

Crigger, Bette-Jane. e-Medicine: policy to shape the future of health care. *Hastings Center Report* 2006 January-February; 36(1): 12-13. Subject: 9.1

Cripe, Larry D. Hope is the thing with feathers. *JAMA: The Journal of the American Medical Association* 2006 October 18; 296(15): 1815-1816. Subject: 20.4.1

Crippen, David; Hawryluck, Laura. Pro/con clinical debate: life support should have a special status among therapies, and patients or their families should have a right to insist on this treatment even if it will not improve outcome. *Critical Care* 2004 August; 8(4): 231-233. Subject: 20.5.1

Crockin, Susan L. The "embryo" wars: at the epicenter of science, law, religion, and politics. *Family Law Quarterly* 2005 Fall; 39(3): 599-632. Subject: 18.5.4

Crockin, Susan L. Reproduction, genetics and the law. *Reproductive BioMedicine Online [electronic]* 2005 June;

10(6): 692-704. Accessed: http://www.rbmonline.com/Article/1726 [2005 December 16]. Subject: 15.2

Crolla, Domenic A. Reflections on the legal, social, and ethical implications of pharmacogenomic research. *Jurimetrics* 2006 Spring; 46(3): 239-248. Subject: 15.1

Cromer, Lisa DeMarni; Freyd, Jennifer J.; Binder, Angela K.; DePrince, Anne P.; Becker-Blease, Kathryn. What's the risk in asking? Participant reaction to trauma history questions compared with reaction to other personal questions. *Ethics and Behavior* 2006; 16(4): 347-362. Subject: 18.5.1

Cross, MargaretAnn. The ethical way in a season of change. *Managed Care* 2005 December; 14(12): 22, 25-27. Subject: 9.3.2

Crow, Karine; Mathson, Lou; Steed, Alicia. Informed consent and truth-telling: cultural directions for healthcare providers. *Journal of Nursing Administration* 2000 March; 30(3): 148-152. Subject: 8.2

Crowinshield, Roy. The orthopaedic profession and industry: conflict or convergence of interests. *Clinical Orthopaedics and Related Research* 2003 July; (412): 8-13. Subject: 9.7

Csillag, Claudio. Brazil approves research with embryo stem cells [news]. *European Journal of Cancer* 2005 May; 41(8): 1102. Subject: 18.5.4

Cüer, Pierre. Can usable sequences extracted from the human genome be patented? = ¿Pueden patentarse secuencias utilizables extraídas del genoma humano? *Law and the Human Genome Review = Revista de Derecho y Genoma Humano* 1995 July-December; (3): 199-209. Subject: 15.8

Cui, Ke-Hui. Three concepts of cloning in human beings. *Reproductive BioMedicine Online [electronic]* 2005 July; 11(1): 16-17. Accessed: http://www.rbmonline.com/Article/1763 [2005 December 16]. Subject: 14.5

Culberson, John; Levy, Cari; Lawhorne, Larry. Do not hospitalize orders in nursing homes: a pilot study. *Journal of the American Medical Directors Association* 2005 January-February; 6(1): 22-26. Subject: 20.5.1

Cullen, David O'Donald. Nature versus nurture: eugenics. *Choice* 2005 November; 43(3): 405-413. Subject: 15.5

Cummings, Nicholas A. Ethics and the allocation of healthcare. *In:* O'Donohue, William; Ferguson, Kyle, eds. Handbook of Professional Ethics for Psychologists: Issues, Questions, and Controversies. Thousand Oaks, Calif.: SAGE Publications; 2003: 115-133. Subject: 9.4

Cummiskey, David. Confucian ethics: responsibilities, rights, and relationships. *Eubios Journal of Asian and International Bioethics* 2006 January; 16(1): 9-21. Subject: 8.1

Cundy, Paul R.; Hassey, Alan. To opt in or out of electronic patient records?: Isle of Wight and Scottish projects are not opt out schemes [letter]. *BMJ: British Medical Journal* 2006 July 15; 333(7559): 146. Subject: 8.3.1

Cupich, Blase J. Abortion and public policy: conditions for the debate. *America* 2006 September 11; 195(6): 19-20. Subject: 12.4.1

Curfman, Gregory D.; Morrissey, Stephen; Drazen, Jeffrey M. Expression of concern reaffirmed [editorial]. *New England Journal of Medicine* 2006 March 16; 354(11): 1193. Subject: 18.2

Curley, Duncan; Sharples, Andrew. Ethical questions to ponder in the European stem cell patent debate. *Journal of Biolaw and Business* 2006; 9(3): 12-16. Subject: 15.8

Curry, S.; Ravelingien, A.; Braeckman, J.; Mortier, F.; Mortier, E.; Kerremans, I. Living patients in a permanent vegetative state as legitimate research subjects [letter and reply]. *Journal of Medical Ethics* 2006 October; 32(10): 606-607, 609-611. Subject: 20.2.1

Curtin, Leah L. Ethics in informatics: the intersection of nursing, ethics, and information technology. *Nursing Administration Quarterly* 2005 October-December; 29(4): 349-352. Subject: 1.3.12

Curtin, Leah L.; Arnold, Lauren. A framework for analysis, Part II. *Nursing Administration Quarterly* 2005 July-September; 29(3): 288-291. Subject: 4.1.3

Curtis, Joy. Multidisciplinary input on institutional ethics committees: a nursing perspective. *QRB: Quality Review Bulletin* 1984 July; 10(7): 199-202. Subject: 20.3.2

Cussac, José Luis González. Genetic manipulation and assisted reproduction in Spain's penal reform = Manipulación genética y reproducción asistida en la reforma penal española. *Law and the Human Genome Review = Revista de Derecho y Genoma Humano* 1995 July-December; (3): 67-97. Subject: 14.1

Custers, Bart. The risks of epidemiological data mining. *In:* Tavani, Herman T., ed. Ethics, Computing, and Genomics. Sudbury, MA: Jones and Bartlett; 2006: 153-165. Subject: 7.1

Cusveller, Bart. Cut from the right wood: spiritual and ethical pluralism in professional nursing practice. *Journal of Advanced Nursing* 1998 August; 28(2): 266-273. Subject: 4.1.3

Cutter, Anthony Mark. Genetic databases and what the rat won't do: what is dignity at law? *In:* Árnason, Gardar; Nordal, Salvör; Árnason, Vilhjálmur, eds. Blood and Data: Ethical, Legal and Social Aspects of Human Genetic Databases. Reykjavík: University of Iceland Press; 2004: 217-222. Subject: 15.1

Cutter, Anthony Mark. To clear or convict? The role of genomics in criminal justice. *Genomics, Society and Policy* 2006 May; 2(1): 1-15. Subject: 15.1

Cutter, Mary Ann G. Managing genetic testing information: legal, ethical and social challenges. *Revista de*

See SUBJECT HEADING KEY FOR SECTION II on inside back cover.

533

Derecho Genoma Humano = Law and the Human Genome Review 1999 July-December; (11): 167-185. Subject: 15.3

Cyranoski, David. Australia lifts ban on cloning [news]. *Nature* 2006 December 14; 442(7121): 799. Subject: 18.5.4

Cyranoski, David. Hwang takes the stand at fraud trial [news]. *Nature* 2006 November 2; 444(7115): 12. Subject: 1.3.9

Cyranoski, David. Named and shamed [news]. *Nature* 2006 May 25; 441(7092): 392-393. Subject: 1.3.9

Cyranoski, David. No end in sight for stem-cell odyssey. *Nature* 2006 February 9; 439(7077): 658-659. Subject: 14.5

Cyranoski, David. Primates in the frame [news]. *Nature* 2006 December 14; 442(7121): 812-813. Subject: 22.2

Cyranoski, David. Verdict: Hwang's human stem cells were all fakes [news]. *Nature* 2006 January 12; 439(7073): 122-123. Subject: 1.3.9

Cyranoski, David; Check, Erika. Koreans admit disguising stem-cell lines [news]. *Nature* 2006 June 15; 441(7095): 790-791. Subject: 18.5.4

Czarkowski, Marek. The protection of patients' rights in clinical trials. *Science and Engineering Ethics* 2006 January; 12(1): 131-138. Subject: 18.2

Czech Republic. Public Defender of Rights / Verejný Ochránce Práv. Final Statement of the Public Defender of Rights in the Matter of Sterilisations Performed in Contravention of the Law and Proposed Remedial Measures. Brno, Czech Republic: Public Defender of Rights, 2005 December 23; 79 p. [Online]. Accessed: http://www.ochrance.cz/documents/doc1142289721.pdf [2006 September 7]. Subject: 11.3

D

d'Agincourt-Canning, Lori. Genetic testing for hereditary breast and ovarian cancer: responsibility and choice. *Qualitative Health Research* 2006 January; 16(1): 97-118. Subject: 15.3

D'Almeida, Michelle; Hume, Roderick F., Jr.; Lathrop, Anthony; Njoku, Adaku; Calhoun,Byron C. Perinatal hospice: family-centered care of the fetus with a lethal condition. *Journal of American Physicians and Surgeons* 2006 Summer; 11(2): 52-55. Subject: 20.4.2

da Silva, Paula Martinho. Genes and patents: will traditional law become outdated? = Genes y patentes: ¿estará desfasado el derecho tradicional? *Law and the Human Genome Review = Revista de Derecho y Genoma Humano* 1995 July-December; (3): 143-152. Subject: 15.8

Daar, Abdallah S.; Sheremeta, Lorraine. The science of stem cells: ethical, legal and social issues. *Experimental and Clinical Transplantation* 2003 December; 1(2): 139-146. Subject: 18.5.4

Dada, Mahomed A.; McQuoid-Mason, David J. Medico-legal aspects of pathology — current dilemmas regarding confidentiality and disclosure. *South African Medical Journal* 2005 November; 95(11): 875-877. Subject: 8.4

Dagg, Paul. Actual case outcome. *Journal of Ethics in Mental Health* 2006 November; 1(1): E10, 1 p. Subject: 8.3.4

Dagg, Paul. John has hepatitis and schizophrenia. *Journal of Ethics in Mental Health* 2006 November; 1(1): E7, 1 p. Subject: 8.3.4

Dahl, E.; Levy, N. The case for physician assisted suicide: how can it possibly be proven? *Journal of Medical Ethics* 2006 June; 32(6): 335-338. Subject: 20.7

Dahl, Edgar. No country is an island: comment on the House of Commons report Human Reproductive Technologies and the Law. *Reproductive BioMedicine Online [electronic]* 2005 July; 11(1): 10-11. Accessed: http://www.rbmonline.com/Article/1830 [2005 December 16]. Subject: 14.3

Dahl, Edgar. Preconception gender selection: a threat to the sex ratio? *Reproductive BioMedicine Online [electronic]* 2005 March; 10(Supplement 1): 116-118. Subject: 14.3

Dahl, Edgar; Hinsch, K.D.; Brosig, B.; Beutel, M. Attitudes towards preconception sex selection: a representative survey from Germany. *Reproductive BioMedicine Online [electronic]* 2004 December; 9(6): 600-603. Subject: 14.3

Dahl, Matthias. "Vollständig bildungs- und arbeitsunfähig" — Kinder- "Euthanasie" während des Nationalsozialismus und die Sterbehilfe-Debatte. *In:* Frewer, Andreas; Eickhoff, Clemens, eds. "Euthanasie" und die aktuelle Sterbehilfe-Debatte: Die historischen Hintergründe medizinischer Ethik. Frankfurt; New York: Campus; 2000: 144-176. Subject: 20.5.2

Dahlberg, John E.; Mahler, Christian C. The Poehlman case: running away from the truth. *Science and Engineering Ethics* 2006 January; 12(1): 157-173. Subject: 1.3.9

Dailard, Cynthia. Beyond the issue of pharmacist refusals: pharmacies that won't sell emergency contraception. *Guttmacher Report on Public Policy* 2005 August; 8(3): 10-12. Subject: 9.7

Dailard, Cynthia. What Lawrence v. Texas says about the history and future of reproductive rights. *Fordham Urban Law Journal* 2004 March; 31(3): 717-723. Subject: 12.4.1

Dalton, Kevin J. Refusal of interventions to protect the life of the viable fetus—a case-based Transatlantic overview. *Medico-Legal Journal* 2006; 74(Part 1): 16-24. Subject: 9.5.5

Dalton, Rex. Trauma trials leave ethicists uneasy [news]. *Nature* 2006 March 23; 440(7083): 390-391. Subject: 18.3

Daly, Barbara J. Pediatric informed consent and assent. *In:* Fedor, Carol A.; Cola, Philip A.; Pierre, Christine, eds.

Responsible Research: A Guide for Coordinators. London; Chicago, IL: Remedics; 2006: 79-92. Subject: 18.5.2

Damschen, Gregor; Gómez-Lobo, Alfonso; Schönecker, Dieter. Sixteen days? A reply to B. Smith and B. Brogaard on the beginning of human individuals [response]. *Journal of Medicine and Philosophy* 2006 April; 31(2): 165-175. Subject: 4.4

Dan, N.G. Professional responsibility: the ethical argument for expert evidence. *Journal of Clinical Neuroscience* 1996 July; 3(3): 216-219. Subject: 7.3

Dane, Francis C.; Parish, David C. Ethical issues in registry research: in-hospital resuscitation as a case study. *Journal of Empirical Research on Human Research Ethics* 2006 December; 1(4): 69-76. Subject: 20.5.1

Danerek, Margaretha; Uden, Giggi; Dykes, Anna-Karin. Sympathetic responsibility in ethically difficult situations. *Acta Obstetricia Gynecologica Scandinavica* 2005 December; 84(12): 1164-1171. Subject: 9.5.5

Daniel, Caroline. Locking the sick out in the cold. *New Statesman (London, England: 1996)* 1997 February 21; 126: 22-23. Subject: 15.3

Daniels, A.U. Dan. Ethics Education at the engineering/medicine interface. *Journal of Investigative Surgery* 1992 July-September; 5(3): 209-218. Subject: 7.2

Daniels, Ken. Ethical considerations in professionals' contribution to policy development in assisted human reproduction. *In:* Sang-yong, Song; Young-Mo, Koo; Macer, Darryl R.J., eds. Asian Bioethics in the 21st Century. Christchurch, NZ: Eubios Ethics Institute, 2002: 358-362. Subject: 14.1

Daniels, Ken. Genetics and artificial procreation in New Zealand. *In:* Meulders-Klein, Marie-Thérèse; Deech, Ruth; Vlaardingerbroek, Paul, eds. Biomedicine, the Family and Human Rights. New York: Kluwer Law International, 2002: 123-132. Subject: 14.1

Daniels, Norman. Decisions about access to health care and accountability for reasonableness. *Journal of Urban Health* 1999 June; 76(2): 176-191. Subject: 9.2

Daniels, Norman. Equity and population health: toward a broader bioethics agenda. *Hastings Center Report* 2006 July-August; 36(4): 22-35. Subject: 9.4

Daniels, Norman. Toward ethical review of health system transformations. *American Journal of Public Health* 2006 March; 96(3): 447-451. Subject: 9.1

Daniels, Norman. Why justice is good for our health. *In:* Lolas Stepke, Fernando; Agar Corbinos, Lorenzo, eds. Interfaces Between Bioethics and the Empirical Social Sciences. Buenos Aires, Argentina: World Health Organization; 2002: 37-52. Subject: 9.1

Daniels, Norman; Flores, Walter; Pannarunothai, Supasit; Ndumbe, Peter N.; Bryant, John H.; Ngulube, T.J.; Wang, Yuankun. An evidence-based approach to benchmarking the fairness of health-sector reform in developing countries. *Bulletin of the World Health Organization* 2005 July; 83(7): 534-540. Subject: 9.1

Danino, Alain Michel; Danino, Isabelle Weber; Moutel, Gregoire; Hervé, Christian; Malka, Gabriel. Non-life-saving human composite allograft: ethical considerations [letter]. *Plastic and Reconstructive Surgery* 2005 January; 115(1): 342- 343. Subject: 19.1

Danis, Marion; Lavizzo-Mourey, Risa. Respecting diversity. *In:* Morrison, R. Sean; Meier, Diane E.; Capello, Carol, eds. Geriatric Palliative Care. New York: Oxford University Press; 2003: 79-90. Subject: 9.5.4

Danish Committee on Scientific Dishonesty. Case of plagiarism: work originating from Denmark, translated into Polish and published in a Polish Journal. Four Polish scientists guilty of scientific dishonesty. *Danish Medical Bulletin* 1996 September; 43(4): 367. Subject: 1.3.9

Darmoni, S.J.; Le Duff, F.; Joubert, M.; Le Beux, P.; Fieschi, M.; Weber, J.; Benichou, J. A preliminary study to assess a French code of ethics for health teaching resources on the Internet. *Studies in Health Technology and Informatics* 2002; 90: 621- 626. Subject: 7.2

Darnill, Stephanie; Gamage, Bernadette. The patient's journey: palliative care — a parent's view. *BMJ: British Medical Journal* 2006 June 24; 332(7556): 1494-1495. Subject: 20.4.2

Darnovsky, Marcy; Jesudason, Sujatha. Sex selection. *In:* Mitcham, Carl, ed. Encyclopedia of Science, Technology, and Ethics. Farmington Hills, MI: Thomson/Gale, 2005: 1758-1761. Subject: 14.3

Darr, Kurt. Terri Schindler Schiavo: end-game. *Hospital Topics* 2005 Spring; 83(2): 29-31. Subject: 20.5.1

Daskalopoulou, Stella S.; Mikhailidis, Dimitri P.; Jacobs, Adam. Exorcising ghosts and unwelcome guests [letters]. *Annals of Internal Medicine* 2006 January 17; 144(2): 149. Subject: 1.3.7

Daugherty, Christopher K.; Fitchett, George; Murphy, Patricia E.; Peterman, Amy H.; Banik, Donald M.; Hlubocky, Fay; Tartaro, Jessica. Trusting God and medicine: spirituality in advanced cancer patients volunteering for clinical trials of experimental agents. *Psycho-Oncology* 2005 February; 14(2): 135-146. Subject: 18.5.1

Dauphinee, W. Dale; Frecker, Richard C. Routinely collected educational data: challenges to ethics and to privacy. *Medical Education* 2005 September; 39(9): 877-879. Subject: 1.3.9

Dausset, Jean. Bioethics and responsibility = Bioética y responsabilidad. *Law and the Human Genome Review = Revista de Derecho y Genoma Humano* 1995 July-December; (3): 23-32. Subject: 2.1

Dauterive, Robin. Was my patient fortunate or forsaken? *Journal of Clinical Ethics* 2006 Spring; 17(1): 90-93. Subject: 8.1

See SUBJECT HEADING KEY FOR SECTION II on inside back cover.

535

Davenport, R. John. Drumming up dollars for stem cell research. *Cell* 2005 December 29; 123(7): 1169-1171. Subject: 18.5.4

Davey, Angela; French, Davina; Dawkins, Hugh; O'Leary, Peter. New mothers' awareness of newborn screening, and their attitudes to the retention and use of screening samples for research purposes. *Genomics, Society and Policy* 2005 December; 1(3): 41-51. Subject: 15.3

Davey, Gareth. Chinese university students' attitudes towards the ethical treatment and welfare of animals. *Journal of Applied Animal Welfare Science* 2006; 9(4): 289-297. Subject: 22.1

Davey, Monica. Ban on most abortions advances in South Dakota; most sweeping ban by a state in years. *New York Times* 2006 February 23; p. A14. Subject: 12.4.1

Davey, Monica. Missouri says it can't comply on executions. *New York Times* 2006 July 15; p. A1, A11. Subject: 20.6

Davey, Monica. South Dakota bans abortion, setting up a battle. *New York Times* 2006 March 7; p. A1, A14. Subject: 12.4.1

Davidhizar, Ruth. Benevolent power. *Journal of Practical Nursing* 2005 Winter; 55(4): 5-9. Subject: 8.1

Davidoff, Frank. Sex, politics, and morality at the FDA: reflections on the Plan B decision. *Hastings Center Report* 2006 March-April; 36(2): 20-25. Subject: 11.1

Davidoff, Frank; Trussell, James. Plan B and the politics of doubt. *JAMA: The Journal of the American Medical Association* 2006 October 11; 296(14): 1775-1777. Subject: 11.1

Davidson, Graham. The ethics of confidentiality: introduction. *Australian Psychologist* 1995 November; 30(3): 153-157. Subject: 8.4

Davidson, Rosemary; Kitzinger, Jenny; Hunt, Kate. The wealthy get healthy, the poor get poorly? Lay perceptions of health inequalities. *Social Science and Medicine* 2006 May; 62(9): 2171-2182. Subject: 9.2

Davies, Christina; Collins, Rory. Confidentiality and consent in medical research: balancing potential risks and benefits of using confidential data. *BMJ: British Medical Journal* 2006 August 12; 333(7563): 349-351. Subject: 18.3

Davies, J.M. Disclosure [editorial]. *Acta Anaesthesiologica Scandinavica* 2005 July; 49(6): 725-727. Subject: 9.8

Davies, Keith G.; Wolf-Phillips, Jonathan. Scientific citizenship and good governance: implications for biotechnology. *Trends in Biotechnology* 2006 February; 24(2): 57-61. Subject: 5.3

Davion, Victoria. Coming down to earth on cloning: an ecofeminist analysis of homophobia in the current debate. *Hypatia: A Journal of Feminist Philosophy* 2006 Fall; 21(4): 58-76. Subject: 14.5

Davis, Carol. Live and let go. *Nursing Standard* 2005 October 26-November 1; 20(7): 16-17. Subject: 20.7

Davis, Eric A.; Maio, Ronald F. Ethical issues in prehospital research. *Prehospital and Disaster Medicine* 1993 January-March; 8(Supplement 1): S11-S14. Subject: 18.3

Davis, F. Daniel; Gianelli, Diane M. News from the President's Council on Bioethics. *Kennedy Institute of Ethics Journal* 2006 December; 16(4): 375-377. Subject: 2.4

Davis, John Jefferson. The moral status of the embryonic human: religious perspectives. *Ethics and Medicine* 2006 Spring; 22(1): 9-21. Subject: 9.5.8

Davis, John K. Surviving interests and living wills. *Public Affairs Quarterly* 2006 January; 20(1): 17-30. Subject: 20.5.4

Davis, Mellar P. Should experimental therapy be made available off-study for terminally ill patients? *Lancet Oncology* 2006 July; 7(7): 531-533. Subject: 20.4.1

Davis, Michael. Codes of ethics. *In:* Mitcham, Carl, ed. Encyclopedia of Science, Technology, and Ethics. Farmington Hills, MI: Thomson/Gale, 2005: 350-353. Subject: 6

Davis, Michael. Conflict of interest. *In:* Mitcham, Carl, ed. Encyclopedia of Science, Technology, and Ethics. Farmington Hills, MI: Thomson/Gale, 2005: 402-404. Subject: 1.3.9

Davis, Michael. Profession and professionalism. *In:* Mitcham, Carl, ed. Encyclopedia of Science, Technology, and Ethics. Farmington Hills, MI: Thomson/Gale, 2005: 1515-1519. Subject: 1.3.1

Davis, Philip M. The ethics of republishing: a case study of Emerald/MCB University Press journals. *Library Resources and Technical Services* 2005 April; 49(2): 72-78. Subject: 1.3.7

Davis, Terry C.; Holcombe, Randall F.; Berkel, Hans J.; Pramanik, Sumona; Divers, Stephen G. Informed consent for clinical trials: a comparative study of standard versus simplified forms. *Journal of the National Cancer Institute* 1998 May 6; 90(9): 668-674. Subject: 18.3

Davis, Walter. Failure to thrive or refusal to adapt? Missing links in the evolution from ethics committee to ethics program. *HEC (Healthcare Ethics Committee) Forum* 2006 December; 18(4): 291-297. Subject: 9.6

Davison, Sara N.; Simpson, Christy. Hope and advance care planning in patients with end stage renal disease: qualitative interview study. *BMJ: British Medical Journal* 2006 October 28; 333(7574): 886-889. Subject: 20.5.4

Dawes, P.J.D.; O'Keefe, L.; Adcock, S. Informed consent: the assessment of two structured interview approaches compared to the current approach. *Journal of*

Subject = NRCBL Primary Classification Number; see inside front cover.

Laryngology and Otology 1992 May; 106(5): 420-424. Subject: 8.3.1

Dawes, Robyn M. The ethical implications of Paul Meehl's work on comparing clinical versus actuarial prediction methods. *Journal of Clinical Psychology* 2005 October; 61(10): 1245-1255. Subject: 9.4

Dawkins, Richard. Collateral damage, Part 1. *Free Inquiry* 2006 December-2007 January; 27(1): 12-14. Subject: 18.5.4

Dawson, A.; Garrard, E. In defense of moral imperialism: four equal and universal prima facie principles. *Journal of Medical Ethics* 2006 April; 32(4): 200-204. Subject: 2.1

Dawson, A.; Paul, Y. Mass public health programmes and the obligation of sponsoring and participating organisations. *Journal of Medical Ethics* 2006 October; 32(10): 580-583. Subject: 9.1

Dawson, Angus J. A messy business: qualitative research and ethical review. *Clinical Ethics* 2006 June; 1(2): 114-116. Subject: 18.4

Dawson, John. Fault-lines in community treatment order legislation. *International Journal of Law and Psychiatry* 2006 November-December; 29(6): 482-492. Subject: 17.1

Dawson, Karen; Trounson, Alan. Ethics of sex selection for family balancing. Why balance families? *Human Reproduction* 1996 December; 11(12): 2577-2578. Subject: 14.3

Dawson, K.J. The storage of human embryos. *Human Reproduction* 1997 January; 12(1): 6. Subject: 14.6

Dawson, Liza; Kass, Nancy E. Views of US researchers about informed consent in international collaborative research. *Social Science and Medicine* 2005 September; 61(6): 1211-1222. Subject: 18.3

Day, Lisa. Boundaries of double effect. *American Journal of Critical Care* 2005 July; 14(4): 334-337. Subject: 2.1

Day, Lisa. Distributive justice and personal responsibility for choices about health. *American Journal of Critical Care* 2006 January; 15(1): 96-98. Subject: 9.2

Day, Michael. Abortion should be made easier, charity says [news]. *BMJ: British Medical Journal* 2006 December 2; 333(7579): 1139. Subject: 12.4.1

Day, Michael. Agency criticises drug trial [news]. *BMJ: British Medical Journal* 2006 June 3; 332(7553): 1290. Subject: 18.1

Day, Michael. Duff's report calls for changes in way drugs are tested [news]. *BMJ: British Medical Journal* 2006 December 16; 333(7581): 1240. Subject: 18.6

Day, Michael. Experts say research on primates is vital to fight disease [news]. *BMJ: British Medical Journal* 2006 December 16; 333(7581): 1235. Subject: 22.2

Day, Michael. Industry association suspends drug company for entertaining doctors. *BMJ: British Medical Journal* 2006 February 18; 332(7538): 381. Subject: 9.7

Day, Michael. US scientists urge overhaul of clinical trials to restore confidence [news]. *BMJ: British Medical Journal* 2006 April 29; 332(7548): 991. Subject: 18.1

Dayton, Cornelia Hughes. Taking the trade: abortion and gender relations in an eighteenth-century New England village. *In:* Kennedy, Kathleen; Ullman, Sharon, eds. Sexual Borderlands: Constructing an American Sexual Past. Columbus: Ohio State University Press; 2003: 50-82. Subject: 12.4.1

de Ángel Yágüez, Ricardo. Prenatal genetic diagnosis and responsibility (Part I) = Diagnósticos genéticos prenatales y responsabilidad (Parte I). *Law and the Human Genome Review = Revista de Derecho y Genoma Humano* 1996 January-June; (4): 93-104. Subject: 15.2

De Anna, Gabriele. Cloning, begetting, and making children. *HEC (Healthcare Ethics Committee) Forum* 2006 June; 18(2): 172-188. Subject: 14.5

de Bouvet, Armelle; Deschamps, Claude; Boitte, Pierre; Boury, Dominique. Bioinformation: the philosophical and ethical issues at stake in a new modality of research practices. *Medicine, Health Care and Philosophy* 2006; 9(2): 201-209. Subject: 15.1

de Briey, Laurent. Euthanasie et autonomie = Euthanasia and autonomy. *Revue Philosophique de Louvain* 2003 February; 101(1): 26-42. Subject: 20.5.1

de Bruyn, Theodore; Elliott, Richard. Compulsory HIV testing after an occupational exposure. *HIV/AIDS Policy and Law Review* 2002 March; 6(3): 1, 24-31. Subject: 9.5.6

de Castro, Leonardo D.; Alvarez, Allen A. Playing God. *In:* Sang-yong, Song; Young-Mo, Koo; Macer, Darryl R.J., eds. Asian Bioethics in the 21st Century. Christchurch, NZ: Eubios Ethics Institute, 2002: 206-213. Subject: 5.1

de Champlain, J.; Patenaude, J. Review of a mock research protocol in functional neuroimaging by Canadian research ethics boards. *Journal of Medical Ethics* 2006 September; 32(9): 530-534. Subject: 18.2

De Cock, Kevin M. HIV testing in the era of treatment scale up. *Health and Human Rights: An International Journal* 2005; 8(2): 31-35. Subject: 9.5.6

de Costa, Caroline M. James Marion Sims: some speculations and a new position. *Medical Journal of Australia* 2003 June 16; 178(12): 660-663. Subject: 7.1

de Costa, Caroline M. Medical abortion for Australian women: it's time. *Medical Journal of Australia* 2005 October 3; 183(7): 378-380. Subject: 12.1

De Dijn, Herman. Euthanasia and pluralism. *In:* Schotsmans, Paul; Meulenbergs, Tom, eds. Euthanasia and Palliative Care in the Low Countries. Dudley, MA: Peeters, 2005: 227-238. Subject: 20.5.1

See SUBJECT HEADING KEY FOR SECTION II on inside back cover.

537

De Francesco, Laura. Genetic profiteering [news]. *Nature Biotechnology* 2006 August; 24(8): 888-890. Subject: 15.1

de Freitas, Sérgio Fernando Torres; Kovaleski, Douglas Francisco; Boing, Antonio Fernando; de Oliveira, Walter Ferreira. Stages of moral development among Brazilian dental students. *Journal of Dental Education* 2006 March; 70(3): 296-306. Subject: 7.2

de Grey, Aubrey D.N.J. The ethical status of efforts to postpone aging: a reply to Hurlbut [editorial]. *Rejuvenation Research* 2005 Fall; 8(3): 129-130. Subject: 20.5.1

De Jonge, Bram; Korthals, Michiel. Vicissitudes of benefit sharing of crop genetic resources: downstream and upstream. *Developing World Bioethics* 2006 December; 6(3): 144-157. Subject: 15.1

de Lacy, Sheryl. Embryo research: is disclosing commercial intent enough? *Human Reproduction* 2006 July; 21(7): 1662-1667. Subject: 18.5.4

de Leeuw, Richard; de Beaufort, Arnout J.; de Kleine, Martin J.; van Harrewijin, Karin; Kollée, Louis A.A. Foregoing intensive care treatment in newborn infants with extremely poor prognoses: a study in four neonatal intensive care units in the Netherlands. *Journal of Pediatrics* 1996 November; 129(5): 661-666. Subject: 20.5.2

de Melo-Martín, Inmaculada. Assisted reproduction technology. *In:* Mitcham, Carl, ed. Encyclopedia of Science, Technology, and Ethics. Farmington Hills, MI: Thomson/Gale, 2005: 123-125. Subject: 14.1

de Melo-Martín, Inmaculada. Furthering injustices against women: genetic information, moral obligations, and gender. *Bioethics* 2006 November; 20(6): 301-307. Subject: 15.3

de Melo-Martín, Inmaculada. Genetic research and technology. *In:* Mitcham, Carl, ed. Encyclopedia of Science, Technology, and Ethics. Farmington Hills, MI: Thomson/Gale, 2005: 841-849. Subject: 15.1

de Melo-Martín, Inmaculada; Briggle, Adam. Birth control. *In:* Mitcham, Carl, ed. Encyclopedia of Science, Technology, and Ethics. Farmington Hills, MI: Thomson/Gale, 2005: 232-237. Subject: 11.1

de Melo-Martín, Inmaculada; Hanks, Craig. Genetics technologies and women: the importance of context. *Bulletin of Science, Technology and Society* 2001 October 1; 21(5): 354-360. Subject: 15.1

de Meyrick, Julian. Approval procedures and passive consent considerations in research among young people. *Health Education* 2005; 105(4): 249-258. Subject: 18.5.2

de Mol, B.A.J.M. New surgical techniques and informed consent — safety first. *Acta Chirurgica Belgica* 2000 August; 100(4): 177-182. Subject: 8.3.1

de Ortúzar, M.G.; Soratti, C.; Velez, I. Bioethics and organ transplantation. *Transplantation Proceedings* 1997 December; 29(8): 3627-3630. Subject: 19.5

de Rosnay, Joël. Biology, power and responsibility. *Diogenes (International Council for Philosophy and Humanistic Studies)* 1980 Spring; (109): 77-91. Subject: 15.1

De Simone, F.; Serratosa, J. Biotechnology, animal health and animal welfare within the framework of European Union legislation. *Revue Scientifique et Technique* 2005 April; 24(1): 89-99. Subject: 22.2

de Sola, Carlos. Privacy and genetic data cases of conflict (I) = Privacidad y datos genéticos. Situaciones de conflicto (I). *Law and the Human Genome = Revista de Derecho y Genoma Humano* 1994 July-December; (1): 173-184. Subject: 15.1

de Vries, R. Ethical concepts regarding the genetic engineering of laboratory animals. *Medicine, Health Care and Philosophy* 2006; 9(2): 211-225. Subject: 15.1

De Vries, Raymond G. Toward a sociology of bioethics [review of Strangers at the Bedside: A History of How Law and Bioethics Transformed Medical Decision Making by David J. Rothman; All Gods Mistakes: Genetic Counseling in a Pediatric Hospital by Charles L. Bosk; Intensive Care: Medical Ethics and the Medical Profession by Robert Zussman; Deciding Who Lives: Fateful Choices in the Intensive-Care Nursery by Renée R. Anspach]. *Qualitative Sociology* 1995 Spring; 18(1): 119-128. Subject: 2.1

De Vries, Raymond; Anderson, Melissa S.; Martinson, Brian C. Normal misbehavior: scientists talk about the ethics of research. *Journal of Empirical Research on Human Research Ethics* 2006 March; 1(1): 43-50. Subject: 1.3.9

De Vries, Raymond; Elliott, Carl. Why disclosure? [editorial]. *JGIM: Journal of General Internal Medicine* 2006 September; 21(9): 1003-1004. Subject: 1.3.9

de Vries, Rob. Genetic engineering and the integrity of animals. *Journal of Agricultural and Environmental Ethics* 2006; 19(5): 469-493. Subject: 15.1

de Wert, Guido. Cascade screening: whose information is it anyway? *European Journal of Human Genetics* 2005 April; 13(4): 397-398. Subject: 15.3

de Wert, Guido. The use of human embryonic stem cells for research: an ethical evaluation. *In:* Rees, Dai; Rose, Steven, eds. The New Brain Sciences: Perils and Prospects. New York: Cambridge University Press; 2004: 213-222. Subject: 18.5.4

de Wolf, Virginia A.; Sieber, Joan E.; Steel, Philip M.; Zarate, Alvan O. Part II: HIPAA and disclosure risk issues. *IRB: Ethics and Human Research* 2006 January-February; 28(1): 6-11. Subject: 8.4

de Wolf, Virginia A.; Sieber, Joan E.; Steel, Philip M.; Zarate, Alvan O. Part III: meeting the challenge when data sharing is required. *IRB: Ethics and Human Research* 2006 March-April; 28(2): 10- 15. Subject: 8.4

Subject = NRCBL Primary Classification Number; see inside front cover.

De Young, Paul; Ladenheim, Kala. Hospital-acquired infection disclosure gains momentum. *NCSL Legisbrief* 2005 October; 13(42): 1-2. Subject: 9.8

Dean, Wesley; Scott, H. Morgan. Emergent infectious diseases. *In:* Mitcham, Carl, ed. Encyclopedia of Science, Technology, and Ethics. Farmington Hills, MI: Thomson/Gale, 2005: 610-614. Subject: 9.1

DeAngelis, Catherine D. The influence of money on medical science [editorial]. *JAMA: The Journal of the American Medical Association* 2006 August 23-30; 296(8): 996-998. Subject: 1.3.9

DeAngelis, Catherine D.; Drazen, Jeffrey M.; Frizelle, Frank A.; Haug, Charlotte; Hoey, John; Horton, Richard; Kotzin, Sheldon; Laine, Christine; Marusic, Ana; Overbeke, A. John P.M.; Schroeder, Torben V.; Sox, Hal C.; Van Der Weyden, Martin B. Clinical trial registration — a statement from the International Committee of Medical Journal Editors. *Archives of Dermatology* 2005 January; 141(1): 76-77. Subject: 18.6

Deaton, Angus. Equity and population health [letter]. *Hastings Center Report* 2006 September-October; 36(5): 5-6. Subject: 9.1

DeBakey, Michael E. The role of government in health care: a societal issue [editorial]. *American Journal of Surgery* 2006 February; 191(2): 145-157. Subject: 9.1

Deber, Raisa B.; Kraetschmer, Nancy; Urowitz, Sara; Sharpe, Natasha. Patient, consumer, client, or customer: what do people want to be called? *Health Expectations* 2005 December; 8(4): 345-351. Subject: 8.1

Debiec, Jacek; Altemus, Margaret. Toward a new treatment for traumatic memories. *Cerebrum: The DANA Forum on Brain Science* 2006 September: 2-11. Subject: 17.1

DeBow, Suzanne; Bubela, Tania; Caulfield, Timothy. Stem cells, politics and the progress paradigm. *Health Law Review* 2006; 15(1): 50-52. Subject: 18.5.4

Debrock, Sophie; Spiessens, Carl; Meuleman, Christel; Segal, Luc; De Loecker, Peter; Meeuwis, Luc; D'Hooghe, Thomas M. New Belgian legislation regarding the limitation of transferable embryos in in vitro fertilization cycles does not significantly influence the pregnancy rate but reduces the multiple pregnancy rate in a threefold way in the Leuven University Fertility Center. *Fertility and Sterility* 2005 May; 83(5): 1572-1574. Subject: 14.4

DeCew, Judith Wagner. Alternatives for protecting privacy while respecting patient care and public health needs. *Ethics and Information Technology* 1999; 1(4): 249-255. Subject: 8.4

DeCew, Judith Wagner. Privacy and policy for genetic research. *Ethics and Information Technology* 2004; 6(1): 5-14. Subject: 15.1

DeCew, Judith Wagner. Privacy and policy for genetic research. *In:* Tavani, Herman T., ed. Ethics, Computing,

and Genomics. Sudbury, MA: Jones and Bartlett; 2006: 121-135. Subject: 15.1

DeCoster, Barry. Avian influenza and the failure of public rationing discussions. *Journal of Law, Medicine and Ethics* 2006 Fall; 34(3): 620-623. Subject: 9.4

DeCoursey, Thomas E. It's difficult to publish contradictory findings [letter]. *Nature* 2006 February 16; 439(7078): 784. Subject: 1.3.9

DeDonato, David M.; Mathis, Rick D. Religious and cultural considerations in military healthcare. *In:* Beam, Thomas E.; Sparacino, Linette R.; Pellegrino, Edmund D.; Hartle, Anthony E.; Howe, Edmund G., eds. Military Medical Ethics. Volume 2. Washington, DC: TMM Publications, Borden Institute, Walter Reed Army Medical Center; 2003: 687-718. Subject: 9.1

Deech, Ruth. A reply from the chairman of the HFEA. *Human Reproduction* 1997 January; 12(1): 5-6. Subject: 14.6

Degen, Peter A. Reflections of a Protestant Christian on the history of informed consent in Germany. *In:* Döring, Ole; Chen, Renbiao, eds. Advances in Chinese Medical Ethics: Chinese and International Perspectives. Hamburg: Institut für Asienkunde; 2002: 73-84. Subject: 8.3.1

Degos, L. Conflicts of interest [editorial]. *Hematology Journal* 2001; 2(2): 69. Subject: 7.3

DeGrazia, David. Moral status, human identity, and early embryos: a critique of the President's approach. *Journal of Law, Medicine, and Ethics* 2006 Spring; 34(1): 49-57. Subject: 2.4

DeGrazia, David. On the question of personhood beyond homo sapiens. *In:* Singer, Peter, ed. In Defense of Animals: The Second Wave. Malden, MA: Blackwell Pub.; 2006: 40-53. Subject: 22.1

DeGrazia, David. Regarding animals: mental life, moral status, and use in biomedical research: an introduction to the special issue. *Theoretical Medicine and Bioethics* 2006; 27(4): 277-284. Subject: 22.2

Degregori, Thomas R. Genetically modified foods. *In:* Mitcham, Carl, ed. Encyclopedia of Science, Technology, and Ethics. Farmington Hills, MI: Thomson/Gale, 2005: 836-838. Subject: 15.1

Deibert, Ryan J.; Goldbaum, Gary; Parker, Theodore R.; Hagan, Holly; Marks, Robert; Hanrahan, Michael; Thiede, Hanne. Increased access to unrestricted pharmacy sales of syringes in Seattle- King County, Washington: structural and individual-level changes, 1996 versus 2003. *American Journal of Public Health* 2006 August; 96(8): 1347-1353. Subject: 9.5.9

Dein, Simon. Race, culture and ethnicity in minority research: a critical discussion. *Journal of Cultural Diversity* 2006 Summer; 13(2): 68-75. Subject: 18.5.1

Dein, Simon; Bhui, Kamaldeep. Issues concerning informed consent for medical research among non-westernized ethnic minority patients in the UK. *Journal of the*

See SUBJECT HEADING KEY FOR SECTION II on inside back cover.

Royal Society of Medicine 2005 August; 98(8): 354-356. Subject: 18.3

Dekkers, Wim. Die Euthanasiedebatte und die Nazi-Ideologie: eine philosophische Analyse einer Diskussion. *In:* Gordijn, Bert; ten Have, Henk, eds. Medizinethik und Kultur: Grenzen medizinischen Handelns in Deutschland und den Niederlanden. Stuttgart: Frommann-Holzboog; 2000: 345-373. Subject: 20.5.1

del Carmen, Marcella G.; Joffe, Steven. Informed consent for medical treatment and research: a review. *Oncologist* 2005 September; 10(8): 636-641. Subject: 8.3.1

del Pozo, Pablo Rodríguez; Fins, Joseph J. Iberian influences on pan-American bioethics: bringing Don Quixote to our shores. *CQ: Cambridge Quarterly of Healthcare Ethics* 2006 Summer; 15(3): 225-238. Subject: 2.1

Delaney, Brendan. Commentary: is society losing control of the medical research agenda. *BMJ: British Medical Journal* 2006 May 6; 332(7549): 1063-1064. Subject: 5.3

Delbanco, Suzanne F.; Stewart, Felicia H.; Koenig, Jacqueline D.; Parker, Molly L.; Hoff, Tina; McIntosh, Mary. Are we making progress with emergency contraception? Recent findings on American adults and health professionals. *Journal of the American Medical Women's Association* 1998 Fall; 53(5, Supplement 2): 242-246. Subject: 11.1

DeLegge, Mark H.; McClave, Stephen A.; DiSario, James A.; Baskin, William N.; Brown, Russel D.; Fang, John C.; Ginsberg Gregory G. Ethical and medicolegal aspects of PEG-tube placement and provision of artificial nutritional therapy. *Gastrointestinal Endoscopy* 2005 December; 62(6): 952-959. Subject: 20.5.1

DeLisi, Lynn E.; Bertisch, Hilary. A preliminary comparison of the hopes of researchers, clinicians, and families for the future ethical use of genetic findings on schizophrenia. *American Journal of Medical Genetics Part B* 2006 January 5; 141(1): 110-115. Subject: 15.3

Delkeskamp-Hayes, Corinna. Freedom-costs of canonical individualism: enforced euthanasia tolerance in Belgium and the problem of European liberalism. *Journal of Medicine and Philosophy* 2006 August; 31(4): 333-362. Subject: 20.5.1

Delkeskamp-Hayes, Corinna. Why patients should give thanks for their disease: traditional Christianity on the joy of suffering. *Christian Bioethics* 2006 August; 12(2): 213-228. Subject: 4.2

Dell'Oro, Roberto. Interpreting clinical judgment: epistemological notes on the praxis of medicine. *In:* Viafora, Corrado, ed. Clinical Bioethics: A Search for the Foundations. Dordrecht: Springer, 2005: 155-168. Subject: 9.1

Delmonico, Francis L.; Burdick, James F. Maximizing the success of transplantation with kidneys from older do-

nors [editorial]. *New England Journal of Medicine* 2006 January 26; 354(4): 411-413. Subject: 19.3

Delmonico, Francis L.; Graham, W.K. Direction of the Organ Procurement and Transplantation Network and United Network for Organ Sharing regarding the oversight of live donor transplantation and solicitation for organs. *American Journal of Transplantation* 2006 January; 6(1): 37-40. Subject: 19.5

DelSignore, Jeanne L. Current guidelines regarding industry-sponsored continuing medical education. *Clinical Orthopaedics and Related Research* 2003 July; (412): 21-27. Subject: 7.2

DeMarco, Joseph P.; Ford, Paul J. Balancing in ethical deliberation: superior to specification and casuistry. *Journal of Medicine and Philosophy* 2006 October; 31(5): 483-497. Subject: 2.1

DeMarco, Joseph P.; Markman, Maurie. The research misconception. *International Journal of Applied Philosophy* 2004 Fall; 18(2): 241-252. Subject: 18.1

DeMaria, Anthony N. Publication bias and journals as policemen. *Journal of the American College of Cardiology* 2004 October 19; 44(8): 1707-1708. Subject: 1.3.7

Demers, Gilles; Griffin, Gilly; De Vroey, Guy; Haywood, Joseph R.; Zurlo, Joanne. Harmonization of animal care and use guidance. *Science* 2006 May 5; 312(5774): 700-701. Subject: 22.2

DeMets, David L.; Fleming, Thomas R. The independent statistician for data monitoring committees. *Statistics in Medicine* 2004 May 30; 23(10): 1513-1517. Subject: 18.2

DeMets, David; Califf, Robert; Dixon, Dennis; Ellenberg, Susan; Fleming, Thomas; Held, Peter; Julian, Desmond; Kaplan, Richard; Levine, Robert; Neaton, James; Packer, Milton; Pocock, Stuart; Rockhold, Frank; Seto, Belinda; Siegel, Jay; Snapinn, Steve; Stump, David; Temple, Robert; Whitley, Richard. Issues in regulatory guidelines for data monitoring committees. *Clinical Trials* 2004; 1(2): 162-169. Subject: 18.2

den Exter, André P. The European Court of Justice and the Keller case: a bridge too far? *Medicine and Law: The World Association for Medical Law* 2006 June; 25(2): 267-271. Subject: 9.2

Denker, H.-W. Potentiality of embryonic stem cells: an ethical problem even with alternative stem cell sources. *Journal of Medical Ethics* 2006 November; 32(11): 665-671. Subject: 18.5.4

Denker, Hans-Werner. Early human development: new data raise important embryological and ethical questions relevant for stem cell research. *Naturwissenschaften* 2004 January; 91(1): 1-21. Subject: 18.5.4

Subject = NRCBL Primary Classification Number; see inside front cover.

Dennehy, Christine. Analysis of patients' rights: dementia and PEG insertion. *British Journal of Nursing* 2006 January 12-25; 15(1): 18-20. Subject: 20.5.1

Dennis, Carina. Australia considers changing laws to allow therapeutic cloning [news]. *Nature Medicine* 2006 February; 12(2): 156. Subject: 18.5.1

Dennis, Carina. Cloning: what now? Mining the secrets of the egg. *Nature* 2006 February 9; 439(7077): 652-655. Subject: 14.5

Dennis, William J.; Furton, Edward J. Personhood and the impaired infant. *Ethics and Medics* 2006 November; 31(11): 1-2. Subject: 4.4

Denny, Colleen C.; Emanuel, Ezekiel J. "Physician-assisted suicide among Oregon cancer patients": a fading issue. *Journal of Clinical Ethics* 2006 Spring; 17(1): 39-42. Subject: 20.7

Denton, David R. Ethical and legal issues related to telepractice. *Seminars in Speech and Language* 2003 November; 24(4): 313-322. Subject: 1.3.12

Denton, Jane; Traub, Tony. A summary of the workshop: handling ART consent. *Human Fertility (Cambridge)* 2005 September; 8(3): 167-168. Subject: 8.3.1

Derbyshire, Stuart W.G. Can fetuses feel pain? *BMJ: British Medical Journal* 2006 April 15; 332(7546): 909-912. Subject: 4.4

DeRenzo, Evan G. Individuals, systems, and professional behavior. *Journal of Clinical Ethics* 2006 Fall; 17(3): 275-288. Subject: 7.2

DeRenzo, Evan G.; Mokwunye, Nneka; Lynch, John J. Rounding: how everyday ethics can invigorate a hospital's ethics committee. *HEC (Healthcare Ethics Committee) Forum* 2006 December; 18(4): 319-331. Subject: 9.6

Derksen, Jim; Chochinov, Harvey Max. Disability and end-of-life care: let the conversation begin. *Journal of Palliative Care* 2006 Autumn; 22(3): 175-182. Subject: 9.5.1

Derse, Arthur R. Emergency research and consent: keeping the exception from undermining the rule. *American Journal of Bioethics* 2006 May-June; 6(3): 36-37; discussion W49-W50. Subject: 18.3

Derse, Arthur R. Limitation of treatment at the end-of-life: withholding and withdrawal. *Clinics in Geriatric Medicine* 2005 February; 21(1): 223-238. Subject: 20.5.1

Desai, Ravi V.; Krishnamurthy, Mahesh; Patel, Harish; Hoffman, David N. Postmortem sperm retrieval: an ethical dilemma [letter]. *American Journal of Medicine* 2004 June 15; 116(12): 858. Subject: 14.1

Deschepper, Reginald; Vander Stichele, Robert; Bernheim, Jan L.; De Keyser, Els; Van Der Kelen, Greta; Mortier, Freddy; Deliens, Luc. Communication on end-of-life decisions with patients wishing to die at home: the making of a guideline for GPs in Flanders, Bel-

gium. *British Journal of General Practice* 2006 January; 56(522): 14-19. Subject: 20.5.1

Detorie, Nicholas. All medical physicists entering the field should have a specific course on research and practice ethics in their educational background: against the proposition. *Medical Physics* 2003 December; 30(12): 3050-3051. Subject: 7.2

Deutsch, Erwin. Limitation of medical research in German law. *Revista de Derecho y Genoma Humano* 2005 July-December; (23): 15-29. Subject: 18.2

DeVeaux, Theresa E. Non-heart-beating organ donation: issues and ethics for the critical care nurse. *Journal of Vascular Nursing* 2006 March; 24(1): 17-21. Subject: 19.5

Deverell, A.S. The patient-physician relationship — a return to paternalism? *South African Medical Journal = Suid Afrikaanse Tydskrif Vir Geneeskunde* 2001 January; 91(1): 42-44. Subject: 8.1

Devereux, John. Re B and J (artificial insemination). *Journal of Law and Medicine* 1998 May; 5(4): 330-332. Subject: 14.2

Devictor, Denis J. Toward an ethics of communication among countries [editorial]. *Pediatric Critical Care Medicine* 2004 May; 5(3): 290-291. Subject: 20.5.2

Devictor, Denis J.; Nguyen, Duc Tinh. Forgoing life-sustaining treatments in children: a comparison between northern and southern European intensive care units. *Pediatric Critical Care Medicine* 2004 May; 5(3): 211-215. Subject: 20.5.2

DeVita, Michael A.; Wicclair, Mark; Swanson, Dennis; Valenta, Cindy; Schold, Clifford. Research involving the newly dead: an institutional response. *Critical Care Medicine* 2003; 31(Supplement 5): S385-S390. Subject: 18.5.1

Devlin, Richard F. Baby M.: the contractual legitimation of misogyny. *Reports of Family Law (3d)* 1988; 10: 4-29. Subject: 14.2

Devolder, K. What's in a name? Embryos, entities, and ANTities in the stem cell debate. *Journal of Medical Ethics* 2006 January; 32(1): 43-48. Subject: 18.5.4

Devolder, Katrien; Harris, John. Compromise and moral complicity in the embryonic stem cell debate. *In:* Athanassoulis, Nafsika, ed. Philosophical Reflections on Medical Ethics. New York: Palgrave Macmillan; 2005: 88-108. Subject: 18.5.4

Devolder, Katrien; Savulescu, Julian. The moral imperative to conduct embryonic stem cell and cloning research. *CQ: Cambridge Quarterly of Healthcare Ethics* 2006 Winter; 15(1): 7-21. Subject: 18.5.4

Dewey, Marc; Schagen, Udo; Eckart, Wolfgang U.; Schönenberger, Eva. Ernst Ferdinand Sauerbruch and his ambiguous role in the period of National Socialism. *Annals of Surgery* 2006 August; 244(2): 315-321. Subject: 7.1

See SUBJECT HEADING KEY FOR SECTION II on inside back cover.

541

Dhai, A. Research ethics review — protecting participants in research. *South African Medical Journal* 2005 August; 95(8): 595-597. Subject: 18.2

Dhondt, Jean-Louis. Implementation of informed consent for a cystic fibrosis newborn screening program in France: low refusal rates for optional testing. *Journal of Pediatrics* 2005 September; 147(3, Supplement): S106-S108. Subject: 9.5.7

di Norcia, Vincent. The ethics in human research ethics [editorial]. *Journal of Empirical Research on Human Research Ethics* 2006 June; 1(2): 1-2. Subject: 18.1

di Norcia, Vincent. Intellectual property and the commercialization of research and development. *Science and Engineering Ethics* 2005 April; 11(2): 203-219. Subject: 1.3.9

Diallo, Dapa A.; Doumbo, Ogobara K.; Plowe, Christopher V.; Wellems, Thomas E.; Emanuel, Ezekial J.; Hurst, Samia A. Community permission for medical research in developing countries. *Clinical Infectious Diseases* 2005 July 15; 41(2): 255-259. Erratum in: Clinical Infectious Diseases 2005 September 15; 41(6): 920. Subject: 18.3

Diamond, Eugene F. The licit use of methotrexate: managing extrauterine gestation. *Ethics and Medics* 2006 March; 31(3): 3. Subject: 9.7

Diamond, Eugene F. Terminal sedation. *Linacre Quarterly* 2006 May; 73(2): 172-175. Subject: 20.5.1

Diamond, Milton; Beh, Hazel Glenn. The right to be wrong: sex and gender decisions. *In:* Sytsma, Sharon E., ed. Ethics and Intersex. Dordrecht: Springer, 2006: 103-113. Subject: 10

Dickens, Bernard. The ethics of "ethics": black and white or shades of grey. *Journal of Ethics in Mental Health* 2006 November; 1(1): E3, 3 p. Subject: 17.1

Dickens, Bernard M. Ethical misconduct by abuse of conscientious objection laws. *Medicine and Law: The World Association for Medical Law* 2006 September; 25(3): 513-522. Subject: 8.1

Dickens, Bernard M. Genetics and artificial procreation in Canada. *In:* Meulders-Klein, Marie-Thérèse; Deech, Ruth; Vlaardingerbroek, Paul, eds. Biomedicine, the Family and Human Rights. New York: Kluwer Law International, 2002: 87-105. Subject: 15.1

Dickens, Bernard M.; Cook, R.J. Adolescents and consent to treatment. *International Journal of Gynecology and Obstetrics* 2005 May; 89(2): 179-184. Subject: 8.3.2

Dickens, Bernard M.; Serour, G.I.; Cook, R.J.; Qiu, R.Z. Sex selection: treating different cases differently. *International Journal of Gynecology and Obstetrics* 2005 August; 90(2): 171-177. Subject: 14.3

Dickenson, Donna. Gender and ethics committees: where's the 'different voice'? *Bioethics* 2006 June; 20(3): 115-124. Subject: 9.6

Dickenson, Donna. Human tissue and global ethics. *Genomics, Society and Policy* 2005 February; 1(1): 41-53. Subject: 19.5

Dickenson, Donna. Ownership, property and women's bodies. *In:* Widdows, Heather; Idiakez, Itziar Alkorta; Cirión, Aitziber Emaldi, eds. Women's Reproductive Rights. New York: Palgrave Macmillan; 2006: 17-32. Subject: 4.4

Dickenson, Donna L. The case for international ethics education. *In:* Tadd, Win, ed. Ethics in Nursing Education, Research and Management. New York: Palgrave Macmillan; 2003: 68-85. Subject: 4.1.1

Dickert, Neal W.; Sugarman, Jeremy. Community consultation: not the problem — an important part of the solution. *American Journal of Bioethics* 2006 May-June; 6(3): 26-28; discussion W46- W48. Subject: 18.6

Dickson-Swift, Virginia; James, Erica L.; Kippen, Sandra. Do university ethics committees adequately protect public health researchers? *Australian and New Zealand Journal of Public Health* 2005 December; 29(6): 576-579, discussion 580-582. Subject: 18.2

Diekema, Douglas S. Conducting ethical research in pediatrics: a brief historical overview and review of pediatric regulations. *Journal of Pediatrics* 2006 July; 149(1, Supplement): S3-S11. Subject: 18.5.2

Diekema, Douglas S. Involuntary sterilization of persons with mental retardation: an ethical analysis. *Mental Retardation and Developmental Disabilities Research Reviews* 2003; 9(1): 21-26. Subject: 11.3

Dierckx de Casterlé, B.; Verpoort, C.; De Bal, N.; Gastmans, C. Nurses' views on their involvement in euthanasia: a qualitative study in Flanders (Belgium). *Journal of Medical Ethics* 2006 April; 32(4): 187-192. Subject: 20.5.1

Dietrich, Frank. Causal responsibility and rationing in medicine. *Ethical Theory and Moral Practice* 2002 March; 5(1): 113-131. Subject: 19.6

Dietz, William H. Needed for NAASO: a code of ethics. *Obesity Research* 1994 March; 2(2): 164-165. Subject: 1.3.9

Dillon, Andrew; Littlejohns, Peter; Minhas, Rubin; Twisselmann, Birte. How much will Herceptin really cost? [letters]. *BMJ: British Medical Journal* 2006 December 9; 333(7580): 1219-1220. Subject: 9.4

Dillon, Kevin J. Significant developments in stem cell research. *Human Reproduction and Genetic Ethics: An International Journal* 2006; 12(1): 24-28. Subject: 18.5.4

Dimond, Bridgit. Colostomy: getting patient consent to treatment for surgery. *British Journal of Nursing* 2006 March 23-April 12; 15(6): 334-335. Subject: 8.3.1

Dimond, Bridgit. Consent to use complementary therapies on critical care wards. *British Journal of Nursing* 2006 September 14-27; 15(16): 893-894. Subject: 8.3.1

Subject = NRCBL Primary Classification Number; see inside front cover.

Dimond, Bridgit. Dermatology: obtaining patient consent in clinical trials. *British Journal of Nursing* 2006 May 11-24; 15(9): 500-501. Subject: 18.3

Dimond, Bridgit. Duty to report: legal implications of nurses stealing from patients. *British Journal of Nursing* 2006 November 23-December 13; 15(21): 1196-1197. Subject: 7.4

Dimond, Bridgit. The law regarding assisted dying for the terminally ill in the UK. *International Journal of Palliative Nursing* 2005 November; 11(11): 582-583. Subject: 20.7

Dimond, Bridgit. Legal aspects of continence: disclosure of a medical condition. *British Journal of Nursing* 2006 April 27-May 10; 15(8): 467-468. Subject: 8.4

Dimond, Bridgit. Mental capacity and professional advice in a patient with dysphagia. *British Journal of Nursing* 2006 May 25-June 7; 15(10): 574-575. Subject: 8.3.3

Dimond, Bridgit. Mental capacity requirement and a patient's right to die. *British Journal of Nursing* 2006 November 9-22; 15(20): 1130-1131. Subject: 20.5.1

Dimond, Bridgit. Rights, resources and health care [editorial]. *Nursing Ethics* 2006 July; 13(4): 335-336. Subject: 8.1

Dimond, Bridgit. What is the law if a patient refuses treatment based on the nurse's race? *British Journal of Nursing* 2006 October 26-November 8; 15(19): 1077-1078. Subject: 8.3.4

Dimond, Brigit. Specialist healthcare law: palliative care. *British Journal of Nursing* 2006 February 9-22; 15(3): 156-157. Subject: 20.5.4

Dinan, Michaela A.; Weinfurt, Kevin P.; Friedman, Joëlle Y.; Allsbrook, Jennifer S.; Gottlieb, Julie; Schulman, Kevin A.; Hall, Mark A.; Dhillon, Jatinder K.; Sugarman, Jeremy. Comparison of conflict of interest policies and reported practices in academic medical centers in the United States. *Accountability in Research* 2006 October-December; 13(4): 325-342. Subject: 1.3.9

Dinc, Leyla; Ulusoy, Mehlika Filiz. How nurses approach ethical problems in Turkey. *International Nursing Review* 1998 September-October; 45(5): 137-139. Subject: 4.1.3

Dines, Alison. Does the distinction between killing and letting die justify some forms of euthanasia? *Journal of Advanced Nursing* 1995 May; 21(5): 911-916. Subject: 20.5.1

Dinnett, Eleanor M.; Mungall, Moira M.B.; Gordon, Claire; Ronald, Elizabeth S.; Gaw, Allan. Offering results to research participants [letter]. *BMJ: British Medical Journal* 2006 March 4; 332(7540): 549-550. Subject: 18.2

Dinwiddie, Stephen H.; Hoop, Jinger; Gershon, Elliot S. Ethical issues in the use of genetic information. *International Review of Psychiatry* 2004 November; 16(4): 320-328. Subject: 15.6

Disilvestro, Russell. Not every cell is sacred: a reply to Charo [response]. *Bioethics* 2006 June; 20(3): 146-157. Subject: 18.5.4

Dissanayake, V.H.W.; Simpson, R.; Jayasekara, R.W. Attitudes towards the new genetic and assisted reproductive technologies in Sri Lanka: a preliminary report. *New Genetics and Society* 2002 March; 21(1): 65-74. Subject: 15.1

District of Columbia. *Laws, statutes, etc.* An act to amend the Human Rights Act of 1977 to prohibit employment discrimination based on genetic information; to prohibit an employer, employment agency, or labor organization from requesting or requiring a genetic test of, or administering a genetic test to, an employee or applicant for employment or membership; to prohibit an employer, employment agency, or labor organization from seeking to obtain, obtaining, or using genetic information of an employee or applicant for employment; to provide an exemption that allows the use of genetic testing or information with the written and informed consent of the employee or applicant for employment to determine the existence of a bona fide occupational qualification, investigate a workers' compensation or disability compensation claim, or determine an employee's susceptibility or exposure to potentially toxic substances in the workplace; to prohibit health benefit plans and health insurers from using genetic information as a condition of eligibility or in setting premium rates; and to prohibit health benefit plans and health insurers from requesting or requiring genetic testing [Approved: 3 January 2005]. Washington, DC: Council of the District of Columbia, 2005. 4 p. [Online]. Accessed: http://www.dccouncil.washington.dc.us/images/00001/20041217111559.pdf [2007 March 9]. Subject: 15.1

Ditto, Peter H.; Hawkins, Nikki A. Advance directives and cancer decision making near the end of life. *Health Psychology* 2005 July; 24(4 Supplement): S63-S70. Subject: 20.5.4

Dixon, Roz. Ethical research with participants who are deaf. *Bulletin of Medical Ethics* 2005 April; (207): 13-19. Subject: 18.5.1

Dixon-Woods, Mary; Jackson, Clare; Windridge, Kate C.; Kenyon, Sara. Receiving a summary of the results of a trial: qualitative study of participants' views. *BMJ: British Medical Journal* 2006 January 28; 332(7535): 206-209. Subject: 18.2

Dixon-Woods, Mary; Williams, S.J.; Jackson, C.J.; Akkad, A.; Kenyon, S.; Habiba, M. Why women consent to surgery, even when they don't want to: a qualitative study. *Clinical Ethics* 2006 September; 1(3): 153-158. Subject: 9.5.5

Djerassi, Carl. Technology and human reproduction: 1950-2050. *Journal of Molecular Biology* 2002 June 14; 319(4): 979-984. Subject: 14.1

See SUBJECT HEADING KEY FOR SECTION II on inside back cover.

543

Doaga, Octavian. Bioethical review in Romania. *In:* Beyleveld, D.; Townend, D.; Wright, J., eds. Research Ethics Committees, Data Protection and Medical Research in European Countries. Hants, England; Burlington, VT: Ashgate; 2005: 215-220. Subject: 18.2

Dobash, Tanya J. Physician-patient sexual contact: the battle between the state and the medical profession. *Washington and Lee Law Review* 1993 Fall; 50(4): 1725-1759. Subject: 7.4

Dobos, Marta; Dioszeghy, Csaba; Hauser, Balazs; Elo, Gabor. Determinant role of education in the ethical aspects of resuscitation: a German/Hungarian comparison. *Bulletin of Medical Ethics* 2005 October-November; (211): 25-30. Subject: 2.3

Dobson, Roger. Study shows that tobacco firms covertly hired scientists [news]. *BMJ: British Medical Journal* 2006 February 11; 332(7537): 321. Subject: 9.5.9

Dockhorn, Robert J. Orphan drugs provide needed treatment options. *Maryland Medicine* 2005 Winter; 6(1): 26-29. Subject: 9.7

Dodds, Susan; Thomson, Colin. Bioethics and democracy: competing roles of national bioethics organisations. *Bioethics* 2006 November; 20(6): 326-338. Subject: 2.4

Dodier, Nicolas. Transnational medicine in public arenas: AIDS treatments in the South. *Culture, Medicine and Psychiatry* 2005 September; 29(3): 285-307. Subject: 9.5.6

Doerflinger, Richard M. Human cloning and embryonic stem cell research after Seoul: examining exploitation, fraud, and ethical problems in the research. Testimony of Richard M. Doerflinger. *National Catholic Bioethics Quarterly* 2006 Summer; 6(2): 339-350. Subject: 18.5.4

Doerflinger, Richard M. The many casualties of cloning. *New Atlantis* 2006 Spring; 12: 60-70. Subject: 14.5

Doerflinger, Richard M. Washington insider. *National Catholic Bioethics Quarterly* 2006 Autumn; 6(3): 413-420. Subject: 18.5.4

Dolan, Timothy; Morlino, Robert; Doyle, Jim. Embryonic stem-cell research. *Origins* 2006 June 15; 36(5): 78-79. Subject: 18.5.4

Dolgin, Janet L. The evolution of the "patient": shifts in attitudes about consent, genetic information, and commercialization in health care. *Hofstra Law Review* 2005 Fall; 34(1): 137-183. Subject: 8.3.1

Dolgin, Janet L. Method, mediations, and the moral dimensions of preimplantation genetic diagnosis. *Cumberland Law Review* 2004-2005; 35(3): 519-542. Subject: 14.4

Dolgin, Janet L. Surrounding embryos: biology, ideology, and politics. *Health Matrix: The Journal of Law-Medicine* 2006 Winter; 16(1): 27-64. Subject: 4.4

Doll, Richard. The role of data monitoring committees. *In:* Duley, Lelia; Farrell, Barbara, eds. Clinical Trials. London: BMJ Books; 2002: 97-104. Subject: 18.2

Dombi, William A. Lessons from Schiavo —beyond the legal. *Caring* 2005 May; 24(5): 28-31. Subject: 20.5.1

Dombrowski, Daniel A. Is the argument from marginal cases obtuse? *Journal of Applied Philosophy* 2006; 23(2): 223-232. Subject: 22.2

Domen, Ronald E. Ethical issues in transfusion medicine: the safety of blood and hematopoietic stem cell donation. *Current Hematology Reports* 2005 November; 4(6): 465-469. Subject: 19.5

Donchin, Anne. Integrating bioethics and human rights: toward a global feminist approach. *In:* Tong, Rosemarie; Donchin, Anne; Dodds, Susan, eds. Linking Visions: Feminist Bioethics, Human Rights, and the Developing World. Lanham, MD: Rowman and Littlefield Publishers; 2004: 31-56. Subject: 2.1

Dondorp, Wybo; Legemaate, Johan; Van de Klippe, Hanneke. The retention of medical records: Dutch Health Council report in favour of statutory change. *European Journal of Health Law* 2004 September; 11(3): 273-282. Subject: 8.4

Donnelly, J. Can adults with cognitive impairment consent to take part in research? *Journal of Wound Care* 2004 July; 13(7): 257-262. Subject: 18.5.7

Donohoe, Martin T. Problem doctors: is there a system-level solution? [letter]. *Annals of Internal Medicine* 2006 June 6; 144(11): 862. Subject: 7.4

Donohue, John W. The stem cell debate: why is there an irreconcilable division between two groups of thoughtful and sympathetic people? *America* 2006 November 13; 195(15): 25-26. Subject: 18.5.4

Donohue, Julie. A history of drug advertising: the evolving roles of consumers and consumer protection. *Milbank Quarterly* 2006; 84(4): 659-699. Subject: 9.7

Donovan, Catherine. Genetics, fathers and families: exploring the implications of changing the law in favour of identifying sperm donors. *Social and Legal Studies* 2006 December; 15(4): 494-510. Subject: 14.2

Doran, E.; Kerridge, I.; McNeil, P.; Henry, David. Empirical uncertainty and moral contest: a qualitative analysis of the relationship between medical specialists and the pharmaceutical industry in Australia. *Social Science and Medicine* 2006 March; 62(6): 1510-1519. Subject: 7.3

Dorff, Elliot N. "These and those are the words of the living God": Talmudic sound and fury in shaping national policy. *In:* Guinn, David E., ed. Handbook of Bioethics and Religion. New York: Oxford University Press, 2006: 143-168. Subject: 2.1

Dorfman, Lori; Wallack, Lawrence; Woodruff, Katie. More than a message: framing public health advocacy to

---

change corporate practices. *Health Education and Behavior* 2005 June; 32(3): 320-336. Subject: 9.1

Döring, Ole. Human genetics and ethics in China. *Eubios Journal of Asian and International Bioethics* 1997 September; 7: 3 p. [Online]. Accessed: http://www.biol.tsukuba.ac.jp/~macer/EJ75/ej75c.html [2005 July 21]. Subject: 15.1

Döring, Ole. Moral development and education in medical ethics: an attempt at a Confucian aspiration. *In:* Döring, Ole; Chen, Renbiao, eds. Advances in Chinese Medical Ethics: Chinese and International Perspectives. Hamburg: Institut für Asienkunde; 2002: 178-194. Subject: 2.3

Döring, Ole. Teaching medical ethics in China, cultural, social and ethical issues. *In:* Sang-yong, Song; Young-Mo, Koo; Macer, Darryl R.J., eds. Asian Bioethics in the 21st Century. Christchurch, NZ: Eubios Ethics Institute, 2002: 255-261. Subject: 2.3

Doron, Israel. Caring for the dying: from a "negative" to a "positive" legal right to die at home. *Care Management Journals* 2005 Spring; 6(1): 22-28. Subject: 20.4.1

Dorr, David A.; Rowan, Belle; Weed, Matt; James, Brent; Clayton, Paul. Physicians' attitudes regarding patient access to electronic medical records. *AMIA Symposium Proceedings* 2003; p. 832. Subject: 8.4

Dörries, Andrea. Genetic prenatal testing: the doctor's and the patient's dilemma. *In:* Glasa, J., ed. Ethics of Human Genetics: Challenges of the (Post) Genomic Era. Bratislava, Slovak Republic: Charis [and] IMEB Foundation; 2002: 107-116. Subject: 15.2

Dorsey, Michael. The new eugenics. *World Watch* 2002 July-August; 15(4): 21-23. Subject: 15.5

Doss, Sonia D. Clinical trial trouble: not responsible for reporting. *Lab Animal* 2006 June; 35(6): 16. Subject: 22.2

Dougherty, Anne Hamilton. Letter to the editor: in defense of the PolyHeme® trial [letter]. *American Journal of Bioethics [Online]* 2006 September-October; 6(5): W35-W37. Subject: 19.4

Douglas, Alison. New role for ethics committees [letter]. *New Zealand Medical Journal* 1993 December 8; 106(969): 528-529. Subject: 18.2

Dow, William H.; Harris, Dean M.; Liu, Zhimei. Differential effectiveness in what are the causes? An example from the drive-through delivery laws. *Journal of Health Politics, Policy and Law* 2006 December; 31(6): 1107-1127. Subject: 9.2

Dowd, M. Denise. Breaching the contract: the ethics of nonpublication of research studies [editorial]. *Archives of Pediatrics and Adolescent Medicine* 2004 October; 158(10): 1014-1015. Subject: 1.3.7

Dowdy, D.W. Partnership as an ethical model for medical research in developing countries: the example of the "implementation trial". *Journal of Medical Ethics* 2006 June; 32(6): 357-360. Subject: 18.5.9

Dowling, Claudia. The visible man: the execution and electronic afterlife of Joseph Paul Jernigan. *Life* 1997 February 20: 41, 44. Subject: 7.2

Downie, Jocelyn. The Canadian agency for the oversight of research involving humans: a reform proposal. *Accountability in Research* 2006 January-March; 13(1): 75-100. Subject: 18.6

Doyal, Len. Dignity in dying should include the legalization of non-voluntary euthanasia [editorial]. *Clinical Ethics* 2006 June; 1(2): 65-67. Subject: 20.5.1

Doyle, Alan; Rawle, Frances; Greenaway, Peter. The UK Biobank. *In:* Sándor, Judit, ed. Society and Genetic Information: Codes and Laws in the Genetic Era. Budapest, Hungary; New York: CEU Press; 2003: 247-263. Subject: 15.1

Doyle, Florence F.; Graunke, Carrie L.; Hildebrandt, Douglas J.; Otto, Robert K.; St. George, Mark C. Act with ethics: Sarbanes-Oxley's role in helping to ensure supply chain integrity. *Materials Management in Health Care* 2005 July; 14(7): 35-40. Subject: 9.3.2

Drake, Amanda L.; Heilig, Lauren F.; Kozak, Katarzyna Z.; Hester, Eric J.; Dellavalle, Robert P. Researcher opinions on human embryonic stem cell issues. *Journal of Investigative Dermatology* 2004 March; 122(3): 855- 856. Subject: 18.5.4

Drane, James F. Stopping nutrition and hydration technologies: a conflict between traditional Catholic ethics and Church authority. *Christian Bioethics* 2006 April; 12(1): 11-28. Subject: 20.5.1

Drane, James F. What is bioethics? A history. *In:* Lolas Stepke, Fernando; Agar Corbinos, Lorenzo, eds. Interfaces Between Bioethics and the Empirical Social Sciences. Buenos Aires, Argentina: World Health Organization; 2002: 15-32. Subject: 2.2

Draper, Heather. Using case studies in clinical ethics. *Clinical Ethics* 2006 March; 1(1): 7-10. Subject: 2.3

Draper, Heather. Why there is no right to know one's genetic origin? *In:* Athanassoulis, Nafsika, ed. Philosophical Reflections on Medical Ethics. New York: Palgrave Macmillan; 2005: 70-87. Subject: 14.1

Draper, Heather; MacDiarmaid-Gordon, Adam; Strumidlo, Laura; Teuten, Bea; Updale, Eleanor. Virtual clinical ethics committee, case 3: confidentiality — what are our obligations to dead patients? *Clinical Ethics* 2006 September; 1(3): 121-129. Subject: 8.4

Draper, Heather; MacDiarmaid-Gordon, Adam; Strumidlo, Laura; Teuten, Bea; Updale, Eleanor. Virtual ethics committee, case 1: should our hospital have a policy of telling patients about near misses? *Clinical Ethics* 2006 March; 1(1): 11-17. Subject: 9.6

Draper, Heather; McDiarmaid-Gordon, Adam; Strumidlo, Laura; Teuten, Bea; Updale, Eleanor. Virtual ethics committee, case 2: can we restrain Ivy for the

See SUBJECT HEADING KEY FOR SECTION II on inside back cover.

545

benefit of others? *Clinical Ethics* 2006 June; 1(2): 68-75. Subject: 17.3

Draper, Heather; MacDiarmaid-Gordon, Adam; Strumidlo, Laura; Teuten, Bea; Updale, Eleanor. Virtual ethics committee, case 4: why can't a dead mother donate a kidney to her son? *Clinical Ethics* 2006 December; 1(4): 183-190. Subject: 19.5

Draper, H.; Ravelingien, A.; Braeckman, J.; Mortier, F.; Mortier, E.; Kerremans, I. Research and patients in a permanent vegetative state [letter and reply]. *Journal of Medical Ethics* 2006 October; 32(10): 607, 609-611. Subject: 20.2.1

Drazen, Jeffrey M. Volunteers at risk [editorial]. *New England Journal of Medicine* 2006 September 7; 355(10): 1060-1061. Subject: 18.1

Dreger, Alice Domurat. Intersex and human rights. *In:* Sytsma, Sharon E., ed. Ethics and Intersex. Dordrecht: Springer, 2006: 73-86. Subject: 10

Dreher, George K. Is this patient really incompetent? *American Family Physician* 2005 January 1; 71(1): 198-199. Subject: 8.3.3

Dreifus, Claudia. An economist examines the business of fertility: a conversation with Debora Spar. *New York Times* 2006 February 28; p. F5, F8. Subject: 14.1

Drenth, Pieter J.D. Responsible conduct in research. *Science and Engineering Ethics* 2006 January; 12(1): 13-21. Subject: 1.3.9

Drescher, Jack. Ethical concerns raised when patients seek to change same-sex attraction. *In:* Shidlo, Ariel; Schroeder, Michael; Drescher, Jack, eds. Sexual Conversion Therapy: Ethical, Clinical, and Research Perspectives. New York: Haworth Medical Press; 2001: 181-208. Subject: 10

Drescher, Jack. Ethical issues in treating gay and lesbian patients. *Psychiatric Clinics of North America* 2002 September; 25(3): 605-621. Subject: 17.1

Dresser, Rebecca. Investigational drugs and the Constitution. *Hastings Center Report* 2006 November-December; 36(6): 9-10. Subject: 18.5.7

Dresser, Rebecca. Pharmaceutical company gifts: from voluntary standards to legal demands. *Hastings Center Report* 2006 May-June; 36(3): 8-9. Subject: 9.7

Dresser, Rebecca. Private-sector research ethics: marketing or good conflicts management? The 2005 John L. Conley Lecture on Medical Ethics. *Theoretical Medicine and Bioethics* 2006; 27(2): 115-139. Subject: 18.1

Dresser, Rebecca. Research participants with mental disabilities: the more things change. . . . *In:* Frost, Lynda E.; Bonnie, Richard J., eds. The Evolution of Mental Health Law. Washington, DC: American Psychological Association; 2001: 57-74. Subject: 18.5.6

Dresser, Rebecca; Jansen, Lynn A. Protection of human subjects and scientific progress: can the two be reconciled? [letter and reply]. *Hastings Center Report* 2006 January-February; 36(1): 7, 9. Subject: 18.1

Dressler, Lynn G.; Juengst, Eric T. Thresholds and boundaries in the disclosure of individual genetic research results. *American Journal of Bioethics* 2006 November-December; 6(6): 18-20; author reply W10-W13. Subject: 15.1

Drew, Christopher; Dewan, Shaila. Accused doctor said to have faced chaos at New Orleans Hospital. *New York Times* 2006 July 20; p. A18. Subject: 7.4

Dreyfuss, Didier. Is it better to consent to an RCT or to care? Muetadeltaepsilonnualphagammaalphanu ("nothing in excess"). *Intensive Care Medicine* 2005 March; 31(3): 345-355. Subject: 18.3

Drought, Theresa S.; Koenig, Barbara A. "Choice" in end-of-life decision making: researching fact or fiction? *Gerontologist* 2002 October; 42(Special Issue 3): 114-128. Subject: 20.4.1

Druart, M.L. Euthanasia. *Acta Chirurgica Belgica* 2002 November-December; 102(6): 365- 367. Subject: 20.5.1

Druart, M.L.; Squifflet, J.-P. Informed consent: principles and recent developments. *Acta Chirurgica Belgica* 2000 August; 100(4): 175-176. Subject: 8.3.1

Du, Zhizheng. An ethical defense for withdrawing medical treatment. *In:* Döring, Ole; Chen, Renbiao, eds. Advances in Chinese Medical Ethics: Chinese and International Perspectives. Hamburg: Institut für Asienkunde; 2002: 306-314. Subject: 20.5.1

Dubler, Nancy Neveloff. Remaining faithful to the promises given: maintaining standards in changing times. *Seton Hall Law Review* 2002; 32(3): 563-572. Subject: 18.2

Dubner, Stephen; Levitt, Steven. Freakonomics. Flesh trade: why not let people sell their organs? *New York Times Magazine* 2006 July 9; p. 20, 21. Subject: 19.5

DuBois, James M. Ethics in behavioral and social science research. *In:* Iltis, Ana Smith, ed. Research Ethics. New York: Routledge, 2006: 102-120. Subject: 18.4

Dubois, Michel Y. The birth of an ethics charter for pain medicine [editorial]. *Pain Medicine* 2005 May-June; 6(3): 201-202. Subject: 6

Dubois, Michel Y.; Banja, John; Brushwood, David; Fine, Perry G.; Gallagher, Rollin M.; Gilbert, Hugh; Hamaty, Daniel; Jansen, Lynn; Joranson, David; Lebovits, Allen H.; Lippe, Philipp M.; Murphy, Timothy F.; Orr, Robert; Rich, Ben A. Ethics Charter from American Academy of Pain Medicine. *Pain Medicine* 2005 May-June; 6(3): 203-212. Subject: 6

Duckler, Lawrence. Moral conduct of an infantry medic [letter]. *Military Medicine* 1999 August; 164(8): R7. Subject: 21.2

Subject = NRCBL Primary Classification Number; see inside front cover.

Dudzinski, Denise M. Compounding vulnerability: pregnancy and schizophrenia. *American Journal of Bioethics [Online].* 2006 March-April; 6(2): W1-W14. Subject: 9.5.3

Dudzinski, Denise M.; Burke, Wylie. Practicing moral medicine: patient care to public health. *American Journal of Bioethics* 2006 March-April; 6(2): 75-76. Subject: 2.1

Dudzinski, Denise M.; Shannon, Sarah E. Competent patients' refusal of nursing care. *Nursing Ethics* 2006 November; 13(6): 608-621. Subject: 8.3.4

Dudzinski, Denise M.; Shannon, Sarah E.; Tong, Rosemarie. Competent refusal of nursing care [case study]. *Hastings Center Report* 2006 March-April; 36(2): 14-15. Subject: 9.5.1

Duff, Gordon. Expert scientific group on phase one clinical trials: interim report. United Kingdom: Expert Scientific Group on Phase One Clinical Trials, 2006 July 20: 71 p. [Online]. Accessed: http://www.dh.gov.uk/assetRoot/04/13/75/69/04137569.pdf [2006 September 12]. Subject: 18.6

Duffy, James. Rediscovering the meaning in medicine: lessons from the dying on the ethics of experience. *Palliative and Supportive Care* 2004 June; 2(2): 207-211. Subject: 20.4.1

Duffy, Sonia A.; Jackson, Frances C.; Schim, Stephanie M.; Ronis, David L.; Fowler, Karen E. Racial/ethnic preferences, sex preferences, and perceived discrimination related to end-of-life care. *Journal of the American Geriatrics Society* 2006 January; 54(1): 150-157. Subject: 20.3.1

Dugger, Celia W. U.S. plan to lure nurses may hurt poor nations. *New York Times* 2006 May 24; p. A1, A12. Subject: 21.6

Duguet, A.M. Genetic research: between freedom in research and the patient's rights: contribution of the Declaration of Helsinki [editorial]. *European Journal of Health Law* 2001 September; 8(3): 203-206. Subject: 15.1

Duke, Katy. Belgian loophole allows Swiss parents a "saviour" baby. *Lancet* 2006 July 29-August 4; 368(9533): 355-356. Subject: 15.2

Dula, Annette; Williams, September. When race matters. *Clinics in Geriatric Medicine* 2005 February; 21(1): 239-253. Subject: 9.5.4

Duncan, O.D.; Parmelee, L.F. Trends in public approval of euthanasia and suicide in the US, 1947-2003. *Journal of Medical Ethics* 2006 May; 32(5): 266-272. Subject: 20.5.1

Duncan, Rony E.; Foddy, Bennett; Delatycki, Martin B. Refusing to provide a prenatal test: can it ever be ethical? *BMJ: British Medical Journal* 2006 November 18; 333(7577): 1066-1068. Subject: 15.2

Duncan, Rony E.; Newson, Ainsley J. Clinical genetics and the problem with unqualified confidentiality. *American Journal of Bioethics* 2006 March-April; 6(2): 41-43. Subject: 8.4

Dundes, Lauren. Is the American public ready to embrace DNA as a crime-fighting tool? A survey assessing public support for DNA database. *Bulletin of Science, Technology and Society* 2001 October 1; 21(5): 369-375. Subject: 15.1

Dunet-Larousse, Emmanuel. L'euthanasie: signification et qualification au regard du droit pénal / Euthanasia: definition and distinctions with regard to criminal law. *Revue de Droit Sanitaire et Social* 1998 April-June; 34(2): 265-283. Subject: 20.5.1

Dunfee, Thomas W. Do firms with unique competencies for rescuing victims of human catastrophes have special obligations? Corporate responsibility and the AIDS catastrophe in sub-Saharan Africa. *Business Ethics Quarterly* 2006 April; 16(2): 185-210. Subject: 9.5.6

Dunn, Laura B.; Candilis, Philip J.; Roberts, Laura Weiss. Emerging empirical evidence on the ethics of schizophrenia research. *Schizophrenia Bulletin* 2006 January; 32(1): 47-68. Subject: 18.5.6

Dunn, Laura B.; Nowrangi, Milap A.; Palmer, Barton W.; Jeste, Dilip V.; Saks, Elyn R. Assessing decisional capacity for clinical research or treatment: a review of instructions. *American Journal of Psychiatry* 2006 August; 163(8): 1323-1334. Subject: 8.3.1

Dunn, Laura B.; Palmer, Barton W.; Keehan, Monique. Understanding of placebo controls among older people with schizophrenia. *Schizophrenia Bulletin* 2006 January; 32(1): 137-146. Subject: 18.3

Dunn, Laura B.; Palmer, Barton W.; Keehan, Monique; Jeste, Dilip V.; Appelbaum, Paul S. Assessment of therapeutic misconception in older schizophrenia patients with a brief instrument. *American Journal of Psychiatry* 2006 March; 163(3): 500-506. Subject: 18.5.6

Dunn, Laura B.; Roberts, Laura Weiss. Emerging findings in ethics of schizophrenia research. *Current Opinion in Psychiatry* 2005 March; 18(2): 111-119. Subject: 18.4

Dusesoi, J. A basic understanding of the judicial procedure. *Acta Chirurgica Belgica* 2000 August; 100(4): 165-168. Subject: 8.5

Duster, Troy. Lessons from history: why race and ethnicity have played a major role in biomedical research. *Journal of Law, Medicine and Ethics* 2006 Fall; 34(3): 487-496. Subject: 9.5.4

DuVal, Gordon; Salmon, Christina. Research note: ethics of drug treatment research with court-supervised subjects. *Journal of Drug Issues* 2004 Fall; 34(4): 991-1005. Subject: 18.5.1

Duvall, Melissa. Pharmacy conscience clause statutes: constitutional religious "accommodations" or unconstitutional "substantial burdens" on women? *American University Law Review* 2006 June; 55(5): 1485-1522. Subject: 11.1

Düwell, Marcus. One moral principle or many? *In:* Rehmann-Sutter, Christoph; Düwell, Marcus; Mieth,

See SUBJECT HEADING KEY FOR SECTION II on inside back cover.

547

Dietmar, eds. Bioethics in Cultural Contexts: Reflections on Methods and Finitude. Dordrecht: Springer, 2006: 93-108. Subject: 2.1

Dvonch, Victoria. Ethical dilemmas: the new is old. *Clinical Orthopaedics and Related Research* 2000 September; (378): 124-128. Subject: 2.2

Dwyer, James. What should the dean do? [case study and commentaries]. *Hastings Center Report* 2006 July-August; 36(4): 16. Subject: 7.2

Dyer, Clare. Code sets out framework for "living wills" [news]. *BMJ: British Medical Journal* 2006 March 18; 332(7542): 623. Subject: 20.5.4

Dyer, Clare. Crime victims are given right to object to disclosure of their medical records to courts [news]. *BMJ: British Medical Journal* 2006 July 15; 333(7559): 115. Subject: 8.4

Dyer, Clare. Judge rules that baby boy should not be allowed to die [news]. *BMJ: British Medical Journal* 2006 March 25; 332(7543): 685. Subject: 20.5.2

Dyer, Clare. Paired kidney transplants to start in the United Kingdom [news]. *BMJ: British Medical Journal* 2006 April 29; 332(7548): 989. Subject: 19.3

Dyer, Clare. Patient is to appeal High Court ruling on breast cancer drug [news]. *BMJ: British Medical Journal* 2006 February 25; 332(7539): 443. Subject: 9.5.5

Dyer, Clare. Third time lucky? [news]. *BMJ: British Medical Journal* 2006 November 25; 333(7578): 1090. Subject: 17.7

Dyer, Clare. Trusts can take cost into account when deciding drug treatment [news]. *BMJ: British Medical Journal* 2006 April 22; 332(7547): 928. Subject: 9.5.5

Dyer, Clare. UK government scraps mental health bill [news]. *BMJ: British Medical Journal* 2006 April 1; 332(7544): 748. Subject: 9.5.3

Dyer, Clare. UK House of Lords rejects physician assisted suicide [news]. *BMJ: British Medical Journal* 2006 May 20; 332(7551): 1169. Subject: 20.7

Dyer, Clare. Woman in PVS can die, rules judge [news]. *BMJ: British Medical Journal* 2006 December 16; 333(7581): 1238. Subject: 20.5.1

Dyer, Clare. Woman loses fight for parents' right to know of abortion advice [news]. *BMJ: British Medical Journal* 2006 January 28; 332(7535): 198. Subject: 12.4.2

Dyer, Owen. British soldiers are "guinea pigs" for new use of blood clotting agent [news]. *BMJ: British Medical Journal* 2006 September 23; 333(7569): 618. Subject: 18.5.8

Dyer, Owen. Force feeding at Guantanamo breaches ethics, doctors say [news]. *BMJ: British Medical Journal* 2006 March 11; 332(7541): 569. Subject: 21.5

Dyer, Owen. GMC hears complaints about UK fertility specialist [news]. *BMJ: British Medical Journal* 2006 March 11; 332(7541): 567. Subject: 14.1

Dyer, Owen. GSK breached marketing code [news]. *BMJ: British Medical Journal* 2006 August 19; 333(7564): 368. Subject: 9.7

Dyer, Owen. Industry group suspends drug company for breaching code [news]. *BMJ: British Medical Journal* 2006 October 7; 333(7571): 717. Subject: 9.7

Dyer, Owen. Patients can't stop their data being put on to NHS "spine" [news]. *BMJ: British Medical Journal* 2006 December 9; 333(7580): 1188. Subject: 1.3.12

Dyer, Owen. Payment offered to injured trial participants has strings attached [news]. *BMJ: British Medical Journal* 2006 April 29; 332(7548): 990. Subject: 18.7

Dyer, Owen. Sex change expert accused of rushing patients into surgery [news]. *BMJ: British Medical Journal* 2006 November 4; 333(7575): 935. Subject: 10

Dykes, Bryan A. Proposed rights of conscience legislation: expanding to include pharmacists and other health care providers. *Georgia Law Review* 2002 Winter; 36(2): 565-597. Subject: 12.1

Dyson, Simon M. "Race," ethnicity and haemoglobin disorders. *Social Science and Medicine* 1998 June 1; 47(1): 121-131. Subject: 15.11

E

Eachempati, Soumitra R.; Hydo, Lynn; Shou, Jian; Barie, Philip S. Sex differences in creation of do-not-resuscitate orders for critically ill elderly patients following emergency surgery. *Journal of Trauma* 2006 January; 60(1): 193-198. Subject: 20.5.1

Easson, Alexandra M. Should research be part of advance care planning? *Critical Care* 2005 February; 9(1): 10-11. Subject: 20.5.4

Eastman, Nigel. Reforming mental health law in England and Wales: the government's recent climb down is not a victory: the real battle is about to begin [editorial]. *BMJ: British Medical Journal* 2006 April 1; 332(7544): 737-738. Subject: 9.5.3

Eastman, N.; Starling, B. Mental disorder ethics: theory and empirical investigation. *Journal of Medical Ethics* 2006 February; 32(2): 94-99. Subject: 4.3

Eastwood, Gregory L. What should the dean do? [case study and commentaries]. *Hastings Center Report* 2006 July-August; 36(4): 14-15. Subject: 7.2

Eaton, Lynn. Ethics group rules on treating premature babies [news]. *BMJ: British Medical Journal* 2006 November 18; 333(7577): 1033. Subject: 20.5.2

Eaton, Lynn. Norwegian researcher admits that his data were faked [news]. *BMJ: British Medical Journal* 2006 January 28; 332(7535): 193. Subject: 1.3.9

Eberl, Jason T.; Koch-Hershenov, Rose; Hershenov, David. The metaphysical nuances of hylomorphism [letter and reply]. *National Catholic Bioethics Quarterly* 2006 Spring; 6(1): 9-12. Subject: 12.3

Echevarria, Laura. RU-486: a bitter pill. *Human Life Review* 2006 Summer-Fall; 32(3-4): 109-117. Subject: 12.1

Eckenwiler, Lisa A. A missed opportunity: the President's Council on Bioethics report on ethical caregiving. *American Journal of Bioethics [Online]*. 2006 March-April; 6(2): W20-W23. Subject: 9.5.2

Eckerdal, Gunnar. Sedation in palliative care — the doctor's perspective. *In:* Tännsjö, Torbjörn, ed. Terminal Sedation: Euthanasia in Disguise? Boston: Kluwer Academic Publishers; 2004: 37-41. Subject: 20.4.1

Eckert, Susan LaRusse; Katzen, Heather; Roberts, J. Scott; Barber, Melissa; Ravdin, Lisa D.; Relkin, Norman R.; Whitehouse, Peter J.; Green, Robert C. Recall of disclosed Apolipoprotein E genotype and lifetime risk estimate for Alzheimer's disease: the REVEAL Study. *Genetics in Medicine* 2006 December; 8(12): 746-751. Subject: 15.2

Ecks, Stefan. Response to Monica Konrad 'Placebo politics: on comparability, interdisciplinarity and international collaborative research'. *Monash Bioethics Review* 2006 October; 25(4): 85-90. Subject: 18.3

Edelmann, Robert J. Surrogacy: the psychological issues. *Journal of Reproductive and Infant Psychology* 2004 May; 22(2): 123-136. Subject: 14.2

Edozien, Leroy C. NHS maternity units should not encourage commercial banking of umbilical cord blood. *BMJ: British Medical Journal* 2006 October 14; 333(7572): 801-804. Subject: 19.4

Edward, Sarah J.L.; Stevens, Andrew J.; Braunholtz, David A.; Lilford, Richard J.; Swift, Teresa. The ethics of placebo-controlled trials: a comparison of inert and active placebo controls. *World Journal of Surgery* 2005 May; 29(5): 610-614. Subject: 18.3

Edwards, James C. Concepts of technology and their role in moral reflection. *In:* Parens, Erik, ed. Surgically Shaping Children: Technology, Ethics, and the Pursuit of Normality. Baltimore, MD: Johns Hopkins University Press; 2006: 51-67. Subject: 9.5.7

Edwards, Jeanette. Incorporating incest: gamete, body and relation in assisted conception. *Journal of the Royal Anthropological Institute* 2004 December; 10(4): 755-774. Subject: 14.1

Edwards, Jeanette. Taking "public understanding" seriously. *New Genetics and Society* 2002 December; 21(3): 315-325. Subject: 14.1

Edwards, Nancy. Legal, ethical, and moral considerations in caring for individuals with Alzheimer's disease. *In:* Cowen, Perle Slavik; Moorhead, Sue, eds. Current Issues in Nursing. 7th ed. St. Louis, MO: Mosby, 2006: 645-651. Subject: 9.5.2

Edwards, R.G. Cloning and cheating [editorial]. *Reproductive BioMedicine Online [electronic]* 2006 February; 12(2): 141. Subject: 1.3.9

Edwards, R.G. Ethics and moral philosophy in the initiation of IVF, preimplantation diagnosis and stem cells. *Reproductive BioMedicine Online [electronic]* 2005 March; 10(Supplement 1): 1-8. Subject: 14.4

Edwards, R.G.; Ahuja, K.K. Legal cases spell big trouble and great opportunities for IVF embryologists. *Reproductive BioMedicine Online [electronic]* 2001 July 2; 2(1): 1 p. Accessed: http://www.rbmonline.com/index.html [2005 June 3]. Subject: 14.4

Edwards, R.G.; Beard, Helen K. Destruction of cryopreserved embryos: U.K. law dictated the destruction of 3000 cryopreserved human embryos. *Human Reproduction* 1997 January; 12(1): 3-5. Subject: 14.6

Edwards, Sarah J.L. Restricted treatments, inducements, and research participation. *Bioethics* 2006 April; 20(2): 77-91. Subject: 18.5.7

Edwards, Steven D.; McNamee, Mike. Why sports medicine is not medicine. *Health Care Analysis: An International Journal of Health Philosophy and Policy* 2006 June; 14(2): 103-109. Subject: 9.5.1

Edwards, T.J.; Finlay, I.; Wilkins, D.C.; Lambert, A.W. Improving risk disclosure during the consent process. *Annals of the Royal College of Surgeons of England* 2004 November; 86(6): 458-462. Subject: 8.3.1

Egan, Jennifer. Wanted: a few good sperm (looking for Mr. Good Sperm). *New York Times Magazine* 2006 March 19; p. 44-51, 66, 81, 98, 100. Subject: 14.2

Egan, Thomas M.; Kotloff, Robert M. Pro/con debate: lung allocation should be based on medical urgency and transplant survival and not on waiting time. *Chest* 2005 July; 128(1): 407-415. Subject: 19.6

Egan, Timothy; Liptak Adam. Fraught issue, but narrow ruling in Oregon suicide case. *New York Times* 2006 January 18; p. A16. Subject: 20.7

Egziabher, Berehan Gebre; Benatar, Soloman; Annas, George J.; Agam, Hasmy; Arya, Sadhana; Menon, Nivedita; Lokaneeta, Jinee; Pratt, Dave; Ho, Mae-Wan; Zhu, Yifei; Blackwelder, Brent; Dubois, Mark; Hayes, Randy; Kennedy, Robert F., Jr.; Knox, John A.; Musil, Robert K.; Passacantando, John; Perrault, Michele; Ritchie, Mark. Views from around the world. *World Watch* 2002 July-August; 15(4): 24-25. Subject: 15.1

Ehni, Hans-Jörg. The definition of adequate care in externally sponsored clinical trials: the terminological controversy about the concept "standard of care". *Science and Engineering Ethics* 2006 January; 12(1): 123-130. Subject: 18.5.9

Ehni, Hans-Jörg; Wiesing, Urban. Placebos in klinischen Versuchsreihen: eine vergleichende Analyse

See SUBJECT HEADING KEY FOR SECTION II on inside back cover.

549

der internationalen Richtlinien = Placebos in clinical research: a comparative analysis of international guidelines. *Ethik in der Medizin* 2006 September; 18(3): 223-227. Subject: 18.3

Ehrlich, J. Shoshanna. Choosing abortion: teens who make the decision without parental involvement. *Gender Issues* 2003 Spring; 21(2): 3-39. Subject: 12.4.2

Eibach, Ulrich. Life history, sin, and disease. *Christian Bioethics* 2006 August; 12(2): 117-131. Subject: 4.2

Eichaker, Peter Q.; Natanson, Charles; Danner, Robert L. Surviving sepsis — practice guidelines, marketing campaigns, and Eli Lilly. *New England Journal of Medicine* 2006 October 19; 355(16): 1640-1642. Subject: 9.7

Eichler, Margrit; Burke, Mary Anne. The BIAS FREE Framework: a new analytical tool for global health research. *Canadian Journal of Public Health* 2006 January-February; 97(1): 63-68. Subject: 18.2

Eide, Brock L.; Eide, Fernette F. The mislabeled child. *New Atlantis* 2006 Spring; 12: 46-59. Subject: 9.5.7

Eide, Karissa. Can a pharmacist refuse to fill birth control prescriptions on moral or religious grounds? *California Western Law Review* 2005 Fall; 42(1): 121-148. Subject: 11.1

Eidelman, L.A.; Jakobson, D.J.; Pizov, R.; Geber, D.; Leibovitz, L.; Sprung, C.L. Forgoing life-sustaining treatment in an Israeli ICU. *Intensive Care Medicine* 1998 February; 24(2): 162-166. Subject: 20.5.1

Eidgenössische Ethikkommission für die Gentechnik im ausserhumanen Bereich = Commission fédérale d'éthique pour le génie génétique dans le domaine non humain = Commissione federale d'etica per l'ingegneria genetica nei settore non umano = Swiss Ethics Committee on Non-Human Gene Technology [ECNH]. Patents on animals and plants: A contribution to discussion. Bern, Switzerland: Swiss Ethics Committee on Non-Human Gene Technology, 2001; 15 p. [Online]. Accessed: http://www.umwelt-schweiz.ch/imperia/md/content/ekah/14.pdf [2006 April 6]. Subject: 15.8

Eidgenössische Ethikkommission für die Gentechnik im ausserhumanen Bereich = Commission fédérale d'éthique pour le génie génétique dans le domaine non humain = Commissione federale d'etica per l'ingegneria genetica nei settore non umano = Swiss Ethics Committee on Non-Human Gene Technology [ECNH]. Statement on putting "the dignity of creation" into concrete terms as part of the planned revision of the Animal Protection Law. Bern, Switzerland: Swiss Ethics Committee on Non-Human Gene Technology, 1999 November 17; 10 p. [Online]. Accessed: http://www.umwelt-schweiz.ch/imperia/md/content/ekah/16.pdf [2006 April 6]. Subject: 22.1

Eidgenössische Ethikkommission für die Gentechnik im ausserhumanen Bereich = Commission fédérale d'éthique pour le génie génétique dans le domaine non

humain = Commissione federale d'etica per l'ingegneria genetica nei settore non umano = Swiss Ethics Committee on Non-Human Gene Technology [ECNH]. Statement on the draft bill of the Federal Law relating to the transplantation of organs, tissues and cells (Transplantation Law, TxG). Bern, Switzerland: Swiss Ethics Committee on Non-Human Gene Technology, 2000 February 28; 11 p. [Online]. Accessed: http://www.umwelt-schweiz.ch/imperia/md/content/ekah/20.pdf [2006 April 6]. Subject: 19.1

Einav, S.; Avidan, A.; Brezis, M.; Rubinow, A. Attitudes of medical practitioners towards "do not resuscitate" orders. *Medicine and Law: World Association for Medical Law* 2006 March; 25(1): 219-228. Subject: 20.3.2

Einsiedel, Edna F. Assessing a controversial medical technology: Canadian public consultations on xenotransplantation. *Public Understanding of Science* 2002 October; 11(4): 315-331. Subject: 19.1

Eisenberg, Rebecca S. Biotech patents: looking backward while moving forward. *Nature Biotechnology* 2006 March; 24(3): 317-319. Subject: 15.8

Eisenstein, Michael. Making ES cells 'ethically sound'. *Nature Methods* 2005 December; 2(12): 891. Subject: 18.5.4

Eiser, C.; Davies, H.; Jenney, M.; Glaser, A. Mothers' attitudes to the randomized controlled trial (RCT): the case of acute lymphoblastic leukaemia (ALL) in children. *Child: Care, Health and Development* 2005 September; 31(5): 517-523. Subject: 18.5.2

Eisman, Michael; Sierles, Frederick S. Medical student exposure to drug company interactions [letter and reply]. *JAMA: The Journal of the American Medical Association* 2006 January 18; 295(3): 281-282. Subject: 7.3

Ek, Eugene T.; Yu, Emma P.; Chan, Jason T.; Love, Bruce R. Nerve injuries in orthopaedics: is there anything more we need to tell our patients? *ANZ Journal of Surgery* 2005 March; 75(3): 132-135. Subject: 8.3.1

Ekamm Ladd, Rosalind; Forman, Edwin. Altruistic motives reconsidered. *American Journal of Bioethics* 2006 September-October; 6(5): 55-56. Subject: 18.3

El-Deiry, Wafik S. Plagiarism is not acceptable in science or for cancer biology and therapy. *Cancer Biology and Therapy* 2005 June; 4(6): 619-620. Subject: 1.3.7

El-Hazmi, Mohsen A.F. Ethics of genetic counseling — basic concepts and relevance to Islamic communities. *Annals of Saudi Medicine* 2004 March-April; 24(2): 84-92. Subject: 15.2

El-Maaytah, M.; Al Kayed, A.; Al Qudah, M.; Al Ahmad, H.; Al-Dabbagh, K.; Jerjes, W.; Al Khawalde, M.; Abu Hammad, O.; Dar Odeh, N.; El-Maaytah, K.; Al Shmailan, Y.; Porter, S.; Scully, C. Willingness of dentists in Jordan to treat HIV-infected patients. *Oral Diseases* 2005 September; 11(5): 318-322. Subject: 9.5.6

El-Shoubaki, H.; Bener, Abdulbari. Public knowledge and attitudes toward organ donation and transplantation: a cross-cultural study. *Transplantation Proceedings* 2005 June; 37(5): 1993-1997. Subject: 19.5

El-Wakeel, H.; Taylor, G.J.; Tate, J.J.T. What do patients really want to know in an informed consent procedure? A questionnaire-based survey of patients in the Bath area, UK. *Journal of Medical Ethics* 2006 October; 32(10): 612-616. Subject: 8.3.1

Elbe, Stefan. Should HIV/AIDS be securitized? The ethical dilemmas of linking HIV/AIDS and security. *International Studies Quarterly* 2006 March; 50(1): 119-144. Subject: 9.5.6

Elbogen, Eric B.; Swartz, Marvin S.; Van Dorn, Richard; Swanson, Jeffrey W.; Kim, Mimi; Scheyett, Anna. Clinical decision making and views about psychiatric advance directives. *Psychiatric Services* 2006 March; 57(3): 350-355. Subject: 17.1

Eldh, Ann Catrine; Ekman, Inger; Ehnfors, Margareta. Conditions for patient participation and non-participation in health care. *Nursing Ethics* 2006 September; 13(5): 503-514. Subject: 8.1

Elding, Christine; Scholes, Julie. Organ and tissue donation: a trustwide perspective or critical care concern? *Nursing in Critical Care* 2005 May-June; 10(3): 129-135. Subject: 19.5

Eldridge, Sandra M.; Ashby, Deborah; Feder, Gene S. Informed patient consent to participation in cluster randomized trials: an empirical exploration of trials in primary care. *Clinical Trials* 2005; 2(2): 91-98. Subject: 18.3

Elford, Kimberly; Lawrence, Carole; Leader, Arthur. Research implications of embryo cryopreservation choices made by patients undergoing in vitro fertilization. *Fertility and Sterility* 2004 April; 81(4): 1154-1155. Subject: 14.4

Elger, Bernice S.; Caplan, Arthur L. Consent and anonymization in research involving biobanks. *EMBO Reports* 2006 July; 7(7): 661-666. Subject: 15.1

Elger, Bernice S.; Harding, Timothy W. Should children and adolescents be tested for Huntington's disease? Attitudes of future lawyers and physicians in Switzerland. *Bioethics* 2006 June; 20(3): 158-167. Subject: 15.3

Elhauge, Einer. The limited regulatory potential of medical technology assessment. *Virginia Law Review* 1996 November; 82(8): 1525-1622. Subject: 9.3.1

Elhence, Priti. Ethical issues in transfusion medicine. *Indian Journal of Medical Ethics* 2006 July-September; 3(3): 87-89. Subject: 19.4

Eliades, Theodore; Athanasiou, Athanasios E.; Papadopulos, Jannis S. Ethics and fraud in science: a review of scientific misconduct and applications to craniofacial research. *World Journal of Orthodontics* 2005 Fall; 6(3): 226-232. Subject: 1.3.9

Elias-Jones, A.C.; Samanta, J. The implications of the David Glass case for future clinical practice in the UK. *Archives of Disease in Childhood* 2005 August; 90(8): 822-825. Subject: 20.5.2

Elks, Martin A. Visual indictment: a contextual analysis of the Kallikak Family photographs. *Mental Retardation* 2005 August; 43(4): 268-280. Subject: 15.5

Ellenberg, Susan S. Scientific and ethical issues in the use of placebo and active controls in clinical trials. *Journal of Bone and Mineral Research* 2003 June; 18(6): 1121-1124. Subject: 18.3

Ellenberg, Susan S.; George, Stephen L. Should statisticians reporting to data monitoring committees be independent of the trial sponsor and leadership? *Statistics in Medicine* 2004 May 30; 23(10): 1503-1505. Subject: 18.2

Ellerin, Bruce E.; Gawande, Atul. Why physicians participate in executions [letter and reply]. *New England Journal of Medicine* 2006 July 6; 355(1): 99-100. Subject: 20.6

Ellerston, Charlotte; Trussell, James; Stewart, Felicia H.; Winikoff, Beverly. Should emergency contraceptive pills be available without prescription? *Journal of the American Medical Women's Association* 1998 Fall; 53(5, Supplement 2): 226-229, 232. Subject: 11.1

Elliot, Ann Christy. Health care ethics: cultural relativity of autonomy. *Journal of Transcultural Nursing* 2001 October; 12(4): 326-330. Subject: 21.7

Elliot, Kevin C. An ethics of expertise based on informed consent. *Science and Engineering Ethics* 2006 October; 12(4): 637-661. Subject: 5.3

Elliot, Richard. Court dismisses constitutional challenge to ban on assisted suicide. *HIV/AIDS Policy and Law Review* 2001; 6(1-2): 35-36. Subject: 20.7

Elliott, Carl. Attitudes, souls, and persons: children with severe neurological impairment. *Mental Retardation and Developmental Disabilities Research Reviews* 2003; 9(1): 16-20. Subject: 9.5.7

Elliott, Carl. The drug pushers. *Atlantic Monthly* 2006 April; 297(3): 82-84, 86, 88-93. Subject: 9.7

Elliott, Douglas. Focus on HIV/AIDS and injection drug use. *Canadian HIV/AIDS Policy and Law Newsletter* 1997-1998 Winter; 3(4)-4(1): 1, 53-57. Subject: 9.5.6

Elliott, Richard. HIV testing and treatment of children. *Canadian HIV/AIDS Policy and Law Newsletter* 1999 Fall-Winter; 5(1): 1, 3-9. Subject: 9.5.6

Elliott, Richard. Medical treatment of children with HIV/AIDS. *Canadian HIV/AIDS Policy and Law Newsletter* 2000 Spring-Summer; 5(2-3): 5-7. Subject: 9.5.6

Elliott, Richard. Ontario appellate court denies HIV-positive man's constitutional claim to medical marijuana. *HIV/AIDS Policy and Law Review* 2002 March; 6(3): 56-58. Subject: 9.5.1

See SUBJECT HEADING KEY FOR SECTION II on inside back cover.

Elliott, Richard. Reform MP proposes compulsory testing. *Canadian HIV/AIDS Policy and Law Newsletter* 2000 Spring-Summer; 5(2-3): 25-27. Subject: 8.3.4

Elliott, Richard. Scaling up HIV testing: human rights and hidden costs. *HIV/AIDS Policy and Law Review* 2006 April; 11(1): 1, 5-10. Subject: 9.5.6

Elliott, Richard. US: appeals court dismisses employment discrimination suit by HIV-positive dental hygienist. *HIV/AIDS Policy and Law Review* 2002 March; 6(3): 70-71. Subject: 9.5.6

Elliott, Richard. US: hospital negligent for failing to warn prior patient of risk of HIV infection by transfusion. *HIV/AIDS Policy and Law Review* 2002 March; 6(3): 71-72. Subject: 9.5.6

Elliott, Richard. US: Supreme Court refuses to hear case of fired HIV-positive dental hygienist. *HIV/AIDS Policy and Law Review* 2003 April; 8(1): 76. Subject: 9.5.6

Ellis, Niki. Employer attitudes to ethics in occupational health. *In:* Westerholm, Peter; Nilstun, Tore; Øvretveit, John, eds. Practical Ethics in Occupational Health. San Francisco: Radcliffe Medical Press; 2004: 263-282. Subject: 16.3

Ellison, George T.H.; Jones, Ian Rees. Social identities and the 'new genetics': scientific and social consequences. *Critical Public Health* 2002; 12(3): 265-282. Subject: 15.1

Ells, Carolyn. Healthcare ethics committees' contribution to review of institutional policy. *HEC (Healthcare Ethics Committee) Forum* 2006 September; 18(3): 265-275. Subject: 9.6

Ellsbury, Kathleen; Carline, Jan D.; Wenrich, Marjorie D. Competing professionalism values among community-based family physicians. *Academic Medicine* 2006 October; 81(10, Supplement): S25-S29. Subject: 4.1.2

Ellwood, David. Late terminations of pregnancy — an obstetrician's perspective. *Australian Health Review* 2005 May; 29(2): 139-142. Subject: 12.5.2

Elsner, D. Just another reproductive technology? The ethics of human reproductive cloning as an experimental medical procedure. *Journal of Medical Ethics* 2006 October; 32(10): 596-600. Subject: 14.5

Elster, Nanette R. ART for the masses? Racial and ethnic inequality in assisted reproductive technologies. *DePaul Journal of Health Care Law* 2005; 9(1): 719-733. Subject: 9.5.4

Elster, Nanette R. Assisted reproductive technologies: contracts, consents, and controversies. *American Journal of Family Law* 2005 Winter; 18(4): 193-199. Subject: 14.1

Elul, Batya; Pearlman, Elizabeth; Sohaindo, Annik; Simonds, Wendy; Westhoff, Carolyn. In-depth interviews with medical abortion clients: thoughts on the method and home administration of misoprostol. *Journal of the American Medical Women's Association* 2000; 55(3, Supplement): 169-172. Subject: 12.5.2

Emanuel, Ezekiel J. The relevance of empirical research for bioethics. *In:* Lolas Stepke, Fernando; Agar Corbinos, Lorenzo, eds. Interfaces Between Bioethics and the Empirical Social Sciences. Buenos Aires, Argentina: World Health Organization; 2002: 99-110. Subject: 2.1

Emanuel, Ezekiel J. Researching a bioethical question. *In:* Gallin, John I., ed. Principles and Practice of Clinical Research. San Diego, CA: Academic Press; 2002: 27-37. Subject: 1.3.9

Emanuel, Ezekiel J.; Wertheimer, Alan. The ethics of influenza vaccination: response [letters]. *Science* 2006 August 11; 313(5788): 758-759. Subject: 9.5.1

Emanuel, Ezekiel J.; Wertheimer, Alan. Who should get influenza vaccine when not all can? *Science* 2006 May 12; 312(5775): 854-855. Subject: 9.4

Emanuel, Linda. Ethics and pain management: an introductory overview. *Pain Medicine* 2001 June; 2(2): 112-116. Subject: 4.4

Emanuel, Linda. Relief of suffering is the business of every discipline [editorial]. *Archives of Internal Medicine* 2006 January 23; 166(2): 149- 150. Subject: 20.4.1

Emanuel, Linda; Iris, Madelyn A.; Webster, James R. Ethical aspects of geriatric palliative care. *In:* Morrison, R. Sean; Meier, Diane E.; Capello, Carol, eds. Geriatric Palliative Care. New York: Oxford University Press; 2003: 55-78. Subject: 9.5.2

Emery, Jon. Is informed choice in genetic testing a different breed of informed decision-making? A discussion paper. *Health Expectations* 2001 June; 4(2): 81-86. Subject: 15.3

Enemark, Christian. United States biodefense, international law, and the problem of intent. *Politics and the Life Sciences* 2005 March-September; 24(1-2): 32-42. Subject: 21.3

Engel, Mylan, Jr. The mere considerability of animals. *Acta Analytica* 2001; 16(27): 89-107. Subject: 22.1

Engelberg, Ruth A.; Patrick, Donald L.; Curtis, J. Randall. Correspondence between patients' preferences and surrogates' understandings for dying and death. *Journal of Pain and Symptom Management* 2005 December; 30(6): 498-509. Subject: 20.4.1

Engelhardt, H. Tristram. Public discourse and reasonable pluralism: rethinking the requirements of neutrality. *In:* Guinn, David E., ed. Handbook of Bioethics and Religion. New York: Oxford University Press, 2006: 169-194. Subject: 21.7

Engelhardt, H. Tristram, Jr. Biological nihilism and modern moral and political theory. *Politics and the Life Sciences* 1988 February; 6(2): 202-205; author's reply 223-225. Subject: 15.9

Engelhardt, H. Tristram, Jr.; Garrett, Jeremy R.; Jotterand, Fabrice. Bioethics and the philosophy of medicine: a thirty-year perspective. *Journal of Medicine and Philosophy* 2006 December; 31(6): 565-568. Subject: 2.1

Engelschion, Sverre. The implementation of Directive 95/46/EC in Norway, especially with regard to medical data. *European Journal of Health Law* 2002 September; 9(3): 189-200. Subject: 8.4

Englert, Y.; Revelard, Ph. Isn't it "who decides" rather than "what to do" with spare embryos? *Human Reproduction* 1997 January; 12(1): 8-10. Subject: 14.6

English, Joel; Klein, Rob; Niehaus, Tess; Ross, Joyce M. Health hazard? *Marketing Health Services* 2005 Winter; 25(4): 14, 16-19. Subject: 9.1

English, Veronica. Autonomy versus protection — who benefits from the regulation of IVF? *Human Reproduction* 2006 December; 21(12): 3044-3049. Subject: 14.4

English, Veronica; Hamm, Danielle; Harrison, Caroline; Sheather, Julian; Sommerville, Ann. Medical governance and the General Medical Council. *Journal of Medical Ethics* 2006 December; 32(12): 743-744. Subject: 2.1

Enserink, Martin. A season of generosity. . .and Jeremiads [news]. *Science* 2006 December 8; 314(5805): 1525. Subject: 18.5.4

Enserink, Martin. Selling the stem cell dream. *Science* 2006 July 14; 313(5784): 160-163. Subject: 9.5.1

Enserink, Martin. WHO panel weighs radical ideas [news]. *Science* 2006 December 1; 314(5804): 1373. Subject: 9.5.6

Eppinette, Matthew; Fergusson, Andrew. Human dignity: still defying devaluation. *Ethics and Medicine* 2006 Spring; 22(1): 5-7. Subject: 4.4

Epps, Charles H., Jr. Ethical guidelines for orthopaedists and industry. *Clinical Orthopaedics and Related Research* 2003 July; (412): 14-20. Subject: 9.7

Epstein, Alex. The "animal rights" movement's cruelty to humans. *Physiologist* 2005 October; 48(5): 223, 225. Subject: 22.1

Epstein, Charles J. Genetic testing: hope or hype? *Genetics in Medicine* 2004 July-August; 6(4): 165-172. Subject: 9.7

Epstein, M. Why effective consent presupposes autonomous authorisation: a counterorthodox argument. *Journal of Medical Ethics* 2006 June; 32(6): 342-345. Subject: 8.3.1

Epstein, Steven. Bodily differences and collective identities: the politics of gender and race in biomedical research in the United States. *Body and Society* 2004 June-September; 10(2-3): 183-204 [Online] Accessed: http://bod.sagepub.com/cgi/reprint/10/2-3/183 [2007 February 6]. Subject: 18.5.3

Epstein, William M. The lighter side of deception research in the social sciences: social work as comedy. *Jour-*

nal of Information Ethics 2006 Spring; 15(1): 11-26. Subject: 18.4

Erbguth, Frank; Lipp, Volker; Nagel, Michael Benedikt. Zum problem ausreichender Gründe für eine Behandlungsbegrenzung [The problem of adequate reasons for limiting treatment. Commentaries I and II]. *Ethik in der Medizin* 2006 June; 18(2): 181-188. Subject: 20.5.1

Erde, E.; Pomerantz, S.C.; Saccocci, M.; Kramer-Feely, V.; Cavalieri, T.A. Privacy and patient-clergy access: perspectives of patients admitted to hospital. *Journal of Medical Ethics* 2006 July; 32(7): 398-402. Subject: 8.4

Erikson, Susan L. Post-diagnostic abortion in Germany: reproduction gone awry, again? *Social Science and Medicine* 2003 May; 56(9): 1987-2001. Subject: 15.2

Eriksson, Stefan; Helgesson, Gert. Potential harms, anonymization, and the right to withdraw consent to biobank research. *European Journal of Human Genetics* 2005 September; 13(9): 1071-1076. Subject: 15.1

Eriksson, Stefan; Helgesson, Gert; Segerdahl, Pär. Provide expertise or facilitate ethical reflection? A comment on the debate between Cowley and Crosthwaite. *Medicine, Health Care and Philosophy* 2006; 9(3): 389-392. Subject: 2.1

Erlen, Judith A. Wanted-nurses: ethical issues and the nursing shortage. *Orthopaedic Nursing* 2004 July-August; 23(4): 289-292. Subject: 4.1.3

Erlen, Judith A. When patients and families disagree. *Orthopaedic Nursing* 2005 July-August; 24(4): 279-282. Subject: 20.5.1

Ersin, Fatma; Cevik, Ebru; Aksoy, Sahin; Aksoy, Nurten. Aging and nursing in Turkey: an ethical perspective. *In:* Sang-yong, Song; Young-Mo, Koo; Macer, Darryl R.J., eds. Asian Bioethics in the 21st Century. Christchurch, NZ: Eubios Ethics Institute, 2002: 118-121. Subject: 9.5.2

Ertman, Martha M. What's wrong with a parenthood market? A new and improved theory of commodification. *North Carolina Law Review* 2003 December; 82(1): 1-59. Subject: 14.1

Erwin, Cheryl. Utopian dreams and harsh realities: who is in control of assisted reproductive technologies in a high-tech world? *Journal of Gender, Race and Justice* 2006 Spring; 9(3): 621-635. Subject: 14.4

Erwin, Cheryl; Philibert, Robert. Shocking treatment: the use of tasers in psychiatric care. *Journal of Law, Medicine, and Ethics* 2006 Spring; 34(1): 116-120. Subject: 9.5.3

Escarce, José J. How does race matter, anyway? [editorial]. *Health Services Research* 2005 February; 40(1): 1-7. Subject: 8.1

Escobar, Mauricio A.; McCullough, Laurence B. Responsibly managing ethical challenges of residency train-

See SUBJECT HEADING KEY FOR SECTION II on inside back cover.

553

ing: a guide for surgery residents, educators, and residency program leaders. *Journal of the American College of Surgeons* 2006 March; 202(3): 531-535. Subject: 7.2

ESHRE Task Force on Ethics and Law; Pennings, G.; de Wert, G.; Shenfield, F.; Cohen, J.; Devroey, P.; Tarlatzis, B. ESHRE Task Force on Ethics and Law 11: posthumous assisted reproduction. *Human Reproduction* 2006 December; 21(12): 3050-3053. Subject: 14.6

Espey, Eve; Ogburn, Tony; Chavez, Alice; Qualls, Clifford; Leyba, Mario. Abortion education in medical schools: a national survey. *American Journal of Obstetrics and Gynecology* 2005 February; 192(2): 640-643. Subject: 12.1

Espiell, Héctor Gros. The common heritage of humanity and the human genome = El patrimonio común de la humanidad y el genoma humano. *Law and the Human Genome Review = Revista de Derecho y Genoma Humano* 1995 July-December; (3): 89-101. Subject: 15.10

Espin, Sherry; Levinson, Wendy; Regehr, Glenn; Baker, G. Ross; Lingard, Lorelei. Error or "act of God"? A study of patients' and operating room team members' perceptions of error definition, reporting, and disclosure. *Surgery* 2006 January; 139(1): 6-14. Subject: 9.8

Esposito, Michael F. Ethical implications of pharmacological enhancement of mood and cognition. *Penn Bioethics Journal* 2005 April 2; 1(1): 4p. [Online]. Accessed: http://www.bioethicsjournal.com [2005 April 19]. Subject: 17.4

Essed, Philomena; Goldberg, David Theo. Cloning cultures: the social injustices of sameness. *Ethnic and Racial Studies* 2002 November 1; 25(6): 1066-1082. Subject: 14.5

Esterhuizen, Philip. Is the professional code still the cornerstone of clinical nursing practice? *Journal of Advanced Nursing* 2006 January; 53(1): 104-110. Subject: 4.1.3

Esteve, Rogette; Halpern, Sheri; Kirloss, Mena; Rosenthal, Andrew. Interview with Dr. Ezekiel Emanuel, Chief of the Department of Clinical Bioethics at the National Institute of Health. *Penn Bioethics Journal* 2005 April 2; 1(1): 5p. [Online]. Accessed: http://www.bioethicsjournal.com [2005 April 19]. Subject: 18.6

Etchegary, Holly. Genetic testing for Huntington's disease: how is the decision taken? *Genetic Testing* 2006 Spring; 10(1): 60-67. Subject: 15.3

Ettorre, Elizabeth. Comparing the practice of reproductive genetics in Greece, UK, Finland, and The Netherlands: constructing "expert" claims while marking "reproductive" time. *In:* Stehr, Nico, ed. Biotechnology Between Commerce and Civil Society. New Brunswick, NJ: Transaction Publishers; 2004: 299-319. Subject: 15.2

Ettorre, Elizabeth; Katz Rothman, Barbara; Steinberg, Deborah Lynn. Feminism confronts the ge-

nome: introduction. *New Genetics and Society* 2006 August; 25(2): 133-142. Subject: 15.10

Etzioni, Amitai. A communitarian approach: a viewpoint on the study of the legal, ethical and policy considerations raised by DNA tests and databases. *Journal of Law, Medicine and Ethics* 2006 Summer; 34(2): 214-221. Subject: 15.1

Eubios Ethics Institute; Asian Bioethics Conference; Song, Sang-Yong; Koo, Young-Moo; Macer, Darryl R. J. Asian bioethics in the 21st century. Christchurch, N.Z.: Eubios Ethics Institute, 2003; 434 p. Subject: 2.1

EURELD Consortium; Bilsen, Johan; Norup, Michael; Deliens, Luc; Miccinesi, Guido; van der Wal, Gerrit; Löfmark, Rurik; Faisst, Karin; van der Heide, Agnes. Drugs used to alleviate symptoms with life shortening as a possible side effect: end-of-life care in six European countries. *Journal of Pain and Symptom Management* 2006 February; 31(2): 111-121. Subject: 20.4.1

European Commission. Directorate General XI [DGXI]; Close, Bryony; Banister, Keith; Baumans, Vera; Bernoth, Eva-Maria; Bromage, Niall; Bunyan, John; Erhardt, Wolff; Flecknell, Paul; Gregory, Neville; Hackbarth, Hansjoachim; Morton, David; Warwick, Clifford. Recommendations for euthanasia of experimental animals: part 1. *Laboratory Animals* 1996; 30: 293-316. [Online]. Accessed: http://www.lal.org.uk/workp.html [2006 October 5]. Subject: 22.2

European Commission. Directorate General XI [DGXI]; Close, Bryony; Banister, Keith; Baumans, Vera; Bernoth, Eva-Maria; Bromage, Niall; Bunyan, John; Erhardt, Wolff; Flecknell, Paul; Gregory, Neville; Hackbarth, Hansjoachim; Morton, David; Warwick, Clifford. Recommendations for euthanasia of experimental animals: part 2. *Laboratory Animals* 1997; 31: 1-32. [Online]. Accessed: http://www.lal.org.uk/workp.html [2006 October 5]. Subject: 22.2

European Parliament. Temporary Committee on Human Genetics and Other New Technologies in Modern Medicine. Final report on the ethical, legal, economic and social implications of human genetics. Strasbourg/Brussels/Luxembourg: European Parliament [A5-0391/2001], 2001 November 8: 1-118. Subject: 15.1

European Society of Gene Therapy [ESGT]. Position paper on social, ethical and public awareness issues in gene therapy. Stockholm, Sweden: European Society of Gene Therapy, 2002 November: 10 p. [Online]. Accessed: http://www.congrex.se/esgt/downloads/position_2.pdf [2006 July 27]. Subject: 15.4

European Society of Human Genetics [ESHG]. Data storage and DNA banking for biomedical research: technical, social and ethical issues. *European Journal of Human Genetics* 2003 December; 11(Supplement 2): S8-S10. Subject: 15.10

Subject = NRCBL Primary Classification Number; see inside front cover.

European Society of Human Genetics [ESHG]. Genetic information and testing in insurance and employment: technical, social and ethical issues. *European Journal of Human Genetics* 2003 December; 11(Supplement 2): S11-S12. Subject: 15.1

European Society of Human Genetics [ESHG]. Population genetic screening programmes: technical, social and ethical issues. *European Journal of Human Genetics* 2003 December; 11(Supplement 2): S5-S7. Subject: 15.3

European Society of Human Genetics [ESHG]; European Society of Human Reproduction and Embryology [ESHRE]. The need for interaction between assisted reproduction technology and genetics: recommendations of the European Societies of Human Genetics and Human Reproduction and Embryology. *Human Reproduction* 2006 August; 21(8): 1971-1973. Subject: 15.2

European Society of Human Genetics [ESHG]. Public and Professional Policy Committee [PPPC]. Genetic information and testing in insurance and employment: technical, social and ethical issues. *European Journal of Human Genetics* 2003 December; 11(12): 909-910. Subject: 15.3

European Society of Human Genetics [ESHG]. Public and Professional Policy Committee [PPPC]. Population genetic screening programmes: technical, social and ethical issues. *European Journal of Human Genetics* 2003 December; 11(12): 903-905. Subject: 15.3

Evans, Audrey E. Medical research: why trouble the patient for informed consent? Commentary. *Medical and Pediatric Oncology* 2002 September; 39(3): 210- 211. Subject: 8.3.2

Evans, Barbara J.; Meslin, Eric M. Encouraging translational research through harmonization of FDA and common rule informed consent requirements for research with banked specimens. *Journal of Legal Medicine* 2006 June; 27(2): 119-166. Subject: 18.3

Evans, Daryl. Cultural lag, economic scarcity, and the technological quagmire of "Infant Doe". *Journal of Social Issues* 1993 Summer; 49(2): 89-113. Subject: 9.4

Evans, David W. Living organ donation needs debate on harm to donors [letter]. *BMJ: British Medical Journal* 2006 October 28; 333(7574): 919. Subject: 19.5

Evans, Emily L.; London, Alex John. Equipoise and the criteria for reasonable action. *Journal of Law, Medicine and Ethics* 2006 Summer; 34(2): 441-450. Subject: 18.2

Evans, Gareth; Harris, Rodney. The ethics of testing for cancer-predisposition genes. *In:* Eeles, R.A., Ponder, B.A.J.; Horwich, A.; Easton, D.F., eds. Genetic Predisposition to Cancer. London: Chapman and Hare; 1996 June: 383-393. Subject: 15.3

Evans, H.M. What's wrong with "retained organs"? Some personal reflections in the afterglow of "Alder Hey". *Journal of Clinical Pathology* 2001 November; 54(11): 824-826. Subject: 19.5

Evans, James P.; Skrzynia, Cécile; Susswein, Lisa; Harlan, Megan. Genetics and the young woman with breast cancer. *Breast Disease* 2005-2006; 23: 17-29. Subject: 15.3

Evans, John H. Between technocracy and democratic legitimation: a proposed compromise position for common morality public bioethics. *Journal of Medicine and Philosophy* 2006 June; 31(3): 213-234. Subject: 2.1

Evans, John H. Religious belief, perceptions of human suffering, and support for reproductive genetic technology. *Journal of Health Politics, Policy and Law* 2006 December; 31(6): 1047-1074. Subject: 14.1

Evans, John H. Stratification in knowledge production: author prestige and the influence of an American academic debate. *Poetics* 2005 April; 33(2): 111-133. Subject: 15.1

Evans, John H. Who legitimately speaks for religion in public bioethics? *In:* Guinn, David E., ed. Handbook of Bioethics and Religion. New York: Oxford University Press, 2006: 61-79. Subject: 2.1

Evans, Martin. Ethical sourcing of human embryonic stem cells — rational solutions? *Nature Reviews Molecular Cell Biology* 2005 August; 6(8): 663-667. Subject: 18.5.4

Evans, Martyn. Reflections on the humanities in medical education. *Medical Education* 2002 June; 36(6): 508-513. Subject: 7.2

Evans, Robert W. The promises and perils of human embryonic stem cell research. *In:* Glasa, J. ed. The Ethics of Human Genetics: Challenges of the (Post) Genomic Era. Bratislava, Slovak Republic: Charis [and] IMEB Foundation; 2002: 181-189. Subject: 18.5.4

Evans, Steven; Block, Jerome B. Ethical issues regarding fee-for-service-funded research within a complementary medicine context. *Journal of Alternative and Complementary Medicine* 2001 December; 7(6): 697-702. Subject: 18.6

Ewing, Charles Patrick. Diagnosing and treating "insanity" on death row: legal and ethical perspectives. *Behavioral Sciences and the Law* 1987 Spring; 5(2): 175-185. Subject: 20.6

Ewy, Gordon A. Cardiac resuscitation — when is enough enough? [editorial]. *New England Journal of Medicine* 2006 August 3; 355(5): 510-512. Subject: 20.5.1

F

Facio, Flavia M. One size does not fit all. *American Journal of Bioethics* 2006 November-December; 6(6): 40-42; author reply W10-W12. Subject: 15.1

Faden, Pamela; Minkler, Meredith; Perry, Martha; Blum, Klaus; Moore, Leroy; Rogers, Judith. Ethical challenges in community based participatory research: a

See SUBJECT HEADING KEY FOR SECTION II on inside back cover.

555

case study from the San Francisco Bay area disability community. *In:* Minkler, Meredith; Wallerstein, Nina, eds. Community Based Participatory Research for Health. San Francisco, CA: Jossey-Bass; 2003: 242-262. Subject: 18.4

Faden, Ruth. Response: reflections on Jay Katz's legacy. *Yale Journal of Health Policy, Law and Ethics* 2006 Summer; 6(2): 451-454. Subject: 18.2

Faden, Ruth. The road to balanced oversight [editorial]. *Science* 2006 August 18; 313(5789): 891. Subject: 5.3

Faden, Ruth R.; Kass, Nancy E. Genetic screening technology: ethical issues in access to tests by employers and health insurance companies. *Journal of Social Issues* 1993 Summer; 49(2): 75-88. Subject: 15.3

Fagerström, Lisbeth. The dialectic tension between 'being' and 'not being' a good nurse. *Nursing Ethics* 2006 November; 13(6): 622-632. Subject: 8.1

Fahey, Charles J. Religious perspectives on access to health care: a Catholic perspective. *Mount Sinai Journal of Medicine* 1997 March; 64(2): 80-83. Subject: 9.2

Fahrenkrog, Aaron R. A comparison of international regulation of preimplantation genetic diagnosis and a regulatory suggestion for the United States. *Transnational Law and Contemporary Problems* 2006 Spring; 15(2): 757-781. Subject: 15.2

Fahrenwald, Nancy L.; Stabnow, Wendy. Sociocultural perspective on organ and tissue donation among reservation-dwelling American Indian adults. *Ethnicity and Health* 2005 November; 10(4): 341-354. Subject: 19.5

Faigman, David L. The right to be let alone: privacy and the problem of defining life and death. *In his:* Laboratory of Justice: The Supreme Court's 200-Year Struggle To Integrate Science and the Law. New York: Times Books/Henry Holt; 2004: 205-250. Subject: 12.4.1

Fairchild, Alysa; Kelly, Karie-Lynn; Balogh, Alex. In pursuit of an artful death: discussion of resuscitation status on an inpatient radiation oncology service. *Supportive Care in Cancer* 2005 October; 13(10): 842-849. Subject: 20.5.1

Fairchild, Amy L. Diabetes and disease surveillance. *Science* 2006 July 14; 313(5784): 175-176. Subject: 9.1

Fairchild, Amy L.; Colgrove, James; Jones, Marian Moser. The challenge of mandatory evacuation: providing for and deciding for. *Health Affairs* 2006 July-August; 25(4): 958-967. Subject: 9.1

Falcâo de Oliveira, Guilherme Freire. Juridical implications on genome knowledge (Part II) = Implicaciones jurídicas del conocimiento del genoma (Parte II). *Revista de Derecho Genoma Humano = Law and the Human Genome Review* 1997 July-December; (7): 59-98. Subject: 15.3

Falcâo de Oliveira, Guilherme Freire. Juridical implications on genome knowledge (Part I) = Impliciones jurídicas del conocimiento del genoma (Parte I). *Revista de*

Derecho Genoma Humano = Law and the Human Genome Review 1997 January-June; (6): 51-62. Subject: 15.10

Falk-Rafael, Adeline. Speaking truth to power: nursing's legacy and moral imperative. *ANS: Advances in Nursing Science* 2005 July-September; 28(3): 212-223. Subject: 4.1.3

Fallberg, Lars. Consequences of the Amsterdam Declaration—a rights revolution in Europe? [editorial]. *European Journal of Health Law* 2003 March; 10(1): 5-10. Subject: 8.3.1

Fallberg, Lars. Do doctors know about their legal responsibilities? [editorial]. *European Journal of Health Law* 2006 June; 13(2): 91-93. Subject: 2.1

Fan, Minsheng. Patients are not ordinary consumers. *In:* Döring, Ole; Chen, Renbiao, eds. Advances in Chinese Medical Ethics: Chinese and International Perspectives. Hamburg: Institut für Asienkunde; 2002: 353-357. Subject: 8.1

Fan, Ruiping. Confucian filial piety and long term care for aged parents. *HEC (Healthcare Ethics Committee) Forum* 2006 March; 18(1): 1-17. Subject: 9.5.2

Fan, Ruiping. Towards a Confucian virtue bioethics: reframing Chinese medical ethics in a market economy. *Theoretical Medicine and Bioethics* 2006; 27(6): 541-566. Subject: 2.1

Fanos, Joanna H.; Spangner, Kerstin A.; Musci, Thomas J. Attitudes toward prenatal screening and testing for Fragile X. *Genetics in Medicine* 2006 February; 8(2): 129-133. Subject: 15.2

Farah, Martha J. Emerging ethical issues in neuroscience. *Nature Neuroscience* 2002 November; 5(11): 1123-1129. Subject: 17.1

Farah, Martha J. Reply to Jedlicka: neuroethics, reductionism and dualism. *Trends in Cognitive Sciences* 2005 April; 9(4): 173. Subject: 17.1

Farahany, Nita; Bernet, William. Behavioral genetics in criminal cases: past, present, and future. *Genomics, Society and Policy* 2006 May; 2(1): 72-79. Subject: 15.6

Farber, Neil J.; Gilibert, Stephanie G.; Aboff, Brian M.; Collier, Virginia U.; Weiner, Joan; Boyer, E. Gil. Physicians' willingness to report impaired colleagues. *Social Science and Medicine* 2005 October; 61(8): 1772-1775. Subject: 7.3

Farber, Neil J.; Simpson, Pamela; Salam, Tabassum; Collier, Virginia U.; Weiner, Joan; Boyer, E. Gil. Physicians' decisions to withhold and withdraw life-sustaining treatment. *Archives of Internal Medicine* 2006 March 13; 166(5): 560-564. Subject: 20.5.1

Farber, Stuart; Shaw, Jim; Mero, Jeff; Maloney, W. Hugh. Withholding resuscitation: a new approach to prehospital end-of-life decisions [letter]. *Annals of Internal Medicine* 2006 November 21; 145(10): 788. Subject: 20.5.1

Subject = NRCBL Primary Classification Number; see inside front cover.

Faria, Miguel A., Jr. Is there a natural right to medical care? [editorial]. *Surgical Neurology* 2005 November; 64(5): 471-473. Subject: 9.2

Farnell, Sheila M. Medical research: why trouble the patient for informed consent? *Medical and Pediatric Oncology* 2002 September; 39(3): 207- 209. Subject: 8.3.2

Farragher, Rachel A.; Laffey, John G. Maternal brain death and somatic support. *Neurocritical Care* 2005; 3(2): 99-106. Subject: 20.2.1

Farragher, R.; Marsh, B.; Laffey, J.G. Maternal brain death — an Irish perspective. *Irish Journal of Medical Science* 2005 October-December; 174(4): 55-59. Subject: 20.2.1

Farrell, Anne-Maree. Is the gift still good? Examining the politics and regulation of blood safety in the European Union. *Medical Law Review* 2006 Summer; 14(2): 155-179. Subject: 19.4

Farrell, Kristen. Human experimentation in developing countries: improving international practices by identifying vulnerable populations and allocating fair benefits. *Journal of Health Care Law and Policy* 2006; 9(1): 136-161. Subject: 18.2

Farthing, Michael J.G. Authors and publication practices. *Science and Engineering Ethics* 2006 January; 12(1): 41-52. Subject: 1.3.9

Fäßler, Peter. Sozialhygiene-Rassenhygiene- Euthanasie: 'Volksgesundheitspflege' im Raum Dresden. *In his:* Dresden unterm Hakenkreuz. Ed. by Reiner Pommerin, Koln: Böhlau Verlag, 1998: 193-207. Subject: 15.5

Faulkner, Alison. Inclusive and empowering. *Mental Health Today* 2005 November; 31-33. Subject: 18.2

Faulstich, Heinz. Die Zahl der "Euthanasie"-Opfer. *In:* Frewer, Andreas; Eickhoff, Clemens, eds. "Euthanasie" und die aktuelle Sterbehilfe-Debatte: Die historischen Hintergründe medizinischer Ethik. Frankfurt; New York: Campus; 2000: 218-234. Subject: 20.5.1

Faunce, Thomas A.; Bolsin, S.N. Fiduciary disclosure of medical mistakes: the duty to promptly notify patients of adverse health care events. *Journal of Law and Medicine* 2005 May; 12(4): 478-482. Subject: 8.2

Faunce, Thomas A.; Gatenby, Paul. Flexner's ethical oversight reprised? Contemporary medical education and the health impacts of corporate globalisation. *Medical Education* 2005 October; 39(10): 1066-1074. Subject: 7.2

Faunce, Thomas A.; Stewart, Cameron. The Messiha and Schiavo cases: third-party ethical and legal interventions in futile care disputes. *Medical Journal of Australia* 2005 September 5; 183(5): 261-263. Subject: 20.5.1

Fauriel, Isabelle; Moutel, Grégoire; Duchange, Nathalie; Montuclard, Luc; Moutard, Marie-Laure; Cochat, Pierre; Hervé, Christian. Decision making concerning life-sustaining treatment in paediatric nephrology: professionals' experiences and values. *Nephrology Dialysis Transplantation* 2005 December; 20(12): 2746-2750. Subject: 20.5.2

Faust, Halley S.; Orentlicher, David. Protection of human subjects and scientific progress: can the two be reconciled? [letter and reply]. *Hastings Center Report* 2006 January-February; 36(1): 5-6, 8- 9. Subject: 18.1

Featherstone, Carol. Testing gene therapy vectors in healthy volunteers [news]. *Molecular Medicine Today* 1997 July; 3(7): 277. Subject: 15.1

Feczko, Josephy; Zarin, Deborah A.; Tse, Tony; Ide, Nicholas C.; Drazen, Jeffrey M.; Wood, Alastair J.J.; Haug, Charlotte; Gøtzsche, Peter C.; Schroeder, Torben V. Clinical trials report card [letter and replies]. *New England Journal of Medicine* 2006 March 30; 354(13): 1426-1429. Subject: 18.2

Feder, Ellen K. Doctor's orders: parents and intersexed children. *In:* Kittay, Eva Feder; Feder, Ellen K., eds. The Subject of Care: Feminist Perspectives on Dependency. Lanham, MD: Rowman and Littlefield Publishers; 2002: 294-320. Subject: 10

Feder, Ellen K. "In their best interests": parents' experience of atypical genitalia. *In:* Parens, Erik, ed. Surgically Shaping Children: Technology, Ethics, and the Pursuit of Normality. Baltimore, MD: Johns Hopkins University Press; 2006: 189-210. Subject: 9.5.7

Feder, Sylvia; Matheny, Roger L.; Loveless, Robert S.; Rea, Thomas D. Withholding resuscitation: a new approach to prehospital end-of-life decisions [editorial]. *Annals of Internal Medicine* 2006 May 2; 144(9): 634-640. Subject: 20.5.1

Feeley, Thomas Hugh; Servoss, Timothy J. Examining college students' intentions to become organ donors. *Journal of Health Communication* 2005 April-May; 10(3): 237-249. Subject: 19.5

Fegran, Liv; Helseth, Solvi; Slettebo, Ashild. Nurses as moral practitioners encountering parents in neonatal intensive care units. *Nursing Ethics* 2006 January; 13(1): 52-64. Subject: 9.5.7

Feinman, Michael; Sher, Geoffrey. Comparing the British and American approaches to regulating ART programmes. *Human Reproduction* 1996 July; 11(7): 1366-1367. Subject: 14.1

Feldman, Eric A. AIDS policy and the politics of rights. *In his:* The Ritual of Rights in Japan: Law, Society, and Health Policy. New York: Cambridge University Press, 2000: 53-81. Subject: 9.5.6

Feldman, Eric A. Asserting rights, legislating death. *In his:* The Ritual of Rights in Japan: Law, Society, and Health Policy. New York: Cambridge University Press, 2000: 82-109. Subject: 20.5.1

Feldman, Eric A. Patients, rights, and protest in contemporary Japan. *In his:* The Ritual of Rights in Japan: Law,

See SUBJECT HEADING KEY FOR SECTION II on inside back cover.

557

Society, and Health Policy. New York: Cambridge University Press, 2000: 38-52. Subject: 9.2

Fellenz, Marc R. Animal experimentation. *In:* Mitcham, Carl, ed. Encyclopedia of Science, Technology, and Ethics. Farmington Hills, MI: Thomson/Gale, 2005: 72-74. Subject: 22.2

Fellenz, Marc R. Animal rights. *In:* Mitcham, Carl, ed. Encyclopedia of Science, Technology, and Ethics. Farmington Hills, MI: Thomson/Gale, 2005: 74-77. Subject: 22.1

Felos, George. Felos on Schiavo. *Stetson Law Review* 2005 Fall; 35(1): 9-15. Subject: 20.5.1

Felten, David L.; Vogt, Thomas; Gunsalus, C.K.; Bruner, Edward M.; Burbules, Nicholas C.; Dash, Leon; Finkin, Matthew; Goldberg, Joseph P.; Greenough, William T.; Miller, Gregory A.; Pratt, Michael G. IRBs: going too far or not far enough? [letters]. *Science* 2006 September 8; 313(5792): 1388-1389. Subject: 18.2

Fennell, Mary L. Racial disparities in care: looking beyond the clinical encounter [editorial]. *Health Services Research* 2005 December; 40(6, Part 1): 1713-1721. Subject: 9.5.4

Fenton, Elizabeth. Liberal eugenics and human nature: against Habermas. *Hastings Center Report* 2006 November-December; 36(6): 35-42. Subject: 15.1

Fenton, Rachel Anne. Catholic doctrine versus women's rights: the new Italian law on assisted reproduction. *Medical Law Review* 2006 Spring; 14(1): 73-107. Subject: 14.4

Ferguson, Robert P.; Rhim, Eugene; Belizaire, Waindel; Egede, Leonard; Carter, Kennita; Langsdale, Thomas. Encounters with pharmaceutical sales representatives among practicing internists. *American Journal of Medicine* 1999 August; 107(2): 149-152. Subject: 7.2

Ferguson, Warren J.; Candib, Lucy M. Culture, language, and the doctor-patient relationship. *Family Medicine* 2002 May; 34(5): 353-361. Subject: 8.1

Fernandez de Casadevante Romani, Carlos. The Convention on the Protection of Human Rights and the Dignity of the Human Being in regard to Applications of Biology and Medicine: Convention on Human Rights and Biomedicine = El Convenio para la Protección de los Derechos Humanos y la Dignidad del Ser Humano con respeto a la aplicación de la Biología y la Medicina: Convención sobre Derechos Humanos y Biomedicina. *Revista de Derecho Genoma Humano = Law and the Human Genome Review* 1997 July-December; (7): 99-112. Subject: 21.1

Fernandez, Conrad V. Publication of ethically suspect research: should it occur? [editorial]. *International Journal for Quality in Health Care* 2005 October; 17(5): 377-378. Subject: 1.3.7

Fernandez, Conrad V.; Weijer, Charles. Obligations in offering to disclose genetic research results. *American Journal of Bioethics* 2006 November-December; 6(6): 44-46. Subject: 15.1

Fernández-Suárez, A.; Cordero Fernández, C.; García Lozano, R.; Pizarro, A.; Garzón, M.; Núñez Roldán, A. Clinical and ethical implications of genetic counselling in familial adenomatous polyposis=Implicaciones clínicas y éticas de consejo genético en la poliposis adenomatosa familiar. *Revista Espanola Enfermedades Digestivas* 2005 September; 97(9): 654- 659; 660-665. Subject: 15.2

Ferrand, E.; Jabre, P.; Fernandez-Curiel, S.; Morin, F.; Vincent-Genod, C.; Duvaldestin, P.; Lemaire, F.; Hervé, C.; Marty, J. Participation of French general practitioners in end-of-life decisions for their hospitalised patients. *Journal of Medical Ethics* 2006 December; 32(12): 683-687. Subject: 20.5.1

Ferraretti, Anna Pia; Pennings, Guido; Gianaroli, Luca; Magli, Maria Cristina. Semen donor recruitment in an oocyte donation programme. *Human Reproduction* 2006 October; 21(10): 2482-2485. Subject: 14.6

Ferree, Myra Marx. Resonance and radicalism: feminist framing in the abortion debates of the United States and Germany. *American Journal of Sociology* 2003 September; 109(2): 304-344. Subject: 12.5.1

Ferreira, Luzitano Brandão. Population genetics and the power of discrimination. *Eubios Journal of Asian and International Bioethics* 2006 January; 16(1): 25-27. Subject: 15.11

Ferrell, Betty. Ethical perspectives on pain and suffering. *Pain Management Nursing* 2005 September; 6(3): 83-90. Subject: 4.4

Ferres, Beverley J. Usual medical practice in the process of obtaining consent to medical procedures for the elderly person. *Journal of Law and Medicine* 1998 May; 5(4): 355-363. Subject: 8.3.3

Ferris, Ann M.; Marquis, Grace S. Bioethics in scientific research: conflicts between subject's equitable access to participate in research and current regulations. *Journal of Nutrition* 2005 April; 135(4): 916-917. Subject: 18.3

Feuillet, Brigitte. The role of ethics committees in relation to French biomedical research: protection of the person and personal data. *In:* Beyleveld, D.; Townend, D.; Wright, J., eds. Research Ethics Committees, Data Protection and Medical Research in European Countries. Hants, England; Burlington, VT: Ashgate; 2005: 55-71. Subject: 18.2

Feuillet-Le Mintier, Brigitte. The journey from ethics to law: the case of euthanasia. *In:* Rehmann-Sutter, Christoph; Düwell, Marcus; Mieth, Dietmar, eds. Bioethics in Cultural Contexts: Reflections on Methods and Finitude. Dordrecht: Springer, 2006: 121-128. Subject: 20.5.1

Feussner, John R.; Burris, James F.; McGlynn, Geraldine; Lavori, Philip W. Enhancing protections for human participants in clinical and health services research — a continuing process. *Medical Care* 2002 September; 40(9, Supplement): V4-V11. Subject: 18.3

Feussner, John R.; Murray, Thomas H. Making informed consent meaningful — a state-of-the-art conference [editorial]. *Medical Care* 2002 September; 40(9, Supplement): V1-V3. Subject: 18.3

Fey, Toby Schonfeld. Regulating radiology: ethical issues in mammography and federal legislation. *Journal of Women's Health and Gender-Based Medicine* 2000 December; 9(10): 1113-1118. Subject: 9.5.5

Fidler, David P. Caught between paradise and power: public health, pathogenic threats, and the axis of illness. *McGeorge Law Review* 2004; 35(1): 45-104. Subject: 9.1

Fidler, David P.; Gostin, Lawrence O. The new international health regulations: an historic development for international law and public health. *Journal of Law, Medicine, and Ethics* 2006 Spring; 34(1): 85-94. Subject: 9.1

Fidler, H.; Thompson, C.; Freeman, A.; Hogan, D.; Walker, G.; Weinman, J. Barriers to implementing a policy not to attempt resuscitation in acute medical admissions: prospective cross sectional study of a successive cohort. *BMJ: British Medical Journal* 2006 February 25; 332(7539): 461-462. Subject: 20.5.1

Fiedler, Leslie A. On infanticide. *Journal of Popular Culture* 1981 Spring; 14: 676-680. Subject: 20.5.2

Field, Charles K.; Kerstein, Morris D. Cost benefit analysis of lower-extremity amputation: ethical considerations. *Wounds* 1993 January-February; 5(1): 10-13. Subject: 9.4

Field, Martha A. Response of Professor Field. *Politics and the Life Sciences* 1991 February; 9(2): 262-268. Subject: 14.2

Fielder, John. The Bioengineer's obligations to patients. *Journal of Investigative Surgery* 1992 July-September; 5(3): 201-208. Subject: 5.2

Fielder, John H. Pharmacists refuse to fill emergency contraception prescriptions. *IEEE Engineering in Medicine and Biology Magazine* 2005 July-August; 24(4): 88-91. Subject: 11.1

Fielder, John H. The Vioxx debacle. *IEEE Engineering in Medicine and Biology Magazine* 2005 March-April; 24(2): 106-109. Subject: 9.7

Fielding, Stephen L.; Edmunds, Emme; Schaff, Eric A. Having an abortion using mifepristone and home misoprostol: a qualitative analysis of women's experiences. *Perspectives on Sexual and Reproductive Health* 2002 January-February; 34(1): 34-40. Subject: 12.5.2

Fields, Gary. Criminal mind: on death row, fate of mentally ill is thorny problem; can states execute inmates made sane only by drugs? medical, legal quandary; a test case is

Mr. Thompson. *Wall Street Journal* 2006 December 14; p. A1, A8. Subject: 20.6

Fields, Helen. What comes next? Scientists are now grappling with a major setback to stem cell research. *U.S. News and World Report* 2006 January 23; 140(3): 56-58. Subject: 18.5.4

Figueiras, Adolfo; Tato, Fernando; Fontaiñas, Jesus; Takkouche, Bahi; Gestal-Otero, Juan Jesus. Physicians' attitudes towards voluntary reporting of adverse drug events. *Journal of Evaluation in Clinical Practice* 2001 November; 7(4): 347-354. Subject: 9.7

Figueroa Yañez, Gonzalo. UNESCO Draft Universal Declaration on the Human Genome = El Proyecto de Declaración Universal sobre el Genoma Humano de la UNESCO. *Revista de Derecho Genoma Humano = Law and the Human Genome Review* 1997 July-December; (7): 113-120. Subject: 15.10

Fijn, Roel; van Epenhuysen, L. Sara; Peijnenburg, A. Jeanne M.; de Jong-van den Berg, Lolkje T.W.; Brouwers, Jacobus R.B.J. Introducing ethics in hospital drug resource allocation decisions: keep expectations modest and beware of unintended effects. Part I: an explorative overview. *Pharmacoepidemiology and Drug Safety* 2002 September; 11(6): 523-527. Subject: 9.7

Fijn, Roel; van Epenhuysen, L. Sara; Peijnenburg, A. Jeanne M.; de Jong-van den Berg, Lolkje T.W.; Brouwers, Jacobus R.B.J. Introducing ethics in hospital drug resource allocation decisions: keep expectations modest and beware of unintended effects. Part II: the use of ethics. *Pharmacoepidemiology and Drug Safety* 2002 October-November; 11(7): 617-620. Subject: 9.7

Fine, Adrian; Fontaine, Bunny; Kraushar, Maryann M.; Rich, Beverly R. Nephrologists should voluntarily divulge survival data to potential dialysis patients: a questionnaire study. *Peritoneal Dialysis International* 2005 May-June; 25(3): 269-273. Subject: 8.3.1

Fine, Robert L.; Whitfield, Jonathan M.; Carr, Barbara L.; Mayo, Thomas W. Medical futility in the neonatal intensive care unit: hope for a resolution. *Pediatrics* 2005 November; 116(5): 1219-1222. Subject: 20.5.2

Finegold, David; Moser, Allison. Ethical decision-making in bioscience firms. *Nature Biotechnology* 2006 March; 24(3): 285-290. Subject: 9.6

Finer, Lawrence B.; Frohwirth, Lori F.; Dauphinee, Lindsay A.; Singh, Susheela; Moore, Ann M. Reasons U.S. women have abortions: quantitative and qualitative perspectives. *Perspectives on Sexual and Reproductive Health* 2005 September; 37(3): 110-118. Subject: 12.5.2

Fink, Max. Is the practice of ECT ethical? *World Journal of Biological Psychiatry* 2005; 6(Supplement 2): 38-43. Subject: 17.5

Finlay, I.G.; Wheatley, Victoria J.; Izdebski, C. The House of Lords Select Committee on the Assisted Dying

See SUBJECT HEADING KEY FOR SECTION II on inside back cover.

559

for the Terminally Ill Bill: implications for specialist palliative care. *Palliative Medicine* 2005 September; 19(6): 444-453. Subject: 20.5.1

Finlay, Ilora. The flip side to 'assisted dying' — why the Lords were wise to reject Lord Joffe's Bill [editorial]. *Clinical Ethics* 2006 September; 1(3): 118-120. Subject: 20.5.1

Finlay, Ilora. Why a third attempt at legislation for physician-assisted suicide in the UK failed. *Lancet Oncology* 2006 July; 7(7): 529-531. Subject: 20.7

Finn, Peter. In Russia, psychiatry is again a tool against dissent. *Washington Post* 2006 September 30; p. A1, A14. Subject: 17.7

Finn, Peter B. The negotiation and development of a clinical trial agreement. *Journal of Biolaw and Business* 2006; 9(2): 21-27. Subject: 18.2

Finnie, Sarah; Foy, Robbie; Mather, Jean. The pathway to induced abortion: women's experiences and general practitioner attitudes. *Journal of Family Planning and Reproductive Health Care* 2006 January; 32(1): 15-18. Subject: 12.5.2

Fins, Joseph J. Clinical pragmatism and the care of brain damaged patients: toward a palliative neuroethics for disorders of consciousness. *Progress in Brain Research* 2005; 150: 565-582. Subject: 17.1

Fins, Joseph J. Neuromodulation, free will and determinism: lessons from the psychosurgery debate. *Clinical Neuroscience Research* 2004 July; 4(1-2): 113-118 [Online]. Accessed: http://www.sciencedirect.com [2007 February 26]. Subject: 17.6

Fins, Joseph J.; Schiff, Nicholas D. Shades of gray: new insights into the vegetative state. *Hastings Center Report* 2006 November-December; 36(6): 8. Subject: 20.5.1

Finucane, Thomas E.; Ancoli-Israel, Sonia; Folks, David G.; Krystal, Andrew D.; McCall, W. Vaughn. Advertising the new hypnotics [letter and reply]. *Journal of the American Geriatrics Society* 2006 January; 54(1): 170-172. Subject: 1.3.7

Firtko, Angela; Jackson, Debra. Do the ends justify the means? Nursing and the dilemma of whistleblowing. *Australian Journal of Advanced Nursing* 2005 September-November; 23(1): 51-56. Subject: 7.3

Fischer, Jennifer. Comparative look at the right to refuse treatment for involuntarily hospitalized persons with a mental illness. *Hastings International and Comparative Law Review* 2006 Winter; 29(2): 153-186. Subject: 8.3.4

Fischer, Johannes. Güter, Tugenden, Pflichten: zum sittlichen Fundament der Medizinethik = Goods, virtues, duties: on the moral foundation of medical ethics. *Ethik in der Medizin* 2006 June; 18(2): 148-163. Subject: 4.1.2

Fischer, Josef E. Surgeons: employees or professionals? [editorial]. *American Journal of Surgery* 2005 July; 190(1): 1-3. Subject: 4.1.2

Fischer, Michael M.J. Ethnographic critique and technoscientific narratives: the old mole, ethical plateaux, and the governance of emergent biosocial polities. *Culture Medicine and Psychiatry* 2001 December; 25(4): 355-393. Subject: 2.1

Fischer, Richard L.; Schaeffer, Kathleen; Hunter, Robert L. Attitudes of obstetrics and gynecology residents toward abortion participation: a Philadelphia area survey. *Contraception* 2005 September; 72(3): 200-205. Subject: 12.5.2

Fischman, Josh. Mix, match, and switch: kidney exchanges between strangers are helping to ease the organ shortage and could save thousands of lives. *U.S. News and World Report* 2006 October 16; 141(14): 74-76. Subject: 19.3

Fisher, Ann Hilton; Hanssens, Catherine; Schulman, David I. The CDC's routine HIV testing recommendation: legally, not so routine. *HIV/AIDS Policy and Law Review* 2006 December; 11(2-3): 17-20. Subject: 9.5.6

Fisher, Anthony. The duties of a Catholic politician with respect to bio-lawmaking. *Notre Dame Journal of Law, Ethics and Public Policy* 2006; 20(1): 89-123. Subject: 12.4.1

Fisher, Celia B. Challenges in constructing a cross-national ethics code for psychologists. *European Psychologist* 2004 December; 9(4): 275-277. Subject: 6

Fisher, Celia B. Clinical trials results databases: unanswered questions. *Science* 2006 January 13; 311(5758): 180-181. Subject: 1.3.9

Fisher, Celia B. Goodness-of-fit ethic for informed consent to research involving adults with mental retardation and developmental disabilities. *Mental Retardation and Developmental Disabilities Research Reviews* 2003; 9(1): 27-31. Subject: 18.3

Fisher, Celia B.; Cea, Christine D.; Davidson, Philip W.; Fried, Adam L. Capacity of persons with mental retardation to consent to participate in randomized clinical trials. *American Journal of Psychiatry* 2006 October; 163(10): 1813-1820. Subject: 18.5.6

Fisher, Ian. Italian poet dies with help from a doctor. *New York Times* 2006 December 22; p. A3. Subject: 20.5.1

Fisher, Jill A. Procedural misconceptions and informed consent: insights from empirical research on the clinical trials industry. *Kennedy Institute of Ethics Journal* 2006 September; 16(3): 251-268. Subject: 18.3

Fisher, Malcolm M.; Raper, Raymond F. Courts, doctors and end-of-life care [editorial]. *Intensive Care Medicine* 2005 June; 31(6): 762-764. Subject: 20.5.1

Fishman, Scott M. The politics of pain and its impact on pain medicine [editorial]. *Pain Medicine* 2005 May-June; 6(3): 199-200. Subject: 4.4

Fisk, Nicholas M.; Roberts, Irene A.G.; Markwald, Roger; Mironov, Vladimir. Can routine commercial cord

---

blood banking be scientifically and ethically justified? *PLoS Medicine* 2005 February; 2(2): 0087-0090. Subject: 19.4

Fissell, Rachel B.; Bragg-Gresham, Jennifer L.; Lopes, Antonio Alberto; Cruz, José Miguel; Fukuhara, Shunichi; Asano, Yasushi; Brown, Wendy Weinstock; Keen, Marcia L.; Port, Friedrich K.; Young, Eric W. Factors associated with "do not resuscitate" orders and rates of withdrawal from hemodialysis in the international DOPPS. *Kidney International* 2005 September; 68(3): 1282-1288. Subject: 20.5.1

Fitzgerald, D.A.; Isaacs, D.; Kemp, A. Scientific ethics committees: a user's guide. *Archives of Disease in Childhood* 2005 December; 90(12): 1249-1250. Subject: 18.2

Fitzgerald, Maureen H.; Phillips, Paul A. Centralized and non-centralized ethics review: a five nation study. *Accountability in Research* 2006 January-March; 13(1): 47-74. Subject: 18.2

Fitzgerald, Maureen H.; Phillips, Paul A.; Yule, Elisa. The research ethics review process and ethics review narrative. *Ethics and Behavior* 2006; 16(4): 377-395. Subject: 18.2

Fitzgibbons, Sean R. Cadaveric organ donation and consent: a comparative analysis of the United States, Japan, Singapore, and China. *ILSA Journal of International and Comparative Law* 1999 Fall; 6(1): 73-105. Subject: 19.5

Fitzpatrick, Erin Elizabeth. Lessons from Starson on consent and capacity. *Health Law in Canada* 2006 June; 26(4): 74-88. Subject: 17.4

Flamigni, Carlo. The embryo question. *Annals of the New York Academy of Sciences* 2001 September; 943: 352-359. Subject: 4.4

Flanagan-Klygis, Erin A.; Sharp, Lisa; Frader, Joel E. Dismissing the family who refuses vaccines: a study of pediatrician attitudes. *Archives of Pediatrics and Adolescent Medicine* 2005 October; 159(10): 929-934. Subject: 9.7

Flanagin, Annette; Fontanarosa, Phil B.; DeAngelis, Catherine D. Update on JAMA's conflict of interest policy. *JAMA: the Journal of the American Medical Association* 2006 July 12; 296(2): 220-221. Subject: 1.3.7

Flanigan, Rosemary. Artificial food and hydration—defending a tradition. *Practical Bioethics* 2006 Spring-Summer; 2(2-3): 11-12. Subject: 20.5.1

Flanigan, Timothy P.; Beckwith, Curt; Carpenter, Charles C.J.; Frieden, Thomas R.; Kellerman, Scott E.; Das-Douglas, Moupali. Public health principles for the HIV epidemic [letter and reply]. *New England Journal of Medicine* 2006 February 23; 354(8): 878. Subject: 9.5.6

Flaum, Tzvi. Living donor organ transplants. *In:* Rosner, Fred, ed. Medicine and Jewish Law. Volume III. Brooklyn, NY: Yashar Books, Inc.; 2005: 131-140. Subject: 19.5

Fleck, Leonard M. The costs of caring: who pays? Who profits? Who panders? *Hastings Center Report* 2006 May-June; 36(3): 13-17. Subject: 9.4

Fleising, Usher. Genetic essentialism, mana, and the meaning of DNA. *New Genetics and Society* 2001 April; 20(1): 43-57. Subject: 15.1

Fleming, John I. Ethics and the Human Genome Diversity Project = La ética y el Proyecto Genoma Humano sobre Diversidad. *Law and the Human Genome Review = Revista de Derecho y Genoma Humano* 1996 January-June; (4): 141-164. Subject: 15.11

Flood, Colleen M. Chaoulli's legacy for the future of Canadian health care policy. *Osgoode Hall Law Journal* 2006 Summer; 44(2): 273-310. Subject: 9.3.1

Flum, David R. Interpreting surgical trials with subjective outcomes: avoiding unSPORTsmanlike conduct. *JAMA: The Journal of the American Medical Association* 2006 November 22-29; 296(20): 2483-2485. Subject: 18.2

Fluss, Sev S. AIDS: toward a regulatory history. *Canadian HIV/AIDS Policy and Law Newsletter* 1995 January; 1(2): 10-11. Subject: 9.5.6

Flynn, Gillian. To test or not: genetic mapping poses ethical dilemmas for employers. *Workforce* 2000 December; 79(12): 108-112. Subject: 15.3

Foddy, Bennett; Savulescu, Julian. Addiction and autonomy: can addicted people consent to the prescription of their drug of addiction? *Bioethics* 2006 February; 20(1): 1-15. Subject: 9.5.9

Foddy, Bennett; Savulescu, Julian. Autonomy, addiction and the drive to pleasure: designing drugs and our biology: a reply to Neil Levy. *Bioethics* 2006 February; 20(1): 21-23. Subject: 9.5.9

Foehl, John C. "How could this happen to me?": sexual misconduct and us. *Journal of the American Psychoanalytic Association* 2005 Summer; 53(3): 957-970. Subject: 7.4

Fogel, Susan Berke; Rivera, Lourdes A. Saving Roe is not enough: when religion controls healthcare. *Fordham Urban Law Journal* 2004 March; 31(3): 725-749. Subject: 12.3

Foglia, Mary Beth; Pearlman, Robert A. Integrating clinical and organizational ethics. *Health Progress* 2006 March-April; 87(2): 31-35. Subject: 9.6

Foley, Kathleen M.; Szalavitz, Maia. Why not a national institute on pain research? *Cerebrum: The Dana Forum on Brain Science* 2006 February: 1-14. Subject: 9.5.1

Foley, Michael. To opt in or out of electronic patient records?: electronic patient record is incompatible with confidentiality [letter]. *BMJ: British Medical Journal* 2006 July 15; 333(7559): 146-147. Subject: 8.3.1

Folkes, Kathryn. Is restraint a form of abuse? *Paediatric Nursing* 2005 July; 17(6): 41-44. Subject: 17.3

See SUBJECT HEADING KEY FOR SECTION II on inside back cover.

561

Follette, William C.; Davis, Deborah; Kemmelmeier, Markus. Ideals and realities in the development and practice of informed consent. *In:* O'Donohue, William; Ferguson, Kyle, eds. Handbook of Professional Ethics for Psychologists: Issues, Questions, and Controversies. Thousand Oaks, Calif.: SAGE Publications; 2003: 195-226. Subject: 8.3.1

Fong, Megan; Braun, Kathryn L.; Chang, R. Mei-Ling. Native Hawaiian preferences for informed consent and disclosure of results from research using stored biological specimens. *Pacific Health Dialog* 2004 September; 11(2): 154-159. Subject: 18.3

Fontanarosa, Phil B.; DeAngelis, Catherine D. JAMA's policy on industry sponsored studies [letter]. *BMJ: British Medical Journal* 2006 January 21; 332(7534): 177. Subject: 1.3.7

Fontenla, M.; Rycroft-Malone, J. Research governance and ethics: a resource for novice researchers. *Nursing Standard* 2006 February 15-21; 20(23): 41-46. Subject: 18.6

Forbes, Ian. States of uncertainty: governing the empire of biotechnology. *New Genetics and Society* 2006 April; 25(1): 69-88. Subject: 15.1

Forbes, James A., Jr. Religious perspectives on access to health care: a Protestant perspective. *Mount Sinai Journal of Medicine* 1997 March; 64(2): 75-79. Subject: 9.1

Ford, Helen L. The effect of consent guidelines on a multiple sclerosis register. *Multiple Sclerosis* 2006 February; 12(1): 104-107. Subject: 8.3.1

Ford, Norman. Human pluripotent stem cell research and ethics. *Monash Bioethics Review* 2006 January; 25(1): 31-41. Subject: 18.5.4

Ford, Paul J.; Kubu, Cynthia S. Stimulating debate: ethics in a multidisciplinary functional neurosurgery committee. *Journal of Medical Ethics* 2006 February; 32(2): 106-109. Subject: 17.5

Ford, Valerie; Furlong, Beth. Health systems and health promotion programs — the necessity of cultural competence: an ethical analysis. *In:* Kronenfeld, Jennie Jacobs, ed. Health Care Services, Racial and Ethnic Minorities and Underserved Populations: Patient and Provider Perspectives. Boston: Elsevier JAI, 2005: 233-243. Subject: 21.7

Foreman, D.M. Attention deficit hyperactivity disorder: legal and ethical aspects. *Archives of Disease in Childhood* 2006 February; 91(2): 192-194. Subject: 9.5.7

Forge, John. Guest editor's introduction: what is bioethics? *Social Alternatives* 2003 Summer; 22(1): 7-11. Subject: 2.1

Forsberg, Ralph P. Teaching virtue theory using a model from nursing. *Teaching Philosophy* 2001 June; 24(2): 155-166. Subject: 4.1.3

Forschner, Maximilian. Menschenwürde, Lebensschutz und biomedizinischer Fortschritt. *In:* Vollmann, Jochen, ed. Medizin und Ethik: Aktuelle ethische Probleme in Therapie und Forschung. Erlangen: Universitätsbund Erlangen-Nürnberg, 2003: 153-180. Subject: 4.4

Forstein, Marshall. Overview of ethical and research issues in sexual orientation therapy. *In:* Shidlo, Ariel; Schroeder, Michael; Drescher, Jack, eds. Sexual Conversion Therapy: Ethical, Clinical, and Research Perspectives. New York: Haworth Medical Press; 2001: 167-179. Subject: 10

Forster, David. Independent institutional review boards. *Seton Hall Law Review* 2002; 32(3): 513-523. Subject: 18.2

Forster, Jean L.; Kahn, Jeffrey P. Ethical challenges in public health education research and practice: introduction. *Health Education and Behavior* 2002 February; 29(1): 12-13. Subject: 7.2

Forsythe, Clarke D.; Presser, Stephen B. The tragic failure of Roe v. Wade: why abortion should be returned to the states. *Texas Review of Law and Politics* 2005 Fall; 10(1): 85-170. Subject: 12.4.2

Fortin, Ernest L. Aristotle and the sociobiologists: an old controversy revived. *Politics and the Life Sciences* 1988 February; 6(2): 205-208; author's reply 223-225. Subject: 15.9

Foss, Tara D. Privacy issues for girls are in the news and in BJN [editorial]. *British Journal of Nursing* 2006 January 26-February 8; 15(2): 65. Subject: 12.4.2

Fost, Norman. Ethical issues in clinical research on fracture prevention in patients with osteoporosis [editorial]. *Journal of Bone and Mineral Research* 2003 June; 18(6): 1110-1115. Subject: 18.3

Fost, Norman. The great stem cell debate: where are we now? Cloning, chimeras, and cash. *WMJ: official publication of the State Medical Society of Wisconsin* 2006 June; 105(4): 16-17. Subject: 14.5

Foster, Andrea L. The bionic CIO. *Chronicle of Higher Education* 2006 June 16; 52(41): A30-A32. Subject: 1.3.12

Foster, C.; Hope, T.; McMillan, J. Submissions from non-existent claimants: the non-identity problem and the law. *Medicine and Law: World Association for Medical Law* 2006 March; 25(1): 159-173. Subject: 4.4

Foster, Claire. Disease, suffering, and sin: one Anglican's perspective. *Christian Bioethics* 2006 August; 12(2): 157-163. Subject: 4.2

Foster, M.W.; Royal, C.D.M.; Sharp, R.R. The routinisation of genomics and genetics: implications for ethical practices. *Journal of Medical Ethics* 2006 November; 32(11): 635-638. Subject: 15.1

Foster, M.W.; Sharp, R.R. Will investments in biobanks, prospective cohorts, and markers of common patterns of variation benefit other populations for drug response and disease susceptibility gene discovery?

Subject = NRCBL Primary Classification Number; see inside front cover.

Pharmacogenomics Journal 2005; 5(2): 75-80. Subject: 15.1

Foster, Morris W. Analyzing the use of race and ethnicity in biomedical research from a local community perspective. *Journal of Law, Medicine and Ethics* 2006 Fall; 34(3): 508-512. Subject: 18.5.1

Foster, Morris W.; Mulvihill, John J.; Sharp, Richard R. Investments in cancer genomes: who benefits and who decides. *American Journal of Public Health* 2006 November; 96(11): 1960-1964. Subject: 15.10

Fouché, Rayvon. Race. *In:* Mitcham, Carl, ed. Encyclopedia of Science, Technology, and Ethics. Farmington Hills, MI: Thomson/Gale, 2005: 1561-1565. Subject: 5.1

Fovargue, S. Editorial. *Clinical Ethics* 2006 June; 1(2): 85. Subject: 20.5.2

Fowler, Esther. An ethical dilemma: is it ever acceptable to lie to a patient? *British Journal of Perioperative Nursing* 2004 October; 14(10): 448-451. Subject: 8.2

Fowler, Kenneth P.; Elpern, David J. Perceptions of a patients' bill of rights: a comparison of Massachusetts and South Carolina. *Journal of the South Carolina Medical Association* 1997 January; 93(1): 21-25. Subject: 9.2

Fox, Anthony W.; Pothmann, Raymund. Clinical trials ethics [letter and reply]. *Headache* 2005 September; 45(8): 1090-1091. Subject: 18.5.2

Fox, Brion J. Framing tobacco control efforts within an ethical context. *Tobacco Control* 2005 August; 14(Supplement 2): ii38-ii44. Subject: 9.5.9

Fox, Daniel M. America's ecumenical health policy: a century of consensus. *Mount Sinai Journal of Medicine* 1997 March; 64(2): 72-74. Subject: 9.1

Fox, Jeffrey L. US biosecurity advisory board faces delicate balancing act [news]. *Nature Biotechnology* 2005 August; 23(8): 905. Subject: 18.6

Fox, Renée C.; Goemaere, Eric. They call it "patient selection" in Khayelitsha: the experience of médecins sans frontières-South Africa in enrolling patients to receive antiretroviral treatment for HIV/AIDS. *CQ: Cambridge Quarterly of Healthcare Ethics* 2006 Summer; 15(3): 302-312. Subject: 9.5.6

Fox, Robin. In the matter of "Baby M": report from the Gruter Institute for Law and Behavioral Research. *Politics and the Life Sciences* 1988 August; 7(1): 77-88. Subject: 14.2

Frader, Joel. Becoming an ethical physician. *Atrium* 2006 Winter; 2: 12-13. Subject: 2.1

Frader, Joel E. Forgoing life support across borders: who decides and why? [editorial]. *Pediatric Critical Care Medicine* 2004 May; 5(3): 289-290. Subject: 20.5.2

France. Comité consultatif national d'éthique pour les sciences de la vie et de la santé. Inégalités d'accès aux soins et dans la participation à la recherche à l'échelle mondiale: problèmes éthiques. *Journal International de Bioéthique = International Journal of Bioethics* 2005 September-December; 16(3-4): 152-153. Subject: 9.2

France. Comité consultatif national d'éthique pour les sciences de la vie et de la santé. Orientation de travailleurs vers un poste comportant un risque. Rôle du médicin du travail et réflexions sur l'ambiguïté du concept d'aptitude. *Journal International de Bioéthique = International Journal of Bioethics* 2005 September-December; 16(3-4): 154-160. Subject: 5.2

France. Comité consultatif national d'éthique pour les sciences de la vie et de la santé. Problèmes éthiques posés par les collections de matériel biologique et les données d'information associées: "biobanques", "biothèques" = Ethical problems posed by biological specimen collections and their associated data: "biobanks", "bioethics". *Journal International de Bioéthique = International Journal of Bioethics* 2005 September-December; 16(3-4): 141-151. Subject: 15.1

Franchitto, N.; Gavarri, L; Telmon, N.; Rougé, D. Comment on the provisions of the French laws of 6 August 2004 and 8 December 2004 relative to the protection of genetic inventions. *Medicine and Law: The World Association for Medical Law* 2006 June; 25(2): 379-387. Subject: 15.8

Francione, Gary L. Equal consideration and the interest of nonhuman animals in continued existence: a response to Professor Sunstein. *University of Chicago Legal Forum* 2006: 231-252. Subject: 22.1

Francis, Theo. Medical dilemma: spread of records stirs patient fears of privacy erosion; Ms.Galvin's insurer studies psychotherapist's notes; a dispute over the rules; complaint tally hits 23,896. *Wall Street Journal* 2006 December 26; p. A1, A8. Subject: 8.4

Franck, Linda S.; Spencer, Caroline. Informing parents about anaesthesia for children's surgery: a critical literature review. *Patient Education and Counseling* 2005 November; 59(2): 117-125. Subject: 9.5.7

Franco, J.G.; Baruff, R.L.R.; Mauri, A.L.; Petersen, C.G.; Carillo, S.V.; Silva, P.; Martinhago, C.D.; Oliveira, J.B.A. Concerns regarding the follow-up on children conceived after assisted reproduction in Latin America. *Reproductive BioMedicine Online [electronic]* 2004 August; 9(2): 127-128. Subject: 14.4

Frank, Erica; Carrera, Jennifer S.; Stratton, Terry; Bickel, Janet; Nora, Lois Margaret. Experiences of belittlement and harassment and their correlates among medical students in the United States: longitudinal survey. *BMJ: British Medical Journal* 2006 September 30; 333(7570): 682-684. Subject: 7.2

Frank, Leonard Roy. The electroshock quotationary. *Ethical Human Psychology and Psychiatry* 2006 Summer; 8(2): 157-177. Subject: 17.5

See SUBJECT HEADING KEY FOR SECTION II on inside back cover.

563

Frank, Pamela; Cruise, Peter L.; Parsons, Sharon K.; Stutes, Ronald; Fruchter, Scott. State, heal thy physicians: an assessment of the Louisiana Natural Death Act. *Journal of Health and Human Services Administration* 2004 Winter; 27(3): 242-275. Subject: 20.5.1

Frank, Robert H. Weighing the true costs and benefits in a matter of life and death (opinion). *New York Times* 2006 January 19; p. C3. Subject: 9.4

Frank, Samuel; Kieburtz, Karl; Holloway, Robert; Kim, Scott Y.H. What is the risk of sham surgery in Parkinson disease clinical trials? A review of published reports. *Neurology* 2005 October 11; 65(7): 1101-1103. Subject: 18.2

Franklin, Deborah. "Come again?" Good medicine requires clarity. *New York Times* 2006 January 24; p. F5. Subject: 8.3.1

Franklin, Lise-Lotte; Ternestedt, Britt-Marie; Nordenfelt, Lennart. Views on dignity of elderly nursing home residents. *Nursing Ethics* 2006 March; 13(2): 130-146. Subject: 9.5.2

Franklin, Sarah. Better by design? *In:* Miller, Paul; Wilsdon, James, eds. Better Humans?: The Politics of Human Enhancement and Life Extension. London: Demos, 2006: 86-94. Subject: 4.5

Franklin, Sarah. Stem cells R us: emergent life forms and the global biological. *In:* Ong, Aihwa; Collier, Stephen J., eds. Global Assemblages: Technology, Politics, and Ethics as Anthropological Problems. Malden, MA: Blackwell Pub.; 2005: 59-78. Subject: 18.5.4

Fraser, Alisdair. Female genital mutilation and Baker Brown [letter]. *Journal of the Royal Society of Medicine* 1997 October; 90(10): 586-587. Subject: 9.5.5

Fraser, J.; Alexander, C. Publish and perish: a case study of publication ethics in a rural community. *Journal of Medical Ethics* 2006 September; 32(9): 526-529. Subject: 1.3.7

Frati, Paola. Organ transplantation from living donors, between bioethics and the law. *Transplantation Proceedings* 2005 July-August; 37(6): 2433-2435. Subject: 19.5

Frawley, Theresa; Begley, Cecily M. Ethical issues in caring for people with carotid artery rupture. *British Journal of Nursing* 2006 January 26-February 8; 15(2): 100-103. Subject: 20.5.1

Freckelton, Ian. Withdrawal of artificial life support [editorial]. *Journal of Law and Medicine* 2004 February; 11(3): 265-268. Subject: 20.5.1

Freda, Margaret Comerford; Kearney, Margaret H. Ethical issues faced by nursing editors. *Western Journal of Nursing Research* 2005 June; 27(4): 487-499. Subject: 1.3.7

Fredriksen, S. Tragedy, utopia and medical progress. *Journal of Medical Ethics* 2006 August; 32(8): 450-453. Subject: 5.1

Freedman, Alfred M.; Halpern, Abraham L. The erosion of ethics and morality in medicine: physician participation in legal executions in the United States. *Law School Review* 1996-1997; 41: 169-188. Subject: 4.1.2

Freedman, Benjamin. Compassionate access to experimental drugs and catastrophic rights. *Canadian HIV/AIDS Policy and Law Newsletter* 1996 October; 3(1): 44-46. Subject: 18.2

Freedman, Robert; Lewis, David A.; Michels, Robert; Pine, Daniel S.; Schultz, Susan K.; Tamminga, Carol T.; Patterson, Sandra L.; McIntyre, John S.; Goldman, Howard H.; Yudofsky, Stuart C.; Hales, Robert E.; Rapaport, Mark H.; Hales, Deborah; Krajeski, James; Kupfer, David J.; Badaracco, Mary Anne; Scully, James H. Jr. Conflict of interest, round 2 [editorial]. *American Journal of Psychiatry* 2006 September; 163(9): 1481-1483. Subject: 1.3.7

Freeman, Anthony. Consciousness. *In:* Mitcham, Carl, ed. Encyclopedia of Science, Technology, and Ethics. Farmington Hills, MI: Thomson/Gale, 2005: 410-411. Subject: 18.4

Freeman, J.M. Ethical theory and medical ethics: a personal perspective. *Journal of Medical Ethics* 2006 October; 32(10): 617-618. Subject: 4.1.2

Freeman, Jerome W. The bedside vigil: love and a question. *South Dakota Journal of Medicine* 2005 May; 58(5): 179-181. Subject: 20.5.4

Freeman, Jerome W.; Schellinger, Ellen; Olsen, Arthur; Harris, Mary Helen; Eidsness, LuAnn. A model for bioethics decision making: C/CPR. *South Dakota Journal of Medicine* 2005 May; 58(5): 195-196. Subject: 2.1

Freeman, Paul B. To err is human . . . sometimes [editorial]. *Optometry* 2006 February; 77(2): 59. Subject: 1.3.7

Freeman, Scott A.; McCall, W. Vaughn. High-risk electroconvulsive therapy and patient autonomy: a response to Dr. McCall's editorial [letter and reply]. *Journal of ECT* 2005 March; 21(1): 52-53. Subject: 17.5

French, Catherine M. Protecting the "right" to choose of women who are incompetent: ethical, doctrinal, and practical arguments against fetal representation. *Case Western Reserve Law Review* 2005 Winter; 56(2): 511-546. Subject: 9.5.3

French, Kathy. In strictest confidence. *Nursing Management* 2005 December; 12(8): 26-29. Subject: 8.3.2

French, Kathy. Young people and sexuality: consent and confidentiality. *Nursing Times* 2006 January 31-February 6; 102(5): 50-51. Subject: 8.1

Freschi, Gina C. Navigating the research exemption's safe harbor: Supreme Court to clarify scope-implications for stem cell research in California. *Santa Clara Computer and High Technology Law Journal* 2005; 21: 855-901. Subject: 5.3

Freshwater, Dawn. Editors and publishing: integrity, trust and faith [editorial]. *Journal of Psychiatric and Mental Health Nursing* 2006 February; 13(1): 1-2. Subject: 1.3.7

Freudenberg, Nicholas. Public health advocacy to change corporate practices: implications for health education practice and research. *Health Education and Behavior* 2005 June; 32(3): 298-319. Subject: 9.1

Freudenburg, William R. Seeding science, courting conclusions: reexamining the intersection of science, corporate cash, and the law. *Sociological Forum* 2005 March; 20(1): 3-33. Subject: 1.3.9

Frewer, Andreas. Die Euthanasie-Debatte in der Zeitschrift Ethik 1922-1938: Zur Anatomie des medizinethischen Diskurses. *In:* Frewer, Andreas; Eickhoff, Clemens, eds. "Euthanasie" und die aktuelle Sterbehilfe-Debatte: Die historischen Hintergründe medizinischer Ethik. Frankfurt; New York: Campus; 2000: 90-119. Subject: 20.5.1

Frewer, Lynn J.; Miles, Susan; Brennan, Mary; Kuznesof, Sharon; Ness, Mitchell; Ritson, Christopher. Public preferences for informed choice under conditions of risk uncertainty. *Public Understanding of Science* 2002 October; 11(4): 363-372. Subject: 5.2

Frey, Harvey S. The ethics of influenza vaccination [letter]. *Science* 2006 August 11; 313(5788): 758. Subject: 9.5.1

Frey, R.G. Intending and causing. *Journal of Ethics* 2005; 9(3-4): 465-474. Subject: 20.5.1

Frey, Ray. Passive death. *In:* Athanassoulis, Nafsika, ed. Philosophical Reflections on Medical Ethics. New York: Palgrave Macmillan; 2005: 198-207. Subject: 20.5.1

Fried, Terri R.; Byers, Amy L.; Gallo, William T.; Van Ness, Peter H.; Towle, Virginia R.; O'Leary, John R.; Dubin, Joel A. Prospective study of health status preferences and changes in preferences over time in older adults. *Archives of Internal Medicine* 2006 April 24; 166(8): 890-895. Subject: 9.5.2

Friedlaender, Jonathan S. Commentary: changing standards of informed consent: raising the bar. *In:* Turner, Trudy R. ed. Biological Anthropology and Ethics: From Repatriation to Genetic Identity. Albany, NY: State University of New York Press; 2005: 263-274. Subject: 15.1

Friedlaender, Michael M. The role of commercial non-related living kidney transplants. *Journal of Nephrology* 2003 November-December; 16(Supplement 7): S10-S15. Subject: 19.3

Friedland, Allen R.; Farber, Neil J.; Collier, Virginia U. Brief report: health care provided by program directors to their resident physicians and families. *JGIM: Journal of General Internal Medicine* 2006 December; 21(12): 1310-1312. Subject: 7.2

Friedman, Amy L. Payment for living organ donation should be legalised. *BMJ: British Medical Journal* 2006 October 7; 333(7571): 746-748. Subject: 19.5

Friedman, Samuel R.; Sherman, Susan G.; Frieden, Thomas R.; Kellerman, Scott E.; Das-Douglas, Moupali. Public health principles for the HIV epidemic [letter and reply]. *New England Journal of Medicine* 2006 February 23; 354(8): 877-878. Subject: 9.5.6

Friend, William B. An introduction to genes and patents = Una introducción a los genes y a las patentes. *Law and the Human Genome Review = Revista de Derecho y Genoma Humano* 1995 July-December; (3): 245-252. Subject: 15.8

Friend, William B. Scientific, ethical and legal perspectives on human genome research: Plenary Session of the Pontifical Academy of Sciences = Perspectivas científicas, éticas y legales de las investigaciones sobre el genoma humano: Sesión Plenaria de la Academia Pontificia de Ciencias, aspectos postorales. *Law and the Human Genome Review = Revista de Derecho y Genoma Humana* 1995 July-December; (3): 221-243. Subject: 15.10

Fries, James F.; Krishnan, Eswar. Equipoise, design bias, and randomized controlled trials: the elusive ethics of new drug development. *Arthritis Research and Therapy* 2004; 6(3): R250-R255. Subject: 9.7

Frikovic, Aleksandra; Gosic, Nada. Practical experience in the work of institutional ethics committees in Croatia on the example of the ethics committee at Clinical Hospital Center Rijeka. *HEC (Healthcare Ethics Committee) Forum* 2006 March; 18(1): 37-48. Subject: 9.6

Frinsina, Michael E. Medical ethics in military biomedical research. *In:* Beam, Thomas E.; Sparacino, Linette R.; Pellegrino, Edmund D.; Hartle, Anthony E.; Howe, Edmund G., eds. Military Medical Ethics. Volume 2. Washington, DC: TMM Publications, Borden Institute, Walter Reed Army Medical Center; 2003: 533-561. Subject: 18.1

Frisina, Michael E. Commentary: the application of medical ethics in biomedical research. *CQ: Cambridge Quarterly of Healthcare Ethics* 2006 Fall; 15(4): 439-441. Subject: 1.3.9

Frist, Bill. Open sesame. Congress must establish boundaries to protect privacy and promote ethical uses of new genetic information. *Forum for Applied Research and Public Policy* 2000 Spring; 15(1): 44-48. Subject: 15.1

Frize, Monique; Yang, Lan; Walker, Robin C.; O'Connor, Annette M. Conceptual framework of knowledge management for ethical decision-making support in neonatal intensive care. *IEEE Transactions on Information Technology in Biomedicine* 2005 June; 9(2): 205-215. Subject: 9.5.7

Froman, Robin D.; Owen, Steven V. Randomized study of stability and change in patients' advance directives. *Research in Nursing and Health* 2005 October; 28(5): 398-407. Subject: 20.5.4

See SUBJECT HEADING KEY FOR SECTION II on inside back cover.

Fry, Craig L.; Hall, Wayne; Ritter, Alison; Jenkinson, Rebecca. The ethics of paying drug users who participate in research: a review and practical recommendations. *Journal of Empirical Research on Human Research Ethics* 2006 December; 1(4): 21-35. Subject: 9.5.9

Fry, Craig L.; Treloar, Carla; Maher, Lisa. Ethical challenges and responses in harm reduction research: promoting applied communitarian ethics. *Drug and Alcohol Review* 2005 September; 24(5): 449-459. Subject: 1.3.9

Fry, C.L.; Madden, A.; Brogan, D.; Loff, B. Australian resources for ethical participatory processes in public health research [letter]. *Journal of Medical Ethics* 2006 March; 32(3): 186. Subject: 18.4

Fry, Sara. Guidelines for making end-of-life decisions. *International Nursing Review* 1998 September-October; 45(5): 143-144, 151. Subject: 20.5.1

Fry, Sara T. Protecting patients from incompetent or unethical colleagues: an important dimension of the nurse's advocacy role. *Journal of Nursing Law* 1997; 4(4): 15-22. Subject: 4.1.3

Fryer, Alan. The genetic testing of children. *Journal of the Royal Society of Medicine* 1997 August; 90(8): 419-421. Subject: 15.3

Fryer-Edwards, Kelly. On cattle and casseroles. *American Journal of Bioethics* 2006 March-April; 6(2): 55-56. Subject: 9.5.1

Fryer-Edwards, Kelly; Fullerton, Stephanie M. Relationships with test-tubes: where's the reciprocity? *American Journal of Bioethics* 2006 November-December; 6(6): 36-38; author reply W10-W12. Subject: 15.1

Fryer-Edwards, Kelly; Wilkins, M. Davis; Baernstein, Amy; Braddock, Clarence H., III. Bringing ethics education to the clinical years: ward ethics sessions at the University of Washington. *Academic Medicine* 2006 July; 81(7): 626-631. Subject: 7.2

Fuchs, Bruce A.; Macrina, Francis L. Use of animals in biomedical experimentation. *In:* Macrina, Francis L., ed. Scientific Integrity: Text and Cases in Responsible Conduct of Research. 3rd ed. Washington, DC: ASM Press; 2005: 127-157. Subject: 22.2

Fuchs-Kittowski, Klaus; Rosenthal, Hans A.; Rosenthal, André. Die Entschlüsselung des Humangenoms — ambivalente Auswirkungen auf Gesellschaft und Wissenschaft = Decoding the human genome — ambivalent effects on society and science. *Erwägen Wissen Ethik* 2005; 16(2): 149-234. Subject: 15.1

Fugh-Berman, Adriane. Carcinogen diagnosis. *Hastings Center Report* 2006 September-October; 36(5): [53]. Subject: 8.2

Fujikawa, Ryan. Federal funding of human embryonic stem cell research: an institutional examination. *Southern California Law Review* 2005 May; 78(4): 1075-1124. Subject: 18.5.4

Fujiki, Norio. Bioethics and medical genetics in Japan. *In:* Sleeboom, Margaret, ed. Genomics in Asia: A Clash of Bioethical Interests? New York: Kegan Paul; 2004: 225-253. Subject: 15.2

Fukuyama, Francis. How to regulate science. *Public Interest* 2002 Winter; 146: 3-22. Subject: 5.3

Fukuyama, Francis. In defense of nature, human and non-human. *World Watch* 2002 July-August; 15(4): 30-32. Subject: 15.1

Fulda, Joseph S. Academics: multiple publications reconsidered II. *Journal of Information Ethics* 2006 Spring; 15(1): 5-7. Subject: 1.3.7

Fulda, Joseph S. Multiple publication reconsidered. *Journal of Information Ethics* 1998 Fall; 7(2): 47-53. Subject: 1.3.7

Fulda, K.G.; Lykens, K. Ethical issues in predictive genetic testing: a public health perspective. *Journal of Medical Ethics* 2006 March; 32(3): 143-147. Subject: 15.3

Fuller, Lisa. Justified commitments? Considering resource allocation and fairness in Medecins sans Frontieres-Holland. *Developing World Bioethics* 2006 May; 6(2): 59-70. Subject: 7.1

Furedy, John J. The decline of the "Euppur si muove" spirit in North American science: professional organizations and PC pressures. *Mankind Quarterly* 1997 Fall-Winter; 38(1-2): 55-66. Subject: 21.1

Furlong, Allannah. Confidentiality with respect to third parties: a psychoanalytic view. *International Journal of Psychoanalysis* 2005 April; 86(Part 2): 375-394. Subject: 8.4

Furness, Peter N. The Human Tissue Act [editorial]. *BMJ: British Medical Journal* 2006 September 9; 333(7567): 512. Subject: 19.5

Furness, Peter N. One-time general consent for research on biological samples: good idea, but will it happen? [letter]. *BMJ: British Medical Journal* 2006 March 18; 332(7542): 665. Subject: 18.3

Furrow, Barry R. Pain management and liability issues. *Hematology/Oncology Clinics of North America* 2002 December; 16(6): 1483-1494. Subject: 20.4.1

Furth, Susan L.; Garg, Pushkal P.; Neu, Alicia M.; Hwang, Wenke; Fivush, Barbara A.; Powe, Neil R. Racial differences in access to the kidney transplant waiting list for children and adolescents with end-stage renal disease. *Pediatrics* 2000 October; 106(4): 756-761. Subject: 19.6

Furton, Edward J. Prospects for pluripotent stem cells: a reply to Communio. *National Catholic Bioethics Quarterly* 2006 Summer; 6(2): 223-232. Subject: 18.5.4

Fuscaldo, Giuliana. Genetic ties: are they morally binding? *Bioethics* 2006 April; 20(2): 64-76. Subject: 14.1

Subject = NRCBL Primary Classification Number; see inside front cover.

Fuyuno, Ichiko; Cyranoski, David. Cash for papers: putting a premium on publication [news]. *Nature* 2006 June 15; 441(7095): 792. Subject: 1.3.7

Fuyuno, Ichiko; Cyranoski, David. Doubts over biochemist's data expose holes in Japanese fraud laws [news]. *Nature* 2006 February 2; 439(7076): 514. Subject: 1.3.9

Fuyuno, Ichiko; Cyranoski, David. Further accusations rock Japanese RNA laboratory [news]. *Nature* 2006 April 6; 440(7085): 720-721. Subject: 1.3.9

G

Gaal, Peter; Belli, Paolo Carlo; McKee, Martin; Szócska, Miklós. Informal payments for health care: definitions, distinctions, and dilemmas. *Journal of Health Politics, Policy and Law* 2006 April; 31(2): 251-293. Subject: 9.3.1

Gaal, Peter; Evetovits, Tamas; McKee, Martin. Informal payment for health care: evidence from Hungary. *Health Policy* 2006 June; 77(1): 86-102. Subject: 9.3.1

Gaba, Aline. Face transplants and the difficulties of obtaining research approval. *Journal of Biolaw and Business* 2006; 9(1): 54-55. Subject: 18.2

Gabard, Donald L. Homosexuality and the Human Genome Project: private and public choices. *Journal of Homosexuality* 1999; 37(1): 25-51. Subject: 10

Gabbard, Glen O. Post-termination sexual boundary violations. *Psychiatric Clinics of North America* 2002 September; 25(3): 593-603. Subject: 17.1

Gable, Lance; Vásquez, Javier; Gostin, Lawrence O.; Jiménez, Heidi V. Mental health and due process in the Americas: protecting the human rights of persons involuntarily admitted to and detained in psychiatric institutions. *Revista panamericana de salud pública/Pan American Journal of Public Health* 2005 October-November; 18(4-5): 366-373. Subject: 17.7

Gabos, Kelly A. The perils of Singleton v. Norris: ethics and beyond. *American Journal of Law and Medicine* 2006; 32(1): 117-132. Subject: 20.6

Gaensslen, R. E. Should biological evidence or DNA be retained by forensic science laboratories after profiling? No, except under narrow legislatively-stipulated conditions. *Journal of Law, Medicine and Ethics* 2006 Summer; 34(2): 375-379. Subject: 15.1

Gaff, Clara L.; Cowan, Ruth; Meiser, Bettina; Lindeman, Geoffrey. Genetic services for men: the preferences of men with a family history of prostate cancer. *Genetics in Medicine* 2006 December; 8(12): 771-780. Subject: 15.3

Gallagher, Ann; Wainwright, Paul. The ethical divide. *Nursing Standard* 2005 October 26-November 1; 20(7): 22-25. Subject: 4.1.3

Gallagher, Janet. Religious freedom, reproductive health care, and hospital mergers. *Journal of the American Medical Women's Association* 1997 Spring; 52(2): 65-68. Subject: 8.1

Gallagher, John A. "Like shining from shook foil": a "virtuous organization" is prepared to test both the body and the soul. *Health Progress* 2006 November-December; 87(6): 18-23. Subject: 9.1

Gallagher, Rollin M. Ethics in pain medicine: good for our health, good for the public health [editorial]. *Pain Medicine* 2001 June; 2(2): 87-89. Subject: 4.4

Gallagher, Thomas H.; Garbutt, Jane M.; Waterman, Amy D.; Flum, David R.; Larson, Eric B.; Waterman, Brian M.; Dunagan, W. Claiborne; Fraser, Victoria J.; Levinson, Wendy. Choosing your words carefully: how physicians would disclose harmful medical errors to patients. *Archives of Internal Medicine* 2006 August 14-28; 166(15): 1585-1593. Subject: 9.8

Gallagher, Thomas H.; Waterman, Amy D.; Garbutt, Jane M.; Kapp, Julie M.; Chan, David K.; Dunagan, W. Claiborne; Fraser, Victoria J.; Levinson, Wendy. US and Canadian physicians' attitudes and experiences regarding disclosing errors to patients. *Archives of Internal Medicine* 2006 August 14-28; 166(15): 1605-1611. Subject: 9.8

Galletti, Matteo. Begetting, cloning and being human: two national commission reports against human cloning from Italy and the U.S.A. *HEC (Healthcare Ethics Committee) Forum* 2006 June; 18(2): 156-171. Subject: 14.5

Galton, D.J. Eugenics: some lessons from the past. *Reproductive BioMedicine Online [electronic]* 2005 March; 10(Supplement 1): 133-136. Subject: 15.5

Galvani, Alison P.; Medlock, Jan; Chapman, Gretchen B. The ethics of influenza vaccination [letter]. *Science* 2006 August 11; 313(5788): 758. Subject: 9.5.1

Gamble, Vanessa Northington. H.R. 5198: The Ethics in Patient Referrals Act: implications for providers. *Journal of Ambulatory Care Management* 1989 May; 12(2): 83-86. Subject: 9.3.2

Gamble, Vanessa Northington. The Tuskegee syphilis study and women's health. *Journal of the American Medical Women's Association* 1997 Fall; 52(4): 195-196. Subject: 18.5.1

Gamble, Vanessa Northington. Trust, medical care, and racial and ethnic minorities. *In:* Satcher, David; Pamies, Rubens J., eds. Multicultural medicine and health disparities. New York: McGraw-Hill, 2006: 437-448. Subject: 9.5.4

Gamble, Vanessa Northington; Stone, Deborah. U.S. policy on health inequities: the interplay of politics and research. *Journal of Health Politics, Policy and Law* 2006 February; 31(1): 93-126. Subject: 9.4

Gammon, Keri. Pandemics and pandemonium: constitutional jurisdiction over public health. *Dalhousie Journal of Legal Studies* 2006; 15: 1-38. Subject: 9.1

See SUBJECT HEADING KEY FOR SECTION II on inside back cover.

567

Gampel, Eric. Does professional autonomy protect medical futility judgments? *Bioethics* 2006 April; 20(2): 92-104. Subject: 8.1

Ganache, Isabelle. "Commercial revolution" of science: the complex reality and experience of genetic and genomic scientists. *Genomics, Society and Policy* 2006 December; 2(3): 96-114. Subject: 15.1

Gandhi, Gursatej. Impact of modern genetics: a Sikh perspective. *In:* Sleeboom, Margaret, ed. Genomics in Asia: A Clash of Bioethical Interests? New York: Kegan Paul; 2004: 51-65. Subject: 15.1

Gänsbacher, Bernd. Policy statement on the social, ethical and public awareness issues in gene therapy. *Journal of Gene Medicine* 2002 November-December; 4(6): 687-691. Subject: 15.4

Ganz, F.D.; Benbenishty, J.; Hersch, M.; Fischer, A.; Gurman, G.; Sprung, C.L. The impact of regional culture on intensive care end of life decision making: an Israeli perspective from the ETHICUS study. *Journal of Medical Ethics* 2006 April; 32(4): 196-199. Subject: 20.5.1

Ganzini, Linda. Response to Denny and Emanuel. *Journal of Clinical Ethics* 2006 Spring; 17(1): 43-45. Subject: 20.7

Ganzini, Linda; Beer, Tomasz M.; Brouns, Matthew; Mori, Motomi; Hsieh, Yi-Ching. Interest in physician-assisted suicide among Oregon cancer patients. *Journal of Clinical Ethics* 2006 Spring; 17(1): 27-38. Subject: 20.5.1

Ganzini, Linda; Goy, Elizabeth R. Influence of mental illness on decision making at the end of life. *In:* Jansen, Lynn A., ed. Death in the Clinic. Lanham, MD: Rowman and Littlefield; 2006: 81-96. Subject: 8.3.3

Ganzini, Linda; Hamilton, N. Gregory; Hamilton, Catherine A. Physician-assisted suicide [letter and reply]. *American Journal of Psychiatry* 2006 June; 163(6): 1109-1110. Subject: 20.7

Ganzini, Linda; Volicer, Ladislav; Nelson, William A.; Fox, Ellen; Derse, Arthur R. Ten myths about decision-making capacity. *Journal of the American Medical Directors Association* 2005 May-June; 6(3 Supplement): S100-S104. Subject: 8.3.3

Gao, Xiangdong; Xu, Yan. Ethical issues in the regulation of population growth and reproduction. *In:* Döring, Ole; Chen, Renbiao, eds. Advances in Chinese Medical Ethics: Chinese and International Perspectives. Hamburg: Institut für Asienkunde; 2002: 327-334. Subject: 13.1

Garanis-Papadatos, Tina; Boukis, Dimitris. Research ethics committees in Greece. *In:* Beyleveld, D.; Townend, D.; Wright, J., eds. Research Ethics Committees, Data Protection and Medical Research in European Countries. Hants, England; Burlington, VT: Ashgate; 2005: 85-91. Subject: 18.2

Garay, Alain. El paciente, el médico y el abogado [The patient, the doctor and the lawyer]. *Persona y Bioética* 1999 February-May; 2(6): 113-122. Subject: 8.1

Garber, Mandy; Arnold, Robert M. Promoting the participation of minorities in research. *American Journal of Bioethics [Online].* 2006 May-June; 6(3): W14-W20. Subject: 18.5.1

Garces-Foley, Kathleen. Hospice and the politics of spirituality. *Omega* 2006; 53(1-2): 117-136. Subject: 20.4.1

Garcia, Jo; Elbourne, Diana; Snowdon, Claire. Equipoise: a case study of the views of clinicians involved in two neonatal trials. *Clinical Trials* 2004; 1(2): 170-188. Subject: 18.2

Garcia, J.L.A. Sin and suffering in a Catholic understanding of medical ethics. *Christian Bioethics* 2006 August; 12(2): 165-186. Subject: 4.2

Garcia, Jorge L.A. A Catholic perspective on the ethics of artificially providing food and water. *Linacre Quarterly* 2006 May; 73(2): 132-152. Subject: 20.5.1

García-Miján, Manuel Lobato. European Patent Office: Decision of 18 January 1995 (Subject Relaxina) = Oficina Europea de Patentes: Decisión de 18 de enero de 1995 (Asunto Relaxina). *Law and the Human Genome Review = Revista de Derecho y Genoma Humano* 1995 July-December; (3): 169-180. Subject: 15.8

García-Sancho, Miguel. The rise and fall of the idea of genetic information (1948-2006). *Genomics, Society and Policy* 2006 December; 2(3): 16-36. Subject: 15.1

Garcia-Velasco, Juan A.; Garrido, Nicolas. How would revealing the identity of gamete donors affect current practice? *Reproductive BioMedicine Online [electronic]* 2005 May; 10(5): 564-566. Accessed: http://www.rbmonline.com/Article/1755 [2005 November 17]. Subject: 14.4

Gardner, William. Compelled disclosure of scientific research data. *Information Society* 2004 April-June; 20(2): 141-146. Subject: 1.3.9

Gardner, William; Lidz, Charles W. Research sponsorship, financial relationships, and the process of research in pharmaceutical clinical trials. *Journal of Empirical Research on Human Research Ethics* 2006 June; 1(2): 11-18. Subject: 1.3.9

Gardner, William; Lidz, Charles W.; Hartwig, Kathryn C. Authors' reports about research integrity problems in clinical trials. *Contemporary Clinical Trials* 2005 April; 26(2): 244-251. Subject: 1.3.9

Garfield, Eugene; McVeigh, Marie; Muff, Marion. Preventing scientific fraud [letter]. *Annals of Internal Medicine* 2006 September 19; 145(6): 472-473. Subject: 1.3.9

Garforth, Kathryn. Canadian "medical necessity" and the right to health. *HIV/AIDS Policy and Law Review* 2003 December; 8(3): 63-69. Subject: 9.2

Garmaise, David. The case for assisted suicide and euthanasia. *Canadian HIV/AIDS Policy and Law Newsletter* 1997 Spring; 3(2-3): 20-23. Subject: 20.7

Garmaise, David. Mandatory HIV testing used to bar potential immigrants. *HIV/AIDS Policy and Law Review* 2003 April; 8(1): 20-21. Subject: 9.5.6

Garmaise, David. Providing assistance in dying: a call for legalization. *Canadian HIV/AIDS Policy and Law Newsletter* 1999 Summer; 4(4): 39-40. Subject: 20.7

Garner, Robert. Animals, medical science and consumer protection. *In his:* Animals, Politics and Morality. 2nd ed. New York: Manchester University Press; 2004: 126-161. Subject: 22.2

Garrafa, Volnei. Crítica bioética: a um nascimento anunciado = Crítica bioética: de un nacimiento anunciado = Bioethical critique: of a foretold birth. *Revista Latinoamericana de Bioética* 2003 January; (4): 18-37. Subject: 14.5

Garside, Ruth; Ayres, Richard; Owen, Mike; Pearson, Virginia A.H.; Roizen, Judith. Anonymity and confidentiality: rural teenagers' concerns when accessing sexual health services. *Journal of Family Planning and Reproductive Health Care* 2002 January; 28(1): 23-26. Subject: 11.2

Garside, Sarah; Maher, John. Assertive Community Treatment (ACT): 23 cases. *Journal of Ethics in Mental Health* 2006 November; 1(1): E6, 4 p. Subject: 17.1

Garzón Díaz, Fabio Alberto. Clonaid: ¿fraude y/o negocio? = Clonaid: fraud and/or business? [editorial]. *Revista Latinoamericana de Bioética* 2003 January; (4): 12-17. Subject: 14.5

Gaskell, George; Ten Eyck, Toby; Jackson, Jonathan; Veltri, Giuseppi. Imagining nanotechnology: cultural support for technological innovation in Europe and the United States. *Public Understanding of Science* 2005 January; 14(1): 81-90. Subject: 5.4

Gason, Alexandra A.; Delatycki, Martin B.; Metcalfe, Sylvia A.; Aitken, MaryAnne. It's "back to school" for genetic screening. *European Journal of Human Genetics* 2006 April; 14(4): 384-389. Subject: 15.3

Gason, A.A.; Aitken, M.A.; Metcalfe, S.A.; Allen, K.J.; Delatycki, M.B. Genetic susceptibility screening in schools: attitudes of the school community towards hereditary haemochromatosis. *Clinical Genetics* 2005 February; 67(2): 166-174. Subject: 15.3

Gastmans, Chris. Caring for dignified end of life in a Christian health care institution: the view of Caritas Catholica Flanders. *In:* Schotsmans, Paul; Meulenbergs, Tom, eds. Euthanasia and Palliative Care in the Low Countries. Dudley, MA: Peeters, 2005: 205-225. Subject: 20.4.1

Gastmans, Chris. Editorial comment. *Nursing Ethics* 2006 May; 13(3): 217-218. Subject: 4.1.3

Gastmans, Chris; Lemiengre, Joke; Dierckx de Casterlé, Bernadette. Role of nurses in institutional ethics policies on euthanasia. *Journal of Advanced Nursing* 2006 April; 54(1): 53-61. Subject: 20.5.1

Gastmans, Chris; Lemiengre, Joke; van der Wal, Gerrit; Schotsmans, Paul; Dierckx de Casterlé, Bernadette. Prevalence and content of written ethics policies on euthanasia in Catholic healthcare institutions in Belgium (Flanders). *Health Policy* 2006 April; 76(2): 169-178. Subject: 20.7

Gastmans, Chris; Milisen, K. Use of physical restraint in nursing homes: clinical-ethical considerations. *Journal of Medical Ethics* 2006 March; 32(3): 148-152. Subject: 9.5.2

Gastmans, Chris; Van Neste, Fernand; Schotsmans, Paul. Pluralism and ethical dialogue in Christian healthcare institutions: the view of Caritas Catholica Flanders. *Christian Bioethics* 2006 December; 12(3): 265-280. Subject: 9.6

Gastmans, Chris; Verpeet, Ellen. 30th anniversary commentary on Esterhuizen P. (1996) Is the professional code still the cornerstone of clinical nursing practice? Journal of Advanced Nursing 23, 25-31. *Journal of Advanced Nursing* 2006 January; 53(1): 111-112. Subject: 4.1.3

Gatensby, Anne. Privacy, property, and social relations in bioinformatics research. *In:* Árnason, Gardar; Nordal, Salvör; Árnason, Vilhjálmur, eds. Blood and Data: Ethical, Legal and Social Aspects of Human Genetic Databases. Reykjavík: University of Iceland Press; 2004: 28-27. Subject: 15.1

Gattellari, Melina; Voigt, Katie J.; Butow, Phyllis N.; Tattersall, Martin H.N. When the treatment goal is not cure: are cancer patients equipped to make informed decisions? *Journal of Clinical Oncology* 2002 January 15; 20(2): 503-513. Subject: 20.5.1

Gatter, Ken. Fixing cracks: a discourse norm to repair the crumbling regulatory structure supporting clinical research and protecting human subjects. *University of Missouri Kansas City Law Review (UMKC)* 2005; 73: 581-641. Subject: 18.6

Gatter, Robert. Conflicts of interest in international human drug research and the insufficiency of international protections. *American Journal of Law and Medicine* 2006; 32(2-3): 351-364. Subject: 18.2

Gattuso, Jami; Hinds, Pamela; Tong, Xin; Srivastava, Kumar. Monitoring child and parent refusals to enrol [sic; enroll] in clinical research protocols. *Journal of Advanced Nursing* 2006 February; 53(3): 319-326. Subject: 18.5.2

Gauthier, C.; Griffin, G. Using animals in research, testing and teaching. *Revue Scientifique et Technique* 2005 August; 24(2): 735-745. Subject: 22.2

Gauthier, Clement. Principles and guidelines for the development of a science- based decision making process fa-

See SUBJECT HEADING KEY FOR SECTION II on inside back cover.

569

cilitating the implementation of the 3Rs by governmental regulators. *ILAR Journal* 2002; 43(Supplement): S99-S104. Subject: 5.3

Gaw, Allan. Beyond consent: the potential for atrocity. *Journal of the Royal Society of Medicine* 2006 April; 99(4): 175-177. Subject: 18.5.1

Gawande, Atul. When law and ethics collide — why physicians participate in executions. *New England Journal of Medicine* 2006 March 23; 354(12): 1221-1229. Subject: 20.6

Gazmararian, Julie A.; Curran, James W.; Parker, Ruth M.; Bernhardt, Jay M.; DeBuono, Barbara A. Public health literacy in America: an ethical imperative. *American Journal of Preventive Medicine* 2005 April; 28(3): 317-322. Subject: 9.1

Gazzaniga, Michael. All clones are not the same (opinion). *New York Times* 2006 February 16; p. A33. Subject: 14.5

Gbadegesin, Segun; Wendler, David. Protecting communities in health research from exploitation. *Bioethics* 2006 September; 20(5): 248-253. Subject: 18.6

Gearhart, John D. The new genetics: stem cell research and cloning. *In:* Miller, Roman J.; Brubaker, Beryl H.; Peterson, James C., eds. Viewing New Creations with Anabaptist Eyes: Ethics of Biotechnology. Telford, PA: Cascadia Pub.; 2005: 21-34. Subject: 18.5.4

Gebhardt, D.O.E.; van Burenlaan, Anna. The generic-patent medicine conflict flares up again in the Netherlands [letter]. *Journal of Medical Ethics* 2006 September; 32(9): 555. Subject: 9.7

Geddes, Colin C.; Rodger, R. Stuart C. Kidneys for transplant [editorial]. *BMJ: British Medical Journal* 2006 May 13; 332(7550): 1105-1106. Subject: 19.6

Geddes, Colin C.; Rodger, R. Stuart C.; Smith, Christopher; Ganai, Anita. Allocation of deceased donor kidneys for transplantation: opinions of patients with CKD. *American Journal of Kidney Diseases* 2005 November; 46(5): 949-956. Subject: 19.6

Geddes, Linda. 'Virgin birth' stem cells bypass ethical objections. *New Scientist* 2006 July 1-7; 191(2558): 19. Subject: 18.5.4

Gee, Rebekah E. Plan B, reproductive rights, and physician activism. *New England Journal of Medicine* 2006 July 6; 355(1): 4-5. Subject: 11.1

Gefenas, Eugenijus. The concept of risk and responsible conduct of research. *Science and Engineering Ethics* 2006 January; 12(1): 75-83. Subject: 1.3.9

Geller, Gail. A "holistic" model of the healing relationship: what would that require of physicians? *American Journal of Bioethics* 2006 March-April; 6(2): 82-85. Subject: 2.1

Geller, Gail; Holtzman, Neil A. A qualitative assessment of primary care physicians' perceptions about the ethical and social implications of offering genetic testing. *Qualitative Health Research* 1995 February; 5(1): 97-116. Subject: 15.2

Geller, Jeffrey L. The evolution of outpatient commitment in the USA: from conundrum to quagmire. *International Journal of Law and Psychiatry* 2006 May-June; 29(3): 234-248. Subject: 17.7

Geller, Jeffrey L.; Fisher, William H.; Grudzinskas, Albert J., Jr.; Clayfield, Jonathan C.; Lawlor, Ted. Involuntary outpatient treatment as "desinstitutionalized coercion": the net-widening concerns. *International Journal of Law and Psychiatry* 2006 November-December; 29(6): 551-562. Subject: 17.7

Geluda, Katia; Bisaglia, Joana Buarque; Moreira, Vivian; Maldonado, Beatriz Motta; Cunha, Antônio J.L.A.; Trajman, Anete. Third-party informed consent in research with adolescents: the good, the bad and the ugly. *Social Science and Medicine* 2005 September; 61(5): 985-988. Subject: 18.3

General Medical Council [GMC](Great Britain). Serious Communicable Diseases. London: General Medical Council, 1998; 14 p. Subject: 9.5.1

Genetic Interest Group [GIG]; Mehta, Pritti. Promoting equity of access to genetic healthcare: a guide to the development of linguistically and culturally competent communication services. London: Genetic Interest Group [GIG], 2005 November: 38 p. [Online]. Accessed: http://gig.org.uk/docs/promotingaccess.pdf [2006 July 26]. Subject: 15.1

Genovese, Elizabeth. Workers' compensation fraud and the physician. *Clinics in Occupational and Environmental Medicine* 2004 May; 4(2): 361-372. Subject: 7.4

Gentleman, Amelia. Doctor in India jailed for telling sex of a fetus. *New York Times* 2006 March 30; p. A15. Subject: 14.3

George, Asha. In search of closure for quinacrine: science and politics in contexts of uncertainty and inequality. *In:* Unnithan-Kumar, Maya, ed. Reproductive Agency, Medicine and the State: Cultural Transformations in Childbearing. New York: Berghahn Books; 2004: 137-160. Subject: 11.3

George, Lloyd. Ethical moment: is it ethical for a dentist to date a patient? *Journal of the American Dental Association* 2005 September; 136(9): 1312-1313. Subject: 8.1

George, Lloyd. Is it ethical for a dentist to date a patient? *Journal of the American Dental Association* 2005 September; 136(9): 1312-1313. Subject: 4.1.1

George, Robert P. Ethics, politics, and genetic knowledge. *Social Research* 2006 Fall; 73(3): 1029-1032. Subject: 4.4

Subject = NRCBL Primary Classification Number; see inside front cover.

George, Sabu M.; Bhat, Mari; Grover, Anil; Vijayvergiya, Rajesh; Jha, Prabhat; Kumar, Rajesh; Dhingra, Neeraj; Bardia, Aditya; Anand, Krishnan; Bhopal, Raj; Somerville, Margaret. Sex ratio in India [letters and reply]. *Lancet* 2006 May 27-June 2; 367(9524): 1725-1729. Subject: 14.3

Georges, Jane M.; Benedict, Susan. An ethics of testimony: prisoner nurses at Auschwitz. *Advances in Nursing Science* 2006 April-June; 29(2): 161-169. Subject: 18.5.5

Georges, Jean-Jacques; Onwuteaka-Philipsen, Bregje D.; van der Heide, Agnes; van der Wal, Gerrit; van der Maas, Paul J. Requests to forgo potentially life-prolonging treatment and to hasten death in terminally ill cancer patients: a prospective study. *Journal of Pain and Symptom Management* 2006 February; 31(2): 100-110. Subject: 20.5.1

Georges, Jean-Jacques; Onwuteaka-Philipsen, Bregje D.; van der Wal, Gerrit; van der Heide, Agnes; van der Maas, Paul J. Differences between terminally ill cancer patients who died after euthanasia had been performed and terminally ill cancer patients who did not request euthanasia. *Palliative Medicine* 2005 December; 19(8): 578-586. Subject: 20.5.1

Geppert, Cynthia M.A.; Arora, Sanjeev. Ethical issues in the treatment of hepatitis C. *Clinical Gastroenterology and Hepatology* 2005 October; 3(10): 937-944. Subject: 9.5.1

Geppert, Cynthia M.A.; Dettmer, Elizabeth; Jakiche, Antonie. Ethical challenges in the care of persons with hepatitis C infection: a pilot study to enhance informed consent with veterans. *Psychosomatics* 2005 September-October; 46(5): 392-401. Subject: 8.3.1

Geraghty, Karen. Guarding the art: Edmund D. Pellegrino. *Virtual Mentor* 2001 October; 3(10): 2p. Subject: 7.1

Geraghty, Karen. Guarding the art: Edmund D. Pellegrino, MD. [photos]. *In:* American Medical Association. ProfessingMedicine: strengthening the ethics and professionalism of tomorrow's physicians. Chicago: American Medical Association; 2001: 96-101. Subject: 4.1.2

Geraghty, Karen. The code as expert witness. *In:* American Medical Association. ProfessingMedicine: strengthening the ethics and professionalism of tomorrow's physicians. Chicago: American Medical Association; 2001: 111-113. Subject: 7.3

Geraghty, Karen. The code as expert witness. *Virtual Mentor* 2001 October; 3(10): 2p. Subject: 2.2

Geraghty, Karen. The obligation to provide charity care. *In:* American Medical Association. ProfessingMedicine: strengthening the ethics and professionalism of tomorrow's physicians. Chicago: American Medical Association; 2001: 57-61. Subject: 9.5.10

Geraghty, Karen. The obligation to provide charity care. *Virtual Mentor* 2001 October; 3(10): 3p. Subject: 9.5.10

Gerards, Janneke H.; Janssen, Heleen L. Regulation of genetic and other health information in a comparative perspective. *European Journal of Health Law* 2006 December; 13(4): 339-398. Subject: 15.1

Gerber, Paul. What can we learn from the Hwang and Sudbø affairs? *Medical Journal of Australia* 2006 June 19; 184(12): 632-635. Subject: 1.3.9

Gerlach, Neil; Hamilton, Sheryl N. From mad scientist to bad scientist: Richard Seed as biogovernmental event. *Communication Theory* 2005 February; 15(1): 78-99. Subject: 5.3

German Society of Human Genetics [GfH]. Commission for Standpoints and Ethical Questions. DNA banking and personal data in biomedical research: technical, social, and ethical questions. *Medizinische Genetik* 2004; 16: 347-350. [Online]. Accessed: http://www.medgenetik.de/sonderdruck/en/DNA%20Banking_engl_060605.pdf [2006 July 31]. Subject: 15.1

German Society of Human Genetics [GfH]. Committee for Public Relations and Ethical Issues. Position paper of the German Society of Human Genetics. *Med Genetik* 1996; 8: 125-130 (13 pages) [Online] Accessed: http://www.medgenetik.de/sonderdruck/en/Position_ paper.pdf [2005 December 2]. Subject: 15.1

German Society of Human Genetics [GfH]. Committee for Public Relations and Ethical Issues. Statement on postnatal predictive genetic diagnosis [position statement]. *Medizinsche Genetik* 1991; 3(2): 10-11. [Online]. Accessed: http://www.medgenetik.de/sonderdruck/en/Predictive_ diagnosis.pdf [2006 July 31]. Subject: 15.3

German Society of Human Genetics [GfH]. Committee for Public Relations and Ethical Issues. Statement on the new Chinese law concerning maternal and child health care. *Medizinische Genetik* 1995; 7: 419 (2 p.). [Online]. Accessed: http://www.medgenetik.de/sonderdruck/en/Chinese_law.pdf [2006 July 31]. Subject: 15.5

Gerntholtz, Liesl. Preventing mother-to-child transmission: landmark decision by South African Court. *HIV/AIDS Policy and Law Review* 2002 March; 6(3): 1, 20-24. Subject: 9.5.6

Gerntholtz, Liesl. South Africa: highest court orders government to provide antiretrovirals to prevent mother-to-child transmission. *HIV/AIDS Policy and Law Review* 2002 December; 7(2-3): 50-52. Subject: 9.5.6

Gerodetti, Natalia. From science to social technology: eugenics and politics in twentieth-century Switzerland. *Social Politics* 2006 Spring; 13(1): 59-88. Subject: 15.5

Gerrish, Kate. Being a 'marginal native': dilemmas of the participant observer. *Nurse Researcher* 1997 Autumn; 5(1): 25-34. Subject: 18.1

See SUBJECT HEADING KEY FOR SECTION II on inside back cover.

571

Gerson, Chad M. Toward an international standard of abortion rights: two obstacles. *Chicago Journal of International Law* 2005; 5: 753-761. Subject: 12.4.1

Gert, Bernard. A brief reply to Carson Strong. *Kennedy Institute of Ethics Journal* 2006 June; 16(2): 195-197. Subject: 2.1

Gert, Bernard. Making the morally relevant features explicit: a response to Carson Strong. *Kennedy Institute of Ethics Journal* 2006 March; 16(1): 59-71. Subject: 2.1

Gert, Bernard. Moral theory and the Human Genome Project. *In:* Tavani, Herman T., ed. Ethics, Computing, and Genomics. Sudbury, MA: Jones and Bartlett; 2006: 33-54. Subject: 15.10

Gert, Bernard; Chiong, Winston. Matters of "life" and "death" [letter and reply]. *Hastings Center Report* 2006 May-June; 36(3): 4, 5-6. Subject: 20.2.1

Gert, Bernard; Culver, Charles M. Therapy and enhancement. *In:* Mitcham, Carl, ed. Encyclopedia of Science, Technology, and Ethics. Farmington Hills, MI: Thomson/Gale, 2005: 1938-1942. Subject: 15.4

Gert, Bernard; Culver, Charles M.; Clouser, K. Danner. Adequate information, competence, and coercion. *In their:* Bioethics: A Systematic Approach. Second edition. New York: Oxford University Press; 2006: 213-236. Subject: 8.3.1

Gert, Bernard; Culver, Charles M.; Clouser, K. Danner. Death. *In their:* Bioethics: A Systematic Approach. Second edition. New York: Oxford University Press; 2006: 283-308. Subject: 20.2.1

Gert, Bernard; Culver, Charles M.; Clouser, K. Danner. Euthanasia. *In their:* Bioethics: A Systematic Approach. Second edition. New York: Oxford University Press; 2006: 309-345. Subject: 20.5.1

Gert, Bernard; Culver, Charles M.; Clouser, K. Danner. Malady. *In their:* Bioethics: A Systematic Approach. Second edition. New York: Oxford University Press; 2006: 129-164. Subject: 4.2

Gert, Bernard; Culver, Charles M.; Clouser, K. Danner. Mental maladies. *APA Newsletters: Newsletter on Philosophy and Medicine* 2006 Spring; 05(2): 20-22. Subject: 4.3

Gert, Bernard; Culver, Charles M.; Clouser, K. Danner. Mental maladies. *In their:* Bioethics: A Systematic Approach. Second edition. New York: Oxford University Press; 2006: 165-190. Subject: 4.3

Gert, Bernard; Culver, Charles M.; Clouser, K. Danner. Paternalism and its justification. *In their:* Bioethics: A Systematic Approach. Second edition. New York: Oxford University Press; 2006: 237-282. Subject: 8.1

Gert, Bernard; Culver, Charles M.; Clouser, K. Danner. Principlism. *APA Newsletters: Newsletter on Philosophy and Medicine* 2006 Spring; 05(2): 16-19. Subject: 2.1

Gert, Bernard; Culver, Charles M.; Clouser, K. Danner. Principlism. *In their:* Bioethics: A Systematic Approach. Second edition. New York: Oxford University Press; 2006: 99-127. Subject: 2.1

Gert, Bernard; Culver, Charles M.; Clouser, K. Danner. What doctors must know about medical practice. *In their:* Bioethics: A Systematic Approach. Second edition. New York: Oxford University Press; 2006: 191-212. Subject: 9.8

Gertz, Renate. Is it 'me' or 'we'? Genetic relations and the meaning of 'personal data' under the Data Protection Directive. *European Journal of Health Law* 2004 September; 11(3): 231-244. Subject: 15.1

Gertz, Renate; Harmon, Shawn; Laurie, Graeme; Pradella, Geoff. Developments in medical law in the United Kingdom in 2005 and 2006. *European Journal of Health Law* 2006 June; 13(2): 143-158. Subject: 20.5.1

Gesang, Bernward. "Enhancement" zwischen Selbstbetrug und Selbstverwirklichung / Enhancement between self-realization and self-deception. *Ethik in der Medizin* 2006 March; 18(1): 10-26. Subject: 4.5

Gethmann, Carl Friedrich. The special status of the human being as a topic of practical philosophy. *In:* Duncker, H.-R.; Prieß, K., eds. On the Uniqueness of Humankind. Berlin; New York: Springer; 2005: 95-105. Subject: 4.4

Getz, Linn; Kirkengen, Anna Luise; Hetlevik, Irene; Sigurdsson, Johann A. Individually based preventive medical recommendations — are they sustainable and responsible? A call for ethical reflection [editorial]. *Scandinavian Journal of Primary Health Care* 2005 June; 23(2): 65-67. Subject: 9.1

Gevers, J.K.M. Terminal sedation: between pain relief, withholding treatment and euthanasia. *Medicine and Law: The World Association for Medical Law* 2006 December; 25(4): 747-751. Subject: 20.5.1

Gevers, Sjef. Abortion legislation and the future of the 'counseling model'. *European Journal of Health Law* 2006 April; 13(1): 27-40. Subject: 12.4.1

Gevers, Sjef. Dementia and the law. *European Journal of Health Law* 2006 September; 13(3): 209-217. Subject: 17.1

Gevers, Sjef. The European Court of Human Rights and the incompetent patients [editorial]. *European Journal of Health Law* 2004 September; 11(3): 225-229. Subject: 20.5.2

Gevers, Sjef. Medical research involving human subjects: towards an international legal framework? [editorial]. *European Journal of Health Law* 2001 December; 8(4): 293-298. Subject: 18.6

Subject = NRCBL Primary Classification Number; see inside front cover.

Gewin, Virginia. Fears rise over leaks of clinical trial results. *Nature* 2005 September 8; 437(7056): 191. Subject: 1.3.9

Ghods, Ahad J. Governed financial incentives as an alternative to altruistic organ donation. *Experimental and Clinical Transplantation* 2004 December; 2(2): 221-228. Subject: 19.5

Ghods, Ahad J.; Nasrollahzadeh, Dariush. Transplant tourism and the Iranian model of renal transplantation program: ethical considerations. *Experimental and Clinical Transplantation* 2005 December; 3(2): 351-354. Subject: 19.3

Ghulam, Amina T.; Kessler, Margrit; Bachmann, Lucas M.; Haller, Urs; Kessler, Thomas M. Patients' satisfaction with the preoperative informed consent procedure: a multicenter questionnaire survey in Switzerland. *Mayo Clinic Proceedings* 2006 March; 81(3): 307-312. Subject: 8.3.1

Giacomini, M.; Cook, D.; DeJean, D.; Shaw, R.; Gedge, E. Decision tools for life support: a review and policy analysis. *Critical Care Medicine* 2006 March; 34(3): 864-870. Subject: 20.5.1

Giarelli, Ellen. Images of cloning and stem cell research in editorial cartoons in the United States. *Qualitative Health Research* 2006 January; 16(1): 61-78. Subject: 14.5

Gibbons, M.C. Common ground: exploring policy approaches to addressing racial disparities from the left and right. *Journal of Health Care Law and Policy* 2006; 9(1): 48-76. Subject: 9.5.4

Gibbs, David C., III. Gibbs on Schiavo. *Stetson Law Review* 2005 Fall; 35(1): 17-29. Subject: 20.5.1

Gibson, Elaine. Medical confidentiality and protection of third party interests. *American Journal of Bioethics* 2006 March-April; 6(2): 23-25. Subject: 8.4

Gibson, Jennifer L.; Martin, Douglas K.; Singer, Peter A. Priority setting in hospitals: fairness, inclusiveness, and the problem of institutional power differences. *Social Science and Medicine* 2005 December; 61(11): 2355-2362. Subject: 9.4

Gibson, Jennifer; Mitton, Craig; Martin, Douglas; Donaldson, Cam; Singer, Peter. Ethics and economics: does programme budgeting and marginal analysis contribute to fair priority setting? *Journal of Health Services Research and Policy* 2006 January; 11(1): 32-37. Subject: 9.4

Gibson, Katie. South Africa: book publisher ordered to pay damages for disclosing women's HIV status. *HIV/AIDS Policy and Law Review* 2005 August; 10(2): 53. Subject: 18.3

Gibson, Katie. Sweden's compulsory confinement order declared a violation of liberty guarantee. *HIV/AIDS Policy and Law Review* 2005 August; 10(2): 49-50. Subject: 9.5.6

Gibson, Mark. Outcomes with assisted reproductive technology: shooting first, asking questions later [editorial]. *Obstetrics and Gynecology* 2004 June; 103(6): 1142-1143. Subject: 14.1

Gibson, T.M. The bioethics of enhancing human performance for spaceflight. *Journal of Medical Ethics* 2006 March; 32(3): 129-132. Subject: 4.5

Gifford, David R; Crausman, Robert S.; Mcintyre, Bruce W. Problem doctors: is there a system-level solution? [letter]. *Annals of Internal Medicine* 2006 June 6; 144(11): 862-863. Subject: 7.4

Gilbert, Donald L.; Buncher, C. Ralph. Assessment of scientific and ethical issues in two randomized clinical trial designs for patients with Tourette's syndrome: a model for studies of multiple neuropsychiatric diagnoses. *Journal of Neuropsychiatry and Clinical Neurosciences* 2005 Summer; 17(3): 324-332. Subject: 18.2

Gilbert, Robert E. Coping with presidential disability: the proposal for a standing medical commission. *Politics and the Life Sciences* 2003 March 22(1): 2-13. Subject: 8.4

Gilbert, Scott F.; Howes-Mischel, Rebecca. 'Show me your original face before you were born': the convergence of public fetuses and sacred DNA. *History and Philosophy of the Life Sciences* 2004; 26(3-4): 377-394. Subject: 4.4

Gilbert, Scott F.; Tyler, Anna L.; Zackin, Emily J. Assisted reproductive technologies: safety and ethical issues. *In their:* Bioethics and the New Embryology: Springboards for Debate. Sunderland, MA: Sinauer Associates; 2005: 71-79. Subject: 14.1

Gilbert, Scott F.; Tyler, Anna L.; Zackin, Emily J. Ethical dilemmas in stem cell therapy. *In their:* Bioethics and the New Embryology: Springboards for Debate. Sunderland, MA: Sinauer Associates; 2005: 159-175. Subject: 18.5.4

Gilbert, Scott F.; Tyler, Anna L.; Zackin, Emily J. Ethics and policies for human cloning. *In their:* Bioethics and the New Embryology: Springboards for Debate. Sunderland, MA: Sinauer Associates; 2005: 125-140. Subject: 14.5

Gilbert, Scott F.; Tyler, Anna L.; Zackin, Emily J. The ethics of animal use in research. *In their:* Bioethics and the New Embryology: Springboards for Debate. Sunderland, MA: Sinauer Associates; 2005: 241-261. Subject: 22.2

Gilbert, Scott F.; Tyler, Anna L.; Zackin, Emily J. New perspectives on old issues: genetic essentialism. *In their:* Bioethics and the New Embryology: Springboards for Debate. Sunderland, MA: Sinauer Associates; 2005: 227-239. Subject: 15.1

Gilbert, Scott F.; Tyler, Anna L.; Zackin, Emily J. New perspectives on old issues: what is "normal"? *In their:* Bioethics and the New Embryology: Springboards for Debate. Sunderland, MA: Sinauer Associates; 2005: 215-225. Subject: 4.2

Gilbert, Scott F.; Tyler, Anna L.; Zackin, Emily J. Philosophical, theological, and scientific arguments. *In*

See SUBJECT HEADING KEY FOR SECTION II on inside back cover.

573

their: Bioethics and the New Embryology: Springboards for Debate. Sunderland, MA: Sinauer Associates; 2005: 31-45. Subject: 4.4

Gilbert, Scott F.; Tyler, Anna L.; Zackin, Emily J. Should we modify the human genome?: should we allow the genetic engineering of human beings? *In their:* Bioethics and the New Embryology: Springboards for Debate. Sunderland, MA: Sinauer Associates; 2005: 199-212. Subject: 15.1

Gilbert, Scott F.; Tyler, Anna L.; Zackin, Emily J. Should we select the sex of our children?: arguments for and against sex selection. *In their:* Bioethics and the New Embryology: Springboards for Debate. Sunderland, MA: Sinauer Associates; 2005: 95-108. Subject: 14.3

Gilbert, Steven G. Ethical, legal, and social issues: our children's future. *NeuroToxicology* 2005 August; 26(4): 521-530. Subject: 9.5.7

Gilbody, S.; Wilson, P.; Watt, I. Benefits and harms of direct to consumer advertising: a systematic review. *Quality and Safety in Health Care* 2005 August; 14: 246-250. Subject: 9.7

Giles, Jim. Animal experiments under fire for poor design [news]. *Nature* 2006 December 21-28; 444(7122): 981. Subject: 22.2

Giles, Jim. Panel clarifies stem-cell rules [news]. *Nature* 2006 March 2; 440(7080): 9. Subject: 18.5.4

Giles, Jim. Stacking the deck [news]. *Nature* 2006 March 16; 440(7082): 270-272. Subject: 1.3.7

Giles, Jim. The trouble with replication [news]. *Nature* 2006 July 27; 442(7101): 344-347. Subject: 1.3.9

Giles, Jim. Warning flag for ethics boards [news]. *Nature* 2006 September 14; 443(7108): 127. Subject: 18.2

Gill, Carol J. Disability, constructed vulnerability, and socially conscious palliative care. *Journal of Palliative Care* 2006 Autumn; 22(3): 183-189. Subject: 9.5.1

Gill, Chandler E.; Taylor, Henry M.; Lin, K.T.; Padaliya, Bimal B.; Newman, William J.; Abramovitch, Anna I.; Richardson, CaraLee R.; Charles, P. David. Difficulty in securing treatment for degenerative hip disease in a patient with Down syndrome: the gap remains open. *Journal of the National Medical Association* 2006 January; 98(1): 93-96. Subject: 9.5.3

Gill, D.G. "Anything you can do, I can do bigger?": the ethics and equity of growth hormone for small normal children. *Archives of Disease in Childhood* 2006 March; 91(3): 270-272. Subject: 9.7

Gillam, L.; Poulakis, Z.; Tobin, S.; Wake, M. Enhancing the ethical conduct of genetic research: investigating views of parents on including their healthy children in a study on mild hearing loss. *Journal of Medical Ethics* 2006 September; 32(9): 537-541. Subject: 15.1

Gilles, Kathy. Uncovering the relationship between IRBs and the HIPAA privacy rule. *Journal of AHIMA* 2004 November-December; 75(10): 48-49, 52, 55-56. Subject: 18.2

Gillett, G. Cyborgs and moral identity. *Journal of Medical Ethics* 2006 February; 32(2): 79-83. Subject: 17.1

Gillick, Muriel R. The ethics of artificial nutrition and hydration—a practical guide. *Practical Bioethics* 2006 Spring-Summer; 2(2-3): 1, 5-7. Subject: 20.5.1

Gillies, John; Sheehan, Mark. Commentary: when should patients be held responsible for their lifestyle choices? [response]. *BMJ: British Medical Journal* 2006 February 4; 332(7536): 279. Subject: 9.5.9

Gillon, Raanan. Families and genetic testing: the case of Jane and Phyllis from a four- principles perspectives. *In:* Ashcroft, Richard; Lucassen, Anneke; Parker, Michael; Verkerk, Marian; Widderhoven, Guy, eds. Case Analysis in Clinical Ethics. New York: Cambridge University Press; 2005: 165-185. Subject: 15.3

Gillon, Raanan. Human reproductive cloning — a look at the arguments against it and a rejection of most of them. *Journal of the Royal Society of Medicine* 1999 January; 92(1): 3-12. Subject: 14.5

Gilman, Daniel. Thou shalt not kill as a defeasible heuristic: law and economics and the debate over physician-assisted suicide. *Oregon Law Review* 2004; 83: 1239-1289. Subject: 20.7

Gilmore, Patricia Davis. An ethical perspective. Waiver of informed consent requirements in certain medical emergencies: ethical dilemmas. *Journal of Nursing Law* 1997; 4(2): 23-39. Subject: 18.3

Gimbel, Ronald W.; Strosberg, Martin A.; Lehrman, Susan E.; Gefenas, Eugenijus; Taft, Frank. Presumed consent and other predictors of cadaveric organ donation in Europe. *Progress in Transplantation* 2003 March; 13(1): 17-23. Subject: 19.5

Gindro, Sandro; Mordini, Emilio. Ethical, legal and social issues in brain research. *Current Opinion in Psychiatry* 1998 September; 11(5): 10 p. [Online]. Accessed: http://gateway.ut.ovid.com [2007 February 26]. Subject: 17.1

Giordano, Simona. Autonomy and control in eating disorders. *In her:* Understanding Eating Disorders: Conceptual and Ethical Issues in the Treatment of Anorexia and Bulimia Nervosa. New York: Oxford University Press; 2005: 211-234. Subject: 9.5.1

Giordano, Simona. Eating or treating? Legal and ethical issues surrounding eating disorders. *In her:* Understanding Eating Disorders: Conceptual and Ethical Issues in the Treatment of Anorexia and Bulimia Nervosa. New York: Oxford University Press; 2005: 179-210. Subject: 9.5.1

Giordano, Simona. Paternalism v. respect for autonomy. *In her:* Understanding Eating Disorders: Conceptual and

---

Ethical Issues in the Treatment of Anorexia and Bulimia Nervosa. New York: Oxford University Press; 2005: 33-57. Subject: 2.1

Giordano, Simona; Harris, John. What is gender equality in sports? *In:* Tamburrini, Claudio; Tännsjö, Torbjörn, eds. Genetic Technology and Sport: Ethical Questions. London; New York: Routledge; 2005: 209-217. Subject: 4.5

Gipson, Chester; Wigglesworth, Carol. A word from USDA and OLAW. *Lab Animal* 2006 June; 35(6): 17. Subject: 22.2

Girbes, Armand R.J. End-of-life decisions in the Netherlands: false euthanasia and false murder [news]. *Intensive Care Medicine* 2005 April; 31(4): 588. Subject: 20.5.1

Girsh, Faye J. Physician aid in dying: a proposed law for California. *Criminal Justice Journal* 1992 Fall; 14(2): 333-344. Subject: 20.5.1

Gitter, Donna M. Am I my brother's keeper? The use of preimplantation genetic diagnosis to create a donor of transplantable stem cells for an older sibling suffering from a genetic disorder. *George Mason Law Review* 2005-2006 Fall/Winter; 13(5): 975-1035. Subject: 15.2

Gitter, Donna M. Ownership of human tissue: a proposal for federal recognition of human research participants' property rights in their biological material. *Washington and Lee Law Review* 2004 Winter; 61(1): 257-345. Subject: 4.4

Giuliani, Michele; Lajolo, Carlo; Rezza, Giovanni; Arici, Claudio; Babudieri, Sergio; Grima, Pierfrancesco; Martinelli, Canio; Tamburrini, Enrica; Vecchiet, Jacopo; Mura, Maria Stella; Cauda, Roberto; Mario, Tumbarello. Dental care and HIV-infected individuals: are they equally treated? *Community Dentistry and Oral Epidemiology* 2005 December; 33(6): 447-453. Subject: 9.5.6

Glad, John. The reviving debate on eugenics: eugenics publications 2003-early 2005 and eugenics data bases. *Mankind Quarterly* 2005 Summer; 45(4): 427-466. Subject: 15.5

Glannon, Walter. Neuroethics. *Bioethics* 2006 February; 20(1): 37-52. Subject: 17.1

Glannon, Walter. 2. Commentary on "John". *Journal of Ethics in Mental Health* 2006 November; 1(1): E9, 1 p. Subject: 8.3.4

Glannon, W. Phase 1 oncology trials: why the therapeutic misconception will not go away. *Journal of Medical Ethics* 2006 May; 32(5): 252-255. Subject: 18.3

Glannon, W. Psychopharmacology and memory. *Journal of Medical Ethics* 2006 February; 32(2): 74-78. Subject: 17.4

Glasa, Jozef. Ethics of pharmacogenetic and pharmacogenomic research: problems and perspectives. *In his:* Ethics of Human Genetics: Challenges of the (Post)

Genomic Era. Bratislava, Slovak Republic: Charis [and] IMEB Foundation; 2002: 153-169. Subject: 15.1

Glasa, Jozef; Miller, Jane. Research ethics committees in Slovakia. *In:* Beyleveld, D.; Townend, D.; Wright, J., eds. Research Ethics Committees, Data Protection and Medical Research in European Countries. Hants, England; Burlington, VT: Ashgate; 2005: 221-227. Subject: 18.2

Glasberg, Ann-Louise; Eriksson, Sture; Dahlqvist, Vera; Lindahl, Elisabeth; Strandberg, Gunilla; Söderberg, Anna; Sørlie, Venke; Norberg, Astrid. Development and initial validation of the stress of conscience questionnaire. *Nursing Ethics* 2006 November; 13(6): 633-648. Subject: 4.1.3

Glaser, John W. "Covering the uninsured" is a flawed moral frame. *Health Progress* 2006 March-April; 87(2): 4-9. Subject: 9.5.10

Glaser, Vicki; Hurlbut, William B. An interview with William B. Hurlbut. *Rejuvenation Research* 2005 Summer; 8(2): 110-122. Subject: 2.1

Glasier, Anna. Emergency contraception: is it worth all the fuss? [editorial]. *BMJ: British Medical Journal* 2006 September 16; 333(7568): 560-561. Subject: 11.1

Glass, Allan R.; Papadakis, Maxine A.; Rattner, Susan L.; Stern, David T. Unprofessional behavior among medical students [letter and reply]. *New England Journal of Medicine* 2006 April 27; 354(17): 1851-1853. Subject: 7.4

Glass, Kathleen Cranley, Carnevale, Franco A. Decisional challenges for children requiring assisted ventilation at home. *HEC (Healthcare Ethics Committee) Forum* 2006 September; 18(3): 207-221. Subject: 8.3.2

Glass, Kathleen Cranley; Orentlicher, David. Protection of human subjects and scientific progress: can the two be reconciled? [letter and reply]. *Hastings Center Report* 2006 January-February; 36(1): 4, 8-9. Subject: 18.1

Glazier, Alexandra K. Donor rights and registries. *Medical Ethics Newsletter [Lahey Clinic]* 2006 Winter; 13(1): 4. Subject: 19.5

Gleeson, Gerald. Why it's wrong to experiment on human embryos. *Social Alternatives* 2003 Summer; 22(1): 33-38. Subject: 18.5.4

Gleicher, Norbert. Reflections and comments on regulations of biotechnologies that touch the beginning of human life. *Journal of Assisted Reproduction and Genetics* 2005 January; 22(1): 41-46. Subject: 5.3

Gleicher, Norbert; Barad, David. The relative myth of elective single embryo transfer. *Human Reproduction* 2006 June; 21(6): 1337-1344. Subject: 14.4

Glenn, David. Blood feud. *Chronicle of Higher Education* 2006 March 3; 52(26): A14-A16, A18. Subject: 18.5.1

Glick, Shimon M.; Casarett, David; Kapo, Jennifer; Caplan, Arthur. Appropriate use of artificial nutrition and

See SUBJECT HEADING KEY FOR SECTION II on inside back cover.

575

hydration [letter and reply]. *New England Journal of Medicine* 2006 March 23; 354(12): 1320-1321. Subject: 20.5.1

Glicksman, Gail Gaisin; Glicksman, Allen. Apples and oranges: a critique of current trends in the study of religion, spirituality, and health. *In:* Guinn, David E., ed. Handbook of Bioethics and Religion. New York: Oxford University Press, 2006: 333-343. Subject: 9.1

Glied, Sherry; Cuellar, Alison. Better behavioral health care coverage for everyone. *New England Journal of Medicine* 2006 March 30; 354(13): 1415-1417. Subject: 9.3.1

Glock, Rosana Soibelmann; Goldim, José Roberto. Informed consent in gerontology. *Eubios Journal of Asian and International Bioethics* 2003 January 13(1): 6-8. Subject: 18.3

Gloth, F. Michael III. The politics of pain: legislative and public policy issues. *In:* Gloth, F.M., ed. Handbook of Pain Relief in Older Adults: An Evidence-Based Approach. Totowa: Humana Press Inc., 2003: 185-205. Subject: 4.4

Glover, D. A suggested code of conduct for editors of peer-reviewed journals. *Journal of Wound Care* 2006 February; 15(2): 85-86. Subject: 1.3.7

Glover, Jacqueline; Lynn, Joanne; Howe, Edmund; McCullough, Laurence; Secundy, Marian; Yeide, Harry. A model for interschool teaching of humanities during clinical training. *Journal of Medical Education* 1984 July; 59(7): 594-596. Subject: 2.3

Glover, Jonathan. Should the child live? Doctors, families and conflict. *Clinical Ethics* 2006 March; 1(1): 52-59. Subject: 20.5.2

Glover-Thomas, N. Treating the vulnerable in England and Wales: the impact of law reform and changing policy. *International Journal of Law and Psychiatry* 2006 January-February; 29(1): 22-35. Subject: 9.5.3

Gluck, John P.; Bell, Jordan B.; Pearson-Bish, Melody. Confronting ethical issues in the use of animals in biomedical and behavioral research: the search for principles. *In:* O'Donohue, William; Ferguson, Kyle, eds. Handbook of Professional Ethics for Psychologists: Issues, Questions, and Controversies. Thousand Oaks, Calif.: SAGE Publications; 2003: 257-274. Subject: 22.2

Godard, Beatrice; Raeburn, Sandy; Pembrey, Marcus; Bobrow, Martin; Farndon, Peter; Ayme, Segolene. Genetic information and testing in insurance and employment: technical, social and ethical issues. *European Journal of Human Genetics* 2003 December; 11(Supplement 2): S123-S142. Subject: 15.3

Godard, Beatrice; Schmidtke, Jorg; Cassiman, Jean-Jacques; Ayme, Segolene. Data storage and DNA banking for biomedical research: informed consent, confidentiality, quality issues, ownership, return of benefits. A professional perspective. *European Journal of Human Genetics* 2003 December; 11(Supplement 2): S88-S122. Subject: 15.10

Godard, Beatrice; ten Kate, Leo; Evers-Kiebooms, Gerry; Ayme, Segolene. Population genetic screening programmes: principles, techniques, practices, and policies. *European Journal of Human Genetics* 2003 December; 11(Supplement 2): S49-S87. Subject: 15.3

Godin, Gaston; Sheeran, P.; Conner, M.; Germain, M.; Blondeau, D.; Gagné, C.; Beaulieu, D.; Naccache, H. Factors explaining the intention to give blood among the general population. *Vox Sanguinis* 2005 October; 89(3): 140-149. Subject: 19.5

Godkin, D. Should children's autonomy be respected by telling them of their imminent death? *Journal of Medical Ethics* 2006 January; 32(1): 24-25. Subject: 8.2

Godlee, Fiona. An international standard for disclosure of clinical trial information [editorial]. *BMJ: British Medical Journal* 2006 May 13; 332(7550): 1107-1108 [see correction in BMJ: British Medical Journal 2006 June 17; 332(7555): 1418]. Subject: 18.2

Godlee, Fiona; Dickersin, Kay. Bias, subjectivity, chance, and conflict of interest in editorial decisions. *In:* Godlee, Fiona; Jefferson, Tom, eds. Peer Review in Health Sciences. 2nd ed. London: BMJ Books; 2003: 91-117. Subject: 1.3.7

Godre, Neha S. Refusing to provide a prenatal test: can it ever be ethical?: Ethics or humanity? *BMJ: British Medical Journal* 2006 December 2; 333(7579): 1174. Subject: 15.2

Goel, Ashish. Ethical issues in international research, Harvard School of Public Health, Boston, USA, 13-17 June 2005. *National Medical Journal of India* 2005 July-August; 18(4): 209. Subject: 18.1

Goel, Ashish; Aggarwal, Praveen. Making choices in an emergency room. *Indian Journal of Medical Ethics* 2006 July-September; 3(3): 105. Subject: 9.4

Goelen, Guido; Rigo, Adelheid; Bonduelle, Maryse; De Greve, Jacques. BRCA 1/2 gene mutation testing-based cancer prevention and the moral concerns of different types of patients. *Annals of the New York Academy of Sciences* 1999; 889: 240-243. Subject: 15.3

Goemaere, Eric. Response to "No shortage of dilemmas". *CQ: Cambridge Quarterly of Healthcare Ethics* 2006 Summer; 15(3): 331-332. Subject: 9.5.6

Goering, Sara. Conformity through cosmetic surgery: the medical erasure of race and disability. *In:* Figueroa, Robert; Harding, Sandra, eds. Science and Other Cultures: Issues in Philosophies of Science and Technology. New York: Routledge; 2003: 172-188. Subject: 9.5.1

Goetz, Thomas. The thin pill. *Wired* 2006 October: 150-157. Subject: 9.7

Gohel, M.S.; Bulbulia, R.A.; Slim, F.J.; Poskitt, K.R.; Whyman, M.R. How to approach major surgery where patients refuse blood transfusion (including Jehovah's

---

Subject = NRCBL Primary Classification Number; see inside front cover.

Witnesses). *Annals of the Royal College of Surgeons of England* 2005 January; 87(1): 3-14. Subject: 19.4

Gold, E. Richard. Gene patents and medical access. *Intellectual Property Forum* 2002 June; 49: 20-27. Subject: 15.8

Gold, Jennifer L. Conflict over conflicts of interest: an analysis of the new NIH rules. *Journal of Law, Medicine, and Ethics* 2006 Spring; 34(1): 105-110. Subject: 1.3.9

Gold, Liza H.; Metzner, Jeffrey L. Psychiatric employment evaluations and the Health Insurance Portability and Accountability Act. *American Journal of Psychiatry* 2006 November; 163(11): 1878-1882. Subject: 8.4

Gold, Mark S. Problem doctors: is there a system-level solution? [letter]. *Annals of Internal Medicine* 2006 June 6; 144(11): 861-862. Subject: 7.4

Gold, Rachel Benson; Sonfield, Adam. Refusing to participate in health care: a continuing debate. *Guttmacher Report* 2000 February; 3(1): 8-11. [Online]. Accessed: http://www.guttmacher.org/pubs/tgr/03/1/gr030108.pdf [2006 November 1]. Subject: 8.1

Goldberg, Alan M.; Hartung, Thomas. Protecting more than animals. *Scientific American* 2006 January; 294(1): 84-91. Subject: 22.2

Goldberg, Aviva. Are dead bodies necessary? Dissecting prosections in anatomy lab. *Atrium* 2005 Spring; 1: 6-7. Subject: 7.2

Goldberg, David J. Dermatologic surgical research and the institutional review board. *Dermatologic Surgery* 2005 October; 31(10): 1317-1322. Subject: 18.2

Goldblatt, David. The gift: when a patient chooses to die. *Perspectives in Biology and Medicine* 2006 Autumn; 49(4): 537-541. Subject: 20.5.1

Goldblatt, David. Must physicians respect an incompetent patient's refusal of treatment? *Medical Ethics Newsletter* 2006 Spring; 13(2): 3. Subject: 8.3.3

Goldblatt, Peter. Evidence will help achieve consensus. *BMJ: British Medical Journal* 2006 January 21; 332(7534): 169. Subject: 8.4

Goldblum, Orin M.; Franzblau, Michael J.; Brennan, Troyen A.; Rothman, David J.; Naughton, James; Cohen, Jordan; Kimball, Harry; Blumenthal, David; Smelser, Neil; Kassirer, Jerome P.; Goldman, JanLori. Academic medical centers and conflicts of interest [letter and reply]. *JAMA: The Journal of the American Medical Association* 2006 June 28; 295(24): 2845-2846, 2848-2849. Subject: 7.3

Goldblum, Peter B.; Martin, David J. Principles for the discussion of life and death options with terminally ill clients with HIV. *Professional Psychology: Research and Practice* 1999 April; 30(2): 187-197. Subject: 20.5.1

Golden, Neville H.; Seigel, Warren M.; Fisher, Martin; Schneider, Marcie; Quijano, Emilyn; Suss, Amy;

Bergeson, Rachel; Seitz, Michele; Saunders, Deborah. Emergency contraception: pediatricians' knowledge, attitudes, and opinions. *Pediatrics* 2001 February; 107(2): 287-292. Subject: 11.1

Golden, Tim. Tough U.S. steps in hunger strike at camp in Cuba; force-feeding detainees; steps to avert a death — lawyers for prisoners protest treatment. *New York Times* 2006 February 9; pl A1, A20. Subject: 21.5

Goldenberg, Saul. Ethical aspects when using animals in research [editorial]. *Pesquisa Odontológica Brasileira/Brazilian Oral Research* 2005 January-March; 19(1): 1-2. Subject: 22.2

Goldie, John; Schwartz, Lisa; McConnachie, Alex; Jolly, Brian; Morrison, Jillian. Can students' reasons for choosing set answers to ethical vignettes be reliably rated? Development and testing of a method. *Medical Teacher* 2004 December; 26(8): 713-718. Subject: 7.2

Goldman, Bruce; Coghlan, Andy. Organs on demand, no embryo needed [news]. *New Scientist* 2006 October 7-13; 192(2572): 8-9. Subject: 18.5.1

Goldman, Steven A. Neurology and the stem cell debate [editorial]. *Neurology* 2005 May 24; 64(10): 1675-1676. Subject: 18.5.4

Goldstein, Irwin. The silver lining of a crisis: the Journal of Sexual Medicine establishes the ethics committee [editorial]. *Journal of Sexual Medicine* 2005 March; 2(2): 161-162. Subject: 1.3.7

Goldstein, Nathan. Financial conflict of interest in biomedical human subject research. *Journal of Biolaw and Business* 2006; 9(1): 26-37. Subject: 18.2

Goldstein, Nathan E.; Concato, John; Bradley, Elizabeth H.; O'Leary, John R.; Fried, Terri R. Doctor-patient communication about prognosis: the influence of race and financial status. *Journal of Palliative Medicine* 2005 October; 8(5): 998-1004. Subject: 8.2

Goldstein, Nathan E.; Lynn, Joanne. Trajectory of end-stage heart failure: the influence of technology and implications for policy change. *Perspectives on Biology and Medicine* 2006 Winter; 49(1): 10-18. Subject: 9.5.2

Golomb, Meredith R.; Garg, Bhuwan P.; Walsh, Laurence E.; Williams, Linda S. Perinatal stroke in baby, prothrombotic gene in mom: does this affect maternal health insurance? *Neurology* 2005 July 12; 65(1): 13-16. Subject: 15.3

Golombok, Susan; Lycett, Emma; MacCallum, Fiona; Jadva, Vasanti; Murray, Clare; Rust, John; Jenkins, Julian; Abdalla, Hossam; Margara, Raoul. Parenting infants conceived by gamete donation. *Journal of Family Psychology* 2004 September; 18(3): 443-452. Subject: 14.2

Golombok, Susan; Murray, Clare; Jadva, Vasanti; MacCallum, Fiona; Lycett, Emma. Families created through surrogacy arrangements: parent-child relation-

See SUBJECT HEADING KEY FOR SECTION II on inside back cover.

577

ships in the first year of life. *Developmental Psychology* 2004 May; 40(3): 400-411. Subject: 14.2

Golombok, Susan; Schulman, Joe; Dahl, Edgar; McLean, Sheila; Doyal, Len; Lotts, Jim; Lockwood, Gillian; Bhargava, Pushpa; McMahan, Jeff; Alikani, Mina; Lotz, Mianna; Te Velde, Egbert; Savulescu, Julian. Discussion (day 2 session 3): ethics of choosing the sex of our offspring. *Reproductive BioMedicine Online [electronic]* 2005 March; 10(Supplement 1): 125-128. Subject: 14.3

Gómez, Euclides Eslava. Controversias sobre muerte cerebral [Controversies in brain death]. *Persona y Bioética* 1999 February-May; 2(6): 43-55. Subject: 20.2.1

Gómez-Lobo, Alfonso. Human cloning: potential and ethical issues. *Estudios Publicos* 2003 Summer; (89): 1-8 [Online]. Accessed: http://www.cepchile.cl/dms/archivo_3180_1626/rev89_gomezlobo_ing.pdf [2007 January 25]. Subject: 14.5

Gonçalves, Ferraz; Marques, Ágata; Rocha, Sónia; Leitão, Pedro; Mesquita, Teresa; Moutinho, Susana. Breaking bad news: experiences and preferences of advanced cancer patients at a Portuguese oncology centre. *Palliative Medicine* 2005 October; 19(7): 526-531. Subject: 8.2

Gonin, P.; Buchholz, C.J.; Pallardy, M.; Mezzina, M. Gene therapy bio-safety: scientific and regulatory issues. *Gene Therapy* 2005 October; 12(Supplement 1): S146-S152. Subject: 15.4

González Barón, Manuel; Gómez Raposo, César; Pinto Marín, Álvaro. Sedation in clinical oncology. *Clinical and Translational Oncology* 2005 August; 7(7): 295-301. Subject: 20.4.1

González, Javier García. Penal regulation of gene technologies in Portugal. A case of normative standstill = Regulación penal de las genotecnologías: Portugal. Un ejemplo de inmovilismo normativo. *Law and the Human Genome Review = Revista de Derecho y Genoma Humano* 1996 July-December; (5): 185-193. Subject: 15.1

González-Pier, Eduardo; Gutiérrez-Delgado, Cristina; Stevens, Gretchen; Barraza-Lloréns, Mariana; Porras-Condey, Raúl; Carvalho, Natalie; Loncich, Kristen; Dias, Rodrigo H.; Kulkarni, Sandeep; Casey, Anna; Murakami, Yuki; Ezzati, Majid; Salomon, Joshua A. Priority setting for health interventions in Mexico's System of Social Protection in Health. *Lancet* 2006 November 4-10; 368(9547): 1608-1618. Subject: 9.4

Good, Grace. Sick to death. *Journal of Clinical Ethics* 2006 Spring; 17(1): 80-82. Subject: 9.5.1

Goodenough, Trudy; Williamson, Emma; Kent, Julie; Ashcroft, Richard. Ethical protection in research: including children in the debate. *In:* Smyth, Marie; Williamson, Emma, eds. Researchers and Their 'Subjects': Ethics, Power, Knowledge and Consent. Bristol, UK: Policy Press; 2004: 55-72. Subject: 15.1

Goodman, Brenda. Judge allows device to be used for monitoring lethal injection. *New York Times* 2006 April 18; p. A18. Subject: 20.6

Goodman, Neville. Animal welfare, human health. *British Journal of Hospital Medicine* 2005 October; 66(10): 593. Subject: 22.2

Goodman, Neville W. Will the new rules for research ethics committees lead to better decisions? *Journal of the Royal Society of Medicine* 2004 April; 97(4): 198-199. Subject: 18.2

Goodman, Robert L.; Carrasquillo, Olveen. The corporate co-author, the ghost writer, and the medical society: an object lesson (June, 2005 issue) [letter]. *JGIM: Journal of General Internal Medicine* 2006 January; 21(1): 102. Subject: 9.7

Goodnough, Abby. Officials clash over mentally ill in Florida jails. *New York Times* 2006 November 15; p. A1, A20. Subject: 17.8

Goodwin, Michele. Assisted reproductive technology and the double bind: the illusory choice of motherhood. *Journal of Gender, Race and Justice* 2005 Fall; 9(1): 1-54. Subject: 14.4

Goodwin, Michele. Bioethical entanglements of race, religion, and AIDS. *In:* Guinn, David E., ed. Handbook of Bioethics and Religion. New York: Oxford University Press, 2006: 363-383. Subject: 9.5.6

Goodwin, Michele. Formalism and the legal status of body parts. *University of Chicago Legal Forum* 2006: 317-388. Subject: 4.4

Goodyear, Michael. Closing the gaps: moving closer to a collaborative culture; comments on disclosure timing: balancing increased transparency and competitive advantage; submission to WHO International Clinical Trials Registry Platform [ICTRP]. Geneva: World Health Organization 2006 March 31: [Online]. Accessed: http://www.who.int/ictrp/007-Michael_Goodyear_31March06.pdf [2006 December 1]. Subject: 18.6

Goodyear, Michael. Learning from the TGN1412 trial [editorial]. *BMJ: British Medical Journal* 2006 March 25; 332(7543): 677-678. Subject: 18.2

Goodyear, Michael D.E. Further lessons from the TGN1412 tragedy: new guidelines call for a change in the culture of research [editorial]. *BMJ: British Medical Journal* 2006 August 5; 333(7562): 270-271. Subject: 18.2

Goodyear, Michael D.E. A model clinical trials agreement [editorial]. *BMJ: British Medical Journal* 2006 November 25; 333(7578): 1083-1084. Subject: 18.2

Goold, Imogen. Tissue donation: ethical guidance and legal enforceability. *Journal of Law and Medicine* 2004 February; 11(3): 331-340. Subject: 19.5

Goold, Susan Dorr; Baum, Nancy M. Define "affordable". *Hastings Center Report* 2006 September-October; 36(5): 22-24. Subject: 9.3.1

Subject = NRCBL Primary Classification Number; see inside front cover.

Goold, Susan Dorr; Stern, David T. Ethics and professionalism: what does a resident need to learn? *American Journal of Bioethics* 2006 July-August; 6(4): 9-17. Subject: 7.2

Gordijn, Bert. Converging NBIC technologies for improving human performance: a critical assessment of the novelty and the prospects of the project. *Journal of Law, Medicine and Ethics* 2006 Winter; 34(4): 726-732. Subject: 15.5

Gordijn, Bert. Die Debatte um Euthanasie in den Niederlanden und Deutschland: ein Vergleich aus historischer Sicht. *In:* Gordijn, Bert; ten Have, Henk, eds. Medizinethik und Kultur: Grenzen medizinischen Handelns in Deutschland und den Niederlanden. Stuttgart: Frommann-Holzboog; 2000: 303-343. Subject: 20.5.1

Gordimer, Nadine. A new racism. *World Watch* 2002 July-August; 15(4): 17. Subject: 9.2

Gordon, Elisa J.; Hamric, Ann B. The courage to stand up: the cultural politics of nurses' access to ethics consultation. *Journal of Clinical Ethics* 2006 Fall; 17(3): 231-254. Subject: 9.6

Gordon, Elisa J.; Harris Yamokoski, Amy; Kodish, Eric. Children, research, and guinea pigs: reflections on a metaphor. *IRB: Ethics and Human Research* 2006 September-October; 28(5): 12-19. Subject: 18.5.2

Gordon, Elisa J.; Prohaska, Thomas R. The ethics of withdrawal from study participation. *Accountability in Research* 2006 October-December; 13(4): 285-309. Subject: 18.3

Gordon, Michael. Ethical and clinical issues in cardiopulmonary resuscitation (CPR) in the frail elderly with dementia: a Jewish perspective. *Journal of Ethics in Mental Health* 2006 November; 1(1): E4, 4 p. Subject: 20.5.1

Gordon, M.; Sheehan, K. Artificial intelligence: making decisions about artificial nutrition and hydration. *Journal of Nutrition, Health and Aging* 2004; 8(4): 254-256. Subject: 20.5.1

Gordon, Richard F. Nazi medical data obtained from concentration camp victims: should it be used? *Delaware Medical Journal* 2005 April; 77(4): 143-150. Subject: 18.5.5

Gorelick, David A. Health Insurance Portability and Accountability Act privacy rule and research consent documents [letter]. *Annals of Internal Medicine* 2006 November 21; 145(10): 790. Subject: 18.3

Gormally, Luke. Terminal sedation and the doctrine of the sanctity of life. *In:* Tännsjö, Torbjörn, ed. Terminal Sedation: Euthanasia in Disguise? Boston: Kluwer Academic Publishers; 2004: 81-91. Subject: 20.4.1

Gostin, Lawrence O. Federal executive power and communicable disease control: CDC quarantine regulations. *Hastings Center Report* 2006 March-April; 36(2): 10-11. Subject: 9.1

Gostin, Lawrence O. HIV screening in health care settings. *JAMA: The Journal of the American Medical Association* 2006 October 25; 296(16): 2023-2025. Subject: 9.5.6

Gostin, Lawrence O. Medical countermeasures for pandemic influenza: ethics and the law. *JAMA: The Journal of the American Medical Association* 2006 February 1; 295(5): 554-556. Subject: 9.1

Gostin, Lawrence O. Physician-assisted suicide: a legitimate medical practice? *JAMA: The Journal of the American Medical Association* 2006 April 26; 295(16): 1941-1943. Subject: 20.7

Gostin, Lawrence O. Property rights and the common good. *Hastings Center Report* 2006 September-October; 36(5): 10-11. Subject: 9.1

Gostin, Lawrence O. Public health strategies for pandemic influenza: ethics and the law. *JAMA: The Journal of the American Medical Association* 2006 April 12; 295(14): 1700-1704. Subject: 9.1

Gostin, Lawrence O.; Hamden, Michael S. Prisoners and medical research. *Chronicle of Higher Education* 2006 November 3; 53(11): B20. Subject: 18.5.5

Gostin, Lawrence O.; Powers, Madison. What does social justice require for the public's health? Public health ethics and policy imperatives. *Health Affairs* 2006 July-August; 25(4): 1053-1060. Subject: 9.1

Gotcher, Robert F. The theology of the body: some reflections on the significance for medical professionals. *Linacre Quarterly* 2006 May; 73(2): 115-131. Subject: 2.1

Gottleib, Michael K. Singleton v. Norris: precursor to Abu Ghraib? The importance of role integrity in medicine. *APA Newsletter on Philosophy and Law* 2005 Fall; 05(1): 11-25. Subject: 20.6

Gottlieb, Michael C. A template for peer ethics consultation. *Ethics and Behavior* 2006; 16(2): 151-162. Subject: 7.3

Gottlieb, Michael K. Executions and torture: the consequences of overriding professional ethics. *Yale Journal of Health Policy, Law and Ethics* 2006 Summer; 6(2): 351-389. Subject: 20.6

Gottweis, Herbert. Human embryonic stem cells, cloning, and the transformation of biopolitics. *In:* Stehr, Nico, ed. Biotechnology Between Commerce and Civil Society. New Brunswick, NJ: Transaction Publishers; 2004: 239-265. Subject: 18.5.4

Gottweis, Herbert; Triendl, Robert. South Korean policy failure and the Hwang debacle. *Nature Biotechnology* 2006 February; 24(2): 141-143. Subject: 14.5

Gøtzsche, Peter C. Research integrity and pharmaceutical industry sponsorship: trial registration, transparency and less reliance on industry trials are essential [editorial].

See SUBJECT HEADING KEY FOR SECTION II on inside back cover.

579

Medical Journal of Australia 2005 June 6; 182(11): 549-550. Subject: 1.3.9

Gøtzsche, Peter C.; Hrobjartsson, Asbjorn; Johansen, Helle Krogh; Haahr, Mette T.; Altman, Douglas G.; Chan, An-Wen. Constraints on publication rights in industry-initiated clinical trials [letter]. *JAMA: The Journal of the American Medical Association* 2006 April 12; 295(14): 1645-1646. Subject: 1.3.7

Gould Halme, Dina; Kessler, David A. FDA regulation of stem-cell-based therapies. *New England Journal of Medicine* 2006 October 19; 355(16): 1730-1735. Subject: 18.5.4

Gould, Donald. Baby doomed to live. *New Statesman (London, England:* 1957) 1972 October 27; 84: 595. Subject: 20.5.2

Gould, Donald. Castrating into conformity. *New Statesman (London, England:* 1957) 1967 October 27; 74: 540. Subject: 9.5.1

Gould, Donald. Conscience of a doctor. *New Statesman (London, England:* 1957) 1967 May 26; 73: 716-717. Subject: 21.2

Gould, Donald. Cool it with a baboon's blood. *New Statesman (London, England:* 1957) 1968 September 27; 76: 390. Subject: 19.1

Gould, Donald. Deciding who shall die. *New Statesman (London, England:* 1957) 1969 January 24; 77: 112. Subject: 19.6

Gould, Donald. Doctors and the public. *New Statesman (London, England:* 1957) 1969 June 6; 77: 793-794. Subject: 19.2

Gould, Donald. Experimenting on patients. *New Statesman (London, England* 1957) 1966 August 19; 72: 256-257. Subject: 18.3

Gould, Donald. Is it too easy to be put away? *New Statesman (London, England:* 1957) 1969 June 27; 77: 906-907. Subject: 17.1

Gould, Donald. New doctor's dilemma. *New Statesman (London, England* 1957) 1967 September 29; 74: 399. Subject: 20.5.1

Gould, Donald. Surgical morals. *New Statesman (London, England:* 1957) 1968 March 1; 75: 266. Subject: 19.1

Gould, Donald. Truth about transplants. *New Statesman (London, England:* 1957) 1968 May 10: 610. Subject: 19.2

Gould, Donald. When doctors should tell. *New Statesman (London, England:* 1957) 1968 November 29; 76: 741-742. Subject: 1.3.7

Goy, Elizabeth R.; Carlson, Bryant; Simpoulos, Nicole; Jackson, Ann; Ganzani, Linda. Determinants of Oregon hospice chaplains' views on physician-assisted suicide. *Journal of Palliative Care* 2006 Summer; 22(2): 83-90. Subject: 20.7

Goy, Elizabeth R.; Jackson, Ann; Harvath, Theresa A.; Miller, Lois L.; Delorit, Molly A.; Ganzini, Linda. Oregon hospice nurses and social workers' assessment of physician progress in palliative care over the past 5 years. *Palliative and Supportive Care* 2003 September; 1(3): 215-219. Subject: 20.4.1

Gozum, Marvin E.; Brennan, Troyen A.; Rothman, David J.; Naughton, James; Cohen, Jordan; Kimball, Harry; Blumenthal, David; Smelser, Neil; Kassirer, Jerome P.; Goldman, JanLori. Academic medical centers and conflicts of interest [letter and reply]. *JAMA: The Journal of the American Medical Association* 2006 June 28; 295(24): 2845, 2848-2849. Subject: 7.3

Grabenstein, John D. The value of immunization for God's people. *National Catholic Bioethics Quarterly* 2006 Autumn; 6(3): 433-442. Subject: 9.1

Grabowski, Henry. Patents, innovation and access to new pharmaceuticals. *Journal of International Economic Law* 2002 December; 5(4): 849-860. Subject: 9.7

Grace, Eric S. Ethical issues. *In his:* Biotechnology Unzipped: Promises and Realities. Revised second edition. Washington, DC: Joseph Henry Press; 2006: 191-223. Subject: 15.1

Grace, Pamela J. The clinical use of placebos: is it ethical? Not when it involves deceiving patients. *AJN: American Journal of Nursing* 2006 February; 106(2): 58-61. Subject: 8.2

Gracia Guillén, Diego. Pharmacogen-ethics. *In:* Lolas Stepke, Fernando; Agar Corbinos, Lorenzo, eds. Interfaces Between Bioethics and the Empirical Social Sciences. Buenos Aires, Argentina: World Health Organization; 2002: 53-65. Subject: 15.1

Gracia, Diego. The foundation of medical ethics in the democratic evolution of modern society. *In:* Viafora, Corrado, ed. Clinical Bioethics: A Search for the Foundations. Dordrecht: Springer, 2005: 33-40. Subject: 2.1

Grady, Christine. Ethical principles in clinical research. *In:* Gallin, John I., ed. Principles and Practice of Clinical Research. San Diego, CA: Academic Press; 2002: 15-26. Subject: 18.1

Grady, Christine. Ethics of vaccine research. *In:* Iltis, Ana Smith, ed. Research Ethics. New York: Routledge, 2006: 22-31. Subject: 18.1

Grady, Christine. Payment of clinical research subjects. *Journal of Clinical Investigation* 2005 July; 115(7): 1681-1687. Subject: 18.2

Grady, Christine; Dickert, Neal; Jawetz, Tom; Gensler, Gary; Emanuel, Ezekiel. An analysis of U.S. practices of paying research participants. *Contemporary Clinical Trials* 2005 June; 26(3): 365-375. Subject: 18.1

Grady, Christine; Hampson, Lindsay A.; Wallen, Gwenyth R.; Rivera-Goba, Migdalia V.; Carrington, Kelli L.; Mittleman, Barbara B. Exploring the ethics of clinical research in an urban community. *American Journal of Public Health* 2006 November; 96(11): 1996-2001. Subject: 18.5.1

Grady, Christine; Horstmann, Elizabeth; Sussman, Jeffrey S.; Hull, Sara Chandros. The limits of disclosure: what research subjects want to know about investigator financial interests. *Journal of Law, Medicine and Ethics* 2006 Fall; 34(3): 592-599. Subject: 18.2

Grady, Denise. As the use of donor sperm increases, secrecy can be a health hazard. *New York Times* 2006 June 6; p. F5, F8. Subject: 14.2

Grady, Denise. Doctors see way to cut risks of suffering in lethal injection. *New York Times* 2006 June 23; p. A1, A24. Subject: 20.6

Grady, Denise. The fuzzy gray place in a killing zone. *New York Times* 2006 August 13; p. WK3. Subject: 20.4.1

Grady, Denise. Lung patients see a new era of transplants. *New York Times* 2006 September 24; p. A1, A30. Subject: 19.6

Grady, Denise. Medical and ethical questions raised on deaths of critically ill patients. *New York Times* 2006 July 20; p. A18. Subject: 20.4.1

Grande, Lydia Feito. Putting ethics in motion: basic elements for analysis of human gene therapy = Poner en marcha la ética: elementos básicos para el análisis de la terapia génica humana. *Law and the Human Genome Review = Revista de Derecho y Genoma Humano* 1996 January-June; (4): 125-139. Subject: 15.4

Grandison, David. Participation of minorities in research and clinical trials. *In:* Satcher, David; Pamies, Rubens J., eds. Multicultural medicine and health disparities. New York: McGraw-Hill, 2006: 449-458. Subject: 18.5.1

Grant, Richard E.; Boylan, Michael. Just end-of-life policies and patient dignity. *American Journal of Bioethics* 2006 September-October; 6(5): 32-33; discussion W30-W32. Subject: 20.5.1

Grant, V.J. Sex predetermination and the ethics of sex selection. *Human Reproduction* 2006 July; 21(7): 1659-1661. Subject: 14.3

Graumann, Sigrid. Die somatische Gentherapie in der Krise: Kritsche Fragen an ein experimentelles Therapiekonzept. *In:* Rehmann-Sutter, Christoph; Müller, Hansjakob, eds. Ethik und Gentherapie: zum praktischen Diskurs um die molekulare Medizin. 2nd ed. Tübingen: Francke Verlag; 2003: 117-133. Subject: 15.4

Graumann, Sigrid. Experts on bioethics in biopolitics. *In:* Rehmann-Sutter, Christoph; Düwell, Marcus; Mieth, Dietmar, eds. Bioethics in Cultural Contexts: Reflections on Methods and Finitude. Dordrecht: Springer, 2006: 175-185. Subject: 2.1

Graumann, Sigrid; Haker, Hille. Some conceptual and ethical comments on egg cell nuclear transfer. *Politics and the Life Sciences* 1998 March; 17(1): 17-19. Subject: 15.4

Gray, Alastair. The advanced nurse practitioner: empowerment in witnessed resuscitation. *In:* Bartter, Karen, ed. Ethical Issues in Advanced Nursing Practice. Boston: Butterworth-Heinemann; 2001: 101-117. Subject: 20.5.1

Gray, David Emmanuel. Decision support and moral sensitivity: must one come at the expense of the other? *American Journal of Bioethics* 2006 May-June; 6(3): 59-62; discussion W51- W53. Subject: 2.1

Gray, Jeremy R.; Thompson, Paul M. Neurobiology of intelligence: science and ethics. *Nature Reviews Neuroscience* 2004 June; 5(6): 471-482. Subject: 17.4

Gray, Ronald H.; Sewankambo, Nelson K.; Wawer, Maria J.; Serwadda, David; Kiwanuka, Noah; Lutalo, Tom. Disclosure of HIV status on informed consent forms presents an ethical dilemma for protection of human subjects. *Journal of Acquired Immune Deficiency Syndromes* 2006 February 1; 41(2): 246-248. Subject: 18.3

Grazi, Richard V. Halachic dilemmas of the process of IVF. *In:* Rosner, Fred, ed. Medicine and Jewish Law. Volume III. Brooklyn, NY: Yashar Books, Inc.; 2005: 25-39. Subject: 14.4

Great Britain. Human Tissue Authority. Human tissue codes of practice. *Bulletin of Medical Ethics* 2005 June-July; (209): 18-24. Subject: 19.5

Great Britain. Parliament. House of Commons Science and Technology Committee. Human reproductive technologies and the law. *Bulletin of Medical Ethics* 2005 May; (208): 13-21. Subject: 18.5.4

Great Britain. Parliament. House of Lords. Assisted dying for the terminally ill bill [HL]. Second Reading. *In:* Parliamentary Debates (Hansard). London: The Stationery Office, 2006 May 12; 681(145): 1184-1296. Subject: 20.7

Great Britain. Parliament. House of Lords. Select Committee. Assisted dying for the terminally ill. *Bulletin of Medical Ethics* 2005 March; (206): 9-11. Subject: 20.7

Greaves, David. Conceptions of persons and dementia. *In his:* The Healing Tradition: Reviving the Soul of Western Medicine. Oxford; San Francisco: Radcliffe Publishing.; 2004: 55-65. Subject: 4.4

Greaves, David. Contrasting perspectives of inequalities in health and in medical care. *In his:* The Healing Tradition: Reviving the Soul of Western Medicine. Oxford; San Francisco: Radcliffe Publishing.; 2004: 99-112. Subject: 9.2

Greco, Dirceu B. Revising the Declaration of Helsinki: ethics vs economics or the fallacy of urgency. *HIV/AIDS Policy and Law Review* 2000; 5(4): 98-101. Subject: 18.3

Greely, Henry T. Knowing sin: making sure good science doesn't go bad. *Cerebrum: The Dana Forum on Brain Science* 2006 June: 1-8. Subject: 17.1

Greely, Henry T. Man and superman. *New Scientist* 2006 August 5-11; 191(2563): 19. Subject: 4.5

See SUBJECT HEADING KEY FOR SECTION II on inside back cover.

581

Greely, Henry T. The revolution in human genetics: implications for human societies. *South Carolina Law Review* 2001 Winter; 52(2): 377-381. Subject: 15.1

Greely, Henry T.; Riordan, Daniel P.; Garrison, Nanibaa' A.; Mountain, Joanna L. Family ties: the use of DNA offender databases to catch offenders' kin. *Journal of Law, Medicine and Ethics* 2006 Summer; 34(2): 248-262. Subject: 15.1

Green, David A.; Nierhoff, Sabine. When doctors participate in torture. *Indian Journal of Medical Ethics* 2006 October-December; 3(4): 128-129. Subject: 21.4

Green, Joshua; Cohen, Jonathan. For the law, neuroscience changes nothing and everything. *Royal Society of London - Series B: Biological Sciences* 2004 November 29; 359(1451): 1775-1785 [Online]. Accessed: http://www.journals.royalsoc.ac.uk/media/dltehetrrr5vtwmlpt6y/contributions/p/f/8/u/pf8u1kjk14u871yu.pdf [2007 February 26]. Subject: 17.1

Green, Lawrence W. Ethics and community-based participatory research: commentary on Minkler. *Health Education and Behavior* 2004 December; 31(6): 698-701. Subject: 18.1

Green, Lee A.; Lowery, Julie C.; Kowalski, Christine P.; Wyszewianski, Leon. Impact of institutional review board practice variation on observational health services research. *Health Services Research* 2006 February; 41(1): 214-230. Subject: 18.2

Green, Nancy S.; Dolan, Siobhan, M.; Murray, Thomas H. Newborn screening: complexities in universal genetic testing. *American Journal of Public Health* 2006 November; 96(11): 1955-1959. Subject: 15.3

Green, Ronald M. For richer or poorer? Evaluating the President's Council on Bioethics. *HEC (Healthcare Ethics Committee) Forum* 2006 June; 18(2): 108-124. Subject: 2.4

Green, Shane K. E³LSI research: an essential element of biodefense. *Biosecurity and Bioterrorism* 2005; 3(2): 128-137. Subject: 21.3

Green, Stephen A.; Bloch, Sidney. 1. Joint commentary on "John". *Journal of Ethics in Mental Health* 2006 November; 1(1): E8, 1 p. Subject: 8.3.4

Greenberg, Julie A. International legal developments protecting the autonomy rights of sexual minorities. *In:* Sytsma, Sharon E., ed. Ethics and Intersex. Dordrecht: Springer, 2006: 87-101. Subject: 10

Greene, Mark. To restore faith and trust: justice and biological access to cellular therapies. *Hastings Center Report* 2006 January-February; 36(1): 57-63. Subject: 18.5.4

Greene, Richard A.; Jenkins, Thomas M.; Wapner, Ronald J. The new genetic era in reproductive medicine: possibilities, probabilities, and problems. *International Journal of Fertility and Women's Medicine* 2001 May-June; 46(3): 169-183. Subject: 14.1

Greene, Wallace. Dispensing medical marijuana: some halachic parameters. *Judaism* 2006 Summer-Fall; 55(1-2): 28-38. Subject: 9.5.1

Greenfield, Bruce H. Reflections of moral dilemmas and patterns of ethical decision making in five clinical physical therapists. *In:* Dinkins, Christine Sorrell; Sorrell, Jeanne Merkle, eds. Listening to the Whispers: Re-Thinking Ethics in Healthcare. Madison, WI: University of Wisconsin Press; 2006: 190-247. Subject: 4.1.1

Greenfield, Debra L. Greenberg v. Miami Children's Hospital: unjust enrichment and the patenting of human genetic material. *Annals of Health Law* 2006 Summer; 15(2): 213-249. Subject: 15.8

Greenfield, Susan A. Biotechnology, the brain and the future. *TRENDS in Biotechnology* 2005 January; 23(1): 34-41. Subject: 17.4

Greenhough, Beth. Decontextualised? Dissociated? Detached? Mapping the networks of bioinformatics exchange. *Environment and Planning* 2006 March; 38(3): 445-463. Subject: 15.10

Greenhouse, Linda. Abortion opponents win dispute. *New York Times* 2006 March 1; p. A14. Subject: 12.4.1

Greenhouse, Linda. Justices reaffirm abortion access for emergencies. *New York Times* 2006 January 19; p. A1, A18. Subject: 12.4.1

Greenhouse, Linda. Justices reject U.S. bid to block assisted suicide; Court, 6-3, says attorney general was wrong in Oregon case. *New York Times* 2006 January 18; p. A1, A16. Subject: 20.7

Greenhouse, Linda. Justices to review federal ban on disputed abortion method; case may hinge on Alito, Court's newest member. *New York Times* 2006 February 22; p. A1, A14. Subject: 12.4.1

Greenley, Rachel Neff; Drotar, Dennis; Zyzanski, Stephen J.; Kodish, Eric. Stability of parental understanding of random assignment in childhood leukemia trials: an empirical examination of informed consent. *Journal of Clinical Oncology* 2006 February 20; 24(6): 891-897. Subject: 18.3

Greenough, Anne; Graham, Helen. Protecting and using patient information: the role of the Caldicott Guardian. *Clinical Medicine* 2004 May-June; 4(3): 246-249. Subject: 8.4

Gregor, Thomas A.; Gross, Daniel R. Guilt by association: the culture of accusation and the American Anthropological Association's investigation of Darkness in El Dorado. *American Anthropologist* 2004 December; 106(4): 687-698. Subject: 18.5.9

Gremmen, Bart. Genomics and the intrinsic value of plants. *Genomics, Society and Policy* 2005 December; 1(3): 1-7. Subject: 15.1

Grentholtz, Liesl; Richter, Marlise. Developments in South African law on HIV/AIDS. *HIV/AIDS Policy and Law Review* 2004 April; 9(1): 57-60. Subject: 9.5.6

Griffith, Ezra E. H. Correction and disclosure. Regarding: Lewis DO, Yeager CA, Blake P, Bard B, Sternziok M: ethics questions raised by the neuropsychiatric, neuropsychological, educational, developmental, and family characteristics of 18 juveniles awaiting execution in Texas. *Journal of the American Academy of Psychiatry and the Law* 2006; 34(2): 142-144. Subject: 1.3.7

Griffith, Richard. Immunisation and the law: compulsion or parental choice? *Nursing Standard* 2003 November 19; 18(10): 39-41. Subject: 8.3.4

Griffith, Richard. Making decisions for incapable adults 1: capacity and best interest. *British Journal of Community Nursing* 2006 March; 11(3): 119-125. Subject: 8.3.3

Griffiths, Paul E.; Stotz, Karola. Genes in the postgenomic era. *Theoretical Medicine and Bioethics* 2006; 27(6): 499-521. Subject: 15.1

Griffiths, Pauline. Being a research participant: the nurse's ethical and legal rights. *British Journal of Nursing* 2006 April 13-26; 15(7): 386-390. Subject: 18.1

Griffiths, Rod. CNEP and research governance. *Lancet* 2006 April 1-7; 367(9516): 1037-1038. Subject: 18.6

Grigoriu, Bogdan-Dragos. Ethical flaws in Romania's health reform [letter]. *Lancet* 2006 June 24-30; 367(9528): 2059. Subject: 19.5

Grimes, David A. Emergency contraception and fire extinguishers: a prevention paradox. *American Journal of Obstetrics and Gynecology* 2002 December; 187(6): 1536-1538. Subject: 11.1

Grimes, David A.; Raymond, Elizabeth G.; Scott Jones, Bonnie. Emergency contraception over-the-counter: the medical and legal imperatives. *Obstetrics and Gynecology* 2001 July; 98(1): 151-155. Subject: 11.1

Grimm, David. A cure for the common trial [news]. *Science* 2006 May 12; 312(5775): 835, 837. Subject: 18.2

Grinbaum, Alexei. Cognitive barriers in perception of nanotechnology. *Journal of Law, Medicine and Ethics* 2006 Winter; 34(4): 689-694. Subject: 5.4

Grisolía, James Santiago. Stem cell grafting for epilepsy: clinical promise and ethical concerns. *Epilepsy and Behavior* 2001 August; 2(4): 318-323. Subject: 12.1

Grisso, Thomas, Vierling, Linda. Minor's consent to treatment: a developmental perspective. *Professional Psychology* 1978 August; 9(3): 412-427. Subject: 8.3.2

Grob, Rachel. Parenting in the genomic age: the "cursed blessing" of newborn screening. *New Genetics and Society* 2006 August; 25(2): 159-170. Subject: 15.2

Grodsky, Jamie A. Genetics and environmental law: redefining public health. *California Law Review* 2005 January; 93(1): 171-269. Subject: 15.1

Groeneveld, Peter W.; Brezis, Mayer; Lehmann, Lisa Soleymani; Pearson, Steven D.; Miller, Franklin G.; Emanuel, Ezekiel J. Medicare requirement for research participation [letters and reply]. *JAMA: The Journal of the American Medical Association* 2006 December 27; 296(24): 2923-2925. Subject: 18.5.7

Groenewegen, Peter P.; Kerssens, Jan J.; Sixma, Herman J.; van der Eijk, Ingrid; Boerma, Wienke G.W. What is important in evaluating health care quality? An international comparison of user views. *BMC Health Services Research* 2005 February 21; 5: 9 p. Subject: 9.8

Groenhout, Ruth. Not without hope: a reformed analysis of sickness and sin. *Christian Bioethics* 2006 August; 12(2): 133-150. Subject: 4.2

Grönvall, Gigi Kwik. A new role for scientists in the Biological Weapons Convention. *Nature Biotechnology* 2005 October; 23(10): 1213-1216. Subject: 21.3

Gros Espiell, Héctor. UNESCO's Draft Universal Declaration on the Human Genome and Human Rights = El Proyecto de Declaración Universal sobre el Genoma Humano y los Derechos de la Persona Humana de la UNESCO. *Revista de Derecho Genoma Humano = Law and the Human Genome Review* 1997 July-December; (7): 121-148. Subject: 15.10

Gross, David E. Presumed dangerous: California's selective policy of forcibly medicating state prisoners with antipsychotic drugs. *University of California Davis Law Review* 2002 January; 35: 483-517. Subject: 17.8

Gross, Jed Adam. Trying the case against bioethics. *American Journal of Bioethics* 2006 May-June; 6(3): 71-73; discussion W51- W53. Subject: 2.1

Gross, Michael. Bioethics and war [editorial]. *CQ: Cambridge Quarterly of Healthcare Ethics* 2006 Fall; 15(4): 341-343. Subject: 2.1

Gross, Michael L. Author's reply to review of Bioethics and Armed Conflict [letter]. *BMJ: British Medical Journal* 2006 December 16; 333(7581): 1272. Subject: 21.2

Gross, Michael L. Medical ethics education: to what ends? *Journal of Evaluation in Clinical Practice* 2001 November; 7(4): 387-397. Subject: 2.3

Grosse, Scott D.; Khoury, Muin J. What is the clinical utility of genetic testing? *Genetics in Medicine* 2006 July; 8(7): 448-450. Subject: 15.3

Grothaus-Day, Cyrene. Criminal conception: behind the white coat. *Family Law Quarterly* 2005 Fall; 39(3): 707-725. Subject: 14.4

Group of Advisers on the Ethical Implications of Biotechnology. The ethical aspects of the fifth research framework program [guideline]. *Politics and the Life Sciences* 1998 March; 17(1): 73-76. Subject: 1.3.9

Groves, Kashina. Justified paternalism: the nature of beneficence in the care of dementia patients. *Penn Bioethics Journal* 2006; 2(2): 17-20. Subject: 17.1

See SUBJECT HEADING KEY FOR SECTION II on inside back cover.

583

Groves, Sara. Health care for the poor and underserved. *In:* Cowen, Perle Slavik; Moorhead, Sue, eds. Current Issues in Nursing. 7th ed. St. Louis, MO: Mosby, 2006: 639-644. Subject: 9.5.10

Gruber, Jonathan. The Massachusetts health care revolution: a local start for universal access. *Hastings Center Report* 2006 September-October; 36(5): 14-19. Subject: 9.2

Gruen, Russell L.; Campbell, Eric G.; Blumenthal, David. Public roles of US physicians: community participation, political involvement, and collective advocacy. *JAMA: The Journal of the American Medical Association* 2006 November 22-29; 296(20): 2467-2475. Subject: 9.1

Gruning, Thilo; Gilmore, Anna B.; McKee, Martin. Tobacco industry influence on science and scientists in Germany. *American Journal of Public Health* 2006 January; 96(1): 20-32. Subject: 5.3

Grunwald, Armin. Nanotechnology — a new field of ethical inquiry? *Science and Engineering Ethics* 2005 April; 11(2): 187-201. Subject: 5.4

Grünwald, Hans W. Hospice care for the terminally ill: an absolute necessity [editorial]. *Cancer Investigation* 2005; 23(3): 283. Subject: 20.4.1

Gruskin, Sofia; Dickens, Bernard. Human rights and ethics in public health [editorial]. *American Journal of Public Health* 2006 November; 96(11): 1903-1905. Subject: 9.1

Grytten, Stein E. Reducing sick leave: swimming upstream — positioning and multiple loyalties. *In:* Westerholm, Peter; Nilstun, Tore; Øvretveit, John, eds. Practical Ethics in Occupational Health. San Francisco: Radcliffe Medical Press; 2004: 133-150. Subject: 16.3

Gu, Shi (Mark). The ethics of placebo-controlled studies on perinatal HIV transmission and its treatment in the developing world. *Penn Bioethics Journal* 2006; 2(2): 21-24. Subject: 18.3

Gudding, Gabriel. The phenotype/genotype distinction and the disappearance of the body. *Journal of the History of Ideas* 1996 July; 57(3): 525-545. Subject: 15.1

Guðmundsson, Sigurður. Doctors and drug companies: the beauty and the beast? [editorial]. *Acta Ophthalmologica Scandinavica* 2005 August; 83(4): 407-408. Subject: 9.7

Guedj, M.; Muñoz Sastre, M.T.; Mullet, E.; Sorum, P.C. Do French lay people and health professionals find it acceptable to breach confidentiality to protect a patient's wife from a sexually transmitted disease? *Journal of Medical Ethics* 2006 July; 32(7): 414-419. Subject: 8.4

Guerrier, M. Hospital based ethics, current situation in France: between "espaces" and committees. *Journal of Medical Ethics* 2006 September; 32(9): 503-506. Subject: 9.6

Guevara, Carlos; Cook, Chad; Herback, Natalie; Pietrobon, Ricardo; Jacobs, Danny O.; Vail, Thomas

Parker. Gender, racial, and ethical disclosure in NIH K-award funded diabetes and obesity clinical trials. *Accountability in Research* 2006 October-December; 13(4): 311-324. Subject: 18.5.1

Guillaume, Agnes. The role of abortion in the fertility transition in Abidjan (Cote d'Ivoire) during the 1990s. *Population* 2003 November-December; 58(6): 657-685. Subject: 12.5.2

Guillemin, Marilys; Gillam, Lynn. Attitudes to genetic testing for deafness: the importance of informed choice. *Journal of Genetic Counseling* 2006 February; 15(1): 51-59. Subject: 15.3

Guillod, Olivier. Recent developments in Swiss health law. *European Journal of Health Law* 2006 June; 13(2): 123-131. Subject: 9.3.1

Guillot-Hurtubise, Bruno. Dentist found guilty of discrimination. *Canadian HIV/AIDS Policy and Law Newsletter* 1995 July; 1(4): 1, 14-15. Subject: 9.5.6

Guimerá, Juan-Felipe Higuera. Juridico-penal considerations on human embryo cloning (I) = Consideraciones jurídico-penales sobre las conductas de clonación en los embriones humanos (I). *Law and the Human Genome = Revista de Derecho y Genoma Humano* 1994 July-December; (1): 49-70. Subject: 14.5

Guinan, Patrick. Medical ethics versus bioethics (a.k.a. principlism). *National Catholic Bioethics Quarterly* 2006 Winter; 6(4): 651-659. Subject: 2.1

Guinan, Patrick. Who is my patient? *Linacre Quarterly* 2006 August; 73(3): 290-292. Subject: 7.1

Guinan, Patrick F. Evaluating Catholic medical ethics books. *Linacre Quarterly* 2006 November; 73(4): 354-360. Subject: 2.1

Guinn, David E. The heart of the matter: religion and spirituality at the end of life. *In:* Guinn, David E., ed. Handbook of Bioethics and Religion. New York: Oxford University Press, 2006: 345-357. Subject: 20.4.1

Guinn, David E.; Keyserlingk, Edward W.; Morton, Wendy. Law and bioethics in Rodriguez v. Canada. *In:* Guinn, David E., ed. Handbook of Bioethics and Religion. New York: Oxford University Press, 2006: 199-220. Subject: 20.5.1

Gunawardana, Nushan P. Refusing to provide a prenatal test: can it ever be ethical?: the darker side of medicine [letter]. *BMJ: British Medical Journal* 2006 December 2; 333(7579): 1174. Subject: 15.2

Gunderman, Richard B.; Engle, William A. Ethics and the limits of neonatal viability [editorial]. *Radiology* 2005 August; 236(2): 427-429. Subject: 20.5.2

Güner, Ahmet. A Book on Medical Ethics in Medieval Islam: Al-Tashwîk Al-Tibbî (Encouraging Medicine) of Abu'l-Alâ Sâid B. Al-Hasan Al-Tabîb (1009-1087 A.C.) [book review]. *Eubios Journal of Asian and International Bioethics* 2006 January; 16(1): 6-9. Subject: 2.2

Subject = NRCBL Primary Classification Number; see inside front cover.

Gunn, Scott; Hashimoto, Satoru; Karakozov, Michael; Marx, Thomas; Tan, Ian K.S.; Thompson, Dan R.; Vincent, Jean-Louis. Ethics roundtable debate: child with severe brain damage and an underlying brain tumour. *Critical Care* 2004 August; 8(4): 213-218. Subject: 20.5.2

Gunnar, William P. The fundamental law that shapes the United States health care system: is universal health care realistic within the established paradigm? *Annals of Health Law* 2006 Winter; 15(1): 151-181. Subject: 9.3.1

Gunning, Thomas G.; Coleman, Terry S. Harmonizing legal and ethical standards for interactions between health care providers and industry. *Fertility and Sterility* 2005 October; 84(4): 861-866. Subject: 7.3

Gunsalus, C.K.; Bruner, Edward M.; Burbules, Nicholas C.; Dash, Leon; Finkin, Matthew; Goldberg, Joseph P.; Greenough, William T.; Miller, Gregory A.; Pratt, Michael G. Mission creep in the IRB world [editorial]. *Science* 2006 June 9; 312(5779): 1441. Subject: 18.2

Guo, Jerry; Xin, Hao. Splicing out the West? [news]. *Science* 2006 November 24; 314(5803): 1232-1235. Subject: 15.4

Gupta, Manju. Occupational risk: the outrageous reaction to HIV positive public safety and health care employees in the workplace. *Journal of Law and Health* 2004-2005; 19(1): 39-73. Subject: 9.5.6

Guptha, S.H.; Owusu-Agyei, P. Ageism in services for transient ischaemic attack and stroke: clinical leadership is key in changing practice [letter]. *BMJ: British Medical Journal* 2006 September 23; 333(7569): 656. Subject: 9.5.2

Gurdon, J.B. Reproductive cloning: past, present and future. *Reproductive BioMedicine Online [electronic]* 2005 March; 10(Supplement 1): 43-44. Subject: 14.5

Gurmankin, Andrea D.; Sisti, Dominic; Caplan, Arthur L. Embryo disposal practices in IVF clinics in the United States. *Politics and the Life Sciences* 2003 September; 22(2): 4-8. Subject: 14.4

Gurnham, David. Losing the wood for the trees: Burke and the Court of Appeal: R (on the application of Oliver Leslie Burke) v. the General Medical Council. *Medical Law Review* 2006 Summer; 14(2): 253-263. Subject: 20.5.1

Gurnham, David. The mysteries of human dignity and the brave new world of human cloning. *Social and Legal Studies* 2005 June; 14(2): 197 [Online]. Accessed: http://sls.sagepub.com/cgi/reprint/14/2/197 [2007 January 23]. Subject: 14.5

Gursahani, Roop. Therapeutic innovation or cynical exploitation [response]. *Indian Journal of Medical Ethics* 2006 October-December; 3(4): 133-134. Subject: 18.5.4

Gurwitz, David; Lunshof, Jeantine E.; Altman, Russ B. A call for the creation of personalized medicine databases. *Nature Reviews Drug Discovery* 2006 January; 5(1): 23-26. Subject: 1.3.12

Gurwitz, Jerry H.; Guadagnoli, Edward; Landrum, Mary Beth; Silliman, Rebecca A.; Wolf, Robert; Weeks, Jane C. The treating physician as active gatekeeper in the recruitment of research subjects. *Medical Care* 2001 December; 39(12): 1339-1344. Subject: 18.2

Gusman, Adam. An appropriate legislative response to cloning for biomedical research: the case against a criminal ban. *Annals of Health Law* 2005 Summer; 14(2): 361-394. Subject: 14.5

Guston, David H. Research integrity. *In:* Mitcham, Carl, ed. Encyclopedia of Science, Technology, and Ethics. Farmington Hills, MI: Thomson/Gale, 2005: 1607-1609. Subject: 1.3.9

Guten, Gary N.; Kohn, Harvey S.; Zoltan, Donald J.; Black, Brian B.; Coran, David L.; Schneider, John A.; Pauers, William. The role of the chief ethics officer in a physician's office. *Clinics in Sports Medicine* 2004 April; 23(2): 243-253. Subject: 2.4

Guterman, Lila. Artificial-blood study has critics seeing red. *Chronicle of Higher Education* 2006 June 16; 52(41): A17. Subject: 18.3

Guterman, Lila. Digging into the roots of research ethics. *Chronicle of Higher Education* 2006 September 1; 53(2): 24-26; 28. Subject: 1.3.9

Guterman, Lila. Guinea pigs in the ER. *Chronicle of Higher Education* 2006 June 16; 52(41): A14-A18. Subject: 18.3

Guterman, Lila. Sense of injustice can lead scientists to act unethically, study finds. *Chronicle of Higher Education* 2006 April 21; 52(33): A21. Subject: 1.3.9

Guterman, Lila. A silent scientist under fire. *Chronicle of Higher Education* 2006 February 3; 52(22): A15, A18-A19. Subject: 18.5.4

Guterman, Lila. The taint of 'misbehavior'. *Chronicle of Higher Education* 2006 February 24; 52(25): A14- A16. Subject: 1.3.9

Gutheil, Thomas G.; Simon, Robert I. Non-sexual boundary crossings and boundary violations: the ethical dimension. *Psychiatric Clinics of North America* 2002 September; 25(3): 585-592. Subject: 17.1

Guyatt, Gordon H.; Mitchell, Alba; Molloy, D. William; Capretta, Rosalie; Horsman, John; Griffith, Lauren. Measuring patient and relative satisfaction with level or aggressiveness of care and involvement in care decisions in the context of life threatening illness. *Journal of Clinical Epidemiology* 1995 October; 48(10): 1215-1224. Subject: 8.1

Guzauskas, Gregory F.; Lebel, Robert Roger. The duty to re-contact for newly appreciated risk factors: Fragile X premutation. *Journal of Clinical Ethics* 2006 Spring; 17(1): 46-52. Subject: 15.3

See SUBJECT HEADING KEY FOR SECTION II on inside back cover.

585

Gyamfi, Cynthia; Berkowitz, Richard L. Responses by pregnant Jehovah's witnesses on health care proxies [reply]. *Obstetrics and Gynecology* 2005 February; 105(2): 442-443. Subject: 8.3.3

Gyamfi, Cynthia; Gyamfi, Mavis M.; Berkowitz, Richard L. Ethical and medicolegal considerations in the obstetric care of a Jehovah's Witness. *Obstetrics and Gynecology* 2003 July; 102(1): 173-180. Subject: 19.4

H

Haack, Susan. Limitation of treatment decisions for unwanted neonate. *Ethics and Medicine* 2006 Fall; 22(3): 139-141. Subject: 20.5.2

Haber, Joram Graf. Philosophic perspectives on access to health care: putting the care into health care. *Mount Sinai Journal of Medicine* 1997 March; 64(2): 96-100. Subject: 9.2

Haber, Paul. Commentary: challenge for doctors and policy makers [response]. *BMJ: British Medical Journal* 2006 February 4; 332(7536): 277-278. Subject: 9.5.9

Habgood, John. A Christian approach to bioethics. *Human Fertility* 2003 August; 6(3): 137-141. Subject: 14.3

Hackam, Daniel G.; Redelmeier, Donald A. Translation of research evidence from animals to humans [letter]. *JAMA: The Journal of the American Medical Association* 2006 October 11; 296(14): 1731-1732. Subject: 22.2

Haddad, Amy. Where do you draw the line between protecting your personal safety and caring for a potentially violent patient? *RN* 2005 May; 68(5): 30. Subject: 8.1

Haddad, Farid Sami. Arab medical ethics. *Studies in History of Medicine* 1982 June; 6: 122-136. Subject: 2.2

Haddow, G. "Because you're worth it?" The taking and selling of transplantable organs. *Journal of Medical Ethics* 2006 June; 32(6): 324-328. Subject: 19.5

Haddow, Gillian. The phenomenology of death, embodiment and organ transplantation. *Sociology of Health and Illness* 2005 January; 27(1): 92-113. Subject: 19.5

Haderka, Jiří F. Assisted Reproduction Law in East European countries = La regulación jurídica de la reproducción asistida humana en los países de Europa oriental. *Law and the Human Genome = Revista de Derecho y Genoma Humano* 1994 July-December; (1): 31-47. Subject: 14.1

Hadfield, S.J. Conscience of the doctor. *Twentieth Century* 1969; 177(1041): 14-17. Subject: 4.1.2

Haesler, Andrew. DNA and policing. *Reform* 2001 Spring; 79: 27-31. Subject: 15.1

Hafferty, Frederic W. Professionalism — the next wave [editorial]. *New England Journal of Medicine* 2006 November 16; 355(20): 2151-2152. Subject: 7.2

Haga, Susanne B. Policy implications of defining race and more by genome profiling. *Genomics, Society and Policy* 2006 May; 2(1): 57-71. Subject: 15.1

Hagelin, Joakim. Use of nonhuman primates in research in Sweden: 25 year longitudinal survey. *ALTEX* 2005; 22(1): 13-18. Subject: 22.2

Hagen, Gregory R. Personal inviolability and public health care: Chaoulli v. Quebec. *Health Law Review* 2006; 14(2): 34-37. Subject: 9.2

Hagen, John D., Jr. Rights talk and its remedies: the jurisprudence of Mary Ann Glendon. *America* 2006 January 2-9; 194(1): 14-16. Subject: 12.4.1

Haidet, Paul; Dains, Joyce E.; Paterniti, Debora A.; Hechtel, Laura; Chang, Tai; Tseng, Ellen; Rogers, John C. Medical student attitudes toward the doctor-patient relationship. *Medical Education* 2002 June; 36(6): 568-574. Subject: 7.2

Haigh, Carol; Neild, Angela; Duncan, Fiona. Balance of power — do patients use researchers to survive hospital? *Nurse Researcher* 2005; 12(4): 71-81. Subject: 18.3

Haimes, Erica. Social and ethical issues in the use of familial searching in forensic investigations: insights from family and kinship studies. *Journal of Law, Medicine and Ethics* 2006 Summer; 34(2): 263-276. Subject: 15.1

Haimes, Erica. What can the social sciences contribute to the study of ethics?: theoretical, empirical and substantive considerations. *In:* Rehmann-Sutter, Christoph; Düwell, Marcus; Mieth, Dietmar, eds. Bioethics in Cultural Contexts: Reflections on Methods and Finitude. Dordrecht: Springer, 2006: 277-298. Subject: 2.1

Haimes, Erica; Luce, Jacquelyne. Studying potential donors' views on embryonic stem cell therapies and preimplantation genetic diagnosis. *Human Fertility (Cambridge, England)* 2006 June; 9(2): 67-71. Subject: 18.5.4

Haimowitz, Stephan. Legal consequences of seclusion and restraint [letter]. *Psychiatric Services* 2006 October; 57(10): 1516. Subject: 17.3

Haisma, H.J.; de Hon, O. Gene doping. *International Journal of Sports Medicine* 2006 April; 27(4): 257-266. Subject: 9.5.1

Haker, Hille. Narrative bioethics. *In:* Rehmann-Sutter, Christoph; Düwell, Marcus; Mieth, Dietmar, eds. Bioethics in Cultural Contexts: Reflections on Methods and Finitude. Dordrecht: Springer, 2006: 353-376. Subject: 2.1

Haker, Hille. Reproductive rights in the twenty-first century. *In:* Widdows, Heather; Idiakez, Itziar Alkorta; Cirión, Aitziber Emaldi, eds. Women's Reproductive Rights. New York: Palgrave Macmillan; 2006: 167-187. Subject: 14.1

Hakki, Murat Metin. European Directive on the Legal Protection of Biotechnological Inventions: scope, status and controversies in a nutshell. *E Law: Murdoch University Electronic Journal of Law* 2004 March; 11(1): 31 p. [Online]. Accessed: http://www.murdoch.edu.au/elaw/

issues/v11n1/hakki_text111.html [2006 August 2]. Subject: 15.8

Halbert, Chanita Hughes; Armstrong, Katrina; Gandy, Oscar H., Jr.; Shaker, Lee. Racial differences in trust in health care providers. *Archives of Internal Medicine* 2006 April 24; 166(8): 896-901. Subject: 9.5.4

Halbert, Chanita Hughes; Gandy, Oscar H., Jr.; Collier, Aliya; Shaker, Lee. Intentions to participate in genetics research among African American smokers. *Cancer Epidemiology, Biomarkers and Prevention* 2006 January; 15(1): 150-153. Subject: 15.1

Halbert, Chanita Hughes; Kessler, Lisa; Stopfer, Jill E.; Domchek, Susan; Wileyto, E. Paul. Low rates of acceptance of BRCA1 and BRCA2 test results among African American women at increased risk for hereditary breast-ovarian cancer. *Genetics in Medicine* 2006 September; 8(9): 576-582. Subject: 15.3

Haldane, John; Lee, Patrick. Aquinas, the embryo and the ethics of abortion. *Philosophy* 2003 March; 78(2): 255-278. Subject: 12.3

Hale, Benjamin. The moral considerability of invasive transgenic animals. *Journal of Agricultural and Environmental Ethics* 2006; 19(4): 337-366. Subject: 15.1

Haley, William E. A commentary — institutional review board approval and beyond: proactive steps to improve ethics and quality in end-of-life research. *Gerontologist* 2002 October; 42(Special Issue 3): 109-113. Subject: 18.5.7

Halfmann, Drew; Rude, Jess; Ebert, Kim. The biomedical legacy in minority health policy-making, 1975-2002. *In:* Kronenfeld, Jennie Jacobs, ed. Health Care Services, Racial and Ethnic Minorities and Underserved Populations: Patient and Provider Perspectives. Boston: Elsevier JAI, 2005: 245-275. Subject: 9.5.4

Hall, Amy Laura. Whose progress? The language of global health. *Journal of Medicine and Philosophy* 2006 June; 31(3): 285-304. Subject: 21.1

Hall, Mark A. A corporate ethic of 'care' in health care. *Seattle Journal for Social Justice* 2004 Fall-Winter; 3(1): 417-428. Subject: 9.1

Hall, Peter. Failed asylum seekers and health care [editorial]. *BMJ: British Medical Journal* 2006 July 15; 333(7559): 109-110. Subject: 9.5.1

Hall, Stephen S. Stem cells: a status report. *Hastings Center Report* 2006 January-February; 36(1): 16-22. Subject: 18.5.4

Hall, Wayne; Carter, Lucy; Morley, Katherine I. Addiction, ethics and scientific freedom. *Addiction* 2003 July; 98(7): 873-874. Subject: 18.5.1

Hallenbeck, James; Goldstein, Mary K. Decisions at the end of life: cultural considerations beyond medical ethics. *Generations: Journal of the American Society on Aging* 1999 Spring; 23(1): 24-29. Subject: 21.7

Haller, Dagmar M.; Sanci, Lena A.; Patton, George C.; Sawyer, Susan M. Practical evidence in favour of mature-minor consent in primary care research [letter]. *Medical Journal of Australia* 2005 October 17; 183(8): 439. Subject: 8.3.1

Haller, Daniel G. JCO and the public trust [editorial]. *Journal of Clinical Oncology* 2006 January 20; 24(3): 323-324. Subject: 1.3.7

Hallowell, Nina; Lawton, Julia. Seeking ethical approval: opening up the lines of communication. *Clinical Ethics* 2006 June; 1(2): 109-113. Subject: 18.4

Hallström, Inger; Elander, Gunnel. Decision-making during hospitalization: parents' and children's involvement. *Journal of Clinical Nursing* 2004 March; 13(3): 367-375. Subject: 8.1

Halperin, Mordechai. Dysfunctional uterine bleeding: new approaches. *In:* Rosner, Fred, ed. Medicine and Jewish Law. Volume III. Brooklyn, NY: Yashar Books, Inc.; 2005: 191-200. Subject: 9.5.5

Halperin, Mordechai. Post-mortem sperm retrieval. *In:* Rosner, Fred, ed. Medicine and Jewish Law. Volume III. Brooklyn, NY: Yashar Books, Inc.; 2005: 41-51. Subject: 14.6

Halpern, Georges M. COX-2 inhibitors: a story of greed, deception and death. *Inflammopharmacology* 2005; 13(4): 419-425. Subject: 9.7

Halpern, Scott D. Decisions devoid of data? *American Journal of Bioethics* 2006 May-June; 6(3): 55-56; discussion W51- W53. Subject: 2.1

Halpern, Scott D. Evidence-based equipoise and research responsiveness [editorial]. *American Journal of Bioethics* 2006 July-August; 6(4): 1-4. Subject: 18.2

Halpern, Scott D.; Hansen-Flaschen, John. Terminal withdrawal of life-sustaining supplemental oxygen. *JAMA: The Journal of the American Medical Association* 2006 September 20; 269(11): 1397-1400. Subject: 20.5.1

Halpern, Scott D.; Karlawish, Jason H.T.; Berlin, Jesse A.; Bacchetti, Peter; Wolf, Leslie E.; Segal, Mark R.; McCulloch, Charles E. Re: "Ethics and sample size" [letter and reply]. *American Journal of Epidemiology* 2005 July 15; 162(2): 195-196. Subject: 18.2

Halvorsen, Juris Marit. The use of biotechnology in medicine with particular regard to questions for family law. *In:* Meulders-Klein, Marie-Thérèse; Deech, Ruth; Vlaardingerbroek, Paul, eds. Biomedicine, the Family and Human Rights. New York: Kluwer Law International, 2002: 459-475. Subject: 5.1

Halweil, Brian. The war of words and images. *World Watch* 2002 July-August; 15(4): 37-39. Subject: 15.1

Halweil, Brian; Bell, Dick. Beyond cloning: the larger agenda of human engineering. *World Watch* 2002 July-August; 15(4): 8-10. Subject: 5.3

See SUBJECT HEADING KEY FOR SECTION II on inside back cover.

Hamano, Kenzo. Should euthanasia be legalized in Japan? The importance of the attitude towards life. *In:* Sang-yong, Song; Young-Mo, Koo; Macer, Darryl R.J., eds. Asian Bioethics in the 21st Century. Christchurch, NZ: Eubios Ethics Institute, 2002: 110-117. Subject: 20.5.1

Hamaty, Daniel. Pain medicine's role in the restoration and reformation of medical ethics. *Pain Medicine* 2001 June; 2(2): 117-120. Subject: 4.4

Hamdan, Aisha. Assisted reproductive technology. *Al Jumuah* 2005 December; 17(11): 24-32. Subject: 14.1

Hameed, Abdul. Medical ethics in medieval Islam. *Studies in Philosophy of Medicine* 1977 March; 1(1): 08-124. Subject: 2.2

Hamel, Oliver; Marchal, Christine; Hervé, Christian. Ethical reflection in dentistry: first steps at the faculty of dental surgery of Toulouse. *Journal of the American College of Dentists* 2006 Fall; 73(3): 36-39. Subject: 4.1.1

Hamel, Ron. Embryonic stem cell research: perilous pursuit? *Health Progress* 2006 September-October; 87(5): 4-5. Subject: 18.5.4

Hamel, Ron. Organizational ethics: why bother? [editorial]. *Health Progress* 2006 November-December; 87(6): 4-5. Subject: 9.1

Hamel, Ron; Panicola, Michael R. Embryonic stem cell research: off limits? *Health Progress* 2006 September-October; 87(5): 23-29. Subject: 18.5.4

Hamilton, Chris. Biodiversity, biopiracy and benefits: what allegations of biopiracy tell us about intellectual property. *Developing World Bioethics* 2006 December; 6(3): 158-173. Subject: 15.8

Hamilton, David P.; Regaldo, Antonio. New questions emerge over stem-cell research claims. *Wall Street Journal* 2006 September 5; p. A15; A19. Subject: 18.5.4

Hamilton, Richard. The law on dying. *Journal of the Royal Society of Medicine* 2002 November; 95(11): 565-566. Subject: 20.5.1

Hammer, Eric T.; Mitcham, Carl. Death and dying. *In:* Mitcham, Carl, ed. Encyclopedia of Science, Technology, and Ethics. Farmington Hills, MI: Thomson/Gale, 2005: 476-481. Subject: 20.1

Hammer, Peter J. Differential pricing of essential AIDS drugs: markets, politics and public health. *Journal of International Economic Law* 2002 December; 5(4): 883-912. Subject: 9.5.6

Hammett, Theodore M. Making the case for health interventions in correctional facilities. *Journal of Urban Health* 2001 June; 78(2): 236-240. Subject: 9.5.1

Hammond, Charles B.; Schwartz, Peter A. Ethical issues related to medical expert testimony. *Obstetrics and Gynecology* 2005 November; 106(5 Part 1): 1055-1058. Subject: 7.3

Hammond, David; Collishaw, Neil E.; Callard, Cynthia. Secret science: tobacco industry research on smoking behaviour and cigarette toxicity. *Lancet* 2006 March 4-10; 367(9512): 781-787. Subject: 9.5.9

Hampson, Lindsay A.; Agrawal, Manish; Joffe, Steven; Gross, Cary P.; Verter, Joel; Emanuel, Ezekiel J. Patients' views on financial conflicts of interest in cancer research trials. *New England Journal of Medicine* 2006 November 30; 355(22): 2330-2337. Subject: 1.3.9

Hampton, James W. End-of-life issues for American Indians: a commentary. *Journal of Cancer Education* 2005 Spring; 20(1 Supplement): 37-40. Subject: 20.4.1

Hampton, Tracy. Are placebos in advanced cancer trials ethically justified? *JAMA: the Journal of the American Medical Association* 2006 July 19; 296(3): 265-266. Subject: 18.3

Hampton, Tracy. Scientists, ethicists ponder challenges in moving stem cell research forward. *JAMA: The Journal of the American Medical Association* 2006 December 6; 296(21): 2542-2543. Subject: 18.5.4

Hampton, Tracy. US stem cell research lagging. *JAMA: The Journal of the American Medical Association* 2006 May 17; 295(19): 2233-2234. Subject: 18.5.4

Han, Juliana. The Tenth Circuit finds a constitutionally protected-right to privacy in prescription drug records. *Journal of Law, Medicine, and Ethics* 2006 Spring; 34(1): 134-136. Subject: 8.4

Han, Paul K.; Arnold, Robert M. Palliative care services, patient abandonment, and the scope of physicians' responsibilities in end-of-life care. *Journal of Palliative Medicine* 2005 December; 8(6): 1238-1245. Subject: 20.4.1

Hanauer, Stephen B. Conflicts of interest. *Nature Clinical Practice. Gastroenterology and Hepatology* 2005 January; 2(1): 1. Subject: 7.4

Hanauer, Stephen B. Institutional review boards: the cost to academic medical centers [editorial]. *Nature Clinical Practice. Gastroenterology and Hepatology* 2005 July; 2(7): 287. Subject: 18.2

Hanauer, Stephen B. Novel potential perils of volunteering for clinical trials [editorial]. *Nature Clinical Practice Gastroenterology and Hepatology* 2005 August; 2(8): 337. Subject: 18.2

Hancock, Debbie. Influenza vaccinations: should they be mandatory for nurses? *MCN: The American Journal of Maternal Child Nursing* 2006 March-April; 31(2): 77. Subject: 9.5.1

Handberg, R.B. Talking about the unspeakable in a secretive institution: health and disability among Supreme Court justices. *Politics and the Life Sciences* 1989 August; 8(1): 70-73. Subject: 8.4

Handelsman, Mitchell M.; Gottlieb, Michael C.; Knapp, Samuel. Training ethical psychologists: an acculturation model. *Professional Psychology: Research and Practice* 2005 February; 36(1): 59-65. Subject: 7.2

Hanford, Jack. Normative ethics in health care. *Ethics and Medicine* 2006 Spring; 22(1): 31-38. Subject: 4.1.2

Hanks, Geoffrey. The proposed Assisted Dying Bill in the UK [editorial]. *Palliative Medicine* 2005 September; 19(6): 441. Subject: 20.5.1

Hanlin, Rebecca. Increasing knowledge flows by linking innovation and health — the case of SAAVI. *Genomics, Society and Policy* 2006 December; 2(3): 37-48. Subject: 9.5.6

Hannay, Alastair. What can philosophers contribute to social ethics? *Topoi* 1998 September; 17(2): 127-136. Subject: 2.1

Hanning, Christopher D.; Rentowl, Patricia. Harmful impact of EU clinical trials directives: trial of alerting drug in fibromyalgia has had to be abandoned. . . [letter]. *BMJ: British Medical Journal* 2006 March 18; 332(7542): 666. Subject: 18.2

Hansen, Lissi; Archbold, Patricia G.; Stewart, Barbara; Westfall, Una Beth; Ganzini, Linda. Family caregivers making life-sustaining treatment decisions: factors associated with role strain and ease. *Journal of Gerontological Nursing* 2005 November; 31(11): 28-35. Subject: 20.5.1

Hanser, Matthew F. Killing, letting die and preventing people from being saved. *Utilitas* 1999 November; 11(3): 277-295. Subject: 20.5.1

Hanson, Clare. Reproductive futures. *In her:* A Cultural History of Pregnancy: Pregnancy, Medicine and Culture, 1750-2000. New York: Palgrave Macmillan; 2004: 146-175. Subject: 14.1

Hanson, Laura C. Honoring Ms. Burke's wishes. *Practical Bioethics* 2006 Spring-Summer; 2(2-3): 13. Subject: 20.5.1

Hanson, Laura C. Honoring Ms. Burke's wishes—a commentary. *Practical Bioethics* 2006 Spring-Summer; 2(2-3): 14-15. Subject: 20.5.1

Hanson, Stephen S. "More on respect for embryos and potentiality: does respect for embryos entail respect for in vitro embryos?". *Theoretical Medicine and Bioethics* 2006; 27(3): 215-226. Subject: 18.5.4

Hansson, Mats G.; Dillner, Joakim; Bartram, Claus R.; Carlson, Joyce A.; Helgesson, Gert. Should donors be allowed to give broad consent to future biobank research? *Lancet Oncology* 2006 March; 7(3): 266-269. Subject: 18.3

Hansson, Sven Ove. Risk ethics. *In:* Mitcham, Carl, ed. Encyclopedia of Science, Technology, and Ethics. Farmington Hills, MI: Thomson/Gale, 2005: 1642-1645. Subject: 2.1

Hansson, Sven Ove. Uncertainty and the ethics of clinical trials. *Theoretical Medicine and Bioethics* 2006; 27(2): 149-167. Subject: 18.2

Hansson, Sven Ove; Björkman, Barbro. Bioethics in Sweden. *CQ: Cambridge Quarterly of Healthcare Ethics* 2006 Summer; 15(3): 285-293. Subject: 15.1

Happe, Kelly E. Heredity, gender and the discourse of ovarian cancer. *New Genetics and Society* 2006 August; 25(2): 171-196. Subject: 9.5.5

Hardcastle, Lorian. Comment: Cilinger C. Centre Hospitalier de Chicoutimi. *Health Law Review* 2006; 14(3): 44-50. Subject: 9.2

Hardwig, John. Rural health care ethics: what assumptions and attitudes should drive the research? *American Journal of Bioethics* 2006 March-April; 6(2): 53-54. Subject: 9.5.1

Hardy, Linda. Informed consent: adolescent minors, surrogate decision- making, and the school nurse. *School Nurse News* 2003 September; 20(4): 28-31. Subject: 9.5.7

Hargreaves, Katrina M.; Stewart, Ruth J.; Oliver, Sandy R. Informed choice and public health screening for children: the case of blood spot screening. *Health Expectations* 2005 June; 8(2): 161-171. Subject: 15.3

Hargrove, Marion D., Jr. A five-step approach to settling a dispute over futile care. *Journal of the Louisiana State Medical Society* 1994 October; 146(10): 439-440. Subject: 20.5.1

Hariharan, Seetharaman; Jonnalagadda, Ramesh; Walrond, Errol; Moseley, Harley. Knowledge, attitudes and practice of healthcare ethics and law among doctors and nurses in Barbados. *BMC Medical Ethics* 2006; 7(7): E7 [Online]. Accessed: http://www.biomedcentral.com/ 1472-6939/7/7 [2006 August 15]. Subject: 2.1

Harley, Karen. The abortion issue and advanced nursing practice. *In:* Bartter, Karen, ed. Ethical Issues in Advanced Nursing Practice. Boston: Butterworth-Heinemann; 2001: 31-50. Subject: 12.3

Harling, Kit. The ethics of risk assessment. *In:* Westerholm, Peter; Nilstun, Tore; Øvretveit, John, eds. Practical Ethics in Occupational Health. San Francisco: Radcliffe Medical Press; 2004: 49-60. Subject: 16.3

Harling, Kit; Westerholm, Peter; Nilstun, Tore. Professional codes of ethics. *In:* Westerholm, Peter; Nilstun, Tore; Øvretveit, John, eds. Practical Ethics in Occupational Health. San Francisco: Radcliffe Medical Press; 2004: 321-329. Subject: 16.3

Harmon, Amy. Are you my sperm donor? Few clinics will say. *New York Times* 2006 January 20; p. A1, A15. Subject: 14.2

Harmon, Amy. Couples cull embryos to halt heritage of cancer. *New York Times* 2006 September 3; p. A1, A20. Subject: 15.2

See SUBJECT HEADING KEY FOR SECTION II on inside back cover.

589

Harmon, Amy. DNA gatherers hit a snag: the tribes don't trust them. *New York Times* 2006 December 10; p. A1, A38. Subject: 15.11

Harmon, Amy. Seeking ancestry and privilege in DNA ties uncovered by tests. *New York Times* 2006 April 12; p. A1, A17. Subject: 15.11

Harmon, Shawn H.E. A penny for your thoughts, a pound for your flesh: implications of recognizing property rights in our own excised body parts. *Medical Law International* 2006; 7(4): 329-353. Subject: 4.4

Harmon, Shawn H.E. The recommendation on research on biological materials of human origin: another brick in the wall. *European Journal of Health Law* 2006 September; 13(3): 293-301. Subject: 15.1

Harmon, Shawn H.E. Solidarity: a (new) ethic for global health policy. *Health Care Analysis: An International Journal of Health Philosophy and Policy* 2006 December; 14(4): 215-236. Subject: 18.2

Haroun, Ansar M. Ethical discussion of informed consent. *Journal of Clinical Psychopharmacology* 2005 October; 25(5): 405-406. Subject: 8.3.1

Haroun, Nasra; Dunn, Laura; Haroun, Ansar; Cadenhead, Kristin S. Risk and protection in prodromal schizophrenia: ethical implications for clinical practice and future research. *Schizophrenia Bulletin* 2006 January; 32(1): 166-178. Subject: 18.5.6

Harper, Cynthia C.; Ellertson, Charlotte E. The emergency contraceptive pill: a survey of knowledge and attitudes among students at Princeton University. *American Journal of Obstetrics and Gynecology* 1995 November; 173(5): 1438-1445. Subject: 11.1

Harper, Cynthia C.; Henderson, Jillian T.; Darney, Philip D. Abortion in the United States. *Annual Review of Public Health* 2005 April; 26: 501-512. Subject: 12.4.1

Harper, Mary G. Ethical multiculturalism: an evolutionary concept analysis. *Advances in Nursing Science* 2006 April-June; 29(2): 110-124. Subject: 1.3.9

Harper, Peter S., ed. The geneticists' manifesto. *In his:* Landmarks in Medical Genetics: Classic Papers with Commentaries. Oxford; New York: Oxford University Press; 2004: 298-301. Subject: 15.5

Harremoës, Poul. Precautionary principle. *In:* Mitcham, Carl, ed. Encyclopedia of Science, Technology, and Ethics. Farmington Hills, MI: Thomson/Gale, 2005: 1474-1479. Subject: 2.1

Harrington, Michael D.; Luebke, D.L.; Lewis, W.R.; Auliso, M.P.; Johnson, N.J. Implantable cardioverter defibrillator (ICD) at end of life #112. *Journal of Palliative Medicine* 2005 October; 8(5): 1056-1057. Subject: 20.5.1

Harris, Evan. Reproductive freedom and the state. *Reproductive BioMedicine Online [electronic]* 2005 March; 10(Supplement 1): 140-143. Subject: 14.1

Harris, Gardiner. F.D.A. approves broader access to next-day pill; sales over the counter; change just for adults — contraceptive still tied to abortion battle. *New York Times* 2006 August 25; p. A1, A18. Subject: 11.1

Harris, Gardiner. F.D.A. dismisses medical benefit from marijuana; political fight widens; agency reply to Congress contradicts '99 report by top scientists. *New York Times* 2006 April 21; p. A1, A23. Subject: 9.5.9

Harris, Gardiner. In article, doctors back ban on drug companies' gifts; concerns cited on quality of patient care. *New York Times* 2006 January 25; p. A14. Subject: 9.7

Harris, Gardiner; Pear, Robert. Drug maker's efforts to compete in lucrative insulin market are under scrutiny. *New York Times* 2006 January 28; p. A14. Subject: 9.7

Harris, John. The moral choice. *New Scientist* 2006 June 17-23; 190(2556): 24. Subject: 15.2

Harris, John. Reproductive liberty, disease and disability. *Reproductive BioMedicine Online [electronic]* 2005 March; 10(Supplement 1): 13-16. Subject: 14.1

Harris, John; Patrizio, Pasquale; Gurdon, John; Strong, Carson; Birnbacher, Dieter; Robertson, John; McLaren, Anne; Holm, Søren; Isasi, Rosario; Edwards, Robert; Lockwood, Gillian; White, Gladys; Galton, David; McMahan, Jeff. Discussion (day 1 session 3): moral philosophy of human reproductive cloning. *Reproductive BioMedicine Online [electronic]* 2005 March; 10(Supplement 1): 56-59. Subject: 14.5

Harris, Sheldon H. Japanese biomedical experimentation during the World-War-II era. *In:* Beam, Thomas E.; Sparacino, Linette R.; Pellegrino, Edmund D.; Hartle, Anthony E.; Howe, Edmund G., eds. Military Medical Ethics. Volume 2. Washington, DC: TMM Publications, Borden Institute, Walter Reed Army Medical Center; 2003: 463-506. Subject: 18.5.5

Harris, Victoria. Electroconvulsive therapy: administration codes, legislation, and professional recommendations. *Journal of the American Academy of Psychiatry and the Law* 2006; 34(3): 406-411. Subject: 17.5

Harrison, Dean; Long, Paul A.; Sedler, Robert A.; Waun, James; Price, Elizabeth; Uhlmann, Michael. Physician-assisted suicide debate at DCL/MSU Fall 1997. *Journal of Medicine and Law* 1997 Fall; 2(1): 85-115. Subject: 20.7

Harrison, Jayne E. Orthodontic clinical trials III: reporting of ethical issues associated with clinical trials published in three orthodontic journals between 1989 and 1998. *Journal of Orthodontics* 2005 June; 32(2): 115-121. Subject: 18.2

Hart, Curtis W. Clinical pragmatism in bioethics: a pastoral approach. *Journal of Religion and Health* 2006 Summer; 45(2): 196-207. Subject: 2.1

Hartling, O.J. Euthanasia — the illusion of autonomy. *Medicine and Law: World Association for Medical Law* 2006 March; 25(1): 189-199. Subject: 20.5.1

Hartshorne, Geraldine. Future regulation of fertility banking in the UK. *Human Fertility* 2003 May; 6(2): 71-73. Subject: 14.6

Harvey, John Collins. The burdens-benefits ratio consideration for medical administration of nutrition and hydration to persons in the persistent vegetative state. *Christian Bioethics* 2006 April; 12(1): 99-106. Subject: 20.5.1

Harvey, John Collins. Clinical ethics: the art of medicine. *In:* Beam, Thomas E.; Sparacino, Linette R.; Pellegrino, Edmund D.; Hartle, Anthony E.; Howe, Edmund G., eds. Military Medical Ethics. Volume 1. Washington, DC: TMM Publications, Borden Institute, Walter Reed Army Medical Center; 2003: 61-104. Subject: 2.1

Harvey, Ken J.; Vitry, Agnes I.; Roughead, Elizabeth; Aroni, Rosalie; Ballenden, Nicola; Faggotter, Ralph. Pharmaceutical advertisements in prescribing software: an analysis. *Medical Journal of Australia* 2005 July 18; 183(2): 75-79. Subject: 9.7

Harvey, Martin. Advance directives and the severely demented. *Journal of Medicine and Philosophy* 2006 February; 31(1): 47- 64. Subject: 20.5.4

Harvey, Rosemary D. Pioneers of genetics: a comparison of the attitudes of William Bateson and Erwin Baur to eugenics. *Notes and Records of the Royal Society of London* 1995 January; 49(1): 105-117. Subject: 15.1

Harvey, S. Marie; Beckman, Linda J.; Branch, Meredith Roberts. The relationship of contextual factors to women's perceptions of medical abortion. *Health Care for Women International* 2002 September; 23(6-7): 654-665. Subject: 12.5.2

Harvey, S. Marie; Beckman, Linda J.; Castle, Mary Ann; Coeytaux, Francine. Knowledge and perceptions of medical abortion among potential users. *Family Planning Perspectives* 1995 September-October; 27(5): 203-207. Subject: 12.5.2

Harvey, S. Marie; Beckman, Linda J.; Satre, Sarah J. Experience and satisfaction with providing methotrexate-induced abortion services among U.S. providers. *Journal of the American Medical Women's Association* 2000; 55 (3, Supplement): 161-163. Subject: 12.1

Harvey, S. Marie; Nichols, Mark D. Development and evaluation of the abortion attributes questionnaire. *Journal of Social Issues* 2005 March; 61(1): 95-107. Subject: 12.5.2

Harvey, S. Marie; Sherman, Christy A.; Bird, Sheryl Thorburn; Warren, Jocelyn. Understanding medical abortion: policy, politics and women's health [policy statement]. *Eugene: University of Oregon. Center for the Study of Women in Society* 2002 Policy Matter #3: 50 p. [Online].

Accessed: http://csws.uoregon.edu/home/policymat3.pdf [2006 October 31]. Subject: 12.1

Harvey-Blakenship, Michele; Hocking, Barbara Ann. Genetic restitution?: DNA, compensation, and biological families. *In:* Tong, Rosemarie; Donchin, Anne; Dodds, Susan, eds. Linking Visions: Feminist Bioethics, Human Rights, and the Developing World. Lanham, MD: Rowman and Littlefield Publishers; 2004: 203-234. Subject: 15.1

Hasegawa, Thomas K.; Matthews, Merrill; Frederiksen, Neil. Pregnancy, x-rays, and risks — the radiology dilemma. Response to ethical dilemma #41. *Texas Dental Journal* 2002 October; 119(10): 1049-1051. Subject: 8.1

Hasegawa, Thomas K.; Matthews, Merrill; Peltier, Bruce. Ethical dilemma #52: transferring records of the demanding patient. *Texas Dental Journal* 2005 July; 122(7): 683-685. Subject: 4.1.1

Hasegawa, Thomas K.; Matthews, Merrill; Peltier, Bruce; Witherspoon, David. The endodontist's painful dilemma. Response to ethical dilemma #36. *Texas Dental Journal* 2001 July; 118(7): 559-562. Subject: 7.3

Hasian, Marouf, Jr. The Internet and the human genome. *Peace Review* 2001 September; 13(3): 375-380. Subject: 15.11

Hasian, Marouf, Jr.; Plec, Emily. The cultural, legal, and scientific arguments in the Human Genome Diversity debate. *Howard Journal of Communications* 2002 October-December; 13(4): 301-319. Subject: 15.10

Hasle, Peter; Limborg, Hans Jorgen. The ethics of workplace interventions. *In:* Westerholm, Peter; Nilstun, Tore; Øvretveit, John, eds. Practical Ethics in Occupational Health. San Francisco: Radcliffe Medical Press; 2004: 61-76. Subject: 16.3

Haslett, D.W. On life, death, and abortion. *Utilitas* 1996 July; 8(2): 159-189. Subject: 12.3

Hasman, Andreas; Holm, Søren. Direct-to-consumer advertising: should there be a free market in healthcare information? *CQ: Cambridge Quarterly of Healthcare Ethics* 2006 Winter; 15(1): 42-49. Subject: 9.7

Hasman, Andreas; Hope, Tony; Østerdal, Lars Peter. Health care need: three interpretations. *Journal of Applied Philosophy* 2006; 23(2): 145-156. Subject: 9.4

Hatfield, Chad. Sin, sickness, and salvation. *Christian Bioethics* 2006 August; 12(2): 199-211. Subject: 4.2

Hathout, H. An Islamic perspective on human genetic and reproductive technologies. *Eastern Mediterranean Health Journal* 2006; 12(Supplement 2): S22-S28 [Online]. Accessed: http://www.emro.who.int/publications/EMHJ/ 12_S2/PDF/3.pdf [2007 January 4]. Subject: 15.1

Hattori, Kenji. East Asian family and biomedical ethics. *In:* Sang-yong, Song; Young-Mo, Koo; Macer, Darryl R.J.,

See SUBJECT HEADING KEY FOR SECTION II on inside back cover.

591

eds. Asian Bioethics in the 21st Century. Christchurch, NZ: Eubios Ethics Institute, 2002: 229-231. Subject: 8.3.1

Hauerwas, Stanley M. Anabaptist eyes on biotechnology. *In:* Miller, Roman J.; Brubaker, Beryl H.; Peterson, James C., eds. Viewing New Creations with Anabaptist Eyes: Ethics of Biotechnology. Telford, PA: Cascadia Pub.; 2005: 243-253. Subject: 2.1

Hausman, Daniel M. Valuing health. *Philosophy and Public Affairs* 2006 Summer; 34(3): 246-274. Subject: 4.2

Haverkamp, Margje H.; van Delden, Johannes J.M. Une mort tres douce: end-of-life decisions in France; reflections from a Dutch perspective. *Medicine, Health Care and Philosophy* 2006; 9(3): 367-376. Subject: 20.4.1

Hawaii. *Laws, statutes, etc.* An act relating to genetic information and genetic testing [Approved: 1 July 2002]. Hawaii: State Legislature, 2002. 3 p. [Online]. Accessed: http://www.capitol.hawaii.gov/session2002/bills/SB2180_hd1_.htm [2007 March 9]. Subject: 15.1

Hawes, Susan; Oakley, Justin. Ethics of using employees' eggs in cloning research. *Nature* 2006 April 20; 440(7087): 992. Subject: 14.5

Hawkins, Jennifer S. Justice and placebo controls. *Social Theory and Practice* 2006 July; 32(3): 467-496. Subject: 18.5.9

Hawryluck, Laura. Research ethics in the intensive care unit: current and future challenges [editorial]. *Critical Care* 2004 April; 8(2): 71-72. Subject: 18.5.1

Hayden, Deborah. Alas, poor Yorick: digging up the dead to make medical diagnoses. *PLoS Medicine* 2005 March; 2(3): 0184-0186. Subject: 20.1

Haydon, J. Genetics: uphold the rights of all clients to informed decision-making and voluntary action. *Nursing Standard* 2005 September 28-October 4; 20(3): 48-51. Subject: 15.3

Hayes, Gregory J. Institutional review boards: balancing conflicting values in research. *In:* O'Donohue, William; Ferguson, Kyle, eds. Handbook of Professional Ethics for Psychologists: Issues, Questions, and Controversies. Thousand Oaks, Calif.: SAGE Publications; 2003: 101-112. Subject: 18.2

Hayes, Richard. The science and politics of genetically modified humans. *World Watch* 2002 July-August; 15(4): 11-12. Subject: 15.1

Hayflick, Leonard. Aging and regenerative medicine. *In:* Mitcham, Carl, ed. Encyclopedia of Science, Technology, and Ethics. Farmington Hills, MI: Thomson/Gale, 2005: 34-37. Subject: 20.5.1

Häyry, Matti. Do regulations address concerns? *In:* Árnason, Gardar; Nordal, Salvör; Árnason, Vilhjálmur, eds. Blood and Data: Ethical, Legal and Social Aspects of Human Genetic Databases. Reykjavík: University of Iceland Press; 2004: 201-207. Subject: 15.1

Häyry, Matti. Public health and human values. *Journal of Medical Ethics* 2006 September; 32(9): 519-521. Subject: 9.1

Häyry, Matti; Takala, Jukka; Jallinoja, Piia; Lötjönen, Salla; Takala, Tuija. Ethicalization in bioscience — a pilot study in Finland. *CQ: Cambridge Quarterly of Healthcare Ethics* 2006 Summer; 15(3): 282-284. Subject: 1.3.9

Hays, Ross M.; Valentine, Jeanette; Haynes, Gerri; Geyer, J. Russell; Villareale, Nanci; McKinstry, Beth; Varni, James W.; Churchill, Shervin S. The Seattle Pediatric Palliative Care Project: effects on family satisfaction and health-related quality of life. *Journal of Palliative Medicine* 2006 June; 9(3): 716-728. Subject: 20.4.2

Hayunga, Eugene G.; Pinn, Vivian W. NIH policy on the inclusion of women and minorities as subjects in clinical research. *In:* Gallin, John I., ed. Principles and Practice of Clinical Research. San Diego, CA: Academic Press; 2002: 145-160. Subject: 18.5.3

Health Council (Netherlands) = Gezondheidsraad (Netherlands); Dondrop, Wybo; de Wert, Guido. Embryonic stem cells without moral pain? *Ethics and Health Monitoring Report* 2005 June 29 ; No. 1: 33 p. [Online]. Accessed: http://www.gr.nl/pdf.php?ID=1270&p=1 [12 February 2007]. Subject: 18.5.4

Healy, David. Did regulators fail over selective serotonin reuptake inhibitors? *BMJ: British Medical Journal* 2006 July 8; 333(7558): 92-95. Subject: 9.7

Healy, David. The new medical oikumene. *In:* Petryna, Adriana; Lakoff, Andrew; Kleinman, Arthur, eds. Global Pharmaceuticals: Ethics, Markets, Practices. Durham: Duke University Press; 2006: 61-84. Subject: 9.7

Healy, David. Psychopharmacology at the interface between the market and the new biology. *In:* Rees, Dai; Rose, Steven, eds. The New Brain Sciences: Perils and Prospects. New York: Cambridge University Press; 2004: 232-248. Subject: 17.4

Healy, Gerald B. Unprofessional behavior: enough is enough. *Laryngoscope* 2006 March; 116(3): 357-358. Subject: 7.4

Healy, Gerald B.; Healy, Lisa H. Honesty is the ONLY policy: physician expert witnesses in the 21st century. *Journal of the American College of Surgeons* 2004 November; 199(5): 741-745. Subject: 7.3

Healy, Lyn; Hunt, Charles; Young, Lesley; Stacey, Glyn. The UK Stem Cell Bank: its role as a public research resource centre providing access to well-characterised seed stocks of human stem cell lines. *Advanced Drug Delivery Reviews* 2005 December 12; 57(13): 1981-1988. Subject: 18.5.4

Heaney, Robert P. Ethical issues in the design of osteoporosis clinical trials: the state of the question. *Journal of*

Subject = NRCBL Primary Classification Number; see inside front cover.

Bone and Mineral Research 2003 June; 18(6): 1117- 1120. Subject: 18.2

Heath, Iona. In defence of ambiguity. *Monash Bioethics Review* 2006 July; 25(3): 26-27. Subject: 4.4

Heathcotte, Brock; Robert, Jason Scott. The strange case of the humanzee patent quest. *National Catholic Bioethics Quarterly* 2006 Spring; 6(1): 51-59. Subject: 15.8

Hebbar, Shripad; Nayak, Sathisha. Ethical issues in laparoscopic hysterectomy. *Indian Journal of Medical Ethics* 2006 January-March; 3(1): 19-20. Subject: 9.5.5

Hedayat, K.M.; Shooshtarizadeh, P.; Raza, M. Therapeutic abortion in Islam: contemporary views of Muslim Shiite scholars and effect of recent Iranian legislation. *Journal of Medical Ethics* 2006 November; 32(11): 652-657. Subject: 12.3

Hedera, Peter. Ethical principles and pitfalls of genetic testing for dementia. *Journal of Geriatric Psychiatry and Neurology* 2001 Winter; 14(4): 213-221. Subject: 15.3

Hedgecoe, Adam. 'At the point at which you can do something about it, then it becomes more relevant': informed consent in the pharmacogenetic clinic. *Social Science and Medicine* 2005 September; 61(6): 1201-1210. Subject: 8.3.1

Hedgecoe, Adam; Martin, Paul. The drugs don't work: expectations and the shaping of the pharmacogenetics. *Social Studies of Science* 2003 June; 33(3): 327-364. Subject: 15.1

Hedgecoe, A.; Carvalho, F.; Lobmayer, P.; Raka, F. Research ethics committees in Europe: implementing the directive, respecting diversity. *Journal of Medical Ethics* 2006 August; 32(8): 483-486. Subject: 18.2

Heffernan, Teresa. Bovine anxieties, virgin births, and the secret of life. *Cultural Critique* 2003 Winter; (53): 116-133. Subject: 15.1

Hegde, R.; Bell, D.; Cole, P. The Jehovah's Witness and dementia: who or what defines 'best interests'? *Anaesthesia* 2006 August; 61(8): 802-806. Subject: 17.1

Hegwer, G.; Fairley, C.; Charrow, J.; Ormond, K.E. Knowledge and attitudes toward a free education and Ashkenazi Jewish Carrier Testing Program. *Journal of Genetic Counseling* 2006 February; 15(1): 61-70. Subject: 15.3

Heikkinen, Anne; Launis, V.; Wainwright, P.; Leino-Kilpi, H. Privacy and occupational health services. *Journal of Medical Ethics* 2006 September; 32(9): 522-525. Subject: 16.3

Heikkinen, Anne; Lemonidou, Chryssoula; Petsios, Konstantinos; Sala, Roberta; Barazzetti, Gaia; Radaelli, Stefania; Leino-Kilpi, Helena. Ethical codes in nursing practice: the viewpoint of Finnish, Greek and Italian nurses. *Journal of Advanced Nursing* 2006 August; 55(3): 310-319. Subject: 4.1.3

Heikkinen, Anne; Wickström, Gustav; Leino-Kilpi, Helena. Understanding privacy in occupational health services. *Nursing Ethics* 2006 September; 13(5): 515-530. Subject: 8.4

Heilbrun, Kirk S. The assessment of competency for execution: an overview. *Behavioural Sciences and the Law* 1987 Autumn; 5(4): 385-396. Subject: 20.6

Heilig, Lauren F.; D'Ambrosia, Renee; Drake, Amanda L.; Dellavalle, Robert P.; Hester, Eric J. A case for informed consent? Indoor UV tanning facility operator's provision of health risks information (United States). *Cancer Causes and Control* 2005 June; 16(5): 557-560. Subject: 8.3.1

Heinonen, Maarit; Oila, Outi; Nordström, Katrina. Current issues in the regulation of human tissue-engineering products in the European Union. *Tissue Engineering* 2005 November-December; 11(11-12): 1905-1911. Subject: 19.5

Heitz, Theresa L.; Kayira, Eric F. Worth its weight in gold: organ transplantation and the new UNOS policies for allocation of hearts and livers. *Journal of Health and Hospital Law* 1997 Fall; 30(3): 195-200. Subject: 19.6

Heland, Melodie. Fruitful or futile: intensive care nurses' experiences and perceptions of medical futility. *Australian Critical Care* 2006 February; 19(1): 25-31. Subject: 20.5.1

Helft, Paul R. An intimate collaboration: prognostic communication with advanced cancer patients. *Journal of Clinical Ethics* 2006 Summer; 17(2): 110-121. Subject: 8.1

Helgason, Höordur Helgi. Informed consent for donating biosamples in medical research — legal requirements in Iceland. *In:* Árnason, Gardar; Nordal, Salvör; Árnason, Vilhjálmur, eds. Blood and Data: Ethical, Legal and Social Aspects of Human Genetic Databases. Reykjavík: University of Iceland Press; 2004: 127-134. Subject: 18.3

Heller, Jan C. Moral mistakes that leaders make. *Health Care Ethics USA* 2006; 14(1): E3 [Online]. Accessed: http://chce.slu.edu/Partnerships_HCE_Intro.html [2006 November 17]. Subject: 9.1

Heller, Jan C.; Wallington, Maria. Cardiology and genomics: an ethical view. *Health Progress* 2006 March-April; 87(2): 51-53. Subject: 15.3

Hellinger, Fred J. The impact of financial incentives on physician behavior in managed care plans: a review of the evidence. *Medical Care Research and Review* 1996 September; 53(3): 294-314. Subject: 9.3.1

Hellsten, Sirkku K. Beyond Europe: rhetoric of reproductive rights in global population policies. *In:* Widdows, Heather; Idiakez, Itziar Alkorta; Cirión, Aitziber Emaldi, eds. Women's Reproductive Rights. New York: Palgrave Macmillan; 2006: 199-213. Subject: 14.1

See SUBJECT HEADING KEY FOR SECTION II on inside back cover.

Helmchen, Hanfried. Forthcoming ethical issues in biological psychiatry. *World Journal of Biological Psychiatry* 2005; 6(Supplement 2): 56-64. Subject: 17.1

Heminger, Justin D. Big abortion: what the antiabortion movement can learn from big tobacco. *Catholic University Law Review* 2005 Summer; 54(4): 1273-1311. Subject: 12.5.1

Hemmerling, Anke; Siedentopf, Friederike; Kentenich, Heribert. Emotional impact and acceptability of medical abortion with mifepristone: a German experience. *Journal of Psychosomatic Obstetrics and Gynaecology* 2005 March; 26(1): 23-31. Subject: 12.1

Hemminki, Akseli; Kellokumpu-Lehtinen, Pirkko-Liisa. Harmful impact of EU clinical trials directive [editorial]. *BMJ: British Medical Journal* 2006 March 4; 332(7540): 501-502. Subject: 18.6

Henderson, Gail E.; Easter, Michele M.; Zimmer, Catherine; King, Nancy M.P.; Davis, Arlene M.; Rothschild, Barbra Bluestone; Churchill, Larry R.; Wilfond, Benjamin S.; Nelson, Daniel K. Therapeutic misconception in early phase gene transfer trials. *Social Science and Medicine* 2006 January; 62(1): 239-253. Subject: 15.4

Henderson, John. Conducting longitudinal epidemiological research in children. *In:* Smyth, Marie; Williamson, Emma, eds. Researchers and Their 'Subjects': Ethics, Power, Knowledge and Consent. Bristol, UK: Policy Press; 2004: 157-174. Subject: 18.5.2

Henderson, Mark; Charter, David; Ahuja, Anjana; Frean, Alexandra. Sperm donors children win the right to trace their fathers. *Times* 2004 January 17; 2p. Subject: 14.2

Hendricks, J.W. Does immunization refusal warrant discontinuing a physician-patient relationship? *Archives of Pediatrics and Adolescent Medicine* 2005 October; 159(10): 994. Subject: 9.7

Heng, Boon Chin. Advances in oocyte cryopreservation technology will eventually blur the ethical and moral boundaries between compensated egg sharing and commercialized oocyte donation. *Reproductive BioMedicine Online [electronic]* 2006 March; 12(3): 280-281. Subject: 14.6

Heng, Boon Chin. Alternative solutions to the current situation of oocyte donation in Singapore. *Reproductive BioMedicine Online [electronic]* 2006 March; 12(3): 286-291. Subject: 19.5

Heng, Boon Chin. Ethical issues in paying for long-distance travel and accommodation expenses of oocyte donors. *Reproductive BioMedicine Online [electronic]* 2005 November; 11(5): 552-553. Subject: 14.4

Heng, Boon Chin. Handing out free travel and accommodation to oocyte donors in lieu of monetary payment: is this ethically justifiable? [letter]. *Medical Hypotheses* 2005; 66(1): 212-213. Subject: 14.1

Heng, Boon Chin. International egg-sharing to provide donor oocytes for clinical assisted reproduction and derivation of nuclear transfer stem cells. *Reproductive BioMedicine Online [electronic]* 2005 December; 11(6): 676-678. Accessed: http://www.rbmonline.com/Article/2024 [2006 July 25]. Subject: 14.2

Heng, Boon Chin. "Reproductive tourism": should locally registered fertility doctors be held accountable for channelling patients to foreign medical establishments? [letter]. *Human Reproduction* 2006 March; 21(3): 840-842. Subject: 14.1

Heng, Boon Chin; Tong, Cao. Refund fertility-treatment costs for donated embryos [letter]. *Nature* 2006 September 7; 443(7107): 26. Subject: 18.5.4

Heng, Boon Chin; Tong, Guo Qing; Pennings, Guido. Mirror exchange of donor gametes should also accommodate scientific research [letter and reply]. *Human Reproduction* 2006 April; 21(4): 1100-1101. Subject: 18.5.4

Henifin, Mary S. New reproductive technologies: equity and access to reproductive health care. *Journal of Social Issues* 1993 Summer; 49(2): 61-74. Subject: 14.1

Henig, Robin Marantz. Looking for the lie: Scientists are using brain imaging and other tools as new kinds of lie detectors. But trickier even than finding the source of deception might be navigating a world without it. *New York Times Magazine* 2006 February 5; p. 47-53, 76, 80. Subject: 17.1

Henig, Robin Marantz. Will we ever arrive at the good death? Almost 40 years after the birth of the hospice movement, and despite the rise of living wills and palliative care, the end of life remains anxious and hypermedicalized. Goldie Gold's struggle, and ours, to come to a dignified end. *New York Times Magazine* 2005 August 7; p. 26-35, 40, 68. Subject: 20.3.1

Henneman, Lidewij; Timmermans, Danielle R.M.; van der Wal, Gerrit. Public attitudes toward genetic testing: perceived benefits and objections. *Genetic Testing* 2006 Summer; 10(2): 139-145. Subject: 15.3

Henry, David A.; Kerridge, Ian H.; Hill, Suzanne R.; McNeill, Paul M.; Doran, Evan; Newby, David A.; Henderson, Kim M.; Maguire, Jane; Stokes, Barrie J.; Macdonald, Graham J.; Day, Richard O. Medical specialists and pharmaceutical industry-sponsored research: a survey of the Australian experience. *Medical Journal of Australia* 2005 June 6; 182(11): 557-560. Subject: 1.3.9

Henry, Linda L. Disclosure of medical errors: ethical considerations for the development of a facility policy and organizational culture change. *Policy, Politics, and Nursing Practice* 2005 May; 6(2): 127-134. Subject: 9.8

Henry, M.S. Uncertainty, responsibility, and the evolution of the physician/patient relationship. *Journal of Medical Ethics* 2006 June; 32(6): 321-323. Subject: 8.1

Henry, Stephen G. Recognizing tacit knowledge in medical epistemology. *Theoretical Medicine and Bioethics* 2006; 27(3): 187-213. Subject: 9.8

Henwood, S.; Wilson, M.A.; Edwards, I. The role of competence and capacity in relation to consent for treatment in adult patients. *British Dental Journal* 2006 January 14; 200(1): 18-21. Subject: 8.3.3

Hepler, Charles D. Balancing pharmacists' conscientious objections with their duty to serve [editorial]. *Journal of the American Pharmacists Association* 2005 July-August; 45(4): 434-436. Subject: 11.1

Herczeg, L.; Szokol, J.; Horvath, G.; Vaszily, M.; Peterffy, A. Open-heart surgery and Jehovah's Witnesses. *Medicine and Law: The World Association for Medical Law* 2006 June; 25(2): 233-239. Subject: 8.3.4

Herissone-Kelly, P. Procreative beneficence and the prospective parent. *Journal of Medical Ethics* 2006 March; 32(3): 166-169. Subject: 15.2

Herissone-Kelly, Peter. Genetic screening, prospective parenthood, and the internal perspective. *In:* Árnason, Gardar; Nordal, Salvör; Árnason, Vilhjálmur, eds. Blood and Data: Ethical, Legal and Social Aspects of Human Genetic Databases. Reykjavík: University of Iceland Press; 2004: 257-262. Subject: 15.2

Herissone-Kelly, Peter. The prohibition of sex selection for social reasons in the United Kingdom: public opinion trumps reproductive liberty? *CQ: Cambridge Quarterly of Healthcare Ethics* 2006 Summer; 15(3): 261-272. Subject: 14.3

Herranz, Gonzalo. Euthanasia: an uncontrollable power over death. *National Catholic Bioethics Quarterly* 2006 Summer; 6(2): 263-269. Subject: 20.5.1

Herrera, C.D. Restraint use and autonomy in psychiatric care. *Journal of Ethics in Mental Health* 2006 November; 1(1): E5, 4 p. Subject: 17.3

Herrera, C.D.; Jansen, Lynn. Protection of human subjects and scientific progress: can the two be reconciled? [letter and reply]. *Hastings Center Report* 2006 January-February; 36(1): 7-8, 9. Subject: 18.3

Herrera, Stephan. Daniel Callahan. *Nature Biotechnology* 2004 December; 22(12): 1495. Subject: 2.2

Herrera, Stephan. Leaders and laggards in the stem cell enterprise [news]. *Nature Biotechnology* 2005 July; 23(7): 775-777. Subject: 18.5.4

Herrling, Paul. Experiments in social responsibility. *Nature* 2006 January 19; 439(7074): 267-268. Subject: 9.7

Herrmann, Beate. Schönheitsideal und medizinische Körpermanipulation: invasive Selbstgestaltung als Ausdruck autonomer Entscheidung oder "sozialer Unterwerfung" = Ideals of beauty and the medical manipulation of the body between free choice and coercion. *Ethik in der Medizin* 2006 March; 18(1): 71-80. Subject: 9.5.1

Hershenov, David B. The death of a person. *Journal of Medicine and Philosophy* 2006 April; 31(2): 107-120. Subject: 20.2.1

Hershenov, David B. Explaining the psychological appeal of viability. *National Catholic Bioethics Quarterly* 2006 Winter; 6(4): 681-686. Subject: 12.3

Hershenov, David; Koch-Hershenov, Rose J. Fission and confusion. *Christian Bioethics* 2006 December; 12(3): 237-254. Subject: 4.4

Herzog, Antonia V.; Frankel, Mark S. A model ethical protocol as a guidance document for human genome research. *Revista de Derecho Genoma Humano = Law and the Human Genome Review* 1999 January-June; (10): 21-40. Subject: 15.11

Heß, Marga. Zur Geschichte der Entschädigung von Euthanasie-Opfern: Gedenken und Handeln. *In:* Frewer, Andreas; Eickhoff, Clemens, eds. "Euthanasie" und die aktuelle Sterbehilfe-Debatte: die historischen Hintergründe medizinischer Ethik. Frankfurt; New York: Campus; 2000: 370-382. Subject: 20.5.1

Hess, David. Cancer. *In:* Mitcham, Carl, ed. Encyclopedia of Science, Technology, and Ethics. Farmington Hills, MI: Thomson/Gale, 2005: 285-288. Subject: 9.5.1

Hess, David. Complementary and alternative medicine. *In:* Mitcham, Carl, ed. Encyclopedia of Science, Technology, and Ethics. Farmington Hills, MI: Thomson/Gale, 2005: 384-387. Subject: 4.1.1

Hessini, Leila. Global progress in abortion advocacy and policy: an assessment of the decade since ICPD. *Reproductive Health Matters* 2005 May; 13(25): 88-100. Subject: 12.1

Hester, D. Micah. Why we must leave our organs to others. *American Journal of Bioethics [Online]* 2006 July-August; 6(4): W23-W28. Subject: 19.5

Hester, D. Micah; Hackler, Chris. Improving medicine through research and the constitutive nature of altruism. *American Journal of Bioethics* 2006 September-October; 6(5): 51-52. Subject: 18.3

Hester, J. David. Intersex and the rhetorics of healing. *In:* Sytsma, Sharon E., ed. Ethics and Intersex. Dordrecht: Springer, 2006: 47-71. Subject: 10

Hewison, Jenny; Haines, Andy. Confidentiality and consent in medical research: overcoming barriers to recruitment in health research. *BMJ: British Medical Journal* 2006 August 5; 333(7562): 300-302. Subject: 18.2

Hewit, David W. Incapable patients and the law [letter]. *BMJ: British Medical Journal* 2006 January 28; 332(7535): 237. Subject: 17.7

See SUBJECT HEADING KEY FOR SECTION II on inside back cover.

595

Hewitt, P.E.; Moore, C.; Soldan, K. vCJD donor notification exercise: 2005. *Clinical Ethics* 2006 September; 1(3): 172-178. Subject: 19.4

Hewlett, Bonnie L.; Hewlett, Barry S. Providing care and facing death: nursing during Ebola outbreaks in central Africa. *Journal of Transcultural Nursing* 2005 October; 16(4): 289-297. Subject: 4.1.3

Hey, Edmund; Chalmers, Iain. Are any of the criticisms of the CNEP trial true? *Lancet* 2006 April 1-7; 367(9516): 1032-1033. Subject: 18.6

Heywood, M.J. The routine offer of HIV counseling and testing: a human right. *Health and Human Rights: An International Journal* 2005; 8(2): 13-19. Subject: 9.5.6

Hickey, Steve. Censorship of medical journals [letter]. *BMJ: British Medical Journal* 2006 July 1; 333(7557): 45. Subject: 1.3.7

Hickman, Larry. Status arguments and genetic research with human embryos. *Southwest Philosophical Review* 1988 January; 4: 45-55. Subject: 18.5.4

Hidalgo, Soraya Nadia. Cloning or serial reproduction of human beings, a twenty-first century alternative? = Clonación o reproducción en serie de seres humanos, ¿una alternativa del siglo XXI? *Law and the Human Genome Review = Revista de Derecho y Genoma Humano* 1996 January-June; (4): 39-58. Subject: 14.5

Hiday, Virginia Aldige. Outpatient commitment: the state of empirical research on its outcomes. *Psychology, Public Policy, and Law* 2003 March-June; 9(1-2): 8-32. Subject: 17.7

Higham, Helen. Artificial nutrition and hydration: managing the practicalities. *Clinical Ethics* 2006 June; 1(2): 86-89. Subject: 20.5.1

Hildén, Hanna-Mari; Honkasalo, Marja-Liisa. Finnish nurses' interpretations of patient autonomy in the context of end-of-life decision making. *Nursing Ethics* 2006 January; 13(1): 41-51. Subject: 20.5.1

Hildén, H-M.; Honkasalo, M-L.; Louhiala, P. Finnish doctors and the realisation of patient autonomy in the context of end of life decision making. *Journal of Medical Ethics* 2006 June; 32(6): 316-320. Subject: 20.4.1

Hilgartner, Stephen. Acceptable intellectual property. *Journal of Molecular Biology* 2002 June 14; 319(4): 943-946. Subject: 5.3

Hilgartner, Stephen. Potential effects of a diminishing public domain in biomedical research data. *In:* Esanu, Julie M.; Uhlir, Paul F., eds. The Role of Scientific and Technical Data and Information in the Public Domain: Proceedings of a Symposium. Washington, DC: National Academies Press; 2002: 133-138. Subject: 18.6

Hill, Edward C. Your morality or mine? An inquiry into the ethics of human reproduction. *American Journal of Obstetrics and Gynecology* 1986 June; 154(6): 1173-1180. Subject: 2.1

Hill, Jill M. Forcina. Hospice utilization: political, cultural, and legal issues. *Journal of Nursing Law* 2005 Winter; 10(4): 216-224. Subject: 20.4.1

Hill, John Lawrence. In defense of enforcement of the surrogate contract: a reply to Field. *Politics and the Life Sciences* 1991 February; 9(2): 253-261. Subject: 14.2

Hill, Kevin P. Free Lunch? [editorial]. *American Journal of Psychiatry* 2006 April; 163(4): 569-570. Subject: 9.7

Hill, Lori R. Response to protocol review scenario: did the right thing. *Lab Animal* 2006 June; 35(6): 15-16. Subject: 22.2

Hilliard, Tom; Chambers, Timothy. The relationship between paediatricians and commerce. *Paediatric Respiratory Reviews* 2006 March; 7(1): 54-59. Subject: 7.3

Hillier, Sheila. Women and population control in China: issues of sexuality, power and control. *Feminist Review* 1988 Spring; (29): 101-113. Subject: 12.5.1

Hillman, Alison A. Human rights and deinstitutionalization: a success story in the Americas. *Revista panamericana de salud pública/Pan American Journal of Public Health* 2005 October-November; 18(4-5): 374-379. Subject: 17.7

Hilton, Sean R.; Slotnick, Henry B. Proto-professionalism: how professionalisation occurs across the continuum of medical education. *Medical Education* 2005 January; 39(1): 58-65. Subject: 4.1.2

Hilyard, Nicholas; Sexton, Sarah. No patents on life. *Forum for Applied Research and Public Policy* 2000 Spring; 15(1): 69-74. Subject: 15.8

Himma, Kenneth Einar. Natural law. *In:* Mitcham, Carl, ed. Encyclopedia of Science, Technology, and Ethics. Farmington Hills, MI: Thomson/Gale, 2005: 1289-1295. Subject: 2.1

Himmelweit, Susan. More than 'a woman's right to choose'? *Feminist Review* 1988 Spring; (29): 38-56. Subject: 12.4.2

Hindley, Carol; Thomson, Ann M. The rhetoric of informed choice: perspectives from midwives on intrapartum fetal heart rate monitoring. *Health Expectations* 2005 December; 8(4): 306-314. Subject: 8.3.1

Hindmarsh, Richard. The problems of genetic engineering. *Peace Review* 2000 December; 12(4): 541-547. Subject: 15.1

Hinkley, Aaron E. Christianity, the culture wars, and bioethics: current debates and controversies in the Christian approach to bioethics. *Christian Bioethics* 2006 December; 12(3): 229-235. Subject: 2.1

Hinton, Veronica J. Ethics of neuroimaging in pediatric development. *Brain and Cognition* 2002 December; 50(3): 455-468. Subject: 17.1

Hinxton Group. An international consortium on stem cells, ethics and law. *Revista de Derecho y Genoma*

Humano = Law and the Human Genome Review 2006 January-June; (24): 251-255. Subject: 18.5.4

Hinxton Group; Faden, Ruth; Donovan, Peter J.; Harris, John; Lovell-Badge, Robin; Mathews, Debra J.H.; Savulescu, Julian; Azariah, Jayapual; Benvenisty, Nissim; Bok, Hilary; Brunelli, Silvia; Campbell, Philip; Chan, Sarah; Cheng, Linzhao; Coles, David; Devolder, Katrien; Finkel, Julia; Friele, Minou; Heyd, David; Honey, Colin; Hyun, Insoo; Isasi, Rosario M.; Kyu Won, Jung; Liao, S. Matthew; McLaren, Anne; Mori, Maurizio; Munthe, Christian; Murdoch, Alison; Nakatsuji, Norio; O'Toole, Chris; Panicker, Mitradas M.; Patterson, Mark; Pedersen, Roger A.; Pera, Martin Frederick; Purnell, Beverly A.; Regenberg, Alan; Qui, Ren-Zong; Romeo-Casabona, Carlos M.; Salter, Brian; Samuelson, Taylor; Santalo, Josep; Saunders, Rhodri; Sheng, Hui Z.; Skene, Loane; Solter, Davor; Stacey, Glyn; Stubing, William C.; Sugarman, Jeremy; Sugden, Andrew M.; Van Steirteghem, Andre; Wallace, Susan E.; Walters, LeRoy B.; Zambidis, Elias T. Consensus statement: the Hinxton Group: an international consortium on stem cells, ethics and law. Baltimore, MD: Johns Hopkins Medical 2006 February 24; 4p. [Online]. Accessed: http://www.hopkinsmedicine.org/bioethics/finalsc.doc [2006 March 3]. Subject: 18.5.4

Hippen, Benjamin. The commerce of the body: the case for kidney markets. *New Atlantis* 2006 Fall; 14: 47-61. Subject: 19.3

Hirsch, Jules. An anniversary for cancer chemotherapy. *JAMA: The Journal of the American Medical Association* 2006 September 27; 296(12): 1518-1520. Subject: 21.3

Hirsch, Paul J. Stem cell research, politics, and bioethics [editorial]. *New Jersey Medicine* 2004 December; 101(12): 7-9. Subject: 18.5.4

Hirschhorn, Kurt. A doctor's perspective. *Mount Sinai Journal of Medicine* 1997 March; 64(2): 105-107. Subject: 9.2

Hirschman, Karen B.; Joyce, Colette M.; James, Bryan D.; Xie, Sharon X.; Karlawish, Jason H.T. Do Alzheimer's disease patients want to participate in a treatment decision, and would their caregivers let them? *Gerontologist* 2005 June; 45(3): 381-388. Subject: 8.3.3

Hirtle, Marie; Knoppers, Bartha M.; Lormeau, Sébastien. Banking of human materials, intellectual property rights and ownership issues; emerging trends in the literature and international policy positions (part II) = Bancos de materiales humanos, derechos de propiedad intelectual y cuestiones relativas a la titularidad: nuevas tendencias en la literatura científica y posiciones en la normativa internacional (Parte II). *Revista de Derecho Genoma Humano = Law and the Human Genome Review* 1997 January-June; (6): 63-83. Subject: 19.5

Hitt, David H. Ethical roles can exist only in an ethical system. *Frontiers of Health Services Management* 1991 Fall; 8(1): 37- 42. Subject: 9.4

Hitt, Jack. Pro-life nation: what happens when you completely criminalize abortion? Over the last eight years, El Salvador has found out. *New York Times Magazine* 2006 April 9; p. 40-47, 62, 72, 74. Subject: 12.4.1

Hjörleifsson, Stefán; Schei, Edvin. Scientific rationality, uncertainty and the governance of human genetics: an interview study with researchers at deCODE genetics. *European Journal of Human Genetics: EJHG* 2006 July; 14(7): 802-808. Subject: 15.1

Hjörleifsson, Stefán; Strand, Roger; Schei, Edvin. Health as a genetic planning project: enthusiasm and second thoughts among biomedical researchers and their research subjects. *Genomics, Society and Policy* 2005 December; 1(3): 52-65. Subject: 15.10

Hlaca, Nenad. Abortion Act and incidence of legal abortions in the Republic of Croatia. *Bulletin of Medical Ethics* 2006 April-May; (214): 26-28. Subject: 12.4.1

Hlaca, Nenad. Genetic counseling and the best interest of the child. *Revista de Derecho Genoma Humano = Law and the Human Genome Review* 1999 July-December; (11): 85-94. Subject: 15.2

Hlaca, Nenad. Human genome and protection of human rights in Croatia. *Revista de Derecho y Genoma Humano = Law and the Human Genome Review* 2006 January-June; (24): 65-73. Subject: 15.3

Ho, Anita. Family and informed consent in multicultural setting. *American Journal of Bioethics* 2006 January-February; 6(1): 26-28; discussion W27-W28. Subject: 8.3.1

Ho, Kwok M.; English, Sonya; Bell, Jeanette. The involvement of intensive care nurses in end-of-life decisions: a nationwide survey. *Intensive Care Medicine* 2005 May; 31(5): 668-673. Subject: 20.5.1

Ho, Wing Wah; Brandfield, Julie; Retkin, Randye; Laraque, Danielle. Complexities in HIV consent in adolescents. *Clinical Pediatrics* 2005 July-August; 44(6): 473-478. Subject: 9.5.6

Hobgood, Cherri; Tamayo-Sarver, Joshua H.; Elms, Andrew; Weiner, Bryan. Parental preferences for error disclosure, reporting, and legal action after medical error in the care of their children. *Pediatrics* 2005 December; 116(6): 1276-1286. Subject: 9.8

Hochhauser, Mark. Paying for research related injuries in the US [letter]. *BMJ: British Medical Journal* 2006 March 11; 332(7541): 610. Subject: 18.1

Hodge, James G. The legal and ethical fiction of "pure" confidentiality. *American Journal of Bioethics* 2006 March-April; 6(2): 21-22. Subject: 8.4

Hodge, James G. Jr.; Gostin, Lawrence O.; Gebbie, Kristine; Erickson, Deborah L. Transforming public health law: the Turning Point Model State Public Health

See SUBJECT HEADING KEY FOR SECTION II on inside back cover.

597

Act. *Journal of Law, Medicine, and Ethics* 2006 Spring; 34(1): 77-84. Subject: 9.1

Hodges, Frederick Mansfield. Bodily integrity in the biotech era: placing human rights and medical ethics in historical context. *In:* Denniston, George C.; Hodges, Frederick Mansfield; Milos, Marilyn Fayre, eds. Flesh and Blood: Perspectives on the Problems of Circumcision in Contemporary Society. New York: Kluwer Academic/Plenum Publishers; 2004: 1-15. Subject: 9.5.7

Hodgson, Helen. Giving the guinea-pigs a voice. *Twentieth Century* 1963 Summer; 172: 110-111. Subject: 18.1

Hoedemaekers, Rogeer; Gordijn, Bert; Hekster, Y.; van Agt, F.;. The complexities of ethical evaluation of genomics research. *HEC (Healthcare Ethics Committee) Forum* 2006 March; 18(1): 18-36. Subject: 15.1

Hoedemaekers, Rogeer; Gordijn, Bert; Pijnenburg, Martien. Does an appeal to the common good justify individual sacrifices for genomic research? *Theoretical Medicine and Bioethics* 2006; 27(5): 415-431. Subject: 15.10

Hoey, John. Editorial independence and the Canadian Medical Association Journal. *New England Journal of Medicine* 2006 May 11; 354(19): 1982-1983. Subject: 1.3.7

Hoeyer, Klaus. Studying ethics as policy: the naming and framing of moral problems in genetic research. *Current Anthropology* 2005 December; 46(supplement 5): S71-S90. Subject: 15.1

Hoeyer, Klaus; Dahlager, Lisa; Lynöe, Niels. Conflicting notions of research ethics. The mutually challenging traditions of social scientists and medical researchers. *Social Science and Medicine* 2005 October; 61(8): 1741-1749. Subject: 1.3.9

Hoeyer, Klaus; Dahlager, Lisa; Lynöe, Niels. Ethical conflicts during the social study of clinical practice: the need to reassess the mutually challenging research ethics traditions of social scientists and medical researchers. *Clinical Ethics* 2006 March; 1(1): 41-45. Subject: 1.3.9

Hoeyer, Klaus; Lynöe, Niels. Is informed consent a solution to contractual problems? A comment on the article '"Iceland Inc"?: On the Ethics of Commercial Population Genomics' by Jon F. Merz, Glenn E. McGee, and Pamela Sankar. *Social Science and Medicine* 2004 March; 58(6): 1211. Subject: 15.10

Hoeyer, Klaus; Tutton, Richard. "Ethics was here": studying the language-games of ethics in the case of UK Biobank. *Critical Public Health* 2005 December; 15(4): 385-397. Subject: 15.1

Höfer, Thomas; Gerner, Ingrid; Gundert-Remy, Ursula; Liebsch, Manfred; Schulte, Agnes; Spielmann, Horst; Vogel, Richard; Wettig, Klaus. Animal testing and alternative approaches for the human health risk assessment under the proposed new European chemicals reg-

ulation. *Archives of Toxicology* 2004 October; 78(10): 549-564. Subject: 22.2

Hoff, Timothy; Hoyt, Adrienne; Therrell, Brad; Ayoob, Maria. Exploring barriers to long-term follow-up in newborn screening programs. *Genetics in Medicine* 2006 September; 8(9): 563-570. Subject: 15.3

Hoffer, L. John. Tube feeding in advanced dementia: the metabolic perspective. *BMJ: British Medical Journal* 2006 December 9; 333(7580): 1214-1215. Subject: 9.5.3

Hoffman, Jan. The last word on the last breath. *New York Times* 2006 October 10; p. F1. Subject: 20.5.1

Hoffman, Paul W. The brethren discuss genetic engineering. *Brethren Life and Thought* 1986 Autumn; 31(4): 201-208. Subject: 15.1

Hoffman, Sharona. "Racially-tailored" medicine unraveled. *American University Law Review* 2005 December; 55(2): 395-452. Subject: 9.5.4

Hoffmann, Diane. Choosing paternalism? *Medical Ethics Newsletter* 2006 Spring; 13(2): 4, 12. Subject: 8.3.1

Hoffmaster, Barry. What does vulnerability mean? *Hastings Center Report* 2006 March-April; 36(2): 38-45. Subject: 8.1

Hoffmaster, Barry; Schrecker, Ted. An ethical analysis of HIV testing of pregnant women and their newborns. *Canadian HIV/AIDS Policy and Law Newsletter* 1999 Summer; 4(4): 5-11. Subject: 9.5.6

Hoffmaster, Barry; Schrecker, Ted. An ethical analysis of the mandatory exclusion of immigrants who test HIV-positive. *HIV/AIDS Policy and Law Review* 2000; 5(4): 1, 42-51. Subject: 9.5.6

Hoffmaster, C. Barry. Against against bioethics. *American Journal of Bioethics* 2006 May-June; 6(3): 53-55; discussion W51- W53. Subject: 2.1

Hofmann, Bjørn. Do biobanks promote paternalism? On the loss of autonomy in the quest for individual independence. *In:* Árnason, Gardar; Nordal, Salvör; Árnason, Vilhjálmur, eds. Blood and Data: Ethical, Legal and Social Aspects of Human Genetic Databases. Reykjavík: University of Iceland Press; 2004: 237-242. Subject: 15.1

Hofmann, Bjørn. Forensic uses and misuses of DNA: a case report from Norway. *Genomics, Society and Policy* 2006 May; 2(1): 129-131. Subject: 15.1

Hofmann, Bjørn; Solbakk, Jan Helge; Holm, Søren. Analogical reasoning in handling emerging technologies: the case of umbilical cord blood biobanking. *American Journal of Bioethics* 2006 November-December; 6(6): 49-57. Subject: 5.1

Hofmann, Bjørn; Solbakk, Jan Helge; Holm, Søren. Teaching old dogs new tricks: the role of analogies in bioethical analysis and argumentation concerning new technologies. *Theoretical Medicine and Bioethics* 2006; 27(5): 397-413. Subject: 15.1

Hofmann, Paul B. Ethical decision making requires collaboration between administrators and clinicians. *Frontiers of Health Services Management* 1991 Fall; 8(1): 31-33. Subject: 9.4

Hofmann, Paul B. Telling patients of mistakes [letter]. *Hastings Center Report* 2006 September-October; 36(5): 7. Subject: 8.2

Hofvander, Yngve. Circumcision of boys: time for doctors to reconsider. *In:* Denniston, George C.; Hodges, Frederick Mansfield; Milos, Marilyn Fayre, eds. Flesh and Blood: Perspectives on the Problems of Circumcision in Contemporary Society. New York: Kluwer Academic/Plenum Publishers; 2004: 109-117. Subject: 9.5.7

Hogerzeil, Hans; Samson, Melanie; Casanovas, Jaume Vidal; Rahmani-Ocora, Ladan. Is access to essential medicines as part of the fulfilment of the right to health enforceable through the courts? *Lancet* 2006 July 22-28; 368(9532): 305-311. Subject: 9.2

Hogle, Linda F. Enhancement technologies and the body. *Annual Review of Anthropology* 2005; 34: 695-716. Subject: 4.5

Hoit, Jeannette D. Who goes first? [editorial]. *American Journal of Speech-Language Pathology* 2005 November; 14(4): 259. Subject: 18.5.1

Hojaij, Carlos Roberto. Ethics for psychiatrists [editorial]. *World Journal of Biological Psychiatry* 2005; 6(2): 66-68. Subject: 4.1.2

Holden, Constance. Schatten: Pitt panel finds 'misbehavior' but not misconduct [news]. *Science* 2006 February 17; 311(5763): 928. Subject: 1.3.9

Holden, Constance. Scientists create human stem cell line from 'dead' embryos [news]. *Science* 2006 September 29; 313(5795): 1869. Subject: 18.5.4

Holden, Constance. Scientists keep some data to themselves [news]. *Science* 2006 January 27; 311(5760): 448. Subject: 1.3.9

Holden, Constance. Scientists object to Massachusetts rules [news]. *Science* 2006 September 8; 313(5792): 1372. Subject: 5.3

Holden, Constance. Senate prepares to vote at last on a trio of stem cell bills [news]. *Science* 2006 July 7; 313(5783): 26-27. Subject: 18.5.4

Holden, Constance. States, foundations lead the way after Bush vetoes stem cell bill. *Science* 2006 July 28; 313(5786): 420-421. Subject: 18.5.4

Holden, Constance. The undisclosed background of a paper on a depression treatment. *Science* 2006 August 4; 313(5787): 598. Subject: 1.3.9

Holdstock, Douglas. Chemical and biological warfare: some ethical dilemmas. *CQ: Cambridge Quarterly of Healthcare Ethics* 2006 Fall; 15(4): 356-365. Subject: 21.3

Holland, Suzanne. It's not what we say, exactly. . .or is it? *American Journal of Bioethics* 2006 November-December; 6(6): 65-66; author reply W13-W14. Subject: 5.1

Hollman, Jay; Kilner, John. Are Christian voices needed in public bioethics debates?: Care for persons with disabilities as a test case. *Ethics and Medicine* 2006 Fall; 22(3): 143-150. Subject: 2.1

Holloway, Karla F.C. Accidental communities: race, emergency medicine, and the problem of PolyHeme. *American Journal of Bioethics* 2006 May-June; 6(3): 7-17; discussion W46- W48. Subject: 19.4

Holm, S. Self inflicted harm — NICE in ethical self destruct mode? [editorial]. *Journal of Medical Ethics* 2006 March; 32(3): 125-126. Subject: 9.4

Holm, S. The WMA on medical ethics — some critical comments. *Journal of Medical Ethics* 2006 March; 32(3): 161-162. Subject: 2.1

Holm, Søren. Embryonic stem cell research and the moral status of human embryos. *Reproductive BioMedicine Online [electronic]* 2005 March; 10(Supplement 1): 63-67. Subject: 18.5.4

Holm, Søren. An empirical approach. *In:* Ashcroft, Richard; Lucassen, Anneke; Parker, Michael; Verkerk, Marian; Widderhoven, Guy, eds. Case Analysis in Clinical Ethics. New York: Cambridge University Press; 2005: 201-211. Subject: 15.3

Holm, Søren. Informed consent and bio-banking of material from children. *Genomics, Society and Policy* 2005 February; 1(1): 16-26. Subject: 15.1

Holm, Søren. Reply to Sandin: the paradox of precaution is not dispelled by attention to context. *CQ: Cambridge Quarterly of Healthcare Ethics* 2006 Spring; 15(2): 184-187. Subject: 5.3

Holm, Søren. What should other healthcare professions learn from nursing ethics. *Nursing Philosophy* 2006 July; 7(3): 165-174. Subject: 4.1.3

Holm, Søren; Williams-Jones, Bryn. Global bioethics — myth or reality? *BMC Medical Ethics [electronic]* 2006; 7:10. 10p. Accessed: http://www.biomedcentral.com/1472-6939/7/10 [nd]. Subject: 2.1

Holman, Julieta Bleichmar; Brendel, David H. The ethics of palliative care in psychiatry. *Journal of Clinical Ethics* 2006 Winter; 17(4): 333-338. Subject: 20.4.1

Holmberg, Lars I.; Wahlberg, Vivian. The process of decision-making on abortion: a grounded theory study of young men in Sweden. *Journal of Adolescent Health* 2000 March; 26(3): 230-234. Subject: 12.5.2

Holmberg, Martin; Emanuel, Ezekiel J.; Wertheimer, Alan. Deciding who should get the flu vaccine [letter and reply]. *Science* 2006 December 8; 314(5805): 1539-1540. Subject: 9.4

See SUBJECT HEADING KEY FOR SECTION II on inside back cover.

599

Holmes-Rovner, Margaret; Wills, Celia E. Improving informed consent — insights from behavioral decision research. *Medical Care* 2002 September; 40(9, Supplement): V30-V38. Subject: 18.3

Holt, Graeme; Wheelan, Kerry; Gregori, Alberto. The ethical implications of recent innovations in knee arthroplasty. *Journal of Bone and Joint Surgery. American Volume* 2006 January; 88(1): 226-229. Subject: 9.5.1

Holt, Kathryn. What do we tell the children? Contrasting the disclosure choices of two HD families regarding risk status and predictive genetic testing. *Journal of Genetic Counseling* 2006 August; 15(4): 253-265. Subject: 15.2

Holtug, Nils. Identity, integrity, and nuclei transplantation. *Politics and the Life Sciences* 1998 March; 17(1): 20-21. Subject: 15.4

Holtzman, Neil A. The diffusion of new genetic tests for predicting disease. *FASEB Journal* 1992 July; 6: 2806-2812. Subject: 15.3

Hongladarom, Soraj. Human cloning in a Thai novel: Wimon Sainimnuan's Amata and Thai cultural attitudes toward biotechnology. *In:* Sleeboom, Margaret, ed. Genomics in Asia: A Clash of Bioethical Interests? New York: Kegan Paul; 2004: 85-105. Subject: 14.5

Hood, Maureen N.; Gugerty, Brian; Levine, Richard; Ho, Vincent B. Computerized information management for institutional review boards. *Computers, Informatics, Nursing* 2005 July-August; 23(4): 190-200. Subject: 18.2

Hood, Robert. AIDS, crisis, and activist science. *In:* Figueroa, Robert; Harding, Sandra, eds. Science and Other Cultures: Issues in Philosophies of Science and Technology. New York: Routledge; 2003: 15-25. Subject: 9.5.6

Hooghiemstra, Theo. The implementation of Directive 95/46/EC in the Netherlands, with special regard to medical data. *European Journal of Health Law* 2002 September; 9(3): 219-227. Subject: 8.4

Hooghiemstra, Theo. Introduction to the special privacy issue. *European Journal of Health Law* 2002 September; 9(3): 181-188. Subject: 8.4

Hook, C. Christopher. The techno sapiens are coming. *Christianity Today* 2004 January; 48(1): 36-40. Subject: 4.5

Hook, C. Christopher; Mueller, Paul S. The Terri Schiavo saga: the making of a tragedy and lessons learned. *Mayo Clinic Proceedings* 2005 November; 80(11): 1449-1460. Subject: 20.5.1

Hook, Mary L. Partnering with patients — a concept ready for action. *Journal of Advanced Nursing* 2006 October; 56(2): 133-143. Subject: 8.1

Hopkin, Michael. 'Vegetative' patient shows signs of conscious thought [news]. *Nature* 2006 September 14; 443(7108): 132-133. Subject: 20.5.1

Hopkin, Michael. Demo backs animal lab in Oxford [news]. *Nature* 2006 March 2; 440(7080): 10-11. Subject: 22.2

Hopkins, Michael M. The hidden research system: the evolution of cytogenetic testing in the National Health Service. *Science as Culture* 2006 September; 15(3): 253-276. Subject: 15.2

Hopkins, Nick; Zeedyk, Suzanne; Raitt, Fiona. Visualising abortion: emotion discourse and fetal imagery in a contemporary abortion debate. *Social Science and Medicine* 2005 July; 61(2): 393-403. Subject: 12.1

Hopkins, Patrick D. Protecting God from science and technology: how religious criticisms of biotechnologies backfire. *Zygon* 2002 June; 37(2): 317-343. Subject: 14.5

Hopkins Tanne, Janice. Researchers funded by NIH are failing to make data available [news]. *BMJ: British Medical Journal* 2006 March 25; 332(7543): 684. Subject: 18.2

Hopson, Laura R.; Hirsh, Emily; Delgado, Joao; Domeier, Robert M.; McSwain, Norman E., Jr.; Krohmer, Jon. Guidelines for withholding or termination of resuscitation in prehospital traumatic cardiopulmonary arrest: a joint position paper from the National Association of EMS Physicians Standards and Clinical Practice Committee and the American College of Surgeons Committee on Trauma. *Prehospital Emergency Care* 2003 January-March; 7(1): 141-146. Subject: 20.5.1

Horlick-Jones, Tom; Walls, John; Rowe, Gene; Pidgeon, Nick; Poortinga, Wouter; O'Riordan, Tim. On evaluating the GM Nation? Public debate about the commercialisation of transgenic crops in Britain. *New Genetics and Society* 2006 December; 25(3): 265-288. Subject: 15.1

Hornig Priest, Susanna. Cloning: a study in news production. *Public Understanding of Science* 2001 January 1; 10(1): 59-69. Subject: 14.5

Horrobin, Steven. Immortality, human nature, the value of life and the value of life extension. *Bioethics* 2006 November; 20(6): 279-292. Subject: 20.5.1

Horst, Maja. Cloning sensations: mass mediated articulation of social responses to controversial biotechnology. *Public Understanding of Science* 2005 April; 14(2): 185-200. Subject: 14.5

Horton, Richard. Trial registers: protecting patients, advancing trust. *Lancet* 2006 May 20-26; 367(9523): 1633-1635. Subject: 18.6

Horton, Richard; Gilmore, Ian. The evolving doctor. *Lancet* 2006 November 18-24; 368(9549): 1750-1751. Subject: 4.1.2

Houkin, Kiyohiro; Nonaka, Tadashi; Oka, Shinnichi; Koyanagi, Izumi. Inadequate website disclosure of surgical outcome of intracranial aneurysms. *Neurologia Medico-Chirurgica* 2005 September; 45(9): 448-453. Subject: 1.3.12

Subject = NRCBL Primary Classification Number; see inside front cover.

Howard, Agnes R. In moral labor. *First Things* 2006 March; (161): 9-12. Subject: 14.1

Howard, Jennifer. Oral history under review. *Chronicle of Higher Education* 2006 November 10; 53(12): A14-A17. Subject: 18.2

Howard, Orion M.; Fairclough, Diane L.; Daniels, Elisabeth R.; Emanuel, Ezekiel J. Physician desire for euthanasia and assisted suicide: would physicians practice what they preach? *Journal of Clinical Oncology* 1997 February; 15(2): 428-432. Subject: 20.7

Howe, Edmund G. Advances in treating (or not treating) intersexed persons: understanding resistance to change. *In:* Sytsma, Sharon E., ed. Ethics and Intersex. Dordrecht: Springer, 2006: 115-137. Subject: 10

Howe, Edmund G. Beyond respect for autonomy. *Journal of Clinical Ethics* 2006 Fall; 17(3): 195-206. Subject: 8.1

Howe, Edmund G. Comment on the CEJA guidelines: treating patients who deny reality. *Journal of Clinical Ethics* 2006 Winter; 17(4): 317-322. Subject: 8.2

Howe, Edmund G. Do we undervalue feelings in patients who are cognitively impaired? *Journal of Clinical Ethics* 2006 Winter; 17(4): 291-301. Subject: 8.1

Howe, Edmund G. Mixed agency in military medicine: ethical roles in conflict. *In:* Beam, Thomas E.; Sparacino, Linette R.; Pellegrino, Edmund D.; Hartle, Anthony E.; Howe, Edmund G., eds. Military Medical Ethics. Volume 1. Washington, DC: TMM Publications, Borden Institute, Walter Reed Army Medical Center; 2003: 331-365. Subject: 2.1

Howe, Edmund G. Patients may benefit from postponing assessment of mental capacity. *Journal of Clinical Ethics* 2006 Summer; 17(2): 99-109. Subject: 8.3.3

Howe, Edmund G. Throwing Jello: a primer on helping patients. *Journal of Clinical Ethics* 2006 Spring; 17(1): 3-14. Subject: 8.1

Howe, P. David. Investigating sports medicine: medical anthropology in context. *In his:* Sport, Professionalism and Pain: Ethnographies of Injury and Risk. New York: Routledge; 2004: 13-32. Subject: 9.5.1

Howell, Joel D. Some thoughts on history and "healing relationships". *American Journal of Bioethics* 2006 March-April; 6(2): 80-82. Subject: 2.1

Howell, Nancy R. Co-creation, co-redemption, and genetics. *American Journal of Theology and Philosophy* 1999 May; 20(2): 147-163. Subject: 15.1

Howsepian, A.A. Must physicians always act in their patient's best interests? *Ethics and Medicine* 2006 Fall; 22(3): 151-161. Subject: 8.3.1

Hoy, Janet; Feigenbaum, Erika. Making the case for ethics consults in community mental health centers. *Community Mental Health Journal* 2005 June; 41(3): 235-250. Subject: 9.6

Hren, Darko; Vujaklija, Ana; Ivaniševic, Ranka; Knezevic, Josip; Marušic, Matko; Marušic, Ana. Students' moral reasoning, Machiavellianism and socially desirable responding: implications for teaching ethics and research integrity. *Medical Education* 2006 March; 40(3): 269-277. Subject: 7.2

Hsin, Dena Hsin-Chen; Macer, Darryl R.J. Heroes of SARS: professional roles and ethics of health care workers. *Journal of Infection* 2004 October; 49(3): 210-215. Subject: 4.1.2

Hsin-Chen, Hsin. Effects of family-centered values in elder's end-of-life decision making—perspectives of seniors in Taiwan and compared to seniors in New Zealand. *Formosan Journal of Medical Humanities* 2006 June; 7(1-2): 179-190. Subject: 20.5.1

Hu, Ching-li. The World Health Organization and its role in bioethics. *In:* Döring, Ole; Chen, Renbiao, eds. Advances in Chinese Medical Ethics: Chinese and International Perspectives. Hamburg: Institut für Asienkunde; 2002: 26-37. Subject: 2.1

Hu, Joan S. Are you alive in there? *Current Surgery* 2004 July-August; 61(4): 393-394. Subject: 20.5.1

Hubben, Joep. Sterbehilfe in den Niederlanden: Das Verhältnis zwischen Gesetzgebung und Rechtsprechung. *In:* Gordijn, Bert; ten Have, Henk, eds. Medizinethik und Kultur: Grenzen medizinischen Handelns in Deutschland und den Niederlanden. Stuttgart: Frommann-Holzboog; 2000: 267-281. Subject: 20.5.1

Huber, Lara. Patientenautonomie als nichtidealisierte "natürliche Autonomie" [Patient autonomy as non-idealized "natural autonomy". *Ethik in der Medizin* 2006 June; 18(2): 133-147. Subject: 8.1

Huber, Sam; Lagay, Faith. Clinical trials in developing countries. *Virtual Mentor* 2001 August; 3(8): 2p. Subject: 18.5.1

Hubert, Robert M.; Freeman, Larry T. Report of the ACA Ethics Committee: 2002-2003. *Journal of Counseling and Development* 2004 Spring; 82(2): 248-251. Subject: 9.6

Hübner, D. Genetic testing and private insurance — a case of "selling one's body"? *Medicine, Health Care and Philosophy* 2006 March; 9(1): 43-55. Subject: 15.3

Hudson, James M.; Bruckman, Amy. "Go away": participant objections to being studied and the ethics of chatroom research. *Information Society* 2004 April-June; 20(2): 127-139. Subject: 1.3.12

Hudson, Kathy L. Embryo biopsy for stem cells: trading old problems for new. *Hastings Center Report* 2006 September-October; 36(5): 50-51. Subject: 18.5.4

Hudson, Kathy L. Genetic testing oversight [editorial]. *Science* 2006 September 29; 313(5795): 1853. Subject: 15.3

See SUBJECT HEADING KEY FOR SECTION II on inside back cover.

601

Hudson, Kathy L.; Murphy, Juli A.; Kaufman, David J.; Javitt, Gail H.; Katsanis, Sara H.; Scott, Joan. Oversight of US genetic testing laboratories. *Nature Biotechnology* 2006 September; 24(9): 1083-1090. Subject: 15.3

Hudson, Michelle. The EU Physical Agents (EMF) Directive and its impact on MRI imaging in animal experiments: a submission by FRAME to the HSE. *ATLA: Alternatives to Laboratory Animals* 2006 June; 34(3): 343-347. Subject: 5.3

Hudson, Michelle; Bhogal, Nirmala. An analysis of the home office statistics of scientific procedures on living animals, Great Britain 2004. *ATLA: Alternatives to Laboratory Animals* 2006 February; 34(1): 85-103. Subject: 22.2

Hug, Kristina. Sources of human embryos for stem cell research: ethical problems and their possible solutions. *Medicina (Kaunas)* 2005; 41(12): 1002-1010. Subject: 18.5.4

Hug, Kristina. Therapeutic perspectives of human embryonic stem cell research versus the moral status of a human embryo—does one have to be compromised for the other? *Medicina (Kaunas)* 2006; 42(2): 107-114. Subject: 18.5.4

Huggins, Eily S. Assisted outpatient treatment: an unconstitutional invasion of protected rights or a necessary government safeguard? *Journal of Legislation* 2004; 30: 305-325. Subject: 8.3.4

Hughes, Henrietta. What is your duty of care? *Journal of Family Planning and Reproductive Health Care* 2005 July; 31(3): 245-246. Subject: 7.3

Hughes, Jonathan. How not to criticize the precautionary principle. *Journal of Medicine and Philosophy* 2006 October; 31(5): 447-464. Subject: 2.1

Hughes, Julian C. Patterns of practice: a useful notion in medical ethics? *Journal of Ethics in Mental Health* 2006 November; 1(1): E2, 5 p. Subject: 17.1

Hughes, Julian C.; Fulford, K.W.M. (Bill). Hurly-burly of psychiatric ethics. *Australian and New Zealand Journal of Psychiatry* 2005 November-December; 39(11-12): 1001-1007. Subject: 17.1

Hui, E.C. The centrality of patient-physician relationship to medical professionalism: an ethical evaluation of some contemporary models. *Hong Kong Medical Journal* 2005 June; 11(3): 222-223. Subject: 8.1

Hui, Edwin C.; Zhiwei, Xu. Freedom, autonomy, reproductive rights and contextualism. *In:* Döring, Ole; Chen, Renbiao, eds. Advances in Chinese Medical Ethics: Chinese and International Perspectives. Hamburg: Institut für Asienkunde; 2002: 98-115. Subject: 14.1

Hull, Richard. "It's a BA-by!". *Free Inquiry* 2006 December-2007 January; 27(1): 27-31. Subject: 18.5.4

Hull, Richard J. Cheap listening? — Reflections on the concept of wrongful disability. *Bioethics* 2006 April; 20(2): 55-63. Subject: 15.2

Hulse, Carl. Senate removes abortion option for young girls. *New York Times* 2006 July 26; p. A1, A15. Subject: 12.4.2

Hulsey, Tara. Prenatal drug use: the ethics of testing and incarcerating pregnant women. *Newborn and Infant Nursing Review* 2005 June; 5(2): 93-96. Subject: 9.5.5

Hulst, Jessie M.; Peters, Jeroen W.B.; van den Bos, Ada; Joosten, Koen F.M.; van Goudoever, Johannes B.; Zimmermann, Luc J.I.; Tibboel, Dick. Illness severity and parental permission for clinical research in a pediatric ICU population. *Intensive Care Medicine* 2005 June; 31(6): 880-884. Subject: 18.5.2

Human Fertilisation and Embryology Authority [HFEA] (Great Britain). Consent to the use and storage of gametes and embryos. London: Human Fertilisation and Embryology Authority, 1996 May; 6 p. Subject: 8.3.1

Human Fertilisation and Embryology Authority [HFEA] (Great Britain). Donor insemination. London: Human Fertilisation and Embryology Authority, 1996 March: 5 p. Subject: 14.2

Human Fertilisation and Embryology Authority [HFEA] (Great Britain). Egg donation. London: Human Fertilisation and Embryology Authority, 1995 January; 7 p. Subject: 14.4

Human Fertilisation and Embryology Authority [HFEA] (Great Britain). Embryo storage. London: Human Fertilisation and Embryology Authority, 1996 May; 6 p. Subject: 14.6

Human Fertilisation and Embryology Authority [HFEA] (Great Britain). Recent deliberations on the case of human fetal oocytes and on pregnancies in post-menopausal women by the British Human Fertilisation and Embryology Authority. *Human Reproduction* 1995 January; 9(12): 239-244. Subject: 14.4

Human Fertilisation and Embryology Authority [HFEA] (Great Britain). The role of the HFEA. London: Human Fertilisation and Embryology Authority, 1995 January: 5 p. Subject: 14.1

Human Fertilisation and Embryology Authority [HFEA] (Great Britain). Sperm and egg donors and the law. London: Human Fertilisation and Embryology Authority, 1995 January: 5 p. Subject: 14.2

Human Fertilisation and Embryology Authority [HFEA] (Great Britain). Treatment clinic: questions to ask. London: Human Fertilisation and Embryology Authority, 1995 January: 10 p. Subject: 14.1

Human Genetics Commission [HGC] (Great Britain). Genetic information, public consultation. Second annual report of the Human Genetics Commission. London: Human Genetics Commission, 2002; 38 p. [Online]. Accessed: http://www.hgc.gov.uk/UploadDocs/DocPub/Document/annualreport_second.pdf [2006 December 19]. Subject: 2.4

Subject = NRCBL Primary Classification Number; see inside front cover.

Human Genetics Commission [HGC] (Great Britain). Our genes, ourselves: towards appropriate genetic testing. Third Annual Report of the Human Genetics Commission. London: Human Genetics Commission, 2003; 63 p. [Online]. Accessed: http://www.hgc.gov.uk/UploadDocs/DocPub/Document/HGC%203rd%20Annual%20Report,%2 0final%20PDF.pdf [2006 December 19]. Subject: 2.4

Human Genetics Commission [HGC] (Great Britain). Public attitudes to human genetic information: People's Panel quantitative study conducted for the Human Genetics Commission. London: Human Genetics Commission, 2001 March. 68 p. [Online]. Accessed: http://www.hgc.gov.uk/UploadDocs/DocPub/Document/morigeneticattitudes.pdf [2006 July 26]. Subject: 15.1

Human Genetics Commission [HGC] (Great Britain). The supply of genetic tests direct to the public: a consultation document. London: Human Genetics Commission, Dept. of Health, 2002 July. 27 p. [Online]. Accessed: http://www.hgc.gov.uk/UploadDocs/DocPub/Document/testingconsultation.pdf [27 July 2006]. Subject: 15.3

Hung, T.; Tong, M.; van Hasselt, C.A. Jehovah's Witnesses and surgery. *Hong Kong Medical Journal* 2005 August; 11(4): 311-312. Subject: 8.3.4

Hunter, David. One-time general consent for research on biological samples: autonomy and majority rules have been misunderstood [letter]. *BMJ: British Medical Journal* 2006 March 18; 332(7542): 665-666. Subject: 18.3

Hunter, Joanna K.; Dean, Tamsin; Gowan, Jenny. Death with dignity: devising a withdrawal of treatment process. *British Journal of Nursing* 2006 February 9-22; 15(3): 138-140. Subject: 20.5.1

Hunter, Kathryn G. DNA as taxable property — the elephant in the room or a red herring? *European Journal of Health Law* 2006 September; 13(3): 263-277. Subject: 15.1

Hunter, Nan D. Managed process, due care: structures of accountability in health care. *Yale Journal of Health Policy, Law and Ethics* 2006 Winter; 6(1): 93-162. Subject: 9.3.2

Hunter, Robert; Cameron, Rosie. Patient involvement in health care will improve quality [letter]. *BMJ: British Medical Journal* 2006 July 15; 333(7559): 147-148. Subject: 8.1

Huntington, Dale; Nawar, Laila; Abdel-Hady, Dalia. Women's perceptions of abortion in Egypt. *Reproductive Health Matters* 1997 May 5; (9): 101-107. Subject: 12.5.2

Huntoon, Lawrence R. The perilous vegetative state [editorial]. *Journal of American Physicians and Surgeons* 2005 Summer; 10(2): 35-36. Subject: 20.5.2

Hurlbut, William. Altered nuclear transfer: scientific, legal, and ethical foundations. *Journal of Contemporary Health Law and Policy* 2006 Spring; 22(2): 458-475. Subject: 14.5

Hurlbut, William B. Framing the future: embryonic stem cells, ethics and the emerging era of developmental biology. *Pediatric Research* 2006 April; 59(4, Part 2): 4R-12R. Subject: 18.5.4

Hurlbut, William B.; George, Robert P.; Grompe, Markus. Seeking consensus: a clarification and defense of altered nuclear transfer. *Hastings Center Report* 2006 September-October; 36(5): 42-50. Subject: 18.5.4

Hurley, Ann C.; Harvey, Rose; Roberts, J. Scott; Wilson-Chase, Chantel; Lloyd, Stephanie; Prest, Janalyn; Lock, Margaret; Horvath, Kathy J.; Green, Robert C. Genetic susceptibility for Alzheimer's disease: why did adult offspring seek testing? *American Journal of Alzheimer's Disease and Other Dementias* 2005 November-December; 20(6): 374-381. Subject: 15.3

Hurst, Irene. The legal landscape at the threshold of viability for extremely premature infants: a nursing perspective, part I. *JONA's Healthcare Law, Ethics, and Regulation* 2006 January-March; 8(1): 20-28. Subject: 20.5.2

Hurst, Irene. The legal landscape at the threshold of viability for extremely premature infants: a nursing perspective, Part II. *Journal of Perinatal and Neonatal Nursing* 2005 July-September; 19(3): 253-262. Subject: 8.3.1

Hurst, Rachel. The perfect crime. *In:* Miller, Paul; Wilsdon, James, eds. Better Humans?: The Politics of Human Enhancement and Life Extension. London: Demos, 2006: 114-121. Subject: 4.5

Hurst, Samia A. "Agreed boundaries": are we asking the right question? [letter]. *Archives of Internal Medicine* 2006 January 9; 166(1): 126- 127. Subject: 20.5.1

Hurst, Samia A.; Chevrolet, Jean-Claude; Loew, François. Methods in clinical ethics: a time for eclectic pragmatism? *Clinical Ethics* 2006 September; 1(3): 159-164. Subject: 9.6

Hurst, Samia A.; Danis, Marion. Indecent coverage? Protecting the goals of health insurance from the impact of co-payments. *CQ: Cambridge Quarterly of Healthcare Ethics* 2006 Winter; 15(1): 107-113. Subject: 9.3.1

Hurst, Samia A.; Mauron, Alex. The ethics of palliative care and euthanasia: exploring common values. *Palliative Medicine* 2006 March; 20(2): 107-112. Subject: 20.4.1

Hurst, Samia; Slowther, Anne-Marie; Forde, Reidun; Pegoraro, Renzo; Reiter-Theil, Stella; Perrier, Arnaud; Garrett-Mayer, Elizabeth; Danis, Marion. Prevalence and determinants of physician bedside rationing: data from Europe. *JGIM: Journal of General Internal Medicine* 2006 November; 21(11): 1138-1143. Subject: 9.4

Hurt, Mark. Doctors as double agents — conflicting loyalties in the contemporary doctor-patient relationship. *Journal of Medicine and Law* 1997 Fall; 2(1): 25-83. Subject: 9.3.2

See SUBJECT HEADING KEY FOR SECTION II on inside back cover.

603

Hurwitz, Brian. Family access to shared genetic information: an analysis of the narrative. *In:* Ashcroft, Richard; Lucassen, Anneke; Parker, Michael; Verkerk, Marian; Widderhoven, Guy, eds. Case Analysis in Clinical Ethics. New York: Cambridge University Press; 2005: 27-43. Subject: 15.3

Hurwitz, Richard L. [A death in the laboratory: the politics of the Gelsinger aftermath] [letter]. *Molecular Therapy* 2001 July; 4(1): 4. Subject: 15.4

Hutchings, Jane; Wrinkler, Jennifer L.; Fuller, Timothy S.; Gardner, Jacqueline S.; Wells, Elisa S.; Downing, Don; Shafer, Rod. When the morning after is Sunday: pharmacist prescribing of emergency contraceptive pills. *Journal of the American Medical Women's Association* 1998 Fall; 53(5, Supplement2): 230-232. Subject: 11.1

Hutchon, David J.R.; Carpenter, Robert James, Jr. Commercial cord blood banking: immediate cord clamping is not safe: public cord blood banking should be more widely adopted [letters]. *BMJ: British Medical Journal* 2006 October 28; 333(7574): 919. Subject: 19.4

Hutson, Stu. Troubling times for embryo gene tests [news]. *New Scientist* 2006 March 18-24; 189(2543): 14-15. Subject: 15.3

Hutt, Leah E. Protecting the protectors: indemnification agreements for REB members. *CMAJ/JAMC: Canadian Medical Association Journal* 2006 November 7; 175(10): 1229-1230. Subject: 18.2

Huxley, Andrew. Testing is necessary on animals as well as in vitro [letter]. *Nature* 2006 January 12; 439(7073): 138. Subject: 22.2

Huxtable, R.; Woodley, J. (When) will they have faces? A response to Agich and Siemionov. *Journal of Medical Ethics* 2006 July; 32(7): 403-404. Subject: 19.1

Hwang, Ann C.; Koyama, Atsuko; Taylor, Diana; Henderson, Jillian T.; Miller, Suellen. Advanced practice clinicians' interest in providing medical abortion: results of a California survey. *Perspectives on Sexual and Reproductive Health* 2005 June; 37(2): 92-97. Subject: 12.5.2

Hwang, Shirley S.; Chang, Victor T.; Cogswell, Janet; Srinivas, Shanthi; Kasimis, Basil. Knowledge and attitudes toward end-of-life care in veterans with symptomatic metastatic cancer. *Palliative and Supportive Care* 2003 September; 1(3): 221-230. Subject: 20.4.1

Hyams, Ross. Who gets to choose? Responses to the foetal/maternal conflict. *E Law: Murdoch University Electronic Journal of Law* 1995 December; 2(3): 8 p. [Online]. Accessed: http://www.murdoch.edu.au/elaw/issues/v2n3/hyams23.html [2006 June 29]. Subject: 9.5.5

Hyder, Adnan A.; Wali, Salman A. Informed consent and collaborative research: perspectives from the develop-

ing world. *Developing World Bioethics* 2006 March; 6(1): 33-40. Subject: 18.3

Hyman, Steven E. Improving our brains? *Biosciences* 2006 March; 1(1): 103-111. Subject: 17.4

Hynds, James. Reconsidering Catholic teaching on withdrawal of artificial nutrition and hydration. *Health Care Ethics USA* 2006; 14(3): E4. Subject: 20.5.1

Hyun, Insoo. Fair payment or undue inducement? *Nature* 2006 August 10; 442(7103): 629-630. Subject: 14.4

Hyun, Insoo. Magic eggs and the frontier of stem cell science. *Hastings Center Report* 2006 March-April; 36(2): 16-19. Subject: 18.5.4

Hyun, Insoo; Griggins, Cynthia; Weiss, Margaret; Robbins, Dorothy; Robichaud, Allyson; Daly, Barbara. When patients do not have a proxy: a procedure for medical decision making when there is no one to speak for the patient. *Journal of Clinical Ethics* 2006 Winter; 17(4): 323-330. Subject: 8.3.3

Hyun, Insoo; Jung, Kyu Won. Human research cloning, embryos, and embryo-life artifacts. *Hastings Center Report* 2006 September-October; 36(5): 34-41. Subject: 18.5.4

Hyun, Insoo; Jung, Kyu Won; Hurlbut, William B.; George, Robert P.; Grompe, Markus. ANT vs. SCNT [letter and reply]. *Hastings Center Report* 2006 November-December; 36(6): 6-7. Subject: 18.5.4

I

Ibanga, Hannah B.; Brookes, Roger H.; Hill, Philip C.; Owiafe, Patrick K.; Fletcher, Helen A.; Lienhardt, Christian; Hill, Adrian V.; Adegbola, Richard A.; McShane, Helen. Early clinical trials with a new tuberculosis vaccine, MVA85A, in tuberculosis-endemic countries: issues in study design. *Lancet Infectious Diseases* 2006 August; 6(8): 522-528. Subject: 18.5.9

Ibarreta, Dolores; Elles, Robert; Cassiman, Jean-Jacques; Rodriguez-Cerezo, Emilio; Dequeker, Elisabeth. Towards quality assurance and harmonization of genetic testing services in the European Union. *Nature Biotechnology* 2004 October; 22(10): 1230-1235. Subject: 15.3

Ibrahim, Darian N. Reduce, refine, replace: the failure of the three R's and the future of animal experimentation. *University of Chicago Legal Forum* 2006: 195-229. Subject: 22.2

Iceland. Supreme Court. Ragnhildur Gumðundsdóttir vs. The State of Iceland. (Thursday, 27 November 2003, No. 151/2003). *European Journal of Health Law* 2004 September; 11(3): 283-291. Subject: 15.1

Icenogle, Daniel L. IRBs, conflict and liability: will we see IRBs in court? Or is it when? *Clinical Medicine and Research* 2003 January; 1(1): 63-68. Subject: 18.2

Idaho. *Laws, statutes, etc.* An act relating to genetic testing privacy; amending title 39, Idaho Code, by the addition of a new chapter 83, title 39, Idaho Code, to provide a short title, to define terms, to set forth restrictions regarding genetic testing information applicable to employers, to provide for a private right of action and to provide for enforcement; and amending section 41-1313, Idaho Code, to prohibit insurers from discriminating on the basis of a genetic test or private genetic information for certain purposes [Approved: 31 March 2006]. Idaho: State Legislature, 2006. 8 p. [Online]. Accessed: http://www3.state.id.us/oasis/2006/S1423.html [2007 March 9]. Subject: 15.3

Iezzoni, Lisa I. Going beyond disease to address disability. *New England Journal of Medicine* 2006 September 7; 355(10): 976-979. Subject: 9.5.1

Iffy, L.; Varadi, V.; Portuondo, N.; Ende, N. Collection of fetal blood for stem cell research and therapy. *Medicine and Law: The World Association for Medical Law* 2006 September; 25(3): 553-561. Subject: 19.4

Ihde, Don. Body. *In:* Mitcham, Carl, ed. Encyclopedia of Science, Technology, and Ethics. Farmington Hills, MI: Thomson/Gale, 2005: 239-242. Subject: 4.4

Ikegaya, H.; Kawai, K.; Kikuchi, Y.; Yoshida, K. Does informed consent exempt Japanese doctors from reporting therapeutic deaths? *Journal of Medical Ethics* 2006 February; 32(2): 114-116. Subject: 8.4

Ikemoto, Lisa C. Race to health: racialized discourses in a transhuman world. *DePaul Journal of Health Care Law* 2005; 9(2): 1101-1129. Subject: 9.5.4

Ikenberg, Hans; Obwegeser, Jörg; Schneider, Volker. Who controls the controllers? [letter and reply]. *Lancet* 2006 August 12-18; 368(9535): 578-579. Subject: 5.2

Iklé, Fred Charles. The deconstruction of death: the coming politics of biotechnology. *National Interest* 2000-2001 Winter; 62: 87-95. Subject: 15.1

Illes, Judy; De Vries, Raymond; Cho, Mildred K.; Schraedley-Desmond, Pam. ELSI priorities for brain imaging. *American Journal of Bioethics [Online].* 2006 March-April; 6(2): W24-W31. Subject: 17.1

Illes, Judy; Kirschen, Matthew P.; Edwards, Emmeline; Stanford, L.R.; Bandettini, Peter; Cho, Mildred K.; Ford, Paul J.; Glover, Gary H.; Kulynych, Jennifer; Macklin, Ruth; Michael, Daniel B.; Wolf, Susan M. Incidental findings in brain imaging research. *Science* 2006 February 10; 311(5762): 783-784. Subject: 18.1

Illes, Judy; Kirschen, Matthew P.; Gabrieli, John D.E. From neuroimaging to neuroethics. *Nature Neuroscience* 2003 March; 6(3): 205. Subject: 17.1

Illes, Judy; Raffin, Thomas A. Neuroethics: an emerging new discipline in the study of brain and cognition. *Brain and Cognition* 2002 December; 50(3): 341-344. Subject: 17.1

Illingworth, R.; Poza, M. Fraud and other misconduct in biomedical research [editorial]. *Neurocirugia* 2005 August; 16(4): 297-300. Subject: 1.3.9

Iltis, Ana Smith. Conducting and terminating randomized clinical trials. *In:* Iltis, Ana Smith, ed. Research Ethics. New York: Routledge, 2006: 86-101. Subject: 18.2

Iltis, Ana Smith. Human subjects research: ethics and compliance. *In:* Iltis, Ana Smith, ed. Research Ethics. New York: Routledge, 2006: 1-21. Subject: 18.1

Iltis, Ana Smith. Lay concepts in informed consent to biomedical research: the capacity to understand and appreciate risk. *Bioethics* 2006 August; 20(4): 180-190. Subject: 18.3

Iltis, Ana Smith. Look who's talking: the interdisciplinarity of bioethics and the implications for bioethics education. *Journal of Medicine and Philosophy* 2006 December; 31(6): 629-641. Subject: 2.1

Iltis, Ana Smith. On the impermissibility of euthanasia in Catholic healthcare organizations. *Christian Bioethics* 2006 December; 12(3): 281-290. Subject: 20.5.1

Inaba, Maskazu; Macer, Darryl R.J. Japanese views of medical biotechnology. *In:* Sang-yong, Song; Young-Mo, Koo; Macer, Darryl R.J., eds. Asian Bioethics in the 21st Century. Christchurch, NZ: Eubios Ethics Institute, 2002: 178-196. Subject: 5.1

Inayatullah, Sohail; Fitzgerald, Jennifer. Gene discourses: politics, culture, law, and futures. *Technological Forecasting and Social Change* 1996 June-July; 52(2-3): 161-183. Subject: 15.1

Incorvati, Giovanni. Xenotransplantation, public responsibility and law. *European Journal of Health Law* 2003 September; 10(3): 295-304. Subject: 19.1

Ingham, Janis Costello. Research ethics 101: the responsible conduct of research. *Seminars in Speech and Language* 2003 November; 24(4): 323-337. Subject: 1.3.9

Inglis, Brian. Guinea pig revolution in medical morality. *Twentieth Century* 1962 Winter; 171: 102-109. Subject: 18.1

Ingram, David. Antidiscrimination, welfare, and democracy: toward a discourse-ethical understanding of disability law. *Social Theory and Practice* 2006 April; 32(2): 213-248. Subject: 9.5.1

Inhorn, Marcia C. Global infertility and the globalization of new reproductive technologies: illustrations from Egypt. *Social Science and Medicine* 2003 May; 56(9): 1837-1851. Subject: 14.1

Inhorn, Marcia C. "He won't be my son" Middle Eastern Muslim men's discourses of adoption and gamete donation. *Medical Anthropology Quarterly* 2006 March; 20(1): 94-120. Subject: 14.4

Institute of Medical Ethics (Great Britain). Working Party on the Ethical Implications of AIDS. AIDS, eth-

See SUBJECT HEADING KEY FOR SECTION II on inside back cover.

605

ics, and clinical trials. *BMJ: British Medical Journal* 1992 September 19; 305(6855): 699-701. Subject: 9.5.6

Institute of Medicine (United States) [IOM]. Committee on Increasing Rates of Organ Donation. Incentives for deceased donation. *In:* Childress, James F.; Liverman, Catharyn T., eds. Organ Donation: Opportunities for Action. Washington, DC: National Academies Press; 2006: 229-262. Subject: 19.5

Institute of Medicine (United States) [IOM]. Committee on Increasing Rates of Organ Donation. Presumed consent. *In:* Childress, James F.; Liverman, Catharyn T., eds. Organ Donation: Opportunities for Action. Washington, DC: National Academies Press; 2006: 205-228. Subject: 19.5

Institute of Medicine (United States) [IOM]. Committee on Increasing Use of Organ Donation. Ethical considerations in living donation. *In:* Childress, James F.; Liverman, Catharyn T., eds. Organ Donation: Opportunities for Action. Washington, DC: National Academies Press; 2006: 263-279. Subject: 19.5

Institute of Medicine (United States) [IOM]. Committee on the Use of Complementary and Alternative Medicine by the American Public. An ethical framework for CAM research, practice, and policy. *In its:* Complementary and Alternative Medicine in the United States. Washington, DC: National Academies Press; 2005: 168-195. Subject: 4.1.1

Interlandi, Jeneen. An unwelcome discovery. Walter DeNino was a young lab technician who analyzed data for his mentor, Eric Poehlman. What he found was that Poehlman was not the scientist he appeared to be. *New York Times Magazine* 2006 October 22; p.98-103. Subject: 1.3.9

International Commission on Occupational Health [ICOH]. International code of ethics for occupational health professionals. Update 2002 March. Rome, Italy: International Commission on Occupational Health. Secretariat General. Update. 2002 March; 26p. [Online]. Accessed: http://www.icohweb.org/core_docs/code_ethics_eng.pdf [2006 October 16]. Subject: 6

International Community of Women Living with HIV/AIDS. The International Community of Women Living with HIV/AIDS: point of view. *Health and Human Rights: An International Journal* 2005; 8(2): 25-26. Subject: 9.5.5

International Council for Laboratory Animal Science [ICLAS]. International harmonisation of guidelines on euthanasia. Nantes, France: International Council for Laboratory Animal Science 2004 November 8: 4 p. [Online]. Accessed: http://www.sciencemag.org/cgi/data/312/5774/700/DC1/1 [2006 October 4]. Subject: 20.5.1

International Council for Laboratory Animal Science [ICLAS]. International harmonisation of guidelines on humane endpoints. Nantes, France: International Council

for Laboratory Animal Science 2005 May 9: 4 p. [Online]. Accessed: http://www.sciencemag.org/cgi/data/312/5774/700/DC1/1 [2006 October 4]. Subject: 22.2

International Council for Laboratory Animal Science [ICLAS]; Demers, G. First ICLAS meeting for the harmonisation of guidelines on the use of animals in science (meeting for harmonisation of guidelines). Nantes, France: Federation of European Laboratory Animal Science Associations [FELASA], Proceedings of the Ninth FELASA Symposium, International Harmonisation of Care and Use Issues 2004 June 13 and 14; section 2: 40-44 [Online]. Accessed: http://www.lal.org.uk/pdffiles/FELASA/Section2.pdf [2006 October 4]. Subject: 22.2

International Stem Cell Forum Ethics Working Party. Ethics issues in stem cell research [letter]. *Science* 2006 April 21; 312(5772): 366-367. Subject: 18.5.4

International Stem Cell Initiative. Steering Committee. The International Stem Cell Initiative: toward benchmarks for human embryonic stem cell research. *Nature Biotechnology* 2005 July; 23(7): 795-797. Subject: 18.5.4

Ionescu, Carmiola. Romanian parents keep HIV secret from infected children. *Lancet* 2006 May 13-19; 367(9522): 1566. Subject: 9.5.6

Ip, Po-Keung. The ethics of human enhancement gene therapy. *In:* Döring, Ole; Chen, Renbiao, eds. Advances in Chinese Medical Ethics: Chinese and International Perspectives. Hamburg: Institut für Asienkunde; 2002: 119-132. Subject: 15.4

Ipas. India Country Office; Ganatra, Bela; Manning, Vinoj; Pallipamulla, Suranjeen Prasad. Medical Abortion in Bihar and Jharkhand: A Study of Service Providers, Chemists, Women and Men. Vasant, Vihar, New Delhi, India: India Country Office, Ipas, 2005; 56 p. [Online]. Accessed: http://www.ipas.org/publications/en/INDMEDAB_E05_en.pdf [2006 March 29]. Subject: 12.5.2

Irish Women's Abortion Support Group. Across the water. *Feminist Review* 1988 Spring; (29): 64-71. Subject: 12.4.2

Irvin, Tracey L. Legal, ethical and clinical implications of prescribing involuntary, life-threatening treatment: the case of the sunshine kid. *Journal of Forensic Sciences* 2003 July; 48(4): 856-860. Subject: 17.8

Irwig, Les; McCaffery, Kirsten; Salkeld, Glenn; Bossuyt, Patrick. Informed choice for screening: implications for evaluation. *BMJ: British Medical Journal* 2006 May 13; 332(7550): 1148-1150. Subject: 9.1

Isasi, Rosario. The human rights perspective. *World Watch* 2002 July-August; 15(4): 32. Subject: 15.1

Isasi, Rosario M.; Annas, George J. To clone alone: the United Nations' Human Cloning Declaration. *Revista de Derecho y Genoma Humano = Law and the Human Ge-*

nome Review 2006 January-June; (24): 13-26. Subject: 14.5

Isasi, Rosario M.; Knoppers, Bartha M. Beyond the permissibility of embryonic and stem cell research: substantive requirements and procedural safeguards. *Human Reproduction* 2006 October; 21(10): 2474-2481. Subject: 18.5.4

Isasi, Rosario; Knoppers, Bartha M. Mind the gap: policy approaches to embryonic stem cell and cloning research in 50 countries. *European Journal of Health Law* 2006 April; 13(1): 9-26. Subject: 18.5.4

Isikoglu, M.; Senol, Y.; Berkkanoglu, M.; Ozgur, K.; Donmez, L.; Stones-Abbasi, A. Public opinion regarding oocyte donation in Turkey: first data from a secular population among the Islamic world. *Human Reproduction* 2006 January; 21(1): 318-323. Subject: 15.2

Itai, K.; Asai,A.; Tsuchiya, Y.; Onishi, M.; Kosugi, S. How do bioethics teachers in Japan cope with ethical disagreement among healthcare university students in the classroom? A survey on educators in charge. *Journal of Medical Ethics* 2006 May; 32(5): 303-308. Subject: 2.3

Itoh, Machiko; Kato, Kazuto. What should scientists do outside the laboratory? Lessons on science communication from the Japanese genome research project. *Genetics, Society, and Policy* 2005 August; 1(2): 80-93. Subject: 1.3.9

Ivanyushkin, A.Y.; Khetagurova, A.K. Palliative care in Russia. *Journal International de Bioéthique = International Journal of Bioethics* 2005 September-December; 16(3-4): 55-63, 169. Subject: 20.4.1

Ivarsson, Bodil; Larsson, Sylvia; Luhrs, Carsten; Sjoberg, Trygve. Extended written pre-operative information about possible complications at cardiac surgery — do the patients want to know? *European Journal of Cardio-thoracic Surgery* 2005 September; 28(3): 407-414. Subject: 8.3.1

Iverson, Amy; Liddell, Kathleen; Fear, Nicole; Hotopf, Matthew; Wessely, Simon. Consent, confidentiality, and the Data Protection Act. *BMJ: British Medical Journal* 2006 January 21; 332(7534): 165-169. Subject: 8.4

Iyer, T.K.K. Kidney donations — Singapore's legislative proposals. *Malayan Law Journal* 1987 July: liii-lxi. Subject: 19.3

Izumi, Shigeko. Bridging western ethics and Japanese local ethics by listening to nurses' concerns. *Nursing Ethics* 2006 May; 13(3): 275-283. Subject: 4.1.3

Izumi, Shigeko; Konishi, Emiko; Yahiro, Michiko; Kodama, Maki. Japanese patients' descriptions of "The Good Nurse": personal involvement and professionalism. *Advances in Nursing Science [electronic]* 2006 April-June; 29(2): E14-E26. Subject: 4.1.3

J

Jack, Andrew. Too close for comfort? [news]. *BMJ: British Medical Journal* 2006 July 1; 333(7557): 13. Subject: 9.7

Jackman, Martha. "The last line of defence for [which?] citizens": accountability, equality, and the right to health in Chaoulli. *Osgoode Hall Law Journal* 2006 Summer; 44(2): 349-375. Subject: 9.3.1

Jackson, Fatimah L.C. Tuskegee experiment. *In:* Mitcham, Carl, ed. Encyclopedia of Science, Technology, and Ethics. Farmington Hills, MI: Thomson/Gale, 2005: 1986-1988. Subject: 18.5.1

Jackson, Grace E. A curious consensus: "brain scans prove disease"? *Ethical Human Psychology and Psychiatry* 2006 Spring; 8(1): 55-60. Subject: 17.1

Jackson, Grace E. Mental health screening in schools: essentials of informed consent. *Ethical Human Psychology and Psychiatry* 2006 Fall-Winter; 8(3): 217-224. Subject: 8.3.2

Jackson, Rebecca; , Bimla Schwartz, Eleanor ; Freedman, Lori; Darney, Philip. Knowledge and willingness to use emergency contraceptive among low-income post-partum women. *Contraception* 2000 June; 61(6): 351-357. Subject: 11.1

Jackson, Thomas R.; Hesketh, Therese; Xing, Zhu Wei. China's one-child family policy [letter and reply]. *New England Journal of Medicine* 2006 February 23; 354(8): 877. Subject: 13.3

Jacob, Marie-Andrée. Another look at the presumed-versus-informed consent dichotomy in postmortem organ procurement. *Bioethics* 2006 November; 20(6): 293-300. Subject: 19.5

Jacob, R.; Clare, I.C.; Holland, A.; Watson, P.C.; Maimaris, C.; Gunn, M. Self-harm, capacity, and refusal of treatment: implications for emergency medical practice. A prospective observational study. *Emergency Medicine Journal* 2005 November; 22(11): 799-802. Subject: 8.3.1

Jacobs, Alice K.; Lindsay, Bruce D.; Bellande, Bruce J.; Fonarow, Gregg C.; Nishimura, Rick A.; Shah, Pravin M.; Annex, Brian H.; Fuster, Valentin; Gibbons, Raymond J.; Jackson, Marcia J.; Rahimtoola, Shahbudin H. Task force 3: disclosure of relationships with commercial interests: policy for educational activities and publications. *Journal of the American College of Cardiology* 2004 October 19; 44(8): 1736-1740. Subject: 7.3

Jacobs, Barbara Bennett; Taylor, Carol. Medical futility in the natural attitude. *ANS: Advances in Nursing Science* 2005 October-December; 28(4): 288-305. Subject: 20.5.1

Jacobs, Barbara Bennett; Taylor, Carol. "Seeing" artificial hydration and nutrition through an ethical lens. *Home Healthcare Nurse* 2005 November; 23(11): 739-742. Subject: 20.5.1

See SUBJECT HEADING KEY FOR SECTION II on inside back cover.

607

Jacobs, Elizabeth A.; Rolle, Italia; Ferrans, Carol Estwing; Whitaker, Eric E.; Warnecke, Richard B. Understanding African Americans' views of the trustworthiness of physicians. *JGIM: Journal of General Internal Medicine* 2006 June; 21(6): 642-647. Subject: 9.5.4

Jacobs, Hollye Harrington. Ethics in pediatric end-of-life care: a nursing perspective. *Journal of Pediatric Nursing* 2005 October; 20(5): 360-369. Subject: 20.4.2

Jacobs, Russell A. Conee and Marquis on contraception. *Southwest Philosophy Review* 2002 July; 18(2): 101-105. Subject: 11.1

Jacobson, Gloria A. Vulnerable research participants: anyone may qualify. *Nursing Science Quarterly* 2005 October; 18(4): 359-363. Subject: 18.3

Jacobson, Michael F. Lifting the veil of secrecy from industry funding of nonprofit health organizations. *International Journal of Occupational and Environmental Health* 2005 October-December; 11(4): 349-355. Subject: 9.1

Jacoby, Liva. The role of altruism in parental decision-making for childhood cancer clinical trials — further questions to explore. *American Journal of Bioethics* 2006 September-October; 6(5): 52. Subject: 18.3

Jacoby, Liva H. For bioethics — the role of empirical research. *American Journal of Bioethics* 2006 May-June; 6(3): 58-59; discussion W51- W53. Subject: 2.1

Jaenisch, Rudolf; Meissner, Alex; Solter, Davor. Politically correct human embryonic stem cells? [letter and reply]. *New England Journal of Medicine* 2006 March 16; 354(11): 1208-1209. Subject: 14.5

Jaenisch, Rudolph. Making the paper: plotting a course through the ethical minefield of stem cells. *Nature* 2006 January 12; 439(7073): ix. Subject: 18.5.4

Jafarey, Aamir. Informed consent: views from Karachi. *Eastern Mediterranean Health Journal/La Revue de Santé de la Méditerranée orientale* 2006; 12(Supplement 1): S50-S55 [Online]. Accessed: http://www.emro.who.int/ Publications/EMHJ/12_S/PDF/8.pdf [2007 January 3]. Subject: 8.3.1

Jaffé, A.; Prasad, S.A.; Larcher, V.; Hart, S. Gene therapy for children with cystic fibrosis — who has the right to choose? *Journal of Medical Ethics* 2006 June; 32(6): 361-364. Subject: 15.4

Jaffe, Gregory. Regulatory slowdown on GM crop decision [letter]. *Nature Biotechnology* 2006 July; 24(7): 748-749. Subject: 15.1

Jain, K.K. Ethical and regulatory aspects of embryonic stem cell research. *Expert Opinion on Biological Therapy* 2005 February; 5(2): 153-162. Subject: 18.5.4

Jairath, Nalini; Donley, Rosemary; Shelton, Deborah; McMullen, Patricia; Grandjean, Cynthia. Nursing and the common good: a clearer definition of the concept could be helpful to all the healing professions. *Health Progress* 2006 November-December; 87(6): 59-63. Subject: 4.1.3

Jakabcin, Ann G. A legal explanation of the advanced medical directive and Maryland living will. *Maryland Medicine* 2005 Spring; 6(2): 33-43. Subject: 20.5.4

Jakušovaite, Irayda; Darulis, ilvinas; ekas, Romualdas. Lithuanian health care in transitional state: ethical problems. *BMC Public Health* 2005 November 9; 5: 117: 8 p. Subject: 9.1

Jallinoja, Piia T. Ethics of clinical genetics: the spirit of the profession and trials of suitability from 1970 to 2000. *Critical Public Health* 2002; 12(2): 103-118. Subject: 15.2

James, Jack E. "Third-party" threats to research integrity in public-private partnerships. *Addiction* 2002 October; 97(10): 1251-1255. Subject: 1.3.9

Jamieson, J.W. The case for cloning. *Mankind Quarterly* 1998 Fall; 39(1): 95-107. Subject: 14.5

Jamieson, J.W. Intellectual ability, evolution and eugenics. *Mankind Quarterly* 1996 Spring-Summer; 36(3 and 4): 381-392. Subject: 15.5

Jan, Stephen; Thompson, Mardi. Proposal: two part payment scheme for live kidney donors [letter]. *BMJ: British Medical Journal* 2006 July 29; 333(7561): 262. Subject: 19.5

Jankowska, Hanna. The Reproductive Rights Campaign in Poland. *Women's Studies International Forum* 1993 May-June; 16(3): 291-296. Subject: 12.5.1

Janofsky, Jeffrey S. Lies and coercion: why psychiatrists should not participate in police and intelligence interrogations. *Journal of the American Academy of Psychiatry and the Law* 2006; 34(4): 472-478. Subject: 4.1.2

Jans, Jan. The Belgian "Act on Euthanasia": clarifying context, legislation, and practice from an ethical point of view". *Journal of the Society of Christian Ethics* 2005 Fall-Winter; 25(2): 163-177. Subject: 20.5.1

Jans, Jan. Churches in the Low Countries on euthanasia: background, argumentation and commentary. *In:* Schotsmans, Paul; Meulenbergs, Tom, eds. Euthanasia and Palliative Care in the Low Countries. Dudley, MA: Peeters, 2005: 175-204. Subject: 20.5.1

Jansen, Lynn A. Hastening death and the boundaries of the self. *Bioethics* 2006 April; 20(2): 105-111. Subject: 20.5.1

Jansen, Lynn A. The problem with optimism in clinical trials. *IRB: Ethics and Human Research* 2006 July-August; 28(4): 13-19. Subject: 18.2

Janssen, A.J.G.M. Informing patients about small risks: a comparative approach. *European Journal of Health Law* 2006 June; 13(2): 159-172. Subject: 8.3.1

Janssen, Fanny; van der Heide, Agnes; Kunst, Anton E.; Mackenbach, Johan P. End-of-life decisions and old-age mortality: a cross-country analysis. *Journal of the American Geriatrics Society* 2006 December; 54(12): 1951-1953. Subject: 20.5.1

Subject = NRCBL Primary Classification Number; see inside front cover.

Janssens, P.M.W.; Simons, A.H.M.; van Kooij, R.J.; Blokzijl, E.; Dunselman, G.A.J. A new Dutch law regulating provision of identifying information of donors to offspring: background, content and impact. *Human Reproduction* 2006 April; 21(4): 852-856. Subject: 14.2

Janvier, Annie; Barrington, Keith J. The ethics of neonatal resuscitation at the margins of viability: informed consent and outcomes. *Journal of Pediatrics* 2005 November; 147(5): 579-585. Subject: 20.5.2

Jasanoff, Sheila. The life sciences and the rule of law. *Journal of Molecular Biology* 2002 June 14; 319(4): 891-899. Subject: 5.3

Jaspers, Patricia; van der Arend, Arie; Wanders, Rinus. Inclusion practice in lung cancer trials. *Nursing Ethics* 2006 November; 13(6): 649-660. Subject: 18.2

Javitt, Gail H. Policy implications of genetic testing: not just for geneticists anymore. *Advances in Chronic Kidney Disease* 2006 April; 13(2): 178-182. Subject: 15.3

Jayaprakash, Azza. Sum of your parts: are there adequate remedies for victims of fraudulent tissue and organ acquisition? *DePaul Journal of Health Care Law* 2006 Spring; 9(3): 1235-1259. Subject: 19.5

Jayson, Gordon; Harris, John. How participants in cancer trials are chosen: ethics and conflicting interests. *Nature Reviews. Cancer* 2006 April; 6(4): 330-336. Subject: 18.2

Jebereanu, Laura. Abortion: pro and contra. *Penn Bioethics Journal* 2006; 2(2): 25-28. Subject: 12.5.2

Jedlicka, Peter. Neuroethics, reductionism and dualism. *Trends in Cognitive Sciences* 2005 April; 9(4): 172-173. Subject: 17.1

Jeffcoate, William J. Should eponyms be actively detached from diseases? [editorial]. *Lancet* 2006 April 22-28; 367(9519): 1296-1297. Subject: 21.4

Jeffords, James M. Confidentiality of medical information: protecting privacy in an electronic age. *Professional Psychology: Research and Practice* 1999 April; 30(2): 115-116. Subject: 8.4

Jendrisak, Martin D.; Hong, B.; Shenoy, S.; Lowell, J.; Desai, N.; Chapman, W.; Vijayan, A.; Wetzel, R.D.; Smith, M.; Wagner, J.; Brennan, S.; Brockmeier, D.; Kappel, D. Altruistic living donors: evaluation for nondirected kidney or liver donation. *American Journal of Transplantation* 2006 January; 6(1): 115-120. Subject: 19.5

Jenkin, Annie; Millward, Jennifer. A moral dilemma in the emergency room: confidentiality and domestic violence. *Accident and Emergency Nursing* 2006 January; 14(1): 38-42. Subject: 8.4

Jenkins, David; Johnston, Lon B. Unethical treatment of gay and lesbian people with conversion therapy. *Families In Society* 2004 October-December; 85(4): 557-561. Subject: 10

Jenkins, David; Price, Bob. Dementia and personhood: a focus for care? *Journal of Advanced Nursing* 1996 July; 24(1): 84-90. Subject: 17.1

Jenkins, Jean F.; Lea, Dale Halsey. Connecting genomics to health benefits: genetic testing. *In their:* Nursing care in the Genomic Era: A Case-Based Approach. Sudbury, MA.: Jones and Bartlett Publishers, 2005: 69-110. Subject: 15.3

Jenkins, Jean F.; Lea, Dale Halsey. Connecting genomics to history. *In their:* Nursing Care in the Genomic Era: A Case-Based Approach. Sudbury, MA: Jones and Bartlett Publishers, 2005: 247-266. Subject: 15.1

Jenkins, Jean F.; Lea, Dale Halsey. Connecting genomics to society: spirituality and religious traditions. *In their:* Nursing Care in the Genomic Era: A Case-Based Approach. Sudbury, MA: Jones and Bartlett Publishers, 2005: 267-285. Subject: 15.1

Jenkins, Jean F.; Lea, Dale Halsey. My hopes and fears: how I feel about genetic research. *In their:* Nursing Care in the Genomic Era: A Case-Based Approach. Sudbury, MA: Jones and Bartlett Publishers, 2005: 287-316. Subject: 15.1

Jenkinson, Crispin; Burton, John S.; Cartwright, Julia; Magee, Helen; Hall, Ian; Alcock, Chris; Burge, Sherwood. Patient attitudes to clinical trials: development of a questionnaire and results from asthma and cancer patients. *Health Expectations* 2005 September; 8(3): 244-252. Subject: 18.5.1

Jennett, Bryan. Thirty years of the vegetative state: clinical, ethical and legal problems. *Progress in Brain Research* 2005; 150: 537-543. Subject: 20.5.1

Jennings, Bruce. Health policy in a new key: setting democratic priorities. *Journal of Social Issues* 1993 Summer; 49(2): 169-184. Subject: 9.4

Jennings, Bruce. The ordeal of reminding: traumatic brain injury and the goals of care. *Hastings Center Report* 2006 March-April; 36(2): 29-37. Subject: 8.3.3

Jennings, Carole P. From science to politics: the stem cell debate [editorial]. *Policy, Politics and Nursing Practice* 2005 February; 6(1): 3-4. Subject: 18.5.4

Jennings, Lance. To enhance, or not to enhance. *Futurist* 2004 March-April; 38(2): 68, 66. Subject: 15.1

Jensen, Eric; Weasel, Lisa H. Abortion rhetoric in American news coverage of the human cloning debate. *New Genetics and Society* 2006 December; 25(3): 305-323. Subject: 14.5

Jenson, Larry. Restoration and enhancement: is cosmetic dentistry ethical? *Journal of the American College of Dentists* 2005 Winter; 72(4): 48-53. Subject: 4.1.1

Jesani, Amar. Medical professionals and interrogation: lies about finding the "truth" [editorial]. *Indian Journal of Medical Ethics* 2006 October-December; 3(4): 116-117. Subject: 21.4

See SUBJECT HEADING KEY FOR SECTION II on inside back cover.

609

Jessiman, Ian; Morgan, Derek. Withdrawing nutrition and hydration [letter and reply]. *Clinical Medicine* 2004 May-June; 4(3): 288. Subject: 20.5.1

Jeste, Dilip V. Can medication-free research ever be ethical in older people with psychotic disorders? *Schizophrenia Bulletin* 2006 April; 32(2): 303-304. Subject: 18.2

Jeste, Dilip V.; Depp, Colin A.; Palmer, Barton W. Magnitude of impairment in decisional capacity in people with schizophrenia compared to normal subjects: an overview. *Schizophrenia Bulletin* 2006 January; 32(1): 121-128. Subject: 18.3

Jette, Alan M. Without scientific integrity, there can be no evidence base. *Physical Therapy* 2005 November; 85(11): 1122-1123. Subject: 1.3.9

Jezewski, Mary Ann; Brown, Jean K.; Wu, Yow-Wu Bill; Meeker, Mary Ann; Feng, Jui-Ying; Bu, Xiaoyan. Oncology nurses' knowledge, attitudes, and experiences regarding advance directives. *Oncology Nursing Forum* 2005 March 5; 32(2): 319-327. Subject: 20.5.4

Jiang, Changmin. Ethical considerations on organ transplantation in China. *Penn Bioethics Journal* 2006; 2(1): 3p. [Online]. Accessed: http://www.bioethicsjournal.com [2006 February 21]. Subject: 19.1

Jiayin, Min. A philosophical meditation on genomics. *In:* Sleeboom, Margaret, ed. Genomics in Asia: A Clash of Bioethical Interests? New York: Kegan Paul; 2004: 201-223. Subject: 15.1

Jochemsen, H.; Hoogland, J.; Polder, J. Maintaining integrity in times of scarce resources. *In:* Viafora, Corrado, ed. Clinical Bioethics: A Search for the Foundations. Dordrecht: Springer, 2005: 139-152. Subject: 9.1

Joffe, Ari R.; Anton, Natalie. Brain death: understanding of the conceptual basis by pediatric intensivists in Canada. *Archives of Pediatrics and Adolescent Medicine* 2006 July; 160: 747-752. Subject: 20.2.1

Joffe, Carole. It's not just abortion, stupid — progressives and abortion. *Dissent* 2005 Winter; 37(2): 91-96. Subject: 12.3

Joffe, Steven. Altruistic discourse and therapeutic misconception in research informed consent. *American Journal of Bioethics* 2006 September-October; 6(5): 53-54. Subject: 18.3

Joh, Elizabeth E. Reclaiming "abandoned" DNA: the Fourth Amendment and genetic privacy. *Northwestern University Law Review* 2006 Winter; 100(2): 857-884. Subject: 15.1

Johannes, Laura. New kidney-transplant rules to benefit blacks. *Wall Street Journal* 2004 February 5; p. D4. Subject: 19.3

Johansen, Sissel; Holen, Jacob C.; Kaasa, Stein; Loge, Jon Håvard; Materstvedt, Lars Johan. Attitudes towards, and wishes for, euthanasia in advanced cancer patients at a palliative medicine unit. *Palliative Medicine* 2005 September; 19(6): 454-460. Subject: 20.5.1

John, T. Jacob. Human rights and public health during pandemic influenza [editorial]. *Indian Journal of Medical Ethics* 2006 January-March; 3(1): 2-3. Subject: 9.1

Johns, Jeanine L. A concept analysis of trust. *Journal of Advanced Nursing* 1996 July; 24(1): 76-83. Subject: 8.1

Johnson, Alissa. Predictive genetic testing of minors. *NCSL Legisbrief* 2006 April-May; 14(19): 1-2. Subject: 15.3

Johnson, Andrea N. The federal psychotherapist-patient privilege, the purported "dangerous patient" exception, and its impact on African American access to mental health services. *Howard Law Journal* 2005; 48(3): 1025-1051. Subject: 8.4

Johnson, Arnold L. Towards a modified cardiopulmonary resuscitation policy. *Canadian Journal of Cardiology* 1998 February; 14(2): 203-208. Subject: 20.5.1

Johnson, Claire. On the subject of human subjects [editorial]. *Journal of Manipulative and Physiological Therapeutics* 2005 February; 28(2): 79-80. Subject: 18.2

Johnson, Dana E.; Thompson, Theodore R.; Aroskar, Mila; Cranford, Ronald E. Baby Doe' rules: there are alternatives. *American Journal of Diseases of Children* 1984 June; 138(6): 523-529. Subject: 20.5.2

Johnson, Kirk. In old mining town, new charges over asbestos; clinic sees pressure to close — company faults diagnoses. *New York Times* 2006 April 22; p. A1, A11. Subject: 16.3

Johnson, Mark E.; Brems, Christiane; Warner, Teddy D.; Roberts, Laura Weiss. The need for continuing education in ethics as reported by rural and urban mental health care providers. *Professional Psychology* 2006 April; 37(2): 183-189. Subject: 2.3

Johnson, Martin H. Escaping the tyranny of the embryo? A new approach to ART regulation based on UK and Australian experiences. *Human Reproduction* 2006 November; 21(11): 2756-2765. Subject: 14.4

Johnson, Matthew S.; Gonzales, Marcia N.; Bizila, Shelley. Responsible conduct of radiology research. Part V. The Health Insurance Portability and Accountability Act and research. *Radiology* 2005 December; 237(3): 757-764. Subject: 18.2

Johnson, Rob. The unique ethics of sports medicine. *Clinics in Sports Medicine* 2004 April; 23(2): 175-182. Subject: 9.5.1

Johnson, Summer. Multiple roles and successes in public bioethics: a response to the public forum critique of bioethics commissions. *Kennedy Institute of Ethics Journal* 2006 June; 16(2): 173-188. Subject: 2.4

Johnson, Summer; Burger, Ingrid. Limitations and justifications for analogical reasoning. *American Journal of*

Bioethics 2006 November-December; 6(6): 59-61; author reply W13-W14. Subject: 5.1

Johnston, Bradley C.; Vohra, Sunita. Investigator-initiated trials are more impartial. *Nature* 2006 September 14; 443(7108): 144. Subject: 1.3.9

Johnston, Carolyn; Holt, Genevieve. The legal and ethical implications of therapeutic privilege — is it ever justified to withhold treatment information from a competent patient? *Clinical Ethics* 2006 September; 1(3): 146-151. Subject: 8.3.1

Johnston, Josephine. Field notes: small. *Hastings Center Report* 2006 November-December; 36(6): inside cover. Subject: 5.3

Johnston, Josephine. Is research in Canada limited to "surplus" embryos? *Health Law Review* 2006; 14(3): 3-13. Subject: 18.5.4

Johnston, Josephine. Paying egg donors: exploring the arguments. *Hastings Center Report* 2006 January-February; 36(1): 28-31. Subject: 14.4

Johnston, K. Wayne; Hertzer, Norman R.; Rutherford, Robert B.; Smith, Robert B., III; Yao, James S.T. Joint council guidelines for disclosure of conflict of interest [editorial]. *Journal of Vascular Surgery* 2000 July; 32(1): 213-215. Subject: 7.3

Johnston, Trevor. In one's own image: ethics and the reproduction of deafness. *Journal of Deaf Studies and Deaf Education* 2005 Fall; 10(4): 426-441. Subject: 9.5.4

Johnstone, Megan-Jane; Kanitsaki, Olga. The ethics and practical importance of defining, distinguishing and disclosing nursing errors: a discussion paper. *International Journal of Nursing Studies* 2006 March; 43(3): 367-376. Subject: 8.2

Johri, Mira; Damschroder, Laura J.; Zikmund-Fisher, Brian J.; Ubel, Peter A. The importance of age in allocating health care resources: does intervention-type matter? *Health Economics* 2005 July; 14(7): 669-678. Subject: 9.5.2

Joly, Yann. Life insurers' access to genetic information: a way out of the stalemate? *Health Law Review* 2006; 14(3): 14-21. Subject: 15.1

Joly, Yann; Knoppers, Bartha M. Pharmacogenomic data sample collection and storage: ethical issues and policy approaches. *Pharmacogenomics* 2006 March; 7(2): 219-226. Subject: 15.10

Jonas, Hans. Technik, Ethik und biogenetische Kunst: Betrachtungen zur neuen Schöpferrolle des Menschen. *In:* Klein, Adolf, ed. Verantwortung in Naturwissenschaft und Technik: ein Textbuch. Bonn: Dümmler; 1989: 83-99. Subject: 15.1

Jones, Andrew G. Profound hypotension: ethical considerations. *Hospital Medicine* 2002 February; 63(2): 92-94. Subject: 5.2

Jones, Caroline. The Department of Health Review of the Human Fertilisation and Embryology Act 1990. *Clinical Ethics* 2006 December; 1(4): 200-204. Subject: 14.4

Jones, Dan. All about me. *New Scientist* 2006 August 19-25; 191(2565): 28-36. Subject: 15.1

Jones, David Albert. Sin, suffering, and the need for theological virtues. *Christian Bioethics* 2006 August; 12(2): 187-198. Subject: 4.2

Jones, D.G. Enhancement: are ethicists excessively influenced by baseless speculations? *Medical Humanities* 2006 December; 32(2): 77-81. Subject: 4.5

Jones, D.G.; Towns, C.R. Navigating the quagmire: the regulation of human embryonic stem cell research. *Human Reproduction* 2006 May; 21(5): 1113-1116. Subject: 18.5.4

Jones, D. Gareth. The emergence of persons. *In:* Jeeves, Michael, ed. From Cells to Souls — and Beyond: Changing Portraits of Human Nature. Grand Rapids, MI: W.B. Eerdmans; 2004: 11-30. Subject: 4.4

Jones, Jackie; Hoffman, Toni. 'I had to act': in conversation with a whistleblower [editorial]. *Australian Journal of Advanced Nursing* 2005 September-November; 23(1): 4-6. Subject: 7.3

Jones, James W.; McCullough, Laurence B.; Richman, Bruce W. Consultation or corruption? The ethics of signing on to the medical-industrial complex. *Journal of Vascular Surgery* 2006 January; 43(1): 192-195. Subject: 7.3

Jones, James W.; McCullough, Laurence B.; Richman, Bruce W. Ethics and commercial insurance. *Journal of Vascular Surgery* 2004 March; 39(3): 692-693. Subject: 9.3.1

Jones, James W.; McCullough, Laurence B.; Richman, Bruce W. The ethics of bylines: would the real authors please stand up? *Journal of Vascular Surgery* 2005 October; 42(4): 816-818. Subject: 1.3.7

Jones, James W.; McCullough, Laurence B.; Richman, Bruce W. The ethics of operating on a family member. *Journal of Vascular Surgery* 2005 November; 42(5): 1033-1035. Subject: 8.1

Jones, James W.; McCullough, Laurence B.; Richman, Bruce W. Ethics of operative scheduling: fiduciary patient responsibilities and more. *Journal of Vascular Surgery* 2003 July; 38(1): 204-205. Subject: 9.5.1

Jones, James W.; McCullough, Laurence B.; Richman, Bruce W. Ethics of professional courtesy. *Journal of Vascular Surgery* 2004 May; 39(5): 1140-1141. Subject: 7.3

Jones, James W.; McCullough, Laurence B.; Richman, Bruce W. Ethics of surgical innovation to treat rare diseases. *Journal of Vascular Surgery* 2004 April; 39(4): 918-919. Subject: 8.3.1

See SUBJECT HEADING KEY FOR SECTION II on inside back cover.

611

Jones, James W.; McCullough, Laurence B.; Richman, Bruce W. Physician-assisted suicide: has it come of age? *Surgery* 2005 July; 138(1): 105-108. Subject: 20.7

Jones, James W.; McCullough, Laurence B.; Richman, Bruce W. Show me the money: the ethics of physicians' income. *Journal of Vascular Surgery* 2005 August; 42(2): 377-379. Subject: 9.3.1

Jones, James W.; McCullough, Laurence B.; Richman, Bruce W. Turf wars: the ethics of professional territorialism. *Journal of Vascular Surgery* 2005 September; 42(3): 587-589. Subject: 7.3

Jones, James W.; McCullough, Laurence B.; Richman, Bruce W. Whodunit? Ghost surgery and ethical billing. *Journal of Vascular Surgery* 2005 December; 42(6): 1239-1241. Subject: 9.8

Jones, Maggie. The mystery of my eggs [PGD]. *New York Times Magazine* 2003 March 16; p. 44-46. Subject: 15.2

Jones, Paul M.; Appelbaum, Paul S.; Siegel, David M. Law enforcement interviews of hospital patients: a conundrum for clinicians. *JAMA: The Journal of the American Medical Association* 2006 February 15; 295(7): 822-825. Subject: 8.3.1

Jones, Rachel K.; Boonstra, Heather. Confidential reproductive health care for adolescents. *Current Opinion in Obstetrics and Gynecology* 2005 October; 17(5): 456-460. Subject: 11.2

Jones, Sian; Davies, Kevin; Jones, Bridie. The adult patient, informed consent and the emergency care setting. *Accident and Emergency Nursing* 2005 July; 13(3): 167-170. Subject: 8.3.1

Jonsen, Albert R. A history of religion and bioethics. *In:* Guinn, David E., ed. Handbook of Bioethics and Religion. New York: Oxford University Press, 2006: 23-36. Subject: 2.2

Jonsen, Albert R. History and future of bioethics. *In:* Rehmann-Sutter, Christoph; Düwell, Marcus; Mieth, Dietmar, eds. Bioethics in Cultural Contexts: Reflections on Methods and Finitude. Dordrecht: Springer, 2006: 13-19. Subject: 2.1

Jonsen, Albert R. "Life is short, Medicine is long": reflections on a bioethical insight. *Journal of Medicine and Philosophy* 2006 December; 31(6): 667-673. Subject: 2.1

Jonsen, Albert R. Nontherapeutic research with children: the Ramsey versus McCormick debate. *Journal of Pediatrics* 2006 July; 149(1, Supplement): S12-S14. Subject: 18.5.2

Joolaee, Soodabeh; Nikbakht-Nasrabadi, Alireza; Parsa-Yekta, Zohreh; Tschudin, Verena; Mansouri, Iman. An Iranian perspective on patients' rights. *Nursing Ethics* 2006 September; 13(5): 488-502. Subject: 9.2

Jordens, C.; Little, M.; Kerridge, I.; McPhee, J. From advance directives to advance care planning: current legal status, ethical rationales and a new research agenda. *Inter-nal Medicine Journal* 2005 September; 35(9): 563-566. Subject: 20.5.4

Jørgensen, Anders W.; Hilden, Jørgen; Gøtzsche, Peter C. Cochrane reviews compared with industry supported meta-analyses and other meta-analyses of the same drugs: systematic review. *BMJ: British Medical Journal* 2006 October 14; 333(7572): 782-785. Subject: 9.7

Jørgensen, Karsten Juhl; Gøtzsche, Peter C. Content of invitations for publicly funded screening mammography. *BMJ: British Medical Journal* 2006 March 4; 332(7540): 538-541. Subject: 9.1

Jorns, Amalia W. Challenging warrantless inspections of abortion providers: a new constitutional strategy. *Columbia Law Review* 2005 June; 105(5): 1563-1596. Subject: 12.4.4

Joseph, Julia. Selling with dignity: organ selling and the safeguarding of human dignity. *Penn Bioethics Journal* 2006; 2(1): 3p. [Online]. Accessed: http://www.bioethicsjournal.com [2006 February 21]. Subject: 19.5

Joshi, Shalaka R. Whose life is it, anyway? The evolving face of euthanasia [editorial]. *Journal of the Association of Physicians of India* 2005 April; 53: 279-281. Subject: 20.5.1

Jost, Timothy Stoltzfus. Racial and ethnic disparities in Medicare: what the Department of Health and Human Services and the Centers for Medicare and Medicaid services can, and should, do. *DePaul Journal of Health Care Law* 2005; 9(1): 667-718. Subject: 9.5.2

Jost, Timothy S. Biotechnology and public policy: an Anabaptist response. *In:* Miller, Roman J.; Brubaker, Beryl H.; Peterson, James C., eds. Viewing New Creations with Anabaptist Eyes: Ethics of Biotechnology. Telford, PA: Cascadia Pub.; 2005: 213-217. Subject: 5.1

Jotkowitz, A.B.; Glick, S. The Groningen protocol: another perspective. *Journal of Medical Ethics* 2006 March; 32(3): 157-158. Subject: 20.5.2

Jotkowitz, Alan. Medical education, managed care and the doctor-patient relationship. *American Journal of Bioethics* 2006 January-February; 6(1): 46-47. Subject: 8.1

Jotkowitz, Alan; Glick, Shimon. Education in professionalism should never end. *American Journal of Bioethics* 2006 July-August; 6(4): 27-28. Subject: 7.2

Jotkowitz, Alan; Steinberg, Avraham. Multiculturalism and end-of-life care: the new Israeli law for the terminally ill patient. *American Journal of Bioethics* 2006 September-October; 6(5): 17-19; discussion W30-W32. Subject: 20.5.1

Jotterand, Fabrice. The politicization of science and technology: its implications for nanotechnology. *Journal of Law, Medicine and Ethics* 2006 Winter; 34(4): 658-666. Subject: 5.4

Subject = NRCBL Primary Classification Number; see inside front cover.

Joyce, Theodore; Kaestner, Robert; Colman, Silvie. Changes in abortions and births and the Texas Parental Notification Law. *New England Journal of Medicine* 2006 March 9; 354(10): 1031- 1038. Subject: 12.4.2

Juengst, Eric T. Developing and delivering new medical technologies: issues beyond access. *Journal of Social Issues* 1993 Summer; 49(2): 201-210. Subject: 5.2

Jukes, Nick. Ukraine and Russia: major InterNICHE outreach: training in alternatives and replacement of animal experiments. *ALTEX: Alternativen zu Experimenten* 2005; 22(4): 269-274. Subject: 22.2

Jukic, Vlado; Goreta, Miroslav; Kozumplik, Oliver; Herceg, Miroslav; Majdancic, eljko; Mu inic, Lana. Implementation of first Croatian Law on Protection of Persons with Mental Disorders. *Collegium Antropologicum* 2005 December; 29(2): 543-549. Subject: 17.7

Jung, Kyu Won; Hyun, Insoo. Oocyte and somatic cell procurement for stem cell research: the South Korean experience. *American Journal of Bioethics [Online].* 2006 January-February; 6(1): W19-W22. Subject: 18.5.4

Juntunen, Juhani. Insurance medicine and work-related diseases: some ethical and legal aspects. *In:* Westerholm, Peter; Nilstun, Tore; Øvretveit, John, eds. Practical Ethics in Occupational Health. San Francisco: Radcliffe Medical Press; 2004: 199-215. Subject: 16.3

Jureidini, Jon. Disease-mongering: a response. *Monash Bioethics Review* 2006 July; 25(3): 24-25. Subject: 4.4

Jürgens, Ralf. Dublin declaration on HIV/AIDS in prisons launched. *HIV/AIDS Policy and Law Review* 2004 April; 9(1): 40-45. Subject: 9.5.6

Jürgens, Ralf. HIV testing and confidentiality: a discussion paper. *Canadian HIV/AIDS Policy and Law Newsletter* 1997 Spring; 3(2-3): 3-7. Subject: 9.5.6

Jürgens, Ralf. HIV testing for peacekeeping forces: legal and human rights issues. *HIV/AIDS Policy and Law Review* 2002 December; 7(2-3): 111-114. Subject: 9.5.6

Jürgens, Ralf. No compulsory HIV-antibody testing of persons accused or convicted of sexual assault. *Canadian HIV/AIDS Policy and Law Newsletter* 1995 April; 1(3): 1, 12-14. Subject: 9.5.6

Jürgens, Ralf. Project begins work on testing and confidentiality issues. *Canadian HIV/AIDS Policy and Law Newsletter* 1996 July; 2(4): 3-7. Subject: 9.5.6

Jürgens, Ralf. Testing of pregnant women: issues and opinions. *Canadian HIV/AIDS Policy and Law Newsletter* 1997 Spring; 3(2-3): 1, 54-60. Subject: 9.5.6

Jürgens, Ralf; Elliot, Richard. Rapid HIV screening at the point of care: legal and ethical issues. *Canadian HIV/AIDS Policy and Law Newsletter* 2000 Spring-Summer; 5(2-3): 28-32. Subject: 9.5.6

Justo, Luis. Doctors, interrogation, and torture [editorial]. *BMJ: British Medical Journal* 2006 June 24; 332(7556): 1462. Subject: 21.4

Justo, Luis; Villareal, Jorgelina. Autonomy as a universal expectation: a review and research proposal. *Eubios Journal of Asian and International Bioethics* 2003 March 13(2): 53-57. Subject: 2.1

Jutel, Annemarie. Conflicted encounters: theoretical considerations in the understanding of disease-mongering. *Monash Bioethics Review* 2006 July; 25(3): 7-23. Subject: 9.7

Jutel, Annemarie. What's in a name? Death before birth. *Perspectives in Biology and Medicine* 2006 Summer; 49(3): 425-434. Subject: 12.1

K

Kachoyeanos, Mary K.; Zollo, Mary Bess. Ethics in pain management of infants and children. *MCN: The American Journal of Maternal Child Nursing* 1995 May-June; 20(3): 142-147. Subject: 9.5.7

Kachuck, Norman J. Challenges and opportunities: what we are learning from the clinical natalizumab experience. *Expert Review of Neurotherapeutics* 2005 September; 5(5): 605-615. Subject: 18.3

Kaczor, Christopher. The violinist and double-effect reasoning. *National Catholic Bioethics Quarterly* 2006 Winter; 6(4): 661-669. Subject: 12.3

Kaebnick, Gregory E. Wonderful children [editorial]. *Hastings Center Report* 2006 November-December; 36(6): 2. Subject: 4.5

Kagu, M.B.; Abjah, U.A.M.; Ahmed, S.G. Awareness and acceptability of prenatal diagnosis of sickle cell anaemia among health professionals and students in North Eastern Nigeria. *Nigerian Journal of Medicine* 2004 January-March; 13(1): 48-51. Subject: 7.1

Kahn, Axel. Clonage thérapeutique, morale et marché [Therapeutic cloning, morality and market]. Unpublished Document 2005 May 8; 3 p. Subject: 18.5.4

Kahn, Axel. Le clonage humain est-il thérapeutique? [Is human cloning therapeutic?]. Unpublished Document 2005 May 8; 5 p. Subject: 18.5.4

Kahn, Axel. Le clonage thérapeutique [Therapeutic cloning]. Unpublished Document 2005 May 8; 5 p. Subject: 18.5.4

Kahn, Charles N. III. Intolerable risk, irreparable harm: the legacy of physician-owned specialty hospitals. *Health Affairs* 2006 January-February; 25(1): 130-133. Subject: 9.3.1

Kahn, Jeffrey. Informed consent in the context of communities. *Journal of Nutrition* 2005 April; 135(4): 918-920. Subject: 18.3

See SUBJECT HEADING KEY FOR SECTION II on inside back cover.

613

Kahn, Jeffrey P. What happens when politics discovers bioethics? *Hastings Center Report* 2006 May-June; 36(3): 10. Subject: 2.1

Kahn, Jonathan. From disparity to difference: how race-specific medicines may undermine policies to address inequalities in health care. *Southern California Interdisciplinary Law Journal* 2005 Fall; 15(1): 105-130. Subject: 15.11

Kahn, Jonathan. Genes, race, and population: avoiding a collision of categories. *American Journal of Public Health* 2006 November; 96(11): 1965-1970. Subject: 9.5.4

Kahn, Jonathan. Patenting race. *Nature Biotechnology* 2006 November; 24(11): 1349-1357. Subject: 15.8

Kahn, Jonathan. Race, pharmacogenomics, and marketing: putting BiDil in context. *American Journal of Bioethics [Online]* 2006 September-October; 6(5): W1-W5. Subject: 15.11

Kahn, Jonathan; Sankar, Pamela. Being specific about race-specific medicine. *Health Affairs* 2006 July-November; (Web Exclusives): 375-377. Subject: 15.11

Kahraman, Semra. Are we talking about the butterflies or a butterfly effect? *Reproductive BioMedicine Online [electronic]* 2005 July; 11(1): 14-15. Accessed: http://www.rbmonline.com/Article/1864 [2005 December 16]. Subject: 14.3

Kahraman, S.; Findikli, N. Effect of Italian referendum on global IVF: a comment from Turkey. *Reproductive BioMedicine Online [electronic]* 2005 December; 11(6): 662-663. Accessed: http://www.rbmonline.com/Article/2052 [2006 July 25]. Subject: 14.4

Kaiser, Irwin H. Reappraisals of J. Marion Sims. *American Journal of Obstetrics and Gynecology* 1978 December 15; 132(8): 878-884. Subject: 7.1

Kaiser, Jocelyn. Court decides tissue samples belong to university, not patients [news]. *Science* 2006 April 21; 312(5772): 346. Subject: 4.4

Kaiser, Jocelyn. House panel finds fault with how NIH handles tissue samples. *Science* 2006 June 23; 312(5781): 1733. Subject: 19.5

Kaiser, Jocelyn. MEDLINE supplements must list corporate ties [news]. *Science* 2006 October 20; 314(5798): 405. Subject: 1.3.7

Kaiser, Jocelyn. NIH rules rile scientists, survey finds [news]. *Science* 2006 November 3; 314(5800): 740. Subject: 1.3.9

Kaiser, Jocelyn. Researchers attack newspaper probe of trials [news]. *Science* 2006 September 22; 313(5794): 1714. Subject: 1.3.9

Kaiser, Jocelyn. Rule to protect records may doom long-term heart study [news]. *Science* 2006 March 17; 311(5767): 1547-1548. Subject: 8.4

Kaiser, Jocelyn. U.S. hospital launches large biobank of children's DNA [news]. *Science* 2006 June 16; 312(5780): 1584-1585. Subject: 15.1

Kaiser, Mario. Drawing the boundaries of nanoscience — rationalizing the concerns? *Journal of Law, Medicine and Ethics* 2006 Winter; 34(4): 667-674. Subject: 5.4

Kakuk, Péter. Genetic information in the age of genohype. *Medicine, Health Care and Philosophy* 2006; 9(3): 325-337. Subject: 15.1

Kalb, Claudia; Rosenberg, Debra; Mummold, Jonathan. Embryonic war: scientists and ethicists put the latest stem-cell 'breakthrough' under the microscope. *Newsweek* 2006 September 4; 148(10): 42-43. Subject: 18.5.4

Kalb, Claudia; Underwood, Anne; Mummolo, Jonathan. Peering into the future. Genetic testing is transforming medicine — and the way families think about their health. As science unlocks the intricate secrets of DNA, we face difficult choices and new challenges. *Newsweek* 2006 December 11; 148(24): 52-54, 56-57, 60-61. Subject: 15.3

Kaldjian, Lauris C.; Jones, Elizabeth W.; Rosenthal, Gary E.; Tripp-Reimer, Toni; Hillis, Stephen L. An empirically derived taxonomy of factors affecting physicians' willingness to disclose medical errors. *JGIM: Journal of General Internal Medicine* 2006 September; 21(9): 942-948. Subject: 9.8

Kalfoglou, Andrea L.; Doksum, Teresa; Bernhardt, Barbara; Geller, Gail; LeRoy, Lisa; Mathews, Debra J.H.; Evans, John H.; Doukas, David J.; Reame, Nancy; Scott, Joan; Hudson, Kathy. Opinions about new reproductive genetic technologies: hopes and fears for our genetic future. *Fertility and Sterility* 2005 June; 83(6): 1612-1621. Subject: 15.2

Kalfoglou, Andrea L.; Scott, Joan; Hudson, Kathy. PGD patients' and providers' attitudes to the use and regulation of preimplantation genetic diagnosis. *Reproductive BioMedicine Online [electronic]* 2005 October; 11(4): 486-496. Subject: 15.2

Kalian, Moshe; Mester, Roberto. Forensic psychiatry corner 3: the issue of anonymity in lay referrals [case study]. *Israel Journal of Psychiatry and Related Sciences* 2004; 41(4): 306-307. Subject: 17.1

Kalichman, Michael. Ethics and science: a 0.1% solution. *Issues in Science and Technology* 2006 Fall; 23(1): 34-36. Subject: 1.3.9

Kalish, R.B.; McCullough, L.B.; Chervenak, F.A. Decision-making about caesarean delivery. *Lancet* 2006 March 18-24; 367(9514): 883-885. Subject: 9.5.5

Kalm, Leah M.; Semba, Richard D. They starved so that others be better fed: remembering Ancel Keys and the Minnesota experiment. *Journal of Nutrition* 2005 June; 135(6): 1347-1352. Subject: 18.5.1

Kalra, Dipak; Gertz, Renate; Singleton, Peter; Inskip, Hazel M. Confidentiality of personal health information used for research. *BMJ: British Medical Journal* 2006 July 22; 333(7560): 196-198. Subject: 18.3

Kaltiala-Heino, Riittakerttu; Välimäki, Maritta. Involuntary commitment in health care: an analysis of the status and rights of involuntarily treated psychiatric patients in comparison with patients treated involuntarily under other acts. *European Journal of Health Law* 2001 December; 8(4): 299-316. Subject: 17.7

Kälvemark Sporrong, Sofia; Höglund, Anna T.; Hansson, Mats G.; Westerholm, Peter; Arnetz, Bengt. "We are white coats whirling round"—moral distress in Swedish pharmacies. *Pharmacy World and Science* 2005 June; 27(3): 223-229. Subject: 9.7

Kamal, R.S. Ethics in medical practice. *Journal of the Pakistan Medical Association* 2004 June; 54(6): 325-327. Subject: 4.1.2

Kamat, Vijaylaxmi. Guiding light at the end of the tunnel [response]. *Indian Journal of Medical Ethics* 2006 July-September; 3(3): 103-104. Subject: 20.5.1

Kaminer, Wendy. Partial-truth abortion bans [op-ed]. *Free Inquiry* 2006 June-July; 26(4): 17-18. Subject: 12.4.1

Kampits, Peter. A case study. *In:* Döring, Ole; Chen, Renbiao, eds. Advances in Chinese Medical Ethics: Chinese and International Perspectives. Hamburg: Institut für Asienkunde; 2002: 427-432. Subject: 20.5.1

Kanamori, Osamu. Ethics of genetic life designs. *In:* Sang-yong, Song; Young-Mo, Koo; Macer, Darryl R.J., eds. Asian Bioethics in the 21st Century. Christchurch, NZ: Eubios Ethics Institute, 2002: 157-164. Subject: 15.1

Kanellopoulou, Nadja K. Gift or duty? A normative discussion for participation in human genetic databases research. *In:* Árnason, Gardar; Nordal, Salvör; Árnason, Vilhjálmur, eds. Blood and Data: Ethical, Legal and Social Aspects of Human Genetic Databases. Reykjavík: University of Iceland Press; 2004: 95-99. Subject: 15.1

Kang, Shinik. Professional medical ethics in Korean context: towards and moral contract. *In:* Sang-yong, Song; Young-Mo, Koo; Macer, Darryl R.J., eds. Asian Bioethics in the 21st Century. Christchurch, NZ: Eubios Ethics Institute, 2002: 294-297. Subject: 4.1.2

Kanhere, Vijay. The Clemenceau debate and occupational health. *Indian Journal of Medical Ethics* 2006 April-June; 3(2): 46-47. Subject: 16.3

Kanis, J.A.; Alexandre, J.M.; Bone, H.G.; Abadie, E.; Brasseur, D.; Chassany, O.; Durrleman, S.; Lekkerkerker, J.F.F.; Caulin, F. Study design in osteoporosis: a European perspective. *Journal of Bone and Mineral Research* 2003 June; 18(6): 1133-1138. Subject: 18.2

Kao, Audiey. Ethics, law, and professionalism: what physicians need to know. *In:* Stern, David Thomas, ed. Measuring Medical Professionalism. New York: Oxford University Press; 2006: 39-52. Subject: 4.1.2

Kao, Audiey. A physician by any other name. *Virtual Mentor* 2001 October; 3(10): 1p. Subject: 8.1

Kapilashrami, M.C. Universal access to health — a rights based approach. *Indian Journal of Public Health* 2005 April-June; 49(2): 48-52. Subject: 9.2

Kaplan, B.; Orvieto, R.; Yogev, Y.; Simon, Y. Social aspects of the new assisted reproduction technologies: attitudes of Israeli gynecologists. *Clinical and Experimental Obstetrics and Gynecology* 2004; 31(4): 285-286. Subject: 14.1

Kaplan, Dana L. Can legislation alone solve America's mental health dilemma? Current state legislative schemes cannot achieve mental health parity. *Quinnipac Health Law* 2004-2005; 8: 325-361. Subject: 17.1

Kaplan, Jay. Commentary: ethical issues surrounding the use of nonhuman primates in biomedical research. *In:* Turner, Trudy R. ed. Biological Anthropology and Ethics: From Repatriation to Genetic Identity. Albany, NY: State University of New York Press; 2005: 79-90. Subject: 22.2

Kaplan, Jonathan. Misinformation, misrepresentation, and misuse of human behavioral genetics research. *Law and Contemporary Problems* 2006 Winter-Spring; 69(1-2): 47-80. Subject: 15.6

Kaplan, Laura Duhan. HIV/AIDS policies: compromising the human rights of women. *In:* Tong, Rosemarie; Donchin, Anne; Dodds, Susan, eds. Linking Visions: Feminist Bioethics, Human Rights, and the Developing World. Lanham, MD: Rowman and Littlefield Publishers; 2004: 235-246. Subject: 9.5.6

Kapp, Marshall B. Drug companies, dollars, and the shaping of American medical practice. *Southern Illinois University Law Journal* 2005 Winter; 29(2): 237-262. Subject: 9.7

Kapp, Marshall B. Informed consent implications of diagnostic evaluations for dementia. *American Journal of Alzheimer's Disease and Other Dementias* 2006 January-February; 21(1): 24-27. Subject: 8.3.3

Kapp, Marshall B. Life-sustaining technologies: value issues. *Journal of Social Issues* 1993 Summer; 49(2): 151-167. Subject: 5.2

Kapp, Marshall B. Protecting human participants in long-term care research: the role of state law and policy. *Journal of Aging and Social Policy* 2004; 16(3): 13-33. Subject: 18.6

Kapterian, Gisele. Harriton, Waller and Australian negligence law: is there a place for wrongful life? *Journal of Law and Medicine* 2006 February; 13(3): 336-351. Subject: 15.2

Kapur, Devesh; McHale, John. Should a cosmopolitan worry about the "brain drain"? *Ethics and International Affairs* 2006; 20(3): 305-320. Subject: 21.6

Karlawish, Jason H.T.; Fox, Ellen; Pearlman, Robert. How changes in health care practices, systems, and re-

See SUBJECT HEADING KEY FOR SECTION II on inside back cover.

615

search challenge the practice of informed consent. *Medical Care* 2002 September; 40(9, Supplement): V12-V19. Subject: 18.3

Karlsen, J.R.; de Faria, P.L.; Solbakk, J.H. To know the value of everything— a critical commentary on B. Björkman and S.O. Hansson's "Bodily rights and property rights". *Journal of Medical Ethics* 2006 April; 32(4): 215-219. Subject: 4.4

Karpa, Kelly Dowhower. Pharmacist critique was ill-formed. *Annals of Pharmacotherapy* 2006 July-August; 40: 1441-1444. Subject: 11.1

Karro, Jonathan; Dent, Andrew W.; Farish, Stephen. Patient perceptions of privacy infringements in an emergency department. *Emergency Medicine Australasia* 2005 April; 17(2): 117-123. Subject: 8.4

Kaser-Boyd, Nancy; Adelman, Howard S.; Taylor, Linda; Nelson, Perry. Children's understanding of risks and benefits of psychotherapy. *Journal of Clinical Child Psychology* 1986; 15(2): 165-171. Subject: 8.3.2

Kaseta, Suzanne. The ethics of population policy: emphasizing female sterilization in the third world. *Einstein Quarterly Journal of Biology and Medicine* 1994; 12(1): 15-20. Subject: 11.3

Kashani, S.; Kinnear, P.; Porter, B. Consent for anaesthesia in cataract surgery [letter]. *Journal of Medical Ethics* 2006 September; 32(9): 555. Subject: 8.3.1

Kaslow, Florence. Ethical problems in mental health practice. *Journal of Family Psychotherapy* 1998; 9(2): 41-54. Subject: 17.2

Kasparian, Nadine A.; Meiser, Bettina; Butow, Phyllis N.; Job, R.F. Soames; Mann, Graham J. Better the devil you know? High-risk individuals' anticipated psychological responses to genetic testing for melanoma susceptibility. *Journal of Genetic Counseling* 2006 December; 15(6): 433-447. Subject: 15.3

Kass-Bartelmes, Barbara L.; Hughes, Ronda. Advance care planning: preferences for care at the end of life. Rockville, MD: Agency for Healthcare Research and Quality [AHRQ], 2003 March; 19 p. [Online]. Accessed: http://www.ahrq.gov/research/ endliferia/endria.pdf [2006 August 30]. Subject: 20.5.4

Kassaw, Kristin; Gabbard, Glen O. The ethics of e-mail communication in psychiatry. *Psychiatric Clinics of North America* 2002 September; 25(3): 665-674. Subject: 1.3.12

Kassirer, Jerome P. Excerpts from: On the Take. *Physician Executive* 2005 March-April; 31(2): 28-32. Subject: 7.1

Kassirer, Jerome P.; Davidoff, Frank; O'Hara, Kathryn; Redelmeier, Donald A. Editorial autonomy of CMAJ. *CMAJ/JAMC: Canadian Medical Association Journal* 2006 March 28; 174(7): 945-950. Subject: 1.3.7

Kast, A. Memorial stones for the souls of animals killed for human welfare in Japan. *Berliner und Munchener Tierarztliche Wochenschrift* 1994 May; 107(5): 166-171. Subject: 22.1

Katz, Katheryn D. Parenthood from the grave: protocols for retrieving and utilizing gametes from the dead or dying. *University of Chicago Legal Forum* 2006: 289-316. Subject: 14.6

Kaufert, Joseph; Commanda, Laura; Elias, Brenda; Grey, Rhoda; Young, T. Kue; Masuzumi, Barney. Evolving participation of Aboriginal communities in health research ethics review: the impact of the Inuvik workshop. *International Journal of Circumpolar Health* 1998 April; 58(2): 134-245. Subject: 18.5.1

Kauffman, Robert P.; Castracane, V. Daniel; Van Hook, Catherine L. Postmenopausal hormone therapy and informed consent: a call for common sense. *Journal of Women's Health* 2005 September; 14(7): 592-594. Subject: 9.5.5

Kaufman, Marc. Plan B battles embroil states; proposals mirror red-blue divide. *Washington Post* 2006 February 27; p. A1, A7. Subject: 11.1

Kaufman, Sharon R. A commentary: hospital experience and meaning at the end of life. *Gerontologist* 2002 October; 42(Special Issue 3): 34-39. Subject: 20.4.1

Kaufman, Sharon R. Death by design. *In her: . . .And a Time to Die: How American Hospitals Shape the End of Life.* New York: Scribner; 2005: 207-235. Subject: 20.5.1

Kaufman, Sharon R. Hidden places: the zone of indistinction as a way of life. *In her: . . .And a Time to Die: How American Hospitals Shape the End of Life.* New York: Scribner; 2005: 273-317. Subject: 20.5.1

Kaufman, Sharon R. Life support. *In her: . . .And a Time to Die: How American Hospitals Shape the End of Life.* New York: Scribner; 2005: 236-272. Subject: 20.5.1

Kaufman, Sharon R. The World War II plutonium experiments: contested stories and their lessons for medical research and informed consent. *Culture, Medicine and Psychiatry* 1997 June; 21(2): 161-197. Subject: 18.5.1

Kauwell, Gail P. Emerging concepts in nutrigenomics: a preview of what is to come. *Nutrition in Clinical Practice* 2005 February; 20(1): 75-87. Subject: 15.10

Kavanagh, Kathryn H. Beyond the individual: healthcare ethics in diverse societies. *In:* Dinkins, Christine Sorrell; Sorrell, Jeanne Merkle, eds. Listening to the Whispers: Re-Thinking Ethics in Healthcare. Madison, WI: University of Wisconsin Press; 2006: 248-309. Subject: 2.1

Kavanaugh, John F. Cloning for Missouri: 'at issue was scientific integrity, not religious fanaticism'. *America* 2006 November 27; 195(17): 8. Subject: 18.5.4

Kavanaugh, John F. Cloning, by whatever name, smells bad. *America* 2006 June 19-26; 194(21): 9. Subject: 14.5

Kavanaugh, Karen; Savage, Teresa; Kilpatrick, Sarah; Kimura, Rob; Hershberger, Patricia. Life support decisions for extremely premature infants: report of a pilot study. *Journal of Pediatric Nursing* 2005 October; 20(5): 347-359. Subject: 20.5.2

Kaveny, M. Cathleen. Diversity and deliberation: bioethics commissions and moral reasoning. *Journal of Religious Ethics* 2006 June; 34(2): 311-337. Subject: 2.4

Kaveny, M. Cathleen. The NBAC report on cloning: a case study in religion, public policy, and bioethics. *In:* Guinn, David E., ed. Handbook of Bioethics and Religion. New York: Oxford University Press, 2006: 221-251. Subject: 2.4

Kaveny, M. Cathleen. Rhetoric, public reason, and bioethics: the President's Council on Bioethics and Human Cloning [review of Human Cloning and Human Dignity: The Report of the President's Council on Bioethics]. *Journal of Law and Politics* 2004 Summer; 20(3): 489-503. Subject: 14.5

Kawar, Amal; Sherlock, Richard. Theoretical issues in the regulation of genetically engineered organisms: the case of deliberate release. *Politics and the Life Sciences* 1989 February; 7(2): 129-134. Subject: 15.7

Kaya, Ayse; Aksoy, Sahin; Simsek, Zeynep; Ozbilge, Hatice; Aksoy, Nurten. An assessment of the level of knowledge of medical and nursing students on HIV/AIDS at Harran University, Sanliurfa/Turkey, and training on ethical aspects of the disease. *In:* Sang-yong, Song; Young-Mo, Koo; Macer, Darryl R.J., eds. Asian Bioethics in the 21st Century. Christchurch, NZ: Eubios Ethics Institute, 2002: 264-267. Subject: 2.3

Kaye, D.H. Behavioral genetics research and criminal DNA databases. *Law and Contemporary Problems* 2006 Winter-Spring; 69(1-2): 259-299. Subject: 15.6

Kaye, D.H. Who needs special needs? On the constitutionality of collecting DNA and other biometric data from arrestees. *Journal of Law, Medicine and Ethics* 2006 Summer; 34(2): 188-198. Subject: 15.1

Kaye, Jane. Broad consent — the only option for population genetic databases? *In:* Árnason, Gardar; Nordal, Salvör; Árnason, Vilhjálmur, eds. Blood and Data: Ethical, Legal and Social Aspects of Human Genetic Databases. Reykjavík: University of Iceland Press; 2004: 103-109. Subject: 15.1

Kaye, Jane. Police collection and access to DNA samples. *Genomics, Society and Policy* 2006 May; 2(1): 16-27. Subject: 15.1

Kaye, Janet M.; Lawton, Powell; Kaye, Donald. Attitudes of elderly people about clinical research on aging. *Gerontologist* 1990 February; 30(1): 100-106. Subject: 18.5.7

Kean, Sam. Bush vetoes bill to loosen policy on stem-cell research. *Chronicle of Higher Education* 2006 July 28; 52(47): A17. Subject: 18.5.4

Kean, Sam. Draft research rules are released [news]. *Chronicle of Higher Education* 2006 September 15; 53(4): A27. Subject: 18.2

Kean, Sam. NIH proposes genetic database [news]. *Chronicle of Higher Education* 2006 September 15; 53(4): A27. Subject: 15.1

Keane, Helen. Moral frameworks, ethical engagement and harm reduction: commentary on 'Ethical challenges and responses in harm reduction research: promoting applied communitarian ethics' by C.L. Fry, C. Treloar and L. Maher. *Drug and Alcohol Review* 2005 November; 24(6): 551-552. Subject: 9.5.9

Kearnes, Matthew; Grove-White, Robin; MacNaghten, Phil; Wilsdon, James; Wynne, Brian. From bio to nano: learning lessons from the UK agricultural biotechnology controversy. *Science as Culture* 2006 December; 15(4): 291-307. Subject: 15.1

Keating, Dominic T.; Nayeem, Kayser; Gilmartin, J.J.; O'Keeffe, Shaun T. Advance directives for truth disclosure. *Chest* 2005 August; 128(2): 1037-1039. Subject: 8.2

Kee, Pei-Teing. Refusal to consent to treatment on religious grounds. *E Law: Murdoch University Electronic Journal of Law* 1995 July; 2(2): 16 p. [Online]. Accessed: http://www.murdoch.edu.au/elaw/issues/v2n2/kee221.html [2006 June 29]. Subject: 8.3.4

Keehan, Carol. Those who don't receive medical care. *Origins* 2006 June 22; 36(6): 81-85. Subject: 9.2

Keenan, Heather T.; Doron, Mia W.; Seyda, Beth A. Comparison of mothers' and counselors' perceptions of predelivery counseling for extremely premature infants. *Pediatrics* 2005 July; 116(1): 104-111. Subject: 8.3.2

Keiper, Adam. The age of neuroelectronics. *New Atlantis* 2006 Winter; 11: 4-41. Subject: 5.1

Keith, Stephen N. Collective bargaining and strikes among physicians. *Journal of the National Medical Association* 1984 November; 76(11): 1117-1121. Subject: 7.1

Keith-Spiegel, Patricia; Koocher, Gerald P.; Tabachnick, Barbara. What scientists want from their research ethics committee. *Journal of Empirical Research on Human Research Ethics* 2006 March; 1(1): 67-81. Subject: 18.2

Keller, Allen S. Torture in Abu Ghraib. *Perspectives in Biology and Medicine* 2006 Autumn; 49(4): 553-569. Subject: 21.4

Keller, F.; Allert, G.; Baitsch, H.; Sponholz, G. Discourse ethics in practical medicine. *Medical Humanities* 2006 December; 32(2): 99-103. Subject: 8.1

See SUBJECT HEADING KEY FOR SECTION II on inside back cover.

617

Kellermann, Arthur; Lynn, Joanne. Withholding resuscitation in prehospital care. *Annals of Internal Medicine* 2006 May 2; 144(9): 692-693. Subject: 20.5.1

Kelley, Carol G.; Lipson, Amy R.; Daly, Barbara J.; Douglas, Sara L. Use of advance directives in the chronically critically ill. *JONA's Healthcare Law, Ethics, and Regulation* 2006 April-June; 8(2): 42-47. Subject: 20.5.4

Kelly, Brian J.; Varghese, Francis T.; Pelusi, Dan. Countertransference and ethics: a perspective on clinical dilemmas in end-of-life decisions. *Palliative and Supportive Care* 2003 December; 1(4): 367-375. Subject: 20.4.1

Kelly, Kevin T. Carhart v. Gonzales: rethinking Stenberg and the partial-birth abortion ban. *Jurimetrics* 2006 Spring; 46(3): 353-372. Subject: 12.4.2

Kelly, Matthew. Critical objections to Michael Steinberg's opt-in system for kidney transplantation. *Penn Bioethics Journal* 2006; 2(1): 3p. [Online]. Accessed: http://www.bioethicsjournal.com [2006 February 21]. Subject: 19.3

Kelly, Paul D. Refusing to provide a prenatal test: can it ever be ethical?: Time to re-think the autonomy of future individuals [letter]. *BMJ: British Medical Journal* 2006 December 2; 333(7579): 1173. Subject: 15.2

Kemelmajer de Carlucci, Aida Rosa. Genetic material and assisted reproduction. Case law reaction (Part I) = Material genético y reproducción asistida. Reacción jurisprudencial (Parte I). *Revista de Derecho Genoma Humano = Law and the Human Genome Review* 1997 January-June; (6): 131-152. Subject: 14.1

Kemelmajer de Carlucci, Aida Rosa. Genetic material and assisted reproduction. Case law reaction (Part II) = Material genético y reproducción asistida. Reacción jurisprudencial (Parte II). *Revista de Derecho Genoma Humano = Law and the Human Genome Review* 1997 July-December; (7): 173-186. Subject: 14.6

Kemmelmeier, Markus; Davis, Deborah; Follette, William C. Seven "sins" of misdirection?: ethical controversies surrounding the use of deception in research. *In:* O'Donohue, William; Ferguson, Kyle, eds. Handbook of Professional Ethics for Psychologists: Issues, Questions, and Controversies. Thousand Oaks, Calif.: SAGE Publications; 2003: 227-256. Subject: 18.3

Kendall, Christopher C. New York v. Sullivan: shhh . . . don't say the "A" word! Another outcome-oriented abortion decision. *John Marshall Law Review* 1990 Summer; 23(4): 753-770. Subject: 12.4.2

Kennedy, Allison M.; Brown, Cedric J.; Gust, Deborah A. Vaccine beliefs of parents who oppose compulsory vaccination. *Public Health Reports* 2005 May-June; 120(3): 252-258. Subject: 9.5.1

Kennedy, Donald. Animal activism: out of control [editorial]. *Science* 2006 September 15; 313(5793): 1541. Subject: 22.1

Kennedy, Donald. Editorial expression of concern [letter]. *Science* 2006 January 6; 311(5757): 36. Subject: 1.3.9

Kennedy, Donald. Responding to fraud [editorial]. *Science* 2006 December 1; 314(5804): 1353. Subject: 1.3.9

Kennedy, Ian; Grubb, Andrew. Abortion. *In their:* Medical Law. 3rd ed. London: Butterworths; 2005: 1405-1491. Subject: 12.4.1

Kennedy, Ian; Grubb, Andrew. Confidentiality. *In their:* Medical Law. 3rd ed. London: Butterworths; 2005: 1047-1136. Subject: 8.4

Kennedy, Ian; Grubb, Andrew. Consent. *In their:* Medical Law. 3rd ed. London: Butterworths; 2005: 575-773. Subject: 8.3.1

Kennedy, Ian; Grubb, Andrew. Consent by others. *In their:* Medical Law. 3rd ed. London: Butterworths; 2005: 774-989. Subject: 8.3.3

Kennedy, Ian; Grubb, Andrew. Contraception and sterilisation. *In their:* Medical Law. 3rd ed. London: Butterworths; 2005: 1139-1210. Subject: 11.2

Kennedy, Ian; Grubb, Andrew. Death and dead bodies. *In their:* Medical Law. 3rd ed. London: Butterworths; 2005: 2191-2263. Subject: 20.2.1

Kennedy, Ian; Grubb, Andrew. Donation and transplant of human tissue and fluids. *In their:* Medical Law. 3rd ed. London: Butterworths; 2005: 1750-1904. Subject: 19.5

Kennedy, Ian; Grubb, Andrew. The end(ing) of life: the competent patient. *In their:* Medical Law. 3rd ed. London: Butterworths; 2005: 1907-2088. Subject: 20.5.1

Kennedy, Ian; Grubb, Andrew. The end(ing) of life: the incompetent patient. *In their:* Medical Law. 3rd ed. London: Butterworths; 2005: 2089-2190. Subject: 20.5.1

Kennedy, Ian; Grubb, Andrew. Medically assisted reproduction. *In their:* Medical Law. 3rd ed. London: Butterworths; 2005: 1211-1404. Subject: 14.1

Kennedy, Ian; Grubb, Andrew. Research. *In their:* Medical Law. 3rd ed. London: Butterworths; 2005: 1665-1749. Subject: 18.6

Kennedy, S.B.; Harris, A.O.; Oudemans, E.; Young, L.; Kollie, J.; Nelson, E.S.; Nisbett, R.A.; Morris, C.; Bartee, N.; George-Williams, E.; Jones, J. Developing capacity to protect human research subjects in a post-conflict, resource-constrained setting: procedures and prospects. *Journal of Medical Ethics* 2006 October; 32(10): 592-595. Subject: 18.6

Kenny, Catherine. Abortion — a reproductive right. *In:* Widdows, Heather; Idiakez, Itziar Alkorta; Cirión, Aitziber Emaldi, eds. Women's Reproductive Rights. New York: Palgrave Macmillan; 2006: 17-32. Subject: 12.1

Kenny, Nuala. Medicine's malaise: the Pellegrino prescription. *American Journal of Bioethics* 2006 March-April; 6(2): 78-80. Subject: 2.1

Kenny, Nuala. Uncharted territory: Hippocratic ethics and health systems [editorial]. *CMAJ/JAMC: Canadian Medical Association Journal* 2006 May 9; 174(10): 1385. Subject: 4.1.2

Kent, Alastair. We can change the future. *EMBO Reports* 2005 September; 6(9): 801-804. Subject: 15.3

Kent, Julie; Faulkner, Alex; Geesink, Ingrid; Fitzpatrick, David. Culturing cells, reproducing and regulating the self. *Body and Society* 2006 June; 12(2): 1-23 [Online]. Accessed: http://bod.sagepub.com/cgi/reprint/ 12/2/1 [2007 January 23]. Subject: 15.1

Kent, Julie; Faulkner, A.; Geesink, I.; FitzPatrick, D. Towards governance of human tissue engineered technologies in Europe: framing the case for a new regulatory regime. *Technological Forecasting and Social Change* 2006 January; 73(1): 41-60. Subject: 15.1

Kent, Julie; Pfeffer, Naomi. Regulating the collection and use of fetal stem cells: they currently lie in a regulatory limbo [editorial]. *BMJ: British Medical Journal* 2006 April 15; 332(7546): 866-867. Subject: 18.5.4

Kenter, M.J.H.; Cohen, A.F. Establishing risk of human experimentation with drugs: lessons from TGN1412. *Lancet* 2006 October 14-20; 368(9544): 1387-1391. Subject: 18.2

Kenyon, Kristi. Routine HIV testing: a view from Botswana. *Health and Human Rights: An International Journal* 2005; 8(2): 21-23. Subject: 9.5.6

Keough, William J. Towards the development of ethical practices in paediatric clinical trials: the special position of the terminally ill child. *Journal of Law and Medicine* 2006 February; 13(3): 370-386. Subject: 20.4.2

Keown, John. Back to the future of abortion law: Roe's rejection of America's history and traditions. *Issues in Law and Medicine* 2006 Summer; 22(1): 3-37. Subject: 12.4.1

Keown, John. Considering physician-assisted suicide: an evaluation of Lord Joffe's assisted dying for the terminally ill bill. London: Care NOT Killing Alliance, 2006. 32 p. Subject: 20.7

Keown, John. Mr. Marty's muddle: a superficial and selective case for euthanasia in Europe. *Journal of Medical Ethics* 2006 January; 32(1): 29-33. Subject: 20.5.1

Keram, Emily A. Will medical ethics be a casualty of the war on terror? [editorial]. *Journal of the American Academy of Psychiatry and the Law* 2006; 34(1): 6-8. Subject: 21.2

Keranen, Lisa. Assessing the seriousness of research misconduct: considerations for sanction assignment. *Accountability in Research* 2006 April-June; 13(2): 179-205. Subject: 1.3.9

Kerr, Anne. Genetics and citizenship. *In:* Stehr, Nico, ed. Biotechnology Between Commerce and Civil Society. New Brunswick, NJ: Transaction Publishers; 2004: 159-174. Subject: 15.1

Kerr, Anne. Genetics and citizenship. *Society* 2003 September-October; 40(6): 44-50. Subject: 15.1

Kerr, Anne. Rights and responsibilities in the new genetics era. *Critical Social Policy* 2003 May; 23(2): 208-226 [Online]. Accessed: http://csp.sagepub.com/cgi/reprint/ 23/2/208 [2007 January 25]. Subject: 15.1

Kerridge, I.H.; McGrath, C.; White, K. One woman's journey is a journey we all may share. *Internal Medicine Journal* 2006 May; 36(5): 323-324. Subject: 8.1

Kerridge, Ian H.; Ankeny, Rachel A.X.; Jordens, Christopher F.C.; Lipworth, Wendy L. Increasing diversity at the cost of decreasing equity? Issues raised by the establishment of Australia's first religiously affiliated medical school. *Medical Journal of Australia* 2005 July 4; 183(1): 28-30. Subject: 7.2

Kershaw, Josephine M. Human rights and undergraduate healthcare management education. *Journal of Health Administration Education* 2005 Fall; 22(4): 459-470. Subject: 21.1

Kerwin, Jeanne; Bauman, Susan. Out-of-hospital do-not-resuscitate (DNR) orders: the New Jersey protocol. *New Jersey Medicine* 2003 November; 100(11): 21-22. Subject: 20.5.1

Kesselheim, Aaron S.; Avorn, Jerry. Biomedical patents and the public's health: is there a role for eminent domain? *JAMA: The Journal of the American Medical Association* 2006 January 25; 295(4): 434-437. Subject: 5.3

Kesselheim, Aaron S.; Mello, Michelle M. Medical-process patents — monopolizing the delivery of health care. *New England Journal of Medicine* 2006 November 9; 355(19): 2036-2041. Subject: 5.3

Kessler, Daniel P.; Summerton, Nicholas; Graham, John R. Effects of the medical liability system in Australia, the UK, and the USA. *Lancet* 2006 July 15-21; 368(9531): 240-246. Subject: 8.5

Kessler, Laura E.; Waehler, Charles A. Addressing multiple relationships between clients and therapists in lesbian, gay, bisexual, transgender communities. *Professional Psychology: Research and Practice* 2005 February; 36(1): 66-72. Subject: 17.2

Kettner, Matthias. "Wunscherfüllende Medizin" zwischen Kommerz und Patientendienlichkeit / "Medicine of desire" between commercialization and patient-centeredness. *Ethik in der Medizin* 2006 March; 18(1): 81-91. Subject: 4.5

Kettner, Matthias. Assistenz zum guten Leben: der Trend zur wunscherfüllenden Medizin / Assistance for a good life: the trend towards wish-fulfilling medicine [editorial]. *Ethik in der Medizin* 2006 March; 18(1): 5-9. Subject: 4.5

Kettner, Matthias. Discourse ethics: Apel, Habermas, and beyond. *In:* Rehmann-Sutter, Christoph; Düwell, Marcus; Mieth, Dietmar, eds. Bioethics in Cultural Con-

See SUBJECT HEADING KEY FOR SECTION II on inside back cover.

619

texts: Reflections on Methods and Finitude. Dordrecht: Springer, 2006: 299-318. Subject: 2.1

Kettner, Matthias. Research ethics committees in Germany. *In:* Beyleveld, D.; Townend, D.; Wright, J., eds. Research Ethics Committees, Data Protection and Medical Research in European Countries. Hants, England; Burlington, VT: Ashgate; 2005: 73-83. Subject: 18.2

Khan, Robyna Irshad. One standard of care for all is not always practical. *Indian Journal of Medical Ethics* 2006 January-March; 3(1): 21-22. Subject: 18.2

Khan, Robyna, I. Paying the price of research. *SciDev.Net (Science and Development Network)* 2004 November 10: 3 pages [Online] Accessed:http://www.scidev.net/dossiers/index.cfm?fuseaction=printarticle&dossier=5&type=3&itemid=331&language-1 [2005 December 2]. Subject: 5.3

Khandekar, Jarardan; Khandekar, Melin. Phase 1 clinical trials: not just for safety anymore? *Archives of Internal Medicine* 2006 July 24; 166(14): 1440-1441. Subject: 18.2

Khanna, Sumant. Response to Dr. Vikram Patel. *Indian Journal of Medical Ethics* 2006 January-March; 3(1): 17-18. Subject: 18.5.6

Khayat, M. Haytham. Research ethics: challenges in the eastern Mediterranean region. *Eastern Mediterranean Health Journal* 2006; 12(Supplement 1): S13-S20 [Online]. Accessed: http://www.emro.who.int/publications/EMHJ/12_S/PDF/3.pdf [2007 January 3]. Subject: 2.1

Khazova, Olga A. Genetics and artificial procreation in Russia. *In:* Meulders-Klein, Marie-Thérèse; Deech, Ruth; Vlaardingerbroek, Paul, eds. Biomedicine, the Family and Human Rights. New York: Kluwer Law International, 2002: 377-391. Subject: 15.1

Khin-Moung-Gyi, Felix A.; Whalen, Matthew. Ethics and human subjects protection. *In:* Fedor, Carol A.; Cola, Philip A.; Pierre, Christine, eds. Responsible Research: A Guide for Coordinators. London; Chicago, IL: Remedics; 2006: 35-48. Subject: 18.2

Khoon, Chan Chee. Genomics, health, and society: a view from the South. *In:* Sleeboom, Margaret, ed. Genomics in Asia: A Clash of Bioethical Interests? New York: Kegan Paul; 2004: 301-316. Subject: 15.1

Khoshnood, Babak; De Vigan, Catherine; Vodovar, Véronique; Bréart, Gérard; Goffinet, François; Blondel, Béatrice. Advances in medical technology and creation of disparities: the case of Down syndrome. *American Journal of Public Health* 2006 December; 96(12): 2139-2144. Subject: 15.2

Khot, U.P.; Vellacott, K.D.; Swarnkar, K.J. Islamic practices: informed consent for stoma [letter]. *Colorectal Disease* 2005 September; 7(5): 529-530. Subject: 8.3.1

Khushf, George. Owning up to our agendas: on the role and limits of science in debates about embryos and brain death. *Journal of Law, Medicine, and Ethics* 2006 Spring; 34(1): 58-76. Subject: 4.4

Kidd, Maria. Ethical considerations in childhood immunizations for the advanced nurse practitioner. *In:* Bartter, Karen, ed. Ethical Issues in Advanced Nursing Practice. Boston: Butterworth-Heinemann; 2001: 66-79. Subject: 9.5.1

Kieniewicz, Piotr H. New frontiers, new dangers: ethical perspective. *In:* Glasa, J. ed. Ethics of Human Genetics: Challenges of the (Post) Genomic Era. Bratislava, Slovak Republic: Charis [and] IMEB Foundation; 2002: 209-223. Subject: 2.1

Kienle, Thomas. New forms of medical data collection — should be complemented by a new European privacy standard? *European Journal of Health Law* 2001 March; 8(1): 27-39. Subject: 8.4

Kietinun, Somboon. Research ethics review in government and academic institutions in Thailand. *Indian Journal of Medical Ethics* 2006 April-June; 3(2): 67-68. Subject: 18.2

Kikuchi, June F. Cultural theories of nursing responsive to human needs and values. *Journal of Nursing Scholarship* 2005; 37(4): 302-307. Subject: 4.1.3

Kilama, W.L. Ethical perspective on malaria research for Africa. *Acta Tropica* 2005 September; 95(3): 276-284. Subject: 18.5.9

Kilgour, David; Matas, David. Response of David Kilgour and David Matas to the Chinese government statement. Ottawa, Ontario, Canada: David Kilgour and David Matas, 2006 July 7; 4 p. [Online]. Accessed: http://investigation.redirectme.net [2006 July 27]. Subject: 19.5

Killien, Marcia; Bigby, Judy Ann; Champion, Victoria; Fernandez-Repollet, Emma; Jackson, Rebecca D.; Kagawa-Singer, Marjorie; Kidd, Kristin; Naughton, Michele J.; Prout, Marianne. Involving minority and underrepresented women in clinical trials: the National Centers of Excellence in Women's Health. *Journal of Women's Health and Gender-Based Medicine* 2000 December; 9(10): 1061-1070. Subject: 18.2

Kim, Dean Y.; Cauduro, Silvania P.; Bohorquez, Humberto E.; Ishitani, Michael B.; Nyberg, Scott L.; Rosen, Charles B. Routine use of livers from deceased donors older than 70: is it justified? *Transplant International* 2005 January; 18(1): 73-77. Subject: 19.5

Kim, Jung Ran; Fisher, Murray John; Elliott, Doug. Attitudes of intensive care nurses towards brain death and organ transplantation: instrument development and testing. *Journal of Advanced Nursing* 2006 March; 53(5): 571-582. Subject: 20.2.1

Kim, Jung Ran; Fisher, Murray; Elliott, Doug. Knowledge levels of Korean intensive care nurses towards brain death and organ transplantation. *Journal of Clinical Nursing* 2006 May; 15(5): 574-580. Subject: 20.2.1

Kim, Ock-Joo; Park, Byung-Joo; Lee, Seung-Mi; Sohn, Dong-Ryul; Shin, Sang-Goo. Current status of the

---

Subject = NRCBL Primary Classification Number; see inside front cover.

institutional review boards in Korea: constitution, operation and policy for protection of research participants. *In:* Sang-yong, Song; Young-Mo, Koo; Macer, Darryl R.J., eds. Asian Bioethics in the 21st Century. Christchurch, NZ: Eubios Ethics Institute, 2002: 17-27. Subject: 18.2

Kim, Ock-Joo; Park, Byung-Joo; Sohn, Dong-Ryul; Lee, Seung-Mi; Shin, Sanfg-Goo. Current status of the institutional review boards in Korea: constitution, operation, and policy for protection of human research participants. *Journal of Korean Medical Science* 2003 February; 18(1): 3-10. Subject: 18.2

Kim, S.Y.H.; Holloway, R.G.; Frank, S.; Beck, C.A.; Zimmerman, C.; Wilson, R.; Kieburtz, K. Volunteering for early phase gene transfer research in Parkinson disease. *Neurology* 2006 April 11; 66(7): 1010-1015. Subject: 15.4

Kim, Scott Y.H. Evidence-based ethics for neurology and psychiatry research. *NeuroRx* 2004 July; 1(3): 372-377. Subject: 18.2

Kim, Scott Y.H. When does decisional impairment become decisional incompetence? Ethical and methodological issues in capacity research in schizophrenia. *Schizophrenia Bulletin* 2006 January; 32(1): 92-97. Subject: 18.5.6

Kim, Scott Y.H.; Frank, Samuel; Holloway, Robert; Zimmerman, Carol; Wilson, Renee; Kieburtz, Karl. Science and ethics of sham surgery: a survey of Parkinson disease clinical researchers. *Archives of Neurology* 2005 September; 62(9): 1357-1360. Subject: 18.2

Kim, Scott Y.H.; Kim, Hyungjin Myra; McCallum, Colleen; Tariot, Pierre N. What do people at risk for Alzheimer disease think about surrogate consent for research? *Neurology* 2005 November 8; 65(9): 1395-1401. Subject: 18.3

Kim, Su Hyun. Confucian bioethics and cross-cultural considerations in health care decision making. *Journal of Nursing Law* 2005 Fall; 10(3): 161-166. Subject: 2.1

Kimmelman, Jonathan; Baylis, Françoise; Glass, Kathleen Cranley. Stem cell trials: lessons from gene transfer research. *Hastings Center Report* 2006 January-February; 36(1): 23-26. Subject: 18.5.4

Kimsma, G.K. Euthanasia for existential reasons. *Medical Ethics Newsletter [Lahey Clinic]* 2006 Winter; 13(1): 1-2, 12. Subject: 20.5.1

Kimsma, Gerrit K.; van Leeuwen, Evert. Euthanasie in den Niederlanden: Historische Entwicklung, Argumente und heutige Lage. *In:* Frewer, Andreas; Eickhoff, Clemens, eds. "Euthanasie" und die aktuelle Sterbehilfe-Debatte: Die historischen Hintergründe medizinischer Ethik. Frankfurt; New York: Campus; 2000: 276-312. Subject: 20.5.1

Kimsma, Gerrit; van Leeuwen, Evert. Euthanasie und Beihilfe zum Suizid in den Niederlanden. *In:* Gordijn, Bert; ten Have, Henk, eds. Medizinethik und Kultur:

Grenzen medizinischen Handelns in Deutschland und den Niederlanden. Stuttgart: Frommann-Holzboog; 2000: 71-103. Subject: 20.5.1

Kindregan, Charles P., Jr.; McBrien, Maureen. Posthumous reproduction. *Family Law Quarterly* 2005 Fall; 39(3): 579-597. Subject: 14.6

King, Dorothy. Lessons learned: what the Terri Schiavo case has taught us thus far. *Health Care Food and Nutrition Focus* 2005 September; 22(9): 1, 3-6. Subject: 20.5.1

King, Jaime Staples; Moulton, Benjamin W. Rethinking informed consent: the case for shared medical decision-making. *American Journal of Law and Medicine* 2006; 32(4): 429-501. Subject: 8.3.1

King, Nancy M.P. The line between clinical innovation and human experimentation. *Seton Hall Law Review* 2002; 32(3): 573-582. Subject: 18.2

King, Nancy M.P.; Orentlicher, David. Protection of human subjects and scientific progress: can the two be reconciled? [letter and reply]. *Hastings Center Report* 2006 January-February; 36(1): 6-7, 8- 9. Subject: 18.1

King, Tekoa L.; Murphy, Patricia Aikins. Editorial policies and publication ethics [editorial]. *Journal of Midwifery and Women's Health* 2006 March-April; 51(2): 69-70. Subject: 1.3.7

Kingma, Stuart. Biomedical ethics: in search of touchstone for tough choices. *Ecumenical Review* 1980 July; 32(3): 273-280. Subject: 2.1

Kingsbury, Brett. A line already drawn: the case for voluntary euthanasia after the withdrawal of life-sustaining hydration and nutrition. *Columbia Journal of Law and Social Problems* 2004 Winter; 38(2): 201-250. Subject: 20.5.1

Kinney, Anita Yeomans; Croyle, Robert T.; Dudley, William N.; Bailey, Christine A.; Pelias, Mary Kay; Neuhausen, Susan L. Knowledge, attitudes, and interest in breast-ovarian cancer gene testing: a survey of a large African-American kindred with a BRCA1 mutation. *Preventive Medicine* 2001 December; 33(6): 543-551. Subject: 15.3

Kinney, Eleanor D.; Clark, Brian Alexander. Provisions for health and health care in the constitutions of the countries of the world. *Cornell International Law Journal* 2004; 37(2): 285-355. Subject: 9.2

Kintisch, Eli. Scientists look to Missouri to show the way on stem cells [news]. *Science* 2006 November 3; 314(5800): 737, 739. Subject: 18.5.4

Kinzie, Susan. Med school owes its existence to many bodies of knowledge. *Washington Post* 2006 December 3; p. A1, A10. Subject: 7.2

Kipnis, Kenneth. A defense defended [letter]. *American Journal of Bioethics [Online]*. 2006 March-April; 6(2): W32-W34. Subject: 8.4

See SUBJECT HEADING KEY FOR SECTION II on inside back cover.

621

Kipnis, Kenneth. A defense of unqualified medical confidentiality. *American Journal of Bioethics* 2006 March-April; 6(2): 7-18. Subject: 8.4

Kipnis, Kenneth. Professional ethics and instructional success. *In:* American Medical Association. ProfessingMedicine: strengthening the ethics and professionalism of tomorrow's physicians. Chicago: American Medical Association; 2001: 21-32. Subject: 2.3

Kipnis, Kenneth. Professional ethics and instructional success. *Virtual Mentor* 2001 November; 3(11): 4p. Subject: 2.3

Kipnis, Kenneth. Taking families seriously enough. *American Journal of Bioethics* 2006 January-February; 6(1): 21-22; discussion W27-W28. Subject: 8.2

Kipnis, Kenneth; King, Nancy M.P.; Nelson, Robert M. An open letter to institutional review boards considering Northfield Laboratories' PolyHeme trial. *American Journal of Bioethics* 2006 May-June; 6(3): 18-21; discussion W49- W50. Subject: 18.2

Kipnis, Kenneth; King, Nancy M.P.; Nelson, Robert M. Trials and errors: barriers to oversight of research conducted under the emergency research consent waiver. *IRB: Ethics and Human Research* 2006 March-April; 28(2): 16-19. Subject: 18.3

Kippax, Susan. A public health dilemma: a testing question. *AIDS Care* 2006 April; 18(3): 230-235. Subject: 9.5.6

Kipper, Delio Jose; Piva, Jefferson Pedro; Garcia, Pedro Celiny Ramos; Einloft, Paulo Roberto; Bruno, Francisco; Lago, Patricia; Rocha, Tais; Schein, Alaor Ernst; Fontela, Patricia Scolari; Gava, Debora Hendler; Guerra, Luciano; Chemello, Keli; Bittencourt, Roney; Sudbrack, Simone; Mulinari, Evandro Freddy; Morais, Joao Feliz Duarte. Evolution of the medical practices and modes of death on pediatric intensive care units in southern Brazil. *Pediatric Critical Care Medicine* 2005 May; 6(3): 258-263. Subject: 20.5.2

Kirby, Michael. HIV vaccine: ethics and human rights. *Canadian HIV/AIDS Policy and Law Newsletter* 2000 Spring-Summer; 5(2-3): 16-20. Subject: 9.5.6

Kirby, Michael. Human freedom and the human genome (Part I). *Revista de Derecho Genoma Humano = Law and the Human Genome Review* 1999 January-June; (10): 107-114. Subject: 15.10

Kirby, Michael. Human freedom and the human genome (Part II). *Revista de Derecho Genoma Humano = Law and the Human Genome Review* 1999 July-December; (11): 71-84. Subject: 15.10

Kirby, Michael. The human genome and patent law. *Reform* 2001 Spring; 79: 10-13, 70. Subject: 15.10

Kirby, Michael. The Human Genome Project and its challenges to society = Proyecto Genoma Humano y su desafio a la sociedad. *Law and the Human Genome Review =* *Revista de Derecho y Genoma Humano* 1996 July-December; (5): 73-85. Subject: 15.10

Kirby, Michael. Meeting our friend, the genome. *Revista de Derecho y Genoma Humano = Law and the Human Genome Review* 1998 January-June; (8): 60-70. Subject: 15.10

Kirby, Michael. Playing God? Owning God? — Patenting and the human genome [forum]. *University of New South Wales Law Journal* 2003; 26(3): 770- 781. Subject: 15.8

Kirk, E.P.; Cregan, K. Ethics of therapeutic cloning [letter and reply]. *Internal Medicine Journal* 2005 August; 35(8): 500-501. Subject: 14.5

Kirklin, Deborah. Humanities in medical training and education. *Clinical Medicine* 2001 January-February; 1(1): 25-27. Subject: 7.2

Kirkman, Maggie. Public health and the challenge of genomics. *Australian and New Zealand Journal of Public Health* 2005 April; 29(2): 163-165. Subject: 15.10

Kirkpatrick, James N.; Kim, Antony Y. Heart failure ethics: overview of an emerging need. *Perspectives on Biology and Medicine* 2006 Winter; 49(1): 1-9. Subject: 9.5.2

Kirschen, Matthew P.; Jaworska, Agnieszka; Illes, Judy. Subjects' expectations in neuroimaging research. *Journal of Magnetic Resonance Imaging* 2006 February; 23(2): 205-209. Subject: 18.3

Kirschner, Kristi L. Unequal stakeholders: "for you, it's an academic exercise; for me, it's my life". *American Journal of Bioethics* 2006 September-October; 6(5): 30-32; discussion W30-W32. Subject: 9.5.1

Kirschner, Kristi L. When written advance directives are not enough. *Clinics in Geriatric Medicine* 2005 February; 21(1): 193-209. Subject: 20.5.4

Kirsner, Robert S.; Federman, Daniel G. The ethical dilemma of population-based medical decision making. *American Journal of Managed Care* 1998 November; 4(11): 1571-1576. Subject: 9.4

Kischer, C. Ward. The American Association of Anatomists and stem cell research. *Linacre Quarterly* 2006 May; 73(2): 164-171. Subject: 18.5.4

Kishore, R.R. Biomedical research and mining of the poor: the need for their exclusion. *Science and Engineering Ethics* 2006 January; 12(1): 175-183. Subject: 18.5.1

Kishore, R.R. Human genome: the promises, concerns and controversies (part I) = El Genoma Humano: promesas, preocupaciones y controversias (Parte I). *Revista de Derecho Genoma Humano = Law and the Human Genome Review* 1997 January-June; (6): 171-180. Subject: 15.1

Kishore, R.R. Human Genome: the promises, concerns and controversies (part II) = El Genoma Humano: promesas, preocupaciones y controversias (Parte II).

Revista de Derecho Genoma Humano = Law and the Human Genome Review 1997 July-December; (7): 189-197. Subject: 15.8

Kiskaddon, Sarah H. Balancing access to participation in research and protection from risks: applying the principle of justice. *Journal of Nutrition* 2005 April; 135(4): 929-932. Subject: 18.2

Kissling, Frances. Does church doctrine trump rape victims' needs? *Conscience* 2006 Autumn; 27(3): 17. Subject: 11.1

Kissling, Frances. Should abortion be prevented? *Conscience* 2006-2007 Winter; 27(4): 13-16. Subject: 12.4.2

Kissling, Frances. The Vatican and reproductive freedom. *Conscience* 2006-2007; 27(Special European Supplement): 20-22. Subject: 14.1

Kitamura, Toshinori. Stress-reductive effects of information disclosure to medical and psychiatric patients. *Psychiatry and Clinical Neurosciences* 2005 December; 59(6): 627-633. Subject: 8.3.1

Kitamura, Toshinori; Kitamura, Fusako. Competency testing in medical and psychiatric practice: legal and psychological concepts and dilemmas. *In:* Takahashi, Takao, ed. Taking Life and Death Seriously: Bioethics from Japan. Amsterdam; Boston: Elsevier JAI; 2005: 113-138. Subject: 17.1

Kitcher, Philip; Cartwright, Nancy. Science and ethics: reclaiming some neglected questions. *Perspectives on Science* 1996 Summer; 4(2): 145-153. Subject: 5.1

Kittay, Eva Feder. The concept of care ethics in biomedicine: the case of disability. *In:* Rehmann-Sutter, Christoph; Düwell, Marcus; Mieth, Dietmar, eds. Bioethics in Cultural Contexts: Reflections on Methods and Finitude. Dordrecht: Springer, 2006: 319-339. Subject: 2.1

Kittay, Eva Feder; Jennings, Bruce; Wasunna, Angela A. Dependency, difference and the global ethic of longterm care. *Journal of Political Philosophy* 2005 December; 13(4): 443-469. Subject: 9.5.1

Kitzinger, Jenny; Williams, Clare. Forecasting science futures: legitimising hope and calming fears in the embryo stem cell debate. *Social Science and Medicine* 2005 August; 61(3): 731-740. Subject: 18.5.4

Kjeldsen, Sverre E.; Narkiewicz, Krzysztof; Cifková, Renata; Mancia, Giuseppe. ESH statement on detection and punishment of abstract fraud and poster plagiarism. *Blood Pressure* 2005; 14(6): 322-323. Subject: 1.3.9

Kjeldsen, Sverre E.; Narkiewicz, Krzysztof; Cifkova, Renata; Mancia, Giuseppe. ESH statement on detection and punishment of abstract fraud and poster plagiarism. *Journal of Hypertension* 2006 January; 24(1): 203-204. Subject: 1.3.9

Kjervik, Diane K. Advance directives: promoting self-determination or hampering autonomy. *In:* Cowen,

Perle Slavik; Moorhead, Sue, eds. Current Issues in Nursing. 7th ed. St. Louis, MO: Mosby, 2006: 652-659. Subject: 20.5.4

Klag, Stefanie; O'Callaghan, Frances; Creed, Peter. The use of legal coercion in the treatment of substance abusers: an overview and critical analysis of thirty years of research. *Substance Use and Misuse* 2005; 40(12): 1777-1795. Subject: 9.5.9

Klampfer, Friderik. Suicide, euthanasia and human dignity. *Acta Analytica* 2001; 16(27): 7-34. Subject: 20.7

Klarenbach, Scott; Garg, Amit X.; Vlaicu, Sorina. Living organ donors face financial barriers: a national reimbursement policy is needed. *CMAJ/JAMC: Canadian Medical Association Journal* 2006 March 14; 174(6): 797-798. Subject: 19.3

Klatt, Edward C.; Florell, Scott R.; Rodgers, George M. Genetic testing in autopsies [letter and reply]. *American Journal of Clinical Pathology* 2000 February; 113(2): 311-312. Subject: 15.3

Kleiman, Mark. The 'brain disease' idea, drug policy and research ethics. *Addiction* 2003 July; 98(7): 871-872. Subject: 18.4

Klein, Renate. Women as body parts in the era of reproductive and genetic engineering. *Health Care for Women International* 1991 October-December; 12(4): 393-405. Subject: 14.4

Kleinfeld, Joshua. Tort law and in vitro fertilization: the need for legal recognition of "procreative injury". *Yale Law Journal* 2005 October; 115(1): 237-245. Subject: 14.4

Kleinman, Carol S. Ethical drift: when good people do bad things. *JONA's Healthcare Law, Ethics, and Regulation* 2006 July-September; 8(3): 72-76. Subject: 4.1.1

Klemp, Jennifer R.; O'Dea, Anne; Chamberlain, Carolyn; Fabian, Carol J. Patient satisfaction of BRCA1/2 genetic testing by women at high risk for breast cancer participating in a prevention trial. *Familial Cancer* 2005; 4(4): 279-284. Subject: 15.3

Klerkx, Greg. The transhumanists as tribe. *In:* Miller, Paul; Wilsdon, James, eds. Better Humans?: The Politics of Human Enhancement and Life Extension. London: Demos, 2006: 59-66. Subject: 4.5

Klick, Jonathan. Econometric analyses of U.S. abortion policy: a critical review. *Fordham Urban Law Journal* 2004 March; 31(3): 751-782. Subject: 12.5.1

Klick, Jonathan. Mandatory waiting periods for abortions and female mental health. *Health Matrix: The Journal of Law-Medicine* 2006 Winter; 16(1): 183-208. Subject: 12.5.3

Kline, A. David. On complicity theory. *Science and Engineering Ethics* 2006 April; 12(2): 257-264. Subject: 1.3.9

See SUBJECT HEADING KEY FOR SECTION II on inside back cover.

Klinnert, Lars. Die kontroverse um die embryonale stammzellforschung — zurück auf der biopolitischen tagesordnung [The controversy about embryonic stem cell research — back on the biopolitical agenda]. *Ethik in der Medizin* 2006 September; 18(3): 273-275. Subject: 18.5.4

Klipstein, Sigal. Preimplantation genetic diagnosis: technological promise and ethical perils. *Fertility and Sterility* 2005 May; 83(5): 1347-1353. Subject: 15.2

Klitzman, Robert. "Post-residency disease" and the medical self: identity, work, and health care among doctors who become patients. *Perspectives in Biology and Medicine* 2006 Autumn; 49(4): 542-552. Subject: 7.3

Klitzman, Robert. Complications of culture in obtaining informed consent. *American Journal of Bioethics* 2006 January-February; 6(1): 20-21; discussion W27-W28. Subject: 8.2

Klitzman, Robert. Genetic testing creates new versions of ancient dilemmas. *New York Times* 2006 January 17; p. F5. Subject: 15.3

Klitzman, Robert. Qualifying confidentiality: historical and empirical issues. *American Journal of Bioethics* 2006 March-April; 6(2): 26-27. Subject: 8.4

Klitzman, Robert. Questions, complexities, and limitations in disclosing individual genetic results. *American Journal of Bioethics* 2006 November-December; 6(6): 34-36; author reply W10-W12. Subject: 15.1

Klitzman, Robert; Kirshenbaum, Sheri; Kittel, Lauren; Morin, Stephen; Daya, Shaira; Mastrogiacomo, Maddalena; Rotheram-Borus, Mary Jane. Naming names: perceptions of name-based HIV reporting, partner notification, and criminalization of non-disclosure among persons living with HIV. *Sexuality Research and Social Policy* 2004; 1(3): 38-57. [Online]. Accessed: http://caliber.ucpress.net/doi/pdf/10.1525/srsp.2004.1.3.38 [2006 November 27]. Subject: 9.5.6

Klontz, Bradley T. Ethical practice of group experiential psychotherapy. *Psychotherapy* 2004 Summer; 41(2): 172-179. Subject: 17.2

Klove, Carole A.; DiBoise, Sarah J.; Pang, Betty; Yarbrough, William C. Informed consent: ethical and legal aspects. *Thoracic Surgery Clinics* 2005 May; 15(2): 213-219. Subject: 8.3.1

Kluge, Eike-Henner W. Competence, capacity, and informed consent: beyond the cognitive-competence model. *Canadian Journal of Aging* 2005 Fall; 24(3): 295-304. Subject: 8.3.1

Klugman, Craig M. Have and have nots. *American Journal of Bioethics* 2006 March-April; 6(2): 63-64. Subject: 9.5.1

Kmietowicz, Zosia. Advertisements highlight MSD's inappropriate hospitality [news]. *BMJ: British Medical Journal* 2006 September 30; 333(7570): 671. Subject: 9.7

Kmietowicz, Zosia. Doctors backtrack on assisted suicide [news]. *BMJ: British Medical Journal* 2006 July 8; 333(7558): 64. Subject: 20.7

Kmietowicz, Zosia. Rules for drug trials should be tightened, say experts [news]. *BMJ: British Medical Journal* 2006 August 5; 333(7562): 276. Subject: 18.2

Kmietowicz, Zosia. Sickle cell screening makes genetic counselling everybody's business [news]. *BMJ: British Medical Journal* 2006 March 11; 332(7541): 570. Subject: 15.3

Knapp, Samuel; VandeCreek, Leon. Ethical and patient management issues with older, impaired drivers. *Professional Psychology: Research and Practice* 2005 April; 36(2): 197-202. Subject: 9.5.2

Knapp, Samuel; VandeCreek, Leon. A principle-based analysis of the 2002 American Psychological Association Ethics Code. *Psychotherapy* 2004 Fall; 41(3): 247-254. Subject: 6

Knestout, Brian P. An essential prescription: why pharmacist-inclusive conscience clauses are necessary. *Journal of Contemporary Health Law and Policy* 2006 Spring; 22(2): 349-382. Subject: 9.7

Knoepffler, Nikolaus. Konfliktfälle am Lebensanfang. *In his:* Menschenwürde in der Bioethik. New York: Springer; 2004: 95-138. Subject: 18.5.4

Knoepffler, Nikolaus. Konfliktfälle am Lebensende. *In his:* Menschenwürde in der Bioethik. New York: Springer; 2004: 139-170. Subject: 20.5.1

Knoepffler, Nikolaus. Konfliktfälle bei gentechnischen Eingriffen am Menschen. *In his:* Menschenwürde in der Bioethik. New York: Springer; 2004: 171-182. Subject: 15.1

Knoppers, Bartha Maria. Geneticism and germ line: between courage and caution. *Politics and the Life Sciences* 1998 March; 17(1): 22-24. Subject: 15.4

Knoppers, Bartha Maria. Genetics and common law. *In:* Meulders-Klein, Marie-Thérèse; Deech, Ruth; Vlaardingerbroek, Paul, eds. Biomedicine, the Family and Human Rights. New York: Kluwer Law International, 2002: 397-414. Subject: 15.1

Knoppers, Bartha Maria. Human genetics: parental, professional and political responsibility. *Health Law Journal* 1993; 1(1): 13-23. Subject: 15.2

Knoppers, Bartha Maria; Fecteau, Claudine. Human genomic databases: a global public good? *European Journal of Health Law* 2003 March; 10(1): 27-41. Subject: 15.10

Knoppers, Bartha Maria; Saginur, Madelaine. The Babel of genetic data terminology. *Nature Biotechnology* 2005 August; 23(8): 925-927. Subject: 15.1

Knoppers, Bartha Maria; Saginur, Madelaine; Cash, Howard. Ethical issues in secondary uses of human biological materials from mass disasters. *Journal of Law, Medicine and Ethics* 2006 Summer; 34(2): 352-365. Subject: 15.1

Knowles, Ann D.; McMahon, Marilyn. Expectations and preferences regarding confidentiality in the psychologist-client relationship. *Australian Psychologist* 1995 November; 30(3): 175-178. Subject: 8.4

Knox, Crissy; Vereb, John A. Allow natural death: a more humane approach to discussing end-of-life directives. *Journal of Emergency Nursing* 2005 December; 31(6): 560-561. Subject: 20.5.1

Knudsen, Lisbeth Ehlert. Workplace genetic screening. *In:* Westerholm, Peter; Nilstun, Tore; Øvretveit, John, eds. Practical Ethics in Occupational Health. San Francisco: Radcliffe Medical Press; 2004: 223-239. Subject: 15.3

Knupp, Jackie. Kant's assessment of motivation in the fulfillment of social obligations. *Penn Bioethics Journal* 2006; 2(2): 29-32. Subject: 8.1

Koch, Douglas D. Refractive lens exchange: ethical considerations in the informed consent process. *Journal of Cataract and Refractive Surgery* 2005 May; 31(5): 863. Subject: 8.3.1

Koch, Douglas D. Truth or consequences. *Journal of Cataract and Refractive Surgery* 2005 September; 31(9): 1679-1680. Subject: 1.3.9

Koch, Hans-Georg. Aktuelle Rechtsfragen der Sterbehilfe im deutschen Recht. *In:* Gordijn, Bert; ten Have, Henk, eds. Medizinethik und Kultur: Grenzen medizinischen Handelns in Deutschland und den Niederlanden. Stuttgart: Frommann-Holzboog; 2000: 225-265. Subject: 20.5.1

Koch, Lene. The government of genetic knowledge. *In:* Lundin, Susanne; Åkesson, Lynn, eds. Gene Technology and Economy. Lund: Nordic Academic Press; 2002: 92-103. Subject: 15.1

Koch, Rose. Conjoined twins and the biological account of personal identity. Unpublished Document, University at Buffalo 2004 November 14: 18 p. Subject: 4.4

Koch, Tom. Bioethics as ideology: conditional and unconditional values. *Journal of Medicine and Philosophy* 2006 June; 31(3): 251-267. Subject: 2.1

Koch, T. Weaponizing medicine: "tutti fratelli," no more. *Journal of Medical Ethics* 2006 May; 32(5): 249-252. Subject: 21.1

Kochiras, Hylarie. Freud said — or Simon says? Informed consent and the advancement of psychoanalysis as a science. *Medicine, Health Care and Philosophy* 2006; 9(2): 227-241. Subject: 17.2

Koch-Hershenov, Rose. Totipotency, twinning, and ensoulment at fertilization. *Journal of Medicine and Philosophy* 2006 April; 31(2): 139-164. Subject: 4.4

Koester, Kimberly A.; Maiorana, Andre; Vernon, Karen; Charlebois, Edwin; Gaffney, Stuart; Lane, Tim; Morin, Stephen F. HIV surveillance in theory and practice: assessing the acceptability of California's non-name HIV surveillance regulations. *Health Policy* 2006 August 22; 78(1): 101-110. Subject: 9.5.6

Koh, Younsuck; Ku, Eun Yong; Koo, Young-Mo; Kim, Ock-Joo; Lee, Soon Haeng; Lee, Sang Il; Han, Oh Su. Ethical issues identified in intensive care units of a university hospital. *In:* Sang-yong, Song; Young-Mo, Koo; Macer, Darryl R.J., eds. Asian Bioethics in the 21st Century. Christchurch, NZ: Eubios Ethics Institute, 2002: 108-109. Subject: 4.1.3

Kohane, Isaac S.; Masys, Daniel R.; Altman, Russ B. The incidentalome: a threat to genomic medicine. *JAMA: the Journal of the American Medical Association* 2006 July 12; 296(2): 212-215. Subject: 15.3

Kohi, Thecla W.; Makoae, Lucy; Chirwa, Maureen; Holzemer, William L.; Phetlhu, Deliwe René; Uys, Leana; Naidoo, Joanne; Dlamini, Priscilla S.; Greeff, Minrie. HIV and AIDS stigma violates human rights in five African countries. *Nursing Ethics* 2006 July; 13(4): 404-415. Subject: 9.5.6

Koivusalo, Meri. The impact of economic globalisation on health. *Theoretical Medicine and Bioethics* 2006; 27(1): 13-34. Subject: 9.1

Kolar, Roman. Animal experimentation. *Science and Engineering Ethics* 2006 January; 12(1): 111-122. Subject: 22.2

Kolata, Gina. Medicare says it will pay, but patients say "no thanks". *New York Times* 2006 March 3; p. C1, C4. Subject: 18.1

Kolata, Gina. Study questions colonoscopy effectiveness. *New York Times* 2006 December 14; p. A36. Subject: 9.5.1

Kolber, Morey J. Stark regulation: a historical and current review of the self-referral laws. *HEC (Healthcare Ethics Committee) Forum* 2006 March; 18(1): 61-84. Subject: 9.3.1

Kolchinsky, Alexander. Evaded bioethics [letter]. *Surgical Neurology* 2000 August; 54(2): 199. Subject: 4.1.2

Koller, Regine. Mind metaphors, neurosciences and ethics. *In:* Rees, Dai; Rose, Steven, eds. The New Brain Sciences: Perils and Prospects. New York: Cambridge University Press; 2004: 71-87. Subject: 17.1

Komel, Radovan. Practical and legal aspects and public debate on ethics in human genetics in Slovenia. *In:* Glasa, J., ed. Ethics of Human Genetics: Challenges of the (Post) Genomic Era. Bratislava, Slovak Republic: Charis [and] IMEB Foundation; 2002: 33-40. Subject: 15.1

Komesaroff, Paul A. Ethical issues in the relationships with industry: an ongoing challenge. New guidelines open for public comment. *Journal of Paediatrics and Child Health* 2005 November; 41(11): 558-560. Subject: 7.3

See SUBJECT HEADING KEY FOR SECTION II on inside back cover.

625

Komesaroff, Paul A. The relationship between law and ethics in medicine. *Internal Medicine Journal* 2001 September-October; 31(7): 413-414. Subject: 2.1

Kompanje, Erwin J.O.; Maas, A.I.R.; Hilhorst, M.T.; Slieker, F.J.A.; Teasdale, G.M. Ethical considerations on consent procedures for emergency research in severe and moderate traumatic brain injury. *Acta Neurochirurgica* 2005 June; 147(6): 633-640. Subject: 18.3

Kompanje, Erwin J.O.; van Zuylen, Lia; van der Rijt, C.C.D. Karin. Morphine is not a sedative and does not shorten life. *Archives of Internal Medicine* 2006 October 9; 166(18): 2047-2048. Subject: 20.4.1

Kon, Alexander A. When parents refuse treatment for their child. *JONA's Healthcare Law, Ethics, and Regulation* 2006 January-March; 8(1): 5-11. Subject: 8.3.2

Kon, Alexander A.; Klug, Michael. Methods and practices of investigators for determining participants' decisional capacity and comprehension of protocols. *Journal of Empirical Research on Human Research Ethics* 2006 December; 1(4): 61-68. Subject: 8.3.3

Kondro, Wayne. Conflicts cause FDA to review advisory committees. *CMAJ/JAMC: Canadian Medical Association Journal* 2006 July 4; 175(1): 23-24. Subject: 9.7

Kondro, Wayne. Dispute over Vioxx study plays out in New England Journal [news]. *CMAJ/JAMC:Canadian Medical Association Journal* 2006 May 9; 174(10): 1397. Subject: 18.2

Konrad, Monica. Placebo politics: on comparability, interdisciplinarity and international collaborative research. *Monash Bioethics Review* 2006 October; 25(4): 67-84. Subject: 18.3

Koo, Mi Jung; Yang, Jae Sub. Reflections on the human dignity in genetics. *In:* Sang-yong, Song; Young-Mo, Koo; Macer, Darryl R.J., eds. Asian Bioethics in the 21st Century. Christchurch, NZ: Eubios Ethics Institute, 2002: 165-171. Subject: 15.1

Koocher, Gerald P. Confidentiality in psychological practice. *Australian Psychologist* 1995 November; 30(3): 158-163. Subject: 8.4

Koocher, Gerald P. Ethics and the advertising of professional services: blame Canada. *Canadian Psychology/Psychologie Canadienne* 2004 May; 45(2): 137-138. Subject: 8.1

Kopala, Beverly; Burkhart, Lisa. Ethical dilemma and moral distress: proposed new NANDA diagnoses. *International Journal of Nursing Terminologies and Classifications* 2005 January-March; 16(1): 3-13. Subject: 4.1.3

Kopelman, Loretta M. Bioethics as a second-order discipline: who is not a bioethicist? *Journal of Medicine and Philosophy* 2006 December; 31(6): 601-628. Subject: 2.1

Kopelman, Loretta M. What is unique about the doctor and patient medical encounter? A moral and economic per-

spective. *American Journal of Bioethics* 2006 March-April; 6(2): 85-88. Subject: 2.1

Kopelman, Loretta M. When should research with infants, children, or adolescents be permitted? *In:* Iltis, Ana Smith, ed. Research Ethics. New York: Routledge, 2006: 121-131. Subject: 18.5.2

Koper, Megan; Bubela, Tania; Caulfield, Timothy; Boon, Heather. Media portrayal of conflicts of interest in herbal remedy clinical trials. *Health Law Review* 2006; 15(1): 9-11. Subject: 4.1.1

Koppelman-White, Elysa. Research misconduct and the scientific process: continuing quality improvement. *Accountability in Research* 2006 July-September; 13(3): 225-246. Subject: 1.3.9

Kordsmeier, Julie. Influenza vaccinations: should they be mandatory for nurses? *MCN: The American Journal of Maternal Child Nursing* 2006 March-April; 31(2): 76. Subject: 9.5.1

Korean Academy of Medical Sciences. Incident of "human cloning" from Kyunghee University Medical Center [editorial]. *Journal of Korean Medical Science* 1999 February; 14(1): 1. Subject: 14.5

Körtner, Ulrich H.J. Frailty: medizinethische Überlegungen zur Gebrechlichkeit des alten Menschen [Frailty: medical ethical considerations about the frailty of the elderly]. *Ethik in der Medizin* 2006 June; 18(2): 108-119. Subject: 9.5.2

Korts, Külliki. Becoming masters of our genes: public acceptance of the Estonian Genome Project. *In:* Árnason, Gardar; Nordal, Salvör; Árnason, Vilhjálmur, eds. Blood and Data: Ethical, Legal and Social Aspects of Human Genetic Databases. Reykjavík: University of Iceland Press; 2004: 187-192. Subject: 15.1

Kostopoulou, V.; Katsouyanni, K. The truth-telling issue and changes in lifestyle in patients with cancer. *Journal of Medical Ethics* 2006 December; 32(12): 693-697. Subject: 8.2

Kothari, Sunil; Kirschner, Kristi. Beyond consent: assent and empowerment in brain injury rehabilitation. *Journal of Head Trauma Rehabilitation* 2003 July-August; 18(4): 379-382. Subject: 8.3.3

Kottow, Michael H. Letter to the editor: a commentary on M.K. Wynia's "Consequentialism and Harsh Interrogations". *American Journal of Bioethics [Online]*. 2006 March-April; 6(2): W36. Subject: 21.4

Kottow, Michael H. Should medical ethics justify violence? *Journal of Medical Ethics* 2006 August; 32(8): 464-467. Subject: 21.2

Kotva, Joseph J. Facing biotechnology as an alternative community of worship, character, and discernment. *In:* Miller, Roman J.; Brubaker, Beryl H.; Peterson, James C., eds. Viewing New Creations with Anabaptist Eyes: Ethics

---

Subject = NRCBL Primary Classification Number; see inside front cover.

of Biotechnology. Telford, PA: Cascadia Pub.; 2005: 261-289. Subject: 5.1

Kozlowski, Lynn T.; Edwards, B.Q. "Not safe" is not enough: smokers have a right to know more than there is no safe tobacco product. *Tobacco Control* 2005 August; 14(Supplement 2): ii3-ii7. Subject: 9.5.9

Kraft, Dina. A hunt for genes that betrayed a desert people. *New York Times* 2006 March 21; p. F1, F4. Subject: 15.11

Kramer, Irwin R. Life and death decisions: a reply to Judge Peccarelli. *John Marshall Law Review* 1990 Summer; 23(4): 569-583. Subject: 20.5.1

Kramers, Cornelis; Deinum, Jaap; Gawande, Atul. Why physicians participate in executions [letter and reply]. *New England Journal of Medicine* 2006 July 6; 355(1): 99-100. Subject: 20.6

Kramlich, Maureen. The abortion debate thirty years later: from choice to coercion. *Fordham Urban Law Journal* 2004 March; 31(3): 783-804. Subject: 12.1

Krause, Joan H. Ethical lawyering in the gray areas: health care fraud and abuse. *Journal of Law, Medicine, and Ethics* 2006 Spring; 34(1): 121-125. Subject: 9.1

Krause-Bachand, Jeanie. Ethical considerations in nursing research. *SCI Nursing* 2002 Fall; 19(3): 136-137. Subject: 18.2

Kremer, H.; Bader, A.; O'Cleirigh, C.; Bierhoff, H.W.; Brockmeyer, N.H. The decision to forgo antiretroviral therapy in people living with HIV — compliance as paternalism or partnership? *European Journal of Medical Research* 2004; 9(2): 61-70. Subject: 9.5.6

Krentel, John Bologna. The Louisiana "human embryo" statute revisited: reasonable recognition and protection for the in vitro fertilized ovum. *Loyola Law Review* 1999 Summer; 45(2): 239-246. Subject: 4.4

Kreß, Hartmut. Gesundheitsschutz und Embryonenschutz in Ethisch-rechtlicher Abwägung. Bericht der Bioethik-Kommission Rheinland-Pfalz zum revisionsbedarf von Embryonenschutz und Stammzellgesetz = Health protection and embryo protection from an ethical-legal perspective. Report of the Bioethics Committee of Rheinland-Pfalz on the need to revise the embryoprotection and stem cell laws. *Ethik in der Medizin* 2006 March; 18(1): 92-99. Subject: 14.1

Kriari-Catranis, Ismini. Human assisted procreation and human rights — the Greek response to the felt necessities of the time. *European Journal of Health Law* 2003 September; 10(3): 271-280. Subject: 14.4

Krimsky, Sheldon. Science, biopolitics, and risk: margins of uncertainty. *Politics and the Life Sciences* 1989 February; 7(2): 140-142. Subject: 15.7

Krishnan, Suneeta. People's voices on justice, equity and health care in India [review of Health Matters by Shikha

Jhingan]. *Indian Journal of Medical Ethics* 2006 July-September; 3(3): 109. Subject: 9.3.1

Kristinsson, Sigurdur. Databases and informed consent: can broad consent legitimate research? *In:* Árnason, Gardar; Nordal, Salvör; Árnason, Vilhjálmur, eds. Blood and Data: Ethical, Legal and Social Aspects of Human Genetic Databases. Reykjavík: University of Iceland Press; 2004: 111-119. Subject: 15.1

Kristjanson, Linda J.; Christakis, Nicholas. Investigating euthanasia: methodological, ethical and clinical considerations [editorial]. *Palliative Medicine* 2005 December; 19(8): 575-577. Subject: 20.5.1

Krizova, Eva. Alternative medicine: a dispute on truth, power, or money? *In:* Rehmann-Sutter, Christoph; Düwell, Marcus; Mieth, Dietmar, eds. Bioethics in Cultural Contexts: Reflections on Methods and Finitude. Dordrecht: Springer, 2006: 197-210. Subject: 4.1.1

Krohmal, Benjamin J.; Sobolski, Gregory K. Commentary: physicians and risk of malevolent use of research. *CQ: Cambridge Quarterly of Healthcare Ethics* 2006 Fall; 15(4): 441-444. Subject: 1.3.9

Krohn, Wolfgang. Enquete commissions. *In:* Mitcham, Carl, ed. Encyclopedia of Science, Technology, and Ethics. Farmington Hills, MI: Thomson/Gale, 2005: 641-644. Subject: 5.3

Krones, Tanja. The scope of the recent bioethics debate in Germany: Kant, crisis, and no confidence in society. *CQ: Cambridge Quarterly of Healthcare Ethics* 2006 Summer; 15(3): 273-281. Subject: 2.1

Krones, Tanja; Neuwonhner, Elke; El Ansari, Susan; Wissner, Thomas; Richter, Gerd. Kinderwunsch und Wunschkinder: Möglichkeiten und Grenzen der in-vitro-fertilisations-Behandlung = Desire for a child and desired children — possibilities and limits of reproductive biomedicine. *Ethik in der Medizin* 2006 March; 18(1): 51-62. Subject: 14.4

Krosnar, Katka. Women forced into sterilisation protest to UN [news]. *BMJ: British Medical Journal* 2006 August 26; 333(7565): 410. Subject: 11.3

Krupp, Brandon H. Ethical issues in forensic medicine in Rhode Island. *Medicine and Health Rhode Island* 2005 December; 88(12): 418-420. Subject: 4.1.2

Kruse, Katherine. Constitutionality of recognizing multiple parental rights in the surrogacy context. *Wisconsin Women's Law Journal* 1992-1993; 7-8: 67-84. Subject: 14.2

Kubar, Olga. Ethical aspects in clinical trials in the CIS, in particular the setting up of ethical committees. *Journal International de Bioéthique = International Journal of Bioethics* 2005 September-December; 16(3-4): 81-87, 172-173. Subject: 18.6

Kubiak, Cinead R. Conflicting interests and conflicting laws: re-aligning the purpose and practice of research eth-

See SUBJECT HEADING KEY FOR SECTION II on inside back cover.

627

ics committees. *Brooklyn Journal of International Law* 2005; 30(2): 759-812. Subject: 18.2

Kubsch, Sylvia M.; Hankerson, Christine; Ghoorahoo, Raschid. Content analysis of holistic ethics. *Complementary Therapies in Clinical Practice* 2005 February; 11(1): 51-57. Subject: 4.1.1

Kuczewski, Mark G. Our cultures, our selves: toward an honest dialogue on race and end of life decisions. *American Journal of Bioethics* 2006 September-October; 6(5): 13-17; discussion W30-W32. Subject: 20.4.1

Kuczewski, Mark G.; Marshall, Patricia. The decision dynamics of clinical research: the context and process of informed consent. *Medical Care* 2002 September; 40(9, Supplement): V45-V54. Subject: 18.3

Kuehn, Bridget M. Group backs emergency contraception. *JAMA: The Journal of the American Medical Association* 2006 June 21; 295(23): 2708-2709. Subject: 11.1

Kuhar, Michael J. Should codes of ethics include expectations of others? [letter]. *Science and Engineering Ethics* 2006 July; 12(3): 413-414. Subject: 6

Kuhn, Duncan M. Problem doctors: is there a system-level solution? [letter]. *Annals of Internal Medicine* 2006 June 6; 144(11): 861. Subject: 7.4

Kuhse, Helga. Why terminal sedation is no solution to the voluntary euthanasia debate. *In:* Tännsjö, Torbjörn, ed. Terminal Sedation: Euthanasia in Disguise? Boston: Kluwer Academic Publishers; 2004: 57-70. Subject: 20.4.1

Kuitenbrouwer, Frank. Privacy and its fallacies [editorial]. *European Journal of Health Law* 2002 September; 9(3): 173-179. Subject: 8.4

Kukla, Rebecca. The limits of lines: negotiating hard medicine choices. *Newsletter on Philosophy and Medicine* 2005 Fall; 05(1): 15-19. Subject: 9.4

Kumar, Nandini K. Bioethics activities in India. *Eastern Mediterranean Health Journal* 2006; 12(Supplement 1): S56-S65 [Online]. Accessed: http://www.emro.who.int/publications/EMHJ/12_S/PDF/9.pdf [2007 January 4]. Subject: 2.3

Kumar, T.C. Anand. Legislation on reproductive technologies in India [editorial]. *Human Reproduction* 1996 April; 11(4): 685. Subject: 14.3

Kuppermann, Miriam; Norton, Mary E. Prenatal testing guidelines: time for a new approach? *Gynecologic and Obstetric Investigation* 2005; 60(1): 6-10. Subject: 15.2

Kurth, Timothy; Cook, Nancy R.; Logroscino, Giancarlo; Diener, Hans-Christoph; Buring, Julie E.; DeAngelis, Catherine D. Unreported financial disclosures in a study of migraine and cardiovascular disease (letters). *JAMA: the Journal of the American Medical Association* 2006 August 9; 296(6): 653-654. Subject: 1.3.7

Kurtzberg, Joanne; Lyerly, Anne Drapkin; Sugarman, Jeremy. Untying the Gordian knot: policies, practices, and ethical issues related to banking of umbilical cord blood. *Journal of Clinical Investigation* 2005 October; 115(10): 2592-2597. Subject: 19.4

Kurzweil, Ray. Nanoscience, nanotechnology, and ethics: promise and peril. *In:* Mitcham, Carl, ed. Encyclopedia of Science, Technology, and Ethics. Farmington Hills, MI: Thomson/Gale, 2005: xli-xlviii. Subject: 5.4

Kuschner, Ware; Lo, Bernard; Rubenfeld, Gordon. Dying patients and palliative sedation [letter and reply]. *JAMA: The Journal of the American Medical Association* 2006 March 15; 295(11): 1250. Subject: 20.4.1

Kushel, Margot B.; Miaskowski, Christine. End-of-life care for homeless patients: "she says she is there to help me in any situation". *JAMA: The Journal of the American Medical Association* 2006 December 27; 296(24): 2959-2966. Subject: 20.4.1

Kusmin, Ben. Swing low, sweet chariot: abandoning the disinterested witness requirement for advance directives. *American Journal of Law and Medicine* 2006; 32(1): 93-116. Subject: 20.5.4

Kuszler, Patricia C. Biotechnology entrepreneurship and ethics: principles, paradigms, and products. *Medicine and Law: The World Association for Medical Law* 2006 September; 25(3): 491-502. Subject: 2.1

Kuther, Tara L.; Posada, Margarita. Children and adolescents' capacity to provide informed consent for participation in research. *In:* Shohov, Serge, P., ed. Advances in Psychology Research, Volume 32. Huntington, N.Y.: Nova Science Publishers; 2004: 163-173. Subject: 18.5.2

Kutukdjian, Georges B. Genética y ética: implicaciones internacionales = Genetics and ethics: international implications. *Revista Latinoamericana de Bioética* 2003 January; (4): 38-55. Subject: 15.1

Kuzu, N.; Ergin, A.; Zencir, M. Patients' awareness of their rights in a developing country. *Public Health* 2006 April; 120(4): 290-296. Subject: 9.2

Kvalheim, Vigdis. The Norwegian model for ethical review of medical research. *In:* Beyleveld, D.; Townend, D.; Wright, J., eds. Research Ethics Committees, Data Protection and Medical Research in European Countries. Hants, England; Burlington, VT: Ashgate; 2005: 163-176. Subject: 18.2

Kvochak, Patricia A. Legal issues. *In:* Gallin, John I., ed. Principles and Practice of Clinical Research. San Diego, CA: Academic Press; 2002: 133-143. Subject: 18.6

Kwak, Jung; Haley, William E. Current research findings on end-of-life decision making among racially or ethnically diverse groups. *Gerontologist* 2005 October; 45(5): 634-641. Subject: 20.5.1

L

La Caze, Adam. Does pharmacogenomics provide an ethical challenge to the utilisation of cost-effectiveness analysis by public health systems? *Pharmacoeconomics* 2005; 23(5): 445-447. Subject: 15.10

La Marne, Paula. Reflexion ethique et formation medicale: soins palliatifs et accompagnement = Ethical reflections and medical education: palliative care and terminal care. *ADSP* 1999 September; (28): 54-56. Subject: 7.2

Lacadena, Juan Ramón. Genetic manipulation offences in Spain's new Penal Code: a genetic commentary = Delitos relativos a la manipulación genética en el nuevo Código Penal español: un comentario genético. *Law and the Human Genome Review = Revista de Derecho y Genoma Humano* 1996 July-December; (5): 195-203. Subject: 15.4

Lachin, John M. Conflicts of interest in data monitoring of industry versus publicly financed clinical trials. *Statistics in Medicine* 2004 May 30; 23(10): 1519-1521. Subject: 18.2

Lachs, John. Researchers and their subjects as neighbors. *Politics and the Life Sciences* 1998 March; 17(1): 24-25. Subject: 15.4

Ladenheim, Kala; Groman, Rachel. State legislative activities related to elimination of health disparities. *Journal of Health Politics, Policy and Law* 2006 February; 31(1): 153-183. Subject: 9.5.4

LaFleur, William R. More information, broader dissent on informed consent. *American Journal of Bioethics* 2006 January-February; 6(1): 15-16. Subject: 8.3.1

Laflin, Molly T.; Glover, Elbert D.; McDermott, Robert J. Publication ethics: an examination of authorship practices. *American Journal of Health Behavior* 2005 November-December; 29(6): 579-587. Subject: 1.3.7

Lafollette, Hugh. Living on a slippery slope. *Journal of Ethics* 2005; 9(3-4): 475-499. Subject: 2.1

LaFrance, Arthur B. Merger of religious and public hospitals: render unto Caesar. . . . *Seattle Journal for Social Justice* 2004 Fall-Winter; 3(1): 229-310. Subject: 9.1

Lagay, Faith. Consent needed to perform procedures on the newly deceased for training purposes. *Virtual Mentor* 2001 August; 3(8): 2p. Subject: 8.3.3

Lagay, Faith. Genetic difference: unfair or only unfortunate? *Virtual Mentor* 2001 November; 3(11): 3p. Subject: 15.4

Lagay, Faith. Genetic disparity: unfortunate or unfair? *In:* American Medical Association. ProfessingMedicine: strengthening the ethics and professionalism of tomorrow's physicians. Chicago: American Medical Association; 2001: 114-117. Subject: 15.1

Lagay, Faith. Physicians' responsibility in the face of patients' irrational decisions. *Virtual Mentor* 2001 September; 3(9): 2p. Subject: 8.3.1

Lagay, Faith. Preimplantation genetic diagnosis. *Virtual Mentor* 2001 August; 3(8): 3p. Subject: 15.2

Lagay, Faith. Resuscitating privacy in emergency settings. *In:* American Medical Association. ProfessingMedicine: strengthening the ethics and professionalism of tomorrow's physicians. Chicago: American Medical Association; 2001: 75-79. Subject: 20.5.1

Lagay, Faith. Resuscitating privacy in emergency settings. *Virtual Mentor* 2001 November; 3(11): 2p. Subject: 8.4

Lagay, Faith. Right to choose patients and duty not to neglect. *Virtual Mentor* 2001 September; 3(9): 2p. Subject: 8.1

Lagerwey, Mary D. The Third Reich in the pages of the American Journal of Nursing, 1932-1950. *Nursing History Review* 2006; 14: 59-87. Subject: 21.4

Lahiri, Debomoy K. Discourse among referees and editors would help [letter]. *Nature* 2006 February 16; 439(7078): 784. Subject: 1.3.9

Lakoff, Andrew. High contact: gifts and surveillance in Argentina. *In:* Petryna, Adriana; Lakoff, Andrew; Kleinman, Arthur, eds. Global Pharmaceuticals: Ethics, Markets, Practices. Durham: Duke University Press; 2006: 111-135. Subject: 9.7

Lakoff, Andrew. The private life of numbers: pharmaceutical marketing in post-welfare Argentina. *In:* Ong, Aihwa; Collier, Stephen J., eds. Global Assemblages: Technology, Politics, and Ethics as Anthropological Problems. Malden, MA: Blackwell Pub.; 2005: 194-213. Subject: 9.7

Lal, Seema. Consent in dentistry. *Pacific Health Dialog* 2003 March; 10(1): 102-105. Subject: 8.3.1

Lalor, Joan; Begley, Cecily. Fetal anomaly screening: what do women want to know? *Journal of Advanced Nursing* 2006 July; 55(1): 11-19. Subject: 15.2

Lam, Stephen T.S. Informed consent in genetic counseling and pediatric genetics. A View from Hong Kong. *In:* Döring, Ole; Chen, Renbiao, eds. Advances in Chinese Medical Ethics: Chinese and International Perspectives. Hamburg: Institut für Asienkunde; 2002: 133-140. Subject: 15.2

Lam, Wendy; Fielding, Richard; Chan, Miranda; Chow, Louis; Ho, Ella. Participation and satisfaction with surgical treatment decision-making in breast cancer among Chinese women. *Breast Cancer Research and Treatment* 2003 July; 80(2): 171-180. Subject: 9.5.5

Lamm, Richard D. The moral imperative of limiting elderly health entitlements. *In:* Altman, Stuart H.; Shactman, David I., eds. Policies for an Aging Society. Baltimore: Johns Hopkins University Press; 2002: 199-216. Subject: 9.4

See SUBJECT HEADING KEY FOR SECTION II on inside back cover.

Landman, Willem A. Legalizing assistance with dying in South Africa. *South African Medical Journal = Suid-Afrikaanse Tydskrif Vir Geneeskunde* 2000 February; 90(2): 113-116. Subject: 20.5.1

Landman, Willem A.; Schüklenk, Udo. Medecins sans Frontieres under the spotlight [editorial]. *Developing World Bioethics* 2006 May; 6(2): iii-iv. Subject: 7.1

Lane, Harlan. Ethnicity, ethics, and the deaf-world. *Journal of Deaf Studies and Deaf Education* 2005 Summer; 10(3): 291-310. Subject: 7.1

Lane, Robert. Safety, identity and consent: a limited defense of reproductive human cloning. *Bioethics* 2006 June; 20(3): 125-135. Subject: 14.5

Langbein, Hermann. Dr. Wirths. *In his:* People in Auschwitz. Chapel Hill: The University of North Carolina Press; 2004: 365-385. Subject: 21.4

Langbein, Hermann. Physicians in the SS. *In his:* People in Auschwitz. Chapel Hill: The University of North Carolina Press; 2004: 333-364. Subject: 21.4

Langdon, I.J.; Hardin, R.; Learmonth, I.D. Informed consent for total hip arthroplasty: does a written information sheet improve recall by patients? *Annals of the Royal College of Surgeons of England* 2002 November; 84(6): 404-408. Subject: 8.3.1

Langdridge, Darren; Blyth, Eric. Regulation of assisted conception services in Europe: implications of the new reproductive technologies for 'the family'. *Journal of Social Welfare and Family Law* 2001 February 1; 23(1): 45-64. Subject: 14.1

Lange, Bernadette. Mutual moral caring actions: a framework for community nursing practice. *Advances in Nursing Science [electronic]* 2006 April-June; 29(2): E45-E55. Subject: 4.1.3

Langley, Laura S.; Blackston, Joseph W. Sperm, egg, and a petri dish: unveiling the underlying property issues surrounding cryopreserved embryos. *Journal of Legal Medicine* 2006 June; 27(2): 167-206. Subject: 14.6

Langlois, Adèle. The governance of genomic information: will it come of age? *Genomics, Society and Policy* 2006 December; 2(3): 49-63. Subject: 15.1

Langston, Anne L.; McCallum, Marilyn; Campbell, Marion K.; Robertson, Clare; Ralston, Stuart H. An integrated approach to consumer representation and involvement in a multicentre randomized controlled trial. *Clinical Trials* 2005; 2(1): 80-87. Subject: 18.2

Lanier, William L. Medical interventions at the end of life: what is appropriate and who is responsible? *Mayo Clinic Proceedings* 2005 November; 80(11): 1411-1413. Subject: 20.5.1

Lansing, Paul; Fricke, Michael. Pharmaceutical advertising to consumers: corporate profits vs. public safety. *Business and Professional Ethics Journal* 2005 Fall; 24(3): 23-26. Subject: 9.7

Lantos, John. The sociobiology of humanism. *Hastings Center Report* 2006 November-December; 36(6): 20-22. Subject: 4.1.2

Lanzafame, Raymond J. Ethics in reporting: truth and the scientific literature [editorial]. *Photomedicine and Laser Surgery* 2004 August; 22(4): 5-6. Subject: 1.3.7

Lappin, Debra R. Clinical research and the new public partnership — a view from the south. *Journal of Rheumatology* 2005 January; 32(Supplement 72): 27-29. Subject: 18.6

Larcher, Vic; Goldman, Ann. Living well and dying well — facing the challenges at a children's hospital. *Clinical Ethics* 2006 September; 1(3): 165-171. Subject: 20.5.2

Larijani, Bagher; Malek-Afzali, Hossein; Zahedi, Farzaneh; Motevaseli, Elaheh. Strengthening medical ethics by strategic planning in the Islamic Republic of Iran. *Developing World Bioethics* 2006 May; 6(2): 106-110. Subject: 2.1

Larijani, B.; Zahedi, F. Changing parameters for abortion in Iran. *Indian Journal of Medical Ethics* 2006 October-December; 3(4): 130-131. Subject: 12.4.1

Larijani, B.; Zahedi, F.; Malek-Afzali, H. Medical ethics in the Islamic Republic of Iran. *Eastern Mediterranean Health Journal* 2005; 11(5 and 6): 1061-1072 [Online]. Accessed: http://www.emro.who.int/publications/emhj/1105_6/PDF/24.pdf [2007 January 4]. Subject: 2.1

Larkin, Gregory Luke; McKay, Mary Pat; Angelos, Peter. Six core competencies and seven deadly sins: a virtues-based approach to the new guidelines for graduate medical education. *Surgery* 2005 September; 138(3): 490-497. Subject: 7.2

Lassen, Jesper; Jamison, Andrew. Genetic technologies meet the public: the discourses of concern. *Science, Technology, and Human Values* 2006 January; 31(1): 8-28. Subject: 15.1

Latham, Stephen R. Some limits of decision-theory in bioethics: rights, ends, and thick concepts. *American Journal of Bioethics* 2006 May-June; 6(3): 56-58; discussion W51- W53. Subject: 2.1

Latson, Larry A. Aortic valvuloplasty in the fetus: technically possible but is it ready for prime time? *Journal of Pediatrics* 2005 October; 147(4): 424-426. Subject: 9.5.8

Lattanzi, Roberto. Research ethics committees in Italy's legal system. *In:* Beyleveld, D.; Townend, D.; Wright, J., eds. Research Ethics Committees, Data Protection and Medical Research in European Countries. Hants, England; Burlington, VT: Ashgate; 2005: 111-125. Subject: 18.2

Lauber, Christoph; Nordt, Carlos; Falcato, Luis; Rössler, Wulf. Can a seizure help? The public's attitude toward electroconvulsive therapy. *Psychiatry Research* 2005 April 15; 134(2): 205-209. Subject: 17.5

Laughlin, Harry H. Report of the Committee to study and to report on the best practical means of cutting off the defective germ-plasm in the American population — Volume I: the scope of the committee's work. Cold Spring Harbor, New York: Eugenics Record Office Bulletin No. 10A 1914; 64 p. Subject: 15.5

Laurence, Desmond R. Compensation for non-negligent harm in trials remains shaky [letter]. *BMJ: British Medical Journal* 2006 February 25; 332(7539): 489-490. Subject: 18.1

Laureys, Steven. Science and society: death, unconsciousness and the brain. *Nature Reviews Neuroscience* 2005 November; 6(11): 899-909. Subject: 20.2.1

Laureys, Steven; Pellas, Frédéric; Van Eeckhout, Philippe; Ghorbel, Sofiane; Schnakers, Caroline; Perrin, Fabian; Berré, Jacques; Faymonville, Marie-Elisabeth; Pantke, Karl-Heinz; Damas, Francois; Lamy, Maurice; Moonen, Gustave; Goldman, Serge. The locked-in syndrome : what is it like to be conscious but paralyzed and voiceless? *Progress in Brain Research* 2005; 150: 495-511. Subject: 9.5.1

Laurie, Graeme; Hunter, Kathryn G. Benefit-sharing and public trust in genetic research. *In:* Árnason, Gardar; Nordal, Salvör; Árnason, Vilhjálmur, eds. Blood and Data: Ethical, Legal and Social Aspects of Human Genetic Databases. Reykjavík: University of Iceland Press; 2004: 323-331. Subject: 15.1

Lauritzen, Paul. Response to Richard B. Miller's "children, ethics, and modern medicine" [book review]. *Journal of Religious Ethics* 2006 March; 34(1): 151-161. Subject: 9.5.7

Lauritzen, Paul; Prusak, Bernard G. The debate over liberal eugenics [letter and reply]. *Hastings Center Report* 2006 March-April; 36(2): 6-7. Subject: 15.5

Lavery, J.V.; Upshur, R.E.; Sharp, R.R.; Hofman, K.J. Ethical issues in international environmental health research. *International Journal of Hygiene and Environmental Health* 2003 August; 206(4-5): 453-463. Subject: 9.1

Lavery, James V.; Van Laethem, Marlene L.P.; Slutsky, Arthur S. Monitoring and oversight in critical care research. *Critical Care* 2004 December; 8(6): 403-405. Subject: 20.5.1

Lavieri, Robert R.; Garner, Samual A. Ethical considerations in the communication of unexpected information with clinical implications. *American Journal of Bioethics* 2006 November-December; 6(6): 46-48. Subject: 15.1

Lavoie, Mireille; De Koninck, Thomas; Blondeau, Danielle. The nature of care in light of Emmanuel Levinas. *Nursing Philosophy* 2006 October; 7(4): 225-234. Subject: 4.1.1

Law Harrison, Lynda. Maintaining the ethic of caring in nursing. *Journal of Advanced Nursing* 2006 May; 54(3): 255-257. Subject: 4.1.3

Law, Nathaniel. Abortion: Supreme Court avoids disturbing abortion precedents by ruling on grounds of remedy —

Ayotte v. Planned Parenthood of Northern New England. *Journal of Law, Medicine and Ethics* 2006 Summer; 34(2): 469-471. Subject: 12.4.1

Lawler, P.G. Assessment of doctors in training: should patients give consent? *BMJ: British Medical Journal* 2006 February 18; 332(7538): 431. Subject: 7.2

Lawler, Peter Augustine. The commerce of the body: is the body property? *New Atlantis* 2006 Fall; 14: 62-72. Subject: 19.5

Lawrence, Dana J.; Johnson, Claire D. On the subject of human subjects [letter and reply]. *Journal of Manipulative and Physiological Therapeutics* 2005 November-December; 28(9): 730-731. Subject: 18.2

Lawrence, Jane. The Indian Health Service and the sterilization of Native American women. *American Indian Quarterly* 2000 Summer; 24(3): 400-419 [Online]. http://muse.jhu.edu/journals/american_indian_quarterly/vo24/24.3lawrence.pdf [2007 February 5]. Subject: 11.3

Lawson, Charles. Patenting genes and gene sequences in Australia. *Journal of Law and Medicine* 1998 May; 5(4): 364-371. Subject: 15.8

Lawton, Graham. The incredibles. *New Scientist* 2006 May 13-19; 190(2551): 32-38. Subject: 4.5

Layne, Linda L. Unhappy endings: a feminist reappraisal of the women's health movement from the vantage of pregnancy loss. *Social Science and Medicine* 2003 May; 56(9): 1881-1891. Subject: 9.5.5

Lazare, Aaron. Apology in medical practice: an emerging clinical skill. *JAMA: The Journal of the American Medical Association* 2006 September 20; 269(11): 1401-1404. Subject: 8.1

Lazarev, Nikolai. The intrinsic value of human life: a critique of Life's Dominion. *E Law: Murdoch University Electronic Journal of Law* 2005 July; 12(1-2): 17 p. [Online]. Accessed: http://www.murdoch.edu.au/elaw/issues/v12n1_2/Lavarev12_1.html [2006 August 2]. Subject: 4.4

Lazaruk, Tina. The CPR question. *Canadian Nurse* 2006 February; 102(2): 22-24; discussion 23-24. Subject: 20.5.1

Lazarus, Arthur. Individual wariness needed to spot biased drug research. *Managed Care* 2005 September; 14(9): 8, 13. Subject: 1.3.9

Lazarus, Arthur. Pharmaceutical policy issues for medical schools. *Psychiatric Services* 2006 February; 57(2): 167. Subject: 7.2

Lazarus, Jeremy A.; Sharfstein, Steven S. Ethics in managed care. *Psychiatric Clinics of North America* 2002 September; 25(3): 561-574. Subject: 2.1

Lazcano-Ponce, Eduardo; Angeles-Llerenas, Angélica; Alvarez-del Río, Asunción; Salazar-Martínez, Eduardo; Allen, Betania; Hernández-Avila, Mauricio; Kraus, Arnoldo. Ethics and communication between physicians and their patients with cancer, HIV/AIDS, and

See SUBJECT HEADING KEY FOR SECTION II on inside back cover.

631

rheumatoid arthritis in Mexico. *Archives of Medical Research* 2004 January-February; 35(1): 66-75. Subject: 8.2

Lazer, David; Mayer-Schönberger, Viktor. Statutory frameworks for regulating information flows: drawing lessons for the DNA data banks from other government data systems. *Journal of Law, Medicine and Ethics* 2006 Summer; 34(2): 366-374. Subject: 15.1

Lazzarini, Zita; Von Kohorn, Jonathan E. Medical ethics and law. *In:* Mayer, Kenneth H.; Pizer, H.F. The AIDS Pandemic: Impact on Science and Society. Boston: Elsevier Academic Press; 2005: 488-510. Subject: 9.5.6

Le Page, Michael. Only drugs can stop sports cheats. *New Scientist* 2006 August 19-25; 191(2565): 18-19. Subject: 4.5

Le Roux, Nadège; Cussenot, Olivier. La génétique au coeur du débat ethique? = Genetics at the heart of the ethical debate? *Progres en Urologie* 2000 November; 10(5): 1053-1084. Subject: 15.1

Lea, Dale Halsey; Williams, Janet; Donahue, M. Patricia. Ethical issues in genetic testing. *Journal of Midwifery and Women's Health* 2005 May-June; 50(3): 234-240. Subject: 15.3

Leach, Gerald. Qualitative birth control. *New Statesman (London, England: 1957)* 1965 June 11: 906. Subject: 15.2

Leask, K. The role of the courts in clinical decision making. *Archives of Disease in Childhood* 2005 December; 90(12): 1256-1258. Subject: 20.5.2

Leather, David A.; Davis, Sarah C. Paediatricians and the pharmaceutical industry: an industry perspective of the challenges ahead. *Paediatric Respiratory Reviews* 2006 March; 7(1): 60-66. Subject: 7.3

Leavitt, Frank J. Compromised autonomy, and Asian autonomy: commentaries on Glock and Goldim, and Dena Hsin-Chen Hsin. *Eubios Journal of Asian and International Bioethics* 2003 January 13(1): 8. Subject: 18.3

Leavitt, Frank J. The international impact of Asian bioethics. *In:* Sang-yong, Song; Young-Mo, Koo; Macer, Darryl R.J., eds. Asian Bioethics in the 21st Century. Christchurch, NZ: Eubios Ethics Institute, 2002: 224-228. Subject: 2.1

Leavitt, Frank J. Is any medical research population not vulnerable? *CQ: Cambridge Quarterly of Healthcare Ethics* 2006 Winter; 15(1): 81-88. Subject: 18.5.1

Leavitt, Sarah A. National Institutes of Health. *In:* Mitcham, Carl, ed. Encyclopedia of Science, Technology, and Ethics. Farmington Hills, MI: Thomson/Gale, 2005: 1271-1274. Subject: 5.1

Lebacqz, Karen. Philosophy, theology, and the claims of justice. *In:* Guinn, David E., ed. Handbook of Bioethics and Religion. New York: Oxford University Press, 2006: 253-263. Subject: 2.1

Lebeer, Guy; De Boeck, Geneviève. Belgian ethics committees and the protection of personal data. *In:* Beyleveld, D.; Townend, D.; Wright, J., eds. Research Ethics Committees, Data Protection and Medical Research in European Countries. Hants, England; Burlington, VT: Ashgate; 2005: 9-25. Subject: 18.2

Lebovits, Allen. Ethics and pain: why and for whom? [editorial]. *Pain Medicine* 2001 June; 2(2): 92-96. Subject: 4.4

Lederer, Susan E. The Cold War and beyond: covert and deceptive American medical experimentation. *In:* Beam, Thomas E.; Sparacino, Linette R.; Pellegrino, Edmund D.; Hartle, Anthony E.; Howe, Edmund G., eds. Military Medical Ethics. Volume 2. Washington, DC: TMM Publications, Borden Institute, Walter Reed Army Medical Center; 2003: 507-531. Subject: 18.5.8

Ledford, Heidi. A breed apart. *Nature* 2006 November 9; 444(7116): 137. Subject: 14.5

LeDoux, Allison. Truth about emergency contraception. *Ethics and Medics* 2006 December; 31(12): 1-2. Subject: 11.1

Lee, Barbara Coombs. Should it be legal for physicians to expedite a death? Yes - what experience teaches about legalization of assisted dying. *Generations: Journal of the American Society on Aging* 1999 Spring; 23(1): 59-60. Subject: 20.7

Lee, Connal; Rogers, Wendy A. Ethics, pandemic planning and communications. *Monash Bioethics Review* 2006 October; 25(4): 9-18. Subject: 9.1

Lee, Martin Lishexian. The inadequacies of absolute prohibition of reproductive cloning. *Journal of Law and Medicine* 2004 February; 11(3): 351-372. Subject: 14.5

Lee, Patrick. Embryonic human beings. *Journal of Contemporary Health Law and Policy* 2006 Spring; 22(2): 424-438. Subject: 4.4

Lee, Patrick; George, Robert P. The first fourteen days of human life. *New Atlantis* 2006 Summer; 13: 61-67. Subject: 18.5.4

Lee, Peter. Patents, paradigm shifts, and progress in biomedical science. *Yale Law Journal* 2004 December; 114(3): 659-695. Subject: 15.8

Lee, Philip R.; Conant, Marcus; Jonsen, Albert R.; Heilig, Steve. Participation in torture and interrogation: an inexcusable breach of medical ethics. *CQ: Cambridge Quarterly of Healthcare Ethics* 2006 Spring; 15(2): 202-203. Subject: 21.4

Lee, Philip; Oliver, Thomas; Benjamin, A.E.; Lee, Dorothy. Politics, health policy, and the American character. *Stanford Law and Policy Review* 2006; 17(1): 7-32. Subject: 9.1

Lee, Pil Ryul. Is the 'pre-embryo' not equivalent to a human being? *In:* Sang-yong, Song; Young-Mo, Koo; Macer, Darryl R.J., eds. Asian Bioethics in the 21st Century.

Christchurch, NZ: Eubios Ethics Institute, 2002: 76-78. Subject: 4.4

Lee, Shui Chuen. Biotechnology and responsibility to future generations: a Confucian perspective. *In:* Sleeboom, Margaret, ed. Genomics in Asia: A Clash of Bioethical Interests? New York: Kegan Paul; 2004: 145-158. Subject: 15.1

Lee, Shui Chuen. A Confucian concept of personhood and its implication for medical ethics. *In:* Döring, Ole; Chen, Renbiao, eds. Advances in Chinese Medical Ethics: Chinese and International Perspectives. Hamburg: Institut für Asienkunde; 2002: 167-177. Subject: 4.4

Lee, Simon J. Craddock. Ethics of articulation: constituting organizational identity in a Catholic hospital system. *In:* Dinkins, Christine Sorrell; Sorrell, Jeanne Merkle, eds. Listening to the Whispers: Re-Thinking Ethics in Healthcare. Madison, WI: University of Wisconsin Press; 2006: 69-137. Subject: 9.1

Leeb-Lundberg, Sara; Kjellberg, Svante; Sydsjö, Gunilla. Helping parents to tell their children about the use of donor insemination (DI) and determining their opinions about open-identity sperm donors. *Acta Obstetricia et Gynecologica Scandinavica* 2006; 85(1): 78-81. Subject: 14.2

Leenaars, Antoon; Connolly, John. Suicide, assisted suicide and euthanasia: international perspectives. *Irish Journal of Psychological Medicine* 2001 March; 18(1): 33-37. Subject: 20.7

Leenen, H.J.J. Assistance to suicide and the European Court of Human Rights/ Court of Justice of the European Communities. *European Journal of Health Law* 2002 September; 9(3): 257-282. Subject: 20.7

Lees, C.; Baumgartner, H. The TRUFFLE study — a collaborative publicly funded project from concept to reality: how to negotiate an ethical, administrative and funding obstacle course in the European Union [editorial]. *Ultrasound in Obstetrics and Gynecology* 2005 February; 25(2): 105-107. Subject: 9.5.8

LeFebour, Patricia A.; Elliot, Douglas. Ontario court rules on notification of blood donors: Canadian AIDS Society v Her Majesty the Queen in Right of Ontario, Dr Richard Schabas and the Canadian Red Cross Society. *Canadian HIV/AIDS Policy and Law Newsletter* 1995 January; 1(2): 1, 13-14. Subject: 19.4

Lefor, Alan T. Scientific misconduct and unethical human experimentation: historic parallels and moral implications. *Nutrition* 2005 July-August; 21(7-8): 878-882. Subject: 1.3.9

Legemaate, Johan. The Dutch Euthanasia Act and related issues. *Journal of Law and Medicine* 2004 February; 11(3): 312-323. Subject: 20.5.1

Leget, C. Boundaries, borders, and limits. A phenomenological reflection on ethics and euthanasia.

Journal of Medical Ethics 2006 May; 32(5): 256-259. Subject: 20.5.1

Lehren, Andrew; Leland, John. Scant drop seen in abortions if parents are told. *New York Times* 2006 March 6; p. A1, A18. Subject: 12.4.2

Lehrman, Sally. A proposition for stem cells. *Scientific American* 2005 September; 293(3): 40, 42. Subject: 18.5.4

Lehtonen, Lasse A.; Halila, Ritva. The general legal responsibility of research ethics committees in Finland. *In:* Beyleveld, D.; Townend, D.; Wright, J., eds. Research Ethics Committees, Data Protection and Medical Research in European Countries. Hants, England; Burlington, VT: Ashgate; 2005: 45-53. Subject: 18.2

Leib, Alden M.; Kowalski, Charles J. Human histological research: is it necessary? Humane? Ethical? *Journal of Periodontology* 2005 July; 76(7): 1207-1210. Subject: 18.1

Leigh, B. Consent — an event or a memory?: A judicial view. *Journal of Bone and Joint Surgery (British volume)* 2006 January; 88(1): 16-18. Subject: 8.3.1

Leino-Kilpi, Helena. 30th anniversary commentary on Esterhuizen P. (1996) Is the professional code still the cornerstone of clinical nursing practice? Journal of Advanced Nursing 23, 25-31. *Journal of Advanced Nursing* 2006 January; 53(1):112-113. Subject: 4.1.3

Leiva, Rene. A brief history of human diploid cell strains. *National Catholic Bioethics Quarterly* 2006 Autumn; 6(3): 443-451. Subject: 9.7

Lekan, Todd M. A pragmatist case for animal advocates on institutional animal care and use committees. *In:* McKenna, Erin; Light, Andrew, eds. Animal Pragmatism: Rethinking Human-Nonhuman Relationships. Bloomington, IN: Indiana University Press; 2004: 193-209. Subject: 22.2

Lemaire, R. Informed consent — a contemporary myth? *Journal of Bone and Joint Surgery (British volume)* 2006 January; 88(1): 2-7. Subject: 8.3.1

Lemke, Thomas. Beyond genetic discrimination. Problems and perspectives of a contested notion. *Genomics, Society and Policy* 2005 December; 1(3): 22-40. Subject: 15.3

Lemmens, Trudo. Compassionate access to experimental drugs: balancing interests and harms. *Canadian HIV/AIDS Policy and Law Newsletter* 1996 October; 3(1): 43-44. Subject: 18.2

Lemmens, Trudo. Euthanasia. *Canadian HIV/AIDS Policy and Law Newsletter* 1995 October; 2(1): 7-9. Subject: 20.5.1

Lemmens, Trudo. A response to the parliamentary sub-committee's report and recommendations. *Canadian HIV/AIDS Policy and Law Newsletter* 1997 Spring; 3(2-3): 40-43. Subject: 18.2

See SUBJECT HEADING KEY FOR SECTION II on inside back cover.

633

Lemmens, Trudo. US appeal courts rule in favour of assisted suicide. *Canadian HIV/AIDS Policy and Law Newsletter* 1996 July; 2(4): 1, 42-43. Subject: 20.7

Lenard, John. Two facets peer review and the proper role of study sections. *Accountability in Research* 2006 July-September; 13(3): 277-283. Subject: 1.3.9

Lenoir, Noëlle. French, European and International Legislation on Bioethics = Normativa francesa, europea e internacional en materia de Bioética. *Law and the Human Genome = Revista de Derecho y Genoma Humano* 1994 July-December; (1): 71-89. Subject: 2.1

Lenoir, Noëlle. Legal and ethical aspects of prenatal diagnosis: the law and current practices in France and certain other countries (Part II) = Aspectos jurídicos y éticos del diagnóstico prenatal: el derecho y las prácticas vigentes en Francia y otros países (y II). *Law and the Human Genome Review = Revista de Derecho y Genoma Humano* 1995 July-December; (3): 123-141. Subject: 15.2

Lenz, Connie. Prescribing a legislative response: educators, physicians, and psychotropic medication for children. *Journal of Contemporary Health Law and Policy* 2005 Fall; 22(1): 72-106. Subject: 17.4

Lenzer, Jeanne. Conflicts of interest are common at FDA [news]. *BMJ: British Medical Journal* 2006 April 29; 332(7548): 991. Subject: 1.3.9

Lenzer, Jeanne. Doctors outraged at Patriot Act's potential to seize medical records [news]. *BMJ: British Medical Journal* 2006 January 14; 332(7533): 69. Subject: 8.4

Lenzer, Jeanne. Researcher received undisclosed payments of $300 000 from Pfizer [news]. *BMJ: British Medical Journal* 2006 December 16; 333(7581): 1237. Subject: 1.3.9

Leo, Jonathan. The SSRI trials in children: disturbing implications for academic medicine. *Ethical Human Psychology and Psychiatry* 2006 Spring; 8(1): 29-41. Subject: 1.3.9

Leonard Hammer. Abortion objection in the United Kingdom within the framework of the European Convention on Human Rights and Fundamental Freedoms. *European Human Rights Law Review* 1999; [1999] 6: 564-575. Subject: 12.3

Leonhardt, David. The choice: a longer life or more stuff. *New York Times* 2006 September 27; p. C1, C7. Subject: 9.8

LePage, Michael. Tools you can trust. *New Scientist* 2006 June 10-16; 190(2555): 38-41. Subject: 15.1

Lerner, Barron H. Beyond informed consent: did cancer patients challenge their physicians in the post-World War II era? *Journal of the History of Medicine and Allied Sciences* 2004 October; 59(4): 507-521. Subject: 8.2

Lerner, Barron H. Choosing a "God Squad," when the mind has faded. *New York Times* 2006 August 29; p. F5. Subject: 9.4

Lerner, Evan. Editorial. *GeneWatch* 2006 November-December; 19(6): 2, 17. Subject: 15.1

Lerner, K. Lee; Lerner, Brenda Wilmoth, eds. Bioethics. *In their:* Medicine, Health, and Bioethics: Essential Primary Sources. Waterville, ME: Thomson Gale; 2006: 433-491. Subject: 2.1

Leroux, Thérèse; Hirtle, Marie; Fortin, Louis-Nicolas. An overview of public consultation mechanisms developed to address the ethical and social issues raised by biotechnology. *Journal of Consumer Policy* 1998 December; 21(4): 445-481. Subject: 5.3

Lesage, Pauline; Portenoy, Russell K. Ethical challenges in the care of patients with serious illness. *Pain Medicine* 2001 June; 2(2): 121-130. Subject: 4.4

Lesch, Walter. Coping with limits: two strategies and their anthropological and ethical implications. *In:* Rehmann-Sutter, Christoph; Düwell, Marcus; Mieth, Dietmar, eds. Bioethics in Cultural Contexts: Reflections on Methods and Finitude. Dordrecht: Springer, 2006: 263-273. Subject: 9.4

Lesch, Walter. Gentherapie und Körperbilder: Anthropologische und ethische Denkanstösse. *In:* Rehmann-Sutter, Christoph; Müller, Hansjakob, eds. Ethik und Gentherapie: zum praktischen Diskurs um die molekulare Medizin. 2nd ed. Tübingen: Francke Verlag; 2003: 251-260. Subject: 15.4

Leslie, Jeff. Lay persons and community values in reviewing animal experimentation. *University of Chicago Legal Forum* 2006: 113-136. Subject: 22.2

Lesnewski, Ruth. Mistakes. *JAMA: The Journal of the American Medical Association* 2006 September 20; 269(11): 1327-1328. Subject: 9.8

Leszczynska, Katarzyna; Dymczyk, K.; Wac, K.; Krajewska, K. Obeying patient's rights on the basis of maternity ward. *Roczniki Akademii Medycznej w Bialymstoku* 2005; 50(Supplement 1): 70-73. Subject: 9.5.5

Levanon, Ayelet; Sobol, Limor; Tzur, Hila. Medical confidentiality and use of medical information in Israel. *Journal of Biolaw and Business* 2006; 9(4): 20-28. Subject: 8.4

Levidow, Les. The GM crops debate: utilitarian bioethics? *Capitalism, Nature, Socialism* 2001 March; 12(1): 44-55. Subject: 15.1

Levin, Alex V. The ethics of surgical innovation: more than one answer? = L'éthique de l'innovation chirurgicale: plus qu'une simple réponse? [editorial]. *Canadian Journal of Ophthalmology* 2005 December; 40(6): 685-688. Subject: 5.2

Levin, Peter J.; McGee, Glenn. Physician, divest thyself [editorial]. *American Journal of Bioethics* 2006 March-April; 6(2): 1-2 [see correction in American Journal of Bioethics 2006 May-June; 6(3): 78]. Subject: 7.3

Subject = NRCBL Primary Classification Number; see inside front cover.

Levin, Phillip D.; Sprung, Charles L. Withdrawing and withholding life-sustaining therapies are not the same. *Critical Care* 2005 June; 9(3): 230-232. Subject: 20.5.1

Levin, Yuval. The moral challenge of modern science. *New Atlantis* 2006 Fall; 14: 32-46. Subject: 5.3

Levine, Aaron. Trends in the geographical distribution of human embryonic stem-cell research. *Politics and the Life Sciences* 2005 September 14; 23(2): 40-45. Subject: 18.5.4

Levine, Aran. Clinical trials research: challenges of patient education and informed consent. *Oncology Nursing Forum* 2005 July; 32(4): 737-739. Subject: 18.3

Levine, Carol. HIPAA and talking with family caregivers: what does the law really say? *AJN: American Journal of Nursing* 2006 August; 106(8): 51-53. Subject: 8.4

LeVine, Harry. Facts, data, and opinion. *In his:* Genetic Engineering: A Reference Handbook. 2nd ed. Santa Barbara, CA: ABC-CLIO, 2006: 141-200. Subject: 15.1

LeVine, Harry. Problems, controversies, and solutions. *In his:* Genetic Engineering: A Reference Handbook. 2nd ed. Santa Barbara, CA: ABC-CLIO, 2006: 47-81. Subject: 15.1

LeVine, Harry. Worldwide perspective. *In his:* Genetic Engineering: A Reference Handbook. 2nd ed. Santa Barbara, CA: ABC-CLIO, 2006: 83-94. Subject: 15.1

Levine, Judith. What human genetic modification means for women. *World Watch* 2002 July-August; 15(4): 26-29. Subject: 15.1

Levine, Phillip B. Abortion policy and the economics of fertility. *Society* 2004 May-June; 41(4): 79-85. Subject: 12.5.1

Levine, Robert J. Empirical research to evaluate ethics committees' burdensome and perhaps unproductive policies and practices : a proposal [editorial]. *Journal of Empirical Research on Human Research Ethics* 2006 September; 1(3): 1-3. Subject: 18.2

Levine, Robert J. Placebo controls in clinical trials of new therapies for osteoporosis. *Journal of Bone and Mineral Research* 2003 June; 18(6): 1154-1159. Subject: 18.3

Levine, Robert J. Placebo controls in clinical trials when there are known effective treatments. *In:* Lolas Stepke, Fernando; Agar Corbinos, Lorenzo, eds. Interfaces Between Bioethics and the Empirical Social Sciences. Buenos Aires, Argentina: World Health Organization; 2002: 79-89. Subject: 18.3

Levinson, Wendy; Laupacis, Andreas. A call for fairness in formulary decisions [editorial]. *Archives of Internal Medicine* 2006 January 9; 166(1): 16-18. Subject: 9.7

Levitt, Mairi. UK Biobank: a model for public engagement? *Genomics, Society and Policy* 2005 December; 1(3): 78-81. Subject: 15.1

Levitt, Mairi; Tomasini, Floris. Bar-coded children: an exploration of issues around the inclusion of children on the England and Wales national DNA database. *Genomics, Society and Policy* 2006 May; 2(1): 41-56. Subject: 15.1

Levitt, Mairi; Weiner, Kate; Goodacre, John. Gene week: a novel way of consulting the public. *Public Understanding of Science* 2005 January; 14(1): 67-79. Subject: 18.6

Levitt, Mairi; Weldon, Sue. Genetic databases and public trust. *In:* Árnason, Gardar; Nordal, Salvör; Árnason, Vilhjálmur, eds. Blood and Data: Ethical, Legal and Social Aspects of Human Genetic Databases. Reykjavík: University of Iceland Press; 2004: 175-179. Subject: 15.1

Levitt, Mairi; Weldon, Sue. A well placed trust? Public perceptions of the governance of DNA databases. *Critical Public Health* 2005 December; 15(4): 311-321. Subject: 15.1

Levy, Neil. Addiction, autonomy and ego-depletion: a response to Bennett Foddy and Julian Savulescu. *Bioethics* 2006 February; 20(1): 16-20. Subject: 9.5.9

Levy, N.; Ravelingien, A.; Braeckman, J.; Mortier, F.; Mortier, E.; Kerremans, I. Respecting rights . . . to death [letter and reply]. *Journal of Medical Ethics* 2006 October; 32(10): 608-609, 609-611. Subject: 20.2.1

Levy, Roger N. Does cost containment create conflict in the care of the elderly patient? *Clinical Orthopaedics and Related Research* 2000 September; (378): 66-70. Subject: 9.5.2

Lewens, T. Distinguishing treatment from research: a functional approach. *Journal of Medical Ethics* 2006 July; 32(7): 424-429. Subject: 18.1

Lewin, Matthew R.; Montauk, Lance; Shalit, Marc; Nobay, Flavia. An unusual case of subterfuge in the emergency department: covert administration of antipsychotic and anxiolytic medications to control an agitated patient. *Annals of Emergency Medicine* 2006 January; 47(1): 75-78. Subject: 8.3.1

Lewis, Carmen E. My computer, my doctor: a constitutional call for federal regulation of cybermedicine. *American Journal of Law and Medicine* 2006; 32(4): 585-609. Subject: 8.1

Lewis, David A.; Michels, Robert; Pine, Daniel S.; Schultz, Susan K.; Tamminga, Carol A.; Freedman, Robert. Conflict of interest [editorial]. *American Journal of Psychiatry* 2006 April; 163(4): 571-573. Subject: 1.3.7

Lewis, Penney. Assisted dying in France: the evolution of assisted dying in France: a third way? *Medical Law Review* 2006 Spring; 14(1): 44-72. Subject: 20.5.1

Lewis, Penney. Medical treatment of dementia patients at the end of life: can the law accommodate the personal identity and welfare problems? *European Journal of Health Law* 2006 September; 13(3): 219-234. Subject: 20.5.4

Lewis, Ricki. Blastomere blasphemy [editorial]. *American Journal of Bioethics* 2006 November-December; 6(6): 1-3. Subject: 18.5.4

See SUBJECT HEADING KEY FOR SECTION II on inside back cover.

635

Lewontin, Richard C. The confusion over cloning. *New York Review of Books* 1997 October 23; 44(16): 20-23. Subject: 14.5

Lex, Joseph Rohan Jr. The physician-pharmaceutical industry relationship. *Journal of Law and Health* 2003-2004; 18(2): 323-342. Subject: 7.3

Lexchin, Joel; Light, Donald W. Commercial influence and the consent of medical journals. *BMJ: British Medical Journal* 2006 June 17; 332(7555): 1444-1447. Subject: 1.3.7

Leydens, Jon A. Plagiarism. *In:* Mitcham, Carl, ed. Encyclopedia of Science, Technology, and Ethics. Farmington Hills, MI: Thomson/Gale, 2005: 1411-1413. Subject: 1.3.9

Li, Benfu. The significance of human embryo stem cell research and its ethical disputes. *In:* Sang-yong, Song; Young-Mo, Koo; Macer, Darryl R.J., eds. Asian Bioethics in the 21st Century. Christchurch, NZ: Eubios Ethics Institute, 2002: 58-60. Subject: 18.5.4

Li, Mingyan; Poovendran, Radha; Narayanan, Sreeram. Protecting patient privacy against unauthorized release of medical images in a group communication environment. *Computerized Medical Imaging and Graphics* 2005 July; 29(5): 367-383. Subject: 8.4

Liang, Bryan A. The bounds of science and ethics. *Journal of Biolaw and Business* 2006; 9(1): 44-45. Subject: 1.3.9

Liang, Bryan A. Medical information, confidentiality, and privacy. *Hematology/Oncology Clinics of North America* 2002 December; 16(6): 1433-1447. Subject: 8.4

Liao, S. Matthew. The embryo rescue case. *Theoretical Medicine and Bioethics* 2006; 27(2): 141-147. Subject: 4.4

Liao, Solomon. Unmet activity of daily living needs: elder mistreatment and ethics in geriatric research [letter]. *Journal of the American Geriatrics Society* 2006 October; 54(10): 1622-1623. Subject: 9.5.2

Liao, Solomon; Arnold, Robert M. The nature of an ethics and law review article: the challenges of a paper on physician-assisted dying [editorial]. *Journal of Palliative Medicine* 2005 June; 8(3): 484-485. Subject: 20.7

Liaschenko, J.; Oguz, N.Y.; Brunnquell, D. Critique of the "tragic case" method in ethics education. *Journal of Medical Ethics* 2006 November; 32(11): 672-677. Subject: 2.3

Libby, Ronald T. Treating doctors as drug dealers: the DEA's war on prescription painkillers. *CATO Institute Policy Analysis* 2005 June 16; (545): 27 p. [Online]. Accessed: http://www.cato.org/pubs/pas/pa545.pdf [2006 November 29]. Subject: 4.4

Liberman, Robert Paul; Smith, Gregory M.; Altenor, Aidan; Davis, Robert H.; LeBel, Janice; Huckshorn, Kevin Ann; Frueh, B. Christopher; Grubaugh, Anouk L.; Robins, Cynthia S. Elimination of seclusion and restraint: a reasonable goal? [letter and replies]. *Psychiatric Services* 2006 April; 57(4): 576-578. Subject: 17.3

Lichterman, Boleslav L. Basic problems of medical ethics in Russia in a historical context. *Journal International de Bioéthique = International Journal of Bioethics* 2005 September-December; 16(3-4): 43-53, 168-169. Subject: 2.2

Lichterman, Boleslav L. Soviet medical ethics (1917-1991). *Journal International de Bioéthique = International Journal of Bioethics* 2005 September-December; 16(3-4): 33-41, 167-168. Subject: 2.2

Lichterman, Boleslav L. Under the shelter of ethics. *Journal International de Bioéthique = International Journal of Bioethics* 2005 September-December; 16(3-4): 77-79, 172. Subject: 18.2

Lichterman, Boleslav L.; Yarovinsky, Michail. Medical ethics in Russia before the October Revolution (1917). *Journal International de Bioéthique = International Journal of Bioethics* 2005 September-December; 16(3-4): 17-32, 166-167. Subject: 2.2

Lichty, Peter D. Human subjects risk in new nanotechnologies? *Protecting Human Subjects* 2006 Spring; (13): 1-4. Subject: 5.2

Liddell, Kathleen; Bion, Julian; Chamberlain, Douglas; Druml, Christiane; Kompanje, Erwin; Lemaire, Francois; Menon, David; Vrhovac, Bozidar; Wiedermann, Christian J. Medical research involving incapacitated adults: implications of the EU Clinical Trials Directive 2001/20/EC. *Medical Law Review* 2006 Autumn; 14(3): 367-417. Subject: 18.2

Liddell, Kathleen; Wallace, Susan. Emerging regulatory issues for human stem cell medicine. *Genomics, Society and Policy* 2005 February; 1(1): 54-73. Subject: 18.6

Liddell, Kathy. Did the watchdog bark, bite or whimper? UK report on the use of personal genetic information. *European Journal of Health Law* 2002 September; 9(3): 243-256. Subject: 15.1

Liddon, Nicole; Pulley, LeaVonne; Cockerham, William C.; Lueschen, Guenther; Vermund, Sten H.; Hook, Edward W. Parents'/guardians' willingness to vaccinate their children against genital herpes. *Journal of Adolescent Health* 2005 September; 37(3): 187-193. Subject: 9.5.7

Lidz, Charles W.; Appelbaum, Paul S. The therapeutic misconception: problems and solutions. *Medical Care* 2002 September; 40(9, Supplement): V55-V63. Subject: 18.3

Lidz, Charles W.; Arnold, Robert M. Rethinking autonomy in long term care. *University of Miami Law Review* 1993 January; 47(3): 603-623. Subject: 8.3.3

Lie, Reidar K.; Emanuel, Ezekiel J.; Grady, Christine. Circumcision and HIV prevention research: an ethical analysis. *Lancet* 2006 August 5-11; 368(9534): 522-525. Subject: 9.5.6

Lienhardt, Christian; Cook, Sharlette V. Conducting clinical trials on tuberculosis in resource-poor countries: imposed science or equally-shared efforts? [editorial]. *International Journal of Tuberculosis and Lung Disease* 2005 September; 9(9): 943. Subject: 18.5.9

Light, Donald W. Be clear about managed care to get clear about doctor-patient relations. *American Journal of Bioethics* 2006 January-February; 6(1): 35-36. Subject: 9.3.2

Ligon, B. Lee. Albert Ludwig Sigesmund Neisser: discoverer of the cause of gonorrhea. *Seminars in Pediatric Infectious Diseases* 2005 October; 16(4): 336-341. Subject: 10

Lilford, Richard J.; Braunholtz, David A. Bayesian perspectives on the ethics of trials. *In:* Duley, Lelia; Farrell, Barbara, eds. Clinical Trials. London: BMJ Books; 2002: 105-120. Subject: 18.2

Lilford, Richard; Girling, Alan; Stevens, Andrew; Almasri, Abdullah; Mohammed, Mohammed A.; Braunholtz, David. Adjusting for treatment refusal in rationing decisions. *BMJ: British Medical Journal* 2006 March 4; 332(7540): 542-544. Subject: 9.4

Lillehammer, Hallvard. Benefit, disability and the non-identity problem. *In:* Gallin, John I., ed. Principles and Practice of Clinical Research. San Diego, CA: Academic Press; 2002: 15-26. Subject: 18.2

Lillehammer, Hallvard. Benefit, disability, and the non-identity problem. *In:* Athanassoulis, Nafsika, ed. Philosophical Reflections on Medical Ethics. New York: Palgrave Macmillan; 2005: 24-43. Subject: 14.1

Lillquist, Erik; Sullivan, Charles A. Legal regulation of the use of race in medical research. *Journal of Law, Medicine and Ethics* 2006 Fall; 34(3): 535-551. Subject: 18.5.1

Lim, Byungmook; Schmidt, Katja; White, Adrian; Ernst, Edzard. Reporting of ethical standards: differences between complementary and orthodox medicine journals? *Wiener Klinische Wochenschrift* 2004 July 31; 116(14): 500- 503. Subject: 1.3.7

Lim, Linda. Singapore cloning bill [news brief]. *Nature Biotechnology* 2004 October; 22(10): 1199. Subject: 14.5

Lin, Chia-Chin; Tsay, Hsiu-Fen. Relationships among perceived diagnostic disclosure, health locus of control, and levels of hope in Taiwanese cancer patients. *Psycho-Oncology* 2005 May; 14(5): 376-385. Subject: 8.2

Lin, Herng-Ching; Kao, Senyeong; Tang, Chao-Hsuin; Yang, Ming-Chin; Lee, Hong-Shen. Factors contributing to patient dumping in Taiwan. *Health Policy* 2006 June; 77(1): 103-112. Subject: 9.3.1

Lin, Ker-Neng; Liao, Yi-Chu; Wang, Pei-Ning; Liu, Hsiu-Chih. Family members favor disclosing the diagnosis of Alzheimer's disease. *International Psychogeriatrics* 2005 December; 17(4): 679-688. Subject: 8.2

Lin, Richard J. Withdrawing life-sustaining medical treatment — a physician's personal reflection. *Mental Retardation and Developmental Disabilities Research Reviews* 2003; 9(1): 10-15. Subject: 20.5.1

Lin, Zhen; Altman, Russ B.; Owen, Art B. Confidentiality in genome research [letter]. *Science* 2006 July 28; 313(5786): 441-442. Subject: 15.10

Lindberg, Michael; Vergara, Cunegundo; Wild-Wesley, Rebecca; Gruman, Cynthia. Physicians-in-training attitudes toward caring for and working with patients with alcohol and drug abuse diagnoses. *Southern Medical Journal* 2006 January; 99(1): 28-35. Subject: 7.2

Lindblad, William J. A matter of ethics [editorial]. *Wound Repair and Regeneration* 2005 May-June; 13(3): 217. Subject: 1.3.9

Lindemann, Hilde. Bioethics' gender. *American Journal of Bioethics [Online]*. 2006 March-April; 6(2): W15-W19. Subject: 2.1

Lindemann, Hilde. The power of parents and the agency of children. *In:* Parens, Erik, ed. Surgically Shaping Children: Technology, Ethics, and the Pursuit of Normality. Baltimore, MD: Johns Hopkins University Press; 2006: 176-188. Subject: 9.5.7

Linder, Erin N. Punishing prenatal alcohol abuse: the problems inherent in utilizing civil commitment to address addiction. *University of Illinois Law Review* 2005; 2005(3): 873-901. Subject: 9.5.5

Lindsay, Ronald A. Gonzales v. Oregon and the politics of medicine. *Kennedy Institute of Ethics Journal* 2006 March; 16(1): 99- 104. Subject: 20.7

Lindsay, Ronald A. Role-differentiated morality: the need to consider institutions, not just individuals. *American Journal of Bioethics* 2006 July-August; 6(4): 70-72. Subject: 18.1

Lindsay, Ronald A. Stem cell research: an approach to bioethics based on scientific naturalism. *Free Inquiry* 2006 December-2007 January; 27(1): 23-26. Subject: 18.5.4

Lindsay, Ronald A. Why should we be concerned with disparate impact? *American Journal of Bioethics* 2006 September-October; 6(5): 23-24; discussion W30-W32. Subject: 9.5.4

Lindseth, Richard E. Ethical issues in pediatric orthopaedics. *Clinical Orthopaedics and Related Research* 2000 September; (378): 61-65. Subject: 8.3.2

Lindström, Irma; Gaston-Johansson, Fannie; Danielson, Ella. Documentation of patients' participation in care at the end of life. *Nursing Ethics* 2006 July; 13(4): 394-403. Subject: 20.4.1

Linford, Steven. Mental health law: compulsory treatment in a general medical setting. *British Journal of Hospital Medicine (London, England)* 2005 October; 66(10): 569-571. Subject: 17.7

See SUBJECT HEADING KEY FOR SECTION II on inside back cover.

637

Lingler, Jennifer Hagerty; Parker, Lisa S.; DeKosky, Steven T.; Schulz, Richard. Caregivers as subjects of clinical drug trials: a review of human subjects protection practices in published studies of Alzheimer's disease pharmacotherapies. *IRB: Ethics and Human Research* 2006 May-June; 28(3): 11-18. Subject: 18.5

Linz, Anthony J.; Haas, Paul F.; Fallon, L. Flemming, Jr.; Metz, Richard J. Impact of concierge care on healthcare and clinical practice. *Journal of the American Osteopathic Association* 2005 November; 105(11): 515-520. Subject: 9.3.1

Linzey, Andrew. Assisted dying: a critique of the theological objections. *Bulletin of Medical Ethics* 2006 April-May; (214): 21-25. Subject: 20.7

Lipkin, K. Michael. Brief report: identifying a proxy for health care as part of routine medical inquiry. *JGIM: Journal of General Internal Medicine* 2006 November; 21(11): 1188-1191. Subject: 20.5.4

Lippi, Donatella; D'Elios, Mario Milco; Benagiano, Marisa; Gensini, Gian Franco. Bioethics under the Tuscan sun. *Bulletin of Medical Ethics* 2005 March; (206): 23-24. Subject: 2.3

Liptak, Adam. Citing risk of missteps, judges set hurdles for lethal injection. *New York Times* 2006 April 12; p. A1, A18. Subject: 20.6

Liptak, Adam. State proposes using device, not doctors, in execution. *New York Times* 2006 April 13; p. A14. Subject: 20.6

Lipton, Peter. Genetic and generic determinism: a new threat to free will? *In:* Rees, Dai; Rose, Steven, eds. The New Brain Sciences: Perils and Prospects. New York: Cambridge University Press; 2004: 88-100. Subject: 15.1

Lipton, Peter. Nuffield Council on Bioethics consultation. *Pharmacogenomics* 2003 January; 4(1): 91-95. Subject: 15.1

Lipworth, Wendy. Navigating tissue banking regulation: conceptual frameworks for researchers, administrators, regulators and policy-makers. *Journal of Law and Medicine* 2005 November; 13(2): 245-255. Subject: 18.3

Lishman, Gordon. Please do not resuscitate: communication is key [letter]. *BMJ: British Medical Journal* 2006 March 11; 332(7541): 609. Subject: 20.5.1

Lissemore, James L. Linkage of genetics and ethics: more crossing over is needed. *Biology of the Cell* 2005 July; 97(7): 599-604. Subject: 15.1

Litt, Iris F. Research with, not on, adolescents: community-based participatory research. *Journal of Adolescent Health* 2003 November; 33(5): 315-316. Subject: 18.5.2

Littenberg, Benjamin; MacLean, Charles D. Passive consent for clinical research in the age of HIPAA. *JGIM: Journal of General Internal Medicine* 2006 March; 21(3): 207-211. Subject: 18.3

Little, George; Kahn, Richard; Green, Ronald M. Parental dreams, dilemmas, and decision-making in Cinéma Vérité. *Journal of Perinatology* 1999 April-May; 19(3): 194-196. Subject: 20.5.2

Little, Miles. Chronic illness and the experience of surviving cancer. *Internal Medicine Journal* 2004 April; 34(4): 201-202. Subject: 9.5.1

Little, M. 'On being both professional and human': a response. *Internal Medicine Journal* 2006 May; 36(5): 319-322. Subject: 8.1

Little, M. Expressing freedom and taking liberties: the paradoxes of aberrant science. *Medical Humanities* 2006 June; 32(1): 32-37. Subject: 1.3.9

Litton, Paul. Defending the distinctions between research and medical care. *American Journal of Bioethics* 2006 July-August; 6(4): 63-66. Subject: 18.2

Liu, Athena. Human embryo cloning prohibited in Hong Kong. *Journal of Assisted Reproduction and Genetics* 2005 December; 22(11-12): 369-378. Subject: 14.5

Liu, Chi-Hong. Impact of assisted reproductive technology on modern medicine. *Journal of the Formosan Medical Association* 2000 February; 99(2): 100-106. Subject: 14.1

Liu, Kimberly E.; Flood, Catherine; Capstick, Valerie. Is an interdisciplinary session on ethics and law in obstetrics and gynaecology effective? *Journal of Obstetrics and Gynaecology Canada* 2005 May; 27(5): 486-490. Subject: 2.3

Livovich, Jeffrey. Ethics in managed care and pain medicine. *Pain Medicine* 2001 June; 2(2): 155-161. Subject: 4.4

Lizza, John P.; Chiong, Winston. Matters of "life" and "death" [letter and reply]. *Hastings Center Report* 2006 May-June; 36(3): 4-5, 5-6. Subject: 20.2.1

Ljungqvist, Arne. The international anti-doping policy and its implementation. *In:* Tamburrini, Claudio; Tännsjö, Torbjörn, eds. Genetic Technology and Sport: Ethical Questions. London; New York: Routledge; 2005: 13-18. Subject: 9.5.1

Llewellyn, David. Penile torts in the courts. *In:* Denniston, George C.; Hodges, Frederick Mansfield; Milos, Marilyn Fayre, eds. Flesh and Blood: Perspectives on the Problems of Circumcision in Contemporary Society. New York: Kluwer Academic/Plenum Publishers; 2004: 69-79. Subject: 9.5.7

Llewellyn, David L., Jr. Licensed to kill: the "death with dignity" initiative. *Criminal Justice Journal* 1992 Fall; 14(2): 309-332. Subject: 20.5.1

Lloyd, Liz. Mortality and morality: ageing and the ethics of care. *Ageing and Society* 2004 March; 24(2): 235-256. Subject: 9.5.2

Lo, Bernard. Advance care planning. *American Journal of Geriatric Cardiology* 2004 November- December; 13(6): 316-320. Subject: 20.5.4

Lo, Bernard. HPV vaccine and adolescents' sexual activity [editorial]. *BMJ: British Medical Journal* 2006 May 13; 332(7550): 1106-1107. Subject: 9.5.1

Lo, Bernard. Strengthening community consultation in critical care and emergency research. *Critical Care Medicine* 2006 August; 34(8): 2236-2238. Subject: 18.6

Lo, Bernard; Groman, Michelle. NBAC recommendations on oversight of human subject research. *Seton Hall Law Review* 2002; 32(3): 493-512. Subject: 18.6

Lo, Bernard; Zettler, Patricia; Cedars, Marcelle I.; Gates, Elena; Kriegstein, Arnold R.; Oberman, Michelle; Reijo Pera, Renee; Wagner, Richard M.; Wuerth, Mary T.; Wolf, Leslie E.; Yamamoto, Keith R. A new era in the ethics of human embryonic stem cell research. *Stem Cells* 2005 November-December; 23(10): 1454-1459. Subject: 18.5.4

Lobo, Rogerio A. ART reporting: the American view. *Human Reproduction* 1996 July; 11(7): 1369-1370. Subject: 14.1

Locher, Julie L.; Bronstein, Janet; Robinson, Caroline O.; Williams, Charlotte, Ritchie, Christine S. Ethical issues involving research conducted with homebound older adults. *Gerontologist* 2006 April; 46(2): 160-164. Subject: 18.5.7

Lock, Margaret. The alienation of body tissue and the biopolitics of immortalized cell lines. *Body and Society* 2001 June-September; 7(2-3): 63-91 [Online] Accessed: http://bod.sagepub.com/cgi/reprint/7/2-3/63 [2007 January 29]. Subject: 15.8

Lock, Margaret. The alienation of body tissue and the biopolitics of immortalized cell lines. *In:* Scheper-Hughes, Nancy; Wacquant, Loïc, eds. Commodifying Bodies. Thousand Oaks, CA: SAGE Publications; 2002: 63-91. Subject: 4.4

Lockwook, Michael. The moral status of the human embryo: implications for IVF. *Reproductive BioMedicine Online [electronic]* 2005 March; 10(Supplement 1): 17-20. Subject: 4.4

Loeben, Greg. Understanding futility: why trust and disparate impact matter as much as what works. *American Journal of Bioethics* 2006 September-October; 6(5): 38-39; discussion W30-W32. Subject: 20.5.1

Loeppky, Rodney D. Control from within? Power, identity, and the Human Genome Project. *Alternatives: Social Transformation and Human Governance* 1998 April-June; 18(2): 205-233. Subject: 15.10

Loewenberg, Samuel. U.S. advisory panel revisits prison research rules. *Lancet* 2006 September 30- October 6; 368(9542): 1143-1144. Subject: 18.5.5

Loewy, Erich H. Sterbehilfe und Euthanasie-Debatte in den Vereinigten Staaten. *In:* Frewer, Andreas; Eickhoff, Clemens, eds. "Euthanasie" und die aktuelle Sterbehilfe-Debatte: Die historischen Hintergründe medizinischer Ethik. Frankfurt; New York: Campus; 2000: 313-335. Subject: 20.5.1

Lohiya, Ghan-Shyam; Tan-Figueroa, Lilia; Crinella, Francis M. End-of-life care for a man with developmental disabilities. *Journal of the American Board of Family Practice* 2003 January-February; 16(1): 58-62. Subject: 20.5.1

Loland, Sigmund. The vulnerability thesis and use of bio-medical technology in sport. *In:* Tamburrini, Claudio; Tännsjö, Torbjörn, eds. Genetic Technology and Sport: Ethical Questions. London; New York: Routledge; 2005: 158-164. Subject: 4.5

Lolas Stepke, Fernando. Empirical social science studies and bioethics: an interface for the regional program on bioethics. *In:* Lolas Stepke, Fernando; Agar Corbinos, Lorenzo, eds. Interfaces Between Bioethics and the Empirical Social Sciences. Buenos Aires, Argentina: World Health Organization; 2002: 11-14. Subject: 2.1

Lomax, James W., II; Karff, Samuel; McKenny, Gerald P. Ethical considerations in the integration of religion and psychotherapy: three perspectives. *Psychiatric Clinics of North America* 2002 September; 25(3): 547-559. Subject: 17.1

London, Alex John. Justice in the Belmont Report and the social division of labor. *APA Newsletters: Newsletter on Philosophy and Medicine* 2006 Spring; 05(2): 5-10. Subject: 18.2

London, Alex John. The moral foundations of equipoise and its role in international research. *American Journal of Bioethics* 2006 July-August; 6(4): 48-51. Subject: 18.5.9

London, Alex John. What is social and global justice to bioethics or bioethics to social and global justice? *Hastings Center Report* 2006 July-August; 36(4): 3. Subject: 2.1

London, Leslie; Rubenstein, Leonard S.; Baldwin-Ragaven, Laurel; Van Es, Adriaan. Dual loyalty among military health professionals: human rights and ethics in times of armed conflict. *CQ: Cambridge Quarterly of Healthcare Ethics* 2006 Fall; 15(4): 381-391. Subject: 21.2

Lone Dog, Leota. Whose genes are they? The Human Genome Diversity Project. *Journal of Health and Social Policy* 1999; 10(4): 51-66. Subject: 15.10

Long, Clarissa. The future of biotechnology: promises and problems. *American Enterprise* 1998 September-October; 9(5): 55-57. Subject: 5.1

Long, Jeffrey C. Commentary: an overview of human subjects research in biological anthropology. *In:* Turner, Trudy R. ed. Biological Anthropology and Ethics: From

See SUBJECT HEADING KEY FOR SECTION II on inside back cover.

639

Repatriation to Genetic Identity. Albany, NY: State University of New York Press; 2005: 275-279. Subject: 18.1

Longenecker, Randall L. The face of overpowering knowledge. *In:* Miller, Roman J.; Brubaker, Beryl H.; Peterson, James C., eds. Viewing New Creations with Anabaptist Eyes: Ethics of Biotechnology. Telford, PA: Cascadia Pub.; 2005: 205-208. Subject: 15.3

Longstaff, Holly; Burgess, Michael; Lewis, Patrick. Comparing methods for ethical consultation for biotechnology related issues. *Health Law Review* 2006; 15(1): 37-38. Subject: 9.6

López, José J. Mapping metaphors and analogies. *American Journal of Bioethics* 2006 November-December; 6(6): 61-63; author reply W13-W14. Subject: 5.1

Lopez, Karen Dunn. Ethics of health care reform: should health care be rationed? *In:* Cowen, Perle Slavik; Moorhead, Sue, eds. Current Issues in Nursing. 7th ed. St. Louis, MO: Mosby, 2006: 611-619. Subject: 9.4

Lopreato, Joseph. Human nature and morality: a sociobiological perspective. *Politics and the Life Sciences* 1988 February; 6(2): 208-213; author's reply 223-225. Subject: 15.9

Lorenz, J.M. Prenatal counseling and resuscitation decisions at extremely premature gestation [editorial]. *Journal of Pediatrics* 2005 November; 147(5): 567-568. Subject: 20.5.2

Lorenz, John M. Ethical dilemmas in the care of the most premature infants: the waters are murkier than ever. *Current Opinion in Pediatrics* 2005 April; 17(2): 186-190. Subject: 20.5.2

Lorenzo, Salomé Santos; González, Aránzazu San José. Second Council of Europe Symposium on Bioethics ('Ethics and Human Genetics') = Segundo Simposio del Consejo de Europa sobre Bioética (<Etica y Genética Humana>). *Law and the Human Genome = Revista de Derecho y Genoma Humano* 1994 July-December; (1): 233-236. Subject: 15.1

Loring, Jeanne F.; Campbell, Cathryn. Intellectual property and human embryonic stem cell research. *Science* 2006 March 24; 311(5768): 1716-1717. Subject: 18.5.4

Lorio, Kathryn Venturatos. The process of regulating assisted reproductive technologies: what we can learn from our neighbors — what translates and what does not. *Loyola Law Review* 1999 Summer; 45(2): 247-268. Subject: 14.1

Lötjönen, Salla. Medical research on patients with dementia — the role of advance directives in European legal instruments. *European Journal of Health Law* 2006 September; 13(3): 235-261. Subject: 20.5.4

Loud, Kelly M. ERISA preemption and patients' rights in the wake of Aetna Health Inc. v. Davila. *Catholic University Law Review* 2005 Spring; 54(3): 1039-1075. Subject: 9.3.2

Loue, Sana. The participation of cognitively impaired elderly in research. *Care Management Journals* 2004 Winter; 5(4): 245-257. Subject: 18.5.7

Louhiala, P.; Hilden, H.-M. Attitudes of Finnish doctors towards euthanasia in 1993 and 2003. *Journal of Medical Ethics* 2006 November; 32(11): 627-628. Subject: 20.5.1

Louw, Stephen J.; Hughes, Julian C. Moral reasoning — the unrealized place of casuistry in medical ethics [editorial]. *International Psychogeriatrics* 2005 June; 17(2): 149-154. Subject: 2.1

Lovell, Anne M. Addiction markets: the case of high-dose Buprenorphine in France. *In:* Petryna, Adriana; Lakoff, Andrew; Kleinman, Arthur, eds. Global Pharmaceuticals: Ethics, Markets, Practices. Durham: Duke University Press; 2006: 136-170. Subject: 9.5.9

Lowbury, Ruth; Kinghorn, George R. Criminal prosecution for HIV transmission [editorial]. *BMJ: British Medical Journal* 2006 September 30; 333(7570): 666-667. Subject: 9.5.6

Lowell, Staci D. Striking a balance: finding a place for religious conscience clauses in contraceptive equity legislation. *Cleveland State Law Review* 2005; 52: 441-465. Subject: 11.1

Lowenfels, Albert B.; Papadakis, Maxine A.; Rattner, Susan L.; Stern, David T. Unprofessional behavior among medical students [letter and reply]. *New England Journal of Medicine* 2006 April 27; 354(17): 1852-1853. Subject: 7.4

Lu, David W.; Matz, Kenneth A. Declining use of the eponym "Reiter's syndrome" in the medical literature, 1998-2003. *Journal of the American Academy of Dermatology* 2005 October; 53(4): 720-723. Subject: 9.5.1

Lübbe, Andreas S. Persisting misconceptions about patients' attitudes at the end of life [editorial]. *Supportive Care in Cancer* 2005 April; 13(4): 203-205. Subject: 20.3.1

Lucas, Peter. Toward a tiered approach to consent in biomedical research. *In:* Árnason, Gardar; Nordal, Salvör; Árnason, Vilhjálmur, eds. Blood and Data: Ethical, Legal and Social Aspects of Human Genetic Databases. Reykjavík: University of Iceland Press; 2004: 79-83. Subject: 18.3

Lucassen, A.; Kaye, J. Genetic testing without consent: the implications of the new Human Tissue Act 2004. *Journal of Medical Ethics* 2006 December; 32(12): 690-692. Subject: 15.3

Lucassen, Anneke. Families and genetic testing: the case of Jane and Phyllis. *In:* Ashcroft, Richard; Lucassen, Anneke; Parker, Michael; Verkerk, Marian; Widdershoven, Guy, eds. Case Analysis in Clinical Ethics. New York: Cambridge University Press; 2005: 7-26. Subject: 15.3

Subject = NRCBL Primary Classification Number; see inside front cover.

Lucassen, Anneke; Parker, Michael. The UK Genethics Club: clinical ethics support for genetic services. *Clinical Ethics* 2006 December; 1(4): 219-223. Subject: 15.1

Lucassen, Anneke; Parker, Michael; Wheeler, Robert. Implications of data protection legislation for family history. *BMJ: British Medical Journal* 2006 February 4; 332(7536): 299-301. Subject: 15.1

Luchins, Daniel J.; Cooper, Amy E.; Hanrahan, Patricia; Heyrman, Mark J. Lawyers' attitudes towards involuntary treatment. *Journal of the American Academy of Psychiatry and the Law* 2006; 34(4): 492-500. Subject: 17.7

Luchsinger, Thomas; Schmid, Hermann. Gentherapie aus juristischer Sicht: Schweizerische und internationale Tendenzen. *In:* Rehmann-Sutter, Christoph; Müller, Hansjakob, eds. Ethik und Gentherapie: zum praktischen Diskurs um die molekulare Medizin. 2nd ed. Tübingen: Francke Verlag; 2003: 169-186. Subject: 15.4

Ludbrook, Philip A.; Clemens, Diane K.; Munson, Ronald; Scannell, Patricia M. Responsible conduct of research. *In:* Schuster, Daniel P.; Powers, William J., eds. Translational and Experimental Clinical Research. Philadelphia, PA: Lippincott Williams and Wilkins; 2005: 163-175. Subject: 18.2

Lueck, Jared C. Roe v. Wade and its Supreme Court progeny. *Journal of Contemporary Legal Issues* 2004; 14(1): 209-214. Subject: 12.4.4

Luginaah, Isaac N.; Yiridoe, Emmanuel K.; Taabazuing, Mary-Margaret. From mandatory to voluntary testing: balancing human rights, religious and cultural values, and HIV/AIDS prevention in Ghana. *Social Science and Medicine* 2005 October; 61(8): 1689-1700. Subject: 9.5.6

Luglié, P.F.; Campus, G.; Lai, V. Ethics: problems of clinical conduct. *Minerva Stomatologica* 2005 September; 54(9): 473-480. Subject: 4.1.2

Lugosi, Charles I. Conforming to the rule of law: when person and human being finally mean the same thing in Fourteenth Amendment jurisprudence. *Issues in Law and Medicine* 2006 Fall-2007 Spring; 22(2-3): 119-303. Subject: 4.4

Lugosi, Charles I. When abortion was a crime: a historical perspective. *University of Detroit Mercy Law Review* 2006 Winter; 83(2): 51-69. Subject: 12.4.2

Lui, S.C.; Weaver, S.M. Attitudes and motives of semen donors and non-donors. *Human Reproduction* 1996 September; 11(9): 2061-2066. Subject: 14.6

Lumpkin, Cristina Arana. Does a pharmacist have the right to refuse to fill a prescription for birth control? *University of Miami Law Review* 2005-2006; 60: 105-130. Subject: 11.1

Lunardi, Valeria Lerch; Peter, Elizabeth; Gastaldo, Denise. Are submissive nurses ethical?: Reflecting on

power anorexia. *Revista Brasileira* 2002 March-April; 55(2): 183-188. Subject: 4.1.3

Lundin, Susanne. The body is worth investing in. *In:* Lundin, Susanne; Åkesson, Lynn, eds. Gene Technology and Economy. Lund: Nordic Academic Press; 2002: 104-115. Subject: 15.1

Lundin, Susanne. Creating identity with biotechnology: the xenotransplanted body as the norm. *Public Understanding of Science* 2002 October; 11(4): 333-345. Subject: 19.1

Lundy, Courtnee. Methods to identify and address the ethical issues associated with managed care. *Penn Bioethics Journal* 2006; 2(2): 3-7. Subject: 9.3.2

Luño, Angel Rodríguez. Ethical reflections on vaccines using cells from aborted fetuses. *National Catholic Bioethics Quarterly* 2006 Autumn; 6(3): 453-459. Subject: 9.5.1

Lunshof, Jeantine E. Lucken in der Regulierung? Zur Kritik der Begutachtungsverfahren. *In:* Rehmann-Sutter, Christoph; Müller, Hansjakob, eds. Ethik und Gentherapie: zum praktischen Diskurs um die molekulare Medizin. Tübingen: Attempto Verlag; 1995: 118-136. Subject: 15.4

Lunshof, Jeantine E. Lücken in der Regulierung?: Zur Kritik der Begutachtungsverfahren. *In:* Rehmann-Sutter, Christoph; Müller, Hansjakob, eds. Ethik und Gentherapie: zum praktischen Diskurs um die molekulare Medizin. 2nd ed. Tübingen: Francke Verlag; 2003: 151-167. Subject: 15.4

Lunshof, Jeantine E.; Simon, Alfred. Die Diskussion um Sterbehilfe und Euthanasie in Deutschland von 1945 bis in die Gegenwart. *In:* Frewer, Andreas; Eickhoff, Clemens, eds. "Euthanasie" und die aktuelle Sterbehilfe-Debatte: Die historischen Hintergründe medizinischer Ethik. Frankfurt; New York: Campus; 2000: 237-249. Subject: 20.5.1

Lunstroth, John. Acting out of ethics: what the open letter asks. *American Journal of Bioethics* 2006 May-June; 6(3): 41-43. Subject: 18.6

Luptak, Marilyn. Social work and end-of-life care for older people: a historical perspective. *Health and Social Work* 2004 February; 29(1): 7-15. Subject: 20.4.1

Lurie, Nicole; Fremont, Allen; Jain, Arvind K.; Taylor, Stephanie L.; McLaughlin, Rebecca; Peterson, Eric; Kong, B. Waine; Ferguson, T. Bruce, Jr. Racial and ethnic disparities in care: the perspectives of cardiologists. *Circulation* 2005 March 15; 111(10): 1264-1269. Subject: 9.5.4

Lurie, Peter; Almeida, Cristina M.; Stine, Nicholas; Stine, Alexander R.; Wolfe, Sidney M. Financial conflict of interest disclosure and voting patterns at Food and Drug Administration drug advisory committee meetings.

See SUBJECT HEADING KEY FOR SECTION II on inside back cover.

641

JAMA: The Journal of the American Medical Association 2006 April 26; 295(16): 1921-1928. Subject: 9.7

Lush, Mary. Who wrote this? [letter]. *New Scientist* 2006 August 19-25; 191(2565): 20. Subject: 1.3.7

Lust, A. Some practical advice concerning a medical lawsuit. *Acta Chirurgica Belgica* 2000 August; 100(4): 160-164. Subject: 8.5

Lutrell, Steven. Mental incapacity and best interests. *In:* Rai, Gurcharan S, ed. Medical Ethics and the Elderly. 2nd ed. San Francisco: Radcliffe Medical Press; 2004: 71-79. Subject: 8.3.3

Luttrell, Steven. Ethical issues and expenditure on health and social care. *In:* Rai, Gurcharan S, ed. Medical Ethics and the Elderly. 2nd ed. San Francisco: Radcliffe Medical Press; 2004: 51-57. Subject: 9.4

Lutzen, Kim; Dahlqvist, Vera; Eriksson, Sture; Norberg, Astrid. Developing the concept of moral sensitivity in health care practice. *Nursing Ethics* 2006 March; 13(2): 187-196. Subject: 4.1.1

Luu, Arlene D. Research examines the minimal risk standard for pediatric research. *Journal of Biolaw and Business* 2006; 9(1): 52-53. Subject: 18.5.2

Luxembourg. Commission Consultative Nationale d'Éthique pour les Sciences de la Vie et de la Santé [CNE]. Avis au sujet de tests de dépistage obligatoires de l'infection par le virus HIV: Avis 1992.1 [Opinion on the subject of compulsory screening tests for infection by the HIV virus: Opinion 1992.1]. Luxembourg: Commission Nationale d'Éthique, 1992 June 12; 9 p. [Online]. Accessed: http://www.cne.public.lu/publications/avis/ 1992_1.pdf [2006 April 7]. Subject: 9.5.6

Luxembourg. Commission Consultative Nationale d'Éthique pour les Sciences de la Vie et de la Santé [CNE]. Avis concernant les articles 7, alinéas 3 et 4, et 43 du projet de loi No 2557 relatif à la protection de la jeunesse: Avis 3/1990 [Opinion 3/1990: Opinion concerning articles 7, line nos. 3 and 4 and 43 of Bill 2557 concerning the protection of youth]. Luxembourg: Commission Nationale d'Éthique, 1990; 18 p. [Online]. Accessed: http://www.cne.public.lu/publications/avis/ 1990_3.PDF [2006 April 7]. Subject: 8.3.2

Luxembourg. Commission Consultative Nationale d'Éthique pour les Sciences de la Vie et de la Santé [CNE]. Avis concernant les directives de la CEE sur la dissémination d'organismes génétiquement modifiés: Avis 2/1990 [Opinion concerning the directives of the CEE on the release of genetically modified organisms: Opinion 2/1990]. Luxembourg: Commission Nationale d'Éthique, 1990; 14 p. [Online]. Accessed: http://www.cne.public.lu/publications/avis/1990_2.PDF [2006 April 7]. Subject: 15.1

Luxembourg. Commission Consultative Nationale d'Éthique pour les Sciences de la Vie et de la Santé [CNE]. Avis concernant un projet de recherche sur les anomalies de l'hémoglobine lors de l'examen prénuptial: Avis 1/1990 [Opinion concerning a research project on the anomalies of hemoglobin at the time of a premarital examination: Opinion 1/1990]. Luxembourg: Commission Nationale d'Éthique, 1990; 2 p. [Online]. Accessed: http://www.cne.public.lu/publications/avis/1990_1.PDF [2006 April 7]. Subject: 15.3

Luxembourg. Commission Consultative Nationale d'Éthique pour les Sciences de la Vie et de la Santé [CNE]. Bref Avis sur le project de loi no. 5448 relatif aux tissus et cellules humains utilisés à des fins thérapeutiques: Avis No 19 [Opinion No. 19: Short opinion on Bill no. 5448 concerning human tissues and cells used for therapeutic ends]. Luxembourg: Commission Nationale d'Éthique, 2005 December 22; 6 p. [Online]. Accessed: http://www.cne.public.lu/publications/avis/Avis_19.pdf [2006 April 7]. Subject: 19.5

Luxembourg. Commission Consultative Nationale d'Éthique pour les Sciences de la Vie et de la Santé [CNE]. Le clonage reproductif d'êtres humains: Avis 2004.1 [Reproductive cloning of humans: Opinion 2004:1]. Luxembourg: Commission Nationale d'Éthique, 2004; 23 p. [Online]. Accessed: http://www.cne.public.lu/publications/avis/2004_1.pdf [2006 April 7]. Subject: 14.5

Lyall, Sarah. British clinic is allowed to deny medicine; decision on cost has broad impact. *New York Times* 2006 February 16; p. A10. Subject: 9.4

Lyall, Sarah. Court backs Briton's right to a costly drug. *New York Times* 2006 April 13; p. A3. Subject: 9.4

Lyman, Bobbi J.; Lee, Susan J.; Ralston, Henry J. Peter, III; Drey, Eleanor A.; Partridge, John Colin; Rosen, Mark A. Fetal pain [letter and reply]. *JAMA: The Journal of the American Medical Association* 2006 January 11; 295(2): 159, 160-161. Subject: 4.4

Lynn, Mary R.; Nelson, Daniel K. Common (mis)perceptions about IRB review of human subjects research. *Nursing Science Quarterly* 2005 July; 16(3): 264-270. Subject: 18.2

Lyons, Edward C. In incognito: the principle of double effect in American Constitutional Law. *Florida Law Review* 2005 July; 57(3): 469-563. Subject: 20.5.1

Lyren, Anne; Kodish, Eric; Lazebnik, Rina; O'Riordan, Mary Ann. Understanding confidentiality: perspectives of African American adolescents and their parents. *Journal of Adolescent Health: Official Publication of the Society for Adolescent Medicine* 2006 August; 39(2): 261-265. Subject: 8.4

Lysaght, Michael J. California's Proposition 71 [editorial]. *Tissue Engineering* 2005 March-April; 11(3-4): xi-xiii. Subject: 18.5.4

Lysaught, M. Therese. And power corrupts . . . religion and the disciplinary matrix of bioethics. *In:* Guinn, David

---

E., ed. Handbook of Bioethics and Religion. New York: Oxford University Press, 2006: 93-127. Subject: 2.1

M

M'charek, Amade. Technologies of similarities and differences, or how to do politics with DNA. *In his:* The Human Genome Diversity Project: An Ethnography of Scientific Practice. Cambridge; New York: Cambridge University Press; 2005: 148-185. Subject: 15.1

Ma, Qiang; Cai, Bingliang; Song, Guofan. The role of the media for medical ethics in China. *In:* Döring, Ole; Chen, Renbiao, eds. Advances in Chinese Medical Ethics: Chinese and International Perspectives. Hamburg: Institut für Asienkunde; 2002: 358-366. Subject: 2.3

Maaroos, Heidi-Ingrid; Tahepold, Heli; Kalda, Ruth. Patient consent rates for video-recording. *Family Practice* 2004 December; 21(6): 706. Subject: 18.3

MacAdam, Philip. New Ontario legislation important for persons living with HIV/AIDS. *Canadian HIV/AIDS Policy and Law Newsletter* 1995 April; 1(3): 10-11. Subject: 9.5.6

MacDonald, Michael G. Attitudes of trainees in suicide intervention toward euthanasia and suicide among the nonterminally ill. *Psychological Reports* 2005 June; 96(3, Part 1): 709-712. Subject: 20.7

Macer, Darryl R.J. The purposes of bioethics education: lessons from Japan and Asia. *In:* Sang-yong, Song; Young-Mo, Koo; Macer, Darryl R.J., eds. Asian Bioethics in the 21st Century. Christchurch, NZ: Eubios Ethics Institute, 2002: 241-250. Subject: 2.3

Macer, Darryl; Inaba, Masakazu; Maekawa, Fumi; Ng, Maryann Chen; Obata, Hiroko. Japanese attitudes toward xenotransplantation. *Public Understanding of Science* 2002 October; 11(4): 347-362. Subject: 19.1

MacFarlane, Phil; Campbell, Norm; McAlister, Finlay A.; Hoey, John. Not all guidelines are created equal [letters and reply]. *CMAJ/JAMC: Canadian Medical Association Journal* 2006 March 14; 174(6): 814-815. Subject: 7.3

Machado, Calixto. The first organ transplant from a brain-dead donor. *Neurology* 2005 June 14; 64(11): 1938-1942. Subject: 20.2.1

Machan, Tibor R. Why human beings may use animals. *Journal of Value Inquiry* 2002; 36(1): 9-14. Subject: 22.1

MacIntosh, Tracy. Ethical considerations for clinical photography in the Global South. *Developing World Bioethics* 2006 May; 6(2): 81-88. Subject: 8.4

Mackay-Sim, Alan. Stem cells— a beginner's guide. *Social Alternatives* 2003 Summer; 22(1): 27-32. Subject: 18.5.4

Mackellar, Calum. Laws and practices relating to euthanasia and assisted suicide in 34 countries of the Council of Europe and the USA. *European Journal of Health Law* 2003 March; 10(1): 63-64. Subject: 20.7

Mackenzie, Robin. Addiction in public health and criminal justice system governance: neuroscience, enhancement and happiness research. *Genomics, Society and Policy* 2006 May; 2(1): 92-109. Subject: 9.5.9

Macklin, Ruth. The Belmont principle of justice: an idea whose time has come. *APA Newsletters: Newsletter on Philosophy and Medicine* 2006 Spring; 05(2): 4-5. Subject: 18.1

Macklin, Ruth. Changing the presumption: providing ART to vaccine research patients. *American Journal of Bioethics [Online].* 2006 January-February; 6(1): W1-W5. Subject: 9.5.6

Macklin, Ruth. The new conservatives in bioethics: who are they and what do they seek? *Hastings Center Report* 2006 January-February; 36(1): 34-43. Subject: 2.1

Macklin, Ruth. No shortage of dilemmas: comment on "they call it 'patient selection' in Khayelitsha". *CQ: Cambridge Quarterly of Healthcare Ethics* 2006 Summer; 15(3): 313-321. Subject: 9.5.6

Macklin, Ruth. Scaling up HIV testing: ethical issues. *Health and Human Rights: An International Journal* 2005; 8(2): 27-30. Subject: 9.5.6

Macklin, Ruth. Unresolved issues in social science medicine. *In:* Lolas Stepke, Fernando; Agar Corbinos, Lorenzo, eds. Interfaces Between Bioethics and the Empirical Social Sciences. Buenos Aires, Argentina: World Health Organization; 2002: 67-78. Subject: 18.4

Maclean, Alasdair R. Advance directives, future selves and decision-making. *Medical Law Review* 2006 Autumn; 14(3): 291-320. Subject: 20.5.4

Maclean, Alisdair. Autonomy, consent and persuasion. *European Journal of Health Law* 2006 December; 13(4): 321-338. Subject: 8.3.1

Maclean, M. Parenthood should not be regarded as a right [debate]. *Archives of Disease in Childhood* 2005 August; 90(8): 782-783. Subject: 14.1

MacLeod, Kendra D.; Whitsett, Stan F.; Mash, Eric J.; Pelletier, Wendy. Pediatric sibling donors of successful and unsuccessful hematopoietic stem cell transplants (HSCT): a qualitative study of their psychosocial experience. *Journal of Pediatric Psychology* 2003 June; 28(4): 223-231. Subject: 19.5

Macnaghten, Phil. Animals in their nature: a case study on public attitudes to animals, genetic modification and "nature". *Sociology* 2004 July 1; 38(3): 533-551. Subject: 15.1

MacNeil, S. Danielle; Fernandez, Conrad V. Informing research participants of research results: analysis of Canadian university based research ethics board policies. *Journal of Medical Ethics* 2006 January; 32(1): 49-54. Subject: 18.2

MacNeil, S. Danielle; Fernandez, Conrad V. Offering results to research participants [editorial]. *BMJ: British*

See SUBJECT HEADING KEY FOR SECTION II on inside back cover.

643

Medical Journal 2006 January 28; 332(7535): 188-189. Subject: 18.2

MacPherson, Cheryl Cox. Healthcare development requires stakeholder consultation: palliative care in the Caribbean. *CQ: Cambridge Quarterly of Healthcare Ethics* 2006 Summer; 15(3): 248-255. Subject: 20.4.1

Madden, Deirdre; McDonagh, Maeve. Research ethics committees in Ireland. *In:* Beyleveld, D.; Townend, D.; Wright, J., eds. Research Ethics Committees, Data Protection and Medical Research in European Countries. Hants, England; Burlington, VT: Ashgate; 2005: 107-109. Subject: 18.2

Madden, William; Carter, Brian S. Physician-soldier: a moral profession. *In:* Beam, Thomas E.; Sparacino, Linette R.; Pellegrino, Edmund D.; Hartle, Anthony E.; Howe, Edmund G., eds. Military Medical Ethics. Volume 1. Washington, DC: TMM Publications, Borden Institute, Walter Reed Army Medical Center; 2003: 269-291. Subject: 2.1

Maehle, Andreas-Holger. Protecting patient privacy or serving public interests? Challenges to medical confidentiality in imperial Germany. *Social History of Medicine* 2003 December; 16(3): 383-401. Subject: 8.4

Maggiore, Salvatore Maurizio; Antonelli, Massimo. Euthanasia, therapeutic obstinacy or something else? An Italian case [news]. *Intensive Care Medicine* 2005 July; 31(7): 997-998. Subject: 20.5.1

Magill, Gerard. Embryonic stem cell research and human therapeutic cloning: maintaining the ethical tension between respect and research. *In:* Iltis, Ana Smith, ed. Research Ethics. New York: Routledge, 2006: 61-85. Subject: 18.5.4

Magill, Gerard. An ethical analysis of the policy implications in the United States emerging from the relationship between human genomics and embryonic stem cell research. *In:* Glasa, J. ed. Ethics of Human Genetics: Challenges of the (Post) Genomic Era. Bratislava, Slovak Republic: Charis [and] IMEB Foundation; 2002: 191-2002. Subject: 18.5.4

Magney, Alix. Cloning me, cloning you: reflections on the ethics of cloning for individuals, families and society. *Social Alternatives* 2003 Summer; 22(1): 19-26. Subject: 14.5

Magnotti, Lauren. Giving a voice to those who can't speak for themselves: toward greater regulation of animal experimentation. *Buffalo Environmental Law Journal* 2006 Spring; 13(2): 179-204. Subject: 22.2

Magnus, David. Blood, sweat and tears. *American Journal of Bioethics* 2006 May-June; 6(3): 1-2. Subject: 18.2

Magnus, David. Stem cell research: the California experience. *Hastings Center Report* 2006 January-February; 36(1): 26-28. Subject: 18.5.4

Magnus, David; Cho, Mildred K. A commentary on oocyte donation for stem cell research in South Korea. *American Journal of Bioethics [Online].* 2006 January-February; 6(1): W23-W24. Subject: 18.5.4

Magnusson, Roger S. The devil's choice: re-thinking law, ethics, and symptom relief in palliative care. *Journal of Law, Medicine and Ethics* 2006 Fall; 34(3): 559-569. Subject: 20.4.1

Magnusson, Roger S. A short history of the next thirty years: genetic testing, clinical care and personal choices [forum]. *University of New South Wales Law Journal* 2003; 26(3): 743-754. Subject: 15.3

Magotra, Ratna. The controversy of drug-eluting cardiac stents. *Indian Journal of Medical Ethics* 2006 January-March; 3(1): 25-26. Subject: 9.7

Magri, Sonia. Research on human embryos and cloning: difficulties of legislating in a changing environment and model approaches to regulation. *Journal of Law and Medicine* 2005 May; 12(4): 483-493. Subject: 18.5.4

Magri, Sonia. Research on human embryos, stem cells and cloning — one year since the passing of Australian legislation: Australia, around the world, and back again. *E Law: Murdoch University Electronic Journal of Law* 2003 December; 10(4): 24 p. [Online]. Accessed: http://www.murdoch.edu.au/elaw/issues/v10n4/magri104.html [2006 June 29]. Subject: 18.5.4

Mahlknecht, Ulrich; Voelter-Mahlknecht, Susanne. Pharmacogenomics: questions and concerns. *Current Medical Research and Opinion* 2005 July; 21(7): 1041-1047. Subject: 15.1

Mahood, S.; Zagozeski, C.; Bradel, T.; Lawrence, K. Pharmaceutical policies in Canadian family medicine training: survey of residency programs. *Canadian Family Physician* 1997 November; 43: 1947-1951. Subject: 7.2

Mahowald, Mark W.; Cramer Bornemann, Michel A. What? Influenced by industry? Not me! [editorial]. *Sleep Medicine* 2005 September; 6(5): 389-390. Subject: 9.7

Maienschein, Jane. The language really matters. *In:* Ruse, Michael; Pynes, Christopher A., eds. The Stem Cell Controversy: Debating the Issues. Amherst, NY: Prometheus Books; 2003: 33-81. Subject: 18.5.4

Main, D.C.J. Offering the best to patients: ethical issues associated with the provision of veterinary services. *Veterinary Record* 2006 January 14; 158(2): 62-66. Subject: 22.1

Maio, Giovanni. Reanimieren oder nicht?: Ethische Überlegungen zur deutschen Diskussion über den Therapieverzicht. *In:* Gordijn, Bert; ten Have, Henk, eds. Medizinethik und Kultur: Grenzen medizinischen Handelns in Deutschland und den Niederlanden. Stuttgart: Frommann-Holzboog; 2000: 105-139. Subject: 20.5.1

Subject = NRCBL Primary Classification Number; see inside front cover.

Maio, Monica. Labor pains: the undue burden of forcing a woman to carry a non-viable fetus to term. *Journal of Law and Family Studies* 2005; 7(2): 459-474. Subject: 12.4.2

Majumdar, Abhik. The right to die: the Indian experience. *Australian Journal of Asian Law* 2004 August; 6(2): 157-175. Subject: 20.5.1

Mak, Yvonne; Elwyn, Glyn. Use of hermeneutic research in understanding the meaning of desire for euthanasia. *Palliative Medicine* 2003; 17(5): 395-402. Subject: 20.5.1

Mak, Yvonne; Elwyn, Glyn. Voices of the terminally ill: uncovering the meaning of desire for euthanasia. *Palliative Medicine* 2005 June; 19(4): 343-350. Subject: 20.5.1

Makin, Andrew. Taking resuscitation decisions in the nursing home setting. *Nursing Times* 2005 October 11-17; 101(41): 28-30. Subject: 20.5.1

Malaviya, Prashant; John, Deborah Roedder; Sternthal, Brian; Barnes, James. Human participants — respondents and researchers [discussion]. *Journal of Consumer Psychology* 2001; 10(1-2): 115-121. Subject: 18.2

Malecha, Wayne. Faith healing exemptions to child protection laws. *Journal of Legislation* 1985; 12: 243-263. Subject: 8.3.4

Malek, Janet. Identity, harm, and the ethics of reproductive technology. *Journal of Medicine and Philosophy* 2006 February; 31(1): 83- 95. Subject: 14.1

Malek, Janet. Informed consent. *In:* Mitcham, Carl, ed. Encyclopedia of Science, Technology, and Ethics. Farmington Hills, MI: Thomson/Gale, 2005: 1016-1019. Subject: 8.3.1

Malek, Janet. Introduction. *Journal of Medicine and Philosophy* 2006 October; 31(5): 441-446. Subject: 2.1

Malek, Janet. Misconduct in science: biomedical science cases. *In:* Mitcham, Carl, ed. Encyclopedia of Science, Technology, and Ethics. Farmington Hills, MI: Thomson/Gale, 2005: 1207-1210. Subject: 1.3.9

Malinowski, Michael J. Could biobanking be a means to include "health care have-nots" in the genomics revolution? *DePaul Journal of Health Care Law* 2005; 9(2): 1005-1022. Subject: 9.5.4

Malinowski, Michael J. A law-policy proposal to know where babies come from during the reproductive revolution. *Journal of Gender, Race and Justice* 2006 Spring; 9(3): 549-568. Subject: 14.4

Mallia, Pierre. Research ethics committees in Malta. *In:* Beyleveld, D.; Townend, D.; Wright, J., eds. Research Ethics Committees, Data Protection and Medical Research in European Countries. Hants, England; Burlington, VT: Ashgate; 2005: 149-152. Subject: 18.2

Mallinger, Julie B.; Fisher, Susan G.; Brown, Theodore; Lamberti, J. Steven. Racial disparities in the use of second-generation antipsychotics for the treatment of schizophrenia. *Psychiatric Services* 2006 January; 57(1): 133-136. Subject: 9.5.4

Malmqvist, Erik. The notion of health and the morality of genetic intervention. *Medicine, Health Care and Philosophy* 2006; 9(2): 181-192. Subject: 15.1

Malone, Ruth E.; Yerger, Valerie B.; McGruder, Carol; Froelicher, Erika. "It's like Tuskegee in reverse": a case study of ethical tensions in institutional review board review of community-based participatory research. *American Journal of Public Health* 2006 November; 96(11): 1914-1919. Subject: 18.2

Maloney, Dennis M. Agency says institutional review board (IRB) did not fulfill duties so agency investigation expands. *Human Research Report* 2006 April; 21(4): 6-7. Subject: 18.2

Maloney, Dennis M. Agency says institutional review board (IRB) failed to warn subjects of significant problems. *Human Research Report* 2006 March; 21(3): 6-7. Subject: 18.2

Maloney, Dennis M. Alternatives to local institutional review board (IRB) system debated. *Human Research Report* 2006 April; 21(4): 1-2. Subject: 18.2

Maloney, Dennis M. Better protection for human subjects is outcome of very early clinical trials. *Human Research Report* 2006 May; 21(5): 1-2. Subject: 18.2

Maloney, Dennis M. Case study: inadequate university response leads to shutdown of human research projects. *Human Research Report* 2006 July; 21(7): 6-7. Subject: 18.2

Maloney, Dennis M. Case study: institutional review board fails to follow numerous regulations. *Human Research Report* 2006 November; 21(11): 6-7. Subject: 18.2

Maloney, Dennis M. Case study: the more a federal office digs, the more problems it finds with the institutional review board (IRB). *Human Research Report* 2006 October; 21(10): 6-7. Subject: 18.5.5

Maloney, Dennis M. Case study: university tries to explain regulatory noncompliance in research. *Human Research Report* 2006 December; 21(12): 6-7. Subject: 18.5.5

Maloney, Dennis M. Defendants agree to multimillion dollar settlement for research subjects. *Human Research Report* 2006 August; 21(8): 8. Subject: 18.5.3

Maloney, Dennis M. Defendants claim that research subjects do not quality [sic; qualify] for a class action lawsuit. *Human Research Report* 2006 February; 21(2): 8. Subject: 18.3

Maloney, Dennis M. The defendants must attempt to find all former research subjects. *Human Research Report* 2006 May; 21(5): 8. Subject: 18.3

Maloney, Dennis M. Federal agency issues new exception to informed consent requirements. *Human Research Report* 2006 July; 21(7): 1-2. Subject: 18.3

See SUBJECT HEADING KEY FOR SECTION II on inside back cover.

645

Maloney, Dennis M. How institutional review boards (IRBs) can handle adverse event reports. *Human Research Report* 2006 January; 21(1): 1-3. Subject: 18.2

Maloney, Dennis M. Human subject protection rules may apply later, even if they don't at first. *Human Research Report* 2006 September; 21(9): 1-2. Subject: 18.5.5

Maloney, Dennis M. In court: court approves settlement between defendants and former research subjects. *Human Research Report* 2006 July; 21(7): 8. Subject: 18.3

Maloney, Dennis M. In court: court says children may have been used like canaries in a mine. *Human Research Report* 2006 December; 21(12): 8. Subject: 18.5.2

Maloney, Dennis M. In court: court says researchers have duty to inform about risks. *Human Research Report* 2006 November; 21(11): 8. Subject: 18.5.2

Maloney, Dennis M. Institutional review board (IRB) did not know about subject problem until after study. *Human Research Report* 2006 May; 21(5): 6-7. Subject: 18.2

Maloney, Dennis M. Institutional review boards (IRBs) and their role in community consultation. *Human Research Report* 2006 November; 21(11): 1-2. Subject: 18.2

Maloney, Dennis M. Institutional review boards (IRBs) must be given adequate information. *Human Research Report* 2006 December; 21(12): 1-2. Subject: 18.2

Maloney, Dennis M. Minority groups as human subjects. *Human Research Report* 2006 February; 21(2): 3. Subject: 18.5.1

Maloney, Dennis M. New advice on special duties for institutional review boards (IRBs). *Human Research Report* 2006 October; 21(10): 1-2. Subject: 18.3

Maloney, Dennis M. No trial needed when financial settlement benefits the former research subjects. *Human Research Report* 2006 April; 21(4): 8. Subject: 18.3

Maloney, Dennis M. Research subject says institutional review board (IRB) was no help. *Human Research Report* 2006 January; 21(1): 7. Subject: 18.2

Maloney, Dennis M. Research subject says institutional review board (IRB) would not answer her questions. *Human Research Report* 2006 February; 21(2): 7. Subject: 18.2

Maloney, Dennis M. Research subjects say institutional review boards (IRBs) must change research review procedures. *Human Research Report* 2006 January; 21(1): 8. Subject: 18.2

Maloney, Dennis M. Research subjects win battle to obtain class action status. *Human Research Report* 2006 March; 21(3): 8. Subject: 18.3

Maloney, Dennis M. University finally can resume human subjects research again [case study]. *Human Research Report* 2006 August; 21(8): 6-7. Subject: 18.2

Maloney, Dennis M. University's medical center ordered to suspend research with prisoners — for starters [case study]. *Human Research Report* 2006 September; 21(9): 6-7. Subject: 18.5.5

Maloney, Michelle. Polishing the mirror: mental health from a Bahá'i perspective. *Journal of Religion and Health* 2006 Fall; 45(3): 405-418. Subject: 4.3

Malpas, P.J. Why tell asymptomatic children of the risk of an adult-onset disease in the family but not test them for it? *Journal of Medical Ethics* 2006 November; 32(11): 639-642. Subject: 15.3

Malpas, Phillipa. The right to remain in ignorance about genetic information—can such a right be defended in the name of autonomy? *New Zealand Medical Journal* 2005 August 12; 118(1220); 8 p. Subject: 15.3

Mamdani, Bashir. Placebos: can you get something for nothing? *Indian Journal of Medical Ethics* 2006 October-December; 3(4): 136-138. Subject: 8.2

Mamdani, Bashir; Mamdani, Meenal. The impact of China's one-child policy. *Indian Journal of Medical Ethics* 2006 July-September; 3(3): 106-108. Subject: 13.3

Mameli, M.; Bortolotti, L. Animal rights, animal minds, and human mindreading. *Journal of Medical Ethics* 2006 February; 32(2): 84-89. Subject: 22.1

Manasse, Henri R., Jr. The other side of the human genome. *American Journal of Health-System Pharmacy* 2005 May 15; 62(10): 1080-1086. Subject: 15.10

Manca, Donna P.; Maher, Peggy; Gallant, Roseanne. Ethical concerns in community practice research. Common concerns encountered by the Alberta family practice research network [editorial]. *Canadian Family Physician* 2006 March; 52: 288-289, 296-298. Subject: 18.1

Mandell, Brian F. New CCJM policy: no manufacturer involvement in the preparation of articles. *Cleveland Clinic Journal of Medicine* 2005 March; 72(3): 169. Subject: 1.3.9

Manfredi, Christopher P.; Maioni, Antonia. "The last line of defence for citizens": litigating private health insurance in Chaoulli v. Quebec. *Osgoode Hall Law Journal* 2006 Summer; 44(2): 249-271. Subject: 9.3.1

Mangan, Katherine. Acting sick. *Chronicle of Higher Education* 2006 September 15; 53(4): A10-A12. Subject: 7.2

Mangan, Katherine S. Researchers raise concerns about secrecy in company-sponsored clinical trials. *Chronicle of Higher Education* 2006 April 7; 52(31): A39. Subject: 18.2

Manickavel, V. Family: another dinosaur? The market driven technological fix: is there a place for family? *In:* Sang-yong, Song; Young-Mo, Koo; Macer, Darryl R.J., eds. Asian Bioethics in the 21st Century. Christchurch, NZ: Eubios Ethics Institute, 2002: 282-86. Subject: 5.1

Mann, Howard. Extensions and refinements of the equipoise concept in international clinical research: would

Benjamin Freedman approve? *American Journal of Bioethics* 2006 July-August; 6(4): 67-69. Subject: 18.5.9

Mann, Howard. How confidential trial negotiations and agreements between the Food and Drug Administration and sponsors marginalize local institutional boards, and what to do about it. *American Journal of Bioethics* 2006 May-June; 6(3): 22-24; discussion W49- W50. Subject: 18.2

Mann, Howard; Shamoo, Adil E. Introduction to special issue of Accountability in Research on the review and approval of biomedical research proposals. *Accountability in Research* 2006 January-March; 13(1): 1-9. Subject: 18.2

Mann, Jonathan. Health and human rights: if not now, when? *American Journal of Public Health* 2006 November; 96(11): 1940-1943. Subject: 9.1

Manna, Claudio; Nardo, Luciano G. Italian law on assisted conception: clinical and research implications. *Reproductive BioMedicine Online [electronic]* 2005 November; 11(5): 532-534. Subject: 14.1

Manninen, B.A. A case for justified non-voluntary active euthanasia: exploring the ethics of the Groningen Protocol. *Journal of Medical Ethics* 2006 November; 32(11): 643-651. Subject: 20.5.1

Manninen, B.A. Medicating the mind: a Kantian analysis of overprescribing psychoactive drugs. *Journal of Medical Ethics* 2006 February; 32(2): 100-105. Subject: 17.4

Manno, Edward M. Nonheart-beating donation in the neurologically devastated patient. *Neurocritical Care* 2005; 3(2): 111-114. Subject: 19.5

Manno, Edward M.; Wijdicks, Eelco F.M. The declaration of death and the withdrawal of care in the neurologic patient. *Neurologic Clinics* 2006 February; 24(1): 159-169. Subject: 20.5.1

Manolio, Teri A. Taking our obligations to research participants seriously: disclosing individual results of genetic research. *American Journal of Bioethics* 2006 November-December; 6(6): 32-34; author reply W10-W12. Subject: 15.1

Månsdotter, Anna; Lindholm, Lars; Lundberg, Michael. Health, wealth and fairness based on gender: the support for ethical principles. *Social Science and Medicine* 2006 May; 62(9): 2327-2335. Subject: 10

Manser, T.; Staender, S. Aftermath of an adverse event: supporting health care professionals to meet patient expectations through open disclosure. *Acta Anaesthesiologica Scandinavica* 2005 July; 49(6): 728-734. Subject: 9.8

Manson, Neil C. What is genetic information, and why is it significant? A contextual, contrastive, approach. *Journal of Applied Philosophy* 2006; 23(1): 1-16. Subject: 15.1

Manthous, Constantine A. Critical care physicians' practices and attitudes and applicable statutes regarding withdrawal of life-sustaining therapies. *Connecticut Medicine* 2005 August; 69(7): 395-400. Subject: 20.5.1

Mantovani, Ferrando. Genetic manipulation, legal interests under threat, control systems and techniques of protection = Manipulaciones genéticas, bienes jurídicos amenazados, sistemas de control y técnicas de tutela. *Law and the Human Genome = Revista de Derecho y Genoma Humano* 1994 July-December; (1): 91-117. Subject: 15.4

Maoz, Arieh. Tampering with nature: an "unended quest". *Eubios Journal of Asian and International Bioethics* 2006 September; 16(5): 140-144. Subject: 5.1

Marasco, Silvana F.; Ibrahim, Joseph E.; Oakley, Justin. Public disclosure of surgeon-specific report cards: current status of the debate. *ANZ Journal of Surgery* 2005 November; 75(11): 1000-1004. Subject: 9.8

Marceau, Emmanuelle. Australia: court orders doctors to pay damages to woman who contracted HIV from her husband [news]. *HIV/AIDS Policy and Law Review* 2003 August; 8(2): 48-51. Subject: 9.5.6

March, Ruth; Cheeseman, Kevin; Doherty, Michael. Pharmacogenetics — legal, ethical and regulatory considerations [editorial]. *Pharmacogenomics* 2001 November; 2(4): 317-327. Subject: 15.1

Marchant, Gary E.; Sylvester, Douglas J. Transnational models for regulation of nanotechnology. *Journal of Law, Medicine and Ethics* 2006 Winter; 34(4): 714-725. Subject: 5.3

Marchant, Jo. Human eggs supply 'ethical' stem cells [news]. *Nature* 2006 June 29; 441(7097): 1038. Subject: 18.5.4

Marco, C.A. Ethical issues of resuscitation: an American perspective. *Postgraduate Medical Journal* 2005 September; 81(959): 608-612. Subject: 20.5.1

Marcoux, Isabelle; Onwuteaka-Philipsen, Bregje D.; Jansen-van der Weide, Marijke C.; van der Wal, Gerrit. Withdrawing an explicit request for euthanasia or physician-assisted suicide: a retrospective study on the influence of mental health status and other patient characteristics. *Psychological Medicine* 2005 September; 35(9): 1265-1274. Subject: 20.5.1

Marcus, Amy Dockser. Patients with rare diseases work to jump-start research; advocacy groups create their own tissue banks to aid in drug development. *Wall Street Journal* 2006 July 11; p. D1, D2. Subject: 19.5

Marcus, Emilie. Retraction controversy [editorial]. *Cell* 2005 October 21; 123(2): 173-175. Subject: 1.3.7

Marcus, Gilbert. The abdication of responsibility: the role of doctors in the Uitenhage unrest. *South African Journal on Human Rights* 1985; 1: 151-154. Subject: 4.1.2

Mareiniss, Darren P.; Casarett, David; Kapo, Jennifer; Caplan, Arthur. Appropriate use of artificial nutrition and hydration [letter and reply]. *New England Journal of Medicine* 2006 March 23; 354(12): 1320-1321. Subject: 20.5.1

Marker, Rita L. Euthanasia and assisted suicide today. *Society* 2006 May-June; 43(4): 59-67. Subject: 20.5.1

See SUBJECT HEADING KEY FOR SECTION II on inside back cover.

647

Markl, Hubert. Man's place in nature: evolutionary past and genomic future. *Journal of Molecular Biology* 2002 June 14; 319(4): 869-876. Subject: 15.1

Markman, Maurie. "Therapeutic intent" in phase 1 oncology trials: a justifiable objective. *Archives of Internal Medicine* 2006 July 24; 166(14): 1446-1448. Subject: 18.2

Markman, Maurie. Assuring the ethical conduct of clinical cancer trials in the developing world. *Cancer* 2006 January 1; 106(1): 1-3. Subject: 18.1

Markman, Maurie. Providing research participants with findings from completed cancer-related clinical trials: not quite as simple as it sounds. *Cancer* 2006 April 1; 106(7): 1421-1424. Subject: 18.3

Markman, Maurie. Reflections on ethical concerns arising from the incorporation of results of randomized trials of antineoplastic therapy into routine clinical practice. *Cancer Investigation* 2005; 23(8): 735-740. Subject: 18.2

Markon, Jerry. Fight intensifies over who acts for children; judge lets teen waive usual cancer care; trial set for August. *Washington Post* 2006 July 26; p. B8. Subject: 8.3.2

Markon, Jerry. Fight over a child's care ends in compromise; Va. judge's order could have forced teen to get chemotherapy. *Washington Post* 2006 August 17; p. A1, A13. Subject: 8.3.4

Markon, Jerry. Who decides child medical care in dispute. *Washington Post* 2006 July 26; p. B1, B8. Subject: 8.3.2

Markovitz, Barry P.; Goodman, Kenneth W. Case reports on the web redux: confidentiality still in jeopardy. *AMIA Symposium Proceedings* 2003; p. 926. Subject: 8.4

Marks, Lee Ann. The "Seymour Report" on Fetal Welfare and the Law in Australia. *E Law: Murdoch University Electronic Journal of Law* 1995 December; 2(3): 4 p. [Online]. Accessed: http://www.murdoch.edu.au/elaw/issues/v2n3/marks23.html [2006 June 29]. Subject: 9.5.8

Marks, Patricia D. Reaching a balance between privacy, privilege and planning: a look at barriers to obtaining information for patients with criminal involvement. *Psychiatric Quarterly* 2004 Summer; 75(2): 127-138. Subject: 8.4

Marks, Ray; Shive, Steven E. Improving our application of the health education code of ethics. *Health Promotion Practice* 2006 January; 7(1): 23-25. Subject: 6

Marks, Thomas C., Jr. A dissenting opinion, Bush v. Schiavo, 885 So. 2d 321 (Fla. 2004). *Stetson Law Review* 2005 Fall; 35(1): 195-205. Subject: 20.5.1

Markus, Karen. The nurse as patient advocate: is there a conflict of interest? *In:* Cowen, Perle Slavik; Moorhead, Sue, eds. Current Issues in Nursing. 7th ed. St. Louis, MO: Mosby, 2006: 620-625. Subject: 4.1.3

Marmor, Theodore R. Canada's Supreme Court and its National Health Insurance Program: evaluating the landmark Chaoulli decision from a comparative perspective. *Osgoode Hall Law Journal* 2006 Summer; 44(2): 311-325. Subject: 9.3.1

Marquis, Don. Abortion and the beginning and end of human life. *Journal of Law, Medicine, and Ethics* 2006 Spring; 34(1): 16-25. Subject: 12.3

Marquis, Don. Does metaphysics have implications for the morality of abortion? *Southwest Philosophy Review* 2002 January; 18(1): 73-78. Subject: 12.3

Marris, Emma. Doctor admits Lancet study is fiction [news]. *Nature* 2006 January 19; 439(7074): 248-249. Subject: 1.3.9

Marris, Emma. An easy way out? *Nature* 2006 June 1; 441(7093): 570-571. Subject: 22.2

Marris, Emma. Grey matter [news]. *Nature* 2006 December 14; 442(7121): 808-810. Subject: 22.2

Marris, Emma. PS I want all the rights [news]. *Nature* 2006 July 13; 442(7099): 118-119. Subject: 1.3.7

Marris, Emma. Sackings put editorial freedom on the spot [news]. *Nature* 2006 March 2; 440(7080): 10-11. Subject: 1.3.7

Marris, Emma. Should journals police scientific fraud? *Nature* 2006 February 2; 439(7076): 520-521. Subject: 1.3.7

Marris, Emma. Will medics' qualms kill the death penalty? [news]. *Nature* 2006 May 4; 441(7089): 8-9. Subject: 20.6

Marris, Emma; Check, Erika. Disgraced cloner's ally is cleared of misconduct [news]. *Nature* 2006 February 16; 439(7078): 768-769. Subject: 1.3.9

Marron, Jonathan M.; Siegler, Mark. Ethical issues in innovative colorectal surgery. *Diseases of the Colon and Rectum* 2005 June; 48(6): 1109-1113. Subject: 18.1

Marsden, Wendy. Analyzing multiple discourses in the establishment of genetic databases. *In:* Árnason, Gardar; Nordal, Salvör; Árnason, Vilhjálmur, eds. Blood and Data: Ethical, Legal and Social Aspects of Human Genetic Databases. Reykjavík: University of Iceland Press; 2004: 167-173. Subject: 15.1

Marsh, Jeffrey L. To cut or not to cut?: a surgeon's perspective on surgically shaping children. *In:* Parens, Erik, ed. Surgically Shaping Children: Technology, Ethics, and the Pursuit of Normality. Baltimore, MD: Johns Hopkins University Press; 2006: 113-124. Subject: 9.5.7

Marsh, Richard. Hard decisions will have to be made: view from intensive care. *BMJ: British Medical Journal* 2006 April 1; 332(7544): 790-791. Subject: 9.4

Marshall, Eliot. Accident prompts a closer look at antibody trials. *Science* 2006 April 14; 312(5771): 172. Subject: 18.6

Subject = NRCBL Primary Classification Number; see inside front cover.

Marshall, Eliot. deCODE adds plagiarism allegation to its case [news]. *Science* 2006 October 27; 314(5799): 580. Subject: 1.3.9

Marshall, Eliot. Lessons from a failed drug trial. *Science* 2006 August 18; 313(5789): 901. Subject: 18.6

Marshall, Jennifer. Life extension research: an analysis of contemporary biological theories and ethical issues. *Medicine, Health Care and Philosophy* 2006; 9(1): 87-96. Subject: 20.5.1

Marshall, Jessica; Aldhous, Peter. Swallowing the best advice? *New Scientist* 2006 October 28-November 3; 192(2575): 18-22. Subject: 9.7

Marshall, Mary Faith; Menikoff, Jerry; Paltrow, Lynn M. Perinatal substance abuse and human subjects research: are privacy protections adequate? *Mental Retardation and Developmental Disabilities Research Reviews* 2003; 9(1): 54-59. Subject: 18.5.3

Marshall, Patricia A. Informed consent in international health research. *Journal of Empirical Research on Human Research Ethics* 2006 March; 1(1): 25-41. Subject: 18.3

Marshall, Patricia A.; Adebamowo, Clement A.; Adeyemo, Adebowale A.; Ogundiran, Temidayo O.; Vekich, Mirjana; Strenski, Teri; Zhou, Jie; Prewitt, Elaine; Cooper, Richard S.; Rotimi, Charles N. Voluntary participation and informed consent to international genetic research. *American Journal of Public Health* 2006 November; 96(11): 1989-1995. Subject: 15.1

Marshall, Patricia A.; Berg, Jessica W. Protecting communities in biomedical research. *American Journal of Bioethics* 2006 May-June; 6(3): 28-30; discussion W46-W48. Subject: 18.6

Marshall, Tom. Informed consent for mammography screening: modelling the risks and benefits for American women. *Health Expectations* 2005 December; 8(4): 295-305. Subject: 8.3.1

Marson, Daniel C.; Savage, Robert; Phillips, Jacqueline. Financial capacity in persons with schizophrenia and serious mental illness: clinical and research ethics aspects. *Schizophrenia Bulletin* 2006 January; 32(1): 81-91. Subject: 18.5.6

Marteau, Theresa M.; Dormandy, Elizabeth; Michie, Susan. A measure of informed choice. *Health Expectations* 2001 June; 4(2): 99-108. Subject: 8.3.1

Martensen, Robert L. Bioethics on the brain. *Medical Humanities Review* 2004 Spring-Fall; 18(1-2): 27-45. Subject: 2.1

Martimo, Kari-Pekka. Workplace health surveillance. *In:* Westerholm, Peter; Nilstun, Tore; Øvretveit, John, eds. Practical Ethics in Occupational Health. San Francisco: Radcliffe Medical Press; 2004: 77-90. Subject: 16.3

Martin, Brian. The politics of a scientific meeting: the origin-of-AIDS debate at the Royal Society. *Politics and the Life Sciences* 2001 September; 20(2): 119-130. Subject: 9.5.6

Martin, Deanna. Abortion consent law before Ind. (Indiana) legislature: doctor would say conception begins life. *Washington Post* 2006 February 12; p. A10. Subject: 12.4.1

Martin, Erika G.; Pollack, Harold A.; Paltiel, A. David. Fact, fiction, and fairness: resource allocation under the Ryan White CARE Act. *Health Affairs* 2006 July-August; 25(4): 1103-1112. Subject: 9.5.6

Martin, Norah. Physician-assisted suicide and euthanasia: weighing feminist concerns. *In:* Fiore, Robin N.; Nelson, Helen Lindemann, eds. Recognition, Responsibility, and Rights: Feminist Ethics and Social Theory. Lanham, MD: Rowman and Littlefield; 2003: 131-142. Subject: 20.5.1

Martin, Paul. Genetic governance: the risks, oversight, and regulation of genetic databases in the UK. *New Genetics and Society* 2001 August; 20(2): 157-183. Subject: 15.1

Martin, Taylor; Rayne, Karen; Kemp, Nate J.; Hart, Jack; Diller, Kenneth R. Teaching for adaptive expertise in biomedical engineering ethics. *Science and Engineering Ethics* 2005 April; 11(2): 257-276. Subject: 2.3

Martindale, Diane. A culture of death. *Scientific American* 2005 June; 292(6): 44, 46. Subject: 20.7

Martinez, Barbara. Health-care consultants reap fees from those they evaluate. *Wall Street Journal* 2006 September 18; p. A1, A14. Subject: 9.3.1

Martins, David S. Compliance rhetoric and the impoverishment of context. *Communication Theory* 2005 February; 15(1): 59-77. Subject: 8.3.4

Martinson, Brian C.; Anderson, Melissa A.; Crain, A. Lauren; De Vries, Raymond. Scientists' perceptions of organizational justice and self-reported misbehaviors. *Journal of Empirical Research on Human Research Ethics* 2006 March; 1(1): 51-66. Subject: 1.3.9

Martone, Marilyn. Traumatic brain injury and the goals of care. *Hastings Center Report* 2006 March-April; 36(2): 3. Subject: 17.1

Martone, Marilyn. What does society owe those who are minimally conscious? *Journal of the Society of Christian Ethics* 2006 Fall-Winter; 26(2): 201-217. Subject: 20.4.1

Marturano, Antonio. Molecular biologists as hackers of human data: rethinking intellectual property rights for bioinformatics research. *In:* Tavani, Herman T., ed. Ethics, Computing, and Genomics. Sudbury, MA: Jones and Bartlett; 2006: 235-245. Subject: 15.1

Marturano, Antonio; Chadwick, Ruth. How the role of computing is driving new genetics' public policy. *Ethics and Information Technology* 2004; 6(1): 43-53. Subject: 15.1

See SUBJECT HEADING KEY FOR SECTION II on inside back cover.

649

Martyn, Susan R.; Jacobs, Lynn Balshone. Legislating advance directives for the terminally ill: the living will and durable power of attorney. *Nebraska Law Review* 1984; 63(4): 779-809. Subject: 20.5.1

Maryland. *Laws, statutes, etc.* An act for the purpose of prohibiting the use of certain genetic information to deny or otherwise affect a health insurance policy or contract; prohibiting the request or requirement of certain genetic information as a basis for issuing or renewing health benefits coverage; prohibiting the disclosure of certain genetic information to certain persons without certain authorization of the individual from whom the genetic information was obtained; identifying certain permissible purposes for disclosure of genetic information; defining certain terms; repealing the termination date of certain provisions of law that relate to the use of genetic tests; and generally relating to prohibiting discrimination on the basis of genetic information in health insurance [Approved: 13 April 1999]. Maryland: General Assembly, 1999. 4 p. [Online]. Accessed: http://mlis.state.md.us/PDF-Documents/1999rs/bills/sb/sb0774t.PDF [2007 March 9]. Subject: 15.1

Marziali, Elsa; Dergal Serafini, Julie M.; McCleary, Lynn. A systematic review of practice standards and research ethics in technology-based home health care intervention programs for older adults. *Journal of Aging and Health* 2005 December; 17(6): 679-696. Subject: 9.8

Masek, Lawrence. A contralife argument against altered nuclear transfer. *National Catholic Bioethics Quarterly* 2006 Summer; 6(2): 235-240. Subject: 14.4

Maskens, A.P. Studies on gene-nutrient interactions in the aetiology of colorectal neoplasia ('ECP-genuine' project): ethical and legal aspects. *European Journal of Cancer Prevention* 2002 February; 11(1): 99-100. Subject: 18.2

Mason, Diana J. In their shoes [editorial]. *AJN: American Journal of Nursing* 2006 October; 106(10): 11. Subject: 7.1

Mason, J.K. Ethical principles and ethical practice [editorial]. *Clinical Ethics* 2006 March; 1(1): 3-6. Subject: 2.1

Mason, Linda. Referral to a National Health Service-funded abortion clinic. *Journal of Family Planning and Reproductive Health Care* 2005 April; 31(2): 117-120. Subject: 12.5.1

Mason, S.; Barrow, H.; Phillips, A.; Eddison, G.; Nelson, A.; Cullum, N.; Nixon, J. Brief report on the experience of using proxy consent for incapacitated adults. *Journal of Medical Ethics* 2006 January; 32(1): 61-62. Subject: 18.3

Massachusetts. Department of Public Health. Public Health Council. Biotechnology Regulations [Approved: 29 August 2006]. *Code of Massachusetts Regulations* 2006; 105: 960.000-009. 4p. [Online]. Accessed: http://www.lawlib.state.ma.us/stemcellregs.html [2007 March 9]. Subject: 18.5.4

Massachusetts. *Laws, statutes, etc.* An act enhancing regenerative medicine in the Commonwealth [Effective: 31 May 2005]. Massachusetts: General Assembly, Acts of 2005 (2005 Session Laws), Chapter 27. Adds Chapter 111L, Biotechnology. 14 p. [Online]. Accessed: http://www.mass.gov/legis/laws/seslaw05/sl050027.htm [2007 March 9]. Subject: 18.5.4

Massachusetts. *Laws, statutes, etc.* An act relative to insurance and genetic testing and privacy protection [Approved: 22 August 2000]. Massachusetts: House Bill 5416, Acts of 2000, Chapter 254. 10 p. [Online]. Accessed: http://www.mass.gov/legis/laws/seslaw00/sl000254.htm [2007 March 9]. Subject: 15.1

Massimo, Luisa M.; Wiley, Thomas J. Randomization, informed consent and physicians' communication skills in pediatric oncology: a delicate balance. *Bulletin du Cancer* 2005 December 1; 92(12): E67-E69. Subject: 18.3

Master, Zubin. Embryonic stem-cell gametes: the new frontier in human reproduction. *Human Reproduction* 2006 April; 21(4): 857-863. Subject: 18.5.4

Masterton, George. Two decades on an ethics committee. *BMJ: British Medical Journal* 2006 March 11; 332(7541): 615. Subject: 18.2

Mastroianni, Anna C. Liability, regulation and policy in surgical innovation: the cutting edge of research and therapy. *Health Matrix: The Journal of Law-Medicine* 2006 Summer; 16(2): 351-442. Subject: 18.6

Materstvedt, Lars Johan. Palliative care on the 'slippery slope' towards euthanasia? *Palliative Medicine* 2003; 17(5): 387-392. Subject: 20.4.1

Matfield, Mark. With one voice: as the European Union updates its legislation on animal experiments, scientists must ensure that lawmakers are well informed. *New Scientist* 2006 November 11-17; 192(2577): 24. Subject: 22.2

Matheny, Gaverick. Utilitarianism and animals. *In:* Singer, Peter, ed. In Defense of Animals: The Second Wave. Malden, MA: Blackwell Pub.; 2006: 13-25. Subject: 22.1

Mather, Charles. The pipeline and the porcupine: alternate metaphors of the physician-industry relationship. *Social Science and Medicine* 2005 March; 60(6): 1323-1334. Subject: 7.3

Mathes, Michele. Terri Schiavo and end-of-life decisions: can law help us out? *Medsurg Nursing* 2005 June; 14(3): 200-202. Subject: 20.5.1

Mathews, Anna Wilde. FDA signals it's open to drug trials that shift midcourse. *Wall Street Journal* 2006 July 10; p. B1, B8. Subject: 18.6

Mathews, Anna Wilde. Fraud, errors taint key study of widely used Sanofi drug; despite some faked results, FDA approves antibiotic; one doctor's cocaine use; company defends safety. *Wall Street Journal* 2006 May 1; p. A1, A12. Subject: 9.7

Mathews, Anna Wilde; Westphal, Sylvia Pagan. Tricky FDA debate: should a risky drug be approved again? *Wall Street Journal* 2006 February 24; p. B1, B4. Subject: 9.7

Mathews, Debra J.; Kalfoglou, Andrea; Hudson, Kathy. Geneticists' views on science policy formation and public outreach. *American Journal of Medical Genetics Part A* 2005 August 30; 137(2): 161-169. Subject: 15.1

Mathews, Debra J.H.; Donovan, Peter; Harris, John; Lovell-Badge; Robin; Savulescu, Julian; Baden, Ruth. Science and law: integrity in international stem cell research collaborations. *Science* 2006 August 18; 313(5789): 921-922. Subject: 18.2

Mathias, Michael B. The competing demands of sport and health: an essay on the history of ethics in sports medicine. *Clinics in Sports Medicine* 2004 April; 23(2): 195-214. Subject: 9.5.1

Matiation, Stefan. HIV/AIDS and aboriginal communities: problems of jurisdiction and discrimination: a review. *Canadian HIV/AIDS Policy and Law Newsletter* 1996 October; 3(1): 1, 47-48. Subject: 9.5.6

Matsuda, Ichiro. Bioethical considerations in neonatal screening: Japanese experiences. *Southeast Asian Journal of Tropical Medicine and Public Health* 2003; 34(Supplement 3): 46-48. Subject: 15.3

Matsuda, Ichiro. Genetic health care services, present and near future in Japan. *Eubios Journal of Asian and International Bioethics* 2003 March 13(2): 57-59. Subject: 15.3

Matta, A.M. Informed consent in medical treatment: conflict or consensus. *Medicine and Law: The World Association for Medical Law* 2006 June; 25(2): 319-339. Subject: 8.3.1

Matteson, Eric L.; Bongartz, Tim. Investigation, explanation, and apology for incomplete and erroneous disclosures [letter]. *JAMA: The Journal of the American Medical Association* 2006 November 8; 296(18): 2205. Subject: 1.3.7

Matthew, Dayna Bowen. A new strategy to combat racial inequality in American health care delivery. *DePaul Journal of Health Care Law* 2005; 9(1): 793-853. Subject: 9.5.4

Matthews, Colin D. ART regulation: the Australian viewpoint. *Human Reproduction* 1996 July; 11(7): 1365-1366. Subject: 14.1

Matthews, Richard S. Indecent medicine: in defense of the absolute prohibition against physician participation in torture. *American Journal of Bioethics [Online].* 2006 May-June; 6(3): W34-W44. Subject: 21.4

Mattick, Karen; Bligh, John. Teaching and assessing medical ethics: where are we now? *Journal of Medical Ethics* 2006 March; 32(3): 181-185. Subject: 2.3

Mattick, Karen; Bligh, John. Undergraduate ethics teaching: revisiting the consensus statement. *Medical Education* 2006 April; 40(4): 329-332. Subject: 7.2

Mattingly, Cheryl. Toward a vulnerable ethics of research practice. *Health (London)* 2005 October; 9(4): 453-471. Subject: 18.2

Mattulat, Martin; Frewer, Andreas. Pathologie, politik und moral: Georg B. Gruber als medizinethiker und die zustimmung zur section [Pathology, politics, and morality: George B. Gruber as medical ethicist and the consent to autopsy]. *Ethik in der Medizin* 2006 September; 18(3): 238-250. Subject: 20.1

Maunder, Judith. The Human Rights Act 1998 — legal implications for those engaged in infertility services. *Human Fertility* 2004 March; 7(1): 5-9. Subject: 14.1

Maurissen, Jacques P.; Gilbert, Steven G.; Sander, Miriam; Beauchamp, Tom L.; Johnson, Shelley; Schwetz, Bernard A.; Goozner, Merrill; Barrow, Craig S. Workshop proceedings: managing conflict of interest in science. A little consensus and a lot of controversy. *Toxicological Sciences* 2005 September; 87(1): 11-14. Subject: 1.3.9

Mauron, Alex. The choosy reaper: from the myth of eternal youth to the reality of unequal death. *EMBO Reports* 2005 July; 6(Special Issue): S67-S71. Subject: 20.5.1

Mauron, Alex. Genomic metaphysics. *Journal of Molecular Biology* 2002 June 14; 319(4): 957-962. Subject: 15.1

Mauron, Alex. Genom-Metaphysik. *In:* Rehmann-Sutter, Christoph; Müller, Hansjakob, eds. Ethik und Gentherapie: zum praktischen Diskurs um die molekulare Medizin. 2nd ed. Tübingen: Francke Verlag; 2003: 237-249. Subject: 15.1

Mauron, Alex. Renovating the house of being: genomes, souls, and selves. *Annals of the New York Academy of Sciences* 2003 October; 1001: 240-252. Subject: 15.1

Mauron, Alex; Rehmann-Sutter, Christoph. Gentherapie: Ein Katalog offener ethischer Fragen. *In:* Rehmann-Sutter, Christoph; Müller, Hansjakob, eds. Ethik und Gentherapie: Zum praktischen Diskurs um die molekulare Medizin. Tübingen: Attempto Verlag; 1995: 22-33. Subject: 15.4

Mavis, Brian E.; Henry, Rebecca C. Being uninformed on informed consent: a pilot survey of medical education faculty. *BMC Medical Education* 2005 April 25; 5(1): 12; 7 p. Subject: 8.3.1

Mavroforou, A.; Giannoukas, A.; Michalodimitrakis, Emmanuel. Consent for organ and tissue retention in British law in the light of the Human Tissue Act 2004. *Medicine and Law: The World Association for Medical Law* 2006 September; 25(3): 427-434. Subject: 19.5

Mavroforou, A.; Michalodimitrakis, E. The British Abortion Act (1967) and the interests of the foetus. *Medicine and Law: World Association for Medical Law* 2006 March; 25(1): 175-188. Subject: 12.4.2

Mavroudis, Constantine. Ethical forces that shape a career in surgery. *American Journal of Surgery* 2005 August; 190(2): 319-323. Subject: 7.1

See SUBJECT HEADING KEY FOR SECTION II on inside back cover.

651

Mavroudis, Constantine; Mavroudis, Constantine D.; Naunheim, Keith S.; Sade, Robert M. Should surgical errors always be disclosed to the patient? *Annals of Thoracic Surgery* 2005 August; 80(2): 399-408. Subject: 9.8

May, Thomas. Bioterror and public health infrastructure: a response to commentators [letter]. *American Journal of Bioethics [Online]*. 2006 January-February; 6(1): W29-W31. Subject: 9.1

May, Thomas. Isolation is not the answer. International scientific collaboration is the best defence against bioterror. *Nature* 2004 June 10; 429(6992): 603. Subject: 21.3

May, William E. The misinterpretation of John Paul II's teaching in Evangelium vitae n. 73. *National Catholic Bioethics Quarterly* 2006 Winter; 6(4): 705-717. Subject: 4.4

May, William F. Deepening a national conversation—my take on the president's council on bioethics. *Practical Bioethics* 2005 Winter; 1(1): 1-3, 7-9. Subject: 2.4

Mayda, Atilla Senih; Özkara, Erdem; Çorapçioglu, Funda. Attitudes of oncologists toward euthanasia in Turkey. *Palliative and Supportive Care* 2005 September; 3(3): 221-225. Subject: 20.5.1

Mayeda, Mayumi. Present state of reproductive medicine in Japan — ethical issues with a focus on those seen in court cases. *BMC Medical Ethics [electronic]* 2006; 7(3): 16p. Accessed: http://www.biomedcentral.com/1472-6939/7/3 [2006 September 12]. Subject: 14.1

Mayer, Dan. A commentary on Maya J. Goldenberg's "The Doctor-Patient Relationship in the Age of Evidence-Based Health Care (and Not the 'Post-Managed Care Era')" [letter]. *American Journal of Bioethics [Online]*. 2006 May-June; 6(3): W45. Subject: 8.1

Mayer, S. Declaration of patent applications as financial interests: a survey of practice among authors of papers on molecular biology in Nature. *Journal of Medical Ethics* 2006 November; 32(11): 658-661. Subject: 1.3.7

Mayle, Kathy. Nurses and ethics consultation: growing beyond a rock and a hard place. *Journal of Clinical Ethics* 2006 Fall; 17(3): 257-259. Subject: 9.6

Maynard, Andrew D.; Aitken, Robert J.; Butz, Tilman; Colvin, Vicki; Donaldson, Ken; Oberdörster, Günter; Philbert, Martin A.; Ryan, John; Seaton, Anthony; Stone, Vicki; Tinkle, Sally S.; Tran, Lang; Walker, Nigel J.; Warheit, David B. Safe handling of nanotechnology [commentary]. *Nature* 2006 November 16; 444(7117): 267-269. Subject: 5.1

Mayo, David J. Some reflections on whether death is bad. *In:* Jansen, Lynn A., ed. Death in the Clinic. Lanham, MD: Rowman and Littlefield; 2006: 17-26. Subject: 20.3.1

Mayor, Susan. Babies born after preimplantation genetic diagnosis need follow-up [news]. *BMJ: British Medical Journal* 2006 February 4; 332(7536): 254. Subject: 15.2

Mayor, Susan. Publicly funded research in the UK must be freely accessible [news]. *BMJ: British Medical Journal* 2006 July 15; 333(7559): 112. Subject: 5.3

Mayor, Susan. Severe adverse reactions prompt call for trial design changes [news]. *BMJ: British Medical Journal* 2006 March 25; 332(7543): 683. Subject: 18.2

Mayor, Susan. Surgery journal bans authors who hide conflicts of interest [news]. *BMJ: British Medical Journal* 2006 January 21; 332(7534): 135. Subject: 1.3.7

Mayrhofer-Reinhartshuber, David; Fitzgerald, Annelies; Fitzgerald, Robert D. Money for consent — psychological consideration. *Annals of Transplantation* 2005; 10(1): 26-29. Subject: 19.5

Maze, Claire D. Martino. Registered nurses' personal rights vs. professional responsibility in caring for members of underserved and disenfranchised populations. *Journal of Clinical Nursing* 2005 May; 14(5): 546-554. Subject: 4.1.3

Mazur, Dennis J.; Hickam, David H. The influence of physician explanations on patient preferences about future health-care states. *Medical Decision Making* 1997 January-March; 17(1): 56-60. Subject: 20.5.4

Mazur, Dennis J.; Hickam, David H. Patients' preferences for risk disclosure and role in decision making for invasive medical procedures. *Journal of General Internal Medicine* 1997 February; 12(2): 114-117. Subject: 8.3.1

McAdam, Catherine; Rai, Gurcharan S. Confidentiality. *In:* Rai, Gurcharan S, ed. Medical Ethics and the Elderly. 2nd ed. San Francisco: Radcliffe Medical Press; 2004: 9-17. Subject: 8.4

McAdam, Jennifer L.; Stotts, Nancy A.; Padilla, Geraldine; Puntillo, Kathleen. Attitudes of critically ill Filipino patients and their families toward advance directives. *American Journal of Critical Care* 2005 January; 14(1): 17-25. Subject: 20.5.4

McCabe, Catherine. Nurse-patient communication: an exploration of patients' experiences. *Journal of Clinical Nursing* 2004 January; 13(1): 41-49. Subject: 8.1

McCabe, Melvina; Morgan, Frank; Curley, Helen; Begay, Rick; Gohdes, Dorothy M. The informed consent process in a cross-cultural setting: is the process achieving the intended result? *Ethnicity and Disease* 2005 Spring; 15(2): 300-304. Subject: 18.3

McCaffery, Margo; Arnstein, Paul. The debate over placebos in pain management: the ASPMN disagrees with a recent placebo position statement. *AJN: American Journal of Nursing* 2006 February; 106(2): 62-65. Subject: 8.2

McCain, Lauren. Informing technology policy decisions: the US Human Genome Project's ethical, legal, and social implications programs as a critical case. *Technology in Society* 2002 January-April; 24(1-2): 111-132. Subject: 15.10

McCall Smith, Alexander. Genetic privacy and discrimination. *In:* Glasa, J., ed. Ethics of Human Genetics: Challenges of the (Post) Genomic Era. Bratislava, Slovak Republic: Charis [and] IMEB Foundation; 2002: 81-87. Subject: 15.3

McCarrick, Theodore. Securing decent health care for all. *Origins* 2006 June 15; 36(5): 65-68. Subject: 9.2

McCarthy, Joan. A pluralist view of nursing ethics. *Nursing Philosophy* 2006 July; 7(3): 157-164. Subject: 4.1.3

McCarthy, Michael. Lethal injection challenged as "cruel and unusual" fate. *Lancet* 2006 March 4-10; 367(9512): 717. Subject: 20.6

McClellan, Frank. Medical malpractice law, morality and the culture wars: a critical assessment of the tort reform movement. *Journal of Legal Medicine* 2006 March; 27(1): 33-53. Subject: 4.4

McClure, Cori A.; Gray, Glenda; Rybczyk, G. Kyle; Wright, Peter F. Challenges to conducting HIV preventative vaccine trials with adolescents. *Journal of Acquired Immune Deficiency Syndrome* 2004 June 1; 36(2): 726-733. Subject: 18.5.2

McComb, Peter. Negotiating consent = Consentement de négociation [editorial]. *Journal of Obstetrics and Gynaecology Canada* 2005 April; 27(4): 317-320. Subject: 7.2

McConnaha, Scott. Catholic teaching and disparities in care. *Health Progress* 2006 January-February; 87(1): 46-50. Subject: 9.4

McConnaha, Scott. Genomics and the ministry: the executive perspective. *Health Progress* 2006 May-June; 87(3): 56-60. Subject: 15.1

McConnel, Charles; Turner, Leigh. Medicine, ageing and human longevity: the economics and ethics of anti-ageing interventions. *EMBO Reports* 2005 July; 6(Special Issue): S59-S62. Subject: 9.5.2

McCormack, Paula. Quality of life and the right to die: an ethical dilemma. *Journal of Advanced Nursing* 1998 July; 28(1): 63-69. Subject: 20.5.1

McCormick, Janice; Kirkham, Sheryl Reimer; Hayes, Virginia. Abstracting women: essentialism in women's health research. *Health Care for Women International* 1998 November-December; 19(6): 495-504. Subject: 18.5.3

McCormick, Richard A. Reproductive technologies: where are we headed? *Loyola Law Review* 1999 Summer; 45(2): 269-285. Subject: 14.1

McCoy, Liza. HIV-positive patients and the doctor-patient relationship: perspectives from the margins. *Qualitative Health Research* 2005 July; 15(6): 791-806. Subject: 9.5.6

McCrary, S. Van; Swanson, Jeffrey W.; Coulehan, Jack; Faber-Langendoen, K.; Olick, Robert S.; Belling, Catherine. Physicians' legal defensiveness in end-of-life treatment decisions: comparing attitudes and knowledge in states with different laws. *Journal of Clinical Ethics* 2006 Spring; 17(1): 15-26. Subject: 20.5.1

McCruden, Patrick; Kuczewski, Mark. Is organizational ethics the remedy for failure to thrive? Toward an understanding of mission leadership. *HEC (Healthcare Ethics Committee) Forum* 2006 December; 18(4): 342-348. Subject: 9.6

McCullough, Laurence B. Getting back to the fundamentals of clinical ethics. *Journal of Medicine and Philosophy* 2006 February; 31(1): 1-6. Subject: 2.1

McCullough, Laurence B. Neonatal ethics at the limits of viability. *Pediatrics* 2005 October; 116(4): 1019-1021. Subject: 20.5.2

McCullough, Laurence B. Practicing preventive ethics — the keys to avoiding ethical conflicts in health care. *Physician Executive* 2005 March-April; 31(2): 18-21. Subject: 7.3

McCullough, Laurence B.; Coverdale, John H.; Chervenak, Frank A. A comprehensive ethical framework for responsibly designing and conducting pharmacologic research that involves pregnant women. *American Journal of Obstetrics and Gynecology* 2005 September; 193(3, Part 2): 901-907. Subject: 18.5.3

McCullough, Laurence B.; Richman, Bruce W.; Jones, James W. Withdrawal of life-sustaining low-burden care. *Journal of Vascular Surgery* 2005 July; 42(1): 176-177. Subject: 20.5.1

McCullough, Laurence B.; Wilson, Nancy L.; Rhymes, Jill A.; Teasdale, Thomas A. Ethical issues in genetics and aging: diagnosis, treatment, and prevention in the era of molecular medicine. *Generations* 2000 Spring; 24(1): 72-78. Subject: 15.1

McDade, William. A racist parent [case study]. *Virtual Mentor* 2001 November; 3(11): 2p. Subject: 8.3.2

McDade, William. The racist parent. *Virtual Mentor* 2001 September; 3(9): 2p. Subject: 8.1

McDaniel, Charlotte; Veledar, Emir; LeConte, Stephen; Peltier, Scott; Maciuba, Agata. Ethical environment, healthcare work, and patient outcomes. *American Journal of Bioethics [Online]* 2006 September-October; 6(5): W17-W29. Subject: 9.1

McDaniel, Patricia A.; Solomon, Gina; Malone, Ruth E. The ethics of industry experimentation using employees: the case of taste-testing pesticide-treated tobacco. *American Journal of Public Health* 2006 January; 96(1): 37-46. Subject: 18.5.1

McDonagh, Eileen. Abortion rights after South Dakota. *Free Inquiry* 2006 June-July; 26(4): 34-38. Subject: 12.4.1

McDonald, Patrick. There's a bug in your head. *Hastings Center Report* 2006 May-June; 36(3): 7. Subject: 8.3.2

See SUBJECT HEADING KEY FOR SECTION II on inside back cover.

653

McDonnell, William M. Will EMTALA changes leave emergency patients dying on the hospital doorstep? *Journal of Health Law* 2005 Winter; 38(1): 77-93. Subject: 9.2

McDowall, Michael A. Ageism in services for transient ischaemic attack and stroke: ageism or cost-benefit analysis? [letter]. *BMJ: British Medical Journal* 2006 September 23; 333(7569): 656. Subject: 9.5.2

McElmurry, Beverly J.; Solheim, Karen; Kishi, Rieko; Coffia, Marcia A.; Woith, Wendy; Janepanish, Poolsuk. Ethical concerns in nurse migration. *Journal of Professional Nursing* 2006 July-August; 22(4): 226-235. Subject: 21.6

McGee, Glenn. Human cloning. *In:* Mitcham, Carl, ed. Encyclopedia of Science, Technology, and Ethics. Farmington Hills, MI: Thomson/Gale, 2005: 938-942. Subject: 14.5

McGee, Glenn. Spare the genes, spoil the child? The not-so-deadly sins of genetic enhancement = ¿Escatimar genes, estropear a los hijos? Los pecados no tan capitales de la mejora genética. *Revista de Derecho Genoma Humano = Law and the Human Genome Review* 1997 July-December; (7): 199-217. Subject: 15.1

McGee, Glenn. Will bioethics take the life of philosophy? [editorial]. *American Journal of Bioethics* 2006 September-October; 6(5): 1-2. Subject: 2.1

McGee, Glenn; McGee, Daniel B. Nuclear meltdown: ethics of the need to transfer genes. *Politics and the Life Sciences* 1998 March; 17(1): 26-28. Subject: 15.4

McGivern, Brenda. Bioethics and the law — the impact of genetic technology on prenatal management. *E Law: Murdoch University Electronic Journal of Law* 1995 December; 2(3): 35 p. [Online]. Accessed: http://www.murdoch.edu.au/elaw/issues/v2n3mcgivern23.html [2006 June 29]. Subject: 15.2

McGlashan, Thomas H. Early detection and intervention in psychosis: an ethical paradigm shift. *British Journal of Psychiatry* 2005 August; 187 (Supplement 48): s113-s115. Subject: 17.1

McGrath, Pam. Multidisciplinary insights on the evolving role of the ethics committee in an Australian regional hospital. *Monash Bioethics Review* 2006 July; 25(3): 59-72. Subject: 9.6

McGrath, Pam; Holewa, Hamish. Ethical decision making in an acute medical ward: Australian findings on dealing with conflict and tension. *Ethics and Behavior* 2006; 16(3): 233-252. Subject: 7.3

McGregor, Joan. No moral absolutes. *American Journal of Bioethics* 2006 March-April; 6(2): 29-30. Subject: 8.4

McGregor, Murray; Moore, Rory. The constitutionality of abortion on request in South Africa. *E Law: Murdoch University Electronic Journal of Law* 1995 December; 2(3): 32 p. [Online]. Accessed: http://www.murdoch.edu.au/elaw/issues/v2n3/moore23.html [2006 June 29]. Subject: 12.4.1

McGuire, Amy L.; Gibbs, Richard A. Currents in contemporary ethics. *Journal of Law, Medicine and Ethics* 2006 Winter; 34(4): 809-812. Subject: 15.1

McHale, Jean. Confidentiality and psychiatry: dilemmas of disclosure [editorial]. *Journal of Forensic Psychiatry* 2000 September; 11(2): 255-259. Subject: 8.4

McHale, Jean V. Law, patient's rights and NHS resource allocation: is Eurostar the answer? *Health Care Analysis: An International Journal of Health Philosophy and Policy* 2006 September; 14(3): 169-183. Subject: 9.4

McHale, J.V. 'Appropriate consent' and the use of human material for research purposes: the competent adult. *Clinical Ethics* 2006 December; 1(4): 195-199. Subject: 18.3

McHenry, L. Ethical issues in psychopharmacology. *Journal of Medical Ethics* 2006 July; 32(7): 405-410. Subject: 17.4

McIlfatrick, S.; Sullivan, K.; McKenna, H. Exploring the ethical issues of the research interview in the cancer context. *European Journal of Oncology Nursing* 2006 February; 10(1): 39-47. Subject: 18.4

McKee, Martin. Values, beliefs, and implications. *In:* Marinker, Marshall, ed. Health Targets in Europe: Polity, Progress and Promise. London: BMJ Books; 2002: 181-205. Subject: 9.1

McKendrick, Jane H.; Bennett, Pamela Aratukutuku. Health research across cultures — an ethical dilemma? *Monash Bioethics Review* 2006 January; 25(1): 64-71. Subject: 21.7

McKenna, Brian G.; Simpson, Alexander I. F.; Coverdale, John H. Outpatient commitment and coercion in New Zealand: a matched comparison study. *International Journal of Law and Psychiatry* 2006 March-April; 29(2): 145-158. Subject: 17.1

McKenna, Phil. Are uterus transplants on the horizon [news]. *New Scientist* 2006 November 11-17; 192(2577): 12. Subject: 19.1

McKenzie, Michael. Genetics and Christianity: an uneasy but necessary partnership. *Christian Research Journal* 1995 Fall; 18: 1-8. Subject: 15.10

McKibben, Bill. Why environmentalists should be concerned. *World Watch* 2002 July-August; 15(4): 40-41. Subject: 15.1

McKinley, James C., Jr. Nicaragua eliminates last exception to strict anti-abortion law. *New York Times* 2006 November 20; p. A5. Subject: 12.4.1

McKinley, Shirley; Rodney, Paddy; Storch, Jan; McAlpine, Heather. The role of ethics in nursing. *Nursing BC* 2004 February; 36(1): 12-16. Subject: 4.1.3

McKinney, Rose; Korn, David. Should an institution that has commercial rights in a new drug or device be allowed to evaluate the technology? *PLoS Medicine* 2005 January; 2(1): 0005-0008. Subject: 9.7

McKnight, Reese. RNA interference: a critical analysis of the regulatory and ethical issues encountered in the development of a novel therapy. *Albany Law Journal of Science and Technology* 2004; 15(1): 73-108. Subject: 15.4

McLachlan, Hugh V. Harris on Quintavalle and the ethics of stem cell research. *Human Reproduction and Genetic Ethics: An International Journal* 2006; 12(2): 66-69. Subject: 18.5.4

McLachlan, John C.; McHarg, Jane. Ethical permission for the publication of routinely collected data. *Medical Education* 2005 September; 39(9): 944-948. Subject: 1.3.9

McLaughlin, Chris. Ethics and spirituality are not synonyms [letter]. *Family Medicine* 2005 November-December; 37(10): 686. Subject: 2.1

McLaughlin, Janice. Screening networks: shared agendas in feminist and disability movement challenges to antenatal screening and abortion. *Disability and Society* 2003 May; 18(3): 297-310. Subject: 15.2

McLean, G.R. Thinking about the living will. *South African Medical Journal* 1995 November; 85(11): 1146-1147. Subject: 20.5.4

McLean, Sheila A.M. De-regulating assisted reproduction: some reflections. *Medical Law International* 2006; 7(3): 233-247. Subject: 14.4

McLean, Sheila A.M. The genetic testing of children. *In:* Sándor, Judit, ed. Society and Genetic Information: Codes and Laws in the Genetic Era. Budapest, Hungary; New York: CEU Press; 2003: 145-160. Subject: 15.3

McLean, Sheila A.M. Mapping the human genome — friend or foe? *Social Science and Medicine* 1994 November; 39(9): 1221-1227. Subject: 15.10

McLean, Sheila A.M. Permanent vegetative state: the legal position. *Neuropsychological Rehabilitation* 2005 July-September; 15(3-4): 237-250. Subject: 20.5.1

McLean, Thomas R. The offshoring of American medicine: scope, economic issues and legal liabilities. *Annals of Health Law* 2005 Summer; 14(2): 205-265. Subject: 21.6

McLeish, Caitríona A. Science and censorship in an age of bio-weapons threat. *Science as Culture* 2006 September; 15(3): 215-236. Subject: 1.3.9

McLellan, Faith; Riis, Povl. Ethical conduct for reviewers of grant applications and manuscripts. *In:* Godlee, Fiona; Jefferson, Tom, eds. Peer Review in Health Sciences. 2nd ed. London: BMJ Books; 2003: 236-247. Subject: 1.3.7

McLeod, Carolyn; Baylis, Françoise. Feminists on the inalienability of human embryos. *Hypatia: A Journal of Feminist Philosophy* 2006 Winter; 21(1): 1-14. Subject: 4.4

McLoughlin, Kris A.; Geller, Jeffrey L. The recovery model and seclusion and restraint [letter]. *Psychiatric Services* 2006 July; 57(7): 1045. Subject: 17.3

McMahan, Jeff. An alternative to brain death. *Journal of Law, Medicine, and Ethics* 2006 Spring; 34(1): 44-48. Subject: 20.2.1

McMahan, Jeff. Killing and equality. *Utilitas* 1995 May; 7(1): 1-29. Subject: 20.5.1

McMahan, Jeff. The morality of screening for disability. *Reproductive BioMedicine Online [electronic]* 2005 March; 10(Supplement 1): 129-132. Subject: 15.3

McMahan, Jeff. Paradoxes of abortion and prenatal injury. *Ethics* 2006 July; 116(4): 625-655. Subject: 12.3

McMahan, Jeff; Cohen, Jacques; Ko, Minoru; Johnson, Martin; Robertson, John; Murphy, Timothy; Brinsden, Peter; Hussein, Fatima; Savulescu, Julian; McLaren, Anne; McLean, Sheila; Harris, John; Schulman, Joe; Edwards, Robert; Pedersen, Roger; Stock, Gregory; Grudzinskas, Gedis; Boivin, Jacky. Discussion (day 2 session 2): modern genetics and the human embryo in vitro. *Reproductive BioMedicine Online [electronic]* 2005 March; 10(Supplement 1): 107-110. Subject: 15.2

McMahon, Marilyn; Knowles, Ann D. Confidentiality in psychological practice: a decrepit concept? *Australian Psychologist* 1995 November; 30(3): 164-168. Subject: 8.4

McMahon, M. Molly; Hurley, Daniel L.; Kamath, Patrick S.; Mueller, Paul S. Medical and ethical aspects of long-term enteral tube feeding. *Mayo Clin Proceedings* 2005 November; 80(11): 1461-1476. Subject: 20.5.1

McMahon, Robin L. An ethical dilemma in a hospice setting. *Palliative and Supportive Care* 2003 March; 1(1): 79-87. Subject: 20.4.1

McMahon, William M.; Baty, Bonnie Jeanne; Botkin, Jeffrey. Genetic counseling and ethical issues for autism. *American Journal of Medical Genetics. Part C, Seminars in Medical Genetics* 2006 February 15; 142(1): 52-57. Subject: 15.2

McMillan, Elizabeth. Joint ventures: a risk to the ministry's moral capital? *Health Progress* 1987 April; 68(3): 54-57, 91. Subject: 9.3.1

McMillan, J.; Sheehan, M.; Austin, D.; Howell, J. Ethics and opportunity costs: have NICE grasped the ethics of priority setting? *Journal of Medical Ethics* 2006 March; 32(3): 127-128. Subject: 9.4

McMinn, Mark R.; Buchanan, Trey; Ellens, Brent M.; Ryan, Molly K. Technology, professional practice, and ethics: survey findings and implications. *Professional Psychology: Research and Practice* 1999 April; 30(2): 165-172. Subject: 4.1.1

See SUBJECT HEADING KEY FOR SECTION II on inside back cover.

655

McMullen, Greg. Breaking the trance? Enabling dissenting views on immortalism. *Health Law Review* 2006; 15(1): 47-49. Subject: 20.3.1

McNamee, M.J.; Edwards, S.D. Transhumanism, medical technology and slippery slopes. *Journal of Medical Ethics* 2006 September; 32(9): 513-518. Subject: 4.5

McNaughton, Heathe Luz; Mitchell, Ellen M.H.; Hernandez, Emilia G.; Padilla, Karen; Blandon, Marta Maria. Patient privacy and conflicting legal and ethical obligations in El Salvador: reporting of unlawful abortions. *American Journal of Public Health* 2006 November; 96(11): 1927-1933. Subject: 12.4.2

McNeil, Donald G., Jr. Tough-talking journal editor faces accusations of leniency. *New York Times* 2006 August 1; p. F1, F3. Subject: 1.3.7

McNeill, Paul M.; Macklin, Ruth; Wasunna, Angela; Komesaroff, Paul A. An expanding vista: bioethics from public health, indigenous and feminist perspectives. *Medical Journal of Australia* 2005 July 4; 183(1): 8-9. Subject: 2.1

McPherson, Stuart; Rees, Colin John. An alcoholic patient who continues to drink: case outcome. *BMJ: British Medical Journal* 2006 February 4; 332(7536): 276. Subject: 9.5.9

McQuillan, Geraldine M.; Pan, Qiyuan; Porter, Kathryn S. Consent for genetic research in a general population: an update on the National Health and Nutrition Examination Survey experience. *Genetics in Medicine* 2006 June; 8(6): 354-360. Subject: 18.3

McQuillen, Michael P.; Tariot, Pierre. Who can say yes (or no) to a physician—and how does the physician know they can? [editorial]. *Neurology* 2005 May 10; 64(9): 1494-1495. Subject: 8.3.1

McQuoid-Mason, David. Pacemakers and end-of-life decisions. *South African Medical Journal* 2005 August; 95(8): 566, 568. Subject: 20.5.1

McSherry, Bernadette. Consenting to shared electronic health records: the proposed HealthConnect system. *Journal of Law and Medicine* 2004 February; 11(3): 269-273. Subject: 8.4

McSherry, Bernadette. The government's duty of care to provide adequate health care to immigration detainees. *Journal of Law and Medicine* 2006 February; 13(3): 281-284. Subject: 9.2

McSherry, Bernadette. Posthumous reproduction. *Journal of Law and Medicine* 2005 August; 13(1): 15-18. Subject: 14.1

McTighe, Maggie. Clinical trial trouble: inform OLAW. *Lab Animal* 2006 June; 35(6): 16-17. Subject: 22.2

McWilliams, Rita; Hebden, Carl W.; Gilpin, Adele M.K. Concept paper: a virtual centralized IRB system. *Accountability in Research* 2006 January-March; 13(1): 25-45. Subject: 18.2

Meador, Helen E.; Zazove, Philip. Health care interactions with deaf culture. *Journal of the American Board of Family Practice* 2005 May-June; 18(3): 218-222. Subject: 8.1

Meador, Kimford J.; Brennan, Troyen A.; Rothman, David J.; Naughton, James; Cohen, Jordan; Kimball, Harry; Blumenthal, David; Smelser, Neil; Kassirer, Jerome P.; Goldman, JanLori. Academic medical centers and conflicts of interest [letter and reply]. *JAMA: The Journal of the American Medical Association* 2006 June 28; 295(24): 2845, 2848-2849. Subject: 7.3

Meaney, Mark E. Lessons from the sustainability movement: toward an integrative decision-making framework for nanotechnology. *Journal of Law, Medicine and Ethics* 2006 Winter; 34(4): 682-688. Subject: 5.4

Medical Research Council (Great Britain) [MRC]. MRC ethics guide. Research involving human participants in developing societies. London: Medical Research Council 2004: 1-8. Subject: 18.5.9

Medical Research Council (Great Britain) [MRC]. Research in developing countries [position statement]. *Bulletin of Medical Ethics* 2005 May; (208): 7-11. Subject: 18.5.9

Meehan, Mary. How the Supremes flunked history. *Human Life Review* 2006 Spring; 32(2): 41-51. Subject: 12.4.1

Meel, B.L. Ethical issues related to HIV/AIDS: case reports. *Journal of Clinical Forensic Medicine* 2005 June; 12(3): 149-152. Subject: 9.5.6

Mehlman, Maxwell J. Dishonest medical mistakes. *Vanderbilt Law Review* 2006 May; 59(4): 1137-1173. Subject: 9.8

Mehta, Michael D.; Gair, Julie J. Social, political, legal and ethical areas of inquiry in biotechnology and genetic engineering. *Technology in Society* 2001 April; 23(2): 241-264. Subject: 15.1

Meichtry, Stacy. Religious order runs drug lab for cures, ethics. *Wall Street Journal* 2006 October 7; p. B1, B8. Subject: 9.7

Meidl, Erik J. A case studies approach to assisted nutrition and hydration. *National Catholic Bioethics Quarterly* 2006 Summer; 6(2): 319-336. Subject: 20.5.1

Meidl, Susan Marie. EIFWAIL and psychological distress: no support for early induction. *Ethics and Medics* 2006 April; 31(4): 1-2. Subject: 15.2

Meier, Barry. Growing debate as doctors train on new devices. *New York Times* 2006 August 1; p. A1, C6. Subject: 7.2

Meier, Barry. Guidant consultant advised company to release data on defects. *New York Times* 2006 March 9; p. C3. Subject: 9.7

Subject = NRCBL Primary Classification Number; see inside front cover.

Meier, Barry. U.S. shields doctor data in implants. *New York Times* 2006 July 10; p. C1, C5. Subject: 8.4

Meier, Diane E. Should it be legal for physicians to expedite a death? No — a change of heart on assisted suicide. *Generations: Journal of the American Society on Aging* 1999 Spring; 23(1): 58, 60. Subject: 20.7

Meier, Diane E.; Myers, Hattie; Muskin, Philip R. When a patient requests help committing suicide. *Generations: Journal of the American Society on Aging* 1999 Spring; 23(1): 61-68. Subject: 20.7

Meier-Kriesche, Herwig-Ulf; Schold, Jesse D.; Gaston, Robert S.; Wadstrom, Jonas; Kaplan, Bruce. Kidneys from deceased donors: maximizing the value of a scarce resource. *American Journal of Transplantation* 2005 July; 5(7): 1725-1730. Subject: 19.6

Meilaender, Gilbert. Gifts of the body. *New Atlantis* 2006 Summer; 13: 25-35. Subject: 19.5

Meilaender, Gilbert. The politics of bioethics: in defense of the Kass Council. *Weekly Standard* 2004 April 12-19; 9(30): 13-14. Subject: 2.4

Meisel, Alan. Ethics and law: physician-assisted dying. *Journal of Palliative Medicine* 2005 June; 8(3): 609-621. Subject: 20.7

Meisel, Alan. Response: from tragedy to catastrophe: lawyers and the bureaucratization of informed consent. *Yale Journal of Health Policy, Law and Ethics* 2006 Summer; 6(2): 479-483. Subject: 8.3.1

Melchert, Timothy P.; Patterson, Michele M. Duty to warn and interventions with HIV-positive clients. *Professional Psychology: Research and Practice* 1999 April; 30(2): 180-186. Subject: 9.5.6

Meldolesi, Anna. Italians scuttle embryo law [news brief]. *Nature Biotechnology* 2005 July; 23(7): 771. Subject: 18.5.6

Mele, V.; Binetti, P. Bioethics, bridge to medical education. *Journal of Biological Regulators and Homeostatic Agents* 2005 January-June; 19(1-2): 49-53. Subject: 2.3

Melgalve, I.; Lazdane, G.; Trapenciere, I.; Shannon, C.; Bracken, H.; Winikoff, B. Knowledge and attitudes about abortion legislation and abortion methods among abortion clients in Latvia. *European Journal of Contraception and Reproductive Health Care* 2005 September; 10(3): 143-150. Subject: 12.5.2

Melisko, Michelle E.; Hassin, Fern; Metzroth, Lauren; Moore, Dan H.; Brown, Beth; Patel, Kiran; Rugo, Hope S.; Tripathy, Debu. Patient and physician attitudes toward breast cancer clinical trials: developing interventions based on understanding barriers. *Clinical Breast Cancer* 2005 April; 6(1): 45-54. Subject: 18.5.3

Mellick, Erica S. Time for Plan B: increasing access to emergency contraception and minimizing conflicts of conscience. *Journal of Health Care Law and Policy* 2006; 9(2): 402-440. Subject: 11.1

Mello, Michelle M.; Studdert, David M.; Brennan, Troyen A. Obesity — the new frontier of public health law. *New England Journal of Medicine* 2006 June 15; 354(24): 2601-2610. Subject: 9.1

Mellon, Brad F. James Drane's More Humane Medicine: a new foundation for twenty-first century bioethics? *Christian Bioethics* 2006 December; 12(3): 301-311. Subject: 2.1

Mellon, Suzanne; Berry-Bobovski, Lisa; Gold, Robin; Levin, Nancy; Tainsky, Michael A. Communication and decision-making about seeking inherited cancer risk information: findings from female survivor-relative focus groups. *Psycho-Oncology* 2006 March; 15(3): 193-208. Subject: 8.1

Melltorp, G.; Nilstun, T. The difference between withholding and withdrawing life-sustaining treatment. *Intensive Care Medicine* 1997 December; 23(12): 1264-1267. Subject: 20.5.1

Melnychuk, Ryan M.; Kenny, Nuala P. Pandemic triage: the ethical challenge. *CMAJ/JAMC: Canadian Medical Association Journal* 2006 November 21; 175(11): 1393-1394. Subject: 9.4

Meltzer, Leslie A. Undesirable implications of disclosing individual genetic results to research participants. *American Journal of Bioethics* 2006 November-December; 6(6): 28-30; author reply W10-W12. Subject: 15.1

Melvin, Louise. Health needs of immigrants: rights to treatment and confidentiality. *Journal of Family Planning and Reproductive Health Care* 2005 October; 31(4): 331-332. Subject: 21.1

Menache, Andre. Primate problem [letter]. *New Scientist* 2006 November 25-December 1; 192(2579): 23. Subject: 22.2

Mendell, Jerry R.; Clark, K. Reed. Risks, benefits, and consent in the age of gene therapy [editorial]. *Neurology* 2006 April 11; 66(7): 964-965. Subject: 15.4

Mendelson, Danuta; Ashby, Michael. The medical provision of hydration and nutrition: two very different outcomes in Victoria and Florida. *Journal of Law and Medicine* 2004 February; 11(3): 282-291. Subject: 20.5.1

Mendelssohn, David C. Both sides now: disclosure of prognosis on dialysis. *Peritoneal Dialysis International* 2005 May-June; 25(3): 238-239. Subject: 8.2

Mendieta, Eduardo. Habermas on human cloning: the debate on the future of the species. *Philosophy and Social Criticism* 2004 September; 30(5-6): 721-743. Subject: 14.5

Mendoza, Fátima Flores. The offence of foetal injuries in Spain's Penal Code of 1995 = El delito de lesiones al feto en el Código español de 1995. *Law and the Human Genome Review = Revista de Derecho y Genoma Humano* 1996 July-December; (5): 157-183. Subject: 9.5.8

See SUBJECT HEADING KEY FOR SECTION II on inside back cover.

Menon, Girish; Cash, Richard. Research involving medical records review: an Indian perspective. *Indian Journal of Medical Ethics* 2006 April-June; 3(2): 55-57. Subject: 18.3

Mensah, George A. Eliminating disparities in cardiovascular health: six strategic imperatives and a framework for action. *Circulation* 2005 March 15; 111(10): 1332-1336. Subject: 9.5.1

Menzel, Paul; Light, Donald W. A conservative case for universal access to healthcare. *Hastings Center Report* 2006 July-August; 36(4): 36-45. Subject: 9.2

Mepham, Ben. Bioethics in the laboratory. *In his:* Bioethics: An Introduction for the Biosciences. Oxford; New York: Oxford University Press; 2005: 357-378. Subject: 1.3.9

Mepham, Ben. Experiments on animals. *In his:* Bioethics: An Introduction for the Biosciences. Oxford; New York: Oxford University Press; 2005: 179-201. Subject: 22.2

Mepham, Ben. Politics and the biosciences. *In his:* Bioethics: An Introduction for the Biosciences. Oxford; New York: Oxford University Press; 2005: 331-355. Subject: 5.1

Mepham, Ben. Reproductive choices. *In his:* Bioethics: An Introduction for the Biosciences. Oxford; New York: Oxford University Press; 2005: 124-149. Subject: 15.3

Mepham, Ben. Risk, precaution and trust. *In his:* Bioethics: An Introduction for the Biosciences. Oxford; New York: Oxford University Press; 2005: 309-330. Subject: 5.2

Mepham, Ben. A time to be born? *In his:* Bioethics: An Introduction for the Biosciences. Oxford; New York: Oxford University Press; 2005: 96-123. Subject: 14.1

Merali, Zeeya. Animal activists flee UK clampdown [news]. *New Scientist* 2006 May 13-19; 190(2551): 6-7. Subject: 22.2

Mercurio, Mark R. The Conscientious Practice Policy: a futility policy for acute care hospitals. *Connecticut Medicine* 2005 August; 69(7): 417-419. Subject: 20.5.1

Mertes, Heidi; Pennings, Guido; Van Steirteghem, André. An ethical analysis of alternative methods to obtain pluripotent stem cells without destroying embryos. *Human Reproduction* 2006 November; 21(11): 2749-2755. Subject: 18.5.7

Merz, J.F.; McGee, G.E.; Sankar, P. Response from Jon F. Merz, Glenn E. McGee, and Pamela Sankar to Hoeyer and Lynöe's commentary on their article "'Iceland Inc.'? On the Ethics of Commercial Genomics". *Social Science and Medicine* 2004 March; 58(6): 1213. Subject: 15.10

Meslin, Eric M. Shifting paradigms in health services research ethics: consent, privacy, and the challenges for IRBs. *JGIM: Journal of General Internal Medicine* 2006 March; 21(3): 279-280. Subject: 18.3

Messinger-Rapport, Barbara J.; Kamel, Hosam K. Predictors of do not resuscitate orders in the nursing home. *Journal of the American Medical Directors Association* 2005 January-February; 6(1): 18-21. Subject: 20.5.1

Mesters, Ilse; Ausems, Marlein; Eichhorn, Sophie; Vasen, Hans. Informing one's family about genetic testing for hereditary non-polyposis colorectal cancer (HNPCC): a retrospective exploratory study. *Familial Cancer* 2005; 4(2): 163-167. Subject: 15.3

Meulenbergs, Tom; Schotsmans, Paul. The sanctity of autonomy?: Transcending the opposition between a quality of life and a sanctity of life ethic. *In their:* Euthanasia and Palliative Care in the Low Countries. Dudley, MA: Peeters, 2005: 121-146. Subject: 4.4

Meyer, Gitte. Journalism and science: how to erode the idea of knowledge. *Journal of Agricultural and Environmental Ethics* 2006; 19(3): 239-252. Subject: 1.3.9

Meyer, Gregg S. Privacy versus progress: the international debate over medical records research. *Nutrition* 1999 January; 15(1): 81-82. Subject: 8.4

Mezza, E.; Consiglio, V.; Soragna, G.; Putaggio, S.; Burdese, M.; Perrotta, L.; Jeantet, A.; Segoloni, G.P.; Piccoli, G.B. CKD patients and erythropoietin: do we need evidence-based informed consent? *International Journal of Artificial Organs* 2005 June; 28(6): 591-599. Subject: 8.3.1

Miah, Andy. Gene doping: the shape of things to come. *In:* Tamburrini, Claudio; Tännsjö, Torbjörn, eds. Genetic Technology and Sport: Ethical Questions. London; New York: Routledge; 2005: 42-53. Subject: 4.5

Miah, Andy. Gene-doping: sport, values, and bioethics. *In:* Glasa, J., ed. Ethics of Human Genetics: Challenges of the (Post) Genomic Era. Bratislava, Slovak Republic: Charis [and] IMEB Foundation; 2002: 171-180. Subject: 15.1

Michalek, Arthur M.; Wicher, Camille C. Conflicts of interest/commitment. *Journal of Cancer Education* 2005 Spring; 20(1): 8-9. Subject: 1.3.9

Michaud, Jean. Bioethics and recent French law developments = Las nuevas leyes francesas sobre Bioética. *Law and the Human Genome Review = Revista de Derecho y Genoma Humano* 1995 July-December; (3): 277-279. Subject: 15.1

Michel, Donna M.; Moss, Alvin H. Communicating prognosis in the dialysis consent process: a patient-centered, guideline-supported approach. *Advances in Chronic Kidney Disease* 2005 April; 12(2): 196-201. Subject: 8.3.1

Michel, L.; Van Damme, H. The challenge of electronic medical prescriptions to the rule of confidentiality and to the respect of patient's privacy. *Acta Chirurgica Belgica* 2005 September-October; 105(5): 455-456. Subject: 8.4

Michelmann, Hans Wilhelm; Wewetzer, Christa; Körner, Uwe. Präkonzeptionelle Geschlechtswahl:

Subject = NRCBL Primary Classification Number; see inside front cover.

medizinische, rechtliche und ethische Aspekte [Preconceptional sex selection; medical, legal, and ethical aspects]. *Ethik in der Medizin* 2006 June; 18(2): 164-180. Subject: 14.2

Michie, Susan; di Lorenzo, Elena; Lane, Ruth; Armstrong, Kevin; Sanderson, Saskia. Genetic information leaflets: influencing attitudes towards genetic testing. *Genetics in Medicine* 2004 July-August; 6(4): 219-225. Subject: 15.3

Mick, JoAnn. The ethical dilemma of medical futility: the case of Mr. X. *Clinical Journal of Oncology Nursing* 2005 October; 9(5): 611-616. Subject: 20.5.1

Middleton, Anna. Parents' attitudes towards genetic testing and the impact of deafness in the family. *In:* Stephens, Dafydd; Jones, Lesley, eds. The Impact of Genetic Hearing Impairment. London; Philadelphia: Whurr; 2005: 11-53. Subject: 15.3

Mieth, Dietmar. The need for ethical evaluation in biomedicine and biopolitics. *In:* Rehmann-Sutter, Christoph; Düwell, Marcus; Mieth, Dietmar, eds. Bioethics in Cultural Contexts: Reflections on Methods and Finitude. Dordrecht: Springer, 2006: 21-43. Subject: 2.1

Mieth, Dietmar. Stem cells: the ethical problems of using embryos for research. *Journal of Contemporary Health Law and Policy* 2006 Spring; 22(2): 439-447. Subject: 18.5.4

Miles, Steven H. A battle for the soul of medicine: medical complicity in torture. *Atrium* 2006 Fall; 3: 7. Subject: 21.4

Miles, Steven H. Medical investigations of homicides of prisoners of war in Iraq and Afghanistan. *Newsletter on Philosophy and Medicine* 2005 Fall; 05(1): 5-14. Subject: 21.4

Miles, Steven H. Medical oaths betrayed. *Washington Post* 2006 July 9; p. B1, B4. Subject: 21.2

Milford, Cecilia; Wassenaar, Douglas; Slack, Catherine. Resources and needs of research ethics committees in Africa: preparations for HIV vaccine trials. *IRB: Ethics and Human Research* 2006 March-April; 28(2): 1-9. Subject: 18.2

Milgram, Stanley. Behavioral study of obedience. *Journal of Abnormal and Social Psychology* 1963 October; 67: 371-378. Subject: 18.4

Miljeteig, Ingrid; Norheim, Ole Frithjof. My job is to keep him alive, but what about his brother and sister? How Indian doctors experience ethical dilemmas in neonatal medicine. *Developing World Bioethics* 2006 March; 6(1): 23-32. Subject: 20.5.2

Millard, Lynda; Hallett, Christine; Luker, Karen. Nurse-patient interaction and decision-making in care: patient involvement in community nursing. *Journal of Advanced Nursing* 2006 July; 55(2): 142-150. Subject: 8.1

Millat, Bertrand; Borie, Frédéric; Fingerhut, Abe. Patient's preference and randomization: new paradigm of evidence-based clinical research. *World Journal of Surgery* 2005 May; 29(5): 596-600. Subject: 18.2

Miller, Courtney. Reflections on protecting conscience for health care providers: a call for more inclusive statutory protection in light of constitutional considerations. *Southern California Review of Law and Social Justice* 2006 Spring; 15(2): 327-362. Subject: 8.1

Miller, Eric C. Listening to the disabled: end-of-life medical decision making and the never competent. *Fordham Law Review* 2006 April; 74(5): 2889-2925. Subject: 20.5.1

Miller, Franklin G. Equipoise and the ethics of clinical research revisited. *American Journal of Bioethics* 2006 July-August; 6(4): 59-61. Subject: 18.2

Miller, Franklin G. Revisiting the Belmont Report: the ethical significance of the distinction between clinical research and medical care. *APA Newsletters: Newsletter on Philosophy and Medicine* 2006 Spring; 05(2): 10-14. Subject: 18.2

Miller, Franklin G.; Joffe, Steven. Evaluating the therapeutic misconception. *Kennedy Institute of Ethics Journal* 2006 December; 16(4): 353-366. Subject: 18.3

Miller, Franklin G.; Wendler, David. The relevance of empirical research in bioethics. *Schizophrenia Bulletin* 2006 January; 32(1): 37-41. Subject: 18.1

Miller, Jed. The unconscionability of conscience clauses: pharmacists' consciences and women's access to contraception. *Health Matrix: The Journal of Law-Medicine* 2006 Winter; 16(1): 237-278. Subject: 9.7

Miller, Jessica Prata. Defining "research" in rural health care ethics. *American Journal of Bioethics* 2006 March-April; 6(2): 59-61. Subject: 9.5.1

Miller, Jessica Prata. Feminist values and bioethics practice: strangers at the bedside? *American Philosophical Association Newsletter on Feminism and Philosophy* 2006 Spring; 5(2): 3-8. [Online]. Accessed: http://www.apaonline.org/publications/newsletters/Vol05n2/Feminism.pdf [18 October 2006]. Subject: 9.6

Miller, Joan F. Opportunities and obstacles for good work in nursing. *Nursing Ethics* 2006 September; 13(5): 471-487. Subject: 7.1

Miller, Judith. Environmental protection and uncertainty: the case of deliberate release of genetically engineered organisms. *Politics and the Life Sciences* 1989 February; 7(2): 142-145. Subject: 15.7

Miller, Patrice Marie; Commons, Michael Lamport; Gutheil, Thomas G. Clinicians' perceptions of boundaries in Brazil and the United States. *Journal of the American Academy of Psychiatry and the Law* 2006; 34(1): 33-42. Subject: 8.1

Miller, Paul; Wilsdon, James. The man who wants to live forever. *In their:* Better Humans?: The Politics of Human

See SUBJECT HEADING KEY FOR SECTION II on inside back cover.

659

Enhancement and Life Extension. London: Demos, 2006: 51-58. Subject: 4.5

Miller, Paul; Wilsdon, James. Stronger, longer, smarter, faster. *In their:* Better Humans?: The Politics of Human Enhancement and Life Extension. London: Demos, 2006: 13-27. Subject: 4.5

Miller, Paul B.; Weijer, Charles. Fiduciary obligation in clinical research. *Journal of Law, Medicine and Ethics* 2006 Summer; 34(2): 424-440. Subject: 8.1

Miller, Paul Steven. Toward truly informed decisions about appearance-normalizing surgeries. *In:* Parens, Erik, ed. Surgically Shaping Children: Technology, Ethics, and the Pursuit of Normality. Baltimore, MD: Johns Hopkins University Press; 2006: 211-226. Subject: 9.5.7

Miller, P.B.; Weijer, C. Trust based obligations of the state and physician-research to patient subjects. *Journal of Medical Ethics* 2006 September; 32(9): 542-547. Subject: 18.1

Miller, Peter. Harm reduction ethics: a promising basis for drug policy. *Drug and Alcohol Review* 2005 November; 24(6): 553-554. Subject: 9.5.9

Miller, Peter; Moore, David; Strang, John. The regulation of research by funding bodies: an emerging ethical issue for the alcohol and other drug sector? *International Journal of Drug Policy* 2006 January; 17(1): 12-16. Subject: 9.5.9

Miller, Richard B. How the Belmont Report fails. *Essays in Philosophy* 2003 June; 4(2): 18 p. [Online]. Accessed: http://www.humboldt.edu/~essays/miller.html [2004 December 20]. Subject: 18.2

Miller, Richard B. On medicine, culture, and children's basic interests: a reply to three critics. *Journal of Religious Ethics* 2006 March; 34(1): 177-189. Subject: 9.5.7

Miller, Robert D. Death and dead bodies. *In his:* Problems in Health Care Law. Ninth edition. Sudbury, MA: Jones and Bartlett Publishers; 2006: 765-787. Subject: 20.2.1

Miller, Robert D. Decision-making concerning individuals. *In his:* Problems in Health Care Law. Ninth edition. Sudbury, MA: Jones and Bartlett Publishers; 2006: 315-425. Subject: 8.3.1

Miller, Robert D. Health care information. *In his:* Problems in Health Care Law. Ninth edition. Sudbury, MA: Jones and Bartlett Publishers; 2006: 427-491. Subject: 8.4

Miller, Robert D. Relationship of patient and provider. *In his:* Problems in Health Care Law. Ninth edition. Sudbury, MA: Jones and Bartlett Publishers; 2006: 279-314. Subject: 8.1

Miller, Robert D. Reproductive issues. *In his:* Problems in Health Care Law. Ninth edition. Sudbury, MA: Jones and Bartlett Publishers; 2006: 737-764. Subject: 14.1

Miller, Roman J. Viewing bioethics through Anabaptist eyes. *In:* Miller, Roman J.; Brubaker, Beryl H.; Peterson, James C., eds. Viewing New Creations with Anabaptist

Eyes: Ethics of Biotechnology. Telford, PA: Cascadia Pub.; 2005: 85-105. Subject: 2.1

Miller, Ronald B. Morbidity and mortality data associated with ESRD and dialysis: should patients be informed? The "truth," the whole truth, and nothing but the truth. . .informing ESRD patients of their prognoses. *Nephrology Nursing Journal* 2005 July-August; 32(4): 441-442. Subject: 8.2

Miller, Victoria A.; Drotar, Dennis; Burant, Christopher; Kodish, Eric. Clinician-parent communication during informed consent for pediatric leukemia trials. *Journal of Pediatric Psychology* 2005 April-May; 30(3): 219-229. Subject: 18.5.2

Miller, Victoria A.; Nelson, Robert M. A developmental approach to child assent for nontherapeutic research. *Journal of Pediatrics* 2006 July; 149(1, Supplement): S25-S30. Subject: 18.3

Mills, Ann E.; Rorty, Mary V.; Spencer, Edward M. Introduction: ethics committees and failure to thrive. *HEC (Healthcare Ethics Committee) Forum* 2006 December; 18(4): 279-286. Subject: 9.6

Mills, Ann E.; Rorty, Mary V.; Werhane, Patricia H. Clinical ethics and the managerial revolution in American healthcare. *Journal of Clinical Ethics* 2006 Summer; 17(2): 181-190. Subject: 9.8

Mills, Catherine. Technology, embodiment and abortion. *Internal Medicine Journal* 2005 July; 35(7): 427-428. Subject: 12.3

Mills, Edward J.; Seely, Dugald; Rachlis, Beth; Griffith, Lauren; Wu, Ping; Wilson, Kumanan; Ellis, Peter; Wright, James R. Barriers to participation in clinical trials of cancer: a meta-analysis and systematic review of patient-reported factors. *Lancet Oncology* 2006 February; 7(2): 141-148. Subject: 18.2

Mills, Edward; Rennie, Stuart; Wu, Zunyou; Sun, Xinhua; Sullivan, Sheena G.; Detels, Roger. HIV testing and individual rights [letter and response]. *Science* 2006 October 20; 314(5798): 417-419. Subject: 9.5.6

Mills, Peter; Whittall, Hugh. "Legal cases spell big trouble and great opportunities for IVF embryologists": a comment from the perspective of the HFEA. *Reproductive BioMedicine Online [electronic]* 2001; 2(3): 1 p. Accessed: http://www.rbmonline.com/index.html [2005 June 3]. Subject: 14.4

Milmore, Don. Hospital ethics committees: a survey in upstate New York. *HEC (Healthcare Ethics Committee) Forum* 2006 September; 18(3): 222-244. Subject: 9.6

Milne, Janet. An analysis of the law of confidentiality with special reference to the counselling of minors. *Australian Psychologist* 1995 November; 30(3): 169-174. Subject: 8.4

Milstein, Arnold; Smith, Mark. America's new refugees — seeking affordable surgery offshore. *New England*

Journal of Medicine 2006 October 19; 355(16): 1637-1640. Subject: 9.3.1

Milton, Constance L. Breaking the rules of the game: ethical implications for nursing practice and education. *Nursing Science Quarterly* 2006 July; 19(3): 207-210. Subject: 4.1.3

Milton, Constance L. The metaphor of nurse as guest with ethical implications for nursing and healthcare. *Nursing Science Quarterly* 2005 October; 18(4): 301-303. Subject: 4.1.3

Milton, Constance L. Symbols and ethics: integrity and the discipline of nursing. *Nursing Science Quarterly* 2005 July; 18(3): 211-214. Subject: 4.1.3

Minhas, Rubin. New ethical framework for pharmaceutical physicians [letter]. *BMJ: British Medical Journal* 2006 April 29; 332(7548): 1034. Subject: 9.7

Minkler, Meredith. Ethical challenges for the "outside" researcher in community-based participatory research. *Health Education and Behavior* 2004 December; 31(6): 684-697. Subject: 18.1

Minkler, Meredith; Fadem, Pamela; Perry, Martha; Blum, Klaus; Moore, Leroy; Rogers, Judith. Ethical dilemmas in participatory action research: a case study from the disability community. *Health Education and Behavior* 2002 February; 29(1): 14-29. Subject: 18.5.6

Minkoff, Howard; Paltrow, Lynn M. The rights of "unborn children" and the value of pregnant women. *Hastings Center Report* 2006 March-April; 36(2): 26-28. Subject: 9.5.5

Minkoff, Howard L.; Berkowitz, Richard. The myth of the precious baby. *Obstetrics and Gynecology* 2005 September; 106(3): 607-609. Subject: 14.1

Minsky, Marvin. Notes on reading Kazuo Ishiguro's "Never Let Me Go" [response]. *Perspectives in Biology and Medicine* 2006 Autumn; 49(4): 628-630. Subject: 14.5

Mintzberg, Henry. Patent nonsense: evidence tells of an industry out of social control. *CMAJ/JAMC: Canadian Medical Association Journal* 2006 August 15; 175(4): 374-376. Subject: 9.7

Miola, J. The relationship between medical law and ethics. *Clinical Ethics* 2006 March; 1(1): 22-25. Subject: 2.1

Miola, José. Autonomy ruled ok?: Al Hamwi v. Johnston and Another. *Medical Law Review* 2006 Spring; 14(1): 108-114. Subject: 15.2

Miola, José. The need for informed consent: lessons from the ancient Greeks. *CQ: Cambridge Quarterly of Healthcare Ethics* 2006 Spring; 15(2): 152-160. Subject: 8.3.1

Miralles, Angela Aparisi. Globalization of bioethics: the task of international commissions. *Georgetown Journal of International Law* 2005 Fall; 37(1): 141-151. Subject: 2.4

Mirarchi, Nina M. Clinical research on the subject with dementia: ethical concerns and research regulation. *Penn Bioethics Journal* 2005 April 2; 1(1): 4p. [Online]. Accessed: http://www.bioethicsjournal.com [2005 April 19]. Subject: 18.3

Miringoff, Marque-Luisa. Dissecting people and ignoring social structure: an analysis of individualism, public policy, and genetic labeling. *Behavioral Sciences and the Law* 1996 Autumn; 14(4): 433-442. Subject: 15.1

Mirkes, Reneé. Is it ethical to generate human-animal chimeras? *National Catholic Bioethics Quarterly* 2006 Spring; 6(1): 109-130. Subject: 15.1

Mirkes, Renée. Newborn screening: toward a just system. *Ethics and Medicine* 2006 Fall; 22(3): 163-175. Subject: 15.3

Misch, Donald A. The physician's counsel. *JAMA: the Journal of the American Medical Association* 2006 July 19; 296(3): 259-260. Subject: 20.5.1

Mishler, Elliot G. Patient stories, narratives of resistance and the ethics of humane care: a la recherche du temps perdu. *Health (London)* 2005 October; 9(4): 431-451. Subject: 8.1

Misje, Aksel H.; Bosnes, V.; Gasdal, O.; Heier, H.E. Motivation, recruitment and retention of voluntary non-remunerated blood donors: a survey-based questionnaire study. *Vox Sanguinis* 2005 November; 89(4): 236-244. Subject: 19.5

Missouri Bishops; Burke, Raymond; Finn, Robert; Gaydos, John; Leibrecht, John; Hermann, Robert; Boland, Raymond. Cloning and embryonic stem-cells: ballot initiative opposed. *Origins* 2006 October 19; 36(19): 293-296. Subject: 14.5

Missouri. *Laws, statutes, etc.* Cloning — use of state funds prohibited [Approved: 10 July 1998; Effective 1 January 1999]. Missouri Revised Statutes, Section 1.217 (28 August 2003) 1 p. [Online]. Accessed: http://www.moga.state.mo.us/statutes/c000-099/0010000217.htm [2007 March 9]. Subject: 14.5

Mitcham, Carl; Briggle, Adam. Life. *In:* Mitcham, Carl, ed. Encyclopedia of Science, Technology, and Ethics. Farmington Hills, MI: Thomson/Gale, 2005: 1128-1131. Subject: 4.4

Mitchell, Christine. "Margaret's" children remember [interview]. *Journal of Clinical Ethics* 2006 Winter; 17(4): 349-357. Subject: 20.4.1

Mitchell, Christine. A mother's death: the story of "Margaret's" children. *Journal of Clinical Ethics* 2006 Winter; 17(4): 331-332. Subject: 20.4.1

Mitchell, Christine; Truog, Robert. When a village is not enough. *Journal of Clinical Ethics* 2006 Spring; 17(1): 79. Subject: 9.5.1

Mitchell, Christopher D. Harmful impact of EU clinical trials directives: . . .while paediatric oncology is being

See SUBJECT HEADING KEY FOR SECTION II on inside back cover.

661

scuppered [letter]. *BMJ: British Medical Journal* 2006 March 18; 332(7542): 666. Subject: 18.2

Mitchell, C. Ben. Human egg "donation" [editorial]. *Ethics and Medicine* 2006 Fall; 22(3): 133-134. Subject: 14.4

Mitchell, David. The importance of being important: euthanasia and critical interests in Dworkin's Life's Dominion. *Utilitas* 1995 November; 7(2): 301-314. Subject: 20.7

Mitchell, Terry Leigh; Baker, Emerance. Community-building versus career-building research: the challenges, risks, and responsibilities of conducting research with Aboriginal and Native American communities. *Journal of Cancer Education* 2005 Spring; 20(1, Supplement): 41-46. Subject: 18.5.1

Mitka, Mike. Approval for pesticide toxicity testing in humans draws criticism [news]. *JAMA: The Journal of the American Medical Association* 2006 March 15; 295(11): 1237-1238. Subject: 18.2

Mitka, Mike. Efforts under way to increase number of potential kidney transplant donors. *JAMA: the Journal of the American Medical Association* 2006 June 14; 295(22): 2588-2589. Subject: 19.3

Mitka, Mike. Guidelines aim to speed drug approval while protecting human subjects [news]. *JAMA: The Journal of the American Medical Association* 2006 March 1; 295(9): 988-989. Subject: 18.2

Mitrany, Edith; Melamed, Yuval. Compulsory treatment of anorexia nervosa. *Israel Journal of Psychiatry and Related Sciences* 2005; 42(3): 185-190. Subject: 9.5.1

Mitrevski, Julia P. Psychotherapist patient privilege. Applying Jaffee v. Redmond: communications to a psychotherapist are not privileged if they occur outside the course of diagnosis or treatment. *Journal of the American Academy of Psychiatry and the Law* 2006; 34(2): 245-246. Subject: 8.4

Mitrevski, Julia P.; Chamberlain, John R. Competence to stand trial and application of Sell standards. Involuntary medication allowed in a nondangerous defendant, to restore competence at trial. *Journal of the American Academy of Psychiatry and the Law* 2006; 34(2): 250-252. Subject: 8.3.3

Miura, Yasuhiko; Asai, Atsushi; Matsushima, Masato; Nagata, Shizuko; Onishi, Motoki; Shimbo, Takuro; Hosoya, Tatsuo; Fukuhara, Shunichi. Families' and physicians' predictions of dialysis patients' preferences regarding life-sustaining treatments in Japan. *American Journal of Kidney Diseases* 2006 January; 47(1): 122-130. Subject: 20.5.1

Miya, Pamela A. Do not resuscitate: when nurses' duties conflict with patients' rights. *Dimensions of Critical Care Nursing* 1984 September-October; 3(5): 293-298. Subject: 20.5.1

Miyagi, Shigehito; Kawagishi, Naoki; Fujimori, Keisei; Sekiguchi, Satoru; Fukumori, Tatsuya;

Akamatsu, Yorihiro; Satomi, Susumu. Risks of donation and quality of donors' life after living donor liver transplantation. *Transplant International* 2005 January; 18(1): 47-51. Subject: 19.5

Miyata, Hiroaki; Shiraishi, Hiromi; Kai, Ichiro. Survey of the general public's attitude toward advance directives in Japan: how to respect patients' preferences. *BMC Medical Ethics* 2006; 7:11. Subject: 20.5.4

Moazam, Farhat. Research and developing countries: hopes and hypes. *Eastern Mediterranean Health Journal/La Revue de Santé de la Méditerranée orientale* 2006; 12(Supplement 1): S30-S36 [Online]. Accessed: http://www.emro.who.int/publications/EMHJ/12_S/PDF/5.pdf [2007 January 3]. Subject: 18.5.9

Moazam, Farhat. "To eat an elephant" [editorial]. *Eastern Mediterranean Health Journal/La Revue de Santé de la Méditerranée orientale* 2006; 12(Supplement 1): S10-S12 [Online]. Accessed: http://www.emro.who.int/publications/EMHJ/12_S/PDF/2.pdf [2007 January 3]. Subject: 2.1

Modell, Stephen M.; Citrin, Toby. Ethics instruction in an issues-oriented course on public health genetics. *Health Education and Behavior* 2002 February; 29(1): 43-60. Subject: 7.2

Modra, Lucy. Prenatal genetic testing kits sold at your local pharmacy: promoting autonomy or promoting confusion? *Bioethics* 2006 September; 20(5): 254-263. Subject: 15.2

Moffic, H. Steven. Managed behavioral healthcare poses multiple ethical challenges for clinicians. *Psychiatric Annals* 2004 February; 34(2): 98-104. Subject: 9.3.2

Mohamed, Mahmoud; Punwani, Manisha; Clay, Marjorie; Appelbaum, Paul. Protecting the residency training environment: a resident's perspective on the ethical boundaries in the faculty-resident relationship. *Academic Psychiatry* 2005 September-October; 29(4): 368-373. Subject: 7.2

Mohammed, Selina A. Moving beyond the "exotic": applying postcolonial theory in health research. *Advances in Nursing Science* 2006 April-June; 29(2): 98-109. Subject: 4.1.3

Mohebbi, Mohammad Reza; Weisleder, Pedro. The right of minors to confidentiality and informed consent [letter and reply]. *Journal of Child Neurology* 2005 May; 20(5): 460-461. Subject: 8.3.2

Mohindra, Raj K.; Hall, Jim A. Desmond's non-NICE choice: dilemmas from drug-eluting stents in the affordability gap. *Clinical Ethics* 2006 June; 1(2): 105-108. Subject: 9.4

Mohl, Paul C. Psychiatric training program engagement with the pharmaceutical industry: an educational issue, not strictly an ethical one. *Academic Psychiatry* 2005 May-June; 29(2): 215-221. Subject: 7.2

Subject = NRCBL Primary Classification Number; see inside front cover.

Mohrmann, Margaret E. Whose interests are they, anyway? [review of Children, Ethics, and Modern Medicine by Richard B. Miller]. *Journal of Religious Ethics* 2006 March; 34(1): 141-150. Subject: 9.5.7

Molinuevo, José L.; Blesa, Rafael. Regulatory issues. *International Psychogeriatrics* 2003; 15(Supplement 1): 283-286. Subject: 18.5.6

Molyneux, C.S.; Peshu, N.; Marsh, K. Trust and informed consent: insights from community members on the Kenyan coast. *Social Science and Medicine* 2005 October; 61(7): 1463-1473. Subject: 18.5.9

Molyneux, C.S.; Wassenaar, D.R.; Peshu, N.; Marsh, K. 'Even if they ask you to stand by a tree all day, you will have to do it (laughter). . .!': community voices on the notion and practice of informed consent for biomedical research in developing countries. *Social Science and Medicine* 2005 July; 61(2): 443-454. Subject: 18.5.9

Molyneux, Maxine. The politics of abortion in Nicaragua: revolutionary pragmatism — or feminism in the realm of necessity? *Feminist Review* 1988 Spring; (29): 114-132. Subject: 12.5.1

Monastersky, Nicole; Landau, Sharon Cohen. Future of emergency contraception lies in pharmacists' hands. *Journal of the American Pharmacists Association* 2006 January-February; 46(1): 84-88. Subject: 11.1

Monastersky, Richard. Harvard scientists to start experiments on cloning human stem cells. *Chronicle of Higher Education* 2006 June 23; 52(42): A18. Subject: 18.5.4

Monastersky, Richard. Science journals must develop stronger safeguards against fraud, panel says. *Chronicle of Higher Education* 2006 December 8; 53(16): A15. Subject: 1.3.9

Monastersky, Richard. A second life for cloning. *Chronicle of Higher Education* 2006 February 3; 52(22): A14, A16-A17. Subject: 18.5.4

Monbiot, George. Exposed: the secret corporate funding behind health research. *Guardian* 2006 February 7 [Online]. Accessed: http://www.guardian.co.uk/print/0,,5393221-103390,00.html [2006 February 8]. Subject: 5.3

Moneymaker, Kathleen. Comfort measures only. *Journal of Palliative Medicine* 2005 June; 8(3): 688. Subject: 20.4.1

Mongodin, Bertrand. Toward an end-of-life "treatment"? *Canadian HIV/AIDS Policy and Law Newsletter* 1996 October; 3(1): 22-23. Subject: 20.5.1

Mongoven, Ann. The war on disease and the war on terror: a dangerous metaphorical nexus? *CQ: Cambridge Quarterly of Healthcare Ethics* 2006 Fall; 15(4): 403-416. Subject: 4.2

Moniz, Helena; Figalgo, Sónia; Vale e Reis, Rafael; Almeida, Rosalvo. The constitution and operation of health ethics committees in Portugal: rights of patients to personal data protection. *In:* Beyleveld, D.; Townend, D.; Wright, J., eds. Research Ethics Committees, Data Protection and Medical Research in European Countries. Hants, England; Burlington, VT: Ashgate; 2005: 189-213. Subject: 18.2

Monsen, Rita Black; Lessick, Mira; MacDonald, Deborah; Jenkins, Jean. International Society of Nurses in Genetics (ISONG) testimony for the Secretary's Advisory Committee on Genetic Testing. *Nursing Outlook* 2000 July-August; 48(4): 185-188. Subject: 4.1.3

Montana. *Laws, statutes, etc.* An act establishing standards for the collection, use, and disclosure of genetic information in issuing insurance; prohibiting insurers from requiring genetic testing except as otherwise required by law; prohibiting discrimination on the basis of genetic traits by insurers, health service corporations, health maintenance organizations, fraternal benefit societies, and other issuers of individual or group policies or certificates of insurance; prohibiting the solicitation of genetic information for nontherapeutic purposes; and amending sections 2-18-812 and 33-31-111, MCA [Approved: 19 April 1999]. Montana: State Legislature, 1999. 5 p. [Online]. Accessed: http://data.opi.state.mt.us/bills/billhtml/HB0111.htm [2007 March 9]. Subject: 15.1

Montazeri, Ali; Haji-Mahmoodi, Mehregan; Jarvandi, Soghra. Breast self-examination: do religious beliefs matter? A descriptive study. *Journal of Public Health Medicine* 2003 June; 25(2): 154-155. Subject: 9.5.5

Monterosso, Leanne; Kristjanson, Linda; Sly, Peter D.; Mulcahy, Mary; Holland, Beng Gee; Grimwood, Sarah; White, Kate. The role of the neonatal intensive care nurse in decision-making: advocacy, involvement in ethical decisions and communication. *International Journal of Nursing Practice* 2005 June; 11(3): 108-117. Subject: 8.1

Montgomery, John H.; Perlis, Roy H.; Nierenberg, Andrew A. Industry funding and author-industry affiliation in clinical trials in psychiatry [letter and reply]. *American Journal of Psychiatry* 2006 June; 163(6): 1110-1111. Subject: 18.1

Montgomery, John Warwick. The human embryo cloning danger in European context. *Philosophia Christi Series 2:* 2002; 4(1): 215-229. Subject: 14.5

Montgomery, Kathryn. The moral status of the (preserved) fetus. *Atrium* 2005 Spring; 1: 3. Subject: 4.4

Montgomery, Robert A.; Gentry, Sommer E.; Marks, William H.; Warren, Daniel S.; Hiller, Janet; Houp, Julie; Zachary, Andrea A.; Melancon, J. Keith; Maley, Warren R.; Rabb, Hamid; Simpkins, Christopher; Segev, Dorry L. Domino paired kidney donation: a strategy to make best use of live non-directed donation. *Lancet* 2006 July 29-August 4; 368(9533): 419-421. Subject: 19.3

Moody, Harry R. Intimations of prolongevity [book reviews]. *Gerontologist* 2004 June; 44(3): 432-436. Subject: 20.5.1

See SUBJECT HEADING KEY FOR SECTION II on inside back cover.

663

Mooney, Chris. Stemming research. *In his:* The Republican War on Science. Rev. ed. New York: BasicBooks, 2006: 195-216. Subject: 18.6

Mooney, Gavin. Communitarian claims and community capabilities: furthering priority setting? *Social Science and Medicine* 2005 January; 60(2): 247-255. Subject: 9.4

Mooney, Gavin. Communitarianism and health economics. *In:* Davis, John B., ed. The Social Economics of Health Care. New York: Routledge; 2001: 40-60. Subject: 9.3.1

Mooney, Gavin. The inefficiency of medical ethics. *In his:* Economics, Medicine and Health Care. Third edition. New York: Prentice Hall/Financial Times; 2003: 61-72. Subject: 9.3.1

Mooney, Gavin. Why not community values in all health research and for all cultures? *Monash Bioethics Review* 2006 January; 25(1): 72-74. Subject: 21.7

Mooney, Pat. Making well people "better". *World Watch* 2002 July-August; 15(4): 13-16, 43. Subject: 15.1

Moor, James H. Using genetic information while protecting the privacy of the soul. *Ethics and Information Technology* 1999; 1(4): 257-263. Subject: 8.4

Moor, James H. Using genetic information while protecting the privacy of the soul. *In:* Tavani, Herman T., ed. Ethics, Computing, and Genomics. Sudbury, MA: Jones and Bartlett; 2006: 109-119. Subject: 8.4

Moore, Adam D. Intellectual property, genetic information, and gene enhancement techniques. *In:* Tavani, Herman T., ed. Ethics, Computing, and Genomics. Sudbury, MA: Jones and Bartlett; 2006: 197-211. Subject: 15.1

Moore, Amanda; Tzovarras, Hunter. 2005-2006 National Health Law Moot Court competition: best brief. *Journal of Legal Medicine* 2006 December; 27(4): 395-425. Subject: 20.5.1

Moore, Andrew. What's in store for animal research in the EU? Researchers should have little to fear from the EU's new animal-welfare directive, but the menace is in the minutiae. *EMBO Reports* 2005 July; 6(7): 606-609. Subject: 22.2

Mor, Eytan; Boas, Hagao. Organ trafficking: scope and ethical dilemma. *Current Diabetes Reports* 2005 August; 5(4): 294-299. Subject: 19.5

Morain, William D. Sometimes both the palates and the ethics are cleft [editorial]. *Annals of Plastic Surgery* 2005 June; 54(6): 681-682. Subject: 15.2

Morain, William D. The stem of our future [editorial]. *Annals of Plastic Surgery* 2005 May; 54(5): 577-578. Subject: 18.5.4

Mordacci, Roberto. Medicine as a practice and the ethics of illness. *In:* Viafora, Corrado, ed. Clinical Bioethics: A Search for the Foundations. Dordrecht: Springer, 2005: 101-113. Subject: 2.1

Mordacci, Roberto. Recognition and respect for persons: a personalistic interpretation of Kant's categorical imperative. *In:* Rehmann-Sutter, Christoph; Düwell, Marcus; Mieth, Dietmar, eds. Bioethics in Cultural Contexts: Reflections on Methods and Finitude. Dordrecht: Springer, 2006: 129-143. Subject: 4.4

Moreland, Lois B. On teaching biopolicy and values in selected reproductive technologies: abortion, in vitro fertilization, and surrogate motherhood. *Politics and the Life Sciences* 1986 August; 5(1): 75-82. Subject: 2.3

Moreno Muñoz, Miguel. The debate on the legal implications of the Human Genome Project: epistemological contributions = Aportaciones epistemológicas al debate sobre las implicaciones jurídicas del Proyecto Genoma Humano. *Revista de Derecho Genoma Humano = Law and the Human Genome Review* 1997 January-June; (6): 181-209. Subject: 15.10

Moreno, Jonathan D. Congress's hybrid problem. *Hastings Center Report* 2006 July-August; 36(4): 12-13. Subject: 18.5.4

Moreno, Jonathan D. Conscience, professionalism and corporate obligation. *Conscience* 2006 Autumn; 27(3): 36-37. Subject: 4.1.2

Moreno, Jonathan D. Ethics committees: beyond benign neglect. *HEC (Healthcare Ethics Committee) Forum* 2006 December; 18(4): 368-369. Subject: 9.6

Moreno, Jonathan D. The name of the embryo. *Hastings Center Report* 2006 September-October; 36(5): 3. Subject: 18.5.4

Moreno, Jonathan D. The role of brain research in national defense. *Chronicle of Higher Education* 2006 November 10; 53(12): B6-B7. Subject: 18.5.8

Moreno, Jonathan D.; Berger, Sam. Taking stem cells seriously. *American Journal of Bioethics* 2006 September-October; 6(5): 6-7. Subject: 18.5.4

Moreno, Jonathan D.; Hynes, Richard O. Guidelines for human embryonic stem cell research. *Nature Biotechnology* 2005 July; 23(7): 793-794. Subject: 18.5.4

Moreno, Jonathan D.; Zuckerman, Connie; London, Alex John. Ethical considerations in the care of patients with neurosurgical disease. *In:* Cottrell, J. and Smith, D., eds. Anesthesia and Neurosurgery, fourth edition. St. Louis: Mosby; 2001: 749-763. Subject: 8.3.1

Morgan, Carol A. Tissue harvesting for cloning: an ethical perspective for veterinarians / Prélèvement de tissus aux fins de clonage: une perspective déontologique à l'intention des vétérinaires. *Canadian Veterinary Journal* 2005 April; 46(4): 358-363. Subject: 14.5

Morgan, Lynn M. "Life begins when they steal your bicycle": cross-cultural practices of personhood at the beginnings and ends of life. *Journal of Law, Medicine, and Ethics* 2006 Spring; 34(1): 8-15. Subject: 4.4

Subject = NRCBL Primary Classification Number; see inside front cover.

Morgan, Lynn M. The rise and demise of a collection of human fetuses at Mount Holyoke College. *Perspectives in Biology and Medicine* 2006 Summer; 49(3): 435-451. Subject: 18.5.4

Morgan, M.A.; Dana, J.; Loewenstein, G.; Zinberg, S.; Schulkin, J. Interactions of doctors with the pharmaceutical industry. *Journal of Medical Ethics* 2006 October; 32(10): 559-563. Subject: 7.3

Morgan, Rose M. Cloning a human. *In her:* The Genetics Revolution: History, Fears, and Future of a Life-Altering Science. Westport, CT: Greenwood Press; 2006: 175-191. Subject: 14.5

Morgan, Rose M. The HGDP debate. *In her:* The Genetics Revolution: History, Fears, and Future of a Life-Altering Science. Westport, CT: Greenwood Press; 2006: 105-128. Subject: 15.10

Morgan, Rose M. Laboratory babies: new biology, old medicine. *In her:* The Genetics Revolution: History, Fears, and Future of a Life-Altering Science. Westport, CT: Greenwood Press; 2006: 55-69. Subject: 14.1

Morgan, Rose M. A major decision. *In her:* The Genetics Revolution: History, Fears, and Future of a Life-Altering Science. Westport, CT: Greenwood Press; 2006: 145-156. Subject: 18.5.4

Morgan, Rose M. Reproductive cloning. *In her:* The Genetics Revolution: History, Fears, and Future of a Life-Altering Science. Westport, CT: Greenwood Press; 2006: 159-173. Subject: 14.5

Morgan, Rose M. Stem-cell research. *In her:* The Genetics Revolution: History, Fears, and Future of a Life-Altering Science. Westport, CT: Greenwood Press; 2006: 131-143. Subject: 18.5.4

Morgan, Rose M. The Warnock report. *In her:* The Genetics Revolution: History, Fears, and Future of a Life-Altering Science. Westport, CT: Greenwood Press; 2006: 55-69. Subject: 14.1

Morgenstern, Leon. Still imperfect: overseeing clinical research [editorial]. *Nutrition* 2005 July-August; 21(7-8): 887-888. Subject: 18.6

Mori, Maurizio. The morality of assisted reproduction of genetic manipulation. *Cadernos de Saúde Pública* 1999; 15(suppl.1): 65-72. Subject: 14.4

Moriaka, Masahiro. When did "bioethics" begin in each country? A proposal of a comparative study. *Eubios Journal of Asian and International Bioethics* 2003 March 13(2): 51. Subject: 2.2

Morioka, Masahiro. Commentary on Bagheri et al. *Eubios Journal of Asian and International Bioethics* 2003 January 13(1): 6. Subject: 19.5

Morioka, Masahiro. Cross-cultural approaches to the philosophy of life in the contemporary world: from bioethics to life studies. *In:* Sleeboom, Margaret, ed. Genomics in Asia: A Clash of Bioethical Interests? New York: Kegan Paul; 2004: 179-199. Subject: 21.1

Morita, Tatsuya; Chinone, Yoshikazu; Ikenaga, Masayuki; Miyoshi, Makoto; Nakaho, Toshimichi; Nishitateno, Kenji; Sakonji, Mitsuaki; Shima, Yasuo; Suenaga, Kazuyuki; Takigawa, Chizuko; Kohara, Hiroyuki; Tani, Kazuyuki; Kawamura, Yasuo; Matsubara, Tatsuhiro; Watanabe, Akihiko; Yagi, Yasuo; Sasaki, Toru; Higuchi, Akiko; Kimura, Hideyuki; Abo, Hirofumi; Ozawa, Taketoshi; Kizawa, Yoshiyuki; Uchitomi, Yosuke. Ethical validity of palliative sedation therapy: a multicenter, prospective, observational study conducted on specialized palliative care units in Japan. *Journal of Pain and Symptom Management* 2005 October; 30(4): 308-319. Subject: 20.4.1

Morita, Toshiko. Nursing of dying patients: from the viewpoint of cultural background of attending death. *In:* Takahashi, Takao, ed. Taking Life and Death Seriously: Bioethics from Japan. Amsterdam; Boston: Elsevier JAI; 2005: 175-208. Subject: 20.4.1

Morland, Iain. Postmodern intersex. *In:* Sytsma, Sharon E., ed. Ethics and Intersex. Dordrecht: Springer, 2006: 319-332. Subject: 10

Morreim, E. Haavi. When research ethics meets business ethics: the AbioCor artificial heart trial. *Organizational Ethics: Healthcare, Business, and Policy* 2006 Spring-Summer; 3(1): 40-45. Subject: 19.2

Morriem, E. Haavi. End-stage heart disease, high-risk research, and competence to consent: the case of the AbioCor artificial heart. *Perspectives on Biology and Medicine* 2006 Winter; 49(1): 19-34. Subject: 18.5.7

Morreim, E. Haavi; Webb, George E.; Gordon, Harvey L.; Brody, Baruch; Casarett, David; Rosenfield, Ken; Sabin, James; Lantos, John D.; Morenz, Barry; Krouse, Robert; Goodman, Stan. Innovation in human research protection: the AbioCor artificial heart trial. *American Journal of Bioethics [Online]* 2006 September-October; 6(5): W6-W16. Subject: 18.2

Morrin, Peter A.F. Death and dying in the Canadian health-care system. *Ontario Medical Review* 1993 December: 55-57. Subject: 20.4.1

Morris, Grant H. Informed consent in psychopharmacology: legal discussion of informed consent [editorial]. *Journal of Clinical Psychopharmacology* 2005 October; 25(5): 403-404. Subject: 8.3.1

Morris, Kathleen. Codes of ethics for nurses and continuing education. *Ohio Nurses Review* 2005 November-December; 80(6): 7. Subject: 6

Morris, Norma; Balmer, Brian. Are you sitting comfortably? Perspectives of the researchers and the researched on "being comfortable". *Accountability in Research* 2006 April-June; 13(2): 111-133. Subject: 18.2

See SUBJECT HEADING KEY FOR SECTION II on inside back cover.

665

Morrison, Laurie J.; Visentin, Laura M.; Kiss, Alex; Theriault, Rob; Eby, Don; Vermeulen, Marian; Sherbino, Jonathan; Verbeek, P. Richard. Validation of a rule for termination of resuscitation in out-of-hospital cardiac arrest. *New England Journal of Medicine* 2006 August 3; 355(5): 478-487. Subject: 20.5.1

Morrissey, Paul E.; Dube, Catherine; Gohh, Reginald; Yango, Angelito; Gautam, Amitabh; Monaco, Anthony P. Good Samaritan kidney donation. *Transplantation* 2005 November 27; 80(10): 1369-1373. Subject: 19.5

Mortimer, Debra. Proprietary rights in body parts: the relevance of Moore's case in Australia. *Monash University Law Review* 1993; 19(1): 217-255. Subject: 15.8

Mortimer, Duncan. On the relevance of personal characteristics in setting health priorities: a comment on Olsen, Richardson, Dolan and Menzel (2003). *Social Science and Medicine* 2005 April; 60(8): 1661-1664. Subject: 9.3.1

Morton, B.; Richardson, A.; Duncan, S. Sudden unexpected death in epilepsy (SUDEP): don't ask, don't tell? *Journal of Neurology, Neurosurgery, and Psychiatry* 2006 February; 77(2): 199-202. Subject: 9.5.1

Morton, Kelly R.; Worthley, Joanna S.; Testerman, John K.; Mahoney, Marita L. Defining features of moral sensitivity and moral motivation: pathways to moral reasoning in medical students. *Journal of Moral Education* 2006 September; 35(3): 387-406. Subject: 7.2

Mosconi, Paola; Colombo, Cinzia; Labianca, Roberto; Apolone, Giovanni. Oncologists' opinions about research ethics committees in Italy: an update, 2004. *European Journal of Cancer Prevention* 2006 February; 15(1): 91-94. Subject: 18.2

Mosconi, Paola; Poli, Paola; Giolo, Antonio; Apolone, Giovanni. How Italian health consumers feel about clinical research: a questionnaire survey. *European Journal of Public Health* 2005 August; 15(4): 372-379. Subject: 18.2

Moseley, Kathryn L.; Silveira, Maria J.; Goold, Susan Dorr. Futility in evolution. *Clinics in Geriatric Medicine* 2005 February; 21(1): 211-222. Subject: 20.5.1

Moseley, Ray; Dobalian, Aram; Hatch, Robert. The problem with advance directives: maybe it is the medium, not the message. *Archives of Gerontology and Geriatrics* 2005 September-October; 41(2): 211-219. Subject: 20.5.4

Moser, David J.; Reese, Rebecca L.; Hey, Clare T.; Schultz, Susan K.; Arndt, Stephan; Beglinger, Leigh J.; Duff, Kevin M.; Andreasen, Nancy C. Using a brief intervention to improve decisional capacity in schizophrenia research. *Schizophrenia Bulletin* 2006 January; 32(1): 116-120. Subject: 18.5.6

Moses, Alan. Intelligent design: playing with the building blocks of biology. *Berkeley Science Review* 2005 Spring; 5(1): 34-40. Subject: 15.1

Moses, Michael F. Casey and its impact on abortion regulation. *Fordham Urban Law Journal* 2004 March; 31(3): 805-815. Subject: 12.4.1

Mosher, Steven W. China's one-child policy: twenty-five years later. *Human Life Review* 2006 Winter; 32(1): 76-101. Subject: 13.3

Moss, Arthur J. Comments on Ethical Issues with Implantable Defibrillators by F. James Brennan. *Pacing and Clinical Electrophysiology* 2004 July; 27(7): 900. Subject: 9.4

Moss, Lenny. The question of questions: what is a gene? Comments on Rolston and Griffiths and Stotz. *Theoretical Medicine and Bioethics* 2006; 27(6): 523-534. Subject: 15.1

Moss, Ralph W. No way to save a life. *New Scientist* 2006 June 3-9; 190(2554): 21. Subject: 20.4.1

Moss, Sheila; Williams, Olwen E.; Hind, Charles R.K. Counselling for an HIV test. *Postgraduate Medical Journal* 1996 February; 72(844): 84-86. Subject: 9.5.6

Mossman, Douglas. Is persecution "medically appropriate?": New law, policy and medicine of involuntary treatment: a comprehensive case problem approach to criminal and civil aspects. *New England Journal on Criminal and Civil Confinement* 2005 Winter; 31(1): 15-80. Subject: 17.8

Mostafa, S.R.A.; El Zeiny, N.A.M.; Tayel, S.E.S.; Moubarak, E.L. What do medical students in Alexandria know about female genital mutilation? *Eastern Mediterranean Health Journal = La Revue de Santé de la Méditerranée orientale* 2006; 12(Supplement 2): S78-S92 [Online]. Accessed: http://www.emro.who.int/publications/emhj/12_S2/PDF/8.pdf [2007 January 4]. Subject: 9.5.5

Moszynski, Peter. Doctors must work in partnership with patients, says GMC [news]. *BMJ: British Medical Journal* 2006 September 9; 333(7567): 513. Subject: 9.8

Motluk, Alison. Science, politics, and morality collide [news]. *New Scientist* 2006 March 18-24; 189(2543): 8-9. Subject: 12.1

Mouradian, Wendy E. What's special about the surgical context? *In:* Parens, Erik, ed. Surgically Shaping Children: Technology, Ethics, and the Pursuit of Normality. Baltimore, MD: Johns Hopkins University Press; 2006: 125-140. Subject: 9.5.7

Moutel, Grégoire; Duchange, Nathalie; Raffi, François; Sharara, Lama I.; Théodorou, Ioannis; Noël, Violaine; de Montgolfier, Sandrine; Callies, Ingrid; Bricaire, François; Hervé, Christian; Leport, Catherine. Communication of pharmacogenetic research results to HIV-infected treated patients: standpoints of professionals and patients. *European Journal of Human Genetics* 2005 September; 13(9): 1055-1062. Subject: 9.5.6

Subject = NRCBL Primary Classification Number; see inside front cover.

Moyer, Anne; Brown, Beth; Gates, Elena; Daniels, Molly; Brown, Halle D.; Kuppermann, Miriam. Decisions about prenatal testing for chromosomal disorders: perceptions of a diverse group of pregnant women. *Journal of Women's Health and Gender-Based Medicine* 1999 May; 8(4): 521-531. Subject: 15.2

Moynihan, Ray. Roche defends buying lavish meals for doctors at Sydney's restaurants [news]. *BMJ: British Medical Journal* 2006 July 22; 333(7560): 169. Subject: 9.7

Mubaraki, Maharukh. The constitutionality of court imposed contraception as a condition of probation. *Criminal Justice Journal* 1992 Fall; 14(2): 385-405. Subject: 11.1

Mudur, Ganapati. Doctors in India prosecuted for sex determination, but few convicted [news]. *BMJ: British Medical Journal* 2006 February 4; 332(7536): 257. Subject: 14.3

Mudur, Ganapati. Indian study sparks debate on the use of placebo in psychiatry trials [news]. *BMJ: British Medical Journal* 2006 March 11; 332(7541): 566. Subject: 18.5.6

Mueller, Paul S.; Koenig, Barbara A. Systematic review of ethics consultation: a route to curriculum development in post-graduate medical education. *American Journal of Bioethics* 2006 July-August; 6(4): 21-23. Subject: 7.2

Muggeridge, Malcolm. My true love hath my heart. *New Statesman (London, England: 1957)* 1968 October 4: 423. Subject: 19.2

Muir, Hazel. Dicing with death. *New Scientist* 2006 July 29-August 4; 191(2562): 38-41. Subject: 9.7

Mulholland, Maureen. Re W (A Minor): autonomy, consent and the anorexic teenager. *Professional Negligence* 1993; 9(1): 21-24. Subject: 8.3.2

Mullen, Richard; Dawson, John; Gibbs, Anita. Dilemmas for clinicians in use of community treatment orders. *International Journal of Law and Psychiatry* 2006 November-December; 29(6): 535-550. Subject: 17.1

Müller, Carola. The status of the extracorporeal embryo in German Law (Part. II). *Revista de Derecho y Genoma Humano* 2005 July-December; (23): 139-165. Subject: 18.5.4

Muller, David. Do NOT resuscitate: a well-orchestrated plan for death ends on a brutal note. *APA [American Philosophical Association] Newsletters: Newsletter on Philosophy and Medicine* 2006 Spring; 05(2): 14-16. Subject: 20.5.4

Müller-Hill, Benno. Human behavioural genetics — past and future. *Journal of Molecular Biology* 2002 June 14; 319(4): 927-929. Subject: 15.6

Müller-Terpitz, Ralf. The "uniqueness" of the human being in constitutional law. *In:* Duncker, H.-R.; Prieß, K., eds. On the Uniqueness of Humankind. Berlin; New York: Springer; 2005: 107-122. Subject: 4.4

Mulley, Albert G., Jr. Developing skills for evidence-based surgery: ensuring that patients make informed decisions. *Surgical Clinics of North America* 2006 February; 86(1): 181-192, xi. Subject: 8.3.1

Mulligan, Elizabeth J.; Claus, Eric D. Psychopharmacology. *In:* Mitcham, Carl, ed. Encyclopedia of Science, Technology, and Ethics. Farmington Hills, MI: Thomson/Gale, 2005: 1542-1545. Subject: 17.4

Mumford, Michael D.; Devenport, Lynn D.; Brown, Ryan P.; Connelly, Shane; Murphy, Stephen T.; Hill, Jason H.; Antes, Alison L. Validation of ethical decision making measures: evidence for a new set of measures. *Ethics and Behavior* 2006; 16(4): 319-345. Subject: 1.3.9

Mundy, Liz. Souls on ice: America's human embryo glut and the unbearable lightness of almost being. *Mother Jones* 2006 July/August; 31(4): 39-45. Subject: 4.4

Mundy, Liza. It's all in the genes, except when it isn't. *Washington Post* 2006 December 17; p. B1, B5. Subject: 14.2

Munro, Cindy L. Genetic technology and scientific integrity. *In:* Macrina, Francis L. Scientific Integrity: Text and Cases in Responsible Conduct of Research. 3rd ed. Washington, DC: ASM Press; 2005: 247-267. Subject: 15.1

Munthe, Christian. Ethical aspects of controlling genetic doping. *In:* Tamburrini, Claudio; Tännsjö, Torbjörn, eds. Genetic Technology and Sport: Ethical Questions. London; New York: Routledge; 2005: 107-125. Subject: 4.5

Murff, Harvey J.; Pichert, James W.; Byrne, Daniel W.; Hedstrom, Christa; Black, Margo; Churchill, Larry; Speroff, Ted. General clinical research center staff nurse perceptions and behaviors regarding informed consent: results of a national survey. *IRB: Ethics and Human Research* 2006 July-August; 28(4): 8-12. Subject: 18.3

Murff, Harvey J.; Pichert, James W.; Byrne, Daniel W.; Hedstrom, Christa; Black, Margo; Churchill, Larry; Speroff, Ted. IRB: Research participants safety and systems factors in general clinical research centers. *Ethics and Human Research* 2006 November-December; 28(6): 8-14. Subject: 18.1

Muroff, Jordana R.; Hoerauf, Sarah L.; Kim, Scott Y.H. Is psychiatric research stigmatized? An experimental survey of the public. *Schizophrenia Bulletin* 2006 January; 32(1): 129-136. Subject: 18.5.1

Murphy, Kevin. A "next generation" ethics committee. *Health Progress* 2006 March-April; 87(2): 26-30. Subject: 9.6

Murphy, Mark C. Pro-choice and presumption: a reply to Kenneth Einar Himma. *Faith and Philosophy* 2003 April; 20(2): 240-242. Subject: 12.3

Murphy, Timothy F. Experiments in gender: ethics at the boundaries of clinical practice and research. *In:* Sytsma, Sharon E., ed. Ethics and Intersex. Dordrecht: Springer, 2006: 139-151. Subject: 10

See SUBJECT HEADING KEY FOR SECTION II on inside back cover.

667

Murphy, Timothy F. Gay science: assisted reproductive technologies and the sexual orientation of children. *Reproductive BioMedicine Online [electronic]* 2005 March; 10(Supplement 1): 102-106. Subject: 10

Murphy, Timothy F. On being downstream from faked scientific reports. *BMJ: British Medical Journal* 2006 March 18; 332(7542): 674. Subject: 1.3.9

Murphy, Timothy F. Would my story get me a kidney? *Hastings Center Report* 2006 March-April; 36(2): inside back cover. Subject: 19.3

Murphy, Timothy F.; Veatch, Robert M. Members first: the ethics of donating organs and tissues to groups. *CQ: Cambridge Quarterly of Healthcare Ethics* 2006 Winter; 15(1): 50-59. Subject: 19.5

Murray, Clare; Golombok, Susan. To tell or not to tell: the decision-making process of egg-donation parents. *Human Fertility* 2003 May; 6(2): 89-95. Subject: 14.4

Murray, Elizabeth; de Zulueta, Paquita. Conscientious objection in medicine: the ethics of responding to bird flu [letter]. *BMJ: British Medical Journal* 2006 February 18; 332(7538): 425. Subject: 8.1

Murray, George. Privacy issues and Plan B: the Canadian Pharmacists Association responds [letter]. *CMAJ/JAMC: Canadian Medical Association Journal* 2006 January 3; 174(1):64-65. Subject: 8.4

Murray, John F.; Rothman, David J. 'The shame of medical research': an exchange [letter and reply]. *New York Review of Books* 2001 May 17; 48(8): 3 p. [Online]. Accessed: http://www.nybooks.com/articles/14239 [2006 October 30]. Subject: 18.2

Murray, Scott A.; Sheikh, Aziz; Thomas, Keri. Advance care planning in primary care [editorial]. *BMJ: British Medical Journal* 2006 October 28; 333(7574): 868-869. Subject: 20.5.4

Murray, Thomas H. Ethical (and political) issues in research with human stem cells. *Novartis Foundation Symposium* 2005; 265: 188-211. Subject: 18.5.4

Murray, Thomas H. Moral reasoning in social context. *Journal of Social Issues* 1993 Summer; 49(2): 185-200. Subject: 2.1

Murtagh, F.E.M.; Thorns, A. Evaluation and ethical review of a tool to explore patient preferences for information and involvement in decision making. *Journal of Medical Ethics* 2006 June; 32(6): 311-315. Subject: 8.1

Murtagh, Ged M. The limits of reproductive decisions. *Human Studies* 2004; 27(4): 417-427. Subject: 14.1

Murthy, Anant; Dixon, Anna; Mossialos, Elias. Genetic testing and insurance. *Journal of the Royal Society of Medicine* 2001 February; 94(2): 57-60. Subject: 15.3

Musher, Daniel M.; Stone, Peter H. Undisclosed conflicts of interest [letter and reply]. *Annals of Internal Medicine* 2006 February 7; 144(3): 225-226. Subject: 1.3.9

Musson, Ruth; Burnapp, Lisa. Human Tissue Act 2004 comes into force. *British Journal of Nursing* 2006 August 10-September 13; 15(15): 804. Subject: 19.5

Muthuswamy, Vasantha. Status of ethical review and challenges in India [editorial]. *Indian Pediatrics* 2005 December; 42(12): 1189-1190. Subject: 18.2

Muylaert, P. The patient's informed consent. Recent evolution of the Case Law. The physician's point of view. *Acta Chirurgica Belgica* 2000 August; 100(4): 151-155. Subject: 8.3.1

Myers, Laura B.; Bulich, Linda A.; Mizrahi, Arielle; Santangelo, Stephen; Lee, Susan J.; Ralston, Henry J. Peter, III; Drey, Eleanor A.; Partridge, John Colin; Rosen, Mark A. Fetal pain [letter and reply]. *JAMA: The Journal of the American Medical Association* 2006 January 11; 295(2): 159, 160-161. Subject: 4.4

Myers, Wade C.; Hall, Richard C.W.; Eth, Spencer. AAPL's new ethics guidelines [letter]. *AAPL (American Academy of Psychiatry and the Law) Newsletter* 2006 April; 31(2): 12-13. Subject: 6

Myhrvold, Trine. The different other — towards an including ethics of care. *Nursing Philosophy* 2006 July; 7(3): 125-136. Subject: 4.1.1

Mykytyn, Courtney Everts. Anti-aging medicine: predictions, moral obligations, and biomedical intervention. *Anthropological Quarterly* 2006 Winter; 79(1): 5-31. Subject: 4.5

Myskja, Bjørn K. The moral difference between intragenic and transgenic modification of plants. *Journal of Agricultural and Environmental Ethics* 2006; 19(3): 225-238. Subject: 15.1

Mystakidou, Kyriaki; Rosenfeld, Barry; Parpa, Efi; Tsilika, Eleni; Katsouda, Emmanuela; Galanos, Antonis; Vlahos, Lambros. The schedule of attitudes toward hastened death: validation analysis in terminally ill cancer patients. *Palliative and Supportive Care* 2004 December; 2(4): 395-402. Subject: 20.4.1

Mystakidou, Kyriaki; Tsilika, E.; Parpa, E.; Katsouda, E.; Vlahos, L. Patterns and barriers in information disclosure between health care professionals and relatives with cancer patients in Greek society. *European Journal of Cancer Care* 2005 May; 14(2): 175-181. Subject: 8.2

N

Naarden, Allan L.; Cissik, John. Informed consent. *American Journal of Medicine* 2006 March; 119(3): 194-197. Subject: 18.3

Naccache, Lionel. Is she conscious? *Science* 2006 September 8; 313(5792): 1395-1396. Subject: 20.5.1

Nachtigall, Robert D.; Becker, Gay; Friese, Carrie; Butler, Anneliese; MacDougall, Kirstin. Parents' conceptualization of their frozen embryos complicates the disposition decision. *Fertility and Sterility* 2005 August; 84(2): 431-434. Subject: 14.6

Nåden, Dagfinn; Sæteren, Berit. Cancer patients' perception of being or not being confirmed. *Nursing Ethics* 2006 May; 13(3): 222-235. Subject: 8.1

Nadler, Richard. Judaism and abortion: the hijacking of a tradition. *Human Life Review* 2006 Winter; 32(1): 43-52. Subject: 12.3

Naef, Rahel. Bearing witness: a moral way of engaging in the nurse-person relationship. *Nursing Philosophy* 2006 July; 7(3): 146-156. Subject: 4.1.3

Nagasako, Elna M.; Kalauokalani, Donna A. Ethical aspects of placebo groups in pain trials: lessons from psychiatry. *Neurology* 2005 December 29; 65(12 Supplement 4): S59-S65. Subject: 18.3

Nagata-Kobayashi, Shizuko; Sekimoto, Miho; Koyama, Hiroshi; Yamamoto, Wari; Goto, Eiji; Fukushima, Osamu; Ino, Teruo; Shimada, Tomoe; Shimbo, Takuro; Asai, Atsushi; Koizumi, Shunzo; Fukui, Tsuguya. Medical student abuse during clinical clerkships in Japan. *JGIM: Journal of General Internal Medicine* 2006 March; 21(3): 212-218. Subject: 7.2

Nagele, Robin Locke. Model conflict-of-interest policies. *Journal of Health Law* 2005 Spring; 38(2): 353-366. Subject: 7.3

Nahman, Michal. Materializing Israeliness: difference and mixture in transnational ova donation. *Science as Culture* 2006 September; 15(3): 199-213. Subject: 15.2

Nahon, Daniella; Pugachova, Inna; Yoffe, Rinat; Levav, Itzhak. The impact of human rights advocacy, mental health legislation and psychiatric reform on the epidemiology of involuntary psychiatric hospitalizations. *Medicine and Law: The World Association for Medical Law* 2006 June; 25(2): 283-295. Subject: 17.7

Naik, Gautam. Surgeons weighty dilemma; wary of extra risk, work, some doctors won't replace knees, hips of obese patients. *Wall Street Journal* 2006 February 28; p. B1, B8. Subject: 8.1

Naimark, David. Clinical discussion of informed consent [editorial]. *Journal of Clinical Psychopharmacology* 2005 October; 25(5): 404-405. Subject: 8.3.1

Nair, Indira. Ethics of care. *In:* Mitcham, Carl, ed. Encyclopedia of Science, Technology, and Ethics. Farmington Hills, MI: Thomson/Gale, 2005: 695-700. Subject: 4.1.1

Nakasone, Ronald Y. Ethics of ambiguity: a Buddhist reflection on the Japanese organ transplant law. *In:* Guinn, David E., ed. Handbook of Bioethics and Religion. New York: Oxford University Press, 2006: 291-303. Subject: 19.1

Nakata, Yoshinori; Okuno-Fujiwara, Masahiro; Goto, Takahisa; Morita, Shigeho. Risk attitudes of anesthesiologists and surgeons in clinical decision making with ex-

pected years of life. *Journal of Clinical Anesthesia* 2000 March; 12(2): 146-150. Subject: 9.4

Nakayama, Susumu. On human dignity: Japan and the west. *In:* Takahashi, Takao, ed. Taking Life and Death Seriously: Bioethics from Japan. Amsterdam; Boston: Elsevier JAI; 2005: 47-64. Subject: 4.4

Nakayama, Takeo; Sakai, Michi; Slingsby, Brian Taylor. Japan's ethical guidelines for epidemiologic research: a history of their development. *Journal of Epidemiology* 2005 July; 15(4): 107-112. Subject: 7.1

Nama, Nosisana; Swartz, Leslie. Ethical and social dilemmas in community-based controlled trials in situations of poverty: a view from a South African project. *Journal of Community and Applied Social Psychology* 2002 July-August; 12(4): 286-297. Subject: 18.5.9

Nandakumar, Saranya. The cloning controversy. *Indian Journal of Medical Ethics* 2006 July-September; 3(3): 93-94. Subject: 1.3.9

Nasim, Anwar. Ethical issues: an Islamic perspective. *In:* Sleeboom, Margaret, ed. Genomics in Asia: A Clash of Bioethical Interests? New York: Kegan Paul; 2004: 29-50. Subject: 15.1

Nathanson, V. Euthanasia, physicians and HIV infected persons [editorial]. *HIV Medicine* 2001 January; 2(1): 1-2. Subject: 20.7

National Advisory Commission on Biomedical Ethics (Switzerland) [NEK-CNE] = Nationale Ethikkommission im Bereich Humanmedizin = Commission nationale d'éthique pour la médecine humaine = Commissione nazionale d'etica per la medicina. Living-Donor Partial Liver Transplantation: The Question of Financing. Bern, Switzerland: Swiss National Advisory Commission on Biomedical Ethics, 2003 October 22; 3 p. Subject: 19.5

National Advisory Commission on Biomedical Ethics (Switzerland) [NEK-CNE] = Nationale Ethikkommission im Bereich Humanmedizin = Commission nationale d'éthique pour la médecine humaine = Commissione nazionale d'etica per la medicina. Preimplantation Genetic Diagnosis:. Bern, Switzerland: Swiss National Advisory Commission on Biomedical Ethics; 2005 December, 19 p. Subject: 15.2

National Advisory Commission on Biomedical Ethics (Switzerland) [NEK-CNE] = Nationale Ethikkommission im Bereich Humanmedizin = Commission nationale d'éthique pour la médecine humaine = Commissione nazionale d'etica per la medicina. Research Involving Human Embryos and Fetuses. Bern, Switzerland: Swiss National Advisory Commission on Biomedical Ethics, 2006 January; 30 p. Subject: 18.5.4

National Bioethics Advisory Commission. Cloning human beings: report and recommendations of the National Bioethics Advisory Commission. *Jurimetrics* 1997 Fall; 38(1): 3-10. Subject: 14.5

See SUBJECT HEADING KEY FOR SECTION II on inside back cover.

669

National Conference of Commissioners on Uniform State Laws. Uniform Health-Care Decisions Act. *Issues in Law and Medicine* 2006 Summer; 22(1): 83-97. Subject: 20.5.1

National Health and Medical Research Council [NHMRC] (Australia). Certifying death: the brain function criterion. Canberra, ACT: The Council, 1997; 25 p. Subject: 20.2.1

National Institutes of Health [NIH] (United States). Draft National Institutes of Health guidelines for research involving human pluripotent stem cells (December 1999). *Cloning* 1999-2000; 1(4): 225-231. Subject: 18.5.4

National Institutes of Health [NIH] (United States). Guidelines for the Conduct of Research in the Intramural Research Program at NIH. Bethesda, MD: National Institutes of Health, 1997 January. [Online]. Accessed: http://www.nih.gov/campus/irnews/guidelines.htm [2006 July 11]; 7 p. Subject: 1.3.9

National Reference Center for Bioethics Literature [NRCBL]. Pharmacists and conscientious objection. *Kennedy Institute of Ethics Journal* 2006 December; 16(4): 379-396. Subject: 9.7

National Society of Genetic Counselors [NSGC] (United States). Code of ethics of the National Society of Genetic Counselors. *Journal of Genetic Counseling* 2006 October; 15(5): 309-311. Subject: 15.2

National Society of Genetic Counselors [NSGC] (United States). Code of Ethics Work Group; Bennett, R.L.; Callanan, N.; Gordon, E.; Karns, L.; Mooney, K.H.; Ruzicka, R.; Schmerler, S.; Weissman, S. Code of ethics of the National Society of Genetic Counselors: Explication of Revisions. *Journal of Genetic Counseling* 2006 October; 15(5): 313-323. Subject: 15.2

National Society of Genetic Counselors [NSGC] (United States). Definition Task Force; Resta, Robert; Bowles Biesecker, Barbara; Bennett, Robin L.; Blum, Sandra; Estabrooks Hahn, Susan; Strecker, Michelle N.; Williams, Janet L. A new definition of genetic counseling: National Society of Genetic Counselors' Task Force report. *Journal of Genetic Counseling* 2006 April; 15(2): 77-83. Subject: 15.2

Nattrass, Nicoli. Rolling out antiretroviral treatment in South Africa: economic and ethical challenges. *In:* van Niekerk, Anton A.; Kopelman, Loretta M., eds. Ethics and AIDS in Africa: The Challenge to Our Thinking. Walnut Creek, CA: Left Coast Press; 2006: 39-52. Subject: 9.5.6

Naughton, Michelle J.; Jones, Alison Snow; Shumaker, Sally A. When practices, promises, profits, and policies outpace hard evidence: the post-menopausal hormone debate. *Journal of Social Issues* 2005 March; 61(1): 159-179. Subject: 9.7

Nauta, Noks. Education in ethics. *In:* Westerholm, Peter; Nilstun, Tore; Øvretveit, John, eds. Practical Ethics in Occupational Health. San Francisco: Radcliffe Medical Press; 2004: 291-306. Subject: 7.2

Nava, Stefano. Ethics, attitude and practice in end-of-life care decision: a European perspective. *Monaldi Archives for Chest Disease* 2004 January-March; 61(1): 50-57. Subject: 20.5.1

Navarrete C.; Victoria Eugenia. Bioética y biotecnología = Bioethics and biotechnology. *Revista Latinoamericana de Bioética* 2003 January; (4): 100-125. Subject: 5.2

Navot, Orit. A historical overview of the developing medical ethics culture in the new Jewish settlement in Israel during the years 1840-1914. *Eubios Journal of Asian and International Bioethics* 2003 March 13(2): 51-53. Subject: 2.2

Nayak, Barun K. Editorial duty and misconduct — keeping an eye. *Indian Journal of Ophthalmology* 2006 March; 54(1): 1-2. Subject: 1.3.7

Nderitu, Terri. Balancing pills and patents: intellectual property and the HIV/AIDS crisis. *E Law: Murdoch University Electronic Journal of Law* 2001 September; 8(3): 14 p. [Online]. Accessed: http://www.murdoch.edu.au/elaw/issues/v8n3/nderitu83_text.html [2006 August 2]. Subject: 9.5.6

Neal, Karama C. Analogical trends in umbilical cord blood legislation in the United States. *American Journal of Bioethics* 2006 November-December; 6(6): 68-70l author reply W13-W14. Subject: 19.4

Neale, Anne Victoria; Schwartz, Kendra L.; Bowman, Marjorie A. Conflict of interest: can we minimize its influence in the biomedical literature? [editorial]. *Journal of the American Board of Family Practice* 2005 September-October; 18(5): 411-413. Subject: 1.3.7

Neame, Alexandra. "What is man?" The politics of representing genetics. *Social Alternatives* 2003 Summer; 22(1): 53-57. Subject: 4.4

Neaves, William B. The ends and means of stem cell research. *Practical Bioethics* 2005 Winter; 1(1): 3-5. Subject: 18.5.4

Nebal, Elizabeth G. Conflict of interest — or conflict of priorities? [editorial]. *New England Journal of Medicine* 2006 November 30; 355(22): 2365-2367. Subject: 1.3.9

Nebraska. *Laws, statutes, etc.* An act relating to genetic testing [Approved: 25 May 2001]. Nebraska: Legislative Bill 432, 97th Legislature. Slip Laws 2001-2002. 7 p. [Online]. Accessed: http://srvwww.unicam.state.ne.us/unicamAllDrafting.html. Subject: 15.3

Nee, P.A.; Griffiths, R.D. Ethical considerations in accident and emergency research. *Emergency Medicine Journal* 2002 September; 19(5): 423-427. Subject: 18.5.1

Needham, Andrea. Patients' right to decide whether to be resuscitated. *Nursing Times* 2005 July 26-August 1; 101(30): 26-27. Subject: 20.5.1

Subject = NRCBL Primary Classification Number; see inside front cover.

Neitzke, Gerald; Charbonnier, Ralph; Diemer, Wolf; May, Arnd T.; Wernstedt, Thela. Göttinger Thesen zur gesetzlichen Regelung des Umgangs mit Patientenverfügung und Vorsorgevollmacht [Göttingen theses on the legal regulation of advance directives and health care powers of attorney]. *Ethik in der Medizin* 2006 June; 18(2): 192-194. Subject: 20.5.4

Nelken, Melissa L. The limits of privilege: the developing scope of federal psychotherapist-patient privilege law. *Review of Litigation* 2000 Winter; 20(1): 1-43 [Online]. Accessed: http://jaffee-redmond.org/articles/nelken.htm [2001 October 17]. Subject: 8.1

Nelson, Erin. Reconceiving pregnancy: expressive choice and legal reasoning. *McGill Law Journal* 2004; 49: 593-634. Subject: 9.5.5

Nelson, John. English court upholds ban on newspaper publishing identity of HIV-positive health-care worker. *HIV/AIDS Policy and Law Review* 2002 July; 7(1): 54-55. Subject: 9.5.6

Nelson, John. HIV-positive child made ward of court after father refuses treatment with antiretroviral drugs. *HIV/AIDS Policy and Law Review* 2002 July; 7(1): 53-54. Subject: 9.5.6

Nelson, John C.; Schwartzberg, Joanne G.; Vergara, Katherine C. The public's and the patient's right to know: AMA commentary on "Public health literacy in America: an ethical imperative". *American Journal of Preventive Medicine* 2005 April; 28(3): 325-326. Subject: 8.3.1

Nelson, Lawrence J. Respect for the developmentally disabled and forgoing life-sustaining treatment. *Mental Retardation and Developmental Disabilities Research Reviews* 2003; 9(1): 3-9. Subject: 9.5.3

Nelson, Leonard J., III. Catholic bioethics and the case of Terri Schiavo. *Cumberland Law Review* 2004-2005; 35(3): 543-574. Subject: 2.1

Nelson, Michelle. Morbidity and mortality data associated with ESRD and dialysis: should patients be informed? Giving hope through information. *Nephrology Nursing Journal* 2005 July-August; 32(4): 440-441. Subject: 8.2

Nelson, Robert M. Imagining the developmentally disabled and mentally retarded: an introduction. *Mental Retardation and Developmental Disabilities Research Reviews* 2003; 9(1): 1-2. Subject: 9.5.3

Nelson, Robert M.; Merz, Jon F. Voluntariness of consent for research — an empirical and conceptual review. *Medical Care* 2002 September; 40(9, Supplement): V69-V80. Subject: 18.3

Nelson, Robert M.; Ross, Lainie Friedman. In defense of a single standard of research risk for all children [editorial]. *Journal of Pediatrics* 2005 November; 147(5): 565-566. Subject: 18.5.2

Nelson, Sarah. Research with psychiatric patients: knowing their own minds? *In:* Smyth, Marie; Williamson,

Emma, eds. Researchers and Their 'Subjects': Ethics, Power, Knowledge and Consent. Bristol, UK: Policy Press; 2004: 91-103. Subject: 18.5.6

Nelson, William A. Defining ethics: how to determine whether a conflict falls under your ethics committee's purview. *Healthcare Executive* 2006 July-August; 21(4): 38-39. Subject: 9.6

Nelson, William A.; Pomerantz, Andrew S.; Weeks, William B. Response to commentaries on "Is there a rural ethics literature?" [letter]. *American Journal of Bioethics [Online]* 2006 July-August; 6(4): W46-W47. Subject: 2.1

Nelson, William; Lushkov, Gili; Pomerantz, Andrew; Weeks, William B. Rural health care ethics: is there a literature? *American Journal of Bioethics* 2006 March-April; 6(2): 44-50. Subject: 9.5.1

Nelson, William; Weeks, William B. Rural and non-rural differences in membership of the American Society of Bioethics and Humanities. *Journal of Medical Ethics* 2006 July; 32(7): 411-413. Subject: 9.6

Nenner, F. A patient's choice [letter]. *Journal of Medical Ethics* 2006 September; 32(9): 554-555. Subject: 8.3.4

Neri, Demetrio. On the concept of eugenics: preliminaries to a critical appraisal. *Cadernos de Saúde Pública* 1999; 15 (suppl. 1): 27-34. Subject: 15.5

Ness, April C. National Institutes of Health enacts final ethics regulations. *Journal of Biolaw and Business* 2006; 9(1): 50-51. Subject: 1.3.9

Nestler, Grit; Steinert, Ralf; Lippert, Hans; Reymond, Marc A. Using human samples in proteomics-based drug development: bioethical aspects. *Expert Review of Proteomics* 2004 June; 1(1): 77-86. Subject: 18.3

Neubauer, Richard L.; Cruess, Sylvia R.; Cruess, Richard L. Paranoia over privacy. *Annals of Internal Medicine* 2006 August 1; 145(3): 228-230. Subject: 8.4

Nevada. *Laws, statutes, etc.* An act relating to genetic information; providing that it is an unlawful employment practice for an employer, a labor organization or an employment agency to discriminate against a person based on genetic information; and providing other matters properly relating thereto [Approved: 9 June 1999]. Nevada: State Legislature, 1999. 2 p. [Online]. Accessed: http://www.leg.state.nv.us/70th/bills/SB/SB16_EN.pdf [2007 March 9]. Subject: 15.3

New Jersey. *Laws, statutes, etc.* An act concerning genetic testing and genetic privacy. New Jersey: Senate Bill 695; Public Laws 1996-1997, Chapter 126. 16 p. [Online]. Accessed http://www.njleg.state.nj.us/9697/Bills/PL96/126_.PDF [9 March 2007]. Subject: 15.1

New Jersey. *Laws, statutes, etc.* An act concerning human stem cell research and supplementing Title 26 of the Revised Statutes and Title 2C of the New Jersey Statutes [Approved: 2 January 2004]. New Jersey: Public Laws 2003, ch. 203. 2 p. [Online]. Accessed: http://www.

See SUBJECT HEADING KEY FOR SECTION II on inside back cover.

671

njleg.state.nj.us/2002/Bills/PL03/203_.PDF [2007 March 9]. Subject: 18.5.4

New Mexico. *Laws, statutes, etc.* An act relating to genetic information; prohibiting the use of genetic information in nonmedical contexts [Approved: 6 April 2005]. New Mexico: State Legislature, 2005. 4 p. [Online]. Accessed: http://legis.state.nm.us/Sessions/05%20Regular/ final/HB0183.pdf [2007 March 9]. Subject: 15.1

New York Academy of Medicine. Committee on Public Health and Committee on Medicine in Society. Statement and resolution on the definition of death [Approved: May 1984]. *Bulletin of the New York Academy of Medicine* 1984 November; 60(9): 955-958. Subject: 20.2.1

New, John G. "Aren't you lucky you have two mamas?": redefining parenthood in light of evolving reproductive technologies and social change. *Chicago-Kent Law Review* 2006; 81(2): 773-808. Subject: 14.1

Newdick, Chris; Derrett, Sarah. Access, equity and the roles of rights in health care. *Health Care Analysis: An International Journal of Health Philosophy and Policy* 2006 September; 14(3): 157-168. Subject: 9.2

Newdick, Christopher. 'Exceptional circumstances' — access to low priority treatments after the Herceptin case. *Clinical Ethics* 2006 December; 1(4): 205-208. Subject: 9.2

Newell, Christopher. Disability, bioethics, and rejected knowledge. *Journal of Medicine and Philosophy* 2006 June; 31(3): 269-283. Subject: 9.5.1

Newland, Shelby E. The role of bioethics in the international prescription drug market: economics and global justice. *Penn Bioethics Journal* 2006; 2(2): 8-12. Subject: 9.7

Newman, A.; Jones, R. Authorship for research papers: ethical and professional issues for short-term researchers. *Journal of Medical Ethics* 2006 July; 32(7): 420-423. Subject: 1.3.7

Newman, Elana; Risch, Elizabeth; Kassam-Adams, Nancy. Ethical issues in trauma-related research: a review. *Journal of Empirical Research on Human Research Ethics* 2006 September; 1(3): 29-46. Subject: 18.4

Newman, Janet; Vidler, Elizabeth. Discriminating customers, responsible patients, empowered users: consumerism and the modernisation of health care. *Journal of Social Policy* 2006 April; 35(2): 193-209. Subject: 9.1

Newson, Ainsley. Should parental refusals of newborn screening be respected? *CQ: Cambridge Quarterly of Healthcare Ethics* 2006 Spring; 15(2): 135-146. Subject: 15.2

Newson, Ainsley J.; Humphries, Steve E. Cascade testing in familial hypercholesterolaemia: how should family members be contacted? *European Journal of Human Genetics* 2005 April; 13(4): 401-408. Subject: 15.3

Ng, Mary Ann Chen; Macer, Darryl. Attitudes toward biotechnology and bioethics in the Philippines: a pilot study. *In:* Sleeboom, Margaret, ed. Genomics in Asia: A Clash of Bioethical Interests? New York: Kegan Paul; 2004: 255-279. Subject: 15.1

Nguyen, Lauren Thuy. The fate of stem cell research and a proposal for future legislative regulation. *Santa Clara Law Review* 2006; 46(2): 419-449. Subject: 18.5.4

Nguyen, Marisa; Ugarte, Carlos; Fuller, Ivonne; Haas, Gregory; Portenoy, Russell K. Access to care for chronic pain: racial and ethnic differences. *Journal of Pain* 2005 May; 6(5): 301-314. Subject: 4.4

Nguyen, Thuan. Science and journalism: never the two shall meet? [letter]. *CMAJ/JAMC: Canadian Medical Association Journal* 2006 April 11; 174(8): 1132. Subject: 11.1

Nguyen, Vinh-Kim. Antiretroviral globalism, biopolitics, and therapeutic citizenship. *In:* Ong, Aihwa; Collier, Stephen J., eds. Global Assemblages: Technology, Politics, and Ethics as Anthropological Problems. Malden, MA: Blackwell Pub.; 2005: 124-144. Subject: 5.1

Nichol, G.; Huszti, E.; Rokosh, J.; Dumbrell, A.; McGowan, J.; Becker, L. Impact of informed consent requirements on cardiac arrest research in the United States: exception from consent or from research? *Resuscitation* 2004 July; 62(1): 3-23. Subject: 18.3

Nicholas, Richard. Ethical considerations in allograft tissue transplantation: a surgeon's perspective. *Clinical Orthopaedics and Related Research* 2005 June; (435): 11-16. Subject: 19.5

Nicholl, David J.; Atkinson, Holly G.; Kalk, John; Hopkins, William; Elias, Elwyn; Siddiqui, Adnan; Cranford, Ronald E.; Sacks, Oliver. Forcefeeding and restraint of Guantanamo Bay hunger strikers [letter]. *Lancet* 2006 March 11-17; 367(9513): 811. Subject: 21.5

Nicholl, David J.; Wilks, Michael. Guantanamo: a call for action: good men need to do something [letter and reply]. *BMJ: British Medical Journal* 2006 April 8; 332(7545): 854-855. Subject: 21.5

Nichols, Alan. Foucault: power, madness and the symbol of the asylum. *Southwest Philosophy Review* 2000 January; 16(1): 133-140. Subject: 4.3

Nichols, Polly S.; Winslow, Gerald. The dating dentist. *General Dentistry* 2005 September-October; 53(5): 324-326. Subject: 7.4

Nichols, Polly S.; Winslow, Gerald. If dentists lack virtue. *General Dentistry* 2005 July-August; 53(4): 254-256. Subject: 4.1.1

Nickel, Philip J. Vulnerable populations in research: the case of the seriously ill. *Theoretical Medicine and Bioethics* 2006; 27(3): 245-264. Subject: 18.5.1

Nicolaides, Kypros H.; Chervenak, Frank A.; McCullough, Laurence B.; Avgidou, Kyriaki; Papageorghiou, Aris. Evidence-based obstetric ethics and informed decision-making by pregnant women about invasive diagnosis after first-trimester assessment of risk for trisomy 21. *American Journal of Obstetrics and Gynecology* 2005 August; 193(2): 322-326. Subject: 15.2

Nicolaidis, Christina. My mother's choice. *JAMA: The Journal of the American Medical Association* 2006 August 23-30; 296(8): 907-908. Subject: 20.7

Nicoletti, Toni A. Quality of care in evaluating the doctor-patient relationship. *American Journal of Bioethics* 2006 January-February; 6(1): 44-45. Subject: 8.1

Nicosia, Francis R. Nazi medicine. *In:* Mitcham, Carl, ed. Encyclopedia of Science, Technology, and Ethics. Farmington Hills, MI: Thomson/Gale, 2005: 1301-1303. Subject: 21.4

Nie, Jing-Bao. Feminist bioethics and the language of human rights in the Chinese context. *In:* Tong, Rosemarie; Donchin, Anne; Dodds, Susan, eds. Linking Visions: Feminist Bioethics, Human Rights, and the Developing World. Lanham, MD: Rowman and Littlefield Publishers; 2004: 73-88. Subject: 2.1

Nie, Jing- Bao. Mainland Chinese people's moral views and experiences of abortion: a brief report. *In:* Döring, Ole; Chen, Renbiao, eds. Advances in Chinese Medical Ethics: Chinese and International Perspectives. Hamburg: Institut für Asienkunde; 2002: 279-289. Subject: 12.5.2

Nie, Jing-Bao. The United States cover-up of Japanese wartime medical atrocities: complicity committed in the national interest and two proposals for contemporary action. *American Journal of Bioethics [Online]*. 2006 May-June; 6(3): W21-W33. Subject: 21.4

Niebrój, L. Genetic medicine: Polish deontological guidelines and the ethical practice of research studies with children. *Human Reproduction and Genetic Ethics: An International Journal* 2006; 12(1): 3-12. Subject: 18.5.2

Nielsen, Linda. Genetic testing and privacy: a European perspective = Pruebas genéticas y derecho a la intimidad: una perspectiva europea. *Law and the Human Genome Review = Revista de Derecho y Genoma Humano* 1996 January-June; (4): 59-76. Subject: 15.3

Nikku, Nina; Eriksson, Bengt Erik. Microethics in action. *Bioethics* 2006 August; 20(4): 169-179. Subject: 2.1

Nilson, Elizabeth G.; Fins, Joseph J. Reinvigorating ethics consultations: an impetus from the "quality" debate. *HEC (Healthcare Ethics Committee) Forum* 2006 December; 18(4): 298-304. Subject: 9.6

Nilssen, Even. Coercion and justice: a critical analysis of compulsory intervention towards adult substance abusers in Scandinavian social law. *International Journal of Social Welfare* 2005 April; 14(2): 134-144. Subject: 9.5.9

Nilstun, Tore; Hermerén, Göran. Human tissue samples and ethics — attitudes of the general public in Sweden to biobank research. *Medicine, Health Care and Philosophy* 2006; 9(1): 81-86. Subject: 15.1

Nilstun, Tore; Øvretveit, John. Ethical analysis. *In:* Westerholm, Peter; Nilstun, Tore; Øvretveit, John, eds. Practical Ethics in Occupational Health. San Francisco: Radcliffe Medical Press; 2004: 37-47. Subject: 16.3

Nilstun, Tore; Westerholm, Peter. Whistleblowing. *In:* Westerholm, Peter; Nilstun, Tore; Øvretveit, John, eds. Practical Ethics in Occupational Health. San Francisco: Radcliffe Medical Press; 2004: 283-290. Subject: 7.4

Niparko, John K.; Levine, Paul A.; Johns, Michael M.E. Our approach to addressing potential conflicts of interest [editorial]. *Archives of Otolaryngology—Head and Neck Surgery* 2005 November; 131(11): 943-944. Subject: 1.3.7

Nippert, Irmgard. International perspectives on abortion and genetic counselling. A European perspective. *In:* Döring, Ole; Chen, Renbiao, eds. Advances in Chinese Medical Ethics: Chinese and International Perspectives. Hamburg: Institut für Asienkunde; 2002: 141-158. Subject: 15.2

Nisbet, Matthew C. The polls — trends: public opinion about stem cell research and human cloning. *Public Opinion Quarterly* 2004 Spring; 68(1): 131-154. Subject: 18.5.4

Nissen, Steven. An audience with . . . Steven Nissen [interview]. *Nature Reviews Drug Discovery* 2006 February; 5(2): 98. Subject: 9.7

Niu, Huei-Chih. Human subject research — ethical and legal approaches for compensation for research induced injury in Taiwan. *In:* Sang-yong, Song; Young-Mo, Koo; Macer, Darryl R.J., eds. Asian Bioethics in the 21st Century. Christchurch, NZ: Eubios Ethics Institute, 2002: 6-15. Subject: 18.1

Nixon, Stephanie A. Critical public health ethics and Canada's role in global health. *Canadian Journal of Public Health* 2006 January-February; 97(1): 32-34. Subject: 9.1

Nnodim, J.O.; Osuji, C.U. Comparison of medical and non-medical student attitudes to social issues in medicine. *Medical Education* 1995 July; 29(4): 273-277. Subject: 7.2

Noble, David W. Preventing scientific fraud [letter]. *Annals of Internal Medicine* 2006 September 19; 145(6): 472. Subject: 1.3.9

Nolan, Carmel. Xenotransplantation — Law and Ethics, by Sheila McLean and Laura Williamson [book review]. *Genomics, Society and Policy* 2006 December; 2(3): 142-144. Subject: 19.1

Nolan, Marie T.; Hughes, Mark; Narendra, Derek Paul; Sood, Johanna R.; Terry, Peter B.; Astrow, Alan B.; Kub, Joan; Thompson, Richard E.; Sulmasy, Daniel P. When patients lack capacity: the roles that patients with terminal diagnoses would choose for their physicians and loved ones in making medical decisions. *Journal of*

See SUBJECT HEADING KEY FOR SECTION II on inside back cover.

Pain and Symptom Management 2005 October; 30(4): 342-353. Subject: 20.4.1

Noland, Lynn R. Informing patients of the risks and benefits of hormone replacement therapy: nephrologists' ethical obligation. *Advances in Chronic Kidney Disease* 2004 October; 11(4): 387-390. Subject: 9.5.5

Noll, Steven. The public face of Southern institutions for the "feeble-minded". *Public Historian* 2005 Spring; 27(2): 25-41. Subject: 17.7

Nõmper, Ants. Estonian Human Research Act and its implementation. *In:* Glasa, J., ed. Ethics of Human Genetics: Challenges of the (Post) Genomic Era. Bratislava, Slovak Republic: Charis [and] IMEB Foundation; 2002: 99-104. Subject: 15.1

Nõmper, Ants. What is wrong with using anonymized data and tissue for research purposes? *In:* Árnason, Gardar; Nordal, Salvör; Árnason, Vilhjálmur, eds. Blood and Data: Ethical, Legal and Social Aspects of Human Genetic Databases. Reykjavík: University of Iceland Press; 2004: 121-126. Subject: 15.1

Nõmper, Ants; Kruuv, Krista. The Estonian Genome Project. *In:* Sándor, Judit, ed. Society and Genetic Information: Codes and Laws in the Genetic Era. Budapest, Hungary; New York: CEU Press; 2003: 213-224. Subject: 15.1

Norbergh, Karl-Gustaf; Helin, Yvonne; Dahl, Annika; Hellzén, Ove; Asplund, Kenneth. Nurses' attitudes towards people with dementia: the semantic differential technique. *Nursing Ethics* 2006 May; 13(3): 264-274. Subject: 17.1

Nord, Erik. Concerns for the worse off: fair innings versus severity. *Social Science and Medicine* 2005 January; 60(2): 257-263. Subject: 4.4

Nord, Erik. Utilitarian decision analysis of informed consent. *American Journal of Bioethics* 2006 May-June; 6(3): 65-67; discussion W51- W53. Subject: 2.1

Nordal, Salvör. Privacy in public. *In:* Árnason, Gardar; Nordal, Salvör; Árnason, Vilhjálmur, eds. Blood and Data: Ethical, Legal and Social Aspects of Human Genetic Databases. Reykjavík: University of Iceland Press; 2004: 249-254. Subject: 8.4

Nordby, Halvor. The analytic-synthetic distinction and conceptual analyses of basic health concepts. *Medicine, Health Care and Philosophy* 2006; 9(2): 169-180. Subject: 4.2

Nordin, Karin; Björk, Jan; Berglund, Gunilla. Factors influencing intention to obtain a genetic test for a hereditary disease in an affected group and in the general public. *Preventive Medicine* 2004 December; 39(6): 1107-1114. Subject: 15.3

Norheim, Ole Frithjof. Soft paternalism and the ethics of shared electronic patient records [editorial]. *BMJ: British Medical Journal* 2006 July 1; 333(7557): 2-3. Subject: 8.3.1

Norman, Douglas J. The kidney transplant wait-list: allocation of patients to a limited supply of organs. *Seminars in Dialysis* 2005 November-December; 18(6): 456-459. Subject: 19.3

Norman, R.; Sellman, D.; Warner, C. Mental capacity, good practice and the cyclical consent process in research involving vulnerable people. *Clinical Ethics* 2006 December; 1(4): 228-233. Subject: 18.3

Normile, Dennis. Panel discredits findings of Tokyo University team [news]. *Science* 2006 February 3; 311(5761): 595. Subject: 1.3.9

Normile, Dennis; Vogel, Gretchen; Couzin, Jennifer. South Korean team's remaining human stem cell claim demolished [news]. *Science* 2006 January 13; 311(5758): 156-157. Subject: 14.5

North American Primary Care Research Group; Society of Teachers of Family Medicine; Hueston, William J.; Mainous, Aarch G., III; Weiss, Barry D.; Macaulay, Aann C.; Hickner, John; Sherwood, Roger A. Protecting participants in family medicine research: a consensus statement on improving research integrity and participants' safety in educational research, community-based participatory research, and practice network research. *Family Medicine* 2006 February; 38(2): 116-120. Subject: 18.3

Northoff, Georg. Neuroscience of decision making and informed consent: an investigation in neuroethics. *Journal of Medical Ethics* 2006 February; 32(2): 70-73. Subject: 8.3.1

Nortvedt, Per. Medical ethics manual: does it serve its purpose? *Journal of Medical Ethics* 2006 March; 32(3): 159-160. Subject: 2.1

Norwegian Medical Association. Guidelines on palliative sedation. *In:* Tännsjö, Torbjörn, ed. Terminal Sedation: Euthanasia in Disguise? Boston: Kluwer Academic Publishers; 2004: 132-133. Subject: 20.4.1

Nosarka, S.; Kruger, T.F. Surrogate motherhood [editorial]. *South African Medical Journal* 2005 December; 95(12): 942, 944, 946. Subject: 14.2

Nosowsky, Rachel; Giordano, Thomas J. The Health Insurance Portability and Accountability Act of 1996 (HIPAA) privacy rule: implications for clinical research. *Annual Review of Medicine* 2006; 57: 575-590. Subject: 8.4

Nosse, Larry J.; Sagiv, Lilach. Theory-based study of the basic values of 565 physical therapists. *Physical Therapy* 2005 September; 85(9): 834-850. Subject: 4.1.1

Nötzoldt, Peter; Walther, Peter Th. The Prussian Academy of Sciences during the Third Reich. *Minerva: A Review of Science, Learning and Policy* 2004; 42(4): 421-444. Subject: 21.4

Subject = NRCBL Primary Classification Number; see inside front cover.

Novotny, Thomas E.; Carlin, D. Ethical and legal aspects of global tobacco control. *Tobacco Control* 2005 August; 14(Supplement 2): ii26-ii30. Subject: 9.5.9

Nowak, Kristin S.; Bankert, Elizabeth A.; Nelson, Robert M. Reforming the oversight of multi-site clinical research: a review of two possible solutions. *Accountability in Research* 2006 January-March; 13(1): 11-24. Subject: 18.2

Nowak, Rachel. Ear implant success sparks culture war. *New Scientist* 2006 November 25-December 1; 192(2579): 16-17. Subject: 9.5.7

Nowak, Rachel. Methuselah moms. *New Scientist* 2006 October 21-27; 192(2574): 46-51. Subject: 14.4

Nowak, Rachel. Not brain-dead, but ripe for transplant. *New Scientist* 2006 August 5-11; 191(2563): 6-7. Subject: 19.5

Nowak, Rachel. When looks can kill: the nip and tuck generation faces a danger far worse than the operation going wrong. *New Scientist* 2006 October 21-27; 192(2574): 18-21. Subject: 9.5.1

Nuffield Council on Bioethics. The ethics of research related to healthcare in developing countries: a follow-up discussion paper. London: Nuffield Council on Bioethics 2005 March 17; 128p. [Online] Accessed: http://www.nuffieldbioethics.org/fileLibrary/pdf/HRRDC_Follow-up_Discussion_Paper001.pdf [2006 September 14]. Subject: 18.5.9

Nuffield Council on Bioethics. Forensic use of bioinformation: ethical issues. Consultation paper. London: Nuffield Council on Bioethics, 2006 November; 28 p. [Online]. Accessed: http://www.nuffieldbioethics.org/fileLibrary/pdf/Consultation_FINAL001.pdf [2006 November 29]. Subject: 15.1

Nunes, Rui. Deafness, genetics and dysgenics. *Medicine, Health Care, and Philosophy* 2006; 9(1): 25-31. Subject: 15.5

Nunnally, Allen C. Intellectual property perspectives in pharmacogenomics. *Jurimetrics* 2006 Spring; 46(3): 249-262. Subject: 15.8

Nusbaum, Julie. Childbirth in modern Athens: the transition from homebirth to hospital birth. *Penn Bioethics Journal* 2006; 2(2): 33-37. Subject: 9.5.5

Nussbaum, Martha C. Long-term care and social justice: a challenge to conventional ideas of the social contract. *In:* Ethical Choices in Long-Term Care. What Does Justice Require? Geneva: World Health Organization, 2002. pp. 31-65 [Online]. Accessed: http://www.who.int/mediacentre/news/notes/ethical_choices.pdf [2006 September 25]. Subject: 9.2

Nussbaum, Martha C. The moral status of animals. *Chronicle of Higher Education* 2006 February 3; 52(22): B6-B8. Subject: 22.1

Nutt, David J. Informed consent — a new approach to drug regulation? [editorial]. *Journal of Psychopharmacology* 2006 January; 20(1): 3-4. Subject: 9.7

Nwomeh, Benedict C.; Waller, Andrea L.; Caniano, Donna A.; Kelleher, Kelly J. Informed consent for emergency surgery in infants and children. *Journal of Pediatric Surgery* 2005 August; 40(8): 1320-1325. Subject: 8.3.2

Nyanzi, Stella; Nyanzi, Barbara; Bessie, Kalina. "Abortion? That's for women!" Narratives and experiences of commercial motorbike riders in south-western Uganda. *African Journal of Reproductive Health* 2005 April; 9(1): 142-161. Subject: 21.1

Nyberg, Kara; Carter, Barrie J.; Chen, Theresa; Dunbar, Cynthia; Flotte, Terrence R.; Rose, Stephen; Rosenblum, Daniel; Simek, Stephanie L.; Wilson, Carolyn. Workshop on long-term follow-up of participants in human gene transfer research. *Molecular Therapy* 2004 December; 10(6): 976-980. Subject: 15.4

Nygren, Sara Lind. Organ donation by incompetent patients: a hybrid approach. *University of Chicago Legal Forum* 2006: 471-502. Subject: 19.5

Nylenna, Magne; Horton, Richard. Research misconduct: learning the lessons. *Lancet* 2006 November 25-December 1; 368(9550): 1856. Subject: 1.3.9

Nylenna, Magne; Simonsen, Sigmund. Scientific misconduct: a new approach to prevention. *Lancet* 2006 June 10-16; 367(9526): 1882-1884. Subject: 1.3.9

Nys, Herman. Comparative health law and the harmonization of patients' rights in Europe. *European Journal of Health Law* 2001 December; 8(4): 317-331. Subject: 9.2

Nys, Herman. A presentation of the Belgian Act on euthanasia against the background of Dutch euthanasia law. *European Journal of Health Law* 2003 September; 10(3): 239-255. Subject: 20.7

Nys, Herman. Recent developments in health law in Belgium. *European Journal of Health Law* 2006 June; 13(2): 95-99. Subject: 20.5.1

Nys, Herman. Towards an international treaty on human rights and biomedicine? Some reflections inspired by UNESCO's Universal Declaration on Bioethics and Human Rights [editorial]. *European Journal of Health Law* 2006 April; 13(1): 5-8. Subject: 2.1

Nys, Thomas R.V.; Nys, Maurits G. Psychiatry under pressure: reflections on psychiatry's drift towards a reductionist biomedical conception of mental illness. *Medicine, Health Care and Philosophy* 2006; 9(1): 107-115. Subject: 4.3

O

O'Brien, Linda A. Establishing and educating a long-term care regional ethics committee: the NJ model.

See SUBJECT HEADING KEY FOR SECTION II on inside back cover.

675

Journal of the American Medical Directors Association 2005 January-February; 6(1): 66-67. Subject: 9.6

O'Brien, Richard L. Moral priorities in a teaching hospital: commentary. *Hastings Center Report* 2006 November-December; 36(6): 13, 14. Subject: 7.2

O'Carroll, R.E.; Whiten, S.; Jackson, D.; Sinclair, D.W. Assessing the emotional impact of cadaver dissection on medical students. *Medical Education* 2002 June; 36(6): 550-554. Subject: 7.2

O'Connor, Mat; Hulatt, Ian; Drake, Linda; Brown, Jane. Means of consent. *Nursing Standard* 2004 May 5; 18(34): 20. Subject: 19.5

O'Day, Ken. Intrinsic value and investment. *Utilitas* 1999 July; 11(2): 194-214. Subject: 12.4.2

O'Donovan, Katherine. Taking a neutral stance on the legal protection of the fetus: Vo v. France. *Medical Law Review* 2006 Spring; 14(1): 115-123. Subject: 4.4

O'Dowd, Adrian. Doctors charged with ensuring dignity for older patients [news]. *BMJ: British Medical Journal* 2006 April 29; 332(7548): 993. Subject: 9.5.2

O'Dowd, Adrian. Society issues guidance on IVF [news]. *BMJ: British Medical Journal* 2006 September 9; 333(7567): 517. Subject: 14.4

O'Keefe, Eileen; Chinouya, Martha. Global migrants, gendered tradition, and human rights: black Africans and HIV in the United Kingdom. *In:* Tong, Rosemarie; Donchin, Anne; Dodds, Susan, eds. Linking Visions: Feminist Bioethics, Human Rights, and the Developing World. Lanham, MD: Rowman and Littlefield Publishers; 2004: 217-234. Subject: 9.5.6

O'Lonergan, Theresa; Zodrow, John J. Pediatric assent: subject protection issues among adolescent females enrolled in research. *Journal of Law, Medicine and Ethics* 2006 Summer; 34(2): 451-459. Subject: 18.5.2

O'Malley, Patricia. The undertreatment of pain: ethical and legal implications for the Clinical Nurse Specialist. *Clinical Nurse Specialist* 2005 September-October; 19(5): 236-237. Subject: 4.4

O'Mathúna, Dónal P. Human dignity in the Nazi era: implications for contemporary bioethics [debate]. *BMC Medical Ethics* 2006; 7(2): 12 p. [Online]. Accessed: http://www.biomedcentral.com/bmcmedethics/ [2006 September 7]. Subject: 21.4

O'Neill, Jill Brace. Professional boundaries in pediatric nursing practice. *Journal of Pediatric Health Care* 1998 July-August; 12(4): 225-227. Subject: 8.1

O'Neill, Onora. Accountability, trust and informed consent in medical practice and research. *Clinical Medicine* 2004 May-June; 4(3): 269-276. Subject: 8.3.1

O'Neill, Onora. DNA and ethics. *In:* Krude, Torsten, ed. DNA: Changing Science and Society. Cambridge, UK;

New York: Cambridge University Press; 2004: 166-182. Subject: 15.1

O'Reilly, R.L.; Gray, J.E. Most important lesson from Starson ignored in article. *Health Law in Canada* 2006 November; 27(2): 36-40. Subject: 17.7

O'Reilly, Richard L.; Keegan, David L.; Corring, Deborah; Shrikhande, Satish; Natarajan, Dhanapal. A qualitative analysis of the use of community treatment orders in Saskatchewan. *International Journal of Law and Psychiatry* 2006 November-December; 29(6): 516-524. Subject: 17.1

O'Rourke, Dennis H.; Hayes, M. Geoffrey; Carlyle, Shawn. The consent process and aDNA research: contrasting approaches in North America. *In:* Turner, Trudy R. ed. Biological Anthropology and Ethics: From Repatriation to Genetic Identity. Albany, NY: State University of New York Press; 2005: 231-240. Subject: 15.1

O'Rourke, Joanne Mcfarland; Roehrig, Stephen; Heeringa, Steven G.; Reed, Beth Glover; Birdsall, William C.; Overcashier, Margaret; Zidar, Kelly. Solving problems of disclosure risk while retaining key analytical uses of publicly released microdata. *Journal of Empirical Research on Human Research Ethics* 2006 September; 1(3): 63-84. Subject: 8.3.1

O'Rourke, Kevin D. The embryo as person. *National Catholic Bioethics Quarterly* 2006 Summer; 6(2): 241-251. Subject: 4.4

O'Rourke, Kevin. Reflections on the papal allocution concerning care for persistent vegetative state patients. *Christian Bioethics* 2006 April; 12(1): 83-97. Subject: 20.5.1

O'Sullivan Burchard, Dorothee J.H. Ethos, ethics, and endeavors: new horizons in family nursing. *Journal of Family Nursing* 2005 November; 11(4): 354-370. Subject: 4.1.3

O'Toole, Brian. St. Louis system has corporate ethics committee. *Health Progress* 2006 March-April; 87(2): 42-45. Subject: 9.6

Oakley, Ann. Eugenics, Social Medicine and the Career of Richard Titmuss in Britain 1935-50. *British Journal of Sociology* 1991 June; 42(2): 165-194. Subject: 15.5

Oakley, Justin. Monash Centre for Human Bioethics: a brief history. *Monash Bioethics Review* 2006 January; 25(1): 85-88. Subject: 2.2

Oakley, Justin. Reproductive cloning and arguments from potential. *Monash Bioethics Review* 2006 January; 25(1): 42-47. Subject: 14.5

Oaks, Laury. Antiabortion positions and young women's life plans in contemporary Ireland. *Social Science and Medicine* 2003 May; 56(9): 1973-1986. Subject: 12.3

Oaks, Laury. Fetal spirithood and fetal personhood: the cultural construction of abortion in Japan. *Women's Studies*

International Forum 1994 September-October; 17(5): 511-523. Subject: 12.5.1

Oberdorfer, Kevin L.J. The lessons of Greenberg: informed consent and the protection of tissue sources' research interests. *Georgetown Law Journal* 2004 November; 93(1): 365-394. Subject: 18.3

Oberlander, Sarah E.; Spencer, Robert J. Graduate students and the culture of authorship. *Ethics and Behavior* 2006; 16(3): 217-232. Subject: 1.3.7

Oberle, Kathleen; Allen, Marion. Ethical considerations for nurses in clinical trials. *Nursing Ethics* 2006 March; 13(2): 180-186. Subject: 18.2

Obi, Samuel N.; Ifebunandu, Ngozi A. Consequences of HIV testing without consent. *International Journal of STD and AIDS* 2006 February; 17(2): 93-96. Subject: 9.5.6

Obiglio, Hugo. Education and Bioethics. *Dolentium Hominum* 1994; 9(3): 53-54. Subject: 2.3

Oderberg, David S. Towards and natural law critique of genetic engineering. *In:* Athanassoulis, Nafsika, ed. Philosophical Reflections on Medical Ethics. New York: Palgrave Macmillan; 2005: 109-134. Subject: 15.1

Odom, Lamar; Garcia, Anthony; Milburn, Pamela. The ethics of capping non-economic damages to control rising healthcare costs: panacea or false and misleading practice? *Leadership in Health Services* 2005; 18(3): i-xi. Subject: 8.5

Oeseburg, Barth; Abma, Tineke A. Care as a mutual endeavour: experiences of a multiple sclerosis patient and her healthcare professionals. *Medicine, Health Care and Philosophy* 2006; 9(3): 349-357. Subject: 8.1

Offit, Kenneth; Sagi, Michal; Hurley, Karen. Preimplantation genetic diagnosis for cancer syndromes. *JAMA: The Journal of the American Medical Association* 2006 December 13; 296(22): 2727-2730. Subject: 15.2

Ogbogu, Ubaka. A review of pressing ethical issues relevant to stem cell translational research. *Health Law Review* 2006; 14(3): 39-43. Subject: 18.5.4

Ogden, Russel. End-of-life summit in Madrid. *Canadian HIV/AIDS Policy and Law Newsletter* 1997-1998 Winter; 3(4)-4(1): 18. Subject: 9.5.6

Ogden, Russel. Ethical review in community-based HIV/AIDS research. *Canadian HIV/AIDS Policy and Law Newsletter* 1999 Fall-Winter; 5(1): 39-40. Subject: 9.5.6

Ogden, Russel. Euthanasia law and policy. *Canadian HIV/AIDS Policy and Law Newsletter* 1995 January; 1(2): 9-10. Subject: 20.5.1

Ogden, Russel. Euthanasia: a reply. *Canadian HIV/AIDS Policy and Law Newsletter* 1996 April; 2(3): 20-22. Subject: 20.5.1

Ogden, Russel. The uncloseting of AIDS-related euthanasia [news]. *Canadian HIV/AIDS Policy and Law Newsletter* 1994 October; 1(1): 14-15. Subject: 9.5.6

Oguamanam, Chidi. From rivalry to rapprochement: biomedicine, complementary alternative medicine (CAM) at ethical crossroads. *HEC (Healthcare Ethics Committee) Forum* 2006 September; 18(3): 245-264. Subject: 4.1.1

Ogundiran, Temidayo O. Africa must come on board with the genomics bandwagon. *Genomics, Society and Policy* 2005 December; 1(3): 66-77. Subject: 15.1

Oguz, N. Yasemin. Research ethics committees in developing countries and informed consent: with special reference to Turkey. *Journal of Laboratory and Clinical Medicine* 2003 May; 141(5): 292-296. Subject: 18.2

Ohio Solid Organ Transplantation Consortium. Substance abuse addendum to patient selection criteria. Worthington, Ohio: Ohio Solid Organ Transplantation Consortium, n.d. [2005?]: 2 p. [Online]. Accessed: http://www.osotc.org/1saa.htm [2006 August 15]. Subject: 19.6

Okie, Susan. Access before approval — a right to take experimental drugs? *New England Journal of Medicine* 2006 August 3; 355(5): 437-440. Subject: 9.7

Okie, Susan. Brave new face. *New England Journal of Medicine* 2006 March 2; 354(9): 889-894. Subject: 19.1

Okie, Susan. Health officials debate ethics of placebo use: medical researchers say guidelines would impair some studies. *Washington Post* 2000 November 24; p. A3. Subject: 18.3

Okie, Susan. Single-cell storm. *New England Journal of Medicine* 2006 October 19; 355(16): 1634-1635. Subject: 18.5.4

Okie, Susan. Stem-cell politics. *New England Journal of Medicine* 2006 October 19; 355(16): 1633-1637. Subject: 18.5.4

Okon, Tomasz R. "Nobody understands": on a cardinal phenomenon of palliative care. *Journal of Medicine and Philosophy* 2006 February; 31(1): 13-46. Subject: 20.4.1

Olakanmi, Ololade. Xenotransplantation: a rational choice? *Penn Bioethics Journal* 2006; 2(2): 38-41. Subject: 19.1

Olbourne, Norman A. The influence of Rogers v. Whitaker on the practice of cosmetic plastic surgery. *Journal of Law and Medicine* 1998 May; 5(4): 334-347. Subject: 8.3.1

Oldham, Paul; Cutter, Anthony Mark. Mapping global status and trends in patent activity for biological and genetic material. *Genomics, Society and Policy* 2006 August; 2(2): 62-91. Subject: 15.8

Oleson, Christopher. Nature, "naturalism", and the immorality of contraception: a critique of Fr. Rhonheimer on condom use and contraceptive intent. *National Catholic Bioethics Quarterly* 2006 Winter; 6(4): 719-721. Subject: 11.1

See SUBJECT HEADING KEY FOR SECTION II on inside back cover.

677

Olick, Robert S. Rationing the flu vaccine. *Journal of Public Health Management and Practice* 2005 July-August; 11(4): 373-374. Subject: 9.4

Olivennes, Francois. Do children born after assisted reproductive technology have a higher incidence of birth defects? *Fertility and Sterility* 2005 November; 84(5): 1325-1326. Subject: 14.4

Oliver, David. Ethics committees: current research ethics forms are an over-reaction that will stifle research [letter]. *BMJ: British Medical Journal* 2006 March 25; 332(7543): 730. Subject: 18.2

Oliver, J. Eric. The politics of pathology: how obesity became an epidemic disease. *Perspectives in Biology and Medicine* 2006 Autumn; 49(4): 611-627. Subject: 9.1

Oliver, Jeffrey. The myth of Thomas Szasz. *New Atlantis* 2006 Summer; 13: 68-84. Subject: 17.1

Olsan, Tobie H. Corporatization and the institutional aspects of morality in home care. *In:* Dinkins, Christine Sorrell; Sorrell, Jeanne Merkle, eds. Listening to the Whispers: Re-Thinking Ethics in Healthcare. Madison, WI: University of Wisconsin Press; 2006: 10-68. Subject: 9.1

Olsen, Douglas P. Should RNs be forced to get the flu vaccine? *AJN: American Journal of Nursing* 2006 October; 106(10): 76-80. Subject: 8.3.4

Olsen, Douglas P.; Dixon, Jane Karpe; Grey, Margaret; Deshefy-Longhi, Terry; Demarest, Jo Cecille. Privacy concerns of patients and nurse practitioners in primary care — an APRNet study. *Journal of the American Academy of Nurse Practitioners* 2005 December; 17(12): 527-534. Subject: 8.4

Olsen, J. Mark. Depression, SSRIs and the supposed obligation to suffer mentally. *Kennedy Institute of Ethics Journal* 2006 September; 16(3): 283-303. Subject: 17.4

Olsen, Jan Abel; Richardson, Jeff; Dolan, Paul; Menzel, Paul. Response to "On the relevance of personal characteristics in setting health care priorities". *Social Science and Medicine* 2005 April; 60(8): 1665-1666. Subject: 9.3.1

Olson, Karen L.; Grannis, Shaun J.; Mandl, Kenneth D. Privacy protection versus cluster detection in spatial epidemiology. *American Journal of Public Health* 2006 November; 96(11): 2002-2008. Subject: 8.4

Olson, L.G.; Terry, W. The missing future tense in medical narrative. *Medical Humanities* 2006 December; 32(2): 88-91. Subject: 8.1

Olson, Maynard V. The Human Genome Project: a player's perspective. *Journal of Molecular Biology* 2002 June 14; 319(4): 931-942. Subject: 15.10

Olson, Michael M.; Sandor, M. Kay; Sierpina, Victor S.; Vanderpool, Harold Y.; Dayao, Patricia. Mind, body, and spirit: family physicians' beliefs, attitudes, and practices regarding the integration of patient spirituality into

medical care. *Journal of Religion and Health* 2006 Summer; 45(2): 234-247. Subject: 7.1

Olson, Sandra F. American Academy of Neurology development of a position on stem cell research [editorial]. *Neurology* 2005 May 24; 64(10): 1674. Subject: 18.5.4

Olsson, Håkan. The commercialization of genes: a patent on breast cancer genes as pilot case. *In:* Lundin, Susanne; Åkesson, Lynn, eds. Gene Technology and Economy. Lund: Nordic Academic Press; 2002: 42-51. Subject: 15.8

Olthuis, Gert; Dekkers, Wim; Leget, Carlo; Vogelaar, Paul. The caring relationship in hospice care: an analysis based on the ethics of the caring conversation. *Nursing Ethics* 2006 January; 13(1): 29-40. Subject: 20.4.1

Olusanya, B.O.; Luxon, L.M.; Wirz, S.L. Ethical issues in screening for hearing impairment in newborns in developing countries. *Journal of Medical Ethics* 2006 October; 32(10): 588-591. Subject: 9.5.7

Omer, Saad B.; Pan, William K.Y.; Halsey, Neal A.; Stokley, Shannon; Moulton, Lawrence H.; Navar, Ann Marie; Pierce, Mathew; Salmon, Daniel A. Nonmedical exemptions to school immunization requirements: secular trends and association of state policies with pertussis incidence. *JAMA: The Journal of the American Medical Association* 2006 October 11; 296(14): 1757-1763. Subject: 9.5.1

Onay, Ozan. The true ramifications of genetic criminality research for free will in the criminal justice system. *Genomics, Society and Policy* 2006 May; 2(1): 80-91. Subject: 15.1

Onder, Robert F. The ethics of placebo-controlled trials: the case of asthma. *Journal of Allergy and Clinical Immunology* 2005 June; 115(6): 1228-1234. Subject: 18.3

Onvomaha Tindana, Paulina; Kass, Nancy; Akweongo, Patricia. The informed consent process in a rural African setting: a case study of the Kassena-Nankana district of Northern Ghana. *IRB: Ethics and Human Research* 2006 May-June; 28(3): 1-6. Subject: 18.3

Onwu, Martin U. The relevance of the principle of cooperation for the ethical debate on embryonic stem cell research and therapies. *Health Care Ethics USA* 2006; 14(1): E5 [Online]. Accessed: http://chce.slu.edu/Partnerships_HCE_Intro.html [2006 November 17]. Subject: 18.5.4

Onwuteaka-Philipsen, Bregje D.; Fisher, Susanne; Cartwright, Colleen; Deliens, Luc; Miccinesi, Guido; Norup, Michael; Nilstun, Tore; van der Heide, Agnes; van der Wal, Gerrit. End-of-life decision making in Europe and Australia. *Archives of Internal Medicine* 2006 April 24; 166(8): 921-929. Subject: 20.5.1

Opel, Douglas J.; Diekema, Douglas S. The case of A.R.: the ethics of sibling donor bone marrow transplantation revisited. *Journal of Clinical Ethics* 2006 Fall; 17(3): 207-219. Subject: 19.5

Oppenheim, D.; Geoerger, B.; Hartmann, O. Ethical issues in pediatric oncology phase I-II trials based on a mother's point of view. *Bulletin du Cancer* 2005 November; 92(11): E57-E60. Subject: 18.5.2

Oppenheim, Elliott B. A doctor's perspective on what the law should be for end-of-life issues. *Journal of Medicine and Law* 1997 Fall; 2(1): 11-18. Subject: 20.5.1

Orenstein, Walter A.; Hinman, Alan R. The immunization system in the United States — the role of school immunization laws. *Vaccine* 1999; 17(Supplement 3): S19-S24. Subject: 9.5.1

Organization for Economic Cooperation and Development [OECD]. Guidance document on the recognition, assessment, and use of clinical signs as humane endpoints for experimental animals used in safety evaluations. Paris: Organization for Economic Cooperation and Development, OECD Environmental Health and Safety Publications 2000 December 20; (19) : 39 p. [Online]. Accessed: http://www.olis.oecd.org/olis/2000doc.nsf/LinkTo/env-jm-mono(2000)7 [2006 October 4]. Subject: 22.2

Oriola, Taiwo A. The propriety of expert ethics testimony in the courtroom: a disclosure. *Journal of Philosophy, Science and Law* 2006 December 11; 6: 1-25. Subject: 7.3

Orlowski, J.P.; Hein, S.; Christensen, J.A.; Meinke, R.; Sincich, T. Why doctors use or do not use ethics consultation. *Journal of Medical Ethics* 2006 September; 32(9): 499-502. Subject: 9.6

Ormond, Kelly E. Disclosing genetic research results: examples from practice. *American Journal of Bioethics* 2006 November-December; 6(6): 30-32; author reply W10-W12. Subject: 15.1

Orobitg, Gemma; Salazar, Carles. The gift of motherhood: egg donation in a Barcelona infertility clinic. *Ethnos* 2005 March; 70(1): 31-52. Subject: 14.4

Orr, Daniel L., II; Curtis, William J. Obtaining written informed consent for the administration of local anesthetic in dentistry. *JADA: Journal of the American Dental Association* 2005 November; 136(11): 1568-1571. Subject: 8.3.1

Orr, Robert D. Clinical ethics consultation: to intubate or not to intubate — Part I of a series. *Today's Christian Doctor* 2006 Fall; 37(3): 30-31. Subject: 9.6

Orr, Robert D. Rules is rules. *American Journal of Bioethics* 2006 May-June; 6(3): 40-41. Subject: 18.6

Orrell, Jon M. To opt in or out of electronic patient records?: integration technology is key to success [letter]. *BMJ: British Medical Journal* 2006 July 15; 333(7559): 146. Subject: 8.3.1

Orton, Colin; Marshall, Christopher; Hendee, William R. Results of publicly-funded scientific research should be immediately available without cost to the public [editorial]. *Medical Physics* 2005 November; 32(11): 3231-3233. Subject: 18.1

Orzalesi, Marcello; Cuttini, Marina. Ethical considerations in neonatal respiratory care. *Biology of the Neonate* 2005; 87(4): 345-353. Subject: 20.5.2

Osberg, Brendan. For your first born child: an ethical defense of the exploitation argument against commercial surrogacy. *Penn Bioethics Journal* 2006; 2(2): 42-45. Subject: 14.2

Osseweijer, Patricia. A new model for science communication that takes ethical considerations into account: the three E-model: entertainment, emotion, and education [letter]. *Science and Engineering Ethics* 2006 October; 12(4): 591-593. Subject: 1.3.9

Ossorio, Pilar N. About face: forensic genetic testing for race and visible traits. *Journal of Law, Medicine and Ethics* 2006 Summer; 34(2): 277-292. Subject: 15.1

Ossorio, Pilar N. Letting the gene out of the bottle: a comment on returning individual research results to participants. *American Journal of Bioethics* 2006 November-December; 6(6): 24-25; author reply W10-W12. Subject: 15.1

Ost, Suzanne. Doctors and nurses of death: a case study of eugenically motivated killing under the Nazi 'euthanasia' programme. *Liverpool Law Review* 2006 April; 27(1): 5-30. Subject: 15.5

Otlowski, Margaret. Essentially yours: the protection of human genetic information in Australia. *GeneWatch* 2006 January-February; 19(1): 9-12. Subject: 15.3

Otlowski, Margaret. Genetic discrimination: meeting the challenges of an emerging issue [forum]. *University of New South Wales Law Journal* 2003; 26(3): 764-769. Subject: 15.3

Otlowski, Margaret F.A.; Williamson, Robert. Ethical and legal issues and the "new genetics". *Medical Journal of Australia* 2003 June 2; 178(11): 582-585. Subject: 15.3

Otto, Sheila. Getting from here to there. *American Journal of Bioethics* 2006 July-August; 6(4): 19-21. Subject: 7.2

Outterson, Kevin. Tragedy and remedy: reparations for disparities in black health. *DePaul Journal of Health Care Law* 2005; 9(1): 735-791. Subject: 9.5.4

Overberg, Kenneth R. Medical ethics. *In his:* Conscience in Conflict: How to Make Moral Choices. 3rd ed. revised. Cincinnati, OH: St. Anthony Messenger Press; 2006: 79-108. Subject: 2.1

Øvretveit, John. Ethical occupational health management and organisation. *In:* Westerholm, Peter; Nilstun, Tore; Øvretveit, John, eds. Practical Ethics in Occupational Health. San Francisco: Radcliffe Medical Press; 2004: 307-319. Subject: 16.3

Øvretveit, John. Ethics, research-informed practice and quality improvement. *In:* Westerholm, Peter; Nilstun, Tore; Øvretveit, John, eds. Practical Ethics in Occupa-

---

See SUBJECT HEADING KEY FOR SECTION II on inside back cover.

679

tional Health. San Francisco: Radcliffe Medical Press; 2004: 23-36. Subject: 16.3

Owen, Adrian M.; Coleman, Martin R.; Boly, Melanie; Davis, Matthew H.; Laureys, Steven; Prickard, John D. Detecting awareness in the vegetative state. *Science* 2006 September 8; 313(5792): 1402. Subject: 20.5.1

Owens, Kelly N.; Harvey-Blankenship, Michelle; King, Mary-Claire. Genomic sequencing in the service of human rights. *International Journal of Epidemiology* 2002 February; 31(1): 53-58. Subject: 15.10

Oye-Adeniran, Boniface A.; Adewole, Isaac F.; Umoh, Augustine V.; Iwere, Ngozi; Gbadegesin, Abidoye. Induced abortion in Nigeria: findings from focus group discussion. *African Journal of Reproductive Health* 2005 April; 9(1): 133-141. Subject: 12.5.2

Ozar, David T. Finding a voice: like individuals, organizations are moral speakers and actors. *Health Progress* 2006 November-December; 87(6): 24-27. Subject: 9.1

Ozar, David T. Towards a more inclusive conception of gender-diversity for intersex advocacy and ethics. *In:* Sytsma, Sharon E., ed. Ethics and Intersex. Dordrecht: Springer, 2006: 17-46. Subject: 10

Özdemir, M. Hakan; Ergönen, Akça T.; Sönmez, Ersel; Can, I. Özgür, Salacin, Serpil. The approach taken by the physicians working at educational hospitals in Ismir towards patient rights. *Patient Education and Counseling* 2006 April; 61(1): 87-91. Subject: 8.1

P

Page, Gayle Giboney. The importance of animal research to nursing science. *Nursing Outlook* 2004 March-April; 52(2): 102-107. Subject: 7.2

Palacios, Marcelo. Report on the Draft Bioethics Convention = Informe sobre el Proyecto de Convenio de Bioética. *Law and the Human Genome Review = Revista de Derecho y Genoma Humano* 1995 July-December; (3): 281-291. Subject: 2.1

Paladin, A. Vanzan. Ethics and neurology in the Islamic world. Continuity and change. *Italian Journal of Neurological Sciences* 1998 August; 19(4): 255-258. Subject: 17.1

Palaganas, Jamie; Civin, Curt I. Two steps forward: keeping the momentum in stem cell research [editorial]. *Stem Cells* 2004; 22(3): 240-241. Subject: 18.5.4

Palda, Valerie A.; Bowman, Kerry W.; McLean, Richard F.; Chapman, Martin G. "Futile" care: do we provide it? Why? A semistructured, Canada-wide survey of intensive care unit doctors and nurses. *Journal of Critical Care* 2005 September; 20(3): 207-213. Subject: 20.5.1

Palma, Enrique Marín. The status of biotechnological inventions in Europe: proposal for a Directive (Part I) = La situación de las invenciones biotecnológicas en Europa: la propuesta de Directiva (Parte I). *Law and the Human Ge-*

nome Review = Revista de Derecho y Genoma Humano 1995 July-December; (3): 261-276. Subject: 15.8

Palma, Enrique Marín. The status of biotechnological inventions in Europe: Proposal for Directives (Part II) = La situación de las invenciones biotecnológicas en Europa: la propuesta de Directiva (Parte II). *Law and the Human Genome Review = Revista de Derecho y Genoma Humano* 1996 January-June; (4): 165-199. Subject: 15.8

Palmer, Barton W.; Jeste, Dilip V. Relationship of individual cognitive abilities to specific components of decisional capacity among middle-aged and older patients with schizophrenia. *Schizophrenia Bulletin* 2006 January; 32(1): 98-106. Subject: 18.5.6

Palmer, Larry I. Response: Jay Katz: from harm to risks. *Yale Journal of Health Policy, Law and Ethics* 2006 Summer; 6(2): 455-464. Subject: 2.1

Palmer, N.; Braunack-Mayer, A.; Rogers, W.; Provis, C.; Cullity, G. Conflicts of interest in divisions of general practice. *Journal of Medical Ethics* 2006 December; 32(12): 715-717. Subject: 7.3

Palmeri, Debera. Directed donation: what is a transplant center to do? *Nephrology Nursing Journal* 2005 November-December; 32(6): 701-702. Subject: 19.5

Palmlund, Ingar. Loyalties in clinical research on drugs: the case of hormone replacement therapy. *Social Science and Medicine* 2006 July; 63(2): 540-551. Subject: 18.5.3

Palombi, Luigi. Patentable subject matter, TRIPS and the European Biotechnology Directive: Australia and patenting human genes [forum]. *University of New South Wales Law Journal* 2003; 26(3): 782-792. Subject: 15.8

Pálsson, Gílsi. The Iceland biogenetic project. *In:* Stehr, Nico, ed. Biotechnology Between Commerce and Civil Society. New Brunswick, NJ: Transaction Publishers; 2004: 277-297. Subject: 15.1

Pálsson, Gísli. Medical databases: the Icelandic case. *In:* Lundin, Susanne; Åkesson, Lynn, eds. Gene Technology and Economy. Lund: Nordic Academic Press; 2002: 22-41. Subject: 15.10

Pálsson, Gísli; Harðardóttir, Kristín E. For whom the cell tolls: debates about biomedicine. *Current Anthropology* 2002 April; 43(2): 271-301. Subject: 15.10

Pálsson, Gísli; Rabinow, Paul. The Iceland controversy: reflections on the transnational market of civic virtue. *In:* Ong, Aihwa; Collier, Stephen J., eds. Global Assemblages: Technology, Politics, and Ethics as Anthropological Problems. Malden, MA: Blackwell Pub.; 2005: 91-103. Subject: 5.1

Pálsson, Gísli; Rabinow, Paul. The Icelandic genome debate. *Trends in Biotechnology* 2001 May 1; 19(5): 166-171. Subject: 15.10

Pan American Health Organization. Women, Health, and Development Program. Gender equity in health. Washington, DC: Pan American Health Organization n.d.

[Online]. Accessed: http://www.paho.org/English/AD/GE/GEHFactSheet.pdf [2006 March 14]. Subject: 9.5.1

Pan American Health Organization. Women, Health and Development Program; Onyango, Christine. Gender equity in health sector reform: a review of the literature. *Pan American Health Organization* 2001 July: 1-42 [Online]. Accessed: http://www.paho.org/English/DPM/GPP/GH/ReformLitReview.pdf [2006 March 14]. Subject: 9.5.1

Pancevski, Bojan. Swiss judge orders HIV positive woman to disclose partners' names [news]. *BMJ: British Medical Journal* 2006 April 8; 332(7545): 809. Subject: 9.5.6

Pandikattu, Kuruvilla. For a collective human future project. *Peace Review* 2000 December; 12(4): 579-585. Subject: 15.10

Pandit, Santishree. Hindu bioethics, the concept of dharma and female infanticide in India. *In:* Sleeboom, Margaret, ed. Genomics in Asia: A Clash of Bioethical Interests? New York: Kegan Paul; 2004: 67-84. Subject: 14.3

Pandya, Sunil K. Bypassing scientific requirements [response]. *Indian Journal of Medical Ethics* 2006 October-December; 3(4): 135. Subject: 18.3

Pandya, Sunil K. The team had no options [response]. *Indian Journal of Medical Ethics* 2006 July-September; 3(3): 102. Subject: 20.5.1

Pang, Alfred H.T.; Lai, K.Y.C.; Bailey, V. Children's consent to psychiatric treatment: all or nothing? *International Journal of Clinical Practice* 1997 September; 51(6): 412-413. Subject: 8.3.2

Pang, Samantha Mei-che. Editorial comment. *Nursing Ethics* 2006 March; 13(2): 103-104. Subject: 20.5.1

Panicola, Michael R.; Hamel, Ronald P. Conscience, cooperation, and full disclosure. *Health Progress* 2006 January-February; 87(1): 52-59. Subject: 15.3

Panno, Joseph. Ethics of animal cloning. *In his:* Animal Cloning: The Science of Nuclear Transfer. New York: Facts of File, 2005: 66-73. Subject: 14.5

Panno, Joseph. Ethics of gene therapy. *In his:* Gene Therapy: Treating Disease by Repairing Genes. New York: Facts on File, 2005: 71-78. Subject: 15.4

Panno, Joseph. The ethics of stem cell research. *In his:* Stem Cell Research: Medical Applications and Ethical Controversy. New York: Facts on File, 2005: 72-80. Subject: 18.5.4

Panno, Joseph. Jesse Gelsinger: down to earth. *In his:* Gene Therapy: Treating Disease by Repairing Genes. New York: Facts on File, 2005: 45-55. Subject: 18.3

Panno, Joseph. Legal issues. *In his:* Animal Cloning: The Science of Nuclear Transfer. New York: Facts on File, 2005: 74-77. Subject: 14.5

Panno, Joseph. Legal issues. *In his:* Gene Therapy: Treating Disease by Repairing Genes. New York: Facts on File, 2005: 79-86. Subject: 15.4

Panno, Joseph. Legal issues. *In his:* Stem Cell Research: Medical Applications and Ethical Controversy. New York: Facts on File, 2005: 81-87. Subject: 18.5.4

Panting, Gerard. The theory of consent. *East African Medical Journal* 2005 July; 82(7 Supplement): S131-S132. Subject: 8.3.1

Papadimos, T.J. Nietzsche's morality: a genealogy of medical malpractice. *Medical Humanities* 2006 December; 32(2): 107-110. Subject: 8.5

Papathanasopoulos, P.G.; Nikolakopoulou, A.; Scolding, N.J. Disclosing the diagnosis of multiple sclerosis. *Journal of Neurology* 2005 November; 252(11): 1307-1309. Subject: 8.2

Pape, Deborah; Manning, Suzanne. The educational ladder model for ethics committees: confidence and change flourishing through core competency development. *HEC (Healthcare Ethics Committee) Forum* 2006 December; 18(4): 305-318. Subject: 9.6

Paradis, Carmen. Equipoise in the real world. *American Journal of Bioethics* 2006 July-August; 6(4): 61-63. Subject: 18.2

Paradis, Carmen. Informing consent: analogies to history-taking. *American Journal of Bioethics* 2006 January-February; 6(1): 24-26; discussion W27-W28. Subject: 8.3.1

Paradise, Jordan. European opposition to exclusive control over predictive breast cancer testing and the inherent implications for U.S. patent law and public policy: a case study of the Myriad Genetics' BRCA patent controversy. *Food and Drug Law Journal* 2004; 59(1): 133-154. Subject: 15.3

Paradiso, Angelo; Bruno, Michele; Cicoria, Onofrio; Digennaro, Maria; Longo, Salvatore; Rinaldi, Michele; Schittulli, Francesco. Analysis of the reasons for accepting or declining participation in genetic research for breast cancer: a hospital-based population study. *Tumori* 2004 July-August; 90(4): 435-436. Subject: 18.1

Parascandola, Mark. Science, industry, and tobacco harm reduction: a case study of tobacco industry scientists' involvement in the National Cancer Institute's Smoking and Health Program, 1964-1980. *Public Health Reports* 2005 May-June; 120(3): 338-349. Subject: 9.5.9

Pardes, Herbert; Lieber, Constance E. Philanthropy for psychiatry [editorial]. *American Journal of Psychiatry* 2006 May; 163(5): 766-767. Subject: 17.1

Pardo, Juan Bautista. Genetic research in the service of mankind: reflections of a lawyer = La investigación genética al servicio del hombre: reflexiones de un jurista. *Law and the Human Genome = Revista de Derecho y*

See SUBJECT HEADING KEY FOR SECTION II on inside back cover.

681

Genoma Humano 1994 July-December; (1): 25-27. Subject: 15.1

Parens, Erik; Asch, Adrienne. Disability rights critique of prenatal genetic testing: reflections and recommendations. *Mental Retardation and Developmental Disabilities Research Reviews* 2003; 9(1): 40-47. Subject: 15.3

Paris, Adeline; Cracowski, Jean-Luc; Maison, Patrick; Radauceanu, Anca; Cornu, Catherine; Hommel, Marc. Impact of French 'Comités de Protection des Personnes' on the readability of informed consent documents (ICD) in biomedical research: more information, but not better information. *Fundamental and Clinical Pharmacology* 2005 June; 19(3): 395-399. Subject: 18.3

Paris, John J.; Cranford, Ronald E. Definition of brain death. *Theology Today* 1983 April; 40(1983-1984): 5-14. Subject: 20.2.1

Paris, John J.; Graham, Neil; Schreiber, Michael D.; Goodwin, Michele. Has the emphasis on autonomy gone too far? Insights from Dostoevsky and parental decisionmaking in NICU. *CQ: Cambridge Quarterly of Healthcare Ethics* 2006 Spring; 15(2): 147-151. Subject: 8.3.2

Paris, John J.; Schreiber, Michael D.; Fogerty, Robert. Rage, rage against the dying of the light: not a metaphor for end-of-life care. *In:* Jansen, Lynn A., ed. Death in the Clinic. Lanham, MD: Rowman and Littlefield; 2006: 118-132. Subject: 20.5.1

Parish, Colin. Profession reacts to allegations of inappropriate control and restraint. *Nursing Standard* 2005 July 20; 19(45): 14-15. Subject: 9.5.3

Park, Park Bae. Teaching medical ethics in the future [discussion]. *Yonsei Medical Journal* 1985 December; 26(2): 139-141. Subject: 7.2

Park, Sang Chul. Reactions to the Hwang scandal [letter]. *Science* 2006 February 3; 311(5761): 606. Subject: 1.3.9

Park, Soo-Mi; Mathur, Raj; Smith, Gordon C.S. Congenital anomalies after treatment for infertility [editorial]. *BMJ: British Medical Journal* 2006 September 30; 333(7570): 665-666. Subject: 14.1

Parker, C. "Misconstructions of self": a response. *Medical Humanities* 2006 December; 32(2): 104-106. Subject: 4.1.1

Parker, Kelly. Pregnant women inmates: evaluating their rights and identifying opportunities for improvements in their treatment. *Journal of Law and Health* 2004-2005; 19(2): 259-295. Subject: 9.5.5

Parker, Lisa S. Best laid plans for offering results go awry. *American Journal of Bioethics* 2006 November-December; 6(6): 22-23; author reply W10-W12. Subject: 15.1

Parker, Lisa S.; Broyles, Lauren Matukaitis. Ethical issues in the conduct of genetic research. *In:* Iltis, Ana Smith, ed. Research Ethics. New York: Routledge, 2006: 32-60. Subject: 15.1

Parker, M. Competence by consequence: ambiguity and incoherence in the law. *Medicine and Law: World Association for Medical Law* 2006 March; 25(1): 1-12. Subject: 8.3.3

Parker, Michael. A conversational approach to the ethics of genetic testing. *In:* Ashcroft, Richard; Lucassen, Anneke; Parker, Michael; Verkerk, Marian; Widderhoven, Guy, eds. Case Analysis in Clinical Ethics. New York: Cambridge University Press; 2005: 149-164. Subject: 15.3

Parker, Michael. A deliberative approach to clinical bioethics. *In:* Viafora, Corrado, ed. Clinical Bioethics: A Search for the Foundations. Dordrecht: Springer, 2005: 61-71. Subject: 2.1

Parker, Michael. The ethics of communication. *In:* Macdonald, Elisbeth, ed. Difficult Conversations in Medicine. New York: Oxford University Press; 2004: 20-31. Subject: 8.1

Parker, Michael. The ethics of evidence-based patient choice. *Health Expectations* 2001 June; 4(2): 87-91. Subject: 8.1

Parker, Michael. The welfare of the child. *Human Fertility* 2005 March; 8(1): 13-17. Subject: 14.4

Parker, Michael. When is research on patient records without consent ethical? *Journal of Health Services Research and Policy* 2005 July; 10(3): 183-186. Subject: 18.3

Parker, Terri L. I didn't even raise my hand: a mother's retrospective journey through end-of-life decisionmaking at the "threshold of viability". *Stetson Law Review* 2005 Fall; 35(1): 207-225. Subject: 20.5.2

Parkes, S.E. Legal aspects of records based medical research. *Archives of Disease in Childhood* 2004 October; 89(10): 899-901. Subject: 18.3

Parkinson, Lynne; Rainbird, Katherine; Kerridge, Ian; Clover, Kerrie; Ravenscroft, Peter; Cavenagh, John; Carter, Gregory. Patients' attitudes towards euthanasia and physician-assisted suicide: a systematic review of the literature published over fifteen years. *Monash Bioethics Review* 2006 October; 25(4): 19-43. Subject: 20.7

Parks, Brian D. The natural-artificial distinction and conjoined twins: a response to Judith Thomson's argument for abortion rights. *National Catholic Bioethics Quarterly* 2006 Winter; 6(4): 671-680. Subject: 4.4

Parks, R.; Warren, P.M.; Boyd, K.M.; Cameron, H.; Cumming, A.; Lloyd-Jones, G. The objective structured clinical examination and student collusion: marks do not tell the whole truth. *Journal of Medical Ethics* 2006 December; 32(12): 734-738. Subject: 7.2

Parmar, Vinay N.; Mayberry, John F. An audit of informed consent in gastroscopy: investigation of a hospital's informed consent procedure in endoscopy by assessing current practice. *European Journal of*

Subject = NRCBL Primary Classification Number; see inside front cover.

Gastroenterology and Hepatology 2005 July; 17(7): 721-724. Subject: 8.3.1

Parr, Douglas. Will nanotechnology make the world a better place? *Trends in Biotechnology* 2005 August; 23(8): 395-398. Subject: 5.4

Parrish, Debra M. On identifying research misconduct respondents [letter]. *Science and Engineering Ethics* 2005 April; 11(2): 171-172. Subject: 1.3.9

Parrot, Anny; Gomez, M.; Herrenschmidt, Maurice; Carnein, Stéphane; Wary, Bernard; Van Der Beken, Jacques. L'euthanasie = Euthanasia. *Overtures* 1999; (93): 2-14. Subject: 20.5.1

Parrott, Roxanne L.; Silk, Kami J.; Dillow, Megan R.; Krieger, Janice L.; Harris, Tina M.; Condit, Celeste M. Development and validation of tools to assess genetic discrimination and genetically based racism. *Journal of the National Medical Association* 2005 July; 97(7): 980-990. Subject: 15.11

Parry, Bronwyn. The new Human Tissue Bill: categorization and definitional issues and their implications. *Genomics, Society and Policy* 2005 February; 1(1): 74-85. Subject: 19.5

Parry, Bronwyn; Gere, Cathy. Contested bodies: property models and the commodification of human biological artefacts. *Science as Culture* 2006 June; 15(2): 139-158. Subject: 19.5

Parry, Jane. Chinese rules on transplantation do not go far enough [news]. *BMJ: British Medical Journal* 2006 April 8; 332(7545): 810. Subject: 19.5

Parry, Odette; Mauthner, Natasha S. Whose data are they anyway? Practical, legal and ethical issues in archiving qualitative research data. *Sociology* 2004 February; 38(1): 139-152. Subject: 5.3

Parsi, Kayhan. Conversation with a famous patient. *Virtual Mentor* 2001 September; 3(9): 2p. Subject: 8.1

Parthasarathy, Shobita. Regulating risk: defining genetic privacy in the United States and Britain. *Science, Technology, and Human Values* 2004 Summer; 29(3): 332-352. Subject: 15.3

Partridge, Ernest. Future generations. *In:* Mitcham, Carl, ed. Encyclopedia of Science, Technology, and Ethics. Farmington Hills, MI: Thomson/Gale, 2005: 807-810. Subject: 2.1

Parturkar, D. Legal and ethical issues in human organ transplantation. *Medicine and Law: The World Association for Medical Law* 2006 June; 25(2):389-398. Subject: 19.5

Pascal, Chris B. Managing data for integrity: policies and procedures for ensuring the accuracy and quality of the data in the laboratory. *Science and Engineering Ethics* 2006 January; 12(1): 23-29. Subject: 1.3.9

Pasotti, Jacopo; Stafford, Ned. It's legal: Italian researchers defend their work with embryonic stem cells [news]. *Nature* 2006 July 20; 442(7100): 229. Subject: 18.5.4

Patel, Cynthia Joan; Shikongo, Armas E.E. Handling spirituality / religion in professional training: experiences of a sample of Muslim psychology students. *Journal of Religion and Health* 2006 Spring: 45(1): 93-112. Subject: 7.2

Patel, P. A natural stem cell therapy? How novel findings and biotechnology clarify the ethics of stem cell research. *Journal of Medical Ethics* 2006 April; 32(4): 235-239. Subject: 18.5.1

Patel, Rajeev; Torres, Robert J.; Rosset, Peter. Genetic engineering in agriculture and corporate engineering in public debate: risk, public relations, and public debate over genetically modified crops. *International Journal of Occupational and Environmental Health* 2005 October-December; 11(4): 428-436. Subject: 15.1

Patel, Salil H. Present and future challenges in medical data management: economics, ethics, and the law. *Studies in Health Technology and Informatics* 2005; 118: 43-51. Subject: 9.1

Patel, Vikram. Ethics of placebo-controlled trial in severe mania. *Indian Journal of Medical Ethics* 2006 January-March; 3(1): 11-12. Subject: 18.3

Patel, Vikram; Saraceno, Benedetto; Kleinman, Arthur. Beyond evidence: the moral case for international mental health [editorial]. *American Journal of Psychiatry* 2006 August; 163(8): 1312-1315. Subject: 9.5.3

Patenaude, Andrea Farkas. The genetic testing of children for cancer susceptibility: ethical, legal, and social issues. *Behavioral Sciences and the Law* 1996 Autumn; 14(4): 393-410. Subject: 15.3

Patenaude, Johane; Cabanac, Julien; de Champlain, Johane. Pan-Canadian study on variations in research ethics boards' reviews of a research project involving placebo use. *Health Law Review* 2006; 14(3): 32-38. Subject: 18.2

Patsopoulos, Nikolaos A.; Analatos, Apostolos A.; Ioannidis, John P.A. Origin and funding of the most frequently cited papers in medicine: database analysis. *BMJ: British Medical Journal* 2006 May 6; 332(7549): 1061-1063. Subject: 5.3

Patterson, Angela. Carey v. Population Services International: minor's rights to access contraceptives. *Journal of Contemporary Legal Issues* 2004; 14(1): 469-475. Subject: 11.2

Patterson, Brodie. Developing a perspective on restraint and the least intrusive intervention. *British Journal of Nursing* 2006 December 14-2007 January 10; 15(22): 1235-1241. Subject: 17.3

Patterson, David. New guidelines on ethical considerations in HIV preventive vaccine research. *Canadian*

See SUBJECT HEADING KEY FOR SECTION II on inside back cover.

683

HIV/AIDS Policy and Law Newsletter 2000 Spring-Summer; 5(2-3): 20-22. Subject: 18.2

Patterson, David. Québec court finds asymptomatic HIV infection a charter "handicap": Hamel v Malaxos [news]. *Canadian HIV/AIDS Policy and Law Newsletter* 1994 October; 1(1): 1,3-4. Subject: 9.5.6

Patterson, David. Resolving legal, ethical, and human rights challenges in HIV vaccine research. *HIV/AIDS Policy and Law Review* 2000; 5(4): 60-66. Subject: 18.2

Patterson, Rachael; George, Katrina. Euthanasia and assisted suicide: a liberal approach versus the traditional moral view. *Journal of Law and Medicine* 2005 May; 12(4): 494-510. Subject: 20.5.1

Pattinson, Shaun D. Figo committee for the ethical aspects of human reproduction and women's health. *Medical Law International* 2006; 7(4): 361-367. Subject: 18.5.4

Pattison, S.; Evans, H.M. Cause for concern: the absence of consideration of public and ethical interest in British public policy. *Journal of Medical Ethics* 2006 December; 32(12): 711-714. Subject: 9.5.7

Patton, Michael F., Jr. Personal identity, autonomy, and advance directives. *Southwest Philosophy Review* 2002 January; 18(1): 65-72. Subject: 20.5.4

Paul, M.; Newns, K.; Creedy, K.V. Some ethical issues that arise from working with families in the National Health Service. *Clinical Ethics* 2006 June; 1(2): 76-81. Subject: 9.5.7

Pauline, Jeffrey S.; Pauline, Gina A.; Johnson, Scott R.; Gamble, Kelly M. Ethical issues in exercise psychology. *Ethics and Behavior* 2006; 16(1): 61-76. Subject: 17.1

Paulson, Henry L. Diagnostic testing in neurogenetics. Principles, limitations, and ethical considerations. *Neurologic Clinics of North America* 2002 August 1; 20(3): 627-643. Subject: 15.3

Paxson, Heather. With or against nature? IVF, gender and reproductive agency in Athens, Greece. *Social Science and Medicine* 2003 May; 56(9): 1853-1866. Subject: 14.4

Paxton, Susan; Gonzales, G.; Uppakaew, K.; Abraham, K.K.; Okta, S.; Green, C.; Nair, K.S.; Merati, T.P.; Thephthien, B.; Marin, M.; Quesada, A. AIDS-related discrimination in Asia. *AIDS Care* 2005 May; 17(4): 413-424. Subject: 9.5.6

Peacock, Stuart; Ruta, Danny; Mitton, Craig; Donaldson, Cam; Bate, Angela; Murtagh, Madeleine. Using economics to set pragmatic and ethical priorities. *BMJ: British Medical Journal* 2006 February 25; 332(7539): 482-485. Subject: 9.4

Pearce, Eugene W.J.; Lewis, Patti. A hospice for the pre-born and newborn. *Health Progress* 2006 September-October; 87(5): 56-61. Subject: 20.5.2

Pearson, Helen. Early embryos can yield stem cells . . . and survive. *Nature* 2006 August 24; 442(7105): 858. Subject: 18.5.4

Pearson, Helen. Ethicists and biologists ponder the price of eggs. *Nature* 2006 August 10; 442(7103): 606-608. Subject: 14.4

Pearson, Helen. Lure of lie detectors spooks ethicists [news]. *Nature* 2006 June 22; 441(7096): 918-919. Subject: 17.1

Pearson, Helen; Abbott, Alison. Stem cells derived from "dead" human embryo [news]. *Nature* 2006 September 28; 443(7110): 376-377. Subject: 18.5.4

Pearson, Megan. The effect of clinical judgment in decision-making: the Mental Health Act 1986 (Vic.) and the Mental Health Review Board. *Ethical Human Psychology and Psychiatry* 2006 Spring; 8(1): 43-53. Subject: 4.3

Pearson, Roger. The concept of heredity in Western thought: part three: the revival of interest in genetics. *Mankind Quarterly* 1995 Fall; 36(1): 73-103. Subject: 15.11

Pearson, Steven D.; Kleinman, Ken; Rusinak, Donna; Levinson, Wendy. A trial of disclosing physicians' financial incentives to patients. *Archives of Internal Medicine* 2006 March 27; 166(6): 623-628. Subject: 7.3

Pearson, Steven D.; Miller, Franklin G.; Emanuel, Ezekiel J. Medicare's requirement for research participation as a condition of coverage: is it ethical? *JAMA: The Journal of the American Medical Association* 2006 August 23-30; 296(8): 988-991. Subject: 18.3

Pearson, Yvette E. Reconfiguring informed consent (with a little help from the capability approach). *American Journal of Bioethics* 2006 January-February; 6(1): 22-24; discussion W27-W28. Subject: 8.3.1

Peccarelli, Anthony M. A moral dilemma: the role of judicial intervention in withholding or withdrawing nutrition and hydration. *John Marshall Law Review* 1990 Summer; 23(4): 537-568. Subject: 20.5.1

Peccarelli, Anthony M. A response to Irwin Kramer's reply. *John Marshall Law Review* 1990 Summer; 23(4): 585-589. Subject: 20.5.1

Pector, Elizabeth A. Ethical issues of high-order multiple births. *Newborn and Infant Nursing Reviews* 2005 June; 5(2): 69-76. Subject: 9.5.5

Pedersen, Paul B. The cultural context of the American Counseling Association code of ethics. *Journal of Counseling and Development* 1997 Winter; 76(1): 23-28. Subject: 6

Pedersen, Roger A. Developments in human embryonic stem cells. *Reproductive BioMedicine Online [electronic]* 2005 March; 10(Supplement 1): 60-62. Subject: 18.5.4

Pedersen, Roger; Holm, Søren; Bortolotti, Lisa; Savulescu, Julian; Brinsden, Peter; Edwards, Robert; Short, Roger; Robertson, John; Lotz, Mianna; Oglivie,

Caroline; Lockwood, Gillian; Onland, Josh; Leather, Suzi. Discussion (day 2 session 1): stem cell outlook. *Reproductive BioMedicine Online [electronic]* 2005 March; 10(Supplement 1): 76-79. Subject: 18.5.4

Pediatric Reference Group; Neonatal Reference Group; Shemie, Sam D.; Doig, Christopher; Dickens, Bernard; Byrne, Paul; Wheelock, Brian; Rocker, Graeme; Baker, Andrew; Seland, T. Peter; Guest, Cameron; Cass, Dan; Jefferson, Rosella; Young, Kimberly; Teitelbaum, Jeanne. Severe brain injury to neurological determination of death: Canadian forum recommendations. *CMAJ/JAMC: Canadian Medical Association Journal* 2006 March 14; 174(6, Supplement): S1-S12. Subject: 20.2.1

Pedley, D.K.; Johnston, M. Death with dignity in the accident and emergency short stay ward [letter]. *Emergency Medicine Journal* 2001 January; 18(supplement 1): 76-77. Subject: 20.5.1

Pegg, Michael S. Overcoming barriers to recruitment in health research: some research ethics committees believe in facilitating ethical research. *BMJ: British Medical Journal* 2006 August 19; 333(7564): 398. Subject: 18.2

Pelias, Mary Kay. Research in human genetics: the tension between doing no harm and personal autonomy. *Clinical Genetics* 2005 January; 67(1): 1-5. Subject: 15.1

Pelias, Mary Z.; DeAngelis, Margaret M. The new genetic technologies: new options, new hope, and new challenges. *Loyola Law Review* 1999 Summer; 45(2): 287-306. Subject: 14.1

Pellegrino, Edmund D. Bioethics and politics: "doing ethics" in the public square. *Journal of Medicine and Philosophy* 2006 December; 31(6): 569-584. Subject: 2.1

Pellegrino, Edmund D. Decisions at the end of life — the abuse of the concept of futility. *Practical Bioethics* 2005 Summer; 1(3): 3-6. Subject: 20.5.1

Pellegrino, Edmund D. The moral foundations of the patient-physician relationship: the essence of medical ethics. *In:* Beam, Thomas E.; Sparacino, Linette R.; Pellegrino, Edmund D.; Hartle, Anthony E.; Howe, Edmund G., eds. Military Medical Ethics. Volume 1. Washington, DC: TMM Publications, Borden Institute, Walter Reed Army Medical Center; 2003: 3-21. Subject: 8.1

Pellegrino, Edmund D. The "telos" of medicine and the good of the patient. *In:* Viafora, Corrado, ed. Clinical Bioethics: A Search for the Foundations. Dordrecht: Springer, 2005: 21-32. Subject: 2.1

Pellegrino, Edmund D. Toward a reconstruction of medical morality. *American Journal of Bioethics* 2006 March-April; 6(2):65-71. Subject: 2.1

Pellicer, Antonio. The Italian law on assisted reproduction: a view from Spain. *Reproductive BioMedicine Online [electronic]* 2005 December; 11(6): 660-661. Accessed:

http://www.rbmonline.com/Article/2060 [2006 July 25]. Subject: 14.1

Peltier, Bruce; Dower, James S. Jr. The ethics of adopting a new drug: articaine as an example. *Journal of the American College of Dentists* 2006 Fall; 73(3): 11-19. Subject: 4.1.1

Pembroke, Neil. Marcelian charm in nursing practice: the unity of agape and eros as the foundation of an ethic of care. *Nursing Philosophy* 2006 October; 7(4): 266-274. Subject: 4.1.1

Pennings, Guido. Commentary on Craft and Thornhill: new ethical strategies to recruit gamete donors. *Reproductive BioMedicine Online [electronic]* 2005; 10(3): 307-309. Subject: 19.5

Pennings, Guido. Questioning the assumptions in the debate on assisted reproduction: comment on the House of Commons report Human Reproductive Technologies and the Law. *Reproductive BioMedicine Online [electronic]* 2005 August; 11(2): 152-154. Accessed: http://www.rbmonline.com/Article/1852 [2006 January 22]. Subject: 14.3

Pennings, Guido; de Wert, Guido M.W.R. Cloned embryos: in search of criteria to determine their moral status. *Nature Review Genetics* 2005 March; 6(3): 161. Subject: 14.5

Pentz, Rebecca. Duty and altruism: alternative analyses of the ethics of sibling bone marrow donation. *Journal of Clinical Ethics* 2006 Fall; 17(3): 227-230. Subject: 19.5

Pérez, S.G.; Gelpi, R.J.; Rancich, A.M. Doctor-patient sexual relationships in medical oaths. *Journal of Medical Ethics* 2006 December; 32(12): 702-705. Subject: 8.1

Perez, Thomas E. Enhancing access to health care and eliminating racial and ethnic disparities in health status: a compelling case for health professions schools to implement race-conscious admissions policies. *Journal of Health Care Law and Policy* 2006; 9(1): 77-104. Subject: 7.2

Pérez-Cárceles, M.D.; Pereñiguez, J.E.; Osuna, E.; Pérez-Flores, D.; Luna, A. Primary care confidentiality for Spanish adolescents: fact or fiction? *Journal of Medical Ethics* 2006 June; 32(6): 329-334. Subject: 9.5.7

Perez-Pena, Richard. New federal policy on H.I.V. testing poses unique local challenge. *New York Times* 2006 October 2; p. B1, B5. Subject: 9.5.6

Perez-Pena, Richard. State still confines mentally ill in nursing homes, suit says. *New York Times* 2006 March 8; p. A1, B6. Subject: 17.8

Perkins, Henry S.; de Souza, Emi Pouce; Cortez, Josie D.; Hazuda, Helen P. Comments on Skrank et al. focus group findings about the influence of culture on communication preferences in end-of-life care [letter]. *JGIM: Journal of General Internal Medicine* 2006 April; 21(4): 399-400. Subject: 20.4.1

See SUBJECT HEADING KEY FOR SECTION II on inside back cover.

685

Perkinson, Margaret A.; Berg-Weger, Marla L.; Carr, David B.; Meuser, Thomas M.; Palmer, Janice L.; Buckles, Virginia D.; Powlishta, Kimberly K.; Foley, Daniel J.; Morris, John C. Driving and dementia of the Alzheimer type: beliefs and cessation strategies among stakeholders. *Gerontologist* 2005 October; 45(5): 676-685. Subject: 17.1

Perlin, Michael L. Therapeutic jurisprudence and outpatient commitment law: Kendra's law as case study. *Psychology, Public Policy, and Law* 2003 March-June; 9(1-2): 183-208. Subject: 17.7

Perna, M.A. "Fair's fair argument" and voluntarism in clinical research: but, is it fair? *Journal of Medical Ethics* 2006 August; 32(8): 478-482. Subject: 18.3

Perneger, T.V. The real ethical problem [editorial]. *International Journal for Quality in Health Care* 2005 October; 17(5): 379. Subject: 18.2

Perpich, Joseph G. The dawn of genomics and regenerative medicine: new paradigms for medicine, the public's health, and society. *Technology in Society* 2004 April-August; 26(2-3): 405-414. Subject: 15.10

Perrett, Roy W. Buddhism, abortion and the middle way. *Asian Philosophy* 2000 July; 10(2): 101-114. Subject: 12.3

Perrett, Roy W. Taking life and the argument from potentiality. *Midwest Studies in Philosophy* 2000 August; 24: 186-198. Subject: 4.4

Perry, Anthony C.F. Nuclear transfer cloning and the United Nations. *Nature Biotechnology* 2004 December; 22(12): 1506-1508. Subject: 14.5

Perry, Baroness of Southwark. A response to reviews by Russell, Festing and Patel, Hendriksen, and Thomas on the Nuffield Council on Bioethics Report, The ethics of research involving animals. *ATLA: Alternatives to Laboratory Animals* 2006 May; 34(2): 255-259. Subject: 22.2

Perry, Joshua E. Biblical biopolitics: judicial process, religious rhetoric, Terri Schiavo and beyond. *Health Matrix: The Journal of Law-Medicine* 2006 Summer; 16(2): 553-630. Subject: 20.5.1

Persaud, Raj. Does smarter mean happier? *In:* Miller, Paul; Wilsdon, James, eds. Better Humans?: The Politics of Human Enhancement and Life Extension. London: Demos, 2006: 129-136. Subject: 4.5

Persson, Ingmar. Peter Singer on why persons are irreplaceable. *Utilitas* 1995 May; 7(1): 55-66. Subject: 4.4

Persson, Ingmar. What's wrong with admiring athletes and other people? *In:* Tamburrini, Claudio; Tännsjö, Torbjörn, eds. Genetic Technology and Sport: Ethical Questions. London; New York: Routledge; 2005: 70-81. Subject: 4.5

Pesut, Barbara. Fundamental or foundational obligation? Problematizing the ethical call to spiritual care in nursing. *Advances in Nursing Science* 2006 April-June; 29(2): 125-133. Subject: 9.1

Peter, Elizabeth. The interplay between the abstract and the particular: research ethics standards and the practice of research as symbolic. *Nursing Science Quarterly* 2006 January; 19(1): 20-24. Subject: 18.2

Peters, June A.; Vadaparampil, Susan T.; Kramer, Joan; Moser, Richard P.; Peterson, Lori Jo; Loud, Jennifer; Greene, Mark H. Familial testicular cancer: interest in genetic testing among high-risk family members. *Genetics in Medicine* 2006 December; 8(12): 760-770. Subject: 15.3

Peters, Ted. Dignity. *In:* Mitcham, Carl, ed. Encyclopedia of Science, Technology, and Ethics. Farmington Hills, MI: Thomson/Gale, 2005: 528-530. Subject: 4.4

Peters, Ted. Playing God. *In:* Mitcham, Carl, ed. Encyclopedia of Science, Technology, and Ethics. Farmington Hills, MI: Thomson/Gale, 2005: 1424-1427. Subject: 15.1

Peters, Thomas G. Racial disparities and transplantation [editorial]. *American Journal of Kidney Diseases* 2005 October; 46(4): 760-762. Subject: 19.6

Petersen, Alan. Securing our genetic health: engendering trust in UK Biobank. *Sociology of Health and Illness* 2005 March; 27(2): 271-292. Subject: 15.1

Petersen, Kerry. Abortion in Australia: a legal misconception. *Australian Health Review* 2005 May; 29(2): 142-145. Subject: 12.4.1

Petersen, Laura A.; Wright, Steven M.; Peterson, Eric D.; Daley, Jennifer. Impact of race on cardiac care and outcomes in veterans with acute myocardial infarction. *Medical Care* 2002 January; 40(1 Supplement): I86-I96. Subject: 9.5.4

Peterson, Candida C.; Siddle, David A.T. Confidentiality issues in psychological research. *Australian Psychologist* 1995 November; 30(3): 187-190. Subject: 8.4

Peterson, James C. So who shall we be? A response to John Gearhart. *In:* Miller, Roman J.; Brubaker, Beryl H.; Peterson, James C., eds. Viewing New Creations with Anabaptist Eyes: Ethics of Biotechnology. Telford, PA: Cascadia Pub.; 2005: 35-38. Subject: 18.5.4

Petryna, Adriana. Globalizing human subjects research. *In:* Petryna, Adriana; Lakoff, Andrew; Kleinman, Arthur, eds. Global Pharmaceuticals: Ethics, Markets, Practices. Durham: Duke University Press; 2006: 33-60. Subject: 18.5.9

Petsko, Gregory A. Color blind. *Genome Biology [electronic]* 2004 November 26; 5(12): 119, 3 p. Accessed: http://genomebiology.com/2004/5/12/119 [2006 January 22]. Subject: 9.5.4

Pettifor, Jean L. Professional ethics across national boundaries. *European Psychologist* 2004 December; 9(4): 264-272. Subject: 6

Pezier, Thomas F. Opting in or out of electronic patient records: debate has missed the boat [letter]. *BMJ: British*

Medical Journal 2006 July 29; 333(7561): 261-262. Subject: 1.3.12

Pfeffer, N.; Kent, J. Consent to the use of aborted fetuses in stem cell research and therapies. *Clinical Ethics* 2006 December; 1(4): 216-218. Subject: 18.3

Phadke, Anant. Restricted availability of free anti-rabies vaccine in public health facilities in India: unethical and criminal. *Indian Journal of Medical Ethics* 2006 April-June; 3(2): 48-49. Subject: 9.5.1

Phaosavasdi, Sukhit; Taneepanichskul, Surasak; Tannirandorn, Yuen; Thamkhantho, Manopchai; Prugsapong, Chumsak; Phupong, Vorapong; Karnjanapitak, Aurchart. What is your opinion on the "medical ethics of medical journal editors"? *Journal of the Medical Association of Thailand* 2005 August; 88(8): 1163-1164. Subject: 1.3.7

Phaosavasdi, Sukhit; Taneepanichskul, Surasak; Tannirandorn, Yuen; Thamkhantho, Manopchai; Pruksapong, Chumsak; Kanjanapitak, Aurchart. Medical ethics for senior medical doctors (episode II). *Journal of the Medical Association of Thailand* 2005 June; 88(6): 867-868. Subject: 4.1.2

Phaosavasdi, Sukhit; Taneepanichskul, Surasak; Tannirandorn, Yuen; Thamkhantho, Manopchai; Pruksapong, Chumsak; Kanjanapitak, Aurchart. Medical ethics and the survival of medical profession. *Journal of the Medical Association of Thailand* 2005 April; 88(4): 563-566. Subject: 4.1.2

Phaosavasdi, Sukhit; Taneepanichskul, Surasak; Tannirandorn, Yuen; Thamkhantho, Manopchai; Pruksapong, Chumsak; Kanjanapitak, Aurchart. Medical ethics for senior medical doctors (episode I). *Journal of the Medical Association of Thailand* 2005 May; 88(5): 708-709. Subject: 4.1.2

Phaosavasdi, Sukhit; Taneepanichskul, Surasak; Tannirandorn, Yuen; Thamkhantho, Manopchai; Pruksapong, Chumsak; Kanjanapitak, Aurchart. Medical ethics for senior medical doctors (episode III). *Journal of the Medical Association of Thailand* 2005 July; 88(7): 1015-1017. Subject: 2.1

Phaosavasdi, Sukhit; Thaneepanichskul, Surasak; Tannirandorn, Yuen; Thamkhantho, Manopchai; Pruksapong, Chumsak; Kanjanapitak, Aurchart; Leong, Hugh. Animals and ethics. *Journal of the Medical Association of Thailand* 2005 February; 88(2): 287-293. Subject: 22.1

Philipov, D.; Andreev, E.; Kharkova, T.; Shkolnikov, V. Induced abortion in Russia: recent trends and underreporting in surveys. *European Journal of Population* 2004; 20(2): 95-117. Subject: 12.5.2

Phillips, Helen. A life or death dilemma. *New Scientist* 2006 July 8-14; 19(2559): 6-7. Subject: 20.5.1

Phillips, Helen. Who is messing with your head? [news]. *New Scientist* 2006 January 21-27; 189(2535): 11. Subject: 17.1

Phillips, Lorraine J.; Phillips, Win. Better reproductive healthcare for women with disabilities: a role for nursing leadership. *Advances in Nursing Science* 2006 April-June; 29(2): 134-151. Subject: 9.5.3

Philpott, Shona. The truth, the whole truth and nothing but the truth? *Nursing New Zealand* 2005 May; 11(4): 16-18. Subject: 8.2

Phipps, Etienne J. What's end of life got to do with it? Research ethics with populations at life's end. *Gerontologist* 2002 October; 42(Special Issue 3): 104-108. Subject: 18.5.7

Phua, Kai-Lit. The Human Genome Project and genetic research: what are the implications for ethics and equity? *Critical Public Health* 2004 June; 14(2): 191-200. Subject: 15.10

Pichini, Simona; Pulido, Marta; García-Algar, Óscar. Authorship in manuscripts submitted to biomedical journals: an author's position and its value [letter]. *Science and Engineering Ethics* 2005 April; 11(2): 173-175. Subject: 1.3.9

Pickens, K.L. Don't judge me by my genes: a survey of federal genetic discrimination legislation. *Tulsa Law Journal* 1998 Fall; 34(1): 161-181. Subject: 15.1

Pickoff, Robert M. Pay for performance — for whom the bell tolls. *Physician Executive* 2005 November-December; 31(6): 12-14. Subject: 9.3.1

Piehler, Henry R. Innovation and change in medical technology: interactions between physicians and engineers. *Journal of Investigative Surgery* 1992 July-September; 5(3): 179-184. Subject: 5.2

Pieterse, Arwen H.; van Dulmen, Sandra; van Dijk, Sandra; Bensing, Jozien M.; Ausems, Margreet G.E.M. Risk communication in completed series of breast cancer genetic counseling visits. *Genetics in Medicine* 2006 November; 8(11): 688-696. Subject: 15.2

Piette, John D.; Bibbins-Domingo, Kirsten; Schillinger, Dean. Health care discrimination, processes of care, and diabetes patients' health status. *Patient Education and Counseling* 2006 January; 60(1): 41-48. Subject: 9.2

Pilcher, Helen. Dial 'E' for ethics [news]. *Nature* 2006 April 27; 440(7088): 1104-1105. Subject: 2.1

Pilcher, Helen. The egg and sperm race. *New Scientist* 2006 October 21-27; 192(2574): 52-54. Subject: 14.4

Pilnick, Alison. What "most people" do: exploring the ethical implications of genetic counselling. *New Genetics and Society* 2002 December; 21(3): 339-350. Subject: 15.2

Pilon, Susan. Learning on the job — the case for mandatory research ethics education for research teams. *Clinical*

See SUBJECT HEADING KEY FOR SECTION II on inside back cover.

687

and Investigative Medicine 2005 April; 28(2): 46-47. Subject: 7.2

Pimple, Kenneth D. Ethics at the interface: a successful online seminar. *Science and Engineering Ethics* 2005 July; 11(3): 495-499. Subject: 1.3.12

Pineda, Rafael Luis. "Contracepción de emergencia" un mal llamado método contraceptivo ["Emergency contraception": a misnamed method of contraception]. *Persona y Bioética* 1999 February-May; 2(6): 1-23. Subject: 11.1

Pinnock, Ralph; Crosthwaite, Jan. When parents refuse consent to treatment for children and young persons. *Journal of Paediatrics and Child Health* 2005 July; 41(7): 369-373. Subject: 9.5.7

Pinto, Maria Cristina Rosamond. Medically assisted procreation: legal framework in Portugal. *Eubios Journal of Asian and International Bioethics* 2006 September; 16(5): 158-160. Subject: 14.4

Pipes, Randolph B.; Holstein, Jaymee E.; Aguirre, Maria G. Examining the personal-professional distinction: ethics codes and the difficulty of drawing a boundary. *American Psychologist* 2005 May-June; 60(4): 325-334. Subject: 6

Pirags, Valdis; Grens, Elmars. The Latvian Genome Project. *In:* Sándor, Judit, ed. Society and Genetic Information: Codes and Laws in the Genetic Era. Budapest, Hungary; New York: CEU Press; 2003: 225-231. Subject: 15.1

Pirakitikulr, Darlyn; Bursztajn, Harold J. The grand inquisitor's choice: comment on the CEJA report on withholding information from patients. *Journal of Clinical Ethics* 2006 Winter; 17(4): 307-311. Subject: 8.1

Pittman, Larry J. A Thirteenth Amendment challenge to both racial disparities in medical treatment and improper physicians' informed consent disclosures. *Saint Louis University Law Journal* 2003 Fall; 48(1): 131-189. Subject: 9.5.4

Place, Michael. Nutrition, hydration and the "persistent vegetative state". *Origins* 2006 May 25; 36(2): 17-24. Subject: 20.5.1

Platt, Priscilla. The individual's right of access to his or her own personal health information. *Health Law in Canada* 2006 March; 26(3): 44-59. Subject: 8.4

Pleat, J.M.; Dunkin, C.S.J.; Davies, C.E.; Ripley, R.M.; Tyler, M.P.H. Prospective survey of factors affecting risk discussion during consent in a surgical specialty. *British Journal of Surgery* 2004 October; 91(10): 1377-1380. Subject: 8.2

Plemmons, Dena K.; Brody, Suzanne A.; Kalichman, Michael W. Student perceptions of the effectiveness of education in the responsible conduct of research. *Science and Engineering Ethics* 2006 July; 12(3): 571-582. Subject: 1.3.9

Ploem, M.C. Towards an appropriate privacy regime for medical data research. *European Journal of Health Law* 2006 April; 13(1): 41-64. Subject: 18.2

Plomer, Aurora. European patent law and ethics [editorial]. *Drug Discovery Today* 2005 July 15; 10(14): 947-948. Subject: 15.8

Plomer, Aurora. Protecting the rights of human subjects in emergency research. *European Journal of Health Law* 2001 December; 8(4): 333-352. Subject: 18.3

Plows, Alexandra; Boddington, Paula. Troubles with biocitizenship? *Genomics, Society and Policy* 2006 December; 2(3): 115-135. Subject: 5.1

Pluhar, Evelyn B. Experimentation on humans and nonhumans. *Theoretical Medicine and Bioethics* 2006; 27(4): 333-355. Subject: 18.1

Pohl, Lynn Marie. Long waits, small spaces, and compassionate care: memories of race and medicine in a mid-twentieth-century southern community. *Bulletin of the History of Medicine* 2000 Spring; 74(1): 107-137. Subject: 9.5.4

Pokorski, Robert J. Genetic information and life insurance risk classification and antiselection (first of two parts). *Journal of Insurance Medicine* 1994-1995 Winter; 26(4): 413-419. Subject: 15.1

Polgar, Stephen; Ng, Joanna. Ethics, methodology and the use of placebo controls in surgical trials. *Brain Research Bulletin* 2005 October 30; 67(4): 290-297. Subject: 18.3

Pollack, Andrew. Genentech caps cost of cancer drug for some patients. *New York Times* 2006 October 12; p C2. Subject: 9.7

Pollack, Andrew. Stanford to ban drug makers' gifts to doctors, even pens. *New York Times* 2006 September 12; p. C2. Subject: 9.7

Pollack, Andrew. Take your pills, all your pills: drug makers nag patients to stay the course. *New York Times* 2006 March 11; p. C1, C13. Subject: 9.7

Pollack, Andrew. The wide, wild world of genetic testing. *New York Times* 2006 September 12; p. NYT4. Subject: 15.3

Pollack, Andrew; Abelson, Reed. Why the data diverge on the dangers of Vioxx: even in medical journals, statistics can be subject to broad interpretation. *New York Times* 2006 May 22; p. C1, C5. Subject: 9.7

Pollack, Andrew; Martin, Andrew. FDA tentatively declares food from cloned animals to be safe; critics say risks have not been fully weighed. *New York Times* 2006 December 29; p. A1, A23. Subject: 14.5

Pollack, Daniel. The capacity of a mentally challenged person to consent to abortion and sterilization. *Health and Social Work* 2005 August; 30(3): 253-257. Subject: 9.5.3

Pollack, David A. Ethical health policy work at the governmental level. *Psychiatric Annals* 2004 February; 34(2): 157, 160-161, 164-166. Subject: 17.1

Pollack, Robert. Natural design and moral constraints in science. *GeneWatch* 2006 July-August; 19(4): 3-7. Subject: 15.5

Pollard, Irina. Bioscience-bioethics and life factors affecting reproduction with special reference to the indigenous Australian population. *Reproduction* 2005 April; 129(4): 391-402. Subject: 7.1

Pomerantz, Andrew M.; Segrist, Dan J. The influence of payment method on psychologists' diagnostic decisions regarding minimally impaired clients. *Ethics and Behavior* 2006; 16(3): 253-263. Subject: 4.3

Pomerantz, Sherry C.; Bhatt, Himani; Brodsky, Nancy L.; Lurie, Deborah; Ciesielski, Janice; Cavalieri, Thomas A. Physicians' practices related to the use of terminal sedation: moral and ethical concerns. *Palliative and Supportive Care* 2004 March; 2(1): 15-21. Subject: 20.4.1

Ponte, Charles D. Comment: pharmacist critique was ill-informed. *Annals of Pharmacotherapy* 2006 July-August; 40: 1475-1476. Subject: 11.1

Ponticelli, Claudio. Altruistic living renal transplantation. *Journal of Nephrology* 2003 November-December; 16(Supplement 7): S6-S9. Subject: 19.3

Pontifical Academy for Life. Moral reflections on vaccines prepared from cells derived from aborted human fetuses. *National Catholic Bioethics Quarterly* 2006 Autumn; 6(3): 541-550. Subject: 9.5.1

Pontifical Academy for Life = Pontificia Academia pro vita. Final communique: ethics of biomedical research. *L'Osservatore Romano* 2003 March 19: 5, 10 [Online]. Accessed: http://www.catholicculture.org/docs/doc_view.cfm?recnum=5083 [2006 September 6]. Subject: 1.3.9

Popovsky, Mark. Dementia and the ethics of decision-making. *Conservative Judaism* 2005 Fall; 58(1): 18-35. Subject: 17.1

Popovsky, Mark. Mental anguish and the permissibility of abortion. *Conservative Judaism* 2006 Summer; 58(4): 3-21. Subject: 12.3

Popp, F.C.; Eggert, N.; Hoy, L.; Lang, S.A.; Obed, A.; Piso, P.; Schlitt, H.J.; Dahlke, M.H. Who is willing to take the risk? Assessing the readiness for living liver donation in the general German population. *Journal of Medical Ethics* 2006 July; 32(7): 389-394. Subject: 19.5

Popp, Richard L.; Smith, Sidney C., Jr. Cardiovascular professionalism and ethics in the modern era. *Journal of the American College of Cardiology* 2004 October 19; 44(8): 1722-1723. Subject: 8.1

Por, Yu Kam. Respecting nature and using human intelligence: elements of a Confucian bioethics. *In:* Sleeboom, Margaret, ed. Genomics in Asia: A Clash of Bioethical Interests? New York: Kegan Paul; 2004: 159-177. Subject: 2.1

Porter, Deborah. Advance directives and the persistent vegetative state in Victoria: a human rights perspective. *Journal of Law and Medicine* 2005 November; 13(2): 256-270. Subject: 20.5.4

Porter, Deborah. The regulation of in-vitro fertilisation: social norms and discrimination. *E Law: Murdoch University Electronic Journal of Law* 1997 September; 4(3): 7 p. [Online]. Accessed: http://www.murdoch.edu.au/elaw/issues/v4n3/port43.html [2006 June 29]. Subject: 14.4

Porter, Gerard. The wolf in sheep's clothing: informed consent forms as commercial contracts. *In:* Árnason, Gardar; Nordal, Salvör; Árnason, Vilhjálmur, eds. Blood and Data: Ethical, Legal and Social Aspects of Human Genetic Databases. Reykjavík: University of Iceland Press; 2004: 85-93. Subject: 15.1

Porter, Gerard; Denning, Chris; Plomer, Aurora; Sinden, John; Torremans, Paul. The patentability of human embryonic stem cells in Europe. *Nature Biotechnology* 2006 June; 24(6): 653-655. Subject: 15.8

Porter, Kamilla K.; Rai, Gurcharan S. Principles of medical ethics. *In:* Rai, Gurcharan S, ed. Medical Ethics and the Elderly. 2nd ed. San Francisco: Radcliffe Medical Press; 2004: 1-7. Subject: 2.1

Portsmouth, Donald. Advance directives. *In:* Rai, Gurcharan S, ed. Medical Ethics and the Elderly. 2nd ed. San Francisco: Radcliffe Medical Press; 2004: 81-89. Subject: 20.5.4

Poses, Roy M.; Silverstein, Scot; Smith, Wally R.; Brennan, Troyen A.; Rothman, David J.; Naughton, James; Cohen, Jordan; Kimball, Harry; Blumenthal, David; Smelser, Neil; Kassirer, Jerome P.; Goldman, JanLori. Academic medical centers and conflicts of interest [letter and reply]. *JAMA: The Journal of the American Medical Association* 2006 June 28; 295(24): 2846-2847, 2848-2849. Subject: 7.3

Post, Jerrold M. Ethical considerations in psychiatric profiling of political figures. *Psychiatric Clinics of North America* 2002 September; 25(3): 635-646. Subject: 17.1

Post, Stephen. Full-spectrum proxy consent for research participation when persons with Alzheimer Disease lose decisional capacities: research ethics and the common good. *Alzheimer Disease and Associated Disorders* 2003 April-June; 17(Supplement 1): S3-S11. Subject: 18.3

Post, Stephen G. Posthumanism. *In:* Mitcham, Carl, ed. Encyclopedia of Science, Technology, and Ethics. Farmington Hills, MI: Thomson/Gale, 2005: 1458-1462. Subject: 4.4

Post, Stephen G. Respectare: moral respect for the lives of the deeply forgetful. *In:* Hughtes, Julian C.; Louw, Stephen J.; Sabat, Steven R., eds. Dementia: Mind, Meaning, and

See SUBJECT HEADING KEY FOR SECTION II on inside back cover.

689

the Person. New York: Oxford University Press, 2006: 223-234. Subject: 9.5.3

Poteliakhoff, Alex. A commitment to peace: a doctor's tale. *Medicine, Conflict and Survival* 2006 January-March; 22(1, Supplement): S3-S55. Subject: 21.2

Potter, Robert L.; Flanigan, Rosemary. A family divided. *Practical Bioethics* 2005 Summer; 1(3): 9. Subject: 20.5.1

Poulton, B.; Ridley, S.; Mackenzie-Ross, R.; Rizvi, S. Variation in end-of-life decision making between critical care consultants. *Anaesthesia* 2005 November; 60(11): 1101-1105. Subject: 20.5.1

Povar, Gail. Are we our brothers' (and sisters') keepers? *Maryland Medicine* 2005 Summer; 6(3): 44, 46. Subject: 7.4

Povar, Gail. The bellicose back patient. *Maryland Medicine* 2004 Winter; 5(1): 34, 37. Subject: 9.4

Powell, Daniel J. Using false claims act as a basis for institutional review board liability. *University of Chicago Law Review* 2002 Summer; 69(3): 1399-1426. Subject: 18.2

Powell, Elizabeth A.; Goldberg Oliver, Rebecca. Abiomed and the AbioCore clinical trials, Part 1. *Organizational Ethics: Healthcare, Business, and Policy* 2006 Spring-Summer; 3(1): 19-32. Subject: 19.2

Powell, Elizabeth A.; Goldberg Oliver, Rebecca. Abiomed and the AbioCor clinical trials, Part 2. *Organizational Ethics: Healthcare, Business, and Policy* 2006 Spring-Summer; 3(1): 33-39. Subject: 19.2

Powell, John; Fitton, Richard; Fitton, Caroline. Sharing electronic health records: the patient view. *Informatics in Primary Care* 2006; 14(1): 55-57. Subject: 9.1

Powell, Tia. Culture and communication: medical disclosure in Japan and the USA Akabayashi and B.T. Slingsby. *American Journal of Bioethics* 2006 January-February; 6(1): 18-20; discussion W27-W28. Subject: 8.2

Powell, Tia. Face transplant: real and imagined ethical challenges. *Journal of Law, Medicine, and Ethics* 2006 Spring; 34(1): 111-115. Subject: 19.1

Powers, Denise V. Perinatal hospice. *Conscience* 2006 Autumn; 27(3): 31-33. Subject: 20.4.2

Powis, Rachel; Stewart, Kevin; Rai, Gurcharan S. Cardiopulmonary resuscitation. *In:* Rai, Gurcharan S, ed. Medical Ethics and the Elderly. 2nd ed. San Francisco: Radcliffe Medical Press; 2004: 61-69. Subject: 20.5.1

Pozos, Robert S. Nazi hypothermia research: should the data be used? *In:* Beam, Thomas E.; Sparacino, Linette R.; Pellegrino, Edmund D.; Hartle, Anthony E.; Howe, Edmund G., eds. Military Medical Ethics. Volume 2. Washington, DC: TMM Publications, Borden Institute, Walter Reed Army Medical Center; 2003: 437-461. Subject: 18.5.5

Po-Wah, Julia Tao Lai. Right-making and wrong-making in surrogate motherhood: a Confucian feminist perspective. *In:* Tong, Rosemarie; Donchin, Anne; Dodds, Susan, eds. Linking Visions: Feminist Bioethics, Human Rights, and the Developing World. Lanham, MD: Rowman and Littlefield Publishers; 2004: 157-179. Subject: 14.2

Prachusilpa, Sukunya; Oumtanee, Areewan. Internet health ethics. *Journal of the Medical Association of Thailand* 2005 January; 88(1): 124-125. Subject: 1.3.12

Prada, Juan Luis Iglesias. The patentability of human genes = La patentabilidad de los genes humanos. *Law and the Human Genome Review = Revista de Derecho y Genoma Humano* 1995 July-December; (3): 103-121. Subject: 15.8

Prainsack, Barbara. "Negotiating life": the regulation of human cloning and embryonic stem cell research in Israel. *Social Studies of Science* 2006 April; 36(2): 173-205 [Online] Accessed: http://sss.sagepub.com/cgi/reprint/36/2/173 [2007 January 23]. Subject: 18.5.4

Prather, Erin. Rx for trouble: prescribing for family, friends discouraged. *Texas Medicine* 2005 July; 101(7): 65-67. Subject: 4.1.2

Pratt, Bridget. "Soft" science in the courtroom?: the effects of admitting neuroimaging evidence into legal proceedings. *Penn Bioethics Journal* 2005 April 2; 1(1): 3p. [Online]. Accessed: http://www.bioethicsjournal.com [2005 April 19]. Subject: 17.1

Premo-Hopkins, Mark W. Between organs and adoption: why pre-embryo donors should not be allowed to discriminate against recipients. *University of Chicago Legal Forum* 2006: 441-470. Subject: 14.6

Prentky, Robert. A sex offender as a patient. *American Family Physician* 2005 October 1; 72(7): 1386, 1389. Subject: 7.1

Prescott, Heather Munro. Using the student body: college and university students as research subjects in the United States during the twentieth century. *Journal of the History of Medicine* 2002 January; 57: 3-38. Subject: 18.5.2

Press, Eyal. My father's abortion war; When the abortion provider Dr. Barnett Slepian was murdered outside Buffalo, one of his colleagues decided to keep his own nearby office open. How America's most polarizing conflict came to my family's doorstep. *New York Times Magazine* 2006 January 22; p. 56-61. Subject: 12.4.3

Press, Nancy. Social construction and medicalization: behavioral genetics in context. *In:* Parens, Erik; Chapman, Audrey R.; Press, Nancy, eds. Wrestling with Behavioral Genetics: Science, Ethics, and Public Conversion. Baltimore, MD: Johns Hopkins University Press; 2006: 131-149. Subject: 15.6

Preston, Julia. Texas hospitals' separate paths reflect the debate on immigration. *New York Times* 2006 July 18; p. A1, A18. Subject: 9.5.9

Price, Andrew. Antibiotics. *In:* Mitcham, Carl, ed. Encyclopedia of Science, Technology, and Ethics. Farmington Hills, MI: Thomson/Gale, 2005: 84-86. Subject: 9.7

Price, Connie C. Decision analysis for a new bioethics. *American Journal of Bioethics* 2006 May-June; 6(3): 62-64; discussion W51- W53. Subject: 2.1

Price, Connie C.; Olufemi Sodeke, Stephen. Letter to the editor: end-of-life care and racial disparities: all social and health care sectors must respond! [letter]. *American Journal of Bioethics [Online]* 2006 September-October; 6(5): W33-W34. Subject: 20.5.1

Price, David M. An ethical perspective. Evaluating managed care. *Journal of Nursing Law* 1998; 5(3): 47-50. Subject: 9.3.2

Prieur, Michael R.; Atkinson, Joan; Hardingham, Laurie; Hill, David; Kernaghan, Gillian; Miller, Debra; Morton, Sandy; Rowell, Mary; Vallely, John F.; Wilson, Suzanne. Stem cell research in a Catholic institution: yes or no? *Kennedy Institute of Ethics Journal* 2006 March; 16(1): 73-98. Subject: 18.5.4

Prigmore, Samantha. End-of-life decisions and respiratory disease. *Nursing Times* 2006 February 14-20; 102(7): 56, 59, 61. Subject: 20.5.1

Proctor, Robert N. Nazi medical ethics: ordinary doctors? *In:* Beam, Thomas E.; Sparacino, Linette R.; Pellegrino, Edmund D.; Hartle, Anthony E.; Howe, Edmund G., eds. Military Medical Ethics. Volume 2. Washington, DC: TMM Publications, Borden Institute, Walter Reed Army Medical Center; 2003: 403-436. Subject: 21.4

Proctor, Robert N. Naziärzte, Rassenmedizin und "lebensunwertes Leben" — von der Ideologie zur "Euthanasie". *In:* Frewer, Andreas; Eickhoff, Clemens, eds. "Euthanasie" und die aktuelle Sterbehilfe-Debatte: Die historischen Hintergründe medizinischer Ethik. Frankfurt; New York: Campus; 2000: 65-89. Subject: 15.5

Programme on Ethical Issues in International Health Research, Department of Population and International Health, Harvard School of Public Health. Innovative therapy or unethical experiment? *Indian Journal of Medical Ethics* 2006 October-December; 3(4): 132. Subject: 18.5.4

Proot, L; Vanderheyden, L. Informed consent [editorial]. *Acta Chirurgica Belgica* 2000 August; 100(4): 149-150. Subject: 8.3.1

Propst, Evan J.; Hales, Sarah; Masellis, Mario; Adejumo, Adebayo O.; Godkin, M. Dianne. The beginning of one's real ethical development. *Clinical and Investigative Medicine* 2006 February; 29(1): 7-9. Subject: 2.1

Prottas, Jeffrey M. Altruism, motivation, and allocation: giving and using human organs. *Journal of Social Issues* 1993 Summer; 49(2): 137-150. Subject: 19.5

Pruchno, Rachel A.; Lemay, Edward P., Jr.; Feild, Lucy; Levinsky, Norman G. Spouse as health care proxy for dialysis patients: whose preferences matter? *Gerontologist* 2005 December; 45(6): 812-819. Subject: 8.3.3

Prudil, Lukas. Privacy and confidentiality — old concept, new challenges. *Medicine and Law: The World Association for Medical Law* 2006 September; 25(3): 573-580. Subject: 8.4

Prudil, Lukás; Kure, Josef. Research ethics committees in the Czech Republic. *In:* Beyleveld, D.; Townend, D.; Wright, J., eds. Research Ethics Committees, Data Protection and Medical Research in European Countries. Hants, England; Burlington, VT: Ashgate; 2005: 31-34. Subject: 18.2

Pruitt, Sandi L.; Mullen, Patricia Dolan. Contraception or abortion? Inaccurate descriptions of emergency contraception in newspaper articles, 1992-2002. *Contraception* 2005 January; 71(1): 14-21. Subject: 11.1

Pruitt, Sandi L.; Mullen, Patricia Dolan. Response to letters to the editor regarding contraception or abortion? Inaccurate descriptions of emergency contraception in newspaper articles, 1992-2002 [letter]. *Contraception* 2005 November; 72(5): 396-397. Subject: 11.1

Pruss, Alexander R. Complicity, fetal tissue, and vaccines. *National Catholic Bioethics Quarterly* 2006 Autumn; 6(3): 461-470. Subject: 9.5.1

Prystay, Cris; Hiebert, Murray; Linebaugh, Kate. Companies face ethical issues over Tamiflu. *Wall Street Journal* 2006 January 16; p. B1, B3. Subject: 9.7

Psaty, Bruce M.; Rennie, Drummond. Clinical trial investigators and their prescribing patterns: another dimension to the relationship between physician investigators and the pharmaceutical industry [editorial]. *JAMA: The Journal of the American Medical Association* 2006 June 21; 295(23): 2787-2790. Subject: 9.7

Psaty, Bruce M.; Weiss, Noel S.; Furberg, Curt D. Recent trials in hypertension: compelling science or commercial speech? *JAMA: The Journal of the American Medical Association* 2006 April 12; 295(14): 1704-1706. Subject: 1.3.9

Pucci, Eugenio; Belardinelli, Natascia; Borsetti, Gabriele; Rodriguez, Daniele; Signorino, Mario. Information and competency for consent to pharmacologic clinical trials in Alzheimer disease: an empirical analysis in patients and family caregivers. *Alzheimer Disease and Associated Disorders* 2001 July- September 15(3): 146-154. Subject: 18.3

Puckrein, Gary. BiDil: from another vantage point. *Health Affairs* 2006 July-November; (Web Exclusives): 368-374. Subject: 15.11

See SUBJECT HEADING KEY FOR SECTION II on inside back cover.

Puckrein, Gary; Yancy, Clyde W. BiDil's impact [letter and response]. *Nature Biotechnology* 2005 November; 23(11): 1343-1344. Subject: 15.1

Puigpelat Marti, Francesca. Sex selection: legal aspects and critical appraisal = La selección de sexo: aspectos jurídicos y valoración crítica. *Revista de Derecho Genoma Humano = Law and the Human Genome Review* 1997 January-June; (6): 85-100. Subject: 14.3

Purdy, Isabell B. Embracing bioethics in neonatal intensive care, part I: evolving toward neonatal evidence-based ethics. *Neonatal Network* 2006 January-February; 25(1): 33-42. Subject: 20.5.2

Purdy, Isabell B.; Wadhwani, Rita T. Embracing bioethics in neonatal intensive care, part II: case histories in neonatal ethics. *Neonatal Network* 2006 January-February; 25(1): 43-53. Subject: 20.5.2

Purdy, Jedediah S. Dolly and Madison. *American Prospect* 1998 May-June; 38: 88-94. Subject: 15.1

Purdy, L. Women's reproductive autonomy: medicalisation and beyond. *Journal of Medical Ethics* 2006 May; 32(5): 287-291. Subject: 12.1

Puri, Vinod K. Death in the ICU: feelings of those left behind. *Chest* 2003 July; 124(1): 11-12. Subject: 20.4.1

Purtilo, Ruth B. Attention to caregivers and hope: overlooked aspects of ethics consultation. *Journal of Clinical Ethics* 2006 Winter; 17(4): 358-363. Subject: 20.4.1

Purtilo, Ruth B. Beyond disclosure: seeking forgiveness [editorial]. *Physical Therapy* 2005 November; 85(11): 1124-1126. Subject: 8.2

Pustovit, Svitlana V. Some methodological aspects of ethics committees' expertise: the Ukrainian example. *Science and Engineering Ethics* 2006 January; 12(1): 85-94. Subject: 9.6

Putnina, Aivita. Population genome project in Latvia: exploring the articulation of agency. *In:* Sándor, Judit, ed. Society and Genetic Information: Codes and Laws in the Genetic Era. Budapest, Hungary; New York: CEU Press; 2003: 233-245. Subject: 15.1

Puzio, Dorothy. An overview of public health in the new millenium: individual liberty vs. public safety. *Journal of Law and Health* 2003-2004; 18(2): 173-198. Subject: 9.1

Q

Qatarneh, Dania; Kashani, Shahram. Local ethics committees and specialised research [letter]. *BMJ: British Medical Journal* 2006 July 29; 333(7561): 261. Subject: 18.2

Qazi, Yureeda. Fabrication: crime in research [letter]. *Lancet* 2006 February 25-March 3; 367(9511): 649. Subject: 1.3.9

Qian, Wang. Chinese perspectives. *In:* Mitcham, Carl, ed. Encyclopedia of Science, Technology, and Ethics.

Farmington Hills, MI: Thomson/Gale, 2005: 317-325. Subject: 1.3.9

Qian, Wang; Qian, Qian. Population policy in China. *In:* Mitcham, Carl, ed. Encyclopedia of Science, Technology, and Ethics. Farmington Hills, MI: Thomson/Gale, 2005: 1456-1458. Subject: 13.3

Qiu, Jane. Mighty mouse [news]. *Nature* 2006 December 14; 442(7121): 814-816. Subject: 22.2

Qiu, Xiangxing; Gao, Zhiyan. A retrospect on fifty years of education in medical ethics and future prospects in China. *In:* Döring, Ole; Chen, Renbiao, eds. Advances in Chinese Medical Ethics: Chinese and International Perspectives. Hamburg: Institut für Asienkunde; 2002: 393-400. Subject: 2.3

Quante, Michael. The indispensability of quality of life. *Human Reproduction and Genetic Ethics: An International Journal* 2006; 12(1): 13-15. Subject: 4.4

Queenan, John T. Elective cesarean delivery [editorial]. *Obstetrics and Gynecology* 2004 June; 103(6): 1135-1136. Subject: 9.5.5

Qui, Renzong. A vision of the role medical ethics could play in transforming Chinese society. *In:* Döring, Ole; Chen, Renbiao, eds. Advances in Chinese Medical Ethics: Chinese and International Perspectives. Hamburg: Institut für Asienkunde; 2002: 3-11. Subject: 2.1

Quick, Oliver. Outing medical errors: questions of trust and responsibility. *Medical Law Review* 2006 Spring; 14(1): 22-43. Subject: 9.8

Quill, Timothy E.; Kimsma, G.K. How much suffering is enough? *Medical Ethics Newsletter* 2006 Spring; 13(2): 10-11. Subject: 4.4

Quill, Timothy E.; Lo, Bernard; Brock, Dan W. Palliative options of last resort: a comparison of voluntary stopping eating and drinking, terminal sedation, physician-assisted suicide, and voluntary active euthanasia. *In:* Tännsjö, Torbjörn, ed. Terminal Sedation: Euthanasia in Disguise? Boston: Kluwer Academic Publishers; 2004: 1-14. Subject: 20.5.1

Quill, Timothy E.; McCann, Robert. Decision making for the cognitively impaired. *In:* Morrison, R. Sean; Meier, Diane E.; Capello, Carol, eds. Geriatric Palliative Care. New York: Oxford University Press; 2003: 332-341. Subject: 8.3.3

Quill, Timothy E.; Meier, Diane E. The big chill — inserting the DEA into end-of-life care. *New England Journal of Medicine* 2006 January 5; 354(1): 1-3. Subject: 20.7

Quinn, Carol. On learning how to care appropriately: a case for developing a model of support for those in need. *In:* Tong, Rosemarie; Donchin, Anne; Dodds, Susan, eds. Linking Visions: Feminist Bioethics, Human Rights, and the Developing World. Lanham, MD: Rowman and Littlefield Publishers; 2004: 105-118. Subject: 4.1.1

Subject = NRCBL Primary Classification Number; see inside front cover.

Quintana, Octavi. Human Rights and Biomedicine Convention: a consensus convention = El Convenio de Derechos Humanos y Biomedicina: un convenio de consenso. *Revista de Derecho Genoma Humano = Law and the Human Genome Review* 1997 July-December; (7): 153-160. Subject: 2.1

R

Rabin, Cara. The medicated self: implications of Prozac on selfhood, embodiment, and identity. *Penn Bioethics Journal* 2006; 2(1): 4p. [Online]. Accessed: http://www.bioethicsjournal.com [2006 February 21]. Subject: 17.4

Rabin, Roni. A new vaccine for girls, but should it be compulsory? *New York Times* 2006 July 18; p. F5, F7. Subject: 9.5.5

Rabin, Sander. The human use of humanoid beings: chimeras and patent law. *Nature Biotechnology* 2006 May; 24(5): 517-519. Subject: 15.8

Rabino, Isaac. Research scientists surveyed on ethical issues in genetic medicine: a comparison of attitudes of US and European researchers. *New Genetics and Society* 2006 December; 25(3): 325-342. Subject: 15.3

Rabkin, Rebecca. From Kierkegaard to Kennedy: existentialist philosophy in the Supreme Court's decision in Planned Parenthood v. Casey and its effect on the right to privacy. *Hastings Constitutional Law Quarterly* 2004 Summer; 31(4): 611-635. Subject: 12.4.4

Racine, E.; Hayes, K. The need for a clinical ethics service and its goals in a community healthcare service centre: a survey. *Journal of Medical Ethics* 2006 October; 32(10): 564-566. Subject: 9.6

Racine, Eric; Gareau, Isabelle; Doucet, Hubert; Laudy, Danielle; Jobin, Guy; Schradeley-Desmond, Pamela. Hyped biomedical science or uncritical reporting? Press coverage of genomics (1992-2001) in Quebec. *Social Science and Medicine* 2006 March; 62(5): 1278-1290. Subject: 15.10

Rackoff, Wayne R.; Papadakis, Maxine A.; Rattner, Susan L.; Stern, David T. Unprofessional behavior among medical students [letter and reply]. *New England Journal of Medicine* 2006 April 27; 354(17): 1852-1853. Subject: 7.4

Radzikowski, Czeslaw. Protection of animal research subjects. *Science and Engineering Ethics* 2006 January; 12(1): 103-110. Subject: 22.2

Rae, Scott B. On the connection between sickness and sin: a commentary. *Christian Bioethics* 2006 August; 12(2): 151-156. Subject: 4.2

Raeburn, J.A. Genetic tests and insurance in the UK. *Reform* 2001 Spring; 79: 32-36, 72. Subject: 15.3

Rafferty, Philip. Roe v. Wade: a scandal upon the court. *Rutgers Journal of Law and Religion* 2005; 7(1): pp. 84

[Online] Accessed: http://org.law.rutgers.edu/publications/law-religion/articles/7_1_1.pdf [2006 December 5]. Subject: 12.4.2

Raffle, Angela E. Information about screening — is it to achieve high uptake or to ensure informed choice? *Health Expectations* 2001 June; 4(2): 92-98. Subject: 9.5.1

Rahmoeller, Glenn. Comments on Ethical Issues with Implantable Defibrillators by F. James Brennan. *Pacing and Clinical Electrophysiology* 2004 July; 27(7): 899. Subject: 9.4

Rai, Gurcharan S.; Blackman, Iva. Ethical issues in dementia. *In:* Rai, Gurcharan S, ed. Medical Ethics and the Elderly. 2nd ed. San Francisco: Radcliffe Medical Press; 2004: 125-137. Subject: 17.1

Rai, Saritha. Union disrupts plan to send ailing workers to India for cheaper medical care. *New York Times* 2006 October 11; p. C6. Subject: 9.3.1

Raine, Rosalind; McIvor, Martin. 9 years on: what progress has been made on achieving UK health-care equity? *Lancet* 2006 October 28-November 3; 368(9546): 1542-1545. Subject: 9.3.1

Räisänen, Ulla; Bekkers, Marie-Jet; Boddington, Paul; Sarangi, Srikant. The causation of disease — the practical and ethical consequences of competing explanations. *Medicine, Health Care and Philosophy* 2006; 9(3): 293-306. Subject: 4.2

Rajput, Vijay; Bekes, Carolyn E. Ethical issues in hospital medicine. *Medical Clinics of North America* 2002 July; 86(4): 869-886. Subject: 2.1

Ralph, Cheryl. Pregnancy in a hemodialysis patient with an ethical/cultural challenge. *CANNT Journal* 2000 January-March; 10(1): 35-38. Subject: 19.3

Ram, N.R. Britain's new preimplantation tissue typing policy: an ethical defense. *Journal of Medical Ethics* 2006 May; 32(5): 278-282. Subject: 15.2

Ram, Natalie. Regulating consent to human embryo research: a critique of Health Canada's proposal. *Health Law Review* 2006; 14(2): 19-27. Subject: 18.3

Ramanathan, Mala; Krishnan, Suneeta; Bhan, Anant. Reporting on the First National Bioethics Conference. *Indian Journal of Medical Ethics* 2006 January-March; 3(1): 27-30. Subject: 2.3

Ramasubbu, K.; Gurm, H.; Litaker, D. Gender bias in clinical trials: do double standards still apply? *Journal of Women's Health and Gender-Based Medicine* 2001 October; 10(8): 757-764. Subject: 18.5.3

Ramer-Chrastek, Joan; Thygeson, Megan V. A perinatal hospice for an unborn child with a life-limiting condition [case study]. *International Journal of Palliative Nursing* 2005 June; 11(6): 274-276. Subject: 15.2

See SUBJECT HEADING KEY FOR SECTION II on inside back cover.

693

Ramírez, Amparo Vélez. La eutanasia: el debat actual [Euthanasia: the current debate]. *Persona y Bioética* 1999 February-May; 2(6): 143-149. Subject: 20.5.1

Ramirez, Anthony. Medicine meets religion in organ donation debate. *New York Times* 2006 November 18; p. B2. Subject: 19.5

Ramsey, Bonnie W. Appropriate compensation of pediatric research participants: thoughts from an Institute of Medicine committee report. *Journal of Pediatrics* 2006 July; 149(1, Supplement): S15-S19. Subject: 18.5.2

Ramsey, Carolyn B. Restructuring the debate over fetal homicide laws. *Ohio State Law Journal* 2006; 67(4): 721-782. Subject: 12.4.2

Ramsey, Joanne. Fit for the 21st century? A review of surrogacy provisions within the Human Fertilisation and Embryology Act 1990. *Medical Law International* 2006; 7(4): 281-307. Subject: 14.2

Ramsey, Sara. The Adults with Incapacity (Scotland) Act — Who knows? Who cares? *Scottish Medical Journal* 2005 February; 50(1): 20-22. Subject: 8.3.3

Ramsey, Scott D.; Yoon, Paula; Moonesinghe, Ramal; Khoury, Muin J. Population-based study for the prevalence of family history of cancer: implications for cancer screening and prevention. *Genetics in Medicine* 2006 September; 8(9): 571-575. Subject: 15.3

Rancich, Ana María; Pérez, Marta Lucia; Morales, Celina; Gelpi, Ricardo Jorge. Beneficence, justice, and lifelong learning expressed in medical oaths. *Journal of Continuing Education in the Health Professions* 2005 Summer; 25(3): 211-220. Subject: 7.2

Randall, Fiona; Downie, R.S. Resuscitation and advance statements. *In their:* The Philosophy of Palliative Care: Critique and Reconstruction. New York: Oxford University Press, 2006: 125-148. Subject: 20.5.1

Randall, Susan. Health care reform and abortion. *Berkeley Women's Law Journal* 1994; 9: 58-76. Subject: 12.1

Randall, Vernellia R. Eliminating racial discrimination in health care: a call for state health care anti-discrimination law. *DePaul Journal of Health Care Law* 2006 Fall; 10(1): 1-25. Subject: 9.5.4

Randolph, A. Raymond. Before Roe v. Wade: Judge Friendly's draft abortion opinion. *Harvard Journal of Law and Public Policy* 2006 Summer; 29(3): 1035-1062. Subject: 12.4.1

Ranson, David. The "born alive" rule. *Journal of Law and Medicine* 2006 February; 13(3): 285-288. Subject: 4.4

Rao, Mala; Clarke, Aileen; Sanderson, Colin; Hammersley, Richard. Patients' own assessments of quality of primary care compared with objective records based measures of technical quality of care: cross sectional study. *BMJ: British Medical Journal* 2006 July 1; 333(7557): 19-22. Subject: 9.8

Rao, Radhika. Preimplantation genetic diagnosis and reproductive equality. *Gender Medicine* 2004 December; 1(2): 64-69. Subject: 15.2

Rapp, Rayna. The thick social matrix for bioethics: anthropological approaches. *In:* Rehmann-Sutter, Christoph; Düwell, Marcus; Mieth, Dietmar, eds. Bioethics in Cultural Contexts: Reflections on Methods and Finitude. Dordrecht: Springer, 2006: 341-351. Subject: 2.1

Rappaport, Richard G. Losing your rights: complications of misdiagnosis [editorial]. *Journal of the American Academy of Psychiatry and the Law* 2006; 34(4): 436-438. Subject: 17.3

Rascher, Wolfgang. Ethische Fragen bei der Behandlung von Früh- und Neugeborenen. *In:* Vollmann, Jochen, ed. Medizin und Ethik: Aktuelle ethische Probleme in Therapie und Forschung. Erlangen: Universitätsbund Erlangen-Nürnberg, 2003: 15-30. Subject: 20.4.2

Rascol, Olivier. Assessing the risk of a necessary harm: placebo surgery in Parkinson disease [editorial]. *Neurology* 2005 October 11; 65(7): 982-983. Subject: 18.3

Rashotte, Judy. Relational ethics in critical care [editorial]. *Australian Critical Care* 2006 February; 19(1): 4-5. Subject: 20.5.2

Rasmussen, Lisa M. Engineering, gerrymandering and expertise in public bioethics. *HEC (Healthcare Ethics Committee) Forum* 2006 June; 18(2): 125-130. Subject: 2.4

Ratanakul, Pinit. Bioethics and AIDS in Thailand: a Buddhist perspective. *In:* Sang-yong, Song; Young-Mo, Koo; Macer, Darryl R.J., eds. Asian Bioethics in the 21st Century. Christchurch, NZ: Eubios Ethics Institute, 2002: 299-301. Subject: 9.5.6

Rautio, Arja; Sunnari, Vappu; Nuutinen, Matti; Laitala, Marja. Mistreatment of university students most common during medical studies. *BMC Medical Education* 2005 October 18; 5(36): 12 p. Subject: 7.2

Ravetz, Jerome R. Taming the technological imperative: a comment. *Politics and the Life Sciences* 1989 February; 7(2): 145-147. Subject: 15.7

Ravichandran, Balaji. AIDS: a cause for optimism? *BMJ: British Medical Journal* 2006 December 2; 333(7579): 1179. Subject: 9.5.6

Ravitsky, Vardit; Wilfond, Benjamin S. Disclosing individual genetic results to research participants. *American Journal of Bioethics* 2006 November-December; 6(6): 8-17. Subject: 15.1

Ray, Pierre F. Ethics and genetics of carrier embryos [letter]. *Human Reproduction* 2006 October; 21(10): 2722-2723. Subject: 15.2

Ray, Susan L. Whistleblowing and organizational ethics. *Nursing Ethics* 2006 July; 13(4): 438-445. Subject: 7.3

Subject = NRCBL Primary Classification Number; see inside front cover.

Ray, Wayne A.; Stein, C. Michael. Reform of drug regulation — beyond an independent drug-safety board. *New England Journal of Medicine* 2006 January 12; 354(2): 194-201. Subject: 9.7

Raz, Aviad E.; Atar, Marcela. Upright generations of the future: tradition and medicalization in community genetics. *Journal of Contemporary Ethnography* 2004 June; 33(3): 296-322 [Online]. Accessed: http://jce.sagepub.com/cgi/reprint/33/3/296 [2007 January 24]. Subject: 15.2

Raza, Mohshin. Collaborative healthcare research: some ethical considerations. *Science and Engineering Ethics* 2005 April; 11(2): 177-186. Subject: 5.3

Read, Cynthia A. Neuroethics society launched. *Cerebrum: The Dana Forum on Brain Science* 2006 July: 1-2. Subject: 17.1

Reamer, Frederic G. Nontraditional and unorthodox interventions in social work: ethical and legal implications. *Families in Society* 2006 April-June; 87(2): 191-197. Subject: 1.3.1

Reardon, Jenny. Group consent and the informed, volitional subject. *In her:* Race to the Finish: Identity and Governance in an Age of Genomics. Princeton, NJ: Princeton University Press; 2005: 98-125. Subject: 15.11

Reardon, Jenny. The Human Genome Diversity Project: a case study in coproduction. *Social Studies of Science* 2001 June; 31(3): 357-388. Subject: 15.10

Redding, Richard E. Bias on prejudice? The politics of research and racial prejudice. *Psychological Inquiry* 2004; 15(4): 289-293. Subject: 18.4

Reddy, Bhavani S. The epidemic of unrelieved chronic pain: the ethical, societal, and regulatory barriers facing opioid prescribing physicians. *Journal of Legal Medicine* 2006 December; 27(4): 427-442. Subject: 4.4

Reddy, Hasini. HIV testing in pregnancy: a duty or a choice? *Canadian HIV/AIDS Policy and Law Newsletter* 1997 Spring; 3(2-3): 7-8. Subject: 9.5.6

Redies, Christoph; Viebig, Michael; Zimmermann, Susanne; Fröber, Rosemarie. Origin of corpses received by the anatomical institute at the University of Jena during the Nazi regime. *Anatomical Record (Part B, New Anatomy)* 2005 July; 285B(1): 6-10. Subject: 21.4

Reding, Raymond. Is it right to promote living donor liver transplantation for fulminant hepatic failure in pediatric recipients? *American Journal of Transplantation* 2005 July; 5(7): 1587-1591. Subject: 19.5

Redman, Barbara K.; Merz, Jon F. Research misconduct policies of high impact biomedical journals. *Accountability in Research* 2006 July-September; 13(3): 247-258. Subject: 1.3.9

Redman, Barbara K.; Templin, Thomas N.; Merz, Jon F. Research misconduct among clinical trial staff. *Science and Engineering Ethics* 2006 July; 12(3): 481-489. Subject: 1.3.9

Redman, B.K. Review of measurement instruments in clinical and research ethics, 1999-2003. *Journal of Medical Ethics* 2006 March; 32(3): 153-156. Subject: 2.1

Reed, Esther D. Property rights, genes, and common good. *Journal of Religious Ethics* 2006 March; 34(1): 41-67. Subject: 15.8

Reeder, Jean M. Withdrawal of life support in a competent patient. *AORN Journal* 1986 September; 44(3): 380, 382, 384. Subject: 20.5.1

Reeleder, David; Martin, Douglas K.; Keresztes, Christian; Singer, Peter A. What do hospital decision-makers in Ontario, Canada, have to say about the fairness of priority setting in their institutions? *BMC Health Services Research [electronic]* 2005 January 21; 5(1): 8; 6 p. Accessed: http://www.biomedcentral.com/1472-6963/5/8 [22 February 2006]. Subject: 9.4

Reese, Kimberly. Family presence at cardiopulmonary resuscitation: considerations in a rehabilitation hospital. *Topics in Stroke Rehabilitation* 2005 Spring; 12(2): 82-88. Subject: 20.5.1

Regalado, Antonio. The great gene grab. *Technology Review* 2000 September-October; 103(5): 48-51, 53, 55. Subject: 15.8

Regalado, Antonio. Scientist's study of brain genes sparks a backlash; Dr. Lahn connects evolution in some groups to IQ; debate on race and DNA; "Speculating is dangerous". *Wall Street Journal* 2006 June 16; p. A1, A12. Subject: 15.1

Regis, Catherine. Direct-to-consumer advertising for prescription drugs in Canada: beyond good or evil. *Health Law Review* 2006; 14(2): 28-33. Subject: 9.7

Regnard, Claud. Please do not resuscitate: solution is flawed [letter]. *BMJ: British Medical Journal* 2006 March 11; 332(7541): 608. Subject: 20.5.1

Regnard, Claud; Randall, Fiona. A framework for making advance decisions on resuscitation. *Clinical Medicine* 2005 July-August; 5(4): 354-360. Subject: 20.5.1

Rehak, Peter. Research ethics committees in Austria. *In:* Beyleveld, D.; Townend, D.; Wright, J., eds. Research Ethics Committees, Data Protection and Medical Research in European Countries. Hants, England; Burlington, VT: Ashgate; 2005: 3-7. Subject: 18.2

Rehmann-Sutter, Christoph. Das soziale Design der Hoffnungen. *In:* Rehmann-Sutter, Christoph; Müller, Hansjakob, eds. Ethik und Gentherapie: zum praktischen Diskurs um die molekulare Medizin. 2nd ed. Tübingen: Francke Verlag; 2003: 275-286. Subject: 15.4

Rehmann-Sutter, Christoph. Keimbahnveränderungen in Nebenfolge?: Ethische Überlegungen zur Abgrenzbarkeit der somatischen Gentherapie. *In:* Rehmann-Sutter, Christoph; Müller, Hansjakob, eds. Ethik und Gentherapie: zum praktischen Diskurs um die

See SUBJECT HEADING KEY FOR SECTION II on inside back cover.

695

molekulare Medizin. Tübingen: Attempto Verlag; 1995: 154-175. Subject: 15.4

Rehmann-Sutter, Christoph. Keimbahnveränderungen in Nebenfolge?: Ethische Überlegungen zur Abgrenzbarkeit der somatischen Gentherapie. *In:* Rehmann-Sutter, Christoph; Müller, Hansjakob, eds. Ethik und Gentherapie: zum praktischen Diskurs um die molekulare Medizin. 2nd ed. Tübingen: Francke Verlag; 2003: 187-205. Subject: 15.4

Rehmann-Sutter, Christoph. Limits of bioethics. *In:* Rehmann-Sutter, Christoph; Düwell, Marcus; Mieth, Dietmar, eds. Bioethics in Cultural Contexts: Reflections on Methods and Finitude. Dordrecht: Springer, 2006: 59-79. Subject: 2.1

Rehmann-Sutter, Christoph. Politik der genetischen Identität: Gute und schlechte Gründe auf Keimbahntherapie zu verzichten. *In:* Rehmann-Sutter, Christoph; Müller, Hansjakob, eds. Ethik und Gentherapie: zum praktischen Diskurs um die molekulare Medizin. 2nd ed. Tübingen: Francke Verlag; 2003: 225-236. Subject: 15.4

Rehmann-Sutter, Christoph. Politik der genetischen Identität: Gute und schlechte Gründe auf Keimbahntherapie zu verzichten. *In:* Rehmann-Sutter, Christoph; Müller, Hansjakob, eds. Ethik und Gentherapie: zum praktischen Diskurs um die molekulare Medizin. Tübingen: Attempto Verlag; 1995: 176-187. Subject: 15.4

Rei, Wenmay; Yeh, Jiunn-Rong. Steering in the tides: National Bioethics Committee as an institutional solution to bio-politics? *In:* Sang-yong, Song; Young-Mo, Koo; Macer, Darryl R.J., eds. Asian Bioethics in the 21st Century. Christchurch, NZ: Eubios Ethics Institute, 2002: 363-375. Subject: 2.1

Reid, Coleen. Medicating "Margaret". *Journal of Clinical Ethics* 2006 Winter; 17(4): 340-343. Subject: 20.4.1

Reidenberg, Marcus M.; Zarin, Deborah A.; Tse, Tony; Ide, Nicholas, C.; Drazen, Jeffrey M.; Wood, Alastair J.J.; Haug, Charlotte; Gøtzsche, Peter C.; Schroeder, Torben V. Clinical trials report card [letter and replies]. *New England Journal of Medicine* 2006 March 30; 354(13): 1428-1429. Subject: 18.2

Reiheld, Alison. Erasure of past: how failure to remember can be a morally blameworthy act. *American Journal of Bioethics* 2006 September-October; 6(5): 25-26; discussion W30-W32. Subject: 9.5.4

Reiheld, Alison. An unexpected opening to teach the impact of interactions between healthcare personnel. *American Journal of Bioethics* 2006 July-August; 6(4): 29-30. Subject: 7.2

Reilly, Michael; Coghlan, Andy. To know or not to know. . . . *New Scientist* 2006 July 22-28; 191(2561): 8-9. Subject: 9.5.6

Reiner, William G. Prenatal gender imprinting and medical decision-making: genetic male neonates with severely inadequate penises. *In:* Sytsma, Sharon E., ed. Ethics and Intersex. Dordrecht: Springer, 2006: 153-163. Subject: 15.2

Reisman, Anna B. Outing the hidden curriculum. *Hastings Center Report* 2006 July-August; 36(4): 9. Subject: 4.1.2

Reitz, S. Maggie; Arnold, Melba; Franck, Linda Gabriel; Austin, Darryl J.; Hill, Diane; McQuade, Lorie J.; Knox, Daryl K.; Slater, Deborah Yarett. Occupational Therapy Code of Ethics (2005). *American Journal of Occupational Therapy* 2005 November-December; 59(6): 639-642. Subject: 6

Reiver, Joanna. The modern art of dying: a history of euthanasia in the United States by Shai J. Lavi [book review]. *Journal of Legal Medicine* 2006 March; 27(1): 109-118. Subject: 20.5.1

Rembis, Michael A. "I ain't been reading while on parole": experts, mental tests, and eugenic commitment law in Illinois, 1890-1940. *History of Psychology* 2004; 7(3): 225-247. Subject: 15.5

Renegar, Gaile; Webster, Christopher J.; Stuerzebecher, Steffen; Harty, Lea; Ide, Susan E.; Balkite, Beth; Rogalski- Salter, Taryn A.; Cohen, Nadine; Spear, Brian B.; Barnes, Diane M.; Brazell, Celia. Returning genetic research results to individuals: points-to-consider. *Bioethics* 2006 February; 20(1): 24-36. Subject: 15.1

Renker, Paula Rinard; Tonkin, Peggy. Women's views of prenatal violence screening: acceptability and confidentiality issues. *Obstetrics and Gynecology* 2006 February; 107(2, Part 1): 348-354. Subject: 9.5.5

Rennie, Drummond. Misconduct and journal peer review. *In:* Godlee, Fiona; Jefferson, Tom, eds. Peer Review in Health Sciences. 2nd ed. London: BMJ Books; 2003: 118-129. Subject: 1.3.7

Rennie, Stuart. Is it ethical to study what ought not to happen? *Developing World Bioethics* 2006 May; 6(2): 71-77. Subject: 7.1

Rennie, Stuart; Behets, Frieda. AIDS care and treatment in Sub-Saharan Africa: implementation ethics. *Hastings Center Report* 2006 May-June; 36(3): 23-31. Subject: 9.5.6

Rennie, Stuart; Behets, Frieda. Desperately seeking targets: the ethics of routine HIV testing in low-income countries. *Bulletin of the World Health Organization* 2006 January; 84(1): 52-57. Subject: 9.5.6

Rentmeester, Christy A. Moral priorities in a teaching hospital: commentary. *Hastings Center Report* 2006 November-December; 36(6): 13-14. Subject: 7.2

Rentmeester, Christy A. What's legal? What's moral? What's the difference? A guide for teaching residents.

American Journal of Bioethics 2006 July-August; 6(4): 31-33. Subject: 7.2

Renzong, Qiu. Bioethics: a search for moral diversity. *Eastern Mediterranean Health Journal* 2006; 12(Supplement 1): S21-S29 [Online]. Accessed: http://www.emro.who.int/publications/EMHJ/12_S/PDF/4.pdf [2007 January 3]. Subject: 2.1

Repenshek, Mark. The mechanism of action in intrauterine devices (IUD) as it relates to physician billing services. *Health Care Ethics USA* 2006; 14(2): E2 [Online]. Accessed: http://chce.slu.edu/Partnerships_HCE_Intro.html [2006 November 17]. Subject: 11.1

Repine, Thomas B.; Lisagor, Philip; Cohen, David J. The dynamics and ethics of triage: rationing care in hard times. *Military Medicine* 2005 June; 170(6): 505-509. Subject: 9.4

Repper-DeLisi, Jennifer; Kilroy, Susan M. "We need to meet". *Journal of Clinical Ethics* 2006 Spring; 17(1): 85-89. Subject: 8.1

Requejo, M. Teresa. Legal analysis of the Spanish basic law 41/2002 on the autonomy of the patient and the rights and obligations with regard to clinical information and documentation. *European Journal of Health Law* 2003 September; 10(3): 257-269. Subject: 8.4

Resnicoff, Steven H. The legal and halachic ramifications of brain death. *In:* Rosner, Fred, ed. Medicine and Jewish Law. Volume III. Brooklyn, NY: Yashar Books, Inc.; 2005: 91-109. Subject: 20.2.1

Resnik, David. Access to affordable medication in the developing world: social responsibility vs. profit. *In:* van Niekerk, Anton A.; Kopelman, Loretta M., eds. Ethics and AIDS in Africa: The Challenge to Our Thinking. Walnut Creek, CA: Left Coast Press; 2006: 111-126. Subject: 9.7

Resnik, David B. Biomedical research in the developing world: ethical issues and dilemmas. *In:* Iltis, Ana Smith, ed. Research Ethics. New York: Routledge, 2006: 132-146. Subject: 5.1

Resnik, David B. Compensation for research-related injuries: ethical and legal issues. *Journal of Legal Medicine* 2006 September; 27(3): 263-287. Subject: 18.3

Resnik, David B. Germ-line manipulations, private industry, and secrecy. *Politics and the Life Sciences* 1998 March; 17(1): 29-30. Subject: 15.4

Resnik, David B. The need for international stem cell agreements. *Nature Biotechnology* 2004 October; 22(10): 1207. Subject: 18.5.4

Resnik, David B.; Jones, Caitlin W. Research subjects with limited English proficiency: ethical and legal issues. *Accountability in Research* 2006 April-June; 13(2): 157-177. Subject: 18.5.9

Resnik, David B.; Orentlicher, David. Protection of human subjects and scientific progress: can the two be recon-

ciled? [letter and reply]. *Hastings Center Report* 2006 January-February; 36(1): 4-5, 8- 9. Subject: 18.3

Resnik, David B.; Portier, Christopher. Pesticide testing on human subjects: weighing benefits and risks. *Environmental Health Perspectives* 2005 July; 113(7): 813-817. Subject: 18.5.1

Resnik, David B.; Shamoo, Adil E.; Krimsky, Sheldon. Fraudulent human embryonic stem cell research in South Korea: lessons learned. *Accountability in Research* 2006 January-March; 13(1): 101- 109. Subject: 18.5.4

Resnik, David B.; Sharp, Richard R. Protecting third parties in human subjects research. *IRB: Ethics and Human Research* 2006 July-August; 28(4): 1-7. Subject: 18.2

Resnik, David B.; Vorhaus, Daniel B. Genetic modification and genetic determinism. *Philosophy, Ethics, and Humanities in Medicine* 2006; 1(9): 11 p. Subject: 15.1

Ressler-Maerlender, Jessamyn; Sorensen, Robyn E. Circumcision: an informed choice. *AWHONN Lifelines* 2005 April-May; 9(2): 146-150. Subject: 9.5.1

Reuben, Adrian. First do no harm. *Hepatology* 2006 February; 43(2, Supplement 1): S243-S249. Subject: 21.4

Reusser, Ruth. The new European Convention on Human Rights and Biomedicine = El nuevo Convenio Europeo sobre Derechos Humanos y Biomedicina. *Revista de Derecho Genoma Humano = Law and the Human Genome Review* 1997 July-December; (7): 161-169. Subject: 2.1

Rew, Lynn; Taylor-Seehafer, Margaret; Thomas, Nancy. Without parental consent: conducting research with homeless adolescents. *Journal of the Society of Pediatric Nurses* 2000 July-September; 5(3): 131-139. Subject: 18.5.2

Reyes, Heathe Luz McNaughton; Hord, Charlotte E.; Mitchell, Ellen M.H.; Blandon, Marta Maria. Invoking health and human rights to ensure access to legal abortion: the case of a nine-year old girl from Nicaragua. *Health and Human Rights: An International Journal* 2006; 9(2): 62-86. Subject: 12.4.2

Reynolds, Sandra M. ORI findings of scientific misconduct in clinical trials and publicly funded research, 1992-2002. *Clinical Trials* 2004; 1(6): 509-516. Subject: 1.3.9

Rhodes, Rosamond. Commentary: the professional obligation of physicians in times of hazard and need. *CQ: Cambridge Quarterly of Healthcare Ethics* 2006 Fall; 15(4): 424-428. Subject: 8.1

Rhodes, Rosamond. The ethical standard of care. *American Journal of Bioethics* 2006 March-April; 6(2): 76-78. Subject: 2.1

Ribas, Salvador Ribas. Empirical studies on healthcare ethics committees in the USA. A bibliographic review. *Formosan Journal of Medical Humanities* 2006 June; 7(1-2): 67-80. Subject: 9.6

See SUBJECT HEADING KEY FOR SECTION II on inside back cover.

697

Ricciardi-von Platen, Alice. Die Wurzeln des Euthanasiegedankens in Deutschland. *In:* Frewer, Andreas; Eickhoff, Clemens, eds. "Euthanasie" und die aktuelle Sterbehilfe-Debatte: Die historischen Hintergründe medizinischer Ethik. Frankfurt; New York: Campus; 2000: 46-64. Subject: 20.5.1

Rice, James A. Taking ourselves seriously: the relevance of Dworkinian principlism in genetic research. *Journal of Philosophy, Science and Law* 2006 March 20; 6: 14 p. Subject: 15.1

Rice, Mary. 'Inappropriate' regulation proposed for tissue engineering. *European Journal of Cancer* 2005 September; 41(14): 2035. Subject: 19.1

Rice, Natalie; Follette, Victoria M. The termination and referral of clients. *In:* O'Donohue, William; Ferguson, Kyle, eds. Handbook of Professional Ethics for Psychologists: Issues, Questions, and Controversies. Thousand Oaks, Calif.: SAGE Publications; 2003: 147-166. Subject: 8.1

Rice, Thomas. Should consumer choice be encouraged in health care? *In:* Davis, John B., ed. The Social Economics of Health Care. New York: Routledge; 2001: 9-39. Subject: 9.1

Rich, Ben A. The doctor as double agent. *Pain Medicine* 2005 September-October; 6(5): 393-395. Subject: 7.1

Rich, Ben A.; Casarett, David; Battin, Margaret P. Ethics forum. 75-year-old man has end-stage prostate cancer with metastases to bone. *Pain Medicine* 2005 November-December; 6(6): 459-463. Subject: 20.4.1

Rich, Robert F.; Ziegler, Julian. Genetic discrimination in health insurance — comprehensive legal solutions for a (not so) special problem? *Indiana Health Law Review* 2005; 2(1): 1-47. Subject: 15.1

Richards, David F. The central role of informed consent in ethical treatment and research with children. *In:* O'Donohue, William; Ferguson, Kyle, eds. Handbook of Professional Ethics for Psychologists: Issues, Questions, and Controversies. Thousand Oaks, Calif.: SAGE Publications; 2003: 377-359. Subject: 18.5.2

Richards, Erica. Loss of potential parenthood as a statutory solution to the conflict between wrongful death remedies and Roe v. Wade. *Washington and Lee Law Review* 2006 Spring; 63(2): 809-848. Subject: 12.4.2

Richards, Norvin. Choosing when to die. *Journal of Ethics* 2005; 9(3-4): 517-531. Subject: 20.1

Richardson, Jeff; McKie, John. Empiricism, ethics and orthodox economic theory: what is the appropriate basis for decision-making in the health sector? *Social Science and Medicine* 2005 January; 60(2): 265-275. Subject: 9.4

Richardson, Lynne D.; Rhodes, Rosamond; Ragin, Deborah Fish; Wilets, Ilene. The role of community consultation in the ethical conduct of research without con-

sent. *American Journal of Bioethics* 2006 May-June; 6(3): 33-35; discussion W46- W50. Subject: 18.3

Richardson, Ruth. Narratives of compound loss: parents' stories from the organ retention scandal. *In:* Hurwitz, Brian; Greenhalgh, Trisha; Skultans, Vieda, eds. Narrative Research in Health and Illness. Malden MA: BMJ Books; 2004: 239-256. Subject: 19.5

Richardson-Tench, Marilyn; Brookes, Alison; Hardley, Andrew. Nursing ethics in practice: issues for perioperative nursing. *Journal of Perioperative Practice* 2006 March; 16(3): 138, 140-143. Subject: 8.3.1

Richman, Kenneth A. A new theory of health: beneficence and recommendations for treatment. *Advances in Mind-Body Medicine* 2005 Summer; 21(2): 8-18. Subject: 4.2

Richmond, David E. The Auckland Hospital ethical committee 1977-1981. *New Zealand Medical Journal* 1983 July 27; 96(736): 569-572. Subject: 18.6

Richmond, Jon; Fletch, Andrew; Van Tongerloo, Robert. The international symposium on regulatory testing and animal welfare: recommendations on best scientific practices for animal care committees and animal use oversight. *ILAR Journal* 2002; 43(Supplement): S129-S132. Subject: 22.2

Richter, Lisa. Corporate sponsorships in dental education: solution or sellout? *CDS Review* 2005 September-October; 98(5): 12-17. Subject: 7.2

Richters, Juliet. Understanding sexual orientation: a plea for clarity. *Reproductive Health Matters* 1998 November; 6(12): 144-149 [Online] Accessed: http://www.sciencedirect.com [2007 January 31]. Subject: 10

Riddell, Mary. We have seen the future: genetically perfect children. What we need to see next are laws and regulations to ensure that time never arrives. *New Statesman (London, England:* 1996) 1997 February 21; 126: 19. Subject: 15.2

Ridker, Paul M. Incomplete financial disclosure for study of funding and outcomes in major cardiovascular trials [letter]. *JAMA: The Journal of the American Medical Association* 2006 June 21; 295(23): 2725-2726. Subject: 1.3.7

Ridker, Paul M.; Torres, Jose. Reported outcomes in major cardiovascular clinical trials funded by for-profit and not-for-profit organization: 2000-2005. *JAMA: The Journal of the American Medical Association* 2006 May 17; 295(19): 2270-2274. Subject: 1.3.9

Ries, Nola M.; Caulfield, Timothy. First pharmacogenomics, next nutrigenomics: genohype or genohealthy? *Jurimetrics* 2006 Spring; 46(3): 281-308. Subject: 15.1

Ries, N.M. Legal rights, constitutional controversies, and access to health care: lessons from Canada. *Medicine and*

Law: World Association for Medical Law 2006 March; 25(1): 45-57. Subject: 9.4

Riessman, Catherine Kohler. Exporting ethics: a narrative about narrative research in South India. *Health (London)* 2005 October; 9(4): 473-490. Subject: 18.5.9

Riessman, Catherine Kohler; Mattingly, Cheryl. Introduction: toward a context-based ethics for social research in health. *Health (London)* 2005 October; 9(4): 427-429. Subject: 18.3

Rietjens, Judith A.C.; van Delden, Johannes J.M.; van der Heide, Agnes; Vrakking, Astrid M.; Onwuteaka-Philipsen, Bregje D.; van der Maas, Paul J.; van der Waal, Gerrit. Terminal sedation and euthanasia. *Archives of Internal Medicine* 2006 April 10; 166(7): 749-753. Subject: 20.4.1

Rifkin, Dena. The elephant in the room. *Hastings Center Report* 2006 March-April; 36(2): 9. Subject: 9.5.1

Riga, Peter J. The authority of the Catholic Church over abortion. *Linacre Quarterly* 2006 May; 73(2): 194-196. Subject: 12.3

Rigby, Heather; Fernandez, Conrad V. Providing research results to study participants: support versus practice of researchers presenting at the American Society of Hematology annual meeting. *Blood* 2005 August 15; 106(4): 1199-1202. Subject: 18.1

Riley, James; Pristave, Robert. Legal mechanisms to protect dialysis patients' end-of-life decisions. *Nephrology News and Issues* 2005 June; 19(7): 53-54. Subject: 20.5.4

Riordan, Sara Hammer; Loescher, Lois J. Medical students' attitudes toward genetic testing of minors. *Genetic Testing* 2006 Spring; 10(1): 68-73. Subject: 15.3

Rios, A.R.; Conesa, C.C.; Ramírez, P.; Rodríguez, M.M.; Parrilla, P. Public attitude toward xenotransplantation: opinion survey. *Transplantation Proceedings* 2004 December; 36(10): 2901-2905. Subject: 19.1

Ripley, Elizabeth B.D. A review of paying research participants: it's time to move beyond the ethical debate. *Journal of Empirical Research on Human Research Ethics* 2006 December; 1(4): 9-20. Subject: 18.1

Ripley, Elizabeth B.D.; Macrina, Frank L.; Markowitz, Monika. Paying clinical research participants: one institution's research ethics committees' perspective. *Journal of Empirical Research on Human Research Ethics* 2006 December; 1(4): 37-44. Subject: 18.1

Ripol Carulla, Santiago. The protection of medical and genetic data in the Council of Europe's normative texts (part II) = La protección de los datos médicos y genéticos en la normativa del Consejo de Europa (Parte II). *Revista de Derecho Genoma Humano = Law and the Human Genome Review* 1997 January-June; (6): 101-127. Subject: 15.1

Risch, Neil; Burchard, Esteban; Ziv, Elad; Tang, Hua. Categorization of humans in biomedical research: genes, race and disease. *Genome Biology* 2002 July 1; 3(7): 1-11. Subject: 18.1

Ritchie, Elspeth Cameron; Mott, Robert L. Military humanitarian assistance: the pitfalls and promise of good intentions. *In:* Beam, Thomas E.; Sparacino, Linette R.; Pellegrino, Edmund D.; Hartle, Anthony E.; Howe, Edmund G., eds. Military Medical Ethics. Volume 2. Washington, DC: TMM Publications, Borden Institute, Walter Reed Army Medical Center; 2003: 805-830. Subject: 9.5.1

Ritchie, James L.; Wolk, Michael J.; Hirshfeld, John W., Jr.; Messer, Joseph V.; Peterson, Eric D.; Prystowsky, Eric N.; Gardner, Timothy J.; Kimball, Harry R.; Popp, Richard L.; Smaha, Lynn; Smith, Sidney C., Jr.; Wann, L. Samuel. Task force 4: appropriate clinical care and issues of "self-referral". *Journal of the American College of Cardiology* 2004 October 19; 44(8): 1740-1746. Subject: 7.3

Ritz, Sarah. The need for parity in health insurance benefits for the mentally and physically disabled: questioning inconsistency between two leading anti-discrimination laws. *Journal of Law and Health* 2003-2004; 18(2): 263-295. Subject: 9.3.1

Rivara, Frederick P.; Christakis, Dimitri A.; Cummings, Peter. Duplicate publication [editorial]. *Archives of Pediatrics and Adolescent Medicine* 2004 September; 158(9): 926. Subject: 1.3.7

Rivera-López, Eduardo. The claim from adoption revisited. *Bioethics* 2006 November; 20(6): 319-325. Subject: 14.1

Rivera-Lopez, Eduardo. Organ sales and moral distress. *Journal of Applied Philosophy* 2006; 23(1): 41-52. Subject: 19.5

Rivlin, Michael M. Can age-based rationing of health care be morally justified? *Mount Sinai Journal of Medicine* 1997 March; 64(2): 113-119. Subject: 9.4

Rizzo, Robert F. Safeguarding genetic information: privacy, confidentiality, and security? *In:* Davis, John B., ed. The Social Economics of Health Care. New York: Routledge; 2001: 257-284. Subject: 15.1

Robb, J. Wesley. The Christian and the new biology. *Encounter* 1981 Summer; 42(3): 197-205. Subject: 15.1

Robert, Jason Scott. Genetics and behavior. *In:* Mitcham, Carl, ed. Encyclopedia of Science, Technology, and Ethics. Farmington Hills, MI: Thomson/Gale, 2005: 849-854. Subject: 15.6

Robert, Jason Scott; Kirk, Dwayne D. Ethics, biotechnology, and global health: the development of vaccines in transgenic plants. *American Journal of Bioethics [Online]* 2006 July-August; 6(4): W29-W41. Subject: 15.1

Roberts, Dorothy E. Legal constraints on the use of race in biomedical research: toward a social justice framework.

See SUBJECT HEADING KEY FOR SECTION II on inside back cover.

699

Journal of Law, Medicine and Ethics 2006 Fall; 34(3): 526-534. Subject: 18.5.1

Roberts, Laura Weiss. Advancing our understanding of the ethics of schizophrenia research: the contribution of conceptual analyses and empirical evidence. *Schizophrenia Bulletin* 2006 January; 32(1): 20-21. Subject: 18.5.6

Roberts, Laura Weiss. Ethics and mental illness research. *Psychiatric Clinics of North America* 2002 September; 25(3): 525-545. Subject: 18.5.6

Roberts, Laura Weiss; Dunn, Laura B.; Green Hammond, Katherine A.; Warner, Teddy D. Do research procedures pose relatively greater risk for healthy persons than for persons with schizophrenia? *Schizophrenia Bulletin* 2006 January; 32(1): 153-158. Subject: 18.5.6

Roberts, Laura Weiss; Geppert, Cynthia M.A. Ethical use of long-acting medications in the treatment of severe and persistent mental illnesses. *Comprehensive Psychiatry* 2004 May-June; 45(3): 161-167. Subject: 17.4

Roberts, Laura Weiss; Geppert, Cynthia M.A.; Warner, Teddy D.; Green Hammond, Katherine A.; Lamberton, Leandrea Prosen. Bioethics principles, informed consent, and ethical care for special populations: curricular needs expressed by men and women physicians-in-training. *Psychosomatics* 2005 September-October; 46(5): 440-450. Subject: 7.2

Roberts, Laura Weiss; Hammond, Katherine Green; Hoop, Jinger. An inverse relationship between perceived harm and participation willingness in schizophrenia research protocols. *American Journal of Psychiatry* 2006 November; 163(11): 2002-2004. Subject: 18.5.6

Roberts, Laura Weiss; McAuliffe, Timothy L. Investigators' affirmation of ethical, safeguard, and scientific commitments in human research. *Ethics and Behavior* 2006; 16(2): 135-150. Subject: 1.3.9

Roberts, Laura Weiss; Warner, Teddy D.; Hammond, Katherine Green; Dunn, Laura B. Assessment by patients with schizophrenia and psychiatrists of relative risk of research procedures. *Psychiatric Services* 2006 November; 57(11): 1629-1635. Subject: 18.5.6

Roberts, Laura Weiss; Warner, Teddy D.; Hammond, Katherine Green; Geppert, Cynthia M.A.; Heinrich, Thomas. Becoming a good doctor: perceived need for ethics training focused on practical and professional development topics. *Academic Psychiatry* 2005 July-August; 29(3): 301-309. Subject: 7.2

Roberts, Laura Weiss; Warner, Teddy D.; Hammond, Katherine Green; Hoop, Jinger G. Views of people with schizophrenia regarding aspects of research: study size and funding sources. *Schizophrenia Bulletin* 2006 January; 32(1): 107-115. Subject: 18.3

Roberts, Melinda A. Supernumerary pregnancy, collective harm, and two forms of the nonidentity problem. *Jour-*

nal of Law, Medicine and Ethics 2006 Winter; 34(4): 776-792. Subject: 4.4

Robertson, Christopher. The consequences of qualified confidentiality. *American Journal of Bioethics* 2006 March-April; 6(2): 31-32. Subject: 8.4

Robertson, Gerald B. Informed consent in Canada: an empirical study. *Osgoode Hall Law Review* 1984 Spring; 22(1): 139-161. Subject: 8.3.1

Robertson, John A. Controversial medical treatment and the right to health care. *Hastings Center Report* 2006 November-December; 36(6): 15-20. Subject: 18.5.7

Robertson, John A. Embryo culture and the "culture of life": Constitutional issues in the embryonic stem cell debate. *University of Chicago Legal Forum* 2006: 1-40. Subject: 4.4

Robertson, John A. Ethics and the future of preimplantation genetic diagnosis. *Reproductive BioMedicine Online [electronic]* 2005 March; 10(Supplement 1): 97-101. Subject: 15.2

Robertson, John A. Regulation of assisted reproduction: the need for flexibility. *Human Reproduction* 1997 January; 12(1): 7-8. Subject: 14.6

Robertson, John A. Schiavo and its (in)significance. *Stetson Law Review* 2005 Fall; 35(1): 101-121. Subject: 20.5.1

Robichaud, Philip. Metaphysics and the morality at the boundaries of life. *Journal of Medicine and Philosophy* 2006 April; 31(2): 97-105. Subject: 4.4

Robins, Robert S.; Rothschild, Henry. Ethical dilemmas of the president's physician. *Politics and the Life Sciences* 1988 August; 7(1): 3-11. Subject: 8.4

Robins, Rosemary. Overburdening risk: policy frameworks and the public uptake of gene technology. *Public Understanding of Science* 2001 January; 10(1): 19-36. Subject: 15.1

Robinson, David; O'Neill, Desmond. Ethics of driving assessment in dementia: care, competence and communication. *In:* Rai, Gurcharan S, ed. Medical Ethics and the Elderly. 2nd ed. San Francisco: Radcliffe Medical Press; 2004: 103-111. Subject: 17.1

Robinson, Ellen M.; Good, Grace; Burke, Suzanne. Talking with Lorraine's mother and sister, five months after her death. *Journal of Clinical Ethics* 2006 Spring; 17(1): 94-96. Subject: 20.3.3

Robinson, Ellen M.; Hamel-Nardozzi, Marguerite. Stories of the silent: advocating for a disabled woman at end of life. *Topics in Stroke Rehabilitation* 2005 Summer; 12(3): 82-86. Subject: 9.5.1

Robinson, Shelby E. Organs for sale? An analysis of proposed systems for compensating organ providers. *University of Colorado Law Review* 1999 Summer; 70(3): 1019-1050. Subject: 19.5

Subject = NRCBL Primary Classification Number; see inside front cover.

Robley, Lois R. Increasing the availability of organs for transplantation: an ethical analysis. *Journal of the Medical Association of Georgia* 1998 April; 87(2): 113-116. Subject: 19.5

Roche, Patricia A.; Annas, George J. DNA testing, banking, and genetic privacy. *New England Journal of Medicine* 2006 August 10; 355(6): 545-546. Subject: 15.3

Rock, Melanie. Discounted lives? Weighing disability when measuring health and ruling on "compassionate" murder. *Social Science and Medicine* 2000; 51(3): 407-417. Subject: 20.5.2

Rock, Patricia J. Eugenics and euthanasia: a cause for concern for disabled people, particularly disabled women. *Disability and Society* 1996 March; 11(1): 121-127. Subject: 9.5.3

Rocker, Graeme M.; Cook, Deborah J.; O'Callaghan, Christopher J.; Pichora, Deborah; Dodek, Peter M.; Conrad, Wendy; Kutsogiannis, Demetrios J.; Heyland, Daren K. Canadian nurses' and respiratory therapists' perspectives on withdrawal of life support in the intensive care unit. *Journal of Critical Care* 2005 March; 20(1): 59-65. Subject: 20.5.1

Rockey, Don C.; Papadakis, Maxine A.; Rattner, Susan L.; Stern, David T. Unprofessional behavior among medical students [letter and reply]. *New England Journal of Medicine* 2006 April 27; 354(17): 1852-1853. Subject: 7.4

Rockhold, Frank W.; Krall, Ronald L. Trial summaries on results databases and journal publication. *Lancet* 2006 May 20-26; 367(9523): 1635-1636. Subject: 18.6

Rockwood, Kenneth. Capacity, population aging and professionalism [editorial]. *CMAJ/JAMC:Canadian Medical Association Journal* 2006 June 6; 174(12): 1689. Subject: 9.5.2

Rodgers, Sandra; Downie, Jocelyn. Abortion: ensuring access [editorial]. *CMAJ/JAMC: Canadian Medical Association Journal* 2006 July 4; 175(1): 9. Subject: 12.1

Rodgers, Willard; Nolte, Michael. Solving problems of disclosure risk in an academic setting: using a combination of restricted data and restricted access methods. *Journal of Empirical Research on Human Research Ethics* 2006 September; 1(3): 85-97. Subject: 8.3.1

Rodriguez, Alina; Tuvemo, Torsten; Hansson, Mats G. Parents' perspectives on research involving children. *Upsala Journal of Medical Sciences* 2006; 111(1): 73-86. Subject: 18.5.2

Rodriguez, Eva; Pinto, Jose Luis. The social value of health programmes: is age a relevant factor? *Health Economics* 2000 October; 9(7): 611-621. Subject: 4.4

Rodriguez, K.L.; Young, A.J. Perceptions of patients in utility or futility of end-of-life treatment. *Journal of Medical Ethics* 2006 August; 32(8): 444-449. Subject: 20.5.1

Rodriguez, Pablo; Shields, Wayne C. Religion and medicine [editorial]. *Contraception* 2005 April; 71(4): 302-303. Subject: 11.1

Rodriguez, Raoul P. Ethics in orthopedic practice [editorial]. *American Journal of Orthopedics* 2002 December; 31(12): 669-670. Subject: 4.1.2

Roelcke, Volker; Hohendorf, Gerrit; Rotzoll, Maike. Psychiatric research and 'euthanasia': the case of the psychiatric department at the University of Heidelberg, 1941-1945. *History of Psychiatry* 1994 December; 5(4:20): 517-532. Subject: 21.4

Roelcke, Volker; Hohendorf, Gerrit; Rotzoll, Maike. Psychiatrische Forschung, "Euthanasie" und der "Neue Mensch": Zur Debatte um Menschenbild und Wersetzungen im Nationalsozialismus. *In:* Frewer, Andreas; Eickhoff, Clemens, eds. "Euthanasie" und die aktuelle Sterbehilfe-Debatte: Die historischen Hintergründe medizinischer Ethik. Frankfurt; New York: Campus; 2000: 193-217. Subject: 18.5.6

Roels, Leo; Kalo, Zoltán; Boesebeck, Detlef; Whiting, James; Wight, Celia. Cost-benefit approach in evaluating investment into donor action: the German case. *Transplant International* 2003 May; 16(5): 321-326. Subject: 19.5

Roff, Sue Rabbitt. Thinking the unthinkable: selling kidneys. *BMJ: British Medical Journal* 2006 July 1; 333(7557): 51. Subject: 19.3

Rogausch, Anja; Prause, Daniela; Schallenberg, Anne; Brockmoller, Jurgen; Himmel, Wolfgang. Patients' and physicians' perspectives on pharmacogenetic testing. *Pharmacogenomics* 2006 January; 7(1): 49-59. Subject: 15.3

Rogawski, Michael A.; Suber, Peter. Support for the NIH public access policy [letter]. *Science* 2006 September 15; 313(5793): 1572. Subject: 1.3.9

Rogers, Alix. Transplantation of ovarian tissue. *Penn Bioethics Journal* 2006; 2(1): 4p. [Online]. Accessed: http://www.bioethicsjournal.com [2006 February 21]. Subject: 14.1

Rogers, Sharon. Why can't I visit? The ethics of visitation restrictions — lessons learned from SARS. *Critical Care* 2004 October; 8(5): 300-302. Subject: 9.1

Rogers, Wendy A. Feminism and public health ethics. *Journal of Medical Ethics* 2006 June; 32(6): 351-354. Subject: 9.1

Rogers, Wendy A. Pressures on confidentiality. *Lancet* 2006 February 18-24; 367(9510): 553-554. Subject: 8.4

Röggla, Georg. Medically enforced feeding of detained asylum seekers on hunger strike [letter]. *Wiener Klinische Wochenschrift* 2005 June; 117(11-12): 436. Subject: 21.5

Roginsky, Martin S.; Handley, Albert. Ethical implications of withdrawal of experimental drugs at the conclusion of phase III trials. *Clinical Research* 1978 December; 26(6): 384-388. Subject: 18.2

See SUBJECT HEADING KEY FOR SECTION II on inside back cover.

701

Roig, Miguel. Commentary: ethical writing should be taught. *BMJ: British Medical Journal* 2006 September 16; 333(7568): 596-597. Subject: 1.3.9

Rold, William J. 30 years after Estelle v. Gamble: a legal retrospective. *CorrectCare* 2006 Summer; 20(3): 7, 18. Subject: 9.5.1

Rolfsen, Michael L.; Bartlett, John G.; Hayden, Frederick G. The ethics of personal stockpiles [letter and reply]. *Annals of Internal Medicine* 2006 February 21; 144(4): 304-305. Subject: 9.2

Rollin, Bernard E. Animal research. *In his:* Science and Ethics. New York: Cambridge University Press; 2006: 99-128. Subject: 22.2

Rollin, Bernard E. Animal welfare. *In:* Mitcham, Carl, ed. Encyclopedia of Science, Technology, and Ethics. Farmington Hills, MI: Thomson/Gale, 2005: 80-83. Subject: 22.1

Rollin, Bernard E. Biotechnology and ethics I: is genetic engineering intrinsically wrong? *In his:* Science and Ethics. New York: Cambridge University Press; 2006: 129-154. Subject: 15.1

Rollin, Bernard E. Biotechnology and ethics II: rampaging monsters and suffering animals. *In his:* Science and Ethics. New York: Cambridge University Press; 2006: 155-184. Subject: 15.1

Rollin, Bernard E. Biotechnology and ethics III: cloning, xenotransplantation, and stem cells. *In his:* Science and Ethics. New York: Cambridge University Press; 2006: 185-214. Subject: 14.5

Rollin, Bernard E. Ethics and research on human beings. *In his:* Science and Ethics. New York: Cambridge University Press; 2006: 66-98. Subject: 18.1

Rollin, Bernard E. Pain and ethics. *In his:* Science and Ethics. New York: Cambridge University Press; 2006: 215-246. Subject: 4.4

Rollin, Bernard E. The regulation of animal research and the emergence of animal ethics: a conceptual history. *Theoretical Medicine and Bioethics* 2006; 27(4): 285-304. Subject: 22.2

Rolston, Holmes, III. What is a gene? From molecules to metaphysics. *Theoretical Medicine and Bioethics* 2006; 27(6): 471-497. Subject: 15.1

Roman, Kathleen M. Risk management assessment: dentists' ethical duty to provide emergency after-hours care. *Dental Assistant* 2005 March-April; 74(2): 30-31, 36. Subject: 8.1

Roman, Linda M.; Metules, Terri J. What we can learn from the Schiavo case. *RN* 2005 August; 68(8): 53-57, 60. Subject: 20.5.1

Romano, L.; de Conciliis, B.; Liguori, M.; Roseto, V. Technical procedure and ethical behaviour in biotechnologies of reproduction = Fare tecnico ed agire etico nelle biotecnologie della riproduzione. *Minerva Ginecologica* 2002 October; 54(5): 403-415. Subject: 14.1

Romeo Casabona, Carlos María. Legal limitations on research and its results? The cloning paradigm = ¿Límites jurídicos a la investigación y sus consecuencias? El paradigma de la clonación. *Revista de Derecho Genoma Humano = Law and the Human Genome Review* 1997 January-June; (6): 21-27. Subject: 14.5

Romero-Ortuño, Román. Access to health care for illegal immigrants in the EU: should we be concerned? *European Journal of Health Law* 2004 September; 11(3): 245-272. Subject: 9.2

Ron-El, R. Assisted reproductive technology and embryo production. *Human Reproduction* 1997 January; 12(1): 10. Subject: 14.6

Root, Michael. The problem of race in medicine. *Philosophy of the Social Sciences* 2001 March; 31(1): 20-39 [Online] Accessed: http://pos.sagepub.com/cgi/reprint/31/1/20 [2007 February 6]. Subject: 9.5.4

Root, Michael. The use of race in medicine as a proxy for genetic differences. *Philosophy of Science* 2003 December; 70(5): 1173-1183. Subject: 15.3

Rose, Hilary. A welcome alert to backdoor germ-line therapy. *Politics and the Life Sciences* 1998 March; 17(1): 34-35. Subject: 15.4

Rose, Nikolas. Becoming neurochemical selves. *In:* Stehr, Nico, ed. Biotechnology Between Commerce and Civil Society. New Brunswick, NJ: Transaction Publishers; 2004: 89-126. Subject: 17.4

Rose, Steven. Brain gain. *In:* Miller, Paul; Wilsdon, James, eds. Better Humans?: The Politics of Human Enhancement and Life Extension. London: Demos, 2006: 69-78. Subject: 4.5

Rosell, Tarris D. After Terri—an ethics of reciprocity. *Practical Bioethics* 2006 Spring-Summer; 2(2-3): 8-10, 12. Subject: 20.5.1

Rosell, Tarris D. An ethics conflict and culture: should this kidney be used? *Pediatric Nursing* 2006 January-February; 32(1): 68-70. Subject: 19.5

Rosen, Gary. What would a clone say? A humanist case against therapeutic cloning. *New York Times Magazine* 2005 November 27; p. 19, 20. Subject: 14.5

Rosen, Jeffrey. The day after Roe. *Atlantic Monthly* 2006 June; 297(5): 56-66. Subject: 12.4.2

Rosen, Michael. Defining death: the interaction of ethics and Halachah. *CCAR Journal: A Reform Jewish Quarterly* 2006 Fall; 53(4): 44-61. Subject: 20.2.1

Rosenberg, Helane S.; Epstein, Yakov M. Equity in egg donation. *Journal of Gender, Race and Justice* 2006 Spring; 9(3): 569-590. Subject: 14.2

Rosenberg, Joshua David. Informed consent and sham surgery as a placebo in fetal cell transplant research for

Parkinson's disease. *Einstein Quarterly Journal of Biology and Medicine* 2003; 20(1): 14-18. Subject: 18.5.4

Rosenblatt, Michael. Is it ethical to conduct placebo-controlled clinical trials in the development of new agents for osteoporosis? An industry perspective. *Journal of Bone and Mineral Research* 2003 June; 18(6): 1142- 1145. Subject: 18.3

Rosendorff, C. Voluntary total fasting: ethical-medical considerations. *World Medical Journal* 1989; 36: 82-83. Subject: 21.5

Rosenstock, Linda. Protecting special interests in the name of "good science". *JAMA: The Journal of the American Medical Association* 2006 May 24-31; 295(20): 2407-2410. Subject: 1.3.9

Rosenthal, Elisabeth. British rethinking test rules after drug trial nearly kills 6. *New York Times* 2006 April 8; p. A1, A6. Subject: 18.6

Rosenthal, Elisabeth. Excommunication is sought for stem cell researchers. *New York Times* 2006 July 1; p. A3. Subject: 18.5.4

Rosenthal, Elisabeth. Inquiries in Britain uncover loopholes in drug trials. *New York Times* 2006 August 3; p. A3. Subject: 18.6

Rosenthal, Joshua P. Politics, culture, and governance in the development of prior informed consent in indigenous communities. *Current Anthropology* 2006 February; 47(1): 119-142. Subject: 18.3

Rosenthal, Mark A.; Sarson-Lawrence, M.; Alt, C.; Arkell, K.; Dodds, M. Ethics committee reviews and mutual acceptance: a pilot study. *Internal Medicine Journal* 2005 November; 35(11): 650-654. Subject: 18.2

Rosenthal, Meredith; Daniels, Norman. Beyond competition: the normative implications of consumer-driven health plans. *Journal of Health Politics, Policy, and Law* 2006 June; 31(3): 671-685. Subject: 9.3.1

Rosenwaks, Zev; Davis, Owen K. On the disposition of cryopreserved human embryos: an opinion. *Human Reproduction* 1997 June; 12(6): 1121. Subject: 14.6

Rosenzweig, Mary; Knudsen, Lisbeth. Research ethics committees in Denmark. *In:* Beyleveld, D.; Townend, D.; Wright, J., eds. Research Ethics Committees, Data Protection and Medical Research in European Countries. Hants, England; Burlington, VT: Ashgate; 2005: 35-39. Subject: 18.2

Roskies, Adina. Neuroethics for the new millenium. *Neuron* 2002 July 3; 35(1): 21-23. Subject: 17.1

Rosner, Fred. Gifts to physicians from drug companies. *In:* Rosner, Fred, ed. Medicine and Jewish Law. Volume III. Brooklyn, NY: Yashar Books, Inc.; 2005: 177-190. Subject: 9.7

Rosner, Fred. Hospice care for the terminally ill: help or hindrance [editorial]. *Cancer Investigation* 2005; 23(3): 281-282. Subject: 20.4.1

Rosner, Fred. Medical confidentiality and patient privacy: the Jewish perspective. *Cancer Investigation* 2006 February; 24(1): 113-115. Subject: 8.4

Rosner, Fred. Pig organs for transplantation: a Jewish view. *In:* Rosner, Fred, ed. Medicine and Jewish Law. Volume III. Brooklyn, NY: Yashar Books, Inc.; 2005: 149-160. Subject: 19.1

Rosner, Fred. Research and/or training on the newly dead: the Jewish perspective. *Mount Sinai Journal of Medicine* 1997 March; 64(2): 120-124. Subject: 7.2

Rosner, Fred. The Terri Schiavo case in Jewish law [op-ed]. *Cancer Investigation* 2005; 23(7): 652. Subject: 20.5.1

Rospigliosi, Enrique Varsi. Genetic Law in Peru = El Derecho genético en el Perú. *Law and the Human Genome Review = Revista de Derecho y Genoma Humano* 1996 July-December; (5): 121-125. Subject: 15.1

Ross, Colin A. Overestimates of the genetic contribution to eating disorders. *Ethical Human Psychology and Psychiatry* 2006 Summer; 8(2): 123-131. Subject: 15.6

Ross, Colin A. The sham ECT literature: implications for consent to ECT. *Ethical Human Psychology and Psychiatry* 2006 Spring; 8(1): 17-28. Subject: 18.3

Ross, Daniel S. The two-faced angel: do Phase I clinical trials have a place in modern hospice? *Penn Bioethics Journal* 2006; 2(2): 46-49. Subject: 18.5.7

Ross, Heather M. Islamic tradition at the end of life. *MedSurg Nursing* 2001 April; 10(2): 83-87. Subject: 20.4.1

Ross, John K.; Ross, Sherry K.; McClung, Bruce A. Ethical decision making and organizational behavior: a case of life and death. *HEC (Healthcare Ethics Committee) Forum* 2006 September; 18(3): 193-206. Subject: 9.1

Ross, Karen. When volunteers are not healthy. *EMBO Reports* 2005 December; 6(12): 1116-1119. Subject: 8.2

Ross, Lainie Friedman. Ethical considerations related to pregnancy in transplant recipients. *New England Journal of Medicine* 2006 March 23; 354(12): 1313-1316. Subject: 19.1

Ross, Lainie Friedman. The ethical limits in expanding living donor transplantation. *Kennedy Institute of Ethics Journal* 2006 June; 16(2): 151-172. Subject: 19.5

Ross, Lainie Friedman. Heterozygote carrier testing in high schools abroad: what are the lessons for the U.S.? *Journal of Law, Medicine and Ethics* 2006 Winter; 34(4): 753-764. Subject: 15.3

Ross, Lainie Friedman. Phase I research and the meaning of direct benefit. *Journal of Pediatrics* 2006 July; 149(1, Supplement): S20-S24. Subject: 18.5.2

See SUBJECT HEADING KEY FOR SECTION II on inside back cover.

703

Ross, Lainie Friedman. Should a PVS patient be a live organ donor? *Medical Ethics Newsletter [Lahey Clinic]* 2006 Winter; 13(1): 3. Subject: 19.5

Ross, Lainie Friedman. What is wrong with the Physician Charter on Professionalism. *Hastings Center Report* 2006 July-August; 36(4): 17-19. Subject: 4.1.2

Ross, Lainie Friedman; Glannon, Walter. A compounding of errors: the case of bone marrow donation between non-intimate siblings. *Journal of Clinical Ethics* 2006 Fall; 17(3): 220-226. Subject: 19.5

Ross, Lainie Friedman; Nelson, Robert M.; Wendler, David; Belsky, Leah; Thompson, Kimberly M.; Emanuel, Ezekiel J. Pediatric research and the federal minimal risk standard [letter and reply]. *JAMA: The Journal of the American Medical Association* 2006 February 15; 295(7): 759-760. Subject: 18.5.2

Ross, Lainie Friedman; Zenios, Stefanos; Thistlethwaite, J. Richard, Jr. Shared decision making in deceased-donor transplant. *Lancet* 2006 July 22-28; 368(9532): 333-337. Subject: 19.6

Rossetti, Jeanette; Fox, Patricia G.; Burns, Kenneth. Advocating for the rights of the mentally ill: a global issue. *International Journal of Psychiatric Nursing Research* 2005 September; 11(1): 1211-1217. Subject: 9.5.3

Rotarius, Timothy; Oetjen, Dawn. The comprehensive organizational plan revisited: building in an ethical component. *Dialysis and Transplantation* 2005 March; 34(3): 150, 152, 157-158,185. Subject: 19.3

Roth, Kevin A. Journal of Histochemistry and Cytochemistry editorial policies and ethical guidelines [editorial]. *Journal of Histochemistry and Cytochemistry* 2006 February; 54(2): 129-130. Subject: 1.3.7

Rothman, Barbara Katz. The consequences of sex selection. *Chronicle of Higher Education* 2006 February 24; 52(25): B16. Subject: 14.3

Rothman, Barbara Katz. A sociological skeptic in the brave new world. *Gender and Society* 1998 October; 12(5): 501-504. Subject: 15.1

Rothman, Kenneth J.; Evans, Stephen. More on JAMA's policy on industry sponsored studies [letter]. *BMJ: British Medical Journal* 2006 February 25; 332(7539): 489. Subject: 18.2

Rothschild, Alan. Gardner; Re BWV: resolved and unresolved issues at end of life. *Journal of Law and Medicine* 2004 February; 11(3): 292-311. Subject: 20.5.1

Rothschild, Barbra Bluestone; Estroff, Sue E.; Churchill, Larry R. The cultural calculus of consent. *Clinical Obstetrics and Gynecology* 2005 September; 48(3): 574-594. Subject: 8.3.1

Rothstein, Mark A. Applications of behavioural genetics: outpacing the science? *Nature Reviews Genetics* 2005 October; 6(10): 793-798. Subject: 15.6

Rothstein, Mark A. Tiered disclosure options promote the autonomy and well-being of research subjects. *American Journal of Bioethics* 2006 November-December; 6(6): 20-21; author reply W10-W13. Subject: 18.3

Rothstein, Mark A.; Schneider, Carl E. Is HIPAA flawed, or unnecessary? [letter and reply]. *Hastings Center Report* 2006 July-August; 36(4): 6-7. Subject: 8.4

Rothstein, Mark A.; Talbott, Meghan K. Compelled disclosure of health information: protecting against the greatest potential threat to privacy. *JAMA: The Journal of the American Medical Association* 2006 June 28; 295(24): 2882-2885. Subject: 8.4

Rothstein, Mark A.; Talbott, Meghan K. The expanding use of DNA in law enforcement: what role for privacy? *Journal of Law, Medicine and Ethics* 2006 Summer; 34(2): 153-164. Subject: 15.1

Roughgarden, Joan. Genetic engineering versus diversity. *In her:* Evolution's Rainbow: Diversity, Gender, and Sexuality in Nature and People. Berkeley: University of California Press; 2004: 306-326. Subject: 15.1

Rouse, Carol Moxley. Paradigms and politics: shaping health care access for sickle cell patients through the discursive regimes of biomedicine. *Culture Medicine and Psychiatry* 2004 September; 28(3): 369-399. Subject: 9.5.4

Rousseau, Paul. The ethics of palliative sedation. *Caring* 2004 November; 23(11): 14-19. Subject: 20.4.1

Rovie, Eric M. Abortion: approaches from virtue. *Auslegung* 2002 Winter-Spring; 25(2): 137-150. Subject: 12.3

Rowan, Andrew N. Animal activism and intimidation of scientists [letter]. *Science* 2006 November 10; 314(5801): 923. Subject: 22.2

Rowe, John W.; Gatz, Margaret. Implications of genetic knowledge for public policy. *Generations: Journal of the American Society of Aging* 2000 Spring; 24(1): 79-83. Subject: 15.1

Rowland, Debran. The reproductive rights of "new medicine.". *In her:* The Boundaries of Her Body: The Troubling History of Women's Rights in America. Naperville, IL: Sphinx Pub.; 2004: 397-460. Subject: 14.1

Rowley, Beverley D.; Baldwin, DeWitt C., Jr.; Bay, R. Curtis; Cannula, Marco. Can professional values be taught? A look at residency training. *Clinical Orthopaedics and Related Research* 2000 September; (378): 110-114. Subject: 7.2

Rowley, Beverley D.; Baldwin, DeWitt C., Jr.; Bay, R. Curtis; Karpman, Robert R. Professionalism and professional values in orthopaedics. *Clinical Orthopaedics and Related Research* 2000 September; (378): 90-96. Subject: 7.2

Roy Choudhury, Shormila; Knapp, Leslie A. A review of international and UK-based ethical guidelines for researchers conducting nontherapeutic genetic studies in developing countries. *European Journal of Human Genetics* 2006 January; 14(1): 9-16. Subject: 18.2

Roy, David. Access to sterile needles for young people under the age of 14: an ethical analysis [letter]. *Canadian HIV/AIDS Policy and Law Newsletter* 1996 April; 2(3): 4. Subject: 9.5.9

Royal College of Physicians of London. Assisted Dying for the Terminally Ill Bill: A Consultation. London: Royal College of Physicians of London, 2006 May 9; 2 p. [Online]. Accessed: http://www.rcplondon.ac.uk/college/statements/statements_assisted_dying_02.htm [2006 August 18]. Subject: 20.7

Royal College of Physicians of London. Clarification of RCP position on the Assisted Dying Bill. London: Royal College of Physicians of London 2004 December 9; 1 p. [Online]. Accessed: http://www.rcplondon.ac.uk/college/statements/statements_assisted_dying_01.htm [2006 August 18]. Subject: 20.7

Royal College of Physicians of London. Human Tissue Bill. Response from the Royal College of Physicians. London: Royal College of Physicians of London 2004 June 16; 4 p. [Online]. Accessed: http://www.rcplondon.ac.uk/college/statements/response_htb.htm [2006 August 18]. Subject: 19.5

Royal College of Physicians of London. Mental Capacity Bill: Briefing from the Royal College of Physicians. London: Royal College of Physicians of London 2004 July 22; 6 p. [Online]. Accessed: http://www.rcplondon.ac.uk/college/statements/response_mcb.htm [2006 August 18]. Subject: 8.3.3

Royal College of Physicians of London. Position statement on the use of animals in medical research. London: Royal College of Physicians of London 2005 April 20; 1 p. [Online]. Accessed: http://www.rcplondon.ac.uk/college/statements/statements_animal_research.htm [2006 August 18]. Subject: 22.2

Royal College of Physicians of London. The relationship between physicians and the biomedical industries: advice of the Royal College of Physicians. London: Royal College of Physicians of London 2004 December 6; 4 p. [Online]. Accessed: http://www.rcplondon.ac.uk/college/statements/advice_biomedIndustry.htm [2006 August 18]. Subject: 9.7

Royal College of Physicians of London. Written evidence to the House of Lords Select Committee on the Assisted Dying for the Terminally Ill Bill [HL]: Written evidence collated by The Royal College of Physicians of London on behalf of The Academy of Medical Royal Colleges. London: Royal College of Physicians of London 2004 September 7; 3 p. [Online]. Accessed: http://www.rcplondon.ac.uk/college/statements/statements_assisted_dying.htm [2006 August 18]. Subject: 20.7

Royal College of Physicians of London. Clinical Effectiveness and Evaluation Unit. HIV testing for patients attending general medical services: national guidelines [and patient card insert]. London: Royal College of Physicians, 2005 March; 10 p. Subject: 9.5.6

Royal College of Physicians of London. Committee on Ethical Issues in Medicine. Response to Patient (Assisted Dying) Bill 2003: Royal College of Physicians Committee on Ethical Issues. London: Royal College of Physicians of London 2003 July 23; 4 p. [Online]. Accessed: http://www.rcplondon.ac.uk/college/statements/padb_response.htm [2006 August 18]. Subject: 20.7

Royal College of Physicians of London; Royal College of Pathologists [RCPath]; British Society for Human Genetics [BSHG]; Farndon, Peter; Douglas, Fiona. Consent and confidentiality in genetic practice: guidance on genetic testing and sharing genetic information. A report of the Joint Committee on Medical Genetics. London: Royal College of Physicians [RCP]; Royal College of Pathologists [RCPath]; British Society of Human Genetics [BSHG], 2006 April; 30 p. Subject: 8.3.1

Roychowdhury, Viveka. Audits of clinical trials in India: a step in the right direction. *Journal of Biolaw and Business* 2006; 9(3): 26-28. Subject: 18.6

Roychowdhury, Viveka. Good clinical practice (GCP) standards: clinical trials in India. An interview with Dr. Urmila Thatte, Head of Clinical Pharmacology, TN Medical College and BYL Nair Hospital. *Journal of Biolaw and Business* 2006; 9(3): 30-31. Subject: 18.6

Royse, Susan D. Implications of genetic testing for sudden cardiac death syndrome. *British Journal of Nursing* 2006 November 9-22; 15(20): 1104-1107. Subject: 15.3

Rozovsky, L.E.; Rozovsky, F.A. The Stephen Dawson case: judging the right to survive. *Canadian Doctor* 1983 June; 49(6): 48-50. Subject: 20.5.2

Rubenstein, Donald S. The fears of looking in the mirror. *Politics and the Life Sciences* 1998 March; 17(1): 31-32. Subject: 15.4

Rubenstein, Leonard S. A new medical ethic: physicians and the fight for human rights. *Harvard International Review* 1998 Summer; 20(3): 54-57. Subject: 21.1

Rubin, Paul. Indian givers: the Havasupai trusted the white man to help with a diabetes epidemic. Instead, ASU tricked them into bleeding for academia. *Phoenix New Times* 2004 May 27; 9 p. [Online]. Accessed: http://www.phoenixnewtimes.com/Issues/2004-05-27/news/feature_print.html [2006 December 28]. Subject: 18.3

Rubin, Philip; Sieber, Joan E. Empirical research on IRBs and methodologies usually associated with minimal risk [editorial]. *Journal of Empirical Research on Human Research Ethics* 2006 December; 1(4): 1-4. Subject: 18.2

Rubin, Susan E.; Grumet, Surah; Prine, Linda. Hospital religious affiliation and emergency contraceptive pre-

See SUBJECT HEADING KEY FOR SECTION II on inside back cover.

705

scribing practices. *American Journal of Public Health* 2006 August; 96(8): 1398-1401. Subject: 11.1

Rudd, Gene. Avoiding pregnancy: "a plan" versus Plan B. *Annals of Pharmacotherapy* 2004 September; 38(9): 1535-1536. Subject: 11.1

Ruddick, William. "Biographical lives" revisited and extended. *Journal of Ethics* 2005; 9(3-4): 501-515. Subject: 20.1

Rudermand, Carly; Tracy, C. Shawn; Benismon, Cécile M.; Bernstein, Mark; Hawryluck, Laura; Zlotnik Shaul, Randi; Upshur, Ross E.G. On pandemics and the duty to care: whose duty? who cares? *BMC Medical Ethics [electronic]* 2006; 7:5. Accessed: http://www.biomedcentral.com/1472-6939/7/5 [nd]. Subject: 8.1

Rudge, David. Do unknown risks preclude informed consent? *Essays in Philosophy* 2003 June; 4(2): 10 p. [Online]. Accessed: http://www.humboldt.edu/~essays/rudge.html [2004 December 24]. Subject: 8.3.1

Rudoren, Jodi. Kansas' top court limits abortion record search; attorney general's inquiry will continue. *New York Times* 2006 February 4; p. A7. Subject: 12.4.1

Rudoren, Jodi. Stem cell work gets states' aid after Bush veto. *New York Times* 2006 July 25; p. A1, A16. Subject: 5.3

Rudze, Laima. Research ethics committees in Latvia. *In:* Beyleveld, D.; Townend, D.; Wright, J., eds. Research Ethics Committees, Data Protection and Medical Research in European Countries. Hants, England; Burlington, VT: Ashgate; 2005: 127-139. Subject: 18.2

Ruebner, Ralph; Reis, Leslie Ann. Hippocrates to HIPAA: a foundation for a federal physician-patient privilege. *Temple Law Review* 2004 Fall; 77(3): 505-576. Subject: 8.4

Ruel, Michael D. Using race in clinical research to develop tailored medications: is the FDA encouraging discrimination or eliminating traditional disparities in health care for African Americans? *Journal of Legal Medicine* 2006 June; 27(2): 225-241. Subject: 18.2

Ruff, Tilman A.; Haikal-Mukhtar, Hadia. Doctors, drugs, information and ethics: a never-ending story [editorial]. *Medical Journal of Australia* 2005 July 18; 183(2): 73-74. Subject: 9.7

Rugemalila, J.B.; Kilama, W.L. Proceedings of the seminar on health research ethics in Africa. *Acta Tropica* 2001 January; 78(Supplement 1): S1-S126. Subject: 18.2

Ruger, Theodore W. The United States Supreme Court and health law: the year in review. *Journal of Law, Medicine and Ethics* 2006 Winter; 34(4): 817-820. Subject: 20.7

Ruipeng, Lei. Is cross-species infection morally irrelevant in xenotransplantation? *In:* Sang-yong, Song; Young-Mo, Koo; Macer, Darryl R.J., eds. Asian Bioethics in the 21st Century. Christchurch, NZ: Eubios Ethics Institute, 2002: 139-140. Subject: 19.1

Ruiz, Amparo; Perez, Inmaculada; Pellicer, Antonio. Cryostorage of human embryos: time to decide. *Human Reproduction* 1996 April; 11(4): 703-705. Subject: 14.6

Rupert, Patricia A.; Kozlowski, Neal F.; Hoffman, Laura A.; Daniels, Denise D.; Piette, Jeanne M. Practical and ethical issues in teaching psychological testing. *Professional Psychology: Research and Practice* 1999 April; 30(2): 209-214. Subject: 18.4

Rurup, Mette L.; Muller, Martien T.; Onwuteaka-Philipsen, Bregje D.; van der Heide, Agnes; van der Wal, Gerrit; van der Maas, Paul J. Requests for euthanasia or physician-assisted suicide from older persons who do not have a severe disease: an interview study. *Psychological Medicine* 2005 May; 35(5): 665-671. Subject: 20.7

Rurup, Mette L.; Onwuteaka-Philipsen, Bregje D.; van der Heide, Agnes; van der Wal, Gerrit; Deeg, Dorly J.H. Frequency and determinants of advance directives concerning end-of-life care in The Netherlands. *Social Science and Medicine* 2006 March; 62(6): 1552-1563. Subject: 20.5.4

Ruse, Michael. Sociobiology. *In:* Mitcham, Carl, ed. Encyclopedia of Science, Technology, and Ethics. Farmington Hills, MI: Thomson/Gale, 2005: 1820-1823. Subject: 15.9

Rushton, J. Philippe. The pioneer fund and the scientific study of human differences. *Albany Law Review* 2002; 66: 207-262. Subject: 15.5

Russano, Jennifer. Is boutique medicine a new threat to American health care or a logical way of revitalizing the doctor-patient relationship? *Washington University Journal of Law and Policy* 2005; 17: 313-340. Subject: 9.3.1

Russell, Alex. A hidden xenophobia of our own? (Does "The Commons" hide a fear of the new diversity genetic engineering might bring?). *World Watch* 2002 September-October; 15(5): 7-8. Subject: 15.1

Russell, Barbara J. It's not just a wound. *Ostomy Wound Management* 2005 April; 51(4): 82-87. Subject: 4.2

Russell, C.; O'Neill, D. Ethicists and clinicians: the case for collaboration in the teaching of medical ethics. *Irish Medical Journal* 2006 January; 99(1): 25-27. Subject: 2.3

Russo, Eugene. Follow the money — the politics of embryonic stem cell research. *PLoS Biology* 2005 July; 3(7): 1167-1171. Subject: 18.5.4

Russo, Gene. Home health tests are 'genetic horoscopes' [news]. *Nature* 2006 August 3; 442(7102): 497. Subject: 15.3

Russo, Nancy Felipe; Denious, Jean E. Controlling birth: science, politics, and public policy. *Journal of Social Issues* 2005 March; 61(1): 181-191. Subject: 13.3

Subject = NRCBL Primary Classification Number; see inside front cover.

Rutkiewicz, Malgorzata. Towards a human rights-based contraceptive policy; a critique of anti-sterilisation law in Poland. *European Journal of Health Law* 2001 September; 8(3): 225-242. Subject: 11.3

Rutledge, Philip; Crookes, David; McKinstry, Brian; Maxwell, Simon R.J. Do doctors rely on pharmaceutical industry funding to attend conferences and do they perceive that this creates a bias in their drug selection? Results from a questionnaire survey. *Pharmacoepidemiology and Drug Safety* 2003 December; 12(8): 663-667. Subject: 9.7

Rutter, Michael. Why is the topic of genes and behavior controversial? *In his:* Genes and Behavior: Nature — Nurture Interplay Explained. Malden, MA; Oxford: Blackwell Pub.; 2006: 1-17. Subject: 15.6

Ryan, Maura. Justice and genetics: whose holy grail? *Health Progress* 2006 May-June; 87(3): 46-56. Subject: 15.1

Ryan, Maura A. The delivery of controversial services: reproductive health and ethical and religious directives. *In:* Guinn, David E., ed. Handbook of Bioethics and Religion. New York: Oxford University Press, 2006: 385-401. Subject: 14.1

Ryan, Rosemary. Palliative care for "Margaret". *Journal of Clinical Ethics* 2006 Winter; 17(4): 344-348. Subject: 20.4.1

Ryder, Richard D. Speciesism in the laboratory. *In:* Singer, Peter, ed. In Defense of Animals: The Second Wave. Malden, MA: Blackwell Pub.; 2006: 87-103. Subject: 22.2

Ryen, Tind Shepper. Human genome organization. *In:* Mitcham, Carl, ed. Encyclopedia of Science, Technology, and Ethics. Farmington Hills, MI: Thomson/Gale, 2005: 942-944. Subject: 15.1

Rynning, Elisabeth. The Swedish system for ethics review of biomedical research and processing of sensitive personal data. *In:* Beyleveld, D.; Townend, D.; Wright, J., eds. Research Ethics Committees, Data Protection and Medical Research in European Countries. Hants, England; Burlington, VT: Ashgate; 2005: 245-270. Subject: 18.2

S

Sabat, Steven R. Capacity for decision-making in Alzheimer's disease: selfhood, positioning and semiotic people. *Australian and New Zealand Journal of Psychiatry* 2005 November-December; 39(11-12): 1030-1035. Subject: 9.5.2

Sabatier, Sandrine. Steering Committee on Bioethics (CDBI): Working Party on Human Genetics (CDBI-CO-GT4). Strasbourg: Council of Europe [COE]. Steering Committee on Bioethics, 1997 October 27: 40 p. [Online]. Accessed: http://www.coe.int/t/e/legal_affairs/ legal_co-operation/bioethics/texts_and_documents/ DIR-JUR(97)13Genetics.pdf [2007 March 5]. Subject: 15.3

Sabin, James. "Disappointing but fair": the connector's challenge. *Hastings Center Report* 2006 September-October; 36(5): 26-28. Subject: 9.2

Sabin, James; Fanelli, Robert; Flaherty, Helen; Istfan, Nawfal; Mariner, Wendy; Barnes, Janet Nally; Pratt, Janey S.A.; Rossi, Laura; Samour, Patricia. Best practice guidelines on informed consent for weight loss surgery patients. *Obesity Research* 2005 February; 13(2): 250-253. Subject: 8.3.1

Sacchini, Dario; Di Pietro, Maria Luisa; Spagnolo, Antonio G. Genetic screening: benefits and pitfalls. *In:* Glasa, J., ed. Ethics of Human Genetics: Challenges of the (Post) Genomic Era. Bratislava, Slovak Republic: Charis [and] IMEB Foundation; 2002: 131-151. Subject: 15.3

Sachedina, Abdulaziz. "No harm, no harassment": major principles of health care in Islam. *In:* Guinn, David E., ed. Handbook of Bioethics and Religion. New York: Oxford University Press, 2006: 265-289. Subject: 2.1

Sachs, Magna Andreen. Sedation — unconsciousness — anaesthesia! What are we talking about? *In:* Tännsjö, Torbjörn, ed. Terminal Sedation: Euthanasia in Disguise? Boston: Kluwer Academic Publishers; 2004: 31-35. Subject: 20.4.1

Sacred Congregation for the Doctrine of the Faith. Declaration on euthanasia. *In:* Tännsjö, Torbjörn, ed. Terminal Sedation: Euthanasia in Disguise? Boston: Kluwer Academic Publishers; 2004: 134-140. Subject: 20.5.1

Sade, Robert M. Issues of social policy and ethics in gene technology. *Methods and Findings in Experimental and Clinical Pharmacology* 1994 September; 16(7): 477-489. Subject: 15.1

Sadler, Troy D.; Zeidler, Dana L. The morality of socioscientific issues: construal and resolution of genetic engineering dilemmas. *Science Education* 2004 January; 88(1): 4-27. Subject: 15.4

Safjan, Marek. L'enseignment de la bioéthique dans la Pologne postcommuniste. *Journal International de Bioéthique = International Journal of Bioethics* 2005 September-December; 16(3-4):97-104, 174. Subject: 2.3

Safranek, Louis; Brugger, E. Christian. Reconsidering ANT-OAR [letter and reply]. *First Things* 2006 October; (166): 5-7. Subject: 18.5.4

Saga, Tadashi. Care for the elderly in Japan: past, present and future. *In:* Takahashi, Takao, ed. Taking Life and Death Seriously: Bioethics from Japan. Amsterdam; Boston: Elsevier JAI; 2005: 139-173. Subject: 9.5.2

Sahm, S.; Will, R.; Hommel, G. What are cancer patients' preferences about treatment at the end of life, and who should start talking about it? A comparison with healthy people and medical staff. *Supportive Care in Cancer* 2005 April; 13(4): 206-214. Subject: 20.4.1

See SUBJECT HEADING KEY FOR SECTION II on inside back cover.

707

Saini, Pushpinder. The doctrine of double effect and the law of murder. *Medico-Legal Journal* 1999; 67(Part 3): 106-120. Subject: 20.5.1

Sakamoto, Hyakudai. Genome, artificial evolution and global community. *In:* Sleeboom, Margaret, ed. Genomics in Asia: A Clash of Bioethical Interests? New York: Kegan Paul; 2004: 135-144. Subject: 15.1

Saks, Elyn R. Competency to refuse psychotropic medication: three alternatives to the law's cognitive standard. *University of Miami Law Review* 1993 January; 47(3): 689-761. Subject: 8.3.3

Saks, Elyn R. Involuntary outpatient commitment. *Psychology, Public Policy, and Law* 2003 March-June; 9(1-2): 94-106. Subject: 17.7

Saks, Elyn R.; Dunn, Laura B.; Palmer, Barton W. Meta-consent in research on decisional capacity: a "Catch-22"? *Schizophrenia Bulletin* 2006 January; 32(1): 42-46. Subject: 18.3

Salako, S.E. The declaration of Helsinki 2000: ethical principles and the dignity of difference. *Medicine and Law: The World Association for Medical Law* 2006 June; 25(2): 341-354. Subject: 18.2

Saleem, Sarah; Fikree, Fariyal F. The quest for small family size among Pakistani women — is voluntary termination of pregnancy a matter of choice or necessity? *Journal of the Pakistan Medical Association* 2005 July; 55(7): 288-291. Subject: 12.5.2

Saliga, Christopher M. Freedom at the end of life: voluntary death versus human flourishing. *National Catholic Bioethics Quarterly* 2006 Summer; 6(2): 253-262. Subject: 20.5.1

Salkever, Stephen G. Final causes and instant cases: a comment. *Politics and the Life Sciences* 1988 February; 6(2): 213-215; author's reply 223-225. Subject: 15.9

Salladay, Susan A. Putting your life on the line. *Nursing* 2006 February; 36(2): 24. Subject: 4.1.3

Salles, Arleen L.F. Bioethics, difference, and rights. *In:* Tong, Rosemarie; Donchin, Anne; Dodds, Susan, eds. Linking Visions: Feminist Bioethics, Human Rights, and the Developing World. Lanham, MD: Rowman and Littlefield Publishers; 2004: 57-72. Subject: 9.5.4

Salmon, Daniel A.; Teret, Stephen P.; MacIntyre, C. Raina; Salisbury, David; Burgess, Margaret A.; Halsey, Neal A. Compulsory vaccination and conscientious or philosophical exemptions: past, present, and future. *Lancet* 2006 February 4-10; 367(9508): 436-442. Subject: 9.5.1

Salter, Brian; Jones, Mavis. Biobanks and bioethics: the politics of legitimation. *Journal of European Public Policy* 2005 August; 12(4): 710-732. Subject: 15.1

Salter, Brian; Jones, Mavis. Regulating human genetics: the changing politics of biotechnology governance in the European Union. *Health, Risk and Society* 2002 November; 4(3): 325-340. Subject: 15.1

Salvage, Jane. More than a makeover is needed to improve nursing's image. *Journal of Advanced Nursing* 2006 May; 54(3): 259-260. Subject: 4.1.3

Samant, Padmaja. Learning to be humane. *Indian Journal of Medical Ethics* 2006 April-June; 3(2): 72. Subject: 12.4.2

Samanta, Ash; Samanta, Jo. Research governance: panacea or problem? *Clinical Medicine* 2005 May-June; 5(3): 235-239. Subject: 18.6

Samerski, Silja. Genetic counseling. *In:* Mitcham, Carl, ed. Encyclopedia of Science, Technology, and Ethics. Farmington Hills, MI: Thomson/Gale, 2005: 838-841. Subject: 15.2

Samerski, Silja. The unleashing of genetic terminology: how genetic counselling mobilizes for risk management. *New Genetics and Society* 2006 August; 25(2): 197-208. Subject: 15.2

Samuel, Gabrielle N.; Ankeny, Rachel A.; Kerridge, Ian H. Mixing metaphors in umbilical cord blood transplantation. *American Journal of Bioethics* 2006 November-December; 6(6): 58-59; author reply W13-W14. Subject: 19.4

Samuels, Alec. Can the doctor do nothing? Can the doctor be compelled to administer treatment? Can the doctor refuse or withhold or withdraw treatment? *Medico-Legal Journal* 2005; 73(Part 3): 112-114. Subject: 20.5.1

Samuels, Alec. Donor anonymity. *Medico-Legal Journal* 2005; 73(Part 2): 71-72. Subject: 14.4

Samuels, Alec. The duty to warn the patient. *British Journal of Neurosurgery* 2005 April; 19(2): 117-119. Subject: 8.3.1

Samuels, Alec. Serious professional misconduct. *Medico-Legal Journal* 2005; 73(Part 4): 166-168. Subject: 7.4

Sanchez-Sweatman, L.R. Reproductive cloning and human health: an ethical, international, and nursing perspective. *International Nursing Review* 2000 March; 47(1): 28-37. Subject: 14.5

Sanci, Lena A.; Sawyer, Susan M.; Kang, Melissa S.-L.; Haller, Dagmar M.; Patton, George C. Confidential health care for adolescents: reconciling clinical evidence with family values. *Medical Journal of Australia* 2005 October 17; 183(8): 410-414. Subject: 8.4

Sanci, Lena A.; Sawyer, Susan M.; Weller, Penny J.; Bond, Lyndal M.; Patton, George C. Youth health research ethics: time for a mature-minor clause? *Medical Journal of Australia* 2004 April 5; 180(7): 336-338. Subject: 18.5.2

Sandberg, David E. Growth hormone treatment for short stature: inferences from FDA decisions and clinical practice. *Atrium* 2006 Fall; 3: 13-15. Subject: 4.5

Sanders, Alan. Assent in medical decision-making with children. *Health Care Ethics USA* 2006; 14(1): E4 [Online]. Accessed: http://chce.slu.edu/Partnerships_HCE_Intro.html [2006 November 17]. Subject: 8.3.2

Sandin, Per. A paradox out of context: Harris and Holm on the precautionary principle. *CQ: Cambridge Quarterly of Healthcare Ethics* 2006 Spring; 15(2): 175-183. Subject: 5.3

Sandler, Ronald; Kay, W.D. The national nanotechnology initiative and the social good. *Journal of Law, Medicine and Ethics* 2006 Winter; 34(4): 675-681. Subject: 5.4

Sandman, Lars; Nordmark, Anders. Ethical conflicts in prehospital emergency care. *Nursing Ethics* 2006 November; 13(6): 592-607. Subject: 9.5.1

Sándor, Judit. Genetic data: old and new challenges in data protection. *In:* Glasa, J., ed. Ethics of Human Genetics: Challenges of the (Post) Genomic Era. Bratislava, Slovak Republic: Charis [and] IMEB Foundation; 2002: 89-97. Subject: 15.3

Sándor, Judit. Research ethics committees in Hungary. *In:* Beyleveld, D.; Townend, D.; Wright, J., eds. Research Ethics Committees, Data Protection and Medical Research in European Countries. Hants, England; Burlington, VT: Ashgate; 2005: 93-105. Subject: 18.2

Sangala, Vanessa. Safe abortion: a woman's right. *Tropical Doctor* 2005 July; 35(3): 130-133. Subject: 12.1

Sanghavi, Darshak M. Wanting babies like themselves, some parents choose genetic defects. *New York Times* 2006 December 5; p. F5, F8. Subject: 15.3

Saniotis, Arthur. Towards an embodiment of environmental bioethics. *Eubios Journal of Asian and International Bioethics* 2006 September; 16(5): 148-151. Subject: 2.1

Sankar, Pamela. Hasty generalisation and exaggerated certainties: reporting genetic findings in health disparities research. *New Genetics and Society* 2006 December; 25(3): 249-264. Subject: 15.1

Sankar, Pamela; Cho, Mildred K.; Wolpe, Paul Root; Schairer, Cynthia. What is in a cause? Exploring the relationship between genetic cause and felt stigma. *Genetics in Medicine* 2006 January; 8(1): 33-42. Subject: 15.3

Sankoorikal, Teena-Ann V. Using scientific advances to conceive the "perfect" donor: the Pandora's box of creating child donors for the purpose of saving ailing family members. *Seton Hall Law Review* 2002; 32(3): 583-616. Subject: 8.3.2

Sanner, Margareta A. Living with a stranger's organ — views of the public and transplant recipients. *Annals of Transplantation* 2005; 10(1): 9-12. Subject: 19.5

Santa Barbara, Joanna. Working for peace through health — ethical values and principles. *Croatian Medical Journal* 2005 December; 46(6): 1007-1009. Subject: 4.1.2

Santarlasci, Benedetta; Messori, Andrea; Pelagotti, Filippo; Trippoli, Sabrina; Vaiani, Monica. Heterogeneity in the evaluation of observational studies by Italian ethics committees. *Pharmacy World and Science* 2005 February; 27(1): 2-3. Subject: 18.2

Santelli, John S.; Speizer, Ilene S.; Avery, Alexis; Kendall, Carl. An exploration of the dimensions of pregnancy intentions among women choosing to terminate pregnancy or initiate prenatal care in New Orleans, Louisiana. *American Journal of Public Health* 2006 November; 96(11): 2009-2015. Subject: 12.5.1

Santora, Marc. In diabetes fight, raising cash and keeping trust. *New York Times* 2006 November 25; p. A1, B4. Subject: 9.5.1

Sarewitz, Daniel. Governance of science. *In:* Mitcham, Carl, ed. Encyclopedia of Science, Technology, and Ethics. Farmington Hills, MI: Thomson/Gale, 2005: 878-882. Subject: 5.3

Sargent, Carolyn; Smith-Morris, Carolyn. Questioning our principles: anthropological contributions to ethical dilemmas in clinical practice. *CQ: Cambridge Quarterly of Healthcare Ethics* 2006 Spring; 15(2): 123-134. Subject: 2.1

Sarmiento, Augusto. The relationship between orthopaedics and industry must be reformed. *Clinical Orthopaedics and Related Research* 2003 July; (412): 38-44. Subject: 9.7

Sarnaik, Ashok P.; Daphtary, Kshama; Sarnaik, Ajit A. Ethical issues in pediatric intensive care in developing countries: combining western technology and eastern wisdom. *Indian Journal of Pediatrics* 2005 April; 72(4): 339-342. Subject: 20.5.2

Sarojini, N.B.; Bhattacharya, Saswati. Such research cannot be in insolation. *Indian Journal of Medical Ethics* 2006 April-June; 3(2): 70. Subject: 1.3.9

Sarra, Janis. Contemporary corporate theory applied to the health care sector: a Canadian perspective. *Seattle Journal for Social Justice* 2004 Fall-Winter; 3(1): 345-385. Subject: 9.1

Sass, Hans-Martin. Ethical dilemma in stem cell research? *Formosan Journal of Medical Humanities* 2006 June; 7(1-2): 19-38. Subject: 18.5.4

Sass, Hans-Martin. Geriatric medicine and care: health literacy, health care and deathbed care. *In:* Döring, Ole; Chen, Renbiao, eds. Advances in Chinese Medical Ethics: Chinese and International Perspectives. Hamburg: Institut für Asienkunde; 2002: 433-443. Subject: 20.5.4

Sass, Hans-Martin; Wang, Yanguang. Geriatric medicine and care: ethical issues in providing and withholding treatment. *In:* Döring, Ole; Chen, Renbiao, eds. Advances in Chinese Medical Ethics: Chinese and International Perspectives. Hamburg: Institut für Asienkunde; 2002: 378-390. Subject: 9.5.2

See SUBJECT HEADING KEY FOR SECTION II on inside back cover.

709

Sassower, Raphael; Grodin, Michael A. Epistemological questions concerning death. *Death Studies* 1986 July-August; 10(4): 341-353. Subject: 20.2.1

Satel, Sally. Death's waiting list. *New York Times* 2006 May 15; p. A21. Subject: 19.5

Satel, Sally; Klick, Jonathan. Are doctors biased? *Policy Review* 2006 April-May; 136: 41-54. Subject: 9.2

Sato, Hajime; Akabayashi, Akira; Kai, Ichiro. Public, experts, and acceptance of advanced medical technologies: the case of organ transplant and gene therapy in Japan. *Health Care Analysis: An International Journal of Health Philosophy and Policy* 2006 December; 14(4): 203-214. Subject: 19.1

Satyapal, K.S. Ethics, transplantation, and the changing role of anatomists. *Clinical Anatomy* 2005 March; 18(2): 150-153. Subject: 19.5

Saucier, Donald A.; Cain, Mary E. The foundation of attitudes about animal research. *Ethics and Behavior* 2006; 16(2): 117-133. Subject: 22.2

Sauer, Mark V. Further HFEA restrictions on egg donation in the UK: two strikes and you're out! *Reproductive BioMedicine Online [electronic]* 2005; 10(4): 431-433. Subject: 14.4

Saugstad, Ola Didrik. When newborn infants are bound to die. *Acta Paediatrica* 2005 November; 94(11): 1535-1537. Subject: 20.5.2

Saul, Stephanie. Doctors object as drug makers learn who's prescribing what. *New York Times* 2006 May 4; p. A1, C4. Subject: 9.7

Saul, Stephanie. Drug makers pay for lunch as they pitch. *New York Times* 2006 July 28; p. A1, C7. Subject: 9.7

Saul, Stephanie. FDA shifts view on next-day pill; moves toward backing its sale over the counter. *New York Times* 2006 August 1; p. A1, A12. Subject: 11.1

Saul, Stephanie. Profit and questions as doctors offer prostate cancer therapy. *New York Times* 2006 December 1; p. A1, C7. Subject: 9.5.1

Saul, Stephanie. Unease on industry's role in hypertension debate. *New York Times* 2006 May 20; p. A1, C9. Subject: 9.7

Saunders, John. Assisted dying: considerations in the continuing debate. *Clinical Medicine* 2005 November-December; 5(6): 543-547. Subject: 20.5.1

Saunders, John. Developing clinical ethics committees. *Clinical Medicine* 2004 May-June; 4(3): 232-234. Subject: 9.6

Saunders, John. Ethics in practice [editorial]. *Clinical Medicine* 2005 July-August; 5(4): 315-316. Subject: 2.1

Saunders, William L., Jr. Lethal experimentation on human beings: Roe's effect on bioethics. *Fordham Urban Law Journal* 2004 March; 31(3): 817-830. Subject: 12.4.1

Saunders, William L., Jr. Washington insider: national developments. *National Catholic Bioethics Quarterly* 2006 Winter; 6(4): 629-636. Subject: 18.5.4

Sauri, Michael. Influence and drug marketing. *Maryland Medicine* 2005 Winter; 6(1): 24-25. Subject: 9.7

Sauri, Michael A. The politics of vaccine production. *Maryland Medicine* 2005 Winter; 6(1): 19-22. Subject: 9.7

Savage, Anne. Confidentiality versus public duty. *Journal of the Royal Society of Medicine* 2006 February; 99(2): 99-100. Subject: 8.4

Savage, Teresa A. Physician-nurse relationships and their effect on ethical nursing practice. *Journal of Clinical Ethics* 2006 Fall; 17(3): 260-265. Subject: 7.3

Saver, Richard S. Medical research oversight from the corporate governance perspective: comparing institutional review boards and corporate boards. *William and Mary Law Review* 2004 November; 46(2): 619-730. Subject: 18.2

Savulescu, Julian. Compulsory genetic testing for APOE Epsilon 4 and boxing. *In:* Tamburrini, Claudio; Tännsjö, Torbjörn, eds. Genetic Technology and Sport: Ethical Questions. London; New York: Routledge; 2005: 136-146. Subject: 15.3

Savulescu, Julian. Conscientious objection in medicine. *BMJ: British Medical Journal* 2006 February 4; 332(7536): 294-297. Subject: 8.1

Savulescu, Julian. New breeds of humans: the moral obligation to enhance. *Reproductive BioMedicine Online [electronic]* 2005 March; 10(Supplement 1): 36-39. Subject: 15.1

Savulescu, Julian. A utilitarian approach. *In:* Ashcroft, Richard; Lucassen, Anneke; Parker, Michael; Verkerk, Marian; Widderhoven, Guy, eds. Case Analysis in Clinical Ethics. New York: Cambridge University Press; 2005: 115-131. Subject: 15.3

Savulescu, Julian; Foddy, Bennett. Comment: genetic test available for sports performance. *British Journal of Sports Medicine* 2005 August; 39(8): 472. Subject: 15.3

Savulescu, Julian; Foddy, Bennett; Rogers, J. What should we say? *Journal of Medical Ethics* 2006 January; 32(1): 7-12. Subject: 8.1

Savulescu, Julian; Hemsley, Melanie; Newson, Ainsley; Foddy, Bennett. Behavioral genetics: why eugenic selection is preferable to enhancement. *Journal of Applied Philosophy* 2006; 23(2): 157-171. Subject: 15.5

Savulescu, Julian; Saunders, Rhodri. The "Hinxton Group" considers transnational stem cell research. *Hastings Center Report* 2006 May-June; 36(3): inside back cover. Subject: 18.5.4

Saw, K. Chee; Wood, Alison M.; Murphy, Karen; Parry, John R.W.; Hartfall, W. Guy. Informed consent: an evaluation of patients' understanding and opinion (with respect to the operation of transurethral resection of prostate). *Journal of the Royal Society of Medicine* 1994 March; 87(3): 143-144. Subject: 8.3.1

Sax, Joanna K. The states "race" with the Federal government for stem cell research. *Annals of Health Law* 2006 Winter; 15(1): 1-36. Subject: 18.5.4

Sayeed, Sadath A. The marginally viable newborn: legal challenges, conceptual inadequacies, and reasonableness. *Journal of Law, Medicine and Ethics* 2006 Fall; 34(3): 600-610. Subject: 20.5.2

Sayers, Gwen M.; Kapembwa, Moses S.; Green, Mary C. Advance refusals: does the law help? *Clinical Ethics* 2006 September; 1(3): 139-145. Subject: 20.5.4

Sayers, G.M.; Lloyd, D.A.; Gabe, S.M. Parenteral nutrition: ethical and legal considerations. *Postgraduate Medical Journal* 2006 February; 82(964): 79-83. Subject: 20.5.1

Sazama, Kathleen. Managing infectious or untested autologous blood components: the ethical dilemma of private rights versus public safety [editorial]. *Archives of Pathology and Laboratory Medicine* 2005 October; 129(10): 1212-1213. Subject: 19.4

Scanlan, Judith M.; Care, W. Dean; Gessler, Sandra. Dealing with the unsafe student in clinical practice. *Nurse Educator* 2001 January-February; 26(1): 23-27. Subject: 7.2

Scanlon, Colleen. Assisted suicide: how nurses should respond. *International Nursing Review* 1998 September-October; 45(5): 152. Subject: 20.7

Scardino, Peter T.; Farley, Suzanne J. The physician and conflict of interest [editorial]. *Nature Clinical Practice. Urology* 2005 March; 2(3): 113. Subject: 7.3

Schachter, Debbie; Kleinman, Irwin; Harvey, William. Informed consent and adolescents. *Canadian Journal of Psychiatry* 2005 August; 50(9): 534-540. Subject: 9.5.7

Schaefer, G. Bradley; Dunston, Georgia M. Health-care disparities in medical genetics. *In:* Satcher, David; Pamies, Rubens J., eds. Multicultural medicine and health disparities. New York: McGraw-Hill, 2006: 471-484. Subject: 15.1

Schäfer, Christof; Herbst, Manfred. Ethical aspects of patient information in radiation oncology: an introduction and a review of the literature. *Strahlentherapie und Onkologie* 2003 July; 179(7): 431-440. Subject: 8.3.1

Schäfer, D.; Kettner, M. Moral concern over cryopreserved human embryos: too much or too little? *Human Reproduction* 1997 January; 12(1): 10-11. Subject: 14.6

Schaffer, Amanda. A philosopher's take on the rhythm method is rattling opponents of abortion. *New York Times* 2006 June 13; p. F5, F8. Subject: 11.1

Schaffer, Randolph L., III; Kulkarni, Sanjay; Harper, Ann; Millis, J. Michael; Cronin, David C., II. The sickest first? Disparities with model for end-stage lever disease-based organ allocation: one region's experience. *Liver Transplantation* 2003 November; 9(11): 1211-1215. Subject: 19.6

Schaller, C.; Kessler, M. On the difficulty of neurosurgical end of life decisions. *Journal of Medical Ethics* 2006 February; 32(2): 65-69. Subject: 20.5.1

Schank, Janet; Slater, Rachel; Banerjee-Stevens, Devjani; Skovholt, Thomas M. Ethics of multiple overlapping relationships. *In:* O'Donohue, William; Ferguson, Kyle, eds. Handbook of Professional Ethics for Psychologists: Issues, Questions, and Controversies. Thousand Oaks, Calif.: SAGE Publications; 2003: 181-193. Subject: 8.1

Scharschmidt, Tiffany; Lo, Bernard. Clinical trial design issues raised during recombinant DNA. Advisory committee review of gene transfer protocols. *Human Gene Therapy* 2006 April; 17(4): 448-454. Subject: 15.4

Schaub, Diana J. Chimeras: from poetry to science. *National Catholic Bioethics Quarterly* 2006 Spring; 6(1): 29-35. Subject: 15.1

Schechter, Alan N. Integrity in research: individual and institutional responsibility. *In:* Gallin, John I., ed. Principles and Practice of Clinical Research. San Diego, CA: Academic Press; 2002: 39-50. Subject: 1.3.9

Scheer, Rebecca. Alberta: new bill will allow for mandatory HIV testing in emergency situations [news]. *HIV/AIDS Policy and Law Review* 2004 April; 9(1): 20-21. Subject: 9.5.6

Schei, Edvin. Doctoring as leadership: the power to heal. *Perspectives in Biology and Medicine* 2006 Summer; 49(3): 393-406. Subject: 8.1

Scheitle, Christopher P. In God we trust: religion and optimism toward biotechnology. *Social Science Quarterly* 2005 December; 86(4): 846-856. Subject: 5.1

Schenker, Joseph G. Assisted reproductive practice: religious perspectives. *Reproductive BioMedicine Online [electronic]* 2005 March; 10(3): 310-319. Accessed: http://www.rbmonline.com/Article/1539 [2005 September 30]. Subject: 14.4

Schenker, Joseph G. Ethical, religious and legal debate on IVF and alternate assisted reproduction. *In:* Masiach, S.; Ben-Rafael, Z.; Laufer, N.; Schenker, J.G., eds. Advances in Assisted Reproductive Technologies. New York: Plenum Press, 1990: 1041-1052. Subject: 14.4

Schenker, Joseph G.; Gdansky, Efraim. Ethical dilemmas in modern obstetrics [editorial]. *Prenatal and Neonatal Medicine* 1998 June; 3(3): 279-280. Subject: 9.5.8

Scheper-Hughes, Nancy. Bodies for sale — whole or in parts. *In:* Scheper-Hughes, Nancy; Wacquant, Loïc, eds.

See SUBJECT HEADING KEY FOR SECTION II on inside back cover.

711

Commodifying Bodies. Thousand Oaks, CA: SAGE Publications; 2002: 1-8. Subject: 4.4

Scheper-Hughes, Nancy. Commodity fetishism in organs trafficking. *In:* Scheper-Hughes, Nancy; Wacquant, Loïc, eds. Commodifying Bodies. Thousand Oaks, CA: SAGE Publications; 2002: 31-62. Subject: 19.5

Scheper-Hughes, Nancy. The global trade in human organs. *Current Anthropology* 2000 April; 41(2): 191-224. Subject: 19.1

Scheper-Hughes, Nancy. The last commodity: post-human ethics and the global traffic in "fresh" organs. *In:* Ong, Aihwa; Collier, Stephen J., eds. Global Assemblages: Technology, Politics, and Ethics as Anthropological Problems. Malden, MA: Blackwell Pub.; 2005: 145-167. Subject: 19.5

Scherer, F.M.; Watal, Jayashree. Post-TRIPS options for access to patented medicines in developing nations. *Journal of International Economic Law* 2002 December; 5(4): 913-939. Subject: 9.7

Scheurich, Neil. The prescriber as moralist: values in the antidepressant debate. *Perspectives in Biology and Medicine* 2006 Spring; 49(2): 199-208. Subject: 17.4

Schicktanz, Silke. Ethical considerations of the human-animal-relationship under conditions of asymmetry and ambivalence. *Journal of Agricultural and Environmental Ethics* 2006; 19(1): 7-16. Subject: 22.1

Schieve, Laura A. The promise of single-embryo transfer [editorial]. *New England Journal of Medicine* 2006 March 16; 354(11): 1190-1193. Subject: 14.4

Schieve, Laura A.; Rasmussen, Sonja A.; Buck, Germaine M.; Schendel, Diana E.; Reynolds, Meredith A.; Wright, Victoria C. Are children born after assisted reproductive technology at increased risk for adverse health outcomes? *Obstetrics and Gynecology* 2004 June; 103(6): 1154-1163. Subject: 14.1

Schildmann, Jan; Cushing, Annie; Doyal, Len; Vollmann, Jochen. Informed consent in clinical practice: pre-registration house officers' knowledge, difficulties and the need for postgraduate training. *Medical Teacher* 2005 November; 27(7): 649-651. Subject: 8.3.1

Schildmann, J.; Doyal, L.; Cushing, A.; Vollmann, J. Decisions at the end of life: an empirical study on the involvement, legal understanding and ethical views of pre-registration house officers. *Journal of Medical Ethics* 2006 October; 32(10): 567-570. Subject: 20.5.1

Schiller, M. Rosita. Ethics in the practice of dietetics. *Topics in Clinical Nutrition* 1997 March; 12(2): 1-11. Subject: 4.1.1

Schiller, M. Rosita. E-cheating: electronic plagiarism. *Journal of the American Dietetic Association* 2005 July; 105(7): 1058, 1060-1062. Subject: 7.2

Schlafly, Andrew L. Legal implications of a link between abortion and breast cancer. *Journal of American Physi-*

cians and Surgeons 2005 Spring; 10(1): 11-14. Subject: 12.1

Schlich-Bakker, Kathryn J.; ten Kroode, Herman F.J.; Ausems, Margreet G.E.M. A literature review of the psychological impact of genetic testing on breast cancer patients. *Patient Education and Counseling* 2006 July; 62(1): 13-20. Subject: 15.3

Schloendorn, John. Making the case for human life extension: personal arguments. *Bioethics* 2006 August; 20(4): 191-202. Subject: 20.5.1

Schlotzhauer, Anna V.; Liang, Bryan A. Definitions and implications of death. *Hematology/Oncology Clinics of North America* 2002 December; 16(6): 1397-1413. Subject: 20.2.1

Schmid, Hermann. Gentherapie aus juristischer Sicht — schweizerische und internationale Tendenzen. *In:* Rehmann-Sutter, Christoph; Müller, Hansjakob, eds. Ethik und Gentherapie: Zum praktischen Diskurs um die molekulare Medizin. Tübingen: Attempto Verlag; 1995: 137-153. Subject: 15.4

Schmidt, Kurt W. Ethische Uberlegungen zur klinischen Durchfuhrung somatischer Gentherapien. *In:* Rehmann-Sutter, Christoph; Müller, Hansjakob, eds. Ethik und Gentherapie: Zum praktischen Diskurs um die molekulare Medizin. Tübingen: Attempto Verlag; 1995: 83-108. Subject: 15.4

Schmidt, Sally D. Cheating: an ethical concern for nursing educators. *Kansas Nurse* 2006 January; 81(1): 1-2. Subject: 7.2

Schmidt, Terri A.; Delorio, Nicole M.; McClure, Katie B. The meaning of community consultation. *American Journal of Bioethics* 2006 May-June; 6(3): 30-32; discussion W46- W50. Subject: 18.6

Schmidt, Ulf. Cold War at Porton Down: informed consent in Britain's biological and chemical warfare experiments. *CQ: Cambridge Quarterly of Healthcare Ethics* 2006 Fall; 15(4): 366-380. Subject: 21.3

Schmidt, Ulf. Kriegsausbruch und "Euthanasie": Neue Forschungsergebnisse zum "Knauer Kind" im Jahre 1939. *In:* Frewer, Andreas; Eickhoff, Clemens, eds. "Euthanasie" und die aktuelle Sterbehilfe-Debatte: Die historischen Hintergründe medizinischer Ethik. Frankfurt; New York: Campus; 2000: 120-143. Subject: 20.5.2

Schmitz, Dagmar; Reinacher, Peter. C. Informed consent in neurology — translating ethical theory into action. *Journal of Medical Ethics* 2006 September; 32(9): 497-498. Subject: 8.3.1

Schmitz, Dagmar; Wiesing, Urban. Just a family medical history? *BMJ: British Medical Journal* 2006 February 4; 332(7536): 297-299. Subject: 15.1

Schmuhl, Hans-Walter. Nationalsozialismus als Argument im aktuellen Medizinethik-Diskurs. Eine Zwischenbilanz. *In:* Frewer, Andreas; Eickhoff, Clemens,

---

eds. "Euthanasie" und die aktuelle Sterbehilfe-Debatte: Die historischen Hintergründe medizinischer Ethik. Frankfurt; New York: Campus; 2000: 385-407. Subject: 2.1

Schneider, Angela J. Genetic enhancement of athletic performance. *In:* Tamburrini, Claudio; Tännsjö, Torbjörn, eds. Genetic Technology and Sport: Ethical Questions. London; New York: Routledge; 2005: 32-41. Subject: 15.4

Schneider, Angela J.; Friedman, Theodore. Ethics and oversight in clinical trials: attempts at gene doping would not conform to accepted ethical standards. *In their:* Gene Doping in Sports: The Science and Ethics of Genetically Modified Athletes. Boston: Elsevier Academic Press, 2006: 51-63. Subject: 18.6

Schneider, Angela J.; Friedman, Theodore. Gene transfer in sports: an opening scenario for genetic enhancement of normal "human traits". *In their:* Gene Doping in Sports: The Science and Ethics of Genetically Modified Athletes. Boston: Elsevier Academic Press, 2006: 37-49. Subject: 4.5

Schneider, Angela J.; Friedman, Theodore. International cooperation and regulation: the Banbury Workshop (2002). *In their:* Gene Doping in Sports: The Science and Ethics of Genetically Modified Athletes. Boston: Elsevier Academic Press, 2006: 65-78. Subject: 15.1

Schneider, Angela J.; Friedman, Theodore. Some ethical aspects of "harm" in sport. *In their:* Gene Doping in Sports: The Science and Ethics of Genetically Modified Athletes. Boston: Elsevier Academic Press, 2006: 89-93. Subject: 15.1

Schneider, Carl E. Drugged. *Hastings Center Report* 2006 July-August; 36(4): 10-11. Subject: 20.5.1

Schneider, Carl E. HIPAA-cracy. *Hastings Center Report* 2006 January-February; 36(1): 10-11. Subject: 8.4

Schneider, Carl E.; Wardle, Lynn D. Genetics and artificial procreation in the U.S.A. *In:* Meulders-Klein, Marie-Thérèse; Deech, Ruth; Vlaardingerbroek, Paul, eds. Biomedicine, the Family and Human Rights. New York: Kluwer Law International, 2002: 55-86. Subject: 15.1

Schneider, John A.; Arora, Vineet; Kasza, Kristen; Van Harrison, R., Humphrey, Holly. Residents' perceptions over time of pharmaceutical industry interactions and gifts and the effect of an educational intervention. *Academic Medicine* 2006 July; 81(7): 595-602. Subject: 7.2

Schneider, Katherine A.; Chittenden, Anu B.; Branda, Kelly J.; Keenan, Meredith A.; Joffe, Steven; Patenaude, Andrea Farkas; Reynolds, Hazel; Dent, Karin; Eubanks, Sonja; Goldman, Jill; Leroy, Bonnie; Warren, Nancy Steinberg; Taylor, Kelly; Vockley, Cate Walsh; Garber, Judy E. Ethical issues in cancer genetics: 1) whose information is it? *Journal of Genetic Counseling* 2006 December; 15(6): 491-503. Subject: 15.3

Schneider, P.L.; Branstedt, K.A. When psychiatry and bioethics disagree about patient decision making capacity (DMC). *Journal of Medical Ethics* 2006 February; 32(2): 90-93. Subject: 17.1

Schneiderman, Lawrence J. Medical ethics and alternative medicine. *Scientific Review of Alternative Medicine* 1998 Spring-Summer; 2(1): 63-66. Subject: 2.1

Schneiderman, Lawrence J.; Gilmer, Todd; Teetzel, Holly D.; Dugan, Daniel O.; Goodman-Crews, Paula; Cohn, Felicia. Dissatisfaction with ethics consultations: the Anna Karenina principle. *CQ: Cambridge Quarterly of Healthcare Ethics* 2006 Winter; 15(1): 101-106. Subject: 9.6

Schniederjan, Stephanie; Donovan, G. Kevin. Ethics versus education: pelvic exams on anesthetized women. *Journal of the Oklahoma State Medical Association* 2005 August; 98(8): 386-388. Subject: 8.3.1

Schnittker, Jason; Liang, Ke. The promise and limits of racial/ethnic concordance in physician-patient interaction. *Journal of Health Politics, Policy and Law* 2006 August; 31(4): 811-838. Subject: 8.1

Schober, Justine. Ethics and futuristic scientific developments concerning genitoplasty. *In:* Sytsma, Sharon E., ed. Ethics and Intersex. Dordrecht: Springer, 2006: 311-317. Subject: 10

Schockenhoff, Eberhard. Töten oder Sterbenlassen: Worauf es in der Euthanasiediskussion ankommt. *In:* Gordijn, Bert; ten Have, Henk, eds. Medizinethik und Kultur: Grenzen medizinischen Handelns in Deutschland und den Niederlanden. Stuttgart: Frommann-Holzboog; 2000: 459-476. Subject: 20.5.1

Schöne-Seifert, Bettina. Danger and merits of principlism: meta-theoretical reflections on the Beauchamp/Childress-approach to biomedical ethics. *In:* Rehmann-Sutter, Christoph; Düwell, Marcus; Mieth, Dietmar, eds. Bioethics in Cultural Contexts: Reflections on Methods and Finitude. Dordrecht: Springer, 2006: 109-119. Subject: 2.1

Schonfeld, Toby L. Reflections on teaching health care ethics on the web. *Science and Engineering Ethics* 2005 July; 11(3): 481-494. Subject: 2.3

Schoot, Tineke; Proot, Ireen; ter Meulen, Ruud; de Witte, Luc. Recognition of client values as a basis for tailored care: the view of Dutch expert patients and family caregivers. *Scandinavian Journal of Caring Sciences* 2005 June; 19(2): 169-176. Subject: 8.1

Schopp, Robert F. Outpatient civil commitment: a dangerous charade or a component of a comprehensive institution of civil commitment? *Psychology, Public Policy, and Law* 2003 March-June; 9(1-2): 33-69. Subject: 17.7

Schorn, Mavis N. Emergency contraception for sexual assault victims: an advocacy coalition framework. *Policy,*

See SUBJECT HEADING KEY FOR SECTION II on inside back cover.

713

Politics and Nursing Practice 2005 November; 6(4): 343-353. Subject: 11.1

Schostak, Zev. Alzheimer's and dementia in the elderly: Halachic perspectives. *Journal of Halacha and Contemporary Society* 2006 Fall; (52): 83-109. Subject: 9.5.3

Schott, Markus. Medical research on humans: regulation in Switzerland, the European Union, and the United States. *Food and Drug Law Journal* 2005; 60(1): 45-77. Subject: 18.6

Schouten, Ronald. Commentary: psychiatric advance directives as tools for enhancing treatment of the mentally ill. *Journal of the American Academy of Psychiatry and the Law* 2006; 34(1): 58-60. Subject: 20.5.4

Schrag, Brian. Research with groups: group rights, group consent, and collaborative research. *Science and Engineering Ethics* 2006 July; 12(3): 511-521. Subject: 18.3

Schramm, Fermin Roland. The Dolly case, the Polly drug, and the morality of human cloning. *Cadernos de Saúde Pública* 1999; 15 (suppl. 1): 51-64. Subject: 14.5

Schroeder, Doris. Benefit sharing: from obscurity to common knowledge [editorial]. *Developing World Bioethics* 2006 December; 6(3): ii. Subject: 15.1

Schroeder, Doris. A child's life or a "little bit of torture"? State-sanctioned violence and dignity. *CQ: Cambridge Quarterly of Healthcare Ethics* 2006 Spring; 15(2): 188-201. Subject: 21.4

Schroeder, Doris; Lasén-Díaz, Carolina. Sharing the benefits of genetic resources: from biodiversity to human genetics. *Developing World Bioethics* 2006 December; 6(3): 135-143. Subject: 15.1

Schroeder, Michael; Shidlo, Ariel. Ethical issues in sexual orientation conversion therapies: an empirical study of consumers. *In:* Shidlo, Ariel; Schroeder, Michael; Drescher, Jack, eds. Sexual Conversion Therapy: Ethical, Clinical, and Research Perspectives. New York: Haworth Medical Press; 2001: 131-166. Subject: 10

Schroeder-Kurth, Traute M. Verfahrensfragen der klinischen Prufung bei somatischer Gentherapie. *In:* Rehmann-Sutter, Christoph; Müller, Hansjakob, eds. Ethik und Gentherapie: Zum praktischen Diskurs um die molekulare Medizin. Tübingen: Attempto Verlag; 1995: 109-117. Subject: 15.4

Schroter, S.; Plowman, R.; Hutchings, A.; Gonzalez, A. Reporting ethics committee approval and patient consent by study design in five general medical journals. *Journal of Medical Ethics* 2006 December; 32(12): 718-723. Subject: 18.3

Schröter, Sonja. Die Heil- und Pflegeanstalt Waldheim in Sachsen 1933-1938. *In her:* Psychiatrie in Waldheim/Sachsen (1716-1946): ein Beitrag zur Geschichte der forensischen Psychiatrie in Deutschland. Franfurt am Main: Mabuse; 2003: 71-120. Subject: 15.5

Schröter, Sonja. Die Heil- und Pflegeanstalt Waldheim in Sachsen 1939-1945. *In her:* Psychiatrie in Waldheim/Sachsen (1716-1946): ein Beitrag zur Geschichte der forensischen Psychiatrie in Deutschland. Franfurt am Main: Mabuse; 2003: 121-192. Subject: 21.4

Schüklenk, Udo. Ethics in bioethics [editorial]. *Bioethics* 2006 September; 20(5): iii. Subject: 2.1

Schüklenk, Udo. Medical professionalism and ideological symbols in doctors' rooms. *Journal of Medical Ethics* 2006 January; 32(1): 1-2. Subject: 8.1

Schüklenk, Udo; Kleinsmidt, Anita. North-south benefit sharing arrangements in bioprospecting and genetic research: a critical ethical and legal analysis. *Developing World Bioethics* 2006 December; 6(3): 122-134. Subject: 15.1

Schulman, Joseph D. Further comment on the House of Commons' report Human Reproductive Technologies and the Law. *Reproductive BioMedicine Online [electronic]* 2005 August; 11(2): 158-160. Accessed: http://www.rbmonline.com/Article/1877 [2006 January 22]. Subject: 14.1

Schulte, Paul A. Interpretation of genetic data for medical and public health uses. *In:* Árnason, Gardar; Nordal, Salvör; Árnason, Vilhjálmur, eds. Blood and Data: Ethical, Legal and Social Aspects of Human Genetic Databases. Reykjavík: University of Iceland Press; 2004: 277-282. Subject: 15.1

Schulze, Thomas G.; Fangerau, Heiner; Propping, Peter. From degeneration to genetic susceptibility, from eugenics to genethics, from Bezugsziffer to LOD score: the history of psychiatric genetics. *International Review of Psychiatry* 2004 November; 16(4): 246-259. Subject: 15.6

Schulz-Baldes, Anette; Splett, Thomas. Entscheidungen am lebensende in der modernen medizin: ethik, recht, ökonomie und klinik [Decisions at the end of life in modern medicine: ethics, law, economics, and clinical practice]. *Ethik in der Medizin* 2006 June; 18(2): 195-200. Subject: 20.5.1

Schulz-Baldes, Annette; Jakovljevic, Anna-Karina. Zur möglichkeit einer kulturübergreifenden bioethik [Possibilities of a cross-cultural bioethics]. *Ethik in der Medizin* 2006 September; 18(3): 261-266. Subject: 2.1

Schwab, Abraham P. Splitting the difference position. *American Journal of Bioethics* 2006 July-August; 6(4): 74-76. Subject: 18.2

Schwab, Abraham P.; Carroll, Kelly A.; Wynia, Matthew K. What is managed care anyway? *American Journal of Bioethics* 2006 January-February; 6(1): 36-37. Subject: 9.3.2

Schwab, A.P. Formal and effective autonomy in healthcare. *Journal of Medical Ethics* 2006 October; 32(10): 575-579. Subject: 8.3.1

Subject = NRCBL Primary Classification Number; see inside front cover.

Schwark, C.; Schellinger, Peter D. Is old age really a reason to withhold thrombolytic therapy? [editorial]. *Journal of Neurology, Neurosurgery, and Psychiatry* 2006 March; 77(3): 289. Subject: 9.5.2

Schwartz, Barry. Apology is integral part of ethics. *Today's FDA* 2005 December; 17(12): 24-26, 28, 30. Subject: 9.8

Schwartz, Barry. Receiving gifts: a conflict of interest discussion. *Journal of the Canadian Dental Association* 2005 September; 71(8): 561-562. Subject: 7.3

Schwartz, Myrna F.; Brecher, Adelyn R.; Whyte, John; Klein, Mary G. A patient registry for cognitive rehabilitation research: a strategy for balancing patients' privacy rights with researchers' need for access. *Archives of Physical Medicine and Rehabilitation* 2005 September; 86(9): 1807-1814. Subject: 18.2; 8.4

Schwartz, Philip H.; Rae, Scott B. An approach to the ethical donation of human embryos for harvest of stem cells. *Reproductive BioMedicine Online [electronic]* 2006 June; 12(6): 771-775. Accessed: http://www.rbmonline.com/Article/2232 [2006 March 24]. Subject: 18.5.4

Schwartz, Robert. When doing the right things means breaking the law — what is the role of the health lawyer? *Journal of Law, Medicine and Ethics* 2006 Fall; 34(3): 624-628. Subject: 7.3

Schwartz, Robert S. The politics and promise of stem cell research. *New England Journal of Medicine* 2006 September 21; 355(12): 1189-1191. Subject: 18.5.4

Schwarz, Pascal. The collection and management of confidential genetic data: an evaluation of deCODE genetics based on the principle of autonomy. *In:* Árnason, Gardar; Nordal, Salvör; Árnason, Vilhjálmur, eds. Blood and Data: Ethical, Legal and Social Aspects of Human Genetic Databases. Reykjavík: University of Iceland Press; 2004: 231-235. Subject: 15.1

Schwerdt, Ruth; Merkel, Reinhard. Schön warm zudecken [Cover up warmly]. *Ethik in der Medizin* 2006 September; 18(3): 251-260. Subject: 20.5.1

Sclar, David. U.S. Supreme Court ruling in Gonzales v. Oregon upholds the Oregon Death with Dignity Act. *Journal of Law, Medicine and Ethics* 2006 Fall; 34(3): 639-645. Subject: 20.5.1

Scott, Anne. "Like editing bits of ourselves": geneticisation and human fate. *New Genetics and Society* 2006 April; 25(1): 109-124. Subject: 4.4

Scott, Christopher Thomas. Chimeras in the crosshairs [news]. *Nature Biotechnology* 2006 May; 24(5): 487-490. Subject: 15.1

Scott, Christy K.; White, William L. Ethical issues in the conduct of longitudinal studies of addiction treatment. *Journal of Substance Abuse Treatment* 2005; 28(Supplement 1): S91-S101. Subject: 9.5.9

Scott, P. Anne. Allocation of resources: issues for nurses. *In:* Tadd, Win, ed. Ethics in Nursing Education, Research and Management. New York: Palgrave Macmillan; 2003: 145-162. Subject: 9.4

Scott, P. Anne. Perceiving the moral dimension of practice: insights from Murdoch, Vetlesen, and Aristotle. *Nursing Philosophy* 2006 July; 7(3): 137-145. Subject: 4.1.3

Scott, Rosamund. Choosing between possible lives: legal and ethical issues in preimplantation genetic diagnosis. *Oxford Journal of Legal Studies* 2006 Spring; 26(1): 153-178. Subject: 15.2

Scott, Russell. Human embryo research: the Australian experience. *Human Reproduction* 1997 November; 12(11): 2342-2343. Subject: 18.5.4

Scott, Timothy. Tricks of the trade. *Ethical Human Psychology and Psychiatry* 2006 Summer; 8(2): 133-146. Subject: 18.2

Scottish Council on Human Bioethics. Embryonic, fetal and post-natal animal-human mixtures: an ethical discussion. *Human Reproduction and Genetic Ethics: An International Journal* 2006; 12(2): 35-60. Subject: 18.5.4

Scottish Council on Human Bioethics. Significant developments in stem cell research. *Journal International de Bioéthique = International Journal of Bioethics* 2005 September-December; 16(3-4): 164. Subject: 18.5.4

Scully, Jackie Leach. Disabled embodiment and an ethic of care. *In:* Rehmann-Sutter, Christoph; Düwell, Marcus; Mieth, Dietmar, eds. Bioethics in Cultural Contexts: Reflections on Methods and Finitude. Dordrecht: Springer, 2006: 247-261. Subject: 4.1.1

Scully, Jackie Leach. Gentherapieethik aus Patientensicht. *In:* Rehmann-Sutter, Christoph; Müller, Hansjakob, eds. Ethik und Gentherapie: zum praktischen Diskurs um die molekulare Medizin. 2nd ed. Tübingen: Francke Verlag; 2003: 207-223. Subject: 15.4

Scully, Jackie Leach. Nothing like a gene. *In:* Neumann-Held, Eva M.; Rehmann-Sutter, Christoph, eds. Genes in Development: Re-reading the Molecular Paradigm. Durham, N.C.: Duke University Press; 2006: 349-364. Subject: 15.1

Scully, Robert; Glynn, Liam. Researching minority groups [letter]. *Lancet* 2006 August 12-18; 368(9535): 575. Subject: 18.5.1

Searight, H. Russell; Gafford, Jennifer. "It's like playing with your destiny": Bosnian immigrants' views of advance directives and end-of-life decision-making. *Journal of Immigrant Health* 2005 July; 7(3): 195-203. Subject: 20.5.4

Sears, David O. A perspective on implicit prejudice from survey research. *Psychological Inquiry* 2004; 15(4): 293-297. Subject: 18.4

See SUBJECT HEADING KEY FOR SECTION II on inside back cover.

715

Sears, Jeanne Marguerite. The payment of research subjects: ethical concerns. *Oncology Nursing Forum* 2001 May; 28(4): 657-663. Subject: 18.2

Sebatier, Sandrine. Ethical questions raised by human genetics. A personal contribution to the preparation of a legal instrument of the Council of Europe on human genetics (Part I). *Revista de Derecho y Genoma Humano = Law and the Human Genome Review* 1998 January-June; (8): 187-203. Subject: 15.1

Sebek, Michael. Some critical notes on Solomon's paper 'The ethical attitude — a bridge between psychoanalysis and analytical psychology'. *Journal of Analytical Psychology* 2002 April; 47(2): 195-201. Subject: 17.2

Secker, Barbara; Goldenberg, Maya J.; Gibson, Barbara E.; Wagner, Frank; Parke, Bob; Breslin, Jonathan; Thompson, Alison; Lear, Jonathan R.; Singer, Peter A. Just regionalization: rehabilitating care for people with disabilities and chronic illnesses. *BMC Medical Ethics [electronic]* 2006; 7:9. Accessed: http://www.biomedcentral.com/1472-6939/7/9 [nd]. Subject: 9.3.1

Sedgwick, Emma. Patients' right to refuse treatment [editorial]. *Hospital Medicine* 2002 April; 63(4): 196-197. Subject: 8.3.4

Sedler, Robert A. The Supreme Court will not overrule Roe v. Wade. *Hofstra Law Review* 2006 Spring; 34(3): 1207-1213. Subject: 12.4.1

Seelig, Michelle D.; Gelberg, Lillian; Tavrow, Paula; Lee, Martin; Rubenstein, Lisa V. Determinants of physician unwillingness to offer medical abortion using mifepristone. *Women's Health Issues* 2006 January-February; 16(1): 14-21. Subject: 8.3.4

Seelman, Katherine D. Assistive technology policy: a road to independence for individuals with disabilities. *Journal of Social Issues* 1993 Summer; 49(2): 115-136. Subject: 9.4

Seers, Kate; Watt-Watson, Judy; Bucknall, Tracey. Challenges of pain management for the 21st century [editorial]. *Journal of Advanced Nursing* 2006 July; 55(1): 4-6. Subject: 4.4

Segal, Mary E.; Sankar, Pamela; Reed, Danielle R. Research issues in genetic testing of adolescents for obesity. *Nutrition Reviews* 2004 August; 62(8): 307-320. Subject: 15.3

Segal, Steven P.; Burgess, Philip M. The utility of extended outpatient civil commitment. *International Journal of Law and Psychiatry* 2006 November-December; 29(6): 525-534. Subject: 17.7

Segerstråle, Ullica. Politics by scientific means and science by political means: Trojan horses in the sociobiology debate. *Science Studies* 2000 June; 13(1): 3-18. Subject: 15.9

Seidman, Guy I. Regulating life and death: the case of Israel's "health basket" committee. *Journal of Contempo-*

rary Health Law and Policy 2006 Fall; 23(1): 9-63. Subject: 9.4

Seifert, Josef. The nature and seven goals of medicine. *Aletheia* 1995-2001; 7: 321-416. Subject: 4.1.2

Selby, Peter; Kapur, Bhushan M.; Hackman, Richard; Koren, Gideon. "No one asked the baby" — an ethical issue in placebo-controlled trials in pregnant smokers. *Canadian Journal of Clinical Pharmacology* 2005 Summer; 12(2): e180-e181. Subject: 18.5.3

Selden, Steven. Transforming Better Babies into Fitter Families: archival resources and the history of American eugenics movement, 1908-1930. *Proceedings of the American Philosophical Society* 2005 June; 149(2): 199-225. Subject: 15.5

Self, Donnie J.; Baldwin, DeWitt C., Jr. Should moral reasoning serve as a criterion for student and resident selection? *Clinical Orthopaedics and Related Research* 2000 September; (378): 115-123. Subject: 7.2

Selgelid, Michael J. Commentary: the ethics of dangerous discovery. *CQ: Cambridge Quarterly of Healthcare Ethics* 2006 Fall; 15(4): 444-447. Subject: 1.3.9

Sellman, Derek. The importance of being trustworthy. *Nursing Ethics* 2006 March; 13(2): 105-115. Subject: 8.1

Senior, Kathryn. Germline gene transfer during gene therapy: reassessing the risks [news]. *Molecular Medicine Today* 1999 September; 5(9): 371. Subject: 15.4

Senn, Stephen J. JAMA's policy does not go far enough [letter]. *BMJ: British Medical Journal* 2006 February 4; 332(7536): 305. Subject: 1.3.7

Sententia, Wrye. Neuroethical considerations: cognitive liberty and converging technologies for improving human cognition. *Annals of the New York Academy of Sciences* 2004 May; 1013: 221-228. Subject: 17.1

Service, Robert F. Synthetic biologists debate policing themselves [news]. *Science* 2006 May 26; 312(5777): 1116. Subject: 15.1

Sethe, Sebastian. Cell line research with UK Biobank: why the new British biobank is not just another population genetic database. *In:* Árnason, Gardar; Nordal, Salvör; Árnason, Vilhjálmur, eds. Blood and Data: Ethical, Legal and Social Aspects of Human Genetic Databases. Reykjavík: University of Iceland Press; 2004: 313-319. Subject: 15.1

Setness, Peter A. Embracing life, accepting limits: a physician's position is unique when a loved one faces death [editorial]. *Postgraduate Medicine* 2003 August; 114(2): 9-10. Subject: 20.5.1

Setness, Peter A. When privacy and the public good collide: does the collection of health data for research harm individual patients? [editorial]. *Postgraduate Medicine* 2003 January; 113(5): 15-16, 19. Subject: 9.1

Subject = NRCBL Primary Classification Number; see inside front cover.

Sevick, Mary Ann; McConnell, Terrance; Muender, Melissa. Conducting research related to treatment of Alzheimer's disease. *Journal of Gerontological Nursing* 2003 February; 29(2): 6-12. Subject: 18.3

Sexton, Sarah. Deceptive promises of cures for diseases. *World Watch* 2002 July-August; 15(4): 18-20. Subject: 9.4

Seyfer, Tara L. An overview of chimeras and hybrids. *National Catholic Bioethics Quarterly* 2006 Spring; 6(1): 37-49. Subject: 15.1

Sfikas, Peter M. HIV in the workplace: Workers' Compensation Act trumps privacy right in Kentucky court case. *Journal of the American Dental Association* 2005 August; 136(8): 1169-1170. Subject: 9.5.6

Sgreccia, Elio. Bioethics centers and committees: cultural origins and current status. *Dolentium Hominum* 1994; 9(2): 50-60. Subject: 2.3

Sgreccia, Elio. Bioética y rehabilitación [Bioethics and rehabilitation]. *Persona y Bioética* 1999 February-May; 2(6): 24-42. Subject: 4.4

Shacter, Hannah. Emergency contraception: balancing a patient's right to medication with a pharmacist's right of conscientious objection. *Penn Bioethics Journal* 2006; 2(1): 3p. [Online]. Accessed: http://www.bioethicsjournal.com [2006 February 21]. Subject: 11.1

Shafer, J.K.; Usilton, Lida J.; Gleeson, Geraldine A. Untreated syphilis in the male Negro. *Public Health Reports* 2006; 121(Supplement 1): 235-241; discussion 234. Subject: 18.5.1

Shaffer, D.N.; Yebei, V.N.; Ballidawa, J.B.; Sidle, J.E.; Greene, J.Y.; Meslin, E.M.; Kimaiyo, S.J.N.; Tierney, W.M. Equitable treatment for HIV/AIDS clinical trial participants: a focus group study of patients, clinical researchers, and administrators in western Kenya. *Journal of Medical Ethics* 2006 January; 32(1): 55-60. Subject: 9.5.6

Shaffer, Nancy. Transgender patients: implications for emergency department policy and practice. *Journal of Emergency Nursing* 2005 August; 31(4): 405-407. Subject: 10

Shah, Ajit; Dickenson, Donna. The Bournewood case and its implications for health and social services. *Journal of the Royal Society of Medicine* 1998 July; 91(7): 349-351. Subject: 8.3.3

Shah, Sonia. Drug trial double standards: why don't people who volunteer for clinical trials in the developing world get the same safeguards as those in the West. *New Scientist* 2006 November 18-24; 192(2578): 22. Subject: 18.5.9

Shaheen, F.A.M.; Kurpad, R.; Al-Attar, B.A.; Al-Khader, A.A. A proposed Saudi approach to the ethical utilization of living unrelated kidney donation. *Transplantation Proceedings* 2005 June; 37(5): 2004-2006. Subject: 19.5

Shahine, Lora K.; Caughey, Aaron B. Preimplantation genetic diagnosis: the earliest form of prenatal diagnosis. *Gynecologic and Obstetric Investigation* 2005; 60(1): 39-46. Subject: 15.2

Shakespeare, Tom. Manifesto for genetic justice. *Social Alternatives* 1999 January; 18(1): 29-32. Subject: 15.5

Shakespeare, Tom. Parental diagnosis, disability equality, and freedom of choice. *Reform* 2001 Spring; 79: 19-21, 71. Subject: 15.1

Shakespeare, Tom W. Refusing to provide a prenatal test: can it ever be ethical?: Rights of future children [letter]. *BMJ: British Medical Journal* 2006 December 2; 333(7579): 1173-1174. Subject: 15.2

Shalev, Moshe. NIH announces final rules on ethics. *Lab Animal* 2005 October; 34(9): 17. Subject: 7.1

Shalev, Moshe. USDA revises policies on licensing of facilities and IACUC membership. *Lab Animal* 2006 June; 35(6): 13. Subject: 22.2

Shalowitz, David I.; Garrett-Mayer, Elizabeth; Wendler, David. The accuracy of surrogate decision makers: a systematic review. *Archives of Internal Medicine* 2006 March 13; 166(5): 493-497. Subject: 8.3.3

Shalowitz, David; Wendler, David. Informed consent for research and authorization under the Health Insurance Portability And Accountability Act privacy rule: an integrated approach. *Annals of Internal Medicine* 2006 May 2; 144(9): 685-688. Subject: 18.3

Shamoo, Adil E. Accountability in research. *In:* Mitcham, Carl, ed. Encyclopedia of Science, Technology, and Ethics. Farmington Hills, MI: Thomson/Gale, 2005: 6-7. Subject: 1.3.9

Shamoo, Adil E. Data audit would reduce unethical behaviour [letter]. *Nature* 2006 February 16; 439(7078): 784. Subject: 1.3.9

Shamoo, Adil E. Letter to the editor: emergency research consent waiver — a proper way. *American Journal of Bioethics [Online]* 2006 July-August; 6(4): W48-W51. Subject: 18.3

Shamoo, Adil E.; Resnik, David B. Ethical issues for clinical research managers. *Drug Information Journal* 2006; 40: 371-383. Subject: 18.2

Shamoo, Adil E.; Resnik, David B. Strategies to minimize risks and exploitation in phase one trials on healthy subjects. *American Journal of Bioethics [Online]*. 2006 May-June; 6(3): W1-W13. Subject: 18.2

Shanawani, H.; Dame, L.; Schwartz, D.A.; Cook-Deegan, R. Non-reporting and inconsistent reporting of race and ethnicity in articles that claim associations among genotype, outcome, and race or ethnicity. *Journal of Medical Ethics* 2006 December; 32(12): 724-728. Subject: 15.11

See SUBJECT HEADING KEY FOR SECTION II on inside back cover.

Shannon, Sarah E. Damage compounded or damage lessened? Disparate impact or the compromises of multiculturalism. *American Journal of Bioethics* 2006 September-October; 6(5): 27-28; discussion W30-W32. Subject: 20.5.1

Shannon, Thomas A. Nutrition and hydration: an analysis of the recent papal statement in the light of the Roman Catholic bioethical tradition. *Christian Bioethics* 2006 April; 12(1): 29-41. Subject: 20.5.1

Shannon, Thomas A. Remaking ourselves? The ethics of stem-cell research. *Commonweal* 1998 December 4; 125: 9-10. Subject: 18.5.4

Shanthi, K. Feminist bioethics and reproductive rights of women in India: myth and reality. *In:* Tong, Rosemarie; Donchin, Anne; Dodds, Susan, eds. Linking Visions: Feminist Bioethics, Human Rights, and the Developing World. Lanham, MD: Rowman and Littlefield Publishers; 2004: 119-132. Subject: 14.1

Shapiro, Carla. Emerging ethical issues in nephrology nursing — Part II. *CANNT Journal* 2000 January-March; 10(1): 23-25. Subject: 19.3

Shapiro, Carla. Our neighbors to the north: a Canadian perspective on perinatal ethics. *Newborn and Infant Nursing Review* 2005 June; 5(2): 82-86. Subject: 9.5.8

Shapiro, Julie. A lesbian centered critique of "genetic parenthood". *Journal of Gender, Race and Justice* 2006 Spring; 9(3): 591-612. Subject: 15.1

Shapiro, Paul. Moral agency in other animals. *Theoretical Medicine and Bioethics* 2006; 27(4): 357-373. Subject: 22.1

Sharfstein, Steven S. American Psychiatric Association clarifies its position on human rights [letter]. *BMJ: British Medical Journal* 2006 July 8; 333(7558): 97-98. Subject: 21.4

Sharma, Geeta; Gold, Heather T.; Chervenak, Frank A.; McCullough, Laurence; Alt, Abigail K.; Chasen, Stephen T. Patient preference regarding first-trimester aneuploidy risk assessment. *American Journal of Obstetrics and Gynecology* 2005 October; 193(4): 1429-1436. Subject: 9.5.5

Sharma, Shridhar. Ethical issues in psychiatric research. *Archives of Indian Psychiatry* 1999; 5(1): 7-9. Subject: 18.2

Sharp, David. Ethics at Porton Down. *Lancet* 2006 August 19-15; 368(9536): 631-632. Subject: 18.5.8

Sharp, Helen M.; Bryant, Karen N. Ethical issues in dysphagia: when patients refuse assessment or treatment. *Seminars in Speech and Language* 2003 November; 24(4): 285-299. Subject: 8.3.4

Sharp, Helen M.; Kuthy, Raymond A.; Heller, Keith E. Ethical dilemmas reported by fourth-year dental students. *Journal of Dental Education* 2005 October; 69(10): 1116-1122. Subject: 4.1.1

Sharp, Richard R.; Foster, Morris W. Clinical utility and full disclosure of genetic results to research participants. *American Journal of Bioethics* 2006 November-December; 6(6): 42-44. Subject: 15.1

Sharp, Richard R.; Yarborough, Mark. Informed trust and the financing of biomedical research. *Journal of Law, Medicine and Ethics* 2006 Summer; 34(2): 460-464. Subject: 1.3.9

Sharpe, Neil F.; Carter, Ronald F. Confidentiality, disclosure, and recontact. *In their:* Genetic Testing: Care, Consent, and Liability. Hoboken, NJ: Wiley-Liss; 2006: 398-424. Subject: 15.3

Sharpe, Neil F.; Carter, Ronald F. New genetics and the protection of information. *In their:* Genetic Testing: Care, Consent, and Liability. Hoboken, NJ: Wiley-Liss; 2006: 425-442. Subject: 15.1

Sharpe, Neil F.; Carter, Ronald F. Prenatal screening and diagnosis. *In their:* Genetic Testing: Care, Consent, and Liability. Hoboken, NJ: Wiley-Liss; 2006: 163-218. Subject: 15.2

Sharpe, Neil F.; Carter, Ronald F. Susceptibility testing. *In their:* Genetic Testing: Care, Consent, and Liability. Hoboken, NJ: Wiley-Liss; 2006: 268-291. Subject: 15.3

Shaul, Randi Zlotnik. Potato, potato, proxy consent, permission — just don't call the whole thing off. *Critical Care* 2005 April; 9(2): 123-124. Subject: 18.3

Shaver, Frances M. Sex work research: methodological and ethical challenges. *Journal of Interpersonal Violence* 2005 March; 20(3): 296-319. Subject: 18.4

Shavers, Vickie L.; Lynch, Charles F.; Burmeister, Leon F. Factors that influence African-Americans' willingness to participate in medical research studies. *Cancer* 2001 January 1; 91(1, Supplement): 233-236. Subject: 18.5.1

Shaw, Alison. Attitudes to genetic diagnosis and to the use of medical technologies in pregnancy: some British Pakistani perspectives. *In:* Unnithan-Kumar, Maya, ed. Reproductive Agency, Medicine and the State: Cultural Transformations in Childbearing. New York: Berghahn Books; 2004: 25-41. Subject: 15.2

Shaw, Sara; Boynton, Petra M.; Greenhalgh, Trisha. Research governance: where did it come from, what does it mean? *Journal of the Royal Society of Medicine* 2005 November; 98(11): 496-502. Subject: 18.6

Shea, John B. Catholic teaching on the human embryo as an object of research. *National Catholic Bioethics Quarterly* 2006 Spring; 6(1): 133-136. Subject: 18.5.4

Shea, John B. The immorality of in vitro fertilization: conception and Catholic moral teaching. *Ethics and Medics* 2006 October; 31(10): 1-2. Subject: 14.4

Shead, N. Will; Dobson, Keith S. Psychology for sale: the ethics of advertising professional services. *Canadian Psy-*

---

chology/Psychologie Canadienne 2004 May; 45(2): 125-136. Subject: 8.1

Shead, N. Will; Dobson, Keith S. Towards more assertive advertising practices: an evolutionary, not revolutionary, step forward. *Canadian Psychology/Psychologie Canadienne* 2004 May; 45(2): 139-140. Subject: 8.1

Sheard, L.; Tompkins, C.N.E.; Wright, N.M.J.; Adams, C.E. Non-commercial clinical trials of a medicinal product: can they survive the current process of research approvals in the UK? *Journal of Medical Ethics* 2006 July; 32(7): 430-434. Subject: 18.5.5

Sheather, Julian. Ethics in the face of uncertainty: preparing for pandemic flu. *Clinical Ethics* 2006 December; 1(4): 224-227. Subject: 9.4

Sheather, Julian. The Mental Capacity Act 2005. *Clinical Ethics* 2006 March; 1(1): 33-36. Subject: 4.3

Sheather, Julian. Sexual relationships between doctors and former patients [editorial]. *BMJ: British Medical Journal* 2006 December 2; 333(7579): 1132. Subject: 7.4

Sheehan, Mark. Is the community consultation requirement necessary? *American Journal of Bioethics* 2006 May-June; 6(3): 38-40; discussion W46- W48. Subject: 18.6

Sheela, S.R.; Latha, M.; Liu, P.; Lem, K.; Kaler, S.G. Copper-replacement treatment for symptomatic Menkes disease: ethical considerations. *Clinical Genetics* 2005 September; 68(3): 278-283. Subject: 9.5.7

Sheikh, Abdul Latif. Pharmaceutical research: paradox, challenge or dilemma? *Eastern Mediterranean Health Journal* 2006; 12(Supplement 1): S42-S49 [Online]. Accessed: http://www.emro.who.int/publications/EMHJ/12_S/PDF/7.pdf [2007 January 3]. Subject: 18.5.9

Shelden, Randall G. Gene warfare. *Social Justice* 2000 Summer; 27(2): 162-167. Subject: 15.5

Sheldon, Tony. Dutch consider excluding costly treatments from health insurance [news]. *BMJ: British Medical Journal* 2006 July 15; 333(7559): 113. Subject: 9.4

Sheldon, Tony. Dutch doctors suspended for use of complementary medicine [news]. *BMJ: British Medical Journal* 2006 April 22; 332(7547): 929. Subject: 4.1.1

Sheldon, Tony. Dutch insurers pay midwives to refer fewer to hospital [news]. *BMJ: British Medical Journal* 2006 November 18; 333(7577): 1034. Subject: 9.5.5

Shelley, Jacob. Deference in the public health context. *Health Law Review* 2006; 15(1): 33-36. Subject: 9.1

Shemie, Sam D.; Baker, Andrew J.; Knoll, Greg; Wall, William; Rocker, Graeme; Howes, Daniel; Davidson, Janet; Pagliarello, Joe; Chambers-Evans, Jane; Cockfield, Sandra; Farrell, Catherine; Glannon, Walter; Gourlay, William; Grant, David; Langevin, Stéphan; Wheelock, Brian; Young, Kimberly; Dossetor, John. Donation after cardiocirculatory death in

Canada. *CMAJ/JAMC: Canadian Medical Association Journal* 2006 October 10; 175(8, Supplement): S1-S24. Subject: 19.5

Shen, Mingxian. Euthanasia and Chinese traditional culture. *In:* Döring, Ole; Chen, Renbiao, eds. Advances in Chinese Medical Ethics: Chinese and International Perspectives. Hamburg: Institut für Asienkunde; 2002: 255-265. Subject: 20.5.1

Shen, Xiaoling; Wang, Zucheng. Cases of informed consent for mental health patients. *In:* Döring, Ole; Chen, Renbiao, eds. Advances in Chinese Medical Ethics: Chinese and International Perspectives. Hamburg: Institut für Asienkunde; 2002: 444-449. Subject: 8.3.3

Shenfield, Françoise. Procreative liberty, or collective responsibility? Comment on the House of Commons report Human Reproductive Technologies and the Law, and on Dahl's response. *Reproductive BioMedicine Online [electronic]* 2005 August; 11(2): 155-157. Accessed: http://www.rbmonline.com/Article/1861 [2006 January 22]. Subject: 14.3

Shenfield, F. Too late for change, too early to judge, but an oxymoron will not solve the problem. *Reproductive BioMedicine Online [electronic]* 2005; 10(4): 433-435. Subject: 19.5

Shenk, David. Money + science = ethics problems on campus. *Nation* 1999 March 22; 268(11): 11-18. Subject: 9.7

Shepardson, Laura B.; Youngner, Stuart J.; Speroff, Theodore; Rosenthal, Gary E. Increased risk of death in patients with do-not-resuscitate orders. *Medical Care* 1999 August; 37(8): 727-737. Subject: 20.5.1

Shepherd, Lois. In respect of people living in a permanent vegetative state — and allowing them to die. *Health Matrix: The Journal of Law-Medicine* 2006 Summer; 16(2): 631-691. Subject: 20.2.1

Shepherd, Lois. Shattering the neutral surrogate myth in end-of-life decisionmaking: Terri Schiavo and her family. *Cumberland Law Review* 2004-2005; 35(3): 575-595. Subject: 20.5.1

Shepherd, Lois. Terri Schiavo and the disability rights community: a cause for concern. *University of Chicago Legal Forum* 2006: 253-273. Subject: 4.4

Sheremeta, Lorraine; Plant, Margo; Knoppers, Bartha Maria. The future of cord blood banking in Canada. *Health Law Review* 2006; 14(3): 51-56. Subject: 19.4

Sheridan, Cormac. Stem cell controversy to stall European tissue and cell therapy rules [news]. *Nature Biotechnology* 2006 May; 24(5): 479-480. Subject: 18.5.4

Sheriff, D.S.; Sheriff, S. Omer. Interventions in reproduction. *Indian Journal of Medical Ethics* 2006 July-September; 3(3): 97-98. Subject: 14.1

Sherlock, Richard. Bioethics. *In:* Mitcham, Carl, ed. Encyclopedia of Science, Technology, and Ethics.

See SUBJECT HEADING KEY FOR SECTION II on inside back cover.

719

Farmington Hills, MI: Thomson/Gale, 2005: 193-200. Subject: 2.1

Sherlock, Richard. Medical ethics. *In:* Mitcham, Carl, ed. Encyclopedia of Science, Technology, and Ethics. Farmington Hills, MI: Thomson/Gale, 2005: 1184-1188. Subject: 2.1

Sherlock, Richard. Nature's end: the theological meaning of the new genetics. *Ethics and Medicine* 2006 Spring; 22(1): 47-56. Subject: 15.1

Sherlock, Richard; Morrey, John D. Ethical issues in transgenics. *Cloning* 2000; 2(3): 137-144. Subject: 15.1

Sherman, Christy A. Emergency contraception: the politics of post-coital contraception. *Journal of Social Issues* 2005 March; 61(1): 139-157. Subject: 11.1

Sherman, Nancy. Holding doctors responsible at Guantánamo. *Kennedy Institute of Ethics Journal* 2006 June; 16(2): 199-203. Subject: 7.4

Sherwin, Susan; Schwartz, Meredith. Resisting the emergence of Bio-Amazons. *In:* Tamburrini, Claudio; Tännsjö, Torbjörn, eds. Genetic Technology and Sport: Ethical Questions. London; New York: Routledge; 2005: 199-204. Subject: 15.4

Sheth, Shirish S. Missing female births in India. *Lancet* 2006 January 21-27; 367(9506): 185-186. Subject: 14.3

Sheth, S.S.; Malpani, A.N. Inappropriate use of new technology: impact on women's health. *International Journal of Gynecology and Obstetrics* 1997 July; 58(1): 159-165. Subject: 5.1

Shi, Chih-Wen; Ganiats, Theodore G. The debate about over-the-counter emergency contraceptive pills. *Journal of Midwifery and Women's Health* 2005 September-October; 50(5): 423-426. Subject: 11.1

Shields, Jon A. Bioethical politics. *Society* 2006 March-April; 43(3): 19-24. Subject: 12.3

Shields, Linda. The nursing shortage and developing countries: an ethical dilemma [editorial]. *Journal of Clinical Nursing* 2005 August; 14(7): 787-788. Subject: 4.1.3

Shih, Fun-Jin; Gau, Meei-Ling; Lin, Yaw-Sheng; Pong, Suang-Jing; Lin, Hung-Ru. Death and help expected from nurses when dying. *Nursing Ethics* 2006 July; 13(4): 360-375. Subject: 20.3.2

Shildrick, Margrit. Genetics, normativity, and ethics: some bioethical concerns. *Feminist Theory* 2004 August; 5(2): 149-165 [Online]. Accessed: http://fty.sagepub.com/cgi/reprint/5/2/149 [2007 January 24]. Subject: 15.1

Shiloh, Shoshana; Gerad, Liora; Goldman, Boleslav. Patients' information needs and decision-making processes: what can be learned from genetic counselees? *Health Psychology* 2006 March; 25(2): 211-219. Subject: 8.1

Shimada, Yasuhiro. Conflict of interest in scientific medical journal [editorial]. *Japanese Journal of Clinical Oncology* 2005 June; 35(6): 363. Subject: 1.3.7

Shinagawa, Shinryo N. Bioethical issues in prenatal sex selection in Japan. *In:* Sang-yong, Song; Young-Mo, Koo; Macer, Darryl R.J., eds. Asian Bioethics in the 21st Century. Christchurch, NZ: Eubios Ethics Institute, 2002: 344-346. Subject: 14.3

Shinoki, Eri; Matsuda, Ichiro. Changes of bioethics perspective of Japanese clinical geneticists about repro-genetics during 1995-2001. *In:* Takahashi, Takao, ed. Taking Life and Death Seriously: Bioethics from Japan. Amsterdam; Boston: Elsevier JAI; 2005: 85-112. Subject: 15.2

Shiva, Vandana. Biopirates and the poor. *World Watch* 2002 July-August; 15(4): 25. Subject: 15.1

Shochet, Ian M.; O'Gorman, J.G. Ethical issues in research on adolescent depression and suicidal behaviour. *Australian Psychologist* 1995 November; 30(3): 183-186. Subject: 18.5.2

Shore, David. Ethical issues in schizophrenia research: a commentary on some current concerns. *Schizophrenia Bulletin* 2006 January; 32(1): 26-29. Subject: 18.5.6

Shorto, Russell. Contra-contraception: a growing number of conservatives see birth control as part of an ailing culture that overemphasizes sex and devalues human life; Is this the beginning of the next culture war? *New York Times Magazine* 2006 May 7; p. 48-55, 68, 83. Subject: 11.1

Shrader-Frechette, Kristin. Gene patents and Lockean constraints. *Public Affairs Quarterly* 2006 April; 20(2): 135-161. Subject: 15.8

Shuchman, Miriam. Delaying generic competition — corporate payoffs and the future of Plavix. *New England Journal of Medicine* 2006 September 28; 355(13): 1297-1300. Subject: 9.7

Shuchman, Miriam; Redelmeier, Donald A. Politics and independence — the collapse of the Canadian Medical Association Journal. *New England Journal of Medicine* 2006 March 30; 354(13): 1337-1339. Subject: 1.3.7

Shugarman, Lisa R.; Lorenz, Karl; Lynn, Joanne. End-of-life care: an agenda for policy improvement. *Clinics in Geriatric Medicine* 2005 February; 21(1): 255-272. Subject: 20.4.1

Shukunami, Ken-ichi.; Nishijima, Koji; Yoshida, Yoshio; Kotsuji, Fumikazu. Responses by pregnant Jehovah's witnesses on health care proxies [letter]. *Obstetrics and Gynecology* 2005 February; 105(2): 442. Subject: 8.3.3

Shultz, Marjorie M. Taking account of ARTs in determining parenthood: a troubling dispute in California. *Washington University Journal of Law and Policy* 2005; 19: 77-128. Subject: 14.1

Shumak, Steven L.; Sen, Mithu; Gregson, Daniel; Lewis, James; Hoey, John. Unnecessary exposure? [letter and response]. *CMAJ/JAMC:Canadian Medical Association Journal* 2006 February 14; 174(4): 499-500. Subject: 8.4

Sibbald, Barbara. Ethics in action: for more than 30 years, Dr. Janet Storch has endeavoured to move ethics out of the textbooks and into nursing practice. *Canadian Nurse* 2005 May; 101(5): 44, 43. Subject: 4.1.3

Sibbald, Barbara. Practising to code. *Canadian Nurse* 2006 February; 102(2): 40, 39. Subject: 4.1.3

Sibbald, Robert W.; Lazar, Neil M. Bench-to-bedside review: ethical challenges for those in directing roles in critical care units. *Critical Care* 2005 February; 9(1): 76-80. Subject: 9.5.1

Siddiqui, Faraz. Assessing the ethicality of pre-implantation genetic diagnosis beyond the discourse of eugenics. *Penn Bioethics Journal* 2006; 2(1): 4p. [Online]. Accessed: http://www.bioethicsjournal.com [2006 February 21]. Subject: 15.2

Side, Katherine. Contract, charity, and honorable entitlement: social citizenship and the 1967 Abortion Act in Northern Ireland after the Good Friday Agreement. *Social Politics* 2006 Spring; 13(1): 89-116. Subject: 12.4.2

Sidel, Victor W.; Levy, Barry S. Physician-soldier: a moral dilemma? *In:* Beam, Thomas E.; Sparacino, Linette R.; Pellegrino, Edmund D.; Hartle, Anthony E.; Howe, Edmund G., eds. Military Medical Ethics. Volume 1. Washington, DC: TMM Publications, Borden Institute, Walter Reed Army Medical Center; 2003: 293-329. Subject: 2.1

Siden, Harold B. The emerging issue of euthanasia [editorial]. *Archives of Pediatric and Adolescent Medicine* 2005 September; 159(9): 887-889. Subject: 20.5.2

Sidle, John E.; Were, Edwin; Wools-Kaloustian, Kara; Chuani, Christine; Salmon, Karen; Tierney, William M.; Meslin, Eric M. A needs assessment to build international research ethics capacity. *Journal of Empirical Research on Human Research Ethics* 2006 June; 1(2): 23-28. Subject: 18.2

Sieber, Joan E. The evolution of best ethical practices in human research [editorial]. *Journal of Empirical Research on Human Research Ethics* 2006 March; 1(1): 1. Subject: 18.1

Sieber, Joan E. Introduction: data sharing and disclosure limitation techniques. *Journal of Empirical Research on Human Research Ethics* 2006 September; 1(3): 47-49. Subject: 8.1

Siegal, Gil; Bonnie, Richard J. Closing the organ gap: a reciprocity-based social contract approach. *Journal of Law, Medicine and Ethics* 2006 Summer; 34(2): 415-423. Subject: 19.5

Siegel, Andrew W. Locating convergence: ethics, public policy, and human stem cell research. *In:* Ruse, Michael; Pynes, Christopher A., eds. The Stem Cell Controversy:

Debating the Issues. Amherst, NY: Prometheus Books; 2003: 271-287. Subject: 18.5.4

Siegel, Jay P.; O'Neill, Robert; Temple, Robert; Campbell, Gregory; Foulkes, Mary A. Independence of the statistician who analyses unblinded data. *Statistics in Medicine* 2004 May 30; 23(10): 1527-1529. Subject: 18.2

Siegel, Mark D. Alone at life's end: trying to protect the autonomy of patients without surrogates or decision-making capacity. *Critical Care Medicine* 2006 August; 34(8): 2238-2239. Subject: 20.5.1

Siegel-Itzkovich, Judy. Cancer organisation hits out at medical research funded by tobacco companies [news]. *BMJ: British Medical Journal* 2006 January 7; 332(7532): 6. Subject: 18.6

Siegel-Itzkovich, Judy. Israel looks into claims of "illegal medical experiment" [news]. *BMJ: British Medical Journal* 2006 July 22; 333(7560): 165. Subject: 1.3.9

Siegel-Itzkovich, Judy. Israeli doctors are arrested in investigation [news]. *BMJ: British Medical Journal* 2006 October 21; 333(7573): 823. Subject: 1.3.9

Siegler, Mark. Lessons from 30 years of teaching clinical ethics. *Virtual Mentor* 2001 October; 3(10): 3p. Subject: 2.3

Siegler, Mark. Lessons from 30 years of teaching clinical medical ethics. *In:* American Medical Association. ProfessingMedicine: strengthening the ethics and professionalism of tomorrow's physicians. Chicago: American Medical Association; 2001: 8-13. Subject: 2.3

Siegrist, Michael. The influence of trust and perceptions of risks and benefits on the acceptance of gene technology. *Risk Analysis* 2000 April; 20(2): 195-203. Subject: 5.2

Sifris, Adiva. Known semen donors: to be or not to be a parent. *Journal of Law and Medicine* 2005 November; 13(2): 230-244. Subject: 14.2

Sigafoos, J. Self-determination: can we let the child determine the 'best' treatment? [editorial]. *Pediatric Rehabilitation* 2006 January-March; 9(1): 1-2. Subject: 9.5.7

Silbergleit, Robert; Watters, Drew; Sayre, Michael R. What treatments are "satisfactory?" Divining regulatory intent and an ethical basis for exception to informed consent for emergency research. *American Journal of Bioethics* 2006 May-June; 6(3): 24-26; discussion W49-W50. Subject: 18.3

Sild, Tarmo; Mullari, Tambet. Population based genetic research: Estonian answer to the legal challenge. *European Journal of Health Law* 2001 December; 8(4): 363-371. Subject: 15.1

Silfen, Molly. I want my information back: evidentiary privilege following the partial birth abortion cases. *Journal of Health Law* 2005 Winter; 38(1): 121-135. Subject: 8.4

See SUBJECT HEADING KEY FOR SECTION II on inside back cover.

721

Sillender, M. Can patients be sure they are fully informed when representatives of surgical equipment manufacturers attend their operations? *Journal of Medical Ethics* 2006 July; 32(7): 395-397. Subject: 8.3.1

Silove, Derrick. The psychiatrist as a political leader in war: does the medical profession have a monitoring role? [editorial]. *Journal of Nervous and Mental Disease* 1995 March; 183(3): 125-126. Subject: 4.1.2

Silva, Mary Cipriano; Ludwick, Ruth. Is the doctor of nursing practice ethical? *Online Journal of Issues in Nursing* 2006; 11(2): 8 p. Subject: 7.2

Silva, Mary Cipriano; Williams, Kathleen O. Managed care and the violation of ethical principles: research vignettes. *In:* Cowen, Perle Slavik; Moorhead, Sue, eds. Current Issues in Nursing. 7th ed. St. Louis, MO: Mosby, 2006: 660-667. Subject: 9.3.2

Silva, Vesta T. In the beginning was the gene: the hegemony of genetic thinking in contemporary culture. *Communication Theory* 2005 February; 15(1): 100-123. Subject: 15.1

Silver, Marc T. Primary prevention implantable cardioverter-defibrillators: economics and ethics. *American Heart Hospital Journal* 2005 Summer; 3(3): 205-206. Subject: 9.3.1

Silverman, Henry J. Withdrawal of feeding-tubes from incompetent patients: the Terri Schiavo case raises new issues regarding who decides in end-of-life decision making [news]. *Intensive Care Medicine* 2005 March; 31(3): 480-481. Subject: 20.5.1

Silverman, Jerald. Clinical trial trouble. *Lab Animal* 2006 June; 35(6): 15. Subject: 22.2

Silverman, Joseph S. A new approach to health system reform: seizing the moral high ground. *Pennsylvania Medicine* 1995 June; 98(6): 28-30. Subject: 9.3.1

Silverman, Paul H. Rethinking genetic determinism: with only 30,000 genes, what is it that makes humans human? *Scientist* 2004 May 24; 18(10): 32-33. Subject: 15.1

Silvers, Anita. Pure enhancement [letter]. *National Catholic Bioethics Quarterly* 2006 Autumn; 6(3): 405-408. Subject: 4.5

Silvers, Anita; Stein, Michael Ashley. Essentially empirical: the roles of biological and legal classification in effectively prohibiting genetic discrimination. *In:* Figueroa, Robert; Harding, Sandra, eds. Science and Other Cultures: Issues in Philosophies of Science and Technology. New York: Routledge; 2003: 129-153. Subject: 15.1

Silverstein, Gerry. Preparing for pandemic influenza. *Lancet* 2006 April 15-21; 367(9518): 1239-1240. Subject: 9.4

Silverstein, Robin P. The ethics of influenza vaccination [letter]. *Science* 2006 August 11; 313(5788): 758. Subject: 9.5.1

Silverton, Louise I. Ethics examined. *Midwifery Today and Childbirth Education* 1994 Summer; (30): 12-13. Subject: 2.1

Sim, Ida; Chan, An-Wen; Gülmezoglu, A. Metin; Evans, Tim; Pang, Tikki. Clinical trial registration: transparency is the watchword. *Lancet* 2006 May 20-26; 367(9523): 1631-1633. Subject: 18.6

Siminoff, Laura A.; Burant, Christopher J.; Ibrahim, Said A. Racial disparities in preferences and perceptions regarding organ donation. *JGIM: Journal of General Internal Medicine* 2006 September; 21(9): 995-1000. Subject: 19.5

Siminoff, Laura A.; Step, Mary M. A communication model of shared decision making: accounting for cancer treatment decisions. *Health Psychology* 2005 July; 24(4 Supplement): S99-S105. Subject: 9.5.1

Simm, Kadri. Benefit-sharing: an inquiry regarding the meaning and limits of the concept in human genetics research. *Genetics, Society, and Policy* 2005 August; 1(2): 29-40. Subject: 15.10

Simmons, Ann. Taking the judgement out of abortion. *Nursing New Zealand* 2005 February; 11(1): 26-27. Subject: 12.5.1

Simon, Alex; Schenker, Joseph G. Ethical consideration of intentioned preimplantation genetic diagnosis to enable future tissue transplantation. *Reproductive BioMedicine Online [electronic]* 2005 March; 10(3): 320-324. Accessed: http://www.rbmonline.com/Article/1615 [2005 September 34]. Subject: 15.2

Simon, Christian; Eder, Michelle; Kodish, Eric; Siminoff, Laura. Altruistic discourse in the informed consent process for childhood cancer clinical trials. *American Journal of Bioethics* 2006 September-October; 6(5): 40-47. Subject: 18.3

Simon, Jürgen. Insurance and genetic testing in Germany and the international context. *In:* Sándor, Judit, ed. Society and Genetic Information: Codes and Laws in the Genetic Era. Budapest, Hungary; New York: CEU Press; 2003: 185-199. Subject: 15.3

Simon, Jürgen; Ravenstein, Christian. Gene tests and employees in an international comparison. *Revista de Derecho y Genoma Humano* 2005 July-December; (23): 167-190. Subject: 15.3

Simon, Laurence. Abnormal psychology textbooks: valid science or political propaganda. *Ethical Human Psychology and Psychiatry* 2006 Summer; 8(2): 101-110. Subject: 17.1

Simoncelli, Tania. Dangerous excursions: the case against expanding forensic DNA databases to innocent persons. *Journal of Law, Medicine and Ethics* 2006 Summer; 34(2): 390-397. Subject: 15.1

Subject = NRCBL Primary Classification Number; see inside front cover.

Simoncelli, Tania; Wallace, Helen. Expanding databases, declining liberties. *GeneWatch* 2006 January-February; 19(1): 3-8, 18. Subject: 15.1

Simonds, Anita K. Ethical aspects of home long term ventilation in children with neuromuscular disease. *Paediatric Respiratory Reviews* 2005 September; 6(3): 209-214. Subject: 9.5.7

Simonstein, Frida. Artificial reproduction technologies (RTs) — all the way to the artificial womb? *Medicine, Health Care and Philosophy* 2006; 9(3): 359-365. Subject: 14.1

Simonstein, Frida. Pressures on women to reproduce and the drive towards assisted reproductive technologies. *Medicine and Law: The World Association for Medical Law* 2006 June; 25(2): 355-363. Subject: 9.5.5

Simonstein, Frida. Stem cells and the ethics of indefinitely prolonged lives. *In:* Sang-yong, Song; Young-Mo, Koo; Macer, Darryl R.J., eds. Asian Bioethics in the 21st Century. Christchurch, NZ: Eubios Ethics Institute, 2002: 65-72. Subject: 4.5

Simpson, Bob. Impossible gifts: bodies, Buddhism and bioethics in contemporary Sri Lanka. *Journal of the Royal Anthropological Institute* 2004 December; 10(4): 839-859. Subject: 19.5

Simpson, Bob. Localising a brave new world: new reproductive technologies and the politics of fertility in contemporary Sri Lanka. *In:* Unnithan-Kumar, Maya, ed. Reproductive Agency, Medicine and the State: Cultural Transformations in Childbearing. New York: Berghahn Books; 2004: 43-57. Subject: 14.1

Simpson, Christopher S.; Hoffmaster, Barry; Dorian, Paul. Downward delegation of implantable cardioverter defibrillator decision-making in a restricted-resource environment: the pitfalls of bedside rationing. *Canadian Journal of Cardiology* 2005 May 15; 21(7): 595-599. Subject: 9.4

Sinaiko, Anna D.; McGuire, Thomas G. Patient inducement, provider priorities, and resource allocation in public mental health systems. *Journal of Health Politics, Policy and Law* 2006 December; 31(6): 1075-1106. Subject: 17.1

Singapore. Bioethics Advisory Committee. Human Stem Cell Research Consultation Paper. Helios, Singapore: Bioethics Advisory Committee, 2001 November 8; 6 p. [Online]. Accessed: http://www.bioethics-singapore.org/resources/pdf/Human%20Stem%20Cell%20Consultation.pdf [2006 March 15]. Subject: 18.5.4

Singapore. Bioethics Advisory Committee. Human Genetics Sub-Committee [HGS]. Human Tissue Research. Consultation Paper. Helios, Singapore: Bioethics Advisory Committee, 2002 February 27; 22 p. [Online]. Accessed: http://www.bioethics-singapore.org/resources/pdf/Human%20Tissue%20Research%20Consultation.pdf [2006 May 1]. Subject: 18.1

Singer, Eleanor; Corning, Amy; Lamias, Mark. The polls — trends: genetic testing, engineering, and therapy: awareness and attitudes. *Public Opinion Quarterly* 1998 Winter; 62(4): 633-664. Subject: 15.1

Singer, Peter. Shopping at the genetic supermarket. *In:* Sang-yong, Song; Young-Mo, Koo; Macer, Darryl R.J., eds. Asian Bioethics in the 21st Century. Christchurch, NZ: Eubios Ethics Institute, 2002: 143-156. Subject: 15.1

Singer, Peter. Stem cell research: the fallacy in Bush's position. *New Jersey Medicine* 2004 December; 101(12): 14-17. Subject: 18.5.4

Singer, Peter. Why the Korean stem-cell controversy matters. *Free Inquiry* 2006 April-May; 26(3): 25-26. Subject: 18.5.4

Singer, Peter; Kuhse, Helga. 1980-2005: bioethics then and now. *Monash Bioethics Review* 2006 January; 25(1): 9-14. Subject: 2.2

Singh, Jerome Amir. The vital importance of implementation ethics. *Hastings Center Report* 2006 May-June; 36(3): 3. Subject: 9.5.6

Singh, Ritupriya; Singh, Kaushal K. Ethical aspects of the tuberculosis programme. *Health Administrator* 2003 January-July; 15(1-2): 156-168. Subject: 9.5.1

Singh, Sameer; Mayahi, Rez. Consent in orthopaedic surgery. *Annals of the Royal College of Surgeons of England* 2004 September; 86(5): 339-341. Subject: 8.3.1

Singh, Swaran P.; Burns, Tom. Race and mental health: there is more to race than racism. *BMJ: British Medical Journal* 2006 September 23; 333(7569): 648-651. Subject: 9.5.4

Singh, Zile; Banerjee, A. HIV/AIDS: social and ethical issues. *Medical Journal of the Armed Forces of India* 2004; 60(2): 107- 108. Subject: 9.5.6

Single, Gregg. United States v. Sell: involuntary administration of antipsychotic medication. Are you dangerous or not? *Journal of Law and Health* 2003-2004; 18(2): 297-321. Subject: 4.3

Singleton, Peter; Wadsworth, Michael. Confidentiality and consent in medical research: consent for the use of personal medical data in research. *BMJ: British Medical Journal* 2006 July 29; 333(7561): 255-258. Subject: 18.3

Sinha, Gunjan. Drug companies accused of stalling tailored therapies [news]. *Nature Medicine* 2006 September; 12(9): 983. Subject: 9.7

Sipr, Kvetoslav. Prenatal diagnosis and respect for autonomy. *In:* Glasa, J., ed. Ethics of Human Genetics: Challenges of the (Post) Genomic Era. Bratislava, Slovak Republic: Charis [and] IMEB Foundation; 2002: 117-121. Subject: 15.2

Sirotin, Nicole; Lo, Bernard. The end of therapeutic privilege? *Journal of Clinical Ethics* 2006 Winter; 17(4): 312-316. Subject: 8.2

See SUBJECT HEADING KEY FOR SECTION II on inside back cover.

Sismondo, Lauren J. GINA, what could you do for me one day?: The potential of the Genetic Information Nondiscrimination Act to protect the American public. *Washington University Journal of Law and Policy* 2006; 21: 459-481. Subject: 15.3

Sisters of St. Francis Health Services, Inc. Management of extrauterine pregnancy [policy statement]. *Ethics and Medics* 2006 March; 31(3): 4. Subject: 9.5.5

Sisti, Dominic A. Health and disease. *In:* Mitcham, Carl, ed. Encyclopedia of Science, Technology, and Ethics. Farmington Hills, MI: Thomson/Gale, 2005: 902-907. Subject: 4.2

Sisti, Dominic A.; Caplan, Arthur L. Back to basics in der post-Gelsinger-Ära: Ethik und Aufsicht der Gentherapieforschung seit dem Todesfall von J. Gelsinger. *In:* Rehmann-Sutter, Christoph; Müller, Hansjakob, eds. Ethik und Gentherapie: zum praktischen Diskurs um die molekulare Medizin. 2nd ed. Tübingen: Francke Verlag; 2003: 135-149. Subject: 15.4

Sites, Brian D.; Lee, Susan J.; Ralston, Henry J. Peter, III; Drey, Eleanor A.; Partridge, John Colin; Rosen, Mark A. Fetal pain [letter and reply]. *JAMA: The Journal of the American Medical Association* 2006 January 11; 295(2): 160-161. Subject: 4.4

Sitter-Liver, Beat. Finitude — a neglected perspective in bioethics. *In:* Rehmann-Sutter, Christoph; Düwell, Marcus; Mieth, Dietmar, eds. Bioethics in Cultural Contexts: Reflections on Methods and Finitude. Dordrecht: Springer, 2006: 45-57. Subject: 2.1

Sittisombut, Sudarat; Love, Edgar J.; Sitthi-amorn, Chitr. Attitudes toward advance directives and the impact of prognostic information on the preference for cardiopulmonary resuscitation in medical inpatients in Chiang Mai University Hospital, Thailand. *Nursing and Health Sciences* 2005 December; 7(4): 243-250. Subject: 20.5.4

Sjöström, Stefan. Invocation of coercion context in compliance communication — power dynamics in psychiatric care. *International Journal of Law and Psychiatry* 2006 January-February; 29(1): 36-47. Subject: 9.5.3

Skene, Loane. Bioscience, community expectations and the law [forum]. *University of New South Wales Law Journal* 2003; 26(3): 799- 806. Subject: 5.3

Skene, Loane. Genetics and artificial procreation in Australia. *In:* Meulders-Klein, Marie-Thérèse; Deech, Ruth; Vlaardingerbroek, Paul, eds. Biomedicine, the Family and Human Rights. New York: Kluwer Law International, 2002: 107-121. Subject: 14.1

Skene, Loane. The Schiavo and Korp cases: conceptualising end-of-life decision-making. *Journal of Law and Medicine* 2005 November; 13(2): 223-229. Subject: 20.5.1

Skinner, S. Rachel; Ng, Cindy; McDonald, Ann; Walters, Tamara. A patient with autism and severe de-pression: medical and ethical challenges for an adolescent medicine unit. *Medical Journal of Australia* 2005 October 17; 183(8): 422-424. Subject: 9.5.7

Skipp, Catharine; Campo-Flores, Arian. What the doctor did: in Katrina's wake, a deadly hospital mystery unfolds. *Newsweek* 2006 July 31; 148(5): 49. Subject: 20.5.1

Skirton, Heather; Frazier, Lorraine Q.; Calvin, Amy O.; Cohen, Marlene Z. A legacy for the children — attitudes of older adults in the United Kingdom to genetic testing. *Journal of Clinical Nursing* 2006 May; 15(5): 565-573. Subject: 15.3

Skjennald, Arnulf. How much should we inform our patients? [editorial]. *Acta Radiologica* 2005 November; 46(7): 662. Subject: 8.3.1

Skloot, Rebecca. Taking the least of you: Most of us have tissue or blood samples on file somewhere, whether we know it or not. What we don't typically know is what research they are being used for and how much money is being made from them. And science may want to keep things that way. *New York Times Magazine* 2006 April 16; p. 38-45, 75, 79, 81. Subject: 19.5

Skouvakis, Fotini Antonia. Defining the undefined: using a best interest approach to decide the fate of cryopreserved preembryos in Pennsylvania. *Penn State Law Review* 2005 Winter; 109(3): 885-905. Subject: 14.6

Skrikerud, Anne Maria. Monozygotic autonomy and genetic privacy. *In:* Árnason, Gardar; Nordal, Salvör; Árnason, Vilhjálmur, eds. Blood and Data: Ethical, Legal and Social Aspects of Human Genetic Databases. Reykjavík: University of Iceland Press; 2004: 243-247. Subject: 15.1

Skultans, Vieda. Varieties of deception and distrust: moral dilemmas in the ethnography of psychiatry. *Health (London)* 2005 October; 9(4): 491-512. Subject: 17.1

Slack, Catherine; Strode, Ann; Grant, Catherine; Milford, Cecilia. Implications of the ethical-legal framework for adolescent HIV vaccine trials — report of a consultative forum. *South African Medical Journal* 2005 September; 95(9): 682-684. Subject: 18.5.2

Slack, C.; Stobie, M.; Milford, C.; Lindegger, G.; Wassenaar, D.; Strode, A.; Ijsselmuiden, C. Provision of HIV treatment in HIV preventive vaccine trials: a developing country perspective. *Social Science and Medicine* 2005 March; 60(6): 1197-1208. Subject: 9.5.6

Slaughter, Louise McIntosh. Genetic testing and discrimination: how private is your information? *Stanford Law and Policy Review* 2006; 17(1): 67-81. Subject: 15.1

Sleeboom, Margaret. The limitations of the Dutch concept of euthanasia. *Eubios Journal of Asian and International Bioethics* 2003 January 13(1): 20-26. Subject: 20.5.1

Sleeboom-Faulkner, Margaret. Chinese concepts of euthanasia and health care. *Bioethics* 2006 August; 20(4): 203-212. Subject: 20.5.1

Slevin, Maurice. Funding of patients' groups. *Lancet* 2006 July 15-21; 368(9531): 202. Subject: 9.5.1

Slingsby, Brian Taylor; Kodama, Satoshi; Akabayashi, Akira. Scientific misconduct in Japan: the present paucity of oversight policy. *CQ: Cambridge Quarterly of Healthcare Ethics* 2006 Summer; 15(3): 294-297. Subject: 1.3.9

Slosar, John Paul. Genomics and neurology: an ethical view. *Health Progress* 2006 January-February; 87(1): 68-72. Subject: 15.3

Slosar, John Paul. Teleology, the modern moral dichotomy, and postmodern bioethics in the 21st century. *In:* Dinkins, Christine Sorrell; Sorrell, Jeanne Merkle, eds. Listening to the Whispers: Re-Thinking Ethics in Healthcare. Madison, WI: University of Wisconsin Press; 2006: 138-189. Subject: 2.1

Slovenko, Ralph. The boundary violation of undue familiarity. *In his:* Psychiatry in Law/Law in Psychiatry. Volume 2. New York: Brunner-Routledge; 2002: 739-763. Subject: 7.4

Slovenko, Ralph. Breach of confidentiality. *In his:* Psychiatry in Law/Law in Psychiatry. Volume 2. New York: Brunner-Routledge; 2002: 689-710. Subject: 8.4

Slovenko, Ralph. Civil commitment (involuntary hospitalization). *In his:* Psychiatry in Law/Law in Psychiatry. Volume 2. New York: Brunner-Routledge; 2002: 555-583. Subject: 17.7

Slovenko, Ralph. Informed consent. *In his:* Psychiatry in Law/Law in Psychiatry. Volume 2. New York: Brunner-Routledge; 2002: 711-738. Subject: 8.3.1

Slovenko, Ralph. Milestones in the evolution of standards for experimental treatment or research. *Medicine and Law: The World Association for Medical Law* 2006 September; 25(3): 523-557. Subject: 18.2

Slovenko, Ralph. Patient and non-patient spouse lawsuits for undue familiarity. *Journal of Psychiatry and Law* 2006 Winter; 34(4): 567-578. Subject: 7.4

Slovenko, Ralph. Right to treatment and right to refuse treatment. *In his:* Psychiatry in Law/Law in Psychiatry. Volume 2. New York: Brunner-Routledge; 2002: 585-618. Subject: 17.8

Slowther, Anne; Boynton, Petra; Shaw, Sara. Research governance: ethical issues. *Journal of the Royal Society of Medicine* 2006 February; 99(2): 65-72. Subject: 18.6

Slowther, Anne-Marie. Medical futility and 'do not attempt resuscitation' orders. *Clinical Ethics* 2006 March; 1(1): 18-20. Subject: 20.5.1

Slowther, Anne-Marie. Patient requests for specific-treatments. *Clinical Ethics* 2006 September; 1(3): 135-137. Subject: 8.1

Slowther, Anne-Marie. The role of the family in patient care. *Clinical Ethics* 2006 December; 1(4): 191-193. Subject: 8.1

Slowther, Anne-Marie. Sharing information in health care: the nature and limits of confidentiality. *Clinical Ethics* 2006 June; 1(2): 82-84. Subject: 8.4

Smagata, David. Workers' compensation claims and disclosure. *Canadian HIV/AIDS Policy and Law Newsletter* 1997-1998 Winter; 3(4)-4(1): 15-16. Subject: 9.5.6

Smart, Andrew. Reporting the dawn of the post-genomic era: who wants to live forever? *Sociology of Health and Illness* 2003 January; 25(1): 24-49. Subject: 1.3.7

Smetanka, C.; Cooper, D.K.C. The ethics debate in relation to xenotransplantation. *Revue Scientifique et Technique* 2005 April; 24(1): 335-342. Subject: 19.1

Smetanka, Stella L. Who will protect the "disruptive" dialysis patient? *American Journal of Law and Medicine* 2006; 32(1): 53-91. Subject: 19.3

Smith, Alexander K.; Ries, Angela Poppe; Zhang, Baohui; Tulsky, James A.; Prigerson, Holly G.; Block, Susan D. Resident approaches to advance care planning on the day of hospital admission. *Archives of Internal Medicine* 2006 August 14-28; 166(15): 1597-1602. Subject: 20.5.4

Smith, Alison P. The Schiavo legacy. *Nursing Economic* 2005 May-June; 23(3): 136-137. Subject: 20.5.4

Smith, Amanda J. J.B. v. M.B. new evidence that contracts need to be reevaluated as the method of choice for resolving frozen embryo disputes. *North Carolina Law Review* 2003 January; 81(2): 878-1011. Subject: 14.6

Smith, Anthony J. Scientific freedom. *Journal of Dental Research* 2004 December; 83(12): 895. Subject: 1.3.9

Smith, David Barton. Healthcare's hidden civil rights legacy. *St. Louis University Law Journal* 2003 Fall; 48(1): 37-60. Subject: 9.5.4

Smith, Gary B.; Poplett, Nicola; Williams, Derek. Staff awareness of a 'do not attempt resuscitation' policy in a district general hospital. *Resuscitation* 2005 May; 65(2): 159-163. Subject: 20.5.1

Smith, George Davey; Frankel, Stephen; Ebrahim, Shah. Rationing for health equity: is it necessary? *Health Economics* 2000 October; 9(7): 575-579. Subject: 9.4

Smith, George P., II. Law, religion and medicine: conjunctive or disjunctive? *Macquarie Law Symposium* 2006: 9-39. Subject: 2.1

Smith, Henry F. Invisible racism. *Psychoanalytic Quarterly* 2006 January; 75(1): 3-19. Subject: 8.1

Smith, Kerri. Caught in the middle [news]. *Nature* 2006 December 14; 442(7121): 811. Subject: 22.2

See SUBJECT HEADING KEY FOR SECTION II on inside back cover.

725

Smith, Martin L. Should possible disparities and distrust trump do-no-harm? *American Journal of Bioethics* 2006 September-October; 6(5): 28-30; discussion W30-W32. Subject: 20.5.1

Smith, Michael E. Let's make the DNA identification database as inclusive as possible. *Journal of Law, Medicine and Ethics* 2006 Summer; 34(2): 385-389. Subject: 15.1

Smith, Peter C. User charges and priority setting in health care: balancing equity and efficiency. *Journal of Health Economics* 2005 September; 24(5): 1018-1029. Subject: 9.4

Smith, Richard. Medical journals are an extension of the marketing arm of pharmaceutical companies. *PLoS Medicine* 2005 May; 2(5): 0364-0366. Subject: 1.3.7

Smith, Richard. The trouble with medical journals. *Journal of the Royal Society of Medicine* 2006 March; 99(3): 115-119. Subject: 1.3.7

Smith, Richard; Raithatha, Nick. Why disclosure of genetic tests for health insurance should be voluntary. *Journal of Health Services Research and Policy* 2006 July; 11(3): 184-186. Subject: 15.3

Smith, Shane; Neaves, William; Teitelbaum, Steven. Adult stem cell treatments for diseases? [letter]. *Science* 2006 July 28; 313(5786): 439. Subject: 5.3

Smith, Vaughan P. Conscientious objection in medicine: doctors' freedom of conscience [letter]. *BMJ: British Medical Journal* 2006 February 18; 332(7538): 425. Subject: 8.1

Smolensky, Kirsten Rabe. Defining life from the perspective of death: an introduction to the Force Symmetry Approach. *University of Chicago Legal Forum* 2006: 41-85. Subject: 4.4

Smolin, David M. Does bioethics provide answers?: Secular and religious bioethics and our procreative future. *Cumberland Law Review* 2004-2005; 35(3): 473-517. Subject: 2.1

Smucker, William D.; Houts, Renate M.; Danks, Joseph H.; Ditto, Peter H.; Fagerlin, Angela; Coppola, Kristen M. Modal preferences predict elderly patients' life-sustaining treatment choices as well as patients' chosen surrogates do. *Medical Decision Making* 2000 July-September; 20(3): 271-280. Subject: 20.5.4

Smyth, Lisa. Narratives of Irishness and the problem of abortion: the X case 1992. *Feminist Review* 1998 Autumn; 60: 61-83. Subject: 12.5.1

Smythe, William E.; Malloy, David C.; Hadjistavropoulos, Thomas; Martin, Ronald R.; Bardutz, Holly A. An analysis of the ethical and linguistic content of hospital mission statements. *Health Care Management Review* 2006 April-June; 31(2): 92-98. Subject: 2.3

Snapinn, Steven; Cook, Thomas; Shapiro, Deborah; Snavely, Duane. The role of the unblinded sponsor statis-

tician. *Statistics in Medicine* 2004 May 30; 23(10): 1531-1533. Subject: 18.2

Snead, O. Carter. Dynamic complementarity: Terri's law and separation of powers principles in the end-of-life context. *Florida Law Review* 2005 January; 57(1): 53-89. Subject: 20.5.1

Sneddon, Andrew. Equality, justice, and paternalism: recentreing debate about physician-assisted suicide. *Journal of Applied Philosophy* 2006; 23(4): 387-404. Subject: 20.7

Sneddon, Andrew. Rawlsian decisionmaking and genetic engineering. *CQ: Cambridge Quarterly of Healthcare Ethics* 2006 Winter; 15(1): 35-41. Subject: 15.4

Snowdon, Claire; Elbourne, Diana; Garcia, Jo. "It was a snap decision": parental and professional perspectives on the speed of decisions about participation in perinatal randomised controlled trials. *Social Science and Medicine* 2006 May; 62(9): 2279-2290. Subject: 18.3

Snyder, Evan Y.; Hinman, Lawrence M.; Kalichman, Michael W. Can science resolve the ethical impasse in stem cell research? *Nature Biotechnology* 2006 April; 24(4): 397-400. Subject: 4.4

Snyder, Evan Y.; Loring, Jeanne F. Beyond fraud — stem-cell research continues. *New England Journal of Medicine* 2006 January 26; 354(4): 321-324. Subject: 1.3.9

Snyder, Graydon F. Bioethics: how will Anabaptists respond? *In:* Miller, Roman J.; Brubaker, Beryl H.; Peterson, James C., eds. Viewing New Creations with Anabaptist Eyes: Ethics of Biotechnology. Telford, PA: Cascadia Pub.; 2005: 218-228. Subject: 2.1

Snyder, Graydon F. Theological reflections on genetic engineering. *Brethren Life and Thought* 1986 Autumn; 31(4): 209-214. Subject: 15.1

Snyder, Steven H.; Byrn, Mary Patricia. The use of prebirth parentage orders in surrogacy proceedings. *Family Law Quarterly* 2005 Fall; 39(3): 633-662. Subject: 14.2

Society for Adolescent Medicine. Guidelines for adolescent health research. *Journal of Adolescent Health* 1995 November; 17(5): 264-269. Subject: 18.5.2

Society for Adolescent Medicine; Santelli, John S.; Rosenfeld, Walter D.; DuRant, Robert H.; Dubler, Nancy; Morreale, Madlyn; English, Abigail; Rogers, Audrey Smith. Guidelines for adolescent health research: a position paper of the society for adolescent medicine. *Journal of Adolescent Health* 1995 November; 17(5): 270-276. Subject: 18.5.2

Society for Assisted Reproductive Technology [SART]. Practice Committee American Society for Reproductive Medicine. Guidelines for advertising by ART programs. *Fertility and Sterility* 2004 September; 82(Supplement 1): S3. Subject: 14.1

Society for Assisted Reproductive Technology [SART]. Practice Committee American Society for Reproductive Medicine. Guidelines on the number of embryos transferred. *Fertility and Sterility* 2004 September; 82(Supplement 1): S1-S2. Subject: 14.4

Society of Nuclear Brain Imaging Council. Ethical clinical practice of functional brain imaging. *Journal of Nuclear Medicine* 1996 July; 37(7): 1256-1259. Subject: 17.1

Sodano, Angelo. The physician and the new evangelization. *Dolentium Hominum* 1994; 9(3): 22-24. Subject: 4.1.2

Sodeke, Stephen O.; Orentlicher, David. Protection of human subjects and scientific progress: can the two be reconciled? [letter and reply]. *Hastings Center Report* 2006 January-February; 36(1): 5, 8-9. Subject: 18.3

Sokalska, Maria. Recent developments in health law in Poland: new law on the removal, storage, and transplantation of cells, tissues, and organs. *European Journal of Health Law* 2006 June; 13(2): 115-122. Subject: 19.5

Sokol, Daniel K. Dissecting "deception". *CQ: Cambridge Quarterly of Healthcare Ethics* 2006 Fall; 15(4): 457-464. Subject: 8.2

Sokol, Daniel K. Time to get streetwise: why medical ethics needs doctors. *BMJ: British Medical Journal* 2006 December 9; 333(7580): 1226. Subject: 2.1

Sokol, Daniel K. Truth-telling in the doctor-patient relationship: a case analysis. *Clinical Ethics* 2006 September; 1(3): 130-134. Subject: 8.2

Sokol, Daniel K. What is false hope? *Journal of Clinical Ethics* 2006 Winter; 17(4): 367-368. Subject: 20.4.1

Sokol, Daniel K.; Bergson, Gilian. Genetic counselling and the "new genetics". *In their:* Medical Ethics and Law: Surviving on the Wards and Passing Exams. London: Trauma Pub., 2005: 133-148. Subject: 15.2

Sokol, Daniel K.; Car, J. Patient confidentiality and telephone consultations: time for a password. *Journal of Medical Ethics* 2006 December; 32(12): 688-689. Subject: 8.4

Solai, Sandra; Dubois-Arber, Françoise; Benninghoff, Fabienne; Benaroyo, Lazare. Ethical reflections emerging during the activity of a low threshold facility with supervised drug consumption room in Geneva, Switzerland. *International Journal of Drug Policy* 2006 January; 17(1): 17-22. Subject: 9.5.9

Solbakk, Jan Helge. Cartharsis and moral therapy II: an Aristotelian account. *Medicine, Health Care and Philosophy* 2006; 9(2): 141-153. Subject: 7.1

Solbakk, Jan Helge. Catharsis and moral therapy I: a Platonic account. *Medicine, Health Care and Philosophy* 2006; 9(1): 57-67. Subject: 2.1

Solbakk, Jan Helge; Holm, Søren; Lobato de Faria, Paula; Harris, Jennifer; Cambon-Thomsen, Anne; Halvorsen, Marit; Stoltenberg, Camilla; Strand,

Roger; Hofmann, Bjørn; Skrikerud, Anne Maria; Karlsen, Jan Reinert. Mapping the language of research-biobanks and health registries: from traditional biobanking to research biobanking. *In:* Árnason, Gardar; Nordal, Salvör; Árnason, Vilhjálmur, eds. Blood and Data: Ethical, Legal and Social Aspects of Human Genetic Databases. Reykjavík: University of Iceland Press; 2004: 299-306. Subject: 15.1

Solomon, Andrew. Our great depression. *New York Times* 2006 November 17; p. A31. Subject: 17.1

Solomon, Deborah. Abortion issue moves to states: shift on federal bench spurs governors, legislators to battle Roe. *Wall Street Journal* 2006 March 9; p. A4. Subject: 12.4.1

Solomon, Mildred Z.; Sellers, Deborah E.; Heller, Karen S.; Dokken, Deborah L.; Levetown, Marcia; Rushton, Cynda; Truog, Robert D.; Fleischman, Alan R. New and lingering controversies in pediatric end-of-life care. *Pediatrics* 2005 October; 116(4): 872-883. Subject: 20.5.2

Somek, Alexander. This is about ourselves: or, what makes genetic discrimination interesting. *In:* Stehr, Nico, ed. Biotechnology Between Commerce and Civil Society. New Brunswick, NJ: Transaction Publishers; 2004: 195-216. Subject: 15.3

Somerville, Margaret A. "Doing ethics" in the context of sharing patients' personal health information. *Canadian Journal on Aging / La Revue Canadienne du Vieillissement* 2004 Fall; 23(3): 197-202. Subject: 8.4

Somfai, Béla. Religious traditions and stem cell research. *In:* Sándor, Judit, ed. Society and Genetic Information: Codes and Laws in the Genetic Era. Budapest, Hungary; New York: CEU Press; 2003: 81-93. Subject: 18.5.4

Sones, Ben. A tale of two countries: parallel visions for informed consent in the United States and the United Kingdom. *Vanderbilt Journal of Transnational Law* 2006 January; 39(1): 253-290. Subject: 8.3.1

Sonfield, Adam. The uses and abuses of science in sexual and reproductive health policy debates. *Guttmacher Report on Public Policy* 2005 November; 8(4): 1-3. Subject: 1.3.9

Sonnenberg, Amnon. Exploring how to tell the truth and preserve hope: can a balance between communication and empathy be calculated? *Clinical Gastroenterology and Hepatology* 2004 June; 2(6): 518-522. Subject: 8.2

SoRelle, Ruth. Who owns your DNA? Who will own it? *Circulation* 2000 February 8; 101(5): e67-e68. Subject: 15.10

Sorenson, Leonard R. On the problematic dimensions of bioethics and the pre-conditions of natural right. *Politics and the Life Sciences* 1988 February; 6(2): 215-220; author's reply 223-225. Subject: 15.9

Sorrell, Jeanne Merkle. Listening in thin places: ethics in the care of persons with Alzheimer's Disease. *Advances in*

See SUBJECT HEADING KEY FOR SECTION II on inside back cover.

727

Nursing Science 2006 April-June; 29(2): 152-160. Subject: 9.5.2

Sorta-Bilajac, Iva; Pessini, Leo; Dobrila-Dintinjana, Renata; Hozo, Izet. Dysthanasia: the (il)legitimacy of artificially postponed death. *Medicinski Arhiv* 2005; 59(3): 199-202. Subject: 20.5.1

Souhami, Robert. Governance of research that uses identifiable personal data: will improve if the public and researchers collaborate to raise standards [editorial]. *BMJ: British Medical Journal* 2006 August 12; 333(7563): 315-316. Subject: 18.6

South Africa. Law Commission. South Africa — national policy on HIV testing and informed consent proposed. *Canadian HIV/AIDS Policy and Law Newsletter* 1997 Spring; 3(2-3): 11-12. Subject: 9.5.6

South Africa. Minister of Health. Choice on Termination of Pregnancy Admendment Bill [B72-2003]. Government Gazette No. 25725 2003 November 13: 1-5. Subject: 12.4.4

South Africa. The Presidency. No. 38 of 2004: Choice of Termination of Pregnancy Amendment Act, 2004 (Assented to 4 February 2005). Government of Gazette, No. 27267, 2005 February 11; (476): 5 p. Subject: 12.4.4

South Carolina. *Laws, statutes, etc.* An act to amend title 38, Code of Laws of South Carolina, 1976, relating to insurance, by adding chapter 93 so as to enact provisions regulating the privacy of genetic information [Approved: 26 May 1998]. South Carolina: General Assembly Bill 535. 4 p. [Online]. Accessed: http://www.scstatehouse.net/sess112_1997-1998/bills/535.htm [2007 March 9]. Subject: 15.1

South Dakota State Medical Association. Committee on Ethics and Judicial Affairs; Holm, Richard P. Prescribing ethics, and self care. *South Dakota Medicine* 2006 February; 59(2): 69. Subject: 9.7

Southall, David P.; Samuels, Martin P. CNEP needs to return. *Lancet* 2006 April 1-7; 367(9516): 1033-1035. Subject: 9.5.7

Southby, Janet R. Nursing ethics and the military. *In:* Beam, Thomas E.; Sparacino, Linette R.; Pellegrino, Edmund D.; Hartle, Anthony E.; Howe, Edmund G., eds. Military Medical Ethics. Volume 2. Washington, DC: TMM Publications, Borden Institute, Walter Reed Army Medical Center; 2003: 661-686. Subject: 4.1.3

Sox, Harold C.; Rennie, Drummond. Preventing scientific fraud [response]. *Annals of Internal Medicine* 2006 September 19; 145(6): 472-473. Subject: 1.3.9

Sox, Harold C.; Rennie, Drummond. Research misconduct, retraction, and cleansing the medical literature: lessons from the Poehlman case. *Annals of Internal Medicine* 2006 April 18; 144(8): 609-613. Subject: 1.3.9

Spalding, Peter M.; Bradley, Richard E. Commercialization of dental education: have we gone too far? *Journal of the American College of Dentists* 2006 Fall; 73(3): 30-35. Subject: 7.2

Spanish Women's Abortion Support Group. Spanish women and the Alton Bill. *Feminist Review* 1988 Spring; (29): 72-74. Subject: 12.4.2

Spar, Debora. Buying our children. Selling our souls?: the commodification of children. *Conscience* 2006 Autumn; 27(3): 14-16. Subject: 14.4

Spar, Debora L. Designing babies: fixing flaws and pursuing perfection. *In her:* The Baby Business: How Money, Science, and Politics Drive the Commerce of Conception. Boston: Harvard Business School Press; 2006: 97-127. Subject: 14.1

Spar, Debora L. Renting wombs for money and love: the emerging market for surrogacy. *In her:* The Baby Business: How Money, Science, and Politics Drive the Commerce of Conception. Boston: Harvard Business School Press; 2006: 69-96. Subject: 14.2

Spar, Debora L. Return to the forbidden past: issues in human cloning. *In her:* The Baby Business: How Money, Science, and Politics Drive the Commerce of Conception. Boston: Harvard Business School Press; 2006: 129-158. Subject: 14.5

Spar, Debora L. Where babies come from: supply and demand in an infant marketplace. *Harvard Business Review* 2006 February; 84(2): 133-140, 142-143. Subject: 14.1

Sparkman, Catherine A. G. Legislating apology in the context of medical mistakes. *AORN Journal* 2005 August; 82(2): 263-264, 266, 269-272. Subject: 9.8

Sparrow, Robert. Cloning, parenthood, and genetic relatedness. *Bioethics* 2006 November; 20(6): 308-318. Subject: 14.5

Sparrow, Robert. Right of the living dead? Consent to experimental surgery in the event of cortical death. *Journal of Medical Ethics* 2006 October; 32(10): 601-605. Subject: 20.2.1

Specter, Michael. Political science: the Bush administration's war on the laboratory. *New Yorker* 2006 March 13: 58, 60-67. Subject: 9.1

Spellecy, Ryan. Unproven or unsatisfactory versus equipoise in emergency research with waived consent. *American Journal of Bioethics* 2006 May-June; 6(3): 44-45. Subject: 18.3

Spence, Des. Research for profit [letter]. *BMJ: British Medical Journal* 2006 May 13; 332(7550): 1155-1156. Subject: 18.1

Spence, Sean A. Patients bearing gifts: are there strings attached? *BMJ: British Medical Journal* 2005 December 24-31; 331(7531): 1527-1529. Subject: 8.1

Spencer, John. Decline in empathy in medical education: how can we stop the rot? [editorial]. *Medical Education* 2004 September; 38(9): 916-920. Subject: 7.2

Subject = NRCBL Primary Classification Number; see inside front cover.

Spencer, Steven S.; Gawande, Atul. Why physicians participate in executions [letter and reply]. *New England Journal of Medicine* 2006 July 6; 355(1): 100. Subject: 20.6

Sperry, Len. Ethical dilemmas in the assessment of clinical outcomes. *Psychiatric Annals* 2004 February; 34(2): 107-113. Subject: 9.3.2

Spielmann, Horst. The future of animal experiments in nutrition research. *Forum of Nutrition* 2003; 56: 297-299. Subject: 22.2

Spier, Raymond E. Reflection on the Budapest Meeting 2005 of the European Ethics Consortium [editorial]. *Science and Engineering Ethics* 2006 October; 12(4): 587-590. Subject: 2.1

Spier, R.E. Vaccines and vaccination. *In:* Mitcham, Carl, ed. Encyclopedia of Science, Technology, and Ethics. Farmington Hills, MI: Thomson/Gale, 2005: 2015-2020. Subject: 9.7

Spigel, Nadine. Euthanasia and physician assisted suicide: effect on the doctor patient relationship. *Penn Bioethics Journal* 2005 April 2; 1(1): 3p. [Online]. Accessed: http://www.bioethicsjournal.com [2005 April 19]. Subject: 8.1

Spike, Jeffrey. Bioethics now. *Philosophy Now* 2006 May-June; 55(6): 7-8 p. [Online]. Accessed: http://www.philosophynow.org/issue55/55spike.htm [2006 December 5]. Subject: 2.1

Spike, Jeffrey P. Human subjects research. *In:* Mitcham, Carl, ed. Encyclopedia of Science, Technology, and Ethics. Farmington Hills, MI: Thomson/Gale, 2005: 960-963. Subject: 18.1

Spike, Jeffrey P. Persistent vegetative state. *In:* Mitcham, Carl, ed. Encyclopedia of Science, Technology, and Ethics. Farmington Hills, MI: Thomson/Gale, 2005: 1396-1399. Subject: 20.5.1

Spike, Jeffrey P. Residency education in clinical ethics and professionalism: not just what, but when, where, and how ought residents be taught? *American Journal of Bioethics* 2006 July-August; 6(4): 23-35. Subject: 7.2

Spinello, Richard A. Property rights in genetic information. *Ethics and Information Technology* 2004; 6(1): 29-42. Subject: 15.8

Spinello, Richard A. Property rights in genetic information. *In:* Tavani, Herman T., ed. Ethics, Computing, and Genomics. Sudbury, MA: Jones and Bartlett; 2006: 213-233. Subject: 15.8

Spital, Aaron. Increasing the pool of transplantable kidneys through unrelated living donors and living donor paired exchanges. *Seminars in Dialysis* 2005 November-December; 18(6): 469-473. Subject: 19.3

Spital, Aaron. More on directed kidney donation by altruistic living strangers: a response to Dr. Hilhorst and his colleagues. *Transplantation* 2005 October 27; 80(8): 1001-1002. Subject: 19.5

Spital, Aaron. More on parental living liver donation for children with fulminant hepatic failure: addressing concerns about competing interests, coercion, consent and balancing acts. *American Journal of Transplantation* 2005 November; 5(11): 2619-2622. Subject: 19.5

Sporrong, Sofia Kävemark; Höglund, Anna T.; Arnetz, Bergt. Measuring moral distress in pharmacy and clinical practice. *Nursing Ethics* 2006 July; 13(4): 416-427. Subject: 4.1.1

Sprague, Robert L.; Mitcham, Carl. Misconduct in science: social science cases. *In:* Mitcham, Carl, ed. Encyclopedia of Science, Technology, and Ethics. Farmington Hills, MI: Thomson/Gale, 2005: 1213-1215. Subject: 1.3.9

Spriggs, Merle. Can children be altruistic research subjects? *American Journal of Bioethics* 2006 September-October; 6(5): 49-50. Subject: 18.3

Springer, Rachelle. Disclosing unanticipated events. *Plastic Surgical Nursing* 2005 October-December; 25(4): 199-201. Subject: 8.2

Spurgeon, David. FDA regulations make it harder to sue drug companies [news]. *BMJ: British Medical Journal* 2006 June 10; 332(7554): 1350. Subject: 9.7

Squire, Charles F.; Asai, Rickland G.; Largent, Beverly A. Is it ethical to criticize other dentists' work? *Journal of the American Dental Association* 2005 June; 136(6): 812-813. Subject: 7.3

Squires, Bruce. Editorial policy: the right to medical information [editorial]. *CMAJ/JAMC: Canadian Medical Association Journal* 2006 September 12; 175(6): 557. Subject: 1.3.9

Srebnik, Debra; Appelbaum, Paul S.; Russo, Joan. Assessing competence to complete psychiatric advance directives with the competence assessment tool for psychiatric advance directives. *Comprehensive Psychiatry* 2004 July-August; 45(4): 239-245. Subject: 17.1

Srebnik, Debra; Kim, Scott Y. Competency for creation, use, and revocation of psychiatric advance directives. *Journal of the American Academy of Psychiatry and the Law* 2006; 34(4): 501-510. Subject: 17.1

Sreenivasan, Gopal; Benatar, Soloman R. Challenges for global health in the 21st century: some upstream considerations. *Theoretical Medicine and Bioethics* 2006; 27(1): 3-11. Subject: 21.1

Srinivasan, Sandhya. The draft national pharmaceuticals policy: concerns relating to data exclusivity and price control [editorial]. *Indian Journal of Medical Ethics* 2006 October-December; 3(4): 118-119. Subject: 9.7

Srinivasan, Sandhya; Loff, Bebe. Medical research in India. *Lancet* 2006 June 17-23; 367(9527): 1962-1964. Subject: 18.5.9

See SUBJECT HEADING KEY FOR SECTION II on inside back cover.

729

Srivastava, Ranjana. No refuge for the ailing. *New England Journal of Medicine* 2006 August 3; 355(5): 443-445. Subject: 9.5.1

St. Louis, Brett. Sport, genetics and the "natural athlete": the resurgence of racial science. *Body and Society* 2003 June; 9(2): 75-95 [Online]. Accessed: http://bod.sagepub.com/cgi/reprint/9/2/75 [2007 January 25]. Subject: 15.1

St. Peter, Christine. Feminist discourse, infertility, and reproductive technologies. *NWSA Journal* 1989 Spring; 1(3): 353-367. Subject: 14.1

Stabell, Aase; Nådan, Dagfinn. Patients' dignity in a rehabilitation ward: ethical challenges for nursing staff. *Nursing Ethics* 2006 May; 13(3): 236-248. Subject: 8.1

Stabile, Bonnie. National determinants of cloning policy. *Social Science Quarterly* 2006 June; 87(2): 449-458. Subject: 14.5

Stabile, Susan J. State attempts to define religion: the ramifications of applying mandatory prescription contraceptive coverage statutes to religious employers. *Harvard Journal of Law and Public Policy* 2005 Summer; 28(3): 741-780. Subject: 11.1

Stack, Austin G.; Martin, David R. Association of patient autonomy with increased transplantation and survival among new dialysis patients in the United States. *American Journal of Kidney Diseases* 2005 April; 45(4): 730-742. Subject: 19.3

Stagno, Susan J.; Zhukovsky, Donna S.; Walsh, Declan. Bioethics: communication and decision-making in advanced disease. *Seminars in Oncology* 2000 February; 27(1): 94-100. Subject: 8.1

Staley, Kristina; Minogue, Virginia. User involvement leads to more ethically sound research. *Clinical Ethics* 2006 June; 1(2): 95-100. Subject: 18.2

Stambolovic, V.; Ðuric, M.; Ðonic, D.; Kelecevic, J.; Rakocevic, Z. Patient-physician relationship in the aftermath of war. *Journal of Medical Ethics* 2006 December; 32(12): 739-742. Subject: 21.2

Stanford, Joseph B.; Larimore, Walter L. Description of emergency contraception in the media [letter]. *Contraception* 2005 November; 72(5): 394-395. Subject: 11.1

Stang, Andreas; Hense, Hans-Werner; Jockel, Karl-Heinz; Turner, Erick H.; Tramer, Martin R. Is it always unethical to use a placebo in a clinical trial? *PLoS Medicine* 2005 March; 2(3): 0177-0180. Subject: 18.3

Stang, Charma; Sheremata, Lorraine. Nanotechnology — a lot of hype over almost nothing? *Health Law Review* 2006; 15(1): 53-55. Subject: 5.4

Stanley, Jay. Societal influences and the ethics of military healthcare. *In:* Beam, Thomas E.; Sparacino, Linette R.; Pellegrino, Edmund D.; Hartle, Anthony E.; Howe, Edmund G., eds. Military Medical Ethics. Volume 2. Washington, DC: TMM Publications, Borden Institute, Walter Reed Army Medical Center; 2003: 719-738. Subject: 9.5.1

Stanton, Jennifer. Renal dialysis: counting the cost versus counting the need. *Clio Medica* 2005; 75: 217-241. Subject: 19.3

Stanton-Ife, John. Resource allocation and the duty to give reasons. *Health Care Analysis: An International Journal of Health Philosophy and Policy* 2006 September; 14(3): 145-156. Subject: 9.4

Stapleton, Renee D.; Nielsen, Elizabeth L.; Engelberg, Ruth A.; Patrick, Donald L.; Curtis, J. Randall. Ethics in cardiopulmonary medicine — association of depression and life-sustaining treatment preferences in patients with COPD. *Chest* 2005 January; 127(1): 328-334. Subject: 20.5.1

Stark, Dennis M. Animal activism and intimidation of scientists [letter]. *Science* 2006 November 10; 314(5801): 923-924. Subject: 22.2

Stark, Dennis M. Laboratory animal-based collaborations and contracts beyond the border. *Lab Animal* 2006 June; 35(6): 37-40. Subject: 22.2

Starks, Helene; Pearlman, Robert A.; Hsu, Clarissa; Back, Anthony L.; Gordon, Judith R.; Bharucha, Ashok J. Why now? Timing and circumstances of hastened deaths. *Journal of Pain and Symptom Management* 2005 September; 30(3): 215-226. Subject: 20.5.1

Starzomski, Rosalie. Ethical issues: to dialyze or not? Is that the question? *CANNT Journal* 2000 October-December; 10(4): 45-46. Subject: 19.3

Statman, Daniel. Human dignity and technology. *In:* Árnason, Gardar; Nordal, Salvör; Árnason, Vilhjálmur, eds. Blood and Data: Ethical, Legal and Social Aspects of Human Genetic Databases. Reykjavík: University of Iceland Press; 2004: 223-228. Subject: 4.4

Steel, Michael. Brain, mind, and person: cloning and questions of identity. *In:* Jeeves, Michael, ed. From Cells to Souls — and Beyond: Changing Portraits of Human Nature. Grand Rapids, MI: W.B. Eerdmans; 2004: 1-10. Subject: 14.5

Stefan, Susan. Silencing the different voice: competence, feminist theory and law. *University of Miami Law Review* 1993 January; 47(3): 763-815. Subject: 4.3

Stein, Ben. When scarcity leads to madness. *New York Times* 2006 September 17; p. BU4. Subject: 21.4

Stein, Dan J. Cosmetic psychopharmacology of anxiety: bioethical considerations. *Current Psychiatry Reports* 2005 August; 7(4): 237-238. Subject: 17.4

Stein, Gary L. Improving our care at life's end: making a difference. *Health and Social Work* 2004 February; 29(1): 77-79. Subject: 20.4.1

Stein, Rob. Health workers' choice debated; proposals back right not to treat. *Washington Post* 2006 January 30; p. A1, A9. Subject: 8.1

Subject = NRCBL Primary Classification Number; see inside front cover.

Stein, Rob. Institute practices reproductive medicine — and Catholicism. *Washington Post* 2006 October 31; p. A14. Subject: 9.5.5

Stein, Rob. A medical crisis of conscience: faith drives some to refuse patients medication or care. *Washington Post* 2006 July 16; p. A1, A6. Subject: 8.3.4

Stein, Rob. Medical practices blend health and faith; doctors, patients distance themselves from care they consider immoral. *Washington Post* 2006 August 31; p. A1, A10. Subject: 8.1

Steinberg, Deborah Lynn. A most selective practice: the eugenic logic of IVF. *Women's Studies International Forum* 1997; 20(1): 33-48. Subject: 15.5

Steinbock, Bonnie. The morality of killing human embryos. *Journal of Law, Medicine, and Ethics* 2006 Spring; 34(1): 26-34. Subject: 18.5.4

Steinbock, Bonnie. Reproductive cloning: another look. *University of Chicago Legal Forum* 2006: 87-111. Subject: 14.5

Steinbrook, Robert. Compensation for injured research subjects. *New England Journal of Medicine* 2006 May 4; 354(18): 1871-1873. Subject: 18.1

Steinbrook, Robert. Egg donation and human embryonic stem-cell research. *New England Journal of Medicine* 2006 January 26; 354(4): 324-326. Subject: 19.5

Steinbrook, Robert. For sale: physicians' prescribing data. *New England Journal of Medicine* 2006 June 29; 354(26): 2745-2747. Subject: 9.7

Steinbrook, Robert. Health care reform in Massachusetts — a work in progress. *New England Journal of Medicine* 2006 May 18; 354(20): 2095-2098. Subject: 9.3.1

Steinbrook, Robert. Imposing personal responsibility for health. *New England Journal of Medicine* 2006 August 24; 355(8): 753-756. Subject: 9.1

Steinbrook, Robert. New technology, old dilemma — monitoring EEG activity during executions. *New England Journal of Medicine* 2006 June 15; 354(24): 2525-2527. Subject: 20.6

Steinbrook, Robert. Public report cards — cardiac surgery and beyond. *New England Journal of Medicine* 2006 November 2; 355(18): 1847-1849. Subject: 9.8

Steinbruner, John. In the name of defence: bioweapons research in the U.S. could trigger just the sort of arms race it is meant to forestall. But that's not the worst of it. *New Scientist* 2006 November 25-December 1; 192(2579): 20. Subject: 21.3

Steinburg, David. The allocation of organs donated by altruistic strangers. *Annals of Internal Medicine* 2006 August 1; 145(3): 197-203. Subject: 19.6

Steiner, Robert. How should we ethically select living kidney donors when they all are at risk? [letter]. *American Journal of Transplantation* 2005 May; 5(5): 1172-1173. Subject: 19.3

Steinert, Tilman; Lepping, Peter; Baranyai, Reka; Hoffmann, Markus; Leherr, Herbert. Compulsory admission and treatment in schizophrenia: a study of ethical attitudes in four European countries. *Social Psychiatry and Psychiatric Epidemiology* 2005 August; 40(8): 635-641. Subject: 17.7

Stemerding, Dirk; Nelis, Annemiek. Cancer genetics and its "different faces of autonomy". *New Genetics and Society* 2006 April; 25(1): 1-19. Subject: 15.2

Stempsey, William E. Emerging medical technologies and emerging conceptions of health. *Theoretical Medicine and Bioethics* 2006; 27(3): 227-243. Subject: 4.2

Stempsey, William E. The geneticization of diagnostics. *Medicine, Health Care and Philosophy* 2006; 9(2): 193-200. Subject: 15.1

Steneck, Nicholas H. Fostering integrity in research: definitions, current knowledge, and future directions. *Science and Engineering Ethics* 2006 January; 12(1): 53-74. Subject: 1.3.9

Steneck, Nicholas H. Office of Research Integrity. *In:* Mitcham, Carl, ed. Encyclopedia of Science, Technology, and Ethics. Farmington Hills, MI: Thomson/Gale, 2005: 1353-1355. Subject: 18.6

Stephen, Sarah. Letters to unborn daughters: exploring the implications of genetic engineering. *Futuris* 2004 March-April; 38(2): 37-39. Subject: 15.1

Stephens, Joe. Harvard research in China is faulted: safety, ethics problems of tests noted. *Washington Post* 2003 March 30: A06. Subject: 1.3.9

Sterba, Sonya K. Misconduct in the analysis and reporting of data: bridging methodological and ethical agendas for change. *Ethics and Behavior* 2006; 16(4): 305-318. Subject: 1.3.9

Sterling, Rene; Henderson, Gail E.; Corbie-Smith, Giselle. Public willingness to participate in and public opinions about genetic variation research: a review of literature. *American Journal of Public Health* 2006 November; 96(11): 1971-1978. Subject: 18.5.1

Stern, David T.; Papadakis, Maxine. The developing physician — becoming a professional. *New England Journal of Medicine* 2006 October 26; 355(17): 1794-1799. Subject: 7.2

Stern, Megan. Dystopian anxieties versus utopian ideals: medicine from Frankenstein to The Visible Human Project and Body Worlds. *Science as Culture* 2006 March; 15(1): 61-84. Subject: 4.4

Steuernagel, Trudy. Marcuse and biotechnology. *Negations* 1998 Winter; 3: 44-55 [Online]. Accessed: http://www.datawranglers.com/negations/issues/98w/steurnagel_01.html [2007 January 31]. Subject: 15.1

See SUBJECT HEADING KEY FOR SECTION II on inside back cover.

731

Stevens, Kenneth R. Emotional and psychological effect of physician-assisted suicide and euthanasia on participating physicians. *Issues in Law and Medicine* 2006 Spring; 21(3): 187-200. Subject: 20.3.2

Stevens, Kenneth R. Emotional and psychological effects of physician-assisted suicide and euthanasia. *Linacre Quarterly* 2006 August; 73(3): 203-216. Subject: 20.7

Stevenson, Keith; Randle, Jacqueline; Grayling, Ian. Inter-group conflict in health care: UK students' experiences of bullying and the need for organisational solutions. *Online Journal of Issues in Nursing* 2006; 11(2): 17 p. Subject: 7.3

Stewart, Moira. Reflections on the doctor-patient relationship: from evidence and experience. *British Journal of General Practice* 2005 October; 55(519): 793-801. Subject: 8.1

Stienstra, Deborah; Chochinov, Harvey Max. Vulnerability, disability, and palliative end-of-life care. *Journal of Palliative Care* 2006 Autumn; 22(3): 166-174. Subject: 20.4.1

Štifanic, Mirko. Mistanasia in a society in transition. *Formosan Journal of Medical Humanities* 2006 June; 7(1-2): 81-89. Subject: 20.3.1

Stiggelbout, A.M.; Elstein, A.S.; Molewijk, B.; Otten, W.; Kievit, J. Clinical ethical dilemmas: convergent and divergent views of two scholarly communities. *Journal of Medical Ethics* 2006 July; 32(7): 381-388. Subject: 2.1

Stiglitz, Joseph E. Scrooge and intellectual property rights: a medical prize fund could improve the financing of drug innovations. *BMJ: British Medical Journal* 2006 December 23-30; 333(7582): 1279-1280. Subject: 5.3

Stiles, Gary L. Wyeth Pharmaceutical's perspective on vaccine production. *Maryland Medicine* 2005 Winter; 6(1): 22-23. Subject: 9.7

Stinson, Sara. Ethical issues in human biology behavioral research and research with children. *In:* Turner, Trudy R. ed. Biological Anthropology and Ethics: From Repatriation to Genetic Identity. Albany, NY: State University of New York Press; 2005: 139-148. Subject: 18.4

Stith, Marah. The semblance of autonomy: treatment of persons with disabilities under the Uniform Health-Care Decisions Act. *Issues in Law and Medicine* 2006 Summer; 22(1): 39-80. Subject: 20.5.1

Stix, Gary. Owning the stuff of life. *Scientific American* 2006 February; 294(2): 76-83. Subject: 15.8

Stoate, Howard. Parliament, ethics and NHS resources [editorial]. *Clinical Ethics* 2006 December; 1(4): 180-182. Subject: 9.2

Stobäus, Ricarda. "Euthanasie" im Nationalsozialismus: Gottfried Ewald und der Protest gegen die "Aktion T4.". *In:* Frewer, Andreas; Eickhoff, Clemens, eds. "Euthanasie" und die aktuelle Sterbehilfe-Debatte: Die historischen Hintergründe medizinischer Ethik. Frankfurt; New York: Campus; 2000: 177-192. Subject: 20.5.1

Stobbart, Lynne; Murtagh, Madeleine; Louw, Stephen J.; Ford, Gary A. Consent for research in hyperacute stroke [editorial]. *BMJ: British Medical Journal* 2006 June 17; 332(7555): 1405-1406. Subject: 18.3

Stobie, Melissa; Strode, Ann; Slack, Cathy. The dilemma of enrolling children in HIV vaccine research in South Africa: what is in 'the child's best interest'? *In:* van Niekerk, Anton A.; Kopelman, Loretta M., eds. Ethics and AIDS in Africa: The Challenge to Our Thinking. Walnut Creek, CA: Left Coast Press; 2006: 190-207. Subject: 18.5.2

Stock, Gregory. Germinal choice technology and the human future. *Reproductive BioMedicine Online [electronic]* 2005 March; 10(Supplement 1): 27-35. Subject: 15.2

Stoerger, Sharon. Sociological ethics. *In:* Mitcham, Carl, ed. Encyclopedia of Science, Technology, and Ethics. Farmington Hills, MI: Thomson/Gale, 2005: 1823-1827. Subject: 5.1

Stolberg, Sheryl Gay. First Bush veto maintains limits on stem cell use; override attempt fails; issue divides G.O.P. — Democrats look ahead to fall elections. *New York Times* 2006 July 20; p. A1, A19. Subject: 18.5.4

Stolberg, Sheryl Gay. Preschool meds: the first clinical trial examining the effects of generic Ritalin on 3- to 5-year-old subjects raises questions not only about the safety of the drug but also about the ethics of testing on ever younger brains. *New York Times Magazine* 2002 November 17; p. 58-61. Subject: 18.5.2

Stolt, Ulrica Gustafsson; Helgesson, Gert; Liss, Per-Erik; Svensson, Tommy; Ludvigsson, Johnny. Information and informed consent in a longitudinal screening involving children: a questionnaire survey. *European Journal of Human Genetics* 2005 March; 13(3): 376-383. Subject: 18.3

Stoltz, Lori; Shap, Louise. HIV testing and pregnancy: medical and legal parameters of the policy debate. *Canadian HIV/AIDS Policy and Law Newsletter* 1999 Spring; 4(2-3): 42-44. Subject: 9.5.6

Stone, Alan A. Forensic ethics and capital punishment: is there a special problem? [editorial]. *Journal of Forensic Psychiatry* 2002 December; 13(3): 487-493. Subject: 20.6

Stone, Alan A. Mental health and the law: the facts and the future. *In:* Deschill, S.; Lebovici, S., eds. The Challenge for Psychoanalysis and Psychotherapy Solutions for the Future. London: Jessica Kingsley Publishers Ltd., 1999: 320-335. Subject: 17.1

Stone, Deborah. Reframing the racial disparities issue for state governments. *Journal of Health Politics, Policy and Law* 2006 February; 31(1): 127-152. Subject: 9.5.4

Subject = NRCBL Primary Classification Number; see inside front cover.

Stone, Margaret A.; Redsell, Sarah A.; Ling, Jennifer T.; Hay, Alastair D. Sharing patient data: competing demands of privacy, trust and research in primary care [interview]. *British Journal of General Practice* 2005 October; 55(519): 783-789. Subject: 8.4

Stone, Tracey J. Making the decision about enrolment in a randomised controlled trial. *In:* Smyth, Marie; Williamson, Emma, eds. Researchers and Their 'Subjects': Ethics, Power, Knowledge and Consent. Bristol, UK: Policy Press; 2004: 35-54. Subject: 18.2

Stones, William. Women, doctors and pain. *In:* Unnithan-Kumar, Maya, ed. Reproductive Agency, Medicine and the State: Cultural Transformations in Childbearing. New York: Berghahn Books; 2004: 103-112. Subject: 4.4

Storch, Janet L. Casualization of nurses and unregulated workers impair ethical practice. *International Nursing Review* 1998 September-October; 45(5): 140-141. Subject: 4.1.3

Stormann, Michael. Genetics and artificial procreation in Austria. *In:* Meulders-Klein, Marie-Thérèse; Deech, Ruth; Vlaardingerbroek, Paul, eds. Biomedicine, the Family and Human Rights. New York: Kluwer Law International, 2002: 367-376. Subject: 14.1

Storrow, Richard F. Quests for conceptions: fertility tourists, globalization and feminist legal theory. *Hastings Law Review* 2005; 57(2): 295-330. Subject: 14.1

Stossel, Thomas; Shaywitz, David. What's wrong with money in science. *Washington Post* 2006 July 2; p. B3. Subject: 1.3.9

Strachan-Bennett, Seonaid. Campaigning nurses — the ethical dilemma. *Nursing Times* 2006 March 14-20; 102(11): 18-19. Subject: 4.1.3

Strand, Edythe A. Clinical and professional ethics in the management of motor speech disorders. *Seminars in Speech and Language* 2003 November; 24(4): 301- 311. Subject: 4.1.1

Strange, Charlie; Moseley, Mary Allison; Jones, Yonge; Schwarz, Laura; Xie, Lianqi; Brantly, Mark L. Genetic testing of minors for alpha1-antitrypsin deficiency. *Archives of Pediatrics and Adolescent Medicine* 2006 May; 160(5): 531-534. Subject: 15.3

STRATA Expert Group. Ethical, legal and social implications of genetic testing: research, development and clinical applications. *European Journal of Health Law* 2004 September; 11(3): 309-317. Subject: 15.3

Strate, John; Kiska, Timothy; Zalman, Marvin. Who favors legalizing physician-assisted suicide? The vote on Michigan's Proposal B. *Politics and the Life Sciences* 2001 September; 20(2): 155-163. Subject: 20.7

Strathern, Marilyn. Still giving nature a helping hand? Surrogacy: a debate about technology and society. *Journal of Molecular Biology* 2002 June 14; 319(4): 985-993. Subject: 14.2

Straus, Stephen E. Unanticipated risk in clinical research. *In:* Gallin, John I., ed. Principles and Practice of Clinical Research. San Diego, CA: Academic Press; 2002: 105-122. Subject: 18.1

Strauss, Bernard S. Getting around. *DNA Repair* 2005 August 15; 4(9): 951-957. Subject: 15.1

Strauss, Ronald G.; Lipton, Karen Shoos. Glucocorticoid stimulation of neutrophil donors: a medical, scientific, and ethical dilemma [editorial]. *Transfusion* 2005 November; 45(11): 1697-1699. Subject: 19.4

Strauss, Ronald P. Ethical and social concerns in facial surgical decision making. *Plastic and Reconstructive Surgery* 1983 November; 72(5): 727-730. Subject: 8.3.4

Streat, Stephen. Clinical review: moral assumptions and the process of organ donation in the intensive care unit. *Critical Care* 2004 October; 8(5): 382-388. Subject: 19.5

Streiffer, Robert. Academic freedom and academic-industry relationships in biotechnology. *Kennedy Institute of Ethics Journal* 2006 June; 16(2): 129-149. Subject: 1.3.9

Streiffer, Robert; Rubel, Alan P.; Fagan, Julie R. Medical privacy and the public's right to vote: what presidential candidates should disclose. *Journal of Medicine and Philosophy* 2006 August; 31(4): 417-439. Subject: 8.4

Streiner, David L.; Saigal, Saroj; Burrows, Elizabeth; Stoskopf, Barbara; Rosenbaum, Peter. Attitudes of parents and health care professionals toward active treatment of extremely premature infants. *Pediatrics* 2001 July; 108(1): 152-157. Subject: 20.5.2

Strode, Ann; Slack, Catherine; Mushariwa, Muriel. HIV vaccine research — South Africa's ethical-legal framework and its ability to promote the welfare of trial participants. *South African Medical Journal* 2005 August; 95(8): 598-601. Subject: 9.5.6

Strong, Carson. Continuing the dialogue: a reply to Bernard Gert. *Kennedy Institute of Ethics Journal* 2006 June; 16(2): 189-194. Subject: 2.1

Strong, Carson. The ethics of human reproductive cloning. *Reproductive BioMedicine Online [electronic]* 2005 March; 10(Supplement 1): 45-49. Subject: 14.5

Strong, Carson. Gamete retrieval after death or irreversible unconsciousness: what counts as informed consent? *CQ: Cambridge Quarterly of Healthcare Ethics* 2006 Spring; 15(2): 161-171. Subject: 14.6

Strong, Carson. Gert's moral theory and its application to bioethics cases. *Kennedy Institute of Ethics Journal* 2006 March; 16(1): 39-58. Subject: 2.1

Strong, Carson. The limited utility of utilitarian analysis. *American Journal of Bioethics* 2006 May-June; 6(3): 67-69; discussion W51- W53. Subject: 2.1

See SUBJECT HEADING KEY FOR SECTION II on inside back cover.

733

Strong, Carson. Preembryo personhood: an assessment of the President's Council arguments. *Theoretical Medicine and Bioethics* 2006; 27(5): 433-453. Subject: 4.4

Stroup, T. Scott; Appelbaum, Paul S. Evaluation of "subject advocate" procedures in the clinical antipsychotic trials of intervention effectiveness (CATIE) schizophrenia study. *Schizophrenia Bulletin* 2006 January; 32(1): 147-152. Subject: 18.5.6

Strous, Rael D. Nazi euthanasia of the mentally ill at Hadamar. *American Journal of Psychiatry* 2006 January; 163(1): 27. Subject: 21.4

Stuart, Kate. Informed consent and the advanced nurse practitioner. *In:* Bartter, Karen, ed. Ethical Issues in Advanced Nursing Practice. Boston: Butterworth-Heinemann; 2001: 80-100. Subject: 8.3.1

Stuck, A.E. Autonomy and appropriate care for older disabled older people: guidelines of the Swiss Academy of Medical Sciences: commentary. *Journal of Nutrition, Health and Aging* 2005 July-August; 9(4): 287. Subject: 9.5.2

Stuhmcke, Anita. For love or money: the legal regulation of surrogate motherhood. *E Law: Murdoch University Electronic Journal of Law* 1995 December; 2(3): 27 p. [Online]. Accessed: http://www.murdoch.edu.au/elaw/issues/v2n3/stuhmcke23.html [2006 June 29]. Subject: 14.2

Stulic, Mathew. Genetic non-discrimination, privacy and property rights. *E Law: Murdoch University Electronic Journal of Law* 2000 June; 7(2): 26 p. [Online]. Accessed: http://www.murdoch.edu.au/elaw/issues/v4n3/stulic72.html [2006 June 29]. Subject: 15.1

Sturges, Melissa L. Who should hold property rights to the human genome? An application of the common heritage of humankind. *American University of International Law Review* 1997; 13(1): 219-261. Subject: 15.8

Sturmey, Peter. Ethical dilemmas and the most effective therapies. *In:* Jacobson, John W.; Foxx, Richard M.; Mulick, James A., eds. Controversial Therapies for Developmental Disabilities: Fad, Fashion, and Science in Professional Practice. Mahwah, NJ: L. Erlbaum Associates; 2005: 435-449. Subject: 9.5.3

Su, Baoq; Macer, Darryl R.J. Ethical dilemmas in genetics and reproductive decisions from the views of Chinese people. *In:* Sang-yong, Song; Young-Mo, Koo; Macer, Darryl R.J., eds. Asian Bioethics in the 21st Century. Christchurch, NZ: Eubios Ethics Institute, 2002: 380-388. Subject: 15.5

Suarez, Isabel Maria Belda; Fernandez-Montoya, Antorio; Fernandez, Andres Rodriguez; Lopez-Berrio, Antorio; Cillero- Penuela, Manuel. How regular blood donors explain their behavior. *Transfusion* 2004 October; 44(10): 1441-1446. Subject: 19.5

Suarez-Almazor, Maria E.; Newman, Catherine; Hanson, John; Bruera, Eduardo. Attitudes of terminally ill cancer patients about euthanasia and assisted suicide: predominance of psychosocial determinants and beliefs over symptom distress and subsequent survival. *Journal of Clinical Oncology* 2002 April 15; 20(8): 2134-2141. Subject: 20.7

Suda, Eiko; Macer, Darryl R.J. Ethical challenges of conducting the Hap Map Genetics project in Japan. *In:* Sang-yong, Song; Young-Mo, Koo; Macer, Darryl R.J., eds. Asian Bioethics in the 21st Century. Christchurch, NZ: Eubios Ethics Institute, 2003: 31-45. Subject: 15.11

Sudore, Rebecca L.; Landefeld, C. Seth; Williams, Brie A.; Barnes, Deborah E.; Lindquist, Karla; Schillinger, Dean. Use of a modified informed consent process among vulnerable patients: a descriptive study. *Journal of General Internal Medicine* 2006 August; 21(8): 867-873. Subject: 18.3

Suen, Lorna K.P.; Lai, C.K.Y.; Wong, T.K.S.; Chow, S.K.Y.; Kong, S.K.F.; Ho, J.L.Y.; Kong, T.K.; Leung, J.S.C.; Wong, I.Y.C. Use of physical restraints in rehabilitation settings: staff knowledge, attitudes and predictors. *Journal of Advanced Nursing* 2006 July; 55(1): 20-28. Subject: 17.3

Sugarman, Jeremy. Lying, cheating and stealing in clinical research [editorial]. *Clinical Trials* 2004; 1(6): 475-476. Subject: 1.3.9

Sugarman, Jeremy; Lavori, Philip W.; Boeger, Maryann; Cain, Carole; Edsond, Robert; Morrison, Vicki; Yeh, Shing Shing. Evaluating the quality of informed consent. *Clinical Trials* 2005; 2(1): 34-41. Subject: 18.3

Sugarman, Jeremy; Levine, Carol; Barnes, Michael R.; Holbrook, Joanna; Feild, John A.; Searls, David B.; Sanseau, Philippe; Ohresser, Marc; Olive, Daniel; Vanhove, Bernard; Watier, Hervé; Focosi, Daniele. Risk in drug trials [correspondence]. *Lancet* 2006 December 23-2007 January 5; 368(9554): 2205-2206. Subject: 18.1

Sugarman, Jeremy; Paasche-Orlow, Michael. Confirming comprehension of informed consent as a protection of human subjects. *Journal of General Internal Medicine* 2006 August; 21(8): 898-899. Subject: 18.3

Sugerman, Noah. Person in PVS: an oxymoronic bioethical issue. *Penn Bioethics Journal* 2006; 2(1): 4p. [Online]. Accessed: http://www.bioethicsjournal.com [2006 February 21]. Subject: 20.5.1

Sujdak Mackiewicz, Birgitta N. Can Catholic facilities justify the use of embryonic stem cell therapies developed from the destruction of human embryos? *Health Care Ethics USA* 2006; 14(2): E3 [Online]. Accessed: http://chce.slu.edu/Partnerships_HCE_Intro.html [2006 November 17]. Subject: 18.5.4

Subject = NRCBL Primary Classification Number; see inside front cover.

Suk, Han Sung. The ethical dilemma of patients in a vegetative state. *International Nursing Review* 1998 September-October; 45(5): 142. Subject: 20.5.1

Sulch, David; Kalra, Lalit. Ethical issues in stroke management. *In:* Rai, Gurcharan S, ed. Medical Ethics and the Elderly. 2nd ed. San Francisco: Radcliffe Medical Press; 2004: 91-101. Subject: 20.5.1

Sullivan, E. Thomas; Juengst, Eric T.; Charo, R. Alta; McCabe, Edward R.B. Risks posed by new biomedical technologies: how do we analyze, communicate and regulate risk? *Medical Ethics Newsletter* 2006 Fall; 13(3): 5-8. Subject: 5.3

Sullivan, Karen. Finding out about ethics: what sources of information do Australian psychologists find useful? *Australian Psychologist* 2005 November; 40(3): 187-189. Subject: 2.1

Sullivan, Mark. Ethical principles in pain management. *Pain Medicine* 2001 June; 2(2): 106-111. Subject: 4.4

Sullivan, Rebecca. An embryonic nation: life against health in Canadian biotechnological discourse. *Communication Theory* 2005 February; 15(1): 39-58. Subject: 15.1

Sullivan, Scott M. A history of extraordinary means. *Ethics and Medics* 2006 November; 31(11): 3-4. Subject: 20.5.1

Sullivan, Scott M. A history of extraordinary means: second of a three-part series. *Ethics and Medics* 2006 October; 31(10): 3-4. Subject: 20.5.1

Sullivan, William M. Confronting moral ambiguity: the struggle for professional ethics. *In his:* Work and Integrity: The Crisis and Promise of Professionalism in America. Second ed. San Francisco, CA: Jossey-Bass; 2005: 257-282, 312-316. Subject: 1.3.1

Sulmasy, Daniel P. Death, dignity, and the theory of value. *In:* Schotsmans, Paul; Meulenbergs, Tom, eds. Euthanasia and Palliative Care in the Low Countries. Dudley, MA: Peeters, 2005: 95-119. Subject: 20.1

Sulmasy, Daniel P. Dignity, vulnerability, and medical error. *Health Progress* 2006 January-February; 87(1): 12-14. Subject: 4.4

Sulmasy, Daniel P. Emergency contraception for women who have been raped: must Catholics test for ovulation, or is testing for pregnancy morally sufficient? *Kennedy Institute of Ethics Journal* 2006 December; 16(4): 305-331. Subject: 9.5.5

Sulmasy, Daniel P. End-of-life care revisited. *Health Progress* 2006 July-August; 87(4): 50-56. Subject: 20.5.1

Sulmasy, Daniel P. The logos of the genome: genomes as parts of organisms. *Theoretical Medicine and Bioethics* 2006; 27(6): 535-540. Subject: 15.1

Sulmasy, Daniel P. On the current state of clinical ethics. *Pain Medicine* 2001 June; 2(2): 97-105. Subject: 9.1

Sulmasy, Daniel P. The science behind the art: empirical research on medical ethics. *In:* Beam, Thomas E.; Sparacino, Linette R.; Pellegrino, Edmund D.; Hartle, Anthony E.; Howe, Edmund G., eds. Military Medical Ethics. Volume 1. Washington, DC: TMM Publications, Borden Institute, Walter Reed Army Medical Center; 2003: 105-126. Subject: 2.1

Sulmasy, Daniel P.; Sood, Johanna R.; Texiera, Kenneth; McAuley, Ruth L.; McGugins, Jennifer; Ury, Wayne A. A prospective trial of a new policy eliminating signed consent for do not resuscitate orders. *JGIM: Journal of General Internal Medicine* 2006 December; 21(12): 1261-1268. Subject: 20.5.1

Sumathipala, Athula. Bioethics in Sri Lanka. *Eastern Mediterranean Health Journal* 2006; 12(Supplement 1): S73-S79 [Online]. Accessed: http://www.emro.who.int/publications/EMHJ/12_S/PDF/11.pdf [2007 January 4]. Subject: 2.1

Summers, David S.; Hentoff, Nat. End-of-life issues [letter and reply]. *Free Inquiry* 2006 October-November; 26(6): 9,11. Subject: 20.7

Sureau, Claude. From transgression to pragmatism in reproductive medicine. *Reproduction, Nutrition, Development* 2005 May-June; 45(3): 307-319. Subject: 14.1

Sureau, C.; Shenfield, F. Oocyte donation by a daughter. *Human Reproduction* 1995 June; 10(6): 1334. Subject: 14.4

Sussman, Michael D. Ethical requirements that must be met before the introduction of new procedures. *Clinical Orthopaedics and Related Research* 2000 September; (378): 15-22. Subject: 18.2

Suthers, G.K.; Armstrong, J.; McCormack, J.; Trott, D. Letting the family know: balancing ethics and effectiveness when notifying relatives about genetic testing for a familial disorder. *Journal of Medical Genetics* 2006 August; 43(8): 665-670. Subject: 15.3

Sutton, A.G. Reasoned and reasonable approaches to ethics in undergraduate medical courses [letter]. *Journal of Medical Ethics* 2006 November; 32(11): 682. Subject: 7.3

Suver, Betsy West. The obstacles to a constitutional partial birth abortion ban: how state legislatures have failed and the shortcomings of President George W. Bush's Partial Birth Abortion Ban Act of 2003. *University of Dayton Law Review* 2004-2005 Fall; 30(1): 149-169. Subject: 12.4.1

Suy, R. Governmental proposals concerning the tights [sic; rights] of the patient. Pandora's box? *Acta Chirurgica Belgica* 2000 August; 100(4): 183-184. Subject: 9.2

Suziedelis, Ann. Nurses: the Rodney Dangerfields of health care? *Health Care Ethics USA* 2006; 14(2): E4 [Online]. Accessed: http://chce.slu.edu/Partnerships_HCE_Intro.html[2006 November 17]. Subject: 4.1.3

See SUBJECT HEADING KEY FOR SECTION II on inside back cover.

Suzuki, David. A little knowledge.... *New Scientist* 2006 September 23-29; 191(2570): 18. Subject: 15.1

Svantesson, Mia; Sjokvist, Peter; Thorsen, Hakan; Ahlstrom, Gerd. Nurses' and physicians' opinions on aggressiveness of treatment for general ward patients. *Nursing Ethics* 2006 March; 13(2): 147-162. Subject: 20.5.1

Svehla, Carolyn J.; Anderson-Shaw, Lisa. Hospital ethics committees: is it time to expand our access to managed care organizations? *JONA's Healthcare Law, Ethics, and Regulation* 2006 January-March; 8(1): 15-19. Subject: 9.6

Svendsen, Mette Nordahl; Koch, Lene. Genetics and prevention: a policy in the making. *New Genetics and Society* 2006 April; 25(1): 51-68. Subject: 15.1

Swanson, Jeffrey W.; Swartz, Marvin S.; Elbogen, Eric B.; Van Dorn, Richard A.; Ferron, Joelle; Wagner, H. Ryan; McCauley, Barbara J.; Kim, Mimi. Facilitated psychiatric advance directives: a randomized trial of an intervention to foster advance treatment planning among persons with severe mental illness. *American Journal of Psychiatry* 2006 November; 163(11): 1943-1951. Subject: 20.5.4

Swanson, Jeffrey W.; Swartz, Marvin; Ferron, Joelle; Elbogen, Eric; Van Dorn, Richard. Psychiatric advance directives among public mental health consumers in five U.S. cities: prevalence, demand, and correlates. *Journal of the American Academy of Psychiatry and the Law* 2006; 34(1): 43-57. Subject: 17.1

Swanson, Jeffrey W.; Van McCrary, S.; Swartz, Marvin S.; Elbogen, Eric B.; Van Dorn, Richard A. Superseding psychiatric advance directives: ethical and legal considerations. *Journal of the American Academy of Psychiatry and the Law* 2006; 34(3): 385-394. Subject: 20.5.4

Swartz, Martha S. "Conscience clauses" or "unconscionable clauses": personal beliefs versus professional responsibilities. *Yale Journal of Health Policy, Law and Ethics* 2006 Summer; 6(2): 269-350. Subject: 9.7

Swartz, Marvin S.; Swanson, Jeffrey W.; Monahan, John. Endorsement of personal benefit of outpatient commitment among persons with severe mental illness. *Psychology, Public Policy, and Law* 2003 March-June; 9(1-2): 70-93. Subject: 17.7

Swartz, Richard D.; Perry, Erica. Medical family: a new view of the relationship between chronic dialysis patients and staff arising from discussions about advance directives. *Journal of Women's Health and Gender-Based Medicine* 1999 November; 8(9): 1147-1153. Subject: 19.3

Swazo, Norman K. Calculating risk/benefit in X-linked severe combined immune deficiency disorder (X-SCID) gene therapy trials: the task of ethical evaluation. *Journal of Medicine and Philosophy* 2006 October; 31(5): 533-564. Subject: 15.4

Swedin, Eric G. Designing babies: a eugenics race with China? *Futurist* 2006 May-June; 40(3): 18-21. Subject: 15.5

Swerdlow, Paul S. Use of humans in biomedical experimentation. *In:* Macrina, Francis L. Scientific Integrity: Text and Cases in Responsible Conduct of Research. 3rd ed. Washington, DC: ASM Press; 2005: 91-126. Subject: 18.1

Swick, Herbert M.; Bryan, Charles S.; Longo, Lawrence D. Beyond the physician charter: reflections on medical professionalism. *Perspectives in Biology and Medicine* 2006 Spring; 49(2): 263-275. Subject: 2.1

Swiss Academy of Medical Sciences; Stuck, Andreas; Amstad, Hermann; Baumann-Hölzle, Ruth; Fankhauser, Angeline; Kesselring, Annemarie; Leuba, Audrey; Rapin, Charles-Henri; Schmitt, Regula; Schönenberg, Hansruedi; Wirz, Urban; Vallotton, Michel. Treatment and care of elderly persons who are in need of care: medical-ethical guidelines and recommendations. *Journal of Nutrition, Health and Aging* 2005 July-August; 9(4): 288-295. Subject: 9.5.2

Swiss Committee on Animal Experimentation; Eidgenössische Ethikkommission für die Gentechnik im ausserhumanen Bereich = Swiss Ethics Committee on Non-Human Gene Technology [ECNH] = Commission fédérale d'éthique pour le génie génétique dans le domaine non humain = Commissione federale d'etica per l'ingegneria genetica nei settore non umano;. The Dignity of Animals: A joint statement by the Swiss Ethics Committee on Non-Human Gene Technology (ECNH) and the Swiss Committee on Animal Experiments (SCAE), concerning a more concrete definition of the dignity of creation with regard to animals. Bern, Switzerland: Swiss Ethics Committee on Non-Human Gene Technology, 2005 May; 12 p. Subject: 22.1

Swiss Society of Medical Genetics [SSGM]. Informed choice in diagnostic genetic testing. Binningen, Switzerland: Swiss Society of Medical Genetics, 2003. 3p [Online]. Accessed: http://www.ssgm.ch/sections/pdf/current/publications/SSGM_eng%20v1.pdf [2006 July 31]. Subject: 15.3

Switankowsky, Irene Sonia. Successful dying for cancer patients. *Humane Health Care International* 2006; 6(2): 3p. Subject: 20.4.1

Swope, Paul. El aborto: un fracaso de communicación [Abortion: a failure of communication]. *Persona y Bioética* 1999 February-May; 2(6): 165-176. Subject: 12.3

Symington, Ian S. Blood-borne viruses as workplace hazards. *In:* Westerholm, Peter; Nilstun, Tore; Øvretveit, John, eds. Practical Ethics in Occupational Health. San Francisco: Radcliffe Medical Press; 2004: 177-187. Subject: 16.3

Synofzik, Matthis. Kognition à la carte? Der Wunsch nach kognitionsverbessernden Psychopharmaka in der

---

Medizin = Cognition on demand? — The wish for cognition-enhancing drugs in medicine. *Ethik in der Medizin* 2006 March; 18(1): 37-50. Subject: 4.5

Sypher, Blake; Hall, Robert T.; Rosencrance, Gregory. Autonomy, informed consent and advance directives: a study of physician attitudes. *West Virginia Medical Journal* 2005 May-June; 101(3): 131-133. Subject: 7.1

Syrett, Keith. Priority-setting and public law: potential realised or unfulfilled? *Medical Law International* 2006; 7(3): 265-279. Subject: 9.4

Sytsma, Sharon E. The ethics of using dexamethasone to prevent virilization of female fetuses. *In:* Sytsma, Sharon E., ed. Ethics and Intersex. Dordrecht: Springer, 2006: 241-258. Subject: 9.5.8

Sytsma, Sharon E. Intersexuality, cultural influences, and cultural relativism. *In:* Sytsma, Sharon E., ed. Ethics and Intersex. Dordrecht: Springer, 2006: 259-270. Subject: 10

Szalai, Julia. Abortion in Hungary. *Feminist Review* 1988 Spring; (29): 98-100. Subject: 12.5.1

Szasz, Thomas. Reply to Battin and Spellecy. *In:* Schaler, Jeffrey A., ed. Szasz Under Fire: The Psychiatric Abolitionist Faces His Critics. Chicago: Open Court; 2004: 291-300. Subject: 20.7

Szebik, Imre. Moral dilemmas of gene transfer techniques. *In:* Sándor, Judit, ed. Society and Genetic Information: Codes and Laws in the Genetic Era. Budapest, Hungary; New York: CEU Press; 2003: 95-100. Subject: 15.4

Szer, J. Democracy or dictatorship at the bedside? [editorial]. *Internal Medicine Journal* 2006 May; 36(5): 275. Subject: 8.1

Szmukler, George; Dawson, John. Commentary: toward resolving some dilemmas concerning psychiatric advance directives. *Journal of the American Academy of Psychiatry and the Law* 2006; 34(3): 398-401. Subject: 20.5.4

Sztybel, David. A living will clause for supporters of animal experimentation. *Journal of Applied Philosophy* 2006; 23(2): 173-189. Subject: 22.2

T

Tabarrok, Alexander; Undis, David J. Response to "Members First: the Ethics of Donating Organs and Tissues to Groups" by Timothy F. Murphy and Robert M. Veatch (CQ Vol 15, No 1). *CQ: Cambridge Quarterly of Healthcare Ethics* 2006 Fall; 15(4): 450-456. Subject: 19.5

Tadd, Win; Clarke, Angela; Lloyd, Llynos; Leino-Kilpi, Helena; Strandell, Camilla; Lemonidou, Chryssoula; Petsios, Konstantinos; Sala, Roberta; Barazzetti, Gaia; Radaelli, Stefania; Zalewski, Zbigniew; Bialecka, Anna; van der Arend, Arie; Heymans, Regien. The value of nurses' codes: European nurses' views. *Nursing Ethics* 2006 July; 13(4): 376-393. Subject: 4.1.3

Taeusch, C.F. Should the doctor testify? *International Journal of Ethics* 1928 July; (38): 401-415. Subject: 7.3

Taft, Lee. Apology and medical mistake: opportunity or foil? *Annals of Health Law* 2005 Winter; 14(1): 55-94. Subject: 8.1

Tai, Michael Cheng-tek. The importance of medical humanity in medical education. *In:* Döring, Ole; Chen, Renbiao, eds. Advances in Chinese Medical Ethics: Chinese and International Perspectives. Hamburg: Institut für Asienkunde; 2002: 401-405. Subject: 2.3

Tai, Michael Cheng-tek. Natural and unnatural — an application of Taoist thought to bioethics. *In:* Sang-yong, Song; Young-Mo, Koo; Macer, Darryl R.J., eds. Asian Bioethics in the 21st Century. Christchurch, NZ: Eubios Ethics Institute, 2002: 122-128. Subject: 2.1

Tai, Michael Cheng-tek. A survey on the effectiveness of bioethics teaching in medical institutes. *Formosan Journal of Medical Humanities* 2006 June; 7(1-2): 133-157. Subject: 7.2

Tait, D.M.; Hardy, J. Consent for investigating and treating adults with cancer. *Clinical Oncology (Royal College of Radiology)* 2006 February; 18(1): 23-29. Subject: 8.3.1

Takahashi, Takao. Introduction: a short history of bioethics in Japan. *In:* Takahashi, Takao, ed. Taking Life and Death Seriously: Bioethics from Japan. Amsterdam; Boston: Elsevier JAI; 2005: 1-18. Subject: 2.2

Takahashi, Takao. A synthesis of bioethics and environmental ethics founded upon the concept of care: toward a Japanese approach to bioethics. *In:* Takahashi, Takao, ed. Taking Life and Death Seriously: Bioethics from Japan. Amsterdam; Boston: Elsevier JAI; 2005: 19-45. Subject: 2.1

Takala, Tuija. Why we should not relax ethical rules in the age of genetics. *In:* Árnason, Gardar; Nordal, Salvör; Árnason, Vilhjálmur, eds. Blood and Data: Ethical, Legal and Social Aspects of Human Genetic Databases. Reykjavík: University of Iceland Press; 2004: 135-140. Subject: 15.1

Talbot, David; Perou, Joan. Ethical issues. *In:* Di Giovanna, Ignazio; Hayes, Gareth, eds. Principles of Clinical Research. Philadelphia: Wrightson Biomedical Pub.; 2001: 63-83. Subject: 18.2

Tallgren, M.; Klepstad, P.; Petersson, J.; Skram, U.; Hynninen, M. Ethical issues in intensive care — a survey among Scandinavian intensivists. *Acta Anaesthesiologica Scandinavica* 2005 September; 49(8): 1092-1100. Subject: 9.4

Talmadge, Stephen A. Who should determine what is best for children in state custody who object to psychotropic medication? *Annals of Health Law* 2006 Summer; 15(2): 183-211. Subject: 8.3.2

Talone, Patricia A. Starting an organizational ethics committee: an ethicist suggests some practical and concrete

See SUBJECT HEADING KEY FOR SECTION II on inside back cover.

737

steps. *Health Progress* 2006 November-December; 87(6): 34-37. Subject: 9.1

Tamburrini, Claudio. Education or genetic blueprints, what's the difference? *In:* Tamburrini, Claudio; Tännsjö, Torbjörn, eds. Genetic Technology and Sport: Ethical Questions. London; New York: Routledge; 2005: 82-90. Subject: 4.5

Tamburrini, Claudio; Tännsjö, Torbjörn. The genetic design of a new Amazon. *In:* Tamburrini, Claudio; Tännsjö, Torbjörn, eds. Genetic Technology and Sport: Ethical Questions. London; New York: Routledge; 2005: 181-198. Subject: 15.4

Tammpuu, Piia. Making genes commonly meaningful: implications of national self-images on human genetic databases. *In:* Árnason, Gardar; Nordal, Salvör; Árnason, Vilhjálmur, eds. Blood and Data: Ethical, Legal and Social Aspects of Human Genetic Databases. Reykjavík: University of Iceland Press; 2004: 161-165. Subject: 15.1

Tamura, Chieko. The family-facilitated approach could be dangerous if there is pressure by family dynamics. *American Journal of Bioethics* 2006 January-February; 6(1): 16-18; discussion W27-W28. Subject: 8.3.1

Tanaka, Tomohiro. Medical business ethics: the HIV-tainted-blood affair in Japan. *In:* Takahashi, Takao, ed. Taking Life and Death Seriously: Bioethics from Japan. Amsterdam; Boston: Elsevier JAI; 2005: 253-273. Subject: 9.5.6

Tanasiewicz, Marta; Bednarski, Jacek; Galazka, Alicja. The truth, misunderstanding or lie? Different forms of doctor-patient relations. *Bulletin of Medical Ethics* 2005 June-July; (209): 13-17. Subject: 8.2

Tang, G.W.; Lau, O.W.K.; Yip, P. Further acceptability evaluation of RU 486 and ONO 802 as abortifacient agents in a Chinese population. *Contraception* 1993 September; 48(3): 267-276. Subject: 12.1

Tang, G.W.K. A pilot study of acceptability of RU 486 and ONO 802 in Chinese population. *Contraception* 1991 November; 44(5): 523-532. Subject: 12.1

Tang, Siew Tzuh; Liu, Tsang-Wu; Lai, Mei-Shu; Liu, Li-Ni; Chen, Chen-Hsiu. Concordance of preferences for end-of-life care between terminally ill cancer patients and their family caregivers in Taiwan. *Journal of Pain and Symptom Management* 2005 December; 30(6): 510-518. Subject: 20.4.1

Tanida, Noritoshi. Breach of information ethics and medical professional ethics during the SARS epidemic in Japan. *Formosan Journal of Medical Humanities* 2006 June; 7(1-2): 57-65. Subject: 8.2

Tanida, Noritoshi. Implications of Japanese religions in the genomic age: a survey on attitudes towards life and death within Shinto, Buddhist and Christian groups. *In:* Sleeboom, Margaret, ed. Genomics in Asia: A Clash of Bioethical Interests? New York: Kegan Paul; 2004: 107-134. Subject: 20.5.1

Tanida, Noritoshi. Implications of Japanese religious views toward life and death in medicine. *In:* Sang-yong, Song; Young-Mo, Koo; Macer, Darryl R.J., eds. Asian Bioethics in the 21st Century. Christchurch, NZ: Eubios Ethics Institute, 2002: 288-93. Subject: 20.5.1

Tanne, Janice Hopkins. FDA appointment is stalled as revelations emerge over Plan B [news]. *BMJ: British Medical Journal* 2006 August 12; 333(7563): 317. Subject: 11.1

Tanne, Janice Hopkins. FDA finally approves plan B — but with restrictions [news]. *BMJ: British Medical Journal* 2006 September 2; 333(7566): 461. Subject: 11.1

Tanne, Janice Hopkins. FDA rejected contraception for political reasons [news]. *BMJ: British Medical Journal* 2006 March 18; 332(7542): 624. Subject: 11.1

Tanne, Janice Hopkins. FDA to clarify rules on advisory committee members [news]. *BMJ: British Medical Journal* 2006 August 5; 333(7562): 278. Subject: 2.4

Tanne, Janice Hopkins. Former FDA commissioner pleads guilty to two charges [news]. *BMJ: British Medical Journal* 2006 October 28; 333(7574): 874. Subject: 9.7

Tanne, Janice Hopkins. NEJM editor gives pretrial evidence in Vioxx case [news]. *BMJ: British Medical Journal* 2006 February 4; 332(7536): 255. Subject: 9.7

Tanne, Janice Hopkins. Science will tighten standards after retracting stem cell papers [news]. *BMJ: British Medical Journal* 2006 December 9; 333(7580): 1189. Subject: 1.3.7

Tanne, Janice Hopkins. Vaccines against cervical cancer provoke US controversy [news]. *BMJ: British Medical Journal* 2006 April 8; 332(7545): 814. Subject: 9.5.7

Tanner, Michael. The wrong road to reform. *Hastings Center Report* 2006 September-October; 36(5): 24-26. Subject: 9.2

Tännsjö, Torbjörn. Genetic engineering and elitism in sport. *In:* Tamburrini, Claudio; Tännsjö, Torbjörn, eds. Genetic Technology and Sport: Ethical Questions. London; New York: Routledge; 2005: 57-69. Subject: 4.5

Tännsjö, Torbjörn. Negotiating ethics in anaesthesia [editorial]. *European Journal of Anaesthesiology* 2005 October; 22(10): 737-740. Subject: 8.1

Tännsjö, Torbjörn. Non-voluntary sterilization. *Journal of Medicine and Philosophy* 2006 August; 31(4): 401-415. Subject: 11.3

Tännsjö, Torbjörn. The sanctity of life and the active/passive distinction: a final reflection. *In:* Tännsjö, Torbjörn, ed. Terminal Sedation: Euthanasia in Disguise? Boston: Kluwer Academic Publishers; 2004: 115-125. Subject: 20.5.1

Tännsjö, Torbjörn. Terminal sedation: a substitute for euthanasia? *In:* Tännsjö, Torbjörn, ed. Terminal Sedation: Euthanasia in Disguise? Boston: Kluwer Academic Publishers; 2004: 15-30. Subject: 20.4.1

Tano, Mervyn L. Interrelationships among native peoples, genetic research, and the landscape: need for further research into ethical, legal, and social issues. *Journal of Law, Medicine and Ethics* 2006 Summer; 34(2): 301-309. Subject: 15.1

Tapp, Ann. Advance directives. *Canadian Nurse* 2006 February; 102(2): 26. Subject: 20.5.4

Tarantola, Daniel. HIV testing: breaking the deadly cycle. *Health and Human Rights: An International Journal* 2005; 8(2): 37-41. Subject: 9.5.6

Tarleton, Beth; Williams, Val; Palmer, Neil; Gramlich, Stacey. 'An equal relationship'?: people with learning difficulties getting involved in research. *In:* Smyth, Marie; Williamson, Emma, eds. Researchers and Their 'Subjects': Ethics, Power, Knowledge and Consent. Bristol, UK: Policy Press; 2004: 73-88. Subject: 18.5.6

Tarn, Derjung M.; Meredith, Lisa S.; Kagawa-Singer, Marjorie; Matsumura, Shinji; Bito, Seiji; Oye, Robert K.; Liu, Honghu; Kahn, Katherine L.; Fukuhara, Shunichi; Wenger, Neil S. Trust in one's physician: the role of ethnic match, autonomy, acculturation, and religiosity among Japanese and Japanese Americans. *Annals of Family Medicine* 2005 July-August; 3(4): 339-347. Subject: 8.1

Tarvydas, Vilia M.; Leahy, Michael J.; Saunders, Jodi L. A comparison of the ethical beliefs of certified rehabilitation counselors and national certified counselors. *Rehabilitation Counseling Bulletin* 2004 Summer; 47(4): 234-246. Subject: 17.1

Tarzian, Anita J.; Hoffmann, Diane E.; Volbrecht, Rose Mary; Meyers, Judy L. The roles of healthcare ethics committee networks in shaping healthcare policy and practices. *HEC (Healthcare Ethics Committee) Forum* 2006 March; 18(1): 85-94. Subject: 9.6

Tattersall, Martin; Kerridge, Ian. The drug industry and medical professionalism [letter]. *Lancet* 2006 January 7-13; 367(9504): 28. Subject: 7.3

Taub, Sara. Images of healing and learning. *Virtual Mentor* 2001 July; 3(7): 2p. Subject: 20.5.1

Taub, Sara; Parsi, Kayhan. The trend toward casual dress and address in the medical profession. *Virtual Mentor* 2001 October; 3(10): 2p. Subject: 8.1

Tauber, Alfred I. In search of medicine's moral guide. *American Journal of Bioethics* 2006 January-February; 6(1): 41-44. Subject: 8.1

Tauber, Alfred I. The moral domain of the medical record: the routine ethics evaluation. *American Journal of Bioethics [Online]* 2006 July-August; 6(4): W1-W16. Subject: 8.1

Tauer, Carol A. The tradition of probabilism and the moral status of the early embryo. *Theological Studies* 1984 March; 45(1): 3-33. Subject: 4.4

Tauh, Sara. "Departed Jan 11, 1983; at peace Dec 26, 1990.". *In:* American Medical Association. ProfessingMedicine: strengthening the ethics and professionalism of tomorrow's physicians. Chicago: American Medical Association; 2001: 108-110. Subject: 20.5.1

Taupitz, Jochen. Genetic analysis and the right to self-determination in German Civil War = Análisis genético y derecho de autodeterminación en el Derecho Civil Alemán. *Law and the Human Genome Review = Revista de Derecho y Genoma Humano* 1996 January-June; (4): 77-90. Subject: 15.3

Tavani, Herman T. Environmental genomics, data mining, and informed consent. *In his:* Ethics, Computing, and Genomics. Sudbury, MA: Jones and Bartlett; 2006: 167-185. Subject: 15.1

Tavani, Herman T. Ethics at the intersection of computing and genomics. *In his:* Ethics, Computing, and Genomics. Sudbury, MA: Jones and Bartlett; 2006: 5-26. Subject: 15.1

Tavani, Herman T. Genomic research and data-mining technology: implications for personal privacy and informed consent. *Ethics and Information Technology* 2004; 6(1): 15-28. Subject: 15.1

Taverne, Dick. The new fundamentalism. *Nature Biotechnology* 2005 April; 23(4): 415-416. Subject: 15.7

Taylor, Bridget. Parental autonomy and consent to treatment. *Journal of Advanced Nursing* 1999 March; 29(3): 570-576. Subject: 8.3.2

Taylor, Bridget. Whose baby is it? The impact of reproductive technologies on kinship. *Human Fertility (Cambridge)* 2005 September; 8(3): 189-195. Subject: 14.1

Taylor, Carol R. Ethics in nursing. *Australian Nursing Journal* 2004 December-2005 January; 12(6): 11. Subject: 4.1.3

Taylor, E.M.; Ramsay, M.P.; Bunton, L. Do our patients understand? A comparison of understanding in adult inpatients and schoolchildren. *New Zealand Medical Journal* 1998 November 27; 111(1078): 449-451. Subject: 8.3.1

Taylor, Gary; Hawley, Helen. Health promotion and the freedom of the individual. *Health Care Analysis: An International Journal of Health Philosophy and Policy* 2006 March; 14(1): 15-24. Subject: 9.1

Taylor, James Stacey. Autonomy, inducements and organ sales. *In:* Athanassoulis, Nafsika, ed. Philosophical Reflections on Medical Ethics. New York: Palgrave Macmillan; 2005: 109-134. Subject: 19.5

Taylor, James Stacey. Black markets, transplant kidneys and interpersonal coercion. *Journal of Medical Ethics* 2006 December; 32(12): 698-701. Subject: 19.5

See SUBJECT HEADING KEY FOR SECTION II on inside back cover.

739

Taylor, James Stacey. Personal autonomy, posthumous harm, and presumed consent policies for organ procurement. *Public Affairs Quarterly* 2006 October; 20(4): 381-404. Subject: 19.1

Taylor, Mark J. Problems with targeting law reform at genetic discrimination. *In:* Árnason, Gardar; Nordal, Salvör; Árnason, Vilhjálmur, eds. Blood and Data: Ethical, Legal and Social Aspects of Human Genetic Databases. Reykjavík: University of Iceland Press; 2004: 347-352. Subject: 15.3

Taylor, Mary Lou. Ethical issues for psychologists in pain management. *Pain Medicine* 2001 June; 2(2): 147-154. Subject: 17.1

Taylor, Richard. Human property: threat or saviour? *E Law: Murdoch University Electronic Journal of Law* 2002 December; 9(4): 14 p. [Online]. Accessed: http://www.murdoch.edu.au/elaw/issues/v9n4/taylor94.html [2006 June 29]. Subject: 4.4

Taymor, Kenneth S.; Scott, Christopher Thomas; Greely, Henry T. The paths around stem cell intellectual property. *Nature Biotechnology* 2006 April; 24(4): 411-413. Subject: 15.8

Teeri, Sari; Leino-Kilpi, Helena; Valimaki, Maritta. Long-term nursing care of elderly people: identifying ethically problematic experiences among patients, relatives and nurses in Finland. *Nursing Ethics* 2006 March; 13(2): 116-129. Subject: 9.5.2

Teisseyre, Nathalie; Mullet, Etienne; Sorum, Paul Clay. Under what conditions is euthanasia acceptable to lay people and health professionals? *Social Science and Medicine* 2005 January; 60(2): 357-368. Subject: 20.5.1

Teitelbaum, Joel B. Health care and civil rights: an introduction. *Ethnicity and Disease* 2005 Spring; 15(2 supplement 2): S2- 27-S2-30. Subject: 9.2

Teka, Telahun; Lulseged, Sileshi. Living by the code in clinical research [editorial]. *Ethiopian Medical Journal* 2005 April; 43(2): 1 p. Subject: 18.2

Templeton, Sarah-Kate. Mother sues for veto on daughter's morning-after pill. *Sunday Times* 2005 May 15: 1 p. [Online]. http://infoweb.newsbank.com/iw-search/we/InfoWeb/?p_action=print&p_docid=10. . . [5 October 2006]. Subject: 11.2

ten Have, Henk. The activities of UNESCO in the area of ethics. *Kennedy Institute of Ethics Journal* 2006 December; 16(4): 333-351. Subject: 2.1

ten Have, Henk. A communitarian approach to clinical bioethics. *In:* Viafora, Corrado, ed. Clinical Bioethics: A Search for the Foundations. Dordrecht: Springer, 2005: 41-51. Subject: 2.1

ten Have, Henk. "A helping and caring profession": medicine as a normative practice. *In:* Viafora, Corrado, ed. Clinical Bioethics: A Search for the Foundations. Dordrecht: Springer, 2005: 75-97. Subject: 2.1

ten Have, Henk. Retos éticos de la nueva biotecnología = Ethical challenges of the new biotechnology. *Revista Latinoamericana de Bioética* 2003 January; (4): 56-79. Subject: 5.2

Tengilimoglu, Dilaver; Kisa, Adnan; Ekiyor, Aykut. The pharmaceutical sales rep/physician relationship in Turkey: ethical issues in an international context. *Health Marketing Quarterly* 2004; 22(1): 21-39. Subject: 9.7

Tengland, Per-Anders. The goals of health work: quality of life, health and welfare. *Medicine, Health Care and Philosophy* 2006; 9(2): 155-167. Subject: 4.4

Tennant, Agnieszka. Define 'better': an interview with bioethicist C. Ben Mitchell. *Christianity Today* 2004 January; 48(1): 42-44. Subject: 5.4

Tennant, Agnieszka. The genome doctor: an interview with Francis Collins. *Christianity Today* 2001 October 1: 42-46. Subject: 15.10

Teno, Joan M. Advance care planning for frail, older persons. *In:* Morrison, R. Sean; Meier, Diane E.; Capello, Carol, eds. Geriatric Palliative Care. New York: Oxford University Press; 2003: 307-313. Subject: 20.5.4

ter Braak, Edith. Patients need not give consent in all clinical education [letter]. *BMJ: British Medical Journal* 2006 March 4; 332(7540): 549. Subject: 7.2

Terry, Nicolas P. Privacy and the health information domain: properties, models and unintended results. *European Journal of Health Law* 2003 September; 10(3): 223-237. Subject: 8.4

Terry, Sharon F.; Terry, Patrick F. A consumer perspective on forensic DNA banking. *Journal of Law, Medicine and Ethics* 2006 Summer; 34(2): 408-414. Subject: 15.1

Tesarik, Jan; Greco, Ermanno. A zygote is not an embryo: ethical and legal considerations. *Reproductive BioMedicine Online [electronic]* 2004 July; 9(1): 4 p. Accessed: http://www.rbmonline.com/index.html [2005 June 3]. Subject: 14.1

Tesoriero, Heather Won. Vioxx doctors wooed by Merck are now its foes. *Wall Street Journal* 2006 March 10; p. B1, B3. Subject: 9.7

Thable, Daman. With great knowledge comes great responsibilities: an examination of genetic discrimination in Canada. *Health Law Review* 2006; 14(3): 22-31. Subject: 15.1

Thall, Peter F.; Estey, Elihu H. Some ethical issues in phase II trials in acute leukemia. *Clinical Advances in Hematology and Oncology* 2005 December; 3(12): 943-948. Subject: 18.2

Thampapillai, Dilan. Court-ordered obstetrical intervention and the rights of a pregnant woman. *Journal of Law and Medicine* 2005 May; 12(4): 455-461. Subject: 9.5.5

Tharyan, Prathap. Placebo-controlled trials in psychiatry on trial. *Indian Journal of Medical Ethics* 2006 January-March; 3(1): 13-16. Subject: 18.3

Tharyan, Prathap. Whose trial is it anyway? Reflections on morality, double standards, uncertainty and criticism in international collaborative health research. *Monash Bioethics Review* 2006 October; 25(4): 51-66. Subject: 18.5.9

Thasler, Wolfgang E.; Schlott, Thilo; Kalkuhl, Arno; Plän, Thomas; Irrgang, Bernhard; Juach, Karl-Walter; Weiss, Thomas S. Human tissue for in vitro research as an alternative to animal experiments: a charitable "honest broker" model to fulfil ethical and legal regulations and to protect research participants. *ATLA: Alternatives to Laboratory Animals* 2006 August; 34(4): 387-392. Subject: 19.5

Thekkuveettil, Anoopkumar. Where is the girl in all the decision making? *Indian Journal of Medical Ethics* 2006 April-June; 3(2): 71. Subject: 1.3.9

Thelen, Mary. End-of-life decision making in intensive care. *Critical Care Nurse* 2005 December; 25(6): 28-38. Subject: 20.5.1

Therrell, Bradford L., Jr. Ethical, legal and social issues in newborn screening in the United States. *Southeast Asian Journal of Tropical Medicine and Public Health* 2003; 34(Supplement 3): 52-58. Subject: 15.3

Thévoz, Jean-Marie. Die Evolution wissenschaftlicher und ethicscher Paradigmen in der Gentherapie. *In:* Rehmann-Sutter, Christoph; Müller, Hansjakob, eds. Ethik und Gentherapie: Zum praktischen Diskurs um die molekulare Medizin. Tübingen: Attempto Verlag; 1995: 34-40. Subject: 15.4

Thibeault, Susan L.; Benninger, Michael. Informed consent in otolaryngology research [editorial]. *Otolaryngology — Head and Neck Surgery* 2005 November; 133(5): 651-653. Subject: 18.3

Thomas, Cordelia. Pre-implantation testing and the protection of the "saviour sibling". *Deakin Law Review* 2004; 9(1): 119-143. Subject: 15.2

Thomas, Cordelia. Preimplantation genetic diagnosis: development and regulation. *Medicine and Law: The World Association for Medical Law* 2006 June; 25(2): 365-378. Subject: 15.2

Thomas, George. Junior doctors, strikes and patient care in public hospitals. *Indian Journal of Medical Ethics* 2006 April-June; 3(2): 44-45. Subject: 4.1.2

Thomas, Hans. ¿Ética pluralismo pueden ir de acuerdo? [Can ethics and pluralism agree?]. *Persona y Bioética* 1999 February-May; 2(6): 89-112. Subject: 14.2

Thomas, J. Mervyn. Responses by pregnant Jehovah's witnesses on health care proxies [letter]. *Obstetrics and Gynecology* 2005 February; 105(2): 441. Subject: 8.3.3

Thomas, Kim. HIV study among pregnant aboriginal women raises concerns. *HIV/AIDS Policy and Law Review* 2002 December; 7(2-3): 33-34. Subject: 9.5.6

Thomas, P.S.; Tan, K.-S.; Yates, D.H. Ethical issues in the relationships involving medicine and industry [letter]. *Internal Medicine Journal* 2005 December; 35(12): 732. Subject: 7.3

Thomasma, David C. Clinical bioethics in a post modern age. *In:* Viafora, Corrado, ed. Clinical Bioethics: A Search for the Foundations. Dordrecht: Springer, 2005: 3-20. Subject: 2.1

Thomasma, David C. Theories of medical ethics: the philosophical structure. *In:* Beam, Thomas E.; Sparacino, Linette R.; Pellegrino, Edmund D.; Hartle, Anthony E.; Howe, Edmund G., eds. Military Medical Ethics. Volume 1. Washington, DC: TMM Publications, Borden Institute, Walter Reed Army Medical Center; 2003: 23-59. Subject: 2.1

Thompson, Alison K.; Faith, Karen; Gibson, Jennifer L.; Upshur, Ross E.G. Pandemic influenza preparedness: an ethical framework to guide decision-making. *BMC Medical Ethics* 2006; 7:12. Subject: 9.1

Thompson, Dan R. What do I tell my patient? *American Journal of Bioethics* 2006 July-August; 6(4): 66-67. Subject: 18.2

Thompson, J.; Ravelingien, A.; Braeckman, J.; Mortier, F.; Mortier, E.; Kerremans, I. Relatives of the living dead [letter and reply]. *Journal of Medical Ethics* 2006 October; 32(10): 607-608, 609-611. Subject: 20.2.1

Thompson, Linda W. Nursing ethics: the ANA code for nurses. *Tennessee Nurse* 1998 December; 61(6): 23, 25-29. Subject: 6

Thompson, Richard E. The hospital ethics committee — then and now. *Physician Executive* 2006 May-June; 32(3): 60-62. Subject: 9.6

Thompson, Richard E. Is pay for performance ethical? *Physician Executive* 2005 November-December; 31(6): 60-62. Subject: 9.3.1

Thompson, Richard E. Lantern of Diogenes: is "honest physician" a 21st century oxymoron? *Physician Executive* 2005 March-April; 31(2): 36-38. Subject: 7.3

Thompson, Richard E. The Terri Schiavo dilemma: an ethics report card with a few surprises. *Physician Executive* 2005 September-October; 31(5): 60-61. Subject: 20.5.1

Thompson, Stephen L.; Salmon, J. Warren. Strikes by physicians: a historical perspective toward an ethical evaluation. *International Journal of Health Services* 2006; 36(2): 331-354. Subject: 9.3.2

Thompson, Trevor D.B.; Barbour, Rosaline S.; Schwartz, Lisa. Health professionals' views on advance directives: a qualitative interdisciplinary study. *Palliative Medicine* 2003; 17(5): 403-409. Subject: 20.5.4

See SUBJECT HEADING KEY FOR SECTION II on inside back cover.

Thompson, W. Grant. The ethics of using placebos. *In his:* The Placebo Effect and Health: Combining Science and Compassionate Care. Amherst, NY: Prometheus Books; 2005: 203-214. Subject: 8.2

Thompson, William. Terri's law: the limit of the Florida legislature to decide an individual's right to die. *New England Journal on Criminal and Civil Confinement* 2005; 31: 485-518. Subject: 20.5.1

Thomson, Alexander N.; White, Gillian Eyres. Attitudes toward sexual contact between general practitioners and their patients. *New Zealand Medical Journal* 1995 June 28; 108(1002): 247-249. Subject: 7.4

Thomson, Colin J.H. Protecting health information privacy in research: how much law do Australians need? *Medical Journal of Australia* 2005 September 19; 183(6): 315-317. Subject: 8.4

Thomson, Colin J.H. Protecting health information privacy in research: what's an ethics committee like yours doing in a job like this? *Journal of Law and Medicine* 2006 February; 13(3): 304-310. Subject: 18.2

Thomson, Elizabeth; McMillan, Ian. Genethics: The Human Genome Project has profound implications for society. Ian McMillan talked to Elizabeth Thomson about its importance for nurses. *Nursing Standard* 1998 December 9-15; 13(12): 21-22. Subject: 15.10

Thorevska, Natalya; Tilluckdharry, Lisa; Tickoo, Sumit; Havasi, Andrea; Amoateng-Adjepong, Yaw; Manthous, Constantine A. Patients' understanding of advance directives and cardiopulmonary resuscitation. *Journal of Critical Care* 2005 March; 20(1): 26-34. Subject: 20.5.4

Thorgeirsdóttir, Sigrídur. The controversy on consent in the Icelandic database case and narrow bioethics. *In:* Árnason, Gardar; Nordal, Salvör; Árnason, Vilhjálmur, eds. Blood and Data: Ethical, Legal and Social Aspects of Human Genetic Databases. Reykjavík: University of Iceland Press; 2004: 67-77. Subject: 15.1

Thorne, C.; Newell, M.L.; Peckham, C.S. Disclosure of diagnosis and planning for the future in HIV-affected families in Europe. *Child: Care, Health and Development* 2000 January; 26(1): 29-40. Subject: 9.5.6

Thorne, Sally; Hislop, T. Gregory; Kuo, Margot; Armstrong, Elizabeth-Anne. Hope and probability: patient perspectives of the meaning of numerical information in cancer communication. *Qualitative Health Research* 2006 March; 16(3): 318-336. Subject: 8.1

Thorne, Sally; Varcoe, Colleen. The tyranny of feminist methodology in women's health research. *Health Care for Women International* 1998 November-December; 19(6): 481-493. Subject: 18.5.3

Thorns, Andrew; Garrard, Eve. Ethical issues in care of the dying. *In:* Ellershaw, John; Wilkinson, Susie, eds. Care of the Dying: A Pathway to Excellence. New York: Oxford University Press; 2003: 62-73. Subject: 20.4.1

Thornton, Hazel. "Empowering" patient choice about participation in trials? *In:* Duley, Lelia; Farrell, Barbara, eds. Clinical Trials. London: BMJ Books; 2002: 121-128. Subject: 18.1

Thornton, T. Judgement and the role of the metaphysics of values in medical ethics. *Journal of Medical Ethics* 2006 June; 32(6): 365-370. Subject: 2.1

Tiefer, Leonore. Sex and disease-mongering: a special case? *Monash Bioethics Review* 2006 July; 25(3): 28-35. Subject: 4.4

Tierney, Alison. The role of research ethics committees. *Nurse Researcher* 1995 September; 3(1): 43-52. Subject: 18.2

Tierney, E. The Nazi hypothermia experiments: forbidden data? [letter]. *Anaesthesia* 2005 April; 60(4): 413. Subject: 18.5.5

Tighe, Mark. Fetuses can feel pain [letter]. *BMJ: British Medical Journal* 2006 April 29; 332(7548): 1036. Subject: 9.5.8

Tijmes, Pieter. Euthanasia in the Netherlands. *In:* Mitcham, Carl, ed. Encyclopedia of Science, Technology, and Ethics. Farmington Hills, MI: Thomson/Gale, 2005: 713-715. Subject: 20.5.1

Tilbury, Farida. Ethical dilemmas: principles and practice in research with African refugees. *Monash Bioethics Review* 2006 January; 25(1): 75-84. Subject: 21.7

Timmermans, Stefan. Death brokering: constructing culturally appropriate deaths. *Sociology of Health and Illness* 2005 November; 27(7): 993-1013. Subject: 20.3.2

Tindell, Deborah R.; Bohlander, Robert W. Participants' naivete and confidentiality in psychological research. *Psychological Reports* 2005 June; 96(3 Part 2): 963-969. Subject: 18.4

Ting, Joseph Yuk Sang; Brennan, Troyen A.; Rothman, David J.; Naughton, James; Cohen, Jordan; Kimball, Harry; Blumenthal, David; Smelser, Neil; Kassirer, Jerome P.; Goldman, JanLori. Academic medical centers and conflicts of interest [letter and reply]. *JAMA: The Journal of the American Medical Association* 2006 June 28; 295(24): 2846, 2848-2849. Subject: 7.3

Tishchenko, P.D. Bioethics in Russia. *Journal International de Bioéthique = International Journal of Bioethics* 2005 September-December; 16(3-4): 67-70, 170. Subject: 2.1

Tishchenko, Pavel. Dimensions of cultural diversity of medical ethics. *In:* Rehmann-Sutter, Christoph; Düwell, Marcus; Mieth, Dietmar, eds. Bioethics in Cultural Contexts: Reflections on Methods and Finitude. Dordrecht: Springer, 2006: 211-227. Subject: 21.7

Subject = NRCBL Primary Classification Number; see inside front cover.

Tober, Diane M. Semen as gift, semen as goods: reproductive workers and the market in altruism. *In:* Scheper-Hughes, Nancy; Wacquant, Loïc, eds. Commodifying Bodies. Thousand Oaks, CA: SAGE Publications; 2002: 137-160. Subject: 14.6

Todres, I. David; Armstrong, Anne; Lally, Patricia; Cassem, Edwin H. Negotiating end-of-life issues. *New Horizons* 1998 November; 6(4): 374-382. Subject: 20.5.1

Toffoli, Luisa; Rudge, Trudy. Organizational predicaments: ethical conditions for nursing research. *Journal of Advanced Nursing* 2006 December; 56(6): 600-606. Subject: 18.1

Toledo-Pereyra, Luis H. Integrity [editorial]. *Journal of Investigative Surgery* 2006 January-February; 19(1): 1-3. Subject: 4.1.2

Tolich, Martin; Fitzgerald, Maureen H. If ethics committees were designed for ethnography. *Journal of Empirical Research on Human Research Ethics* 2006 June; 1(2): 71-78. Subject: 18.6

Tollefsen, Christopher. Fission, fusion, and the simple view. *Christian Bioethics* 2006 December; 12(3): 255-263. Subject: 4.4

Tollefsen, Christopher. The President's Council on Bioethics: overview and assessment. *HEC (Healthcare Ethics Committee) Forum* 2006 June; 18(2): 99-107. Subject: 2.4

Toller, Claire A. Stark; Budge, Marc M. Compliance with and understanding of advance directives among trainee doctors in the United Kingdom. *Journal of Palliative Care* 2006 Autumn; 22(3): 141-146. Subject: 20.5.4

Tomasevic, Luka. Challenges of global bioethics and biotechnology. *Formosan Journal of Medical Humanities* 2006 June; 7(1-2): 39-55. Subject: 2.1

Tomasini, Floris. Exploring ethical justification for self-demand amputation. *Ethics and Medicine* 2006 Summer; 22(2): 99-115. Subject: 4.3

Tomlinson, Tom. Ethical issues. *In:* Kuebler, Kim K.; Davis, Mellar P.; Moore, Crystal Dea, eds. Palliative Practices: An Interdisciplinary Approach. St. Louis, MO: Elsevier Mosby; 2005: 291-307. Subject: 20.5.1

Tomova, Sylvia. Research ethics committees in Bulgaria. *In:* Beyleveld, D.; Townend, D.; Wright, J., eds. Research Ethics Committees, Data Protection and Medical Research in European Countries. Hants, England; Burlington, VT: Ashgate; 2005: 27-30. Subject: 18.2

Tomycz, N.D. A profession selling out: lamenting the paradigm shift in physician advertising. *Journal of Medical Ethics* 2006 January; 32(1): 26-28. Subject: 8.1

Tong, Rosemarie. Feminist perspectives, global bioethics, and the need for moral language translation skills. *In:* Tong, Rosemarie; Donchin, Anne; Dodds, Susan, eds. Linking Visions: Feminist Bioethics, Human Rights, and the Developing World. Lanham, MD: Rowman and Littlefield Publishers; 2004: 89-104. Subject: 2.1

Tong, S.; Olsen, J. The threat to scientific integrity in environmental and occupational medicine. *Occupational and Environmental Medicine* 2005 December; 62(12): 843-846. Subject: 1.3.9

Tongan, Anthony; Adam, Mary B. Ethics involved in simulation-based medical planning. *Ethics and Medicine* 2006 Spring; 22(1): 23-29. Subject: 4.1.2

Tonti-Filippini, Nicholas. New issues in organ donation. *Linacre Quarterly* 2006 November; 73(4): 326-343. Subject: 19.5

Tonti-Filippini, Nicholas; Fleming, John I.; Pike, Gregory K.; Campbell, Ray. Ethics and human-animal transgenesis. *National Catholic Bioethics Quarterly* 2006 Winter; 6(4): 689-704. Subject: 19.1

Toom, Victor. DNA fingerprinting and the right to inviolability of the body and bodily integrity in the Netherlands: convincing evidence and proliferating body parts. *Genomics, Society and Policy* 2006 December; 2(3): 64-74. Subject: 15.1

Topbas, Murat; Çan, G.; Can, M.A.; Özgün, S. Outmoded attitudes toward organ donation among Turkish health care professionals. *Transplantation Proceedings* 2005 June; 37(5): 1998-2000. Subject: 19.5

Tope, Rosie; Koskinen, Marja-Kaarina. Quality assurance — an ethical responsibility? *In:* Tadd, Win, ed. Ethics in Nursing Education, Research and Management. New York: Palgrave Macmillan; 2003: 163-191. Subject: 9.8

Torda, A. How far does a doctor's 'duty of care' go? *Internal Medicine Journal* 2005 May; 35(5): 295-296. Subject: 8.1

Torjuul, Kirsti; Sorlie, Venke. Nursing is different than medicine: ethical difficulties in the process of care in surgical units. *Journal of Advanced Nursing* 2006 November; 56(4): 404-413. Subject: 8.1

Toscani, Franco; Farsides, Calliope. Deception, Catholicism, and hope: understanding problems in the communication of unfavorable prognoses in traditionally-Catholic countries. *American Journal of Bioethics [Online]*. 2006 January-February; 6(1): W6-W18. Subject: 8.2

Tovino, Stacey A. Hospital chaplaincy under the HIPAA Privacy rule: health care or "just visiting the sick"? *Indiana Health Law Review* 2005; 2(1): 49-92. Subject: 9.1

Tovino, Stacey A.; Winslade, William J. A primer on the law and ethics of treatment, research, and public policy in the context of severe traumatic brain injury. *Annals of Health Law* 2005 Winter; 14(1): 1-53. Subject: 20.5.2

Townell, Nick. Quality of life after donor nephrectomy: is better after laparoscopy than the mini incision technique [editorial]. *BMJ: British Medical Journal* 2006 July 29; 333(7561): 209-210. Subject: 19.5

See SUBJECT HEADING KEY FOR SECTION II on inside back cover.

743

Townend, David M.R. Who owns genetic information? *In:* Sándor, Judit, ed. Society and Genetic Information: Codes and Laws in the Genetic Era. Budapest, Hungary; New York: CEU Press; 2003: 125-144. Subject: 15.1

Townsley, Michael; Smith, Chloe; Pease, Ken. First impressions count: serious detections arising from criminal justice samples. *Genomics, Society and Policy* 2006 May; 2(1): 28-40. Subject: 15.1

Trachtman, Howard. The law of mass action. *American Journal of Bioethics* 2006 July-August; 6(4): 72-74. Subject: 18.2

Trachtman, Howard. The secret sharer [letter]. *American Journal of Bioethics [Online].* 2006 March-April; 6(2): W35. Subject: 8.4

Tracy, C. Shawn; Drummond, Neil; Ferris Lorraine E.; Globerman, Judith; Hébert, Philip C.; Pringle, Dorothy M.; Cohen, Carole A. To tell or not to tell? Professional and lay perspectives on the disclosure of personal health information in community-based dementia care. *Canadian Journal on Aging = La Revue Canadienne du Vieillissement* 2004 Fall; 23(3): 203-215. Subject: 8.4

Traiman, Leland. Guidelines but no guidance: GaySpermBank.com vs. FDA. *Journal of Gender, Race and Justice* 2006 Spring; 9(3): 613-620. Subject: 14.2

Trehan, Nidhi; Crowhurst, Isabel. Minority groups and reproductive rights: coerced sterilisation and female genital mutilation in Europe. *In:* Widdows, Heather; Idiakez, Itziar Alkorta; Cirión, Aitziber Emaldi, eds. Women's Reproductive Rights. New York: Palgrave Macmillan; 2006: 88-108. Subject: 11.3

Treloar, A.J. Advance directives: limitations upon their applicability in elderly care. *International Journal of Geriatric Psychiatry* 1999 December; 14(12): 1039-1043. Subject: 20.5.4

Tremain, Shelley. Reproductive freedom, self-regulation, and the government of impairment in utero. *Hypatia: A Journal of Feminist Philosophy* 2006 Winter; 21(1): 35-53. Subject: 15.3

Tremaine, William J.; Carlson, Marilyn R.; Isaacs, Kim L.; Motil, Kathleen J.; Robuck, Patricia R.; Wurzelmann, John I. Ethical issues, safety, and data integrity in clinical trials. *Inflammatory Bowel Diseases* 2005 November; 11(Supplement 1): S17-S21. Subject: 18.2

Trent, Ronald J.A. Essentially yours: the protection of human genetic information in Australia — the impact on clinical practice and the 'new genetics'. *University of New South Wales Law Journal* 2003; 26(3): 807- 812. Subject: 15.3

Trevena, L.; Irwig, L.; Barratt, A. Impact of privacy legislation on the number and characteristics of people who are recruited for research: a randomised controlled trial. *Journal of Medical Ethics* 2006 August; 32(8): 473-477. Subject: 18.2

Trías, Encarna Roca. The perplexities of law: mysteries of embryos = El derecho perplejo: los misterios de los embriones. *Law and the Human Genome = Revista de Derecho y Genoma Humano* 1994 July-December; (1): 119-148. Subject: 4.4

Tribbensee, Nancy E.; Claiborn, Charles D. Confidentiality in psychotherapy and related contexts. *In:* O'Donohue, William; Ferguson, Kyle, eds. Handbook of Professional Ethics for Psychologists: Issues, Questions, and Controversies. Thousand Oaks, Calif.: SAGE Publications; 2003: 287-300. Subject: 17.2

Trimmel, Michael; Lattacher, Helene; Janda, Monika. Voluntary whole-blood donors, and compensated platelet donors and plasma donors: motivation to donate, altruism and aggression. *Transfusion and Apheresis Science* 2005 October; 33(2): 147-155. Subject: 19.4

Tripp, J.; McGregor, D. Withholding and withdrawing of life sustaining treatment in the newborn. *Archives of Disease in Childhood. Fetal Neonatal Edition* 2006 January; 91(1): F67-F71. Subject: 20.5.2

Trivedi, Amal N.; Ayanian, John Z. Perceived discrimination and use of preventive health services. *JGIM: Journal of General Internal Medicine* 2006 June; 21(6): 553-558. Subject: 9.5.1

Trontelj, Joze. Research ethics committees in Slovenia. *In:* Beyleveld, D.; Townend, D.; Wright, J., eds. Research Ethics Committees, Data Protection and Medical Research in European Countries. Hants, England; Burlington, VT: Ashgate; 2005: 229-232. Subject: 18.2

Trotochaud, Karen. Ethical issues and access to healthcare. *Journal of Infusion Nursing* 2006 May-June; 29(3): 165-170. Subject: 9.2

Trotter, Griffin. Bioethics and deliberative democracy: five warnings from Hobbes. *Journal of Medicine and Philosophy* 2006 June; 31(3): 235-250. Subject: 2.1

Trotter, Griffin. Interpreting scientific data ethically: a frontier for research ethics. *In:* Iltis, Ana Smith, ed. Research Ethics. New York: Routledge, 2006: 165-177. Subject: 18.2

Trotter, Griffin. What the trough breaks. *American Journal of Bioethics [Online].* 2006 January-February; 6(1): W25-W26. Subject: 2.1

Truog, Robert D. Increasing the participation of children in clinical research [editorial]. *Intensive Care Medicine* 2005 June; 31(6): 760-761. Subject: 18.5.2

Truog, Robert D. Will ethical requirements bring critical care research to a halt? *Intensive Care Medicine* 2005 March; 31(3): 338-344. Subject: 18.3

Truog, Robert D.; Cochrane, Thomas I. The truth about "donation after cardiac death". *Journal of Clinical Ethics* 2006 Summer; 17(2): 133-136. Subject: 19.5

Truog, Robert D.; Mitchell, Christine. Futility — from hospital policies to state laws. *American Journal of Bioethics* 2006 September-October; 6(5): 19-21; discussion W30-W32. Subject: 20.5.1

Truscott, Derek; Goodkey, Lori. Ethical principles of the psychology profession and involuntary commitment. *In:* O'Donohue, William; Ferguson, Kyle, eds. Handbook of Professional Ethics for Psychologists: Issues, Questions, and Controversies. Thousand Oaks, Calif.: SAGE Publications; 2003: 167-180. Subject: 17.7

Tsai, D. F-C. The WMA Medical Ethics Manual [book review]. *Journal of Medical Ethics* 2006 March; 32(3): 163. Subject: 2.1

Tsai, Daniel F.C. The two-dimensional concept of Confucian personhood in biomedical practice. *In:* Döring, Ole; Chen, Renbiao, eds. Advances in Chinese Medical Ethics: Chinese and International Perspectives. Hamburg: Institut für Asienkunde; 2002: 195-213. Subject: 8.1

Tsai, Daniel Fu-Chang; Chen, Ding-Shinn. What should the dean do? [case study and commentaries]. *Hastings Center Report* 2006 July-August; 36(4): 15. Subject: 7.2

Tsang, Lincoln. Legal and ethical status of stem cells as medicinal products. *Advanced Drug Delivery Reviews* 2005 December 12; 57(13): 1970-1980. Subject: 18.5.4

Tschudin, Verena. Cultural and historical perspectives on nursing and ethics: listening to each other — report of the conference in Taipei, Taiwan, 19 May 2005, organized by ICNE and Nursing Ethics. *Nursing Ethics* 2006 May; 13(3): 304-322. Subject: 4.1.3

Tschudin, Verena. How nursing ethics as a subject changes: an analysis of the first 11 years of publication of the journal Nursing Ethics. *Nursing Ethics* 2006 January; 13(1): 65-85. Subject: 4.1.3

Tschudin, Verena. 30th anniversary commentary on Esterhuizen P. (1996) Is the professional code still the cornerstone of clinical nursing practice? Journal of Advanced Nursing 23, 25-31. *Journal of Advanced Nursing* 2006 January; 53(1): 113. Subject: 4.1.3

Tsioumanis, Assterios; Mattas, Konstadinos; Tsioumani, Elsa. The ugly curve — genetic screening into the 21st century. *In:* Árnason, Gardar; Nordal, Salvör; Árnason, Vilhjálmur, eds. Blood and Data: Ethical, Legal and Social Aspects of Human Genetic Databases. Reykjavík: University of Iceland Press; 2004: 263-268. Subject: 15.6

Tsolova, Svetla. Patients' rights in Bulgaria. *European Journal of Health Law* 2003 September; 10(3): 281-293. Subject: 8.3.1

Tsotsi, N.M.; Rudolph, M.J. Informed consent in oral health care. *East African Medical Journal* 2005 April; 82(4): 216-220. Subject: 8.3.1

Tsuchiya, Aki; Williams, Alan. A "fair innings" between the sexes: are men being treated inequitably? *Social Science and Medicine* 2005 January; 60(2): 277-286. Subject: 9.4

Tsyboulsky, Vadim B. Patients' rights in Russia. *European Journal of Health Law* 2001 September; 8(3): 257-263. Subject: 9.2

Tuch, Bernard E.; Scott, Hayley; Armati, Patricia J.; Tabiin, Muhammad T.; Wang, Liping P. Use of human fetal tissue for biomedical research in Australia, 1994-2002. *Medical Journal of Australia* 2003 November 17; 179(10): 547- 550. Subject: 18.5.4

Tucker, Andrew M. Ethics and the professional team physician. *Clinics in Sports Medicine* 2004 April; 23(2): 227-241. Subject: 9.5.1

Tucker, Diane C.; Acton, Ronald, T.; Press, Nancy; Ruggiero, Andrea; Reiss, Jacob A.; Walker, Ann P.; Wenzel, Lari; Harrison, Barbara; Fadojutimi-Akinsiku, Margaret; Harrison, Helen; Adams, Paul; Crabb, Jennifer A.; Anderson, Roger; Thomson, Elizabeth. Predictors of belief that genetic test information about hemochromatosis should be shared with family members. *Genetic Testing* 2006 Spring; 10(1): 50-59. Subject: 15.3

Tucker, Jonathan B.; Zilinskas, Raymond A. The promise and perils of synthetic biology. *New Atlantis* 2006 Spring; 12: 25-45. Subject: 5.3

Tucker, Philip. Good faith: in search of a unifying principle for the doctor-patient relationship. *Journal of Law and Medicine* 1998 May; 5(4): 372-391. Subject: 8.1

Tuckett, Anthony G. Residents' rights and nurses' ethics in the Australian nursing home. *International Nursing Review* 2005 September; 52(3): 219-224. Subject: 9.2

Tuech, Jean-Jacques; Moutel, Gregoire; Pessaux, Patrick; Thoma, Veronique; Schraub, Simon; Herve, Christian. Disclosure of competing financial interests and role of sponsors in phase III cancer trials. *European Journal of Cancer* 2005 October; 41(15): 2237-2240. Subject: 7.3

Tuffs, Annette. Germany will penalise cancer patients who do not undergo regular screening [news]. *BMJ: British Medical Journal* 2006 October 28; 333(7574): 877. Subject: 9.1

Tuffs, Annette. Sponsorship of patients' groups by drug companies should be made transparent [news]. *BMJ: British Medical Journal* 2006 December 16; 333(7581): 1238. Subject: 9.1

Tuite, Helen; Browne, Katherine; O'Neill, Desmond. Prisoners in general hospitals: doctors' attitudes and practice [letter]. *BMJ: British Medical Journal* 2006 March 4; 332(7540): 548-549. Subject: 9.5.1

Tulloch, Gail. A feminist utilitarian perspective on euthanasia: from Nancy Crick to Terri Schiavo. *Nursing Inquiry* 2005 June; 12(2): 155-160. Subject: 20.5.1

See SUBJECT HEADING KEY FOR SECTION II on inside back cover.

745

Tumber, M.B.; Dickersin, K. Publication of clinical trials: accountability and accessibility. *Journal of Internal Medicine* 2004 October; 256(4): 271-283. Subject: 18.2

Tuohey, John. Ethics consultation in Portland. *Health Progress* 2006 March-April; 87(2): 36-41. Subject: 9.6

Tupasela, Aaro. Locating tissue collections in tissue economies — deriving value from biomedical research. *New Genetics and Society* 2006 April; 25(1): 33-49. Subject: 15.10

Turiel, Judith Steinberg. End of life. *In her:* Our Parents, Ourselves: How American Health Care Imperils Middle Age and Beyond. Berkeley: University of California Press; 2005: 179-224. Subject: 20.5.1

Turiel, Judith Steinberg. Health-care rationing: taking it personally. *In her:* Our Parents, Ourselves: How American Health Care Imperils Middle Age and Beyond. Berkeley: University of California Press; 2005: 143-178. Subject: 9.4

Turkoski, Beatrice B. Home care and hospice ethics: using the code for nurses as a guide. *Home Healthcare Nurse* 2000 May; 18(5): 308-317. Subject: 4.1.3

Turner, D.D. Just another drug? A philosophical assessment of randomised controlled studies on intercessory prayer. *Journal of Medical Ethics* 2006 August; 32(8): 487-490. Subject: 18.1

Turner, Danielle; Sahakian, Barbara. The cognition-enhanced classroom. *In:* Miller, Paul; Wilsdon, James, eds. Better Humans?: The Politics of Human Enhancement and Life Extension. London: Demos, 2006: 79-85. Subject: 4.5

Turner, Danielle C.; Sahakian, Barbara J. Neuroethics of cognitive enhancement. *BioSocieties* 2006 March; 1(1): 113-123. Subject: 17.4

Turner, Trudy R. Commentary: data sharing and access to information. *In:* Turner, Trudy R. ed. Biological Anthropology and Ethics: From Repatriation to Genetic Identity. Albany, NY: State University of New York Press; 2005: 281-287. Subject: 15.1

Turner, Trudy R.; Nelson, Jeffrey D. Darkness in El Dorado: claims, counter-claims, and the obligations of researchers. *In:* Turner, Trudy R. ed. Biological Anthropology and Ethics: From Repatriation to Genetic Identity. Albany, NY: State University of New York Press; 2005: 165-183. Subject: 18.5.9

Turner, William B. Putting the contract into contractions: reproductive rights and the founding of the republic. *Wisconsin Law Review* 2005; 2005(6): 1535-1610. Subject: 14.1

Turney, Jon. More life. *In:* Miller, Paul; Wilsdon, James, eds. Better Humans?: The Politics of Human Enhancement and Life Extension. London: Demos, 2006: 95-103. Subject: 4.5

Turney, Lyn. Paternity secrets: why women don't tell. *Journal of Family Studies* 2005 October; 11(2): 227-248. Subject: 14.1

Turone, Fabio. Italian court upholds ban on pre-implantation diagnosis [news]. *BMJ: British Medical Journal* 2006 November 4; 333(7575): 934. Subject: 15.2

Turone, Fabio. Italy debates end of life decisions [news]. *BMJ: British Medical Journal* 2006 October 7; 333(7571): 719. Subject: 20.5.1

Twiss, Sumner B. On cross-cultural conflict and pediatric intervention [review of "Children, Ethics, and Modern Medicine" by Richard B. Miller]. *Journal of Religious Ethics* 2006 March; 34(1): 163-175. Subject: 9.5.7

Tyminski, Marie Ortman. The current state of advance directive law in Ohio: more protective of provider liability than patient rights. *Journal of Law and Health* 2004-2005; 19(2): 411-449. Subject: 20.5.4

Tyrer, Peter. Combating editorial racism in psychiatric publications [editorial]. *British Journal of Psychiatry* 2005 January; 186: 1-3. Subject: 1.3.7

Tyson, Jon E.; Stoll, Barbara J. Evidence-based ethics and the care and outcome of extremely premature infants. *Clinics in Perinatology* 2003 June; 30(2): 363-387. Subject: 9.5.7

Tzamalouka, Georgia S.; Papadakaki, Maria; Soultatou, Pelagia; Chatzifotiou, Sevasti; Tarlatzis, Basil; Chliaoutakis, Joannes El. Predicting human cloning acceptability: a national Greek survey on the beliefs of the public. *Journal of Assisted Reproduction and Genetics* 2005 October; 22(9-10): 315-322. Subject: 14.5

Tzamalouka, Georgia S.; Soultatou, Pelagia; Papadakaki, Maria; Chatzifotiou, Sevasti; Tarlatzis, Basil; Chliaoutakis, Joannes El. Identifying the public's knowledge and intention to use human cloning in Greek urban areas. *Journal of Assisted Reproduction and Genetics* 2005 February; 22(2): 47-56. Subject: 14.5

Tzeng, Huey-Ming; Yin, Chang-Yi. Comment. *Nursing Ethics* 2006 May; 13(3): 219-221. Subject: 8.1

Tzeng, Huey-Ming; Yin, Chang-Yi. Demands for religious care in the Taiwanese health system. *Nursing Ethics* 2006 March; 13(2): 163-179. Subject: 8.1

Tzeng, Huey-Ming; Yin, Chang-Yi. Nurses' fears and professional obligations concerning possible human-to-human avian flu. *Nursing Ethics* 2006 September; 13(5): 455-470. Subject: 8.1

U

Ubel, Peter A. Is information always a good thing? Helping patients make "good" decisions. *Medical Care* 2002 September; 40(9, Supplement): V39-V44. Subject: 8.3.1

Ubel, Peter A. Tough questions, even harder answers [editorial]. *JGIM: Journal of General Internal Medicine* 2006 November; 21(11): 1209-1210. Subject: 9.4

Subject = NRCBL Primary Classification Number; see inside front cover.

Ude-Koeller, Susanne; Müller, Luise; Wiesemann, Claudia. Junge oder Mädchen? Elternwunsch, Geschlechtswahl und geschlechtskorrigierende Operationen bei Kindern mit Störungen der Geschlechtsentwicklung = Girl or boy? — Parents' preferences, choice of sex, and sex reassignment surgery for children with disorders of sex development. *Ethik in der Medizin* 2006 March; 18(1): 63-70. Subject: 10

Ueki, Satoshi. Informed consent eine rechtsvergleichende betrachtung des arzthaftungsrechts. *Kansai University Review of Law and Politics* 1996 March; (17): 1-9. Subject: 8.3.1

Uhl, George R. Are over-simplified views of addiction neuroscience providing too simplified ethical considerations? *Addiction* 2003 July; 98(7): 872-873. Subject: 18.5.1

Ulmer, Nicholas C. Doctors and the death penalty: hippocratic and hypocritical? *Christianity and Crisis* 1981 April 13; 41: 109-119. Subject: 20.6

Ulrich, Hans G. Ethische Konflikte bei der Präimplantationsdiagnostik (Preimplantation-Genetic-Diagnosis). *In:* Vollmann, Jochen, ed. Medizin und Ethik: Aktuelle ethische Probleme in Therapie und Forschung. Erlangen: Universitätsbund Erlangen-Nürnberg, 2003: 31-59. Subject: 15.2

Um, Young-Rhan. Dispute over scientific research involving human embryos in South Korea. *In:* Sang-yong, Song; Young-Mo, Koo; Macer, Darryl R.J., eds. Asian Bioethics in the 21st Century. Christchurch, NZ: Eubios Ethics Institute, 2002: 56-57. Subject: 18.5.4

UNAIDS Reference Group on HIV/AIDS and Human Rights. Ensuring a rights-based approach to HIV testing. *Health and Human Rights: An International Journal* 2005; 8(2): 43-44. Subject: 9.5.6

Ungar, David; Joffe, Steven; Kodish, Eric. Children are not small adults: documentation of assent for research involving children. *Journal of Pediatrics* 2006 July; 149(1, Supplement): S31-33. Subject: 18.3

Union of American Hebrew Congregations. Committee on Bio-Ethics. Allocation of Scarce Medical Resources: Program Guide VII. New York, NY: Union of American Hebrew Congregations, 1994 Autumn; 61 p. Subject: 9.4

Union of American Hebrew Congregations. Committee on Bio-Ethics. Autonomy: My Right to Live or Die: Bioethics Program/Case Study: Case Study II. New York, NY: Union of American Hebrew Congregations, 1989 April; 30 p. Subject: 20.5.1

Union of American Hebrew Congregations. Committee on Bio-Ethics. Cloning: Bioethics Program/Case Study: Program Guide X. New York, NY: Union of American Hebrew Congregations, 1998 Summer; 66 p. Subject: 14.5

Union of American Hebrew Congregations. Committee on Bio-Ethics. Genetic Screening and the Human Genome Project: Bioethics Program/Case Study: Program Guide V. New York, NY: Union of American Hebrew Congregations, 1992 Spring; 35 p. Subject: 15.3

Union of American Hebrew Congregations. Committee on Bio-Ethics. Genetic Testing: Bioethics Study Guide XII. New York, NY: Union of American Hebrew Congregations, 2001; 70 p. Subject: 15.3

Union of American Hebrew Congregations. Committee on Bio-Ethics. Infertility and Assisted Reproduction: Bioethics Program/Case Study: Study Guide XI. New York, NY: Union of American Hebrew Congregations, 1999 Autumn; 95 p. Subject: 14.1

Union of American Hebrew Congregations. Committee on Bio-Ethics. The Living Will/Medical Directive: Bioethics Program/Case Study: Case Study IV. New York, NY: Union of American Hebrew Congregations, 1991 Winter; 41 p. Subject: 20.5.4

Union of American Hebrew Congregations. Committee on Bio-Ethics. The Role of Pain and Suffering in Decision Making: Bioethics Program/Case Study: Program Guide VIII. New York, NY: Union of American Hebrew Congregations, 1996 Winter; 38 p. Subject: 4.4

Union of American Hebrew Congregations. Committee on Bio-Ethics. Termination of Treatment: Bioethics Program Case Study: Case Study III. New York, NY: Union of American Hebrew Congregations, 1990 April; 28 p. Subject: 20.5.1

Union of American Hebrew Congregations. Committee on Bio-Ethics. A Time to Be Born: Bioethics Program/Case Study: Program Guide I. New York, NY: Union of American Hebrew Congregations, 1998 Fall: 35 p. Subject: 14.1

Union of American Hebrew Congregations. Committee on Bio-Ethics. Voluntary Active Euthanasia — Assisted Suicide: Bioethics Program/Case Study: Bio-Ethics Case VI. New York, NY: Union of American Hebrew Congregations, 1993 Summer; 47 p. Subject: 20.5.1

Union of American Hebrew Congregations. Committee on Bio-Ethics; United States. Health Resources and Services Administration (HRSA). Organ Donation and Transplantation: Bioethics Program/Case Study: Program Guide IX. New York, NY: Union of American Hebrew Congregations, 1997 Spring; 111 p. Subject: 19.1

United Kingdom. Department of Health. HSC 2000/028: resuscitation policy. London: Department of Health. Health Service Circular 2000 September: 2 p. [Online]. Accessed: http://www.dh.gov.uk/assetRoot/04/01/21/84/04012184.pdf [2006 October 3]. Subject: 20.5.1

United Kingdom. Department of Health. Chief Medical Officer's Expert Group Reviewing the Potential of Developments on Stem Cell Research and Cell Nuclear Replacement to Benefit Human Health. Stem cell re-

See SUBJECT HEADING KEY FOR SECTION II on inside back cover.

747

search: medical progress with responsibility: executive summary. *Cloning* 2000; 2(2): 91-96. Subject: 18.5.4

United Kingdom. Office of the Secretary of State for Health. Government response to the recommendations made in the Chief Medical Officer's Expert Group report: "Stem Cell Research: Medical Progress with Responsibility". *Cloning* 2000; 2(2): 97-100. Subject: 18.5.4

United Nations Educational, Scientific, and Cultural Organization [UNESCO]. Universal declaration on bioethics and human rights. *Bulletin of Medical Ethics* 2005 October-November; (211): 11-15. Subject: 2.1

United Nations Educational, Scientific, and Cultural Organization [UNESCO]. General Conference. Universal declaration on bioethics and human rights. *Revista de Derecho y Genoma Humano* 2005 July-December; (23): 227-237. Subject: 2.1

United Nations Educational, Scientific, and Cultural Organization [UNESCO]. International Bioethics Committee. Outline of a declaration on the human genome and its protection in relation to human dignity and human rights = El Borrador de Declaración sobre el genoma humano y su protección en relación con la dignidad humana y los derechos humanos. *Law and the Human Genome Review = Revista de Derecho y Genoma Humano* 1995 July-December; (3): 303-307. Subject: 15.10

United Nations. Expert group meeting on disability-sensitive policy and programme monitoring and evaluation; Avard, Denise. Human genetics research and practice: implications for people with disabilities. New York: United Nations Headquarters. Expert group meeting on disability-sensitive policy and programme monitoring and evaluation; 2002 January 14; 9 p. [Online]. Accessed: http://www.un.org/esa/socdev/enable/disid2001e.htm#top [2006 August 15]. Subject: 15.10

United Nations. Office of the High Commissioner for Human Rights. Principles of medical ethics relevant to the role of health personnel, particularly physicians, in the protection of prisoners and detainees against torture and other cruel, inhuman or degrading treatment or punishment. Geneva: United Nations Office of the High Commissioner for Human Rights, 1982 December 18: 2 p. [Online]. Accessed: http://www.ohchr.org/english/law/medicalethics.htm [2007 January 31]. Subject: 21.1

United States. Congress. An act for the relief of the parents of Theresa Marie Schiavo. Washington, DC: U.S. G.P.O., 2005. 2 p. [Online]. Accessed: http://frwebgate.access.gpo.gov/cgi-bin/getdoc.cgi?dbname=109_cong_public_laws& docid=f:publ003.109.pdf [2007 March 2]. Subject: 20.5.3

United States. Congress. An act to prohibit the procedure commonly known as partial-birth abortion. Washington, DC: U.S. G.P.O., 2003. 8 p. [Online]. Accessed: http://frwebgate.access.gpo.gov/cgi-bin/getdoc.cgi?

dbname=108_cong_public_laws&docid=f:publ105.108.pdf [2007 November 5]. Subject: 12.4.4

United States. Congress. An act to protect infants who are born alive. Washington, DC: U.S. G.P.O., 2002. 1 p. [Online]. Accessed: http://frwebgate.access.gpo.gov/cgi-bin/getdoc.cgi?dbname=107_cong_public_laws&docid=f:publ207.107.pdf[2007 March 2]. Subject: 12.4.4

United States. Congress. United States Leadership Against HIV/AIDS, Tuberculosis, and Malaria Act of 2003. [approved: 2003 May 27]. United States: Public Law 108-025 [HR 1298], 117 Stat. 2003 May 27: 711-750 [Online]. Accessed: http://frwebgate.access.gpo.gov/cgi- bin/getdoc/cgi?dbname=108_cong_public_laws&docid=f:publ025.108.pdf [2006 February 22]. Subject: 9.5.6

United States. Congress. House. A bill to amend the Controlled Substances Act to promote pain management and palliative care without permitting assisted suicide and euthanasia, and for other purposes. Washington, DC: U.S. G.P.O., 2000. 12 p. [Online]. Accessed: http://frwebgate.access.gpo.gov/cgi-bin/getdoc.cgi?dbname=106_cong_bills&docid= f:h5544ih.txt.pdf [2007 March 2]. Subject: 20.4.1

United States. Congress. House. A bill to amend the Federal Food, Drug, and Cosmetic Act to prohibit the approval of any drug that infringes the right to life, and for other purposes. Washington, DC: U.S. G.P.O., 2005. 2 p. [Online]. Accessed: http://frwebgate.access.gpo.gov/cgi-bin/getdoc.cgi?dbname=109_cong_bills&docid=f:h3553ih.txt.pdf [2006 June 7]. Subject: 9.7

United States. Congress. House. A bill to amend the Federal Food, Drug, and Cosmetic Act with respect to drug advertising, and for other purposes. Washington, DC: U.S. G.P.O., 2005. 9. [Online]. Accessed: http://frwebgate.access.gpo.gov/cgi-bin/useftp.cgi?IPaddress=162.140.64.21&filename=h3950ih.pdf&directory=/diskb/wais/data/109_cong_bills [2006 June 7]. Subject: 9.7

United States. Congress. House. A bill to amend the Internal Revenue Code of 1986 to allow tax credits to holders of stem cell research bonds. Washington, DC: U.S. G.P.O., 2005. 14 p. [Online]. Accessed: http://frwebgate.access.gpo.gov/cgi-bin/useftp.cgi?IPaddress=162.140.64.21&filename=h1650ih.pdf&directory=/diskb/wais/data/109_cong_bills [2006 May 6]. Subject: 18.5.4

United States. Congress. House. A bill to amend the Public Health Service Act to establish an independent office to be known as the Office for Protection of Human Research Subjects, and to assign to such Office responsibility for administering regulations regarding the protection of human subjects in Federal research projects. Washington, DC: U.S. G.P.O., 2000. 11 p. [Online]. Accessed: http://frwebgate.access.gpo.gov/cgi-bin/getdoc.cgi?dbname=106_cong_bills&docid= f:h3569ih.txt.pdf[2007 March 2]. Subject: 18.2

United States. Congress. House. A bill to amend the Public Health Service Act to prohibit health discrimination against individuals and their family members on the basis of genetic information, and for other purposes. Washington, DC: U.S. G.P.O., 2003. 7 p. [Online]. Accessed: http://frwebgate.access.gpo.gov/cgi-bin/useftp.cgi? IPaddress=162.140.64.21&filename=h3636ih.pdf& directory=/disk2/wais/data/108_cong_bills [2006 November 20]. Subject: 15.3

United States. Congress. House. A bill to amend the Public Health Service Act to prohibit the solicitation or acceptance of tissue from fetuses gestated for research purposes, and for other purposes. Washington, DC: U.S. G.P.O., 2006. 3 p. [Online]. Accessed: http://frwebgate.access. gpo.gov/cgi-bin/useftp.cgi?IPaddress=162.140.64.21&fil ename=h5719ih.pdf&directory=/diskb/wais/data/ 109_cong_bills [2006 December 4]. Subject: 18.5.4

United States. Congress. House. A bill to amend the Public Health Service Act to provide for a program at the National Institutes of Health to conduct and support research in the derivation and use of human pluripotent stem cells by means that do not harm human embryos, and for other purposes. Washington, DC: U.S. G.P.O., 2005. 5 p. [Online]. Accessed: http://frwebgate.access.gpo.gov/cgi-bin/ useftp.cgi?IPaddress=162.140.64.21&filename= h3144ih.pdf&directory=/diskb/wais/data/109_cong_bills [2006 May 10]. Subject: 18.5.4

United States. Congress. House. A bill to amend the Public Health Service Act to provide for human embryonic stem cell research. Washington, DC: U.S. G.P.O., 2005. 4 p. [Online]. Accessed: http//frwebgate.access.gpo/cgi-bin/ useftp.cgi?IPaddress=162.140.64.21&filename= h810ih.pdf&directory=/diskb/wais/data/109_cong_bills [2006 May 10]. Subject: 18.5.4

United States. Congress. House. A bill to amend the Public Health Service Act with respect to the protection of human subjects in research. Washington, DC: U.S. G.P.O., 2000. 35 p. [Online]. Accessed: http://frwebgate.access. gpo.gov/cgi-bin/getdoc.cgi?dbname=106_cong_bills& docid= f:h4605ih.txt.pdf [2007 March 2]. Subject: 18.2

United States. Congress. House. A bill to amend the Public Health Service Act with respect to the protection of human subjects in research. Washington, DC: U.S. G.P.O., 2006. 35 p. [Online]. Accessed: http://frwebgate.access. gpo.gov/cgi-bin/useftp.cgi?IPaddress=162.140.64.21& filename=h5578ih.pdf&directory=/diskb/wais/data/ 109_cong_bills [2006 July 17]. Subject: 18.2

United States. Congress. House. A bill to amend title 18, United States Code, and the Uniform Code of Military Justice to protect unborn children from assault and murder, and for other purposes. Washington, DC: U.S. G.P.O., 2001. 7 p. [Online]. Accessed: http://frwebgate.access. gpo.gov/cgi-bin/getdoc.cgi?dbname=107_cong_bills& docid= f:h503ih.txt.pdf [2007 March 2]. Subject: 4.4

United States. Congress. House. A bill to amend title 18, United States Code, to prevent the transportation of minors in circumvention of certain laws relating to abortion.

Washington, DC: U.S. G.P.O., 2005. 10 p. [Online]. Accessed: http://frwebgate.access.gpo.gov/cgi-bin/useftp. cgi?IPaddress=162.140.64.21&filename=h748ih.p df& directory=/diskb/wais/data/109_cong_bills [2006 July 24]. Subject: 12.4.2

United States. Congress. House. A bill to amend title 18, United States Code, to prohibit human cloning. Washington, DC: U.S. G.P.O., 2003. 5 p. [Online]. Accessed: http://frwebgate.access.gpo.gov/cgi-bin/getdoc.cgi? dbname=108_cong_bills&docid= f:h234ih.txt. pdf [2007 March 8]. Subject: 14.5

United States. Congress. House. A bill to authorize the use of Federal funds for research on human embryonic stem cells irrespective of the date on which such stem cells were derived, and for other purposes. Washington, DC: U.S. G.P.O., 2005. 4 p. [Online]. Accessed: http://frwebgate.access.gpo.gov/cgi-bin/useftp.cgi? IPaddress=162.140.64.21&filename=h162ih.pdf& directory=/diskb/wais/data/109_cong_bills [2006 June 7]. Subject: 18.5.4

United States. Congress. House. A bill to derive human pluripotent stem cell lines using techniques that do not knowingly harm embryos. Washington, DC: U.S. G.P.O., 2006. 4 p. [Online]. Accessed: http://frwebgate.access. gpo.gov/cgi-bin/useftp.cgi?IPaddress=162.140.64.21& filename=h5526ih.pdf&directory=/diskb/wais/data/ 109_cong_bills [2006 December 14]. Subject: 18.5.4

United States. Congress. House. A bill to ensure that women seeking an abortion are fully informed regarding the pain experienced by their unborn child. Washington, DC: U.S. G.P.O., 2006. 23 p. [Online]. Accessed: http://frwebgate.access.gpo.gov/cgi-bin/useftp.cgi? IPaddress=162.140.64.21&filename=h6099ih.pdf&di rectory=/diskb/wais/data/109_cong_bills [2006 November 20]. Subject: 12.4.2

United States. Congress. House. A bill to establish limitations with respect to disclosure and use of genetic information, and for other purposes. Washington, DC: U.S. G.P.O.; 1997. 8 p. [Online]. Accessed: http://frwebgate.access. gpo.gov/cgi-bin/useftp.cgi?IPaddress=162.140.64.122& filename=h341ih.pdf&directory=/diskc/wais/data/ 105_cong_bills [2007 March 5]. Subject: 15.1

United States. Congress. House. A bill to establish limitations with respect to disclosure and use of genetic information in connection with group health plans and health insurance coverage, to provide for consistent standards applicable in connection with hospital care and medical services provided under title 38 of the United States Code, to prohibit employment discrimination on the basis of genetic information and genetic testing, and for other purposes. Washington, DC: U.S. G.P.O.; 1998. 22 p. [Online]. Accessed: http://frwebgate.access.gpo.gov/cgi-bin/useftp. cgi?IPaddress=162.140.64.122&filename=h3299ih. pdf&directory=/diskc/wais/data/105_cong_bills [2007 March 6]. Subject: 15.1

See SUBJECT HEADING KEY FOR SECTION II on inside back cover.

749

United States. Congress. House. A bill to prevent abusive practices by pharmaceutical benefit managers (PBMs). Washington, DC: U.S. G.P.O., 2006. 2 p. [Online]. Accessed: http://frwebgate.access.gpo.gov/cgi-bin/useftp.cgi?IPaddress=162.140.64.21&filename=h5979ih.pdf&directory=/diskb/wais/data/109_cong_bills [2006 November 27]. Subject: 9.7

United States. Congress. House. A bill to prohibit certain abortions. Washington, DC: U.S. G.P.O., 2005. 2 p. [Online]. Accessed: http://frwebgate.access.gpo.gov/cgi-bin/useftp.cgi?IPaddress=162.140.64.21&filename=h3746ih.pdf&directory=/diskb/wais/data/109_cong_bills [2006 June 7]. Subject: 12.4.2

United States. Congress. House. A bill to prohibit discrimination by group health plans and employers based on genetic information. Washington, DC: U.S. G.P.O., 2006. 10 p. [Online]. Accessed: http://frwebgate.access.gpo.gov/cgi-bin/useftp.cgi?IPaddress=162.140.64.21&filename=h6125ih.pdf&directory=/diskb/wais/data/109_cong_bills [2006 November 1]. Subject: 15.3

United States. Congress. House. A bill to prohibit discrimination on the basis of genetic information with respect to health insurance. Washington, DC: U.S. G.P.O., 2001. 69 p. [Online]. Accessed: http://frwebgate.access.gpo.gov/cgi-bin/getdoc.cgi?dbname=107_cong_bills&docid= f:h602ih.txt. pdf [2007 March 8]. Subject: 15.3

United States. Congress. House. A bill to prohibit discrimination on the basis of genetic information with respect to health insurance. Washington, DC: U.S. G.P.O., 2003, 75 p. [Online]. Accessed: http://frwebgate.access.gpo.gov/cgi-bin/useftp.cgi?IPaddress=162.140.64.21&filename=h1910ih.pdf&directory=/disk2/wais/data/108_cong_bills [2006 November 27]. Subject: 15.3

United States. Congress. House. A bill to prohibit discrimination on the basis of genetic information with respect to health insurance and employment. Washington, DC: U.S. G.P.O., 2005. 81 p. [Online]. Accessed: http://frwebgate.access.gpo.gov/cgi-bin/useftp.cgi?IPaddress=162.140.64.21&filename=h1227ih.pdf&directory=/diskb/wais/data/109_cong_bills [2006 December 6]. Subject: 15.3

United States. Congress. House. A bill to prohibit health insurance and employment discrimination against individuals and their family members on the basis of predictive genetic information or genetic services. Washington, DC: U.S. G.P.O., 1999. 70 p. [Online]. Accessed: http://frwebgate.access.gpo.gov/cgi-bin/getdoc.cgi?dbname=106_cong_bills&docid= f:h2457ih.txt.pdf [2007 March 8]. Subject: 15.3

United States. Congress. House. A bill to prohibit human cloning. Washington, DC: U.S. G.P.O., 2005. 4 p. [Online]. Accessed: http://frwebgate.access.gpo.gov/cgi-bin/useftp.cgi?IPaddress=162.140.64.21&filename=

h3932ih.pdf&directory=/diskb/wais/data/109_cong_bills [2006 November 21]. Subject: 14.5

United States. Congress. House. A bill to prohibit human cloning and protect stem cell research. Washington, DC: U.S. G.P.O., 2005. 11 p. [Online]. Accessed: http://frwebgate.access.gpo.gov/cgi-bin/useftp.cgi?IPaddress=162.140.64.21&filename=h1822ih.pdf&directory=/diskb/wais/data/109_cong_bills [2006 May 10]. Subject: 14.5

United States. Congress. House. A bill to promote safe and ethical clinical trials of drugs and other test articles on people overseas. Washington, DC: U.S. G.P.O., 2006. 11 p. [Online]. Accessed: http://frwebgate.access.gpo.gov/cgi-bin/useftp.cgi?IPaddress=162.140.64.21&filename=h5641ih.pdf&directory=/diskb/wais/data/109_cong_bills [2006 July 17]. Subject: 18.5.9

United States. Congress. House. A bill to protect the privacy of health information in the age of genetic and other new technologies, and for other purposes. Washington, DC: U.S. G.P.O., 1999. 73 p. [Online]. Accessed: http://frwebgate.access.gpo.gov/cgi-bin/getdoc.cgi?dbname=106_cong_bills&docid= f:h2878ih.txt.pdf [2007 March 8]. Subject: 8.4

United States. Congress. House. A bill to provide for programs that reduce the need for abortion, help women bear healthy children, and support new parents. Washington, DC: U.S. G.P.O., 2006. 46 p. [Online]. Accessed: http://frwebgate.access.gpo.gov/cgi-bin/useftp.cgi?IPaddress=162.140.64.21&file name=h6145ih.pdf&directory=/diskb/wais/data/109_cong_bills [2006 December 05]. Subject: 9.5.5

United States. Congress. House. A bill to provide for the provision by hospitals of emergency contraceptives to women who are survivors of sexual assault. Washington, DC: U.S. G.P.O., 2005. 7 p. [Online]. Accessed: http://frwebgate.access.gpo.gov/cgi-bin/useftp.cgi?IPaddress=162.140.64.21&file name=h2928ih.pdf&directory=/diskb/wais/data/109_cong_bills [2006 November 27]. Subject: 11.1

United States. Congress. House. A bill to provide individuals with access to health information of which they are a subject, ensure personal privacy with respect to health-care-related information , impose criminal and civil penalties for unauthorized use of protected health information , to provide for the strong enforcement of these rights, and to protect States' rights. Washington, DC: U.S. G.P.O., 1999. 81 p. [Online]. Accessed: http://frwebgate.access.gpo.gov/cgi-bin/getdoc.cgi?dbname=106_cong_bills&docid= f:h1057ih.txt.pdf [2007 March 2]. Subject: 8.4

United States. Congress. House. A bill to provide that human life shall be deemed to exist from conception. Washington, DC: U.S. G.P.O., 2005. 4 p. [Online]. Accessed: http://frwebgate.access.gpo.gov/cgi-bin/useftp.cgi?IPaddress=162.140.64.21&file name=h776ih.pdf&

Subject = NRCBL Primary Classification Number; see inside front cover.

directory=/diskb/wais/data/109_cong_bills [2006 November 27]. Subject: 4.4

United States. Congress. House. A bill to provide the Department of Justice the necessary authority to apprehend, prosecute, and convict individuals committing animal enterprise terror. 109th Congress, 1st Session, H.R. 4239. Introduced by Mr. Petri on 2005 November 4. Referred to the Committee on the Judiciary; 7p. Subject: 22.2

United States. Congress. House. A bill to require the Commissioner of Food and Drugs to determine whether to allow the marketing of Plan B as a prescription drug for women 15 years of age or younger and a nonprescription drug for women 16 years of age or older. Washington, DC: U.S. G.P.O., 2005. 7 p. [Online]. Accessed: http://frwebgate.access.gpo.gov/cgi-bin/useftp.cgi?IPaddress=162.140.64.21&filename=h4229ih.pdf&directory=/diskb/wais/data/109_cong_bills [2006 November 21]. Subject: 11.1

United States. Congress. House. A bill to suspend further implementation of the Department of Defense anthrax vaccination program until the vaccine is determined to be safe and effective and to provide for a study by the National Institutes of Health of that vaccine. Washington, DC: U.S. G.P.O., 1999. 8 p. [Online]. Accessed: http://frwebgate.access.gpo.gov/cgi-bin/getdoc.cgi?dbname=106_cong_bills&docid= f:h2548ih.txt.pdf [2007 March 2]. Subject: 9.7

United States. Congress. House. A bill to provide for parental notification and intervention in the case of a minor seeking an abortion. Washington, DC: U.S. G.P.O., 2005. 4 p. [Online]. Accessed: http://frwebgate.access.gpo.gov/cgi-bin/getdoc.cgi?dbname=109_cong_bills&docid = f:h2971ih.txt.pdf [2006 June 7]. Subject: 12.4.2

United States. Congress. House. A bill to require prescription drug manufacturers, packers, and distributors to disclose certain gifts provided in connection with detailing, promotional, or other marketing activities, and for other purposes. Washington, DC: U.S. G.P.O., 2006. 5 p. [Online]. Accessed: http://frwebgate.access.gpo.gov/cgi-bin/useftp.cgi?IPaddress=162.140.64.21&filename=h4718ih.pdf&directory=/diskb/wais/data/109_cong_bills [2006 June 7]. Subject: 9.7

United States. Congress. Senate. An act to amend the Federal Food, Drug, and Cosmetics Act to authorize the Food and Drug Administration to require certain research into drugs used in pediatric patients. Washington, DC: U.S. G.P.O., 2003. 22 p. [Online]. Accessed: http://frwebgate.access.gpo.gov/cgi-bin/useftp.cgi?IPaddress=162.140.64.21&filename=s650es.pdf&directory=/disk2/wais/data/108_cong_bills [2006 December 15]. Subject: 18.5.2

United States. Congress. Senate. An act to amend title 18, United States Code, to prohibit taking minors across State lines in circumvention of laws requiring the involvement of parents in abortion decisions. Washington, DC: U.S.

G.P.O., 2006. 6 p. [Online]. Accessed: http://frwebgate.access.gpo.gov/cgi-bin/useftp.cgi?IPaddress=162.140.64.21&filename=s403es.pdf&directory=/diskb/wais/data/109_cong_bills [2006 July 25]. Subject: 12.4.2

United States. Congress. Senate. An act to prohibit discrimination on the basis of genetic information with respect to health insurance and employment. Washington, DC: U.S. G.P.O., 2003. 86 p. [Online]. Accessed: http://frwebgate.access.gpo.gov/cgi-bin/useftp.cgi?IPaddress=162.140.64.21&filename=s1053es.pdf&directory=/disk2/wais/data/108_cong_bills [2006 November 27]. Subject: 15.3

United States. Congress. Senate. A bill to amend the Federal Food, Drug, and Cosmetic Act to create a new three-tiered approval system for drugs, biological products, and devices that is responsive to the needs of seriously ill patients, and for other purposes. Washington, DC: U.S. G.P.O., 2005. 24 p. [Online]. Accessed: http://frwebgate.access.gpo.gov/cgi-bin/useftp.cgi?IPaddress=162.140.64.21&filename=s1956is.pdf&directory=/diskb/wais/data/109_cong_bills [2006 November 21]. Subject: 5.3

United States. Congress. Senate. A bill to amend the Public Health Service Act to improve the health and healthcare of racial and ethnic minority and other health disparity populations. Washington, DC: U.S. G.P.O., 2006. 131 p. [Online]. Accessed: http://frwebgate.access.gpo.gov/cgi-bin/useftp.cgi?IPaddress=162.140.64.21& filename=s4024is.pdf&directory=/diskb/wais/data/109_cong_bills [2006 December 5]. Subject: 9.5.4

United States. Congress. Senate. A bill to amend the Public Health Service Act to prohibit human cloning. Washington, DC: U.S. G.P.O., 2003. 5 p. [Online]. Accessed: http://frwebgate.access.gpo.gov/cgi-bin/getdoc.cgi?dbname=108_cong_bills&docid=f:s245is.txt. pdf [2007 March 8]. Subject: 14.5

United States. Congress. Senate. A bill to amend the Public Health Service Act to prohibit the solicitation or acceptance of tissue from fetuses gestated for research purposes, and for other purposes. Washington, DC: U.S. G.P.O., 2006. 3 p. [Online]. Available http://frwebgate.access.gpo.gov/cgi-bin/useftp.cgi?IPaddress=162.140.64.21&filename=s3504is.pdf&directory=/diskb/wais/data/109_cong_bills [2006 July 17]. Subject: 4.4

United States. Congress. Senate. A bill to amend the Public Health Service Act to provide for human embryonic stem cell research. Washington, DC: U.S. G.P.O., 2005. 3 p. [Online]. Accessed: http://frwebgate.access.gpo.gov/cgi-bin/useftp.cgi?IPaddress=162.140.64.88&filename=s471is.pdf&directory=/diskb/wais/data/109_cong_bills [2006 May 10]. Subject: 18.5.4

United States. Congress. Senate. A bill to amend Title 18, United States Code, to prohibit human chimeras. Washington, DC: U.S. G.P.O., 2005. 5 p. [Online]. Accessed: http://frwebgate.access.gpo.gov/cgi-bin/getdoc.cgi?

See SUBJECT HEADING KEY FOR SECTION II on inside back cover.

751

dbname=109_cong_bills&docid= f:s659is.txt.pdf [2006 April 28]. Subject: 15.1

United States. Congress. Senate. A bill to amend title 18, United States Code, to prohibit taking minors across State lines in circumvention of laws requiring the involvement of parents in abortion decisions. Washington, DC: U.S. G.P.O., 2005. 5 p. [Online]. Accessed: http://frwebgate. access.gpo.gov/cgi-bin/useftp.cgi?IPaddress=162.140. 64.21&filename=s403pcs.pdf&directory=/diskb/wais/ data/109_cong_bills [2006 July 17]. Subject: 12.4.2

United States. Congress. Senate. A bill to amend titles 10 and 18, United States Code, to protect unborn victims of violence. Washington, DC: U.S. G.P.O., 2001. 7 p. [Online]. Accessed: http://frwebgate.access.gpo.gov/cgi-bin/ getdoc.cgi?dbname=107_cong_bills&docid= f:s480is.txt.pdf [2007 March 2]. Subject: 4.4

United States. Congress. Senate. A bill to ban human cloning while protecting stem cell research. Washington, DC: U.S. G.P.O., 2002. 3 p. [Online]. Accessed: http://frwebgate.access.gpo.gov/cgi-bin/getdoc.cgi? dbname=107_cong_bills&docid= f:s1893is.tx t.pdf [2007 March 8]. Subject: 14.5

United States. Congress. Senate. A bill to clarify Federal law to prohibit the dispensing, distribution, or administration of a controlled substance for the purpose of causing, or assisting in causing, the suicide, euthanasia, or mercy killing of any individual. Washington, DC: U.S. G.P.O., 2006. 5 p. [Online]. Accessed: http://frwebgate.access. gpo.gov/cgi-bin/useftp.cgi?IPaddress=162.140.64.21& filename=s3788is.pdf&directory=/diskb/wais/data/ 109_cong_bills. Subject: 20.7

United States. Congress. Senate. A bill to derive human pluripotent stem cells using techniques that do not knowingly harm embryos. Washington, DC: U.S. G.P.O., 2006. 4 p. [Online]. Available http://frwebgate.access. gpo.gov/cgi-bin/useftp.cgi?IPaddress=162.140.64.21& filename=s2754is.pdf&directory=/diskb/wais/data/ 109_cong_bills [2006 July 17]. Subject: 18.5.4

United States. Congress. Senate. A bill to ensure that women seeking an abortion are fully informed regarding the pain experienced by their unborn child. Washington, DC: U.S. G.P.O., 2005. 21 p. [Online]. Accessed: http:// frwebgate.access.gpo.gov/cgi-bin/useftp.cgi? IPaddress=162.140.64.21&filename=s51is.pdf& directory=/diskb/wais/data/109_cong_bills [2006 May 8]. Subject: 12.4.2

United States. Congress. Senate. A bill to establish certain duties for pharmacies when pharmacists employed by the pharmacies refuse to fill valid prescriptions for drugs or devices on the basis of personal beliefs, and for other purposes. Washington, DC: U.S. G.P.O., 2005. 7 p. [Online]. Accessed: http://frwebgate.access.gpo.gov/cgi-bin/ useftp.cgi?IPaddress=162.140.64.21&filename= s809is.pdf&directory=/diskb/wais/data/109_cong_bills [2006 November 21]. Subject: 9.7

United States. Congress. Senate. A bill to improve access to and appropriate utilization of valid, reliable and accurate molecular genetic tests by all populations thus helping to secure the promise of personalized medicine for all Americans. Washington, DC: U.S. G.P.O., 2006. 43 p. [Online]. Accessed: http://frwebgate.access.gpo.gov/cgi-bin/ getdoc.cgi?dbname=109_cong_bills&docid= f:s3822is.txt.pdf [2006 July 17]. Subject: 15.1

United States. Congress. Senate. A bill to prohibit discrimination on the basis of genetic information with respect to health insurance. Washington, DC: U.S. G.P.O., 1999. 27 p. [Online]. Accessed: http://frwebgate.access. gpo.gov/cgi-bin/getdoc.cgi?dbname=106_cong_bills& docid= f:s543is.txt. pdf [2007 March 8]. Subject: 15.1

United States. Congress. Senate. A bill to prohibit discrimination on the basis of genetic information with respect to health insurance. Washington, DC: U.S. G.P.O.; 2001. 28 p. [Online]. Accessed: http://frwebgate.access. gpo.gov/cgi-bin/useftp.cgi?IPaddress=162.140.64.31& filename=s382is.pdf&directory=/disk2/wais/data/ 107_cong_bills [2007 March 6]. Subject: 15.1

United States. Congress. Senate. A bill to prohibit discrimination on the basis of genetic information with respect to health insurance and employment. Washington, DC: U.S. G.P.O., 2001. 73 p. [Online]. Accessed: http:// frwebgate.access.gpo.gov/cgi-bin/getdoc.cgi? dbname=107_cong_bills&docid= f:s318is.txt. pdf [2007 March 8]. Subject: 15.1

United States. Congress. Senate. A bill to prohibit discrimination on the basis of genetic information with respect to health insurance and employment. Washington, DC: U.S. G.P.O., 2002. 45 p. [Online]. Accessed: http:// frwebgate.access.gpo.gov/cgi-bin/getdoc.cgi? dbname=107_cong_bills&docid= f:s1995is.tx t.pdf [2007 March 8]. Subject: 15.1

United States. Congress. Senate. A bill to prohibit discrimination on the basis of genetic information with respect to health insurance and employment. Washington, DC: U.S. G.P.O., 2005. 85 p. [Online]. Accessed: http:// frwebgate.access.gpo.gov/cgi-bin/useftp.cgi? IPaddress=162.140.64.21&file name=s306es.pdf& directory=/diskb/wais/data/109_cong_bills. Subject: 15.3

United States. Congress. Senate. A bill to prohibit health insurance and employment discrimination against individuals and their family members on the basis of predictive genetic information or genetic services. Washington, DC: U.S. G.P.O., 1999. 70 p. [Online]. Accessed: http:// frwebgate.access.gpo.gov/cgi-bin/getdoc.cgi? dbname=106_cong_bills&docid= f:s1322is.tx t.pdf [2007 March 8]. Subject: 15.1

United States. Congress. Senate. A bill to prohibit human cloning. Washington, DC: U.S. G.P.O., 2005. 4 p. [Online]. Accessed: http://frwebgate.access.gpo.gov/cgi-bin/ useftp.cgi?IPaddress=162.140.64.21&file name=

Subject = NRCBL Primary Classification Number; see inside front cover.

s1520is.pdf&directory=/diskb/wais/data/109_cong_bills [2006 November 21]. Subject: 14.5

United States. Congress. Senate. A bill to prohibit human cloning and protect stem cell research. Washington, DC: U.S. G.P.O., 2003. 11 p. [Online]. Accessed: http://frwebgate.access.gpo.gov/cgi-bin/getdoc.cgi?dbname=108_cong_bills&docid= f:s303is.txt.pdf [2007 March 8]. Subject: 14.5

United States. Congress. Senate. A bill to prohibit human cloning and protect stem cell research. Washington, DC: U.S. G.P.O., 2005. 11 p. [Online]. Accessed: http://frwebgate.access.gpo.gov/cgi-bin/useftp.cgi?IPaddress=162.140.64.21&file name=s876is.pdf&directory=/diskb/wais/data/109_cong_bills [2006 May 10]. Subject: 14.5

United States. Congress. Senate. A bill to promote pain management and palliative care without permitting assisted suicide and euthanasia, and for other purposes. Washington, DC: U.S. G.P.O., 2000. 12 p. [Online]. Accessed: http://frwebgate.access.gpo.gov/cgi-bin/getdoc.cgi?dbname=106_cong_bills&docid= f:s2607is.txt.pdf [2007 March 02]. Subject: 20.4.1

United States. Congress. Senate. A bill to protect, consistent with Roe v. Wade, a woman's freedom to choose to bear a child or terminate a pregnancy, and for other purposes. Washington, DC: U.S. G.P.O., 2006. 8 p. [Online]. Accessed: http://frwebgate.access.gpo.gov/cgi-bin/getdoc.cgi?dbname=109_cong_bills&docid=f:s2593is.txt.pdf [2006 June 7]. Subject: 12.4.2

United States. Congress. Senate. A bill to protect the genetic privacy of individuals, and for other purposes. Washington, DC: U.S. G.P.O., 1996. 42 p. [Online]. Accessed: http://frwebgate.access.gpo.gov/cgi-bin/getdoc.cgi?dbname=104_cong_bills&docid=f:s1898is.txt.pdf [2007 March 8]. Subject: 15.1

United States. Congress. Senate. A bill to provide individuals with access to health information of which they are a subject, ensure personal privacy with respect to health-care-related information, impose criminal and civil penalties for unauthorized use of protected health information, to provide for the strong enforcement of these rights, and to protect State's rights. Washington, DC: U.S. G.P.O., 1999. 81 p. [Online]. Accessed: http://frwebgate.access.gpo.gov/cgi-bin/getdoc.cgi?dbname=106_cong_bills&docid= f:s573is.txt.pdf [2007 March 2]. Subject: 8.4

United States. Congress. Senate. A bill to provide individuals with access to health information of which they are the subject, ensure personal privacy with respect to personal medical records and health care-related information, impose criminal and civil penalties for unauthorized use of personal health information, and to provide for the strong enforcement of these rights. Washington, DC: U.S. G.P.O., 1997. 78 p. [Online]. Accessed: http://frwebgate.access.gpo.gov/cgi-bin/getdoc.cgi?dbname=105_cong_bills&docid= f:s1368is.txt.pdf [2007 March 2]. Subject: 8.4

United States. Congress. Senate. Expressing the sense of the Senate concerning Griswold v. Connecticut. Washington, DC: U.S. G.P.O., 2005. 4 p. [Online]. Accessed: http://frwebgate.access.gpo.gov/cgi-bin/useftp.cgi?IPaddress=162.140.64.21&file name=sr162is.pdf&directory=/diskb/wais/data/109_cong_bills [2006 June 7]. Subject: 11.1

United States. Court of Appeals. First Circuit. Abbott v. Bragdon [Date of Decision: 1997 March 5]. *Federal Reporter*, 3d Series 1997; 107: 934-949. Subject: 9.5.6

United States. Court of Appeals. Ninth Circuit. Planned Parenthood of Idaho v. Wasden [Date of Decision: 2004 July 16]. *Federal Reporter*, 3d Series, 2004; 376: 908-944. Subject: 12.4.4

United States. Department of Education. Protection of human subjects; final regulations. *Federal Register* 1997 November 26; 62(228): 63219-63222 [Online] Accessed: http://frwebgate.access.gpo.gov/cgi-bin/multidb.cgi [2005 December 27]. Subject: 18.5.2

United States. Department of Health and Human Services [DHHS]. Health and Human Services Policy for Protection of Human Subjects Research — HHS Final Rule. *Federal Register* 1994 June 1; 59(104): 28276. Subject: 18.6

United States. Department of Health and Human Services [DHHS]. Protection of human research subjects: delay of effective date. *Federal Register* 2001 May 18; 66(97): 27599 [Online]. Accessed: http://frwebgate.access.gpo. gov/cgi-bin/multidb.cgi [2005 December 27]. Subject: 18.6

United States. Department of Health and Human Services [DHHS] [and] National Science Foundation [NSF] (United States) [and] United States. Department of Transportation [DOT]. Federal policy for the protection of human subjects; final rule; technical amendments. *Federal Register* 2005 June 23; 70(120): 36325-36328 [Online] Accessed: http://frwebgate.access.gov.gpo/cgi-bin/multidb.cgi [2005 December 28]. Subject: 18.6

United States. Department of Health and Human Services [DHHS]. Center for Mental Health Service, Substance Abuse and Mental Health Services Administration. Substance Abuse and Mental Health Services Administration; requirements applicable to protection and advocacy of individuals with mental illness; final rule. *Federal Register* 1997 October 15; 62(199): 53548-53571. [Online]. Accessed: http://frwebgate.access.gpo.gov/cgi-bin/ multidb.cgi [2005 December 28]. Subject: 17.1

United States. Department of Health and Human Services [DHHS]. Indian Health Service [IHS]. Indian Health Service multiple project assurance (mpa) for compliance with DHHS regulations for the protection of human subjects (45 CFR 46) as amended. Rockville, MD: Indian Health Service; 24 pages [Online]. Accessed:

See SUBJECT HEADING KEY FOR SECTION II on inside back cover.

753

http://www.ihs.gov/medicalprograms/research/pdf%5F
files/mpa%2Dihs2. pdf [2006 January 6]. Subject: 18.5.1

United States. Department of Health and Human Services [DHHS]. Office of the Secretary. Exemption of Certain Research and Demonstration Projects From Regulations for Protection of Human Research Subjects: Final Rule. *Federal Register* 1983 March 4; 48(44): 9266-9270. Subject: 18.6

United States. Department of Health and Human Services [DHHS]. Office of the Secretary. Protection of Human Subjects; Compensating for Research Injuries; Request for Comments on Report of the President's Commission for the Study of Ethical Problems in Medicine and Biomedical and Behavioral Research. *Federal Register* 1982 November 23; 47(226): 52880-52930. Subject: 18.1

United States. Department of Health and Human Services [DHHS]. Food and Drug Administration [FDA]. Human cells, tissues, and cellular and tissue-based products; establishment registration and listing. *Federal Register* 2001 January 19; 66(13): 5447-5469 [Online] Accessed: http://frwebgate.access.gpo.gov/cgi-bin/getdoc.cgi?dbname=2001_register&docid=01-1126-filed.pdf [2006 September 6]. Subject: 19.5

United States. Department of Veterans Affairs. Medical: advance health care planning. Final rule. *Federal Register* 2005 November 30; 70(229): 71772-71774. Subject: 20.5.4

United States. District Court, District of Maine. Bragdon v. Abbott [Date of Decision: 22 December 1995]. *Federal Supplement* 1995; 912: 580-596. Subject: 9.5.6

United States. District Court, Middle District of Tennessee. Craft v. Vanderbilt University [Date of Decision: 19 August 1998]. *Federal Supplement*, 2d Series, 1998; 18: 786-798. Subject: 18.5.3

United States. Environmental Protection Agency [EPA]. Human testing; advance notice of proposed rulemaking. *Federal Register* 2003 May 2; 68(88): 24410-24416 [Online]. Accessed: http://frwebgate.access.gpo.gov/cgi-bin/ multidb.cgi [2005 December 27]. Subject: 18.6

United States. Food and Drug Administration [FDA]. Protection of human subjects. *Federal Register* 2000 December 27; 65(249): 81739 [Online]. Accessed: http://frwebgate.access.gpo.gov/cgi-bin/multidb.cgi [2005 December 27]. Subject: 18.6

United States. Food and Drug Administration [FDA]. Protection of human subjects; informed consent verification. *Federal Register* 1996 November 5; 61(215): 57278-57280 [Online] Accessed: http://frwebgate.access.gpo.gov/cgi-bin/multidb.cgi [12 December 2005]. Subject: 18.3

United States. Food and Drug Administration [FDA]. Protection of human subjects; informed consent; technical amendment. *Federal Register* 1999 March 8; 64(44): 10942-10943 [Online] Accessed: http://frwebgate.access.gpo.gov/cgi-bin/multidb.cgi [27 December 2005]. Subject: 18.3

United States. Food and Drug Administration [FDA]. Guidance for institutional review boards, clinical investigations, and sponsors: exception from informed consent requirements for emergency research: draft guidance. Rockville, MD: Food and Drug Administration, 2006 July; 26 p. [Online]. Accessed: http://www.fda.gov/OHRMS/DOCKETS/98fr/06d-0331-gdl0001.pdf [2006 September 1]. Subject: 18.3

United States. Government Accountability Office [GAO]; Kutz, Gregory. Nutrigenetic Testing: Tests Purchased from Four Web sites Mislead Consumers. Testimony before the Special Committee on Aging, U.S. Senate. Statement of Gregory Kutz, Managing Director Forensic Audits and Special Investigations. Washington, DC: Government Accountability Office [GAO], 2006 July 27; 23 p. [Online]. Accessed: http://www.gao.gov/cgi-bin/getrpt?GAO-06-977T [2006 August 3]. Subject: 15.3

United States. *Laws, statutes, etc.* Chemical and biological warfare program. Reports to Congress. United States Code 1994; Title 50: Section 1511. [Online]. Accessed: http://frwebgate4.access.gpo.gov/cgi-bin/waisgate.cgi?WAISdocID=8628003093+0+0+ 0&WAISaction= retrieve [2007 March 2]. Subject: 21.3

United States. *Laws, statutes, etc.* Chemical and biological warfare program. Use of human subjects for testing of chemical or biological agents by Department of Defense; accounting to Congressional committees with respect to experiments and studies; notification of local civilian officials. United States Code 1994; Title 50: Section 1520. [Online]. Accessed: http://frwebgate1.access.gpo.gov/cgi-bin/waisgate.cgi?WAISdocID=862184395128+0+0+0&WAISaction=retrieve [2007 March 2]. Subject: 21.3

United States. *Laws, statutes, etc.* Health insurance for aged and disabled. Limitation on certain physician referrals. United States Code 2003; Title 42: Section 1395nn. [Online]. Accessed: http://frwebgate1.access.gpo.gov/cgi-bin/waisgate.cgi?WAISdocID=862834393531+0+0+0&WAISaction=retrieve [2007 March 2]. Subject: 7.3

United States. Public Health Service [PHS]. Protection of Human Subjects; Reports of the President's Commission for the Study of Ethical Problems in Medicine and Biomedical and Behavioral Research; Notice of availability of reports and request for public comment. *Federal Register* 1983 July 28; 48(146): 34408-34412. Subject: 18.6

United States. Social Security Administration. Office of Hearings and Appeals. In the Case of Judith C. Hart, Claim for Parent's Insurance Benefits: Notice of Decision — Fully Favorable [Date of Decision: 27 March 1997]. Unpublished Document. New Orleans, LA: SSA Office of Hearings and Appeals, 1997 March 27: 16 p. [+ 48 p. appended]. Subject: 14.2

United States. Supreme Court. Gonzales v. Oregon [Date of Decision: 17 January 2006]. Slip Opinion, No. 04-623, 57 p., 2006. Subject: 20.7

United States. Supreme Court; Lindsay, Ronald A.; Dick, Rebecca P. Alberto Gonzales, Attorney General, et al., v. State of Oregon, et al. On Writ of Certiorari to the United States Court of Appeals for the Ninth Circuit. Brief for Amici Curiae in Support of Respondents. Subject: 20.7

University of Bristol, Domestic Violence Research Group. Domestic violence and research ethics. *In:* Smyth, Marie; Williamson, Emma, eds. Researchers and Their 'Subjects': Ethics, Power, Knowledge and Consent. Bristol, UK: Policy Press; 2004: 195-210. Subject: 18.5.3

University of Cape Town. Maternal and Child Health Information and Resource Centre, Child Health Unit. The Choice on Temination of Pregnancy Act, 1996: we consider the provisions of the new Act, its role in improving public health and its implementation. *MCH News* 1996 December; (4): 6-8. Subject: 12.4.1

University of Pittsburgh. Summary Investigative Report on Allegations of Possible Scientific Misconduct on the Part of Gerald P. Schatten, Ph.D., February 8, 2006. Pittsburgh, PA: University of Pittsburgh, 2006 February 8; 9. p. [Online]. Accessed: http://newsbureau.upmc.com/ PDF/Final%20Public%20Report%202.08.pdf. Subject: 1.3.9

Unnithan-Kumar, Maya. Conception technologies, local healers and negotiations around childbearing in Rajasthan. *In:* Unnithan-Kumar, Maya, ed. Reproductive Agency, Medicine and the State: Cultural Transformations in Childbearing. New York: Berghahn Books; 2004: 59-81. Subject: 9.5.5

Unschuld, Paul U. Modern societies, medical ethics and HIV/AIDS. *In:* Döring, Ole; Chen, Renbiao, eds. Advances in Chinese Medical Ethics: Chinese and International Perspectives. Hamburg: Institut für Asienkunde; 2002: 57-72. Subject: 9.5.6

Unsworth-Webb, John. Potential termination of pregnancy in a non-consenting minor. *Nursing Ethics* 2006 July; 13(4): 428-437. Subject: 12.3

Updale, Eleanor. The challenge of lay membership of clinical ethics committees. *Clinical Ethics* 2006 March; 1(1): 60-62. Subject: 9.6

Upvall, Michele; Hashwani, S. Negotiating the informed-consent process in developing countries: a comparison of Swaziland and Pakistan. *International Nursing Review* 2001 September; 48(3): 188-192. Subject: 18.5.9

Uranga, Amelia Martín. European legislation on genetically modified organisms = La normativa en Europa sobre los organismos modificados genéticamente. *Law and the Human Genome Review = Revista de Derecho y Genoma Humano* 1996 July-December; (5): 205-223. Subject: 15.1

Urbina, Ian. Panel suggests using inmates in drug trials. *New York Times* 2006 August 13; p. A1, A21. Subject: 18.5.5

Üstun, Cagatay. Passive euthanasia [letter]. *Nursing Ethics* 2006 May; 13(3): 323-324. Subject: 20.5.1

Uys, Leana R. Are ethics committees always ethical? *International Journal of Nursing Practice* 2006 February; 12(1): 1-2. Subject: 18.2

V

Vahrman, Julian. Placebo controls [letter]. *Journal of the Royal Society of Medicine* 1995 October; 88(10): 603. Subject: 9.6

Valapour, Maryam. Donation after cardiac death: consent is the issue, not death. *Journal of Clinical Ethics* 2006 Summer; 17(2): 137-138. Subject: 19.5

Valdez-Martinez, Edith; Turnbull, Bernardo; Garduno-Espinosa, Juan; Porter, John D.H. Descriptive ethics: a qualitative study of local research ethics committees in Mexico. *Developing World Bioethics* 2006 May; 6(2): 95-105. Subject: 18.2

Valiathan, M.S. Ethical issues in the practice of medicine. *Indian Journal of Chest Diseases and Allied Sciences* 2006 January-March; 48(1): 7-11. Subject: 2.1

Väliverronen, Esa. Expert, healer, reassurer, hero and prophet: framing genetics and medical scientists in television news. *New Genetics and Society* 2006 December; 25(3): 233-247. Subject: 15.1

Valmassoi, G.; Mazzon, D. Informed consent to proposed course of medical treatment: recent case law stances. *Minerva Anestesiologica* 2005 November; 71(11): 659-669. Subject: 8.3.1

van Bogaert, Louis-Jacques. Rights of and duties to non-consenting patients — informed refusal in the developing world. *Developing World Bioethics* 2006 March; 6(1): 13-22. Subject: 8.3.4

van Delden, Johannes J.M. Terminal sedation: different practice, different evaluations. *In:* Tännsjö, Torbjörn, ed. Terminal Sedation: Euthanasia in Disguise? Boston: Kluwer Academic Publishers; 2004: 103-113. Subject: 20.4.1

van den Akker, Olga. Genetic and gestational surrogate mothers' experience of surrogacy. *Journal of Reproductive and Infant Psychology* 2003 May; 21(2): 145-161. Subject: 14.2

van den Akker, Olga. A review of family donor constructs: current research and future directions. *Human Reproduction Update* 2006 March; 12(2): 91-101. Subject: 14.4

van den Akker, Olga B.A. A longitudinal pre-pregnancy to post-delivery comparison of genetic and gestational surrogate and intended mothers: confidence and genealogy.

See SUBJECT HEADING KEY FOR SECTION II on inside back cover.

755

Journal of Psychosomatic Obstetrics and Gynaecology 2005 December; 26(4): 277-284. Subject: 14.2

van den Berg, Matthijs; Timmermans, Danielle, R.M.; Kleinveld, Johanna H.; Garcia, Elisa; van Vugt, John M.G.; van der Wal, Gerrit. Accepting or declining the offer of prenatal screening for congenital defects: test uptake and women's reasons. *Prenatal Diagnosis* 2005 January; 25(1): 84-90. Subject: 15.3

van den Broek, Nynke. The problem of unsafe abortions [editorial]. *Tropical Doctor* 2005 July; 35(3): 129. Subject: 12.1

Van den Hof, Michiel; Wilson, R. Douglas. Obstetric ultrasound: is it time for informed consent? = Echographie obstetricale: le temps est-il venu d'avoir recours au consentement eclaire? [editorial]. *Journal of Obstetrics and Gynaecology Canada* 2005 June; 27(6): 569-571. Subject: 8.3.1

van den Hoonaard, Will C. Trends in Canadian sociology master's theses in relation to research ethics review, 1995-2004. *Journal of Empirical Research on Human Research Ethics* 2006 December; 1(4): 77-88. Subject: 18.2

van den Hoonaard, Will C.; Connolly, Anita. Anthropological research in light of research ethics review: Canadian master's theses, 1995-2004. *Journal of Empirical Research on Human Research Ethics* 2006 June; 1(2): 59-69. Subject: 18.6

van den Hoven, Jeroen. Privacy. *In:* Mitcham, Carl, ed. Encyclopedia of Science, Technology, and Ethics. Farmington Hills, MI: Thomson/Gale, 2005: 1490-1492. Subject: 8.4

van der Arend, Arie J.G. Euthanasia and assisted suicide in The Netherlands: clarifying the practice and the nurse's role. *International Nursing Review* 1998 September-October; 45(5): 145-151. Subject: 20.5.1

van der Arend, Arie J.G. Research ethics committees and the nurse's role. *In:* Tadd, Win, ed. Ethics in Nursing Education, Research and Management. New York: Palgrave Macmillan; 2003: 116-141. Subject: 18.2

van der Arend, Arie J.G.; Smits, Marie-Josee. Ethics education: does it make for practice? *In:* Tadd, Win, ed. Ethics in Nursing Education, Research and Management. New York: Palgrave Macmillan; 2003: 86-100. Subject: 4.1.3

van der Steen, Jenny T.; Ooms, Marcel E.; Ribbe, Miel W.; van der Wal, Gerrit. Decisions to treat or not to treat pneumonia in demented psychogeriatric nursing home patients: evaluation of a guideline. *Alzheimer Disease and Associated Disorders* 2001 July-September; 15(3): 119-128. Subject: 9.4

van der Steen, Jenny T.; van der Wal, Gerrit; Mehr, David R.; Ooms, Marcel E.; Ribbe, Miel W. End-of-life decision making in nursing home residents with dementia and pneumonia: Dutch physicians' intentions regarding hastening death. *Alzheimer Disease and Associated Disor-*

ders 2005 July-September; 19(3): 148-155. Subject: 20.5.1

Van Der Weyden, Martin B. Ethics committees and guardianship legislation [letter]. *Medical Journal of Australia* 2003 October 6; 179(7): 390. Subject: 8.3.3

Van Der Weyden, Martin B. Retrospective ethical approval [reply]. *Medical Journal of Australia* 2001 September 3; 175(5): 286. Subject: 9.5.5

van Dijk, Mara; Widdershoven, Guy A.M.; Meershoek, Agnes M. Reporting euthanasia: physicians' experiences with a Dutch regional evaluation committee. *In:* Schotsmans, Paul; Meulenbergs, Tom, eds. Euthanasia and Palliative Care in the Low Countries. Dudley, MA: Peeters, 2005: 71-82. Subject: 20.5.1

Van Dorn, Richard A.; Elbogen, Eric B.; Redlich, Allison D.; Swanson, Jeffrey W.; Swartz, Marvin S.; Mustillo, Sarah. The relationship between mandated community treatment and perceived barriers to care in persons with severe mental illness. *International Journal of Law and Psychiatry* 2006 November-December; 29(6): 495-506. Subject: 17.1

van Gend, David. Prometheus, Pandora and the myths of cloning. *Human Life Review* 2006 Summer-Fall; 32(3-4): 15-27. Subject: 14.5

Van Gijn, J. Euthanasia and trust [letter]. *Clinical Medicine* 2005 May-June; 5(3): 299. Subject: 20.5.1

van Hilvoorde, Ivo. Sport and genetics: moral and educational considerations regarding 'athletic predestination.'. *In:* Tamburrini, Claudio; Tännsjö, Torbjörn, eds. Genetic Technology and Sport: Ethical Questions. London; New York: Routledge; 2005: 91-103. Subject: 4.5

van Korlaar, I.M.; Vossen, C.Y.; Rosendaal, F.R.; Bovill, E.G.; Naud, S.; Cameron, L.D.; Kaptein, A.A. Attitudes toward genetic testing for thrombophilia in asymptomatic members of a large family with heritable protein C deficiency. *Journal of Thrombosis and Haemostasis* 2005 November; 3(11): 2437-2444. Subject: 15.3

van Leeuwen, Evert; Kimsma, Gerrit. Probleme im Zusammenhang mit der ethischen Rechtfertigung zur medizinischen Sterbehilfe: Auseinandersetzung mit der Euthanasie und ärztlichen Suizidbeihilfe. *In:* Gordijn, Bert; ten Have, Henk, eds. Medizinethik und Kultur: Grenzen medizinischen Handelns in Deutschland und den Niederlanden. Stuttgart: Frommann-Holzboog; 2000: 433-457. Subject: 20.5.1

van Luijn, H.E.M.; Aaronson, N.K.; Keus, R.B.; Musschenga, A.W. The evaluation of the risks and benefits of phase II cancer clinical trials by institutional review boards (IRB) members: a case study. *Journal of Medical Ethics* 2006 March; 32(3): 170-176. Subject: 18.2

van Niekerk, Anton A. Mother-to-child transmission of HIV/AIDS in Africa: ethical problems and perspectives.

In: van Niekerk, Anton A.; Kopelman, Loretta M., eds. Ethics and AIDS in Africa: The Challenge to Our Thinking. Walnut Creek, CA: Left Coast Press; 2006: 141-159. Subject: 18.5.3

van Niekerk, Anton A. Principles of global distributive justice and the HIV/AIDS pandemic: moving beyond Rawls and Buchanan. *In:* van Niekerk, Anton A.; Kopelman, Loretta M., eds. Ethics and AIDS in Africa: The Challenge to Our Thinking. Walnut Creek, CA: Left Coast Press; 2006: 84-110. Subject: 9.5.6

Van Norman, Gail A.; Palmer, Susan K.; Jackson, Stephen H. The ethical role of medical journal editors [letter]. *Anesthesia and Analgesia* 2005 February; 100(2): 603-604. Subject: 1.3.9

van Oorschot, B.; Simon, A. Importance of the advance directive and the beginning of the dying process from the point of view of German doctors and judges dealing with guardianship matters: results of an empirical survey. *Journal of Medical Ethics* 2006 November; 32(11): 623-626. Subject: 20.5.4

Van Overstraeten, M.; Michel, Luc. The protection of the patient's private life: a vast normative landscape. First part. *Acta Chirurgica Belgica* 2005 September-October; 105(5): 457-463. Subject: 8.4

Van Overstraeten, M.; Michel, Luc. The protection of the patient's private life: the computer challenge. Second part. *Acta Chirurgica Belgica* 2005 September-October; 105(5): 464-470. Subject: 8.4

Van Rinsum, Henk J.; Tangwa, Godfrey, B. Colony of genes, genes of the colony: diversity, differences and divide. *Third World Quarterly* 2004 September; 25(6): 1031-1043. Subject: 15.10

Van Riper, Kristi K.; Hellerstedt, Wendy L. Emergency contraceptive pills: dispensing practices, knowledge and attitudes of South Dakota pharmacists. *Perspectives on Sexual and Reproductive Health* 2005 March; 37(1): 19-24. Subject: 11.1

van Ryn, Michelle; Burgess, Diana; Malat, Jennifer; Griffin, Joan. Physicians' perceptions of patients' social and behavioral characteristics and race disparities in treatment recommendations for men with coronary artery disease. *American Journal of Public Health* 2006 February; 96(2): 351- 357. Subject: 9.5.4

Van Steendam, Guido; Dinnyés, András; Mallet, Jacques; Meloni, Rolando; Casabona, Carlos Romeo; González, Jorge Guerra; Kure, Josef; Szathmáry, Eörs; Vorstenbosch, Jan; Molnár, Péter; Edbrooke, David; Sándor; Oberfrank, Ferenc; Cole-Turner, Ron; Hargittai, István; Littig, Beate; Ladikas, Miltos; Mordini, Emilio; Roosendaal, Hans E.; Salvi, Maurizio; Gulyás, Balázs; Malpede, Diana. Summary: the Budapest Meeting 2005 intensified networking on ethics of science: the case of reproductive cloning, germline gene therapy, and human dignity. *Science and Engineering Ethics* 2006 July; 12(3): 415-420. Subject: 15.1

Van Steendam, Guido; Dinnyés, András; Mallet, Jacques; Meloni, Rolando; Casabona, Carlos Romeo; González, Jorge Guerra; Kure, Josef; Szathmáry, Eörs; Vorstenbosch, Jan; Molnár, Péter; Edbrooke, David; Sándor, Judit; Oberfrank, Ferenc; Cole-Turner, Ron; Hargittai, István; Littig, Beate; Ladikas, Miltos; Mordini, Emilio; Roosendaal, Hans E.; Salvi, Maurizio; Gulyás, Balázs; Malpede, Diana. The Budapest Meeting 2005 intensified networking on ethics of science: the case of reproductive cloning, germline gene therapy and human dignity. *Science and Engineering Ethics* 2006 October; 12(4): 731-793. Subject: 14.5

van Veen, Ben-Evert. Human tissue bank regulations [letter]. *Nature Biotechnology* 2006 May; 24(5): 496-498. Subject: 19.5

van Voorhees, Alexander. Truth in testing laws: a shot in the arm for designer gene tests. *Health Matrix: The Journal of Law-Medicine* 2006 Summer; 16(2): 797-829. Subject: 15.3

van Wijmen, Frans C.B.; de Wert, Guido M.W.R. Genetics and artificial procreation in the Netherlands. *In:* Meulders-Klein, Marie-Thérèse; Deech, Ruth; Vlaardingerbroek, Paul, eds. Biomedicine, the Family and Human Rights. New York: Kluwer Law International, 2002: 275-300. Subject: 14.1

van Willigenburg, Theo. Tod, wo ist dein Stachel?: eine internatistische Sicht des Wertes des Lebens und der Drohung des Todes. *In:* Gordijn, Bert; ten Have, Henk, eds. Medizinethik und Kultur: Grenzen medizinischen Handelns in Deutschland und den Niederlanden. Stuttgart: Frommann-Holzgoog; 2000: 477-494. Subject: 20.5.1

van Zuuren, Florence J.; van Manen, Eeke. Moral dilemmas in neonatology as experienced by health care practitioners: a qualitative approach. *Medicine, Health Care and Philosophy* 2006; 9(3): 339-347. Subject: 20.5.2

Vancouver Coastal Health Corporate Ethics Committee. How to make allocation decisions: a theory and test questions. *Healthcare Management Forum* 2005 Spring; 18(1): 32-33. Subject: 9.4

VandeKieft, Gregg. Who decides? An ethics case consult for Terri Schiavo. *American Journal of Hospice and Palliative Medicine* 2005 May-June; 22(3): 175-177. Subject: 20.5.1

Vandenbroucke, Amy. Case brief: physician assisted suicide. *DePaul Journal of Health Care Law* 2005; 9(1): 893-904. Subject: 20.7

Vandenbroucke, Amy. HIV and organ donation: Illinois' solution to organ donation shortages. *DePaul Journal of Health Care Law* 2006 Spring; 9(3): 1285-1316. Subject: 19.5

See SUBJECT HEADING KEY FOR SECTION II on inside back cover.

757

Vandervort, Lucinda. Reproductive choice: screening policy and access to the means of reproduction. *Human Rights Quarterly* 2006 May; 28(2): 438-464. Subject: 14.1

Varelius, Jukka. Autonomy, wellbeing, and the case of the refusing patient. *Medicine, Health Care and Philosophy* 2006; 9(1): 117-125. Subject: 8.3.4

Varelius, Jukka. The value of autonomy in medical ethics. *Medicine, Health Care and Philosophy* 2006; 9(3): 377-388. Subject: 2.1

Varelius, Jukka. Voluntary euthanasia, physician-assisted suicide, and the goals of medicine. *Journal of Medicine and Philosophy* 2006 April; 31(2): 121-137. Subject: 20.7

Vargas-Parada, Laura; Kawa, Simon; Salazar, Alberto; Mazon, Juan Jose; Flisser, Ana. Informed consent in clinical research at a general hospital in Mexico: opinions of the investigators. *Developing World Bioethics* 2006 March; 6(1): 41-51. Subject: 18.3

Vargese, Sunny T.; George, Sapna Ann. Doctors and the electronic media [letter]. *Indian Journal of Medical Ethics* 2006 October-December; 3(4): 145. Subject: 8.4

Varone, Frédéric; Rothmayr, Christine; Montpetit, Eric. Regulating biomedicine in Europe and North America: a qualitative comparative analysis. *European Journal of Political Research* 2006 March; 45(2): 317-343. Subject: 14.4

Varsha. DNA fingerprinting in the criminal justice system: an overview. *DNA and Cell Biology* 2006 March; 25(3): 181-188. Subject: 15.1

Vasgird, Daniel R. Resisting power and influence: a case study in virtue ethics. *Journal of Empirical Research on Human Research Ethics* 2006 June; 1(2): 19-22. Subject: 18.2

Vassy, Carine. From a genetic innovation to mass health programmes: the diffusion of Down's Syndrome prenatal screening and diagnostic techniques in France. *Social Science and Medicine* 2006 October; 63(8): 2041-2051. Subject: 15.3

Vassy, Carine. How prenatal diagnosis became acceptable in France. *Trends in Biotechnology* 2005 May; 23(5): 246-249. Subject: 15.2

Vaughan, N.J.A.; Fogarty, L. Confidentiality and diabetes 'registers' — a dilemma? *Diabetic Medicine* 2000 August; 17(8): 563-564. Subject: 8.4

Veach, Patricia McCarthy; LeRoy, Bonnie S.; Bartels, Dianne M. Behaving ethically. *In their:* Facilitating the Genetic Counseling Process: A Practice Manual. New York: Springer, 2003: 222-241. Subject: 15.2

Veach, Patricia McCarthy; LeRoy, Bonnie S.; Bartels, Dianne M. National Society of Genetic Counselors Code of Ethics. *In their:* Facilitating the Genetic Counseling Process: A Practice Manual. New York: Springer, 2003: 285-287. Subject: 15.2

Veatch, Robert M. Allocating health resources ethically: new roles for administrators and clinicians. *Frontiers of Health Services Management* 1991 Fall; 8(1): 3-29. Subject: 9.4

Veatch, Robert M. Assessing Pellegrino's reconstruction of medical morality. *American Journal of Bioethics* 2006 March-April; 6(2): 72-75. Subject: 2.1

Veatch, Robert M. Benevolent lies: fallible universalism and the quest for an international standard. *Formosan Journal of Medical Humanities* 2006 June; 7(1-2): 3-18. Subject: 8.2

Veatch, Robert M. How philosophy of medicine has changed medical ethics. *Journal of Medicine and Philosophy* 2006 December; 31(6): 585-600. Subject: 2.1

Veatch, Robert M. Organ exchanges: fairness to the O-blood group [editorial]. *American Journal of Transplantation* 2006 January; 6(1): 1-2. Subject: 19.5

Veatch, Robert M. Reply. *Frontiers of Health Services Management* 1991 Fall; 8(1): 43-44. Subject: 9.4

Veatch, Robert M. Why researchers cannot establish equipoise. *American Journal of Bioethics* 2006 July-August; 6(4): 55-57. Subject: 18.2

Vedantam, Shankar. Comparison of schizophrenia drugs often favors firm funding study. *Washington Post* 2006 April 12; p. A1, A6. Subject: 17.4

Vedantam, Shankar. Group says FDA, advisory panels show bias toward drug approvals. *Washington Post* 2006 August 29; p. A13. Subject: 5.3

Veidebaum, Toomas. Research ethics in Estonia. *In:* Beyleveld, D.; Townend, D.; Wright, J., eds. Research Ethics Committees, Data Protection and Medical Research in European Countries. Hants, England; Burlington, VT: Ashgate; 2005: 41-43. Subject: 18.2

Velleman, J. David. Against the right to die. *In:* Jansen, Lynn A., ed. Death in the Clinic. Lanham, MD: Rowman and Littlefield; 2006: 49-65. Subject: 20.5.1

Verástegui, Emma L. Consenting of the vulnerable: the informed consent procedure in advanced care patients in Mexico. *BMC Medical Ethics* 2006; 7(13): 12p. Subject: 18.3

Verbeek, Jos; Hulshof, Carel. Work disability assessment in the Netherlands. *In:* Westerholm, Peter; Nilstun, Tore; Øvretveit, John, eds. Practical Ethics in Occupational Health. San Francisco: Radcliffe Medical Press; 2004: 105-114. Subject: 16.3

Verhagen, A.A.E. Developments with regard to end-of-life decisions in newborns [editorial]. *West Indian Medical Journal* 2005 October; 54(5): 277-278. Subject: 20.5.2

Verhagen, A.A.E. End of life decisions in newborns in the Netherlands: medical and legal aspects of the Groningen

---

Subject = NRCBL Primary Classification Number; see inside front cover.

protocol. *Medicine and Law: The World Association for Medical Law* 2006 June; 25(2): 399-407. Subject: 20.5.2

Verhagen, A.A.E.; Sauer, P.J.J. End-of-life decisions in newborns: an approach from the Netherlands. *Pediatrics* 2005 September; 116(3): 736-739. Subject: 20.5.1

Verkerk, Marian. A feminist care-ethics approach to genetics. *In:* Ashcroft, Richard; Lucassen, Anneke; Parker, Michael; Verkerk, Marian; Widderhoven, Guy, eds. Case Analysis in Clinical Ethics. New York: Cambridge University Press; 2005: 133-148. Subject: 15.3

Verkerk, M.A.; Buise, R.V.; van Berkestijn, Th.M.G.; Doxiadis, Spyros A.; Riis, Povl; Moerkerk, H. Medical ethics. *In:* Hermans, H.E.G.M.; Casparie, A.F.; Paelinck, J.H.P., eds. Health Care in Europe After 1992. Brookfield, VT: Ashgate, 1992: 89-107. Subject: 2.1

Verlinsky, Yury. Designing babies: what the future holds. *Reproductive BioMedicine Online [electronic]* 2005 March; 10(Supplement 1): 24-26. Subject: 14.1

Vermaas, Albert. Forced HIV-testing: a blessing for the physician or a worst case scenario for the patient? *Medicine and Law: The World Association for Medical Law* 2006 June; 25(2): 241-247. Subject: 8.4

Vermeersch, E. The Belgian law on euthanasia: the historical and ethical background. *Acta Chirurgica Belgica* 2002 November-December; 102(6): 394- 397. Subject: 20.7

Vernon, Martin J. Informed consent. *In:* Rai, Gurcharan S, ed. Medical Ethics and the Elderly. 2nd ed. San Francisco: Radcliffe Medical Press; 2004: 19-31. Subject: 8.3.1

Vernon, Martin J.; Gaillemin, Olivier. Decisions on life-sustaining therapy: nutrition and fluid. *In:* Rai, Gurcharan S, ed. Medical Ethics and the Elderly. 2nd ed. San Francisco: Radcliffe Medical Press; 2004: 33-48. Subject: 20.5.1

Vernooij-Dassen, Myrra J.F.J.; Osse, Bart H.P.; Schade, Egbert; Grol, Richard P.T.M. Patient autonomy problems in palliative care: systematic development and evaluation of a questionnaire. *Journal of Pain and Symptom Management* 2005 September; 30(3): 264-270. Subject: 20.4.1

Verpeet, Ellen; Dierckx de Casterlé, Bernadette; Lemiengre, Joke; Gastmans, Chris. Belgian nurses' views on codes of ethics: development, dissemination, implementation. *Nursing Ethics* 2006 September; 13(5): 531-545. Subject: 4.1.3

Verweij, Marcel. Die Debatte in Sachen Nichtreanimations-entscheidungen in den Niederlanden. *In:* Gordijn, Bert; ten Have, Henk, eds. Medizinethik und Kultur: Grenzen medizinischen Handelns in Deutschland und den Niederlanden. Stuttgart: Frommann-Holzboog; 2000: 141-158. Subject: 20.5.1

Verweij, Marcel; Dawson, Angus. Ethical principles for collective immunisation programmes. *Vaccine* 2004 August 13; 22(23-24): 3122-3126. Subject: 9.5.1

Vesilind, P. Aarne. Medicine, technology, and ethics: a historical perspective. *Journal of Investigative Surgery* 1992 July-September; 5(3): 171-178. Subject: 5.2

Vester, A.E.; Christensen, E.F.; Andersen, S.K.; Tonnesen, E. Ethical and practical problems in blood sampling for research purposes during pre-hospital emergencies. *Acta Anaesthesiologica Scandinavica* 2005 November; 49(10): 1540-1543. Subject: 18.3

Viafora, Corrado. The ethical function in the health care institutions: clinical ethics committees. *In:* Viafora, Corrado, ed. Clinical Bioethics: A Search for the Foundations. Dordrecht: Springer, 2005: 181-192. Subject: 9.6

Vick, Catherine C.; Finan, Kelly R.; Kiefe, Catarina; Neumayer, Leigh; Hawn, Mary T. Variation in Institutional Review processes for a multisite observational study. *American Journal of Surgery* 2005 November; 190(5): 805-809. Subject: 18.2

Vick, Hannah M. Embryonic stem cell research: ethically wrong treatment of the tiniest of humans. *Concerned Women for America* 2000 May 1: 5 pages [Online] Accessed:http://www.cwfa.org/printerfriendly.asp?id=1423 &department=cwa&categoryid=life [2005 November 30]. Subject: 18.5.4

Vick, Katherine R. Stem cell research debate shifting to the courts. *Journal of Biolaw and Business* 2006; 9(1): 56-57. Subject: 18.5.4

Victoroff, Michael S. When personal and professional collide. *Managed Care* 2005 August; 14(8): 18, 21. Subject: 9.7

Vieta, Eduard; Carné, Xavier. The use of placebo in clinical trials on bipolar disorder: a new approach for an old debate. *Psychotherapy and Psychosomatics* 2005; 74(1): 10-16. Subject: 18.3

Vig, Elizabeth K.; Taylor, Janelle S.; Starks, Helene; Hopley, Elizabeth K.; Fryer-Edwards, Kelly. Beyond substituted judgment: how surrogates navigate end-of-life decision-making. *Journal of American Geriatrics Society* 2006 November; 54(11): 1688-1693. Subject: 8.3.3

Vince, T.; Petros, A. Should children's autonomy be respected by telling them of their imminent death? *Journal of Medical Ethics* 2006 January; 32(1): 21-23. Subject: 8.2

Vincent, Jean-Louis. Outcome and ethics in severe brain damage. *Progress in Brain Research* 2005; 150: 555-563. Subject: 20.5.1

Vincent, Jean-Louis. Withdrawing may be preferable to withholding. *Critical Care* 2005 June; 9(3): 226-229. Subject: 20.5.1

Vincent, Jean-Louis; Berre, J.; Creteur, J. Withholding and withdrawing life prolonging treatment in the intensive care unit: a current European perspective. *Chronic Respiratory Disease* 2004; 1(2): 115-120. Subject: 20.5.1

Vineis, Paolo. The tension between ethics and evidence-based medicine. *In:* Viafora, Corrado, ed. Clinical

See SUBJECT HEADING KEY FOR SECTION II on inside back cover.

759

Bioethics: A Search for the Foundations. Dordrecht: Springer, 2005: 131-137. Subject: 9.8

Vining, Therese W. Assisted suicide: where do advanced practice nurses stand? *Journal of Nursing Law* 1997; 4(2): 17-22. Subject: 20.7

Virginia. *Laws, statutes, etc.* An act to amend an reenact section 38.2-613 of the Code of Virginia and to amend the Code of Virginia by adding a section numbered 38.2-508.4 relating to insurance; genetic information privacy [Approved 6 April 1996; Expires 1 July 1998]. Virginia: Senate Bill 335; Acts of Assembly, Chapter 704. [Online]. 5 p. Accessed http://leg1.state.va.us/cgi-bin/legp504.exe? 961+ful+CHAP0704 [2007 March 9]. Subject: 15.1

Virt, Günter. Unity and variety of ethical principles: human dignity endangered. *Human Reproduction and Genetic Ethics: An International Journal* 2006; 12(2): 61-65. Subject: 4.4

Vischer, Robert K. Conscience in context: pharmacist rights and the eroding moral marketplace. *Stanford Law and Policy Review* 2006; 17(1): 83-119. Subject: 9.7

Visco, Frances M.; Skolnick, Mark; Collins, Francis S. Commentary on the ASCO Statement on Genetic Testing for Cancer Susceptibility. *Journal of Clinical Oncology* 1996 May; 14(5): 1737-1740. Subject: 15.3

Vittabai, Baby Flankitt; Azaria, Jayapaul; Macer, Darryl R.J. Bioethics education and awareness in schools in Tamil Nadu, India. *In:* Sang-yong, Song; Young-Mo, Koo; Macer, Darryl R.J., eds. Asian Bioethics in the 21st Century. Christchurch, NZ: Eubios Ethics Institute, 2002: 268-277. Subject: 2.3

Vivat, Bella. Situated ethics and feminist ethnography in a west of Scotland hospice. *In:* Bondi, Liz et al., eds. Subjectivities, Knowledges, and Feminist Geographies: The Subjects and Ethics of Social Research. Lanham, MD: Rowman and Littlefield, 2002: 236-252. Subject: 4.1.3

Vlassov, Vasiliy. Russian medicine and the Nuremberg trials. *European Journal of Public Health* 2006 June; 16(3): 229. Subject: 2.2

Vogel, F. Human genetics: the molecular revolution and its ethical consequences. *International Journal of Human Genetics* 2001; 1(1): 1-9. Subject: 15.1

Vogel, Gretchen. Ethical oocytes: available for a price. *Science* 2006 July 14; 313(5784): 155. Subject: 14.6

Vogel, Gretchen. Fraud investigation clouds paper on early cell fate [news]. *Science* 2006 December 1; 314(5804): 1367-1368. Subject: 1.3.9

Vogel, Gretchen. Scientists derive line from single embryo cell. *Science* 2006 August 25; 313(5790): 1031. Subject: 19.1

Vogel, Laurent. The ethics of health and safety services: a trade union perspectives. *In:* Westerholm, Peter; Nilstun, Tore; Øvretveit, John, eds. Practical Ethics in Occupa-

tional Health. San Francisco: Radcliffe Medical Press; 2004: 253-261. Subject: 16.3

Vogel, Lawrence. Natural law Judaism?: The genesis of bioethics in Hans Jonas, Leo Strauss, and Leon Kass. *Hastings Center Report* 2006 May-June; 36(3): 32-44. Subject: 2.1

Vogeli, Christine; Yucel, Recai; Bendavid, Eran; Jones, Lisa M.; Anderson, Melissa S.; Louis, Karen Seashore; Campbell, Eric G. Data withholding and the next generation of scientists: results of a national survey. *Academic Medicine* 2006 February; 81(2): 128-136. Subject: 1.3.9

Vohra, Sameer S. An American Muslim's right to die: incorporating Islamic law into the debate. *Journal of Legal Medicine* 2006 September; 27(3): 341-359. Subject: 20.5.1

Volandes, Angelo. Envying Cinderella and the future of medical enhancements. *Medical Humanities* 2006 December; 32(2): 73-76. Subject: 4.5

Volandes, Angelo E.; Abbo, Elmer D. Toward a reconstruction of a professional medical morality. *American Journal of Bioethics* 2006 March-April; 6(2): 88-89. Subject: 2.1

Volker, Deborah Lowe. Assisted suicide and the domain of nursing practice. *Journal of Nursing Law* 1998; 5(1): 39-50. Subject: 20.7

Volker, Deborah Lowe; Kahn, David; Penticuff, Joy H. Patient control and end-of-life care Part I: the advanced practice nurse perspective. *Oncology Nursing Forum* 2004 September 17; 31(5): 945-953. Subject: 20.4.1

Volker, Deborah Lowe; Kahn, David; Penticuff, Joy H. Patient control and end-of-life care Part II: the patient perspective. *Oncology Nursing Forum* 2004 September 17; 31(5): 954-960. Subject: 20.4.1

Volkov, Ilia. A part of life, a part of me, and "the quality of life". *Journal of Clinical Ethics* 2006 Summer; 17(2): 191-192. Subject: 4.4

Vollmann, Jochen. Die deutsche Diskussion über ärztliche Tötung auf Verlangen und Beihilfe zum Suizid: Eine Übersicht medizinethischer und rechtlicher Aspekte. *In:* Gordijn, Bert; ten Have, Henk, eds. Medizinethik und Kultur: Grenzen medizinischen Handelns in Deutschland und den Niederlanden. Stuttgart: Frommann-Holzgoog; 2000: 31-70. Subject: 20.5.1

Vollmann, Jochen. Patientselbstbestimmung und "aktive Sterbehilfe": Klinische und ethische Probleme. *In:* Vollmann, Jochen, ed. Medizin und Ethik: Aktuelle ethische Probleme in Therapie und Forschung. Erlangen: Universitätsbund Erlangen-Nürnberg, 2003: 107-123. Subject: 20.5.1

Vollmar, Lewis C. Military medicine in war: the Geneva Conventions today. *In:* Beam, Thomas E.; Sparacino, Linette R.; Pellegrino, Edmund D.; Hartle, Anthony E.; Howe, Edmund G., eds. Military Medical Ethics. Volume

Subject = NRCBL Primary Classification Number; see inside front cover.

2. Washington, DC: TMM Publications, Borden Institute, Walter Reed Army Medical Center; 2003: 739-771. Subject: 2.1

Vollmar, Lewis C., Jr. Development of the laws of war as they pertain to medical units and their personnel. *Military Medicine* 1992 May; 157(5): 231-236. Subject: 4.1.2

Volokh, Eugene. Slippery slope arguments. *In:* Mitcham, Carl, ed. Encyclopedia of Science, Technology, and Ethics. Farmington Hills, MI: Thomson/Gale, 2005: 1783-1785. Subject: 2.1

Vrakking, Astrid M.; van der Heide, Agnes; Arts, Willem Frans; Pieters, Rob; van der Voort, Edwin; Rietjens, Judith A.C.; Onwuteaka-Philipsen, Bregje D.; van der Maas, Paul J.; van der Wal, Gerrit. Medical end-of-life decisions for children in the Netherlands. *Archives of Pediatric and Adolescent Medicine* 2005 September; 159(9): 802-809. Subject: 20.5.2

W

Wachbroit, Robert. Normality and the significance of difference. *In:* Parens, Erik; Chapman, Audrey R.; Press, Nancy, eds. Wrestling with Behavioral Genetics: Science, Ethics, and Public Conversion. Baltimore, MD: Johns Hopkins University Press; 2006: 235-253. Subject: 15.6

Wachbroit, Robert. Research as a profession. *Philosophy and Public Policy Quarterly* 2006 Winter-Spring; 26(1-2): 18-20. Subject: 1.3.9

Waddell, James P. Informed consent [editorial]. *Canadian Journal of Surgery* 2005 August; 48(4): 269. Subject: 18.3

Wade, Christopher H.; Kalfoglou, Andrea L. When do genetic researchers have a duty to recontact study participants? *American Journal of Bioethics* 2006 November-December; 6(6): 26-27; author reply W10-W12. Subject: 15.1

Wade, Nicholas. Cancer study was made up, journal says. *New York Times* 2006 January 19; p. A16. Subject: 1.3.9

Wade, Nicholas. In new method for stem cells, viable embryos; objections to use remain; development could raise the level of debate in midterm elections. *New York Times* 2006 August 24; p. A1, A23. Subject: 5.3

Wade, Nicholas. It may look authentic; here's how to tell it isn't: a scientific journal shows the way in a new offensive against fraud. *New York Times* 2006 January 24; p. F1, F6. Subject: 1.3.9

Wade, Nicholas. The quest for the $1,000 human genome: DNA sequencing in the doctor's office? At birth? It may be coming closer. *New York Times* 2006 July 18; p. F1, F3. Subject: 15.10

Wade, Nicholas. Science academy creating panel to monitor stem-cell research. *New York Times* 2006 February 16; p. A21. Subject: 1.3.9

Wade, Nicholas. Some scientists see shift in stem cell hopes. *New York Times* 2006 August 14; p. A18. Subject: 5.3

Wade, Nicholas. University panel faults cloning co-author. *New York Times* 2006 February 11; p. A12. Subject: 14.5

Wade, Nicholas; Sang-Hun, Choe. Human cloning was all faked, Koreans report. *New York Times* 2006 January 10; p. A1, A12. Subject: 1.3.9

Wadman, Meredith. Agency accused of 'illusion of integrity' [news]. *Nature* 2006 September 21; 443(7109): 252-253. Subject: 1.3.9

Wadman, Meredith. Drive for drugs leads to baby clinical trials. *Nature* 2006 March 23; 440(7083): 406-407. Subject: 18.2

Wadman, Meredith. Earlier drug test on people could be unsafe, critics warn [news]. *Nature Medicine* 2006 February; 12(2): 153. Subject: 18.6

Wadman, Meredith. A few good scientists. *Nature Medicine* 2006 September; 12(9): 986-987. Subject: 1.3.9

Wadman, Meredith. London's disastrous drug trial has serious side effects for research [news]. *Nature* 2006 March 23; 440(7083): 388-389. Subject: 18.2

Wadman, Meredith. Neal Barnard. *Nature Medicine* 2006 June; 12(6): 602. Subject: 22.2

Wadman, Meredith. The quiet rise of the clinical contractor. *Nature* 2006 May 4; 441(7089): 22-23. Subject: 18.1

Wadman, Meredith. Spitzer sues drug giant for deceiving doctors [news]. *Nature* 2004 June 10; 429(6992): 589. Subject: 9.7

Wadman, Meredith; Abbott, Alison. A long week in stem-cell politics. . . [news]. *Nature* 2006 July 27; 442(7101): 335. Subject: 18.5.4

Wager, Elizabeth; Herxheimer, Andrew. Peer review and the pharmaceutical industry. *In:* Godlee, Fiona; Jefferson, Tom, eds. Peer Review in Health Sciences. 2nd ed. London: BMJ Books; 2003: 130-139. Subject: 1.3.7

Wagner, Andrew L. Vertebroplasty and the randomized study: where science and ethics collide [editorial]. *AJNR: American Journal of Neuroradiology* 2005 August; 26(7): 1610-1611. Subject: 18.2

Wagner, Gorm; Bondil, Pierre; Dabees, Khalid; Dean, John; Fourcroy, Jean; Gingell, Clive; Kingsberg, Sheryl; Kothari, Prakash; Rubio-Aurioles, Eusebio; Ugarte, Fernando; Navarrete, R. Vela. Ethical aspects of sexual medicine. *Journal of Sexual Medicine* 2005 March; 2(2): 163-168. Subject: 10

Wagner, H. Ryan; Swartz, Marvin S.; Swanson, Jeffrey W.; Burns, Barbara J. Does involuntary outpatient commitment lead to more intensive treatment? *Psychology, Public Policy, and Law* 2003 March-June; 9(1-2): 145-158. Subject: 17.7

See SUBJECT HEADING KEY FOR SECTION II on inside back cover.

761

Wahn, Eve. An update on Olivieri: what difference did it make? *Health Law in Canada* 2006 June; 26(4): 61-70. Subject: 18.3

Wahrman, Miryam Z. Fruit of the womb: artificial reproductive technologies and Jewish law. *Journal of Gender, Race and Justice* 2005 Fall; 9(1): 109-136. Subject: 14.4

Wailoo, Allan; Anand, Paul. The nature of procedural preferences for health-care rationing decisions. *Social Science and Medicine* 2005 January; 60(2): 223-236. Subject: 9.4

Wakley, Gill. The conduct of colleagues. *Journal of Family Planning and Reproductive Health Care* 2005 April; 31(2): 156-157. Subject: 7.3

Walcher-Andris, Elfriede. Ethische Aspekte des pharmakologischen "cognition enhancement" am Beispiel des Gebrauchs von Psychostimulanzien durch Kinder und Jugendliche / Ethical aspects of pharmacological cognition enhancement and the use of psychostimulants by children and young persons. *Ethik in der Medizin* 2006 March; 18(1): 27-36. Subject: 4.5

Waldau, Paul. Religion and animals. *In:* Singer, Peter, ed. In Defense of Animals: The Second Wave. Malden, MA: Blackwell Pub.; 2006: 69-83. Subject: 22.1

Waldman, Ellen. Cultural priorities revealed: the development and regulations of assisted reproduction in the United States and Israel. *Health Matrix: The Journal of Law-Medicine* 2006 Winter; 16(1): 65-106. Subject: 21.7

Wales, Heathcote W.; Hiday, Virginia Aldigé. PLC or TLC: is outpatient commitment the/an answer? *International Journal of Law and Psychiatry* 2006 November-December; 29(6): 451-468. Subject: 17.1

Walin, Laura. The regulation of genetic research and the commercialisation of its results in Finland. *Medical Law International* 2006; 7(4): 309-328. Subject: 18.6

Walker, Francis O. Cultivating simple virtues in medicine. *Neurology* 2005 November 22; 65(10): 1678-1680. Subject: 2.1

Walker, Rebecca L. Human and animal subjects of research: the moral significance of respect versus welfare. *Theoretical Medicine and Bioethics* 2006; 27(4): 305-331. Subject: 22.2

Wall, L. Lewis. The medical ethics of Dr. J. Marion Sims: a fresh look at the historical record. *Journal of Medical Ethics* 2006 June; 32(6): 346-350. Subject: 18.5.1

Wall, L. Lewis; Brown, Douglas. Refusals by pharmacists to dispense emergency contraception: a critique. *Obstetrics and Gynecology* 2006 May; 107(5): 1148-1151. Subject: 11.1

Wall, L. Lewis; Brown, Douglas. Regarding zygotes as persons: implications for public policy. *Perspectives in Biology and Medicine* 2006 Autumn; 49(4): 602-610. Subject: 4.4

Wallace, Helen. Permanently detained: as the U.K.'s database expands, crimes solved with DNA drop. *GeneWatch* 2006 November-December; 19(6): 13-18. Subject: 15.1

Waller-Wise, Renece. Conscientious objection: do nurses have the right to refuse to provide care? *AWHONN Lifelines* 2005 August-September; 9(4): 283-286. Subject: 8.1

Walley, Tom. Using personal health information in medical research. *BMJ: British Medical Journal* 2006 January 21; 332(7534): 130-131. Subject: 8.4

Walsh, Kieran. Diva [case study]. *Advances in Health Sciences Education: Theory and Practice* 2005; 10(1): 81-84. Subject: 7.2

Walsh, Raoul A.; Cholowski, Krystyna; Tzelepis, Flora. Surveying university students: variability in ethics committee requirements [letter]. *Australian and New Zealand Journal of Public Health* 2006 February; 30(1): 84-85. Subject: 9.6

Walter, James J. The bioengineering of planet Earth: some scientific, moral, and theological considerations. *New Theology Review* 2002 August; 15: 41-54. Subject: 15.1

Walter, James J. A Catholic reflection on embryonic stem cell research. *Linacre Quarterly* 2006 August; 73(3): 255-263. Subject: 18.5.4

Walter, James J. Medical futility—an ethical issue for clinicians and patients. *Practical Bioethics* 2005 Summer; 1(3): 1, 6-8. Subject: 20.5.1

Walter, Robert J. Medicine's goals and the prophetic tradition. *Health Progress* 2006 September-October; 87(5): 40-45. Subject: 4.1.2

Walters, LeRoy B. Ethical issues in biotechnology: human embryonic stem cell research and the Anabaptist vision. *In:* Miller, Roman J.; Brubaker, Beryl H.; Peterson, James C., eds. Viewing New Creations with Anabaptist Eyes: Ethics of Biotechnology. Telford, PA: Cascadia Pub.; 2005: 122-135. Subject: 18.5.4

Walters, LeRoy B. The ethics of human gene therapy. *Brethren Life and Thought* 1986 Autumn; 31(4): 215-222. Subject: 15.1

Walters, LeRoy B. Major events and publications related to the birth of bioethics, 1925-1975 with special attention to the Anglican contribution. *Anglican Theological Review* 1999 Fall; 81(4): 631-650. Subject: 2.2

Walthall, Arron. Legal pressure to incorporate pharmacogenetics in the U.K. *Jurimetrics* 2006 Spring; 46(3): 263-279. Subject: 9.7

Walther, Frans J. Withholding treatment, withdrawing treatment, and palliative care in the neonatal intensive care unit. *Early Human Development* 2005 December; 81(12): 965-972. Subject: 20.5.2

Walther, J.-U. Genetische Beratung und ihre Normen. Ethische Überlegungen [Genetic counselling in a

---

Subject = NRCBL Primary Classification Number; see inside front cover.

sociocultural framework. Ethical considerations]. *Monatsschrift Kinderheilkunde* 2004; 152: 1217-1224. Subject: 15.2

Waltho, Simon. Response to Westin and Nilstun. *Health Care Analysis: An International Journal of Health Philosophy and Policy* 2006 June; 14(2): 119-122. Subject: 2.1

Waltman, Patricia A.; Schenk, Laura K. Neonatal ethical decision making: where does the NNP fit in? *Neonatal Network* 1999 December; 18(8): 27-32. Subject: 20.5.2

Waltz, Emily. Informed consent issues hobble cancer genome scheme [news]. *Nature Medicine* 2006 July; 12(7): 719. Subject: 15.10

Waltz, Emily. New York's scheme to track diabetes stirs privacy concerns [news]. *Nature Medicine* 2006 February; 12(2): 155. Subject: 8.4

Waltz, Emily. US court rules to allow experimental drugs for dying patients [news]. *Nature Medicine* 2006 June; 12(6): 596. Subject: 18.5.7

Wancata, Andrew. No value for a pound of flesh: extending market-inalienability of the human body. *Journal of Law and Health* 2003-2004; 18(2): 199-228. Subject: 4.4

Wang, Qizhi. Misconduct: China needs university ethics courses. *Nature* 2006 July 13; 442(7099): 132. Subject: 1.3.9

Wang, Yanguang. Chinese 'eugenics': definition, practice and cultural values. *In:* Sleeboom, Margaret, ed. Genomics in Asia: A Clash of Bioethical Interests? New York: Kegan Paul; 2004: 281-299. Subject: 15.5

Wang, Yanguang. Chinese ethical views on embryo stem (ES) cell research. *In:* Sang-yong, Song; Young-Mo, Koo; Macer, Darryl R.J., eds. Asian Bioethics in the 21st Century. Christchurch, NZ: Eubios Ethics Institute, 2002: 49-55. Subject: 18.5.4

Wang, Yanguang. Some policy recommendations based on the principle of strategic tolerance concerning HIV/AIDS in China. *In:* Döring, Ole; Chen, Renbiao, eds. Advances in Chinese Medical Ethics: Chinese and International Perspectives. Hamburg: Institut für Asienkunde; 2002: 298-305. Subject: 9.5.6

Wang, Yifang. Ideals and ethics: the concept of 'the art of humaneness' is not reliable. *In:* Döring, Ole; Chen, Renbiao, eds. Advances in Chinese Medical Ethics: Chinese and International Perspectives. Hamburg: Institut für Asienkunde; 2002: 266-275. Subject: 2.2

Warburton, Damian. Confidentiality and HIV: ethical issues in the care of patients with HIV. *British Journal of Hospital Medicine (London)* 2005 September; 66(9): 525-528. Subject: 9.5.6

Ward, Andrew. The concept of underinsurance: a general typology. *Journal of Medicine and Philosophy* 2006 October; 31(5): 499-531. Subject: 9.3.1

Ward, Frances R. Parents and professionals in the NICU: communication within the context of ethical decision mak-

ing — an integrative review. *Neonatal Network* 2005 May-June; 24(3): 25-33. Subject: 8.3.2

Wardak, Ahson; Gorman, Michael E. Using trading zones and life cycle analysis to understand nanotechnology regulation. *Journal of Law, Medicine and Ethics* 2006 Winter; 34(4): 695-703. Subject: 5.4

Waring, Justin J. Beyond blame: cultural barriers to medical incident reporting. *Social Science and Medicine* 2005 May; 60(9): 1927-1935. Subject: 9.8

Warne, Garry; Bhatia, Vijayalakshmi. Intersex, east and west. *In:* Sytsma, Sharon E., ed. Ethics and Intersex. Dordrecht: Springer, 2006: 183-205. Subject: 10

Warner, Carol M. Genetic engineering of human eggs and embryos: prelude to cloning. *Politics and the Life Sciences* 1998 March; 17(1): 33-34. Subject: 15.4

Warner, Teddy D.; Monaghan-Geernaert, Pamela; Battaglia, John; Brems, Christiane; Johnson, Mark E.; Roberts, Laura Weiss. Ethical considerations in rural health care: a pilot study of clinicians in Alaska and New Mexico. *Community Mental Health Journal* 2005 February; 41(1): 21-33. Subject: 9.5.1

Warnke, Patrick H. Repair of a human face by allotransplantation. *Lancet* 2006 July 15-21; 368(9531): 181-183. Subject: 19.1

Warnock, Mary. Genetics. *In her:* Nature and Mortality: Recollections of a Philosopher in Public Life. New York: Continuum; 2003: 69-110. Subject: 18.5.4

Warnock, Mary. Human fertilization and embryology. *In her:* Nature and Morality: Recollections of a Philosopher in Public Life. New York: Continuum; 2003: 69-110. Subject: 18.5.4

Warnock, Mary. Man and other animals. *In her:* Nature and Morality: Recollections of a Philosopher in Public Life. New York: Continuum; 2003: 149-177. Subject: 22.2

Washington. *Laws, statutes, etc.* An act relating to genetic testing as a condition of employment; and adding a new section to chapter 49.44 of the Revised Code of Washington [Approved: 11 March 2004]. Washington: State Legislature, 2004. 3 p. [Online]. Accessed: http://www.leg.wa.gov/pub/billinfo/2003-04/Pdf/Bills/Session%20Law%202004/6180.SL.pdf [2007 March 9]. Subject: 15.3

Washofsky, Mark. Halachah, aggadah, and Reform Jewish bioethics: a response. *CCAR Journal: A Reform Jewish Quarterly* 2006 Summer; 53(3): 81-106. Subject: 2.1

Wasley, Paula. Psychologists debate ethics of their involvement in interrogations. *Chronicle of Higher Education* 2006 September 1; 53(2): 28. Subject: 17.1

Wasserman, David. This old house: the human genome and human body as objects of historic preservation. *Politics and the Life Sciences* 2003 March 22(1): 43-47. Subject: 15.1

See SUBJECT HEADING KEY FOR SECTION II on inside back cover.

763

Wasserman, David; Hellman, Deborah S.; Wachbroit, Robert. Physicians as researchers: difficulties with the "similarity position". *American Journal of Bioethics* 2006 July-August; 6(4): 57-59. Subject: 18.2

Wasserman, Jason; Clair, Jeffery Michael; Ritchey, Ferris J. Racial differences in attitudes toward euthanasia. *Omega* 2005-2006; 52(3):263-287. Subject: 20.5.1

Wasson, Katherine. Altruism and pediatric oncology trials: it does not tip the decision-making scales. *American Journal of Bioethics* 2006 September-October; 6(5): 48. Subject: 18.3

Wasson, Katherine; Cook, David. Pellegrino and medicine: a critical revision. *American Journal of Bioethics* 2006 March-April; 6(2): 90-91. Subject: 2.1

Wasson, Katherine; Cook, E. David; Helzlsour, Kathy. Direct-to-consumer online genetic testing and the four principles: an analysis of the ethical issues. *Ethics and Medicine* 2006 Summer; 22(2): 83-91. Subject: 15.3

Wasti, Sabahat A.; Bhatti, Sajid Z. Guantanamo: a call for action: doctors should not treat detainees only to render them fit to further abuse [letter]. *BMJ: British Medical Journal* 2006 April 8; 332(7545): 855. Subject: 21.4

Waterhouse, Tessa; Pollard, Andrew. Clinical trials: consent in children [editorial]. *Expert Review of Vaccines* 2005 February; 4(1): 1-3. Subject: 18.5.2

Waterston, T. A general paediatrician's practice in children's rights. *Archives of Disease in Childhood* 2005 February; 90(2): 178-181. Subject: 8.3.2

Watkins, Peter. On the use of human tissue after death [editorial]. *Clinical Medicine* 2004 September-October; 4(5): 393-394. Subject: 7.1

Watkins, Sylvia. Migration of healthcare professionals: practical and ethical considerations. *Clinical Medicine* 2005 May-June; 5(3): 240-243. Subject: 21.6

Watson, A.R. Ethics support in clinical practice. *Archives of Disease in Childhood* 2005 September; 90(9): 943-946. Subject: 9.6

Watson, Alison. Ethical dilemma: an elderly man and getting home. *Perspectives* 2005 Winter; 29(4): 13-15. Subject: 9.5.2

Watson, Jean. Can an ethic of caring be maintained? *Journal of Advanced Nursing* 2006 May; 54(3): 257-259. Subject: 4.1.3

Watson, Jean. Caring science: belonging before being as ethical cosmology. *Nursing Science Quarterly* 2005 October; 18(4): 304-305. Subject: 4.1.3

Watson, Jean. Caring theory as an ethical guide to administrative and clinical practices. *JONA's Healthcare Law, Ethics, and Regulation* 2006 July-September; 8(3): 87-93. Subject: 4.1.1

Watson, Katie. A conversation with Mary Stainton: power dynamics and informed consent [interview]. *Atrium* 2006 Fall; 3: 16-17. Subject: 8.3.2

Watson, Katie. Jarred and jarring: the unfolding history of a museum of anatomy. *Atrium* 2005 Spring; 1: 1-3. Subject: 4.4

Watson, Katie. Pascal's wager 2.0. *Atrium* 2006 Winter; 2: 9-11. Subject: 20.5

Watson, Katie. Sterilization of people with disabilities today. *Atrium* 2006 Fall; 3: 17, 21. Subject: 11.3

Watson, Max. Harmful impact of EU clinical trials directives: . . .and so has trial of melatonin in cancer related weight loss. . . [letter]. *BMJ: British Medical Journal* 2006 March 18; 332(7542): 666. Subject: 18.2

Watson, Michael S.; Mann, Marie Y.; Lloyd-Puryear, Michele A.; Rinaldo, Piero; Howell, R. Rodney. Newborn screening: toward a uniform screening panel and system. Executive summary. *Genetics in Medicine* 2006 May; 8(Supplement 1): 1S-11S. Subject: 9.5.7

Watson, Michael S.; Mann, Marie Y.; Lloyd-Puryear, Michele A.; Rinaldo, Piero; Howell, R. Rodney. Newborn screening: toward a uniform screening panel and system. Main report. *Genetics in Medicine* 2006 May; 8(Supplement 1): 12S-52S. Subject: 9.5.7

Watson, Nigel; Halamka, John. Patients should have to opt out of national electronic care records. *BMJ: British Medical Journal* 2006 July 1; 333(7557): 39-42. Subject: 8.3.1

Watson, Peter Y.; Musial, Joseph L.; Khandewal, Akshay K.; Buckley, John D.; Brennan, Troyen A.; Rothman, David J.; Naughton, James; Cohen, Jordan; Kimball, Harry; Blumenthal, David; Smelser, Neil; Kassirer, Jerome P.; Goldman, JanLori. Academic medical centers and conflicts of interest [letter and reply]. *JAMA: The Journal of the American Medical Association* 2006 June 28; 295(24): 2847-2848, 2848-2849. Subject: 7.3

Watson, Roger. Editorial: should studies without ethical permission be published in JCN? *Journal of Clinical Nursing* 2006 March; 15(3): 251. Subject: 1.3.7

Watson, Rory. Cancer group denies company funding will influence its agenda [news]. *BMJ: British Medical Journal* 2006 October 28; 333(7574): 874. Subject: 9.1

Watts, Cara D. Asking adolescents: does a mature minor have a right to participate in health care decisions? *Hastings Women's Law Journal* 2005 Summer; 16(2): 221-249. Subject: 8.3.2

Watts, Geoff. Combating chaos [news]. *BMJ: British Medical Journal* 2006 September 30; 333(7570): 674. Subject: 9.6

Watts, Geoff. Will UK biobank pay off? [news]. *BMJ: British Medical Journal* 2006 May 6; 332(7549): 1052. Subject: 15.1

Subject = NRCBL Primary Classification Number; see inside front cover.

Watts, Nelson B. Is it ethical to use placebos in osteoporosis clinical trials? *Current Osteoporosis Reports* 2004 March; 2(1): 31-36. Subject: 18.3

Wax, Amy L. Technology assessment and the doctor-patient relationship. *Virginia Law Review* 1996 November; 82(8): 1641-1662. Subject: 9.3.1

Wax, Joseph R.; Cartin, Angelina; Pinette, Michael G.; Blackstone, Jacquelyn. Patient choice cesarean: an evidence-based review. *Obstetrical and Gynecological Survey* 2004 August; 59(8): 601-616. Subject: 9.5.5

Wazana, Ashley; Primeau, Francois. Ethical considerations in the relationship between physicians and the pharmaceutical industry. *Psychiatric Clinics of North America* 2002 September; 25(3): 647-663. Subject: 9.7

Weait, Matthew; Azad, Yusef. The criminalization of HIV transmission in England and Wales: questions of law and policy. *HIV/AIDS Policy and Law Review* 2005 August; 10(2): 1, 5-12. Subject: 9.5.6

Weaver, Glenn. Embodied spirituality: experiences of identity and spiritual suffering among persons with Alzheimer's dementia. *In:* Jeeves, Michael, ed. From Cells to Souls — and Beyond: Changing Portraits of Human Nature. Grand Rapids, MI: W.B. Eerdmans; 2004: 77-101. Subject: 9.5.2

Weber, David O. Unethical business practices in U.S. health care alarm physician leaders. *Physician Executive* 2005 March-April; 31(2): 6-13. Subject: 9.1

Webster, Andrew. Social science ethics: the changing context for research. *Clinical Ethics* 2006 March; 1(1): 39-40. Subject: 1.3.9

Webster, Dianne. Storage and use of residual dried blood spots. *Southeast Asian Journal of Tropical Medicine and Public Health* 2003; 34(Supplement 3): 49-51. Subject: 15.3

Webster, Paul. Canadian researchers respond to CMAJ crisis. *Lancet* 2006 April 8-14; 367(9517): 1133-1134. Subject: 1.3.7

Webster, Paul. CMAJ editors dismissed amid calls for more editorial freedom. *Lancet* 2006 March 4-10; 367(9512): 720. Subject: 1.3.7

Wechsler, Harlan J. Religious perspectives on access to health care: a Jewish perspective. *Mount Sinai Journal of Medicine* 1997 March; 64(2): 84-89. Subject: 9.4

Wechter, David; Masek, Lawrence. ANT and the contralife argument [letter and reply]. *National Catholic Bioethics Quarterly* 2006 Winter; 6(4): 617-618. Subject: 14.4

Weckert, John. The control of scientific research: the case of nanotechnology. *In:* Tavani, Herman T., ed. Ethics, Computing, and Genomics. Sudbury, MA: Jones and Bartlett; 2006: 323-339. Subject: 5.4

Weeden, Jeffrey Lawrence. Genetic liberty, genetic property: protecting genetic information. *Ave Maria Law Review* 2006 Summer; 4(2): 611-664. Subject: 15.8

Weel, Andre N.H.; Kelder, Marja J. Sickness absence management. *In:* Westerholm, Peter; Nilstun, Tore; Øvretveit, John, eds. Practical Ethics in Occupational Health. San Francisco: Radcliffe Medical Press; 2004: 115-131. Subject: 16.3

Wegener, Stephen T. The rehabilitation ethic and ethics. *Rehabilitation Psychology* 1996; 41(1): 5-17. Subject: 9.4

Wehlte, Christian. Über die "Heiligkeit des Lebens" — Zur Vernachlässigung soziokultureller Dimensionen in der Euthanasie-Diskussion. *In:* Frewer, Andreas; Eickhoff, Clemens, eds. "Euthanasie" und die aktuelle Sterbehilfe-Debatte: Die historischen Hintergründe medizinischer Ethik. Frankfurt; New York: Campus; 2000: 336-355. Subject: 4.4

Weijer, Charles. Clinical trials. *In:* Mitcham, Carl, ed. Encyclopedia of Science, Technology, and Ethics. Farmington Hills, MI: Thomson/Gale, 2005: 347-350. Subject: 18.1

Weijer, Charles. The ethical analysis of risk in intensive care unit research. *Critical Care* 2004 April; 8(2): 85-86. Subject: 18.3

Weijer, Charles. The ethics of placebo-controlled trials. *Journal of Bone and Mineral Research* 2003 June; 18(6): 1150-1153. Subject: 18.3

Weijer, Charles; LeBlanc, Guy J. The balm of Gilead: is the provision of treatment to those who seroconvert in HIV prevention trials a matter of moral obligation or moral negotiation? *Journal of Law, Medicine and Ethics* 2006 Winter; 34(4): 793-808. Subject: 18.5.1

Weikart, Richard. Eugenics. *In:* Mitcham, Carl, ed. Encyclopedia of Science, Technology, and Ethics. Farmington Hills, MI: Thomson/Gale, 2005: 707-710. Subject: 15.5

Weil, Elizabeth. Breeder reaction: does everybody have the right to have a baby? And who should pay when nature alone doesn't work? *Mother Jones* 2006 July/August; 31(4): 33-37. Subject: 14.1

Weil, Elizabeth. What if it's (sort of) a boy and (sort of) a girl? *New York Times Magazine* 2006 September 24; p. 48-53. Subject: 10

Weil, Elizabeth. A wrongful birth? *New York Times Magazine* 2006 March 12; p. 48-53. Subject: 11.4

Weil, Jon; Ormond, Kelly; Peters, June; Peters, Kathryn; Bowles Biesecker, Barbara; LeRoy, Bonnie. The relationship of nondirectiveness to genetic counseling: report of a workshop at the 2003 NSGC Annual Education Conference. *Journal of Genetic Counseling* 2006 April; 15(2): 85-93. Subject: 15.2

Weimar, Willem; Zuidema, Willij; de Klerk, Marry; Haase-Kromwijk, Bernadette; Ijzermans, Jan. Altruis-

See SUBJECT HEADING KEY FOR SECTION II on inside back cover.

765

tic kidney donation. *Lancet* 2006 September 16-22; 368(9540): 987. Subject: 19.5

Weinberg, Aviva. Pediatric cochlear implants: the great debate. *Penn Bioethics Journal* 2005 April 2; 1(1): 4p. [Online]. Accessed: http://www.bioethicsjournal.com [2005 April 19]. Subject: 9.5.7

Weinfurt, Kevin P.; Dinan, Michaela A.; Allsbrook, Jennifer S.; Friedman, Joëlle Y.; Hall, Mark A.; Schulman, Kevin A.; Sugarman, Jeremy. Policies of academic medical center for disclosing financial conflicts of interest to potential research participants. *Academic Medicine* 2006 February; 81(2): 113-118. Subject: 18.2

Weinfurt, Kevin P.; Friedman, Joëlle Y.; Allsbrook, Jennifer S.; Dinan, Michaela A.; Hall, Mark A.; Sugarman, Jeremy. Views of potential research participants on financial conflicts of interest: barriers and opportunities for effective disclosure. *JGIM: Journal of General Internal Medicine* 2006 September; 21(9): 901-906. Subject: 18.2

Weinfurt, Kevin P.; Friedman, Joëlle Y.; Dinan, Michaela A.; Allsbrook, Jennifer S.; Hall, Mark A.; Dhillon, Jatinder K.; Sugarman, Jeremy. Disclosing conflicts of interest in clinical research: views on institutional review boards, conflict of interest committees, and investigators. *Journal of Law, Medicine and Ethics* 2006 Fall; 34(3): 581-591. Subject: 18.2

Weinstein, James N. The missing piece: embracing shared decision making to reform health care [editorial]. *Spine* 2000 January; 25(1): 1-4. Subject: 8.1

Weinstein, James N. Partnership: doctor and patient: advocacy for informed choice vs. informed consent. *Spine* 2005 February 1; 30(3): 269-271. Subject: 8.3.1

Weisbrot, David. Mad science or modern miracles? *Reform* 2001 Spring; 79: 5-9. Subject: 15.3

Weiss Roberts, Laura. Ethical philanthropy in academic psychiatry. *American Journal of Psychiatry* 2006 May; 163(5): 772-778. Subject: 17.1

Weiss Roberts, Laura; Geppert, Cynthia M.A.; Coverdale, John; Louie, Alan; Edenharder, Kristin. Ethical and regulatory considerations in educational research [editorial]. *Academic Psychiatry* 2005 Spring; 29(1): 1-5. Subject: 17.1

Weiss, Kenneth M. Coming to terms with human variation. *Annual Review of Anthropology* 1998; 27: 273-300. Subject: 15.11

Weiss, Marcia J. Beware! Uncle Sam has your DNA; legal fallout from its use and misuse in the U.S. *Ethics and Information Technology* 2004; 6(1): 55-63. Subject: 15.1

Weiss, Rick. "Serious misconduct" by NIH expert found: scientist did not report sending tissues to drug firm and getting paid, report says. *Washington Post* 2006 June 14; p. A6. Subject: 1.3.9

Weiss, Rick. Government health researchers pressed to share data at no charge. *Washington Post* 2006 March 10; p. A17. Subject: 1.3.9

Weiss, Rick. Human embryos in Britain may be screened for cancer risk. *Washington Post* 2006 May 11; p. A12. Subject: 15.3

Weiss, Rick. The power to divide: stem cells could launch a new era of medicine, curing deadly diseases with custom-made tissues and organs. But science may take a backseat to politics in deciding if — and where — that hope will be realized. *National Geographic* 2005 July; 208(1): 2-7, 15-17, 22-23, 26-27. Subject: 18.5.4

Weiss, Sheila. "Essay Review: Racial Science and Genetics at the Kaiser Wilhelm Society". *Journal of the History of Biology* 2005 Summer; 38(2): 367-379. Subject: 21.4

Weiss, Sheila F. Is biotechnological medicine a curse or a blessing? Lessons learned from the international eugenics movement, 1900-1945. *In:* Döring, Ole; Chen, Renbiao, eds. Advances in Chinese Medical Ethics: Chinese and International Perspectives. Hamburg: Institut für Asienkunde; 2002: 85-97. Subject: 15.5

Weissman, David. Do not resuscitate orders: a call for reform. *Virtual Mentor* 2001 July; 3(7): 3p. Subject: 20.5.1

Weissman, Irving L. Politic stem cells. *Nature* 2006 January 12; 439(7073): 145, 147-148. Subject: 18.5.4

Weisz, Victoria; Robbennolt, Jennifer K. Risks and benefits of pediatric bone marrow donation: a critical need for research. *Behavioral Sciences and the Law* 1996 Autumn; 14(4): 375-391. Subject: 19.5

Weithorn, Lois A.; Scherer, David G. Children's involvement in research participation decisions: psychological considerations. *In:* Gordin, M.; Glantz, L., eds. Children as Research Subjects. Oxford University Press; 1994: 133-179. Subject: 18.5.2

Weiting, Mark W.; Mevis, Howard; Zuckerman, Joseph D. The role of industry in Internet education. *Clinical Orthopaedics and Related Research* 2003 July; (412): 28-32. Subject: 7.2

Welchman, Jennifer. Is pragmatism chauvinistic? Dewey on animal experimentation. *In:* McKenna, Erin; Light, Andrew, eds. Animal Pragmatism: Rethinking Human-Nonhuman Relationships. Bloomington, IN: Indiana University Press; 2004: 179-192. Subject: 22.2

Weldon, Sue; Levitt, Mairi. "Public databases and privat(ized) property?": a UK study of public perceptions of privacy in relation to population based human genetic databases. *In:* Árnason, Gardar; Nordal, Salvör; Árnason, Vilhjálmur, eds. Blood and Data: Ethical, Legal and Social Aspects of Human Genetic Databases. Reykjavík: University of Iceland Press; 2004: 181-186. Subject: 15.1

Welie, Jos V.M. Is dentistry a profession? Part 1. Professionalism defined. *Journal of the Canadian Dental Association* 2004 September; 70(8): 529-532. Subject: 4.1.1

Subject = NRCBL Primary Classification Number; see inside front cover.

Welie, Jos V.M. Is dentistry a profession? Part 2. The hallmarks of professionalism. *Journal of the Canadian Dental Association* 2004 October; 70(9): 599-602. Subject: 4.1.1

Welie, Jos V.M. Is dentistry a profession? Part 3. Future challenges. *Journal of the Canadian Dental Association* 2004 November; 70(10): 675-678. Subject: 4.1.1

Welie, Sander P.K.; Berghmans, Ron L.P. Inclusion of patients with severe mental illness in clinical trials: issues and recommendations surrounding informed consent. *CNS Drugs* 2006; 20(1): 67-83. Subject: 18.3

Welin, Stellan. The value of life. *In:* Lundin, Susanne; Åkesson, Lynn, eds. Gene Technology and Economy. Lund: Nordic Academic Press; 2002: 85-91. Subject: 15.1

Wellbery, Caroline. Emergency contraception: an ongoing debate [editorial]. *American Family Physician* 2004 August 15; 70(4): 655-659. Subject: 11.1

Wells, Frank. Fraud and misconduct in clinical research. *In:* Di Giovanna, Ignazio; Hayes, Gareth, eds. Principles of Clinical Research. Philadelphia: Wrightson Biomedical Pub.; 2001: 507-528. Subject: 1.3.9

Welsh, Johnathan R. In whose 'best interests'? Ethical issues involved in the moral dilemmas surrounding the removal of sexually abused adolescents from a community-based residential treatment unit to a locked, forensic adult psychiatric unit. *Journal of Advanced Nursing* 1998 January; 27(1): 45-51. Subject: 17.7

Welsh, Rick; Ervin, David. Precaution as an approach to technology development: the case of transgenic crops. *Science, Technology, and Human Values* 2006 March; 31(2): 153-172. Subject: 15.7

Wendler, David. Assent in paediatric research: theoretical and practical considerations. *Journal of Medical Ethics* 2006 April; 32(4): 229-234. Subject: 18.5.2

Wendler, David. Clinical research, clinical tragedies and the assumption of responsibility. *Organizational Ethics: Healthcare, Business, and Policy* 2006 Spring-Summer; 3(1): 46-49. Subject: 18.3

Wendler, David. One-time general consent for research on biological samples. *BMJ: British Medical Journal* 2006 March 4; 332(7540): 544-547. Subject: 8.3.1

Wendler, David. One-time general consent for research on biological samples: is it compatible with the Health Insurance Portability And Accountability Act? *Archives of Internal Medicine* 2006 July 24; 166(14): 1449-1452. Subject: 18.3

Wendler, David; Emanuel, Ezekiel J. What is a "minor" increase over minimal risk? *Journal of Pediatrics* 2005 November; 147(5): 575-578. Subject: 18.5.2

Wendler, David; Shah, Seema. How can medical training and informed consent by reconciled with volume-outcome data? *Journal of Clinical Ethics* 2006 Summer; 17(2): 149-157. Subject: 7.2

Wendorf, Barbara. Ethical decision-making in quality assurance. *QRB: Quality Review Bulletin* 1982 January; 8(1): 4-6. Subject: 2.3

Wenger, Ashley A. Fetal pain legislation: subordinating sound medical findings to moral and political agendas. *Journal of Legal Medicine* 2006 December; 27(4): 459-476. Subject: 12.5.3

Wenger, Nanette K.; Weber, Michael A.; Scheidt, Stephen. Hippocrates, Maimonides, and end-of-life issues [editorial]. *American Journal of Geriatric Cardiology* 2004 November-December; 13(6): 291-292. Subject: 20.5.1

Wenger, Neil S.; Lieberman, Jay R. Achieving informed consent when patients appear to lack capacity and surrogates. *Clinical Orthopaedics and Related Research* 2000 September; (378): 78-82. Subject: 8.3.1

Wenger, Neil S.; Lieberman, Jay R. The orthopaedic surgeon and industry: ethics and industry incentives. *Clinical Orthopaedics and Related Research* 2000 September; (378): 39-43. Subject: 9.7

Wenkel, David H. Separation of conjoined twins and the principle of double effect. *Christian Bioethics* 2006 December; 12(3): 291-300. Subject: 9.5.1

Werner, Perla; Carmel, Sara; Ziedenberg, Hanna. Nurses' and social workers' attitudes and beliefs about and involvement in life-sustaining treatment decisions. *Health and Social Work* 2004 February; 29(1): 27-35. Subject: 20.3.2

Werner, Rachel M.; Asch, David A.; Polsky, Daniel. Racial profiling: the unintended consequences of coronary artery bypass graft report cards. *Circulation* 2005 March 15; 111(10): 1257-1263. Subject: 9.5.4

Werntoft, Elisabet; Edberg, Anna-Karin; Rooke, Liselotte; Hermeren, Goran; Elmstahl, Solve; Hallberg, Ingalill Rahm. Older people's views of prioritization in health care. The applicability of an interview study. *Journal of Clinical Nursing* 2005 September; 14(8B): 64-74. Subject: 5.1

Werntoft, Elisabet; Hallberg, Ingalill Rahn; Elmståhl, Sölve; Edberg, Anna-Karin. Older people's views of prioritization in health care. *Aging Clinical and Experimental Research* 2005 October; 17(5): 402-411. Subject: 9.4

Wesley, Carol A. Social Work and End-of-Life Decisions: Self-Determination and the Common Good. *Health and Social Work* 1996 May; 21(2): 115-121. Subject: 20.5.1

West, Chad. Economics and ethics in the genetic engineering of animals. *Harvard Journal of Law and Technology* 2006 Spring; 19(2): 413-442. Subject: 22.2

West, John C. Medical malpractice/battery. Various causes of action available in 'ghost surgery' case. *Journal of Healthcare Risk Management* 2004; 24(1): 31-32. Subject: 8.5

See SUBJECT HEADING KEY FOR SECTION II on inside back cover.

767

West, J. Andrew. Defining the limits of conscientious objection in health care. *Newsletter on Philosophy and Law* 2005 Fall; 05(1): 25-34. Subject: 12.4.3

Westerveld, H.E.; Briet, J.W.; Houwaart, E.S.; Legemaate, J.; Meerman, T.J.A.M.; Breetvelt, E.J.; van der Wall, E. Dutch medical oath. *Netherlands Journal of Medicine* 2005 October; 63(9): 368-371. Subject: 6

Westin, Alan F. Public attitudes toward electronic health records. *AHIP Coverage* 2005 July-August; 46(4): 22-25. Subject: 8.4

Westin, Lars; Nilstun, Tore. Principles help to analyse but often give no solution — secondary prevention after a cardiac event. *Health Care Analysis: An International Journal of Health Philosophy and Policy* 2006 June; 14(2): 111-117. Subject: 2.1

Westin, Lars; Nilstun, Tore. Principlism revisited: response to Simon Waltho. *Health Care Analysis: An International Journal of Health Philosophy and Policy* 2006 December; 14(4): 247-248. Subject: 2.1

Westmoreland, Timothy M.; Watson, Kathryn R. Redeeming hollow promises: the case for mandatory spending on health care for American Indians and Alaska Natives. *American Journal of Public Health* 2006 April; 96(4): 600-605. Subject: 9.5.4

Weston, Christine M.; O'Brien, Linda A.; Goldfarb, Neil I.; Roumm, Adam R.; Isele, William P.; Hirschfeld, Kathryn. The NJ SEED project: evaluation of an innovative initiative for ethics training in nursing homes. *Journal of the American Medical Directors Association* 2005 January-February; 6(1): 68-75. Subject: 9.6

Wettstein, Robert M. Ethics and forensic psychiatry. *Psychiatric Clinics of North America* 2002 September; 25(3): 623-633. Subject: 17.1

Whaley, Arthur L. Ethnicity/race, ethics, and epidemiology. *Journal of the National Medical Association* 2003 August; 95(8): 736-742. Subject: 9.5.1

Wheeler, Robert. Gillick or Fraser? A plea for consistency over competence in children [editorial]. *BMJ: British Medical Journal* 2006 April 8; 332(7545): 807. Subject: 9.5.7

Whelan, Jo. Sex is for fun: IVF is for children. *New Scientist* 2006 October 21-27; 192(2574): 42-45. Subject: 14.4

Whetten, Kathryn; Leserman, Jane; Whetten, Rachel; Ostermann, Jan; Thielman, Nathan; Swartz, Marvin; Stangl, Darlene. Exploring lack of trust in care providers and the government as a barrier to health service use. *American Journal of Public Health* 2006 April; 96(4): 716-721. Subject: 9.5.6

While, Alison. First steps towards ethical research. *Practice Nurse* 1998 February 20; 15(3): 135-138. Subject: 18.1

Whitaker, Stuart. Health examinations on new employment: ethical issues. *In:* Westerholm, Peter; Nilstun, Tore;

Øvretveit, John, eds. Practical Ethics in Occupational Health. San Francisco: Radcliffe Medical Press; 2004: 91-104. Subject: 16.3

White, Caroline. Fertility treatment regulator steps up warning about multiple births [news]. *BMJ: British Medical Journal* 2006 June 10; 332(7554): 1353. Subject: 14.4

White, Douglas B.; Curtis, J. Randall; Lo, Bernard; Luce, John M. Decisions to limit life-sustaining treatment for critically ill patients who lack both decision-making capacity and surrogate decision-makers. *Critical Care Medicine* 2006 August; 34(8): 2053-2059. Subject: 20.5.1

White, Earl D., II. Reflections on the success of hospital ethics committees in my health system. *HEC (Healthcare Ethics Committee) Forum* 2006 December; 18(4): 349-356. Subject: 9.6

White, Gladys B. Analogical power and Aristotle's model of persuasion. *American Journal of Bioethics* 2006 November-December; 6(6): 67-68; author reply W13-W14. Subject: 19.4

White, Karolyn; McGrath, Catherine; Kerridge, Ian. Multicultural medicine: ethical issues encountered when perspectives differ. *Eubios Journal of Asian and International Bioethics* 2006 January; 16(1): 4-6. Subject: 21.7

White, Katherine A. Crisis of conscience: reconciling religious health care providers' beliefs and patients' rights. *Stanford Law Review* 1999 July; 51(6): 1703-1749. Subject: 9.2

White, Mary Terrell. Diagnosing PVS and minimally conscious state: the role of tacit knowledge and intuition. *Journal of Clinical Ethics* 2006 Spring; 17(1): 62-71. Subject: 20.5.1

White, Mary Terrell. Religious and spiritual concerns in genetic testing and decision making: an introduction for pastoral and genetic counselors. *Journal of Clinical Ethics* 2006 Summer; 17(2): 158-167. Subject: 15.2

White, Matthew. Conscience clauses for pharmacists: the struggle to balance conscience rights with the rights of patients and institutions. *Wisconsin Law Review* 2005; 2005(6): 1611-1648. Subject: 11.1

White, Robert M. Misinformation and misbeliefs in the Tuskegee Study of Untreated Syphilis fuel mistrust in the healthcare system [editorial]. *Journal of the National Medical Association* 2005 November; 97(11): 1566-1573. Subject: 18.5.1

White, S.A.; Prasad, K.R. Liver transplantation from non-heart beating donors: a promising way to increase the supply of organs. *BMJ: British Medical Journal* 2006 February 18; 332(7538): 376-377. Subject: 19.1

White, S.M.; Baldwin, T.J. The Mental Capacity Act 2005 — implications for anaesthesia and critical care. *Anaesthesia* 2006 April; 61(4): 381-389. Subject: 8.3.3

White, S.M.; Baldwin, T.J. Withholding life-prolonging treatment [letter]. *Anaesthesia* 2005 April; 60(4): 417-418. Subject: 20.5.1

Whitehouse, Peter J. The end of Alzheimer disease II: commentary on "Decisions to treat or not to treat pneumonia in demented psychogeriatric nursing home patients". *Alzheimer Disease and Associated Disorders* 2001 July-September; 15(3): 118. Subject: 9.4

Whiteman, David C. Privacy and medical research [editorial]. *Internal Medicine Journal* 2005 August; 35(8): 441-442. Subject: 8.4

Whiteman, David C.; Clutton, Cathy; Hill, David. Australian public's view on privacy and health research [letter]. *BMJ: British Medical Journal* 2006 May 27; 332(7552): 1274. Subject: 18.1

Whitney, Simon N.; Ethier, Angela M.; Frugé, Ernest; Berg, Stacey; McCullough, Laurence B.; Hockenberry, Marilyn. Decision making in pediatric oncology: who should take the lead? The decisional priority in pediatric oncology model. *Journal of Clinical Oncology* 2006 January 1; 24(1): 160-165. Subject: 9.4

Whittaker, Elvi. Adjudicating entitlements: the emerging discourses of research ethics boards. *Health (London)* 2005 October; 9(4): 513-535. Subject: 18.2

Whyte, Susan Reynolds; van der Geest, Sjaak; Hardon, Anita. Drug vendors and their market: the commodification of health. *In their:* Social Lives of Medicines. New York: Cambridge University Press; 2002: 79-90. Subject: 9.7

Whyte, Susan Reynolds; Whyte, Michael A.; Meinert, Lotte; Kyaddondo, Betty. Treating AIDS: dilemmas of unequal access in Uganda. *In:* Petryna, Adriana; Lakoff, Andrew; Kleinman, Arthur, eds. Global Pharmaceuticals: Ethics, Markets, Practices. Durham: Duke University Press; 2006: 240-262. Subject: 9.5.6

Wicclair, Mark R. Pharmacies, pharmacists, and conscientious objection. *Kennedy Institute of Ethics Journal* 2006 September; 16(3): 225-250. Subject: 9.7

Wicclair, Mark R. Training on newly deceased patients: an ethical analysis. *In:* Jansen, Lynn A., ed. Death in the Clinic. Lanham, MD: Rowman and Littlefield; 2006: 135-154. Subject: 7.2

Wicclair, Mark R.; Gosman, Gabriella. Abortion. *In:* Mitcham, Carl, ed. Encyclopedia of Science, Technology, and Ethics. Farmington Hills, MI: Thomson/Gale, 2005: 1-6. Subject: 12.1

Wicher, Camille P.; Michalek, Arthur M. When is informed consent not enough? *Journal of Cancer Education* 2005 Spring; 20(1): 9-10. Subject: 18.3

Wichman, Alison, Kalyan, Dev N.; Abbott, Lura J.; Wesley, Robert; Sandler, Alan L. Protecting human subjects in the NIH's Intramural Research Program: a draft instrument to evaluate convened meetings of its IRBs. *IRB:*

Ethics and Human Research 2006 May-June; 28(3): 7-10. Subject: 18.2

Wichman, Alison; Sandler, Alan L. Institutional review boards. *In:* Gallin, John I., ed. Principles and Practice of Clinical Research. San Diego, CA: Academic Press; 2002: 51-62. Subject: 18.2

Wichmann, H.-E. Genetic epidemiology in Germany — from biobanking to genetic statistics. *Methods of Information in Medicine* 2005; 44(4): 584-589. Subject: 15.1

Widdershoven, Guy. Interpretation and dialogue in hermeneutic ethics. *In:* Ashcroft, Richard; Lucassen, Anneke; Parker, Michael; Verkerk, Marian; Widderhoven, Guy, eds. Case Analysis in Clinical Ethics. New York: Cambridge University Press; 2005: 57-75. Subject: 15.3

Widdershoven, Guy A.M. Beyond autonomy and beneficience: the moral basis of euthanasia in the Netherlands. *In:* Schotsmans, Paul; Meulenbergs, Tom, eds. Euthanasia and Palliative Care in the Low Countries. Dudley, MA: Peeters, 2005: 83-93. Subject: 20.5.1

Widdershoven, G. Commentary: euthanasia in Europe: a critique of the Marty report. *Journal of Medical Ethics* 2006 January; 32(1): 34-35. Subject: 20.5.1

Widdows, Heather. The impact of new reproductive technologies on concepts of genetic relatedness and non-relatedness. *In:* Widdows, Heather; Idiakez, Itziar Alkorta; Cirión, Aitziber Emaldi, eds. Women's Reproductive Rights. New York: Palgrave Macmillan; 2006: 151-164. Subject: 14.1

Widiger, Thomas A.; Rorer, Leonard. The Responsible psychotherapist. *American Psychologist* 1984 May; 39(5): 503-515. Subject: 17.2

Wiebe, Ellen R.; Trouton, Konia J.; Fielding, Stephen L.; Klippenstein, Jodine; Henderson, Angela. Antichoice attitudes to abortion in women presenting for medical abortions. *Journal of Obstetrics and Gynaecology Canada* 2005 March; 27(3): 247-250. Subject: 12.5.2

Wiegle, Thomas C. The biotechnology of sex preselection: social issues in a public policy context. *Policy Studies Review* 1985 February; 4(3): 445-460. Subject: 14.3

Wiens, Arlene G. Biotechnology through a nursing ethics lens. *In:* Miller, Roman J.; Brubaker, Beryl H.; Peterson, James C., eds. Viewing New Creations with Anabaptist Eyes: Ethics of Biotechnology. Telford, PA: Cascadia Pub.; 2005: 187-192. Subject: 4.1.3

Wiesemann, Claudia; Dahl, Matthias. Forschung mit Kindern und Jugendlichen: Ist eine neue rechtliche Regelung notwendig? *In:* Vollmann, Jochen, ed. Medizin und Ethik: Aktuelle ethische Probleme in Therapie und Forschung. Erlangen: Universitätsbund Erlangen-Nürnberg, 2003: 83-106. Subject: 18.5.2

Wiesing, Urban. Reanimieren/Nicht Reanimieren aus philosophischer Sicht. *In:* Gordijn, Bert; ten Have, Henk,

See SUBJECT HEADING KEY FOR SECTION II on inside back cover.

769

eds. Medizinethik und Kultur: Grenzen medizinischen Handelns in Deutschland und den Niederlanden. Stuttgart: Frommann-Holzboog; 2000: 375-390. Subject: 20.5.1

Wiggins, Kenneth R. Medicaid and the enforceable right to receive medical assistance: the need for a definition of "medical assistance". *William and Mary Law Review* 2006 February; 47(4): 1487-1512. Subject: 9.3.1

Wikler, Daniel. Polls and focus groups in bioethics: the case of resource allocation. *In:* Lolas Stepke, Fernando; Agar Corbinos, Lorenzo, eds. Interfaces Between Bioethics and the Empirical Social Sciences. Buenos Aires: World Health Organization; 2002: 91-98. Subject: 9.4

Wilan, Ken. Finding the moral high ground [news]. *Nature Biotechnology* 2006 March; 24(3): 237-239. Subject: 9.7

Wilansky, Daniel P. Civil rights: prisoners' right to treatment information under Pabon v. Wright. *Journal of Law, Medicine and Ethics* 2006 Winter; 34(4): 831-832. Subject: 8.3.1

Wilbanks, John. Another reason for opening access to research. *BMJ: British Medical Journal* 2006 December 23-30; 333(7582): 1306-1308. Subject: 1.3.9

Wilkes, Lesley; Cert, Renal; Beale, Barbara. Role conflict: appropriateness of a nurse researcher's actions in the clinical field. *Nurse Researcher* 2005; 12(4): 57-70. Subject: 18.2

Wilkie, Tom. When man plays God. *New Statesman (London, England:* 1996) 1998 June 12; 127(4389): 14-15. Subject: 15.1

Wilkinson, D. Is it in the best interests of an intellectually disabled infant to die? *Journal of Medical Ethics* 2006 August; 32(8): 454-459. Subject: 20.5.2

Wilkinson, Jan. Commentary: what's all the fuss about? *BMJ: British Medical Journal* 2006 July 1; 333(7557): 42-43. Subject: 8.3.1

Wilkinson, Stephen. 'Designer babies', instrumentalisation and the child's right to an open future. *In:* Athanassoulis, Nafsika, ed. Philosophical Reflections on Medical Ethics. New York: Palgrave Macmillan; 2005: 44-69. Subject: 14.1

Wilkinson, Stephen. Biomedical research and the commercial exploitation of human tissue. *Genomics, Society and Policy* 2005 February; 1(1): 27-40. Subject: 19.5

Wilkinson, Stephen. Eugenics, embryo selection, and the Equal Value Principle. *Clinical Ethics* 2006 March; 1(1): 46-51. Subject: 15.5

Wilkinson, Sue; Kitzinger, Celia. Whose breast is it anyway? A feminist consideration of advice and 'treatment' for breast cancer. *Women's Studies International Forum* 1993 May-June; 16(3): 229-238. Subject: 9.5.5

Wilks, Michael. Guantanamo: a call for action [editorial]. *BMJ: British Medical Journal* 2006 March 11; 332(7541): 560-561. Subject: 21.4

Will, Jonathan F. My God, my choice: the mature minor doctrine and adolescent refusal of live-saving or sustaining medical treatment based upon religious beliefs. *Journal of Contemporary Health Law and Policy* 2006 Spring; 22(2): 233-300. Subject: 8.3.2

Willems, S.; De Maesschalck, S.; Devuegele, M.; Derese, A.; De Maeseneer, J. Socio-economic status of the patient and doctor-patient communication: does it make a difference? *Patient Education and Counseling* 2005 February; 56(2): 139-146. Subject: 8.3.1

Williams, Alan. Thinking about equity in health care. *Journal of Nursing Management* 2005 September; 13(5): 397-402. Subject: 9.4

Williams, Anne. Ethics and action research. *Nurse Researcher* 1995 March; 2(3): 49-59. Subject: 18.1

Williams, Anne. Pitfalls on the road to ethical approval. *Nurse Researcher* 1997 Autumn; 5(1): 15-22. Subject: 18.2

Williams, Carolyn. Australian attitudes to DNA sample banks and genetic screening. *Current Medical Research and Opinion* 2005 November; 21(11): 1773-1775. Subject: 15.1

Williams, Charmaine C. Ethical considerations in mental health research with racial and ethnic minority communities. *Community Mental Health Journal* 2005 October; 41(5): 509-520. Subject: 18.5.1

Williams, Clare; Alderson, Priscilla; Farsides, Bobbie. 'Drawing the line' in prenatal screening and testing: health practitioners' discussions. *Health Risk and Society* 2002 March; 4(1): 61-75. Subject: 15.2

Williams, Clare; Sandall, Jane; Lewando-Hundt, Gillian; Heyman, Bob; Spencer, Kevin; Grellier, Rachel. Women as moral pioneers? Experiences of first trimester antenatal screening. *Social Science and Medicine* 2005 November; 61(9): 1983-1992. Subject: 9.5.5

Williams, Garrath. Bioethics and large-scale biobanking: individualistic ethics and collective projects. *Genetics, Society, and Policy* 2005 August; 1(2): 50-66. Subject: 15.1

Williams, John R. Medical ethics in contemporary clinical practice. *Journal of the Chinese Medical Association* 2005 November; 68(11): 495-499. Subject: 2.1

Williams, John R. The physician's role in the protection of human research subjects. *Science and Engineering Ethics* 2006 January; 12(1): 5-12. Subject: 8.1

Williams, John R. Response to reviews of the World Medical Association Medical Ethics Manual. *Journal of Medical Ethics* 2006 March; 32(3): 164-165. Subject: 2.1

Williams, Mark E. Internet organ solicitation, explained. *Advances in Chronic Kidney Disease* 2006 January; 13(1): 70-75. Subject: 19.5

Williams, Mark E.; Kitsen, Jenny. The involuntarily discharged dialysis patient: conflict (of interest) with providers. *Advances in Chronic Kidney Disease* 2005 January; 12(1): 107-112. Subject: 19.3

Williams, M.R.; Hegde, S.; Norton, M.R. Informed consent and surgeons in training: do patients consent to allow surgical trainees to operate on them? *Annals of the Royal College of Surgeons of England* 2004 November; 86(6): 465. Subject: 8.3.1

Williams, Sloan R. A case study of ethical issues in genetic research: the Sally Hemings-Thomas Jefferson story. *In:* Turner, Trudy R. ed. Biological Anthropology and Ethics: From Repatriation to Genetic Identity. Albany, NY: State University of New York Press; 2005: 185-208. Subject: 15.1

Williams, Susan G. How do the elderly and their families feel about research participation? *Geriatric Nursing* 1993 January-February; 14(1): 11-14. Subject: 18.5.7

Williamson, Alan R. Gene patents: socially acceptable monopolies or an unnecessary hindrance to research? *Trends in Genetics* 2001 November; 17(11): 670-673. Subject: 15.8

Williamson, Bob. The Walter C. Randall Lecture: embryos, cloning people and stem cell research. *Physiologist* 2005 December; 48(6): 295, 297. Subject: 18.5.4

William-Jones, Bryn. "Be ready against cancer, now": direct-to-consumer advertising for genetic testing. *New Genetics and Society* 2006 April; 25(1): 89-107. Subject: 15.3

Willis, Gordon. Cognitive interviewing as a tool for improving the informed consent process. *Journal of Empirical Research on Human Research Ethics* 2006 March; 1(1): 9-23. Subject: 18.3

Willison, Donald J.; Kapral, Moira K.; Peladeau, Pierrot; Richards, Janice R.A.; Fang, Jiming; Silver, Frank L. Variation in recruitment across sites in a consent-based clinical data registry: lessons from the Canadian Stroke Network. *BMC Medical Ethics* 2006; 7(6): E6 [Online]. Accessed: http://www.biomedcentral.com/1472-6939/7/6 [2006 August 15]. Subject: 18.2

Willmott, L.; White, B. A model for decision making at the end-of-life: Queensland and beyond. *Medicine and Law: World Association for Medical Law* 2006 March; 25(1): 201-217. Subject: 20.5.1

Willmott, L.; White, Ben; Howard, Michelle. Overriding advance refusals of life-sustaining medical treatment. *Medicine and Law: The World Association for Medical Law* 2006 December; 25(4): 647-661. Subject: 20.5.4

Willmott, Lindy; White, Ben. Charting a course through difficult legislative waters: tribunal decisions on life-sustaining measures. *Journal of Law and Medicine* 2005 May; 12(4): 441-454. Subject: 20.5.1

Willmott, Lindy; White, Ben; Cooper, Donna. The Schiavo decision: emotional, but legally controversial? *Bond Law Review* 2006 June; 18(1): 132-159. Subject: 20.5.1

Wilmut, Ian. Recent stem cell research poses several challenges [editorial]. *Cloning and Stem Cells* 2006 Summer; 8(2): 67-68. Subject: 18.5.1

Wilmut, Ian; Dominko, Tanja. Government encouragement for therapeutic cloning [editorial]. *Cloning* 2000; 2(2): 53-54. Subject: 18.5.4

Wils, Jean-Pierre. Body, perception and identity. *In:* Rehmann-Sutter, Christoph; Düwell, Marcus; Mieth, Dietmar, eds. Bioethics in Cultural Contexts: Reflections on Methods and Finitude. Dordrecht: Springer, 2006: 231-245. Subject: 4.4

Wilson, Elizabeth. End-of-life decisions by GPs. *Family Medicine* 2005 March; 37(3): 221. Subject: 7.2

Wilson, Frederic S. Continuing medical education: ethical collaboration between sponsor and industry. *Clinical Orthopaedics and Related Research* 2003 July; (412): 33-37. Subject: 7.2

Wilson, Jennifer Fisher. Health Insurance Portability and Accountability Act privacy rule causes ongoing concerns among clinicians and researchers. *Annals of Internal Medicine* 2006 August 15; 145(4): 313-316. Subject: 8.4

Wilson, Leland. Toward regulating genetic engineering. *Brethren Life and Thought* 1986 Autumn; 31(4): 241-248. Subject: 15.1

Wilson, Mark H. The CMA's legitimation crisis [letter]. *BMJ: British Medical Journal* 2006 April 8; 332(7545): 854. Subject: 1.3.7

Wilson, Nick; Thomson, George. Tobacco taxation and public health: ethical problems, policy responses. *Social Science and Medicine* 2005 August; 61(3): 649-659. Subject: 9.5.9

Wilson, Philip K. Confronting "hereditary" disease: eugenic attempts to eliminate tuberculosis in progressive era America. *Journal of Medical Humanities* 2006 Spring; 27(1): 19-37. Subject: 15.1

Wilson, Robin Fretwell. Nanotechnology: the challenge of regulating known unknowns. *Journal of Law, Medicine and Ethics* 2006 Winter; 34(4): 704-713. Subject: 5.4

Wilson, Sarah. Biobanks and the "social" in social justice. *In:* Árnason, Gardar; Nordal, Salvör; Árnason, Vilhjálmur, eds. Blood and Data: Ethical, Legal and Social Aspects of Human Genetic Databases. Reykjavík: University of Iceland Press; 2004: 333-338. Subject: 15.1

Wilson, Scott T.; Stanley, Barbara. Ethical concerns in schizophrenia research: looking back and moving forward. *Schizophrenia Bulletin* 2006 January; 32(1): 30-36. Subject: 18.5.6

Winch, Sarah. Constructing a morality of caring: codes and values in Australian carer discourse. *Nursing Ethics* 2006 January; 13(1): 5-16. Subject: 8.1

Winckler, Susan C.; Gans, John A. Conscientious objection and collaborative practice: conflicting or complemen-

See SUBJECT HEADING KEY FOR SECTION II on inside back cover.

771

tary initiatives? *Journal of the American Pharmacists Association* 2006 January-February; 46(1): 12-13. Subject: 11.1

Wing, A.J. Organs for transplantation: should the UK follow Belgium? [editorial]. *Journal of the Royal Society of Medicine* 1996 December; 89(12): 661-662. Subject: 19.5

Winick, Bruce J. Competency to consent to treatment: the distinction between assent and objection. *In:* Wexler, David B.; Winick, Bruce J. Essays in Therapeutic Jurisprudence. Durham, NC: Carolina Academic Press, 1991: 41-81. Subject: 8.3.3

Winick, Bruce J. Competency to consent to voluntary hospitalization: a therapeutic jurisprudence analysis of Zinermon v. Burch. *In:* Wexler, David B.; Winick, Bruce J. Essays in Therapeutic Jurisprudence. Durham, NC: Carolina Academic Press, 1991: 83-132. Subject: 8.3.3

Winick, Bruce J. Outpatient commitment: a therapeutic jurisprudence analysis. *Psychology, Public Policy, and Law* 2003 March-June; 9(1-2): 107-144. Subject: 17.7

Winick, Bruce J. Psychotropic medication in the criminal trial process: the constitutional and therapeutic implications of Riggins v. Nevada. *New York Law School Journal of Human Rights* 1993 Symposium; 10(Part 3): 637-709. Subject: 4.3

Winickoff, David E.; Neumann, Larissa B. Towards a social contract for genomics: property and the public in the "biotrust" model. *Genomics, Society and Policy* 2005 December; 1(3): 8-21. Subject: 15.10

Winker, Margaret A. Race and ethnicity in medical research: requirements meet reality. *Journal of Law, Medicine and Ethics* 2006 Fall; 34(3): 520-525. Subject: 18.5.1

Winkler, David I. Conceptual issues in the definition of death: a guide to public policy. *In:* Rosner, Fred, ed. Medicine and Jewish Law. Volume III. Brooklyn, NY: Yashar Books, Inc.; 2005: 111-129. Subject: 20.2.1

Winner, Langdon. Are humans obsolete? *Hedgehog Review* 2002 Fall; 4(3): 25-44 [Online]. Accessed: http://etext.lib.virginia.edu/etcbin/toccer-hh?id= WinObso4-3.xml&images=images/modeng&data= /texts/english/modeng/parsed&tag=public∂=all [29 January 2007]. Subject: 5.1

Winslade, William; McKinney, E. Bernadette. The ethical health lawyer. *Journal of Law, Medicine and Ethics* 2006 Winter; 34(4): 813-816. Subject: 8.2

Winston, Cynthia E.; Kittles, Rick A. Psychological and ethical issues related to identity and inferring ancestry of African Americans. *In:* Turner, Trudy R. ed. Biological Anthropology and Ethics: From Repatriation to Genetic Identity. Albany, NY: State University of New York Press; 2005: 209-229. Subject: 15.11

Winter, Karen. The participation rights of looked after children in their health care: a critical review of the re-

search. *International Journal of Children's Rights* 2006; 14(1): 77-95. Subject: 9.5.7

Winter, Robert B. Innovation in surgical technique: the story of spine surgery. *Clinical Orthopaedics and Related Research* 2000 September; (378): 9-14. Subject: 2.2

Wiseman, David. Medical resource allocation as a function of selected patient characteristics. *Journal of Applied Social Psychology* 2006 March; 36(3): 683-689. Subject: 9.4

Wiseman, Oliver J.; Wijewardena, M.; Calleary, J.; Masood, J.; Hill, J.T. 'Will you be doing my operation doctor?' Patient attitudes to informed consent. *Annals of the Royal College of Surgeons of England* 2004 November; 86(6): 462-464. Subject: 8.3.1

Wisemann, Claudia. The contributions of medical history to medical ethics: the case of brain death. *In:* Rehmann-Sutter, Christoph; Düwell, Marcus; Mieth, Dietmar, eds. Bioethics in Cultural Contexts: Reflections on Methods and Finitude. Dordrecht: Springer, 2006: 187-196. Subject: 20.2.1

Wiser, James L. The good life and the life sciences. *Politics and the Life Sciences* 1988 February; 6(2): 220-222; author's reply 223-225. Subject: 15.9

Witek-Janusek, Linda. Commentary on the importance of animal research to nursing science. *Nursing Outlook* 2004 March-April; 52(2): 108-110. Subject: 7.2

Withers, Rob. Reading the genes. *In:* Ashcroft, Richard; Lucassen, Anneke; Parker, Michael; Verkerk, Marian; Widderhoven, Guy, eds. Case Analysis in Clinical Ethics. New York: Cambridge University Press; 2005: 95-114. Subject: 15.3

Witkowski, Jan A.; Miller, Henry I.; Conko, Gregory. Should we make a fuss? [letters]. *Nature Biotechnology* 2006 August; 24(8): 899-900. Subject: 15.7

Wittes, Janet. Playing safe and preserving integrity: making the FDA model work. *Statistics in Medicine* 2004 May 30; 23(10): 1523-1525. Subject: 18.2

Wofford, James L.; Ohl, Christopher A. Teaching appropriate interactions with pharmaceutical company representatives: the impact of an innovative workshop on student attitudes. *BMC Medical Education [electronic]* 2005 February 8; 5(1): 5; 7 p. Accessed: http://www. biomedcentral.com/1472-6920/5/5 [2006 February 22]. Subject: 7.2

Wohn, D. Yvette; Normile, Dennis. Korean cloning scandal: prosecutors allege elaborate deception and missing funds [news]. *Science* 2006 May 19; 312(5776): 980-981. Subject: 14.5

Woien, Sandra; Rady, Mohamed Y.; Verheijde, Joseph L.; McGregor, Joan. Organ procurement organizations internet enrollment for organ donation: abandoning informed consent. *BMC Medical Ethics* 2006; 7(14): 9p. Subject: 19.5

Subject = NRCBL Primary Classification Number; see inside front cover.

Wojtasiewicz, Mary Ellen. Damage compounded: disparities, distrust, and disparate impact in end-of-life conflict resolution policies. *American Journal of Bioethics* 2006 September-October; 6(5): 8-12. Subject: 20.4.1

Wolbring, Gregor. A disability rights approach to genetic discrimination. *In:* Sándor, Judit, ed. Society and Genetic Information: Codes and Laws in the Genetic Era. Budapest, Hungary; New York: CEU Press; 2003: 161-184. Subject: 15.3

Wolbring, Gregor. The unenhanced underclass. *In:* Miller, Paul; Wilsdon, James, eds. Better Humans?: The Politics of Human Enhancement and Life Extension. London: Demos, 2006: 122-128. Subject: 4.5

Wolf, G. Portrayal of negative qualities in a doctor as a potential teaching tool in medical ethics and humanism: Journey to the End of Night by Louis-Ferdinand Céline. *Postgraduate Medical Journal* 2006 February; 82(964): 154-156. Subject: 7.2

Wolf, Leslie E.; Croughan, Mary; Lo, Bernard. The challenges of IRB review and human subjects protections in practice-based research. *Medical Care* 2002 June; 40(6): 521-529. Subject: 18.2

Wolf, Leslie E.; Walden, Janice Ferrara; Lo, Bernard. Human subjects issues and IRB review in practice-based research. *Annals of Family Medicine* 2005 May-June; 3(Supplement 1): S30-S37. Subject: 18.2

Wolf, Leslie E.; Zandecki, Jolanta. Sleeping better at night: investigators' experiences with certificates of confidentiality. *IRB: Ethics and Human Research* 2006 November-December; 28(6): 1-7. Subject: 18.2

Wolf, Susan M. Debating the use of racial and ethnic categories in research. *Journal of Law, Medicine and Ethics* 2006 Fall; 34(3): 483-486. Subject: 18.5.1

Wolf, Susan M. Physician-assisted suicide. *Clinics in Geriatric Medicine* 2005 February; 21(1): 179-192. Subject: 20.7

Wolf, Susan M. Response: doctor and patient: an unfinished revolution. *Yale Journal of Health Policy, Law and Ethics* 2006 Summer; 6(2): 485-500. Subject: 8.3.1

Wolfberg, Adam J. Genes on the web — direct-to-consumer marketing of genetic testing. *New England Journal of Medicine* 2006 August 10; 355(6): 543-545. Subject: 15.3

Wolfberg, Douglas M.; Wirth, Stephen R. Do EMS ride-along programs violate patient privacy? How to ensure your program measures up to HIPAA's privacy rule. *JEMS: A Journal of Emergency Medical Services* 2006 January; 31(1): 36-41. Subject: 8.4

Wolff, Jonathan; Boyd, Kenneth. Animal rights and wrongs. *New Scientist* 2006 March 11-17; 189(2542): 20. Subject: 22.2

Wolfslast, Gabriele. Rechtliche Neuordnung der Tötung auf Verlangen? *In:* Vollmann, Jochen, ed. Medizin und Ethik: Aktuelle ethische Probleme in Therapie und Forschung. Erlangen: Universitätsbund Erlangen-Nürnberg, 2003: 125-151. Subject: 20.7

Wolfson, Adam. Biodemocracy in America. *Public Interest* 2002 Winter; 40(146): 23-37. Subject: 15.1

Wolfson, Jay. The rule in Terri's case: an essay on the public death of Theresa Marie Schiavo. *Stetson Law Review* 2005 Fall; 35(1): 39-47. Subject: 20.5.1

Wolfson, Rachel K.; Kahana, Madelyn D.; Nachman, James B.; Lantos, John. Extracorporeal membrane oxygenation after stem cell transplant: clinical decision-making in the absence of evidence. *Pediatric Critical Care Medicine* 2005 March; 6(2): 200-203. Subject: 19.4

Wolinsky, Howard. Bioethics for the world. *EMBO Reports* 2006 April; 7(4): 354-358. Subject: 6

Wolinsky, Howard. Disease mongering and drug marketing: does the pharmaceutical industry manufacture diseases as well as drugs? *EMBO Reports* 2005 July; 6(7): 612-614. Subject: 9.7

Wolinsky, Howard. Do-it-yourself diagnosis. *EMBO Reports* 2005 September; 6(9): 805-807. Subject: 15.3

Woliver, Laura R. Abortion politics: discourses on lives. *In her:* The Political Geographies of Pregnancy. Urbana: University of Illinois Press; 2002: 82-114. Subject: 12.4.1

Woliver, Laura R. Adoption and surrogacy: children as commodities, wombs for rent. *In her:* The Political Geographies of Pregnancy. Urbana: University of Illinois Press; 2002: 115-135. Subject: 14.1

Woliver, Laura R. The Human Genome Project: designer genes. *In her:* The Political Geographies of Pregnancy. Urbana: University of Illinois Press; 2002: 45-81. Subject: 15.3

Woliver, Laura R. New reproductive technologies: medicalization of pregnancy, birth, reproduction, and infertility. *In her:* The Political Geographies of Pregnancy. Urbana: University of Illinois; 2002: 27-44. Subject: 14.1

Wolk, Michael J.; Popp, Richard L.; Smith, Sidney C., Jr.; DeMaria, Anthony N. President's page: the trust imperative: ethical choice always puts patient first. *Journal of the American College of Cardiology* 2004 October 19; 44(8): 1709-1711. Subject: 7.3

Wolpert, Lewis. Is science dangerous? *Journal of Molecular Biology* 2002 June 14; 319(4): 969-972. Subject: 1.3.9

Wolpert, Lewis. The Medawar Lecture 1998: is science dangerous? *Philosophical Transactions of the Royal Society of London. Series B, Biological Sciences* 2005 June 29; 360(1458): 1253-1258. Subject: 5.1

Wolthers, O.D. A questionnaire on factors influencing children's assent and dissent to non-therapeutic research. *Journal of Medical Ethics* 2006 May; 32(5): 292-297. Subject: 18.5.2

See SUBJECT HEADING KEY FOR SECTION II on inside back cover.

773

Wong, Alvin. The ethics of HEK 293. *National Catholic Bioethics Quarterly* 2006 Autumn; 6(3): 473-495. Subject: 18.5.4

Wong, Benjamin. Eugenics from an East Asian perspective. *Mankind Quarterly* 2002 Spring; 42(3): 231-262. Subject: 15.5

Wonkam, Ambroise; Njamnshi, Alfred K.; Angwafo, Fru F., III. Knowledge and attitudes concerning medical genetics amongst physicians and medical students in Cameroon (sub-Saharan Africa). *Genetics in Medicine* 2006 June; 8(6): 331-338. Subject: 15.3

Wood, Alastair J.J. A proposal for radical changes in the drug-approval process. *New England Journal of Medicine* 2006 August 10; 355(6): 618-623. Subject: 9.7

Wood, Alastair J.J.; Darbyshire, Janet. Injury to research volunteer — the clinical-research nightmare. *New England Journal of Medicine* 2006 May 4; 354(18): 1869-1871. Subject: 18.1

Wood, Diana F. Bullying and harassment in medical schools [editorial]. *BMJ: British Medical Journal* 2006 September 30; 333(7570): 664-665. Subject: 7.2

Wood, Robert W.; Hopkins, Sharon G.; Peppert, John F.; Jourden, Jack. The Washington state "name-to-code" HIV reporting system: a public health perspective. *Journal of Public Health Management and Practice* 2002; 8(6): 1-14. Subject: 9.5.6

Woodcock, Tom; Wheeler, Robert. Glass v. United Kingdom and Burke v. General Medical Council. Judicial interpretations of European Convention Rights for patients in the United Kingdom facing decisions about life-sustaining treatment limitations [news]. *Intensive Care Medicine* 2005 June; 31(6): 885. Subject: 20.5.1

Woodring, Barbara C. The role of the staff nurse in protecting children and families involved in research. *Journal of Pediatric Nursing* 2004 August; 19(4): 311-313. Subject: 18.5.2

Woods, Bob; Pratt, Rebekah. Awareness in dementia: ethical and legal issues in relation to people with dementia. *Aging and Mental Health* 2005 September; 9(5): 423-429. Subject: 17.1

Woods, John. Privatizing death: metaphysical discouragements of ethical thinking. *Midwest Studies in Philosophy* 2000 August; 24: 199-218. Subject: 20.1

Woods, Simon. Terminal sedation: a nursing perspective. *In:* Tännsjö, Torbjörn, ed. Terminal Sedation: Euthanasia in Disguise? Boston: Kluwer Academic Publishers; 2004: 43-56. Subject: 20.4.1

Woods, Simon; Sandman, Lars. Continental philosophy and nursing ethics. *In:* Tadd, Win, ed. Ethics in Nursing Education, Research and Management. New York: Palgrave Macmillan; 2003: 14-34. Subject: 4.1.3

Woodsong, Cynthia; MacQueen, Kathleen; Namey, Emily; Sahay, Seema; Morrar, Neetha; Mlingo, Mar-garet; **Meheldale, Sanjay.** Women's autonomy and informed consent in microbicides clinical trials. *Journal of Empirical Research on Human Research Ethics* 2006 September; 1(3): 11-26. Subject: 18.5.3

Woogara, Jay. Privacy and dignity of cancer patients: a qualitative study of patients privacy in UK National Health Service patient care settings. *Journal of Cancer Education* 2005 Summer; 20(2): 119-123. Subject: 8.4

Woolf, Lord. The medical profession and justice. *Journal of the Royal Society of Medicine* 1997 July; 90(7): 364-367. Subject: 9.8

Woolhandler, Steffie; Himmelstein, David U. The new Massachusetts health reform: half a step forward and three steps back. *Hastings Center Report* 2006 September-October; 36(5): 19-21. Subject: 9.2

Woolley, Karen L.; Ely, Julie A.; Woolley, Mark J.; Findlay, Leigh; Lynch, Felicity A.; Choi, Yoonah; McDonald, Jane M. Declaration of medical writing assistance in international peer-reviewed publications [letter]. *JAMA: The Journal of the American Medical Association* 2006 August 23-30; 296(8): 932-934. Subject: 1.3.7

Woolley, S. Children of Jehovah's Witnesses and adolescent Jehovah's Witnesses: what are their rights? *Archives of Disease in Childhood* 2005 July; 90(7): 715-719. Subject: 8.3.4

Woolley, S. Jehovah's Witnesses in the emergency department: what are their rights? *Emergency Medicine Journal* 2005 December; 22(12): 869-871. Subject: 8.3.4

Worrall, Bradford B.; Chen, Donna T.; Brown, Robert D., Jr.; Brott, Thomas G.; Meschia, James F. A survey of the SWISS researchers on the impact of sibling privacy protections on pedigree recruitment. *Neuroepidemiology* 2005; 25(1): 32-41. Subject: 15.1

Worth, Heather. Unconditional hospitality: HIV, ethics and the refugee 'problem'. *Bioethics* 2006 September; 20(5): 223-232. Subject: 9.5.6

Worthington, Roger. Standards of healthcare and respecting children's rights. *Journal of the Royal Society of Medicine* 2006 April; 99(4): 208-210. Subject: 9.5.7

Woteki, Catherine E. Ethics opinion: conflicts of interest in presentations and publications and dietetics research. *Journal of the American Dietetic Association* 2006 January; 106(1): 27-31. Subject: 7.4

Woywodt, Alexander; Haubitz, Marion; Haller, Hermann; Matteson, Eric L. Wegener's granulomatosis. *Lancet* 2006 April 22-28; 367(9519): 1362-1366. Subject: 21.4

Wray, Julie. Confidentiality and teenage pregnancy — the affinity gap. *RCM Midwives* 2005 December; 8(12): 493. Subject: 8.3.2

Wright, Alexi A.; Katz, Ingrid T. Home testing for HIV. *New England Journal of Medicine* 2006 February 2; 354(5): 437-440. Subject: 9.5.6

Wright, Alexi A.; Katz, Ingrid T. Roe versus reality — abortion and women's health. *New England Journal of Medicine* 2006 July 6; 355(1): 1-3, 5-9. Subject: 12.4.1

Wright, Evangeline. Mind-control experimentation: a travesty of human rights in the United States. *Journal of Gender, Race and Justice* 2005 Fall; 9(1): 211-239. Subject: 17.3

Wright, Jessica; Gordijn, Bert. Medical research on human subjects and RECs in the Netherlands. *In:* Beyleveld, D.; Townend, D.; Wright, J., eds. Research Ethics Committees, Data Protection and Medical Research in European Countries. Hants, England; Burlington, VT: Ashgate; 2005: 153-161. Subject: 18.2

Wright, LaTonia Denise. Violating professional boundaries. *Nursing* 2006 March; 36(3): 52-54. Subject: 8.1

Wright, Sarah; Waters, Rachel; Nicholls, Vicky. Ethical considerations in service-user-led research: strategies for Living Project. *In:* Smyth, Marie; Williamson, Emma, eds. Researchers and Their 'Subjects': Ethics, Power, Knowledge and Consent. Bristol, UK: Policy Press; 2004: 19-34. Subject: 18.5.6

Wroe, Abigail L.; Bhan, Angela; Salkovskis, Paul; Bedford, Helen. Feeling bad about immunising our children. *Vaccine* 2005 February 10; 23(12): 1428-1433. Subject: 9.5.1

Wu, Guosheng. Misconduct: forum should not be used to settle scores. *Nature* 2006 July 13; 442(7099): 132. Subject: 1.3.9

Wu, Zunyou; Sun, Xinhua; Sullivan, Sheena G.; Detels, Roger. HIV testing in China. *Science* 2006 June 9; 312(5779): 1475-1476. Subject: 9.5.6

Wunder, Michael. Medizin und Gewissen — Die neue Euthanasie-Debatte in Deutschland vor dem historischen und internationalen Hintergrund. *In:* Frewer, Andreas; Eickhoff, Clemens, eds. "Euthanasie" und die aktuelle Sterbehilfe-Debatte: Die historischen Hintergründe medizinischer Ethik. Frankfurt; New York: Campus; 2000: 250-275. Subject: 20.5.1

Wunsch, Hannah; Harrison, David A.; Harvey, Sheila; Rowan, Kathryn. End-of-life decisions: a cohort study of the withdrawal of all active treatment in intensive care units in the United Kingdom. *Intensive Care Medicine* 2005 June; 31(6): 823-831. Subject: 20.5.1

Wurth, Gene R.; Sherr, Judy H.; Coffman, Thomas M. Orthopaedic research and education foundation and industry. *Clinical Orthopaedics and Related Research* 2003 July; (412): 54-56. Subject: 9.7

Wynaden, Dianne; Orb, Angelica. Impact of patient confidentiality on carers of people who have a mental disorder. *International Journal of Mental Health Nursing* 2005 September; 14(3): 166-171. Subject: 8.4

Wynen, A. The physician and torture. *World Medical Journal* 1982 March-April; 28(2): 18-19. Subject: 4.1.2

Wynia, Matthew K. Consequentialism and outrageous options: response to commentary on "Consequentialism and Harsh Interrogations". *American Journal of Bioethics [Online]*. 2006 March-April; 6(2): W37. Subject: 21.4

Wynia, Matthew K. Ethics and public health emergencies: rationing vaccines. *American Journal of Bioethics* 2006 November-December; 6(6): 4-7. Subject: 9.4

Wynia, Matthew K. Markets and public health: pushing and pulling vaccines into production. *American Journal of Bioethics* 2006 May-June; 6(3): 3-6. Subject: 9.1

Wynia, Matthew K. Risk and trust in public health: a cautionary tale. *American Journal of Bioethics* 2006 March-April; 6(2): 3-6. Subject: 9.1

Wynia, Matthew K. Routine screening: informed consent, stigma and the waning of HIV exceptionalism. *American Journal of Bioethics* 2006 July-August; 6(4): 5-8. Subject: 9.1

Wynn, Susan G.; Wolpe, Paul Root. The majority view of ethics and professionalism in alternative medicine. *Journal of the American Veterinary Medical Association* 2005 February 15; 226(4): 516-520. Subject: 22.1

Wynne, Louis. Dr. Szasz's gauntlet: a critical review of the work of American psychiatry's most vocal gadfly. *Ethical Human Psychology and Psychiatry* 2006 Summer; 8(2): 111-122. Subject: 17.1

Wyoming. *Laws, statutes, etc.* An act relating to group health insurance; limiting the use of genetic testing results by group insurers as specified; and providing for an effective date [Approved: 2003 March 3]. Wyoming: State Legislature, 2003. 3 p. [Online]. Accessed: http://legisweb.state.wy.us/2003/enroll/hb0024.pdf [2007 March 9]. Subject: 15.1

Wyse, D. George. Conflict of interest — draining the swamp means confronting alligators [editorial]. *Journal of Interventional Cardiac Electrophysiology* 2005 June; 13(1): 5-7. Subject: 7.3

W., Barbara. Counter attack [letter]. *Canadian Medical Association Journal* 2006 January 17; 174(2): 211-212. Subject: 11.1

X

Xin, Hao. Gendicine's efficacy: hard to translate [news]. *Science* 2006 November 24; 314(5803): 1233. Subject: 15.4

Xin, Hao. Online sleuths challenge cell paper [news]. *Science* 2006 December 15; 314(5806): 1669. Subject: 1.3.9

Xin, Hao. Scandals shake Chinese science. *Science* 2006 June 9; 312(5779): 1464-1466. Subject: 1.3.9

See SUBJECT HEADING KEY FOR SECTION II on inside back cover.

775

Y

Yadwad, B.S.; Gouda, H. Consent — its medico legal aspects. *Journal of the Association of Physicians in India* 2005 October; 53: 891-894. Subject: 8.3.1

Yaes, Robert J.; Gawande, Atul. Why physicians participate in executions [letter and reply]. *New England Journal of Medicine* 2006 July 6; 355(1): 99-100. Subject: 20.6

Yagüe, Francisco Lledó. Compulsory paternity: on the recent 19 January 1994 judgement of the Spanish Constitutional Court = La paternidad forzada: a propósito de la reciente sentencia del Tribunal Constitucional de 19 enero de 1994. *Law and the Human Genome = Revista de Derecho y Genoma Humano* 1994 July-December; (1): 197-202. Subject: 15.1

Yágüez, Ricardo de Ángel. Prenatal genetic diagnosis and responsibility (Part II) = Diagnósticos genéticos prenatales y responsabilidad (Parte II). *Law and the Human Genome Review = Revista de Derecho y Genoma Humano* 1996 July-December; (5): 129-143. Subject: 15.2

Yahata, Hideyuki. Moral thinking about the embryo-fetus period: reconsidering the problems of identity and existence. *In:* Takahashi, Takao, ed. Taking Life and Death Seriously: Bioethics from Japan. Amsterdam; Boston: Elsevier JAI; 2005: 65-84. Subject: 4.4

Yamalik, Nermin. Dentist-patient relationship and quality care 4. Professional information and informed consent. *International Dental Journal* 2005 October; 55(5): 342-344. Subject: 8.3.1

Yamin, Alicia Ely; Rosenthal, Eric. Out of the shadows: using human rights approaches to secure dignity and well-being for people with mental disabilities. *PLoS Medicine* 2005 April; 2(4): 0296-0298. Subject: 9.5.3

Yan, Qingshan. Removing obstacles — ethics of the public welfare payments for the disabled. *In:* Döring, Ole; Chen, Renbiao, eds. Advances in Chinese Medical Ethics: Chinese and International Perspectives. Hamburg: Institut für Asienkunde; 2002: 315-321. Subject: 9.5.1

Yanes, Pedro. Personal insurance and genetic information (I) = Seguros de personas e información genética (I). *Law and the Human Genome = Revista de Derecho y Genoma Humano* 1994 July-December; (1): 185-194. Subject: 15.1

Yang, Huanming. In the name of humanity — a brief introduction to the Universal Declaration on the Human Genome and Human Rights. *In:* Döring, Ole; Chen, Renbiao, eds. Advances in Chinese Medical Ethics: Chinese and International Perspectives. Hamburg: Institut für Asienkunde; 2002: 38-53. Subject: 15.1

Yang, Xiangzhong. Hwang's fraud adds impetus to ES cell research [letter]. *Nature Biotechnology* 2006 April; 24(4): 393. Subject: 1.3.9

Yang, Xiangzhong. A simple system of checks and balances to cut fraud [letter]. *Nature* 2006 February 16; 439(7078): 782. Subject: 1.3.9

Yano, Eiji. Japanese spousal smoking study revisited: how a tobacco industry funded paper reached erroneous conclusions. *Tobacco Control* 2005 August; 14(4): 227-235. Subject: 1.3.9

Yanos, Philip T.; Ziedonis, Douglas M. The patient-oriented clinician-researcher: advantages and challenges of being a double agent. *Psychiatric Services* 2006 February; 57(2): 249-253. Subject: 18.4

Yarhouse, Mark A. Ethical issues in considering "religious impairment" in diagnosis. *Mental Health, Religion and Culture* 2003 July; 6(2): 131-147. Subject: 17.1

Yarhouse, Mark A.; Throckmorton, Warren. Ethical issues in attempts to ban reorientation therapies. *Psychotherapy: Theory/Research/Practice/Training* 2002 Spring; 39(1): 66-75. Subject: 10

Yentis, S.M. When lecturers need patient consent. *BMJ: British Medical Journal* 2006 May 6; 332(7549): 1100. Subject: 8.3.1

Yentis, S.M.; Dawson, A.J. Medical studies with 'no material ethical issues' — an unhelpful, confusing and potentially unethical suggestion. *Clinical Ethics* 2006 December; 1(4): 234-236. Subject: 18.2

Yeo, Gwen. Ethical considerations in Asian and Pacific Island elders. *Clinics in Geriatric Medicine* 1995 February; 11(1): 139-151. Subject: 21.7

Yeoman, A.D.; Dew, M.J.; Das, L.; Rajapaksa, S. Role of cognitive function in assessing informed consent for endoscopy. *Postgraduate Medical Journal* 2006; 82(963): 65-69 [Online]. Accessed: http://pmj.bmjjournals.com/cgi/reprint/82/963/65 [2006 March 7]. Subject: 8.3.1

Yew, Y.W.; Saw, Seang-Mei; Pan, J.C.-H.; Shen, H.M.; Lwin, M.; Yew, M.-S.; Heng, W.-J. Knowledge and beliefs on corneal donation in Singapore adults. *British Journal of Ophthalmology* 2005 July; 89(7): 835-840. Subject: 19.5

Young, Diony. Confrontation in Kansas City: elective cesareans and maternal choice [editorial]. *Birth* 2000 September; 27(3): 153-155. Subject: 9.5.5

Young, John. Ageism in services for transient ischaemic attack and stroke [editorial]. *BMJ: British Medical Journal* 2006 September 9; 333(7567): 508-509. Subject: 9.5.2

Young, John D.; Bianco, Richard W.; Fung, John J.; Lackner, Andrew A. Animal activism and intimidation of scientists [letter]. *Science* 2006 November 10; 314(5801): 923. Subject: 22.2

Young, John L. Commentary: it's all about the fundamentals. *Journal of the American Academy of Psychiatry and the Law* 2006; 34(4): 479-481. Subject: 4.1.2

Subject = NRCBL Primary Classification Number; see inside front cover.

Young, Lorraine E. Scientific hazards of human reproductive 'cloning'. *Human Fertility* 2003 May; 6(2): 59-63. Subject: 14.5

Youngner, Stuart J. Brain death. *In:* Mitcham, Carl, ed. Encyclopedia of Science, Technology, and Ethics. Farmington Hills, MI: Thomson/Gale, 2005: 245-247. Subject: 20.2.1

Youngner, Stuart J.; O'Toole, Elizabeth; Stellato, Tom. Two times what? Quantity and quality of life in tube feeding decisions [editorial]. *Journal of General Internal Medicine* 1997 February; 12(2): 134-135. Subject: 20.5.1

Youngner, Stuart; Chiong, Winston. Matters of "life" and "death" [letter and reply]. *Hastings Center Report* 2006 May-June; 36(3): 5, 5-6. Subject: 20.2.1

Youngs, Robin; Kenyon, Guy. Maintaining ethical standards in medical publishing [editorial]. *Journal of Laryngology and Otology* 2006 January; 120(1): 1-2. Subject: 1.3.7

Yu, Kaiming; Wang, Defen; Lin, Meili; Wang, Shixiong; Ren, Zaoriu; Qiu, Weiqin. Ethical issues of genetic counseling and artificial abortion. *In:* Döring, Ole; Chen, Renbiao, eds. Advances in Chinese Medical Ethics: Chinese and International Perspectives. Hamburg: Institut für Asienkunde; 2002: 421-426. Subject: 12.3

Yu, Kam-por. The alleged Asian values and their implications for bioethics. *In:* Sang-yong, Song; Young-Mo, Koo; Macer, Darryl R.J., eds. Asian Bioethics in the 21st Century. Christchurch, NZ: Eubios Ethics Institute, 2002: 232-237. Subject: 21.7

Yu, Victor Y. Is neonatal intensive care justified in all preterm infants? *Croatian Medical Journal* 2005 October; 46(5): 744-750. Subject: 9.5.7

Yucel, Aylin; Gecici, O.; Emul, M.; Oyar, O.; Gulsoy, U.K.; Dayanir, Y.O.; Acar, M.; Degirmenci B.; Haktanir, A. Effect of informed consent for intravascular contrast material on the level of anxiety: how much information should be given? *Acta Radiologica* 2005 November; 46(7): 701-707. Subject: 8.3.1

Yudin, Boris. Human life: genetic or social construction. *Journal International de Bioéthique = International Journal of Bioethics* 2005 September-December; 16(3-4): 89-96, 173-174. Subject: 15.6

Yudin, Boris. Values of preservation and values of change in bioethics. *Journal International de Bioéthique = International Journal of Bioethics* 2005 September-December; 16(3-4): 71-75, 170-171. Subject: 2.1

Z

Zachariah, Rony; Janssens, Vincent; Ford, Nathan. Do aid agencies have an ethical duty to comply with researchers? A response to Rennie. *Developing World Bioethics* 2006 May; 6(2): 78-80. Subject: 7.1

Zajtchuk, Joan T. Military medicine in humanitarian missions. *In:* Beam, Thomas E.; Sparacino, Linette R.; Pellegrino, Edmund D.; Hartle, Anthony E.; Howe, Edmund G., eds. Military Medical Ethics. Volume 2. Washington, DC: TMM Publications, Borden Institute, Walter Reed Army Medical Center; 2003: 773-804. Subject: 9.5.1

Zaltzman, Jeffrey S. Kidney transplantation in Canada: unequal access. *CMAJ/JAMC: Canadian Medical Association Journal* 2006 August 29; 175(5): 489-490. Subject: 19.6

Zamir, Tzachi. Killing for knowledge. *Journal of Applied Philosophy* 2006; 23(1): 17-40. Subject: 22.2

Zamir, Tzachi. The moral basis of animal-assisted therapy. *Society and Animals: Journal of Human-Animal Studies* 2006; 14(2): 179-199. Subject: 22.1

Zamiska, Nicholas. Scientist rebels against WHO over bird flu [Ilaria Capua]. *Wall Street Journal* 2006 March 13; p B1, B2. Subject: 1.3.9

Zamudio, Stacy. Institutional review boards: the structural and cultural obstacles encountered in human biological research. *In:* Turner, Trudy R. ed. Biological Anthropology and Ethics: From Repatriation to Genetic Identity. Albany, NY: State University of New York Press; 2005: 149-163. Subject: 18.2

Zaner, Richard M. On evoking clinical meaning. *Journal of Medicine and Philosophy* 2006 December; 31(6): 655-666. Subject: 2.1

Zanskas, Steve; Coduti, Wendy. Eugenics, euthanasia, and physician assisted suicide: an overview for rehabilitation professionals. *Journal of Rehabilitation* 2006 January-March; 72(1): 27-34. Subject: 15.5

Zarate, Alvan O.; Zayatz, Laura. Essentials of the disclosure review process: a federal perspective. *Journal of Empirical Research on Human Research Ethics* 2006 September; 1(3): 51-62. Subject: 8.3.1

Zarocostas, John. UN questions China over organ harvesting [news]. *BMJ: British Medical Journal* 2006 October 14; 333(7572): 770. Subject: 19.5

Zatti, Paolo. The right to choose one's health. *In:* Viafora, Corrado, ed. Clinical Bioethics: A Search for the Foundations. Dordrecht: Springer, 2005: 115-129. Subject: 4.2

Zawawi, Majdah. Third party involvement in the reproductive process: comparative aspects of the legal and ethical approaches to surrogacy. *In:* Sang-yong, Song; Young-Mo, Koo; Macer, Darryl R.J., eds. Asian Bioethics in the 21st Century. Christchurch, NZ: Eubios Ethics Institute, 2002: 389-401. Subject: 14.2

Zebrowski, Robin L. Altering the body: nanotechnology and human nature. *International Journal of Applied Philosophy* 2006 Fall; 20(2): 229-246. Subject: 5.4

Zerby, Stephen A.; Thomas, Christopher R. Legal issues, rights, and ethics for mental health in juvenile justice.

See SUBJECT HEADING KEY FOR SECTION II on inside back cover.

Child and Adolescent Psychiatric Clinics of North America 2006 April; 15(2): 373-390. Subject: 17.1

Zernike, Kate. F.D.A.'s report illuminates wide divide on marijuana. *New York Times* 2006 April 22; p. A11. Subject: 9.5.9

Zhai, Xiaomei. How should the issue of homosexuality be regarded in Chinese medical ethics? *In:* Döring, Ole; Chen, Renbiao, eds. Advances in Chinese Medical Ethics: Chinese and International Perspectives. Hamburg: Institut für Asienkunde; 2002: 290-297. Subject: 10

Zhai, Xiaomei. Informed consent in medical research involving human subjects in China. *In:* Sang-yong, Song; Young-Mo, Koo; Macer, Darryl R.J., eds. Asian Bioethics in the 21st Century. Christchurch, NZ: Eubios Ethics Institute, 2002: 4-5. Subject: 18.3

Zhai, Xiaomei; Döring, Ole. A method to study medical ethics. *In:* Döring, Ole; Chen, Renbiao, eds. Advances in Chinese Medical Ethics: Chinese and International Perspectives. Hamburg: Institut fur Asienkunde; 2002: 409-416. Subject: 2.3

Zhang, Bao-Hong. The completion of the human genome nucleotide sequence raises privacy concerns [letter]. *Bulletin of the World Health Organization* 2000; 78(11): 1373. Subject: 15.1

Zhang, Daqing. Medicine as virtuous conduct: assessing the tradition of Chinese medical ethics. *In:* Döring, Ole; Chen, Renbiao, eds. Advances in Chinese Medical Ethics: Chinese and International Perspectives. Hamburg: Institut für Asienkunde; 2002: 233-254. Subject: 2.1

Zhang, Xinqing. Germ-line gene therapy from the lens of Confucian ethics. *In:* Sang-yong, Song; Young-Mo, Koo; Macer, Darryl R.J., eds. Asian Bioethics in the 21st Century. Christchurch, NZ: Eubios Ethics Institute, 2002: 61-64. Subject: 15.4

Zhou, Jianping. Ethics and practice of family planning and reproductive health in China. *In:* Döring, Ole; Chen, Renbiao, eds. Advances in Chinese Medical Ethics: Chinese and International Perspectives. Hamburg: Institut für Asienkunde; 2002: 322-326. Subject: 11.1

Zhu, Yongming. Ethical issues of blood transfusion and bone marrow transplantation in China. *In:* Döring, Ole; Chen, Renbiao, eds. Advances in Chinese Medical Ethics: Chinese and International Perspectives. Hamburg: Institut für Asienkunde; 2002: 367-377. Subject: 19.1

Ziegler, Stephen J.; Jackson, Robert A. Who's not afraid of Proposal B?: an analysis of exit-poll data from Michigan's vote on physician-assisted suicide. *Politics and the Life Sciences* 2004 March; 23(1): 42-48. Subject: 20.7

Zientek, David M. The impact of Roman Catholic moral theology on end-of-life care under the Texas Advance Directives Act. *Christian Bioethics* 2006 April; 12(1): 65-82. Subject: 20.5.1

Zikmund-Fisher, Brian J.; Sarr, Brianna; Fagerlin, Angela; Ubel, Peter A. A matter of perspective: choosing for others differs from choosing for yourself in making treatment decisions. *JGIM: Journal of General Internal Medicine* 2006 June; 21(6): 618-622. Subject: 8.1

Zilberberg, Julie M. A boy or a girl: is any choice moral?: The ethics of sex selection and sex preselection in context. *In:* Tong, Rosemarie; Donchin, Anne; Dodds, Susan, eds. Linking Visions: Feminist Bioethics, Human Rights, and the Developing World. Lanham, MD: Rowman and Littlefield Publishers; 2004: 147-156. Subject: 14.3

Zimmerman, Burke K. Commentary on Kawar and Sherlock. *Politics and the Life Sciences* 1989 February; 7(2): 148-153. Subject: 15.7

Zimmerman, Richard K. If pneumonia is the "old man's friend", should it be prevented by vaccination? An ethical analysis. *Vaccine* 2005 May 31; 23(29): 3843-3849. Subject: 9.5.1

Zimmermann, Volker. Die "Heiligkeit des Lebns" — Geschichte der Euthanasie in Grundzügen. *In:* Frewer, Andreas; Eickhoff, Clemens, eds. "Euthanasie" und die aktuelle Sterbehilfe-Debatte: Die historischen Hintergründe medizinischer Ethik. Frankfurt; New York: Campus; 2000: 27-45. Subject: 20.5.1

Zimmermann-Acklin, Markus. "Der Schrecken nutzt sich ab" — Zur Wechselwirkung von Geschichte und Ethik in der gegenwärtigen Euthanasie-Diskussion. *In:* Frewer, Andreas; Eickhoff, Clemens, eds. "Euthanasie" und die aktuelle Sterbehilfe-Debatte: Die historischen Hintergründe medizinischer Ethik. Frankfurt; New York: Campus; 2000: 448-470. Subject: 20.5.1

Zindrick, Michael R. Orthopaedic surgery and Food and Drug Administration off-label uses. *Clinical Orthopaedics and Related Research* 2000 September; (378): 31-38. Subject: 9.7

Zink, Margo R.; Potter, Jeanne; Chirlin, Kristi. Ethical issues and resources for nurses across the continuum. *In:* Cowen, Perle Slavik; Moorhead, Sue, eds. Current Issues in Nursing. 7th ed. St. Louis, MO: Mosby, 2006: 626-632. Subject: 4.1.3

Zink, Sheldon. Organ transplants. *In:* Mitcham, Carl, ed. Encyclopedia of Science, Technology, and Ethics. Farmington Hills, MI: Thomson/Gale, 2005: 1371-1373. Subject: 19.1

Zink, Sheldon; Wertlieb, Stacey; Kimberly, Laura. Informed consent. *Progress in Transplantation* 2005 December; 15(4): 371-378. Subject: 18.3

Zion, Deborah. Clinical research, vulnerability and exploitation [editorial]. *Monash Bioethics Review* 2006 October; 25(4): 1-2. Subject: 18.5.9

Zipkin, Daniella A.; Steinman, Michael A. Response to "interactions between pharmaceutical representatives and doctors in training: a thematic review" [letter]. *JGIM:*

Journal of General Internal Medicine 2006 January; 21(1): 103. Subject: 9.7

Zlotowitz, Bernard M.; Golden, Gerald S.; Koretzky, Roselyn B. Termination of treatment: case no. 1 [study topic with commentaries]. *Journal of Psychology and Judaism* 1996 Spring; 20(1): 3-22. Subject: 20.5.1

Zoloth, Laurie. Learning a practice of uncertainty: clinical ethics and the nurse. *In:* Cowen, Perle Slavik; Moorhead, Sue, eds. Current Issues in Nursing. 7th ed. St. Louis, MO: Mosby, 2006: 668-678. Subject: 4.1.3

Zoloth, Laurie. The gaze toward the beautiful dead: considering ethical issues raised by the Body Worlds exhibit. *Atrium* 2005 Spring; 1: 5-6. Subject: 4.4

Zoloth, Laurie; Zoloth, Stephen. Don't be chicken: bioethics and avian flu [editorial]. *American Journal of Bioethics* 2006 January-February; 6(1): 5-8. Subject: 9.1

Zoltan, Andrew. Jacobson revisited: mandatory polio vaccination as an unconstitutional condition. *George Mason Law Review* 2005 Spring; 13(3): 735-765. Subject: 9.7

Zonana, Howard. Torture and interrogation by psychiatrists. *American Academy of Psychiatry and the Law* 2006 September; 31(3): 5-9. Subject: 21.4

Zongliang, Xu. Ethical challenges of human genome diversity research. *Eubios Journal of Asian and International Bioethics* 2003 January 13(1): 8-10. Subject: 15.10

Zorn, Jean-René. About the HFEA patients' guide to donor insemination and in-vitro fertilization (IVF) clinics — are we crossing the Rubicon? *Human Reproduction* 1996 July; 11(7): 1367-1368. Subject: 14.1

Zuber, Rebecca Friedman. Compliance with the Medicare conditions of participation: patient rights. *Home Healthcare Nurse* 2005 August; 23(8): 490-494. Subject: 9.3.1

Zucker, A. Medical ethics as therapy. *Medical Humanities* 2006 June; 32(1): 48-52. Subject: 2.3

Zucker, Kenneth J.; Spitzer, Robert L. Was the gender identity disorder of childhood diagnosis introduced into DSM-III as a backdoor maneuver to replace homosexuality? A historical note. *Journal of Sex and Marital Therapy* 2005 January-February; 31(1): 31-42. Subject: 10

Zuckerman, Connie. Looking beyond the law to improve end-of-life care. *Generations: Journal of the American Society on Aging* 1999 Spring; 23(1): 30-35. Subject: 20.5.1

Zuckerman, Diana M. FDA advisory committees: does approval mean safety? Washington, DC: National Research Center for Women and Families, 2006; 48 p.[Online]. Accessed: http://www.center4research.org/pdf/FDA_Report_9-2006.pdf [2006 September 28]. Subject: 9.7

Zutlevics, Tamara. Should ART be offered to HIV-serodiscordant and HIV-serocordant couples: an ethical discussion? *Human Reproduction* 2006 August; 21(8): 1956-1960. Subject: 14.4

Zutlevics, T.L.; Henning, P.H. Obligation of clinicians to treat unwilling children and young people: an ethical discussion. *Journal of Paediatrics and Child Health* 2005 December; 41(12): 677-681. Subject: 8.1

Zwart, Hub. The Language of God: a Scientist Presents Evidence for Belief, by Francis Collins [book review]. *Genomics, Society and Policy* 2006 December; 2(3): 136-141. Subject: 15.10

Zwi, Anthony B.; Grove, Natalie J.; Kelly, Paul; Gayer, Michelle; Ramos-Jimenez, Pilar; Sommerfeld, Johannes. Child health in armed conflict: time to rethink. *Lancet* 2006 Junes 10-16; 367(9526): 1886-1888. Subject: 9.5.7

Zwi, Anthony B.; McNeill, Paul M.; Grove, Natalie J. Commentary: responding more broadly and ethically. *CQ: Cambridge Quarterly of Healthcare Ethics* 2006 Fall; 15(4): 428-431. Subject: 8.1

Zwick, Michael. Genetic engineering: risks and hazards as perceived by the German public. *New Genetics and Society* 2000 December; 19(3): 269-281. Subject: 15.1

Zwillich, Todd. USA confronts looming organ-shortage crisis. *Lancet* 2006 August 12-18; 368(9535): 567-568. Subject: 19.5

Anonymous

Abortion and our culture: an interview with Eyal Press. *Free Inquiry* 2006 June-July; 26(4): 8. Subject: 12.1

Abortion rights in Latin America [editorial]. *New York Times* 2006 January 6; p. A20. Subject: 12.4.1

Abortion ruling in Colombia [editorial]. *New York Times* 2006 May 24; p. A26. Subject: 12.4.1

Agency proposes safeguards for children in clinical trials. *Human Research Report* 2006 June; 21(6): 1-2. Subject: 18.5.2

A.M. Carr-Saunders on eugenics and the declining birth rate. *Population and Development Review* 2004 March; 30(1): 147-157. Subject: 15.5

Amateur night [editorial]. *Nature* 2006 May 4; 441(7089): 2. Subject: 20.6

Appendix: submission made by FoA to the expert working group studying the TGN1412 incident. *ATLA: Alternatives to Laboratory Animals* 2006 June; 34(3): 354-356. Subject: 18.2

The appropriateness of criminal law to prevent misguided genetic interventions = Sobre la idoneidad del Derecho penal para prevenir intervenciones genéticas desviadas. *Law and the Human Genome Review = Revista de Derecho y Genoma Humano* 1996 July-December; (5): 15-17. Subject: 15.1

Are journals doing enough to prevent fraudulent publication? [editorial]. *CMAJ/JAMC: Canadian Medical Associ-*

See SUBJECT HEADING KEY FOR SECTION II on inside back cover.

779

ation Journal 2006 February 14; 174(4): 431. Subject: 1.3.9

Artificial feeding for a child with a degenerative disorder: a family's view. *Archives of Disease in Childhood* 2005 September; 90(9): 979. Subject: 20.5.1

As evolution intended. *New Scientist* 2006 August 26-September 1; 19(2566): 25. Subject: 4.5

Assisted reproductive technologies hit all time high [editorial]. *Lancet* 2006 July 1-7; 368(9529): 2. Subject: 14.4

The assisted-suicide decision [editorial]. *New York Times* 2006 January 19; p. A22. Subject: 20.7

Australia relaxes ban on stem cell research [news]. *BMJ: British Medical Journal* 2006 December 16; 333(7581): 1236. Subject: 18.5.4

Australia — lenient sentence in euthanasia case. *Canadian HIV/AIDS Policy and Law Newsletter* 1996 July; 2(4): 25-26. Subject: 20.5.1

Australia—doctors admit to performing assisted suicide and euthanasia [news]. *Canadian HIV/AIDS Policy and Law Newsletter* 1997-1998 Winter; 3(4)-4(1): 47. Subject: 20.5.1

Avoiding conflict of interest: a challenge for leaders in all professions. *Health Care Food and Nutrition Focus* 2005 November; 22(11): 9-12. Subject: 7.3

Beautification and fraud [editorial]. *Nature Cell Biology* 2006 February; 8(2): 101-102. Subject: 1.3.9

The Belgian act on euthanasia of May 28th, 2002. *European Journal of Health Law* 2003 September; 10(3): 329-335. Subject: 20.7

Beyond IVF: should parents be free to decide what is acceptable? [editorial]. *New Scientist* 2006 October 21-27; 192(2574): 5. Subject: 14.1

Bioethics at the bench [editorial]. *Nature* 2006 April 27; 440(7088): 1089-1090. Subject: 2.1

Board approves position statement on the rights of the HIV-positive nurse [news]. *Pennsylvania Nurse* 1996 July; 51(7): 11. Subject: 9.5.6

Britain: report suggests no care for early babies. *New York Times* 2006 November 15; p. A8. Subject: 20.5.2

Case timeline. *In:* Caplan, Arthur L.; McCartney, James J.; Sisti, Dominic A., eds. The Case of Terri Schiavo: Ethics at the End of Life. Amherst, NY: Prometheus Books; 2006: 325-345. Subject: 20.5.1

Cash-per-publication. . . [editorial]. *Nature* 2006 June 15; 441(7095): 786. Subject: 1.3.7

China: people living with HIV complain about conduct of medical research [news]. *HIV/AIDS Policy and Law Review* 2004 April; 9(1): 31-32. Subject: 18.3

Chinese Embassy's Statement on the Issue of Falun Gong. Beijing: Ministry of Foreign Affairs, 2006 July 26; 2 p.

[Online]. Accessed: http://www.chinaembassycanada.org/eng/xwdt/t265055.htm [2006 July 27]. Subject: 19.5

Choice policies must focus on reducing health inequalities [editorial]. *Lancet* 2006 January 14-20; 367(9505): 85. Subject: 9.3.1

Clinical trials in children, for children [editorial]. *Lancet* 2006 June 17-23; 367(9527): 1953. Subject: 18.5.2

Le clonage thérapeutique: mythes et perspectives [Therapeutic cloning: myths and perspectives]. Unpublished Document 2005 May 8; 5 p. Subject: 18.5.4

Code of ethics for the health education profession. *Health Education and Behavior* 2002 February; 29(1): 11. Subject: 6

Come veto or high water [editorial]. *Nature* 2006 July 27; 442(7101): 329. Subject: 18.5.4

Compassionate access to investigational therapies. *Canadian HIV/AIDS Policy and Law Newsletter* 1996 October; 3(1): 1, 41-43. Subject: 9.5.6

Condoms and the Vatican [editorial]. *Lancet* 2006 May 13-19; 367(9522): 1550. Subject: 9.5.6

Conflict between the law and ethics while researching. *Indian Journal of Medical Ethics* 2006 April-June; 3(2): 69. Subject: 1.3.9

Considerations of the Holy See on human cloning. *United Nations: General Assembly* 2004 October 7; A/C.6/59/INF/1: 4 p. [Online]. Accessed: http://daccessdds.un.org/doc/UNDOC/LTD/N04/541/26/PDF/N0454126.pdf?OpenElement [2007 February 12]. Subject: 14.5

Constitutional law — abortion rights — Fourth Circuit declares Virginia partial birth infanticide statute unconstitutional per se. — Richmond Medical Center for Women v. Hicks, 409 F.3d 619 (4th Cir.), reh'g and reh'g en banc denied, 422 F.3d 160 (4th Cir. 2005). *Harvard Law Review* 2005 December; 119(2): 685-692. Subject: 12.4.1

Cow-human chimaera for stem cells faces UK ban [news brief]. *Nature* 2006 December 21-28; 444(7122): 983. Subject: 18.5.4

Dealing with disclosure [editorial]. *Nature Medicine* 2006 September; 12(9): 979. Subject: 1.3.9

Deaths after RU-486 [editorial]. *New York Times* 2006 April 10; p. A22. Subject: 12.1

The debate on establishing a Taiwan biobank. *Formosan Journal of Medical Humanities* 2006 June; 7(1-2): 1-2. Subject: 15.1

Declaration of Gijón: against the use of biological weapons. *Eubios Journal of Asian and International Bioethics* 2006 January; 16(1): 2-3. Subject: 21.3

Declaration of Indigenous Peoples of the Western Hemisphere regarding the Human Genome Diversity Project. Phoenix (Arizona), on February 19 of 1995 = Declaración de los Pueblos Indígenas del Hemisferio Occidental en relación con el Proyecto de Diversidad del Genoma Hum-

---

Subject = NRCBL Primary Classification Number; see inside front cover.

ano. Fénix (Arizona), 19 de febrero de 1995. *Law and the Human Genome Review = Revista de Derecho y Genoma Humano* 1996 January-June; (4): 209-211. Subject: 15.11

Did nurses have duty to tell pt. what happened? *Nursing Law's Regan Report* 2005 November; 46(6): 1. Subject: 8.2

Disclosure of confidential information: amendments to the Code of Ethics of Nurses. *Perspective Infirmiere* 2005 September-October; 3(1): 9. Subject: 6

Disclosure of medical errors. *Annals of Emergency Medicine* 2004 March; 43(3): 432. Subject: 6

Discrimination and human rights abuse in Russia. *Canadian HIV/AIDS Policy and Law Newsletter* 1999 Fall-Winter; 5(1): 22-27. Subject: 9.5.6

The dissent in Richmond Medical Center v. Hicks in the Fourth Circuit Court of Appeals. *Issues in Law and Medicine* 2006 Spring; 21(3): 239-259. Subject: 20.4.3

Do researchers learn to practice misbehavior? [letter]. *Hastings Center Report* 2006 March-April; 36(2): 4. Subject: 1.3.9

DoD issues guidance for medical personnel dealing with detainees. *Military Medicine* 2005 Summer; (Supplement): 10-11. Subject: 21.2

The Domesday project [editorial]. *New Scientist* 2006 January 21-27; 189(2535): 5. Subject: 15.1

Don't shoot the messenger [editorial]. *New Scientist* 2006 June 17-23; 190(2556): 5. Subject: 7.3

Drop the c-word [news]. *New Scientist* 2006 October 21-27; 192(2574): 7. Subject: 14.5

Drugs tests on trial [news]. *Nature* 2006 April 20; 440(7087): 970. Subject: 18.2

Dying to live [editorial]. *Nature Medicine* 2006 June; 12(6): 593. Subject: 18.5.7

Editorial. *Bulletin of Medical Ethics* 2005 April; (207): 1. Subject: 21.1

Editorial. *Bulletin of Medical Ethics* 2005 December-2006 January; (212): 1. Subject: 18.2

Editorial. *Canadian HIV/AIDS Policy and Law Newsletter* 1999 Spring; 4(2-3): 3-4. Subject: 9.5.6

Effective implementation of the Human Tissue Act [editorial]. *Lancet* 2006 September 9-15; 368(9539): 891. Subject: 19.5

El Salvador: legislature removes law allowing pre-employment HIV testing [news]. *HIV/AIDS Policy and Law Review* 2002 December; 7(2-3): 49. Subject: 9.5.6

The elephant in the room: a biotech trial that went awry [editorial]. *Nature* 2006 December 14; 442(7121): 790. Subject: 18.1

Empirical studies in bioethics [review]. *Bulletin of Medical Ethics* 2005 March; (206): 13-22. Subject: 20.5.1

End-of-life groups in spat over names [news]. *Bulletin of Medical Ethics* 2005 December-2006 January; (212): 3. Subject: 20.7

End-of-life lawmaking [editorial]. *New York Times* 2006 April 23; p. CY17. Subject: 20.5.4

Enforcement Procedure for Occupational Therapy Code of Ethics (2000). *American Journal of Occupational Therapy* 2000 November-December; 54(6): 617-621. Subject: 6

The ethical and legal debate on the Human Genome Diversity Project: are all the perspectives reconcilable? = El debate ético y jurídico en torno al Proyecto Genoma Humano sobre Diversidad ¿son conciliables todas las perspectivas? [editorial]. *Law and the Human Genome Review = Revista de Derecho y Genoma Humano* 1996 January-June; (4): 13-15. Subject: 15.11

Ethical issues in prescribing an antipsychotic medication following neuroleptic malignant syndrome. *Psychiatric Annals* 2005 March; 35(3): 201-202. Subject: 17.4

Ethics and fraud [editorial]. *Nature* 2006 January 12; 439(7073): 117-118. Subject: 1.3.9

Ethics and ICT implants in humans [news]. *Bulletin of Medical Ethics* 2005 March; (206): 3-4. Subject: 17.1

The ethics of brain science: open your mind. *Economist* 2002 May 25; 363(8274): 5 p. [Online]. Accessed: http://web.ebscohost.com/ehost/delivery?vid=8&hid=5&sid=c902ab2a-0616-456 [2006 November 27]. Subject: 17.1

Ethics of preimplantation genetic diagnosis for cancer. *Lancet Oncology* 2006 August; 7(8): 611. Subject: 15.2

The ethics of premature delivery [editorial]. *Lancet* 2006 November 25-December 1; 368(9550): 1844. Subject: 20.5.2

European court of human rights: ECHR 2003/1 Case of Pichon and Sajous v. France, 2 October 2001, no. 49853/99. *European Journal of Health Law* 2003 March; 10(1): 66-69. Subject: 12.3

Euthanasia: a "kit" sold in Belgian pharmacies. *Prescrire International* 2005 October; 14(79): 197. Subject: 20.5.1

Fill this prescription. *Scientific American* 2005 October; 293(4): 6. Subject: 9.7

Finding fraud in China [editorial]. *Nature* 2006 June 1; 441(7093): 549-550. Subject: 1.3.9

Flickers of consciousness [editorial]. *Nature* 2006 September 14; 443(7108): 121-122. Subject: 20.5.1

Foolish vaccine exemptions [editorial]. *New York Times* 2006 October 12; p. A28. Subject: 8.3.2

Fraud and the role of the NHS nurse. *British Journal of Nursing* 2006 June 22-July 12; 15(12): 655. Subject: 7.4

Full clinical trial disclosure needed: expert [news]. *CMAJ/JAMC: Canadian Medical Association Journal* 2006 July 18; 175(2): 140-141. Subject: 9.8

See SUBJECT HEADING KEY FOR SECTION II on inside back cover.

781

Funding of patients' groups [editorial]. *Lancet* 2006 July 1-7; 368(9529): 2. Subject: 9.7

Genes for sale? = ¿Genes a la venta? [editorial]. *Revista de Derecho y Genoma Humano = Law and the Human Genome Review* 1998 January-June; (8): 15-18. Subject: 15.1

The genetic starting line. *Economist* 2000 July 1; 356: 21-22. Subject: 15.10

Genome privacy [editorial]. *Nature Medicine* 2006 July; 12(7): 717. Subject: 15.10

Guiding regulatory reform in reproduction and genetics. *Harvard Law Review* 2006 December; 2: 574-596. Subject: 14.1

HIV: compulsory testing and falling incidence? [editorial]. *Lancet* 2006 April 8-14; 367(9517): 1118. Subject: 9.5.6

HIV testing and confidentiality: final report. *Canadian HIV/AIDS Policy and Law Newsletter* 1999 Spring; 4(2-3): 74. Subject: 9.5.6

Hospital charged with dumping homeless patient. *New York Times* 2006 November 17; p. A29. Subject: 9.5.10

House passes abortion bill on minors. *New York Times* 2006 September 27; p. A23. Subject: 12.4.1

How does PLoS medicine manage competing interests? [editorial]. *PLoS Medicine* 2005 March; 2(3): 0171-0172. Subject: 1.3.7

Human cloning and scientific corruption: the South Korea scandal and the future of the stem cell debate. *New Atlantis* 2006 Winter; 11: 113-117. Subject: 14.5

Human Genome Research Act (Latvia, 2003). *In:* Sándor, Judit, ed. Society and Genetic Information: Codes and Laws in the Genetic Era. Budapest, Hungary; New York: CEU Press; 2003: 375-388. Subject: 15.1

Hungary: a fight every step of the way for voluntary, anonymous, and free tests [news]. *HIV/AIDS Policy and Law Review* 2004 August; 9(2): 35. Subject: 9.5.6

Illuminating BiDil [editorial]. *Nature Biotechnology* 2005 August; 23(8): 903. Subject: 15.1

International Workshop on Legal Aspects of the Human Genome Project. Bilbao Declaration (Spain) = Reunión Internacional sobre el Derecho ante el Proyecto Genoma Humano. La Declaración de Bilbao. *Law and the Human Genome = Revista de Derecho y Genoma Humano* 1994 July-December; (1): 205-209. Subject: 15.10

Is this the bionic man? [editorial]. *Nature* 2006 July 13; 442(7099): 109. Subject: 5.1

Japan's research conduct [editorial]. *Nature* 2006 February 9; 439(7077): 634. Subject: 1.3.9

Last rights [editorial]. *Nature* 2006 June 1; 441(7093): 550. Subject: 22.2

Legal and ethical norms in the field of genetics: a selection of international and national legal documents, reports, and policy recommendations. *In:* Sándor, Judit, ed. Society and

Genetic Information: Codes and Laws in the Genetic Era. Budapest, Hungary; New York: CEU Press; 2003: 267-281. Subject: 15.1

Lethal injection on trial [editorial]. *Lancet* 2006 March 4-10; 367(9512): 703. Subject: 20.6

A letter from the children. *Journal of Clinical Ethics* 2006 Winter; 17(4): 339. Subject: 20.4.1

Manitoba pharmacists' association clarifies Plan B regulations [news]. *CMAJ/JAMC:Canadian Medical Association Journal* 2006 April 11; 174(8): 1078. Subject: 11.1

Matter of ethics. *Economist* 1967 September 30; 224: 1170. Subject: 20.5.1

A matter of life and death [news]. *Nature* 2006 December 14; 442(7121): 807. Subject: 22.2

Medicine: organ donation. *National Catholic Bioethics Quarterly* 2006 Winter; 6(4): 769-775. Subject: 19.5

Memory enhancement — a neuroethical dilemma [editorial]. *Lancet* 2006 August 19-15; 368(9536): 620. Subject: 17.1

The minimally conscious state: a call for guidelines [editorial]. *Lancet* 2006 July 15-21; 368(9531): 176. Subject: 20.5.1

Morals and the mind [review of The Ethical Brain, by Michael Gazzaniga]. *New Atlantis* 2006 Winter; 11: 121-125. Subject: 17.1

National Committee on Assisted Human Reproduction: a promising first step = Comisión Nacional de Reproducción Asistida: un primer paso prometedor [editorial]. *Revista de Derecho Genoma Humano = Law and the Human Genome Review* 1999 January-June; (10): 15-18. Subject: 14.1

Neuroethics needed [editorial]. *Nature* 2006 June 22; 441(7096): 907. Subject: 17.1

New international prospects for human rights and the human genome [editorial] = Nuevas perspectivas para los derechos humanos y el genoma humano en el ámbito internacional. *Revista de Derecho Genoma Humano = Law and the Human Genome Review* 1997 July-December; (7): 15-21. Subject: 15.1

The new threat to your medical privacy. *Consumer Reports* 2006 March; 71(3): 39-42. Subject: 8.4

New York policy on HIV testing of newborns. *Canadian HIV/AIDS Policy and Law Newsletter* 1996 January; 2(2): 15. Subject: 9.5.6

NIH and FDA seek to increase oversight of gene therapy research [news]. *Journal of Investigative Medicine* 2000 May; 48(3): 169-171. Subject: 18.6

93rd Interparliamentary Conference. Bioethics: an international challenge for the protection of human rights = 93a. Conferencia Interparlamentaria. La Bioética: un reto internacional para la protección de los derechos humanos. *Law and the Human Genome Review = Revista de Derecho*

Subject = NRCBL Primary Classification Number; see inside front cover.

y Genoma Humano 1995 July-December; (3): 299-301. Subject: 2.1

No easy answers [editorial]. *Nature* 2006 May 18; 441(7091): 255. Subject: 15.2

North Carolina, using medical monitoring device, executes killer. *New York Times* 2006 April 22; p. A13. Subject: 20.6

Not for sale at any price [editorial]. *Lancet* 2006 April 8-14; 367(9517): 1118. Subject: 19.5

One of a kind [editorial]. *New Scientist* 2006 July 1-7; 191(2558): 5. Subject: 18.5.4

Ontario pharmacists drop Plan B screening form [news]. *Canadian Medical Association Journal* 2006 January 17; 174(2): 149-150. Subject: 11.1

An open debate [editorial]. *Nature* 2006 December 14; 442(7121): 789-790. Subject: 22.2

Oral argument in Gonzales v. Oregon. *Issues in Law and Medicine* 2006 Spring; 21(3): 213-237. Subject: 20.7

Our conflicted medical journals [editorial]. *New York Times* 2006 July 23; p. WK11. Subject: 1.3.7

The patentability of human genes: a necessary debate (with imagination) = La patentabilidad de genes humanos: un debate necesario (con imaginación) [editorial]. *Law and the Human Genome Review = Revista de Derecho y Genoma Humano* 1995 July-December; (3): 15-19. Subject: 15.8

Peer review and fraud [editorial]. *Nature* 2006 December 21-28; 444(7122): 971-972. Subject: 1.3.7

Phase 1 drug trial disaster [news]. *Bulletin of Medical Ethics* 2006 February-March; (213): 3-5. Subject: 18.6

The plaintiff as person: cause lawyering, human subject research, and the secret agent problem. *Harvard Law Review* 2006 March; 119(5): 1510-1531. Subject: 18.3

Playing down the risks of a drug [editorial]. *New York Times* 2006 December 19; p. 32. Subject: 9.7

Poaching nurses from the developing world [editorial]. *Lancet* 2006 June 3-9; 367(9525): 1791. Subject: 21.6

Policing ourselves [editorial]. *Nature* 2006 May 25; 441(7092): 383. Subject: 15.1

Position statement on assisted suicide approved. *Canadian HIV/AIDS Policy and Law Newsletter* 1995 July; 1(4): 11. Subject: 20.7

The power of the media [interviews]. *Atrium* 2006 Fall; 3: 8-11. Subject: 1.3.7

Principles of occupational therapy ethics. *American Journal of Occupational Therapy* 1984 December 1; 38(12): 799-802. Subject: 6

Proceed with caution [editorial]. *Nature Biotechnology* 2005 July; 23(7): 763. Subject: 14.5

Proceed with caution [editorial]. *New Scientist* 2006 October 14-20; 192(2573): 5. Subject: 21.3

Proposed international guidelines on ethical issues in medical genetics and genetic services (Part I). *Revista de Derecho y Genoma Humano = Law and the Human Genome Review* 1998 January-June; (8): 219-233. Subject: 15.1

Rationing is essential in tax-funded health systems. *Lancet* 2006 October 21-27; 368(9545): 1394. Subject: 9.3.1

Recommendations of the Danish Council of Ethics on the patentability of human genes = Recomendaciones del Consejo Danés de Etica sobre la patentabilidad de los genes humanos. *Law and the Human Genome Review = Revista de Derecho y Genoma Humano* 1995 July-December; (3): 297-298. Subject: 15.8

Reconsidering ethics in research. *Protecting Human Subjects* 2006 Spring; (13): 6. Subject: 18.2

Refusal to artificially inseminate 'unmarried' lesbian. *Nursing Law's Regan Report* 2005 December; 46(7): 1. Subject: 14.2

Reporting euthanasia in Holland [news]. *European Journal of Cancer Care* 2003 December; 12(4): 302. Subject: 20.5.1

Research agenda. *Journal of Empirical Research on Human Research Ethics* 2006 September; 1(3): 9-10. Subject: 18.2

Research agendas: an invitation to readers. *Journal of Empirical Research on Human Research Ethics* 2006 June; 1(2): 3-5. Subject: 18.1

Research agendas: an invitation to readers. *Journal of Empirical Research on Human Research Ethics* 2006 March; 1(1): 5-6. Subject: 18.1

Research ethics committees; good clinical practice; advance directives [policy statements]. *Bulletin of Medical Ethics* 2005 June-July; (209): 8-11. Subject: 18.2

Research in developing countries. *Protecting Human Subjects* 2006 Spring; (13): 7. Subject: 18.2

Resisting terrorism [editorial]. *Nature* 2006 September 14; 443(7108): 122. Subject: 22.2

Response to the so called "China's organ harvesting report". Beijing: Ministry of Foreign Affairs, 2006 July 6; 1 p. [Online]. Accessed: http://www.chinaembassycanada.org/eng/xwdt/t261810.htm [2006 July 31]. Subject: 19.5

The rights of the child in the context of HIV/AIDS. *Canadian HIV/AIDS Policy and Law Newsletter* 1997-1998 Winter; 3(4)-4(1): 59. Subject: 9.5.7

Risks and ethics of gene transfer. *Reproductive BioMedicine Online [electronic]* 2005 March; 10(3): 309 Accessed: http://www.rbmonline.com [2005 September 30]. Subject: 15.4

Routine testing for the AIDS virus [editorial]. *New York Times* 2006 September 25; p. A24. Subject: 9.5.6

Sacking of CMAJ editors is deeply troubling [editorial]. *Lancet* 2006 March 4-10; 367(9512): 704. Subject: 1.3.7

See SUBJECT HEADING KEY FOR SECTION II on inside back cover.

Safe drug testing in prisons [editorial]. *New York Times* 2006 August 23; p. A22. Subject: 18.5.5

Safeguards for donors [editorial]. *Nature* 2006 August 10; 442(7103): 601. Subject: 14.4

Seducing the medical profession [editorial]. *New York Times* 2006 February 2; p. A22. Subject: 9.7

Should a doctor tell? *Economist* 1971 March 13; 238: 25. Subject: 8.4

Southall's CNEP trial more than stands up to scrutiny [editorial]. *Lancet* 2006 April 1-7; 367(9516): 1030. Subject: 18.6

Spain's Constitutional Court and assisted reproduction techniques = El Tribunal Constitucional español y las técnicas de reproducción asistada. *Revista de Derecho Genoma Humano = Law and the Human Genome Review* 1999 July-December; (11): 15-17. Subject: 14.1

Spanish Constitutional Court. Ruling of 19 of December 1996. The challenge on the grounds of inconstitutionality against Law 42/1988, of 28 December, regulating the donation and use of human embryos and foetuses or the cells, tissues or organs therefrom. *Revista de Derecho y Genoma Humano = Law and the Human Genome Review* 1998 January-June; (8): 119-133. Subject: 19.5

A special relationship [editorial]. *New Scientist* 2006 October 28-November 3; 192(2575): 5. Subject: 9.7

Stand up and be counted [editorial]. *New Scientist* 2006 March 4-10; 189(2541): 5. Subject: 22.2

Standards for papers on cloning [editorial]. *Nature* 2006 January 19; 439(7074): 243. Subject: 1.3.7

Standing up for stem cell research [editorial]. *New York Times* 2006 July 18; p. A20. Subject: 18.5.4

Statement on stem cell research issued by the Johns Hopkins University. *South African Medical Journal* 2004 September; 94(9): 739-740. Subject: 18.5.4

Statement on the Principled Conduct of Genetic Research. Statement approved by HUGO Council on 21 March 1996, Heidelberg (Federal Republic of Germany) = Declaración sobre los Principios de Actuación en la Investigación Genética. Aprobada por el Consejo de HUGO en Heidelberg (República Federal de Alemania), 21 marzo de 1996. *Law and the Human Genome Review = Revista de Derecho y Genoma Humano* 1996 July-December; (5): 235-237. Subject: 15.10

Stem cells without embryo loss [editorial]. *New York Times* 2006 August 26; p. A14. Subject: 19.1

Striking the right balance between privacy and public good [editorial]. *Lancet* 2006 January 28-February 3; 367(9507): 275. Subject: 8.4

Task Force Report on Genetic Information and Health Insurance = Informe del Grupo Trabajo sobre Información

Genética y Seguros de Salud. *Law and the Human Genome = Revista de Derecho y Genoma Humano* 1994 July-December; (1): 221-232. Subject: 15.1

Terri Schiavo and beyond [news]. *Bulletin of Medical Ethics* 2005 March; (206): 5-6. Subject: 20.7

Togo: abortion legalized in rape and incest. *New York Times* 2006 December 29; p. A15. Subject: 12.4.2

Towards better biosecurity [editorial]. *Nature* 2006 April 6; 440(7085): 715. Subject: 21.3

Trialists should tell participants result, but how? [editorial]. *Lancet* 2006 April 1-7; 367(9516): 1030. Subject: 18.3

UK: court orders publication ban in case of HIV-positive health-care worker [news]. *HIV/AIDS Policy and Law Review* 2002 March; 6(3): 74. Subject: 9.5.6

A universal code of ethics falls badly short [editorial]. *Lancet* 2006 January 14-20; 367(9505): 86. Subject: 1.3.9

University's defense against noncompliance charges begin to fail [case study]. *Human Research Report* 2006 June; 21(6): 6-7. Subject: 18.2

Urgent changes needed for authorisation of phase I trials [editorial]. *Lancet* 2006 April 15-21; 367(9518): 1214. Subject: 18.6

US judge: inadequate medical care for HIV-positive prisoners is a violation of rights. *HIV/AIDS Policy and Law Review* 2004 August; 9(2): 48-49. Subject: 9.2

US—doctor settles HIV-testing case for $10,000 [news]. *Canadian HIV/AIDS Policy and Law Newsletter* 1996 October; 3(1): 40. Subject: 9.5.6

Was this 'irreversible coma' really irreversible? *Nursing Law's Regan Report* 2006 January; 46(8): 1. Subject: 20.5.2

What should the dean do? [case study and commentaries]. *Hastings Center Report* 2006 July-August; 36(4): 14. Subject: 7.2

When doctors hide medical errors [editorial]. *New York Times* 2006 September 9; p. A14. Subject: 9.8

When informed consent is not required for research. *Human Research Report* 2006 June; 21(6): 3. Subject: 18.3

Who said murder? [editorial]. *New Scientist* 2006 July 29-August 4; 191(2562): 3. Subject: 18.5.4

Winners and losers: routine HIV testing is on the cards. Who will it really help? [editorial]. *New Scientist* 2006 July 22-28; 191(2561): 5. Subject: 9.5.6

Writing a new ending for a story of scientific fraud [editorial]. *Lancet* 2006 January 7-13; 367(9504): 1. Subject: 1.3.9

Subject = NRCBL Primary Classification Number; see inside front cover.

SECTION III:
MONOGRAPHS

SUBJECT ENTRIES

Section III: Monographs Contents*

Only those classes with entries in this volume appear on this Contents list.

SECTION III: MONOGRAPHS
SUBJECT ENTRIES

1.1 PHILOSOPHICAL ETHICS

Appiah, Kwame Anthony. THE ETHICS OF IDENTITY. Princeton, NJ: Princeton University Press, 2005. 358 p. ISBN 0-691-12036-6. [BJ1031 .A64 2005] (1.1; 21.7)

Audi, Robert. PRACTICAL REASONING AND ETHICAL DECISION. London/New York: Routledge, 2006. 249 p. ISBN 0-415-36463-9. (Gift of the publisher.) [BC177 .A84 2006] (1.1)

Calhoun, Cheshire, ed. SETTING THE MORAL COMPASS: ESSAYS BY WOMEN PHILOSOPHERS. Oxford/New York: Oxford University Press, 2004. 384 p. ISBN 0-19-515475-4. (Studies in Feminist Philosophy series.) [BJ1395 .S48 2004] (1.1; 1.3.5; 10; 21.1; 21.4)

Chong, Kim-chong; Tan, Sor-hoon; and Ten, C.L., eds. THE MORAL CIRCLE AND THE SELF: CHINESE AND WESTERN PERSPECTIVES. Chicago: Open Court, 2003. 307 p. ISBN 0-8126-9535-6. [BJ69 .M66 2003] (1.1; 1.3.1; 4.4; 21.7)

Derrida, Jacques. ETHICS, INSTITUTIONS, AND THE RIGHT TO PHILOSOPHY. Lanham, MD: Rowman & Littlefield, 2002. 111 p. ISBN 0-7425-0903-6. (Culture and Politics Series. Translation from the French, edited and with commentary by Peter Pericles Trifonas of: *Des humanitâes et de la discipline philosophique.*) [B2430 .D483 H8613 2002] (1.1; 1.3.1; 21.1)

Fiore, Robin N. and Nelson, Hilde Lindemann, eds. RECOGNITION, RESPONSIBILITY, AND RIGHTS: FEMINIST ETHICS AND SOCIAL THEORY. Lanham, MD: Rowman & Littlefield, 2003. 233 p. ISBN 0-7425-1443-9. (Feminist Constructions series.) [BJ1395 .R43 2003] (1.1; 4.4; 8.1; 9.5.5; 10; 20.5.1; 20.7; 21.1)

Friedman, Marilyn. AUTONOMY, GENDER, POLITICS. Oxford/New York: Oxford University Press, 2003. 248 p. ISBN 0-19-513851-1. (Studies in Feminist Philosophy series.) [B808.67 .F75 2003] (1.1; 1.3.5; 10; 21.7)

Gardiner, Stephen M., ed. VIRTUE ETHICS, OLD AND NEW. Ithaca, NY: Cornell University Press, 2005. 222 p. ISBN 0-8014-8968-7. (Proceedings of a conference held at the University of Canterbury in May 2002.) [BJ1521 .V566 2002] (1.1)

Hauser, Marc D. MORAL MINDS: HOW NATURE DESIGNED OUR UNIVERSAL SENSE OF RIGHT AND WRONG. New York: Ecco, 2006. 489 p. ISBN 0-06-078070-3. [BJ1012 .H348 2006] (1.1; 1.3.1)

Hoverman, J. Russell. THE LANDSCAPE WITHIN: AN INQUIRY ON THE STRUCTURE OF MORALITY. New York: Peter Lang, 1994. 157 p. ISBN 0-8204-2235-5. (International Healthcare Ethics Series; Vol. 1. ISSN 1073-5771.) [BJ1311 .H68 1994] (1.1; 15.9)

Madsen, Richard and Strong, Tracy B., eds. THE MANY AND THE ONE: RELIGIOUS AND SECULAR PERSPECTIVES ON ETHICAL PLURALISM IN THE MODERN WORLD. Princeton, NJ: Princeton University Press, 2003. 372 p. ISBN 0-691-09993-6. (Ethikon Series in Comparative Ethics.) [BJ69 .M26 2003] (1.1; 1.2; 10)

Nelson, Hilde Lindemann. DAMAGED IDENTITIES, NARRATIVE REPAIR. Ithaca, NY: Cornell University Press, 2001. 204 p. ISBN 0-8014-8740-4. [BJ45 .N45 2001] (1.1; 4.4; 7.1; 10; 17.1)

Neusner, Jacob and Chilton, Bruce D., eds. ALTRUISM IN WORLD RELIGIONS. Washington, DC: Georgetown University Press, 2005. 202 p. ISBN 1-58901-065-5. (Gift of the publisher.) [BJ1474 .A475 2005] (1.1; 1.2)

Nussbaum, Martha C. FRONTIERS OF JUSTICE: DISABILITY, NATIONALITY, SPECIES MEMBERSHIP. Cambridge, MA: Belknap Press of Harvard University Press, 2006. 487 p. ISBN 0-674-01917-2. (The Tanner Lectures on Human Values series. Gift of the publisher.) [HM671 .N87 2006] (1.1; 1.3.1; 1.3.5; 9.5.1; 9.5.3; 22.1)

Petronio, Sandra. BOUNDARIES OF PRIVACY: DIALECTICS OF DISCLOSURE. Albany: State University of New York Press, 2002. 268 p. ISBN 0-7914-5516-5. (SUNY Series in Communication Studies.) [BF697.5 .S427 P48 2002] (1.1; 8.4)

Potter, Nancy Nyquist. HOW CAN I BE TRUSTED? A VIRTUE THEORY OF TRUSTWORTHINESS. Lanham, MD: Rowman & Littlefield, 2002. 193 p. ISBN 0-7425-1151-0. (Feminist Constructions series.) [BJ1500 .T78 P68 2002] (1.1)

See inside front cover for NRCBL Classification Scheme

Shun, Kwong-Loi and Wong, David B., eds. CONFUCIAN ETHICS: A COMPARATIVE STUDY OF SELF, AUTONOMY, AND COMMUNITY. Cambridge/New York: Cambridge University Press, 2004. 228 p. ISBN 0-521-79657-1. [BL1853 .C66 2004] (1.1; 1.3.1; 1.3.5; 4.4; 21.1)

Tallis, Raymond. THE KNOWING ANIMAL: A PHILOSOPHICAL INQUIRY INTO KNOWLEDGE AND TRUTH. Edinburgh: Edinburgh University Press, 2005. 330 p. ISBN 0-7486-1953-4. [BD161 .T29 2005] (1.1)

1.2 RELIGIOUS ETHICS

Bial, Henry. ACTING JEWISH: NEGOTIATING ETHNICITY ON THE AMERICAN STAGE & SCREEN. Ann Arbor: University of Michigan Press, 2005. 195 p. ISBN 0-472-06908-X. (Gift of Max M. and Marjorie B. Kampelman.) [PN1590 .J48 B53 2005] (1.2)

Bucar, Elizabeth M. and Barnett, Barbra, eds. DOES HUMAN RIGHTS NEED GOD? Grand Rapids, MI: William B. Eerdmans, 2005. 391 p. ISBN 0-8028-2905-8. (The Eerdmans Religion, Ethics, and Public Life series.) [BL65 .H78 D64 2005] (1.2; 21.1)

Coppa, Frank. THE PAPACY, THE JEWS, AND THE HOLOCAUST. Washington, DC: Catholic University of America Press, 2006. 353 p. ISBN 0-8132-1449-1. (Gift of Max M. and Marjorie B. Kampelman.) [BM535 .C677 P3 2006] (1.2; 21.4)

Dougherty, Jude P. THE LOGIC OF RELIGION. Washington, DC: Catholic University of America Press, 2003. 178 p. ISBN 0-8132-1308-8. [BL51 .D68 L6 2003] (1.2; 1.3.5)

Flach, Frederic. FAITH, HEALING, AND MIRACLES. New York: Hatherleigh Press, 2000. 230 p. ISBN 1-57826-100-7. [BT732.5 .F537 2000] (1.2; 9.1)

Haynes, Stephen R. THE BONHOEFFER PHENOMENON: PORTRAITS OF A PROTESTANT SAINT. Minneapolis: Fortress Press, 2004. 280 p. ISBN 0-8006-3652-X. [BX4827 .B57 H396 2004] (1.2)

Haynes, William F., Jr. and Kelly, Geffrey B. IS THERE A GOD IN HEALTH CARE? TOWARD A NEW SPIRITUALITY OF MEDICINE. New York: Haworth Pastoral Press, 2006. 222 p. ISBN 0-7890-2867-0. [R725.55 .H39 2006] (1.2; 4.1.1; 4.4; 8.1; 9.1; 9.5.1)

Hollenbach, David. THE COMMON GOOD AND CHRISTIAN ETHICS. Cambridge/New York: Cambridge University Press, 2002. 269 p. ISBN 0-521-89451-4. (New Studies in Christian Ethics series.) [BJ1249 .H578 2002] (1.2; 1.3.1)

Idel, Moshe. KABBALAH AND EROS. New Haven, CT: Yale University Press, 2005. 371 p. ISBN 0-300-10832-X. (Gift of Max M. and Marjorie B. Kampelman.) [BM526 .I337 2005] (1.2; 10)

Iwry, Samuel. TO WEAR THE DUST OF WAR: FROM BIALYSTOK TO SHANGHAI TO THE PROMISED LAND: AN ORAL HISTORY. New York: Palgrave Macmillan, 2004. 214 p. ISBN 1-4039-6576-5. (Edited by L.J.H. Kelley.

Palgrave Studies in Oral History series. Gift of Max M. and Marjorie B. Kampelman.) [DS135 .P63 I895 2004] (1.2; 21.1; 21.4; Biography)

Kass, Leon R. THE BEGINNING OF WISDOM: READING GENESIS. Chicago: University of Chicago Press, 2003. 700 p. ISBN 0-226-42567-3. (Originally published: Free Press, New York, 2003. Gift of Max M. and Marjorie B. Kampelman.) [BS1235.53 .K37 2003] (1.2)

Levinas, Emmanuel. NEW TALMUDIC READINGS. Pittsburgh, PA: Duquesne University Press, 1999. 133 p. ISBN 0-8207-0297-8. (Translation from the French by Richard A. Cohen of: *Nouvelles Lectures Talmudiques*; Les Editions de Minuit, 1996. Gift of Max M. and Marjorie B. Kampelman.) [BM504.3 .L48613 1999] (1.2)

Lewy, Guenter. THE CATHOLIC CHURCH AND NAZI GERMANY. New York: Da Capo Press, 2000. 416 p. ISBN 0-306-80931-1. [BX1536 .L4 1999] (1.2; 1.3.5; 15.5; 21.2; 21.4)

Matt, Daniel C., translation and commentary. THE ZOHAR, VOLUME 1. Stanford, CA: Stanford University Press, 2004. 500 p. ISBN 0-8047-4747-4. (Pritzker edition. Text includes some words in Hebrew and Aramaic. Gift of Max M. and Marjorie B. Kampelman.) [BM525 .A52 M37 2004 v.1] (1.2)

Matt, Daniel C., translation and commentary. THE ZOHAR, VOLUME 2. Stanford, CA: Stanford University Press, 2004. 460 p. ISBN 0-8047-4868-3. (Pritzker edition. Text includes some words in Hebrew and Aramaic. Gift of Max M. and Marjorie B. Kampelman.) [BM525 .A52 M37 2004 v.2] (1.2)

Matt, Daniel C., translation and commentary. THE ZOHAR, VOLUME 3. Stanford, CA: Stanford University Press, 2006. 586 p. ISBN 0-8047-5210-9. (Pritzker Edition. Text includes some words in Hebrew and Aramaic. Gift of Max M. and Marjorie B. Kampelman.) [BM525 .A52 M37 2004 v.3] (1.2)

Neusner, Jacob. QUESTIONS AND ANSWERS: INTELLECTUAL FOUNDATIONS OF JUDAISM. Peabody, MA: Hendrickson Publishers, 2005. 254 p. ISBN 1-56563-865-4. (Gift of Max M. and Marjorie B. Kampelman.) [BM496.5 .N48165 2005] (1.2)

Overberg, Kenneth R. CONSCIENCE IN CONFLICT: HOW TO MAKE MORAL CHOICES. Cincinnati, OH: St. Anthony Messenger Press, 2006. 160 p. ISBN 0-86716-723-8. (Third edition. Publisher's address: 28 W. Liberty Street, Cincinnati, OH 45202-6498. Gift of the publisher.) [BJ1249 .O92 2006] (1.2; 1.3.1; 2.1; 10)

Patterson, David and Roth, John K., eds. FIRE IN THE ASHES: GOD, EVIL, AND THE HOLOCAUST. Seattle: University of Washington Press, 2005. 350 p. ISBN 0-295-98547-X. (The Pastora Goldner Series in Post-Holocaust Studies.) (Gift of Max M. and Marjorie B. Kampelman.) [BT93 .F57 2005] (1.2; 4.4; 21.4)

Numbers in ( ) = NRCBL Classification Numbers

Prywes, Moshe and Chertok, Haim. PRISONER OF HOPE. Hanover, NH: Published by University Press of New England [for] Brandeis University Press, 1996. 371 p. ISBN 0-87451-653-6. (Tauber Institute for the Study of European Jewry Series; No. 22. Foreword by Elie Weisel. Gift of Max M. and Marjorie B. Kampelman.) [DS135 .P63 P7913 1995] (1.2; 7.2; 21.2; 21.4; Biography)

Reinhart, A. Kevin. BEFORE REVELATION: THE BOUNDARIES OF MUSLIM MORAL THOUGHT. Albany: State University of New York Press, 1995. 255 p. ISBN 0-7914-2290-9. (SUNY Series in Middle Eastern Studies.) [BP166.1 .R45 1995] (1.2)

Rittner, Carol and Roth, John K., eds. "GOOD NEWS" AFTER AUSCHWITZ? CHRISTIAN FAITH WITHIN A POST-HOLOCAUST WORLD. Macon, GA: Mercer University Press, 2001. 215 p. ISBN 0-86554-701-7. (Gift of Max M. and Marjorie B. Kampelman.) [BT93 .G66 2001] (1.2; 21.4)

Sachar, Howard M. A HISTORY OF THE JEWS IN THE MODERN WORLD. New York: Alfred A. Knopf, 2005. 831 p. ISBN 0-375-41497-5. ("This is a Borzoi Book." Gift of Max M. and Marjorie B. Kampelman.) [DS124 .S18 2005] (1.2)

Sarfatti, Michele. THE JEWS IN MUSSOLINI'S ITALY: FROM EQUALITY TO PERSECUTION. Madison: University of Wisconsin Press, 2006. 396 p. ISBN 0-299-21730-2. (George L. Mosse Series in Modern European Cultural and Intellectual History. Translation from the Italian by John and Anne C. Tedeschi of: *Ebrei nell'Italia fascista*. Gift of Max M. and Marjorie B. Kampelman.) [DS135 .I8 S22613 2006] (1.2; 21.4)

Saunders, Nicholas. DIVINE ACTION AND MODERN SCIENCE. Cambridge/New York: Cambridge University Press, 2002. 234 p. ISBN 0-521-52416-4. (Gift of Max M. and Marjorie B. Kampelman.) [BL240.3 .S34 2002] (1.2; 5.1)

Spitzer, Joseph. A GUIDE TO THE ORTHODOX JEWISH WAY OF LIFE FOR HEALTHCARE PROFESSIONALS. London: J. Spitzer, 2005. 84 p. ISBN 0-9532343-1-2. (Third revised edition. Publisher's address: The Surgery, 62 Cranwich Road, London N16 5JF. Gift of Max M. and Marjorie B. Kampelman.) [BM538 .H43 S65 2002] (1.2; 4.4; 7.1; 9.1; 10; 20.1)

Sposato, Jeffrey S. THE PRICE OF ASSIMILATION: FELIX MENDELSSOHN AND THE NINETEENTH-CENTURY ANTI-SEMITIC TRADITION. Oxford/New York: Oxford University Press, 2006. 228 p. ISBN 0-19-514974-2. (Gift of Max M. and Marjorie B. Kampelman.) [ML410 .M5 S66 2006] (1.2)

1.3.1 APPLIED AND PROFESSIONAL ETHICS (GENERAL)

Singer, Peter and Mason, Jim. THE WAY WE EAT: WHY OUR FOOD CHOICES MATTER. [Emmaus, PA]: Rodale, 2006. 328 p. ISBN 1-57954-889-X. [TX357 .S527 2006] (1.3.1; 1.3.11; 16.1; 22.3)

Stephenson, Joan; Ling, Lorraine; Burman, Eva; and Cooper, Maxine, eds. VALUES IN EDUCATION. London/New York: Routledge, 1998. 223 p. ISBN 0-415-15738-2. [LC268 .V263 1998] (1.3.1; 1.3.3; 21.1; 21.7)

Sullivan, William M. WORK AND INTEGRITY: THE CRISIS AND PROMISE OF PROFESSIONALISM IN AMERICA. San Francisco: Jossey-Bass, 2005. 327 p. ISBN 0-7879-7458-7. (Second edition.) [BJ1725 .S85 2005] (1.3.1; 1.3.2; 1.3.3; 1.3.5; 4.1.2; 21.1)

1.3.2 APPLIED AND PROFESSIONAL ETHICS: BUSINESS

Levine, Aaron. MORAL ISSUES OF THE MARKETPLACE IN JEWISH LAW. Brooklyn, NY: Yashar Books, 2005. 616 p. ISBN 1-933143-09-6. (Yashar Ethics Series; Vol. III. Gift of Max M. and Marjorie B. Kampelman.) [KBM920 .L49 2005] (1.3.2; 1.2)

1.3.3 APPLIED AND PROFESSIONAL ETHICS: EDUCATION

Keohane, Nannerl O. HIGHER GROUND: ETHICS AND LEADERSHIP IN THE MODERN UNIVERSITY. Durham, NC: Duke University Press, 2006. 284 p. ISBN 0-8223-3786-X. (Gift of the publisher.) [LB2341 .K39 2006] (1.3.3)

Strike, Kenneth A.; Anderson, Melissa S.; Curren, Randall; Van Geel, Tyll; Pritchard, Ivor; and Robertson, Emily. ETHICAL STANDARDS OF THE AMERICAN EDUCATIONAL RESEARCH ASSOCIATION: CASES AND COMMENTARY. Washington, DC: American Educational Research Association, 2002. 193 p. ISBN 0-935302-28-X. [LB1028.25 .U6 E83 2002] (1.3.3; 1.3.7; 6; 18.5.1)

1.3.5 APPLIED AND PROFESSIONAL ETHICS: GOVERNMENT/CRIMINAL JUSTICE

Batt, John. STOLEN INNOCENCE: A MOTHER'S FIGHT FOR JUSTICE: THE STORY OF SALLY CLARK. London: Ebury Press, 2004. 336 p. ISBN 0-09-190070-0. (1.3.5; 7.3; 20.5.2)

Bergerson, Andrew Stuart. ORDINARY GERMANS IN EXTRAORDINARY TIMES: THE NAZI REVOLUTION IN HILDESHEIM. Bloomington: Indiana University Press, 2004. 312 p. ISBN 0-253-34465-4. (Gift of Max M. and Marjorie B. Kampelman.) [DD901 .H66 B47 2004] (1.3.5; 21.4)

Christman, John and Anderson, Joel, eds. AUTONOMY AND THE CHALLENGES TO LIBERALISM: NEW ESSAYS. Cambridge/New York: Cambridge University Press, 2005. 383 p. ISBN 0-521-83951-3. [JC574 .A86 2005] (1.3.5; 1.1)

Gelvin, James L. THE ISRAEL-PALESTINE CONFLICT: ONE HUNDRED YEARS OF WAR. Cambridge/New York: Cambridge University Press, 2005. 294 p. ISBN

0-521-61804-5. (Gift of Max M. and Marjorie B. Kampelman.) [DS119.7 .G3895 2005] (1.3.5; 21.2)

Novak, David. THE JEWISH SOCIAL CONTRACT: AN ESSAY IN POLITICAL THEOLOGY. Princeton, NJ: Princeton University Press, 2005. 257 p. ISBN 0-691-12210-5. (New Forum Books series. Gift of Max M. and Marjorie B. Kampelman.) [BM538 .S7 N68 2005] (1.3.5; 1.2)

Pringle, Heather. THE MASTER PLAN: HIMMLER'S SCHOLARS AND THE HOLOCAUST. New York: Hyperion, 2006. 463 p. ISBN 0-7868-6886-4. (Gift of the publisher.) [DD247 .H46 P75 2006] (1.3.5; 15.5; 21.4; Biography)

Zertal, Idith. ISRAEL'S HOLOCAUST AND THE POLITICS OF NATIONHOOD. Cambridge/New York: Cambridge University Press, 2005. 236 p. ISBN 0-521-85096-7. (Cambridge Middle East Studies series; No. 21. Translation from the Hebrew by Chaya Galai of: *Ha'Umah ve Ha'Mavet, Historia, Zikaron, Politika*; Dvir Publishing House, 2002. Gift of Max M. and Marjorie B. Kampelman.) [D804.348 .Z4713 2005] (1.3.5; 21.4)

1.3.6 APPLIED AND PROFESSIONAL ETHICS: INTERNATIONAL AFFAIRS

Sutch, Peter. ETHICS, JUSTICE, AND INTERNATIONAL RELATIONS: CONSTRUCTING AN INTERNATIONAL COMMUNITY. London/New York: Routledge, 2001. 224 p. ISBN 0-415-23274-0. (Routledge Advances in International Relations and Politics series; Vol. 13.) [JZ1306 .S88 2001] (1.3.6; 1.3.1)

1.3.7 APPLIED AND PROFESSIONAL ETHICS: JOURNALISM/MASS MEDIA

Day, Louis Alvin. ETHICS IN MEDIA COMMUNICATIONS: CASES AND CONTROVERSIES. Belmont, CA: Thompson/Wadsworth, 2003. 468 p. ISBN 0-534-56235-3. (Fourth edition.) [P94 .D39 2003] (1.3.7; 1.1; 1.3.2; 1.3.12; 6; 8.4)

1.3.9 APPLIED AND PROFESSIONAL ETHICS: SCIENTIFIC RESEARCH

Macrina, Francis L. SCIENTIFIC INTEGRITY: TEXT AND CASES IN RESPONSIBLE CONDUCT OF RESEARCH. Washington, DC: ASM; Distributed by: Malden, MA: Blackwell, 2005. 402 p. ISBN 1-55581-318-6. (Third edition.) [Q180.5 .M67 M33 2005] (1.3.9; 1.3.7; 5.3; 15.1; 18.1; 18.3; 22.2)

Rollin, Bernard E. SCIENCE AND ETHICS. Cambridge/New York: Cambridge University Press, 2006. 292 p. ISBN 0-521-67418-2. (Gift of the publisher.) [R852 .R67 2006] (1.3.9; 4.4; 5.3; 14.5; 15.1; 18.1; 18.5.4; 19.1; 22.2)

1.3.12 APPLIED AND PROFESSIONAL ETHICS: INFORMATION TECHNOLOGY

Kluge, Eike-Henner W. THE ETHICS OF ELECTRONIC PATIENT RECORDS. New York: Peter Lang, 2001. 182 p. ISBN 0-8204-5259-9. (International Healthcare Ethics series; Vol. 6.) [R864 .K58 2001] (1.3.12; 8.2; 8.4)

Langford, Duncan, ed. INTERNET ETHICS. New York: St. Martin's Press, 2000. 257 p. ISBN 0-312-23279-9. [TK5105.875 .I57 I547 2000] (1.3.12; 1.1; 1.3.5)

Schultz, Robert A. CONTEMPORARY ISSUES IN ETHICS AND INFORMATION TECHNOLOGY. Hershey, PA: IRM Press, 2006. 208 p. ISBN 1-59140-780-X. (Gift of the publisher.) [BJ995 .S38 2006] (1.3.12; 1.1; 5.1; 5.3)

Woodbury, Marsha Cook. COMPUTER AND INFORMATION ETHICS. Champaign, IL: Stipes Publishing, 2003. 356 p. ISBN 1-58874-155-9. [QA76.9 .M65 W66 2003] (1.3.12; 1.1; 1.3.2; 6)

2.1 BIOETHICS (GENERAL)

American Medical Association [AMA]. PROFESSING MEDICINE: STRENGTHENING THE ETHICS AND PROFESSIONALISM OF TOMORROW'S PHYSICIANS. Chicago: American Medical Association, 2001. 141 p. ISBN 1-57947-279-6. ("Commemorative issue of: *Virtual Mentor*, AMA's online ethics journal; www.virtualmentor.org.") [R724 .P738 2001] (2.1; 4.1.2; 7.1; 8.1)

Athanassoulis, Nafsika, ed. PHILOSOPHICAL REFLECTIONS ON MEDICAL ETHICS. Basingstoke [England]/New York: Palgrave/Macmillan, 2005. 210 p. ISBN 1-4039-4527-6. (Gift of the publisher.) [R725.5 .P48 2005] (2.1; 1.1; 4.4; 14.1; 15.1; 18.5.4; 19.5; 20.5.1)

Azariah, Jayapaul; Azariah, Hilda; and Macer, Darryl R.J., eds. BIOETHICS IN INDIA. Christchurch, New Zealand: Eubios Ethics Institute, 1998. 403 p. ISBN 0-908897-10-3. (Proceedings of the International Bioethics Workshop in Madras: Bioethical Management of Biogeoresources, 16-19 January 1997, University of Madras. Gift of the publisher.) [QH332 .I57 1998] (2.1; 1.2; 1.3.9; 2.3; 4.4; 15.1; 16.1; 20.3.1; 22.1; 22.2)

Baron, Jonathan. AGAINST BIOETHICS. Cambridge, MA: MIT Press, 2006. 236 p. ISBN 0-262-02596-5. (Basic Bioethics Series. Gift of the publisher.) [R725.5 .B25 2006] (2.1; 1.1; 4.3; 4.4; 4.5; 8.4; 9.4; 9.7; 15.1; 18.2; 19.5; 20.5.1; 20.7)

Bauzon, Stéphane. LA PERSONNE BIOJURIDIQUE. Paris: Presses Universitaires de France [PUF], 2006. 184 p. ISBN 2-13-055591-8. (Essais-débats, Quadrige series. ISSN 0291-0489. Gift of the author.) (2.1; 4.4; 5.2; 6; 9.3.1; 14.5; 18.2; 18.3; 19.5)

Bennett, Belinda. LAW AND MEDICINE. Sydney, NSW: LBC Information Services, 1997. 191 p. ISBN 0-455-21456-5.

[KU1520 .B46 1997] (2.1; 7.4; 8.3.1; 8.4; 12.4.1; 14.1; 15.1; 18.1; 19.5; 20.5.1)

Cahill, Lisa Sowle. THEOLOGICAL BIOETHICS: PARTICIPATION, JUSTICE, AND CHANGE. Washington, DC: Georgetown University Press, 2005. 310 p. ISBN 1-58901-075-2. (Moral Traditions Series. Gift of the publisher.) [R725.56 .C34 2005] (2.1; 1.2)

Caplan, Arthur L. SMART MICE, NOT SO SMART PEOPLE: AN INTERESTING AND AMUSING GUIDE TO BIOETHICS. Lanham, MD: Rowman & Littlefield, 2007. 210 p. ISBN 0-7425-4171-1. (Gift of the publisher.) [R724 .C344 2007] (2.1)

Daniel, Eileen L., ed. TAKING SIDES: CLASHING VIEWS IN HEALTH AND SOCIETY. Dubuque, IA: McGraw Hill, 2006. 393 p. ISBN 0-07-354561-9. (Seventh edition. Contemporary Learning Series. Gift of the publisher.) [RA776.9 .T35 2006] (2.1; 1.2; 1.3.1; 1.3.5; 1.3.11; 9.1; 9.3.1; 9.4; 9.5.5; 9.5.9; 9.7; 10; 15.1; 18.5.4; 20.5.1; 20.7)

Dinkins, Christine Sorrell and Sorrell, Jeanne Merkle, eds. LISTENING TO THE WHISPERS: RE-THINKING ETHICS IN HEALTHCARE. Madison: University of Wisconsin Press, 2006. 330 p. ISBN 0-299-21650-0. (Interpretive Studies in Healthcare and the Human Sciences series; Vol. 5. Gift of the publisher.) [R724 .L57 2006] (2.1; 1.2; 1.3.2; 9.1; 21.7)

Gert, Bernard; Culver, Charles M.; and Clouser, K. Danner. BIOETHICS: A SYSTEMATIC APPROACH. Oxford/New York: Oxford University Press, 2006. 359 p. ISBN 0-19-515906-3. (Second edition. Gift of the publisher.) [R724 .G46 2006] (2.1; 2.3)

Gill, Robin. HEALTH CARE AND CHRISTIAN ETHICS. Cambridge/New York: Cambridge University Press, 2006. 229 p. ISBN 0-521-85723-6. (New Studies in Christian Ethics series; Vol. 26.) [R725.56 .G55 2006] (2.1; 1.2; 9.4; 9.5.6; 15.1; 20.5.1)

Gross, Michael L. BIOETHICS AND ARMED CONFLICT: MORAL DILEMMAS OF MEDICINE AND WAR. Cambridge, MA: MIT Press, 2006. 384 p. ISBN 0-262-57226-5. (Basic Bioethics series. Gift of the publisher.) [R724 .G76 2006] (2.1; 1.3.5; 4.4; 8.3.1; 8.4; 9.4; 20.5.1; 21.2; 21.3; 21.4)

Guinn, David E., ed. HANDBOOK OF BIOETHICS AND RELIGION. Oxford/New York: Oxford University Press, 2006. 437 p. ISBN 0-19-517873-4. (Gift of the publisher.) [R725.55 .H36 2006] (2.1; 1.2; 2.2; 2.4; 5.3; 9.5.6; 14.1; 14.5; 18.5.4; 19.1; 20.5.1; 20.7; 21.7)

Judson, Karen; Harrison, Carlene; and Hicks, Sharon. LAW AND ETHICS FOR MEDICAL CAREERS. New York: McGraw-Hill, 2006. 350 p. ISBN 0-07-301869-1. (Fourth edition.) (2.1; 8.1; 8.3.1; 8.4; 8.5; 9.1; 9.5.7; 15.1; 20.1)

Kennedy, Ian and Grubb, Andrew. MEDICAL LAW. Oxford/New York: Oxford University Press, 2005. 2303 p. ISBN 0-406-90325-5. (Third edition.) [KD3395 .K46 2005] (2.1; 7.4; 8.3.1; 8.3.2; 8.3.3; 8.3.4; 8.4; 9.2; 9.7; 11.2; 11.3; 12.4.1; 14.1; 18.2; 19.5; 20.2.1; 20.5.1; 20.5.4)

Knoepffler, Nikolaus. MENSCHENWÜRDE IN DER BIOETHIK. Berlin/New York: Springer, 2004. 220 p. ISBN 3-540-21455-0. [R724 .K585 2004] (2.1; 4.4; 18.5.4; 20.4.1)

Koterski, Joseph W., ed. LIFE AND LEARNING XII: PROCEEDINGS OF THE TWELFTH UNIVERSITY FACULTY FOR LIFE CONFERENCE AT AVE MARIA LAW SCHOOL 2002. Washington, DC: University Faculty for Life, 2003. 374 p. (ISSN 1097-0878.) [HQ767.15 .U55a 2002] (2.1; 1.2; 4.4; 9.5.5; 9.5.8; 10; 12.3; 12.4.2; 12.5.1; 14.1; 14.5; 21.1)

Kuhse, Helga and Singer, Peter, eds. BIOETHICS: AN ANTHOLOGY. Malden, MA: Blackwell, 2006. 738 p. ISBN 1-4051-2947-6. (Second edition. Blackwell Philosophy Anthologies series; No. 9. Gift of the publisher.) [R724 .B4582 2006] (2.1; 2.3)

Mappes, Thomas A. and DeGrazia, David. BIOMEDICAL ETHICS. Boston: McGraw-Hill, 2006. 723 p. ISBN 0-07-297644-6. (Sixth edition. Gift of the publisher.) [R724 .B49 2006] (2.1; 2.3)

Mason, J.K.; Smith, R.A. McCall; and Laurie, G.T. LAW AND MEDICAL ETHICS. London: Butterworths LexisNexis, 2002. 704 p. ISBN 0-406-94995-6. (Sixth edition.) [K3601 .M38 2002] (2.1)

Practical Ethics. ACTA ANALYTICA: PHILOSOPHY AND PSYCHOLOGY 2001; 16(27): 7-203. ISBN 3-89754-199-8. (ISSN 0353-5150.) (2.1; 1.1; 1.3.5; 1.3.6; 4.4; 8.1; 8.2; 14.5; 15.1; 15.3; 20.5.1; 20.7; 21.2; 22.1; 22.2)

Puri, Basant K.; Brown, Robert A.; McKee, Heather J.; and Treasaden, Ian H. MENTAL HEALTH LAW: A PRACTICAL GUIDE. London: Hodder Arnold; Distributed in the U.S. by: New York: Oxford University Press, 2005. 254 p. ISBN 0-340-88503-3. (Gift of the publisher.) [KD3412 .M47 2005] (2.1; 1.3.5; 4.3; 6; 7.4; 8.3.1; 9.5.2; 9.5.3; 9.5.7; 17.1; 17.7; 20.7; 21.7)

Rehmann-Sutter, Christoph; Düwell, Marcus; and Mieth, Dietmar, eds. BIOETHICS IN CULTURAL CONTEXTS: REFLECTIONS ON METHODS AND FINITUDE. New York: Springer New York, 2006. 384 p. ISBN 1-4020-4240-X. (International Library of Ethics, Law, and the New Medicine series; Vol. 28. Gift of the publisher.) [QH332 .B51727 2006] (2.1; 1.1; 2.2; 4.1.1; 4.4.; 5.3; 7.1; 20.2.1; 20.5.1; 20.5.2; 21.1; 21.7)

Rosner, Fred and Schulman, Robert, eds. MEDICINE AND JEWISH LAW, VOLUME III. Brooklyn, NY: Yashar Books, 2005. 208 p. ISBN 1-933143-07-X. (Proceedings of the conference "Modern Medicine and Jewish Law", held 14-15 February 1999 at the Lincoln Square Synagogue in New York City under the auspices of the Association of Orthodox Jewish Scientists. Gift of Max M. and Marjorie B. Kampelman.) [BM538 .H43 M43 v.3] (2.1; 1.2; 9.7; 14.1; 14.5; 15.3; 19.1; 19.5; 20.2.1; 22.2)

Takahashi, Takao, ed. TAKING LIFE AND DEATH SERIOUSLY: BIOETHICS FROM JAPAN. Amsterdam/Boston: Elsevier JAI, 2005. 335 p. ISBN 0-7623-1206-8. (Advances in Bioethics; Vol. 8. ISSN 1479-3709.) [R724 .T35

See inside front cover for NRCBL Classification Scheme

2005] (2.1; 2.2; 4.3; 4.4; 9.5.2; 15.1; 16.1; 17.1; 20.1; 20.3.1; 20.3.2; 21.1)

Tettamanzi, Dionigi. DIZIONARIO DI BIOETICA. Casale Monferrato (Allessandria): Piemme, 2002. 457 p. ISBN 88-384-6521-5. (2.1; Reference)

Tippett, Victoria. MEDICAL ETHICS AND LAW: AN INTRODUCTION. Oxford/San Francisco: Radcliffe Publishing, 2004. 156 p. ISBN 1-85775-894-3. (Forewords by Richard Ashcroft and Raanan Gillon.) [KF2905 .T57 2004] (2.1; 2.3)

Tong, Rosemarie; Donchin, Anne; and Dodds, Susan, eds. LINKING VISIONS: FEMINIST BIOETHICS, HUMAN RIGHTS, AND THE DEVELOPING WORLD. Lanham, MD: Rowman & Littlefield, 2004. 260 p. ISBN 0-7425-3279-8. (Studies in Social, Political, and Legal Philosophy series.) [R724 .L55 2004] (2.1; 1.3.5; 9.1; 9.5.4; 9.5.5; 9.5.6; 9.5.7; 10; 14.1; 14.2; 14.3; 15.1; 15.8; 21.1)

UNESCO. International Bioethics Committee. PROCEEDINGS: INTERNATIONAL BIOETHICS COMMITTEE OF UNESCO (IBC), EIGHTH SESSION. [Paris, France]: Division of the Ethics of Science and Technology, UNESCO, 2002. 2 volumes. (September 2001. "...the Eighth Session of the International Bioethics Committee (IBC) was held at UNESCO Headquarters in Paris, from 12 to 14 September 2001. Volume 2 has title: *Actes: Comité International de Bioéthique de l'UNESCO (CIB), huitieme session = Proceedings: International Bioethics Committee of UNESCO (IBC), Eighth Session.*" Gift of LeRoy Walters.) (2.1; 2.3; 2.4; 5.3; 8.4; 15.1; 15.8; 18.3)

Viafora, Corrado, ed. CLINICAL BIOETHICS: A SEARCH FOR THE FOUNDATIONS. Dordrecht/Boston: Springer, 2005. 206 p. ISBN 1-4020-3592-6. (International Library of Ethics, Law, and the New Medicine series; Vol. 26.) [R724 .C5254 2005] (2.1; 1.1; 1.3.1; 4.1.2; 8.1; 9.4; 9.6; 9.8)

Walters, LeRoy; Kahn, Tamar Joy; and Goldstein, Doris Mueller, eds. BIBLIOGRAPHY OF BIOETHICS, VOLUME 32. Washington, DC: Kennedy Institute of Ethics, Georgetown University, 2006. 803 p. ISBN 1-883913-13-6. (ISSN 0363-0161.) [Z6675 .E8 W34 v.32] (2.1; Reference)

Warnock, Mary. NATURE AND MORTALITY: RECOLLECTIONS OF A PHILOSOPHER IN PUBLIC LIFE. London/New York: Continuum, 2003. 225 p. ISBN 0-8264-5940-4. [B1674 .W333 A3 2003] (2.1; 1.3.5; 9.5.7; 12.1; 14.1; 15.1; 20.5.1; 22.2; Biography)

2.2 BIOETHICS: HISTORY OF HEALTH ETHICS

Lerner, K. Lee and Lerner, Brenda Wilmoth, eds. MEDICINE, HEALTH, AND BIOETHICS: ESSENTIAL PRIMARY SOURCES. Farmington Hills, MI: Thomson Gale, 2006. 513 p. ISBN 1-4144-0623-1. (Social Issues Primary Sources Collection series.) (Gift of the publisher.) [R724 .M313 2006] (2.2; 16.1; 21.1; Reference)

Percival, Thomas and Pellegrino, Edmund D. [introduction]. MEDICAL ETHICS, OR, A CODE OF INSTITUTES AND PRECEPTS, ADAPTED TO THE PROFESSIONAL CONDUCT OF PHYSICIANS AND SURGEONS. Birmingham, AL: The Classics of Medicine Library, 1985. 52 p. (Facsimile reprint. Originally published: Manchester [England]: Printed by S. Russell for J. Johnson and R. Bickerstaff, 1803. "This special edition...has been privately printed for the members of The Classics of Medicine Library.") [R724 .P4 1985] (2.2)

2.3 BIOETHICS: EDUCATION/PROGRAMS

Macer, Darryl R.J., ed. A CROSS-CULTURAL INTRODUCTION TO BIOETHICS. Bangkok, Thailand: Eubios Ethics Institute, 2006. 283 p. ISBN 0-908897-23-5. (Publisher's address: c/o UNESCO Bangkok, 920 Sukhumvit Road, Prakanong, Bangkok 10110, Thailand. Gift of the publisher.) (2.3; 2.1; 15.1; 16.1; 17.1; 21.7)

Mepham, Ben. BIOETHICS: AN INTRODUCTION FOR THE BIOSCIENCES. Oxford/New York: Oxford University Press, 2005. 386 p. ISBN 0-19-926715-4. [QH332 .M47 2005] (2.3; 1.1; 1.3.11; 2.1; 5.2; 14.1; 15.1; 16.1; 21.1; 22.2)

Sang-yong, Song; Young-Mo, Koo; and Macer, Darryl R.J., eds. ASIAN BIOETHICS IN THE 21ST CENTURY. Christchurch, New Zealand: Eubios Ethics Institute, 2003. 434 p. ISBN 0-908897-19-7. (The Conference was held under the auspices of the Asian Bioethics Association, the Korean Bioethics Association, the Korean Society for Medical Ethics Education, and the Korean Association of Institutional Review Boards.) [QH332 .A85 2002] (2.3; 2.1; 2.4; 5.3; 14.3; 14.5; 15.1; 15.3; 16.1; 18.2; 18.3; 18.5.1; 18.5.4; 19.1; 20.3.1; 20.5.1; 20.7; 21.1; 21.7; 22.2)

3.1 PHILOSOPHY OF BIOLOGY (GENERAL)

Tallis, Raymond. THE HAND: A PHILOSOPHICAL INQUIRY INTO HUMAN BEING. Edinburgh: Edinburgh University Press, 2003. 364 p. ISBN 0-7486-1738-8. [BF908 .T35 2003] (3.1; 4.4)

Wilson, Edward O. NATURE REVEALED: SELECTED WRITINGS, 1949-2006. Baltimore, MD: Johns Hopkins University Press, 2006. 719 p. ISBN 0-8018-8329-6. (Gift of the publisher.) [QL568 .F7 W63 2006] (3.1; 15.9)

3.2 EVOLUTION AND CREATION

Baker, Catherine and Miller, James B., ed. THE EVOLUTION DIALOGUES: SCIENCE, CHRISTIANITY, AND THE QUEST FOR UNDERSTANDING. Washington, DC: Program of Dialogue on Science, Ethics, and Religion/ American Association for the Advancement of Science, 2006. 208 p. ISBN 0-87168-709-7. [BL263 .B25 2006] (3.2; 1.2)

Corning, Peter A. HOLISTIC DARWINISM: SYNERGY, CYBERNETICS, AND THE BIOECONOMICS OF EVOLUTION. Chicago: University of Chicago Press, 2005. 546 p. ISBN 0-226-11616-6. (Gift of the publisher.) [JC336 .C848 2005] (3.2; 1.3.2; 1.3.12; 15.9)

Numbers in ( ) = NRCBL Classification Numbers

Dembski, William A., ed. DARWIN'S NEMESIS: PHILLIP JOHNSON AND THE INTELLIGENT DESIGN MOVEMENT. Downers Grove, IL: IVP Academic/Leicester, England: InterVarsity Press, 2006. 357 p. ISBN 0-8308-2836-2. (Foreword by Senator Rick Santorum. Gift of the publisher.) [BT1220 .D28 2006] (3.2; 1.2; Biograghy)

Eldredge, Niles. DARWIN: DISCOVERING THE TREE OF LIFE. New York: W.W. Norton, 2005. 256 p. ISBN 0-393-05966-9. [QH31 .D2 E43 2005] (3.2; Biography)

Hösle, Vittorio and Illies, Christian, eds. DARWINISM & PHILOSOPHY. Notre Dame, IN: University of Notre Dame Press, 2005. 392 p. ISBN 0-268-03073-1. [B818 .D26 2005] (3.2; 3.1)

Larson, Edward J. EVOLUTION: THE REMARKABLE HISTORY OF A SCIENTIFIC THEORY. New York: Modern Library, 2004. 337 p. ISBN 0-697-64288-9. (A Modern Library Chronicles Book series; No. 17.) [QH361 .L27 2004] (3.2; 1.2; 5.1; 15.1; 15.5)

Ruse, Michael. DARWINISM AND ITS DISCONTENTS. Cambridge/New York: Cambridge University Press, 2006. 316 p. ISBN 0-521-82947-X. (Gift of the publisher.) [QH371 .R755 2006] (3.2; 1.1; 1.2)

4.1.1 PHILOSOPHY OF MEDICINE, NURSING, & OTHER HEALTH PROFESSIONS

Birnbaum, Raoul. THE HEALING BUDDHA. Boston: Shambhala, 1989. 289 p. ISBN 1-57062-612-X. (Revised edition.) [BQ4690 .B5 B57 1989] (4.1.1; 1.2; 4.2)

D'Cruz, Len; Mills, Simon; and Holmes, David. LEGAL ASPECTS OF GENERAL DENTAL PRACTICE. Edinburgh/New York: Elsevier/Churchill Livingstone, 2006. 110 p. ISBN 0-443-10038-1. (Dental Updates Series. Foreword by Kevin Lewis.) [RK58.7 .D372 2006] (4.1.1; 8.1; 8.3.1; 8.4; 9.8)

Haller, John S. THE HISTORY OF AMERICAN HOMEOPATHY: THE ACADEMIC YEARS, 1820-1935. New York: Pharmaceutical Products Press, 2005. 444 p. ISBN 0-7890-2660-0. [RX51 .H34 2005] (4.1.1; 7.1)

Makely, Sherry. PROFESSIONALISM IN HEALTH CARE: A PRIMER FOR CAREER SUCCESS. Upper Saddle River, NJ: Pearson Prentice Hall, 2005. 134 p. + 1 CD-ROM. ISBN 0-13-114509-6. (Second edition. Revised edition of: *The Health Care Worker's Primer on Professionalism*; 2000. System requirements for accompanying CD-ROM: Windows 98 or newer and Macintosh 9.X and OSX.) [R725.5 .M35 2005] (4.1.1; 7.3; 9.8)

Meulendbeld, G. Jen, ed. [and] Leslie, Julia, ed. MEDICAL LITERATURE FROM INDIA, SRI LANKA AND TIBET [AND] RULES AND REMEDIES IN CLASSICAL INDIAN LAW. Leiden: E.J. Brill, 1991. 137 p. + 90 p. ISBN 90-04-09522-5. (Panels of the VIIth World Sanskrit Conference series; Vol. 8 and Vol. 9.) (2 volumes in 1.) [R605 .W67 1987] (4.1.1)

Tovey, Philip; Easthope, Gary; and Adams, Jon, eds. THE MAINSTREAMING OF COMPLEMENTARY AND ALTERNATIVE MEDICINE: STUDIES IN SOCIAL CONTEXT. London/New York: Routledge, 2004. 180 p. ISBN 0-415-26700-5. [R733 .M357 2004] (4.1.1; 1.3.2; 7.1; 7.3; 9.1.3; 9.8; 16.3)

Welie, Jos V.M., ed. JUSTICE IN ORAL HEALTH CARE: ETHICAL AND EDUCATIONAL PERSPECTIVES. Milwaukee, WI: Marquette University Press, 2006. 370 p. ISBN 0-87462-670-6. (Marquette Studies in Philosophy series; No. 47. Gift of the publisher.) [RK52.7 .J87 2006] (4.1.1; 1.1; 2.3; 6; 7.2; 9.3.1; 9.4; 9.5.4; 9.5.10; 21.1)

4.1.2 PHILOSOPHY OF MEDICINE

Montgomery, Kathryn. HOW DOCTORS THINK: CLINICAL JUDGMENT AND THE PRACTICE OF MEDICINE. Oxford/New York: Oxford University Press, 2006. 246 p. ISBN 0-19-518712-1. (4.1.2; 7.1; 8.1)

Tallis, Raymond. HIPPOCRATIC OATHS: MEDICINE AND ITS DISCONTENTS. London: Atlantic Books, 2004. 342 p. ISBN 1-84354-127-0. [R723 .T25 2004] (4.1.2; 7.1; 9.1)

Willis, James. FRIENDS IN LOW PLACES. Oxon, OX: Radcliffe Medical Press, 2001. 214 p. ISBN 1-85775-404-2. (Foreword by Michael O'Donnell.) (4.1.2)

4.1.3 PHILOSOPHY OF NURSING

Bartter, Karen, ed. ETHICAL ISSUES IN ADVANCED NURSING PRACTICE. Oxford/Boston: Butterworth Heinemann, 2001. 141 p. ISBN 0-7506-4955-0. [RT85 .E795 2001] (4.1.3; 8.3.1; 9.5.7; 9.7; 11.2; 12.3; 20.5.1; 20.5.4)

Cowen, Perle Slavik and Moorhead, Sue, [eds.]. CURRENT ISSUES IN NURSING. St. Louis, MO: Mosby/Elsevier, 2006. 865 p. ISBN 0-323-03652-X. (Seventh edition.) [RT63 .C87 2006] (4.1.3; 1.3.5; 1.3.12; 4.1.1; 7.2; 7.3; 9.3.1; 9.3.2; 9.5.2; 9.5.5; 9.5.7; 9.8; 17.1; 20.4.1; 21.1)

Dimond, Bridgit. LEGAL ASPECTS OF NURSING. Harlow, England/New York: Pearson Education, 2005. 746 p. ISBN 0-582-82278-5. (Fourth edition.) [KD2968 .N8 D56 2005] (4.1.3; 2.1)

Guido, Ginny Wacker. LEGAL AND ETHICAL ISSUES IN NURSING. Upper Saddle River, NJ: Pearson Prentice Hall, 2006. 532 p. ISBN 0-13-171762-6. (Fourth edition.) [KF2915 .N8 G85 2006] (4.1.3; 7.4; 8.3.1; 8.4; 9.3.1; 20.5.4)

Hendrick, Judith. LAW AND ETHICS. Cheltenham: Nelson Thornes, 2004. 289 p. ISBN 0-7487-7541-2. (Foundations in Nursing and Health Care Series.) [RT85 .H458 2004] (4.1.3; 2.1; 8.3.1; 8.4; 8.5; 9.2; 9.5.2; 9.5.5; 9.5.7; 9.5.8; 11.3; 12.1; 17.1; 18.1; 20.1)

Holland, Stephen, ed. INTRODUCING NURSING ETHICS: THEMES IN THEORY AND PRACTICE. Salisbury: APS, 2004. 212 p. ISBN 1-9038772-2-9. (Publisher's address: The Old School, Tollard Royal, Salisbury, Wiltshire SP5 5PW; Web: http://www.apspublishing.co.uk.) [RT85 .I687

2004] (4.1.3; 1.1; 2.3; 4.4; 7.2; 8.3.1; 8.4; 9.1; 9.4; 12.3; 17.3; 18.1; 20.5.1; 21.7)

Iyer, Patricia W., ed. [and] American Association of Legal Nurse Consultants. LEGAL NURSE CONSULTING: PRINCIPLES AND PRACTICE. Boca Raton, FL: CRC Press, 2002. 1132 p. ISBN 0-8493-1418-6. (Second edition.) [KF2915 .N8 L35 2003] (4.1.3; 1.3.2; 1.3.5; 2.1; 7.3; 8.5)

Johnstone, Megan-Jane. BIOETHICS: A NURSING PERSPECTIVE. Sydney/New York: Churchill Livingstone, [2004]. 420 p. ISBN 0-7295-3726-9. (Fourth edition.) [RT85 .J663 2004] (4.1.3; 2.1)

Nestel, Sheryl. OBSTRUCTED LABOUR: RACE AND GENDER IN THE RE-EMERGENCE OF MIDWIFERY. Vancouver: UBC Press, 2006. 200 p. ISBN 0-7748-1220-6. (Gift of the publisher.) [RG950 .N47 2006] (4.1.3; 7.3; 9.5.4; 9.5.5; 10)

O'Brien, Mary Elizabeth. THE NURSE'S CALLING: A CHRISTIAN SPIRITUALITY OF CARING FOR THE SICK. New York: Paulist Press, 2001. 141 p. ISBN 0-8091-4009-8. [RT85.2 .O367 2001] (4.1.3; 1.2)

Webb, Val. FLORENCE NIGHTINGALE: THE MAKING OF A RADICAL THEOLOGIAN. St. Louis, MO: Chalice Press, 2002. 363 p. ISBN 0-8272-1032-9. [BL50 .N473 W43 2002] (4.1.3; 1.2; Biography)

4.2 CONCEPT OF HEALTH

Cha, Dia. HMONG AMERICAN CONCEPTS OF HEALTH, HEALING, AND CONVENTIONAL MEDICINE. New York: Routledge, 2003. 240 p. ISBN 0-415-94495-3. (Studies in Asian Americans series.) [RA418.5 .T73 C48 2003] (4.2; 1.2; 4.1.1; 7.1; 9.5.4; 21.7)

Duffin, Jacalyn. LOVERS AND LIVERS: DISEASE CONCEPTS IN HISTORY. Toronto/Buffalo, NY: University of Toronto Press, 2005. 229 p. ISBN 0-8020-3805-0. (The 2002 Joanne Goodman Lectures series. Gift of the publisher.) [RA418 .D83 2005] (4.2; 4.1.2; 4.3)

4.3 CONCEPT OF MENTAL HEALTH

Brendel, David H. HEALING PSYCHIATRY: BRIDGING THE SCIENCE/HUMANISM DIVIDE. Cambridge, MA: MIT Press, 2006. 178 p. ISBN 0-262-02594-9. (Basic Bioethics series. Foreword by T.M. Luhrmann. Gift of the publisher.) [RC455.2 .E8 B74 2006] (4.3; 3.1; 7.1; 17.1)

British Medical Association [and] Law Society (Great Britain). ASSESSMENT OF MENTAL CAPACITY: GUIDANCE FOR DOCTORS AND LAWYERS. London: BMJ Books, 2004. 236 p. ISBN 0-7279-1671-8. (Second edition. "This report outlines the current legal requirements in England and Wales concerning assessment of mental capacity. Practical guidelines on the medical assessment of capacity are included.") [KD737 .B7 2004] (4.3; 1.3.5; 8.3.1; 8.3.3; 8.3.4; 9.5.3; 17.1; 18.3; 18.5.6)

Hughes, Julian C.; Louw, Stephen J., and Sabat, Steven R., eds. DEMENTIA: MIND, MEANING, AND THE PERSON. Oxford/New York: Oxford University Press, 2006. 310 p.

ISBN 0-19-856615-8. (International Perspectives in Philosophy and Psychiatry series. Gift of the publisher.) [RC521 .D45564 2006] (4.3; 1.1; 1.2; 4.4; 9.5.2)

Pickering, Neil. THE METAPHOR OF MENTAL ILLNESS. Oxford/New York: Oxford University Press, 2006. 194 p. ISBN 0-19-853088-9. (International Perspectives in Philosophy and Psychiatry series. Gift of the publisher.) [RC437.5 .P53 2006] (4.3; 4.1.2; 7.1; 17.1)

Schopp, Robert F. COMPETENCE, CONDEMNATION, AND COMMITMENT: AN INTEGRATED THEORY OF MENTAL HEALTH LAW. Washington, DC: American Psychological Association, 2001. 291 p. ISBN 1-55798-745-9. (The Law and Public Policy: Psychology and the Social Sciences series.) (4.3; 1.3.5; 7.3; 8.3.4; 10; 17.7; 17.8)

Whitehouse, Peter J.; Maurer, Konrad; and Ballenger, Jesse F., eds. CONCEPTS OF ALZHEIMER DISEASE: BIOLOGICAL, CLINICAL, AND CULTURAL PERSPECTIVES. Baltimore, MD: Johns Hopkins University Press, 2000. 321 p. ISBN 0-8018-6233-7. [RC523 .C657 2000] (4.3; 7.1; 8.1; 9.1; 9.5.2; 15.1; 17.1; 21.7)

4.4 QUALITY/VALUE OF LIFE/PERSONHOOD

Bennett, Gillian. BODIES: SEX, VIOLENCE, DISEASE, AND DEATH IN CONTEMPORARY LEGEND. Jackson: University Press of Mississippi, 2005. 313 p. ISBN 1-57806-789-8. (Gift of the publisher.) [GR78 .B46 2005] (4.4; 7.1; 9.5.6; 10; 19.1; 19.4; 19.5)

Carr, Alison; Higginson, Irene J.; and Robinson, Peter G., eds. QUALITY OF LIFE. London: BMJ Books, 2003. 133 p. ISBN 0-7279-1544-4. [RA407 .Q32 2003] (4.4; 5.1; 7.1; 8.1; 9.5.7)

Collste, Göran. IS HUMAN LIFE SPECIAL? RELIGIOUS AND PHILOSOPHICAL PERSPECTIVES ON THE PRINCIPLE OF HUMAN DIGNITY. Bern/New York: Peter Lang, 2002. 233 p. ISBN 3-906769-26-7 [Germany]; ISBN 0-8204-5893-7 [US]. [BD450 .C62 2002] (4.4; 1.1; 1.2; 2.1)

Dormandy, Thomas. THE WORST OF EVILS: THE FIGHT AGAINST PAIN. New Haven: Yale University Press, 2006. 547 p. ISBN 0-300-11322-6. (Gift of the publisher.) [RB127 .D67 2006] (4.4; 1.2; 7.1; 9.7; 20.4.1; 21.7)

Duncker, H.-R. and Prieß, K. ON THE UNIQUENESS OF HUMANKIND. Berlin/New York: Springer-Verlag, 2005. 122 p. ISBN 3-540-23981-2. (Wissenschaftsethik und Technikfolgenbeurteilung series; Bd. 25. Proceedings from a conference, *The Uniqueness of Humankind: Über die Sonderstellung des Menschen,* held 28-30 March 2001 in Bad Neuenahr-Ahrweiler.) [BD450 .O54 2005] (4.4; 1.1; 3.2; 10; 15.1)

Ethical Issues and Dilemmas Faced by Today's Pain Practitioner: A Bioethical Primer. PAIN MEDICINE 2001 June; 2(2): 87-175. (ISSN 1526-2375.) (4.4; 2.1; 4.1.2; 7.1; 7.2; 7.3; 8.3.1; 9.1; 9.3.2; 9.5.1; 9.6; 9.8; 17.1; 18.2; 18.3; 20.4.1; 20.5.1; 20.7)

Longhurst, Robyn. BODIES: EXPLORING FLUID BOUND-ARIES. London/New York: Routledge, 2001. 166 p. ISBN 0-415-18967-5. (Critical Geographies series.) [HM636 .L65 2001] (4.4; 10)

Mailis-Gagnon, Angela and Israelson, David. BEYOND PAIN: MAKING THE MIND-BODY CONNECTION. Ann Arbor: University of Michigan Press, 2005. 274 p. ISBN 0-472-03082-5. (Foreword by Oliver Sacks. First published by: Viking Canada, 2003.) [RB127 .M334 2005] (4.4; 3.1; 7.1)

Martin, Raymond and Barresi, John. THE RISE AND FALL OF SOUL AND SELF: AN INTELLECTUAL HISTORY OF PERSONAL IDENTITY. New York: Columbia University Press, 2006. 383 p. ISBN 0-231-13744-3. [BD438.5 .M375 2006] (4.4; 1.1; 1.2)

Mathieu, Bertrand. THE RIGHT TO LIFE IN EUROPEAN CONSTITUTIONAL AND INTERNATIONAL CASE-LAW. Strasbourg: Council of Europe, 2006. 124 p. ISBN 92-871-5867-3. (Europeans and Their Rights series. Also published in French as: Le droit à la vie; ISBN 92-871-5866-5. English version distributed in the U.S. and Canada by: Manhattan Publishing Group, 468 Albany Post Road, Croton-on-Hudson, NY 10520; Web: http://www.manhattanpublishing.com. Gift of the publisher.) [KJC5132 .M375 2006] (4.4; 8.3.4; 11.4; 12.4.1; 14.5; 18.5.4; 20.5.1; 20.6; 20.7; 21.1)

Stiftung Deutsches Hygiene-Museum [and] Deutsche Behindertenhilfe-Aktion Mensche e.V. DER (IM-)PERFEKTE MENSCH: VOM RECHT AUF UNVOLLKOMMENHEIT. Ostfildern-Ruit: Hatje Cantz, 2001. 261 p. ISBN 3-7757-0997-5. (An exhibition catalog with illustrated essays that provide an overview of normalcy from the early new high period to the present. Edited by Helga Raulff. Exhibit held at the Deutsches Hygiene-Museum, 20 December 2000-12 August 2001.) [NX650 .H72 I67 2001] (4.4; 4.2; 4.3; 9.5.1; 9.5.3)

Tallis, Raymond. I AM: A PHILOSOPHICAL INQUIRY INTO FIRST-PERSON BEING. Edinburgh: Edinburgh University Press, 2004. 350 p. ISBN 0-7486-1951-8. [BD438.5 .T35 2004] (4.4; 3.1)

4.5 ENHANCEMENT

Miller, Paul and Wilsdon, James, eds. BETTER HUMANS? THE POLITICS OF HUMAN ENHANCEMENT AND LIFE EXTENSION. London: Demos, 2006. 139 p. ISBN 1-84180-155-0. (Demos Collection series; No. 21.) [TP248.23 .B48 2006] (4.5; 5.3; 15.1; 20.5.1)

5.1 SCIENCE, TECHNOLOGY AND SOCIETY (GENERAL)

Budinger, Thomas F. and Budinger, Miriam D. ETHICS OF EMERGING TECHNOLOGIES: SCIENTIFIC FACTS AND MORAL CHALLENGES. Hoboken, NJ: John Wiley & Sons, 2006. 496 p. ISBN 0-471-69212-3. (Gift of the publisher.) [T14 .B784 2006] (5.1; 1.1; 1.3.2; 1.3.9; 1.3.11; 1.3.12; 2.1; 4.5;

9.6; 9.7; 14.1; 14.5; 15.1; 15.4; 15.7; 16.1; 18.1; 18.5.4; 20.5.1; 22.2)

Collins, Francis S. THE LANGUAGE OF GOD: A SCIENTIST PRESENTS EVIDENCE FOR BELIEF. New York: Free Press, 2006. 294 p. ISBN0-7432-8639-1. [BL240.3 .C66 2006] (5.1; 1.2; 3.2; 15.1)

Figueroa, Robert and Harding, Sandra G., eds. SCIENCE AND OTHER CULTURES: ISSUES IN PHILOSOPHIES OF SCIENCE AND TECHNOLOGY. New York: Routledge, 2003. 276 p. ISBN 0-415-93992-5. [Q175 .S4172 2003] (5.1; 21.7)

Higgs, Eric; Light, Andrew; and Strong, David, eds. TECHNOLOGY AND THE GOOD LIFE? Chicago: University of Chicago Press, 2000. 392 p. ISBN 0-226-33387-6. [T14 .T386 2000] (5.1; 1.1; 1.3.11; 1.3.12; 16.1)

Iles, Greg. THE FOOTPRINTS OF GOD. New York: Pocket Star Books, 2004, c2003. 528 p. ISBN 0-7434-5414-6. ("In a secret goverment lab, America's top scientists work on Trinity–a supercomputer that could surpass the power of the human mind. As the project's ethicist, Dr. David Tennant works in a firestorm of limitless science and ruthless ambition. After a fellow scientist is murdered, David uncovers who the killer is. Desperate, he turns to Rachel Weiss, the psychiatrist probing the nightmares that have plagued him since joining the project, and both are forced to flee for their lives. Pursued around the globe, David and Rachel piece together the truth behind Project Trinity, and the apocalyptic power it possesses. But Trinity's countdown has already begun, and humanity is now held hostage by a form of life that cannot be destroyed. The only hope for survival lies in the shocking connection that exists between Trinity and David's tortured mind. Mankind's future hangs in the balance–and the price of failure is extinction.") [PS3559 .L47 F66 2004] (5.1; 1.3.12; 4.5; 20.5.1; Fiction)

Jeeves, Malcolm, ed. FROM CELLS TO SOULS — AND BEYOND: CHANGING PORTRAITS OF HUMAN NATURE. Grand Rapids, MI: William B. Eerdmans, 2004. 252 p. ISBN 0-8028-0985-5. [BL240.3 .F75 2004] (5.1; 1.2; 4.4; 14.5; 15.1; 17.1)

Mitcham, Carl, ed. ENCYCLOPEDIA OF SCIENCE, TECHNOLOGY, AND ETHICS. Detroit: Macmillan Reference USA, 2005. 4 volumes. [2378 p.]. ISBN 0-02-865831-0 [set]; ISBN 0-02-865832-9 [Vol. 1]; ISBN 0-02-865833-7 [Vol. 2]; ISBN 0-02-865834-5 [Vol. 3]; ISBN 0-02-865901-5 [Vol. 4]. [Q175.35 .E53 2005] (5.1; 1.3.1; 1.3.4; 1.3.9; 1.3.12; 2.1; 15.1; Reference)

Montaigne, Fen. MEDICINE BY DESIGN: THE PRACTICE AND PROMISE OF BIOMEDICAL ENGINEERING. Baltimore, MD: Johns Hopkins University Press, 2006. 229 p. ISBN 0-8018-8347-4. (Gift of the publisher.) [R856 .M595 2006] (5.1; 7.1; 9.1; 15.1; POP)

Nelson, Sue, and Hollingham, Richard. HOW TO CLONE THE PERFECT BLONDE: USING SCIENCE TO MAKE YOUR WILDEST DREAMS COME TRUE. Philadelphia: Quirk Books,

2004. 271 p. ISBN 1-59474-008-9. [Q162 .N42 2004] (5.1; 4.4; 4.5; 20.1)

Science and Society. EMBO REPORTS 2005 July; 6(Special Issue): S1-S83. (ISSN 1469-221X.) (5.1; 1.1; 1.2; 1.3.7; 4.4; 4.5; 5.3; 9.3.1; 9.5.2; 14.5; 18.5.1; 20.5.1)

Shurkin, Joel N. BROKEN GENIUS: THE RISE AND FALL OF WILLIAM SHOCKLEY, CREATOR OF THE ELECTRONIC AGE. New York: London/Macmillan, 2006. 297 p. ISBN 1-4039-8815-3. [TK140 .S466 S58 2006] (5.1; 1.3.12; 14.6; 15.5; Biography)

Stebbins, Michael. SEX, DRUGS AND DNA: SCIENCE'S TABOOS CONFRONTED. London/New York: Macmillan, 2006. 350 p. ISBN 1-4039-9342-4. [Q162 .S825 2006] (5.1; 1.2; 1.3.7; 3.2; 9.3.1; 10; 14.5; 15.1; 15.6; 18.5.4; 21.3)

Winnick, Pamela R. A JEALOUS GOD: SCIENCE'S CRUSADE AGAINST RELIGION. Nashville, TN: Nelson Current, 2005. 334 p. ISBN 1-5955-5019-4. [BL240.3 .W57 2005] (5.1; 1.2; 1.3.9; 5.3)

World Commission on the Ethics of Scientific Knowledge and Technology [COMEST] [and] United Nations Educational, Scientific and Cultural Organization [UNESCO]. PROCEEDINGS: FOURTH SESSION: BANGKOK, THAILAND, 23-25 MARCH 2005. Paris: United Nations Educational, Scientific and Cultural Organization, 2005. 135 p. (Gift of Darryl Macer.) (5.1; 1.3.3; 1.3.11; 9.2; 15.1; 16.1; 21.1; 22.1)

5.2 TECHNOLOGY ASSESSMENT

Bennett, Peter and Calman, Kenneth, eds. RISK COMMUNICATION AND PUBLIC HEALTH. Oxford/New York: Oxford University Press, 2001. 272 p. ISBN 0-19-850899-9. (Oxford Medical Publications series.) [RA423.2 .R55 2001] (5.2; 1.3.5; 1.3.7; 1.3.11; 5.3; 9.1; 15.1; 16.1; 22.3)

Berry, Dianne C. RISK, COMMUNICATION AND HEALTH PSYCHOLOGY. Berkshire/New York: Open University Press, 2004. 173 p. ISBN 0-335-21315-0. [RA423.2 .B47 2004] (5.2; 7.1; 8.1; 8.3.1)

Morgan, M. Granger; Fischhoff, Baruch; Bostrom, Ann; and Atman, Cynthia J. RISK COMMUNICATION: A MENTAL MODELS APPROACH. Cambridge/New York: Cambridge University Press, 2002. 351 p. ISBN 0-521-00256-7. [T10.68 .R58 2002] (5.2; 5.3; 9.5.6; 16.1)

Pidgeon, Nick; Kasperson, Roger E.; and Slovic, Paul, eds. THE SOCIAL AMPLIFICATION OF RISK. Cambridge/New York: Cambridge University Press, 2003. 448 p. ISBN 0-521-52044-4. [HM1101 .S63 2003] (5.2; 1.3.5; 1.3.7; 5.3; 9.5.6; 16.1; 16.2; 22.3)

Slovic, Paul. THE PERCEPTION OF RISK. London/Sterling, VA: Earthscan, 2000. 473 p. ISBN 1-85383-528-5. (Risk, Society and Policy Series.) [BJ637 .R57 S57 2000] (5.2; 1.3.5; 4.4; 5.3; 9.5.7; 9.5.9; 10; 16.2; 17.1)

Sunstein, Cass R. RISK AND REASON: SAFETY, LAW, AND THE ENVIRONMENT. Cambridge/New York: Cambridge University Press, 2002. 342 p. ISBN 0-521-01625-8. [HD61 .S86 2002] (5.2; 5.3; 16.1)

Titterton, Mike. RISK AND RISK TAKING IN HEALTH AND SOCIAL WELFARE. London/Philadelphia: Jessica Kingsley, 2005. 160 p. ISBN 1-85302-482-1. [RA427.3 .T56 2005] (5.2; 1.3.10; 4.3; 9.1; 9.5.2; 9.5.7; 9.5.10; 10)

5.3 SOCIAL CONTROL OF SCIENCE/TECHNOLOGY

Brown, Nik and Webster, Andrew. NEW MEDICAL TECHNOLOGIES AND SOCIETY: REORDERING LIFE. Cambridge/Malden, MA: Polity, 2004. 216 p. ISBN 0-7456-2724-2. [RA418.5 .M4 B76 2004] (5.3; 4.4; 7.1; 19.1; 20.1; 22.2)

Dew, Kevin and Fitzgerald, Ruth, eds. CHALLENGING SCIENCE: ISSUES FOR NEW ZEALAND SOCIETY IN THE 21ST CENTURY. Palmerston North, New Zealand: Dunmore Press, 2004. 286 p. ISBN 0-86469-458-X. (Publisher's address: PO Box 5115; Web: http://www.dunmore.co.nz.) [Q127 .N3 C48 2004] (5.3; 1.3.3; 5.1; 5.2; 15.1; 21.7)

Deyo, Richard A. and Patrick, Donald L. HOPE OR HYPE: THE OBSESSION WITH MEDICAL ADVANCES AND THE HIGH COST OF FALSE PROMISES. New York: AMACOM, 2005. 335 p. ISBN 0-8144-0845-1. (Gift of the publisher.) [RA418.5 .M4 D49 2005] (5.3; 1.3.7; 5.2; 9.1; 9.3.1; 9.7)

Dyens, Ollivier. METAL AND FLESH: THE EVOLUTION OF MAN: TECHNOLOGY TAKES OVER. Cambridge, MA: MIT Press, 2001. 120 p. ISBN 0-262-04200-2. (Leonardo Books series. Translation from the French by Evan J. Bibbee and Ollivier Dyens of: *Chair et métal.*) [HM846 .D9413 2001] (5.3; 1.3.12; 4.4)

Epstein, Richard A. OVERDOSE: HOW EXCESSIVE GOVERNMENT REGULATION STIFLES PHARMACEUTICAL INNOVATION. New Haven, CT: Yale University Press, 2006. 283 p. ISBN 0-300-11664-0. ("An Institute for Policy Innovation Book.") (5.3; 1.3.2; 1.3.5; 9.7)

Flynn, James; Slovic, Paul; and Kunreuther, Howard, eds. RISK, MEDIA, AND STIGMA: UNDERSTANDING PUBLIC CHALLENGES TO MODERN SCIENCE AND TECHNOLOGY. London/Sterling, VA: Earthscan, 2001. 399 p. ISBN 1-85383-700-8. (Risk, Society, and Policy Series.) [P96 .T42 R56 2001] (5.3; 1.3.2; 1.3.5; 1.3.7; 5.2; 9.5.6; 9.7; 16.1; 16.2; 21.3; 22.3)

Herzig, Rebecca M. SUFFERING FOR SCIENCE: REASON AND SACRIFICE IN MODERN AMERICA. New Brunswick, NJ: Rutgers University Press, 2005. 194 p. ISBN 0-8135-3662-6. [Q127 .U6 H396 2005] (5.3; 4.4; 7.1)

Joss, Simon and Durant, John, eds. PUBLIC PARTICIPATION IN SCIENCE: THE ROLE OF CONSENSUS CONFERENCES IN EUROPE. London: Science Museum with the support of the European Commission Directorate General XII, 1995. 144 p. ISBN 0-901805-85-8. [Q127 .E86 P83 1995] (5.3; 5.2)

Numbers in ( ) = NRCBL Classification Numbers

Mooney, Chris. THE REPUBLICAN WAR ON SCIENCE. New York: Basic Books, 2005. 357 p. ISBN 0-465-04676-2. [Q175.52 .U5 M66 2006] (5.3; 1.3.5; 3.2; 10; 16.1; 18.5.4; 21.1)

National Research Council (United States). Steering Committee on the Role of Scientific and Technical Data and Information in the Public Domain. THE ROLE OF SCIENTIFIC AND TECHNICAL DATA AND INFORMATION IN THE PUBLIC DOMAIN: PROCEEDINGS OF A SYMPOSIUM. Washington, DC: National Academies Press, 2003. 226 p. ISBN 0-309-08850-X. (Edited by Julie M. Esanu and Paul F. Uhlir. "The symposium was held on September 5-6, 2002, at the National Academies in Washington, D.C." Also available on the Web at: http://www.nap.edu.) [Q223 .S96 2002] (5.3; 1.3.3; 1.3.9; 1.3.12)

Ong, Aihwa and Collier, Stephen J., eds. GLOBAL ASSEMBLAGES: TECHNOLOGY, POLITICS, AND ETHICS AS ANTHROPOLOGICAL PROBLEMS. Malden, MA: Blackwell, 2005. 494 p. ISBN 1-4051-2358-3. [HM831 .G49 2005] (5.3; 1.3.12; 3.1; 9.7; 13.3; 15.11; 18.5.4; 19.5; 21.1; 21.7)

Stehr, Nico, ed. BIOTECHNOLOGY: BETWEEN COMMERCE AND CIVIL SOCIETY. New Brunswick, NJ: Transaction, 2004. 376 p. ISBN 0-7658-0224-4. (Proceedings of a conference held at the Kulturwissenschaftliche Institut, Essen, Germany in September 2004.) [TP248.23 .B5625 2004] (5.3; 1.3.7; 1.3.12; 5.1; 13.1; 14.1; 14.5; 15.1; 15.8; 15.10; 18.5.4; 21.1)

White, Michael. THE FRUITS OF WAR: HOW MILITARY CONFLICT ACCELERATES TECHNOLOGY. London/New York: Simon & Schuster, 2005. 374 p. ISBN 0-7432-2024-2. [U42 .W45 2005] (5.3; 1.3.12; 16.2; 21.2)

6 CODES OF/POSITIONS STATEMENTS ON PROFESSIONAL ETHICS

Fisher, Celia B. DECODING THE ETHICS CODE: A PRACTICAL GUIDE FOR PSYCHOLOGISTS. Thousand Oaks, CA: Sage, 2003. 283 p. ISBN 0-7619-2619-4. [BF76.4 .F57 2003] (6; 1.3.1; 1.3.7; 1.3.9; 7.2; 8.4; 9.8; 10; 17.1)

7.1 SOCIOLOGY OF HEALTH CARE (GENERAL)

Benson, Evelyn Rose. AS WE SEE OURSELVES: JEWISH WOMEN IN NURSING. Indianapolis, IN: Center Nursing Publishing, 2001. 196 p. ISBN 1-930538-05-7. (Gift of Max M. and Marjorie B. Kampelman.) (7.1; 1.2; 4.1.3; Biography)

Bourdelais, Patrice. EPIDEMICS LAID LOW: A HISTORY OF WHAT HAPPENED IN RICH COUNTRIES. Baltimore, MD: Johns Hopkins University Press, 2006. 176 p. ISBN 0-8018-8295-8. (Translation from the French by Bart K. Holland of: *Les épidémies terrassées: une histoire de pays riches*; Éditions de La Martinière, Paris, 2003.) [RA650.6 .A1 B6813 2006] (7.1; 9.1; 9.5.1; 9.5.6; 21.1)

Brim, Orville Gilbert; Ryff, Carol D.; and Kessler, Ronald C., eds. HOW HEALTHY ARE WE? A NATIONAL STUDY OF WELL-BEING AT MIDLIFE. Chicago: University of Chicago Press, 2004. 687 p. ISBN 0-226-07475-7. (John D. and Catherine T. MacArthur Foundation Series on Mental Health and Development.) [BF724.6 .H69 2004] (7.1; 4.4; 17.1)

Burns, Gene. THE MORAL VETO: FRAMING CONTRACEPTION, ABORTION, AND CULTURAL PLURALISM IN THE UNITED STATES. Cambridge/New York: Cambridge University Press, 2005. 340 p. ISBN 0-521-60984-4. [HN90 .M6 B87 2005] (7.1; 11.1; 12.5.1; 12.5.2; 15.5; 21.7)

Campo, Rafael. THE POETRY OF HEALING: A DOCTOR'S EDUCATION IN EMPATHY, IDENTITY, AND DESIRE. New York: W.W. Norton, 1997. 270 p. ISBN 0-393-04009-7. [R154 .C26 A3 1997] (7.1; 8.1; 9.5.6; Biography)

Collins, Harry and Pinch, Trevor. DR. GOLEM: HOW TO THINK ABOUT MEDICINE. Chicago: University of Chicago Press, 2005. 246 p. ISBN 0-226-11366-3. [RC81 .C695 2005] (7.1; 1.3.9; 4.1.1; 8.2; 9.1; 9.5.1; 9.5.6; 20.1)

Davis, Corney and Schaefer, Judy, eds. BETWEEN THE HEARTBEATS: POETRY & PROSE BY NURSES. Iowa City: University of Iowa Press, 1995. 225 p. ISBN 0-87745-517-1. (Gift of Warren Reich.) [PS508 .N87 B48 1995] (7.1; 8.1)

Fleischhauer, Kurt and Hermerén, Göran. GOALS OF MEDICINE IN THE COURSE OF HISTORY AND TODAY: A STUDY IN THE HISTORY AND PHILOSOPHY OF MEDICINE. Stockholm: Kungl. Vitterhets Historie och Antikvitets Akademien [Royal Academy of Letters, History and Antiquities]; Distributed by: Almqvist & Wiksell International, 2006. 479 p. ISBN 91-7402-353-5. (Publisher's address: PO Box 15200, SE-104 65 Stockholm. Gift of the publisher.) (7.1; 1.2; 2.2; 4.1.2; 9.1; 11.1; 12.1; 15.1; 15.5)

Greaves, David. THE HEALING TRADITION: REVIVING THE SOUL OF WESTERN MEDICINE. Oxford/San Francisco: Radcliffe, 2004. 166 p. ISBN 1-85775-963-X. [R133 .G74 2004] (7.1; 4.1.2; 4.2; 4.3; 4.4)

Greenhalgh, Susan. UNDER THE MEDICAL GAZE: FACTS AND FICTIONS OF CHRONIC PAIN. Berkeley: University of California Press, 2001. 371 p. ISBN 0-520-22398-5. [RB127 .G745 2001] (7.1; 4.1.1; 4.4; 8.1; 10; Biography)

Hart, Gerald D. ASCLEPIUS: THE GOD OF MEDICINE. London/Lake Forest, IL: Royal Society of Medicine Press, 2000. 262 p. ISBN 1-85315-409-1. [R135 .H375 2000] (7.1; 4.1.2)

Helman, Cecil, ed. DOCTORS AND PATIENTS: AN ANTHOLOGY. Abingdon, Oxon: Radcliffe Medical Press, 2003. 162 p. ISBN 1-85775-993-1. [PN6071 .P45 D63 2003] (7.1; 8.1; Fiction)

Hutt, Patrick; Heath, Iona; and Neighbour, Roger. CONFRONTING AN ILL SOCIETY: DAVID WIDGERY, GENERAL PRACTICE, IDEALISM AND THE CHASE FOR CHANGE. Oxon/San Francisco: Radcliffe, 2005. 120 p. ISBN 1-85775-910-9. (Foreword by Richard Smith.) [R489 .W3965 H88 2005] (7.1; 9.1; Biography)

Justman, Stewart. SEEDS OF MORTALITY: THE PUBLIC AND PRIVATE WORLDS OF CANCER. Chicago: Ivan R. Dee, 2003. 219 p. ISBN 1-56663-498-9. [RC262 .J876 2003] (7.1; 9.5.1)

Kelly, John. THE GREAT MORALITY: AN INTIMATE HISTORY OF THE BLACK DEATH. London/New York: Harper Perennial, 2006. 364 p. ISBN 0-00-715070-9. (First published in Great Britain by: Fourth Estate, 2005.) (7.1; 9.5.1)

Kronenfeld, Jennie Jacobs, ed. SOCIAL INEQUALITIES, HEALTH AND HEALTH CARE DELIVERY. Amsterdam/Boston: JAI/Elsevier Science, 2002. 234 p. ISBN 0-7623-0957-1. (Research in the Sociology of Health Care series; Vol. 20.) [RA418 .R48 v.20] (7.1; 9.1; 9.3.1; 9.5.4; 9.5.5; 9.5.10; 9.8)

Linton, Derek S. EMIL VON BEHRING: INFECTIOUS DISEASE, IMMUNOLOGY, AND SERUM THERAPY. Philadelphia: American Philosophical Society, 2005. 580 p. ISBN 0-87169-255-4. (Memoirs of the American Philosophical Society Held at Philadelphia for Promoting Useful Knowledge series; Vol. 255. ISSN 0065-9738.) [Q11 .P612 v.255] (7.1; 9.1; 18.1; Biography)

National Research Council (United States). Panel on DHHA Collection of Race and Ethnicity Data. ELIMINATING HEALTH DISPARITIES: MEASUREMENT AND DATA NEEDS. Washington, DC: National Academies Press, 2004. 294 p. ISBN 0-309-09231-0. (Edited by Michele ver Ploeg and Edward Perrin. Also available on the Web at: http://www.nap.edu.) [RA418.3 .U6 E45 2004] (7.1; 9.1; 9.5.4)

Ober, K. Patrick. MARK TWAIN AND MEDICINE: "ANY MUMMERY WILL CURE". Columbia: University of Missouri Press, 2003. 362 p. ISBN 0-8262-1502-5. (Mark Twain and His Circle Series.) [PS1342 .M43 O24 2003] (7.1)

Padden, Carol and Humphries, Tom. INSIDE DEAF CULTURE. Cambridge, MA: Harvard University Press, 2005. 208 p. ISBN 0-674-01506-1. [HV2545 .P35 2005] (7.1; 5.3; 9.5.1)

Rollins, Peter C. and Smith, Alan, eds. SHAKESPEARE'S THEORIES OF BLOOD, CHARACTER, AND CLASS: A FESTSCHRIFT IN HONOR OF DR. DAVID SHELLEY BERKELEY. New York: Peter Lang, 2001. 244 p. ISBN 0-8204-4518-5. (Studies in Shakespeare series; Vol. 12.) ("Publications of David S. Berkeley.") [PR3069 .B58 S48 2001] (7.1; 15.5; 15.6)

Rosenberg, Charles E., ed. RIGHT LIVING: AN ANGLO-AMERICAN TRADITION OF SELF-HELP MEDICINE AND HYGIENE. Baltimore, MD: Johns Hopkins University Press, 2003. 236 p. ISBN 0-8018-7189-1. [RC81 .R57 2003] (7.1; 1.3.7; 9.1; 10; POP)

Shuman, Joel and Volck, Brian. RECLAIMING THE BODY: CHRISTIANS AND THE FAITHFUL USE OF MODERN MEDICINE. Grand Rapids, MI: Brazos Press, 2006. 173 p. ISBN 1-58743-127-0. (The Christian Practice of Everyday Life series.) (Gift of the publisher.) [BT732 .S482 2006] (7.1; 1.2; 2.1; 4.4; 9.1)

Snyder, Sharon L. and Mitchell, David T. CULTURAL LOCATIONS OF DISABILITY. Chicago: University of Chicago Press, 2006. 245 p. ISBN 0-226-76732-9. [HV1568 .S69 2006] (7.1; 1.3.5; 9.5.1; 9.5.3; 15.5)

Valencius, Conevery Bolton. THE HEALTH OF THE COUNTRY: HOW AMERICAN SETTLERS UNDERSTOOD THEMSELVES AND THEIR LAND. New York: Basic Books, 2002. 388 p. ISBN 0-465-08987-9. [RA792 .V354 2002] (7.1; 1.3.11; 16.1)

7.2 EDUCATION FOR HEALTH CARE PROFESSIONALS

Institute of Medicine (United States). Board on Health Sciences Policy. Committee on Institutional and Policy-level Strategies for Increasing the Diversity of the U.S. Health Care Workforce. IN THE NATION'S COMPELLING INTEREST: ENSURING DIVERSITY IN THE HEALTH-CARE WORKFORCE. Washington, DC: National Academies Press, 2004. 409 p. ISBN 0-309-09125-X. (Edited by Brian D. Smedley, Adrienne Stith Butler, and Lonnie R. Bristow. Also available on the Web at: http://www.nap.edu.) [R745 .I5 2004] (7.2; 9.1; 9.3.1; 21.7)

8.1 PATIENT RELATIONSHIPS (GENERAL)

Coulter, Angela. THE AUTONOMOUS PATIENT: ENDING PATERNALISM IN MEDICAL CARE. London: The Nuffield Trust; Published by: London: TSO (The Stationery Office), 2002. 121 p. ISBN 0-11-703056-2. (8.1; 9.1; 9.8)

Forman, Jane Harriet. THE PHYSICIAN-PATIENT RELATIONSHIP: VIEWS OF ADULTS WITH LIFE-THREATENING ILLNESS. Ann Arbor, MI: ProQuest Information and Learning/UMI, 2001. 296 p. (Publication No. AAT-3030161. Dissertation (D.Sc.)—Johns Hopkins University, School of Hygiene and Public Health, 2001.) (8.1; 7.1; 9.5.1; 9.5.6; 17.1)

Hind, Charles R.K., ed. COMMUNICATION SKILLS IN MEDICINE. London: BMJ Publishing Group, 1997. 161 p. ISBN 0-7279-1152-X. [R727.3 .H559 1997] (8.1; 8.3.3; 9.5.1; 9.5.3; 9.5.6; 9.5.7; 10; 20.1; 20.2.1; 20.5.1)

Horton, Richard. SECOND OPINION: DOCTORS, DISEASES AND DECISIONS IN MODERN MEDICINE. London: Granta Books, 2003. 582 p. ISBN 1-86207-587-5. [R727.3 .H67 2003] (8.1; 1.3.11; 4.2; 4.4; 9.5.6; 9.7; 15.1; 15.10; 20.5.1; 21.2; 21.3)

Hunink, M.G. Myriam; Glasziou, Paul p.; Siegel, Joanna E.; Weeks, Jane C.; Pliskin, Joseph S.; Elstein, Arthur S.; and Weinstein, Milton C. DECISION MAKING IN HEALTH AND MEDICINE: INTEGRATING EVIDENCE AND VALUES. Cambridge/New York: Cambridge University Press, 2001. 388 p. ISBN 0-521-77029-7. (Includes a CD-ROM of supplemental materials.) [R723.5 .D39 2001] (8.1; 4.4; 9.4; 9.8)

Hurwitz, Brian; Greenhalgh, Trisha; and Skultans, Vieda, eds. NARRATIVE RESEARCH IN HEALTH AND ILLNESS. London: BMJ Books/Blackwell, 2004. 446 p. ISBN

0-7279-1792-7. [R727 .N27 2004] (8.1; 1.2; 7.1; 9.5.1; 9.5.7; 17.1; 19.5; 20.4.1)

Jonsen, Albert R.; Siegler, Mark; and Winslade, William J. CLINICAL ETHICS: A PRACTICAL APPROACH TO ETHICAL DECISIONS IN CLINICAL MEDICINE. New York: McGraw-Hill Medical, 2006. 227 p. ISBN 0-07-144199-9. (Sixth edition. Gift of the publisher.) [R724 .J66 2006] (8.1; 2.1; 2.3; 4.4; 8.3.1; 8.4; 9.6; 20.2.1; 20.5.1)

Kittay, Eva Feder and Feder, Ellen K. THE SUBJECT OF CARE: FEMINIST PERSPECTIVES ON DEPENDENCY. Lanham, MD: Rowman & Littlefield, 2002. 382 p. ISBN 0-7425-1363-7. (Feminist Constructions series.) [HQ1206 .S9 2002] (8.1; 1.1; 1.3.2; 7.1; 9.5.2; 9.5.3; 9.5.5; 9.5.7; 9.5.10; 10; 21.1)

Morrow, Jason. AWAKENING TO HUMANITY: SOURCES OF MORAL AUTHORITY AND RESPONSIVENESS IN DOCTOR-PATIENT RELATIONSHIPS. Ann Arbor, MI: ProQuest Information and Learning/UMI, 2004. 270 p. (Publication No. AAT-3124646. Dissertation, (Ph.D.)—Graduate School of Biomedical Sciences, University of Texas at Galveston, 2004.) (8.1; 4.4; 9.5.6)

Ofri, Danielle. INCIDENTAL FINDINGS: LESSONS FROM MY PATIENTS IN THE ART OF MEDICINE. Boston: Beacon Press, 2005. 181 p. ISBN 0-8070-7266-4. [R705 .O38 2005] (8.1; 7.1; 17.1)

Tauber, Alfred I. PATIENT AUTONOMY AND THE ETHICS OF RESPONSIBILITY. Cambridge, MA: MIT Press, 2005. 328 p. ISBN 0-262-70112-X. (Basic Bioethics series. Gift of the publisher.) [R727.42 .T38 2005] (8.1; 1.1; 4.4)

Weir, Al B. WHEN YOUR DOCTOR HAS BAD NEWS: SIMPLE STEPS TO STRENGTH, HEALING & HOPE. Grand Rapids, MI: Zondervan, 2003. 191 p. ISBN 0-310-24742-X. (Foreword by Joni Eareckson Tada.) [R726.5 .W45 2003] (8.1; 1.2; 7.1; 17.1)

8.2 TRUTH DISCLOSURE

Peters, David, ed. UNDERSTANDING THE PLACEBO EFFECT IN COMPLEMENTARY MEDICINE: THEORY, PRACTICE AND RESEARCH. Edinburgh/New York: Churchill Livingstone, 2001. 235 p. ISBN 0-443-06031-2. [RM331 .U52 2001] (8.2; 4.1.1; 18.3)

Surbone, Antonella. FROM TRUTH TELLING TO TRUTH MAKING IN MEDICINE. Ann Arbor, MI: ProQuest Information & Learning/UMI, 2004. 388 p. (Publication Order No. AAT-3125027. Dissertation, (Ph.D.)—Fordham University, 2004.) (8.2; 4.2; 8.1; 9.5.5; 15.3)

Thompson, W. Grant. THE PLACEBO EFFECT AND HEALTH: COMBINING SCIENCE AND COMPASSIONATE CARE. Amherst, NY: Prometheus Books, 2005. 350 p. ISBN 1-59102-275-4. [R726.5 .T488 2005] (8.2; 4.1.1; 7.1; 8.1; 17.2; 18.3)

8.3.1 INFORMED CONSENT (GENERAL)

Merz, Jon Frederick. TOWARD A STANDARD OF DISCLOSURE FOR MEDICAL INFORMED CONSENT: DEVELOPMENT AND DEMONSTRATION OF A DECISION-ANALYTIC METHODOLOGY. Ann Arbor, MI: University Microfilms International [UMI], 1991. 122 p. (Publication No. AAT-9202919. Dissertation, (Ph.D. in Engineering and Public Policy)—Carnegie Mellon University, 1991.) (8.3.1; 5.2; 7.1)

8.4 CONFIDENTIALITY

Beyleveld, Deryck; Townend, David; Rouillé-Mirza, Ségolène; and Wright, Jessica, eds. IMPLEMENTATION OF THE DATA PROTECTION DIRECTIVE IN RELATION TO MEDICAL RESEARCH IN EUROPE. Aldershot, Hants, England/Burlington, VT: Ashgate, 2004. 473 p. ISBN 0-7546-2369-6. (Data Protection and Medical Research in Europe: PRIVIREAL series.) [KJE6229 .R43 I485 2004] (8.4; 1.3.5; 1.3.12; 18.2; 21.1)

Beyleveld, D.; Townend, D.; Rouillé-Mirza, S.; and Wright, J., eds. THE DATA PROTECTION DIRECTIVE AND MEDICAL RESEARCH ACROSS EUROPE. Aldershot, Hants/Burlington, VT: Ashgate, 2004. 252 p. ISBN 0-7546-2367-X. (Data Protection and Medical Research in Europe: PRIVIREAL series.) [KJE6229 .R43 D38 2004] (8.4; 9.1; 18.2; 21.1)

Confidentiality Issues in Psychology. AUSTRALIAN PSYCHOLOGIST 1995 November; 30(3): 153-190. (ISSN 0005-0067.) (8.4; 1.3.12; 4.3; 6; 7.1; 8.1; 8.3.1; 9.3.1; 9.5.6; 9.5.7; 9.5.9; 10; 17.2; 18.2; 18.4; 18.5.2; 20.7)

8.5 MALPRACTICE

Woods, Michael S. and Brucker, Hilda J. HEALING WORDS: THE POWER OF APOLOGY IN MEDICINE. Oak Park, IL: Doctors in Touch, 2004. 89 p. ISBN 0-9755196-0-3. (Publisher's address: 1100 Lake Street, Suite 230, zip 60301.) (8.5; 2.1; 8.1)

9.1 HEALTH CARE (GENERAL)

Adams, Lee; Amos, Mary; and Munro, James, eds. PROMOTING HEALTH: POLITICS & PRACTICE. London/Thousand Oaks, CA: Sage, 2002. 209 p. ISBN 0-7619-6834-2. [RA427.8 .P762 2002] (9.1; 7.1; 9.5.1; 9.5.4; 9.5.5; 9.5.10; 16.1; 21.1)

Baggott, Rob; Allsop, Judith; and Jones, Kathryn. SPEAKING FOR PATIENTS AND CARERS: HEALTH CONSUMER GROUPS AND THE POLICY PROCESS. New York: Palgrave Macmillan, 2005. 349 p. ISBN 0-333-96829-8. [RA395 .G6 B346 2005] (9.1; 1.3.5; 1.3.7; 7.1; 9.7)

Blane, David; Brunner, Eric; and Wilkinson, Richard, eds. HEALTH AND SOCIAL ORGANIZATION: TOWARDS A HEALTH POLICY FOR THE TWENTY-FIRST CENTURY. London/New York: Routledge, 1996. 326 p. ISBN 0-415-13070-0. [RA418.3 .G7 H43 1996] (9.1; 7.1; 9.5.1; 21.1)

Cogan, John F.; Hubbard, R. Glenn; and Kessler, Daniel p. HEALTHY, WEALTHY, AND WISE: FIVE STEPS TO A BETTER HEALTH CARE SYSTEM. Washington, DC: AEI Press [and] Stanford, CA: Hoover Institution, 2005. 130 p. ISBN 0-8447-7178-3. [RA395 .A3 C633 2005] (9.1; 1.3.5; 7.1; 8.5; 9.3.1; 9.8)

Great Britain. Department of Health. VALUING PEOPLE: A NEW STRATEGY FOR LEARNING DISABILITY FOR THE 21ST CENTURY: A WHITE PAPER. London: Stationery Office, 2001. 142 p. ISBN 0-10-150862-X. (Command Paper series; No. 5086.) [HV3008 .G7 G78 2001] (9.1; 1.3.5; 7.1; 9.5.1; 9.5.3; 9.5.7; 9.8)

Harrison, Jamie; Innes, Rob; and van Zwanenberg, Tim, eds. REBUILDING TRUST IN HEALTHCARE. Oxon, United Kingdom: Radcliffe Medical Press, 2003. 198 p. ISBN 1-85775-938-9. [RA485 .R432 2003] (9.1; 1.3.7; 7.2; 7.4; 8.1; 9.5.7; 9.8; 19.5; 20.1)

Health Inequalities [and] Priority Setting. HEALTH ECONOMICS 2000 October; 9(7): 565-641. (ISSN 1057-9230.) (9.1; 1.3.5; 7.1; 9.3.1; 9.4; 9.5.9; 9.5.10; 9.7; 16.1; 17.1)

Hervey, Tamara K. and McHale, Jean V. HEALTH LAW AND THE EUROPEAN UNION. Cambridge/New York: Cambridge University Press, 2004. 469 p. ISBN 0-521-60524-5. (Law in Context series.) [KJE6206 .H47 2004] (9.1; 1.3.12; 2.1; 8.4; 9.4; 9.7; 14.5; 15.1; 18.5.4; 21.1)

Institute of Medicine (United States). Committee on Health Literacy. HEALTH LITERACY: A PRESCRIPTION TO END CONFUSION. Washington, DC: National Academies Press, 2004. 345 p. ISBN 0-309-09117-9. (Edited by Lynn Nielsen-Bohlman, Allison Panzer, and David Kindig. Contains the following commissioned papers: *The Relationship Between Health Literacy and Medical Costs*, David H. Howard; *Improving Chronic Disease Care for Populations with Limited Health Literacy*, Dean Schillinger; and *Outside the Clinician-Patient Relationship: A Call to Action for Health Literacy*, Barry D. Weiss.) [RA440 .H43 2004] (9.1; 7.1)

Isaacs, Stephen L. and Knickman, James R., eds. TO IMPROVE HEALTH AND HEALTH CARE, VOLUME VI: THE ROBERT WOOD JOHNSON FOUNDATION ANTHOLOGY. San Francisco: Jossey-Bass, 2003. 287 p. ISBN 0-7879-6311-9. [RA440.87 .U6 T626 2003] (9.1; 9.5.7; 9.5.9; 20.4.1)

La Forgia, Gerard M., ed. HEALTH SYSTEM INNOVATION IN CENTRAL AMERICA: LESSONS AND IMPACT OF NEW APPROACHES. Washington, DC: The International Bank for Reconstruction and Development / The World Bank, 2005. 213 p. ISBN 0-8213-6278-X. (Gift of The World Bank.) [RA395 .C35 H34 2005] (9.1; 9.3.1; 9.5.1; 9.5.7; 9.8; 21.1)

Marinker, Marshall, ed. SENSE AND SENSIBILITY IN HEALTH CARE. London: BMJ Publishing Group, 1996. 281 p. ISBN 0-7279-1111-2. [RA395 .G6 S46 1996] (9.1; 1.3.7; 1.3.12; 8.1)

McFarlane, Lawrie and Prado, Carlos. THE BEST-LAID PLANS: HEALTH CARE'S PROBLEMS AND PROSPECTS. Mon-

treal: McGill-Queen's University Press, 2002. 196 p. ISBN 0-7735-2365-0. (9.1; 9.2; 9.3.1; 9.3.2; 9.5.2)

Miller, Robert D., ed. PROBLEMS IN HEALTH CARE LAW. Sudbury, MA: Jones and Bartlett, 2006. 899 p. ISBN 0-7637-4555-3. (Ninth edition. Gift of the publisher.) [KF3825 .M53 2006] (9.1; 1.3.5; 1.3.12; 8.1; 8.3.4; 9.3.1; 9.5.1; 9.5.2; 9.5.10; 14.1; 19.5; 20.1; 20.2.1)

Morone, James A. and Jacobs, Lawrence R., eds. HEALTHY, WEALTHY, AND FAIR: HEALTH CARE AND THE GOOD SOCIETY. New York: Oxford University Press, 2005. 382 p. ISBN 0-19-517066-0. [RA418.3 .U6 H436 2005] (9.1; 1.3.5; 7.1; 9.3.1; 9.5.10)

National Research Council (United States). Committee on the Review and Assessment of the HIH's Strategic Research Plan and Budget to Reduce and Ultimately Eliminate Health Disparities. EXAMINING THE HEALTH DISPARITIES RESEARCH PLAN OF THE NATIONAL INSTITUTES OF HEALTH: UNFINISHED BUSINESS. Washington, DC: National Academies Press, 2006. 304 p. ISBN 0-309-10121-2. (Edited by Gerald E. Thomson, Faith Mitchell, and Monique B. Williams. Also available on the Web at: http://www.nap.edu.) [RA418.3 .U6 E93 2006] (9.1; 1.3.5; 7.1; 9.3.1; 9.5.4)

Oakley, Ann and Barker, Jonathan, eds. PRIVATE COMPLAINTS AND PUBLIC HEALTH: RICHARD TITMUSS ON THE NATIONAL HEALTH SERVICE. Bristol: Policy Press, 2004. 247 p. ISBN 1-86134-560-7. [RA485 .T57 2004] (9.1; 7.1)

Patel, Kant and Rushefsky, Mark. HEALTH CARE POLITICS AND POLICY IN AMERICA. Armonk, NY: M.E. Sharpe, 2006. 506 p. ISBN 0-7656-1479-0. (Third edition.) [RA395 .A3 P285 2006] (9.1; 5.1; 7.1; 8.5; 9.3.1; 9.3.2; 9.5.2; 9.5.4; 9.5.10; 9.7; 20.5.1; 21.1; Reference)

Powers, Madison and Faden, Ruth. SOCIAL JUSTICE: THE MORAL FOUNDATIONS OF PUBLIC HEALTH AND HEALTH POLICY. New York: Oxford University Press, 2006. 229 p. ISBN 0-19-518926-4. (Issues in Biomedical Ethics series.) (Gift of the publisher.) [RA427.25 .P69 2006] (9.1; 1.1; 1.3.5; 9.3.1; 9.4)

Professor Z. LIFE MEANS NOTHING BEHIND THE GREEN WALL: A NOVEL. Caldwell, ID: Physician's Publishing, 2002. 320 p. ISBN 0-9665240-5-5. ("The Park Hospital in Brooklyn, New York City. Two established top knives lead the local Medical-Surgical Mafia. They control the medical board, bully the hospital president, intimidate the chairman of surgery, elevate their cronies, repress their enemies and extort dollar-producing referrals. They also systematically kill their patients through sloppy and negligent practice but remain beyond scrutiny for many years. Until Professor Z arrives... This novel invites you to join the chaotic daily life of a surgical department. Participants in surgical operations, rounds, quality assurance and mortality & morbidity conferences. The pages of this book bear witness to extreme malpractice, negligence, greed and corruption; whistleblowing, witch hunting, friendships, and treachery.") (9.1; 7.3; 7.4; 8.5; 9.8; Fiction)

Richmond, Julius B. and Fein, Rashi. THE HEALTH CARE MESS: HOW WE GOT INTO IT AND WHAT IT WILL TAKE TO GET OUT. Cambridge, MA: Harvard University Press, 2005. 307 p. ISBN 0-674-01924-5. (Foreword by Jimmie Carter.) [RA395 .A3 R53 2005] (9.1; 1.3.5; 7.1; 9.2; 9.3.1; 9.3.2; 9.5.2; 9.5.10)

Ritvo, Roger A.; Ohlsen, Joel D.; and Holland, Thomas P. ETHICAL GOVERNANCE IN HEALTH CARE: A BOARD LEADERSHIP GUIDE FOR BUILDING AN ETHICAL CULTURE. Chicago: Health Forum, 2004. 106 p. ISBN 1-55648-320-1. (Foreword by Sr. Mary Roch Rocklage, RSM.) [RA427.25 .R55 2004] (9.1; 1.3.2)

Schroeder, Christopher H. and Steinzor, Rena, eds. A NEW PROGRESSIVE AGENDA FOR PUBLIC HEALTH AND THE ENVIRONMENT: A PROJECT OF THE CENTER FOR PROGRESSIVE REGULATION. Durham, NC: Carolina Academic Press, 2005. 222 p. ISBN 1-59460-082-1. (Gift of the publisher.) [RA566.3 .N487 2005] (9.1; 1.3.5; 16.1; 21.1)

Segen, Joseph. CONCISE DICTIONARY OF MODERN MEDICINE. New York: McGraw-Hill, 2006. 765 p. ISBN 0-8385-1535-5. (9.1; Reference)

Sidell, Moyra; Jones, Linda; Katz, Jeanne; Peberdy, Alyson; and Douglas, Jenny, eds. DEBATES AND DILEMMAS IN PROMOTING HEALTH: A READER. Houndsmills, Basingstoke, Hampshire/New York: Palgrave Macmillan in association with The Open University, 2003. 440 p. ISBN 1-4039-0228-3. (Second edition.) [RA427.8 .D43 2003] (9.1; 1.3.12; 7.1; 9.5.2; 9.5.4; 9.5.5; 9.5.6; 10; 21.1)

Stanley, David and Reed, Jan. OPENING UP CARE: ACHIEVING PRINCIPLED PRACTICE IN HEALTH AND SOCIAL CARE INSTITUTIONS. London: Arnold, 1999. 144 p. ISBN 0-340-70591-4. (9.1; 1.3.2; 9.8)

Sulmasy, Daniel p. THE REBIRTH OF THE CLINIC: AN INTRODUCTION TO SPIRITUALITY IN HEALTH CARE. Washington, DC: Georgetown University Press, 2006. 246 p. ISBN 1-58901-095-7. (Gift of the publisher.) [R725.55 .S83 2006] (9.1; 1.2; 4.4; 8.1; 20.4.1)

Symposium: Health Care in America: A New Generation of Challenges. STANFORD LAW AND POLICY REVIEW 2006; 17(1): 1-197. (ISSN 1044-4386.) (9.1; 1.1; 5.2; 7.1; 7.2; 7.3; 8.1; 8.3.4; 9.3.1; 9.3.2; 9.4; 9.5.2; 9.5.10; 9.7; 15.1; 15.3)

Weissert, Carol S. and Weissert, William G. GOVERNING HEALTH: THE POLITICS OF HEALTH POLICY. Baltimore, MD: Johns Hopkins University Press, 2006. 452 p. ISBN 0-8018-8432-2. (Third edition. Gift of the publisher.) [RA395 .A3 W45 2006] (9.1; 1.3.5; 9.5.2; 9.7; 21.1)

9.2 RIGHT TO HEALTH CARE

Derickson, Alan. HEALTH SECURITY FOR ALL: DREAMS OF UNIVERSAL HEALTH CARE IN AMERICA. Baltimore, MD: Johns Hopkins University Press, 2005. 240 p. ISBN 0-8018-8081-5. [RA395 .A3 D47 2005] (9.2; 7.1; 9.1; 9.3.1)

9.3.1 HEALTH CARE ECONOMICS (GENERAL)

Callahan, Daniel and Wasunna, Angela A. MEDICINE AND THE MARKET: EQUITY V. CHOICE. Baltimore, MD: Johns Hopkins University Press, 2006. 320 p. ISBN 0-8018-8339-3. [RA410.53 .C352 2006] (9.3.1; 9.1; 9.3.2; 9.7; 21.1)

Davis, John B., ed. THE SOCIAL ECONOMICS OF HEALTH CARE. London/New York: Routledge, 2001. 290 p. ISBN 0-415-25162-1. (Advances in Social Economics series.) [RA410.5 .S63 2001] (9.3.1; 7.1; 8.4; 9.1; 9.3.2; 9.4; 9.5.2; 15.3)

Funigiello, Philip J. CHRONIC POLITICS: HEALTH CARE SECURITY FROM FDR TO GEORGE W. BUSH. Lawrence: University Press of Kansas, 2005. 395 p. ISBN 0-7006-1399-4. [RA412.2 .F86 2005] (9.3.1; 7.1; 9.1; 9.5.2; 21.1)

Geyman, John. SHREDDING THE SOCIAL CONTRACT: THE PRIVATIZATION OF MEDICARE. Monroe, ME: Common Courage Press, 2006. 322 p. ISBN 1-56751-376-X. [RA410.5 .G485 2006] (9.3.1; 1.3.5; 9.1; 9.4; 9.5.2; 21.1)

Gottret, Pablo and Schieber, George. HEALTH FINANCING REVISITED: A PRACTITIONER'S GUIDE. Washington, DC: World Bank, 2006. 318 p. ISBN 0-8213-6585-1. (Gift of the publisher.) [RA410.5 .G68 2006] (9.3.1; 7.1; 21.1)

Hall, George M. A TIDE IN THE AFFAIRS OF MEDICINE: NATIONAL HEALTH INSURANCE AS THE AUGURY OF PROFESSIONALISM. St. Louis, MO: Warren H. Green, 2004. 136 p. ISBN 0-87527-536-2. [RA412.2 .H34 2004] (9.3.1)

Jacobs, Philip and Rapoport, John. THE ECONOMICS OF HEALTH AND MEDICAL CARE. Sudbury, MA: Jones and Bartlett, 2004. 438 p. ISBN 0-7637-2595-1. (Fifth edition.) [RA410 .J32 2004] (9.3.1; 5.2)

Kling, Arnold. CRISIS OF ABUNDANCE: RETHINKING HOW WE PAY FOR HEALTH CARE. Washington, DC: Cato Institute, 2006. 110 p. ISBN 1-930865-89-9. [RA410.53 .K586 2006] (9.3.1; 5.2; 9.1; 9.4)

Marcinko, David Edward and Hetico, Hope Rachel, eds. DICTIONARY OF HEALTH INSURANCE AND MANAGED CARE. New York: Springer Publishing Company, 2006. 360 p. ISBN 0-8261-4994-4. [RA413 .D53 2006] (9.3.1; 9.3.2; Reference)

Mooney, Gavin. ECONOMICS, MEDICINE AND HEALTH CARE. Harlow, England/New York: Prentice Hall/Financial Times, 2003. 147 p. ISBN 0-273-65157-9. (Third edition.) [RA410 .M66 2003] (9.3.1; 1.1; 2.1; 9.1; 9.4)

Pollock, Allyson M.; Leys, Colin; et al. NHS PLC: THE PRIVATISATION OF OUR HEALTH CARE. London/New York: Verso, 2004. 271 p. ISBN 1-84467-011-2. [RA412.5 .G7 P656 2004] (9.3.1; 9.1; 9.5.2)

Rettenmaier, Andrew J. and Saving, Thomas R., eds. MEDICARE REFORM: ISSUES AND ANSWERS. Chicago: University of Chicago Press, 1999. 224 p. ISBN 0-226-71013-0. (Bush School Series in the Economics of Public Policy; Vol. 1.) [RA412.3 .M444 1999] (9.3.1; 9.5.2)

9.3.2 MANAGED CARE

Enthoven, Alain C. and Tollen, Laura A., eds. TOWARD A 21ST CENTURY HEALTH SYSTEM: THE CONTRIBUTIONS AND PROMISE OF PREPAID GROUP PRACTICE. San Francisco: Jossey-Bass, 2004. 284 p. ISBN 0-7879-7309-2. (Foreword by William L. Roper.) [RA413.5 .U5 T69 2004] (9.3.2; 9.3.1; 9.8)

9.4 ALLOCATION OF HEALTH CARE RESOURCES

Anand, Paul and Dolan, Paul, eds. *Equity, Capabilities and Health*. SOCIAL SCIENCE AND MEDICINE 2005 January; 60(2): 219-368. (ISSN 0277-9536.) (9.4; 1.3.1; 4.4; 7.1; 9.2; 10; 15.1; 15.7; 19.5; 20.5.1; 20.7)

Matthews, Eric and Russell, Elizabeth. RATIONING MEDICAL CARE ON THE BASIS OF AGE: THE MORAL DIMENSIONS. Abingdon, Oxon/Seattle, WA: Radcliffe, 2005. 159 p. ISBN 1-84619-000-2. (Foreword by Kenneth Boyd.) [RA413.7 .A4 M27 2005] (9.4; 9.1; 9.3.1; 9.5.2)

9.5.1 HEALTH CARE FOR SPECIFIC DISEASES/GROUPS (GENERAL)

Adelson, Betty M. DWARFISM: MEDICAL AND PSYCHOSOCIAL ASPECTS OF PROFOUND SHORT STATURE. Baltimore, MD: Johns Hopkins University Press, 2005. 342 p. ISBN 0-8018-8122-6. (Gift of the publisher.) [RB140.3 .A33 2005] (9.5.1; 4.4; 7.1; 9.5.7; 15.1; 17.1; Reference)

Burack-Weiss, Ann. THE CAREGIVER'S TALE: LOSS AND RENEWAL IN MEMOIRS OF FAMILY LIFE. New York: Columbia University Press, 2006. 189 p. ISBN 0-231-12159-8. (Gift of the publisher.) [RA645.3 .B86 2006] (9.5.1; 7.1; 8.1; 9.5.6; 9.5.9; 17.1)

Colgrove, James. STATE OF IMMUNITY: THE POLITICS OF VACCINATION IN TWENTIETH-CENTURY AMERICA. Berkeley: University of California Press [and] New York: Milbank Memorial Fund, 2006. 332 p. ISBN 0-520-24749-3. (California/Milbank Books on Health and the Public series; Vol. 16. Gift of the publisher.) [RA638 .C64 2006] (9.5.1; 7.1; 9.1; 9.7; 21.1)

Epstein, Samuel S. CANCER-GATE: HOW TO WIN THE LOSING CANCER WAR. Amityville, NY: Baywood, 2005. 377 p. ISBN 0-89503-354-2. (Policy, Politics, Health and Medicine Series.) [RA645 .C3 E67 2005] (9.5.1; 1.3.5; 1.3.11; 5.2; 9.1; 9.5.5; 21.1; 22.3)

Glynn, Ian and Glynn, Jenifer. THE LIFE AND DEATH OF SMALLPOX. New York: Cambridge University Press, 2004. 278 p. ISBN 0-521-84542-4. (Published in the UK by: Profile Books, London.) (9.5.1; 7.1; 9.7; 21.3)

Holland, Walter W. and Stewart, Susie. SCREENING IN DISEASE PREVENTION: WHAT WORKS? Abingdon, Oxon: Radcliffe, 2005. 168 p. ISBN 1-85775-770-X. (European Observatory on Health Systems and Policies series. "This book is a co-publication between The Nuffield Trust and the European Observatory on Health Systems and Policies.") [RA427.5 .H65 2005] (9.5.1; 9.1; 9.5.2; 9.5.5; 9.5.7; 15.3; 21.1)

Howe, P. David. SPORT, PROFESSIONALISM AND PAIN: ETHNOGRAPHIES OF INJURY AND RISK. London/New York: Routledge, 2004. 222 p. ISBN 0-415-24730-6. [RC1210 .H69 2004] (9.5.1; 1.3.1; 4.4; 7.1)

Institute of Medicine (United States). Committee on Disability in America: A New Look. WORKSHOP ON DISABILITY IN AMERICA: A NEW LOOK: SUMMARY AND BACKGROUND PAPERS. Washington, DC: National Academies Press, 2006. 275 p. ISBN 0-309-10090-9. (Edited by Marilyn J. Field, Alan M. Jette, and Linda Martin. "Based on a Workshop for the Committee on Disability in America: A New Look." Also available on the Web at: http://www.nap.edu.) [HV1553 .W67 2005] (9.5.1; 4.2; 7.1; 9.1; 9.5.3; 9.5.7; 16.1; 17.1)

Kane, Robert L.; Priester, Reinhard; and Totten, Annette M. MEETING THE CHALLENGE OF CHRONIC ILLNESS. Baltimore, MD: Johns Hopkins University Press, 2005. 302 p. ISBN 0-8018-8209-5. (Foreword by Edward Wagner.) [RA644.5 .K36 2005] (9.5.1; 1.3.7; 5.1; 7.1; 8.1; 9.3.1; 9.8)

Kleinman, Arthur and Watson, James L., eds. SARS IN CHINA: PRELUDE TO PANDEMIC? Stanford, CA: Stanford University Press, 2006. ISBN 0804753148. (Gift of the publisher.) [RA644 .S17 S275 2006] (9.5.1; 7.1; 9.1; 21.1; 21.7)

Panno, Joseph. CANCER: THE ROLE OF GENES, LIFESTYLE, AND ENVIRONMENT. New York: Facts on File, 2005. 162 p. ISBN 0-8160-4950-5. (The "New Biology" series.) [RC262 .P35 2005] (9.5.1; 15.1; 16.1; 18.1; 21.1; Reference)

Sacks, Oliver. A LEG TO STAND ON. New York: HarperPerennial, 1987, c1984. 222 p. ISBN 0-06-097082-0. (Reprint. Originally published: Summit Books, New York, 1984. Gift of Warren Reich.) [RC339.52 .S23 A35 1990] (9.5.1; Biography)

Salzman, Mark. LYING AWAKE. New York: Vintage Books, 2000. 181 p. ISBN 0-375-70606-2. ("In a Carmelite monastery outside present-day Los Angeles, life goes on in a manner virtually unchanged for centuries. Sister John of the Cross has spent years there in the service of God, but lately her life has been electrified by her ever more frequent visions of God's radiance. Sister John's waking dreams have led her toward the deepest religious ecstasy she has ever known, and have allowed her life and writings to become an example of the rewards of devotion for her fellow supplicants. But her visions are accompanied by shattering headaches, and when a doctor reveals that they may be dangerous, she faces a devastating choice. For if her spiritual gifts are symptoms of illness rather than grace,

---

Numbers in ( ) = NRCBL Classification Numbers

will a "cure" mean the end of her visions and a soul once again at odds with the world?") [PS3569 .A4627 L95 2001] (9.5.1; 1.2; Fiction)

Smart, Julie. DISABILITY, SOCIETY, AND THE INDIVIDUAL. Austin, TX: PRO-ED, 2001. 357 p. ISBN 0-944480-28-4. (Reprint. Originally published: Gaithersburg, MD: Aspen, 2001; ISBN 0-834216019.) [HV1568 .S63 2003] (9.5.1; 4.2; 4.3; 4.4; 7.1; 9.5.3; 17.1)

Walters, Mark Jerome. SIX MODERN PLAGUES AND HOW WE ARE CAUSING THEM. Washington, DC: Island Press/Shearwater Books, 2003. 212 p. ISBN 1-55963-714-5. [RA653 .W34 2003] (9.5.1; 9.5.6; 22.3)

Wheelwright, Jeff. THE IRRITABLE HEART: THE MEDICAL MYSTERY OF THE GULF WAR. New York: W.W. Norton, 2001. 427 p. ISBN 0-393-01956-X. [RB152.7 .W48 2001] (9.5.1; 1.3.5; 3.1; 17.1; 21.2; 21.3)

Wister, Andrew V. BABY BOOMER HEALTH DYNAMICS: HOW ARE WE AGING? Toronto/Buffalo, NY: University of Toronto Press, 2005. 253 p. ISBN 0-8020-8635-7. [RA408 .B33 W58 2005] (9.5.1; 7.1; 9.4; 9.5.2; 9.5.9)

9.5.2 HEALTH CARE FOR THE AGED

Altman, Stuart H. and Shactman, David I., eds. POLICIES FOR AN AGING SOCIETY. Baltimore, MD: Johns Hopkins University Press, 2002. 402 p. ISBN 0-8018-6907-2. [HQ1064 .U5 P62 2002] (9.5.2; 9.1; 9.3.1; 9.4; 21.1)

Gass, Thomas Edward. NOBODY'S HOME: CANDID REFLECTIONS OF A NURSING HOME AIDE. Ithaca, NY: ILR Press/Cornell University Press, c2004, 2005. 189 p. ISBN 0-8014-7261-X. (Culture and Politics of Health Care Work series.) [RA645.3 .G376 2004] (9.5.2; 9.3.1; 9.4)

Harris, Diana K. and Benson, Michael L. MALTREATMENT OF PATIENTS IN NURSING HOMES: THERE IS NO SAFE PLACE. Binghamton, NY: Haworth Pastoral Press, 2006. 146 p. ISBN 0-7890-2326-1. (Gift of the publisher.) [RA997 .H357 2006] (9.5.2; 1.3.5; 7.1; 9.8; 17.1; 17.3)

Koenig, Harold G. and Lawson, Douglas M. FAITH IN THE FUTURE: HEALTHCARE, AGING, AND THE ROLE OF RELIGION. Philadelphia: Templeton Foundation Press, 2004. 216 p. ISBN 1-932031-35-9. [RA564.8 .K625 2004] (9.5.2; 1.2; 9.1; 9.3.1)

Levenson, Rose [and] King Edward's Hospital Fund for London. AUDITING AGE DISCRIMINATION: A PRACTICAL AP-PROACH TO PROMOTING EQUALITY IN HEALTH AND SOCIAL CARE. London: King's Fund, 2003. 68 p. ISBN 1-85717-472-0. (Policy into Practice Guide series.) [RA399 .A1 L484 2003] (9.5.2; 9.1)

Nelson, Todd D., ed. AGEISM: STEREOTYPING AND PREJU-DICE AGAINST OLDER PERSONS. Cambridge, MA: MIT Press, 2002. 372 p. ISBN 0-262-64057-0. ("A Bradford Book.") [HQ1061 .A42442 2002] (9.5.2; 7.1; 21.7)

Panno, Joseph. AGING: THEORIES AND POTENTIAL THERA-PIES. New York: Facts on File, 2005. 157 p. ISBN

0-8160-4951-3. (The "New Biology" series.) [QP86 .P33 2005] (9.5.2; 7.1; 15.4; Reference)

Silin, Peter S. NURSING HOMES: THE FAMILY'S JOURNEY. Baltimore, MD: Johns Hopkins University Press, 2001. 296 p. ISBN 0-8018-6625-1. [RC954.3 .S556 2001] (9.5.2; 7.1; 8.1; 9.5.1; 17.1; 20.4.1; 20.5.4; POP)

Turiel, Judith Steinberg. OUR PARENTS, OURSELVES: HOW AMERICAN HEALTH CARE IMPERILS MIDDLE AGE AND BE-YOND. Berkeley: University of California Press, 2005. 306 p. ISBN 0-520-24524-5. [RA564.8 .T87 2005] (9.5.2; 4.4; 9.1; 9.4; 9.7; 17.1; 20.4.1; 20.5.1; 20.7)

9.5.3 HEALTH CARE FOR MENTALLY DISABLED PERSONS

Swinton, John, ed. CRITICAL REFLECTIONS ON STANLEY HAUERWAS' THEOLOGY OF DISABILITY: DISABLING SOCI-ETY, ENABLING THEOLOGY. Binghamton, NY: Haworth Pastoral Press, 2004. 205 p. ISBN 0-7890-2722-4. (Simul-taneously published as: *Journal of Religion, Disability & Health*, Volume 8, Numbers 3-4, 2004.) [BT732.4 .C66 2004] (9.5.3; 1.2; 2.1; 4.1.1; 4.4)

9.5.4 HEALTH CARE FOR MINORITIES

Kronenfeld, Jennie Jacobs. HEALTH CARE SERVICES, RA-CIAL AND ETHNIC MINORITIES AND UNDERSERVED POPULA-TIONS: PATIENT AND PROVIDER PERSPECTIVES. Amsterdam/Boston: Elsevier JAI, 2005. 295 p. ISBN 0-7623-1249-1. (Research in the Sociology of Health Care series; Vol. 23. ISSN 0275-4959.) [RA393 .H43 2005] (9.5.4; 7.1; 7.2; 9.1; 9.3.1; 9.5.2; 9.5.5; 9.5.7; 10; 14.1; 17.1; 21.7)

National Research Council (United States). Division of Behavioral and Social Sciences and Education. Committee on Population. Panel on Race, Ethnicity, and Health in Later Life. CRITICAL PERSPECTIVES ON RACIAL AND ETH-NIC DIFFERENCES IN HEALTH IN LATE LIFE. Washington, DC: National Academies Press, 2004. 735 p. ISBN 0-309-09211-6. (Edited by Norman B. Anderson, Rodolfo A. Bulatao, and Barney Cohen. Also available on the Web at: http://www.nap.edu.) [RA564.8 .C75 2004] (9.5.4; 7.1; 9.5.2; 15.1; 17.1; 21.7)

Torres, M. Idalí and Cernada, George P., eds. SEXUAL AND REPRODUCTIVE HEALTH PROMOTION IN LATINO POPULA-TIONS = PARTERAS, PROMOTORAS Y POETAS: CASE STUDIES ACROSS THE AMERICAS. Amityville, NY: Baywood, 2003. 352 p. ISBN 0-89503-276-7. [RG136 .S475 2003] (9.5.4; 9.1; 9.5.5; 9.5.6; 10; 11.1; 14.1; 21.1; 21.7)

9.5.5 HEALTH CARE FOR WOMEN

Abusharaf, Rogaia Mustafa, ed. FEMALE CIRCUMCISION: MULTICULTURAL PERSPECTIVES. Philadelphia: University of Pennsylvania Press, 2006. 287 p. ISBN 0-8122-3924-5. (Pennsylvania Studies in Human Rights series. Rose Fitz-gerald Kennedy Collection on Women, Infants and Chil-dren. Gift of the publisher.) [GN645 .F43 2006] (9.5.5; 1.2; 9.5.7; 10; 21.7)

Chavkin, Wendy and Chesler, Ellen. WHERE HUMAN RIGHTS BEGIN: HEALTH, SEXUALITY, AND WOMEN IN THE NEW MILLENNIUM. New Brunswick, NJ: Rutgers University Press, 2005. 309 p. ISBN 0-8135-3657-X. (Rose Fitzgerlad Kennedy Collection on Women, Infants and Children. Gift of the publisher.) [HQ766.15 .W46 2005] (9.5.5; 1.2; 9.5.6; 9.5.7; 10; 12.5.1; 14.1; 21.1; 21.7)

Frank, Gelya. VENUS ON WHEELS: TWO DECADES OF DIALOGUE ON DISABILITY, BIOGRAPHY, AND BEING FEMALE IN AMERICA. Berkeley: University of California Press, 2000. 284 p. ISBN 0-520-21716-0. (Rose Fitzgerald Kennedy Collection on Women, Infants and Children.) [HV3021 .W66 F73 2000] (9.5.5; 7.1; 9.5.1; Biography)

Freeman, Michael, ed. CHILDREN, MEDICINE AND THE LAW. Aldershot, Hants/Burlington, VT: Ashgate, 2005. 678 p. ISBN 1-84014-754-7. (International Library of Medicine, Ethics and Law series. Rose Fitzgerald Kennedy Collection on Women, Infants and Children. Gift of the publisher.) (9.5.5; 1.1; 4.3; 8.3.2; 9.2; 9.5.6; 10; 11.3; 14.1; 15.2; 15.3; 18.5.2; 19.5)

Guenther, Lisa. THE GIFT OF THE OTHER: LEVINAS AND THE POLITICS OF REPRODUCTION. Albany: State University of New York Press, 2006. 190 p. ISBN 0-7914-6848-8. (SUNY Series in Gender Theory. Rose Fitzgerald Kennedy Collection on Women, Infants and Children. Gift of the publisher.) [HQ1206 .G838 2006] (9.5.5; 4.4; 10; 14.1)

Kitzinger, Sheila. THE NEW EXPERIENCE OF CHILDBIRTH. London: Orion Publishing Group, 2004. 248 p. ISBN 0-75286-137-9. (Rose Fitzgerald Kennedy Collection on Women, Infants and Children.) (9.5.5; 9.5.7; 14.1; POP)

Kukla, Rebecca. MASS HYSTERIA: MEDICINE, CULTURE, AND MOTHERS' BODIES. Lanham, MD: Rowman & Littlefield, 2005. 251 p. ISBN 0-7425-3358-1. (Explorations in Bioethics and the Medical Humanities series. Rose Fitzgerlad Kennedy Collection on Women, Infants and Children.) [HQ1206 .K785 2005] (9.5.5; 7.1; 10; 17.1)

Momoh, Comfort, ed. FEMALE GENITAL MUTILATION. Oxford/Seattle, WA: Radcliffe, 2005. 172 p. ISBN 1-85775-693-2. (Forewords by Dame Karlene Davis and Christine McCafferty. Rose Fitzgerald Kennedy Collection on Women, Infants and Children.) [GN484 .F353 2005] (9.5.5; 7.1; 9.5.7; 10; 21.7)

Petchesky, Rosalind Pollack. GLOBAL PRESCRIPTIONS: GENDERING HEALTH AND HUMAN RIGHTS. London/New York: Zed Books in association with United Nations Research Institute for Social Development, 2003. 306 p. ISBN 1-84277-004-7. [RA778 .P476 2003] (9.5.5; 9.1; 9.2; 9.5.6; 10; 21.1; 21.7)

White, Arlette Campbell; Merrick, Thomas W.; and Yazbeck, Abdo S. REPRODUCTIVE HEALTH: THE MISSING MILLENNIUM DEVELOPMENT GOAL. Washington, DC: World Bank, 2006. 208 p. ISBN 0-8213-6613-0. (Gift of the publisher. Rose Fitzgerald Kennedy Collection on Women, Infants and Children.) [RG133 .W48 2006] (9.5.5; 7.1; 9.1; 9.3.1; 9.4; 9.5.10; 14.1; 21.1)

Widdows, Heather; Idiakez, Itziar Alkorta; and Cirión, Aitziber Emaldi, eds. WOMEN'S REPRODUCTIVE RIGHTS. New York: Palgrave/Macmillan 2006. 241 p. ISBN 1-4039-4993-X. (Women's Rights in Europe series. Rose Fitzgerald Kennedy Collection on Women, Infants and Children. Gift of the publisher.) [HQ1236.5 .E85 W645 2006] (9.5.5; 9.5.4; 9.5.7; 12.5.1; 14.1; 15.1; 15.2; 21.1)

9.5.6 HEALTH CARE FOR HIV INFECTION AND AIDS

Ainsworth, Martha; Vaillancourt, Denise A.; and Gaubatz, Judith Hahn. COMMITTING TO RESULTS: IMPROVING THE EFFECTIVENESS OF HIV/AIDS ASSISTANCE: AN OED EVALUATION OF THE WORLD BANK'S ASSISTANCE FOR HIV/AIDS CONTROL. Washington, DC: World Bank, 2005. 250 p. ISBN 0-8213-6388-3. (World Bank Operations Evaluation Studies series. Also available on the Web at: http://www.worldbank.org/oed/aids. Gift of the publisher.) [HC60 .A4575 2005] (9.5.6; 7.1; 9.1; 9.3.1; 9.8; 21.1)

Fan, Hung Y.; Conner, Ross F.; and Villarreal, Luis p. AIDS: SCIENCE AND SOCIETY. Boston: Jones and Bartlett, 2004. 229 p. ISBN 0-7637-0086-X. (Fourth edition. Jones and Bartlett Series in Biology.) (9.5.6; 7.1)

Feldman, Eric A. THE RITUAL OF RIGHTS IN JAPAN: LAW, SOCIETY, AND HEALTH POLICY. Cambridge/New York: Cambridge University Press, 2000. 219 p. ISBN 0-521-77964-2. (Cambridge Studies in Law and Society series.) [KNX3098 .F45 2000] (9.5.6; 1.1; 1.3.5; 8.3.1; 8.3.3; 10; 19.5; 20.2.1; 20.3.1)

Godinho, Joana; Renton, Adrian; Vinogradov, Viatcheslav; Novotny, Thomas; Rivers, Mary-June; Gotsadze, George; and Bravo, Mario. REVERSING THE TIDE: PRIORITIES FOR HIV/AIDS PREVENTION IN CENTRAL ASIA. Washington, DC: World Bank, 2005. 186 p. ISBN 0-8213-6230-5. (World Bank Working Paper series; No. 54. Gift of the publisher.) [RA643.86 .A783 R48 2005] (9.5.6; 7.1; 9.1; 9.5.9)

Long, Thomas L. AIDS AND AMERICAN APOCALYPTICISM: THE CULTURAL SEMIOTICS OF AN EPIDEMIC. Albany: State University of New York Press, 2005. 242 p. ISBN 0-7914-6168-8. (SUNY Series in the Sociology of Culture.) [RA643.83 .L66 2004] (9.5.6; 1.2; 7.1)

Mayer, Kenneth H. and Pizer, H.F., eds. THE AIDS PANDEMIC: IMPACT ON SCIENCE AND SOCIETY. Amsterdam/Boston: Elsevier Academic Press, 2005. 537 p. ISBN 0-12-465271-9. [RA643.8 .A435 2005] (9.5.6; 5.3; 9.1; 9.3.1; 9.5.9; 9.7; 10; 21.1)

Over, Mead; Heywood, Peter; Gold, Julian; Gupta, Indrani; Hira, Subhash; Marseille, Elliot [and] World Bank. Human Development Network. HIV/AIDS TREATMENT AND PREVENTION IN INDIA: MODELING THE COST AND CONSEQUENCES. Washington, DC: World Bank, 2004. 121 p. + 1 CD-ROM. ISBN 0-8213-5657-7. (Health, Nutrition, and Population Series.) ("This title projects the future implications of three alternative AIDS treatment financing policies for the health burden of AIDS in India and for its overall health expenditures. Written by an inter-disciplinary team of AIDS experts, the book presents new data on the supply and demand for antiretroviral treatment in India and new models of the epidemiological effects and the financial costs of alternative policies." CD-ROM contains background papers in Microsoft Word format. Gift of the publisher.) [RA643.86 .I42 H58 2004] (9.5.6; 1.3.5; 5.2; 5.3; 7.1; 9.1; 9.3.1; 9.7)

Palliative Care in the Age of HIV/AIDS. JOURNAL OF THE ROYAL SOCIETY OF MEDICINE 2001 September; 94(9): 428-498. (ISSN 0141-0768.) (9.5.6; 1.2; 2.2; 4.4; 7.2; 9.1; 9.3.1; 9.4; 9.5.4; 9.5.5; 9.5.9; 9.5.10; 9.7; 9.8; 20.4.1; 20.5.1; 20.7)

Schüklenk, Udo, ed. AIDS: SOCIETY, ETHICS AND LAW. Aldershot, Hants/Burlington, VT: Ashgate, 2001. 556 p. ISBN 0-7546-2103-0. (International Library of Medicine, Ethics and the Law series.) [RC607 .A26 A3566 2001] (9.5.6; 7.1; 8.1; 8.3.1; 8.4; 9.4; 9.5.5; 9.5.7; 9.7; 10; 16.3; 18.2; 18.5.1; 20.7; 21.1)

Smith, Raymond, A. and Siplon, Patricia D. DRUGS INTO BODIES: GLOBAL AIDS TREATMENT ACTIVISM. Westport, CT: Praeger, 2006. 196 p. ISBN 0-275-98325-0. (Afterword by Alan Berkman. Gift of the publisher.) [RA643.8 .S65 2006] (9.5.6; 9.7; 21.1)

Van Niekerk, Anton A. and Kopelman, Loretta M., eds. ETHICS & AIDS IN AFRICA: THE CHALLENGE TO OUR THINK-ING. Walnut Creek, CA: Left Coast Press, 2006. 222 p. ISBN 1-59874-071-7. (Foreword by Justice Edwin Cameron.) [RA643.86 .A35 E84 2005] (9.5.6; 1.3.2; 9.3.1; 9.5.5; 9.5.7; 9.7; 18.3; 18.5.2; 21.1)

World Bank. PREVENTING HIV/AIDS IN THE MIDDLE EAST AND NORTH AFRICA: A WINDOW OF OPPORTUNITY TO ACT. Washington, DC: World Bank, 2005. 86 p. ISBN 0-8213-6264-X. (Orientations in Development Series. Gift of the publisher.) [RA643.86 .M628 P74 2005] (9.5.6; 7.1; 9.1; 9.3.1; 21.1)

9.5.7 HEALTH CARE FOR MINORS

Boswell-Penc, Maia. TAINTED MILK: BREASTMILK, FEMI-NISMS, AND THE POLITICS OF ENVIRONMENTAL DEGRADA-TION. Albany: State University of New York Press, 2006. 212 p. ISBN 0-7914-6720-1. (Rose Fitzgerald Kennedy Collection on Women, Infants and Children. Gift of the publisher.) [RJ216 .B67 2006] (9.5.7; 1.3.2; 9.5.4; 9.5.5; 9.5.6; 10; 16.1)

McDermott, Jeanne. BABYFACE: A STORY OF HEART AND BONES. New York: Penguin Books, 2000. 261 p. ISBN 0-14-200033-7. (Gift of Warren Reich.) [RD763 .M346 2002] (9.5.7; Biography)

Parens, Erik, ed. SURGICALLY SHAPING CHILDREN: TECH-NOLOGY, ETHICS, AND THE PURSUIT OF NORMALITY. Balti-more: Johns Hopkins University Press, 2006. 274 p. ISBN 0-8018-8305-9. (Gift of the publisher. Rose Fitzgerald Kennedy Collection on Women, Infants and Children.) [RD137 .S846 2006] (9.5.7; 4.2; 4.4; 5.3; 8.3.2; 10; 17.1)

9.5.8 HEALTH CARE FOR EMBRYOS AND FETUSES

Sperling, Daniel. MANAGEMENT OF POST-MORTEM PREG-NANCY: LEGAL AND PHILOSOPHICAL ASPECTS. Aldershot, Hampshire/Burlington, VT: Ashgate, 2006. 159 p. ISBN 0-7546-4304-2. (Gift of the publisher. Rose Fitzgerald Kennedy Collection on Women, Infants and Children.) [K642 .S64 2006] (9.5.8; 1.1; 4.4; 8.1; 8.3.3; 9.5.5; 10; 12.4.2; 19.5; 20.2.1; 20.5.4)

9.5.9 HEALTH CARE FOR SUBSTANCE ABUSERS/USERS OF CONTROLLED SUBSTANCES

Midanik, Lorraine T. BIOMEDICALIZATION OF ALCOHOL STUDIES: IDEOLOGICAL SHIFTS AND INSTITUTIONAL CHAL-LENGES. New Brunswick, NJ: Aldine Transaction, 2006. 170 p. ISBN 0-202-30835-9. [RC565 .M432 2006] (9.5.9; 4.2; 7.1; 9.1; 9.3.1; 15.6; 17.1; 18.5.1)

Musto, David F. and Korsmeyer, Pamela. THE QUEST FOR DRUG CONTROL: POLITICS AND FEDERAL POLICY IN A PE-RIOD OF INCREASING SUBSTANCE ABUSE, 1963-1981. New Haven, CT: Yale University Press, 2002. 312 p. + 1 CD-ROM. ISBN 0-300-09036-6. (CD-ROM includes searchable drug policy documents.) [HV5825 .M845 2002] (9.5.9; 1.3.5; 7.1; 9.1; 21.1)

National Center on Addiction and Substance Abuse at Co-lumbia University. WOMEN UNDER THE INFLUENCE. Balti-more, MD: John Hopkins University Press, 2006. 292 p. ISBN 0-8018-8228-1. (Foreword by Joseph A. Califano, Jr. Gift of the publisher.) [RC564.5 .W65 W66 2006] (9.5.9; 9.1; 9.5.5; 9.5.7; 9.5.8)

Rabin, Robert L. and Sugarman, Stephen D., eds. REGU-LATING TOBACCO. Oxford/New York: Oxford University Press, 2001. 299 p. ISBN 0-19-514756-1. [HD9136 .R43 2001] (9.5.9; 1.3.2; 1.3.5; 9.1; 9.5.7)

Reid, Roddey. GLOBALIZING TOBACCO CONTROL: ANTI-SMOKING CAMPAIGNS IN CALIFORNIA, FRANCE, AND JAPAN. Bloomington, IN: Indiana University Press, 2005. 310 p. ISBN 0-253-21809-8. (Tracking Globalization se-ries.) [RA1242 .T6 R435 2005] (9.5.9; 1.3.5; 1.3.7; 7.1; 9.1; 21.7)

Tracy, Sarah W. ALCOHOLISM IN AMERICA: FROM RECON-STRUCTION TO PROHIBITION. Baltimore, MD: Johns Hopkins University Press, 2005. 357 p. ISBN 0-8018-8119-6. [RC565.7 .T73 2005] (9.5.9; 4.2; 7.1; 15.5; 15.6)

Warner, Kenneth E., ed. TOBACCO CONTROL POLICY. San Francisco: Jossey-Bass/John Wiley & Sons, 2006. 590 p. ISBN 0-7879-8745-X. (Robert Wood Johnson Foundation Series on Health Policy. Foreword by Risa Lavizzo-Mourey. Gift of the publisher.) [HV5760 .T65 2006] (9.5.9; 1.3.5; 1.3.7; 7.1; 9.3.1; 9.5.7; 16.3)

9.5.10 HEALTH CARE FOR INDIGENTS

Gwatkin, Davidson R.; Wagstaff, Adam; and Yazbeck, Abdo S., eds. REACHING THE POOR WITH HEALTH, NUTRITION, AND POPULATION SERVICES: WHAT WORKS, WHAT DOESN'T, AND WHY. Washington, DC: World Bank, 2005. 353 p. ISBN 0-8213-5961-4. [RA418.5 .P6 R43 2005] (9.5.10; 7.1; 9.5.5; 9.5.6; 9.8; 21.7)

9.7 DRUGS AND PHARMACEUTICAL INDUSTRY

Critser, Greg. GENERATION RX: HOW PRESCRIPTION DRUGS ARE ALTERING AMERICAN LIVES, MINDS, AND BODIES. Boston: Houghton Mifflin, 2005. 308 p. ISBN 0-618-39313-7. [RM263 .C75 2005] (9.7; 1.3.2; 7.1; 9.1; 9.3.1; POP)

DeGrandpre, Richard. THE CULT OF PHARMACOLOGY: HOW AMERICA BECAME THE WORLD'S MOST TROUBLED DRUG CULTURE. Durham, NC: Duke University Press, 2006. 294 p. ISBN 0-8223-3881-5. (Gift of the publisher.) [RM263 .D44 2006] (9.7; 1.3.5; 7.1; 9.5.9; 17.4)

Dukes, Graham. THE LAW AND ETHICS OF THE PHARMACEUTICAL INDUSTRY. Amsterdam/Boston: Elsevier, 2006. 409 p. ISBN 0-444-51868-1. [K3636 .D853 2006] (9.7; 1.3.5; 9.3.1; 9.8; 12.1; 21.1)

Goldberg, Richard and Lonbay, Julian, eds. PHARMACEUTICAL MEDICINE, BIOTECHNOLOGY AND EUROPEAN LAW. Cambridge/New York: Cambridge University Press, 2000. 241 p. ISBN 0-521-79249-5. [KJC6191 .P48 2000] (9.7; 1.3.12; 5.3; 15.8; 21.1)

Harper, Jonathan. COUNTERFEIT MEDICINES: SURVEY REPORT. Strasbourg: Council of Europe, 2006. 239 p. ISBN 92-871-5863-0. (Distributed in the U.S. and Canada by: Manhattan Publishing Company, 468 Albany Post Road, Croton-on-Hudson, NY 10520; Web: http://www. manhattanpublishing.com. Gift of the publisher.) [HV5840 .E8 H37 2006] (9.7; 7.1; 21.1)

Kelly, William N. PRESCRIBED MEDICATIONS AND THE PUBLIC HEALTH: LAYING THE FOUNDATION FOR RISK REDUCTION. New York: Pharmaceutical Products Press, 2006. 355 p. ISBN 0-7890-2361-X. (Gift of the publisher.) [RM146.5 .K45 2006] (9.7; 9.1; 9.8)

Link, Kurt. THE VACCINE CONTROVERSY: THE HISTORY, USE, AND SAFETY OF VACCINATIONS. Westport, CT: Praeger, 2005. 196 p. ISBN 0-275-98472-9. [RA638 .L565 2005] (9.7; 5.2; 7.1; 9.5.1)

McTavish, Jan R. PAIN AND PROFITS: THE HISTORY OF THE HEADACHE AND ITS REMEDIES IN AMERICA. New Brunswick, NJ: Rutgers University Press, 2004. 239 p. ISBN 0-8135-3441-0. [RB128 .M386 2004] (9.7; 1.3.2; 4.4; 9.5.1)

Petryna, Adriana; Lakoff, Andrew; and Kleinman, Arthur, eds. GLOBAL PHARMACEUTICALS: ETHICS, MARKETS, PRACTICES. Durham, NC: Duke University Press, 2006. 301 p.

ISBN 0-8223-3741-X. (Gift of the publisher.) [HD9665.5 .G56 2006] (9.7; 7.1; 9.3.1; 9.5.6; 18.1; 21.1)

Reidy, Jamie. HARD SELL: THE EVOLUTION OF A VIAGRA SALESMAN. Kansas City, MO: Andrews McMeel, 2005. 210 p. ISBN 0-7407-5039-9. [HF5439 .D75 R45 2005] (9.7; POP)

Weber, Leonard J. PROFITS BEFORE PEOPLE? ETHICAL STANDARDS AND THE MARKETING OF PRESCRIPTION DRUGS. Bloomington: Indiana University Press, 2006. 206 p. ISBN 0-253-34748-3. (Bioethics and the Humanities series. Gift of the publisher.) [HD966.5 .W43 2006] (9.7; 1.3.2; 6; 7.2; 7.3; 9.3.1; 18.6)

9.8 QUALITY OF HEALTH CARE

Edwards, Adrian and Elwyn, Glyn, eds. EVIDENCE-BASED PATIENT CHOICE: INEVITABLE OR IMPOSSIBLE? Oxford/New York: Oxford University Press, 2001. 331 p. ISBN 0-19-263194-2. [R723.7 .E96 2001] (9.8; 1.3.12; 5.2; 7.1; 7.2; 8.1; 9.3.1)

Godlee, Fiona and Jefferson, Tom, eds. PEER REVIEW IN HEALTH SCIENCES. London: BMJ Books, 2003. 367 p. ISBN 0-7279-1685-8. (Second edition.) [R118.6 .P44 2003] (9.8; 1.3.7; 1.3.12; 7.3; 7.4; 9.7)

Klick, Jonathan and Satel, Sally. THE HEALTH DISPARITIES MYTH: DIAGNOSING THE TREATMENT GAP. Washington, DC: AEI Press/American Enterprise Institute, 2006. 81 p. ISBN 0-8447-7192-9. [RA418.3 .U6 K65 2006] (9.8; 7.1; 8.1; 9.1; 9.5.4; 9.5.10)

Morath, Julianne and Turnbull, Joanne E. TO DO NO HARM: ENSURING PATIENT SAFETY IN HEALTH CARE ORGANIZATIONS. San Francisco: Jossey-Bass, 2005. 354 p. ISBN 0-7879-6770-X. [R729.8 .M665 2005] (9.8; 8.1; 8.2; 9.1; 9.7)

Nash, David B. and Goldfarb, Neil I., eds. THE QUALITY SOLUTION: THE STAKEHOLDER'S GUIDE TO IMPROVING HEALTH CARE. Sudbury, MA: Jones and Bartlett, 2006. 321 p. ISBN 0-7637-2748-2. (Gift of the publisher.) [RA399 .A3 Q35 2006] (9.8; 1.3.12; 7.1; 7.2; 8.1; 9.1; 9.3.1; 9.5.2)

Nguyen, Anh Vu and Nguyen, Dung A. LEARNING FROM MEDICAL ERRORS: LEGAL ISSUES. Abingdon, UK: Radcliffe, 2005. ISBN 18577576X. (Companion volume to: *Learning from Medical Errors: Clinical Problems*. Gift of the publisher.) [R729.8 .N48 2005] (9.8; 7.1; 8.5)

10 SEXUALITY/GENDER

Bem, Sandra Lipsitz. THE LENSES OF GENDER: TRANSFORMING THE DEBATE ON SEXUAL INEQUALITY. New Haven, CT: Yale University Press, 1993. 244 p. ISBN 0-300-06163-3. [QH1075 .B45 1993] (10)

Cuomo, Chris. THE PHILOSOPHER QUEEN: FEMINIST ESSAYS ON WAR, LOVE, AND KNOWLEDGE. Lanham, MD: Rowman & Littlefield, 2002. 161 p. ISBN 0-7425-1381-5. (Femi-

---

Numbers in ( ) = NRCBL Classification Numbers

nist Constructions series.) [HQ1190 .C866 2003] (10; 1.1; 16.1; 21.2)

Jung, Patricia Beattie; Hunt, Mary E.; and Balakrisnan, Radhika, eds. GOOD SEX: FEMINIST PERSPECTIVES FROM THE WORLD'S RELIGIONS. New Brunswick, NJ: Rutgers University Press, 2001. 220 p. ISBN 0-8135-2884-4. [BL458 .G647 2001] (10; 1.2; 21.1)

Kennedy, Kathleen and Ullman, Sharon, eds. SEXUAL BORDERLANDS: CONSTRUCTING AN AMERICAN SEXUAL PAST. Columbus: Ohio State University Press, 2003. 360 p. ISBN 0-8142-5107-2. (Women and Health: Cultural and Social Perspectives series.) [HQ18 .U5 S488 2003] (10)

Rudacille, Deborah. THE RIDDLE OF GENDER: SCIENCE, ACTIVISM, AND TRANSGENDER RIGHTS. New York: Pantheon, 2005. 355 p. ISBN 0-375-42162-9. [HQ77.95 .U6 R83 2005] (10)

Scarth, Fredrika. THE OTHER WITHIN: ETHICS, POLITICS, AND THE BODY IN SIMONE DE BEAUVOIR. Lanham, MD: Rowman & Littlefield, 2004. 195 p. ISBN 0-7425-3476-6. (Feminist Constructions series.) [HQ1190 .S293 2004] (10; 1.1; 4.4; 14.1)

Smith, Bonnie G. and Hutchison, Beth, eds. GENDERING DISABILITY. New Brunswick, NJ: Rutgers University Press, 2004. 314 p. ISBN 0-8135-3373-2. ("Based on scholarship presented at a three-day conference, *Gender and Disability Studies*, organized by the Institute for Research on Women (IRW) at Rutgers University, March 1-3, 2001.") [HV1569.3 .W65 G46 2004] (10; 4.4; 7.1; 9.5.1; 9.5.5; 21.1)

Sytsma, Sharon E., ed. ETHICS AND INTERSEX. Dordrecht/New York: Springer, 2006. 336 p. ISBN 1-4020-4313-9. (International Library of Ethics, Law, and the New Medicine series; Vol. 29. Gift of the publisher.) [RC883 .E84 2006] (10; 1.2; 9.5.7; 15.1; 17.1; 18.5.2; 21.7)

White, Mel. STRANGER AT THE GATE: TO BE GAY AND CHRISTIAN IN AMERICA. New York: Penguin Group, 1995, c1994. 347 p. ISBN 0-452-27381-1. ("A Plume Book.") [BX9896 .Z8 W45 1995] (10; 1.2)

Wilson, Glenn and Rahman, Qazi. BORN GAY: THE PSYCHOBIOLOGY OF SEX ORIENTATION. London: Peter Owen, 2005. 176 p. ISBN 0-7206-1223-3. [RC451.4 .G39 W55 2005] (10; 7.1; 15.6; 17.1)

11.1 CONTRACEPTION (GENERAL)

Farmer, Ann. PROPHETS & PRIESTS: THE HIDDEN FACE OF THE BIRTH CONTROL MOVEMENT. London: Saint Austin Press, 2002. 188 p. ISBN 1-901157-62-8. (Publisher's address: 296 Brockley Road, postal code SE4 2RA.) [HQ766 .F286 2002] (11.1; 9.5.5; 9.5.10; 13.3; 15.5)

Tham, S. Joseph. THE MISSING CORNERSTONE: REASONS WHY COUPLES CHOOSE NATURAL FAMILY PLANNING IN THEIR MARRIAGE. Hamden, CT: Circle Press, 2003. 203 p. ISBN 0-9651601-9-X. (Publisher's address: 33 Rossotto

Drive, zip 06514. Gift of the author.) [HQ766.3 .S53 2003] (11.1; 1.2; 10; 14.1)

12.1 ABORTION (GENERAL)

Dyer, Frederick N. THE PHYSICIANS' CRUSADE AGAINST ABORTION. Sagamore Beach, MA: Science History Publications, 2005. 354 p. ISBN 0-88135-378-7. [HQ767.5 .U5 P49 2005] (12.1; 1.3.7; 4.4; 7.1; 12.4.3; 12.5.2)

Faúndes, Aníbal and Barzelatto, José. THE HUMAN DRAMA OF ABORTION: A GLOBAL SEARCH FOR CONSENSUS. Nashville, TN: Vanderbilt University Press, 2006. 200 p. ISBN 0-8265-1526-6. (Gift of the publisher.) [HQ767 .F38 2006] (12.1; 2.1; 7.1; 9.1; 9.5.5; 12.3; 12.4.1; 12.5.2; 21.7)

World Health Organization. SAFE ABORTION: TECHNICAL AND POLICY GUIDANCE FOR HEALTH SYSTEMS. Geneva: World Health Organization, 2003. 106 p. ISBN 92-4-159034-3. [RG734 .S23 2003] (12.1; 9.1; 9.5.5; 9.8; 12.4.2)

12.3 ABORTION: MORAL AND RELIGIOUS ASPECTS

Driscoll, Margaret and Faugno, Emily. SAVING WOMEN AND INFANTS FROM ABORTION: A DANCE IN THE RAIN. New York: Paulist Press, 2006. 83 p. ISBN 0-8091-4393-3. (Gift of the publisher.) [HQ767.5 .D75 2006] (12.3; 12.5.3)

Koterski, Joseph W., ed. LIFE AND LEARNING V: PROCEEDINGS OF THE FIFTH UNIVERSITY FACULTY FOR LIFE CONFERENCE JUNE 1995 AT MARQUETTE UNIVERSITY. Washington, DC: University Faculty for Life, 1996. 400 p. ISBN 1-886387-03-6. [HQ767.15 .U55a 1995] (12.3; 1.2; 2.1; 7.1; 10; 12.4.2; 13.3; 20.4.1; 20.5.1; 21.1)

Koterski, Joseph W., ed. LIFE AND LEARNING VIII: PROCEEDINGS OF THE EIGHTH UNIVERSITY FACULTY FOR LIFE CONFERENCE, JUNE 1998 AT THE UNIVERSITY OF TORONTO. Washington, DC: University Faculty for Life, 1999. 515 p. ISBN 1-886387-06-0. [HQ767.15 .U55a 1998] (12.3; 1.2; 1.3.5; 2.1; 2.2; 4.4; 7.1; 10; 11.3; 12.4.2; 15.5; 20.5.1; 20.6; 20.7; 21.1)

Torr, James D., ed. ABORTION: OPPOSING VIEWPOINTS. Farmington Hills, MI: Greenhaven Press/Thomson Gale, 2006. 192 p. ISBN 0-7377-2922-8. (Opposing Viewpoints series. Gift of the publisher.) [HQ767.15 .A23 2006] (12.3; 4.4; 9.5.5; 12.4.2; 12.5.1; 15.2; 18.5.4; 21.1)

12.4.2 ABORTION: LEGAL ASPECTS/ INTERESTS OF WOMAN/FETUS/FATHER

Mersky, Roy M. and Liebert, Tobe, comps. A DOCUMENTARY HISTORY OF THE LEGAL ASPECTS OF ABORTION IN THE UNITED STATES: STENBERG V. CARHART. Buffalo, NY: William S. Hein, 2003. 2 volumes. ISBN 0-8377-3436-3. (Documentary History of the Legal Aspects of Abortion in the United States series; No. 6.) [KF228 .S784 D63 2003] (12.4.2; 10; 12.3)

12.5.1 ABORTION: SOCIAL ASPECTS (GENERAL)

Ariss, Mary Rachel. THE RECYCLED FETUS: ETHICS OF WASTE AND GIFT EXCHANGE IN NEW REPRODUCTIVE TECHNOLOGIES. Ann Arbor, MI: ProQuest Information and Learning/UMI, 2001. 310 p. ISBN 0-612-69052-0. (Publication No. AAT-NQ699052. Dissertation, (S.J.D.)—University of Toronto, 2001.) [KF3827 .D66 A75 2002] (12.5.1; 4.4; 5.3; 9.3.1; 10; 12.4.2; 14.1; 14.4; 19.1; 19.5)

12.5.2 ABORTION: DEMOGRAPHIC SURVEYS

Smyth, Lisa. ABORTION AND NATION: THE POLITICS OF REPRODUCTION IN CONTEMPORARY IRELAND. Aldershot, Hants/Burlington, VT: Ashgate, 2005. 187 p. ISBN 0-7546-3592-9. [HQ767.5 .I73 S69 2005] (12.5.2; 1.3.5; 2.2; 7.1; 9.5.5; 10; 14.1; 21.1)

13.3 POPULATION POLICY

Mumford, Stephen D. THE LIFE AND DEATH OF NSSM 200: HOW THE DESTRUCTION OF POLITICAL WILL DOOMED A U.S. POPULATION POLICY. Research Triangle Park, NC: Center for Research on Population and Security, 1996. 580 p. ISBN 0-937307-05-X. (Publisher's address: PO Box 13067, zip 27709; tel.: 919-933-7491.) [HB883.5 .M85 1996] (13.3; 1.2; 1.3.5; 1.3.7; 12.5.2; 21.1)

14.1 REPRODUCTION/REPRODUCTIVE TECHNOLOGIES (GENERAL)

Bhattacharyya, Swasti. MAGICAL PROGENY, MODERN TECHNOLOGY: A HINDU BIOETHICS OF ASSISTED REPRODUCTIVE TECHNOLOGY. Albany: State University of New York Press, 2006. 161 p. ISBN 0-7914-6792-9. [BL1215 .B55 B43 2006] (14.1; 1.2; 2.1; 7.1)

Creating Life? Examining the Legal, Ethical, and Medical Issues of Assisted Reproductive Technologies [Part 2]. JOURNAL OF GENDER, RACE AND JUSTICE 2006 Spring; 9(3): 443-635. (ISSN 1550-7815.) (14.1; 2.4; 4.4; 5.3; 8.4; 8.5; 9.8; 10; 14.2; 15.1; 15.2; 19.5; 19.6)

Gilbert, Scott F.; Tyler, Anna L.; and Zackin, Emily J. BIOETHICS AND THE NEW EMBRYOLOGY: SPRINGBOARDS FOR DEBATE. Sunderland, MA: Sinauer Associates; Distributed by: W.H. Freeman, 2005. 299 p. ISBN 0-7167-7345-7. [RG133.5 .G555 2005] (14.1; 4.4; 14.3; 14.5; 15.4; 18.5.4; 19.5)

Hawthorne, Susan and Klein, Renate, eds. ANGELS OF POWER AND OTHER REPRODUCTIVE CREATIONS. West Melbourne, Australia: Spinifex Press, 1991. 260 p. ISBN 1-875559-00-0. (Publisher's address: 4/49-59 Stanley Street, West Melbourne 2003.) [PR9614.5 .W6 A53 1991] (14.1; 7.1; 10; 15.1; Fiction)

Jackson, Timothy p., ed. THE MORALITY OF ADOPTION: SOCIAL-PSYCHOLOGICAL, THEOLOGICAL, AND LEGAL PERSPECTIVES. Grand Rapids, MI: William B. Eerdmans, 2005. 337 p. ISBN 0-8028-2979-1. (Religion, Marriage, and Family series.) [HV875.55 .M67 2005] (14.1; 1.2; 14.4; 14.6; 21.7)

Knudsen, Lara M. REPRODUCTIVE RIGHTS IN A GLOBAL CONTEXT: SOUTH AFRICA, UGANDA, PERU, DENMARK, UNITED STATES, VIETNAM, JORDAN. Nashville, TN: Vanderbilt University Press, 2006. 289 p. ISBN 0-8265-1528-2. (Gift of the publisher.) [QH766 .K65 2006] (14.1; 7.1; 9.5.5; 10; 11.1; 12.1; 21.7)

Maier, Barbara. ETHIK IN GYNÄKOLOGIE UND GEBURTSHILFE: ENTSCHEIDUNGEN ANHAND KLINISCHER FALLBEISPIELE. Berlin: Springer, 2000. 294 p. ISBN 3-540-67304-0. (Gift of Warren Shibles.) (14.1; 2.1; 12.4.1; 14.4; 15.2)

McHaffie, Hazel E. DOUBLE TROUBLE: A STORY OF ASSISTED REPRODUCTION. Oxford/Seattle, WA: Radcliffe, 2005. 258 p. ISBN 1-85775-669-X. (Living Literature Series. "The Halleys are a close, successful, loving family. But relationships become increasingly complex following the marriages of identical twins Nicholas and Michael. Darker secrets and hidden emotions are revealed when an unplanned pregnancy and a surrogacy arrangement lead to discoveries which challenge their moral values and jeopardise their happiness. This story probes beneath society's superficial acceptance of fertility treatment, revealing the potential for pain, distorted relationships, and far-reaching consequences, both medical and moral." Gift of the publisher.) [PR6063 .C517 D68 2005] (14.1; 14.2; Fiction)

Meulders-Klein, Marie Thérèse; Deech, Ruth; and Vlaardingerbroek, Paul, eds. BIOMEDICINE, THE FAMILY AND HUMAN RIGHTS. The Hague/New York: Kluwer Law International, 2002. 638 p. ISBN 90-411-1627-3. (Text in English and French.) [K3611 .A77 B56 2002] (14.1; 1.3.5; 9.5.7; 15.1; 17.1; 21.1)

National Health and Medical Research Council (Australia). Australian Health Ethics Committee. ETHICAL GUIDELINES ON THE USE OF ASSISTED REPRODUCTIVE TECHNOLOGY IN CLINICAL PRACTICE AND RESEARCH. Canberra, ACT: National Health and Medical Research Council, 2004. 70 p. ISBN 1-86496-271-2. (September 2004. "Endorsed by NHMRC for public release in September 2004." Available from: National Health and Medical Research Council Publications; email: nhmrc.publications@nhmrc.gov.au; Web: http://www.nhmrc.gov.au. Also available on the Web at: http://www.nhmrc.gov.au/publications/_files/e56.pdf.) (14.1; 6; 8.3.1; 14.2; 14.3; 14.6; 15.2; 18.5.4)

Obermeyer, Carla Makhlouf, ed. CULTURAL PERSPECTIVES ON REPRODUCTIVE HEALTH. Oxford/New York: Oxford University Press, 2001. 333 p. ISBN 0-19-924689-0. (International Studies in Demography series. "Based on a seminar organised by the Reproductive Health Committee of the International Union for the Scientific Study of Population at Kwa Maritane, South Africa in June 1997.")

Numbers in ( ) = NRCBL Classification Numbers

[HQ766.5 .D44 C8 2001] (14.1; 5.2; 7.1; 9.5.5; 10; 11.1; 12.1; 13.3; 15.1; 21.7)

Reproduction Gone Awry. SOCIAL SCIENCE AND MEDICINE 2003 May; 56(9): 1831-1986. (ISSN 0277-9536.) (14.1; 1.2; 4.1.3; 7.1; 8.1; 8.3.4; 9.1; 9.5.5; 10; 11.1; 12.3; 13.3; 14.2; 14.4; 15.2; 15.3; 21.7)

Revelli, Alberto; Tur-Kaspa, Ilan; Holte, Jan Gunnar; and Massobrio, Marco, eds. BIOTECHNOLOGY OF HUMAN RE-PRODUCTION. New York: Parthenon Publishing Group, 2003. 464 p. ISBN 1-84214-132-5. [RG133.5 .B566 2003] (14.1; 14.4; 14.5; 14.6; 15.1; 18.5.4; 19.1)

Rothstein, Mark A.; Murray, Thomas H.; Kaebnick, Gregory E.; and Majumder, Mary Anderlik, eds. GENETIC TIES AND THE FAMILY: THE IMPACT OF PATERNITY TESTING ON PARENTS AND CHILDREN. Baltimore, MD: Johns Hopkins University Press, 2005. 244 p. ISBN 0-8018-8193-5. [HQ755.85 .G473 2005] (14.1; 8.1; 9.5.7; 15.1)

Schaffer, Patricia. HOW BABIES AND FAMILIES ARE MADE: THERE IS MORE THAN ONE WAY! Berkeley, CA: Tabor Sarah Books, 1988. 52 p. ISBN 0-935079-17-3. (Juvenile literature. Illustrated by Suzanne Corbett. "Summary: Surveys the different ways in which children are conceived, develop, are born, and become parts of families, examining special situations such as artificial insemination, cesarean births, and families with adopted children or stepchildren.") [HQ53 .S3 1988] (14.1; 10; POP)

Spar, Debora L. THE BABY BUSINESS: HOW MONEY, SCIENCE, AND POLITICS DRIVE THE COMMERCE OF CONCEPTION. Boston: Harvard Business School Press, 2006. 299 p. ISBN 1-59139-620-4. [RG133.5 .S666 2006] (14.1; 1.3.5; 7.1; 9.3.1; 14.2; 14.5; 15.2)

Unnithan-Kumar, Maya, ed. REPRODUCTIVE AGENCY, MEDICINE AND THE STATE: CULTURAL TRANSFORMATIONS IN CHILDBEARING. New York: Berghahn Books, 2004. 255 p. ISBN 1-57181-648-8. (Fertility, Reproduction, and Sexuality series; Vol. 3. Gift of the publisher.) [RG133.5 .R456 2004] (14.1; 4.4; 7.1; 9.1; 9.5.5; 14.4; 15.2; 19.5; 21.1; 21.7)

14.2 ARTIFICIAL INSEMINATION AND SURROGACY

Weisberg, D. Kelly. THE BIRTH OF SURROGACY IN ISRAEL. Gainesville: University Press of Florida, 2005. 291 p. ISBN 0-8130-2809-4. (14.2; 1.3.5; Reference)

14.5 CLONING

Dudley, William, ed. CLONING. Farmington Hills, MI: Greenhaven Press/Thomson Gale, 2006. 112 p. ISBN 0-7377-3196-6. (Writing the Critical Essay series. Gift of the publisher.) [QH442.2 .C5646 2006] (14.5; 2.3; 15.1; 18.5.4; 22.2; Reference)

Haddix, Margaret Peterson. DOUBLE IDENTITY. New York: Simon & Schuster Books for Young Readers, 2005. 218 p. ISBN 0-689-87374-3. (Juvenile literature. "As Bethany approaches her thirteenth birthday, her parents begin acting more oddly than usual: Her mother cries constantly, and her father barely lets Bethany out of his sight. Then one morning he hustles the entire family into the car, drives across several state lines—and leaves Bethany with an aunt she never knew existed. Bethany has no idea what's going on. She's worried that her mom and dad are running from some kind of trouble, but she can't find out because they won't tell her where they are going. Bethany's only clue is a few words she overheard her father tell her aunt Myrlie: 'She doesn't know anything about Elizabeth.' But Aunt Myrlie won't tell Bethany who Elizabeth is, and she won't explain why people in her small town react to Bethany as if they've seen a ghost. The mystery intensifies when Bethany gets a package from her father containing four different birth certificates from four states. with four different last names—and thousands of dollars in cash. And when a stranger man shows up asking questions, Bethany realizes she's not the only one who's desperate to unravel the secrets of her past.") [PS3558 .A3118 D68 2005] (14.5; Fiction)

Ishiguro, Kazuo. NEVER LET ME GO. New York: Alfred A. Knopf, 2005. 288 p. ISBN 1-4000-4339-5. ("From the Booker Prize-winning author of *The Remains of the Day* and *When We Were Orphans*, comes an unforgettable edge-of-your-seat mystery that is at once heartbreakingly tender and morally courageous about what it means to be human. Hailsham seems like a pleasant English boarding school, far from the influences of the city. Its students are well tended and supported, trained in art and literature, and become just the sort of people the world wants them to be. But, curiously, they are taught nothing of the outside world and are allowed little contact with it. Within the grounds of Hailsham, Kathy grows from schoolgirl to young woman, but it's only when she and her friends Ruth and Tommy leave the safe grounds of the school (as they always knew they would) that they realize the full truth of what Hailsham is.") [PR6059 .S5 N48 2005] (14.5; 19.5; Fiction)

Panno, Joseph. ANIMAL CLONING: THE SCIENCE OF NUCLEAR TRANSFER. New York: Facts on File, 2005. 164 p. ISBN 0-8160-4947-5. (The "New Biology" series.) [QH442.2 .P26 2005] (14.5; 2.2; 15.1; 19.1; 22.2; 22.3; Reference)

Raël. YES TO HUMAN CLONING: IMMORTALITY THANKS TO SCIENCE! London/Los Angeles: Tagman Press, 2001. 172 p. ISBN 0-903571-05-7. (14.5; 1.2; 1.3.11; 1.3.12; 4.4; 5.1; 15.1; 16.1; 20.5.1)

Wilmut, Ian and Highfield, Roger. AFTER DOLLY: THE USES AND MISUSES OF HUMAN CLONING. New York: W.W. Norton, 2006. 335 p. ISBN 0-393-06066-7. [QH442.2 .W544 2006] (14.5; 2.2; 14.1; 18.5.4; 22.2; 22.3)

14.6 CRYOBANKING OF SPERM, OVA, OR EMBRYOS

Plotz, David. THE GENIUS FACTORY: THE CURIOUS HISTORY OF THE NOBEL PRIZE SPERM BANK. New York: Random House, 2005. 262 p. ISBN 1-4000-6124-5. [HQ761 .P56 2005] (14.6; 14.2; 15.6; 19.5)

15.1 GENETICS, MOLECULAR BIOLOGY AND MICROBIOLOGY (GENERAL)

Burt, Austin and Trivers, Robert. GENES IN CONFLICT: THE BIOLOGY OF SELFISH GENETIC ELEMENTS. Cambridge, MA: Belknap Press of Harvard University Press, 2006. 602 p. ISBN 0-674-01713-7. [QH447.8 .S45 B87 2006] (15.1)

Chiu, Lisa Seachrist. WHEN A GENE MAKES YOU SMELL LIKE A FISH...AND OTHER TALES ABOUT THE GENES IN YOUR BODY. Oxford/New York: Oxford University Press, 2006. 219 p. ISBN 0-19-516994-8. (Illustrations by Judith A. Seachrist.) [QH431 .C474 2006] (15.1)

Danchin, Antoine. THE DELPHIC BOAT: WHAT GENOMES TELL US. Cambridge, MA: Harvard University Press, 2002. 368 p. ISBN 0-674-00930-4. (Translation from the French by Alison Quayle of: *La barque de Delphes*; Editions Odile Jacob, 1998.) [QH447 .D3613 2002] (15.1)

Distin, Kate. THE SELFISH MEME: A CRITICAL REASSESS-MENT. Cambridge/New York: Cambridge University Press, 2005. 231 p. ISBN 0-521-60627-6. [HM621 .D57 2005] (15.1; 3.2; 21.7)

Duncan, David Ewing. THE GENETICIST WHO PLAYED HOOPS WITH MY DNA: ...AND OTHER MASTERMINDS FROM THE FRONTIERS OF BIOTECH. New York: William Morrow/HarperCollins, 2005. 273 p. ISBN 0-06-053738-8. [QH429 .D86 2005] (15.1; 5.1; Biography)

Ferenczi, Andrea. GENETICS, GENE-ETHICS: INTERVIEWS WITH HUNGARIAN SCIENTISTS. Edinburgh: Handsel/Budapest: Harmat, 2001. 163 p. ISBN 1-871828-61-9 [Handsel]; ISBN 963-9148-50-4 [Harmat]. (English translation by András Falus. Orders in the UK: Handsel Press, Millfield, Boat of Garten, PH24 3BY, Scotland; orders outside of the UK: Harmat Kiadó, Bukarest utca 3, H-1114 Budapest, Hungary.) [QH431 .F474 2001] (15.1; 5.3; 14.5; 19.1; 22.2)

Forum: Genetics and the Law. UNIVERSITY OF NEW SOUTH WALES LAW JOURNAL 2003; 26(3): 741-812. (ISSN 0313-0096.) (15.1; 1.3.5; 2.2; 4.5; 5.1; 5.2; 5.3; 8.2; 8.3.1; 8.4; 9.3.1; 9.5.4; 11.4; 15.3; 15.8; 18.2; 21.1)

Franceschi, Magali. DROIT ET MARCHANDISATION DE LA CONNAISSANCE SUR LES GÈNES HUMAINS. Paris: CNRS Éditions, 2004. 247 p. ISBN 2-271-06200-4. (CNRS droit series.) [K3611 .G46 F73 2004] (15.1; 1.3.9; 5.2; 5.3; 9.3.1)

Fujiki, Norio; Sudo, Masakatsu; and Macer, Darryl, eds. BIOETHICS AND THE IMPACT OF GENOMICS IN THE 21ST CENTURY: PHARMACOGENOMICS, DNA POLYMORPHISM AND MEDICAL GENETICS SERVICES. Christchurch, New Zealand: Eubios Ethics Institute, 2001. [175 p. + 170 p.]. ISBN 0-908897-17-0. (Text in English and Japanese.) (15.1; 1.3.12; 2.1; 2.3; 2.4; 6; 9.3.1; 9.7; 14.1; 14.5; 15.2; 15.3; 15.5; 15.10; 18.5.4; 21.1; 21.7)

Glover, Jonathan. CHOOSING CHILDREN: GENES, DISABIL-ITY, AND DESIGN. Oxford: Clarendon Press/New York: Ox-

ford University Press, 2006. 120 p. ISBN 0-19-929092-X. (Uehiro Series in Practical Ethics. Gift of the publisher.) [RJ47.3 .G556 2006] (15.1; 4.5; 9.5.7; 15.2; 15.5)

Grace, Eric S. BIOTECHNOLOGY UNZIPPED: PROMISES AND REALITIES. Washington, DC: Joseph Henry Press, 2006. 240 p. ISBN 0-309-09621-9. (Revised second edition.) [TP248.15 .G73 2006] (15.1; 1.3.11; 15.7; 15.8; 16.1; 22.3)

Harper, Peter S., ed. LANDMARKS IN MEDICAL GENETICS: CLASSIC ARTICLES WITH COMMENTARIES. Oxford/New York: Oxford University Press, 2004. 307 p. ISBN 0-19-515930-6. (Oxford Monographs on Medical Genetics series; No. 51.) [RB155 .L345 2004] (15.1; 9.5.3; 10; 15.10)

Hyde, Margaret O. and Setaro, John F. MEDICINE'S BRAVE NEW WORLD: BIOENGINEERING AND THE NEW GENETICS. Brookfield, CT: Twenty-First Century Books, 2001. 143 p. ISBN 0-7613-1706-6. (Juvenile literature.) [R855.4 .H833 2001] (15.1; 14.1; 14.5; 18.5.4; 19.1)

Isaac, Grant E. AGRICULTURAL BIOTECHNOLOGY AND TRANSATLANTIC TRADE: REGULATORY BARRIERS TO GM CROPS. Wallingford, Oxon, UK/New York: CABI, 2002. 303 p. ISBN 0-85199-580-2. [HD9999 .G452 I83 2002] (15.1; 1.3.11; 15.7; 21.1)

Joseph, Jay. THE GENE ILLUSION: GENETIC RESEARCH IN PSYCHIATRY AND PSYCHOLOGY UNDER THE MICROSCOPE. New York: Algora, 2004. 407 p. ISBN 0-87586-343-4. [RC455.4 .G4 J67 2004] (15.1; 2.2; 15.6; 17.1; 18.5.6)

Kahn, Axel and Papillon, Fabrice. LE SECRET DE LA SALAMANDRE: LA MÉDECINE EN QUÊTE D'IMMORTALITÉ. Paris: Nil, 2005. 366 p. ISBN 2-84111-281-0. [QP90.2 .K34 2005] (15.1; 14.5; 15.4; 18.5.4; 22.2)

Keller, Evelyn Fox. REFIGURING LIFE: METAPHORS OF TWENTIETH-CENTURY BIOLOGY. New York: Columbia University Press, 1995. 134 p. ISBN 0-231-10205-4. (The Wellek Library Lectures at the University of California, Irvine series.) [QH428 .K45 1995] (15.1; 3.2)

Keynes, Milo; Edwards, A.W.F.; and Peel, Robert, eds. A CENTURY OF MENDELISM IN HUMAN GENETICS: PROCEEDINGS OF A SYMPOSIUM ORGANIZED BY THE GALTON INSTITUTE AND HELD AT THE ROYAL SOCIETY OF MEDICINE, LONDON, 2001. Boca Raton: CRC Press, 2004. 161 p. ISBN 0-415-32960-4. [QH428 .C46 2004] (15.1)

Krude, Torsten, ed. DNA: CHANGING SCIENCE AND SOCIETY. Cambridge/New York: Cambridge University Press, 2004. 193 p. ISBN 0-521-82378-1. (Darwin College Lectures series.) [QP624 .D615 2004] (15.1; 1.3.5; 5.1)

Lacey, Hugh. VALUES AND OBJECTIVITY IN SCIENCE: THE CURRENT CONTROVERSY ABOUT TRANSGENIC CROPS. Lanham, MD: Lexington Books, 2005. 289 p. ISBN 0-7391-1141-8. [Q175 .L158 2005] (15.1; 1.3.11; 5.1; 15.7)

Numbers in ( ) = NRCBL Classification Numbers

LeVine, Harry. GENETIC ENGINEERING: A REFERENCE HANDBOOK. Santa Barbara, CA: ABC-CLIO, 2006. 313 p. ISBN 1-85109-860-7. (Second edition. Contemporary World Issues series.) [TP248.6 .L4 2006] (15.1; 5.3; 21.1; Biography; Reference)

Marks, Graham. ZOO. London: Bloomsbury, 2005. 265 p. ISBN 0-7475-7733-1. ("After seventeen-year-old Cam Stewart escapes from the kidnappers who took him from right in front of his San Diego home, he continues a dangerous adventure that includes finding a mysterious chip in his arm which leads him to question his identity." Gift of the publisher.) [PR6063 .A65 Z3 2005] (15.1; 4.5; 15.5; Fiction)

Morgan, Rose M. THE GENETICS REVOLUTION: HISTORY, FEARS, AND FUTURE OF A LIFE-ALTERING SCIENCE. Westport, CT: Greenwood Press, 2006. 219 p. ISBN 0-313-33672-5. (Gift of the publisher.) [RB155 .M673 2006] (15.1; 14.4; 14.5; 15.11; 18.5.4)

National Research Council (United States). Commitee on Genomics Databases for Bioterrorism Threat Agents. SEEKING SECURITY: PATHOGENS, OPEN ACCESS, AND GENOME DATABASES. Washington, DC: National Academies Press, 2004. 74 p. ISBN 0-309-09305-8. (Also available on the Web at: http://www.nap.edu.) [QH447 .N38 2004] (15.1; 1.3.12; 21.2; 21.3)

Neumann-Held, Eva M. and Rehmann-Sutter, Christoph, eds. GENES IN DEVELOPMENT: RE-READING THE MOLECULAR PARADIGM. Durham, NC: Duke University Press, 2006. 378 p. ISBN 0-8223-3667-7. (Gift of the publisher.) [QH453 .G47 2006] (15.1; 3.1; 3.2; 15.6)

Noble, Denis. THE MUSIC OF LIFE: BIOLOGY BEYOND THE GENOME. Oxford/New York: Oxford University Press, 2006. 153 p. ISBN 0-19-929573-5. [QH501 .N633 2006] (15.1; 3.1)

Nuffield Council on Bioethics. THE USE OF GENETICALLY MODIFIED CROPS IN DEVELOPING COUNTRIES: A FOLLOW-UP DISCUSSION PAPER. London: Nuffield Council on Bioethics, 2004. 122 p. ISBN 1-904384-07-2. (January 2004. Available from: Nuffield Council on Bioethics, 28 Bedford Square, London WC1B 3JS. Also available on the Web at: http://www.nuffieldbioethics.org.) [SB123.57 .N84 2004] (15.1; 1.3.11; 5.3; 21.1)

Paarlberg, Robert L. THE POLITICS OF PRECAUTION: GENETICALLY MODIFIED CROPS IN DEVELOPING COUNTRIES. Baltimore, MD: Johns Hopkins University Press, 2001. 181 p. ISBN 0-8018-6823-8. (Published for the International Food Policy Research Institute.) [SB123.57 .P33 2001] (15.1; 1.3.5; 1.3.11; 5.3; 21.1)

Pence, Gregory E. DESIGNER FOOD: MUTANT HARVEST OR BREADBASKET OF THE WORLD? Lanham, MD: Rowman & Littlefield, 2002. 235 p. ISBN 0-7425-0839-0. [TP248.65 .F66 P46 2002] (15.1; 1.3.11; 15.7; 16.1; 22.3; POP)

Pinstrup-Andersen, Per and Shiøler, Ebbe. SEEDS OF CONTENTION: WORLD HUNGER AND THE GLOBAL CONTROVERSY OVER GM CROPS. Baltimore, MD: Johns Hopkins

University Press, 2000. 164 p. ISBN 0-8018-6826-2. [HD9000.5 .P564 2001] (15.1; 1.3.2; 1.3.11; 9.5.10; 15.7; 21.1)

Radetzki, Marcus; Radetzki, Marian; and Juth, Niklas. GENES AND INSURANCE: ETHICAL, LEGAL AND ECONOMIC ISSUES. Cambridge/New York: Cambridge University Press, 2003. 170 p. ISBN 0-521-83090-7. (Cambridge Law, Medicine and Ethics series.) [HG8771 .R33 2003] (15.1; 1.3.12; 5.2; 7.1; 8.4; 9.1; 9.3.1; 15.3; 21.1)

Rajan, Kaushik Sunder. BIOCAPITAL: THE CONSTITUTION OF POSTGENOMIC LIFE. Durham, NC: Duke University Press, 2006. 343 p. ISBN 0-8223-3720-7. (Gift of the publisher.) [HD9999 .B442 S86 2006] (15.1; 1.3.2; 1.3.5; 1.3.12; 9.3.1; 9.7)

Ridley, Matt. FRANCIS CRICK: DISCOVERER OF THE GENETIC CODE. New York: Atlas Books/HarperCollins, 2006. 213 p. ISBN 0-06-082333-X. (Eminent Lives series.) [QH429.2 .C75 R53 2006] (15.1; 3.1; Biography)

Rowell, Andrew. DON'T WORRY, IT'S SAFE TO EAT: THE TRUE STORY OF GM FOOD, BSE & FOOT AND MOUTH. London/Sterling, VA: Earthscan, 2003. 268 p. ISBN 1-85383-932-9. [TP248.65 .F66 R69 2003] (15.1; 1.3.11; 5.3; 22.3)

Sándor, Judit, ed. SOCIETY AND GENETIC INFORMATION: CODES AND LAWS IN THE GENETIC ERA. Budapest/New York: Central European University Press, 2003. 422 p. ISBN 963-9241-75-X. (CPS Books series. ISSN 1587-6942.) [QH438.7 .S63 2003] (15.1; 1.2; 1.3.12; 5.1; 6; 8.4; 9.3.1; 9.5.7; 15.3; 15.4; 15.5; 15.10; 15.11; 18.5.4; 21.1)

Scheuerle, Angela. UNDERSTANDING GENETICS: A PRIMER FOR COUPLES AND FAMILIES. Westport, CT: Praeger, 2005. 209 p. ISBN 0-275-98189-4. [RB155 .S283 2005] (15.1; 9.5.7; 9.5.8; 15.2; 15.3)

Silva, Vesta T. RE-PRODUCING A GENETIC SELF: MEDIA REPRESENTATIONS OF GENETIC REPRODUCTIVE TECHNOLOGIES. Ann Arbor, MI: ProQuest Information & Learning/UMI, 2004. 213 p. (Publication Order No. AAT-3129340. Dissertation, (Ph.D. in Communication Studies)—University of Iowa, 2004.) (15.1; 1.3.7; 5.3; 14.2; 14.4; 14.5; 15.6)

Smith, Gina. THE GENOMICS AGE: HOW DNA TECHNOLOGY IS TRANSFORMING THE WAY WE LIVE AND WHO WE ARE. New York: AMACOM, 2005. 262 p. ISBN 0-8144-0843-5. [QH437 .S654 2005] (15.1; 1.3.5; 9.5.2; 14.5; 15.3; 15.4; 15.5; 15.10; 20.5.1)

Stephens, Dafydd and Jones, Lesley, eds. THE IMPACT OF GENETIC HEARING IMPAIRMENT. London/Philadelphia: Whurr, 2005. 247 p. ISBN 1-86156-437-6. (Published in association with GENDEAF (European Thematic Network on Genetic Deafness.) [RF292 .I47 2005] (15.1; 7.1; 9.5.1; 9.5.2; 9.5.7; 17.1)

Tamburrini, Claudio and Tannsjö, Torbjörn, eds. GENETIC TECHNOLOGY AND SPORT: ETHICAL QUESTIONS. London/New York: Routledge, 2005. 223 p. ISBN 0-415-34237-6. (Ethics and Sport series. Gift of the publisher.) [RC1230 .G46 2005] (15.1; 1.3.1; 4.5; 9.5.9; 9.7; 10; 21.1)

Tavani, Herman T., ed. ETHICS, COMPUTING, AND GENOMICS. Sudbury, MA: Jones and Bartlett, 2006. 356 p. ISBN 0-7637-3620-1. (Gift of the publisher.) [QH441.2 .E47 2006] (15.1; 1.3.9; 1.3.12; 7.1; 8.3.1; 8.4; 15.8; 15.10; 16.1)

Wailoo, Keith and Pemberton, Stephen. THE TROUBLED DREAM OF GENETIC MEDICINE: ETHNICITY AND INNOVATION IN TAY-SACHS, CYSTIC FIBROSIS, AND SICKLE CELL DISEASE. Baltimore, MD: Johns Hopkins University Press, 2006. 249 p. ISBN 0-8018-8326-1. [RB155.5 .W35 2006] (15.1; 9.5.1; 9.5.4; 15.4; 21.7)

15.2 GENETIC COUNSELING/PRENATAL DIAGNOSIS

Body, G.; Perrotin, F.; Guichet, A.; Paillet, C.; Descamps, p.; Aubron, F.; et al. LA PRATIQUE DU DIAGNOSTIC PRÉNATAL. Paris: Masson, 2001. 400 p. ISBN 2-225-83671-X. (Hors collection series.) [RG628 .P72 2001] (15.2; 9.5.8)

Franklin, Sarah and Roberts, Celia. BORN AND MADE: AN ETHNOGRAPHY OF PREIMPLANTATION GENETIC DIAGNOSIS. Princeton, NJ: Princeton University Press, 2006. 256 p. ISBN 0-691-12193-1. (In-formation Series.) (15.2; 5.3; 7.1)

Jenkins, Jean F. and Lea, Dale Halsey. NURSING CARE IN THE GENOMIC ERA: A CASE-BASED APPROACH. Sudbury, MA: Jones and Bartlett, 2005. 411 p. ISBN 0-7637-3325-3. [RB155.7 .J46 2005] (15.2; 1.2; 4.1.3; 4.4; 7.1; 8.1; 9.7; 15.3; 17.1)

Skirton, Heather and Patch, Christine. GENETICS FOR HEALTHCARE PROFESSIONALS: A LIFESTAGE APPROACH. Oxford: BIOS Scientific, 2002. 207 p. ISBN 1-85996-043-X. [RB155 .S557 2002] (15.2; 9.5.5; 9.5.7; 15.3)

Veach, Patricia McCarthy; LeRoy, Bonnie S.; and Bartels, Dianne M. FACILITATING THE GENETIC COUNSELING PROCESS: A PRACTICAL MANUAL. New York: Springer-Verlag, 2003. 308 p. ISBN 0-387-00330-4. [RB155.7 .V434 2003] (15.2; 1.3.12; 6; 8.1)

Vieth, Andreas. GESUNDHEITSZWECKE UND HUMANGENETIK: MEDIZINETHISCHE ARGUMENTE FÜR DIE BINDUNG PRÄDIKTIVER GENTESTS AN GESUNDHEITSZWECKE. Paderborn: Mentis, 2004. 319 p. ISBN 3-89785-171-7. (Based on the conference "Prädiktive genetische Tests: 'Health Purposes'" held in 1997 at the Institut für Wissenschaft und Ethik.) [RB155.6 .V546 2004] (15.2; 2.1; 15.3; Reference)

15.3 GENETIC SCREENING/TESTING

Gilbar, Roy. THE STATUS OF THE FAMILY IN LAW AND BIOETHICS: THE GENETIC CONTEXT. Aldershot, Hants/Burlington, VT: Ashgate, 2005. 270 p. ISBN 0-7546-4545-2. (Gift of the publisher.) [KD3410 .I54 G55 2005] (15.3; 2.1; 5.2; 8.1; 8.3.1; 8.4; 15.1)

Sharpe, Neil F. and Carter, Ronald F. GENETIC TESTING: CARE, CONSENT, AND LIABILITY. Hoboken, NJ: Wiley-Liss, 2006. 594 p. ISBN 0-471-64987-2. [RB155.6 .S74 2006] (15.3; 5.2; 8.1; 8.3.1; 8.4; 9.5.1; 9.5.5; 9.5.7; 15.2; 17.1)

Special Issue: Informed Choice in Screening. HEALTH EXPECTATIONS 2001 June; 4(2): 79-135. (ISSN 1369-6513.) (15.3; 1.1; 1.3.1; 5.2; 7.1; 8.1; 8.3.1; 9.1; 9.4; 9.5.1; 15.2; 18.5.1)

15.4 GENE THERAPY/TRANSFER

Panno, Joseph. GENE THERAPY: TREATING DISEASE BY REPAIRING GENES. New York: Facts on File, 2005. 172 p. ISBN 0816049483. (The "New Biology" series.) [RB155.8 .P36 2005] (15.4; 9.5.1; 18.2; 18.3; Reference)

Schneider, Angela J. and Friedmann, Theodore. GENE DOPING IN SPORTS: THE SCIENCE AND ETHICS OF GENETICALLY MODIFIED ATHLETES. Amsterdam/Boston: Elsevier Academic Press, 2006. 116 p. ISBN 0-12-017651-3. (Advances in Genetics series; Vol. 51.) [RC1230 .S25 2006] (15.4; 1.3.1; 4.5; 9.7; 18.2; 18.5.1)

15.5 EUGENICS

Bruinius, Harry. BETTER FOR ALL THE WORLD: THE SECRET HISTORY OF FORCED STERILIZATION AND AMERICA'S QUEST FOR RACIAL PURITY. New York: Alfred A. Knopf, 2006. 401 p. ISBN 0-375-41371-5. [HQ755.5 .U5 B78 2006] (15.5; 1.3.5; 2.2; 11.3; 21.4)

Cleminson, Richard. ANARCHISM, SCIENCE AND SEX: EUGENICS IN EASTERN SPAIN, 1900-1937. Bern/New York: Peter Lang, 2000. 287 p. ISBN 3-906765-57-1 [Germany]; ISBN 0-8204-5097-9 [United States]. [HQ755.5 .S7 C54 2000] (15.5; 1.3.5; 2.2; 10)

Corcos, Alain F. THE MYTH OF THE JEWISH RACE: A BIOLOGIST'S POINT OF VIEW. Bethlehem, PA: Lehigh University Press, 2005. 170 p. ISBN 0-934223-79-3. [DS143 .C675 2005] (15.5; 1.2; 21.4)

Holmes, Sarah Catherine. LEFTIST LITERATURE AND THE IDEOLOGY OF EUGENICS DURING THE AMERICAN DEPRESSION. Ann Arbor, MI: ProQuest Information & Learning/UMI, 2002. 137 p. (Publication Order No. AAT-3053107. Dissertation, (Ph.D. in English)—University of Rhode Island, 2002.) [PS228 .E8 H64 2002] (15.5; 2.2; 7.1)

Peel, Robert A. and Galton, Francis, Sir. HUMAN PEDIGREE STUDIES: PROCEEDINGS OF A CONFERENCE ORGANISED BY THE GALTON INSTITUTE, LONDON, 1998. London: The

Galton Institute, 1999. 117 p. ISBN 0-9504066-4-3. (15.5; 15.1)

Rodriguez, Julia. CIVILIZING ARGENTINA: SCIENCE, MEDICINE, AND THE MODERN STATE. Chapel Hill: University of North Carolina Press, 2006. 306 p. ISBN 0-8078-5669-X. (Gift of the publisher.) [F2847 .R639 2006] (15.5; 1.3.5; 5.3; 9.5.5; 10)

15.6 BEHAVIORAL GENETICS

Coll, Cynthia García; Bearer, Elaine L.; and Lerner, Richard M., eds. NATURE AND NURTURE: THE COMPLEX INTERPLAY OF GENETIC AND ENVIRONMENTAL INFLUENCES ON HUMAN BEHAVIOR AND DEVELOPMENT. Mahwah, NJ: Lawrence Erlbaum Associates, 2004. 253 p. ISBN 0-8058-4387-6. [QH438.5 .N38 2004] (15.6; 3.1; 7.1; 21.7)

Grafen, Alan and Ridley, Mark, eds. RICHARD DAWKINS: HOW A SCIENTIST CHANGED THE WAY WE THINK: REFLECTIONS BY SCIENTISTS, WRITERS, AND PHILOSOPHERS. Oxford/New York: Oxford University Press, 2006. 283 p. ISBN 0-19-929116-0. [QH31 .D39 R53 2006] (15.6; 3.2; 15.9)

Peel, Robert and Zeki, Mazin, ed. HUMAN ABILITY: GENETIC AND ENVIRONMENTAL INFLUENCES: PROCEEDINGS OF A CONFERENCE ORGANISED BY THE GALTON INSTITUTE, LONDON, 2005. London: Galton Institute, 2006. 108 p. ISBN 0-9546570-0-4. (Publisher's address: 19 Northfields Prospect, Northfields, London SW18 1PE.) [BF431 .H816 2006] (15.6)

Roubertoux, Pierre L. EXISTE-T-IL DES GÈNES DU COMPORTEMENT? Paris: Odile Jacob, 2004. 385 p. ISBN 2-7381-1545-4. [QH457 .R678 2004] (15.6; POP)

Rutter, Michael. GENES AND BEHAVIOR: NATURE-NURTURE INTERPLAY EXPLAINED. Malden, MA: Blackwell, 2006. 280 p. ISBN 1-4051-1061-9. [QH457 .R88 2006] (15.6)

15.7 BIOHAZARDS OF GENETIC RESEARCH

den Nijs, H.C.M.; Dartsch, D.; and Sweet, J., eds. INTROGRESSION FROM GENETICALLY MODIFIED PLANTS INTO WILD RELATIVES. Oxfordshire/Cambridge, MA: CABI, 2004. 403 p. ISBN 0-85199-816-X. (Proceedings of a conference held in Amsterdam, January 2003.) [SB123.57 .I78 2004] (15.7; 1.3.11; 15.1; 16.1)

National Research Council (United States) [and] Institute of Medicine (United States). Committee on Identifying and Assessing Unintended Effects of Genetically Engineered Foods on Human Health. SAFETY OF GENETICALLY ENGINEERED FOODS: APPROACHES TO ASSESSING UNINTENDED HEALTH EFFECTS. Washington, DC: National Academies Press, 2004. 235 p. ISBN 0-309-09209-4. (Also available on the Web at: http://www.nap.edu.) [TP248.65 .F66 S245 2004] (15.7; 1.3.11; 15.1)

15.8 GENETIC PATENTS

Grubb, Philip W. PATENTS FOR CHEMICALS, PHARMACEUTICALS AND BIOTECHNOLOGY: FUNDAMENTALS OF GLOBAL LAW, PRACTICE AND STRATEGY. Oxford/New York: Oxford University Press, 2004. 511 p. ISBN 0-19-927378-2. (Fourth edition.) [T211 .G76 2004] (15.8; 1.3.2; 1.3.11; 9.3.1; 9.7; 15.1; 21.1; 22.2)

Lundin, Susanne and Åkesson, Lynn, eds. GENE TECHNOLOGY AND ECONOMY. Lund: Nordic Academic Press, 2002. 117 p. ISBN 91-89116-25-9. (Publisher's address: Box 1206, SE-221 05 Lund, Sweden.) [QH442 .G453 2002] (15.8; 1.3.11; 1.3.12; 4.4; 15.5; 18.1)

Naimark, Arnold and Yamada, Ron [and] Canadian Biotechnology Advisory Committee. Expert Working Party on Human Genetic Materials, Intellectual Property and the Health Sector = Comité consultatif canadien de la biotechnologie. Rapport du Groupe de travail d'experts sur la matériel génétique humain, la propriété intellectuelle et le secteur de la santé. HUMAN GENETIC MATERIALS: MAKING CANADA'S INTELLECTUAL PROPERTY REGIME WORK FOR THE HEALTH OF CANADIANS: REPORT OF THE EXPERT WORKING PARTY ON HUMAN GENETIC MATERIALS, INTELLECTUAL PROPERTY AND THE HEALTH SECTOR = MATÉRIEL GÉNÉTIQUE HUMAIN: METTRE LE RÉGIME CANADIEN DE PROPRIÉTÉ INTELLECTUELLE AU SERVICE DE LA SANTÉ DES CANADIENS. Ottawa: Canadian Biotechnology Advisory Council, 2005. [68 p. + 77 p.]. ISBN 0-662-41898-0 [English]; ISBN 0-662-70454-1 [French]. (October 2005. Text in English with French on inverted pages. Available from: Canadian Biotechnology Advisory Committee (CBAC), 255 Albert Street, Ottawa, Ontario K1A 0H5; tel.: 866-748-2222; fax: 613-946-2847. Also on the Web at: http://cbac-cccb.ca/epic/internet/incbac-cccb.nsf/en/h_ah00094e.html [English]; http://cbac-cccb.ca/epic/internet/incbac-cccb.nsf/fr/h_ah00094f.html [French].) (15.8; 5.3; 9.5.1; 15.1)

15.10 GENOME MAPPING

Macer, Darryl R.J., ed. ETHICAL CHALLENGES AS WE APPROACH THE END OF THE HUMAN GENOME PROJECT. Christchurch, New Zealand: Eubios Ethics Institute, 2000. 123 p. ISBN 0-908897-15-4. [QH332 .E67 2000] (15.10; 1.1; 1.2; 1.3.11; 5.3; 9.1; 13.1; 15.4; 15.5; 15.11; 21.1)

15.11 GENETICS AND HUMAN ANCESTRY

Árnason, Gardar; Nordal, Salvör; and Árnason, Vilhjálmur, eds. BLOOD & DATA: ETHICAL, LEGAL AND SOCIAL ASPECTS OF HUMAN GENETIC DATABASES. Reykjavík: University of Iceland Press [and] Centre for Ethics, 2004. 352 p. ISBN 9979-54-593-3. (Published for the International ELSAGEN Conference, University of Iceland, Reykjavík, 25-28 August 2004.) [RB155 .B662 2004] (15.11; 1.3.5; 1.3.12; 2.1; 4.4; 5.3; 7.1; 8.4; 9.3.1; 15.3; 15.5; 15.10; 18.5.1; 19.5; 21.1)

M'charek, Amade. THE HUMAN GENOME DIVERSITY PROJECT: AN ETHNOGRAPHY OF SCIENTIFIC PRACTICE. Cambridge/New York: Cambridge University Press, 2005. 213 p. ISBN 0-521-53987-0. (Cambridge Studies in Society and the Life Sciences series.) [QH455 .M385 2005] (15.11; 5.3; 22.2)

Turner, Trudy R., ed. BIOLOGICAL ANTHROPOLOGY AND ETHICS: FROM REPATRIATION TO GENETIC IDENTITY. Albany: State University of New York Press, 2005. 327 p. ISBN 0-7914-6296-X. [GN62 .B55 2005] (15.11; 1.3.1; 6; 15.1; 18.2; 18.3; 18.4; 18.5.2; 22.1)

Wade, Nicholas. BEFORE THE DAWN: RECOVERING THE LOST HISTORY OF OUR ANCESTORS. New York: Penguin Press, 2006. 312 p. ISBN 1-59420-079-3. [GN281 .W33 2006] (15.11; 3.2)

16.1 ENVIRONMENTAL QUALITY (GENERAL)

Benson, John. ENVIRONMENTAL ETHICS: AN INTRODUCTION WITH READINGS. London/New York: Routledge, 2000. 295 p. ISBN 0-415-21236-7. (Philosophy & the Human Situation Series.) [GE42 .B46 2000] (16.1; 10; 21.7)

Bocking, Stephen. NATURE'S EXPERTS: SCIENCE, POLITICS, AND THE ENVIRONMENT. New Brunswick, NJ: Rutgers University Press, 2004. 298 p. ISBN 0-8135-3398-8. [GE170 .B65 2004] (16.1; 1.3.5; 5.1; 5.3)

Chapple, Christopher Key, ed. JAINISM AND ECOLOGY: NONVIOLENCE IN THE WEB OF LIFE. Cambridge, MA: Distributed by the Harvard University Press for the Center for the Study of World Religions, Harvard Divinity School, 2002. 252 p. ISBN 0-945454-34-1. (Religions of the World and Ecology series.) [BL1375 .H85 J35 2002] (16.1; 1.2)

De Silva, Padmasiri. ENVIRONMENTAL PHILOSOPHY AND ETHICS IN BUDDHISM. New York: St. Martin's Press, 1998. 194 p. ISBN 0-312-21316-6. (Published in Great Britain by: Macmillan Press, Basingstoke, 1998; ISBN 0-333-67906-7.) [BQ4570 .E23 D35 1998] (16.1; 1.2)

Easton, Thomas A. and Goldfarb, Theodore D., eds. TAKING SIDES: CLASHING VIEWS ON CONTROVERSIAL ENVIRONMENTAL ISSUES. New York: McGraw-Hill/Dushkin, 2004. 437 p. ISBN 0-07-293317-8. (Tenth edition. Taking Sides series. ISSN 1091-8825.) [QH75 .T27 2004] (16.1; 1.3.5; 1.3.11; 9.5.4; 13.2; 15.1; 16.2)

Grim, John A., ed. INDIGENOUS TRADITIONS AND ECOLOGY: THE INTERBEING OF COSMOLOGY AND COMMUNITY. Cambridge, MA: Distributed by Harvard University Press for the Center for the Study of World Religions, Harvard Divinity School, 2001. 754 p. ISBN 0-945454-28-7. (Religions of the World and Ecology series.) [GN470.2 .I53 2001] (16.1; 1.2; 1.3.11; 5.3)

Hossay, Patrick. UNSUSTAINABLE: A PRIMER FOR GLOBAL ENVIRONMENTAL AND SOCIAL JUSTICE. London/New York: Zed Books, 2006. 280 p. ISBN 1-84277-657-6. (Gift of the publisher.) [GE42 .H67 2006] (16.1; 9.5.10; 21.1)

Pellow, David Naguib and Brulle, Robert J., eds. POWER, JUSTICE, AND THE ENVIRONMENT: A CRITICAL APPRAISAL OF THE ENVIRONMENTAL JUSTICE MOVEMENT. Cambridge, MA: MIT Press, 2005. 339 p. ISBN 0-262-66193-4. (Urban and Industrial Environments series.) (Gift of the publisher.) [GE180 .P686 2005] (16.1; 1.1; 9.5.4; 9.5.10; 21.1)

Vaughn, Jacqueline and Cortner, Hanna J. GEORGE W. BUSH'S HEALTHY FORESTS: REFRAMING THE ENVIRONMENTAL DEBATE. Boulder: University of Colorado Press, 2005. 231 p. ISBN 0-87081-820-1. [SD565 .S85 2005] (16.1; 1.3.5)

16.3 OCCUPATIONAL HEALTH

Institute of Medicine (United States). Committee on the Work Environment for Nurses and Patient Safety. THE RICHARD AND HINDA ROSENTHAL LECTURES 2003: KEEPING PATIENTS SAFE: TRANSFORMING THE WORK ENVIRONMENT OF NURSES. Washington, DC: National Academies Press, 2005. 32 p. ISBN 0-309-09441-0. (Edited by Ann Page. The Richard and Hinda Rosenthal Lectures series; 2003. "The Rosenthal lecture included in this volume captures a panel discussion on the IOM report *Keeping Patients Safe : Transforming the Work Environment of Nurses.*" Also available on the Web at: http://www.nap.edu.) [RT87 .S24 K4473 2005] (16.3; 4.1.3; 5.2; 8.1; 9.8)

O'Brien, Ruth. CRIPPLED JUSTICE: THE HISTORY OF MODERN DISABILITY POLICY IN THE WORKPLACE. Chicago: University of Chicago Press, 2001. 288 p. ISBN 0-226-61660-6. [HD7256 .U5 O27 2001] (16.3; 1.3.5; 1.3.8; 7.1; 9.5.1)

17.1 THE NEUROSCIENCES AND MENTAL HEALTH THERAPIES (GENERAL)

Ackerman, Sandra J. HARD SCIENCE, HARD CHOICES: FACTS, ETHICS, AND POLICIES GUIDING BRAIN SCIENCE TODAY. New York: Dana Press, 2006. 152 p. ISBN 1-932594-02-7. (The Dana Foundation Series on Neuroethics. Gift of the publisher.) [QP376 .A233 2006] (17.1; 1.3.12; 4.5; 9.7; 15.1; 17.4)

Ballenger, Jesse F. SELF, SENILITY, AND ALZHEIMER'S DISEASE IN MODERN AMERICA: A HISTORY. Baltimore, MD: Johns Hopkins University Press, 2006. 236 p. ISBN 0-8018-8276-1. [RC523 .B25 2006] (17.1; 4.4; 7.1; 9.5.2)

Bhugra, Dinesh and Cochrane, Ray, eds. PSYCHIATRY IN MULTICULTURAL BRITAIN. London: Gaskell/Royal College of Psychiatrists, 2001. 367 p. ISBN 1-901242-45-5. (Distributed in North America by: American Psychiatric Press.) (17.1; 1.3.5; 7.1; 7.2; 9.5.2; 9.5.4; 9.5.7; 9.5.9; 9.8; 21.7)

Bush, Shane S.; Connell, Mary A.; and Denney, Robert L. ETHICAL PRACTICE IN FORENSIC PSYCHOLOGY: A SYSTEMATIC MODEL FOR DECISION MAKING. Washington, DC: American Psychological Association, 2006. 196 p. ISBN 1-59147-395-0. (Gift of the publisher.) [RA1148 .B86 2006] (17.1; 1.3.1; 1.3.5; 6; 7.3; 7.4; 8.1)

Numbers in ( ) = NRCBL Classification Numbers

Eastman, Nigel and Peay, Jill, eds. LAW WITHOUT EN-FORCEMENT: INTEGRATING MENTAL HEALTH AND JUSTICE. Oxford/Portland, OR: Hart, 1999. 238 p. ISBN 1-901362-75-2. [KD3412 .L38 1999] (17.1; 1.3.5; 4.3; 8.3.1; 17.7)

Ethics in Psychiatry. PSYCHIATRIC CLINICS OF NORTH AMERICA 2002 September; 25(3): 509-674. (ISSN 0193-953X.) (17.1; 1.3.5; 1.3.2; 1.3.12; 2.2; 4.1.1; 8.1; 8.4; 9.3.1; 10; 18.3; 18.5.6)

Fisher, William H., ed. COMMUNITY-BASED INTERVEN-TIONS FOR CRIMINAL OFFENDERS WITH SEVERE MENTAL ILLNESS. New York: JAI/Elsevier Science, 2003. 220 p. ISBN 0-7623-0972-5. (Research in Community and Mental Health series; Vol. 12.) [RA790 .A1 R48 v.12] (17.1; 1.3.5; 4.3; 7.1; 17.4; 17.7)

Frost, Lynda E. and Bonnie, Richard J., eds. THE EVOLU-TION OF MENTAL HEALTH LAW. Washington, DC: Ameri-can Psychological Association, 2001. 336 p. ISBN 1-55798-746-7. (Law and Public Policy: Psychology and the Social Sciences series.) [KF3828 .E94 2001] (17.1; 1.3.5; 4.3; 9.3.1; 9.3.2; 17.2; 17.7; 20.6)

Josephson, Allan M. and Peteet, John R., eds. HANDBOOK OF SPIRITUALITY AND WORLDVIEW IN CLINICAL PRACTICE. Washington, DC: American Psychiatric Publishing, 2004. 179 p. ISBN 1-58562-104-8. [RC489 .R46 H365 2004] (17.1; 1.2; 21.7)

Koenig, Harold G. FAITH AND MENTAL HEALTH: RELIGIOUS RESOURCES FOR HEALING. Philadelphia: Templeton Foun-dation Press, 2005. 343 p. ISBN 1-932031-91-X. [RC489 .S676 K64 2005] (17.1; 1.2)

Kramer, Peter D. AGAINST DEPRESSION. New York: Vi-king, 2005. 353 p. ISBN 0-670-03405-3. [RC537 .K725 2005] (17.1; 7.1; 17.4; POP)

Levine, Bruce E. COMMONSENSE REBELLION: DEBUNKING PSYCHIATRY, CONFRONTING SOCIETY: AN A TO Z GUIDE TO REHUMANIZING OUR LIVES. New York: Continuum, 2001. 331 p. ISBN 0-8264-1315-3. [RC437.5 .L477 2001] (17.1; 1.3.12; 4.3; 5.1; 15.6; 17.3; 17.4)

Martin, Mike W. FROM MORALITY TO MENTAL HEALTH: VIRTUE AND VICE IN A THERAPEUTIC CULTURE. Ox-ford/New York: Oxford University Press, 2006. 234 p. ISBN 0-19-530471-3. (Practical and Professional Ethics Series. Gift of the publisher.) [RC458 .M265 2006] (17.1; 1.1; 1.3.5; 4.3; 9.5.9; 17.2)

McHugh, Paul R. THE MIND HAS MOUNTAINS: REFLEC-TIONS ON SOCIETY AND PSYCHIATRY. Baltimore, MD: Johns Hopkins University Press, 2006. 249 p. ISBN 0-8018-8249-4. (Gift of the publisher.) [RC458 .M33 2006] (17.1; 2.1; 4.1.2; 7.1; 8.1; 20.5.1; 20.7)

Mitchell, Robert. DOCUMENTATION IN COUNSELING RE-CORDS. Alexandria, VA: American Counseling Associa-tion, 2001. 97 p. ISBN 1-55620-179-6. (Second edition. ACA Legal Series. Publisher's address: 5999 Stevenson Avenue, zip 22304.) [RC466 .M57 2001] (17.1; 1.3.10; 1.3.12; 9.5.9; 10)

Morrall, Peter and Hazelton, Mike, eds. MENTAL HEALTH: GLOBAL POLICIES AND HUMAN RIGHTS. London/Philadel-phia: Whurr/Taylor & Francis, 2004. 196 p. ISBN 1-86156-388-4. [RA394 .M46 2004] (17.1; 9.1; 21.1)

O'Donohue, William and Ferguson, Kyle, eds. HANDBOOK OF PROFESSIONAL ETHICS FOR PSYCHOLOGISTS: ISSUES, QUESTIONS, AND CONTROVERSIES. Thousand Oaks, CA: Sage, 2003. 474 p. ISBN 0-7619-1189-8. [BF76.4 .H36 2003] (17.1; 1.1; 1.3.1; 6; 8.1; 8.2; 8.3.1; 8.3.2; 8.4; 9.4; 9.5.2; 9.5.3; 9.5.4; 9.5.7; 10; 17.7; 18.2; 18.3; 18.5.2; 22.2)

Rees, Dai and Rose, Steven, eds. THE NEW BRAIN SCI-ENCES: PERILS AND PROSPECTS. Cambridge/New York: Cambridge University Press, 2004. 301 p. ISBN 0-521-53714-2. [RC341 .N53 2004] (17.1; 4.4; 15.6; 17.4; 18.5.4)

Rose, Steven. THE FUTURE OF THE BRAIN: THE PROMISE AND PERILS OF TOMORROW'S NEUROSCIENCE. Oxford/New York: Oxford University Press, 2005. 344 p. ISBN 0-19-515420-7. [QP376 .R679 2005] (17.1; 4.4; 15.6; 17.4; POP)

Suzuki, Akihito. MADNESS AT HOME: THE PSYCHIATRIST, THE PATIENT, AND THE FAMILY IN ENGLAND, 1820-1860. Berkeley: University of California Press, 2006. 259 p. ISBN 0-520-24580-6. (Medicine and Society series; No. 13.) (17.1; 7.1; 8.1)

Tancredi, Laurence R. HARDWIRED BEHAVIOR: WHAT NEU-ROSCIENCE REVEALS ABOUT MORALITY. Cambridge/New York: Cambridge University Press, 2005. 226 p. ISBN 0-521-86001-6. [BJ45.5 .T36 2005] (17.1; 1.1; 10)

Toporek, Rebecca L.; Gerstein, Lawrence H.; Fouad, Nadya A.; Roysircar, Gargi; and Israel, Tania, eds. HAND-BOOK FOR SOCIAL JUSTICE IN COUNSELING PSYCHOLOGY: LEADERSHIP, VISION, AND ACTION. Thousand Oaks, CA: Sage, 2006. 617 p. ISBN 1-4129-1007-2. (Gift of the pub-lisher.) [BF637 .C6 H3115 2006] (17.1; 1.1; 1.3.3; 9.5.5; 9.5.6; 9.5.10; 10; 16.1; 21.1; 21.7)

Wexler, David B. and Winick, Bruce J. ESSAYS IN THERA-PEUTIC JURISPRUDENCE. Durham, NC: Carolina Academic Press, 1991. 322 p. ISBN 0-89089-459-0. [KF3828 .W485 1991] (17.1; 1.3.5; 4.3; 8.3.1; 8.5; 17.2)

17.2 PSYCHOTHERAPY

Hart, Thomas. HIDDEN SPRING: THE SPIRITUAL DIMENSION OF THERAPY. Minneapolis, MN: Fortress Press, 2002. 164 p. ISBN 0-8006-3576-0. (Second edition.) [RC489 .R46 H37 2002] (17.2; 1.2)

Jenkins, Peter, ed. LEGAL ISSUES IN COUNSELLING & PSY-CHOTHERAPY. London/Thousand Oaks, CA: Sage, 2002. 195 p. ISBN 0-7619-5481-3. (Ethics in Practice Series.) [KD2965 .P75 L44 2002] (17.2; 1.3.5; 1.3.12; 7.4; 8.4; 10; 21.1)

Peteet, John R. DOING THE RIGHT THING: AN APPROACH TO MORAL ISSUES IN MENTAL HEALTH TREATMENT. Washington, DC: American Psychiatric Publishing, 2004. 125 p. ISBN 1-58562-083-1. [RC455.2 .E8 P467 2004] (17.2; 1.1)

Schank, Janet A. and Skovholt, Thomas M. ETHICAL PRACTICE IN SMALL COMMUNITIES: CHALLENGES AND REWARDS FOR PSYCHOLOGISTS. Washington, DC: American Psychological Association, 2006. 241 p. ISBN 1-59147-346-2. (Psychologists in Independent Practice series. Gift of the publisher.) [BF76.4 .S33 2006] (17.2; 1.3.1; 6)

17.4 PSYCHOPHARMACOLOGY

Dworkin, Ronald W. ARTIFICIAL HAPPINESS: THE DARK SIDE OF THE NEW HAPPY CLASS. New York: Carroll & Graf, 2006. 343 p. ISBN 0-78671-714-9. (17.4; 1.2; 4.1.1)

Kalikow, Kevin T. YOUR CHILD IN THE BALANCE: AN INSIDER'S GUIDE FOR PARENTS TO THE PSYCHIATRIC MEDICINE DILEMMA. New York: CDS Books, 2006. 276 p. ISBN 1-59315-359-7. [RJ504.7 .K35 2006] (17.4; 4.3; 5.2; 9.5.7; 17.1; 17.3)

18.1 HUMAN EXPERIMENTATION (GENERAL)

Coleman, Carl H.; Menikoff, Jerry A.; Goldner, Jesse A.; and Dubler, Nancy Neveloff. THE ETHICS AND REGULATION OF RESEARCH WITH HUMAN SUBJECTS. Newark, NJ: LexisNexis, 2005. 746 p. + appendices. ISBN 1-58360-798-6. [KF3827 .M38 E86 2005] (18.1; 2.2; 8.4; 9.3.1; 15.1; 18.2; 18.3; 18.5.1; 18.5.2; 18.5.3; 18.5.4; 18.5.5; 18.5.6)

Coleman, Carl H.; Menikoff, Jerry A.; Goldner, Jesse A.; and Dubler, Nancy Neveloff. THE ETHICS AND REGULATION OF RESEARCH WITH HUMAN SUBJECTS: TEACHER'S MANUAL. Newark, NJ: LexisNexis, 2005. 219 p. ISBN 3-6204-0005-9. [KF3827 .M38 E86 2005] (18.1; 2.2; 8.4; 9.3.1; 15.1; 18.2; 18.3; 18.5.1; 18.5.2; 18.5.3; 18.5.4; 18.5.5.; 18.5.6)

Duley, Lelia and Farrell, Barbara, eds. CLINICAL TRIALS. London: BMJ Books, 2002. 133 p. ISBN 0-7279-1599-1. [R853 .C55 C57 2002] (18.1; 18.2)

Gallin, John I. PRINCIPLES AND PRACTICE OF CLINICAL RESEARCH. San Diego, CA: Academic Press, 2002. 493 p. ISBN 0-12-274065-3. [R850 .G35 2002] (18.1; 1.3.7; 1.3.9; 1.3.12; 4.4; 5.3; 7.1; 9.3.1; 9.7; 18.2; 18.5.2; 18.5.3; 22.2)

Halpern, Sydney A. LESSER HARMS: THE MORALITY OF RISK IN MEDICAL RESEARCH. Chicago: University of Chicago Press, 2004. 232 p. ISBN 0-226-31451-0. (Morality and Society Series.) [R853 .H8 H357 2004] (18.1; 1.3.9; 5.2; 9.5.7; 9.7; 18.2; 18.3; 18.5.2; 18.6; 22.2)

Iltis, Ana Smith, ed. RESEARCH ETHICS. New York: Routledge, 2006. 181 p. ISBN 0-415-70158-9. (Routledge Annals of Bioethics series; Vol. 1.) [R853 .H8 R45 2006]

(18.1; 1.3.9; 9.3.1; 9.7; 14.5; 18.2; 18.3; 18.4; 18.5.1; 18.5.2; 18.5.4; 18.5.9)

Minkler, Meredith and Wallerstein, Nina, eds. COMMUNITY BASED PARTICIPATORY RESEARCH FOR HEALTH. San Francisco: Jossey-Bass, 2003. 490 p. ISBN 0-7879-6457-3. [RA440.85 .C65 2003] (18.1; 1.3.12; 5.3; 7.1; 9.1; 9.3.1; 9.5.4; 9.8; 18.2)

Nesbitt, Lori A. CLINICAL RESEARCH: WHAT IT IS AND HOW IT WORKS. Boston: Jones and Bartlett, 2004. 274 p. ISBN 0-7637-3136-6. [R850 .N47 2004] (18.1; 5.2; 9.3.1; 9.7; 18.2; 18.3; 18.5.1)

18.2 HUMAN EXPERIMENTATION: POLICY GUIDELINES/INSTITUTIONAL REVIEW BOARDS

Bankert, Elizabeth A. and Amdur, Robert J. INSTITUTIONAL REVIEW BOARD: MANAGEMENT AND FUNCTION. Sudbury, MA: Jones and Bartlett, 2006. 530 p. ISBN 0-7637-3049-1. [R852.5 .A46 2006] (18.2; 6; 7.3; 8.4; 18.3; 18.5.1; Reference)

Beyleveld, D.; Townend, D; and Wright, J., eds. RESEARCH ETHICS COMMITTEES, DATA PROTECTION AND MEDICAL RESEARCH IN EUROPEAN COUNTRIES. Aldershot, Hants, England/Burlington, VT: Ashgate, 2005. 315 p. ISBN 0-7546-4350-6. (Data Protection and Medical Research in Europe series.) [KJE6229 .R43 R474 2005] (18.2; 1.3.5; 1.3.12; 8.4; 21.1)

Di Giovanna, Ignazio and Hayes, Gareth, eds. PRINCIPLES OF CLINICAL RESEARCH. Petersfield, UK/Philadelphia: Wrightson Biomedical, 2001. 558 p. ISBN 1-871816-45-9. (Published in association with the Institute of Clinical Research (UK). Publisher's address: Ash Barn House, Winchester Road, Stroud, Petersfield, Hampshire, postal code GU32 3PN.) [RM301.27 .P75 2001] (18.2; 1.3.9; 7.1; 7.4; 9.3.1; 9.7)

Fedor, Carol; Philip A. Cola; and Pierre, Christine, eds. RESPONSIBLE RESEARCH: A GUIDE FOR COORDINATORS. London/Chicago: Remedica Publishing, 2006. 219 p. ISBN 1-901346-68-4. (Publisher's address: Commonwealth House, 1 New Oxford Street, postal code WC1A 1NU. Gift of the publisher.) [R853 .C55 R47 2006] (18.2; 8.3.2; 9.8; 18.3; 18.5.2)

Issues in Data Monitoring and Interim Analysis of Trials. HEALTH TECHNOLOGY ASSESSMENT 2005 March; 9(7): iii-223. (ISSN 1366-5278. Special Issue.) (18.2; 7.1; 7.3; 9.3.1)

Jastone, Lee O., ed. FEDERAL PROTECTION FOR HUMAN RESEARCH SUBJECTS: AN ANALYSIS OF THE COMMON RULE AND ITS INTERACTIONS WITH FDA REGULATIONS AND THE HIPAA PRIVACY RULE. New York: Novinka Books/Nova Science, 2006. 108 p. ISBN 1-59454-725-4. [KF3827 .M38 F43 2006] (18.2; 1.3.5; 2.2; 6; 7.4; 8.4; 18.3; 18.5.1)

Mulay, Marilyn. A STEP-BY-STEP GUIDE TO CLINICAL TRIALS. Boston: Jones & Bartlett, 2001. 143 p. ISBN

0-7637-1569-7. [R853 .C55 M84 2001] (18.2; 9.3.1; 18.3; 18.5.1)

Royal College of Psychiatrists. Working Party on Guidelines for Researchers and for Research Ethics Committees on Psychiatric Research Involving Human Participants. GUIDELINES FOR RESEARCHERS AND RESEARCH ETHICS COMMITTEES ON PSYCHIATRIC RESEARCH INVOLVING HUMAN PARTICIPANTS. London: Gaskell, 2001. 52 p. ISBN 1-901242-53-1. (Council Report series; No. CR82.) [RC455.2 .E8 R694 2001] (18.2; 4.3; 8.3.2; 171; 18.3; 18.5.2)

Shapiro, S.; Dinger, J.; and Scriba, p., eds. ENABLING RISK ASSESSMENT IN MEDICINE: FAREWELL SYMPOSI[UM] FOR WERNER-KARL RAFF = WEGE ZUR RISIKOBESTIMMUNG IN DER MEDIZIN: ABSCHIEDSSYMPOSIUM FÜR WERNER-KARL RAFF. Münster: Lit [and] New Brunswick, [NJ]: Distributed in North America by: Transaction Publishers, 2004. 150 p. ISBN 3-8258-7250-5. (Ethik in der Praxis: Studien = Practical Ethics: Studies series; Bd. 21.) (18.2; 5.2; 9.7)

Spiegelhalter, David J.; Abrams, Keith R.; and Myles, Jonathan p. BAYESIAN APPROACHES TO CLINICAL TRIALS AND HEALTH-CARE EVALUATION. Chichester/Hoboken, NJ: John Wiley & Sons, 2004. 391 p. ISBN 0-471-49975-7. [R853 .S7 S66 2004] (18.2; 5.2; 7.1)

18.3 HUMAN EXPERIMENTATION: INFORMED CONSENT

Lay Public's Understanding of Equipoise and Randomisation in Randomised Controlled Trials. HEALTH TECHNOLOGY ASSESSMENT 2005 March; 9(8): iii-177. (ISSN 1366-5278. Special Issue.) (18.3; 7.1; 8.1; 9.4; 18.2)

18.5.2 RESEARCH ON NEWBORNS AND MINORS

Ross, Lainie Friedman. CHILDREN IN MEDICAL RESEARCH: ACCESS VERSUS PROTECTION. Oxford: Clarendon Press/New York: Oxford University Press, 2006. 285 p. ISBN 0-19-927328-6. (Issues in Biomedical Ethics series. Rose Fitzgerald Kennedy Collection on Women, Infants and Children. Gift of the publisher.) [RJ85 .R66 2006] (18.5.2; 2.2; 8.3.2; 9.2; 9.3.1; 9.5.4; 18.2; 18.3)

18.5.4 RESEARCH ON EMBRYOS AND FETUSES

Bellomo, Michael. THE STEM CELL DIVIDE: THE FACTS, THE FICTION, AND THE FEAR DRIVING THE GREATEST SCIENTIFIC, POLITICAL, AND RELIGIOUS DEBATE OF OUR TIME. New York: AMACOM, 2006. 262 p. ISBN 0-8144-0881-8. (Gift of the publisher.) [QH588 .S83 B45 2006] (18.5.4; 1.2; 1.3.5; 14.5; 15.1; 19.4)

Devolder, Katrien. THE ETHICS AND REGULATION OF HUMAN EMBRYONIC STEM CELL RESEARCH: A CRITICAL ANALYSIS OF THE DEBATE. Ghent, Belgium: Department of Philosophy and Moral Sciences, Ghent University, 2005.

221 p. (Gift of the author.) (18.5.4; 1.3.5; 4.4; 9.1; 14.4; 15.1; 19.5)

Panno, Joseph. STEM CELL RESEARCH: MEDICAL APPLICATIONS AND ETHICAL CONTROVERSY. New York: Facts on File, 2005. 178 p. ISBN 0-8160-4949-1. (The "New Biology" series.) [QH588 .S83 P36 2005] (18.5.4; 1.1; 1.3.2; 4.4; 9.5.1; 15.1; Reference)

Ruse, Michael and Pynes, Christopher A., eds. THE STEM CELL CONTROVERSY: DEBATING THE ISSUES. Amherst, NY: Prometheus Books, 2003. 308 p. ISBN 1-59102-030-1. (Contemporary Issues series.) [QH587 .S723 2003] (18.5.4; 1.2; 1.3.9; 2.4; 4.4; 9.1; 18.5.1; 21.1; 22.2)

Scott, Christopher Thomas. STEM CELL NOW: FROM THE EXPERIMENT THAT SHOOK THE WORLD TO THE NEW POLITICS OF LIFE. New York: Pi Press, 2005. 243 p. ISBN 0-13-173798-8. [QH588 .S83 S35 2006] (18.5.4; 1.2; 4.4; 14.1; 15.1; 21.1)

18.5.8 RESEARCH ON MILITARY AND GOVERNMENT PERSONNEL

Moreno, Jonathan D. MIND WARS: BRAIN RESEARCH AND NATIONAL DEFENSE. New York: Dana Press, 2006. 210 p. ISBN 1-932594-16-7. (Gift of the publisher.) [UH399.5 .M67 2006] (18.5.8; 1.3.5; 17.1; 17.4; 18.4)

18.5.9 RESEARCH ON FOREIGN NATIONALS

Shah, Sonia. THE BODY HUNTERS: TESTING NEW DRUGS ON THE WORLD'S POOREST PATIENTS. New York: The New Press, 2006. 242 p. ISBN 1-56584-912-4. (Gift of the publisher.) [RA401 .D44 S53 2006] (18.5.9; 9.5.6; 9.5.10; 9.7; 18.2; 18.3; 21.1)

19.1 ARTIFICIAL AND TRANSPLANTED ORGANS OR TISSUES (GENERAL)

Kureishi, Hanif. THE BODY. London: Faber and Faber, 2002. 266 p. ISBN 0-571-20972-6. ("What if you were middle-aged and were offered the chance to trade in your sagging flesh for a much younger and more pleasing model? This is the situation in which the main character of *The Body* finds himself. Taking the plunge, he embarks on an odyssey of hedonism, but soon regrets what he has left behind, as the responsibilities he thought he had sloughed off now begin to come home to him. Sinister forces are pursuing him, wanting to take possession of his 'body', leaving him in a no man's land, uncertain which way to turn.") [PR6061 .U68 B78 2002] (19.1; 4.4; 7.1; 9.5.2; Fiction)

McLean, Sheila A.M. and Williamson, Laura. XENOTRANSPLANTATION: LAW AND ETHICS. Aldershot, Hants/Burlington, VT: Ashgate, 2005. 281 p. ISBN 0-7546-2379-3. (Gift of the publisher.) [KD3409 .M36 2005] (19.1; 22.2)

Price, David, ed. ORGAN AND TISSUE TRANSPLANTATION. Aldershot, Hampshire/Burlington, VT: Ashgate, 2006.

559 p. ISBN 0-7546-2539-7. (The International Library of Medicine, Ethics and Law series. Gift of the publisher.) [RD120.7 .O65 2006] (19.1; 1.1; 8.3.1; 8.3.3; 9.1; 9.3.1; 18.5.1; 19.5; 19.6; 20.2.1; 20.5.2; 21.1; 22.2)

Sharp, Lesley A. BODIES, COMMODITIES, AND BIOTECHNOLOGIES: DEATH, MOURNING, AND SCIENTIFIC DESIRE IN THE REALM OF HUMAN ORGAN TRANSFER. New York: Columbia University Press, 2007. 129 p. ISBN 0-231-13838-5. (Leonard Hastings Schoff Memorial Lectures series. Gift of the publisher.) [GT497 .U6 S53 2007] (19.1; 4.4; 5.3; 7.1; 9.3.1; 20.3.1; 22.2)

Sharp, Lesley A. STRANGE HARVEST: ORGAN TRANSPLANTS, DENATURED BODIES, AND THE TRANSFORMED SELF. Berkeley: University of California Press, 2006. 307 p. ISBN 0-520-24786-8. (Gift of the publisher.) [RD120.7 .S49 2006] (19.1; 4.4; 7.1; 19.5; 20.2.1)

19.2 ARTIFICIAL AND TRANSPLANTED HEARTS

Burg, Mark and Koules, Oren, producers. JOHN Q. [s.l., DE]: New Line Productions, 2002. 1 color videocassette [VHS]. (112 mins.) ("Oscar winner Denzel Washington stars as John Q. Archivald, an everyday man forced to take drastic measures in a desperate situation. When his young son collapses, John Q. and his wife learn that their only child needs a heart transplant. Without enough health insurance or money to cover the operation, it seems that they are out of options...John Q. takes matters into his own hands in the race against time to save his son's life.") (19.2; 9.3.1)

McRae, Donald. EVERY SECOND COUNTS: THE RACE TO TRANSPLANT THE FIRST HUMAN HEART. New York: G.P. Putnam's Sons, 2006. 356 p. ISBN 0-399-15341-1. (Gift of the publisher.) [RD598.35 .T7 M45 2006] (19.2; 7.1; Biography)

19.3 ARTIFICIAL AND TRANSPLANTED KIDNEYS

Cafaro, Janice A. FROM PERSONAL TRAGEDY TO PUBLIC PROBLEM: MIRACLE TECHNOLOGIES AND END-STAGE RENAL DISEASE POLICY, 1960-1972. Ann Arbor, MI: University Microfilms International [UMI], 1998. 206 p. (Publication No. AAT-9833869. Dissertation, (Ph.D. in History)—Case Western Reserve University, 1998.) [RC903 .C34 1998] (19.3; 1.3.5; 1.3.7; 2.2; 4.4; 5.3; 9.1; 9.3.1; 9.5.2)

Moazam, Farhat. BIOETHICS AND ORGAN TRANSPLANTATION IN A MUSLIM SOCIETY: A STUDY IN CULTURE, ETHNOGRAPHY, AND RELIGION. Bloomington: Indiana University Press, 2006. 264 p. ISBN 0-253-34782-3. (Bioethics and the Humanities series. Gift of the publisher.) [RD575 .M62 2006] (19.3; 1.2; 2.1; 7.1; 8.1; 19.5)

19.4 BLOOD TRANSFUSION

Casebeer, Adrianne Waldman. GIVING BLOOD: AN EXPLORATION OF THE DETERMINANTS OF THE GIFT RELATIONSHIP. Ann Arbor, MI: ProQuest Information and Learning/UMI,

2002. 293 p. (Publication No. AAT-3053602. Dissertation, (Ph.D. in Public Affairs)—University of Colorado at Denver, 2002.) (19.4; 7.1; 9.3.1; 19.5)

19.5 DONATION/PROCUREMENT OF ORGANS/TISSUES

Cheney, Annie. BODY BROKERS: INSIDE AMERICA'S UNDERGROUND TRADE IN HUMAN REMAINS. New York: Broadway Books, 2006. 205 p. ISBN 0-7679-1733-2. [RD129.5 .C4554 2006] (19.5; 7.2; 9.3.1; 18.6; 20.1)

Goodwin, Michele. BLACK MARKETS: THE SUPPLY AND DEMAND OF BODY PARTS. Cambridge/New York: Cambridge University Press, 2006. 294 p. ISBN 0-521-85280-3. (Gift of the publisher.) [RD120.7 .G66 2006] (19.5; 1.1; 2.1; 4.4; 8.3.1; 9.3.1)

Institute of Medicine (United States). Board on Health Sciences Policy. Committee on Increasing Rates of Organ Donation. ORGAN DONATION: OPPORTUNITIES FOR ACTION. Washington, DC: National Academies Press, 2006. 339 p. ISBN 0-309-10114-X. (Committee chaired by James F. Childress. Also available on the Web at: http://www.nap.edu.) [RD129.5 .O74 2006] (19.5; 1.3.2; 7.1; 8.3.1; 9.1; 9.3.1)

Waldby, Catherine and Mitchell, Robert. TISSUE ECONOMIES: BLOOD, ORGANS, AND CELL LINES IN LATE CAPITALISM. Durham, NC: Duke University Press, 2006. 231 p. ISBN 0-8223-3770-3. (Science and Cultural Theory series. Gift of the publisher.) [RD127 .W35 2006] (19.5; 8.3.1; 9.3.1; 15.1; 21.1)

20.1 DEATH AND DYING (GENERAL)

Charmaz, Kathy; Howarth, Glennys; and Kellehear, Allan, eds. THE UNKNOWN COUNTRY: DEATH IN AUSTRALIA, BRITAIN, AND THE USA. Basingstoke, Hampshire: Macmillan Press/New York: St. Martin's Press, 1997. 268 p. ISBN 0-333-67041-8 [UK]; ISBN 0-312-16545-5 [US]. [HQ1073 .U55 1997] (20.1; 2.1; 7.1; 9.5.5; 9.5.6; 9.5.9; 20.3.1; 20.7; 21.2; 21.7)

Long, Susan Orpett. FINAL DAYS: JAPANESE CULTURE AND CHOICE AT THE END OF LIFE. Honolulu: University of Hawai'i Press, 2005. 287 p. ISBN 0-8248-2964-6. [HQ1073.5 .J3 L65 2005] (20.1; 7.1; 8.2; 19.1; 20.3.1; 20.4.1; 20.5.1; 21.7)

O'Kelly, Eugene and Postman, Andrew. CHASING DAYLIGHT: HOW MY FORTHCOMING DEATH TRANSFORMED MY LIFE. New York: McGraw-Hill, 2006. 179 p. ISBN 0-07-147172-3. [BF789 .D4 O44 2006] (20.1; 9.5.1; 17.1; 20.3.1; Biography)

Ullmann, Linn. GRACE. New York: Alfred A. Knopf, 2005. 130 p. ISBN 1-4000-4285-2. (Translation from the Norwegian by Barbara Haveland of: *Nåde*; Forlaget Oktober AS, Oslo, 2002. "When Johan was a boy, he bargained with Death, and in good time Death obligingly took his father. And when Johan was miserably married, Death kindly took his equine first wife, leaving him a tidy sum.

But now, with the Reaper coming for *him*, Johan cries out for certainties, for control, for dignity. He enlists his adoring second wife, the grace of his otherwise mean existence, to be, "when he couldn't fight any longer," his reluctant angel of death. But as he drifts away into melancholic, hallucinatory recollection, the bonds of their mutual devotion gradually dissolve and the living and the dying begin their inevitable divergence. And as Johan, his wife beside him, slips under the solitary shadow he fears most, we are made to witness the muted tragedy of the Scandinavian way—now more and more our own way—of dying.") [PT8951.31 .L56 T513 2005] (20.1; 20.3.1; Fiction)

20.2.1 DEFINITION/DETERMINATION OF DEATH (GENERAL)

Lizza, John p. PERSONS, HUMANITY, AND THE DEFINITION OF DEATH. Baltimore, MD: Johns Hopkins University Press, 2006. 212 p. ISBN 0-8018-8250-8. [RA1063 .L59 2006] (20.2.1; 4.4; 21.7)

20.3.1 ATTITUDES TOWARD DEATH (GENERAL)

Gilbert, Sandra M. DEATH'S DOOR: MODERN DYING AND THE WAYS WE GRIEVE. New York: W.W. Norton, 2006. 580 p. ISBN 0-393-05131-5. (Gift of the publisher.) [HQ1073 .G54 2006] (20.3.1; 7.1)

Mander, Rosemary. LOSS AND BEREAVEMENT IN CHILD-BEARING. London/New York: Routledge, 2006. 238 p. ISBN 0-415-35411-0. (Second edition. Gift of the publisher.) [RG648 .M345 2006] (20.3.1; 9.5.5; 9.5.8; 12.5.1; 17.1; 20.1)

20.4.1 CARE OF THE DYING PATIENT (GENERAL)

Ellershaw, John and Wilkinson, Susie, eds. CARE OF THE DYING: A PATHWAY TO EXCELLENCE. Oxford/New York: Oxford University Press, 2003. 214 p. ISBN 0-19-850933-2. [R726.8 .C369 2003] (20.4.1; 1.2; 7.2; 8.1)

End-of-Life Care in the Modern Era. CLINICS IN GERIATRIC MEDICINE 2005 February; 21(1): 1-272. (ISSN 0749-0690.) (20.4.1; 4.2; 4.4; 7.2; 8.1; 8.3.3; 9.1; 9.3.1; 9.4; 9.5.2; 9.5.4; 9.8; 20.5.1; 21.1)

Gerstenkorn, Uwe. HOSPIZARBEIT IN DEUTSCHLAND: LEBENSWISSEN IM ANGESICHT DES TODES. Stuttgart: Kohlhammer, 2004. 352 p. ISBN 3-17-018222-6. (Diakoniewissenschaft series; Bd. 10. Thesis, (doctoral)—Ludwig-Maximilians-Universität, München, 2003. Gift of Warren Shibles.) [R726.8 .G477 2004] (20.4.1; 1.2)

Jansen, Lynn A., ed. DEATH IN THE CLINIC. Lanham, MD: Rowman & Littlefield, 2006. 164 p. ISBN 0-7425-3510-X. (Practicing Bioethics series. Gift of the publisher.) [R726 .D442 2006] (20.4.1; 2.1; 8.1; 9.5.2; 17.1; 20.2.1; 20.3.1; 20.5.1)

Katz, Jeanne Samson and Peace, Sheila, eds. END OF LIFE IN CARE HOMES: A PALLIATIVE APPROACH. Oxford/New York: Oxford University Press, 2003. 205 p. ISBN 0-19-851071-3. [R726.8 .E535 2003] (20.4.1; 9.5.2)

Kaufman, Sharon R. ...AND A TIME TO DIE: HOW AMERICAN HOSPITALS SHAPE THE END OF LIFE. New York: Scribner, 2005. 400 p. ISBN 0-7432-6476-2. ("A Lisa Drew Book.") [R726.8 .K385 2005] (20.4.1; 4.4; 9.1; 9.5.2; 20.3.1; 21.1)

Kelly, David F. MEDICAL CARE AT THE END OF LIFE: A CATHOLIC PERSPECTIVE. Washington, DC: Georgetown University Press, 2006. 180 p. ISBN 1-58901-112-0. (Gift of the publisher.) [R725.56 .K46 2006] (20.4.1; 1.2; 8.3.1; 8.3.3; 20.5.1; 20.5.4; 20.7)

Kuebler, Kim K.; Davis, Mellar P.; and Moore, Crystal Dea. PALLIATIVE PRACTICES: AN INTERDISCIPLINARY APPROACH. New York: Elsevier Mosby, 2005. 491 p. ISBN 0-323-02821-7. [R726.8 .K85 2005] (20.4.1; 1.2; 4.4; 9.5.1; 9.7; 20.5.1; 21.7)

McNamara, Beverley. FRAGILE LIVES: DEATH, DYING AND CARE. Buckingham/Philadelphia: Open University Press, 2001. 165 p. ISBN 0-335-20899-1. [HQ1073 .M425 2001] (20.4.1; 7.1; 17.1; 20.3.1; 20.5.1)

Meier, Diane E. and Morrison, R. Sean, eds. *Care at the End of Life: Restoring a Balance.* GENERATIONS: JOURNAL OF THE AMERICAN SOCIETY ON AGING 1999 Spring; 23(1): 4-98. (ISSN 0738-7806.) (20.4.1; 1.2; 4.4; 8.1; 9.3.1; 9.5.2; 17.1; 20.3.1; 20.5.1; 20.5.4; 20.7)

Monroe, Barbara and Oliviere, David, eds. PATIENT PARTICIPATION IN PALLIATIVE CARE: A VOICE FOR THE VOICELESS. Oxford/New York: Oxford University Press, 2003. 206 p. ISBN 0-19-851581-2. [R726.8 .P365 2003] (20.4.1; 1.2; 1.3.10; 8.1; 9.8; 17.1; 21.7)

Morrison, R. Sean; Meier, Diane E.; and Capello, Carol, eds. GERIATRIC PALLIATIVE CARE. Oxford/New York: Oxford University Press, 2003. 430 p. ISBN 0-19-514191-1. [R726.8 .G475 2003] (20.4.1; 4.4; 8.1; 8.3.3; 9.1; 9.4; 9.5.2; 20.5.1; 20.5.4; 21.7)

Randall, Fiona and Downie, R.S. THE PHILOSOPHY OF PALLIATIVE CARE: CRITIQUE AND RECONSTRUCTION. Oxford/New York: Oxford University Press, 2006. 236 p. ISBN 0-19-856736-7. [R726.8 .R35 2006] (20.4.1; 1.1; 1.2; 4.1.2; 4.4; 9.4; 17.1; 20.5.1; 20.5.4)

Saunders, Cicely M. CICELY SAUNDERS: SELECTED WRITINGS 1958-2004. Oxford/New York: Oxford University Press, 2006. 300 p. ISBN 0-19-857053-8. (Introduction by David Clark.) [R726.8 .S279 2006] (20.4.1; 2.2; 4.4; 7.1; 9.5.1; 9.7; 20.5.1)

Stanworth, Rachel. RECOGNIZING SPIRITUAL NEEDS IN PEOPLE WHO ARE DYING. Oxford/New York: Oxford University Press, 2004. 255 p. ISBN 0-19-852511-7. [R726.8 .S678 2005] (20.4.1; 1.2; 4.1.3; 7.1; 8.1; 17.1; 20.3.1)

20.4.2 CARE OF THE DYING CHILD

Bearison, David J. WHEN TREATMENT FAILS: HOW MEDI-CINE CARES FOR DYING CHILDREN. Oxford/New York: Oxford University Press, 2006. 289 p. ISBN 0-19-515612-9. [RJ249 .B43 2006] (20.4.2; 4.4; 7.1; 8.1; 17.1; 20.5.2)

Guyer, Ruth Levy. BABY AT RISK: THE UNCERTAIN LEGA-CIES OF MEDICAL MIRACLES FOR BABIES, FAMILIES AND SO-CIETY. Sterling, VA: Capital Books, 2006. 161 p. ISBN 1-933102-26-8. (Capital Currents Book series. Gift of the publisher.) [RG600 .G89 2006] (20.4.2; 4.4; 5.1; 8.1; 9.5.7; 20.5.2; 20.5.4)

20.5.1 PROLONGATION OF LIFE AND EUTHANASIA (GENERAL)

Amarasekara, Kumar and Bagaric, Mirko. EUTHANASIA, MORALITY AND THE LAW. New York: Peter Lang, 2002. 161 p. ISBN 0-8204-5667-5. (Teaching Texts in Law and Politics series; Vol. 19.) [K3611 .E95 B34 2002] (20.5.1; 1.1; 1.2; 4.4; 8.1; 20.7)

Caplan, Arthur L.; McCartney, James J.; Sisti, Dominic A., eds. THE CASE OF TERRI SCHIAVO: ETHICS AT THE END OF LIFE. Amherst, NY: Prometheus Books, 2006. 352 p. ISBN 1-59102-398-X. (Foreword by Jay Wolfson. Gift of the publisher.) [R726 .C357 2006] (20.5.1; 1.2; 1.3.5; 4.4; 8.1; 20.2.1; 20.4.1; 20.5.4; Biography)

Colby, William H. UNPLUGGED: RECLAIMING OUR RIGHT TO DIE IN AMERICA. New York: AMACOM Books, 2006. 272 p. ISBN 0-8144-0882-6. (Gift of the publisher.) [R726 .C637 2006] (20.5.1; 1.2; 1.3.5; 4.4; 8.1; 20.4.1; 20.5.4)

Cosic, Miriam. THE RIGHT TO DIE? AN EXAMINATION OF THE EUTHANASIA DEBATE. Sydney: New Holland, 2003. 295 p. ISBN 1-86436-809-8. (Publisher's address: 14 Aquatic Drive, Frenchs Forest, NSW 2086, Australia.) [R726 .C6765 2003] (20.5.1; 4.4; 20.4.1; 21.1)

Dowbiggin, Ian. A CONCISE HISTORY OF EUTHANASIA: LIFE, DEATH, GOD AND MEDICINE. New York: Rowman & Littlefield, 2005. 163 p. ISBN 0-7425-3110-4. (Critical Issues in History series.) [R726 .D688 2005] (20.5.1; 1.2; 2.2; 7.1; 8.1; 20.7)

Fridell, Ron. CRUZAN V. MISSOURI AND THE RIGHT TO DIE DEBATE: DEBATING SUPREME COURT DECISIONS. Berkeley Heights, NJ: Enslow Publishers, 2005. 128 p. ISBN 0-7660-2356-7. (Debating Supreme Court Decisions series. Juvenile literature.) [KF228 .C78 F75 2005] (20.5.1; 8.3.3; 20.7)

Fuhrman, Mark. SILENT WITNESS: THE UNTOLD STORY OF TERRI SCHIAVO'S DEATH. New York: William Morrow, 2005. 255 p. ISBN 0-06-085337-9. [R726 .F8275 2005] (20.5.1; 8.1; 20.4.1; Biography)

Reflections on and Implications of Schiavo. STETSON LAW REVIEW 2005 Fall; 35(1): 1-205. (ISSN 0739-9731.) (20.5.1; 1.2; 1.3.5; 1.3.7; 1.3.8; 2.1; 2.4; 4.4; 8.3.3)

Schiavo, Michael. TERRI: THE TRUTH. New York: Dutton, 2006. 360 p. ISBN 0-525-94946-1. [R726 .S338 2006] (20.5.1; 1.2; 1.3.5; 20.4.1; 21.1; Biography)

Schindler, Mary and Schindler, Robert. A LIFE THAT MAT-TERS: THE LEGACY OF TERRI SCHIAVO—A LESSON FOR US ALL. New York: Warner Books, 2006. 251 p. ISBN 0-446-57987-4. [R726 .S339 2006] (20.5.1; 8.1; 20.4.1; Biography)

Schotsmans, Paul and Meulenbergs, Tom, eds. EUTHANA-SIA AND PALLIATIVE CARE IN THE LOW COUNTRIES. Leuven/Dudley, MA: Peeters, 2005. 264 p. ISBN 90-429-1556-0. (Ethical Perspectives Monograph Series; No. 3. Gift of the editors.) [R726 .E7865 2005] (20.5.1; 1.1; 1.2; 4.4; 8.1; 20.4.1; 20.7)

Solomon, Lewis D. THE QUEST FOR HUMAN LONGEVITY: SCIENCE, BUSINESS, AND PUBLIC POLICY. New Brunswick, NJ: Transaction, 2006. 197 p. ISBN 0-7658-0300-3. (20.5.1; 1.3.2; 1.3.9; 4.5; 5.3; 9.5.2; 9.7; 15.1)

White, Stephen. KILL ME: A NOVEL. New York: Dutton, 2006. 402 p. ISBN 0-525-94930-5. ("What if you could choose when to die? But once you decide, you can't change your mind. Ever. No matter what... Relentlessly paced and intelligent, *Kill Me* brings Alan Gregory face-to-face with the most challenging case of his career. A man walks into Dr. Gregory's practice playing a game of cat and mouse, slowly revealing a progression of deadly secrets while trying to influence how the game will end.") [PS3573 .H47477 K55 2006] (20.5.1; 20.4.1; 20.7; Fiction)

Woodward, John, ed. THE RIGHT TO DIE. Detroit, MI: Greenhaven Press, 2006. 94 p. ISBN 0-7377-3440-X. (At Issue series. Gift of the publisher.) [KF3827 .E87 R58 2006] (20.5.1; 1.2; 1.3.5; 2.3; 4.4; 8.1; 20.7; POP)

20.5.2 ALLOWING MINORS TO DIE

Mifflin, Pauline Challinor. SAVING VERY PREMATURE BA-BIES: KEY ETHICAL ISSUES. Edinburgh/New York: Books for Midwives, 2003. 246 p. ISBN 0-7506-5412-0. [RJ250 .M54 2003] (20.5.2; 4.4; 8.1; 9.4; 9.5.7; 12.1)

O'Malley, Suzanne. THE UNSPEAKABLE CRIME OF ANDREA YATES: "ARE YOU THERE ALONE?" New York: Pocket Star Books, 2005. 404 p. ISBN 0-7434-6629-2. [HV6541 .U62 H686 2005] (20.5.2; 1.2; 1.3.8; 4.3; 17.1; 20.6)

20.5.4 LIVING WILLS/ADVANCE DIRECTIVES

Advance Care Planning. AMERICAN JOURNAL OF GERIAT-RIC CARDIOLOGY 2004 November-December; 13(6): 291-328. (ISSN 1076-7460.) (20.5.4; 5.2; 8.1; 8.3.1; 8.3.3; 9.4; 9.5.2; 17.1; 20.4.1; 20.5.1)

20.6 CAPITAL PUNISHMENT

Martinez, J. Michael; Richardson, William D.; and Hornsby, D. Brandon, eds. THE LEVIATHAN'S CHOICE: CAPI-TAL PUNISHMENT IN THE TWENTY-FIRST CENTURY. Lanham,

---

Numbers in ( ) = NRCBL Classification Numbers

MD: Rowman & Littlefield, 2002. 408 p. ISBN 0-8476-9731-2. [HV8694 .L475 2002] (20.6; 1.1; 1.2; 21.1)

Owens, Erik C.; Carlson, John D.; and Elshtain, Eric p., eds. RELIGION AND THE DEATH PENALTY: A CALL FOR RECKONING. Grand Rapids, MI: William B. Eerdmans, 2004. 294 p. ISBN 0-8028-2172-3. (Eerdmans Religion, Ethics, and Pubic Life Series.) [HV8694 .R455 2004] (20.6; 1.2; 1.3.8)

Prejean, Helen. THE DEATH OF INNOCENTS: AN EYEWITNESS ACCOUNT OF WRONGFUL EXECUTIONS. New York: Random House, 2005. 310 p. ISBN 0-679-44056-9. [HV8699 .U5 P745 2005] (20.6)

Symposium: The Death Penalty and Mental Illness. CATHOLIC UNIVERSITY LAW REVIEW 2005 Summer; 54(4): 1113-1193. (ISSN 0008-8390.) (20.6; 9.5.3; 17.1)

20.7 SUICIDE/ASSISTED SUICIDE

Chapman, Simon and Leeder, Stephen, eds. THE LAST RIGHT? AUSTRALIANS TAKE SIDES ON THE RIGHT TO DIE. Melbourne, Victoria: Mandarin, 1995. 160 p. ISBN 1-86330-504-1. (Gift of Warren Reich.) [R726 .L378 1995] (20.7; 7.1; 20.3.1; 20.5.1)

Gorsuch, Neil M. THE FUTURE OF ASSISTED SUICIDE AND EUTHANASIA. Princeton, NJ: Princeton University Press, 2006. 311 p. ISBN 0-691-12458-2. (New Forum Books series. Gift of the publisher.) [R726 .G65 2006] (20.7; 1.1; 2.2; 4.4; 8.1; 20.5.1)

Great Britain. Parliament. House of Lords. Select Committee on the Assisted Dying for the Terminally Ill Bill. ASSISTED DYING FOR THE TERMINALLY ILL BILL [HL]. London: Stationery Office, 2005. 2 volumes. [148 p.+ 737 p.]. ISBN 0-10-400650-1 [Vol. 1]; ISBN 0-10-400649-8 [Vol. 2]. (Volume I: *Report*; publication no. HL Paper 86-I. Volume 2: *Evidence*; publication no. HL Paper 86-II. Available from: The Stationery Office (TSO), PO Box 29, Norwich NR3 1GN; tel: 0870-600-5522; fax: 0870-600-5533; Web: http://www.tso.co.uk/bookshop. Also available on the Web at: http://www.publications.parliament.uk/pa/ld200405/ldselect/ldasdy/86/86i.pdf.) [KD3410 .E88 A2 2005] (20.7; 7.1; 8.1; 20.3.2; 20.5.1)

Nicol, Neal and Wylie, Harry. BETWEEN THE DYING AND THE DEAD: DR. JACK KEVORKIAN'S LIFE AND THE BATTLE TO LEGALIZE EUTHANASIA. Madison: Terrace Books/University of Wisconsin Press, 2006. 273 p. ISBN 0-299-21710-8. (Gift of the publisher.) [R726 .N53 2006] (20.7; 8.1; 20.4.1; 20.5.1; Biography)

Preston, Tom. PATIENT-DIRECTED DYING: A CALL FOR LEGALIZED AID IN DYING FOR THE TERMINALLY ILL. New York: iUniverse, 2006. 180 p. ISBN 0-595-38144-8. (Available from: iUniverse, 2021 Pine Lake Road, Guide 100, Lincoln, NE 68512; Web: http://www.iuniverse.com.) (20.7; 8.2; 20.4.1; 20.5.1)

Special Issue: Ethic Commission of Royal Belgian Society for Surgery: Opinion Concerning the Law on Euthanasia, *September 23, 2002.* ACTA CHIRURGICA BELGICA 2002 November-December; 102(6): 363-419. (ISSN 0001-5458. Text in English, French and Flemish. Gift of L. Michel.) (20.7; 2.1; 20.5.1)

21.1 INTERNATIONAL AND POLITICAL DIMENSIONS OF BIOLOGY AND MEDICINE (GENERAL)

Aginam, Obijiofor. GLOBAL HEALTH GOVERNANCE: INTERNATIONAL LAW AND PUBLIC HEALTH IN A DIVIDED WORLD. Toronto/Buffalo, NY: University of Toronto Press, 2005. 202 p. ISBN 0-8020-8000-6. [K3570 .A35 2005] (21.1; 9.1; 9.7)

Bennett, Belinda, ed. HEALTH, RIGHTS AND GLOBALISATION. Aldershot, Hants/Burlington, VT: Ashgate, 2006. 403 p. ISBN 0-7546-2590-7. (The International Library of Medicine, Ethics and Law series. Gift of the publisher.) [RA441 .H444 2006] (21.1; 1.1; 2.1; 5.3; 9.1; 9.3.1; 9.4; 9.5.5; 9.5.6; 9.7; 10; 12.1; 14.1; 21.7)

Bernasconi, Robert and Lott, Tommy L., eds. THE IDEA OF RACE. Indianapolis, IN: Hackett, 2000. 213 p. ISBN 0-87220-458-8. (Hackett Readings in Philosophy series.) [GN269 .I34 2000] (21.1; 3.2; 4.4; 15.5)

Boehmer, Ulrike. THE PERSONAL AND THE POLITICAL: WOMEN'S ACTIVISM IN RESPONSE TO THE BREAST CANCER AND AIDS EPIDEMICS. Albany: State University of New York Press, 2000. 208 p. ISBN 0-7914-4550-X. [RC280 .B8 B62 2000] (21.1; 7.1; 9.5.5; 9.5.6; 10)

Dershowitz, Alan. RIGHTS FROM WRONGS: A SECULAR THEORY OF THE ORIGINS OF RIGHTS. New York: Basic Books, 2004. 261 p. ISBN 0-465-01713-4. [JC571 .D3985 2004] (21.1; 1.1; 1.2; 1.3.5; 4.4; 16.1; 19.1; 22.1)

Honderich, Ted. AFTER THE TERROR. Edinburgh: Edinburgh University Press, 2003. 195 p. ISBN 0-7486-1668-3. (Expanded, revised edition.) [HM665 .H66 2003] (21.1; 1.3.5)

MacDonald, Théodore H. THIRD WORLD HEALTH: HOSTAGE TO FIRST WORLD WEALTH. Oxford, UK/Seattle, WA: Radcliffe Publishing, 2005. 297 p. ISBN 1-85775-769-6. (Foreword by Desmond M. Tutu. Gift of the publisher.) [RA441.5 .M32 2005] (21.1; 1.3.2; 9.1; 9.5.6; 9.5.7; 9.5.9; 9.5.10; 9.7; 16.1)

Marinker, Marshall, ed. HEALTH TARGETS IN EUROPE: POLITY, PROGRESS AND PROMISE. London: BMJ Books, 2002. 240 p. ISBN 0-7279-1642-4. [RA395 .E85 H43 2002] (21.1; 9.1)

Tesón, Fernando. HUMANITARIAN INTERVENTION: AN INQUIRY INTO LAW AND MORALITY. Ardsley, NY: Transnational Publishers, 2005. 456 p. ISBN 1-57105-248-8. (Third edition, updated and revised.) [JX4481 .T32 2005] (21.1; 1.1; 1.3.5; 1.3.6)

21.2 WAR

Berquist, Jon L., ed. STRIKE TERROR NO MORE: THEOLOGY, ETHICS, AND THE NEW WAR. St. Louis, MO: Chalice Press, 2002. 355 p. ISBN 0-8272-3454-6. [BT736.15 .S77 2002] (21.2; 1.2; 21.1)

21.3 CHEMICAL AND BIOLOGICAL WEAPONS

Biological Terrorism: Understanding the Threat, Preparation, and Medical Response. DM/DISEASE-A-MONTH 2000 February; 46(2): 129-190. (ISSN 0011-5029.) (21.3; 9.1; 21.2)

Charles, Daniel. MASTER MIND: THE RISE AND FALL OF FRITZ HABER, THE NOBEL LAUREATE WHO LAUNCHED THE AGE OF CHEMICAL WARFARE. New York: Ecco/HarperCollins, 2005. 313 p. ISBN 0-06-056272-2. [QD22 .H15 C48 2005] (21.3; 1.3.9; 1.3.11; 21.2; 21.4; Biography)

Cordesman, Anthony H. THE CHALLENGE OF BIOLOGICAL TERRORISM. Washington, DC: CSIS Press, 2005. 208 p. ISBN 0-89206-477-3. (CSIS Significant Issues Series; Vol. 27, No. 7. Available from: Center for Strategic and International Studies, 1800 K Street, NW, Washington, DC 20006; tel: 202-775-3119.) [HV6433.35 .C67 2005] (21.3; 1.3.5; 1.3.11; 21.2)

Naff, Clay Farris, ed. BIOLOGICAL WEAPONS. Detroit, MI: Greenhaven Press/Thomas Gale, 2006. 191 p. ISBN 0-7377-3183-4. (Contemporary Issues Companion series. Gift of the publisher.) [UG447.8 .B573 2006] (21.3; 1.3.5; 9.5.1; 18.5.5; 21.2; POP)

National Research Council (United States). Committee on Biological Threats to Agricultural Plants and Animals. COUNTERING AGRICULTURAL BIOTERRORISM. Washington, DC: National Academies Press, 2003. 169 p. ISBN 0-309-08545-4. ("The study was a collaborative effort of the NRC Board on Agriculture and National Resources and the Board on Life Sciences." Also available on the Web at: http://www.nap.edu.) [UG447.8 .N37 2003] (21.3; 1.3.11; 22.3)

Reminick, Gerald. NIGHTMARE IN BARI: THE WORLD WAR II LIBERTY SHIP POISON GAS DISASTER AND COVERUP. Palo Alto, CA: Glencannon Press, 2001. 266 p. ISBN 1-889901-21-0. [D763 .I82 B377 2001] (21.3; 21.2)

Wheelis, Mark; Rózsa, Lajos; and Dando, Malcolm, eds. DEADLY CULTURES: BIOLOGICAL WEAPONS SINCE 1945. Cambridge, MA: Harvard University Press, 2006. 479 p. ISBN 0-674-01699-8. (Gift of the publisher.) [UG447.8 .D43 2006] (21.3; 1.3.11; 21.1; 21.2; 22.1)

World Health Organization. PUBLIC HEALTH RESPONSE TO BIOLOGICAL AND CHEMICAL WEAPONS: WHO GUIDANCE. Geneva: World Health Organization, 2004. 340 p. ISBN 92-4-154615-8. (Second edition of: *Health Aspects of Chemical and Biological Weapons: Report of a WHO*

Group of Consultants; 1970.) [UG447 .W66 2004] (21.3; 5.2; 9.1; 16.1; 21.2)

21.4 TORTURE AND GENOCIDE

Amnesty International. COMBATING TORTURE: A MANUAL FOR ACTION. London: Amnesty International Publications, 2003. 335 p. ISBN 0-86210-323-1. [K5410 .T6 C66 2003] (21.4; 1.3.5; 1.3.6)

Chang, Iris. THE RAPE OF NANKING: THE FORGOTTEN HOLOCAUST OF WORLD WAR II. New York: Penguin Books, 1997. 290 p. ISBN 0-14-027744-7. [DS796 .N2 C44 1998] (21.4; 10; 21.2)

Dietrich, Donald J., ed. CHRISTIAN RESPONSES TO THE HOLOCAUST: MORAL AND ETHICAL ISSUES. Syracuse, NY: Syracuse University Press, 2003. 217 p. ISBN 0-8156-3029-8. (Religion, Theology, and the Holocaust series. Gift of Max M. and Marjorie B. Kampelman.) [BT93 .C495 2003] (21.4; 1.2; 1.3.5; 15.5)

Lang, Berel. POST-HOLOCAUST: INTERPRETATION, MISINTERPRETATION, AND THE CLAIMS OF HISTORY. Bloomington: Indiana University Press, 2005. 200 p. ISBN 0-253-21728-8. (Jewish Literature and Culture series. Gift of Max M. and Marjorie B. Kampelman.) [D804.348 .L36 2005] (21.4)

Levinson, Sanford, ed. TORTURE: A COLLECTION. Oxford/New York: Oxford University Press, 2004. 342 p. ISBN 0-19-530646-5. (21.4; 1.3.5)

Lipstadt, Deborah E. HISTORY ON TRIAL: MY DAY IN COURT WITH DAVID IRVING. New York: Ecco/Harper Collins, 2005. 346 p. ISBN 0-06-059376-8. [KD379.5 .I78 L57 2005] (21.4; 1.3.5; 1.3.8; 15.5)

Lower, Wendy. NAZI EMPIRE-BUILDING AND THE HOLOCAUST IN UKRAINE. Chapel Hill: University of North Carolina Press in association with the United States Holocaust Memorial Museum, 2005. 307 p. ISBN 0-8078-2960-9. (Gift of Max M. and Marjorie B. Kampelman.) [DK508.833 .L69 2005] (21.4; 1.3.5; 21.2)

Monroe, Kristen Renwick. THE HAND OF COMPASSION: PORTRAITS OF MORAL CHOICE DURING THE HOLOCAUST. Princeton, NJ: Princeton University Press, 2004. 361 p. ISBN 0-691-11863-9. (Gift of Max M. and Marjorie B. Kampelman.) [D804.65 .M66 2004] (21.4; 1.1)

Mulisch, Harry. CRIMINAL CASE 40/61, THE TRIAL OF ADOLF EICHMANN: AN EYEWITNESS ACCOUNT. Philadelphia: University of Pennsylvania Press, 2005. 178 p. ISBN 0-8122-3861-3. (Personal Takes series. Translation from the Dutch by Robert Naborn of: *De Zaak 40/61: Een Reportage*, Uitgeverij de Bezige Bij, Amsterdam, 1961. Gift of Max M. and Marjorie B. Kampelman.) [DD247 .E5 M813 2005] (21.4; 1.3.5; 1.3.7)

Patterson, David and Roth, John K., eds. AFTER-WORDS: POST-HOLOCAUST STRUGGLES WITH FORGIVENESS, RECONCILIATION, JUSTICE. Seattle: University of Washington Press, 2004. 275 p. ISBN 0-295-98406-6. (Pastora

---

Numbers in ( ) = NRCBL Classification Numbers

Goldner Series in Post-Holocaust Studies. Gift of Max M. and Marjorie B. Kampelman.) [D804.3 .A38 2004] (21.4; 1.2)

Weissmark, Mona Sue. JUSTICE MATTERS: LEGACIES OF THE HOLOCAUST AND WORLD WAR II. Oxford/New York: Oxford University Press, 2004. 198 p. ISBN 0-19-515757-5. (Gift of Max M. and Marjorie B. Kampelman.) [D804.44 .W45 2004] (21.4; 1.1; 17.1; 21.2)

Wilshire, Bruce. GET 'EM ALL! KILL 'EM! GENOCIDE, TERRORISM, RIGHTEOUS COMMUNITIES. Lanham, MD: Lexington Books, 2006. 199 p. ISBN 0-7391-0873-5. (Gift of the publisher.) [HV6322.7 .W55 2005] (21.4; 1.2; 1.3.5; 15.5)

21.6 INTERNATIONAL MIGRATION OF HEALTH PROFESSIONALS

Kingma, Mireille. NURSES ON THE MOVE: MIGRATION AND THE GLOBAL HEALTH CARE ECONOMY. Ithaca, NY: ILR Press/Cornell University Press, 2006. 275 p. ISBN 0-8014-7259-8. (The Culture and Politics of Health Care Work series. Gift of the publisher.) [RT89.3 .K56 2006] (21.6; 4.1.3; 9.3.1; 21.7)

21.7 CULTURAL PLURALISM

Ghosh, Partha and Khan, Shahid Anis. TRANSCULTURAL GERIATRICS: CARING FOR ELDERLY PEOPLE OF INDO-ASIAN ORIGIN. Oxford/Seattle, WA: Radcliffe, 2005. 168 p. ISBN 1-85775-745-9. [RA448.5 .A83 G46 2005] (21.7; 4.1.1; 7.1; 9.5.2; 9.5.4; 20.3.1)

Kurzer, Paulette. MARKETS AND MORAL REGULATION: CULTURAL CHANGE IN THE EUROPEAN UNION. Cambridge/New York: Cambridge University Press, 2001. 210 p. ISBN 0-521-00395-4. (Themes in European Governance series.) [HF5474 .A2 K87 2001] (21.7; 1.3.5; 7.1; 9.1; 9.5.9; 10; 12.4.1)

Rundle, Anne; Carvalho, Maria; and Robinson, Mary, eds. CULTURAL COMPETENCE IN HEALTH CARE: A PRACTICE GUIDE. San Francisco: Jossey-Bass, 1999. 234 p. ISBN 0-7879-6221-X. ("An earlier version of this book was previously published in hard binder format under the title: *Honoring Patient Preferences*.") [RA418.5 .T73 H65 2002] (21.7; 1.2; 9.5.4; 9.8; Reference)

Satcher, David; Pamies, Rubens J.; and Woelfl, Nancy N., [eds.]. MULTICULTURAL MEDICINE AND HEALTH DISPARITIES. New York: McGraw-Hill, 2006. 577 p. ISBN 0-07-143680-4. [RA418.5 .T73 M855 2006] (21.7; 1.2; 4.4; 7.1; 9.1; 9.5.1; 9.5.4; 9.5.6; 9.5.9; 9.8; 15.1; 17.1; 18.5.1; 19.5)

Üstün, T. Bedirhan; Chatterji, Somnath; Bickenbach, Jerome E.; Trotter II, Robert T.; Room, Robin; Rehm, Jurgen; and Saxena, Shekhar, eds. DISABILITY AND CULTURE: UNIVERSALISM AND DIVERSITY. Seattle: Hogrefe & Huber, 2001. 328 p. ISBN 0-88937-239-X. (Published on behalf of the World Health Organization.) [RA1055.5 .D564 2001] (21.7; 4.3; 7.1; 9.5.1; 9.5.3; 9.5.9)

22.1 ANIMAL WELFARE (GENERAL)

Arluke, Arnold. JUST A DOG: UNDERSTANDING ANIMAL CRUELTY AND OURSELVES. Philadelphia: Temple University Press, 2006. 221 p. ISBN 1-59213-472-6. (Animals, Culture, and Society series. Gift of the publisher.) [HV4708 .A756 2006] (22.1)

Beers, Diane L. FOR THE PREVENTION OF CRUELTY: THE HISTORY AND LEGACY OF ANIMAL RIGHTS ACTIVISM IN THE UNITED STATES. Athens: Swallow Press/Ohio University Press, 2006. 312 p. ISBN 0-8040-1087-0. (Gift of the publisher.) [HV4764 .B44 2006] (22.1; 22.2)

Salem, Deborah J. and Rowan, Andrew N., eds. THE STATE OF THE ANIMALS II, 2003. Washington, DC: Humane Society Press, 2003. 253 p. ISBN 0-9658942-7-4. (Public Policy Series.) [HV4708 .S719 2003] (22.1; 1.2; 1.3.11; 22.2; 22.3)

Salem, Deborah J. and Rowan, Andrew N., eds. THE STATE OF THE ANIMALS III, 2005. Washington, DC: Humane Society Press, 2005. 155 p. ISBN 0-9748400-5-X. (Publisher's address: 2100 L Street, NW; zip 20037; tel.: 202-452-1100; website: http://www.hsus.org.) [HV4708 .S719 2005] (22.1; 22.2; 22.3)

Singer, Peter, ed. IN DEFENSE OF ANIMALS: THE SECOND WAVE. Malden, MA: Blackwell, 2006. 248 p. ISBN 1-4051-1941-1. (Gift of the publisher.) [HV4711 .I6 2006] (22.1; 1.1; 1.2; 1.3.2; 1.3.7; 4.4; 22.2; 22.3)

Turner, Jacky and D'Silva, Joyce, eds. ANIMALS, ETHICS AND TRADE: THE CHALLENGE OF ANIMAL SENTIENCE. London/Sterling, VA: Earthscan, 2006. 286 p. ISBN 1-84407-255-X. (Gift of the publisher.) [HV4704 .A52 2006] (22.1; 1.2; 21.1; 22.2; 22.3)

22.2 ANIMAL EXPERIMENTATION

National Research Council (United States). Institute for Laboratory Animal Reseach. Committee on Guidelines for the Humane Transportation of Laboratory Animals. GUIDELINES FOR THE HUMANE TRANSPORTATION OF RESEARCH ANIMALS. Washington, DC: National Academies Press, 2006. 141 p. ISBN 0-309-10110-7. (Also available on the Web at: http://www.nap.edu.) [SF406.7 .G85 2006] (22.2; 5.3; 7.1)

Schuppli, Catherine Anne. THE ROLE OF THE ANIMAL ETHICS COMMITTEE IN ACHIEVING HUMANE ANIMAL EXPERIMENTATION. Ann Arbor, MI: ProQuest Information and Learning/UMI, 2004. 162 p. ISBN 0-612-90265-X. (Publication No. AAT-NQ90265. Dissertation, (Ph.D.)—University of British Columbia, 2004.) (22.2)

22.3 ANIMAL PRODUCTION

Stull, Donald D. and Broadway, Michael J. SLAUGHTERHOUSE BLUES: THE MEAT AND POULTRY INDUSTRY IN NORTH AMERICA. Belmont, CA: Thomson/Wadsworth, 2004. 172 p. ISBN 0-534-61303-9. (Case Studies on Contemporary Social Issues series.) [HD9415 .S78 2004] (22.3)

NEW JOURNAL SUBSCRIPTIONS

CLINICAL ETHICS 2006 March; 1(1). Quarterly. ISSN 1477-7509. (Publisher's address: Royal Society of Medicine Press Ltd., 1 Wimpole Street, London W1G 0AE; Website: http://www.rsmpress.co.uk/ce.htm.) (2.1; 8.1)

ORGANIZATIONAL ETHICS: HEALTHCARE, BUSINESS, AND POLICY 2004 Spring; 1(1). 2/year. ISSN 1541-1036. Publisher's address: Organizational Ethics: Healthcare, Business, and Policy, 138 West Washington Street, Suite 403, Hagerstown, MD 21740; tel. (within U.S.): 800-654-8188; fax: 240-420-0037; Website: http://www.organizationalethics.com.) (9.1; 1.3.2; 2.1; 9.3.2)

NEW PUBLICATIONS FROM THE KENNEDY INSTITUTE OF ETHICS

Walters, LeRoy; Kahn, Tamar Joy; and Goldstein, Doris Mueller, eds. BIBLIOGRAPHY OF BIOETHICS, VOLUME 32. Washington, DC: Kennedy Institute of Ethics, Georgetown University, 2006. 803 p. ISBN 1-883913-13-6. (ISSN 0363-0161.) [Z6675 .E8 W34 v.32] (2.1; Reference)

SECTION IV:
MONOGRAPHS

TITLE INDEX

SECTION IV: MONOGRAPHS TITLE INDEX

A

Abortion and Nation: The Politics of Reproduction in Contemporary Ireland. *Section III:* 12.5.2—Smyth, Lisa.

Abortion: Opposing Viewpoints. *Section III:* 12.3—Torr, James D., ed.

Acta Analytica: Philosophy and Psychology 2001; 16(27). *Section III:* 2.1—Practical Ethics.

Acta Chirurgica Belgica 2002 November-December; 102(6). *Section III:* 20.7—Special Issue: Ethic Commission of Royal Belgian Society for Surgery: Opinion Concerning the Law on Euthanasia, September 23, 2002.

Acting Jewish: Negotiating Ethnicity on the American Stage & Screen. *Section III:* 1.2—Bial, Henry.

After Dolly: The Uses and Misuses of Human Cloning. *Section III:* 14.5—Wilmut, Ian and Highfield, Roger.

After the Terror. *Section III:* 21.1—Honderich, Ted.

After-Words: Post-Holocaust Struggles with Forgiveness, Reconciliation, Justice. *Section III:* 21.4—Patterson, David and Roth, John K., eds.

Against Bioethics. *Section III:* 2.1—Baron, Jonathan.

Against Depression. *Section III:* 17.1—Kramer, Peter D.

Ageism: Stereotyping and Prejudice against Older Persons. *Section III:* 9.5.2—Nelson, Todd D., ed.

Aging: Theories and Potential Therapies. *Section III:* 9.5.2—Panno, Joseph.

Agricultural Biotechnology and Transatlantic Trade: Regulatory Barriers to GM Crops. *Section III:* 15.1—Isaac, Grant E.

AIDS and American Apocalypticism: The Cultural Semiotics of an Epidemic. *Section III:* 9.5.6—Long, Thomas L.

AIDS Pandemic: Impact on Science and Society, The. *Section III:* 9.5.6—Mayer, Kenneth H. and Pizer, H.F., eds.

AIDS: Science and Society. *Section III:* 9.5.6—Fan, Hung Y.; Conner, Ross F.; and Villarreal, Luis P.

AIDS: Society, Ethics and Law. *Section III:* 9.5.6—Schüklenk, Udo, ed.

Alcoholism in America: From Reconstruction to Prohibition. *Section III:* 9.5.9—Tracy, Sarah W.

Altruism in World Religions. *Section III:* 1.1—Neusner, Jacob and Chilton, Bruce D., eds.

American Journal of Geriatric Cardiology 2004 November-December; 13(6). *Section III:* 20.5.4—Advance Care Planning.

Anarchism, Science and Sex: Eugenics in Eastern Spain, 1900-1937. *Section III:* 15.5—Cleminson, Richard.

. . . And a Time to Die: How American Hospitals Shape the End of Life. *Section III:* 20.4.1—Kaufman, Sharon R.

Angels of Power and Other Reproductive Creations. *Section III:* 14.1—Hawthorne, Susan and Klein, Renate, eds.

Animal Cloning: The Science of Nuclear Transfer. *Section III:* 14.5—Panno, Joseph.

Animals, Ethics and Trade: The Challenge of Animal Sentience. *Section III:* 22.1—Turner, Jacky and D'Silva, Joyce, eds.

Artificial Happiness: The Dark Side of the New Happy Class. *Section III:* 17.4—Dworkin, Ronald W.

As We See Ourselves: Jewish Women in Nursing. *Section III:* 7.1—Benson, Evelyn Rose.

Asclepius: The God of Medicine. *Section III:* 7.1—Hart, Gerald D.

Asian Bioethics in the 21st Century. *Section III:* 2.3—Sang-yong, Song; Young-Mo, Koo; and Macer, Darryl R.J., eds.

Assessment of Mental Capacity: Guidance for Doctors and Lawyers. *Section III:* 4.3—British Medical Association [and] Law Society (Great Britain).

Assisted Dying for the Terminally Ill Bill [HL]. *Section III:* 20.7—Great Britain. Parliament. House of Lords. Select Committee on the Assisted Dying for the Terminally Ill Bill.

Auditing Age Discrimination: A Practical Approach to Promoting Equality in Health and Social Care. *Section*

III: 9.5.2—Levenson, Rose; King Edward's Hospital Fund for London.

Australian Psychologist 1995 November; 30(3). *Section III:* 8.4—Confidentiality Issues in Psychology.

Autonomous Patient: Ending Paternalism in Medical Care, The. *Section III:* 8.1—Coulter, Angela.

Autonomy and the Challenges to Liberalism: New Essays. *Section III:* 1.3.5—Christman, John and Anderson, Joel, eds.

Autonomy, Gender, Politics. *Section III:* 1.1—Friedman, Marilyn.

Awakening to Humanity: Sources of Moral Authority and Responsiveness in Doctor-Patient Relationships. *Section III:* 8.1—Morrow, Jason.

B

Baby at Risk: The Uncertain Legacies of Medical Miracles for Babies, Families and Society. *Section III:* 20.4.2—Guyer, Ruth Levy.

Baby Boomer Health Dynamics: How Are We Aging? *Section III:* 9.5.1—Wister, Andrew V.

Baby Business: How Money, Science, and Politics Drive the Commerce of Conception, The. *Section III:* 14.1—Spar, Debora L.

Babyface: A Story of Heart and Bones. *Section III:* 9.5.7—McDermott, Jeanne.

Bayesian Approaches to Clinical Trials and Health-Care Evaluation. *Section III:* 18.2—Spiegelhalter, David J.; Abrams, Keith R.; and Myles, Jonathan P.

Before Revelation: The Boundaries of Muslim Moral Thought. *Section III:* 1.2—Reinhart, A. Kevin.

Before the Dawn: Recovering the Lost History of Our Ancestors. *Section III:* 15.11—Wade, Nicholas.

Beginning of Wisdom: Reading Genesis, The. *Section III:* 1.2—Kass, Leon R.

Best-Laid Plans: Health Care's Problems and Prospects, The. *Section III:* 9.1—McFarlane, Lawrie and Prado, Carlos.

Better for All the World: The Secret History of Forced Sterilization and America's Quest for Racial Purity. *Section III:* 15.5—Bruinius, Harry.

Better Humans? The Politics of Human Enhancement and Life Extension. *Section III:* 4.5—Miller, Paul and Wilsdon, James, eds.

Between the Dying and the Dead: Dr. Jack Kevorkian's Life and the Battle to Legalize Euthanasia. *Section III:* 20.7—Nicol, Neal and Wylie, Harry.

Between the Heartbeats: Poetry & Prose by Nurses. *Section III:* 7.1—Davis, Corney and Schaefer, Judy, eds.

Beyond Pain: Making the Mind-Body Connection. *Section III:* 4.4—Mailis-Gagnon, Angela and Israelson, David.

Bibliography of Bioethics, Volume 32. *Section III:* 2.1—Walters, LeRoy; Kahn, Tamar Joy; and Goldstein, Doris Mueller, eds.

Biocapital: The Constitution of Postgenomic Life. *Section III:* 15.1—Rajan, Kaushik Sunder.

Bioethics: A Nursing Perspective. *Section III:* 4.1.3—Johnstone, Megan-Jane.

Bioethics: A Systematic Approach. *Section III:* 2.1—Gert, Bernard; Culver, Charles M.; and Clouser, K. Danner.

Bioethics: An Anthology. *Section III:* 2.1—Kuhse, Helga and Singer, Peter, eds.

Bioethics: An Introduction for the Biosciences. *Section III:* 2.3—Mepham, Ben.

Bioethics and Armed Conflict: Moral Dilemmas of Medicine and War. *Section III:* 2.1—Gross, Michael L.

Bioethics and Organ Transplantation in a Muslim Society: A Study in Culture, Ethnography, and Religion. *Section III:* 19.3—Moazam, Farhat.

Bioethics and the Impact of Genomics in the 21st Century: Pharmacogenomics, DNA Polymorphism and Medical Genetics Services. *Section III:* 15.1—Fujiki, Norio; Sudo, Masakatsu; and Macer, Darryl, eds.

Bioethics and the New Embryology: Springboards for Debate. *Section III:* 14.1—Gilbert, Scott F.; Tyler, Anna L.; and Zackin, Emily J.

Bioethics in Cultural Contexts: Reflections on Methods and Finitude. *Section III:* 2.1—Rehmann-Sutter, Christoph; Düwell, Marcus; and Mieth, Dietmar, eds.

Bioethics in India. *Section III:* 2.1—Azariah, Jayapaul; Azariah, Hilda; and Macer, Darryl R.J., eds.

Biological Anthropology and Ethics: From Repatriation to Genetic Identity. *Section III:* 15.11—Turner, Trudy R., ed.

Biological Weapons. *Section III:* 21.3—Naff, Clay Farris, ed.

Biomedical Ethics. *Section III:* 2.1—Mappes, Thomas A. and DeGrazia, David.

Biomedicalization of Alcohol Studies: Ideological Shifts and Institutional Challenges. *Section III:* 9.5.9—Midanik, Lorraine T.

Biomedicine, the Family and Human Rights. *Section III:* 14.1—Meulders-Klein, Marie Thérèse; Deech, Ruth; and Vlaardingerbroek, Paul, eds.

Biotechnology: Between Commerce and Civil Society. *Section III:* 5.3—Stehr, Nico, ed.

Section III arranged by NRCBL Classification Number, then Author or Title

Biotechnology of Human Reproduction. *Section III:* 14.1—Revelli, Alberto; Tur-Kaspa, Ilan; Holte, Jan Gunnar; and Massobrio, Marco, eds.

Biotechnology Unzipped: Promises and Realities. *Section III:* 15.1—Grace, Eric S.

Birth of Surrogacy in Israel, The. *Section III:* 14.2—Weisberg, D. Kelly.

Black Markets: The Supply and Demand of Body Parts. *Section III:* 19.5—Goodwin, Michele.

Blood & Data: Ethical, Legal and Social Aspects of Human Genetic Databases. *Section III:* 15.1—Árnason, Gardar; Nordal, Salvör; and Árnason, Vilhjálmur, eds.

Bodies, Commodities, and Biotechnologies: Death, Mourning, and Scientific Desire in the Realm of Human Organ Transfer. *Section III:* 19.1—Sharp, Lesley A.

Bodies: Exploring Fluid Boundaries. *Section III:* 4.4—Longhurst, Robyn.

Bodies: Sex, Violence, Disease, and Death in Contemporary Legend. *Section III:* 4.4—Bennett, Gillian.

Body, The. *Section III:* 19.1—Kureishi, Hanif.

Body Brokers: Inside America's Underground Trade in Human Remains. *Section III:* 19.5—Cheney, Annie.

Body Hunters: Testing New Drugs on the World's Poorest Patients, The. *Section III:* 18.5.9—Shah, Sonia.

Bonhoeffer Phenomenon: Portraits of a Protestant Saint, The. *Section III:* 1.2—Haynes, Stephen R.

Born and Made: An Ethnography of Preimplantation Genetic Diagnosis. *Section III:* 15.2—Franklin, Sarah and Roberts, Celia.

Born Gay: The Psychobiology of Sex Orientation. *Section III:* 10—Wilson, Glenn and Rahman, Qazi.

Boundaries of Privacy: Dialectics of Disclosure. *Section III:* 1.1—Petronio, Sandra.

Broken Genius: The Rise and Fall of William Shockley, Creator of the Electronic Age. *Section III:* 5.1—Shurkin, Joel N.

C

Cancer: The Role of Genes, Lifestyle, and Environment. *Section III:* 9.5.1—Panno, Joseph.

Cancer-Gate: How to Win the Losing Cancer War. *Section III:* 9.5.1—Epstein, Samuel S.

Care of the Dying: A Pathway to Excellence. *Section III:* 20.4.1—Ellershaw, John and Wilkinson, Susie, eds.

Caregiver's Tale: Loss and Renewal in Memoirs of Family Life, The. *Section III:* 9.5.1—Burack-Weiss, Ann.

Case of Terri Schiavo: Ethics at the End of Life, The. *Section III:* 20.5.1—Caplan, Arthur L.; McCartney, James J.; Sisti, Dominic A., eds.

Catholic Church and Nazi Germany, The. *Section III:* 1.2—Lewy, Guenter.

Catholic University Law Review 2005 Summer; 54(4). *Section III:* 20.6—Symposium: The Death Penalty and Mental Illness.

Century of Mendelism in Human Genetics: Proceedings of a Symposium Organized by the Galton Institute and Held at the Royal Society of Medicine, London, 2001, A. *Section III:* 15.1—Keynes, Milo; Edwards, A.W.F.; and Peel, Robert, eds.

Challenge of Biological Terrorism, The. *Section III:* 21.3—Cordesman, Anthony H.

Challenging Science: Issues for New Zealand Society in the 21st Century. *Section III:* 5.3—Dew, Kevin and Fitzgerald, Ruth, eds.

Chasing Daylight: How My Forthcoming Death Transformed My Life. *Section III:* 20.1—O'Kelly, Eugene and Postman, Andrew.

Children in Medical Research: Access versus Protection. *Section III:* 18.5.2—Ross, Lainie Friedman.

Children, Medicine and the Law. *Section III:* 9.5.5—Freeman, Michael, ed.

Choosing Children: Genes, Disability, and Design. *Section III:* 15.1—Glover, Jonathan.

Christian Responses to the Holocaust: Moral and Ethical Issues. *Section III:* 21.4—Dietrich, Donald J., ed.

Chronic Politics: Health Care Security from FDR to George W. Bush. *Section III:* 9.3.1—Funigiello, Philip J.

Cicely Saunders: Selected Writings 1958-2004. *Section III:* 20.4.1—Saunders, Cicely M.

Civilizing Argentina: Science, Medicine, and the Modern State. *Section III:* 15.5—Rodriguez, Julia.

Clinical Bioethics: A Search for the Foundations. *Section III:* 2.1—Viafora, Corrado, ed.

Clinical Ethics: A Practical Approach to Ethical Decisions in Clinical Medicine. *Section III:* 8.1—Jonsen, Albert R.; Siegler, Mark; and Winslade, William J.

Clinical Research: What It Is and How It Works. *Section III:* 18.1—Nesbitt, Lori A.

Clinical Trials. *Section III:* 18.1—Duley, Lelia and Farrell, Barbara, eds.

Clinics in Geriatric Medicine 2005 February; 21(1). *Section III:* 20.4.1—End-of-Life Care in the Modern Era.

Cloning. *Section III:* 14.5—Dudley, William, ed.

Combating Torture: A Manual for Action. *Section III:* 21.4—Amnesty International.

Committing to Results: Improving the Effectiveness of HIV/AIDS Assistance: An OED Evaluation of the World Bank's Assistance for HIV/AIDS Control. *Section III:* 9.5.6—Ainsworth, Martha; Vaillancourt, Denise

A.; and Gaubatz, Judith Hahn; World Bank. Operations Evaluation Department.

Common Good and Christian Ethics, The. *Section III:* 1.2—Hollenbach, David.

Commonsense Rebellion: Debunking Psychiatry, Confronting Society: An A to Z Guide to Rehumanizing Our Lives. *Section III:* 17.1—Levine, Bruce E.

Communication Skills in Medicine. *Section III:* 8.1—Hind, Charles R.K., ed.

Community Based Participatory Research for Health. *Section III:* 18.1—Minkler, Meredith and Wallerstein, Nina, eds.

Community-Based Interventions for Criminal Offenders with Severe Mental Illness. *Section III:* 17.1—Fisher, William H., ed.

Competence, Condemnation, and Commitment: An Integrated Theory of Mental Health Law. *Section III:* 4.3—Schopp, Robert F.

Computer and Information Ethics. *Section III:* 1.3.12—Woodbury, Marsha Cook.

Concepts of Alzheimer Disease: Biological, Clinical, and Cultural Perspectives. *Section III:* 4.3—Whitehouse, Peter J.; Maurer, Konrad; and Ballenger, Jesse F., eds.

Concise Dictionary of Modern Medicine. *Section III:* 9.1—Segen, Joseph.

Concise History of Euthanasia: Life, Death, God and Medicine, A. *Section III:* 20.5.1—Dowbiggin, Ian.

Confronting an Ill Society: David Widgery, General Practice, Idealism and the Chase for Change. *Section III:* 7.1—Hutt, Patrick; Heath, Iona; and Neighbour, Roger.

Confucian Ethics: A Comparative Study of Self, Autonomy, and Community. *Section III:* 1.1—Shun, Kwong-Loi and Wong, David B., eds.

Conscience in Conflict: How to Make Moral Choices. *Section III:* 1.2—Overberg, Kenneth R.

Contemporary Issues in Ethics and Information Technology. *Section III:* 1.3.12—Schultz, Robert A.

Counterfeit Medicines: Survey Report. *Section III:* 9.7—Harper, Jonathan; Council of Europe.

Countering Agricultural Bioterrorism. *Section III:* 21.3—National Research Council (United States). Committee on Biological Threats to Agricultural Plants and Animals.

Criminal Case 40/61, the Trial of Adolf Eichmann: An Eyewitness Account. *Section III:* 21.4—Mulisch, Harry.

Crippled Justice: The History of Modern Disability Policy in the Workplace. *Section III:* 16.3—O'Brien, Ruth.

Crisis of Abundance: Rethinking How We Pay for Health Care. *Section III:* 9.3.1—Kling, Arnold.

Critical Perspectives on Racial and Ethnic Differences in Health in Late Life. *Section III:* 9.5.4—National Research Council (United States). Division of Behavioral and Social Sciences and Education. Committee on Population. Panel on Race, Ethnicity, and Health in Later Life.

Critical Reflections on Stanley Hauerwas' Theology of Disability: Disabling Society, Enabling Theology. *Section III:* 9.5.3—Swinton, John, ed.

Cross-Cultural Introduction to Bioethics, A. *Section III:* 2.3—Macer, Darryl R.J., ed.; Eubios Ethics Institute.

Cruzan v. Missouri and the Right to Die Debate: Debating Supreme Court Decisions. *Section III:* 20.5.1—Fridell, Ron.

Cult of Pharmacology: How America Became the World's Most Troubled Drug Culture, The. *Section III:* 9.7—DeGrandpre, Richard.

Cultural Competence in Health Care: A Practice Guide. *Section III:* 21.7—Rundle, Anne; Carvalho, Maria; and Robinson, Mary, eds.

Cultural Locations of Disability. *Section III:* 7.1—Snyder, Sharon L. and Mitchell, David T.

Cultural Perspectives on Reproductive Health. *Section III:* 14.1—Obermeyer, Carla Makhlouf, ed.

Current Issues in Nursing. *Section III:* 4.1.3—Cowen, Perle Slavik and Moorhead, Sue, [eds.].

D

Damaged Identities, Narrative Repair. *Section III:* 1.1—Nelson, Hilde Lindemann.

Darwin: Discovering the Tree of Life. *Section III:* 3.2—Eldredge, Niles.

Darwin's Nemesis: Phillip Johnson and the Intelligent Design Movement. *Section III:* 3.2—Dembski, William A., ed.

Darwinism and Its Discontents. *Section III:* 3.2—Ruse, Michael.

Darwinism & Philosophy. *Section III:* 3.2—Hösle, Vittorio and Illies, Christian, eds.

Data Protection Directive and Medical Research Across Europe, The. *Section III:* 8.4—Beyleveld, D.; Townend, D.; Rouillé-Mirza, S.; and Wright, J., eds.

Deadly Cultures: Biological Weapons Since 1945. *Section III:* 21.3—Wheelis, Mark; Rózsa, Lajos; and Dando, Malcolm, eds.

Death in the Clinic. *Section III:* 20.4.1—Jansen, Lynn A., ed.

Death of Innocents: An Eyewitness Account of Wrongful Executions, The. *Section III:* 20.6—Prejean, Helen.

Death's Door: Modern Dying and the Ways We Grieve. *Section III:* 20.3.1—Gilbert, Sandra M.

Debates and Dilemmas in Promoting Health: A Reader. *Section III:* 9.1—Sidell, Moyra; Jones, Linda; Katz, Jeanne; Peberdy, Alyson; and Douglas, Jenny, eds.

Decision Making in Health and Medicine: Integrating Evidence and Values. *Section III:* 8.1—Hunink, M.G. Myriam; Glasziou, Paul P.; Siegel, Joanna E.; Weeks, Jane C.; Pliskin, Joseph S.; Elstein, Arthur S.; and Weinstein, Milton C.

Decoding the Ethics Code: A Practical Guide for Psychologists. *Section III:* 6—Fisher, Celia B.

Delphic Boat: What Genomes Tell Us, The. *Section III:* 15.1—Danchin, Antoine.

Dementia: Mind, Meaning, and the Person. *Section III:* 4.3—Hughes, Julian C.; Louw, Stephen J., and Sabat, Steven R., eds.

Designer Food: Mutant Harvest or Breadbasket of the World? *Section III:* 15.1—Pence, Gregory E.

Dictionary of Health Insurance and Managed Care. *Section III:* 9.3.1—Marcinko, David Edward and Hetico, Hope Rachel, eds.

Disability and Culture: Universalism and Diversity. *Section III:* 21.7—Üstün, T. Bedirhan; Chatterji, Somnath; Bickenbach, Jerome E.; Trotter II, Robert T.; Room, Robin; Rehm, Jurgen; and Saxena, Shekhar, eds.

Disability, Society, and the Individual. *Section III:* 9.5.1—Smart, Julie.

Divine Action and Modern Science. *Section III:* 1.2—Saunders, Nicholas.

Dizionario di bioetica. *Section III:* 2.1—Tettamanzi, Dionigi.

DM/Disease-A-Month 2000 February; 46(2). *Section III:* 21.3—Biological Terrorism: Understanding the Threat, Preparation, and Medical Response.

DNA: Changing Science and Society. *Section III:* 15.1—Krude, Torsten, ed.

Doctors and Patients: An Anthology. *Section III:* 7.1—Helman, Cecil, ed.

Documentary History of the Legal Aspects of Abortion in the United States: Stenberg v. Carhart, A. *Section III:* 12.4.2—Mersky, Roy M. and Liebert, Tobe, comps.

Documentation in Counseling Records. *Section III:* 17.1—Mitchell, Robert.

Does Human Rights Need God? *Section III:* 1.2—Bucar, Elizabeth M. and Barnett, Barbra, eds.

Doing the Right Thing: An Approach to Moral Issues in Mental Health Treatment. *Section III:* 17.2—Peteet, John R.

Don't Worry, It's Safe to Eat: The True Story of GM Food, BSE & Foot and Mouth. *Section III:* 15.1—Rowell, Andrew.

Double Identity. *Section III:* 14.5—Haddix, Margaret Peterson.

Double Trouble: A Story of Assisted Reproduction. *Section III:* 14.1—McHaffie, Hazel E.

Dr. Golem: How to Think About Medicine. *Section III:* 7.1—Collins, Harry and Pinch, Trevor.

Droit et marchandisation de la connaissance sur les gènes humains. *Section III:* 15.1—Franceschi, Magali.

Drugs into Bodies: Global AIDS Treatment Activism. *Section III:* 9.5.6—Smith, Raymond, A. and Siplon, Patricia D.

Dwarfism: Medical and Psychosocial Aspects of Profound Short Stature. *Section III:* 9.5.1—Adelson, Betty M.

E

Economics, Medicine and Health Care. *Section III:* 9.3.1—Mooney, Gavin.

Economics of Health and Medical Care, The. *Section III:* 9.3.1—Jacobs, Philip and Rapoport, John.

Eliminating Health Disparities: Measurement and Data Needs. *Section III:* 7.1—National Research Council (United States). Panel on DHHA Collection of Race and Ethnicity Data.

EMBO Reports 2005 July; 6(Special Issue). *Section III:* 5.1—Science and Society.

Emil von Behring: Infectious Disease, Immunology, and Serum Therapy. *Section III:* 7.1—Linton, Derek S.

Enabling Risk Assessment in Medicine: Farewell Symposi[um] for Werner-Karl Raff = Wege zur Risikobestimmung in der Medizin: Abschiedssymposium für Werner-Karl Raff. *Section III:* 18.2—Shapiro, S.; Dinger, J.; and Scriba, P., eds.

Encyclopedia of Science, Technology, and Ethics. *Section III:* 5.1—Mitcham, Carl, ed.

End of Life in Care Homes: A Palliative Approach. *Section III:* 20.4.1—Katz, Jeanne Samson and Peace, Sheila, eds.

Environmental Ethics: An Introduction with Readings. *Section III:* 16.1—Benson, John.

Environmental Philosophy and Ethics in Buddhism. *Section III:* 16.1—De Silva, Padmasiri.

Epidemics Laid Low: A History of What Happened in Rich Countries. *Section III:* 7.1—Bourdelais, Patrice.

Essays in Therapeutic Jurisprudence. *Section III:* 17.1—Wexler, David B. and Winick, Bruce J.

See inside front cover for NRCBL Classification Scheme

F

Female Genital Mutilation. *Section III:* 9.5.5—Momoh, Comfort, ed.

Final Days: Japanese Culture and Choice at the End of Life. *Section III:* 20.1—Long, Susan Orpett.

Fire in the Ashes: God, Evil, and the Holocaust. *Section III:* 1.2—Patterson, David and Roth, John K., eds.

Florence Nightingale: The Making of a Radical Theologian. *Section III:* 4.1.3—Webb, Val.

Footprints of God, The. *Section III:* 5.1—Iles, Greg.

For the Prevention of Cruelty: The History and Legacy of Animal Rights Activism in the United States. *Section III:* 22.1—Beers, Diane L.

Fragile Lives: Death, Dying and Care. *Section III:* 20.4.1—McNamara, Beverley.

Francis Crick: Discoverer of the Genetic Code. *Section III:* 15.1—Ridley, Matt.

Friends in Low Places. *Section III:* 4.1.2—Willis, James.

From Cells to Souls— and Beyond: Changing Portraits of Human Nature. *Section III:* 5.1—Jeeves, Malcolm, ed.

From Morality to Mental Health: Virtue and Vice in a Therapeutic Culture. *Section III:* 17.1—Martin, Mike W.

From Personal Tragedy to Public Problem: Miracle Technologies and End-Stage Renal Disease Policy, 1960-1972. *Section III:* 19.3—Cafaro, Janice A.

From Truth Telling to Truth Making in Medicine. *Section III:* 8.2—Surbone, Antonella.

Frontiers of Justice: Disability, Nationality, Species Membership. *Section III:* 1.1—Nussbaum, Martha C.

Fruits of War: How Military Conflict Accelerates Technology, The. *Section III:* 5.3—White, Michael.

Future of Assisted Suicide and Euthanasia, The. *Section III:* 20.7—Gorsuch, Neil M.

Future of the Brain: The Promise and Perils of Tomorrow's Neuroscience, The. *Section III:* 17.1—Rose, Steven.

G

Gendering Disability. *Section III:* 10—Smith, Bonnie G. and Hutchison, Beth, eds.

Gene Doping in Sports: The Science and Ethics of Genetically Modified Athletes. *Section III:* 15.4—Schneider, Angela J. and Friedmann, Theodore.

Gene Illusion: Genetic Research in Psychiatry and Psychology Under the Microscope, The. *Section III:* 15.1—Joseph, Jay.

Gene Technology and Economy. *Section III:* 15.8—Lundin, Susanne and Åkesson, Lynn, eds.

Gene Therapy: Treating Disease by Repairing Genes. *Section III:* 15.4—Panno, Joseph.

Generation Rx: How Prescription Drugs Are Altering American Lives, Minds, and Bodies. *Section III:* 9.7—Critser, Greg.

Generations: Journal of the American Society on Aging 1999 Spring; 23(1). *Section III:* 20.4.1 . Meier, Diane E. and Morrison, R. Sean, eds.

Genes and Behavior: Nature-Nurture Interplay Explained. *Section III:* 15.6—Rutter, Michael.

Genes and Insurance: Ethical, Legal and Economic Issues. *Section III:* 15.1—Radetzki, Marcus; Radetzki, Marian; and Juth, Niklas.

Genes in Conflict: The Biology of Selfish Genetic Elements. *Section III:* 15.1—Burt, Austin and Trivers, Robert.

Genes in Development: Re-reading the Molecular Paradigm. *Section III:* 15.1—Neumann-Held, Eva M. and Rehmann-Sutter, Christoph, eds.

Genetic Engineering: A Reference Handbook. *Section III:* 15.1—LeVine, Harry.

Genetic Technology and Sport: Ethical Questions. *Section III:* 15.1—Tamburrini, Claudio and Tannsjö, Torbjörn, eds.

Genetic Testing: Care, Consent, and Liability. *Section III:* 15.3—Sharpe, Neil F. and Carter, Ronald F.

Genetic Ties and the Family: The Impact of Paternity Testing on Parents and Children. *Section III:* 14.1—Rothstein, Mark A.; Murray, Thomas H.; Kaebnick, Gregory E.; and Majumder, Mary Anderlik, eds.

Geneticist Who Played Hoops with My DNA: . . . and Other Masterminds from the Frontiers of Biotech. *Section III:* 15.1—Duncan, David Ewing.

Genetics for Healthcare Professionals: A Lifestage Approach. *Section III:* 15.2—Skirton, Health and Patch, Christine.

Genetics, Gene-Ethics: Interviews with Hungarian Scientists. *Section III:* 15.1—Ferenczi, Andrea.

Genetics Revolution: History, Fears, and Future of a Life-Altering Science, The. *Section III:* 15.1—Morgan, Rose M.

Genius Factory: The Curious History of the Nobel Prize Sperm Bank, The. *Section III:* 14.6—Plotz, David.

Genomics Age: How DNA Technology Is Transforming the Way We Live and Who We Are, The. *Section III:* 15.1—Smith, Gina.

George W. Bush's Healthy Forests: Reframing the Environmental Debate. *Section III:* 16.1—Vaughn, Jacqueline and Cortner, Hanna J.

Geriatric Palliative Care. *Section III:* 20.4.1—Morrison, R. Sean; Meier, Diane E.; and Capello, Carol, eds.

Germans, Jews and the Claims of Modernity. *Section III:* 1.2—Hess, Jonathan M.

Gesundheitszwecke und Humangenetik: Medizinethische Argumente für die Bindung prädiktiver Gentests an Gesundheitszwecke. *Section III:* 15.2—Vieth, Andreas.

Get 'Em All! Kill 'Em! Genocide, Terrorism, Righteous Communities. *Section III:* 21.4—Wilshire, Bruce.

Gift of the Other: Levinas and the Politics of Reproduction, The. *Section III:* 9.5.5—Guenther, Lisa.

Giving Blood: An Exploration of the Determinants of the Gift Relationship. *Section III:* 19.4—Casebeer, Adrianne Waldman.

Global Assemblages: Technology, Politics, and Ethics as Anthropological Problems. *Section III:* 5.3—Ong, Aihwa and Collier, Stephen J., eds.

Global Health Governance: International Law and Public Health in a Divided World. *Section III:* 21.1—Aginam, Obijiofor.

Global Pharmaceuticals: Ethics, Markets, Practices. *Section III:* 9.7—Petryna, Adriana; Lakoff, Andrew; and Kleinman, Arthur, eds.

Global Prescriptions: Gendering Health and Human Rights. *Section III:* 9.5.5—Petchesky, Rosalind Pollack.

Globalizing Tobacco Control: Anti-smoking Campaigns in California, France, and Japan. *Section III:* 9.5.9—Reid, Roddey.

Goals of Medicine in the Course of History and Today: A Study in the History and Philosophy of Medicine. *Section III:* 7.1—Fleischhauer, Kurt and Hermerén, Göran.

"Good News" after Auschwitz? Christian Faith within a Post-Holocaust World. *Section III:* 1.2—Rittner, Carol and Roth, John K., eds.

Good Sex: Feminist Perspectives from the World's Religions. *Section III:* 10—Jung, Patricia Beattie; Hunt, Mary E.; and Balakrisnan, Radhika, eds.

Governing Health: The Politics of Health Policy. *Section III:* 9.1—Weissert, Carol S. and Weissert, William G.

Grace. *Section III:* 20.1—Ullmann, Linn.

Great Morality: An Intimate History of the Black Death, The. *Section III:* 7.1—Kelly, John.

Guide to the Orthodox Jewish Way of Life for Healthcare Professionals, A. *Section III:* 1.2—Spitzer, Joseph.

Guidelines for Researchers and Research Ethics Committees on Psychiatric Research Involving Human Participants. *Section III:* 18.2—Royal College of Psychiatrists. Working Party on Guidelines for Researchers and for Research Ethics Committees on Psychiatric Research Involving Human Participants.

Guidelines for the Humane Transportation of Research Animals. *Section III:* 22.2—National Research Council (United States). Institute for Laboratory Animal Reseach. Committee on Guidelines for the Humane Transportation of Laboratory Animals.

H

Hand: A Philosophical Inquiry into Human Being, The. *Section III:* 3.1—Tallis, Raymond.

Hand of Compassion: Portraits of Moral Choice during the Holocaust, The. *Section III:* 21.4—Monroe, Kristen Renwick.

Handbook for Social Justice in Counseling Psychology: Leadership, Vision, and Action. *Section III:* 17.1—Toporek, Rebecca L.; Gerstein, Lawrence H.; Fouad, Nadya A.; Roysircar, Gargi; and Israel, Tania, eds.

Handbook of Bioethics and Religion. *Section III:* 2.1—Guinn, David E., ed.

Handbook of Professional Ethics for Psychologists: Issues, Questions, and Controversies. *Section III:* 17.1—O'Donohue, William and Ferguson, Kyle, eds.

Handbook of Spirituality and Worldview in Clinical Practice. *Section III:* 17.1—Josephson, Allan M. and Peteet, John R., eds.

Hard Science, Hard Choices: Facts, Ethics, and Policies Guiding Brain Science Today. *Section III:* 17.1—Ackerman, Sandra J.

Hard Sell: The Evolution of a Viagra Salesman. *Section III:* 9.7—Reidy, Jamie.

Hardwired Behavior: What Neuroscience Reveals about Morality. *Section III:* 17.1—Tancredi, Laurence R.

Healing Buddha, The. *Section III:* 4.1.1—Birnbaum, Raoul.

Healing Psychiatry: Bridging the Science/Humanism Divide. *Section III:* 4.3—Brendel, David H.

Healing Tradition: Reviving the Soul of Western Medicine, The. *Section III:* 7.1—Greaves, David.

Healing Words: The Power of Apology in Medicine. *Section III:* 8.5—Woods, Michael S. and Brucker, Hilda J.

Health and Social Organization: Towards a Health Policy for the Twenty-first Century. *Section III:* 9.1—Blane, David; Brunner, Eric; and Wilkinson, Richard, eds.

Health Care and Christian Ethics. *Section III:* 2.1—Gill, Robin.

Health Care Mess: How We Got Into It and What It Will Take to Get Out, The. *Section III:* 9.1—Richmond, Julius B. and Fein, Rashi.

Health Care Politics and Policy in America. *Section III:* 9.1—Patel, Kant and Rushefsky, Mark.

Health Care Services, Racial and Ethnic Minorities and Underserved Populations: Patient and Provider

Last Right? Australians Take Sides on the Right to Die, The. *Section III:* 20.7—Chapman, Simon and Leeder, Stephen, eds.

Law and Ethics. *Section III:* 4.1.3—Hendrick, Judith.

Law and Ethics for Medical Careers. *Section III:* 2.1—Judson, Karen; Harrison, Carlene; and Hicks, Sharon.

Law and Ethics of the Pharmaceutical Industry, The. *Section III:* 9.7—Dukes, Graham.

Law and Medical Ethics. *Section III:* 2.1—Mason, J.K.; Smith, R.A. McCall; and Laurie, G.T.

Law and Medicine. *Section III:* 2.1—Bennett, Belinda.

Law Without Enforcement: Integrating Mental Health and Justice. *Section III:* 17.1—Eastman, Nigel and Peay, Jill, eds.

Learning from Medical Errors: Legal Issues. *Section III:* 9.8—Nguyen, Anh Vu and Nguyen, Dung A.

Leftist Literature and the Ideology of Eugenics During the American Depression. *Section III:* 15.5—Holmes, Sarah Catherine.

Leg to Stand On, A. *Section III:* 9.5.1—Sacks, Oliver.

Legal and Ethical Issues in Nursing. *Section III:* 4.1.3—Guido, Ginny Wacker.

Legal Aspects of General Dental Practice. *Section III:* 4.1.1—D'Cruz, Len; Mills, Simon; and Holmes, David.

Legal Aspects of Nursing. *Section III:* 4.1.3—Dimond, Bridgit.

Legal Issues in Counselling & Psychotherapy. *Section III:* 17.2—Jenkins, Peter, ed.

Legal Nurse Consulting: Principles and Practice. *Section III:* 4.1.3—Iyer, Patricia W., ed.; American Association of Legal Nurse Consultants.

Lenses of Gender: Transforming the Debate on Sexual Inequality, The. *Section III:* 10—Bem, Sandra Lipsitz.

Lesser Harms: The Morality of Risk in Medical Research. *Section III:* 18.1—Halpern, Sydney A.

Leviathan's Choice: Capital Punishment in the Twenty-First Century, The. *Section III:* 20.6—Martinez, J. Michael; Richardson, William D.; and Hornsby, D. Brandon, eds.

Life and Death of NSSM: How the Destruction of Political Will Doomed a U.S. Population Policy, The. *Section III:* 13.3—Mumford, Stephen D.

Life and Death of Smallpox, The. *Section III:* 9.5.1—Glynn, Ian and Glynn, Jenifer.

Life and Learning V: Proceedings of the Fifth University Faculty for Life Conference June 1995 at Marquette University. *Section III:* 12.3—Koterski, Joseph W., ed.

Life and Learning VIII: Proceedings of the Eighth University Faculty for Life Conference, June 1998 at the University of Toronto. *Section III:* 12.3—Koterski, Joseph W., ed.

Life and Learning XII: Proceedings of the Twelfth University Faculty for Life Conference at Ave Maria Law School 2002. *Section III:* 2.1—Koterski, Joseph W., ed.

Life Means Nothing Behind the Green Wall: A Novel. *Section III:* 9.1—Professor Z.

Life That Matters: The Legacy of Terri Schiavo—A Lesson for Us All, The. *Section III:* 20.5.1—Schindler, Mary and Schindler, Robert.

Linking Visions: Feminist Bioethics, Human Rights, and the Developing World. *Section III:* 2.1—Tong, Rosemarie; Donchin, Anne; and Dodds, Susan, eds.

Listening to the Whispers: Re-Thinking Ethics in Healthcare. *Section III:* 2.1—Dinkins, Christine Sorrell and Sorrell, Jeanne Merkle, eds.

Logic of Religion, The. *Section III:* 1.2—Dougherty, Jude P.

Loss and Bereavement in Childbearing. *Section III:* 20.3.1—Mander, Rosemary.

Lovers and Livers: Disease Concepts in History. *Section III:* 4.2—Duffin, Jacalyn.

Lying Awake. *Section III:* 9.5.1—Salzman, Mark.

M

Madness at Home: The Psychiatrist, the Patient, and the Family in England, 1820-1860. *Section III:* 17.1—Suzuki, Akihito.

Magical Progeny, Modern Technology: A Hindu Bioethics of Assisted Reproductive Technology. *Section III:* 14.1—Bhattacharyya, Swasti.

Mainstreaming of Complementary and Alternative Medicine: Studies in Social Context, The. *Section III:* 4.1.1—Tovey, Philip; Easthope, Gary; and Adams, Jon, eds.

Maltreatment of Patients in Nursing Homes: There Is No Safe Place. *Section III:* 9.5.2—Harris, Diana K. and Benson, Michael L.

Management of Post-Mortem Pregnancy: Legal and Philosophical Aspects. *Section III:* 9.5.8—Sperling, Daniel.

Many and the One: Religious and Secular Perspectives on Ethical Pluralism in the Modern World, The. *Section III:* 1.1—Madsen, Richard and Strong, Tracy B., eds.

Mark Twain and Medicine: "Any Mummery Will Cure". *Section III:* 7.1—Ober, K. Patrick.

Markets and Moral Regulation: Cultural Change in the European Union. *Section III:* 21.7—Kurzer, Paulette.

Mass Hysteria: Medicine, Culture, and Mothers' Bodies. *Section III:* 9.5.5—Kukla, Rebecca.

Master Mind: The Rise and Fall of Fritz Haber, the Noble Laureate Who Launched the Age of Chemical Warfare. *Section III:* 21.3—Charles, Daniel.

Master Plan: Himmler's Scholars and the Holocaust, The. *Section III:* 1.3.5—Pringle, Heather.

Medical Care at the End of Life: A Catholic Perspective. *Section III:* 20.4.1—Kelly, David F.

Medical Ethics and Law: An Introduction. *Section III:* 2.1—Tippett, Victoria.

Medical Ethics, or, A Code of Institutes and Precepts, Adapted to the Professional Conduct of Physicians and Surgeons. *Section III:* 2.2—Percival, Thomas and Pellegrino, Edmund D. [introduction].

Medical Law. *Section III:* 2.1—Kennedy, Ian and Grubb, Andrew.

Medical Literature from India, Sri Lanka and Tibet [and] Rules and Remedies in Classical Indian Law. *Section III:* 4.1.1—Meulendbeld, G. Jen, ed. [and] Leslie, Julia, ed.

Medicare Reform: Issues and Answers. *Section III:* 9.3.1—Rettenmaier, Andrew J. and Saving, Thomas R., eds.

Medicine and Jewish Law, Volume III. *Section III:* 2.1—Rosner, Fred and Schulman, Robert, eds.

Medicine and the Market: Equity v. Choice. *Section III:* 9.3.1—Callahan, Daniel and Wasunna, Angela A.

Medicine by Design: The Practice and Promise of Biomedical Engineering. *Section III:* 5.1—Montaigne, Fen.

Medicine, Health, and Bioethics: Essential Primary Sources. *Section III:* 2.2—Lerner, K. Lee and Lerner, Brenda Wilmoth, eds.

Medicine's Brave New World: Bioengineering and the New Genetics. *Section III:* 15.1—Hyde, Margaret O. and Setaro, John F.

Meeting the Challenge of Chronic Illness. *Section III:* 9.5.1—Kane, Robert L.; Priester, Reinhard; and Totten, Annette M.

Menschenwürde in der Bioethik. *Section III:* 2.1—Knoepffler, Nikolaus.

Mental Health: Global Policies and Human Rights. *Section III:* 17.1—Morrall, Peter and Hazelton, Mike, eds.

Mental Health Law: A Practical Guide. *Section III:* 2.1—Puri, Basant K.; Brown, Robert A.; McKee, Heather J.; and Treasaden, Ian H.

Metal and Flesh: The Evolution of Man: Technology Takes Over. *Section III:* 5.3—Dyens, Ollivier.

Metaphor of Mental Illness, The. *Section III:* 4.3—Pickering, Neil.

Mind Has Mountains: Reflections on Society and Psychiatry, The. *Section III:* 17.1—McHugh, Paul R.

Mind Wars: Brain Research and National Defense. *Section III:* 18.5.8—Moreno, Jonathan D.

Missing Cornerstone: Reasons Why Couples Choose Natural Family Planning in Their Marriage, The. *Section III:* 11.1—Tham, S. Joseph.

Moral Circle and the Self: Chinese and Western Perspectives, The. *Section III:* 1.1—Chong, Kim-chong; Tan, Sor-hoon; and Ten, C.L., eds.

Moral Issues of the Marketplace in Jewish Law. *Section III:* 1.3.2—Levine, Aaron.

Moral Minds: How Nature Designed Our Universal Sense of Right and Wrong. *Section III:* 1.1—Hauser, Marc D.

Moral Veto: Framing Contraception, Abortion, and Cultural Pluralism in the United States, The. *Section III:* 7.1—Burns, Gene.

Morality of Adoption: Social-Psychological, Theological, and Legal Perspectives, The. *Section III:* 14.1—Jackson, Timothy P., ed.

Multicultural Medicine and Health Disparities. *Section III:* 21.7—Satcher, David; Pamies, Rubens J.; and Woelfl, Nancy N., [eds.].

Music of Life: Biology Beyond the Genome, The. *Section III:* 15.1—Noble, Denis.

Myth of the Jewish Race: A Biologist's Point of View, The. *Section III:* 15.5—Corcos, Alain F.

N

Narrative Research in Health and Illness. *Section III:* 8.1—Hurwitz, Brian; Greenhalgh, Trisha; and Skultans, Vieda, eds.

Nature and Mortality: Recollections of a Philosopher in Public Life. *Section III:* 2.1—Warnock, Mary.

Nature and Nurture: The Complex Interplay of Genetic and Environmental Influences on Human Behavior and Development. *Section III:* 15.6—Coll, Cynthia García; Bearer, Elaine L.; and Lerner, Richard M., eds.

Nature Revealed: Selected Writings, 1949-2006. *Section III:* 3.1—Wilson, Edward O.

Nature's Experts: Science, Politics, and the Environment. *Section III:* 16.1—Bocking, Stephen.

Nazi Empire-Building and the Holocaust in Ukraine. *Section III:* 21.4—Lower, Wendy.

Never Let Me Go. *Section III:* 14.5—Ishiguro, Kazuo.

New Brain Sciences: Perils and Prospects, The. *Section III:* 17.1—Rees, Dai and Rose, Steven, eds.

New Experience of Childbirth, The. *Section III:* 9.5.5—Kitzinger, Sheila.

Section III arranged by NRCBL Classification Number, then Author or Title

New Medical Technologies and Society: Reordering Life. *Section III:* 5.3—Brown, Nik and Webster, Andrew.

New Progressive Agenda for Public Health and the Environment: A Project of the Center for Progressive Regulation, A. *Section III:* 9.1—Schroeder, Christopher H. and Steinzor, Rena, eds.

New Talmudic Readings. *Section III:* 1.2—Levinas, Emmanuel.

NHS plc: The Privatisation of Our Health Care. *Section III:* 9.3.1—Pollock, Allyson M.; Leys, Colin; et al.

Nightmare in Bari: The World War II Liberty Ship Poison Gas Disaster and Coverup. *Section III:* 21.3—Reminick, Gerald.

Nobody's Home: Candid Reflections of a Nursing Home Aide. *Section III:* 9.5.2—Gass, Thomas Edward.

Nurse's Calling: A Christian Spirituality of Caring for the Sick, The. *Section III:* 4.1.3—O'Brien, Mary Elizabeth.

Nurses on the Move: Migration and the Global Health Care Economy. *Section III:* 21.6—Kingma, Mireille.

Nursing Care in the Genomic Era: A Case-Based Approach. *Section III:* 15.2—Jenkins, Jean F. and Lea, Dale Halsey.

Nursing Homes: The Family's Journey. *Section III:* 9.5.2—Silin, Peter S.

O

Obstructed Labour: Race and Gender in the Re-Emergence of Midwifery. *Section III:* 4.1.3—Nestel, Sheryl.

On the Uniqueness of Humankind. *Section III:* 4.4—Duncker, H.-R. and Prieß, K.

Opening Up Care: Achieving Principled Practice in Health and Social Care Institutions. *Section III:* 9.1—Stanley, David and Reed, Jan.

Ordinary Germans in Extraordinary Times: The Nazi Revolution in Hildesheim. *Section III:* 1.3.5—Bergerson, Andrew Stuart.

Organ and Tissue Transplantation. *Section III:* 19.1—Price, David, ed.

Organ Donation: Opportunities for Action. *Section III:* 19.5—Institute of Medicine (United States). Board on Health Sciences Policy. Committee on Increasing Rates of Organ Donation.

Other Within: Ethics, Politics, and the Body in Simone de Beauvoir, The. *Section III:* 10—Scarth, Fredrika.

Our Parents, Ourselves: How American Health Care Imperials Middle Age and Beyond. *Section III:* 9.5.2—Turiel, Judith Steinberg.

Overdose: How Excessive Government Regulation Stifles Pharmaceutical Innovation. *Section III:* 5.3—Epstein, Richard A.

P

Pain and Profits: The History of the Headache and Its Remedies in America. *Section III:* 9.7—McTavish, Jan R.

Pain Medicine 2001 June; 2(2). *Section III:* 4.4—Ethical Issues and Dilemmas Faced by Today's Pain Practitioner: A Bioethical Primer.

Palliative Practices: An Interdisciplinary Approach. *Section III:* 20.4.1—Kuebler, Kim K.; Davis, Mellar P.; and Moore, Crystal Dea.

Papacy, the Jews, and the Holocaust, The. *Section III:* 1.2—Coppa, Frank.

Patents for Chemicals, Pharmaceuticals and Biotechnology: Fundamentals of Global Law, Practice and Strategy. *Section III:* 15.8—Grubb, Philip W.

Patient Autonomy and the Ethics of Responsibility. *Section III:* 8.1—Tauber, Alfred I.

Patient Participation in Palliative Care: A Voice for the Voiceless. *Section III:* 20.4.1—Monroe, Barbara and Oliviere, David, eds.

Patient-Directed Dying: A Call for Legalized Aid in Dying for the Terminally Ill. *Section III:* 20.7—Preston, Tom.

Peer Review in Health Sciences. *Section III:* 9.8—Godlee, Fiona and Jefferson, Tom, eds.

Perception of Risk, The. *Section III:* 5.2—Slovic, Paul.

Personal and the Political: Women's Activism in Response to the Breast Cancer and AIDS Epidemic, The. *Section III:* 21.1—Boehmer, Ulrike.

Personne biojuridique, La. *Section III:* 2.1—Bauzon, Stéphane.

Persons, Humanity, and the Definition of Death. *Section III:* 20.2.1—Lizza, John P.

Pharmaceutical Medicine, Biotechnology and European Law. *Section III:* 9.7—Goldberg, Richard and Lonbay, Julian, eds.

Philosopher Queen: Feminist Essays on War, Love, and Knowledge, The. *Section III:* 10—Cuomo, Chris.

Philosophical Reflections on Medical Ethics. *Section III:* 2.1—Athanassoulis, Nafsika, ed.

Philosophy of Palliative Care: Critique and Reconstruction, The. *Section III:* 20.4.1—Randall, Fiona and Downie, R.S.

Physician-Patient Relationship: Views of Adults with Life-Threatening Illness, The. *Section III:* 8.1—Forman, Jane Harriet.

Physicians' Crusade Against Abortion, The. *Section III:* 12.1—Dyer, Frederick N.

Placebo Effect and Health: Combining Science and Compassionate Care, The. *Section III:* 8.2—Thompson, W. Grant.

Poetry of Healing: A Doctor's Education in Empathy, Identity, and Desire, The. *Section III:* 7.1—Campo, Rafael.

Policies for an Aging Society. *Section III:* 9.5.2—Altman, Stuart H. and Shactman, David I., eds.

Politics of Precaution: Genetically Modified Crops in Developing Countries, The. *Section III:* 15.1—Paarlberg, Robert L.

Post-Holocaust: Interpretation, Misinterpretation, and the Claims of History. *Section III:* 21.4—Lang, Berel.

Power, Justice, and the Environment: A Critical Appraisal of the Environmental Justice Movement. *Section III:* 16.1—Pellow, David Naguib and Brulle, Robert J., eds.

Practical Reasoning and Ethical Decision. *Section III:* 1.1—Audi, Robert.

La pratique du diagnostic prénatal. *Section III:* 15.2—Body, G.; Perrotin, F.; Guichet, A.; Paillet, C.; Descamps, P.; Aubron, F.; et al.

Prescribed Medications and the Public Health: Laying the Foundation for Risk Reduction. *Section III:* 9.7—Kelly, William N.

Preventing HIV/AIDS in the Middle East and North Africa: A Window of Opportunity to Act. *Section III:* 9.5.6—World Bank.

Price of Assimilation: Felix Mendelssohn and the Nineteenth-Century Anti-Semitic Tradition, The. *Section III:* 1.2—Sposato, Jeffrey S.

Principles and Practice of Clinical Research. *Section III:* 18.1—Gallin, John I.

Principles of Clincal Research. *Section III:* 18.2—Di Giovanna, Ignazio and Hayes, Gareth, eds.

Prisoner of Hope. *Section III:* 1.2—Prywes, Moshe and Chertok, Haim.

Private Complaints and Public Health: Richard Titmuss on the National Health Service. *Section III:* 9.1—Oakley, Ann and Barker, Jonathan, eds.

Problems in Health Care Law. *Section III:* 9.1—Miller, Robert D., ed.

Proceedings: Fourth Session: Bangkok, Thailand, 23-25 March 2005. *Section III:* 5.1—World Commission on the Ethics of Scientific Knowledge and Technology [COMEST] [and] United Nations Educational, Scientific and Cultural Organization [UNESCO].

Proceedings: International Bioethics Committee of UNESCO (IBC), Eighth Session. *Section III:* 2.1—UNESCO. International Bioethics Committee.

Professing Medicine: Strengthening the Ethics and Professionalism of Tomorrow's Physicians. *Section III:* 2.1—American Medical Association [AMA].

Professionalism in Health Care: A Primer for Career Success. *Section III:* 4.1.1—Makely, Sherry.

Profits before People? Ethical Standards and the Marketing of Prescription Drugs. *Section III:* 9.7—Weber, Leonard J.

Promoting Health: Politics & Practice. *Section III:* 9.1—Adams, Lee; Amos, Mary; and Munro, James, eds.

Prophets & Priests: The Hidden Face of the Birth Control Movement. *Section III:* 11.1—Farmer, Ann.

Psychiatric Clinics of North American 2002 September; 25(3). *Section III:* 17.1—Ethics in Psychiatry.

Psychiatry in Multicultural Britain. *Section III:* 17.1—Bhugra, Dinesh and Cochrane, Ray, eds.

Public Health Response to Biological and Chemical Weapons: WHO Guidance. *Section III:* 21.3—World Health Organization.

Public Participation in Science: The Role of Consensus Conferences in Europe. *Section III:* 5.3—Joss, Simon and Durant, John, eds.; Science Museum [and] Commission of the European Communities. Directorate-General for Science, Research, and Development.

Q

Quality of Life. *Section III:* 4.4—Carr, Alison; Higginson, Irene J.; and Robinson, Peter G., eds.

Quality Solution: The Stakeholder's Guide to Improving Health Care, The. *Section III:* 9.8—Nash, David B. and Goldfarb, Neil I., eds.

Quest for Drug Control: Politics and Federal Policy in a Period of Increasing Substance Abuse, 1963-1981, The. *Section III:* 9.5.9—Musto, David F. and Korsmeyer, Pamela.

Quest for Human Longevity: Science, Business, and Public Policy, The. *Section III:* 20.5.1—Solomon, Lewis D.

Questions and Answers: Intellectual Foundations of Judaism. *Section III:* 1.2—Neusner, Jacob.

R

Rape of Nanking: The Forgotten Holocaust of World War II, The. *Section III:* 21.4—Chang, Iris.

Rationing Medical Care on the Basis of Age: The Moral Dimensions. *Section III:* 9.4—Matthews, Eric and Russell, Elizabeth.

Reaching the Poor with Health, Nutrition, and Population Services: What Works, What Doesn't, and Why. *Section III:* 9.5.10—Gwatkin, Davidson R.; Wagstaff, Adam; and Yazbeck, Abdo S., eds.

Rebirth of the Clinic: An Introduction to Spirituality in Health Care, The. *Section III:* 9.1—Sulmasy, Daniel P.

Rebuilding Trust in Healthcare. *Section III:* 9.1—Harrison, Jamie; Innes, Rob; and van Zwanenberg, Tim, eds.

Reclaiming the Body: Christians and the Faithful Use of Modern Medicine. *Section III:* 7.1—Shuman, Joel and Volck, Brian.

Recognition, Responsibility, and Rights: Feminist Ethics and Social Theory. *Section III:* 1.1—Fiore, Robin N. and Nelson, Hilde Lindemann, eds.

Recognizing Spiritual Needs in People Who Are Dying. *Section III:* 20.4.1—Stanworth, Rachel.

Recycled Fetus: Ethics of Waste and Gift Exchange in New Reproductive Technologies, The. *Section III:* 12.5.1—Ariss, Mary Rachel.

Refiguring Life: Metaphors of Twentieth-Century Biology. *Section III:* 15.1—Keller, Evelyn Fox.

Regulating Tobacco. *Section III:* 9.5.9—Rabin, Robert L. and Sugarman, Stephen D., eds.

Religion and the Death Penalty: A Call for Reckoning. *Section III:* 20.6—Owens, Erik C.; Carlson, John D.; and Elshtain, Eric P., eds.

Re-Producing a Genetic Self: Media Representations of Genetic Reproductive Technologies. *Section III:* 15.1—Silva, Vesta T.

Reproductive Agency, Medicine and the State: Cultural Transformations in Childbearing. *Section III:* 14.1—Unnithan-Kumar, Maya, ed.

Reproductive Health: The Missing Millennium Development Goal. *Section III:* 9.5.5—White, Arlette Campbell; Merrick, Thomas W.; and Yazbeck, Abdo S.

Reproductive Rights in a Global Context: South Africa, Uganda, Peru, Denmark, United States, Vietnam, Jordan. *Section III:* 14.1—Knudsen, Lara M.

Republican War on Science, The. *Section III:* 5.3—Mooney, Chris.

Research Ethics. *Section III:* 18.1—Iltis, Ana Smith, ed.

Research Ethics Committees, Data Protection and Medical Research in European Countries. *Section III:* 18.2—Beyleveld, D.; Townend, D; and Wright, J., eds.

Responsible Research: A Guide for Coordinators. *Section III:* 18.2—Fedor, Carol; Philip A. Cola; and Pierre, Christine, eds.

Reversing the Tide: Priorities for HIV/AIDS Prevention in Central Asia. *Section III:* 9.5.6—Godinho, Joana; Renton, Adrian; Vinogradov, Viatcheslav; Novotny, Thomas; Rivers, Mary-June; Gotsadze, George; and Bravo, Mario; World Bank.

Richard and Hinda Rosenthal Lectures 2003: Keeping Patients Safe: Transforming the Work Environment of Nurses, The. *Section III:* 16.3—Institute of Medicine (United States). Committee on the Work Environment for Nurses and Patient Safety.

Richard Dawkins: How a Scientist Changed the Way We Think: Reflections by Scientists, Writers, and Philosophers. *Section III:* 15.6—Grafen, Alan and Ridley, Mark, eds.

Riddle of Gender: Science, Activism, and Transgender Rights, The. *Section III:* 10—Rudacille, Deborah.

Right Living: An Anglo-American Tradition of Self-Help Medicine and Hygiene. *Section III:* 7.1—Rosenberg, Charles E., ed.

Right to Die, The. *Section III:* 20.5.1—Woodward, John, ed.

Right to Die? An Examination of the Euthanasia Debate, The. *Section III:* 20.5.1—Cosic, Miriam.

Right to Life in European Constitutional and International Case-Law, The. *Section III:* 4.4—Mathieu, Bertrand.

Rights from Wrongs: A Secular Theory of the Origins of Rights. *Section III:* 21.1—Dershowitz, Alan.

Rise and Fall of Soul and Self: An Intellectual History of Personal Identity, The. *Section III:* 4.4—Martin, Raymond and Barresi, John.

Risk and Reason: Safety, Law, and the Environment. *Section III:* 5.2—Sunstein, Cass R.

Risk and Risk Taking in Health and Social Welfare. *Section III:* 5.2—Titterton, Mike.

Risk Communication: A Mental Models Approach. *Section III:* 5.2—Morgan, M. Granger; Fischhoff, Baruch; Bostrom, Ann; and Atman, Cynthia J.

Risk, Communication and Health Psychology. *Section III:* 5.2—Berry, Dianne C.

Risk Communication and Public Health. *Section III:* 5.2—Bennett, Peter and Calman, Kenneth, eds.

Risk, Media, and Stigma: Understanding Public Challenges to Modern Science and Technology. *Section III:* 5.3—Flynn, James; Slovic, Paul; and Kunreuther, Howard, eds.

Ritual of Rights in Japan: Law, Society, and Health Policy, The. *Section III:* 9.5.6—Feldman, Eric A.

Role of Scientific and Technical Data and Information in the Public Domain: Proceedings of a Symposium, The. *Section III:* 5.3—Esanu, Julie M. and Uhlir, Paul F., eds.; National Research Council (United States). Steering Committee on the Role of Scientific and Technical Data and Information in the Public Domain.

Role of the Animal Ethics Committee in Achieving Humane Animal Experimentation, The. *Section III:* 22.2—Schuppli, Catherine Anne.

S

Safe Abortion: Technical and Policy Guidance for Health Systems. *Section III:* 12.1—World Health Organization.

Safety of Genetically Engineered Foods: Approaches to Assessing Unintended Health Effects. *Section III:* 15.7—National Research Council (United States) [and] Institute of Medicine (United States). Committee on Identifying and Assessing Unintended Effects of Genetically Engineered Foods on Human Health.

SARS in China: Prelude to Pandemic? *Section III:* 9.5.1—Kleinman, Arthur and Watson, James L., eds.

Saving Very Premature Babies: Key Ethical Issues. *Section III:* 20.5.2—Mifflin, Pauline Challinor.

Saving Women and Infants from Abortion: A Dance in the Rain. *Section III:* 12.3—Driscoll, Margaret and Faugno, Emily.

Science and Ethics. *Section III:* 1.3.9—Rollin, Bernard E.

Science and Other Cultures: Issues in Philosophies of Science and Technology. *Section III:* 5.1—Figueroa, Robert and Harding, Sandra G., eds.

Scientific Integrity: Text and Cases in Responsible Conduct of Research. *Section III:* 1.3.9—Macrina, Francis L.

Screening in Disease Prevention: What Works? *Section III:* 9.5.1—Holland, Walter W. and Stewart, Susie.

Second Opinion: Doctors, Diseases and Decisions in Modern Medicine. *Section III:* 8.1—Horton, Richard.

Secret de la salamandre: la médecine en quête d'immortalité, Le. *Section III:* 15.1—Kahn, Axel and Papillon, Fabrice.

Seeds of Contention: World Hunger and the Global Controversy over GM Crops. *Section III:* 15.1—Pinstrup-Andersen, Per and Shiøler, Ebbe.

Seeds of Mortality: The Public and Private Worlds of Cancer. *Section III:* 7.1—Justman, Stewart.

Seeking Security: Pathogens, Open Access, and Genome Databases. *Section III:* 15.1—National Research Council (United States). Commitee on Genomics Databases for Bioterrorism Threat Agents.

Self, Senility, and Alzheimer's Disease in Modern America: A History. *Section III:* 17.1—Ballenger, Jesse F.

Selfish Meme: A Critical Reassessment, The. *Section III:* 15.1—Distin, Kate.

Sense and Sensibility in Health Care. *Section III:* 9.1—Marinker, Marshall, ed.

Setting the Moral Compass: Essays by Women Philosophers. *Section III:* 1.1—Calhoun, Cheshire, ed.

Sex, Drugs and DNA: Science's Taboos Confronted. *Section III:* 5.1—Stebbins, Michael.

Sexual and Reproductive Health Promotion in Latino Populations = Parteras, Promotoras y Poetas: Case Studies Across the Americas. *Section III:* 9.5.4—Torres, M. Idalí and Cernada, George P., eds.

Sexual Borderlands: Constructing an America Sexual Past. *Section III:* 10—Kennedy, Kathleen and Ullman, Sharon, eds.

Shakespeare's Theories of Blood, Character, and Class: A Festschrift in Honor of Dr. David Shelley Berkeley. *Section III:* 7.1—Rollins, Peter C. and Smith, Alan, eds.

Shredding the Social Contract: The Privatization of Medicare. *Section III:* 9.3.1—Geyman, John.

Silent Witness: The Untold Story of Terri Schiavo's Death. *Section III:* 20.5.1—Fuhrman, Mark.

Six Modern Plagues and How We Are Causing Them. *Section III:* 9.5.1—Walters, Mark Jerome.

Slaughterhouse Blues: The Meat and Poultry Industry in North America. *Section III:* 22.3—Stull, Donald D. and Broadway, Michael J.

Smart Mice, Not So Smart People: An Interesting and Amusing Guide to Bioethics. *Section III:* 2.1—Caplan, Arthur L.

Social Amplification of Risk, The. *Section III:* 5.2—Pidgeon, Nick; Kasperson, Roger E.; and Slovic, Paul, eds.

Social Economics of Health Care, The. *Section III:* 9.3.1—Davis, John B., ed.

Social Inequalities, Health and Health Care Delivery. *Section III:* 7.1—Kronenfeld, Jennie Jacobs, ed.

Social Justice: The Moral Foundations of Public Health and Health Policy. *Section III:* 9.1—Powers, Madison and Faden, Ruth.

Social Science and Medicine 2003 May; 56(9). *Section III:* 14.1—Reproduction Gone Awry.

Social Science and Medicine 2005 January; 60(2). *Section III:* 9.4 . Anand, Paul and Dolan, Paul, eds.

Society and Genetic Information: Codes and Laws in the Genetic Era. *Section III:* 15.1—Sándor, Judit, ed.

Speaking for Patients and Carers: Health Consumer Groups and the Policy Process. *Section III:* 9.1—Baggott, Rob; Allsop, Judith; and Jones, Kathryn.

Sport, Professionalism and Pain: Ethnographies of Injury and Risk. *Section III:* 9.5.1—Howe, P. David.

Stanford Law and Policy Review 2006; 17(1). *Section III:* 9.1—Symposium: Health Care in America: A New Generation of Challenges.

State of Immunity: The Politics of Vaccination in Twentieth-Century America. *Section III:* 9.5.1—Colgrove, James.

State of the Animals II, 2003, The. *Section III:* 22.1—Salem, Deborah J. and Rowan, Andrew N., eds.

State of the Animals III, 2005, The. *Section III:* 22.1—Salem, Deborah J. and Rowan, Andrew N., eds.; Humane Society of the United States.

Status of the Family in Law and Bioethics: The Genetic Context, The. *Section III:* 15.3—Gilbar, Roy.

Stem Cell Controversy: Debating the Issues, The. *Section III:* 18.5.4—Ruse, Michael and Pynes, Christopher A., eds.

Stem Cell Divide: The Facts, the Fiction, and the Fear Driving the Greatest Scientific, Political, and Religious Debate of Our Time, The. *Section III:* 18.5.4—Bellomo, Michael.

Stem Cell Now: From the Experiment That Shook the World to the New Politics of Life. *Section III:* 18.5.4—Scott, Christopher Thomas.

Stem Cell Research: Medical Applications and Ethical Controversy. *Section III:* 18.5.4—Panno, Joseph.

Step-by-Step Guide to Clinical Trials, A. *Section III:* 18.2—Mulay, Marilyn.

Stetson Law Review 2005 Fall; 35(1). *Section III:* 20.5.1—Reflections on and Implications of Schiavo.

Stolen Innocence: A Mother's Fight for Justice: The Story of Sally Clark. *Section III:* 1.3.5—Batt, John.

Strange Harvest: Organ Transplants, Denatured Bodies, and the Transformed Self. *Section III:* 19.1—Sharp, Lesley A.

Stranger at the Gate: To Be Gay and Christian in America. *Section III:* 10—White, Mel.

Strike Terror No More: Theology, Ethics, and the New War. *Section III:* 21.2—Berquist, Jon L., ed.

Subject of Care: Feminist Perspectives on Dependency, The. *Section III:* 8.1—Kittay, Eva Feder and Feder, Ellen K.

Suffering for Science: Reason and Sacrifice in Modern America. *Section III:* 5.3—Herzig, Rebecca M.

Surgically Shaping Children: Technology, Ethics, and the Pursuit of Normality. *Section III:* 9.5.7—Parens, Erik, ed.

T

Tainted Milk: Breastmilk, Feminisms, and the Politics of Environmental Degradation. *Section III:* 9.5.7—Boswell-Penc, Maia.

Taking Life and Death Seriously: Bioethics from Japan. *Section III:* 2.1—Takahashi, Takao, ed.

Taking Sides: Clashing Views in Health and Society. *Section III:* 2.1—Daniel, Eileen L., ed.

Taking Sides: Clashing Views on Controversial Environmental Issues. *Section III:* 16.1—Easton, Thomas A. and Goldfarb, Theodore D., eds.

Technology and the Good Life? *Section III:* 5.1—Higgs, Eric; Light, Andrew; and Strong, David, eds.

Terri: The Truth. *Section III:* 20.5.1—Schiavo, Michael.

Theological Bioethics: Participation, Justice, and Change. *Section III:* 2.1—Cahill, Lisa Sowle.

Third World Health: Hostage to First World Wealth. *Section III:* 21.1—MacDonald, Théodore H.

Tide in the Affairs of Medicine: National Health Insurance as the Augury of Professionalism, A. *Section III:* 9.3.1—Hall, George M.

Tissue Economies: Blood, Organs, and Cell Lines in Late Capitalism. *Section III:* 19.5—Waldby, Catherine and Mitchell, Robert.

To Do No Harm: Ensuring Patient Safety in Health Care Organizations. *Section III:* 9.8—Morath, Julianne and Turnbull, Joanne E.

To Improve Health and Health Care, Volume VI: The Robert Wood Johnson Foundation Anthology. *Section III:* 9.1—Isaacs, Stephen L. and Knickman, James R., eds.

To Wear the Dust of War: From Bialystok to Shanghai to the Promised Land: An Oral History. *Section III:* 1.2—Iwry, Samuel.

Tobacco Control Policy. *Section III:* 9.5.9—Warner, Kenneth E., ed.

Torture: A Collection. *Section III:* 21.4—Levinson, Sanford, ed.

Toward a Standard of Disclosure for Medical Informed Consent: Development and Demonstration of a Decision-Analytic Methodology. *Section III:* 8.3.1—Merz, Jon Frederick.

Toward a 21st Century Health System: The Contributions and Promise of Prepaid Group Practice. *Section III:* 9.3.2—Enthoven, Alain C. and Tollen, Laura A., eds.

Transcultural Geriatrics: Caring for Elderly People of Indo-Asian Origin. *Section III:* 21.7—Ghosh, Partha and Khan, Shahid Anis.

Troubled Dream of Genetic Medicine: Ethnicity and Innovation in Tay-Sachs, Cystic Fibrosis, and Sickle Cell Disease, The. *Section III:* 15.1—Wailoo, Keith and Pemberton, Stephen.

U

Under the Medical Gaze: Facts and Fictions of Chronic Pain. *Section III:* 7.1—Greenhalgh, Susan.

Understanding Genetics: A Primer for Couples and Families. *Section III:* 15.1—Scheuerle, Angela.

See inside front cover for NRCBL Classification Scheme

Understanding the Placebo Effect in Complementary Medicine: Theory, Practice and Research. *Section III:* 8.2—Peters, David, ed.

University of New South Wales Law Journal 2003; 26(3). *Section III:* 15.1—Forum: Genetics and the Law.

Unknown Country: Death in Australia, Britain, and the USA, The. *Section III:* 20.1—Charmaz, Kathy; Howarth, Glennys; and Kellehear, Allan, eds.

Unplugged: Reclaiming Our Right to Die in America. *Section III:* 20.5.1—Colby, William H.

Unspeakable Crime of Andrea Yates: "Are You There Alone?", The. *Section III:* 20.5.2—O'Malley, Suzanne.

Unsustainable: A Primer for Global Environmental and Social Justice. *Section III:* 16.1—Hossay, Patrick.

Use of Genetically Modified Crops in Developing Countries: A Follow-up Discussion Paper, The. *Section III:* 15.1—Nuffield Council on Bioethics.

V

Vaccine Controversy: The History, Use, and Safety of Vaccinations, The. *Section III:* 9.7—Link, Kurt.

Values and Objectivity in Science: The Current Controversy about Transgenic Crops. *Section III:* 15.1—Lacey, Hugh.

Values in Education. *Section III:* 1.3.1—Stephenson, Joan; Ling, Lorraine; Burman, Eva; and Cooper, Maxine, eds.

Valuing People: A New Strategy for Learning Disability for the 21st Century: A White Paper. *Section III:* 9.1—Great Britain. Department of Health.

Venus on Wheels: Two Decades of Dialogue on Disability, Biography, and Being Female in America. *Section III:* 9.5.5—Frank, Gelya.

Virtue Ethics, Old and New. *Section III:* 1.1—Gardiner, Stephen M., ed.

W

Way We Eat: Why Our Food Choices Matter, The. *Section III:* 1.3.1—Singer, Peter and Mason, Jim.

When a Gene Makes You Smell Like a Fish. . . and Other Tales about the Genes in Your Body. *Section III:* 15.1—Chiu, Lisa Seachrist.

When Treatment Fails: How Medicine Cares for Dying Children. *Section III:* 20.4.2—Bearison, David J.

When Your Doctor Has Bad News: Simple Steps to Strength, Healing & Hope. *Section III:* 8.1—Weir, Al B.

Where Human Rights Begin: Health, Sexuality, and Women in the New Millennium. *Section III:* 9.5.5—Chavkin, Wendy and Chesler, Ellen.

Women Under the Influence. *Section III:* 9.5.9—National Center on Addiction and Substance Abuse at Columbia University.

Women's Reproductive Rights. *Section III:* 9.5.5—Widdows, Heather; Idiakez, Itziar Alkorta; and Cirión, Aitziber Emaldi, eds.

Work and Integrity: The Crisis and Promise of Professionalism in America. *Section III:* 1.3.1—Sullivan, William M.

Workshop on Disability in America: A New Look: Summary and Background Papers. *Section III:* 9.5.1—Institute of Medicine (United States). Committee on Disability in America: A New Look.

Worst of Evils: The Fight Against Pain, The. *Section III:* 4.4—Dormandy, Thomas.

X

Xenotransplantation: Law and Ethics. *Section III:* 19.1—McLean, Sheila A.M. and Williamson, Laura.

Y

Yes to Human Cloning: Immortality Thanks to Science! *Section III:* 14.5—Raël.

Your Child in the Balance: An Insider's Guide for Parents to the Psychiatric Medicine Dilemma. *Section III:* 17.4—Kalikow, Kevin T.

Z

Zohar, Volume 1, The. *Section III:* 1.2—Matt, Daniel C., translation and commentary.

Zohar, Volume 2, The. *Section III:* 1.2—Matt, Daniel C., translation and commentary.

Zohar, Volume 3, The. *Section III:* 1.2—Matt, Daniel C., translation and commentary.

Zoo. *Section III:* 15.1—Marks, Graham.

BIBLIOGRAPHY OF BIOETHICS
SUBJECT HEADING KEY FOR SECTION II

Section II lists the primary classification number for each document. To find the full citation in Section I, or to find documents on the same subject, refer to the list below, which indicates all possible subject headings for each primary classification number appearing in Section II.

1.3.1	Professional Ethics
1.3.7	Journalism and Publishing
1.3.9	Biomedical Research/ Research Ethics and Scientific Misconduct
1.3.12	Telemedicine and Informatics
2.1	Bioethics and Medical Ethics, *or its subdivisions:* /Legal Aspects, /Philosophical Perspectives, *or* /Religious Perspectives
2.2	Bioethics and Medical Ethics/ History
2.3	Bioethics and Medical Ethics/ Education
2.4	Bioethics and Medical Ethics/ Commissions
4.1.1	Professional Ethics
4.1.2	Philosophy of Medicine
4.1.3	Nursing Ethics and Philosophy
4.2	Health, Concept of
4.3	Mental Health, Concept of
4.4	Quality and Value of Life
4.5	Enhancement
5.1, 5.2	Biomedical Research
5.3	Biomedical Research/ Social Control of Science and Technology
5.4	Nanotechnology
6	Codes of Ethics
7.1	Sociology of Medicine
7.2	Medical Education
7.3	Professional Professional Relationship
7.4	Malpractice and Professional Misconduct
8.1	Patient Relationships
8.2	Truth Disclosure
8.3.1	Informed Consent
8.3.2	Informed Consent/ Minors
8.3.3	Informed Consent /Incompetents
8.3.4	Treatment Refusal
8.4	Confidentiality
8.5	Malpractice and Professional Misconduct
9.1	Health Care, *or* Public Health
9.2	Right to Health Care
9.3.1	Health Care/ Health Care Economics
9.3.2	Health Care/ Health Care Economics/ Managed Care Programs
9.4	Resource Allocation
9.5.1	Care for Specific Groups
9.5.2	Care for Specific Groups/ Aged
9.5.3	Care for Specific Groups/ Mentally Disabled
9.5.4	Care for Specific Groups/ Minorities
9.5.5	Care for Specific Groups/ Women
9.5.6	AIDS *or its subdivisions:* /Confidentiality, /Human Experimentation, *or* /Legal Aspects
9.5.7	Care for Specific Groups/ Minors
9.5.8	Care for Specific Groups/ Fetuses
9.5.9	Care for Specific Groups/ Substance Abusers
9.5.10	Care for Specific Groups/ Indigents
9.6	Ethicists and Ethics Committees
9.7	Drug Industry
9.8	Health Care/ Health Care Quality
10	Sexuality
11.1, 11.2, 11.4	Contraception
11.3	Sterilization
12.1	Abortion
12.3	Abortion/ Moral and Religious Aspects
12.4.1, 12.4.2, 12.4.3, 12.4.4	Abortion/ Legal Aspects
12.5.1, 12.5.2, 12.5.3	Abortion/ Social Aspects
13.1, 13.3	Population Policy
14.1	Reproductive Technologies
14.2	Artificial Insemination and Surrogate Mothers
14.3	Sex Determination
14.4	In Vitro Fertilization
14.5	Cloning *or its subdivision:* Cloning /Legal Aspects